THE PASSION OF

TALES OF THE SOUTH PACIFIC!

THE SWEEP OF

HAWAII!

CARAVANS

James A. Michener's magnificent new novel of a restless, adventure-seeking Bryn Mawr girl who disappears in Afghanistan, and of the American diplomatic attaché who is assigned to search for her in that strange, exotic land.

"Fascinating . . . an imaginative journey to a barbarous land little changed in centuries, plus a heady mixture of adventure, scenery and sex stirred by a master hand."

Minneapolis Tribune

(OVER)

"THE SEVERITY, THE VASTNESS AND

"A RATTLING GOOD ADVENTURE YARN" Chicago Tribune

"In the grand manner . . . the Michener trademark—realism and deft, crisp descriptive passages." Pittsburgh Press

---

"An extraordinary novel . . . the mountains sing and the deserts writhe in a kind of spasmodic horror of deathlessness. The caravansaries come to life; the old nomadic trails across the mountains spring into existence; the wildness and the ruggedness of the land are communicated to the reader . . . excellent . . . brilliant." The New York Times

---

ANOTHER MICHENER TRIUMPH WITH

THE POETRY OF A FARAWAY LAND"*

"In CARAVANS, Mr. Michener has done for Afghanistan what his last book did for Hawaii and his first one did for the South Pacific."

*New York Herald Tribune

"Michener casts his usual spell. He has a wonderful empathy for the wild and free and an understanding of the reasons behind the kind of cruelty that goes with it . . . romantic and adventurous."

Newsday

"Frightening . . . vivid and colorful. The vast desert with its shifting sands, camel trains and bands of nomads that fires the imagination."

Columbus Dispatch

RAVE REVIEWS FROM COAST TO COAST!

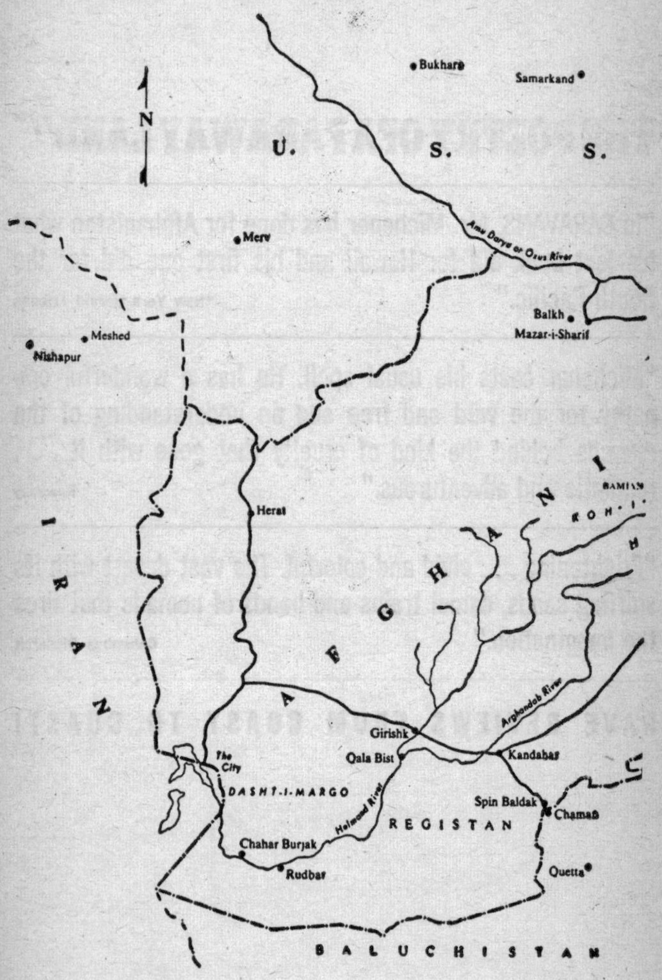

N
Bukhara
Samarkand
U.
S.
S.
Merv
Amu Darya or Oxus River
Balkh
Mazar-i-Sharif
Meshed
Nishapur
Herat
I R A N
A F G H A N I
BAMIAN
KOH-I-
H
Arghandab River
Girishk
Qala Bist
Kandahar
The City
DASHT-I-MARGO
Helmand River
Spin Baldak
Chaman
REGISTAN
Chahar Burjak
Rudbar
Quetta
BALUCHISTAN

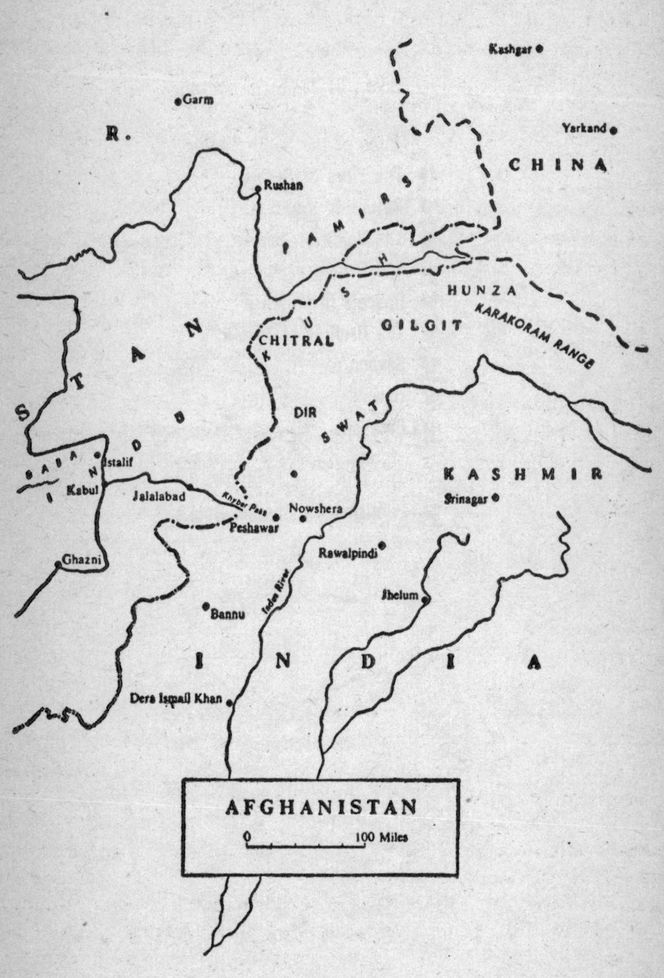

Kashgar
Garm
R.
Yarkand
CHINA
Rushan
PAMIRS
HINDU KUSH
HUNZA
KARAKORAM RANGE
GILGIT
CHITRAL
AFGHANISTAN
DIR
SWAT
BABA
Istalif
KASHMIR
Kabul
Jalalabad
Khyber Pass
Nowshera
Srinagar
Peshawar
Rawalpindi
Ghazni
Jhelum
Bannu
Indus River
INDIA
Dera Ismail Khan
AFGHANISTAN
0
100 Miles

Books by James A. Michener

Tales of the South Pacific
The Fires of Spring
Return to Paradise
The Voice of Asia
The Bridge at Andau
Rascals in Paradise
The Bridges at Toko-Ri
Sayonara
Hawaii
Caravans

Published by Bantam Books

CARAVANS

A NOVEL BY

JAMES A. MICHENER

*This low-priced Bantam Book
has been completely reset in a type face
designed for easy reading, and was printed
from new plates. It contains the complete
text of the original hard-cover edition.*
NOT ONE WORD HAS BEEN OMITTED.

CARAVANS

*A Bantam Book / published by arrangement with
Random House, Inc.*

PRINTING HISTORY

*Random House edition published August 1963
2nd printing . . . August 1963
3rd printing . . . August 1963
4th printing . . . January 1964
Book-of-the-Month Club edition published August 1963
Bantam edition published September 1964
2nd printing
3rd printing*

*Quotation on pages 53-54 from the 11th Edition Encyclopaedia
Britannica, published in 1910. Reprinted by permission.*

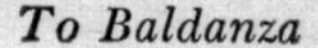

To Baldanza

1

On a bleak wintry morning some years ago I was summoned to the office of our naval attaché at the American embassy in Kabul. Captain Verbruggen looked at me with an air of frustration and growled, "Damn it all, Miller, two weeks ago the ambassador ordered you to settle this mess about the saddle shoes. Last night the Afghanistan government made another protest . . . this time official. I want you, by three o'clock this afternoon, to hand me . . ."

I interrupted to report: "Sir, a much more serious matter has come up. Last night a dispatch arrived. I've assembled the data for you."

I shoved before him a leather portfolio jammed with papers. Across the face of the portfolio was stamped the gold inscription, "For the Ambassador," and since our embassy owned only two such folders, what went into them was apt to be important.

"Can't it wait till the ambassador gets back from Hong Kong?" Captain Verbruggen asked hopefully, for even though he was our acting ambassador he preferred to temporize.

I disappointed him. "It's got to be handled now."

"What's it deal with?" he asked, for he was a self-made man who disliked reading.

Carefully folding back the leather cover, I pointed

to a cable from Washington. "Senior senator from Pennsylvania. Demands an answer. Immediately."

Verbruggen, a rugged, bald-headed man in his sixties, snapped to attention, as if the senator from Pennsylvania had entered the room. "What's he want?" He still refused to do any unnecessary reading.

"The Jaspar girl," I said.

With a disgusted reflex Verbruggen slammed shut the portfolio. "For seventeen months," he complained, "this embassy has been plagued by the Jaspar girl. I'm here to help a nation climb out of the Dark Ages, and that's the job I'm trying to do. But I'm pestered with saddle shoes and Jaspar idiots. There's nothing more I can think of to do on this case," he concluded firmly, shoving the papers to me.

But I forced the papers back to his side of the desk. "You've got to read the dispatch," I warned.

Gingerly he lifted the leather cover and peeked at the peremptory message from Washington. When he saw that even the Secretary of State had involved himself in the matter, he snapped to attention and pulled the paper before him. Slowly he read aloud:

> "It is imperative that I be able to supply the senior senator from Pennsylvania with full details regarding the whereabouts and condition of Ellen Jaspar. All previous reports from your embassy are judged inadequate and unacceptable. If necessary, detail your best men to this problem as it involves many collateral considerations. Am I correct in remembering that Mark Miller speaks the native language? If so, consider assigning him to this project at once and have him report promptly, sparing no effort."

Captain Verbruggen leaned back, blew air from puffed-up cheeks and once again shoved the folder to me. "Looks like it's been taken out of my hands," he said with relief. "Better get to work, son."

I lifted the portfolio from his desk and said, "I have been working, sir. Ever since I arrived."

"In a very desultory way," he suggested pleasantly. My boss could never forgo the obvious, which was why he was stuck off in Afghanistan, one of the most inconspicuous nations on earth. In 1946 it was just emerging from the bronze age, a land incredibly old, incredibly tied to an ancient past. At the embassy we used to say, "Kabul today shows what Palestine was like at the time of Jesus." In many ways, our attaché was an ideal man for Afghanistan, for he too was only just emerging from his own bronze age.

Yet I liked him. He was a rough, wily businessman who had made a minor fortune in the used-car racket, and a place for himself in the Democratic party in Minnesota. Four times he had helped elect Franklin D. Roosevelt, and although I was a strong Republican, I respected Verbruggen's tested loyalty. He had given the Democrats some sixty thousand dollars and they had given him Afghanistan.

He was almost entitled to it. While still a civilian he had made himself into a rough-and-ready yachtsman, for boating was his principal hobby, and when World War II struck, he volunteered to help the navy manage its shore installations. By merit and drive he had risen from lieutenant to navy captain and had made significant contributions to the building of our great bases at Manus and Samar. He was a tough bullet-head and men respected him; he had courage, and I could prove it.

My name is not really Mark Miller. By rights it's Marcus Muehler, but in the 1840's when my ancestors fled Germany they decided with that foresight which distinguishes my family that a Jewish name would not be helpful in America, so they translated *muehler* into its English equivalent, and henceforth we were Millers.

As usual, my family was right. The fact that my name was Miller and my face wholly un-Jewish enabled me to succeed at Groton and Yale, so that when in 1942 the United States navy was looking for a few acceptable Jewish officers to avoid having many unacceptable ones forced upon them, they grabbed me with relief and were happy when most of my shipmates never realized that I was Jewish. In how many wardrooms was I assured by amateur anthropologists, "I can spot a kike every time."

Captain Verbruggen, under whom I served at Manus, watched me for three weeks, then said, "Miller, you're the kind of kid who ought to be in Intelligence. You've got brains." And he personally fought with the brass on the island until he found me a good berth. In 1945, when our State Department also became eager to pick up a few Jewish career men with table manners, my former boss remembered me, and in one exciting week he switched me from lieutenant, junior grade, to State Department officer, very junior grade.

Then came the problem of where State should put me, for the typical embassy doubted that I would fit in. For example, I wouldn't be welcome in Cairo or Baghdad, where the citizens hated Jews, or, as it happened, in Paris, where many of our staff felt the same way. At this point Captain Verbruggen, now serving as naval attaché in Afghanistan, reported that he knew Mark Miller, and that I was a well-behaved Jew who would be a credit to the country. "In fact," he said in a cable that was passed widely throughout the department, "some of my best friends are Jews," and he got me. His courage gained the gratitude of President Truman and a nod from the Secretary of State. To everyone's relief I was working out reasonably well, so that Captain Verbruggen looked on me with a certain pride. I was one of his ideas that hadn't turned sour, which could not be said for all of them.

"I haven't been a ball of fire on the Jaspar girl," I confessed, "but when the cable arrived I got everything together. I've reviewed the files and I think I know what's got to be done next."

"What?"

"At four this afternoon I'm seeing Shah Khan. At

his home. He talks better there, and if anyone knows where the Jaspar girl is, he does."

"Will he tell you?" Captain Verbruggen countered suspiciously.

"In Afghanistan I expect no one to tell me anything, and what they do tell me, I distrust."

"You're learning." The captain laughed. He looked at his watch and said, "If you've already studied the file, and if you're going to meet Shah Khan at four . . ."

"I'd better get to work on the saddle shoes," I anticipated.

"You'd better. Those damned mullahs are off again on a big religious kick." I was always surprised at Captain Verbruggen's use of the vernacular. He read widely—magazines, not books—and acquired strange phrases. "The mullahs from the mountain districts stormed into town yesterday," he continued, "and they got wind, somehow, of the saddle shoes and they're demanding that our Marine guards be sent home."

"You aren't going to let a few mad priests dictate our policy, sir?"

"The one thing I refuse to get mixed up in is a bunch of fanatic Muslim priests. You don't know them the way I do. Already they're putting a lot of pressure on the Afghan government. I may have to lose my Marines."

"What am I to do?"

"You speak the language. Go down to the bazaar. See what's actually happening."

"Very good, sir."

"And, Miller, if there's any good reason for getting rid of the Marines, let me know right away. Their time's almost up and it might be a friendly gesture on our part to get them out of here. Placate the mullahs at no real expense to ourselves."

I was equally surprised at the precise vocabulary my boss could use when he wished to. "I don't like the idea of placating a bunch of mullahs," I objected stubbornly.

"You won't be," he replied. "I'll accept responsibility, and we'll all be further ahead if I do."

I nodded deferentially and rose to go, tucking the Jaspar papers under my arm, but at the door I was stopped by a command from the acting ambassador. "Let me know what Shah Khan thinks," he said.

I laughed. "There must be twelve million people in Afghanistan who would like to know what Shah Khan thinks. I'm sure I won't be the one to find out." I left the room, then called back, "But I'll let you know what he doesn't tell me."

In 1946 the American embassy in Afghanistan required no large staff, for in those hesitant days the big lend-lease program that was to mark the future had not yet been visualized. We who did serve in the strange and sometimes forbidding city were forced by circumstance to be a closely knit group, because at that time Kabul provided positively nothing for foreigners: no hotels that we could use, no cinema of any kind, no newspapers, no radio with European programs, no restaurants available to visitors, no theaters, no cafés, no magazines. No public meetings were allowed, nor were we permitted any kind of normal social life with our Afghan hosts, for this was prohibited by the Afghans. We were thus driven in upon ourselves and if we wanted entertainment or social life we had to provide it ourselves, looking principally to the personnel attached to the English, French, Italian, Turkish and American embassies. At the end of a long, confining winter during which the city was snowbound, we searched hungrily for any diversion and were delighted when the people at the English embassy, always the most inventive where living overseas was concerned, came up with the idea of reading plays aloud before informal audiences.

Therefore, when I got back to my office in the two-story white building which served as our embassy, I was not surprised to find our pool secretary, Miss Maxwell of Omaha, typing furiously and somewhat irritated when I asked for the well-thumbed papers on the saddle shoes.

"They're over there," she snapped without looking up.

"Could you get them?" I asked.

"Please, Mr. Miller," she protested. "I'm just finishing the play for tonight."

"I'm sorry," I said, finding the papers for myself.

"The reading's tonight," she explained, "and I'm responsible for all of Act Three. The British girls are doing Act One, which is the longest, and one of the Italian girls is typing Act Two. She's finished. I guess they never do any work at the Italian embassy," she sighed.

"You go ahead," I said consolingly, and I noticed that she had in her machine not only the original copy but seven carbons as well. "See that I get one of the first three," I cautioned. "I can't read those last carbons."

"On my machine they're all right," Miss Maxwell assured me. "It's the Italian typewriters that won't strike off seven copies." I noticed that Miss Maxwell was using a German machine, and it did make seven usable copies.

I took the saddle-shoe papers to my inner office and started to leaf through them, but the top page arrested me, for it said briefly, "Afghan agents have warned us that if the Marines continue to molest the saddle shoes, there will be a murder in the bazaar." This moved the whole matter up several notches in gravity, so I asked Miss Maxwell to summon my Afghan aide, Nur Muhammad, who came quietly into the room.

He was a good-looking, lithe young man of thirty-two, dressed in a western-style blue suit which fitted badly. He had black hair, dark skin, deep-set eyes, a big Afghan nose and extremely white teeth, which he showed rarely. He was a moody, sensitive person who during the two years he had worked at the American embassy had taught himself to speak English. It was generally known that he was in the employ of the Afghanistan government.

"Sit down, Nur," I said. With grave attention to protocol he sat in the chair I indicated, smoothed his trousers, then folded his hands in his lap.

"Yes, sahib?" he said with a deft combination of willingness to help and studiousness not to appear too eager.

"It's about the saddle shoes," I began, and Nur Muhammad relaxed. "You've heard about the latest intelligence?" I continued.

Nur Muhammad betrayed nothing. He was far too smart to be trapped into admitting that he knew anything. He insisted that I speak first. Then he would react to what I had said. "What intelligence?" he asked blandly.

I opened the manila folder on the case and looked at the ominous report. "Some of your people have warned us that if the Marines continue to . . . Well, they say molest. Nur Muhammad, do you think our Marines have molested anyone?"

Before Nur could reply my door was opened by a handsome young American Marine who had won battle stars on Guadalcanal and Iwo Jima and who now enjoyed, as his reward, an easy job as one of our two military guards in the embassy. He stepped in smartly, handed me some papers, turned professionally, and disappeared. His uniform, I remember, was immaculate and his shoes were shined.

When he was gone Nur Muhammad replied cautiously, "I wouldn't say by your standards the young men have molested. But Ramadan is approaching. The mullahs gain more voice each day. It is they who believe there has been molestation and if they believe this, Mr. Miller . . ."

I showed him the report. At the suggestion of murder he drew in his breath.

"Yes," I said. "Murder." Nur Muhammad carefully replaced the paper, then straightened his trousers once more.

"I would not ignore the mullahs," Nur Muhammad warned. "You see, as Ramadan approaches they wish to reinforce their power. To remind us of that power."

"Suppose these suspicions continued? Suppose the Marine you just saw did . . . well . . . molest?" I added quickly, "You understand, I'm not for one minute granting that any Marine did molest."

"You made your position clear on that point," Nur Muhammad agreed effusively.

"But suppose the mullahs thought otherwise? Whom would they murder?"

Without a moment's reflection Nur replied, "The saddle shoes, of course."

"The saddle shoes!" I gasped.

"Of course. I must explain, Miller Sahib. In the past the mullahs loved to murder the ferangi, but whenever they murdered a ferangi it caused much trouble for Afghanistan. So they've had to quit."

I was always bemused by the Afghan word for *foreigner*. When the first Asian students saw this ugly word, with its even uglier connotations, the unaccustomed combination of *g* and *n* perplexed them, so they invented an expressive pronunciation which included all the letters, heavily fraught with hatred, envy and contempt. Some pronounced it *ferangi,* with a hard *g,* some *faranji,* others *foreggin,* but it meant the same.

"The mullahs will not murder the ferangi," Nur Muhammad assured me.

"I think we should go down to the bazaar right now," I suggested.

"I do not think I should go, Miller Sahib. My presence would endanger your effectiveness and mine."

"I agree, but I'd like to have you there, if danger should erupt."

"What danger can erupt in a Kabul bazaar?" Nur Muhammad asked deprecatingly.

"We just agreed. Murder."

"But not to a ferangi," Nur assured me, and he declined to join me, returning to his regular duties.

When he had gone I called Security to request that our two Marines be excused from duty, and although I met with loud protest, my threat to involve the acting ambassador turned the trick. From my window I watched the two clean-cut battle heroes hurrying toward the exit gate. I summoned Miss Maxwell and informed her, "I'll be in the bazaar."

"Good," she replied, grabbing her hat. "I'll deliver the copies of the play."

I went to the exit gate and asked the guard to hail me a ghoddy, and in a few minutes a driver pulled up with the world's most uncomfortable taxi: a horse-drawn two-seater in which the driver perched comfortably in front on a hair cushion, while the passengers clung precariously to a sloping wooden seat that faced backward. Thin strips of old automobile tires tacked to wooden wheels enabled the ghoddy to travel over the rough, frozen streets.

I've been told that diplomats and military men remember with nostalgia the first alien lands in which they served, and I suppose this is inevitable; but in my case I look back upon Afghanistan with special affection because it was, in those days, the wildest, weirdest land on earth and to be a young man in Kabul was the essence of adventure. Now, as I jogged along in the ghoddy on an unbelievable mission, I thought again of the violent land and the even more violent contradictions that surrounded me.

The city of Kabul, perched at the intersection of caravan trails that had functioned for more than three thousand years, was hemmed in on the west by the Koh-i-Baba range of mountains, nearly seventeen thousand feet high, and on the north by the even greater Hindu Kush, one of the major mountain massifs of Asia. In the winter these powerful ranges were covered with snow, so that one could never forget that he was caught in a kind of bowl whose rim was composed of ice and granite.

Kabul, pronounced Cobble by all who have been there, Kaboul by those who have not, was shaped like a large capital U lying on its side, with the closed end to the east where the Kabul River flowed down to the Khyber Pass, and the open end to the west facing the Koh-i-Baba. The central part of the U was occupied by a rather large hill, which in my home state of Massachusetts would have been called a mountain. The American embassy and most European quarters lay in the northern leg of the U, which I was now leaving, while the bazaar, the mosques, and the vivid life of the city lay in the southern leg, to which I was heading.

As we made our way toward the center of Kabul I was reminded of the first contradiction that marked Afghanistan. The men I saw on the streets looked much more Jewish than I. They were tall, dark of skin, lithe, with flashing black eyes and prominent Semitic noses. They took great pride in their claim to be descendants of the lost tribes of Israel, who were supposed to have reached these mountain plateaus during the Diaspora. But at the same time the Afghans remembered that the ancient name of their country was Aryana, and in the volatile 1930's they were adopted by Adolf Hitler as the world's first Aryans and his special wards. The proud Afghans were able to accept both accolades without discrimination and consequently boasted that while it was true that they were born of the Jewish tribe, the Ben-i-Israel, once they reached Afghanistan they had ceased being Jews and had founded the Aryan race. It made as much sense as what some of their friends were propounding elsewhere.

The dress of Afghan men was striking. The few educated men and officials dressed like Nur Muhammad: western clothes with fur-collared overcoats and handsome iridescent caps of karakul, shaped either like American Legion overseas caps or like fezzes. Other men wore the national costume: sandals which allowed toes to drag in the snow, baggy white pants of Arab derivation, an enormous white shirt whose tails were worn outside and reached below the knees to flap in the breeze, richly patterned vest, overcoat of some heavy western cloth, and a dirty turban, one of whose ends trailed over the shoulder. If they were tribesmen from the hills, they also carried rifles and sometimes wore bandoleers well studded with cartridges. I doubt if you could have found a national capital anywhere in the world where so many men walked the streets fully armed, for in addition to their rifles most of the tribesmen carried daggers as well. Civilization in Afghanistan, as represented by officials who wore the karakul cap, existed on a very narrow margin of survival.

During my first days in Afghanistan I had noticed that whenever I saw a pair of these fierce tribesmen down from the hills, men who had probably killed in mountain ambush, one of the couple behaved in a very masculine manner while his partner was sure to have feminine traits. He walked in mincing steps, kept a handkerchief in one hand, and carried a winter flower between his teeth. Usually the feminine partner wore a little rouge or eye makeup and always he walked holding the hand of his more rugged partner.

A further glance at the streets of Kabul explained why this was so. There were no women visible. I had been in the country more than a hundred days and had yet to see a woman. I had been entertained in important homes, like that of Shah Khan, but never had I been allowed to see any of the women who lived there. It was this phenomenon that accounted for the curious behavior of the men: having removed all women from public life, the Afghans realized that feminine traits were nevertheless desirable and so allocated them to men. On the frozen streets of Kabul I saw just as many feminine actions as I would have seen on the boulevards of Paris, except that here men performed them.

Of course, it isn't accurate to say that I saw no women. Frequently as the ghoddy plugged along I saw emerging from towering walls, whose gates were always guarded, vague moving shapes enshrouded in cloth from head to toe. They were women, obliged by Afghan custom never to appear in public without a chaderi, the Muslim covering that provides only a tiny rectangle of embroidered lace through which the wearer can see but cannot be seen. We were told by educated Afghan men, most of whom despised the chaderi, that the imposition damaged the health and the eyesight of the women, but it persisted. At the age of thirteen all females were driven into this seclusion, from which they never escaped.

I must admit, however, that these ghostly figures, moving through the city in shrouds that were often beautifully pleated and made of costly fabric, imparted a grave sexuality to life. There was a mysteriousness in meeting them and wondering what kind of human being resided inside the cocoon, and rarely have I been as aware of women, or as fascinated by them, as I was in Afghanistan, where I saw none.

It was midmorning when the ghoddy dropped me at the little fortress-like mosque with two white minarets that stood by the river in the heart of the city, and I noticed at the doorway to the mosque three mullahs—tall, gaunt, unkempt men with flowing beards and fierce eyes—who appeared to be guarding the holy place and condemning me, a non-Muslim, for passing so near. When I looked at them politely, they stared back with undisguised hatred and I thought: These are the men who rule Afghanistan!

At this moment one of them, obviously down from the hills, spied something behind me that alarmed him, and he began screaming imprecations in Pashto. Encouraged by his protests, the other two mullahs started running at me, and I hurriedly ducked aside to let them pass. When they had gone, like scarecrows in their long gowns and flying beards, I looked after them to see what had so agitated them, and I discovered that our typist, Miss Maxwell, had driven to town in the embassy jeep and was now hurrying along the public sidewalk with her eight copies of the play we were to read that night. The country mullah had spotted her, a woman without a chaderi, and felt obliged to assault her for this violation of faith. He and his companions, giving no thought to the fact that Miss Maxwell was ferangi, bore down upon her screaming and cursing.

Before I could protect her, the three tall mullahs, their beards and hooked noses making them caricatures of religious frenzy, had swarmed upon her and were beating her with their fists. What was worse—then and in retrospect—they began spitting at her, and rheum from their lips trickled across her terrified face.

I dashed through the crowd that had gathered and began grabbing the mullahs, shouting in Pashto, "Stop it, you fools! She's ferangi!"

I was saved by the fact that I knew the language; the holy men fell back, startled that I could speak to them in Pashto, whereas had I been a mere ferangi who had struck a priest they might have incited the crowd to kill me. A policeman ambled up, never swiftly for he did not wish to become involved with mullahs, and said quietly, "Look here, men. We're in Kabul, not the mountains. Let the woman alone." And the three fanatic mullahs withdrew to guard once more the mosque at the river's edge.

Miss Maxwell, terrorized by the sudden attack, proved herself a brave girl and refused to cry. I wiped the spit from her face and said, "Forget them. They're madmen. I'll find your driver."

I looked about for the embassy car and discovered the Afghan driver lounging unconcernedly along the river wall, from where he had watched the incident.

He was sure that I or somebody would halt the fanatical mullahs and that his charge, Miss Maxwell, wasn't going to get seriously hurt, so he saw no good reason to risk his neck brawling with idiot mullahs.

He now sauntered over. "Must I take Miss Maxwell back to the embassy?" he asked in Pashto.

"The Italian embassy," I explained.

"Be careful," he warned me. "The mullahs are dangerous these days."

Before he drove Miss Maxwell away, I congratulated her upon the self-control she had exhibited. People back home made jokes about the softness of Americans, but they should have seen Miss Maxwell that March day in Kabul.

When she was gone, I wandered over to the bazaar, a nest of narrow streets in the crowded section of the city, where almost everything was for sale, much of it stolen from warehouses in Delhi, Isfahan and Samarkand. I derived perverse pleasure from the assurance that new India, ancient Persia and revolutionary Russia were alike impotent to halt the hereditary thieves of Central Asia. When Darius the Persian marched through Kabul five hundred years before the birth of Christ, this same bazaar was selling practically the same goods stolen from the same ancient cities.

There were, of course, a few modern improvements. Gillette razor blades were in good supply, as were surgical scissors from Göttingen in Germany. One enterprising merchant had penicillin and aspirin, while another had imported from a rifled G.I. warehouse in Bombay cans of Campbell's soup and spark plugs for American cars, of which there were beginning to be a few on the deeply rutted streets of Kabul.

But it was the faces that made me think I was back in the days of Alexander the Great, when Afghanistan, astonishing as it now seemed, was a distant satrapy of Athens, a land of high culture long before England was properly discovered or any of the

Americas civilized. In these faces there was a sense of potential fire, of almost maniacal intensity, and wherever I looked there were the mysterious forms of women, shrouded in flimsy robes which hid even their eyes.

I was watching the movement of these alluring figures, wondering as a young man should what form was sequestered beneath the robes, when I became aware—how I cannot even now explain—of two young women who moved with tantalizing grace. How did I know they were young women? I don't know. How did I know they were beautiful, and aching with sexual desire, and gay and lively? I don't know. But I do know that these creatures, whatever their age or appearance, were positively alluring in their mysteriousness.

One was dressed in an expensive, pleated chaderi of fawn-colored silk; the other was in gray. At first I thought they were trying to attract me, so when they passed very close I whispered in Pashto, "You little girls be careful. The mullahs are watching."

They stopped in astonishment, turned to look out of the bazaar toward the three gaunt mullahs, then giggled and hurried on. When I turned to look after them, I saw that they were wearing American-style saddle shoes. These must be the girls who had been reported as meeting our two Marine guards in the bazaar, and from my memory of the dashing manner in which the Marines had left our embassy compound, and from the saucy way in which the girls had moved past me, I suspected that matters of substantial moment were afoot, and that the impending meeting of these young people might lead to tragedy.

I therefore set out to follow the girls, and I cursed Nur Muhammad for not being on hand to help. The girls were not moving fast, and from time to time I was able to catch glimpses of them, two figures shrouded in expensive silk, exquisite in their movements, and wearing saddle shoes. They became the personification of sexual desire—attractive, dangerous, evanescent—as they moved gracefully through the bazaar, looking, hoping.

I followed them into the alleyways where karakul caps were sold, those silvery gray hats that made Afghan men seem so handsome and ferangi so ridiculous. "Sahib, cap! Cap!" the merchants cried, falling back with laughter when I said regretfully in Pashto, "It takes a handsome man to wear karakul."

Now the shrouded girls moved lazily, wasting time in the fruit stalls where precious melons from the south were available, and in the dark stalls where cloth from India was on sale. I do not think they were aware of me, following them at a distance, but the movement of those gay, abandoned saddle shoes fascinated me, and I well understood how our two Marines had fallen under the spell of these lively girls.

For a moment I lost them. I turned into a street where there were shops with metal goods—bronze, tin, stainless steel and silver—but the girls were not there. Fearing something not easily described, I hurried back to the fabric center, and finding no one there I turned toward a little alley which led to what seemed a dead end. On chance, I stepped that way and saw a perplexing, haunting sight.

Against the dead-end wall leaned our two American Marines, in bright uniform. Against them, their backs to me, were pressed the two Afghan girls, their chaderies thrown back, their unseen lips pressed eagerly against those of the Marines. The girl in gray had allowed her dress to be pulled partly away, and in the wintry air I could see her naked shoulders. I have never seen human beings so passionately intertwined, and I became aware of the fact that the girls had begun to loosen the uniforms of the Marines and to adjust to the results.

It was at this moment that I saw, from the corner of my eye, the three gaunt mullahs moving through the bazaar, intent upon finding the girls. It would be some moments before they reached this alley, and they might not see it. On the other hand, they might.

"You fools!" I shouted in Pashto, running down the alley. "This way! At once!"

I tried to grab the two girls, partly, I suppose, in order to see what Afghan women looked like with the chaderi removed, but they eluded me, and when they finally did face me, the shrouds were back in place and the girls were as mysterious, as silent as ever.

"The mullahs?" they asked in real fear.

"Yes! Hurry!"

I started to lead them to what I thought was safety, but the two couples, having surmounted the language barrier, had somehow planned their own escape routes, for in an instant the girls vanished down a narrow pathway that led away from the approaching mullahs, while the two Marines vaulted the seemingly unscalable wall, and I was left alone in the cul-de-sac. I heard the angry mullahs behind me, whipping up a crowd, and on the spur of the moment I had the presence of mind to start urinating against the wall.

This even the mullahs understood, and I heard them cry in frustration from the other end of the alley, "The evil girls must be here." When I made my way through the crowd, I saw along the farther edge two shrouded figures, one in a fawn-colored chaderi, one in gray, drifting easily away from the bazaar. Their silken shrouds flowed in the wintry wind like the robes of Grecian goddesses, and along the snowy footpaths I watched the saddle shoes depart. I was aching with the mystery of sex, with the terrible allure that such undulating figures could evoke. I wanted to run after the girls and protest madly in Pashto that I needed them, that with the Marines gone I would like to make love with them, even in the hurried corner of a bazaar where men paused to urinate.

For the Marines would have to leave Afghanistan. That was clear. Regretfully I watched the girls disappear, then realized with some shame that I was inwardly pleased that the Marines would be sent home. I dismissed the unworthy thought and looked for a ghoddy. To my surprise one appeared promptly, occupied by Nur Muhammad, who had come down to survey matters from a distance.

"Trouble?" he asked blandly, pointing to the mullahs, who were haranguing a crowd near the entrance to the bazaar.

"Just escaped," I reported. "A miracle."

I climbed onto the sloping seat of the ghoddy and we drove back toward the embassy. As the horse clip-clopped over the frozen mud that served as a road in Kabul, I noticed once more the little open ditches that lined most streets in the city. In them ran the public drinking water, since underground pipes were unknown in Afghanistan. But in the same ditches the citizens also urinated, pitched dead dogs, brushed teeth and washed all food that would be later eaten by the citizens, including ferangi stationed in the American and European embassies. I shuddered.

Ahead of me a man from the mountains, carbine slung over his back, squatted over the ditch and defecated, while not ten yards away a cook's helper, dressed like Nur Muhammad, unconcernedly washed the meat that would be served that night in the French embassy.

"A thing like that is a national disgrace," Nur said bitterly.

"Does the government know who the girls are? The saddle shoes, I mean?"

"Rumors whisper that one is Shah Khan's granddaughter."

"Does the old man know?" I probed.

"He's the one who protested to the ambassador."

"Is his granddaughter pretty?"

"They say she's a beauty," Nur replied. "I haven't met anyone who's seen her."

"Is it true that Shah Khan has openly stated he's opposed to the chaderi?" I asked, trying to review our intelligence on the man I was shortly to see.

"Of course. That's why the mullahs tried to murder him last Ramadan."

"I have to be there at four," I repeated. Nur said he'd have the jeep ready, and I hurried to report to Captain Verbruggen. We arranged for the two Marines to be shipped out of the country that afternoon. They would ride an open truck down the long, perilous mountain passes to Peshawar, at the Indian end of the Khyber Pass. And in the years ahead they would relate such memories of Afghanistan as would inspire other young men to serve in distant nations.

❁

2

Kabul was superb at the end of winter, particularly when the late afternoon sun rushed toward some rendezvous in Persia, to the west; for then the normal drabness of the miserable mud homes was masked in snow, and the solitary figures with carbines who moved across the empty fields outside of town bore an epic quality which captivated the eye. No stranger, at such a moment, could forget that he was in Asia.

Shah Khan lived well to the west, in a forbidding fortress hidden behind massive surrounding walls at least fifteen feet high. It must have required the forced labor of hundreds of convicts for many months to build the walls alone, for they enclosed many acres. This redoubtable establishment, complete with turrets and its own minaret, lay in the shadow of the beautiful Koh-i-Baba mountains, which were now snow-covered, reminding the foreigner that during the winter this city was practically inaccessible, unless one wished to risk his life on sloping mountain passes where each year many trucks were lost.

At the fortress gate through which one entered to visit Shah Khan there hung a bell cord, at which Nur Muhammad tugged vigorously, sending an echo through the frosty air. Normally the heavy gate would have been operated by some superannuated warrior who had served the owner in his youth, but when Nur yanked the cord a second time I thought I heard the pounding of horses' hoofs. Then, instead of the miserly half-inch through which the guards customarily peered at intending visitors, the gates were slammed violently open and a handsome man of thirty-six, astride a pawing white horse, greeted us.

"Mark Miller! Enter!" he cried in English. He was Moheb Khan, son of the Shah, educated at Oxford and at the Wharton School of Finance and Commerce. He held a responsible position in the Foreign Office, but on this day was affecting the dress of a prosperous mountain man, for he wore sheepskin trousers, an expensive embroidered vest, a long Russian-style fur coat, and a silver-gray karakul cap. He was clean-shaven, sharp-eyed and urbane, the educated Afghan at his best. I had talked with Moheb Khan several times before and had found him sophisticated in learning, dignified in bearing, and arrogant in judgment. He was tall and slim, with a large head marked by wavy black hair in which he took special pride. I respected him as one of the cleverest men I knew.

Whenever I was with Moheb I appreciated anew the fact that the future history of Afghanistan, if left to Afghans, would be determined by the struggle between the many bearded mullahs from the hills and the few young experts like Moheb, with degrees from Oxford or the Sorbonne or the Massachusetts Institute of Technology. I was not at all sure how the contest would eventuate, but it was clear that not only I but also all the people of all the embassies prayed that Moheb Khan and his young associates might win.

"Where'd you get the horse?" I asked, walking into the great compound, which in the nineteenth century had housed thousands of men during the frequent sieges.

"Look at the brand!" he cried, reaching down to shake my hand. "Pardon the glove," he added, "but I'm afraid to drop the reins."

He pointed to the horse's left flank, where a scrawling W had been burned deep into the hair and skin.

"I don't get it," I said.

"Think, Miller!"

"W," I repeated aloud. "I don't know any ranch with that brand."

"It's sentimental!" Moheb laughed. "Think! Think!"

I could not guess what the cryptic brand was intended to signify, and when Nur Muhammad edged the jeep into the compound, the horse shied and darted off across the snowy plain—it would be ridiculous to call that huge expanse of land a garden—and I could well observe the fine horsemanship that Moheb Khan exhibited.

He brought the dashing animal back to the jeep, to familiarize the horse with the sound of a motor car, then leaped with agility to the ground beside me and cupped his hands near my right knee, all in one marvelously synchronized movement. "You ride," he commanded.

There was something that no stranger ever became accustomed to in Afghanistan: the peremptory command of the educated Afghan. "You ride!" a friend said, and you got the feeling that if you didn't leap on the horse immediately one of those omnipresent carbines was going to go off. So I threw my right foot into the cupped hands and, leaping upward to match his strong lift, I was astride the white horse.

At Groton I had taken horsemanship, and I could ride passably well, but it quickly became apparent that I was not going to tell this horse what to do. Yet the semi-wild animal loved the feel of a man on his back, for he tore across the huge field in such a way as to blend his movements with mine. I thought: He wants to frighten me, but he also wants me on hand so that there'll be someone to frighten. He did not exactly ignore the reins, nor did he respond quickly. Like a willful child he must have thought: If I pay no attention to him, this rider may forget the whole thing. But when I quietly insisted that he obey my commands, he accommodated himself to them, tardily and with a trace of rebellion. He was a superb horse, and I brought him back to the jeep, where Moheb Khan stood talking with Nur Muhammad.

When the horse was close to the idling jeep, Moheb suddenly reached for the accelerator with his hand, jammed it down so that the engine exploded once or twice, thus sending the horse high in the air. Fortunately I had not yet dropped the reins, and I tugged at them fiercely to bring the frightened beast back under control. I was furious with Moheb for this reckless act—training his horse at my peril—and on the spur of the moment I dug my heels into the flanks of the white beast and we tore across the open land, turning and twisting and cavorting for some minutes. At the end of our exciting ride I brought the horse back to the jeep and called sternly, "Nur Muhammad, turn off the engine."

But before he could do so, Moheb Khan again jammed the accelerator pedal to the floor. This time I held the horse steady, then threw the reins to Moheb. "He's a good horse," I said.

"You're a good rider, Miller. Better than any American I've seen yet." I laughed and he asked, "You don't fathom the brand?"

"Who can fathom the brain of an Afghan?" I joked.

"Not I," Moheb confessed. "But your failure does surprise me."

"Where'd you get the horse?" I asked again, as we walked toward the main house, an imposing mud-walled castle around which clustered twelve or thirteen smaller buildings.

"Some traders brought him down from the north. Said they got him over the Oxus in Russia. I had a man from the Russian embassy out one afternoon and the horse did seem to recognize Russian commands."

"Splendid beast," I said, "Russian or whatever."

Moheb Khan led me through the rugged door of

the main house, whose mud walls were more than thirty inches thick. I said, "They must keep you cool in summer."

Moheb replied, "More important, they withstood British cannon for eleven days." He pointed to spots where there were deep indentations. With an imperial afterthought, he indicated to Nur Muhammad where he should wait, then took me in to see his father.

Shah Khan—his name could be translated as Sir Mister and was hardly a name at all—was a slim patrician who had served as adviser to three successive kings. He was thin and gray, wore a trim mustache, expensive Harris tweeds tailored in London, and a heavy gold watch chain across his vest. Normally he spoke Persian, but in dealing with foreigners, he preferred French, for he had attended the Sorbonne; but he was also competent in English, German and Pashto, the language of the countryside. Like all educated Afghans, Shah Khan looked to France as the source of culture, to Germany as the source of military instruction, to America as the source of canned goods, and to England as the fountainhead of duplicity. Nevertheless, it was with the latter country that Afghanistan had always maintained its closest ties, like a husband who hates his wife yet would be lost if she deserted him.

One of the reasons why Shah Khan had taken a liking to me, and confided in me when he refused to do so with other Americans, was that although I could not speak Persian I did speak French, and he could thus indulge his obsession that diplomacy must be conducted only in that language. Today we would speak French.

The room in which we talked was important in the history of Afghanistan and essential to any understanding of the modern nation. Here had occurred spectacular murders which altered the course of dynasty, protracted sieges, secret councils and, strangest of all, Christian weddings under the sponsorship of

Shah Khan. They took place whenever some exile from Europe wished to marry a Christian girl from one of the embassies, for there often were no Christian ministers available in Kabul.

It was a rocky fortress of a room, built by a German architect, furnished by a Danish merchant who sold only the best, and decorated by a Frenchman who spent eleven thousand dollars in shipping charges alone. On one wall there was a Picasso, but nothing the French decorator had devised could alter the Germanic heaviness of the room, and it remained a typical Afghan salon.

On the low table from Copenhagen lay copies of the *London Illustrated News,* the *Manchester Guardian, Newsweek,* the *Reader's Digest* and six or seven French magazines. Against one wall stood a huge Gramophone with numerous speakers, for Shah Khan loved music, as did his son, Moheb. Another wall contained the principal British, Italian, French and American encyclopedias, as well as novels in five or six different languages.

Shah Khan, who could be as Afghan as his room, asked bluntly, "What do you wish to discuss?"

I showed him the leather folder and replied, "Our government is demanding that we report where Ellen Jaspar is."

"They've been doing that for the better part of a year," Shah Khan parried. He sat deep in a leather chair which his grandfather had purchased in Berlin. Not even the French decorator had been able to banish it from the room, but he had succeeded in staining the leather an objectionable red.

"But this time, Your Excellency, it isn't merely the government who demands. It's the senator from Pennsylvania."

"Is that important?" the old Afghan parried.

"Well," I fumbled. "Let's say that in America a senator has the same powers that you have in Kabul.

Now suppose you sent the embassy in Paris an inquiry. Wouldn't you expect an answer?"

"I certainly would. Moheb, did you know the senator from Pennsylvania?"

"Which one?" Moheb asked quickly. He rattled off the names of the two senators. "I liked them both."

"Are they significant men?" his father asked.

"Very," Moheb replied. The young man was an unusual Afghan, in that while he was a devout Muslim, he also drank alcohol, and he now poured me a drink of whiskey. His father, a Muslim of the old school, felt obliged to reprove his son because the drinking took place before a Christian. Accordingly he spoke harshly in Pashto, whereupon I replied in the same language, "Let the blame be upon me, Your Excellency." This reminder that I spoke not only French but also the Afghan language softened the old man.

"You feel, Monsieur Miller, that this time something must be done."

"Indeed, or we shall all be reprimanded. Perhaps called home."

"Let us suffer the evils that we know rather than flee to those we know not of," Shah Khan replied, paraphrasing Hamlet in French. "Have you new material about this unfortunate girl?"

I checked with Shah Khan and his alert son the facts that our embassy knew about Ellen Jaspar and Nazrullah. In the autumn of 1942 the Afghan government had sent a fine young man from Kabul to the Wharton School, the business end of the University of Pennsylvania, in Philadelphia. This Nazrullah, who was then twenty-four—eight years younger than Moheb Khan—came from a good Kabul family, was bright, good-looking and endowed with a very comfortable expense account which allowed him to buy, from a Philadelphia used-car dealer, a Cadillac convertible painted red.

The young Afghan cut a swath in Philadelphia society. He was seen everywhere—Merion, Bryn Mawr,

New Hope. At the same time, the solid engineering degree he had earned in Germany prepared him to work for high marks at the Wharton School.

Moheb added, "In spite of his enthusiastic social life, Nazrullah was an honor student. I kept tabs on him, since I was serving in the embassy in Washington at the time."

"Didn't Nazrullah's time at the Wharton School overlap yours?" Shah Khan asked.

"No," Moheb explained. "Don't you remember? You sent him to Wharton because I'd done fairly well there."

I pointed excitedly at Moheb and shouted in English, "That's it! The W stands for Wharton!"

"Exactly!" Moheb shouted back, and we raised our glasses.

"What's this foolishness?" old Shah Khan asked from the depths of his red leather chair.

"Your son branded his white horse with a W. In honor of his degree from Wharton," I explained.

"Preposterous," Shah Khan growled, plainly irritated by his son's noisy drinking.

"Nazrullah was offered half a dozen jobs in America," Moheb added, "but he preferred to help us out here at home."

"Where'd he meet the Jaspar girl?" Shah Khan asked, fingering his gold chain.

"Those were the years," Moheb reminded us, "when there weren't too many American men available. Nazrullah . . ."

"What's his last name?" I interrupted.

"Just Nazrullah," Moheb replied. "Like so many Afghans, he has no last name. As to the girl. She was a junior at Bryn Mawr. I think he may have met her while he was playing tennis at Merion. She came from a good family in Dorset, Pennsylvania."

"Where's that?" I asked, finding it strange to be asking an Afghan about American geography.

"Small town in Penns County," Moheb explained. "North of Philadelphia."

"They didn't get married in Dorset," I explained to Shah Khan.

"I should say not!" Moheb agreed vociferously. "Her family raised bloody hell. Bryn Mawr did the same. You know what that girl did? In the middle of the war she went to England, wangled her way to India, and came up the Khyber Pass in a donkey caravan. She was married here in Kabul."

"It was a brilliant wedding," Shah Khan remembered. "Have you a picture of the girl, Monsieur Miller?"

From my files I produced several photographs of Ellen Jaspar. As a sophomore at Bryn Mawr she had played in Shakespeare—Olivia in *Twelfth Night*—a thin, good-looking blonde and apparently graceful. In her junior year she sang in the chorus that co-operated with Fritz Reiner in doing Beethoven's *Ninth Symphony,* and in her surplice with her blond hair peeking from under her cap she looked angelic. There were pictures of her and Nazrullah, she a lovely white and he a romantic brown. And there was one picture of her when she graduated from high school, wide-eyed and smiling, yet somehow apprehensive. I had known a thousand girls like Ellen Jaspar; they adorned the campuses at Radcliffe, Smith and Holyoke. They all did well in English, poorly in mathematics, indifferently in philosophy. They were the vibrant, exciting girls who would seriously consider, in the middle of their junior year, marrying a young man from Afghanistan or Argentina or Turkestan. Most of them, in their senior year, developed more sense and married young men from Denver or Mobile or Somerville, outside of Boston.

"What made her different?" Shah Khan asked.

"We have the reports. Her father says he begged her not to do this thing, and all she would reply was that she was fed up with Dorset, Pennsylvania, and that she would rather die on the sands of the desert than marry the young man from that town who had been courting her."

"Is Dorset so bad?" the old Afghan asked. "I knew many small towns in France, and they weren't exciting, but they weren't bad, either."

"I used to drive out to Dorset," Moheb Khan replied. "I remember it as a lovely American town. Rather colonial in architecture, I recall."

"But you didn't live there," the old man reflected.

"As a matter of fact, I did," Moheb corrected. "For three days. Ellen and Nazrullah drove me up one Friday afternoon. He wanted the Jaspars to see that in Afghanistan we had many young men who spoke well. It was an agonizing weekend."

"The Jaspars took the whole thing rather dimly?" I asked.

Moheb was about to reply when I received the distinct sensation that some additional person had entered the room. A presence of some kind seemed to hover near me in the heavy battle-room and I thought I saw old Shah Khan looking over my shoulder and shaking his head. I turned in the direction of whoever it was who might be receiving the message, and there was no one. But I did see something I had not noticed when I first arrived in the room. In the hallway, thrown across a chair as an American child might throw her raincoat, lay a fawn-colored chaderi.

"Dimly?" Moheb was echoing. "The Jaspars looked at Nazrullah and me as if we had leprosy."

"What did Mr. Jaspar work at?" I asked. "Wasn't it insurance?"

"Yes. He had that sweet, affable nature that insurance men around the world acquire," Moheb replied. "I liked him, and his wife was equally pleasant. He was also chairman, I believe, of the local draft board. A position of responsibility."

"Later on," Shah Khan inquired, "didn't you advise the Jaspars against an Afghan marriage?"

"Yes. I met them in Philadelphia, and I brought along our ambassador from Washington, and the four of us . . . Nazrullah and Ellen knew nothing of this meeting and did not attend. We discussed the matter quite frankly."

"You told them the truth?" I asked.

"Completely. As I recall, our ambassador was rather unhappy and thought the explicitness of my explanation unnecessary. Told me later I might have damaged our nation's reputation. I told the Jaspars that if their daughter married Nazrullah, when she reached Kabul her American passport would be taken away and she could never thereafter leave Afghanistan, no matter what the excuse, without her husband's permission. That she was an Afghan then and forever, and that she surrendered all claim to protection from America."

"You told them that as clearly as you are telling me?" Shah Khan asked.

"Yes."

"What did they say?"

"Mrs. Jaspar began to cry."

"Did you warn them about Afghan salaries and living conditions?" I asked.

"I did. Most explicitly," Moheb assured me. "I said, 'Mr. Jaspar, Ellen mustn't be deceived by the fact that in America Nazrullah drives a Cadillac and I a Mercedes. Our government is very generous to us as long as we're abroad, but when we go home Nazrullah and I will get jobs that pay no more than twenty American dollars a month.' "

"Did they believe you?"

"They saw the cars and were sure I was lying. In Dorset, Pennsylvania, as in Kabul, cupidity is the same. The Jaspars were convinced that Nazrullah was very rich."

"What does he earn now?" I asked.

The Khans conversed in Pashto and agreed that Nazrullah and his American bride had begun with a salary of twenty-one dollars a month and that it had now grown to twenty-seven, more or less.

"And I explained the housing," Moheb continued. "I said that for much of her life Ellen would live in a hovel, surrounded by women who despised her for not wearing the chaderi . . ."

"Is it true, Your Excellency," I asked, "that Afghanistan may soon discard the chaderi?"

The old man leaned back in his red leather chair and replied, "You Americans seem inordinately preoccupied with the chaderi. Look!" and he pointed to the chair in the hall. "My own granddaughter wears the chaderi and her mother graduated from the Sorbonne." I looked again at the fawn-colored shroud.

"Does your granddaughter enjoy doing so?" I asked.

"We do not concern ourselves about that," Shah Khan replied.

"But the Russians do," I responded, touching a sore point with the old man. "They say they will force you to set your women free, as they have done theirs."

I knew instinctively that he wanted to speak further on this point, that he agreed with me and the Russians that the chaderi must go or revolution come, but he stopped the conversation with this observation: "I learned today that the young woman from your embassy, Miss Maxwell, was assaulted by three mullahs from the hills. You rescued her, I believe. Then you know how powerful these fanatics still are. The chaderi will remain."

"I assured the Jaspars," Moheb continued, "that Ellen would not have to wear one, but that Nazrullah's family would hate her if she didn't. I also warned them that if Ellen appeared in public without the chaderi, mullahs might spit at her." His voice grew harsh as he added, "Miller Sahib, I told the Jaspars of every fact relating to ferangi wives in Afghanistan, and later on I told Ellen herself. I was as honest as a man could be. I warned her that if she married Nazrullah she would become a woman without a country, a woman without a judge to protect her, a woman with no human rights at all, an animal . . . an animal." He rose and walked with great agitation up and down the fortress room. "And I remember exactly what I said, Miller, because a year later I had to tell another girl, from Baltimore this time, the same dismal story, and this girl had sense enough not to marry me, but your damned Miss Jaspar went ahead and married Nazrullah, and now senators are trying to find out where she is."

He fell into a chair, poured himself a drink and reflected, "This preposterous Afghan government. It says, 'When young Afghans go abroad they must live like gentlemen.' So the government provides huge expense accounts and we buy Cadillacs. What allowance do you suppose I got when I was at the Wharton School? One thousand dollars every month. No wonder the girls wanted to marry us. But when that same government brought me home, you know the salary I got—twenty-one dollars a month. Right now, Nazrullah heads an irrigation project west of Kandahar and earns twenty-seven dollars a month . . . more or less."

"Is his wife with him?" I asked bluntly.

"Which wife?" Shah Khan asked.

I was startled. "What do you mean, which wife?"

"Didn't you tell the Jaspars about that?" Shah Khan asked his son.

"There are some things an Afghan doesn't discuss in a foreign country," Moheb replied.

"Was Nazrullah married before he went to America?" I pressed.

"He had a family wife, of course," Shah Khan explained. "But that signifies nothing."

"That's not in the file," I protested.

"Enter it now," the old man said. "Nazrullah was married before he met the American girl. That should put the Jaspars at ease." As soon as he had said this, he apologized. "I'm sorry, Miller Sahib. That was ungenerous. I'm as worried as the Jaspars must be. Where is their daughter? They haven't heard from her, you tell me, in more than thirteen months? What a terrible burden on good parents."

The old man began to cry, and wiped tears from his dark eyes. Afghans, I had learned, were very apt to cry on little notice, but these tears were real.

When he had mastered his weeping he added in a beautiful French whisper, "Our family showed the same prudence as Nazrullah's. Before we allowed Moheb to leave for England we married him to a local girl from a good Muslim family. We reasoned, 'Later on, if he also marries an English girl, no harm will be done. When he works in Kabul he'll have a Muslim family and when he's sent to Europe he'll have an attractive English wife.' I remember discussing the matter with Nazrullah's parents. We promised, 'We won't allow the boys to leave home till they've had one or two Afghan babies.' It worked very well."

"Did you explain that to the Baltimore girl?" I asked Moheb.

"No," he replied honestly, "but I suppose it was what drove me to describe so frankly the other drawbacks of life in Afghanistan."

I put my hands squarely on the leather folder and said, "All right, where can the Jaspar girl be?"

Shah Khan ordered a glass of orangeade, a foul sweet drink which abstemious Afghans took in place of alcohol. It was brought, of course, by a befezzed man, for in a country adhering to the chaderi, men must do much of the work usually done by women.

"I've been pondering this problem," Shah Khan reflected. "It isn't easy to obtain news from a city as far away as Kandahar, but we manage. We find that Nazrullah and his American wife . . . you understand that his Muslim wife stays here in Kabul with the children?"

"More than one child?" I asked.

"Yes, he had one before he went to the Wharton School and one after he got back."

I pondered this, then pointed out, "But he must have been living with the Jaspar girl when he had the second child?"

"Of course. But he also had responsibilities to his Afghan wife. She merited consideration."

"So he gave her another baby?" I asked.

"It's difficult to comprehend our attitude toward women," Shah Khan confessed. "We cherish them. We love them. We protect them. And we dedicate most of our poetry to them. But we don't want them cluttering up our lives."

"I'd think that two wives would do just that," I demurred.

"My life is one of the most uncluttered I know," Shah Khan assured me quietly, "yet I have four wives."

"Four?" I asked.

Something in the way I looked at the old man amused him, for he said quietly, "You Americans picture a man with four wives as leaping from bed to bed till he drops of exhaustion. It isn't like that . . . not at all. Fact is, in some ways I'm worse off than the average American businessman. He marries young, outgrows his wife and gets rid of her. I can't. When a girl marries me, she leaves her home forever and I can't send her back. I've got to support her in my home the rest of her life, unless I divorce her, which would be a public disgrace. So as the years go by I move these good women, one by one, into back bedrooms. In energy and money the American and the Afghan systems cost about the same."

Moheb interrupted, "The Muslim attitude toward women was a response to historical forces, and the interesting thing is that these same forces are acting now to make America polygamous."

Before I could challenge this surprising theory, Shah Khan observed, "Moheb's right. Islam was born in a period when war and ambuscade killed off our men. Each family had a burdensome surplus of women, and Muhammad, with his superbly practical mind, saw there were only three ways of dealing with the matter. Either you converted the needless women into marketplace whores, or edged them into ritual celibacy, or portioned them out as extra wives. Muhammad, always the most moral of men, shuddered at prostitution and gave the women legal status as wives. He chose the flawless solution."

"How does this apply to America?" I asked.

Shah Khan ignored my question. "So under our system I've had to take care of many women . . . wives, brothers' wives, grandmothers. By the way, Miller Sahib, do you know anything of a Quaker school near Philadelphia called the George School? We're thinking of sending my granddaughter Siddiqa there. The other girls have always gone to Paris."

Cautiously I asked, "How old is Siddiqa?"

"How old is she?" Shah Khan asked.

"Seventeen," Moheb replied. "She prefers things American and we thought . . ."

"It's a good school," I said. "Coeducational. Boys and girls."

"It isn't a convent?" Shah Khan asked with some surprise.

"Oh, no!"

"That takes care of America," Shah Khan growled. "Off she goes to Paris. But what Moheb said earlier is true. The forces that drove Islam to plural marriage will operate throughout the world. In France, for example, I thought their handling of the problem was pathetic . . . mistresses, liaisons, scandal, murder."

"But Moheb referred to America," I pointed out.

The young diplomat sipped his whiskey, then reflected, "Do you know the thing which impressed me most in America? The frightening excess of women over men. In some cities like Washington and New York the situation was scandalous."

"You were there during wartime," I pointed out.

"And peacetime," he reminded me. "You not only have more women than men in the population, but you also have an increasing number of young men who remove themselves from the marriage market. Homosexuality, Oedipus complexes, withdrawal from competition, psychological crippling . . ."

Shah Khan interrupted to observe gently, "The point is, Miller Sahib, that brilliant young men like you come to Afghanistan and say, 'Such a quaint land beset by such quaint problems.' When I go to France or Moheb to America we make exactly the same observation."

"And the most quaint," Moheb laughed, "is the way in which your society pretends to be shocked when some man is caught with two wives, legal or otherwise. What do you expect a girl to do when she realizes there aren't enough husbands to go around? Grab someone else's . . . I would."

Since I had not come to Shah Khan's for a lecture on the shortcomings of my country, I asked abruptly, "Then Ellen Jaspar was last heard of in Kandahar?"

"Not exactly," Shah Khan replied. "We know she was there, because one day some mullahs attacked her on the street. Not wearing the chaderi. She distinguished herself by fighting back, and her husband joined her. Between them they kicked the devil out of the mullahs, and I'm glad they did."

"Must have made her popular in Kandahar," I suggested.

"Didn't matter one way or the other," Shah Khan laughed. "Most of us in government are bloody well fed up with mullahs, but we don't know what to do about them. At any rate, her outburst didn't harm Nazrullah's chances, for shortly he was promoted to the best engineering job in the country. Set up headquarters in the old fortress at Qala Bist."

The old man's eyes misted over at the mention of

this great name in Afghan history and he asked, "Monsieur Miller, have you ever seen Qala Bist?"

I hadn't, but I refrained from comment because I didn't want to get the old patriot off on a tirade about the vanished glories of Afghanistan. My trick didn't work, for he said quietly, "This fantastic arch rising from the desert and reflected in the river. It's as beautiful an arch as there is in the world. I much prefer it to Ctesiphon. No one recalls when it was built, but the building it was attached to must have been immense. There's a fort nearby which surely housed ten thousand men, and an abandoned city of perhaps half a million. Now we don't even remember what the city was named."

"What's he doing at Qala Bist?" I asked, for I had learned at previous meetings that when Shah Khan started talking about the lost glories of Afghanistan, reaching back long before the days of Alexander the Great, there was no stopping him. In fact, I had acquired much of my Afghan history from such reminiscences, for unlike those of other men, the reflections of old Shah Khan were founded in fact. If he said Qala Bist had once been a city of half a million, it had been, and now even the history of the city was lost.

"Nazrullah and his American wife went there for preliminary work on our big irrigation project," Shah Khan explained.

Moheb added, "We know that she reached Qala Bist, for we had letters from them. But that was nine months ago."

"What would your guess be?" I asked.

"Judging from what's happened to other ferangi wives"—both Moheb and his father used the word *ferangi* no matter what language they were speaking —"three things could have taken place. Miss Jaspar could have killed herself in despair, or she could have been locked up by her husband with no possibility of escape, not even to send a letter. Or she could have tried to run away. There's a British railroad station, you know, at Chaman, but we've asked there and she didn't reach Chaman."

"Your guess?" I insisted.

"Putting myself in Nazrullah's place," Moheb ventured, "I would suggest these lines of possibility. Nazrullah was very kind to his American wife and tried to soften all the blows her vanity received. He took her as quickly as possible away from his domineering family, where his women must have made her life unbearable. At Kandahar he reasoned with her and helped her adjust to living on mud floors on twenty-seven dollars a month. She wanted to go back to America, but he refused permission, as was his right, and after a series of dreadful scenes she decided to run away on her own account and perished before she reached the frontier. It's happened before."

"But why hasn't Nazrullah reported these matters?" I asked.

"For two reasons," Moheb Khan replied, bowing to his father's judgment. "First, she is only a woman and nothing to get excited about. When he gets back to Kabul he'll explain everything. Second, because he truly loved Ellen Jaspar and still thinks she may have survived and will come back to him."

We sat silent for some minutes and I noticed that the wintry darkness had enveloped us, stealing down from the Koh-i-Baba on icy blasts of wind that ripped across the plain which lay between the fortress walls. Snow eddied in the darkness like the passage of a white horse, and we were alone in the massive room of a massive fort that had withstood shocks from the Koh-i-Baba and from other quarters.

"Would you object, Khan Sahib, if I went to Kandahar and Qala Bist? Some very important Americans insist upon knowing."

"If I were your age, Miller Sahib," the old man replied, "I should have gone to Kandahar long ere this."

"I have your permission, then?"

"My blessing. In spite of the rude comments of my son, we Afghans do get excited about beautiful women. And if she is a ferangi woman, we respect those ferangi who get excited about her, too."

To my own surprise, I asked abruptly, "Shah Khan, have you a photograph of your granddaughter, Siddiqa? The one who wants to go to school in America?"

"No," the old man replied. "We true Muslims don't like photography. It seems a violation of our religious principles. An intrusion on the essence of a man."

"And especially a woman?" I laughed.

"Yes, it is quite contrary to the spirit of the chaderi. But I will tell you this, Monsieur Miller, she is an unusually pretty girl, and she is the child whom you caught kissing the soldier in the bazaar this morning."

I was shocked by his knowledge of an event which I supposed that I alone had witnessed. "The Marines are already on their way to the Khyber Pass," I mumbled.

"If they had not been expelled," Shah Khan replied evenly, proving that his intelligence service covered Americans as well as Afghans, "I would not now be talking with you. Moheb, get Monsieur Miller's jeep."

When the younger man had left, old Shah Khan rose from his leather chair and walked with me to the door. I looked past him for a moment, staring at the fawn-colored chaderi, and the former sensation of overpowering sexuality repossessed me, and I felt dizzy, as if the shroud were exuding its own perfume.

"These damned girls!" The old man laughed. "They douse their chaderies with cheap French essence. To make the boys notice them more. Smell this!" And he picked up the fawn chaderi and smothered my face with it. The perfume was heavy and clung to my nostrils after he had withdrawn the silk.

The old warrior put his arm about me and said,

"Monsieur Miller, concerning the Jaspar girl. We do have one bit of additional information. Perhaps I shouldn't call it information. Nothing but absurd speculation, I suspect. Anyway, it's so bizarre, really, that I won't suffer myself to repeat it. Perhaps it represents what happened, but when you get to Kandahar you'll undoubtedly hear the rumor. So you judge for yourself."

"You won't tell me?" I begged.

"I would abhor having in your file my name even remotely attached to such a rumor. I've my reputation to consider. But you're a younger man. You can risk such embarrassments, and I wish you Godspeed." I was always astonished to rediscover that Muslims shared our God in exactly the form we used Him. There it was, old Shah Khan wishing me Godspeed, and there could be no doubt that he was referring to the One God.

"Papers authorizing your travel to Kandahar and wherever else you may have to go in the area will be at your office in the morning," the old man assured me.

"Thank you, Shah Khan," I replied, and when he opened the door leading to the waiting jeep I saw his son, Moheb Khan, once more upon the white horse, leaping and twisting and roaring off across the snow. As he disappeared in a cloud of flakes I thought: That must be the only horse in the world branded with a W for the Wharton School in Philadelphia.

3

In Afghanistan almost every building bears jagged testimony to some outrage. Some, like the walled fortress now owned by Shah Khan, were built to withstand sieges, and did so many times. Others were the scenes of horrible murder and retaliation. In distant areas, scars still remained of Alexander the Great or Genghis Khan or Tamerlane or Nadir Shah, of Persia. Was there ever a land so overrun by terror and devastation as Afghanistan?

Yet of all the buildings which testified to acts of violence none was more evocative than the group that huddled within the British compound, for here scenes of terrible defeat and massacre had taken place, here loyalties were betrayed, here brave men died with daggers across their throats, and the fact that the British still maintained friendly relations with Afghanistan was tribute to English resilience.

In 1946 the British compound was probably the most civilized center in Afghanistan, a fortress of its own well out into the country, with its private gardens, tennis courts and restaurants. It was here that the European community, in which the Americans were grudgingly included, met on long winter evenings to read plays. Tonight, fresh from the typewriters of the English, Italian and American embassies, in that order, the play was to be *Born Yesterday,* a boisterous comedy which had opened in New York only the month before. Ingrid, a stately Swedish girl, was scheduled to read the part of Billie Dawn. An Englishman who imagined that he could talk like an American gangster was to be Harry Brock, and I was to read the part of the *New Republic* reporter.

Italians, Frenchmen and the Turkish ambassador's wife completed the cast, and looking back upon such readings I am still impressed by the intellectual pleasure we had when the snow was so high in Kabul. We were, in a very real sense, cut off from everything that civilized men and women had come to take for granted: books, magazines, theaters, hotels, music. All we had were our own personalities, with what understandings and memories we had acquired through the years; and it was reassuring to discover what a vivid social life was possible under those circumstances. Never have I known better wit nor more exciting conversation than in the crowded little rooms of Kabul. Never have I known a group of people to be so self-sufficient, so enchanting as human beings. In those years I used to see the same two dozen people night after night, and they were rewarding beyond expectation, partly because any escape from them or their individualities was impossible.

On this night our reading—in which we were peremptorily handed pieces of paper we had not seen before and directed to read specific parts, growing into them as the night progressed—was delayed because Miss Maxwell, from my office, was late in arriving, and since she had typed Act Three and was to read one of the minor parts, we felt the least we could do was to wait for her. However, our host, the British ambassador, found Miss Maxwell's tardiness embarrassing since he was at the moment entertaining Sir Herbert Chinnery, the stiff, mustachioed Inspector Ordinary for Asia, whose duty it was to report on conditions at the British embassy in Afghanistan as he had just done for the embassy in Persia, and it was important that Sir Herbert be pleased.

"Don't worry," Sir Herbert said graciously, putting us all at ease. "I've learned that Americans are rarely punctual."

I replied that I was sure Miss Maxwell must have met with some misfortune—temporary, I hoped—for she had that very morning risen at six in order to type her share of the play and had then, at some risk to herself, insisted upon delivering it to the Italian embassy, to which Signorina Risposi could testify. "As a matter of fact," I concluded, "in performing her duty Miss Maxwell was subjected to harsh treatment at the hands of three mullahs . . ."

"The usual?" Sir Herbert asked.

"Spitting, jostling, curses in Pashto," I explained.

"That's the second time it's happened this week," the ambassador said.

"I've a mind to advise Whitehall," Sir Herbert confided, "that all English girls in Kabul go into chaderi immediately."

"Oh, dear, no!" squealed a peaches-and-cream English girl called Gretchen Askwith. "Oh, Sir Herbert. No, I beg you."

It always seemed to me that the British went a little far in their coyness, but Gretchen Askwith was quite the loveliest of the unmarried white girls in Kabul, and it ill behooved me to think poorly of her, for although there were six or eight eligible young European men among the various embassies, I appeared to be the one most likely to win Gretchen's attention . . . that is, if she didn't discover that I was Jewish, a fact which none of the ferangi embassies yet knew.

There was not good blood between the British and the Americans in Afghanistan. The English tolerated us, and that's about all. Captain Verbruggen was thought to be a great bore and unlettered as well. Our secretaries were too pretty and too highly paid. Our Marines were undisciplined. And men like me were much too brash. In fact, about the only thing American that impressed the British was my ability to speak Pashto, but this was diminished by the fact that three of their chaps did too, including one chinless young man who spoke Russian and Persian as well. Still, we were tolerated because our kitchens served excellent food and our bars were generally open.

"There she is now!" Sir Herbert cried, with that boyish excitement that even the oldest Englishmen often retain, but when the door opened it was not Miss Maxwell but an unexpected guest, Moheb Khan. He was now dressed in a blue Bond Street pin-stripe worsted, with handsome brown leather shoes and a London shirting. He had transformed himself into a most proper diplomat, and in this guise presented himself to the ambassador.

"On three occasions, sir, you've asked me to these readings. May I choose my own time?"

"My dear fellow, you honor us!"

"I hear the play's very funny. I'd not have known about it except that I stopped by the Italian embassy and was told of its merit by Signorina Risposi." He bowed toward the Italian typist, who was quite plump.

"She told you the truth," Sir Herbert interrupted. "Our man in Washington saw it last month. Laughed so much he airmailed me a script."

There was a moment of emptiness, into which the Swedish girl said loudly, "Couldn't we start? Miss Maxwell doesn't participate until Act Two."

"I think it would be better if we waited," Sir Herbert insisted. "After all, the dear girl did much of the typing, Mr. Miller informs me."

Miss Askwith added, "And after her bout with the mullahs . . ."

"Do you think the mullahs are gaining ground in their battle for control?" Sir Herbert asked Moheb Khan.

"No," the Afghan replied cautiously. "On the other hand, they're not losing ground, either."

"Some time ago there was talk of discarding the chaderi," Sir Herbert suggested, and our discussion proceeded from that point. I had found, even in my short stay, that Afghanistan had two topics of conversation which were positively guaranteed to excite participation: the chaderi and the latest cure for diarrhea, for with the kind of drinking water available in Kabul, this latter scourge was sooner or later bound to infect everyone. Sure enough, not long after the chaderi was disposed of I heard Signorina Risposi advising the group.

"A German doctor has invented something much better than entero-vioform. It's called sulfas, I believe. Developed during the war."

"Does it work?" the Swedish girl was asking.

"My theory," Sir Herbert interrupted, "has always been to fill the lower bowel with some bland bulk producer like one of the new mucils. You'd be surprised how this slows down the bowel action."

"Really?" the Turkish ambassador's wife pursued. "I've relied on entero-vioform, and it seems to concentrate rather effectively on the upper bowel. But when it fails, it fails."

The dialogue now switched to French, for one of the scientists in that country had developed a radically new drug which the French ambassador's wife was explaining, and I thought: This must be the only capital in the world where a sophisticated international audience can discuss with all seriousness the control of the upper and lower bowel. Yet no aspect of Afghan life was more significant than this, for when the virulent Asiatic diarrhea, known locally as the Kabul Trots, struck, it was not like a stomach ache back home. It was a sickness which nauseated, embarrassed, debilitated and outraged the human body. In a land where toilet facilities were not excessive, diarrhea was a scourge, and I was willing to gamble that not a single person in that softly lit room, lined with books, was without his or her secret vial of pills and even more secret roll of personal toilet paper.

"What do you do for the disease?" the French ambassador's wife asked Moheb Khan in French.

"It's very simple," Moheb replied in lilting English. "You Europeans are always shocked at our open water supply into which little boys urinate. Or worse. But what happens? From drinking such water most of our children die, and that's neither a curse nor a blessing. They die and that's that. So the life expectancy in Afghanistan is about twenty-three years. But that figure doesn't mean what it says, not really. For if by chance you are one of the babies who does not die, you are inoculated against positively everything. Look about you. See the large number of our men who live to an extreme old age. With the women, I can assure you, it is the same. If you drink our water till you are seven, nothing can kill you but a bullet." He thumped his chest and laughed.

A rotund English doctor, on temporary duty in Kabul, said quietly, "You know, of course, he's not teasing. Take poliomyelitis, which strikes so many children in an antiseptic country like America . . ."

"Here no child gets polio," Moheb Khan insisted. "But you Europeans who come to us later in life, when you've not had the inoculations our water imparts . . . How many cases have we had of polio among the Europeans?"

"Many, even in my time," the fat doctor concurred.

There was a sound at the door, and in a moment Miss Maxwell appeared, flushed from the deep cold and from some experience which had left her stunned. "It's too much!" she cried in a kind of wild exhilaration.

"What happened?" many voices cried.

"This morning," she said excitedly. "The three mullahs screaming at me."

"We know about that unfortunate affair," Sir Herbert said consolingly.

"I didn't mind it," Miss Maxwell said. "I left Omaha to see Afghanistan, and I love it." Seeing Moheb she ran to him and took his hands. "What do you suppose I just saw? Not two hundred yards from the embassy?"

"More mullahs?" Moheb asked quietly.

"Wolves!" Miss Maxwell reported. "Yes, a huge pack of wolves. They were running across an open field where the snow was thick."

"The storms have driven them down from the mountains," Moheb Khan explained. "At this time of the year . . ."

"Would they attack . . . a man?" someone asked.

"They're ravenously hungry," Moheb replied. "In the morning you may hear . . . Well, they are wolves, down from the Hindu Kush."

The concept of wild wolves, running in a pack through the outskirts of Kabul, running until they found a straggler, either animal or human, cast a spell of terror over the group that had gathered to read a comedy. We felt chilly, and Sir Herbert directed his Afghan houseboy to throw on more logs. We felt very close to each other, and our group became more compact. Miss Maxwell, I am glad to say, did not try to monopolize the center of attention. She simply reported, "They were not at all like the wolves in Walt Disney. They were animals, great shaggy, terrifying animals."

"Did they have long teeth?" Signorina Risposi asked.

"I don't know. At such a moment . . . You know, they dashed right at our car. If I'd been driving I don't know what I'd have done. But our boy, Sadruddin, was in charge and he blew the horn sharply. Like one huge animal with many legs they swerved away and disappeared."

"Where?" the Swedish girl asked.

"Toward town," Miss Maxwell said, pointing toward where we all lived.

"It's one reason why we built high walls," Moheb Khan reflected in French.

"This is a land of startling contrasts," the French ambassador agreed.

"Do the wolves surprise you?" Moheb asked the general audience in English. "Before we read the play, tell me. Do the wolves surprise you?"

"No," the French ambassador replied in English. "When we come to Kabul we expect . . . Well, we expect the Hindu Kush."

"But we are never prepared for what we expect," Sir Herbert observed. He, too, was willing to postpone the reading of the play. After all, in winter in Kabul it mattered little when a party broke up . . . ten o'clock, or one, or four. "I remember when I was stationed in India. It was before the war." He didn't say, "They were good days, those," but we knew he intended us to think so. "I was hunting in Kashmir and I announced one day that I was going out with my native bearers to bag me a Kashmiri brown bear.

"A man in the bar at Srinagar, a total stranger, asked, 'Are you quite sure you want to shoot a Kashmiri bear, Sir Herbert?' I replied that I intended doing so, and doubtless my manner implied that I was irritated with his question."

The Afghan servant came in to place upon the fire a few precious logs, and each of us drew closer to someone else, for the wind outside was audible. "The stranger rejected my rebuff and asked again, 'Sir Herbert, do you know anything of the Kashmiri bear?' I replied, with some irritation, 'It's a bear. I've seen it at the zoo in Simla. Roger Whatshisname shot one.' The man pressed me, 'But have you shot one?'

" 'No,' I replied, and the man said sternly, 'Then you have no right to have an opinion upon this matter. Sir Herbert, you must not shoot this particular bear, really you mustn't.' I thanked him for his pains and marched out of the bar, but on the way to the shoot, one of my guides asked me in Kashmiri if I had ever hunted the bears of his country, and when I said no, he suggested that we go back. This so whetted my appetite that I spurred the horses and we came to that part of Kashmir where the brown bears are to be found.

"We hunted for some time and saw nothing, but toward dusk we came upon a thicket, and although I didn't get a clear sight on the beast, I could see it was a bear, and I let fly. I didn't kill the bear, and more's the pity, for I had wounded it mortally."

Sir Herbert stopped his narrative, and for a moment I thought he had undertaken in his telling rather more than he had anticipated. He did not want to continue, that was obvious, but he took a gulp of whiskey and said, "I suppose no one in this room has ever heard a Kashmiri bear. He has a voice like a human being . . . like a woman in extreme pain. When he is wounded, he beats his way through the thicket crying like a stricken mother. You can almost hear the words. He moans and wails and is obviously about to die of mortal pain. It is . . ." He fumbled for words, extended his right hand and punched the air. "It is . . ."

From a place near the fire Lady Margaret said, "It is shattering to the mind. Sir Herbert wanted to leave the thicket, but the bearers warned him that he must finish off the bear. That was his duty. So he plunged in—the men told me—but the bear had limped off into the deeper woods." Husband and wife fell silent, and we listened to the rising wind, blowing down the last of the winter's blizzards.

"I tracked that sobbing bear for about an hour," Sir Herbert said quietly. "It was easy, because constantly the beast screamed and wept. It was positively uncanny. That bear was not an animal. It was all the grieved things that men shoot, the partridges, the deer, the rabbits. I tell you, that bear spoke to me, crying out in its pain. I finally found it exhausted by a tree. Even as I came upon it, it wept new laments. By God, I tell you that bear . . ."

"Did you shoot him?" the French ambassador asked in French.

"Yes. I don't know how, but I did. Then I rushed back to Srinagar to find the man who had warned me in the bar, but he was gone."

"What is the point of this story, Sir Herbert?" Moheb Khan asked. "Surely if tonight we shoot a wolf it will not behave so."

"The point is, Moheb Khan, that none of us in this room was prepared for what we expected in Afghanistan. You, Miss Maxwell, didn't your government in Washington hand you a neatly typed report on Kabul? Mean temperature. Dress warmly. Expect dysentery."

"Yes," Miss Maxwell laughed.

"And it was all the truth, wasn't it?"

"Yes."

"But did it prepare you for today? Getting up at six to type a play because you wanted to be here with us? Being assaulted by mullahs in the bazaar? Seeing wolves rushing at your car?"

"No," Miss Maxwell said calmly. "The reports in Washington did not prepare me for any of that. I never dreamed that I could find a room anywhere in the world as warm, as human as this one. Almost everyone I care for deeply is right here, tonight. As for the mullahs and the wolves, I wasn't prepared for them, either. Right now I don't believe they happened."

"Exactly what I meant," Sir Herbert said, holding his hands up toward the group. "Reality in no way prepared me for the Kashmiri bears. I'm sure that dreadful incident never happened. But, Miss Maxwell, sometime years from now, those wolves will be as real to you as that stricken bear is to me. And to each of us, years from now, Afghanistan will be real, too."

"You make it sound far too difficult to understand my country," Moheb Khan contradicted. "It's very easy, really. All you have to do is read what Colonel

Sir Hungerford Holdich said about us in the Eleventh Edition of the Encyclopaedia Britannica." He pronounced the names with exaggerated precision.

"What are you saying?" the Swedish girl asked in French.

"With your permission," Moheb Khan said, bowing to Sir Herbert and taking down from the library shelf Volume I of the Britannica. Opening it to the article on Afghanistan he read in a sardonic accent:

> "The Afghans, inured to bloodshed from childhood, are familiar with death, and audacious in attack, but easily discouraged by failure; excessively turbulent and unsubmissive to law or discipline; apparently frank and affable in manner, especially when they hope to gain some object, but capable of the grossest brutality when that hope ceases. They are unscrupulous in perjury, treacherous, vain and insatiable, passionate in vindictiveness, which they will satisfy at the cost of their own lives and in the most cruel manner. Nowhere is crime committed on such trifling grounds, or with such general impunity, though when it is punished the punishment is atrocious. Among themselves the Afghans are quarrelsome, intriguing and distrustful; estrangements and affrays are of constant occurrence; the traveler conceals and misrepresents the time and direction of his journey. The Afghan is by breed and nature a bird of prey. If from habit and tradition he respects a stranger within his threshold, he yet considers it legitimate to warn a neighbor of the prey that is afoot, or even to overtake and plunder his guest after he has quitted his roof. The repression of crime and the demand of taxation he regards alike as tyranny. The Afghans are eternally boasting of their lineage, their independence and their prowess. They look on the Afghans as the first of nations, and each man looks on himself as the equal of any Afghan.

"Now that's all one paragraph, mind you," Moheb Khan warned us, "and I used to wonder how long it would take me to acquire the attributes I was, as a typical Afghan, supposed to have. Crafty, lying, deceitful I was, but what do you suppose kept me from qualifying? That troublesome bit about the bird of prey. How does one transform himself into a bird of prey? Well, I gave up on that first paragraph, but the next one offered hope. May I continue?"

"Proceed," Sir Herbert said.

Moheb Khan smiled, adjusted the heavy volume and read on:

> "They are capable of enduring great privation, and make excellent soldiers under British discipline, though there are but few in the Indian army. Sobriety and hardiness characterize the bulk of the people, though the higher classes are too often stained with deep and degrading debauchery. The first impression made by the Afghan is favorable. The European, especially if he come from India, is charmed by their apparently frank, openhearted, hospitable and manly manners; but the charm is not of long duration, and he finds that the Afghan is as cruel and crafty as he is independent."

With a flourish, Moheb Khan slammed the encyclopedia shut and stared at the readers. "You know, there's a funny thing about this. It was written by an Englishman who was totally perplexed as to how we Afghans had managed to thrash the living daylights out of English armies . . . twice. The man who wrote this must have perched himself on a stool in a little room and thought for some time: What kind of men are these Afghans, that they can defeat our armies? And he composed the description of a man who was as unlike an Englishman as possible, and then he wrote it properly in this big book, which I first read at Oxford. And what was my reaction? At that time? I was proud that a ferangi had seen so deeply into my character and had written with such respect. Today, when I am older, these seem like words of hatred or ignorance. They are not. They are profound words of respect from a scholar who simply had to know how we Afghans generated our capacity to fight. Never forget that marvelous peroration: 'the charm is not of long duration, and he finds that the Afghan is as cruel and crafty as he is independent.' "

"Moheb!" I cried. "You've memorized the passage, haven't you?"

"Only the favorable parts," he laughed.

"You think 'cruel and crafty' one of the good parts?" Miss Askwith inquired.

"When you use those characteristics to defend the end word of the sentence, they're good," Moheb replied. "Always remember the end word, Miss Askwith. Independent." Then he laughed easily and said, "But through trying years you English have come to know me as your trusted friend. Otherwise, how would I dare read such an English passage inside these walls, where twice my cruel and crafty ancestors murdered every Englishman resident in Kabul? In 1841 we did that evil thing, and in 1879 we played an encore, and I think it damned gracious of you even to have me here."

"Don't think we English forget the massacres," Sir Herbert said gravely. "It lends a certain spice to life in Kabul. Within these red and crumbling walls. Sort of like living in Hiroshima when an airplane flies overhead."

"I think we should get on with the reading," I suggested.

"He's to be the star," a young British officer teased. He was my principal rival for the attentions of Miss Gretchen Askwith.

"As a matter of fact," one of the Frenchmen said in French, "he's supposed to kiss Ingrid."

"I am," I said eagerly, "and I'd appreciate it if we got to that part before morning."

"Wise boy," Ingrid laughed. "In the morning I look dreadful."

It was in this mood that the reading began. During the first act, the voices seemed strange, for the Englishman who was supposed to be Harry Brock remained an Oxford aesthete, and Ingrid could be no more than a Swedish beauty with prominent breasts, while the others remained themselves, including me, who never transmuted myself into anything but an eager young man from the American embassy. But the fire was warm. The audience was attentive. And outside there was the smell of wolves, and no one could forget that he was in Afghanistan in the deep of winter, far, far from what he knew as civilization. I think even Moheb Khan was affected by the experience, for at the end of the first act he asked, "Sir Herbert, have the evenings I missed been as good as this?"

"Since I've been here they have," the Englishman replied. "Three weeks ago we read *Murder in the Cathedral.* I was asked to be Thomas à Becket."

"Oh, I should like to have seen that!" Moheb cried. "American college folk are very fond of T. S. Eliot. They adore him as a fellow citizen who became a poet, and respect him for having had the character to flee America, which they would like to do, but can't."

I'm afraid I had fallen rather deeply into the part I was reading, that of the intellectual reporter from the *New Republic,* and I said, "Like Eliot, you fled America, Moheb, but unlike him you regret it every minute."

"Agreed!" the affable Afghan cried. "If there's one thing I like it's fast cars and a sense of irresponsibility. In America I had both, and every day I work here in Afghanistan I regret their passing." He raised his palms in a gesture of submission, then added, "But at some point in our lives, we must grow up."

"I am sure your country will," I replied evenly. Moheb, rather pleased with his earlier remarks, flushed slightly but nodded pleasantly, for he was not the kind of fighter who refused to accept his adversary's blows; he rather respected the man who could strike back.

"Will anyone have more spiced rum?" the ambassador inquired, and as the servants refilled our drinks, and as the fire grew brighter, we reformed our group and the reading of Act Two commenced. By now we were more accustomed to our roles, and the audience accepted whatever peculiarities we exhibited. If tonight Harry Brock spoke not Brooklynese but an exaggerated Oxford—one as bad as the other, I thought —we were willing to accept this convention, and when Ingrid cried, "Would you do me a favor, Harry? Drop dead?" she sounded exactly like the dumb blonde of all countries, of all time. By the end of the act we had created, there in the old fortress, that ambience which dramatists seek but which so often eludes them. Actors and audience were one, moving together and accepting each other as equals. Partly, I think, it was because each person in that warm, quiet room knew that if he did not achieve some kind of satisfaction from our play, there was nothing else in Afghanistan to which he could escape. Either he attained catharsis now, or he was self-sentenced to days of non-participation. So each of us reached out to the other, made overtures that normally we would not have made, because each knew that for the forthcoming sixteen or eighteen months we would find joy with our repetitive neighbors, or we would find no joy at all. That was why life in Kabul—sans roads, sans movies, sans news, sans everything—was so profoundly meaningful. We probed the secrets of a few rather than glossing over the chance acquaintanceship of many, and each new thing we discovered about our colleagues uncovered new significance. For example, I had never imagined that glamorous Ingrid owned such a naughty wit.

The conversation that developed after Act Two was much different from that which followed Act One. Somehow, the play had insinuated itself into our intellect and had taken command. We poor inadequate readers had transcended ourselves, and the characters we were purporting to create had actually come to life. Harry Brock and his aspiring blonde were with us in the stout-walled embassy.

"We could use a few of your type in our country," Moheb Khan said to the Englishman playing the part of the junk dealer, and he meant not the actual Oxford boy but his play part, the junk dealer.

"There's a great deal to be said about good old Harry that isn't said in this play," the Englishman agreed. "Miller, how much of the building of America is to be credited to men like our Harry?"

"A good deal, I should imagine, and I think it's rather clever of you to discover the fact. You've not been in America, have you?"

"No, but reading this part makes one recall how inevitably one thinks of Harry Brock as the archetype American. We excoriate him, just as this play does, but we forget that he is also the life force of the nation, whether any of us likes him or not."

Miss Gretchen Askwith threw palpitations into the hearts of various young men by observing, "Really, Mark, you read your part exceedingly well. Have you studied dramatics?"

"In school I was in *Outward Bound.*"

"We intended reading that," Sir Herbert interrupted, "but the younger group thought it terribly dated. Do you agree, Miller?"

"I'm afraid I do, but I also think we should read it. It's fun."

"British, isn't it?" Sir Herbert asked.

I did not respond to Sir Herbert's question, for I was looking at Gretchen, and there in the crowded room I had a distinct premonition that Gretchen and I would be thrown together increasingly in Kabul . . . that it would become automatic for all hostesses to invite "Gretchen and Mark," and that sometime in the next years all would be asked to Shah Khan's great compound, where a tent would be erected and where Moheb Khan would ride up on his white horse to serve as my best man while the marriage was performed.

It was an inevitable progression, Gretchen Askwith and Mark Miller to the altar in Afghanistan; but as I looked at her and saw her blushing, for she must have been entertaining the same premonition of inevitability, her face was obliterated and I saw only a fawn chaderi, smelling of perfume, and a pair of American saddle shoes, and I heard the name Siddiqa, and I looked at Siddiqa's uncle, Moheb Khan, and I knew that it would never happen that I should marry Gretchen Askwith, no matter how inevitable our courtship. I longed to see the hidden face of Siddiqa Khan. I was mesmerized by the flowing movement of her chaderi, by the exquisite sense of sex this child had somehow managed to evoke.

Sir Herbert repeated his question: "Isn't *Outward Bound* a British play?"

"I don't know," I replied. "I always supposed it was by a sentimental American who wanted to sound British."

"You may be right," Sir Herbert replied with the thin smile that served him as a laugh.

The reading of Act Three recaptured the intensity that we had created in Act Two. The laughter at our jokes was rather more explosive than it should have been, and my courting of Miss Ingrid more emotionally received. A good many people in the room were wondering what was going to happen to Ingrid—the person, not the character—and it gave our play an adventitious prurience to have me, one of the unmarried men, attracted to her, even in make-believe.

As we ended our reading there was genuine applause. Our audience was grateful that for a few hours we had provided them with escape, and when the snowy winds whirling down from the Hindu Kush whistled outside, the gratitude increased. I knew there would arise, as had arisen before, a longing not to shatter the illusion of the night, and that we would sit around for hours and talk, hoping to extend the human warmth we had created.

We were astonished, therefore, when Moheb Khan said rather explosively, "Miss Ingrid, may I drive you home?"

The Swedish girl smiled graciously at the Afghan and replied, "Yes."

Within a moment Moheb had his coat and hers. He summoned his driver from the kitchen quarters where all the Afghan drivers were resting, and from the manner in which Ingrid nestled into her fur coat and then onto the arm of Moheb Khan, we intuitively knew that she had allowed the part she had been playing to influence her normal personality. There could be little doubt that Moheb and Ingrid would be bedded down that night. When the door opened and we caught the snowy blast and saw Ingrid move even closer, that last little doubt was erased.

When the door closed, one of the Frenchmen asked, "But isn't Moheb Khan already married?"

"He has two wives," one of the Englishwomen volunteered.

"Both Afghan?"

"Of course. He wanted to marry an American, but it didn't come off."

No one could have anticipated where this line of conversation might lead, but it was forestalled, and properly so, by Sir Herbert, who said, rather petulantly, I thought, "We really ought to read *Outward Bound*. I'll offer myself as the bartender." There was an immediate flurry of casting and a determination as to which secretaries would type out the required copies of which acts. Miss Maxwell, indestructible American that she was, offered to do the longest and others fell in line.

Then Sir Herbert said, "For the young lovers we'll have Gretchen and Mark." The audience looked at us as if we had been set apart, and my former sensation of the inevitability of love in Afghan surroundings returned. Gretchen smiled, a wonderful British smile with white teeth and flushed cheeks. There was a moment of painful indecision, which I fractured by suggesting, "May I drive you home, Gretchen?"

My question was so parallel to Moheb Khan's, the situation was so transparent, that Gretchen flushed again, then laughed prettily and said, "Sir Herbert, you must keep them from talking about us, too."

Sir Herbert grew red, looked at Lady Margaret, then said, "I think you should know by now that in Kabul any pretty unmarried girl is fair game for all sorts of speculation. Are you riding with Mark?"

"Yes," Gretchen snapped saucily. "Yes, I am. Just the way Ingrid went with Moheb." She did not yet have her coat on, but she grabbed my arm possessively.

Sir Herbert smiled wanly and said, "I dare say Freddy and Karl will be damned unhappy about your decision."

"At the next reading I'll ride home with Freddy and Karl," she laughed, slipping into the coat which an Afghan servant held for her.

Lady Margaret interrupted. "But at the next reading you and Mark are to be lovers."

Gretchen flashed her wittiest smile at her superior's wife. "Lady Margaret, haven't you noticed? At the end of a reading the actress is so irritated with her stage lover that she wishes to have no more to do with him. After all, in our play tonight Ingrid and Mark were lovers. But she made no move to go home with Mark. By the time the next reading's finished, I'll be fed to here with dear Mark." With her hand she made a line across her eyebrows. "Tonight, he is my gallant champion, to keep me from the wolves." To my surprise, she leaned forward and kissed me on the cheek.

"Bravo, Gretchen!" Lady Margaret applauded.

"Looks as if you're losing your secretary to the Yanks," Sir Herbert huffed at the ambassador, as I led Gretchen to the jeep which Nur Muhammad had driven up.

Not all the British hands could find quarters in the embassy grounds, ample though they were, and some lived in Kabul proper, in a spacious walled house west of the public square. It was quite the liveliest spot in town, filled with laughter, ponderous jokes which the British overseas so love, and a fairy-tale kind of make-believe which has enabled them to live in reasonable relaxation in almost any portion of the globe. I was often in this house and I remember it now mostly as a center of things hearty. When I first came to know it and its occupants I wondered how a man ever got an English girl into bed. What did they do with her hockey stick? How did he halt her from making very witty jokes about nothing? Now, as I started to ride homeward with one of the prettiest English girls I had ever met, I was bothered by the same questions.

But as we rode over the winding trail that led from the embassy to Kabul, and as we saw to our left the soaring mountains of the Hindu Kush, outlined in snowy moonlight, the trivial problems of courtship left us, and we were two strangers from alien lands traveling across one of the high plateaus of the world. Gretchen moved closer to me, and we held hands as our jeep approached the first houses of Kabul.

Then we saw lights—actual flaming torches—as men hurried to and fro and a wagon with horses approached. There was a crowd in the road, and Nur Muhammad left the jeep to find out what had happened. In a moment he returned to report without inflection, "The wolves found an old man."

It must have ended quickly. Fifteen to twenty wolves, by local count, had struck the man and torn him to pieces within a few minutes. Now they were raging somewhere to the east and soldiers were out to shoot a few, after which the others would retreat. Nur Muhammad drove the jeep past the scene of mutilation and we reached the English dormitory.

Pretty Gretchen said, "Will you come in?" and I

said I would, for I knew that on the morning following a reading no one would get to his office promptly, and in the English house there would be fun and good talk and kissing beneath the stairs. But when I started in, I saw Nur Muhammad sitting in the jeep and I said, "Nur, you can go home. I'll walk across the park." But he said, "You mustn't. They haven't shot the wolves yet." And from the east we heard sounds and could tell that something was rushing down the narrow streets, and I did not want to be in the English house that night.

"I'll take Nur Muhammad home," I apologized. "He's been working since dawn."

Almost as if relieved of a heavy burden Gretchen said, "I do think that's best," and I bounded, with improper haste I reflected later, into the jeep.

"Let's find the wolves," I cried to Nur, and we spurred the jeep east of the American embassy and along one narrow street after another until we were on the edge of town, with soldiers well to the south. They were moving slowly northward, hoping to come upon the animals, and we could see lights moving mysteriously along the edge of the river.

We stayed there in the snowy moonlight for some time, alone on the edge of an ancient city with the Hindu Kush rising to our left and the immensity of Asia all about us: to the east the Khyber Pass, to the north the Oxus River and the plains of Samarkand, to the south the bazaars of Kandahar and the limitless deserts of Baluchistan, and to the west the strange lake that vanishes in air, and the minarets of Shiraz and Isfahan. It was a moment of immensity in which I sensed the hugeness of Central Asia, that semi-world with a chaderi over its face, and just as the chaderi of Siddiqa had contained its own perfume, now the crisp, silent night with the flickering lights along the river possessed its particular power. It was the smell of frozen fields, biting on the nostril, the aroma of the bazaar, great and filthy even in the night, and the clean, sweet smell of pine trees that hid behind garden walls. Those were moments I shall never forget, when the vastness of Asia, whose distant mountain passes had sent us the wolves, was borne in upon me and I wondered how I had been lucky enough to draw an assignment in Kabul, the most remote of capitals.

My reverie was broken by shots to the south; gun-flashes could be seen. The soldiers must be near at hand. I remember distinctly that at that moment, when the light of the guns added illumination to the crystal, snowy night, I thought: It was nights like this that the Russian writers spoke of, the white nights of Russia. It was a vagrant thought, shattered by a rush of sound.

Moving up from the river, across fields that were now barren, came the wolves: fifteen, eighteen, they were so close-packed I could not count. They seemed not to be running. They were moving as one giant animal, its heads looking out from side to side and finding no food. It was a terrifying, possessive animal that moved across the snow, a force driven by forces outside itself, an embodiment of Asia and the great mountains.

One of the wolves must have smelled Nur and me, for the pack suddenly veered directly toward us, but when its leaders saw not men but the mechanical jeep, whose headlights now exploded with brilliance, the animals shifted course without visible decision, and the gray pack slipped off into the frozen night.

"Here they are!" Nur Muhammad shouted, and the soldiers rushed up. Some shots were fired and I remember mumbling to myself: "I hope they got away."

The Afghan soldiers came to the jeep and conversed with Nur and me for a few minutes, pleased at meeting a ferangi who could speak Pashto. Their officer arrived later in a staff car and it was agreed to leave two men on watch. "It will soon be spring," the officer said in Pashto, "and we'll have no more wolves. Till next year."

It was now about four in the morning, but there would be no sign of daylight for many hours, and Nur started to drive me home, but I said impulsively, "Let's go to the English house!" and we did and as I had suspected the lights were not yet extinguished, and when I knocked on the door the English girls were not surprised to see me. Some men were there talking about the play and I created a stir when I said, "We've been out chasing the wolves. We saw them on the eastern edge of the city."

"Were they fearful?" Gretchen asked, and she seemed then immensely pretty, and I told her of the wolves and of the soldier who said it would soon be spring, and as I had anticipated earlier there was fine English fun, and good talk, and kissing beneath the stairs.

4

Next morning I was awakened by Nur Muhammad beating on my door and crying, "Miller Sahib! Captain Verbruggen has called a meeting for eleven!"

I rose hastily, doused my eyes in cold water and waited for Nur to push open the door with his pot of boiling water for my shave. My face luxuriated in the soothing water, and as I scraped my beard, I asked, "How much time?"

"It's past ten," he warned, and I looked into the hall to greet him, brown, well shaved, dressed in western clothes and karakul cap, waiting to lead me to our breakfast. This morning he was bursting with a special pride. "I'm also to attend His Excellency's meeting," he confided, and I saw that he had used my shoe box to freshen his shoes as well as mine. Such things he was not required to do. He was my official helper at the embassy, but he was a married man and had asked if he could augment his salary by overseeing the servants at my house. "Otherwise, sahib, they'll steal you blind. They're Afghans, you know."

I lived in one of the new houses on the far side of the public park that dominated the north arm of Kabul: to the west lay the British dormitory, within walking distance, while to the east stood the American embassy, also close at hand. When I had finished shaving I slipped into an Afghan robe and went onto the roof of my house to view once more a scene far more important to me than either the British dormitory or the American embassy. I wished to inspect the mountains and thus remind myself of where I was.

I looked first to the west, where the poetic Koh-i-Baba mountains stood shimmering in the sunlight, so near they could almost be felt, so graceful and varied that they seemed like Gothic sculpture rather than real mountains. To the north stood the great, somber Hindu Kush, heavy and foreboding. They had been named, local legend insisted, The Hindu Killers because of what they had done to the natives of India who tried to cross them seeking the profitable trade of Samarkand. Whenever during my working day I caught a glimpse of the Hindu Kush I felt that I was in direct link with the heartland of Asia.

For to the east these master mountains of Afghanistan joined the Pamirs, the impenetrable, mysterious massif that guarded the meeting place of nations; and these in turn led to the Karakorams, most inaccessible of the Asian mountains, on whose flanks lived the Hunza people, the Gilgits and the Kashmiris. South of the Karakorams came the Himalayas themselves on their eastward sweep down the spine of Asia.

Thus each morning when I greeted the mountains I felt myself in contact not only with Afghanistan but with the entire continent of Asia and with my own past: the wartime flights over the Himalayas into China; the intelligence mission into Gilgit, perched in the clouds; the great sea battles off the eastern flank of Asia; and now my job with the State Department in Kabul. I breathed deeply half a dozen times, imagined the ponderous ballet of the mountains as they swept across Asia, and went down to where Nur Muhammad and the servants had arranged breakfast.

For his eleven-o'clock meeting Captain Verbruggen had collected the four members of our staff best informed on the Ellen Jaspar affair. Richardson of Intelligence was there, a tweedy, pipe-smoking gentleman who affected a British-type mustache and who was favorably known for talking sense, primarily because he refused to give any opinion unless it was fortified by documents. He had reached the State Department via the F.B.I. and was an expert in security and Russian intentions. We supposed that he had been assigned to Afghanistan only briefly in order to study the southern flank of Russia where it impinged on Afghanistan. He felt the case of the Jaspar girl to be an intrusion and frequently said so. But now he sat confidently, his hands folded on his own intelligence file, just waiting for us to ask him questions.

Nexler, the subtle brains of the embassy, was also present, a self-effacing man in his late forties and the only one on our staff who enjoyed secure status in the real hierarchy of State. Unlike the rest of us, he had not come to the department from some other job; he had always been a diplomat and found subtle pleasure in reminding us of the gap that existed between him and us. He was an expert in masking his opinions, but we suspected that he deplored the naval attaché as a political hack, held Richardson in contempt as a kind of F.B.I. precinct cop, and regretted me as an unavoidable error in a department that had been forced to recruit untested men to fill new posts. He suffered Kabul in silence, waiting for the day when he would be transferred to a real embassy, say Buenos Aires or Vienna. London and Paris would come later. In the meantime his strategy in Kabul was to speak as little as possible.

Nur Muhammad and I completed the group, and it was to me that Captain Verbruggen spoke first: "Shah Khan's office delivered the papers, so you're free to head for Kandahar."

"I'll go down tomorrow," I said.

"Good. What do you expect to find?"

"Yesterday Shah Khan suggested three different

things that could have happened. First theory. She killed herself."

"Is that likely?" Verbruggen asked.

"It's possible. She must have been shocked by the life she was required to lead in Afghanistan. I know I was shocked yesterday by some of the things Moheb Khan said."

"He's the one in the Foreign Office?" Verbruggen asked.

"Yes. Moheb told me something that isn't in our reports. Nazrullah married an Afghan wife before he left for America and had a baby with her."

"We knew that," Richardson said complacently, tapping the file with his pipe.

I was irritated that he had kept information from me. "Did you also know," I asked, "that after Nazrullah and Ellen Jaspar were married, his Afghan wife lived with them and she had a second baby? This could well have caused Miss Jaspar to kill herself. Remember, three years ago the Allison girl did."

The Americans in the room winced at the memory of that dismal affair, and Richardson asked, "Wouldn't we have heard about a suicide?"

"I asked about the lack of information, and what do you suppose Moheb answered? She was only a woman, and when Nazrullah gets back to Kabul he'll tell us all we need to know."

"What were the other guesses?" Verbruggen asked.

I thought: Look at Nexler wincing. A career diplomat would say, "What are the other hypotheses?" I prefer Verbruggen's way.

"Second theory," I said. "She's been locked up by her husband and we won't see her for some years. Remember that this occurred with that English girl Sanderson and that Dutch girl . . ."

"Vonderdonk," Richardson filled in promptly.

"Do you take such a hypothesis seriously?" Verbruggen asked as Nexler raised his eyebrows.

"I certainly do. It's happened before."

Richardson sucked his pipe, then observed cautiously, "Evidence I've collected supports the belief that Nazrullah loved his American wife, did all he could to make her happy. I find no parallel with the Sanderson and Vonderdonk girls. Their husbands hated them and kept them locked up eight or nine years to prove it. I reject this theory completely."

"We're rejecting nothing," Verbruggen said firmly. "This is Afghanistan and no one of us here can project himself inside the Afghan mind. How do you know what Nazrullah might do?"

Richardson nodded amiably, dragged on his pipe, then asked, "Let's concede that he's keeping her locked up. Where? A city like Kandahar? An outpost like Qala Bist?" We looked at one another.

"Excuse me, sir," Nur Muhammad interrupted. "I've reviewed all recent cases of such personal imprisonment. Without exception the jail turned out to be the home of the husband's mother. If you surround a ferangi wife with half a dozen women in chaderi they not only can keep her hidden, they enjoy doing it."

Captain Verbruggen looked at Nur Muhammad as if to say: Whatever we pay you, son, it's worth it. Aloud he asked, "Have we checked the mother's home?"

"Everything possible," Nur replied. "Not a single clue."

Nexler spoke for the first time. "But didn't your government also check in the Sanderson and Vonderdonk cases?"

"They did," Nur confessed, "and they found nothing. But Nazrullah's family is much more modern than the ones involved in those cases."

"Would you rule out the possibility that she's hidden, right here in Kabul?" Verbruggen pressed.

"No," Nur responded quickly. "After all, it was Your Excellency who reminded us that this is Afghanistan. But I do think it most unlikely." The acting ambassador nodded. American officials were not supposed to be addressed as Your Excellency, and by no stretch of protocol did Captain Verbruggen warrant the honorific, but I noticed that all who were so addressed were pleased with the courtesy and reluctant to admonish.

Nexler asked quietly, "Is there no way to visit the family home and check for ourselves?"

The naval attaché turned sharply to his colleague and snapped, "You overlook three factors. In Afghanistan a home is a fort, and if we try to barge in they'll shoot us. The country has no habeas corpus. And most important, Miss Jaspar is no longer of any legal concern to the American government."

"Perhaps we should tell that to the senator from Pennsylvania," Nexler observed dryly.

"He can bully us about the girl," the acting ambassador complained, "but there's not a damned thing we can do to bully the Afghan government. What's the third guess?"

"Shah Khan advised us to consider an eventuality which has also occurred in the past. Miss Jaspar has run away. Trying to reach the British railway station at Chaman. If so, two things may have happened. She reached Chaman, which we know she didn't do because we've checked. She died in the desert, which is the way the two earlier cases ended."

"I don't have their cases," Richardson protested.

"Before your time," I said, and he retreated behind his pipe.

"That finishes your report?" Verbruggen asked.

"Yes, sir," I replied with a finality I did not feel. There remained the matter of Shah Khan's implausible rumor, which he had refused to share with me, but for the moment I concealed this because I wanted our group to explore logical conjectures before speculating on wild improbabilities.

"I'd like to point out," Verbruggen growled with that down-to-earth realism which characterized him, "that your first alternative contains two alternatives of its own, one of which you overlooked. Miller says Shah Khan suggested Miss Jaspar may have committed suicide. I suggest she may have been murdered . . . by Nazrullah."

Nur Muhammad, whom I expected to rise in defense of his countryman, quickly agreed with the logic of this hypothesis. "Not impossible," he said firmly. Then he added, "But I've studied Nazrullah, and it's unlikely he would murder a ferangi."

The acting ambassador nodded. "From what I know of him, most unlikely. But I raise the possibility."

"Thank you, sir," I replied. "As you know, I've never seen Nazrullah, but from what I've read of him he's not the murdering type."

"We're leaping to some rather broad conclusions," Verbruggen cautioned. "Let's all get back to facts."

Richardson coughed and said, "I have a complete report on the Jaspar girl. Naval Intelligence and F.B.I. helped us out." He opened his file ceremoniously, looked at Nexler, and asked, "May I start reading?" Without waiting for consent he began:

> "Ellen Jaspar, born in Dorset, Pennsylvania, 1922. Father's in real estate and insurance. She has one brother, three years younger. He seems normal in every way. Enlisted in the army and did well. Now a sophomore at Penn State. We include a photograph of the Jaspars taken in 1943, the year before our subject met the gentleman from Afghanistan."

Richardson detached the photograph and said, "If you're looking for the All-American family, here it is. Even have a collie and a Buick."

When the photograph reached me I saw a family which could have come from any part of America: mother a bit plump but well dressed; father taller and solid-looking; son ill at ease in pants a little too tight; collie dog well cared for; Buick recently polished; daughter . . .

"She's much prettier than most foreign women who marry Afghans," Nur Muhammad reacted.

To my surprise Richardson laid down his pipe and said, "I'd date that one. She's stunning."

I looked again. At twenty, Ellen Jaspar was the typical sophomore at a good girls' college like Bryn Mawr. She was lean, well groomed, an attractive blonde, which must have made her additionally impressive to Nazrullah. No one would mistake her for the brain of the campus; she was too good-looking for that. Nor would anyone pick her as the hottest thing at the Saturday dance; she was too intelligent for that. She was, to use a phrase then coming into use, well-scrubbed, for even in the picture she was conspicuously neat, and one felt that she had not prettied herself up for the photograph.

Captain Verbruggen took charge of the picture and asked, "Is there any possible clue as to why she would marry an Afghan?"

Richardson had seen something in the photograph the rest of us had missed, and he said, "She looks to me like a girl who would often whine, 'Oh, Mother!' " Verbruggen, who had a daughter, chuckled, and Richardson continued, "We all know that girls of twelve are driven to anguish by their parents' inadequacies. Thank God this passes. But this girl looks as if she'd maintained this attitude right into her twenties."

I studied the photograph again, and I must admit that I could hear her crying, "Really, Mother!"

The acting ambassador asked, "Do the reports substantiate this?"

"Yes," Richardson replied. "Ellen Jaspar attended public school in Dorset through her sophomore year, and did well. Then she grew discontented with everything and her parents transferred her to a good private school in Philadelphia, where she also did well."

"All-around girl?" Verbruggen asked, implying that only such girls did well.

"Oh, yes!" Richardson assured him. "Hockey, glee

club, tried out for the senior play. Boys took her to dances and in the summer she was counselor at a camp. Well adjusted."

"Any desire to travel?"

"None evident, but she did excel in nature work. Led the camp in this respect."

"College the same?" Verbruggen asked. "Hockey, singing, dramatics?"

"You've hit," Richardson said, as Nexler sat silent, looking straight ahead. "Except that in college her singing became good enough for her to join a semi-professional chorus that sang with the Philadelphia Orchestra."

The acting ambassador leaned back and looked at the roof. "Where does the flaw come in? That she would enter such a marriage?"

"We've gone rather deeply into that," Richardson replied. "First clue we get is from an interview with one of her high-school steadies. Boy who did well in the navy. He told the investigator:

> " 'When Ellen came home from boarding school she was pretty stuck up, not socially I mean, because she always stayed a neat kid and we all liked her, but she said screwy things like, "This town is a real bore," and "Can you imagine living the rest of your life in Dorset and going to the country club every Saturday night? Big deal." She talked this way so much that I stopped dating her.' "

Richardson dropped the paper, smiled reflectively and added, "That's his version. The facts seem to be the other way around. It was Ellen who stopped dating him. At least that's what the others reported."

"Is Dorset so bad?" the acting ambassador probed.

"I asked for a report on that," Richardson replied. "Fine town. Good families, good churches, good schools. It's no Tobacco Road, that's for sure. Pearl Buck lives in the next county and so does Oscar Hammerstein. He's the one who wrote *Oklahoma.*

There's a little theater not far away. I'd say Dorset was way above average. But when Ellen reached Bryn Mawr her antagonism increased. One of her roommates . . . And here's a point I'd like to emphasize. Not a single person we interviewed said, 'I knew all along she'd do something screwy.' This fact alone is noteworthy. In every investigation you expect to meet the joker who foresaw everything four years ahead of anybody else. In her case, no. Listen to this:

> "Miss Jaspar's first college roommate told us, 'Ellen Jaspar was a dear, sweet kid. She was loyal, responsive, and trustworthy. We had three dandy years together and whatever she's done, she's done with her eyes open. And if you come back and say she's committed murder I'm not going to say, it was in her all along. Nothing but essential goodness was in this girl.'
>
> "Her second roommate gave us a somewhat different version. 'Ellen could grow quite bitter about what she called "the inescapable nothingness" of life in her family. She dreaded going back home to marry or live. I'd been to her home several times and I loved the place. Old town, old houses, real good people with lots to do. I didn't understand her antipathy, but I can assure you it was real. Once she exploded, "In Dorset they don't turn back the clocks. They shoot the man who invented clocks." She told me she was determined never to go back there to live, but I used to ask her, "Don't you think New York and Chicago are just as goopy?" She said, "Maybe so. But there must be some place in the world that's different." I never understood her bitterness.' "

"I'm terrified!" Captain Verbruggen cried. "Sounds just like my daughter." He passed around a picture of an intense, good-looking junior from Sarah Lawrence. "You see any difference?" he joked.

"There was this difference," Richardson replied. "In her sophomore year at Bryn Mawr, Ellen stopped dating. Told her roommate, 'I'm not going to marry some jerk whose big vision of life is selling insurance in Dorset, Pennsylvania.' We also have an instructive report from a boy who went to Haverford. Did very well in the army. He told us:

" 'Ellen Jaspar was a real winner. She had a world of class. I took her to several dances in her freshman year and she was practically what you'd call a clock-stopper. Very popular with the gang. Real human too. If she hadn't turned so difficult in her sophomore year something big could have developed. At least I was willing to make the try. What it was that changed her I'll never know. At first I blamed myself, but later on I ran into a lot of chicks who just couldn't get things straight. But I'll take the blame for the bust-up, because I always felt somebody else might have kept Ellen on the track. But I will admit this. I wasn't the man to do it.' "

"It must have been about then that she met Nazrullah," the acting ambassador observed. "How'd it happen?"

Richardson, who rather enjoyed the limelight, went through involved motions lighting his pipe, then explained, "Her first roommate covers that:

" 'In March, 1944, there was this Saturday dance at the Wharton School and some joker invited four of us to go in to Philly. Well, actually he called me and asked me to bring along three warm bodies. So even though Ellen wasn't dating at the time I said, "Come along. You may meet a glamorous Frenchman." The idea struck her fancy and on the spur of the moment she joined us. We went in by train, and at the station my date met me with a jalopy, but there beside him was this dark-skinned fellow with a red Cadillac convertible and a turban. It was too much. Ellen took one look at him, and that was that. They saw one another a lot, then this other Afghanistan gentleman came up from the embassy in Washington and they all went up to Dorset to meet Ellen's folks. It must have been a real fiasco. She came back swearing that she would rather die on the sands of the desert than marry some Dorset jerk. She left college before exams and that was the last I heard of her, except for one week end that summer. She appeared at my home in Connecticut sort of breathless. Nazrullah had gone back to Afghanistan without her, but she had a passport and a couple of hundred dollars. She needed another twelve hundred dollars. Like a fool I let her have it. I've never heard from her since.' "

"Neither has anybody else," Captain Verbruggen growled. "What did her father say?" Richardson was ready with a summary:

" 'My name is Thomas Shalldean Jaspar. I own an important real estate and insurance business in Dorset, Pennsylvania, where my family has lived for seven generations. My wife is Esther Johnson Jaspar, and her family . . .' "

"We can skip the begats," the acting ambassador snapped, so Richardson casually discarded a page and resumed reading:

" 'My wife and I have tried to remember anything that might explain our daughter's behavior, but we come up with nothing. There is no explanation. She was a good girl, never gave us a bit of trouble till her sophomore year in high school, when she got fed up with everything in Dorset, including her parents.

" 'When she reached Bryn Mawr we breathed a little easier, for she fell in with two of the nicest roommates a girl could have and also met some nice boys at Haverford College. Then everything went sour. Refused to date. Didn't go out much, and was downright hateful when she came home, which wasn't often. Her behavior was ridiculous.' "

Here Richardson stopped, drew on his pipe, and observed, "I'm not going to read all of this, but one thing does strike me every time I review it. Whenever

Mr. Jaspar comes up against anything unusual, unknown or unfamiliar he describes it as ridiculous. He and his wife seem to have had a rather rigorous definition of what was not ridiculous, and God help anything that fell outside their pattern."

"Thank you for your profound analysis," Captain Verbruggen said. At a normal embassy such sarcasm from an acting ambassador could blight a career, but in Kabul, an irregular post at best, we worked under an irregular discipline which allowed a rather broad latitude for jokes. Verbruggen's wisecrack was directed at himself as much as at Richardson, who laughed easily.

"Excuse me, sir," I interrupted, "but I think we may have the clue we're looking for in *ridiculous*. Since Mr. Jaspar stigmatized everything out of the ordinary with that word, his daughter was compelled by an urge to outrage the system. What was the most ridiculous thing she could do? Find herself an Afghan with a turban and a red Cadillac convertible."

"My dear Miller," Captain Verbruggen said slowly, "when I observed that Richardson's analysis was profound I meant just that, because frankly, what he pointed out had missed me. Now you have made it completely obvious, and I thank you, too."

Richardson relit his pipe, smiled at me and suggested, "Perhaps we should get back to Mr. Jaspar, who seems to have been a completely dull gentleman. Certainly his report is."

> " 'At a well-chaperoned dance held at the Wharton School, a fine institution in Philadelphia, Ellen met a young man from Afghanistan and before we had even heard about him she had fallen in love with him. We put detectives on his trail and found that he had a Cadillac, got good grades in college, and that he had been in Germany during the early days of the war. We reported this to the F.B.I. but they said he was cleared and was not a spy. After his examinations the young man . . .' "

Richardson paused and said, "You'll notice that Mr. Jaspar refuses to use Nazrullah's name. Probably considered it ridiculous."

Nur Muhammad observed, "More likely he was confused because Nazrullah had no last name." Captain Verbruggen looked up in approval and Richardson continued reading from Mr. Jaspar's report:

> " 'You know the rest. Week before exams Ellen ran away from college and we don't know where she went. She wasn't with the young man, because the detectives kept track of him until he sailed for Afghanistan. Later she turned up at her roommate's in Connecticut with a little money and a passport. She borrowed twelve hundred dollars, which I later repaid, and then went to England. How she managed this we don't know, because at this time ordinary people couldn't get to England . . . I suppose the world is impressed by ridiculous adventurers, especially if they're pretty girls. We haven't heard a word from her since February, 1945.' "

Richardson shook his head dolefully. "No use reading the rest. Poor fellow never had a clue."

"Any reports from Bryn Mawr?" Captain Verbruggen asked.

"Certainly." Richardson brightened, shuffling a new set of papers into position. "Deans, professors, counselors all report the same: Ellen Jaspar presented no problems." Satisfied with the completeness of his responses, the intelligence officer folded his file and smiled.

During the former F.B.I. man's report I had been impressed by the detached air assumed by Nexler, the State Department career man. Now he coughed modestly, produced from an inside pocket a letter which he unfolded with care, and said, "In this case it isn't quite proper to claim that no one had foresight. I made some inquiries at Harvard University, where a Bryn Mawr professor is spending his sabbatical. A routine check by our people there . . ." He turned condescendingly to Richardson and said in an offhand way, "After the meeting I'll give you the letter. It could prove relevant."

Richardson was justifiably furious that information had been withheld from him, but he masked his anger behind the ritual of lighting his pipe. "I'd like to hear what you've turned up," he said with studied amiability.

"Probably of no consequence," Nexler replied deprecatingly. "Comes from an assistant professor of music your people overlooked at the time. Here's what he says now.

> " 'I'm not surprised at what you tell me about the behavior of Ellen Jaspar, and without wishing to appear omniscient I must say that I foresaw almost everything that you report. In fact, I shared my predictions with her parents, but they paid no attention.
>
> " 'When Ellen first joined our group she struck me as one destined for tragedy, but I was not satisfied then nor am I now that *tragedy* was the word I sought. I saw her as a girl of good intention who was determined to disaffiliate herself from our society, and I wondered if she were strong enough to find something better to rely on.
>
> " 'I met her for the first time during the opening of college in 1941. Without my asking she said, "I want to get as far away from Dorset, Pennsylvania, as I can." She spoke with transparent hatred, which did not disturb me at the time, for I encounter many young people who feel this way during their first year of college. But Ellen plunged into the field of medieval music with such intensity that I knew it was not the music she sought. I took the trouble to check with her other professors, and they found her to be normal and above average in performance. I therefore had to conclude that what I had witnessed was merely some temporary aberration.

" 'But when Ellen returned in her second year with increased bitterness, claiming that the world seemed pointless, as if it were interested only in a perpetual Saturday night dance at some cosmic country club, I began to take her malaise more seriously, and I asked my wife to talk with her. Ellen brought her young Haverford boy to dine with us and we found him charming, but were forced to agree with her that his ambitions were as ordinary as her father's.

" 'My wife and I became so convinced that Ellen would fall into serious trouble that in the spring of 1943 we wrote a letter to her parents. We said—and signed it jointly lest it be thought that I was in some way enamored of the girl, as male professors sometimes are with erratic and attractive girls—that we were convinced Ellen might be in for serious psychological disturbance unless a solid attempt was made to reconcile her to her family and her society as represented by her home town. This brought her parents down upon us in full fury. They pointed out that I was not head of my department, that Ellen was doing well in her real subjects, and that it was ridiculous for an assistant professor of music to presume, etc., etc.

" 'This was not the first time I had heard this distinction between real subjects and mine, and I confess that I was always irritated by people who raised the issue. Therefore, when Mr. Jaspar shouted for the third time that my letter was ridiculous I quickly confessed that it probably was and asked him to forget the whole affair, which he did. In fact, that December he sent me a Christmas card, and three months later, in early 1944, his daughter met the boy from Afghanistan.

" 'So far as I know I was the only person with whom Ellen discussed her intention of marrying the young visitor. I took her immediately to talk with my wife, and we in turn called in the young man to interrogate him. He impressed us as one of the finest foreign students we had ever met, and if Ellen has fallen into trouble through her association with him, we cannot say, "We told you so." We must say exactly the opposite. We told Ellen, "He's a fine person, but he will not solve your problem." "What is my problem?" she asked, and I said, "You have the disease that eats at our world. You cannot find peace in old conventions and beliefs, yet you are not sufficiently committed to anything to forge new ones for yourself." She looked at me and said, "You may be right. But wouldn't my going with Nazrullah be a step in the right direction?" I told her it would solve nothing, but on the other hand it would not make things worse. That's the last discussion we had.

" 'When you find Ellen you will find that it is not Nazrullah who has wronged her but she who has wronged Nazrullah.

" 'I'll close this informal report with one observation. Ellen Jaspar is sick with the disease that is beginning to infect our ablest young people. She has disaffiliated herself from the beliefs that gave our society its structure in the past, but she has found no new structure upon which she can rely for that support which every human life requires.' "

Primly Nexler handed the letter to Richardson, who accepted it without comment, but Verbruggen blustered, "I'd have acted precisely as the Jaspars did. If my daughter gets A's and B's in her real subjects and a music professor sends me a letter as garbled as that, I'll be as stupefied as the Jaspars were." Then he stared at me with his big, blunt face and demanded, "Miller, does that letter make any sense to you?"

Having heard what he had just said, I didn't want to insult him, so I equivocated. "It's part of the picture, sir."

"What a hell of an answer!" he exploded. "As a father my reaction was the one I just gave. But as an outsider, trying to get a focus on this thing, the music professor's letter is the only one that makes sense." Nexler smiled with satisfaction.

Abruptly Verbruggen turned to Nur Muhammad and said, "Nur, we brought you here today for a fresh look at an old problem. Considering what you've heard, what do you make of it?"

Nur Muhammad was one of the indefinable Afghans who turned up at all embassies. He learned English—or French or German or Turkish as required—had a fair education, quickly made himself invaluable, and was surely in the pay of the Afghan government, to which he reported secretly. Nur was an agreed-upon convenience, for he told the Afghans what we wanted them to know; and through him the Afghans leaked official secrets to us. He had been invited to this morning's meeting to warn the Afghan government that we expected full cooperation in Kandahar.

Nur, who acted as if he did not know that we suspected him of being a government agent, cleared his throat and said cautiously, "Your Excellency, I cling to these fundamentals. Miss Jaspar is not held prisoner here in Kabul. Nazrullah did not murder her. She may be a prisoner at Qala Bist, but that seems unlikely, because remember what I said. Only women can keep a ferangi wife prisoner. Men cannot. I therefore conclude that she has run away to the British at Chaman and has died in the attempt."

"Why haven't we been informed?" Verbruggen growled.

"Nazrullah hopes that she may still be found alive. And remember one thing, Your Excellency. You're not fighting the Afghan government on this matter. It's not a case of Shah Khan withholding information. He too is perplexed."

"Well," Verbruggen warned, "look after Miller in the south. We haven't time to worry about another missing American."

"He shall be my special charge," Nur Muhammad assured him, and from the manner in which the acting ambassador had spoken Nur realized that it was time for him to depart. Graciously, he withdrew.

As soon as Nur was gone, Verbruggen said to me, "While you're down there, there's another matter I want you to look into. Several of the embassies may go together to hire a doctor. We want a ferangi, of course. We've been advised there's a German practicing in Kandahar. What's his name?"

Richardson consulted a memorandum and replied, "Otto Stiglitz."

The acting ambassador continued, "Seems to be a refugee who fled Nazi Germany. But he might have come here to escape British or Russian courts trying war criminals. Anyway, the Italians recommend him as an excellent doctor and if he is, we might work out something. Check him out. Maybe he'll know something about our girl, too."

I looked about the room to insure that no Afghan personnel had entered unexpectedly, then said, "There's one more matter to discuss, sir. Yesterday as I was leaving, Shah Khan took me aside and whispered that he had recently received a rumor regarding Ellen Jaspar so bizarre that he refused even to discuss it. Didn't want it in our files under his name. At any rate, a rumor has arisen substantial enough to survive a trip from Kandahar to Kabul, but so ridiculous . . ."

"You're using Mr. Jaspar's word," the acting ambassador pointed out. "Shah Khan said bizarre. I suppose they mean the same."

"Anyone care to guess what the rumor might have been?" I asked.

"You've obviously been thinking about it all night," Verbruggen pointed out. "You speak."

"Could Ellen have murdered Nazrullah? And is the Afghan government hushing it up?"

Richardson shook his head. "Shah Khan is the Afghan government."

Verbruggen was not so easily satisfied. "Has any American seen Nazrullah alive?"

"Yes," Richardson replied, consulting his notes. "That irrigation expert from Colorado, Professor

Pritchard, reported that on his way to ascertain water flow along the Persian border he had talked with Nazrullah at Qala Bist."

"Would he have known Nazrullah if he saw him?"

"His letter refers to him as a fine young man with a beard who graduated from the Wharton School. Must have been Nazrullah."

"Next guess," the acting ambassador snapped.

"Could she have defected to Russia?" I asked. This was 1946 and most Americans would have viewed my question with amazement, for in the States it was not yet recognized that Russia was our major enemy. In Afghanistan, living next door to Russia as we did, we knew.

"The thought's been going through my head," the acting ambassador replied. The Kabul dispatches of 1946 and 1947, if they are ever published, are going to make our staff look like a group of military geniuses. Partly this was because Richardson, our intelligence man, saw things very clearly; partly because Captain Verbruggen had a feeling for military matters; and partly because all of us on the staff could add two and two.

"We know that the Afghans hate communism," I argued, "especially its attitude on religion, but we also know that secret Russian missions have been operating in this country. Now if an American woman let it be known that she was fed up with America and Afghanistan . . . well, mightn't the Russians approach her?"

Richardson tried to light his pipe and said offhandedly, "You'd probably be on better grounds if you investigated the likelihood that she defected to the Chinese. Don't forget that lands controlled by the Chinese Communists touch Afghanistan on the north."

"I think we're up the wrong tree," Captain Verbruggen said. "If she had gone over to either Russia or

China, those governments would use that fact to embarrass us. They haven't done so."

"On the other hand, sir," I argued, "this girl's whole personality, her attitude toward her home . . . Everything indicates the kind of person who might turn traitor."

The acting ambassador refused comment and changed the line of discussion radically. "Any chance she's in Europe? Why couldn't she be toasting her heels in Venice with some Italian grand duke?"

Richardson treated this with contempt. "The chances of an American girl's entering India without being noticed, then sailing from Karachi or Bombay, are just not measurable. Can't be done. You want to call the British embassy to check?"

"I withdraw," Verbruggen surrendered. There was silence, after which he turned to me, saying, "You find out what happened, Miller."

"I'll do my best, sir," I said briskly.

"You'll find out," he growled, "or you'll damned well be back in the navy." The group laughed and Richardson left, followed by Nexler. When we were alone Captain Verbruggen put his arm about me and said, "Miller, it would be a feather in my cap if we could get this Jaspar thing cleared up before the old man gets back from Hong Kong."

"I'll do my damnedest," I promised.

"On the other hand," he cautioned, "don't rush things. This is your first big mission. Ask a lot of questions. Learn the country. Don't be afraid of looking stupid, because one of these days we could be driven into war across this terrain, and you'd be the only American who'd ever seen parts of it. Keep your eyes open."

"I will."

Suddenly he cried, with real emotion, "God, I wish I was going in your place. Good luck, kid."

As I left his office I thought: Nexler's dying to get to Paris and Richardson wants to get back to Washington. But Verbruggen and I love Afghanistan. Who cares about the dysentery and the loneliness? For I knew that Afghanistan was the toughest assignment on record. Here was the post which sooner or later tested a man, and for me the preliminaries were over. I was about to plunge into one of the world's great cauldrons.

5

While it was still dark, Nur Muhammad helped me pack the jeep for the trip to Kandahar. We stowed our extra tins of motor oil, the precautionary spark plugs, the rope, an extra jack, sleeping bags and medical supplies. We had requisitioned from the embassy four cases of army K-rations, two spare tires and some jugs of boiled water for drinking. Seeing us on that wintry morning, you would not have guessed that we were embarking on a routine trip from the capital of a sovereign nation to the secondary metropolis nearby. We looked more like adventurers about to set forth in some dubious caravan, which we were.

Before we left Kabul, where wolves had again made forays down narrow streets, I asked Nur if he would drive me past the home of Nazrullah's family, and he obliged. It lay in the southern arm of the city, on the way to Kandahar, and when we drew up before its tall, fast-bound wooden gate, studded with ancient nails and bolts, I realized that I was once more facing the portal of an Afghan fortress. The surrounding mud walls were many feet high, so that nothing inside was visible. No agency in Afghanistan other than force was entitled to break its way into these confines, in which a woman could be kept hidden indefinitely without the assent of any but her jailers.

While we sat in the car inspecting the silent and forbidding gate, we became aware of someone inside the walls who had been alerted by our presence, and after a while a feeble light, obviously from an open flame, was seen glimmering through the chinks in the weatherbeaten gate. The light stopped moving. Someone on the other side was staring at us through the gate. No one spoke.

After several minutes I whispered to Nur, "You suppose they know who we are?"

"They know," he replied. "The jeep means ferangi."

"Why don't we ask where Ellen is?" I suggested, certain that Nur would dismiss the proposal as fruitless. To my surprise he shrugged his shoulders, descended from the jeep and went dutifully to the gate. Even though the unseen watcher must have followed his approach, nothing happened. Finally Nur surrendered and went through the formality of tugging the bell cord.

Inside the stout wall there was a clangor and the light moved. After the customary interval the small one-person doorway that had been cut into one of the larger gates swung open and a thin man swathed in rags and a dirty turban peered out. While Nur spoke in Pashto he listened impassively, then shook his head no. The little door squeaked shut in the darkness and between the chinks I could see the flickering light disappear.

"They don't know where she is," Nur reported, and in our strong headlights I caught my last glimpse of the mysterious wall.

The road from Kabul south to Kandahar was about three hundred miles long and had been in existence for some three thousand years. Judging from its condition at the end of winter in 1946, the last repairs must have been completed at least eight hundred years ago, for each mile of the road involved a particular adventure.

The potholes were so deep that we could travel at

no more than twenty, and wherever water had seeped under the rocks, the entire roadbed vanished and we had to set out across rutted fields until the antique roadway reestablished itself. In the darkness we passed many vehicles disabled, their passengers sleeping unconcernedly until spare parts could be procured from Kabul on foot.

Promptly at six, for we were in the vernal equinox, the sun rose over the eastern hills and illuminated the noble, desolate landscape of central Afghanistan. Far to the west stood the Koh-i-Baba range, white in majesty and completely impenetrable as long as snow preempted the passes. Nearer at hand stood an occasional home, a low, mud-brick affair entirely surrounded by walls along whose tops thorns had been trained to grow and broken bottles implanted. Close to the road stretched shreds of fields which in good years might produce scattered crops; but usually rain stayed in the mountains and the farmer's work proved fruitless.

The dominant aspect of the landscape was its color. Everything not covered with snow was brown: the mountains, the mud walls, the land where nothing grew. The human stragglers on their way to Kabul seemed all a dirty brown. Once their shirts, hanging to their knees, must have been white, but much wear and little laundry had rendered them brown. Even the dogs were brown.

We stopped once to watch a group of men playing with one of these dogs, but the beast knew we were strangers and began snarling, whereupon the men picked up small rocks and with prodigious accuracy threw at the animal until he retreated. "I should think they'd injure the dog," I protested, but Nur pointed out that none of the stones had been thrown with force.

"They love their scrawny dogs," he assured me. "Kill an Afghan's dog and he'll track you through the Hindu Kush."

To travel from Kabul to Kandahar at the time of equinox—we were starting our journey on the twenty-first of March, the last day of winter, the first of spring—was comparable to traveling from the snowbound mountains of New York to the spring-drenched warmth of Virginia, for as we moved south we rushed headlong into the Asian spring, and we traveled from snow to flowers. Before the first morning had passed we were seeing blue flowers beside the road and yellow birds speeding across brown fields. The great bleak plains, so recently under snow, were beginning to look almost alluring.

Our first stopping point was the ancient capital of Afghanistan, the storied city of Ghazni, and I use the word *storied* with care, because when it was announced that I had drawn Afghanistan as my first diplomatic post I studied what I could of local history and no existing city captured my imagination as Ghazni did, for from its many-towered walls there had issued in the year 1000, a convenient date to remember, a barbaric conqueror of unmatched vigor. He was known as Mahmud of Ghazni, and every year for more than a quarter of a century this fearful Afghan had led his armies down through the Khyber Pass and onto the plains of India, where he was not once defeated nor even successfully resisted.

The chroniclers said of him, "Mahmud kept the cities of India tethered in the sun like fat cows, which he came regularly to milk." He murdered thousands, swept up the riches of a continent, and transformed his ugly little Afghan city of Ghazni into one of the contemporary centers of education, wealth and power.

I remember that on the day when I first encountered his name, one of the most lustrous in Asian history—comparable perhaps to Charlemagne in Europe—I interrupted my studies to ask some twenty other graduate students then joining the State Department if they had ever heard of Mahmud of Ghazni, and none knew the name. I think it was then that I realized how completely unknown a land Afghanistan was, and I discovered to my chagrin that even learned people were vaguely of the opinion that Afghanistan was an alternate name for Ethiopia. Many of my friends assumed I had been assigned to Africa.

Well, I learned who Mahmud of Ghazni was, and now with Nur Muhammad's guidance I was approaching his city. What a drab, desolate disappointment it was from a distance, a scrawny collection of mean brown buildings surrounded by an ugly mud wall. From where I first saw Ghazni, it looked like a nondescript collection of cattle barns. There were no trees, no cooling river, no spacious approach. It was to remain my major disillusionment in Afghanistan, this dreary, almost forsaken jumble of mud huts that had once been the capital of much of the world.

But when we reached the wall there were compensations, and I must confess that when I stood before the great south gate I did feel a stirring of imagination and an echo, however remote, of the imperial Mahmud. The gate was huge and excellently built. It was protected by two stout round towers whose battlements were slotted for rifle fire and whose windows were mere slits for the accommodation of guns. To stand outside this gate amid a throng of travelers, seeking admission to the city, imparted a sense of history, and I could believe that it was from the security of these walls that Mahmud had issued on his yearly forays.

And when we had edged our jeep through the gates and into the narrow streets, even the dimmest mind could perceive that we were no longer in Kabul, where the embassies provided a spurious international flavor and where German engineers had at least brought the river under control. In Ghazni there were no German engineers and we were in the most ancient part of Asia.

In the little square in which we finally found ourselves, an earthen, unpaved square bordered by dusty shops and a filthy restaurant, every man we saw was dressed in dirty white trousers, knee-length shirt, western-style vest, shabby overcoat and voluminous turban. All wore open-toed sandals of ragged leather, and there was not a karakul cap to be seen. Nor were there any women, not even in chaderi. Men walked by lugging skins and furs, bladders filled with goats' milk, grapes and melons from the south, bundles of charcoal, and odds and ends of country produce. Compared to the bazaar at Kabul, this was mean indeed, for color was lacking, and movement, and foreign goods; but it was impressive in a timeless way and I was not unhappy when Nur parked the jeep and told me to guard it while he went searching for a place to stay, for the road was so bad that we could not hope to make Kandahar in one day and to stop south of Ghazni was unthinkable.

I had been studying the mean little square for perhaps ten minutes when I found myself surrounded by Afghans in tattered clothes, ordinary men from the city who were interested in the ferangi. They were pleased when I spoke Pashto and were telling me that in the Ghazni area it had been a bad winter with little food when Nur Muhammad returned. As he did so, the crowd mysteriously dispersed, and I supposed that Nur had reprimanded them, but I saw that what had scared them off was the approach of two mullahs, tall, bearded men in dark robes and scowls of intense hatred. They marched up to the jeep, which they knew to be alien to their interests, and began berating it, not me.

Their fury abated when I spoke to them in Pashto, explaining that I was their friend. Granted this assurance, they relaxed their animosity and began discussing my trip with me. They proved to be pleasant men, and under Nur's careful persuasion they actually started laughing and the crowd regathered. Nur assured them that the ferangi would not molest the girls of Ghazni nor would he drink alcohol. They bowed as they departed, and Nur whispered, "Mullahs could be handled . . . if we had enough time."

Nur now called a little boy to lead me to the front of the hotel while he drove the jeep to a compound in the back, where it could be locked up and guarded during our stay in Ghazni. The boy, dressed in pitiful rags, shuffled along a narrow alley and brought me finally to my first Afghan hotel, which I approached with real excitement. I will say merely that it had no glass in any window, no lock on any door, no water, no heat, no food, no bed, no bedclothes, and no flooring but earth. It did, however, possess one characteristic that made it memorable: on the dirt floor of our room were piled five of the most beautiful Persian rugs I had ever seen. They had been woven in Russia at the ancient city of Samarkand and had been smuggled into Afghanistan by itinerant traders who had hauled them over mountains and across deserts. They were poems in thread, three reddish blue and two in stunning white and gold. They had lain on the hotel floor for many years, where the extreme dryness had kept them from rotting, and they seemed now as colorful as when they left the loom. They made the hotel livable and I was dismayed when Nur Muhammad began unloading every item of our cargo, including the two spare tires, onto them.

"Don't lug that stuff in here!" I protested.

"What shall I do with it?" he asked.

"Leave it in the jeep," I said.

"In the jeep?" Nur gasped. "They'd steal everything we own."

"You hired two men with shotguns," I argued.

"They're to see that nobody steals the wheels," Nur explained. "Miller Sahib, if we left these spare tires in the jeep, the guards would sell them in ten minutes."

I was disgusted and said, "I'm hungry. Let's go out and get some food."

"We can't both go," Nur replied.

"Why not? The mullahs know you're here as my friend."

"I mean the room. We can't leave it unguarded. One of us has to stay."

I looked out the back window, a mere slit for rifle fire, and pointed to the two big, bearded guards lolling in the empty jeep. "Let's put one of them in the room."

"Them!" Nur exploded. "They'd steal everything we have and shoot us when we got back."

"Then why are you paying them?" I demanded.

"To keep the wheels on the jeep," Nur repeated.

I couldn't hide my irritation, so Nur took me to the front window, another rifle slot, and showed me the hotel courtyard, where forty or fifty hungry-looking tribesmen had gathered. "Miller Sahib," Nur whispered, "they're just waiting for us to leave this room."

It was decided that I should eat first, and it was about three in the afternoon when I returned to the square seeking a restaurant. I use the word loosely, for all I could find was the filthy corner café I had seen earlier. It contained one rickety table, three chairs and a water bottle whose sides could not be seen for flyspecks. Its aroma, however, was another matter, for I had grown partial to Afghan food and this café had some of the best. The waiter, a man in an unbelievably tattered overcoat and green turban, brought me a chunk of nan, a kind of thick, crunchy tortilla made of coarse, nutritious flour and baked in slabs the size of snowshoes. It was, most of us thought, the best bread we had ever eaten, for it was baked in clay ovens over charcoal and tasted of the fields where the wheat had grown. The waiter also plopped down a large dish of pilau, a steaming mixture of barley, cracked wheat, onions, raisins, pine nuts, orange peel and shreds of roast lamb. On these two dishes, nan and pilau, I would exist during my entire trip, and I would never tire of either.

As I ate, men with whom I had been talking earlier

reassembled about me. Two sat on the frail chairs. Others stood behind me, and from time to time I offered them chunks of nan, which they used as scoops to attack the pilau. Perhaps seven or eight men thus dipped their fingers into my meal with me, and we developed that camaraderie which is so marked a feature of Afghan life. As I was paying for my meal and bidding my guests good-by, some men in long coats ran across the square, shouting. I did not understand their words and was about to return to the hotel so that Nur could eat, when the men around me became very excited and tugged at my sleeve. I was to follow them. Together we trailed the first men across the square and out of the gates of the city. I remember thinking that I should return to Nur Muhammad, but some evil genius kept me running and soon I was in the midst of a mob converging on a spot outside the gates where a heavy stake had been driven into the earth.

On the far side of the stake, which rose to a height of seven feet, stood four mullahs, including the two who had accosted me earlier. They were mournful, aloof and terrifying. In their beards and turbans they seemed like patriarchs of old, and I was assailed by the uneasy feeling that I had intruded upon some Biblical scene which should have terminated twenty-five centuries ago. The lean, angry mullahs were from the Old Testament. The string of camels placidly grazing by the crumbling walls were of an ancient time, and the crowd of turbaned men, their faces brown from sun, their beards gray with desert dust, could have been waiting for some religious rite in Nineveh or Babylon.

As I looked hurriedly about I could detect only one note that indicated we were in the twentieth century. Outside the gates of Ghazni, jammed into a crumbling fragment of wall that may once have formed part of a fort guarding the imperial city, stood a telegraph pole which carried three precarious wires from Ghazni to Kabul. What I was about to witness could thus have been telegraphed to the whole world in a matter of minutes, but no one in Ghazni, except perhaps Nur Muhammad, would have considered it worthy of report.

The mullahs were praying, and the declining afternoon sun threw handsome shadows athwart their faces. The prayer stopped. From the nearby gates marched four soldiers bearing carbines and bandoleers, leading between them a hesitant, barefooted figure covered by a coarse white chaderi. In Kabul I had seen pleated chaderies of exquisite cloth with embroidered peepholes for the eyes, and the savageness of the custom was temporarily overlooked; but in Ghazni this chaderi was a coarse, dirty white shroud and the opening no more than a tiny square of cheap mosquito netting.

I was not told who hid inside the chaderi, but it had to be a woman, for so far as I knew men never wore the shroud. Whoever it was must have seen the looks of bitter hatred that greeted her as she passed.

When the soldiers reached the stake, they inexpertly drove several nails into it and lashed their prisoner's hands to these nails, at the same time securing her ankles to the bottom of the stake. When they stepped back, the dirty white chaderi fell completely over the bare feet and the prisoner was wholly masked. She was still free, however, to look out upon the world of hate-filled faces.

Now the four mullahs prayed, and the crowd responded in a ritual I did not understand; but this was followed by a speech from one of the mullahs who had accosted me in the square, and what he said was in Pashto, and this I understood clearly, though what it signified I was not then competent to guess. He shouted mournfully, "This is the woman taken in adultery! This is the whore of Ghazni! This is the raging insult to all men who revere God!" He ended and I stared at the shrouded figure, trying to anticipate what her punishment was to be. If she heard the charge, she did not tremble.

Another mullah stepped forward and cried, "We have studied the case of this woman taken in adultery and she is guilty. We submit her to the judgment of the men of Ghazni." His companions assented, and the first mullah led the bearded men back through the gates of Ghazni and we saw them no more.

I had turned to watch the mullahs and did not see what happened next, but I heard a thudding sound and a gasp. I looked around quickly in time to see that a rather large stone had apparently struck the woman and had fallen at her feet. The gasp must have come from her.

Now the men at my right, the ones who had eaten with me and brought me to the scene, knelt to find stones, and the smaller rocks they discarded, but soon all were armed, and with the same skill that I had seen directed at the dog, they began throwing at the shrouded figure. From all sides stones whizzed toward the stake, and most struck, and it was obvious that punishment for adultery in Afghanistan was severe.

The woman refused to cry out, but a cheer soon rose from the crowd. One powerful man had found an especially good stone, large and jagged, and he threw this with force, aiming it carefully at her body, and it struck so violently in her abdomen that soon the first blood of the afternoon showed through the chaderi. It was this that brought the cheer, but I remember thinking how indecent it was that a human body which none could see should send its blood through the interstices of a shroud and deposit it in sunlight as testimony of punishment.

Another stone of equal size struck the woman's shoulder. It brought both blood and cheers. I felt sickness in my throat and thought: Who halts the punishment?

Then I almost fainted. A large man with unerring aim pitched a jagged rock of some size and caught the woman in the breast. Blood spurted through the torn chaderi and at last the woman uttered a piercing scream. I wanted to run away, but I was hemmed in by maniacs and I had been warned by many accounts that for a foreigner to make one mistake at such a scene might lead to his being killed. I prayed that the men had had enough, and then I saw why the soldiers had hammered the nails in the stake. They kept the ropes from slipping, and when the prisoner fainted, her bloodstained chaderi going all limp, these nails prevented her from falling to the ground.

Surely, I thought, the soldiers will release her now. But they watched impassively while men from all sides gathered fresh ammunition.

The sagging body was struck eight or nine times in the next fusillade, but mercifully the woman could not have known. Now a burly man shouted that he had found the perfect rock and others must stand clear. The crowd obeyed and watched breathlessly as he took careful aim, whirled his arm, and launched his missile with ugly force. It flashed across the fifteen yards separating the men from their target and sped accurately as intended, striking the unconscious woman in the face. Quick blood marked the spot and the crowd cheered.

The blow was so terrible that it wrenched the prisoner's hands from the nails and allowed her to collapse in a heap about the stake. As she did so the crowd broke loose and rushed to the fallen body, smashing it with boulders which no man, however powerful, could have thrown from a distance. Again and again they dropped the huge rocks on the fallen body until they crushed it completely, continuing the wild sport until they had built a small mound of stones over the scene, as a pauper family in the desert might have marked a burial.

In a state of shock I returned through the gates of Ghazni. I passed the restaurant where the fellowship had been so congenial and was greeted by the men who had thrown the largest rocks. They were gathering to discuss the execution and congratulate each other upon expert performances. I got to the hotel to find that Nur Muhammad, realizing I had been sidetracked, had sent a boy for some pilau, which he had eaten with greasy fingers. He was now asleep on the Persian rugs, but when I entered the room he wakened like a prudent guard.

"Why are you so white?" he asked.

"A woman taken in adultery," I mumbled.

"Stones?" he asked.

"Yes."

Nur beat the rugs, then put his hands over his face. "What a terrible disgrace! My poor country!"

"It was horrible," I said weakly. "How can you permit it?"

He sat up, cross-legged on the rug, while I sank down on the spare tires. "Don't you suppose we're ashamed?" he asked. "Moheb Khan . . . the king? If they'd seen this . . ."

"Why don't they stop it?" I demanded angrily.

"If they tried to stop it, Miller Sahib, the men you watched today and their brothers in the hills would storm Kabul and kill you and me and Moheb Khan and the king, too."

"Impossible!" I cried.

"They've done so in the past," Nur insisted. "In Kabul we have perhaps two thousand educated Afghans who know that things like this must end. In Kandahar maybe five hundred. But in Ghazni none. We're outnumbered twelve million madmen to three thousand . . . perhaps five thousand. I'm not sorry you saw the execution, Miller Sahib. You'll understand my country better."

"Will things go on like this indefinitely?" I asked.

"No," Nur said firmly. "Across the Oxus people just like us used to behave the way you saw today. Public executions supervised by mullahs were common in places like Samarkand. But the Communists from

Moscow and Kiev said they had to stop. The chaderi was outlawed. Women were freed. Miller, we have ten years to halt these terrible things. If we don't . . . Russia's going to come down and stop them for us."

"Does the government realize this?"

"Of course. Do you think men like Shah Khan are stupid? The government knows it. But twelve million citizens don't." Nur rose and stamped impatiently about the room, picking his way through our scattered gear. "Don't you understand the problems that face a man like me? Right now in Ghazni, a few hours' journey from Kabul, every man who participated in that stoning fully expects to continue doing so for the rest of his life. If you told them tonight that you were going to halt all this, they would kill you."

I was suddenly assaulted by a terrifying premonition and I leaped off the spare tires to grab Nur by the arm. "Is this what happened to Ellen Jaspar?"

Nur relaxed and started laughing. "No, Miller Sahib. If that had happened we'd have known in Kabul."

I said, "I feel sick. Let's take a walk."

"I can't leave the goods," he protested.

"Call one of the guards," I said sharply. "I've got to get out of this town."

"Go ahead. I'll stay here and guard the things."

"I'm afraid to go alone," I said honestly.

"You're wise," Nur agreed, and against his better judgment he started to summon one of the guards. Then he paused to ask, "You assume responsibility for this?" I said I did.

Nur told the bearded warrior, with gun and bandoleer, "If one thing is missing when we return, you'll be shot. Understand?" The fierce renegade nodded and when we left we heard him piling our goods against the door to keep out would-be intruders.

We walked through the square, where the enthusiastic executioners hailed me again, and down to the gate, where I could see the ominous stake rising from the mound of rocks. Dogs were nosing at the blood.

"How long will the body remain?" I asked.

"They'll take it away tonight," Nur assured me. Then he said fervently, "One thing you must understand, Miller Sahib. Today's execution must have looked like a riot. It wasn't. Mullahs study these cases with care and no decision is reached casually. Strictly speaking, what you saw was a planned, legal act of justice. But a horrifying one."

We turned away from the funeral mound and walked south along an old caravan route until we had lost sight of Ghazni. We must have covered four miles when I saw off to the east an unfamiliar sight: something that looked like a flock of large black birds assembled on an empty plain, and I expected the huge birds to take wing; but as we moved closer I saw that we had come upon a tribe of nomads who move back and forth across Afghanistan with the seasons.

"Povindahs!" Nur exclaimed with marked excitement. Running ahead, he called, "Look at those women!"

From a distance I watched the nomad women, dressed in black with flashing jewelry. They moved with fierce grace—I can call it nothing else—and wore no chaderi. They were free, the wild nomads who traveled the upland plateaus of Asia. The sun was setting now, and its red rays illuminated their dark faces, lending them an animal quality of absorbed preoccupation with the world about them. For more than three thousand years their ancestors had moved back and forth across the boundaries of Asia and no one had found a way to stop them.

In their annual passage across Afghanistan the Povindahs must have looked with disgust at the way the Afghans imprisoned their women, hiding them in sacks and treating them like chattels, while at the same time the Povindah women were free to move about as they wished.

"They're an insult to your whole system," I told Nur.

"You're right," he agreed. "But the price they pay for this freedom is appalling."

"They look fairly happy to me."

"They're completely ostracized. When they move through our country they remain a people apart."

"Then why were you so excited when you spotted them?"

Nur laughed. "Afghan men are lured to these black tents like flies to honey. Many of my friends have tried to spend the night in there." He pointed to the tents where the women moved. "But the Povindah men are watchful to keep us away."

One such nomad rode up to us now, on a brown horse. He was a tall dark-faced man with mustaches and a flowing turban. Across his chest were bandoleers and with one arm he pointed a rifle at us casually and said in Pashto, "Keep away!" Nur spoke with him for a moment and he replied graciously, but at the end he repeated his warning. "Keep away!" Spurring his horse, he rode back to the tents.

"He suspected we were government officials."

"Where do they go from here?" I asked.

"They follow the melting snow."

We started to leave when I saw from the corner of my eye a figure in red dart out from one of the tents and disappear behind another, as a bright-colored bird will flash through trees in spring. I turned to look more carefully and was rewarded when a young girl, dressed all in red and bangles, reappeared chasing a goat, but before I could see her well, she disappeared again and I thought: She reminds me of Siddiqa. Like Shah Khan's granddaughter she seemed a person of unusual grace and sexual suggestion.

Nur Muhammad, who missed little, which was why the Afghan government employed him to be employed by the American government, chuckled and asked, "Fascinating, isn't she?"

"Why does she wear red?"

"Shows she's not married . . ."

"Look!" I cried. From behind the tent nearest us the wayward goat burst free and ran directly at us. Hot after him came the determined girl, and some forty yards from where we stood she tackled the animal, rolling him in the dust. I saw her dark skin, her flashing eyes, and two long pigtails which swung in the sunlight as she wrestled with the goat. I could understand the fascination felt by the Afghan men for such a person, and as we watched she skillfully led the goat back to its tether.

"Makes me feel good to know that such people are also a part of Afghanistan," I observed as we walked away.

"They're not our people," Nur corrected. "In the winter they go to India. In the summer they go north. They use us only as a corridor."

"What country do they belong to?" I asked.

"I never considered the matter," Nur replied. "Legally, I suppose they're Indians."

It was night when we approached the Ghazni gate, on whose ramparts flickering lights moved back and forth. It was a solemn moment, at the end of day, when the ancient city was settling down for sleep, and we paused to watch the towers etched in the glow from some improvised fire where travelers outside the city were roasting a sheep. In after years, whenever I have thought of an Afghan city it has been Ghazni, looming in the darkness.

When we passed the scene of the execution Nur Muhammad begged, "Don't look again, Miller Sahib. This is our shame." And we returned to the square, where shadowy lights illuminated the corner café. We took our seats at the table and good-natured men elbowed up to us to discuss the day's events; and against my will I found myself entangled with these bewildered, half-savage men who were fighting the contemporary world, yet who were so hungry to know about America. They ate our nan and shared our pilau. They told us of the problems facing Ghazni—the food supply, the taxes and the cost of horses—and at the end of our meal they walked with us to our hotel, where they entered and sat for hours, cross-legged on the Persian rugs, talking . . . talking . . .

6

Shortly after dawn we left Ghazni, passing on the way the scene of execution, from which the stake had been removed, for wood in Afghanistan was precious. The stones, however, were left conveniently scattered in case another culprit should be apprehended.

We had been on the road for less than an hour when I discovered an important fact about Afghanistan which none of my reading had discussed; yet it was so fundamental that if one missed its significance he missed the meaning of this country. I refer to the bridges of Afghanistan.

When we came to the first one I did not appreciate its importance. It was a beautiful bridge, built in the early 1900's, I judged, by some expert engineer. It was well designed, contained good stonework and was ornamented by four crenelated towers. Unfortunately, a recent flood had eaten away the approaches to the bridge, leaving it an isolated structure that now served no useful purpose. To cross the river we had to leave the road, descend by gullies to the river, ford it, and reverse the process until we climbed back onto the road. Obviously, in time of storm traffic on the road would halt, but I remember thinking, while fording the river: That's a handsome bridge . . . almost a work of art.

Thirty minutes later we came upon an even more beautiful bridge, with eight towers done in the most sturdy style, a kind of military Gothic common to old French and German towns. It was a splendid structure and I studied it with some care, for which I had ample time since its approaches had also been washed away. We were thus forced once more to ford the river, and I could see the bridge from below.

The stonework was exemplary; the joints were interesting because I could not detect how they were sealed. It looked as if the architect had depended upon the skill of his cutters to give him a joint which held of its own friction and weight. Moreover the structure was well designed, with the eight towers adding a striking note. It was a bridge to admire, and only the advent of some unexpected flood had rendered it useless.

But when we came to the third fine bridge and found its approaches gone too, I grew irritated and asked Nur Muhammad, "Are all the bridges like this?"

"They are," he said sadly.

"Why?"

"We call them 'Bridges Afghan Style.' They can't be used."

"What happened?" I demanded.

"Afghanistan's folly," he said, and it was obvious that he wished to drop the matter.

At the seventh washed-out bridge we had to ford a river much deeper than we had anticipated and got stuck in the middle with our bottoms wet and our engine useless, waiting till a truck came along to haul us out. We had nothing to do but study the bridge overhead, and it was perhaps the loveliest of all: its arch was graceful, its turrets solid, its brickwork neat, and its impression substantial.

"Beautiful bridge," I admitted grudgingly. "Who built it?"

"A German. One of the worst tragedies that ever hit our nation."

It was a pleasure to talk with Nur, for he spoke

idiomatic English while I was fairly competent in Pashto; for practice we liked a system whereby I spoke in his language and he replied in mine, but when discussing complex subjects each used his own language. To an outsider our conversation would be confusing, for often we switched languages in midsentence. Now, with my bottom wet and cold, I was angry and spoke in harsh Pashto.

"What happened with these bridges, Nur?"

He replied in careful Pashto. "A disaster. We were taking our first step out of the Dark Ages and the Germans said, 'It's stupid to have your two major cities unconnected by a road.' They arranged a big loan and gave us experts who surveyed the road and showed how it could be built. When the king saw the survey, very neatly drawn with little pictures, he approved and said, 'We're a modern country now. We must have a modern road.' Then he asked who would build the bridges, and the Germans lent us a learned professor-architect who had built many bridges, and the work started."

Nur pointed up at the bridge. "He was a brilliant man who demanded the best. Look at that brickwork. You don't find much of that in Afghanistan. It was his idea to mark each bridge with distinctive turrets and ornamentation, for he told us, 'A bridge is more than a bridge. It's a symbol connecting past and present.' He said that towers and intricate brickwork were part of the Afghan soul. In a famous speech he gave in Kabul he said that he had taken the idea of towers from the family forts that mark Afghanistan."

"I didn't see the relationship," I remarked, but Nur pointed down the river toward a private fort and then I knew what the professor-architect had been after.

"He built some twenty bridges," Nur explained as we sat in the cold river—and I mean in the river, for the jeep kept settling—"and all the time he was working, a handful of Afghans like Shah Khan and my father kept warning him, 'Doctor, that bridge is fine for a well-controlled European river, but has anyone told you about our Afghan rivers in the spring?' He replied angrily that he had built bridges over some of the finest rivers in Europe . . . much greater rivers, he assured us, than these trivial desert streams."

Nur looked sadly at the bridge and said in English, "You understand, of course, that this all happened before I was born." Then he explained in Pashto, "But I remember my father telling us later, 'We went to the government and warned them, "Those German bridges will not stand up against our rivers in the spring." ' They were told, 'You think you're smart enough to tell a German how to do his job? A man who has built bridges all over Europe?' My father replied that he had never seen a European river and it looked to him as if the German had never seen an Afghan river, and there the matter was left."

The jeep settled deeper and Nur said in English, "Shah Khan is a learned man and a brave one. In those days he was without the dignity of his present position, but he refused to drop the matter. He told the Germans"—and here Nur Muhammad reverted to Pashto—" 'These bridges are far more important to us than they are to you. They're our first contact with the western world. If they succeed, we who want to modernize this nation will succeed. If they fail, dreadful consequences may follow. Now please, Professor-Architect, listen when I tell you that sometimes in the spring what you call our trivial desert streams roar out of the mountains two miles wide. They move boulders as big as houses. They destroy everything not perched on a hill. And the next day they're little streams again. Professor, build us big broad bridges and leave off the pretty towers.'

"The German professor was furious that Shah Khan would dare speak to him directly. He insisted that a meeting of government be convened, at which he made an impassioned speech. 'I want to tell you that I have sunk my pillars to bedrock. I have built as no bridges in Afghanistan have ever been built before. When the floods that Shah Khan speaks of meet my bridges not one bridge will fall down.' I must say that Shah Khan was a fighter. He replied, 'Professor-Architect, you're entirely right. The bridges will not fall down. Of that I'm convinced. But the rivers of Afghanistan, like the people of Afghanistan, never attack the enemy head on. Your stout bridges are like the British army. Their soldiers were ten times better than ours . . . better fed . . . better armed. But we didn't march up to the British in double file so they could shoot us down. In a thousand tricky ways we surrounded them. They protested, "This is no decent way to fight," and we destroyed them. Our rivers will destroy your bridges, Professor-Architect, because they're European bridges and they're not prepared to fight Afghan rivers. What we want, Professor-Architect, are tricky Afghan bridges.'

"The German replied, 'A bridge is a bridge,' and Shah Khan shouted, 'Not in Afghanistan.' The quarrel was taken to the king himself, and he ordered Shah Khan to shut up. The German ambassador explained everything by pointing out that Shah Khan had been educated in France and was thus emotionally unstable.

"So the bridges were built, and the next year there were no spring floods. For eighteen months we enjoyed a wonderful road between Kabul and Kandahar, and Afghanistan was spurting to catch up with the world. In that second winter there was a great snowfall in the mountains followed by an unusually warm spring, which sent towering floods down the gullies, moving boulders as big as houses. When these floods struck the bridges, the German was proved right. His stone pillars stood fast, as he had predicted. The bridges were as strong as he said. But they were so narrow in span that our rivers simply went around them. All the approaches were gouged out and the bridges stood isolated."

"Why not rebuild the approaches?" I asked.

"We did," Nur replied. "Another flood took them out. So we rebuilt again. Another flood. My father calculated that to keep the bridges operating would require a hundred thousand men working around the year. So after the third flood the government said, 'Let them go. Who needs bridges?' And the dream road that was to have bound our nation together remained an aching monument to the folly of man."

"What happened to the professor?" I asked.

"After the first flood he traveled from Kabul to Kandahar, refusing to believe what he saw. 'I've built a hundred bridges over some of the greatest rivers in Europe,' he shouted. He stood in the middle of one little stream two feet deep and wailed, 'How could this little puddle wash out a bridge?' He refused, even then, to see the boulders which that little puddle had moved down from the mountain."

"Did he leave the country?"

"No, he went back to Kabul and boasted to everyone who would listen that not a single one of his pillars had been destroyed. He made himself what the English call 'quite a bore.' He insisted upon explaining about the bridges. The German embassy finally called him in, and what they said we never found out, but that night he went to his room and blew his brains out."

Nur shook his head sadly, still waiting for a truck to appear. "You can't imagine the tragedy those bridges became. Whenever the government wanted to do some new thing the mullahs and the mountain chiefs would laugh: 'Remember the German bridges!' You're an American and you may not like Germans since you fought them twice, but in Afghanistan they were wonderful people. Most of what we have that's good came from the Germans, but after the bridges even they were held in suspicion. Their effectiveness was chopped in half. Those damned bridges!"

He shook his head, then asked, "By the way, you're

meeting a German doctor in Kandahar, aren't you?"

"How did you know?" I asked.

As soon as I uttered the words I could have kicked myself. Perhaps it was the coldness of the river that had made me thoughtless, but the damage was done. Nur stammered, "Well, I just know."

It was a rule in Afghan-American relations that neither side would embarrass the other regarding spies like Nur Muhammad on their side and Richardson on ours. It's true that Nur had slipped when he let me know that somehow or other he had found out that one of my missions in Kandahar was to inspect Dr. Otto Stiglitz; he should have kept his mouth shut. But once he did betray himself, I should never have challenged him. I had humiliated a good friend and an able spy. I was sorry.

He recovered by saying, "In a few miles . . . if we ever get out of this river . . . you'll see a bridge that my father and Shah Khan built. You'll laugh at it, but it's stood for more than thirty years."

A truck finally arrived and shouting men plunged into the river with ropes, which they attached to our front axle. With relative ease they pulled us free, then refused pay. We offered them cigarettes, which gratified them, and with much laughter they assured us that the rivers to the south would give no trouble. "But in two more weeks. Whooo, whooo! Floods everywhere. Road washed out for six or seven days."

When we resumed our journey Nur Muhammad said, "So if I tell you, Miller Sahib, that we have an Afghan way of doing things, and it works, please don't think I'm being obstinate. It's just possible that it does work."

"On the other hand," I argued, "if your country operates on unique solutions which no outsider can possibly understand, and if you use that as an excuse for doing nothing, then Russia will surely move in and make the changes for you."

"That's the battle we're engaged in, you and I,"

Nur agreed. "May we complete the job before Russia takes over."

"My government's policy is to help you," I said.

"But do be reasonable on one thing, Miller Sahib. We'll soon be in Kandahar, and you'll be forming opinions about Nazrullah. Let me assure you, he's on our side. He understands these matters better than either of us. Don't antagonize him at the beginning. If we destroy men like him, Afghanistan is lost."

"I don't want to destroy him," I snapped. "I want to find out where his wife is."

"So do I," Nur promised. "But in the Afghan way."

I was about to make an acid reply when Nur stopped our jeep at the bridge his father had built across one of the lesser streams, which the Germans had left for later. It was a silly affair that looked like a roller coaster at a run-down amusement park. It was built of wood and showed no evidence of European beauty, but it looked good for a hundred years. I thought: If a German professor-architect designed a bridge like this they'd hang him from the Brandenburger Tor.

"The secret," Nur pointed out, "is the big dips in the road before you reach the bridge itself. See how they work?"

"Not exactly," I replied.

With his forefinger he drew in the dust on the jeep windshield a profile of the bridge, showing a level road which dipped sharply, rose again to cross the bridge, then dipped on the other side. Nur's diagram looked like a scraggly capital W. "You might call it an Afghan bridge. It says to the river, 'I want to cross you, but I know I mustn't pinch you in. So when you want to run wild, go down the dips in the road and leave me alone. The rest of the year I'll leave you alone.' Silly, but it works."

Hesitantly I asked, "But during the flood you can't use the road?"

"Of course not," Nur agreed. "But if you allow the

river its way, it closes the road only once or twice a year. Who needs a road all year? Maybe it's better to give it a rest."

I thought of six good answers to this evasion, but I was constrained from using them by one overriding fact: while crossing rivers which the German had tried to conquer my bottom was wet, but while crossing on the tricky Afghan bridge my bottom was dry, and things had been this way for nearly fifty years. I kept my mouth shut.

We were about to resume our journey when a truck came down the road from Ghazni bearing a strange group of men who were dressed in vivid clothes of many colors and who wore their black hair long in the manner of ancient Greek page boys: thick bangs in front, elsewhere a shoulder-length bob. The faces of the men were aquiline and paler than those of the normal Afghan. All were handsome but there was one young man not yet in his twenties, I judged, who was positively beautiful. At first I wasn't sure he was a man and I must have pointed toward him as the truck crossed the bridge, for in Pashto he screamed a very filthy phrase, which caused his truckmates to cheer his insolence. In acknowledgment he made a pretty gesture like a girl, but he was startled when I shouted back in Pashto a phrase equally obscene. He laughed with gusto, moving his head so that his long hair flashed in the sunlight. Then he pointed at me with a languid, graceful arm and shouted, "I know what the ferangi wants, but he can't have it." Once more the men in the truck applauded their special member, and proceeded on their way to Kandahar.

"Who were they?" I asked.

"A dancing team," Nur replied. "They tour the country all year."

"The long hair?"

"Traditional. Judging from their clothes they must be a pretty good team."

We had completed most of the trip to Kandahar

when we overtook a young man in his early twenties, conspicuous because he wore not only the customary baggy pants and long shirt, but also a tattered overcoat made originally for a woman. It must have been a beautiful coat, with long flaring panels and a tight waist, and looked as if it might have come from Paris. Wine-red in color, it still possessed an air of grace.

I asked Nur to stop and we invited the young fellow to join us and his eyes widened with pleasure. He climbed in the back and adjusted his coat carefully over the spare tires on which he had to crouch.

"Ever been in a car before?" I asked in Pashto.

"No. It's exciting."

"Going to Kandahar?"

"Yes. To the spring festival."

"Ever been before?"

"No," he replied with a flashing smile. "But I've heard of Kandahar. Who hasn't?"

"Where do you live?"

"In the hills. Badakshar."

"I don't know it," I said to Nur, who with four or five pinpoint questions developed that it was several hundred miles north.

"Must be a dump," he said in English.

"Good place?" I asked in Pashto.

"Oh, yes!" the young man replied warmly. "Last year we had a good crop. In the autumn I sold a horse to the Povindahs as they went south. So I am coming to Kandahar with some money, I can tell you."

As soon as he said this he realized that his boasting might cost him his life, for he did not know who we were, and travelers were frequently murdered when it was known they had money. No doubt it had sometimes happened near Badakshar, and he looked at us fearfully.

"Shut your mouth, you fool," Nur snapped. "This time you're lucky. We're from the government."

The young man sighed and fell silent, but I asked him, "Where'd you get your coat?"

He was a congenial fellow who enjoyed talk, so he said quickly, "It's been in my family for many years. My father wore it to Kabul once. I haven't been to Kabul, but my brother wore it to Herat, which is a large city, he says."

"Where'd your father get the coat?"

The young man refused to answer and Nur Muhammad asked, "He killed a man for it, didn't he?" The traveler said nothing and Nur continued. "A stranger came through the mountains wearing this coat and your father got hungry for it. So he shot him, eh?"

I turned around to look at the young man, across whose face had come a beatific smile. He said, "You government men know everything, don't you? How to raise sheep. How to pay taxes. What roads to build. But you don't know about this coat, do you?" He chuckled and in sheer pleasure wrapped his arms a little tighter about himself.

"Who killed who?" Nur pressed.

The young man laughed openly and wagged his finger at Nur. "No, no, Mr. Government! That's one thing you're not going to know. And before you ask any more questions stop the car and I'll walk."

"Take it easy," Nur said.

"All right," the young man said gravely. "But forget about the coat."

We rode in silence for some miles, then heard a gasp from the rear of the jeep, for our rider had spotted some of the minarets of Kandahar. "It's the city!" he cried.

At first I saw nothing, but gradually the outlines of Kandahar, much older than Kabul, stood out against the horizon, and as we approached the walls I could not say who was the more excited, the young man with the European coat or the man from the American embassy about to engage in his first diplomatic mission.

We dropped our passenger in the middle of the city, a sprawling, dirty, camel-train metropolis whose mud walls looked as they had in the time of Darius the Persian. Nur found us a place to stay, much better than the hole in Ghazni but without the Persian rugs, and when the jeep was under armed guard I said, "Since you already know I'm here to see Dr. Stiglitz, could you find where he lives?"

"Now?" Nur asked.

"Now," I repeated, and he soon returned to lead me down a mean, narrow street where from one dirty mud wall projected the sign

DOKTOR
UNIVERSITY OF MUNICH

"Want me to stay with you?" Nur asked.

"No thanks."

"Kandahar is rougher than Kabul," Nur warned.

"I can handle myself," I assured him and entered the doctor's quarters.

The waiting room startled me. It was a small, dirt-floored, misshapen room with one bench and two very old chairs, on which sat men in turbans. One rose to offer me his seat, but I said in Pashto, "I'll stand," and the bronzed faces stared at me. Finally one asked, "Ferangi?" and I replied "American." The staring continued.

After some minutes the door leading to the doctor's office opened and a turbaned man departed. The next patient in line moved in to see the doctor and he must have said that there was a ferangi outside, for the door quickly burst open and a man of middle years and middle height rushed out, not to see me but to inspect me.

"Who are you?" he demanded in crisp, accented English. I gave my name and he drew back suspiciously. "What do you want?"

I tried to say that I'd wait until he was through, but he interrupted, shouting in Pashto, "These damned Americans come here demanding special privilege. They always do. Well, he must wait in line till all of you are finished . . . all of you."

In Pashto I said, "When you're through, Doctor."

My use of the language did not impress him. He stepped back, eyed me coldly and asked cautiously, "What is it you want?"

"Did you ever treat the American wife of Nazrullah?"

He glared at me, drew a protective shell of some kind about himself, and returned to his office, slamming the crude wooden door. In a flash he was back in the waiting room shouting in Pashto, "He must wait in line like all of you . . . to the very end." Once more he slammed the door.

By the time the last Afghan had seen the doctor, darkness had fallen and I was left alone in the shadowy waiting room. The wooden door creaked open and Dr. Stiglitz said graciously, "Now perhaps we can talk."

He did not invite me to his office, but he did leave the door open so that some light from the single unshaded electric bulb entered our room. He was balding, with a blond-gray German crew cut, and he had a pipe. He looked more frightened than bellicose, and his forehead was deeply wrinkled. "Yes, I treated Madame Nazrullah. Not quite a year ago. Sit down." He invited me to take one of the rickety chairs while he sat wearily on the other. "Be careful of the chair," he warned. "In Afghanistan wood is so scarce that any chair is a treasure. You can't imagine the trouble I had finding that door. I shouldn't have slammed it so, but visitors make me nervous." He made a conscious effort to relax and asked with some show of generosity, "Now what do you wish to know?"

Before I could speak, the door to the street opened and a thin Afghan in his fifties entered, followed by a chaderi. The woman stood obediently near the door while the man bowed and pleaded with the doctor. "My wife is ill," the man whispered.

"All right," Stiglitz growled in what I thought was an offensive manner. "She's late, but I'll help her." With no enthusiasm he returned to his office, and I moved my chair aside to let the woman follow, but she was left standing in the outer room and it was the nervous husband who joined the doctor. Stiglitz, seeing my surprise, said, "You'd better come in here. He wouldn't like you alone with his wife, and what happens may interest you."

So the American visitor, the German doctor and the Afghan husband consulted in the inner room while the sick woman remained standing by the door of the waiting room. "Tell her she can sit down," the doctor began, and the husband went to his wife, who obediently sat on the floor.

While he was gone I had an opportunity to inspect the doctor's office. It was a dirty little mud-floored room with practically no medical equipment and one cupboard containing flyspecked bottles of pills. There was a desk made of packing crates and the swinging, glaring electric light bulb.

The husband returned and Stiglitz asked, "Now what's wrong?"

"Pains in the stomach, Doctor."

"Fever?"

"Yes."

"High?"

"No, medium."

"Does she vomit?"

"No."

"Pregnant?"

"The midwife says no."

"Is her period regular?"

"I don't know."

"Find out," Stiglitz ordered, and the husband dutifully returned to the other room, where he sat on the floor to consult with his veiled wife.

While he was gone I asked, "Don't you examine her?"

"A wife? In chaderi? I'd be shot."

The husband returned and said his wife's periods had been regular, so the examination proceeded. Six times the husband was ordered to ask his wife intimate questions regarding her health and six times he relayed his understanding of her answers to the doctor. Once, when the man was gone, Stiglitz confided, "The real evil of this system comes when the husband thinks his wife's symptoms reflect discredit on him. He suppresses the information. And if the apothecary charges too much for the medicine I prescribe he simply doesn't buy it."

"What happens to the woman?" I asked.

"She dies," he replied without emotion. "That is, she dies a little sooner than otherwise."

The husband now decided that he had told Dr. Stiglitz all that was relevant and he waited for the doctor's decision. "It's an amazing thing," Stiglitz said in English, "but after a while you instinctively know what ails the woman and you probably do her as much good as if you'd taken her pulse and temperature." In Pashto he instructed the husband what medication to buy for his wife and the man laid down a pitiful fee, which the doctor accepted. When the man went to inform his wife he left the door open and I could see him kneel beside her and console and reassure her, with obvious love etched on his face. His wife, who must have been seriously ill under the chaderi, breathed deeply two or three times, then rose and followed her husband out of the office.

"Now about Madame Nazrullah," Dr. Stiglitz began. "Since you're interested in her you must be from the American embassy."

"I am."

"And you've been sent down here to spy on me?"

"No," I lied.

"You're lying. Right this minute you're thinking,

What's a man like Stiglitz doing in a hole like Kandahar? Go ahead and spy on me and I'll spy on you."

Before I could reply, Stiglitz hopped up, ran to the door leading to the street, and barred it. When this was done he sat on one of the chairs, using it in reversed position so that its unsteady back formed a chin rest. "Young man," he said. "Will you please bring me my pipe?" He was tired and he looked it.

I joined him in the waiting room and studied him as he lit his pipe. His hands were nervous, but I remembered that this was the end of a long day. His close-cropped head was a little larger than normal, and his hard blue eyes looked at all things with a blend of cynicism and challenge. He was inclined toward plumpness and was clearly no self-reliant German superman. I was disposed to like his quick honesty and felt intuitively that he ought to move to Kabul, where the various embassies could provide him with patients well able to pay. As he had foreseen, the major question in my mind as I studied him was, "What's a man like this doing in a hole like Kandahar?"

"Nazrullah's wife lived in this region for a little more than a year," he reported grudgingly. "Why are you interested?"

"She's disappeared."

"What?" he asked with real surprise.

"Yes. Her parents haven't heard from her in thirteen months."

He began to laugh, not heartily but in disgust. "You Americans! My parents haven't heard from me in four years but they don't go running to the German embassy."

"With an American woman married to an Afghan the problem is somewhat different," I said sharply.

"Any ferangi who marries an Afghan does so with her eyes alert," Stiglitz replied impatiently. "I treated Madame Nazrullah several times."

"What for?" I asked.

Stiglitz looked at me coldly. "She was a well-adjusted, likable young woman. Quite happy with her husband and he with her. I've grown to respect Nazrullah as one of the finest Afghans. Say, Herr Miller, are you hungry?"

"I am."

"You eat pilau and nan?"

"At every chance."

"Good. I'm starved." Then, for the first time, I saw him hesitate, as if he were unsure of himself. "Herr Miller, may I be very rude?"

"You may."

"I wish that the invitation I just extended could mean what it would in Germany. That I was taking you to dinner. Frankly, Herr Miller . . . You saw the fee they pay here."

"I'm taking you to dinner," I assured him.

"No! My own dinner I can afford. But sometimes you ferangi eat like such pigs . . ."

He summoned a watchman, who appeared from a room in the back carrying a rifle and two daggers. Carefully Stiglitz locked the cupboard with its pitiful supply of drugs, then unbarred the door, which the watchman locked behind us as soon as we had left. Stiglitz led me to the public square, which contained an eating place of better than average appearance.

Cautiously he asked, "Do you like beer?"

"Not particularly."

"Good," he sighed with real relief. "I manage to find a few bottles each month and it makes life bearable. So if you don't mind I'll not offer you one. Why don't you have an orange?"

"I usually drink tea."

"Better for you," he laughed uneasily.

When our meal was served, the waiter produced from some well-protected corner a bottle of lukewarm German beer, which Dr. Stiglitz attended to personally. With meticulous care he pried away the top, quickly pressing his mouth over the foaming bottle to catch each drop that would otherwise have been wasted. Next he took a long, slow, satisfying draught, closed his eyes, and placed the bottle reverently on the table close to his right hand.

"What would you have said," I asked, "if I had liked beer?"

He opened his eyes slowly and winked. "I'd have said, 'How unfortunate. In Kandahar the mullahs allow no alcohol,' and right now we'd both be drinking tea. I won't try to explain, Herr Miller, but this is my only contact with Europe. It's so precious . . ."

"Would you have any guess as to why Nazrullah's wife disappeared?"

"I'm not satisfied she has."

"Any rumors?"

"I give no credence to rumors."

"That means you've heard some."

"Herr Miller, I hadn't even heard she was missing."

"You hadn't?"

"Why should I?" he asked impatiently. "They left here last July to work at Qala Bist. Haven't seen them since."

"Was she all right . . . when you knew her?"

"All right?" he asked angrily, licking his fingers. "Who's all right? Maybe she was planning to murder her husband and have a baby by a camel. Who can you point to in Afghanistan and say, 'That one's all right'? She was healthy, she laughed more than she cried, and she was well groomed."

"How do you know about the crying?"

"I don't. Every time I saw her she was laughing."

It was obvious that he intended the interrogation to end, but I could not resist one final question. "Did you know her by her western name?"

Dr. Stiglitz threw down the piece of nan he had been using as a fork and sputtered, "No more! Eat!" He took a long swig of beer.

This relaxed him and he asked philosophically, "Herr Miller, have you ever speculated as to why it was such a terrible punishment in these lands to cut off the hand of a thief? No? The awful part about it was that they always cut off the right hand. Look around this restaurant and see if that gives you an idea."

There were perhaps fifteen eating areas in the dusty room and at each men were eating pilau, but I didn't see the connection. Stiglitz pointed out, "They're all eating with their right hands. See!" He pointed to a rug on which five bearded Afghans were digging freely from a common bowl, and each used his right hand. The left never appeared in motion.

"I don't understand."

"Only the right hand is allowed in the food bowl," Stiglitz said ponderously, like a German professor, "because when a man goes to the toilet he must always wipe himself with his left hand. In lands where there is little water, this is a prudent rule." He took another drink of beer and reflected, "It was a terrifying punishment, to cut off a man's right hand. Automatically it banished him from the food bowl."

I was about to ask the point of this story when I saw two men rigging a string of lights across one corner of the square. "What goes on over there?" I asked.

"That's for the dance," he explained. "Spring festival brings out the dancing boys, the dirty little monsters."

I described the team I'd seen on the truck and he banged his empty beer bottle. "That's the kind. They're all alike. Filthy animals."

"The ones I saw looked fairly clean," I protested.

"Clean? Yes. Even perfumed. But they're cruel little pederasts . . . sodomites. When they come to town they create a great evil."

"You astonish me," I gulped.

"I shouldn't. If you have a society where women are forbidden, men must volunteer for the female functions."

"I was remarking on that the other day. But not in this context."

"This is the context that counts," Stiglitz snapped. "Our handsome dancing boys are all dirty little whores. How could they otherwise afford the clothes they wear?"

The lights were now in position and a stage was being marked off, about which began to cluster several hundred men in turbans and a few in karakul caps. From an alley which was to serve as dressing room a man in his fifties, whom I recognized from the truck, appeared to make a speech.

"Let's go see the little monsters," Stiglitz proposed, and we walked slowly across the square to join the crowd. We were in time to hear the speaker assure us that he had brought to Kandahar the finest troupe of dancers in Afghanistan, who had just finished a season in Kabul, where they had danced for the king. Five musicians came on stage, older men who played flutes, drums and a bucket-like fiddle containing at least twenty strings. The music had a standard Oriental, wailing quality, but also a fierce rhythm quite alien to countries like China and Japan. This was the throbbing music of the upland plateaus, a modification of Indian, Mongol and Greek strains. As sound it was attractive; as rhythm it was compelling.

"I've grown fond of the music," Stiglitz said, "and these men are good." They played for some minutes and induced in the crowd a subtle change. Men stopped talking. Bodies began swaying, and a sense of excitement became almost tangible. Then, with a shout, two young men in candy-striped costumes leaped out of the alley and began a whirling dance in which their long hair stood out straight from their heads. They were unlike western dancers, more controlled in their torsos, but more abandoned in the way they used their extremities and their heads.

I whispered to Stiglitz, "Do you deny they're artists?"

"It's their other skills I object to," he snapped.

During the first half-hour the star of the troupe did not appear and the interval was filled with flying bodies and wild music. The audience seemed to grow impatient and it was clear they were waiting for the young man who had insulted me on the bridge, and I too was waiting for him. The master of ceremonies knew this and took advantage of our anticipation by sending his musicians among the crowd to collect donations in their karakul fezzes.

"What do I give?" I asked the doctor.

"As little as possible," he growled, and I saw him throw in a few small coins, which caused the musician to sneer at him as a ferangi. I contributed a bill and gained a professional, ingratiating smile.

The musicians reassembled and the master announced that we were now to see what we had been waiting for, the premier dancer of Afghanistan. The long thin drums, with goat leather at either end, began throbbing and flutes scurried up and down the register. The music halted and from the alley appeared, in the slowest of rhythmic steps, the young man who had made such an impression on me that morning.

He was dressed in a tunic cut from some rare purple fabric threaded with gold. His trousers were gray whipcord that flowed about his legs as he danced, and his turban was of pale blue silk, its free end flying out from his left shoulder. At this stage of the dance his extraordinary hair was held in place by the turban, but at his shoulders it was free to twist and move in the flickering lights. He was a young man of extreme physical beauty, and I was repelled by him for the reason that he knew he was beautiful and intended using this beauty to create confusion.

The tempo of the music increased, but now the audience did not move and the solitary dancer began to shift his body and his feet more deftly. I noticed that he kept lagging behind the beat of the music, as if he were too languid to keep up, and this gave his dance a quality of sexual boredom and lethargy.

Then the musicians began to shout and hammer their drums in planned frenzy, giving the impression that the boy was being driven to dance more rapidly, and as he did so the end of his turban pulled loose and was soon expanded into a flash of color and a hypnotic gyration that I had to admit was thrilling. No woman in a steamy hall, loosening her garments one by one, ever generated more excitement than this young man did in twirling away his blue turban until his furious black hair was free to whirl out in great circles parallel to the earth. He now intensified his rhythm until he was beating the earth like a drum, his head twisting in ecstasy.

Dr. Stiglitz, who refused to acknowledge his spell, growled, "Probably his last year."

"He's not twenty!" I protested. "He could dance thirty more years."

"You forget. His job isn't dancing. He's here to attract customers for a troupe of nasty little boys. When they grow too old to attract these swine," he said, indicating the silent, panting watchers, "they're through, and that sweet little man playing the fiddle finds himself ten more teen-age mountain boys who enjoy sodomy."

I felt a little sick at this scientific appraisal of what I was seeing, but such thoughts were banished when I looked across the stage to see in the front row the young man from Badakshar, who stood mesmerized, swaying back and forth in his tattered European coat. I tried to attract his attention, but he was enchanted and could not take his eyes from the young dancer, who now entered the final portion of his performance.

Elbowing my way through the crowd to speak with the young mountaineer, I incurred bitter remarks from Afghans who were similarly bewitched by the exciting dancer, but I ignored them and came at last to the youth from Badakshar. "He's good, eh?" I asked in Pashto.

He did not hear me. He was not aware that anyone had joined him, for he was captivated by the expert who now whirled about the stage in wide circles, his hair flashing in the night, his gold and purple costume rippling like crests of sand in a windswept desert.

I poked the young mountaineer, and he blinked his eyes. Finally he was able to focus on me, as if from a distance, and he muttered weakly, "Without wings, he flies." Having uttered this, he returned to his trance and watched as the dancer leaped and gyrated into a furious finale. Now even I had to pay attention, for I did not believe that a human body could move so fast and yet maintain control. The drums exploded and the flutes ran riot. There was a flash of hair and wild eyes and grinning mouth and golden cloth. The dance ended. At my side the young mountaineer gasped and said, "In Badakshar we saw no dance like that." I wished him good night, but I fear he heard no words.

7

When I awakened in the morning I saw Nur Muhammad perched on the spare tires, a mirror propped against a knee, a can of hot water at his side, shaving contentedly, for in the hotel at Kandahar there was no bathroom. After admiring his dexterity for some minutes I said in English, "That dancing boy we met on the bridge put on a terrific performance."

"The one who cursed you?" Nur asked.

"Stiglitz said they were all sodomites."

"They are," Nur said methodically. "But the police watch them."

I pondered my next question for some time, then asked, hesitantly, in Pashto, "Nur, would you tell me what you know about Stiglitz?"

He continued shaving, inspected his chin as if today a good shave were important, then dried his face with ostentatious care. Apparently Nur had anticipated this question before we left Kabul and had consulted with government officials as to how he should answer. Carefully he replied, "We first heard of Otto Stiglitz in February of last year. That's 1945. Without any warning he crossed the border from Persia. Had no valid papers and was arrested in Herat. Never been to Kabul. He did carry with him papers that claimed a doctor's degree in medicine from some German university."

"His sign says Munich."

"I believe it was. When the war ended we directed our ambassador in Paris to investigate the matter and he satisfied himself that Stiglitz was a legitimate doctor. His degree was authentic. As I recall, we received a copy of his university record. It was impressive."

"But it's so difficult to get permission to enter Afghanistan," I pointed out. Since we were speaking in Pashto I automatically used the standard pronunciation, as if the word contained no *gh* sound at all. To us who worked or lived in the country, it was Afanistan. "How could an ordinary man like Stiglitz just walk in?"

"You forget," Nur pointed out. "He wasn't an ordinary man. He was a doctor, and we need doctors. He was also a German, and we've always needed Germans. Forgetting the unhappy experience with the bridges, our nation has been built by Germans. We're sometimes called 'The Germany of Asia,' and we're not going to turn away German refugees now."

"You believe he was a Nazi?"

"Weren't they all . . . legally?" Nur asked quietly, as he began to pack away his shaving gear and offer me the hot water.

"That's all you know?" I pressed.

"Obviously, he came to Kandahar and opened shop as a doctor. Local people advise us he's very good. At any rate, we're glad to have him and I suppose he'll stay here for many years."

"Why do you say that?"

"For most Germans, Afghanistan is the end of their road. From here there are few places they can go."

"Not even back to Germany?"

"There least of all."

"How many German nationals have you in the country?" I asked, with a kind of morbid fascination, for although I was no professional German-hater I did have to acknowledge that had I been a citizen of that country in 1937 I would now be dead. And my relatives and many of my friends would also be dead. And since I'm a man who has always found joy in my association with relatives and friends, the thought of their being mutilated and starved and dead was not only morally repulsive. It scared the very devil out of me. Instinctively I feared Germans and always will.

I don't think this sprang from an unhealthy preoccupation with death. From early childhood I had been prepared by my parents to face the fact that people died, and I knew that one day I would; but Jews have a love of continuity—which accounted in part for the delight I took in the history of Afghanistan—and prior to World War II, whenever I thought of myself as dead, I thought of future Millers continuing. "There'll always be some Miller who has tickets to Symphony Hall," I assured myself, and if I weren't among them my absence would be regrettable but not tragic; but if Millers and Goldbergs and Sharps and Weinsteins were not there—if all were gone—it would be unbearable. Had my family not emigrated from Germany we would now all be dead, and I could not ignore that fact.

These personal reflections kept me from hearing all of Nur's reply, but I did catch the figure of more than six hundred Germans reaching Afghanistan, some with exalted credentials.

"All Nazis?"

"That's a matter of definition. Many were decent men and women who hated Hitler and who had scars on their backs and minds to prove it. I talked about this with Moheb Khan . . ." Again I lost what he was saying, for his phrase "I talked about this with Moheb Khan" didn't jibe with my experience of the two men. Whenever I had been with Moheb in the presence of Nur, the former had treated Nur like a servant. Apparently there was much I didn't comprehend about Afghan espionage and I supposed that some day

I would find that Nur was Moheb Khan's younger brother or nephew to the king.

"If Stiglitz is so good, why doesn't he come to Kabul?"

"An understanding we have with all refugees. They've got to settle in different parts of the country. Where they're needed. If he proves himself in Kandahar, he could be invited to Kabul."

"Then he's not free to move around?"

"You aren't free to move around," he pointed out. "You had to get permission from Shah Khan."

"I'm an outsider."

"So's Stiglitz. Until he proves himself."

"Is he doing so?"

"Yes." Obviously, Nur wished to say no more on this subject.

But I asked, "What's the average Afghan pay for a visit to a doctor?"

"Possibly eight cents."

"So the refugees don't get rich?"

"Not in Kandahar." Again he ended the conversation, then added with cool calculation, "But if later on he could move to Kabul, then perhaps he'd be able to serve the diplomatic community. Perhaps even officially. And for that he'd receive good pay."

"Do you suppose Dr. Stiglitz would consider coming to Kabul?"

Nur looked straight at me as he filled my shaving mug with hot water. "I should imagine that he dreams of nothing else."

"Could you give me an opinion as to how long his apprenticeship in Kandahar will be?"

"That will be decided by our government . . . and yours, if you should be thinking of employing Stiglitz as embassy doctor." I made no comment.

I was amused when Stiglitz and Nur met at lunch that day. The German was much more careful with Nur than he had been with me, for he quickly guessed that Nur might be an official with some power in

Kabul. "It's a pleasure to meet Your Excellency," Stiglitz said ingratiatingly.

"I'm not an excellency, sad to confess," Nur parried. "I'm Miller Sahib's driver."

Stiglitz looked carefully at Nur's western shoes, western suit and expensive karakul cap and decided not to fall into that trap. "I must congratulate Herr Miller on having one of the finest drivers in Afghanistan. I wish I spoke English as well as you, Nur Sahib."

"I wish I were a doctor with a fine degree from Munich," Nur replied, and the pudgy German radiated gratification.

In succeeding days I saw a good deal of Stiglitz, and the more I saw the more assured I became that the embassies would be getting a good doctor if they got him, and I decided to help engineer his promotion to Kabul. We often ate together, he jealously guarding his bottle of beer, I asking questions by the score, and he was willing to permit this because I paid for the meals.

My questioning assured me of one thing: Stiglitz was no Nazi. He had a humanitarian attitude toward medicine and an understanding of what it could do to alleviate mental as well as physical suffering. He was hungry for philosophical discussion and each night dined with me on nan and pilau, then accompanied me to see the dances, after which we talked till midnight as he smoked his pipe.

One memory of Stiglitz persists when I recall those exciting days in Kandahar: his outspoken disgust over the dancing troupe and the lead dancer in particular. "They're a blot on Afghanistan," he railed, pronouncing the name of his new land like a native. "They represent a deep malaise. By God, they ought to get the women out of chaderi and put this country on a normal psychological basis."

One day at lunch we were discussing this with Nur and he laughed tolerantly. "Every ferangi who comes here has some one thing that ought to be done right away. Dr. Stiglitz says, 'Get the women out of chaderi.' The French ambassador says, 'Educate two thousand more medical men.' The American ambassador tells us, 'Pipe water into the city from the hills.' And the Russians say, 'Pave your streets.' Do you know really what we must do first?"

"What?" Stiglitz asked eagerly. This was the kind of conversation he liked.

"All of them," Nur replied. "Yes! Laugh! But we've got to move the entire nation ahead on all possible fronts. And that requires more brains and more courage than we have available. Pray for us when you go to sleep."

"I've been praying that you'd take me to the house where Nazrullah lives when he's in Kandahar," I said.

"I completed arrangements yesterday." Nur bowed. "Will you join us, Doctor?"

"I would be honored," he said formally. He was about to dig into his pocket for some change when a pleasant thought struck him. "Is the ferangi paying for this lunch?"

"I am," I said. No refugees worried so constantly about money as the Germans. He sighed with relief when I produced the money, and I noticed that just before the bill was totaled he grabbed an extra piece of nan, which he munched as we hiked through the streets.

Nur led us to the typical walled house, where the inevitable gate watcher inspected us grudgingly, then allowed us to pass. The establishment contained no unusual feature: it had a garden, some fruit trees, mud walls, some Persian rugs, and a male servant. There was a big colored photograph of the king and on the table three very old copies of *Time*. The furniture was upholstered in a bilious pink mohair.

Then something quite different happened. From one of the doors appeared an apparently young woman in a pale blue silk chaderi. Dr. Stiglitz showed amazement when he saw the shroud worn indoors, as did Nur Muhammad, who introduced me as the gentleman from the American embassy. In Pashto the shrouded figure said, "I am proud to welcome you to Nazrullah's house." Then she whispered to Nur, who nodded assent, and she called for a male servant, who appeared with two children, a girl four years old and a boy only a few months old.

"Nazrullah's children," Nur said approvingly. "The oldest is the age of my youngest."

"How many children have you?" I asked Nur.

"Three," he replied.

"Is your wife Afghan?"

"It's none of your business," Dr. Stiglitz snapped.

"She's from the north," Nur said obligingly.

It was obvious that we were speaking among ourselves because the presence of the woman in chaderi embarrassed us. Normally any Afghan man advanced enough to bring a ferangi into his home for presentation to his wife would tell her, "You can remove the chaderi, dear." And Mrs. Nazrullah must have wanted to do so. But she was restrained by the fact that Nur Muhammad was an official of the government and might be a man committed to retaining the chaderi. To protect her husband, she had to remain covered.

Nur, on the other hand, was known to me positively as an enlightened Afghan who wanted to see the chaderi go, and he was certainly inclined personally to say to Mrs. Nazrullah, "With us you can drop the chaderi," but he was afraid that someone might report his action to Kabul, and he was not sufficiently well placed in government to establish his own rules.

So two people who knew the chaderi was doomed were thus locked into positions where pragmatically they defended it. I broke the impasse by asking, in English, for I had no idea how a man addressed a woman whom he couldn't see, "Why didn't Mrs. Nazrullah accompany her husband to Qala Bist?"

"Ask her," Nur said, so I restated my question in Pashto.

"There were no quarters for us," she replied softly. It was a curious sensation, hearing words issuing from a shroud.

"I understand," I said, but at the same time I remarked to myself: Ellen Jaspar found quarters.

"Do be seated, gentlemen," she said as the servant appeared with four glasses of orange drink. I wondered: How's she going to drink with a chaderi on?

"We'll be seeing your husband soon," I said. "Can we take him anything?"

"You're very thoughtful," she replied in what I detected as embarrassment. Then she laughed charmingly, and I saw by the wall a box of things already waiting for us to take to Qala Bist.

"Nur's been here before me," I said with what gallantry I could command.

"Yes," she said easily. "He arranged it yesterday, but I'm pleased you have the same idea. I wouldn't want Nur to exceed his prerogatives." Her use of words was so precise that I had to readjust my concept of the Nazrullah triangle. His Afghan wife was no barefoot desert girl hurriedly acquired to have babies which would extend the family line.

"Can you speak other than Pashto?" I inquired.

"French." Then slowly, and with pride, she added, "And a little English."

"Wisely so," Stiglitz grunted. "Some day she'll be an ambassador's wife."

Mrs. Nazrullah didn't hear this and Nur repeated the compliment in Pashto. The veiled figure laughed, then turned to the doctor and asked, "Do you speak French?"

"Yes," Stiglitz replied.

"Do you, Miller Sahib?"

"Yes, madame," I nodded.

"Then why don't we all use that language?" she asked in good French. I looked at Nur, and Madame Nazrullah assured me, "Oh, Nur speaks better French than I."

I must have looked startled, for Nur explained, "Where do you suppose I worked before I worked with you? French embassy." I thought: When the Afghans get hold of a good man they see he gets a practical education.

Dr. Stiglitz remarked, "You come back in three years, Herr Miller. Your man Nur will be speaking Russian."

"Well," Madame Nazrullah said with that hands-folded, businesslike way women can adopt, "I've been told why you're here, Miller Sahib, and I wish I could help you. But I haven't any idea where my husband's other wife has gone."

"Isn't she with him?" I asked.

"I think not," she said.

"And she's not here?"

Madame Nazrullah laughed pleasantly. "No, we haven't had any ferangi wives walled up here in Kandahar for weeks and weeks."

"Forgive me," I said.

"But I suppose if you went back a few years, you might find an example or two. So your suspicions are excusable."

"Thank you."

"I do want to assure you of one thing, and please believe me as a friend who would do neither you nor Ellen harm. She never fought with me. I never humiliated her. During the short time we shared a house in Kabul we behaved like sisters. She used to sing to my daughter."

"Had she been warned—a second wife, I mean?"

"Of course!" the shrouded figure laughed. "On the day we met she kissed me and said, 'You're Karima. Nazrullah told me all about you.' "

"I can't believe it," I said flatly. "No American girl . . ."

Nur interrupted. "Don't speak like that, Miller Sahib. Is what Karima says any more difficult to believe than other things we already know to be true?"

"No. I apologize."

"I know how difficult it must be to understand my country," Madame Nazrullah said softly. "But in your report cling to this fact, Miller Sahib. In Nazrullah's home Ellen was treated with love and respect. She treated us in the same manner."

"Does that include Nazrullah's mother . . . and sisters?"

"For two hours each afternoon Ellen took lessons in Pashto from Nazrullah's mother. She was an adorable girl and our family loved her . . . all of us." She rose, bowed graciously and started to leave. Her orange drink remained untouched.

"One more question, please," I pleaded. "Have you any guess, no matter how bizarre . . ."

"As to what happened? No. But I will assure you of this. Whatever Ellen did was an act of intelligence. She willed it to occur just as it did occur, for she was in possession of all her faculties and they were extraordinary. She was a brilliant, wonderful person, and if evil has come to her I am bereft, because there is one other thing you must know." She hesitated and I believe she was crying, for she put her right hand to her mouth, or so I judged, for the chaderi masked her motions. "When Nazrullah brought her to Kandahar and left me behind in Kabul, it was Ellen who insisted that I rejoin them. When I arrived she met me and said, 'I was so homesick for the little girl.' Between us, Miller Sahib, there was only love."

She left the room, then reconsidered and said from the door, "Possibly she asked me to come to Kandahar because she knew I could have children and apparently she couldn't. Dr. Stiglitz will confirm that."

The lady in the shroud, whatever her complexion or beauty, bowed and we saw her no more. When she had gone I said, "I expected a barefoot nomad from the Hindu Kush."

"Her sister went to school in Bordeaux," Nur observed.

I turned to Stiglitz and said, "About the matter of having children . . ."

In disgust Stiglitz barked something in German which I did not understand. He turned to leave the house, then snapped in Pashto, "Such matters are no concern of an embassy." Abruptly he left us and stalked off, and I could see that he must have fled Germany for good reason. He was an honest, hard, opinionated man and for him life under the Nazis must have been hell.

Slyly Nur observed, "His way of confirming what Karima said."

"Think so?"

"Include it in your report," Nur advised. "You won't be far wrong."

That evening Nur and I missed Dr. Stiglitz at dinner, but after our nan and pilau we wandered across the square to watch the dancers and I told Nur, "You could take this troupe to New York right now and they'd be a sensation."

"Is that true?" he asked skeptically.

"Of course. That lead dancer could fit into any ensemble I ever saw. Do you realize how good he is?"

"Look!" Nur chuckled during one of the intermissions. "Overcoat Sahib." And there was the young man from Badakshar, still stupefied by the dancer who "without wings, he flies."

My comment about the troupe saddened Nur, in a way I could not have predicted. "In many things we have great talent in Afghanistan. I've heard old men in the hills who could tell long stories better than most of the European novels I read. You say the dancers are good. Do you realize how miserable it is to grow up in a country where there's no outlet for talent?" I felt it best not to comment on this, but Nur asked, "Is it true that in Russia they take dancing teams like this and sometimes give them medals and even send them to Paris?"

"Of course," I replied. "All countries do. In the

middle of the war I was in China, where they fought the Japanese all day and went to Chinese opera at night. The Chinese were no better dancers than these men."

"Is that true?" Nur mused. Again, the idea depressed him.

But next morning we received another view of the dancing team, for while I was seated on the spare tires, shaving, I heard my name called in the courtyard. One of the armed guards who had been sleeping in our jeep was announcing that a visitor had come to see me, so I wrapped a towel around my neck and went to the slit window. The visitor was Dr. Stiglitz.

"Let him in!" I called in Pashto.

In a moment the German doctor joined us. "Want to see something unique? Probably nowhere else in the world to see it."

"What's up?"

"Didn't you hear the commotion . . . about four this morning?"

"Yes," Nur replied. "Fighting in the streets. I put it down as a brawl."

"You were half right," Stiglitz said. "It started as a brawl."

"What about?" Nur asked.

"The usual. Men got to fighting over the dancing boys. Particularly the one Herr Miller admired."

"The one I said could succeed in New York," I reminded Nur.

"He succeeded last night," Stiglitz said wryly. "Two men were fighting over him. It ended in murder."

Nur Muhammad swore in Pashto. "Another of those?"

"Yes," Stiglitz replied in Pashto. "I warned our American friend that this boy was evil . . . evil. You never understood, did you, Herr Miller?"

"I didn't anticipate murder," I admitted in Pashto, and for the remainder of the terrifying incident in which we were to participate we continued to speak that language.

Nur Muhammad must have guessed what we were about to witness, but I didn't, for nothing in my reading about Afghanistan, nor even the grisly events in Ghazni, had prepared me for the public square in Kandahar that lovely spring morning. Dr. Stiglitz, having witnessed such an event in Herat, knew what was afoot, and on our short walk to the square asked us to stop by his office, where the armed guard admitted us to a doubly locked trunk from which Stiglitz produced a Leica camera. Testing it by snapping Nur and me in his consulting room, he slung the camera over his shoulder and put on a karakul cap. Then he led us to the square.

Where the dancers had performed the night before, a large group of men had gathered, but now the string of lights was gone and the bare earth glistened rock-like in the sun. To one side stood an elderly man, the focus of all attention. He seemed not to be a distinguished citizen, for his sandals and shirt were tattered and his vest was nearly in shreds, but he commanded attention if only because of the noble manner in which he bore himself. He was surrounded by the mob, yet not a part of it, and all who came close to him offered deference, which he accepted as hereditary right. He was obviously one of the causes why the mob had gathered.

When the sun was well up, there was a beating of drums, not intended as the passionate accompaniment to dancing, for they were somber and of a different timbre, intended to announce the arrival of eight uniformed policemen, grim and forbidding in appearance. In pairs they marched to compass points previously marked by piles of pebbles, and then I saw that each pair had a mallet and a short stake, which was driven into the ground, leaving about eight inches showing.

The drums throbbed again, and from the alley that

had been used as a dressing room appeared two mullahs, small, roundish men with clean-shaved faces, quite unlike the gaunt beak-nosed mullahs of the hills. They signaled the drums to cease, whereupon they prayed, first one, then the other. I did not catch all their words, but they seemed to be cleansing the minds of those who were about to participate in a time-honored rite. They also prayed that each of us, seeing this thing, would henceforth respect the commands of God and the precepts of His chosen Prophet. When their prayers ended, the drums beat again and a shackled man, obviously a prisoner, was led forth.

"It's the young man with the coat!" I cried.

Nur said, "From Badakshar!" Then he cautioned me to remain silent, while Dr. Stiglitz busied himself taking photographs of the procession.

The young man from the hills was in a daze. I doubt that he understood what was happening or had happened. He had come to Kandahar with a year's savings and had been engulfed in a whirlpool beyond his comprehension. The guards moved him about as if he were merely an animal.

"Is he the murderer?" I whispered to Nur.

A man to the left explained, "Last night, when the dancing ended, the prisoner tried to buy the dancing boy. But a policeman had already spoken for him. The mountain boy refused to understand that the dancer could not be his. In a blind fury he killed the policeman. Everyone saw him do it. There's no question of guilt. Only of punishment."

"What's the punishment to be?" I asked.

"I wish you weren't going to see it," Nur replied.

"Are you staying?"

"What happens . . . I must report," he said with resignation.

The two mullahs went to the bedazed mountain man and said, "You have committed murder." The prisoner was unable to acknowledge the charge. I didn't know what to expect next.

The mullahs moved to a man whom I had not seen before, a fat fellow with a karakul cap, and asked, "Does the government wish to assume control of this case?"

The fat official replied, "This is a crime of passion. The government is not concerned in any way with this case." He nodded to the mullahs and departed.

Next the mullahs moved to the elderly man in the badly torn vest and announced, "Gul Majid, this prisoner has murdered your son. By the law of the Prophet, he is handed to you for punishment. Do you, Gul Majid, accept this responsibility?"

The old man stepped forward with great dignity, raised his eyes so that they stared directly at the young man, and announced in a clear voice, "I accept the prisoner."

The mullahs said a final prayer, beseeching justice and mercy, and we saw them no more.

The men who had been guarding the prisoner shoved him forward until he was almost touching the old man, and it was now a matter solely between the young murderer and the elderly father of the murdered man, a morality play conceived by desert people thousands of years ago and honored by them through countless generations. State and church alike had withdrawn. It was the guilty and the bereaved, standing face to face, and the crowd, which formed a significant part in this reenactment of the passion play, remained tense and silent until the old man cried in a loud voice, "Let the prisoner be tied!"

At this the crowd broke into a shout of wild approval, and I heard Nur whispering in Pashto, "I wish to God that just once there could be mercy." On this day there was to be vengeance, not mercy.

The young murderer was whisked to the stakes, stretched upon the ground face-up and lashed by ankles and wrists until he was spread-eagled in the manner of St. Andrew at his crucifixion. No further attempt was made to keep this a religious ceremony;

we were about to participate in retribution, sure and implacable.

When the young man was securely tied, the guards who had done the job stepped away, to be replaced by a cordon of police, brother officers to the murdered man. They stood at intervals about the prisoner, close enough together to prevent a riot but far enough apart to provide everyone with a clear view. The crowd grew silent and men elbowed their way forward to find good spots from which to view the spectacle.

The father of the dead policeman now stepped forward and stood at the feet of the staked-out prisoner. He mumbled a short prayer, then shouted boldly, "Give me the scimitar." I'm not sure you would translate his word as *scimitar,* but at least it wasn't the word for *sword,* and from his band of associates a man stepped forward with a rusty old nineteenth-century bayonet. In a clear voice the old man shouted, "My grandfather captured this from the British at the siege of Kandahar." The crowd cheered.

I looked down at the young man, who appeared not to comprehend what was happening, for his eyes were glassy and remained in the trance that he had entered at the time of the murder, when he was battling for the favors of the dancing boy. But when the old man's address to the public ended and he knelt beside the young man's head, the prisoner at last saw the rusty bayonet and began to scream.

It was a horrifying, animal scream that came from far back in the history of human development. It was, I thought, exactly the right kind of scream for such a scene, for it put us all solidly in the animal category. "No! No!" screamed the staked-out young man, but we had passed the time for words.

The old man steadied himself, twisted his left hand in the victim's hair, and pulled his neck taut. With the rusty bayonet in his right hand he began sawing at his prisoner's throat, and with each awful passage of the bayonet, the boy's head twisted back and forth, while terrible screams emanated from the throat which had not yet been severed. I thought I would vomit.

Then, by the grace of God, a figure hurried out from the crowd and intervened with the old man. The insanity stopped. I breathed again.

The intruder was Dr. Stiglitz, and he argued with the old man in Pashto, but the impassioned executioner failed to comprehend and looked at the German in bewilderment. Then I saw Stiglitz point to the camera and say in a clear voice which I and the others could hear, "If you work from the other side, the light will be better."

The old man shrugged his shoulders and Stiglitz asked harshly, "You want your picture taken, don't you?" At last the executioner understood, and I watched aghast as he switched his position and started cutting from the other side. The sun was unobstructed.

With four powerful drags of the bayonet the old man slashed the victim's throat and silenced the horrible cries. Then he continued bearing down until the cartilage and bone were severed, whereupon with some awkwardness and fatigue from his exertion he rose, keeping his left hand twisted in the victim's hair, and marched triumphantly about the circle, showing each of us the death's head.

When the old man came to me, I had to look away and found myself looking directly at the sodomite dancer whose alluring performance had launched the tragedy. His face was enraptured as he followed the passage of the severed head. His clothes were as neat as ever and he smelled of perfume. When he caught me staring at him with loathing he flashed his most ingratiating smile and whispered in Pashto, "It was horrible, wasn't it?"

"Herr Miller!" I heard a voice calling. Dr. Stiglitz had seen the sybaritic dancer standing beside me and had come for a picture of us. He worked on the focus for a moment, while the dancer, accustomed to having his picture taken, assumed a dramatic pose and I looked astounded in my karakul cap. I still have the picture, and it serves to remind me that what I have described did happen.

Nur and I walked silently across the square to the restaurant, but I was too shocked to want food. Before long the doctor joined us and said, as if nothing had happened, "I'll have a bottle of beer. Nur can't join me because he's Muslim and you don't like beer." When another of the precious bottles was produced, Stiglitz observed, "I'll have two good reasons to get to Kabul eventually. You don't have these public executions up there, but you do have German beer."

"If the execution appalled you," I asked weakly, "why did you photograph it so carefully?"

"I believe we should have a record," he replied. "All historical processes should be recorded. In a few years what you saw today will vanish. Nur Muhammad will see to that."

"But when you stopped the old man . . . Surely, you could have prevailed upon him."

"Me?" Stiglitz cried. "They'd have killed me."

"They would have," Nur agreed.

"But to ask him to switch sides. God, it's ghoulish."

"I altered nothing," he replied, carefully prying the cap off his bottle of beer.

I was choked with moral rage, and then I began laughing. Deep, gusty, cackling laughter overtook me, and although both Nur and Stiglitz tried to stop me, they couldn't, for I was pointing across the restaurant to the public square, where the old man who had conducted the execution was marching home. In his right hand he held the historic bayonet which had avenged family dishonor, while in his left he held the hand of the sodomite dancer, who walked along bowing to the approval of the crowd. It was not this incongruous mating which had caused me to burst into uncontrolled laughter. At the scene of the execution the old man had discarded his sorely tattered vest and he was now wearing the dead man's overcoat, that beautiful, torn and ravaged but still serviceable woman's coat from Paris. It fitted his spare body well, and he actually looked dapper in his new garment.

"Wait!" I called as he passed, and the old man stopped. "Doctor!" I shouted. "Get a picture of this, too," and I struck a pose between the unlikely pair.

When I rejoined my table Nur Muhammad was so angry that he cast aside his role of polite government aide. "Why did you do that?" he demanded bitterly.

"It was so goddamned ridiculous," I said, suddenly ashamed of myself.

"You're using Mr. Jaspar's word," Nur said acidly.

"What's that? Who?" Stiglitz asked, carefully putting away his camera.

"A friend of Miller Sahib's. Every time he confronts something he doesn't understand he calls it ridiculous."

"I'm sorry," I said.

"Some years ago a Frenchman took a series of excellent photographs . . . in Alabama . . . of a lynching. Was that ridiculous?"

"I was laughing because my nerves were shot," I explained lamely.

"Good. I think that now you may be ready to discuss your problem seriously."

"What do you mean by that?" I asked angrily.

"You've seen the terror of my nation. Now let's talk about Ellen Jaspar."

"I'm willing," I said in some bewilderment.

"Let's have no more diversions. No more amusing yourself with old men in public."

"I apologized," I snapped.

"Good," Nur said grudgingly. "When you ridiculed the old fool and the evil young man I thought . . ."

"I think it was the coat . . . It rounded out the story."

"I've forgotten the incident," Nur said. "Don't you remember it as the way we live in Afghanistan."

"We can talk frankly, then?" I asked.

"You always could, with me," Nur replied.

"The other day when I spoke with Shah Khan he confided that he had heard rumors that something extremely bizarre had happened to Ellen Jaspar . . . so bizarre, in fact, that he wouldn't even repeat the rumor."

"What rumor?" Dr. Stiglitz interrupted.

"The one I asked you about the first night."

"I told you. I have no speculation," he growled, returning to his beer.

"Have you?" I asked Nur.

"As I told you before, she's run away and perished."

"You're honestly convinced that she didn't die at the hands of fanatical mullahs?"

Nur was plainly irritated. "Miller Sahib," he protested, "you asked me that last week in Ghazni, and I swore it could not have happened. Don't you take my word for anything?"

"What we just saw," I said quietly, pointing toward the headless corpse which would lie on the ground till sundown, "permits a man to check answers, doesn't it?"

"Not when the answers have already been verified," Nur replied.

"But the mullahs?" I repeated.

Nur laughed pleasantly. "Those two mullahs happen to be among the finest men in our priesthood. They were acting in strict accordance with Afghan custom, but they know public executions like this can't continue indefinitely. And when it comes time for men like you and me to end them, they'll be on our side."

"They will?" I asked incredulously.

"Of course. I've a brother who's a mullah and a lot better citizen than I am."

"I'd like to meet him," I said brusquely.

"When we get back to Kabul, you will. Miller, you miss the secret of Afghanistan if you think that Islam is a religion which condones what you've just seen."

"It's a damned fine religion," Dr. Stiglitz interrupted in Pashto, where the oath was more colorful. "Matter of fact, I became a Muslim last year."

"You did?" I asked in undisguised surprise.

"Why not? This is my home from now on. It's an exciting country with a profound religion."

"You've surrendered Christianity?" I asked with an abhorrence which I didn't try to mask.

"I repeat," he began in Pashto. Then for some inexplicable reason he started speaking French. "I repeat," he said in French, "why not? A religion is not something eternal. It's got to function in a given time in a given place. If it doesn't function, it's no good and you'd better get another. Have you ever considered how your Christianity functioned in Germany? The total perversion of society it permitted? The mass executions? The horrible betrayal of humanity? I swore when I reached Herat, 'If Christianity can't do any better than it did in Munich, I'll take whatever religion they use here. It can't be worse.' Actually, it works out rather well."

Nur added something that astounded me. "I suppose you know that Ellen Jaspar also became a Muslim?"

Before I could speak, Dr. Stiglitz said, "Sensible girl. We talked about it the last time I saw her. She said she found great solace in her new faith. Called it 'a desert faith.' When I asked her what she meant by that, she said that Christianity had become a convenient ritual for those who overeat on Saturday, commit adultery on Saturday night, and play golf on Sunday." Ellen's description, when delivered in French, sounded witty, ugly and profound. "She said she needed a religion much closer to original sources. One thing she said impressed me. She pointed out that Islam, Christianity and Judaism all started in the desert, where God seems closer, and life and death are more mysterious. She said that we are all essentially desert animals and that life is meant to be harsh. When we live in an oasis like Philadelphia or Munich we become degenerate and lose touch with our origins."

"Would you return to Munich . . . if you were free to do so?" I asked.

Dr. Stiglitz looked at me with contempt. Nothing he had so far said implied that he was barred from returning to Germany, but his self-committal to a new world permitted only one conclusion, and I had publicly stated it. He was angry with me for having done so and replied in German, "No, I would never return to Germany." Then he translated into Pashto.

At this point the pilau was served, a rich, steaming dish with extra pine nuts and raisins, and although immediately after the beheading I had been repelled by the thought of food, with the passage of time I had grown hungry, and we three dug into it with our fingers, achieving a kind of hard brotherhood as we did. Dr. Stiglitz was then forty, Nur Muhammad was thirty-two and I twenty-six, but because each of us had a certain integrity which he was willing to protect, we were growing to respect one another, and I was happy to be with them. Indeed, I was proud to be with them, eating in communion after a ritual execution.

"You must not think of Islam as a religion of the desert," Nur warned. "It has much vitality and the world has not yet heard the last of it."

I was driven to ask an impertinent question. "If a new state of Israel is fashioned out of the desert, will you Muslims be able to accept it?"

"You can trust the Jews to look after themselves," Stiglitz said bluntly, and the brotherhood that had been burgeoning collapsed. I was shocked that a German refugee would make such a statement publicly, but what followed shocked me even more: "And if they should need help, men like you and me would help them. They deserve a country of their own." He returned to his beer.

"The Muslims won't like it," Nur reflected, "particularly the Arabs. I won't like it. I don't want Jews taking part of my homeland. But the alternatives I like even less. We Muslims will give the Jews a little . . . not much, but a little."

After a while I remarked, "We have no proof at the embassy that Ellen Jaspar became a Muslim."

"Many ferangi wives do," Nur replied. "We see no reason for official comment one way or the other."

"They do?" I asked.

"Of course. You Christians always think that conversion goes one way. Right here you see proof to the contrary. Dr. Stiglitz from Germany and Ellen Jaspar from Philadelphia."

I began to laugh again, this time nonhysterically. "What about that beer?" I asked, pointing at the half-empty bottle.

"A German can be many things," Stiglitz explained robustly. "A Catholic, a Jew, a Lutheran, a Muslim. But always he's a beer drinker. I have a dispensation from the mullah . . . the one you saw today. He's an understanding liberal."

[illegible] like each son. We [illegible] wind gave the [illegible] a [illegible] [illegible] not much but a [illegible].

After a while a crowd [illegible]. We have to [illegible] at the [illegible] that [illegible] appear becomes a [illegible].

"[illegible]," I [illegible]. "We [illegible] the [illegible] and [illegible] the [illegible]. [illegible] they [illegible]."

"Of course. [illegible] that [illegible] [illegible]."

I began to [illegible] [illegible] in which I was traveling, the Helmand, which started in the Koh-i-Baba west of Kabul, and the Arghandab, which flowed down past Kandahar [illegible] that they [illegible] to [illegible] across the desert and [illegible] the most ancient [illegible] civilization developed [illegible] [illegible] I would have [illegible] had I not known that [illegible] and that [illegible] jeep had vanished [illegible].

[illegible] lay only seventy miles west of [illegible] many of those miles [illegible] Muhammad had our jeep [illegible] before [illegible] we drove out of Kandahar with the [illegible] of [illegible]. We must have made an impressive [illegible], for we had now discarded [illegible] and [illegible] dressed like desert Afghans, except [illegible] caps. I was impressed by the [illegible] through fruit groves and [illegible] each protected by high mud walls [illegible] at the corners.

"What are the boxes for?" I asked.

[illegible] laughed and said, "Those are [illegible]."

8

Two substantial rivers ran through the part of Afghanistan in which I was traveling, the Helmand, which started in the Koh-i-Baba west of Kabul, and the Arghandab, which flowed down past Kandahar. It was at Qala Bist that they met to combine forces for a dash across the desert, and it was at this confluence, in the most ancient times, that a powerful civilization developed. From the way Shah Khan had described it, I would have wanted to see Qala Bist even had I not known that Nazrullah was working there and that Ellen Jaspar had vanished from that point.

The ruins lay only seventy miles west of Kandahar, but since many of those miles were across open desert, Nur Muhammad had our jeep packed before dawn and we drove out of Kandahar with the first rays of sun. We must have made an impressive one-jeep caravan, for we had now discarded western clothes and were dressed like desert Afghans, except that we kept our karakul caps. I was impressed by the road west, for it led through fruit groves and well-established farms, each protected by high mud walls with box-like structures at the corners.

"What are the boxes for?" I asked.

Nur laughed and said, "Those are melon fields."

"I still don't get the boxes."

"They're for the lookouts," he explained. "Growing melons in Afghanistan is extremely difficult. During the entire month they're ripening the farmer has to station armed men at each field to shoot thieves."

I must have looked as if I thought he was teasing, for he added gravely, "My father raised melons, and at the age of nine I stood night watch with a shotgun. Otherwise every melon would have been stolen."

"Why do you permit such thievery?" I asked.

"We're a brigand society," Nur said. "Our king doesn't rule in Kabul the way your president rules in Washington. In this country we murder kings."

We had now reached the village of Girishk, where we were to leave the pleasant melon patches and turn south across the desert. For me this was a rare moment, for we were about to enter upon the great world-desert that sweeps from Central India across Arabia, through Egypt, over the Sahara and on to Morocco, where it is finally halted by the Atlantic Ocean. I had not previously seen this enormous desert, and now as the early sun showed me the windswept land and the burning rocks I knew I was entering a new world. This was the universe of shifting sand, the mournful camel chewing sideways, the men in dirty white. I remember with great clarity my first impression of this vast desert and my astonishment at its enormous vistas.

The segment which we had struck was in some ways an ideal introduction, for it was both smaller than the better-known deserts of Arabia, Egypt and Libya—less than two hundred miles on a side—and more savage. It had no oasis, no vegetation and no protective rocks. It was a bleak, barren waste across which the wind howled perpetually, and to be lost on it meant death, a fact which was amply proved each year, and it was from this remorseless character that the Afghan desert had obtained its lurid name, which I hesitate to repeat, since it sounds so exhibitionistic: The Dasht-i-Margo, the Desert of Death.

We had traversed the dangerous wastes for about two hours when we saw ahead a sight that I knew was coming but which nevertheless startled me. Rising from the desert, along the shores of the Helmand River, stood the arch of Qala Bist, an enormous clay-brick structure rising high in the air. A thousand years ago it had formed part of some Muslim edifice, but even the memory of the mosque was lost. Yet there the arch stood, so tall it seemed impossible that a desert people had built it. It was the more surprising because it was an unsupported arch, a lofty, soaring flight of brick composed in beautiful proportions, and when we stopped the car to admire it I told Nur, "You had some architects in the old days."

"Wait till you see over there," Nur laughed, and as we approached the suspended arch I began to see the outline of a great deserted city: walls that crept up from the river and enclosed enormous areas, turrets of majestic size, and battlements that once accommodated thousands of soldiers.

"What is it?" I asked.

"Nobody knows."

"You mean it's just there?"

"It's one of our smaller deserted cities," Nur assured me. Pointing westward across the desert he said, "On the other side, where the Helmand disappears, there's an empty city seventy miles long. No one knows who built it, either, but there it is."

"What do you mean, where the Helmand disappears?"

"This river," he said, indicating the powerful flow at our feet. "Out in the desert it just disappears."

"Into what?" I asked.

"Into air. The Desert of Death is so dry that the river runs into a lake that just dries up." I looked at him suspiciously and realized he was not teasing, so I dropped the matter, but the city before me could not be casually dismissed.

"Who built this?" I probed.

"It's always been here," Nur laughed.

"No name?"

"No. Qala Bist is our modern name for the arch."

"It's a masterpiece. If we had something like this in America, we'd make it a national park."

"You started about a thousand years too late to have something like this," Nur laughed. "We do have some ideas, of course. Possibly it was the winter capital of Mahmud of Ghazni. He was rich enough to have built it. But I agree with the experts who argue that it must have been here for a long time before Mahmud's day."

"And that's all that's known?"

"You see what I see," Nur replied defensively. "There was a great city in the desert, and now even its history is gone."

The idea tantalized me and I was about to say, I'm going to find out what happened here, when I saw on the ramparts above me a young man in his late twenties, dressed in desert costume and turban. He was waving to us and Nur cried, "It's Nazrullah," and I saw that he wore a mustache and beard. On the city wall he made a fine figure and could have been a young captain of the guard a thousand years ago.

"Eh, Nazrullah!" Nur shouted. "I've brought an American with me . . . from the embassy." This news somewhat deflated the young man on the wall, for he ceased waving; but then his pleasure at seeing visitors overcame any hesitancy, and he scrambled down from the high wall and ran forward to greet us.

"Nur Muhammad!" he cried with real pleasure, and they embraced in a manner that satisfied me that my driver was no ordinary Afghan. Nazrullah then turned to me and said in English, smiling warmly, "You are welcome to my humble abode, such as it is, four hundred rooms."

We laughed and Nur said in Pashto, "This one speaks our language. And he's come to spy you out for the evil fellow you are." It was apparent that Nur desperately wanted us to get along.

Nazrullah extended his hand and said generously, "You're most welcome! Drive this way. We've cut a breach in the wall and you can bring your jeep into the city." And he led us to the opening.

There he climbed in with us, for his camp site was far inside the walls—three-quarters of a mile, I judged—and as we traveled I tried to study both Nazrullah and his extraordinary city. He was an attractive fellow, not so tall as I but more wiry and better co-ordinated. He had a mercurial brilliance, in both gesture and speech. His hair was rather long, possibly because barbers were rare in Qala Bist, but he was extremely clean, even though he was living under unusual conditions. He seemed a well-organized man and I could understand the high regard in which Moheb Khan, Nur Muhammad and Dr. Stiglitz held him.

The deserted city was equally impressive. Stout walls many feet thick and sometimes twenty feet high swept over rolling ground for some eight or nine miles, enclosing an area which once contained substantial farm lands, water systems and separate villages for menials. The brick city itself was a confusion of palaces, minarets, fortresses and what must have been administrative centers. I can best describe it this way: By the time I had seen one complete set of related buildings I thought: This is the city. But it wasn't, for it was connected by ramparts and forts to a larger segment, and this was repeated six or seven times.

After a considerable drive we reached a large field contained within the walls, and here Nazrullah had pitched his tents, from which he was conducting surveys of the area that was to be irrigated by water taken from the Helmand River. He had at his disposal two jeeps, three engineers and four servants. No women were evident, but one tent, finer than the others, must have been the one in which Ellen Jaspar had lived when she came to Qala Bist nine months ago, and where possibly she still remained. I tried cautiously to study this tent without attracting attention, but I failed, for Nazrullah volunteered, "That's where I live. Let's unload your gear."

"Don't let us inconvenience you," I apologized.

"You're my first guests from Kabul," he replied expansively. "Of course you'll stay with me." He threw back the flaps of his tent and bade us enter. I remember two things: the floor was covered by an expensive Persian rug, and on the desk stood a portrait of Ellen Jaspar dressed in the surplice she wore when singing Beethoven's *Ninth* with the Philadelphia Orchestra. Nazrullah made no comment about the photograph.

He indicated where we were to sleep and sent his servants to fetch our gear, which they unpacked for stowing in cardboard trunks which Nazrullah had acquired in the bazaar, but as they worked I saw in another corner a trunk made of leather, stamped with the initials E.J. It was locked, so I could not tell whether it was empty or full, but it seemed to be waiting for its owner to return.

Nazrullah now took us to a tent some distance from the others, and here, seated on rugs, we had our inevitable lunch of nan and pilau, but this was different, because near the tent the cook was operating an oven that must have been more than a thousand years old, and for the first time I saw how nan was baked. A conical mound of clay, looking exactly like a beehive with the top cut off, rose above a shallow pit in which charcoal was kept burning. The opening of the beehive gave access to the inner sides, which sloped over the coals, and it was against these sloping sides that the raw dough was fixed, though why it did not fall onto the coals I never understood. I asked Nazrullah and he said, "By trial and error the desert people developed this stove three or four thousand years ago. The dough is just sticky enough to cling to the sides and the fire is cool enough not to bake the bread too quickly. It's obviously impossible, but it works." The hot bread was delicious.

After the meal, when our greasy fingers had been washed by servants, we returned to Nazrullah's tent, where he said reflectively, "It's been my salvation, living here on the edge of the desert. After Germany and America, it's reminded me of what Afghanistan is. Do you know what it is?" he asked me directly.

"Until I saw the Desert of Death I thought I knew. A mountainous land marked by inhabitable valleys and plateaus."

"Precisely. That's what I thought it was. But four-fifths of our nation looks like what you see outside these walls. Desert, cut by rivers. And wherever we can lead those rivers onto the desert, we're rewarded a thousandfold. Before you came here, Miller, did you realize that the Afghan is probably the world's best irrigation expert?"

I said I hadn't and he continued, "We waste hardly a drop of water. The skill of our peasants is unbelievable. They take a little stream coming out of the mountains and lead it hundreds of yards to irrigate a field, then take it back to its main bed so that others can borrow it farther down the mountainside. One insignificant stream will be used many times."

"I've never seen that," I replied.

"My job is to do on a grand scale with the Helmand what the farmers do so well with little streams. We're going to build a gigantic dam up in the hills and capture all the water you see going to waste out there."

The concept had inflamed his imagination, and with boundless vitality he rushed us out of the tent and over to the city, where we passed through silent streets that must once have been glorious with ribbons from India and furs from Russia. We climbed stairs that were almost as good now as when erected and came to a vast reception hall, its walls still marked with murals, then entered the battlements which troops could have used that night. Nazrullah moved quickly, for he was familiar with the ancient city, but I was tardy because I wanted to absorb the implied splendor of the place. It was incredible that men had ruled here whose dynasties were forgotten, that a city of this magnitude could have perished without leaving in the records even the name by which its enemies described it. As I caught up with Nazrullah on the battlement I said, "Must give you an eerie feeling, living in a place like this."

"It does. No matter how indifferent you are to history, when you live here you speculate."

"Any conclusions?"

"None. I don't have to solve the past." He pointed down to the river that ran along the foot of the wall on which we stood. "My job is to get water out of that river."

"What'll you do with it when you get it?"

He pointed beyond the river to the bleak desert, where wind was churning up the sand, and I supposed that he was going to say that farther out lay an arable district. Instead he replied, "What looks like desert down there is potential farmland. Wherever we can lead the water, we can grow crops. When we're through, this land will be as valuable as it was when this city supported perhaps half a million people. They lived by irrigation."

"You think so?"

"Look!" he cried with infectious enthusiasm, and he intended that I look upstream where old embankments proved that the Helmand has once before been tapped for irrigation purposes, but I saw instead a curious procession of tall mounds that led away from our city toward a group of small mountains some twenty miles to the east. The mounds had obviously been made by man, because they appeared at regular quarter-mile intervals, and since each was of considerable size, and there were eighty or more visible, I was looking at a project of magnitude, whatever it was.

"What are you staring at?" Nazrullah asked.

"That chain of mounds," I replied.

Nazrullah thought for a moment, then banged his right fist enthusiastically into his left palm and cried, "Miller, are you game for something exciting?"

"The ambassador told me to look around."

"You'll be the only American who's ever done this." He ran to a point from which he could call to Nur Muhammad: "Nur, you want to go with us through the karez?" He pronounced the strange word in one syllable to rhyme with *breeze,* and it had an instant effect upon Nur.

"Not me! And if Miller Sahib has any sense, he won't go either."

"He's already volunteered," Nazrullah shouted enthusiastically, "and if he goes, you'll be shamed."

"I stand before my ancestors shamed," Nur laughed. "You uphold the honor of Afghanistan. I'm a coward."

We hurried through the deserted city and climbed into one of Nazrullah's jeeps, which he raced expertly through the breached wall and onto the desert. Soon we were pulled up beside one of the mounds, which was built of mud brick rising to a height of fifteen feet or more. A crude ladder led to the top.

When we had climbed it, I saw inside another ladder, much longer than the first, leading down to darkness. Nazrullah dropped a pebble, which splashed in water, far below us, and I realized that we were perched atop a shaft which led to an underground stream.

"Down we go!" Nazrullah cried like a college boy, and I watched his excited face, its beard covered with dust, disappear. I followed, and when I reached bottom found myself standing on a narrow edge of earth bordering a clear stream of water only faintly illuminated by sunlight seeping down the shaft.

"Is each of the mounds like this?" I asked.

"Yep," Nazrullah replied, proud of his American colloquialism. "It's an underground irrigation system bringing water down from the hills. You game to crawl through to the next mound?" He must have seen my apprehension, for he flashed on a light and added, "We've cleaned it out for just such expeditions."

I looked at the low ceiling of the tunnel and discovered that once we left the mound, which permitted us to stand, we would be walking in very stooped positions—duck-walking, we had called it as children—and I wasn't sure my legs would take it. "You won't feel it . . . in a quarter of a mile," Nazrullah assured me.

"Here we go," I cried, more bravely than I felt, and bent over to creep duck-wise into the tunnel.

My back quickly began to ache and, as I feared, my leg muscles became numb, but lithe Nazrullah was pushing ahead with such enthusiasm that I had to follow. At midpoint we could begin to see slight indications of light from the next mound and this encouraged me to bear my pain; it also permitted me to see the construction of the tunnel. Its ceiling was protected in no way and was held in place merely by the cohesion of clay, and whenever I bumped it with my head, bits of earth splashed into the water. I thought: This thing could collapse at any moment, and I began to feel my throat constricting.

Fortunately, we reached the next mound and I was able to stand erect. My feet were soaking wet and my back creaked as I stretched it, but I was too stiff to want to climb the ladder immediately, so we stood in the small shaft of light and breathed the cool air.

"Now you understand why Nur refused the invitation," Nazrullah laughed.

"I'm glad I came. Who invented the idea?"

"Maybe the Persians. More likely the Afghans. It's the best way known to transport water across a desert. If we tried to do it on the surface, the sun would evaporate it all."

"How old is the tunnel?"

"Assuming that it was used by the city, which it probably was, the hole we're standing in could have been dug twelve or thirteen hundred years ago."

"Let's get out of here!" I cried.

"Of course, it's been redug many times. The tunnels do collapse," he said brightly.

"I wondered about that as we were crawling through," I replied.

Nazrullah held the ladder by one hand and said, "The karez system was very costly of human life. Water experts would go to the mountains and dig at likely points . . . sometimes seventy feet down, but because they were experts they usually found water. They would then calculate where that particular level would work itself to the surface, and they would dig these underground tunnels for ten to twenty miles, following the natural line of the water's flow."

"Why didn't the ceilings fall in?" I asked.

"They did, frequently. The one we crawled under could collapse at any moment," he said without emotion. "In desert regions men who worked the karez formed a special caste. They lived under special laws, ate special food, had extra women. Mullahs and police were powerless to molest them, for generally they lived short lives and when they died, usually of suffocation, for they never shored up the ceilings and trusted to luck, their few possessions and their women were passed along to the next karez man."

I was beginning to feel the approach of claustrophobia and started up the ladder, increasing my speed when I saw how fragile the clay bricks were under which we had been standing. When I regained freedom I gasped deeply, then saw Nazrullah smiling, his beard gray with dust. "Lucky I didn't tell you that when we were halfway through," he apologized.

"That tunnel is going to fall on me every time I go to sleep for the next month." I laughed thinly.

"I've thought of that myself," Nazrullah confided. "After a series of collapses they often had to beat the men with whips to drive them back into the karez. At the beginning of the system the kings ordained that any boy born to a karez man had to inherit the job. In some districts they were branded at birth."

"You live in a rugged land," I remarked, shivering in the hot sun.

Nazrullah climbed down the outside ladder and sat with me in the shadow of the mound. "It is a cruel land," he admitted. "The existence of this karez reminds us how cruel. But even today in Afghanistan I could show you things that would shock you."

"I've seen some of them," I assured him.

"What?" he asked suspiciously.

"In Ghazni . . . a woman stoned to death. In Kandahar a young man committed murder over a dancing boy. They cut off his head . . . with a rusty bayonet."

"You've been initiated," Nazrullah said without inflection. He seemed wholly composed, but his inner tension was betrayed by quick gestures and the nervous movement of his beard. "I force myself down to the karez occasionally so that I may remember the heritage of human suffering we're trying to eradicate. If I'd known you'd seen the executions I wouldn't have dragged you into the tunnel, but I find I can't talk with ferangi who haven't had some similar experience."

"I've had three now," I said. "We can talk."

"I think we can," he agreed, "and I'd like to say two things. It will require some words, but like your journey through the karez, it may be worth it.

"I went to Germany at the age of twenty. Before that I'd been educated by private tutors whose main job, it seems to me now, was to impress me with the moral depravity of Afghanistan and the timeless glory of Europe. I knew no better than to accept their indoctrination at face value and reported to Germany fully prepared to exhibit my tutors' prejudices. But when I reached Göttingen I found that the true barbarians were not the primitives who stone women in Ghazni—and we have some real primitives in this country—but the Germans. From 1938 through 1941

I remained as their guest, to witness the dreadful degeneration of a culture which might once have been what my tutors claimed but was now a garish travesty. Believe me, Miller, I learned more in Germany than you'll ever learn in Afghanistan.

"As you know, I went from Germany to Philadelphia, where half the people thought I was a Negro. What I didn't learn in Germany, you taught me. Why do you suppose I wear this beard? Before I grew it I made a six-week experiment. I decided to be a Negro . . . lived in Negro hotels, ate in their restaurants, read their papers and dated Negro girls. It was an ugly, ugly life, being a Negro in your country . . . maybe not so bad as being a Jew in Germany, but a lot worse than being an Afghan in Ghazni. To prove to Philadelphians I wasn't a Negro, I grew this beard and wore a turban, which I had never worn at home.

"My education was worth every penny my government paid for it, because after six years in Göttingen and Philadelphia I positively hungered to get home and go to work. Miller, we can build here just as good a society as the Germans or the Americans have built in their surroundings."

I looked at his surroundings: a bleak desert, a muddy river, blazing empty hills, an abandoned city. Because I had seen Afghanistan, I appreciated the Herculean task he had set himself.

"The second thing I want to say is this," he continued with fervor. "Having made my transition from a boy who wanted to escape Afghanistan to a man who fought to get back, I find daily joy in being here. Imagine, at twenty-eight I can be appointed head of a project that will revolutionize this part of Asia. In Philadelphia a man at a cocktail party offered me the stirring job of helping to sell shoes. 'You're enthusiastic,' the man said. 'Women will go for that beard.' Miller, I'm here in the desert because I want to be here. I want to stir the earth like the karez men stirred theirs . . . fundamentally . . . in the bowels . . . at the bottom of the ladder in a deep hole. And if the ceiling collapses on me, I don't give a damn."

There was another moment of tension, then he laughed and said, "We'd better drive back," but when we tried to enter the jeep, the metal was so hot we could not touch it, for we were really in the desert, and if the ancient karez men had not dug their perilous tunnels, water could never have crossed this land and the city could not have existed.

In the days that followed, Nazrullah talked eagerly about all aspects of life in Afghanistan, but whenever I broached the subject of his wife, he was adept in putting me off. Ellen was not at Qala Bist, however; of that I was satisfied. If Nazrullah did not respond to my overtures on the subject, he did take every opportunity to let me see the kind of man he was, and as I watched him with the engineers and the workers I knew that I was observing a man who had matured far beyond his years.

He had an enviable capacity to elicit from others their best efforts. I understood why the shoe company in Philadelphia had wanted to hire him and why a German engineering firm, looking to the future, had recently written to ask if he would represent them in Asia. He had a quick smile, an infectious wit and a generosity of spirit that was engaging, and I could now understand his effect upon a junior at Bryn Mawr, bored by her native surroundings. It was reasonable that Ellen Jaspar had fallen in love with him, but it was not reasonable that she should now, because of him, be in serious trouble, if indeed she were alive.

In a way, I was sorry that I had interviewed Nazrullah's Afghan wife in Kandahar, for if that silken, shrouded voice had not convinced me that she and Ellen had been friends, it would now be easy to conclude that only the shock of discovering a previous marriage had unnerved Ellen. But if relationships were as placid as reported, and if Nazrullah were as congenial as he seemed, what dark force operating on this trio could have occasioned tragedy?

It was also interesting for me to compare Nazrullah with Nur. The former had been set free psychologically by his travels abroad, while Nur was still uncertain of himself, because of an insular limitation which he was working desperately to correct. Nazrullah utilized a broad, frontal approach to problems and for an Afghan was markedly outspoken, partly because he was honest and partly because he lacked the ability to maneuver, whereas Nur was a master of manipulation. The big difference, however, lay in their concept of what process would lead to their country's salvation. Nur, the traditionalist, whose brother was an enlightened mullah, felt that Afghanistan would be saved through the rededication of the individual and the moral regeneration of Islam. Nazrullah, in our long talks in the tent, argued that what happened to the Muslim religion was no great concern of his. From having studied various religions at first hand, he suspected that any of the three great desert religions, Islam, Christianity or Judaism, was as good as any other but that Islam was rather better fitted for the social structure of Afghanistan. "But what's going to save this nation is the creation of a contemporary world—a new economic system, a real representative form of government, dams, roads, farms . . . the things that we can create."

As he said this he snapped his fingers and cried, "Miller, to show you what I mean, I'm going to take you to the site of the new dam. How soon can you start?"

Nur protested that the location was too far away, but Nazrullah would not listen. "You've got to go there anyway. Saddle up the jeeps!" He dashed about camp and within fifteen minutes had a major expedition assembled. "You're going to see the future of Afghanistan!" he promised.

We roared out of the old walls in a caravan of three

jeeps because Nazrullah felt that any penetration of the desert in machines was so inherently perilous that group protection was advisable, but on this day nothing happened. We reached the junction town of Girishk, from which we struck off across forbidding land on a trail that jeeps could barely negotiate. Finally we ground to a halt at a goat trail, where we left the jeeps under guard while we climbed on foot to a high elevation, from which we could see, far below us, the roaring Helmand River as it carried the spring thaw through a narrow cleft in the mountains.

"To build a dam, a great dam such as the American and German experts advise," Nazrullah cried, pointing with a stick, "requires two things, a gorge and a mountain close by. Down there you see the gorge, with steep, solid walls, and over there you see one hell of a mountain."

"What's the relationship?" Nur asked.

"You build a road from the mountain to the gorge. Then you lead that road over a temporary bridge that crosses the gorge, high up in the air. Then you dynamite the mountain rock by rock and haul it in trucks to the bridge, where you drop the rocks into the river. And after you do this day and night for three or four years, you have a dam."

He showed us where the road would be built and where the bridge would be slung, high above the rapids. "For seven months trucks will dump rocks off that bridge and nothing will happen, because the river will wash our boulders downstream as if they were straw. But one day the rocks will begin to hold, and the river will start to back up—just a little. But on that day we have it strangled. Then we can do with it what we will."

He called for his field glasses, which enabled me to see bench marks already cut into the cliff north of where the dam would be and other marks south, many feet above the present water level. "Any idea what that's to be?" he asked, and when I admitted my ignorance he replied, "That's the tunnel. While we're throwing in the rock, we're also digging that tunnel, and when the river starts to back up, it gradually rises to that level, and runs away through the tunnel. Then we move in hundreds of trucks and throw thousands of tons of rock into the ravine, pack them with earth and after some years concrete the exposed face and find ourselves with a dam."

It was difficult to visualize the completed dam, it was of such magnitude, but Nazrullah had surveyed the ground so often that to him the gigantic structure already existed. Pointing to a mark hundreds of feet above the river he said, "The water will rise to there. We'll collect the floods in the spring, when they aren't needed in the fields, and release them in the summer, when they are. And the beauty of this system is that every pound of water that drops through our tunnel will generate electricity which we'll send over the mountains to Kandahar."

Remembering that primitive city I predicted, "In Kandahar they won't be using much electricity."

"Ah! That's where you're wrong!" Nazrullah cried. "In Germany we made a study of fifteen primitive societies"—I liked his using the word *primitive;* our ambassador had forbidden us to do so, claiming it insulted the Afghans—"and we found that when irrigation dams were built in primitive areas, the financial experts always fought against wasting the money to add generators at the same time. They argued, 'The people are so primitive they'll have no use for electricity.' In every instance, within five years the original output of electricity, which the experts had called wasteful, was being utilized and further capacity was required. If we can get electricity to Kandahar, they'll find ways of using it. Progress creates its own dynamics."

The concept was so new to me that I asked for an illustration of a primitive society where this had happened. "I'll give you a classic," he said instantly. "The Tennessee Valley Authority."

"I'd hardly call Tennessee primitive," I argued with some asperity.

"I would," he replied flatly. "The hill region anyway. I made a study of it, on the spot, and in its way, compared to New York, it's as primitive as Girishk compared to Kabul. And the T.V.A. found it couldn't make electricity fast enough."

I was not satisfied with his description of part of my country as primitive, having always reserved that word for other nations, but I was impressed by his excitement about his job and the poetic insights he brought to it. For example, he stared down at the river which now ran wild through the gorge and said softly, "Isn't it a gripping idea, Miller, that on the day we drop our first load of rock into that turbulent river it'll have no idea of what's happening? Rocks like that have been falling off the cliffs for a million years, and it's washed them aside. But these rocks will be different. They'll be the beginning of something not even that river is strong enough to halt. And we will continue . . ." He hammered the air with his fist, visualizing the enormous aggregation of rock that would ultimately jam that gorge and tame the river.

He turned to Nur and me with dancing eyes. "Each day we must throw similar rocks into the human river of Afghanistan. Here a school, there a road, down in the gorge a dam. So far our human river isn't aware that it's been touched. But we shall never halt until we've modified it completely."

As I looked down at the turbulent Helmand, rushing freely between the cliffs, it seemed to symbolize the wild freedom of Afghanistan, and I said half to myself, "It's rather a pity that such a river must be brought under control."

Nazrullah grabbed me by the arm and whipped me about. "What did you say?" he demanded.

"I said, It's a shame such a river has to be dammed."

"That's incredible," he muttered, not in surprise or anger or any other emotion that I could recognize. "That's really incredible, Miller." He snapped his fingers, tugged at his beard and stared at me as if trying to reassemble fragments. "Those are the exact words Ellen said while standing here." He bit his forefinger, then added with impatience, "You damned Americans are so sentimental. You've organized your own land to the limit, but you criticize others who want to organize theirs."

"I was speaking symbolically," I protested.

"So was Ellen," he snapped. "What you both meant was, The more modern Tennessee becomes, the nicer it would be to keep Afghanistan a primitive place where we could come to observe the peasants. Well, Miller, we're going to change it . . . profoundly."

"I want you to. Perhaps Ellen meant that old-fashioned ways are always better. A lot of Americans believe that nonsense. But I don't."

"What do you believe?"

"That it's always sad to see freedom lost. As for change, that's why we have an American embassy in Kabul. To help you make the changes, yet stay free."

"You'd better help," he warned. "Because if you try to hold us back, Russia will be eager to jump in and help us."

"To what?" I asked, but he had turned away and now stamped angrily down the mountain trail. When he reached the jeeps he jumped into one and roared down the dangerous trail to Girishk, leaving Nur and me to ride with an assistant engineer, who drove us back to Qala Bist. But often as our jeeps passed and repassed on the desert I caught sight of Nazrullah, brooding in silence, the knuckles of his left fist pressed against his bearded chin.

9

Our caravan had barely come in sight of Qala Bist when we spotted a strange jeep speeding at us from the walled city, throwing a cloud of dust across the desert. It was Dr. Stiglitz, driven by an Afghan military officer, coming out to intercept us as quickly as possible.

"Where's Nazrullah?" the German shouted as he drew close.

"He's back there," I cried.

The four jeeps drew together in the desert and Stiglitz said in German, "I bring you bad news."

He and Nazrullah continued talking in German, but I caught the fact that something had happened to the American engineer Pritchard, who had crossed the Desert of Death some months before to measure the spring flow of the Helmand River. I waited impatiently while the two discussed the problem, and finally they took cognizance of me. "Sorry, Herr Miller. My visit really concerns you."

"How?"

"There's an official message for you," Nazrullah replied, and he spoke to the Afghan officer, who handed me a paper containing directions which the American embassy had phoned down to Kandahar military headquarters that morning. It said:

Miller. Proceed immediately to The City, thence to Chahar, where Pritchard broke his leg three weeks ago. See if the German Dr. Stiglitz can accompany you at our expense, but travel in at least two jeeps because earlier investigators dispatched by the Afghan government have not been heard from. Obtain fullest local advice before attempting journey.

It was signed by Verbruggen and I could imagine his rough, worried voice on the telephone. I asked Stiglitz, "You know what's in the message?"

"Of course."

"You'll go?"

"I'm here."

"How much?" Before he could reply I led him away from the others, where he stood silent for some moments. I was certain he had guessed why I had called on him in Kandahar and I knew he wanted me to carry back a good report which might enable him to jump from Kandahar to Kabul, so he would be disposed to request a low fee in hopes of winning my favor; on the other hand he was a trained doctor and proud of his German degree, in addition to which the cost of German beer in Kandahar was not trivial, so that he had reasons for asking a substantial fee. It was a delicate problem, and the poor pudgy man was not equal to solving it. I grew ashamed of myself, especially since I was a Jew and he a German.

"I'm sorry, Doctor," I said. "I should've spoken first. Two hundred dollars plus twenty dollars for each day beyond five that we're out."

Stiglitz breathed deeply, and I judged that my offer was more generous than he had dared to demand. "I accept!" he said, continuing with profuse thanks which became almost embarrassing. "You've no idea, Herr Miller, how those damned Afghans rob me for my beer."

"Agreed." Then I asked the Afghan soldier, "Are you driving us?"

"He is not!" Nazrullah protested. "I am." He drew his staff about him and shot a series of questions: "What's the state of the moon?" "Which of our jeeps is in best condition?" "Miller, will you turn over your K-rations to us?" "Water, crowbars, tow ropes?" When he had satisfactory answers he looked at his watch and said, "We'll leave Qala Bist in forty minutes. We're taking Miller's jeep and mine. Nur Muhammad to drive one. I'll drive the other. Stiglitz and Miller the only passengers. I want everything assembled in front of my tent at once. O.K.?"

He jumped in his jeep and sped for Qala Bist, leading us through the ponderous wall and across the fields to the camp. As he ran for his tent he shouted, "Nur, stay with me," and in the next minutes I watched two Afghan gentlemen assume command of an expedition that could turn out disastrously if anything went wrong. Nur, who understood jeeps, took care of matters in that area, while Nazrullah checked the logistics, then supervised the packing. "Turbans for the ferangi!" Nazrullah shouted, and one of the engineers solved this by lifting two from the heads of the servants. "You'll need it," Nur assured me as I packed mine.

It was still several hours before dark when we approached our loaded jeeps, where Nazrullah consulted for the last time with his staff and with the Afghan officer. Taking a map he drew a tentative line from Qala Bist across the desert to an extended area marked simply The City. There he turned his line south until it reached the remote village of Chahar. "We'll be going this way," he announced in Pashto, "and if anything should happen, I promise I won't be far off this route." He watched while Nur and the officer traced the route on their maps.

"Now," Nazrullah asked sharply, "where do you think the missing men could be?"

He stared at his staff, at Nur, at the officer. The

latter spoke: "Ten days ago we sent two men in a jeep . . ."

"One jeep?" Nazrullah asked, tugging his beard.

"Yes."

"Great Jesus Christ!" Nazrullah snapped, uttering an oath quite inappropriate for a Muslim, something he had picked up at the Wharton School. "One jeep?" He stabbed at the map. "Driving across that?"

"Yes," the officer replied, unruffled. "They left Kandahar ten days ago, drove to Girishk, and started across the desert on this course." On Nazrullah's map he drew a firm line which converged on our projected course about halfway across the desert.

Nazrullah reflected and said, "With the lines running that way we might spot them anywhere during the second half."

I added, "If they're broken down, they'll probably have a flag waving that we can see."

Nazrullah looked at me with compassion, then asked, "Did they know the desert?"

"Yes."

"They the type who follow instructions?"

"Best men we had."

Nazrullah studied the map for some minutes. "I want you to change my route just a little. We'll drop up here and take a look." He drew a jog to the north, almost off the desert, and said, "We'll never be far from this route. Salaam aleikum." With that he spun his wheels in a tight circle and sped for the wall. In a few moments we were entering the desert, headed west for the setting sun, a simple caravan of two jeeps, each marked by high poles from which fluttered large squares of white cloth.

The Afghan Dasht-i-Margo was not a desert in the accustomed sense, for although it did contain vast unbroken stretches of sand, it was also an accumulation of shaly detritus laid down by deteriorating mountains which had eroded through millions of years, so that across the desert we found bands of this shale sometimes half a mile wide along which our jeeps could race at forty miles an hour, while we saw on either side the glorious sweep of traditional dunes that characterize the usual desert.

An additional feature marked this desert: When we were well into its heart we could not see a single thing growing nor any shred of human existence. There were no lichens on the rock, no seedlings in crevices, no shrubs, no birds, no gullies touched with a little water, no lizards, no eagles, no oases of any kind. There were no fence poles nor relics of forgotten homes nor even stones laid in a row. There was only the most blazing, heat-racked emptiness I had ever seen. I remember thinking once, when we were surrounded by dunes: In the polar regions they at least have frozen water and insects. Here there's nothing . . . except heat.

"How hot is it?" I asked Nur.

"Hundred and thirty, but it isn't the thermometer that worries us," he said as he studied the desolate landscape. "It's the wind." He checked some drifting sand and said, "Wind's thirty miles an hour. Later it'll grow to fifty. That's what kills you on the desert."

I now began to appreciate the flags that Nazrullah had provided for our jeeps, for as our caravan moved across the desert we were frequently separated, since neither driver could be sure that what looked like a potential road would turn out to be so; and often it was the driver in second position who found the successful trail, whereas what had looked good to the first man had turned into a wall of impenetrable sand. When this happened, the unsuccessful driver would whirl about, look for his companion's flag, and set off in hot pursuit. Neither waited for the other, but each felt responsible for seeing that the separation did not become too great.

"Is it possible to work your way into a real dead end?" I asked.

"Sure. Probably what happened to the missing men. In this business you need that other flag."

We had been on the road for well over an hour when Nazrullah, whose jeep was now in the lead, stopped abruptly and waited for us to join him. He signaled for silence, then pointed to a small herd of gazelles—not more than fifteen—that had penetrated these dreadful wastes where I had been unable to see a shred of forage but where they were acquainted with hidden areas that no man had yet identified.

At first I didn't understand why the gazelles fascinated me, but I sat spellbound watching the small, delicate animals standing gracefully on the face of the burning desert. What could they be doing? What did they signify? Afghanistan had untold valleys where an animal could find forage. Why were they here? And why was I so moved by seeing them?

One of their lookouts spotted us, and with a disembodied grace the small animals leaped, exploded in the dying sunlight, twisted, turned and fled like wraiths across the desert. I had never before seen such flawless motion, and as they sped away like the sound of retreating music, one female, small and without horns, ran toward us with a breathless poetry, then saw the jeeps and turned in mid-air, throwing her sharp hoofs to one side as she changed direction. As she did this marvelous thing, I was forced to cry out, for I saw that she was colored like the chaderi Moheb Khan's niece had worn, and she was not an animal at all, she was not a gazelle, but the embodiment of the hunger I felt. In this cruel land of recurring ugliness, where only men were seen, the gazelle reminded me of womanliness, of girls at a dance, of the mystery of half the world. I watched her go in matchless grace, darting this way and that until she vanished behind a distant dune, and there were tears in my eyes and I felt I could not tolerate the awful loneliness of the desert. I was lost in Asia. I was forsaken on the high roof of the world and the gazelles had been a sighing, drifting premonition.

Then I heard Nazrullah saying, "They must have come down from the caravanserai," and we took out our maps to discover that we were near the jog that Nazrullah had drawn to the north. "There's a chance the other two might have made for the caravanserai." And we turned north.

The sun was just setting when we reached the top of a dune from which we could look down upon one of the sights that has always inspired the traveler in Asia: a walled caravanserai looming out of the dusk at the end of a long journey. It remains unforgettable: a gaunt, square, mud-walled sanctuary built around a central open space where animals of the caravan were sheltered. One leg of the wall comprised a fort devoid of windows but well supplied in recent centuries with slit holes for rifle fire. Entrance was by a solitary gate, a handsome structure built in fine Arabic proportions. The serai had been erected hundreds of years ago, possibly even in the days of Muhammad, and through the centuries had served continuously, for it stood at the edge of the desert near the end of a little gully in which grass grew and stagnant water accumulated, and to it had come, as we now came, thousands of caravans needing protection for the night. It was a rule of the desert that whoever succeeded in entering a serai was safe for the night, no matter what antagonist he encountered inside, and there must have been many stirring tales of blood enemies who shared sanctuary here under unexpected circumstances.

As we approached the gate, Nazrullah halted the jeeps and he and Nur debarked to study, on hands and knees, all the surrounding sand, entering the walls to continue their search. After a while they reappeared and said, "They didn't get this far."

I hoped that this was a sign that we were to move on, for whereas I had found the ruins at Qala Bist so immense as to be commanding, I found this old deserted caravanserai a place of brooding quiet that was in a sense terrifying. Possibly I was still influenced by the gazelles, possibly by the haunting loneliness of a desert twilight, but the idea that a wayside inn had once flourished here but had now lost its reason for being was at the moment too gloomy for my acceptance.

"Are we leaving?" I asked hopefully.

"We'll eat here," Nazrullah replied, and he took us to the fort, where he and the doctor began laying out blankets on the earthen floor. Nur lit two Coleman lamps, whose incandescent glow showed the high roof of the caravanserai to good effect, and if anything were calculated to make me feel gloomier than I already did, it was the way the flickering light threw enormous shadows on the mud walls. I thought: Genghis Khan could come through that door, and he'd be right at home.

Two-thirds of the way down the hall, a stout circular column about twelve feet in diameter rose from the floor and continued through the roof. It was built neither of wood nor of mud but of plaster, and our lights played upon its uneven surfaces in exciting patterns. "That's a beautiful column," I remarked. "What's it used for?"

"Famous, too," Nazrullah replied without looking.

"What for?"

"Manner of construction," he replied.

"What's unusual, the plaster?"

"The insides."

Dr. Stiglitz interrupted. "What's inside?" he asked, and years later when I reconstructed that night I became convinced that somehow he knew what the answer was going to be.

"It's not pleasant," Nazrullah cautioned. "Want to hear it before dinner?" When I said yes, he continued, "Some time around 1220, Genghis Khan . . ."

"I just thought of him!" I cried.

"How so?" Nur asked.

"I was looking at those shadows and thought, If Genghis Khan came in now, I wouldn't be surprised."

"He was here," Nazrullah laughed.

"What about the pillar?" Stiglitz asked.

"Genghis Khan destroyed Afghanistan. In one assault on The City he killed nearly a million people. That's not a poetic figure. It's fact. In Kandahar the slaughter was enormous. Some refugees fled to this caravanserai . . . this room. They were sure the Mongols wouldn't find them here, but they did." His voice resumed its flatness.

"And the pillar?" Stiglitz pressed.

"First Genghis erected a pole right through the roof. Then the Mongols took their prisoners and tied their hands. Laid the first batch on the floor over there and lashed their feet to the pole. All around. That's why the pillar is twelve feet across."

"Then what?" Stiglitz asked, perspiration standing on his forehead.

"They just kept on laying the prisoners down, one layer on top of the other until they reached the roof. They didn't kill a single person that day, the Mongols, but they kept soldiers stationed with sticks to push back the tongues when they protruded. And while the pillar of people was still living—those that hadn't been pressed to death—they called in masons to plaster over the whole affair. If you'd scrape away the plaster you'd find skulls. But the government takes a dim view of scraping. It's a kind of national monument. The Caravanserai of the Tongues."

No one spoke. The meal was ready but no one seemed hungry, so finally Nazrullah said, "I tell you these things only to explain the terrible burdens under which Afghanistan has labored. Our major cities have been destroyed so many times. Do you know what I expect . . . seriously? When a thousand men like me have rebuilt Kabul and made it as great as The City once was, either the Russians or the Americans will come with their airplanes and bomb it to rubble."

"Wait a minute!" I protested.

"I'm not speaking against Americans . . . or Russians. You won't destroy us in anger. Genghis Khan wasn't angry at us when he destroyed The City. Neither was Tamerlane or Nadir Shah or Baber. And I'm not downcast because we're doomed to be destroyed again." He shrugged his shoulders. "It's inevitable. We go on building while we can."

He laughed and inspected the cans that lay opened on the blankets. "I for one love American K-rations. But please, gentlemen, you must see to it that Nur Muhammad and I get ones that contain no pork."

"Tonight," I said with some embarrassment, "everyone has pork and beans."

"Then Nur and I shall make a great show of picking out one shred of pork each and placing it upon your plate . . . thus. 'Please take this pork from us, Miller Sahib, because we are Muslims.' But the rest of the pork I shall jolly well keep on my plate, because I love it." We ate as a family group, two Muslims, a renegade Christian and a Jew, and my sense of loneliness was erased, but when it came time to clean the dishes I noticed that Dr. Stiglitz, who sat facing the pillar, had eaten little.

It was after our meal that I learned with pleasure that we would not stay in the serai but were pushing across the desert in the cooler night air. As I left the refuge I said, "One nice thing about it. It's the only building I've seen that I can date. It was here in 1220."

"Probably been rebuilt since then," Nazrullah said without further comment.

We went into the night and for the first time in my life I saw the stars hanging low over the desert, for the atmosphere above us contained no moisture, no dust, no impediment of any kind. It was probably the cleanest air man knows and it displayed the stars as no other could. Not even at Qala Bist, which stood by the river, had air been so pure. The stars seemed enormous, but what surprised me most was the fact that they dropped right to the horizon, so that to the east some rose out of dunes while to the west others crept beneath piles of shale.

While I was staring at the unfamiliar stars, Nazrullah borrowed a light and wrote the following note on a scrap of paper in Persian, Pashto and English:

> On the evening of April 11, 1946, we stopped here to seek evidence of the missing soldiers but found nothing.

Using a sharp piece of shale, he wedged the message into the door and we started up the gully to the desert.

Then I understood why Nazrullah had halted our caravan at the serai; while we were listening to the explanation of the pillar the burning wind had abated and the moon had brightened and was nearly full. It now stood well above the horizon, a huge center of light which made our trip across the desert possible. It was an unworldly experience, with moonlight reflecting from the dunes as if it were day. I noticed that we now traveled at less than twenty-five miles an hour, and since the path looked just as good as it had in the afternoon when we did over forty, I asked why and Nur explained, "At night we can't spot the gotch."

"The what?" I asked.

"Gotch. A flaky white substance that comes in big patches. I think you call it gypsum."

"That's worth something, gypsum. It occurs in piles?"

"Desert's full of it, always in patches. That's where Genghis Khan got his plaster for the pillar."

"So that's what gypsum's used for," I mused.

"Mixed with water it's useful," Nur cautioned, "but don't hit it when it's dry."

At this point we heard a horn blowing insistently, and I looked about for Nazrullah's flag. It was stationary in a valley ahead and he was signaling us not to follow. "He's trapped in gotch," Nur said. "In this light you can't see the stuff."

"Did we pass some this afternoon?"

"Acres of it," Nur assured me. "But then it was no trouble."

We parked our jeep and hiked ahead to where Nazrullah was stuck. "Nothing serious," he said. "The wheels slow down . . . pooosh."

I knelt to feel the gotch and found it a flaky powder, very soft to the fingers and providing no traction for a spinning wheel. "Here's the rope," Nazrullah cried. "Give me a little tug."

We edged our jeep carefully forward, attached the rope, and with no trouble pulled Nazrullah free. When he drew up beside us he warned, "If you hit this stuff at more than twenty-five you may break a nose."

"If we do hit," Nur added, "protect your face. We stop very suddenly."

It was now our turn to lead, and we set forth upon one of the few flawless journeys a man can take: to be moving over the desert at night when the great stars are overhead and a white moon illuminates the ghostly world; to be rising suddenly from a depression and on the crest to see a great sweep of desert appearing like a cross between a blizzard of snow and a garden of white flowers in spring; to watch the rise and fall of dunes as they make their poetic march across the shadowy horizon. Most impressive was the silence, the absolute silence of the desert at night. No insects marred it, no night birds whispered, there was no echo of wind nor sound of distant thunder. If we stopped to reconnoiter, we could hear Nazrullah's jeep chattering unseen behind some hill, and I remember once when we had worked ourselves into a cul-de-sac of sweeping dunes how the sound of our engine echoed from each as we tried to fight our way to passages that did not exist. We were hemmed in by floating sand, but as we studied our position I caught sight of Nazrullah's flag whisking past us on the correct road.

We had proceeded thus some forty miles deeper into

the desert when I thought I spied something unusual off to the north. I watched it for some minutes and at first took it to be a pile of shale. Then I drew Nur Muhammad's attention, but he had been concentrating so intently on gotch that at first he saw nothing. Finally his eyes adjusted and when they did so he said, "It's a jeep!" And I saw that he was right.

We then faced the problem of how to flag down Nazrullah, who was well ahead of us. We could drive faster, but that might pitch us into gotch. We could blow our horn, but would they hear? I suggested, "Let me get down and stand here, so that you can find the jeep when you come back."

Nur looked at me in horror. "In the desert?" he asked.

He flashed his headlights, whereupon Nazrullah's jeep promptly turned about, and when he had joined us, he asked, "What's up?"

"Miller found the jeep," Nur replied. Then he added, "He suggested that he get down and wait here till I caught you."

Nazrullah looked at me and groaned. "My God!" Then he looked toward the ghostly jeep and said, "I hate to go up there."

Slowly we drove north and it soon became apparent that we were entering a huge concentration of gotch. Nazrullah called out, "Drive back and plant your flag on the hard surface." We did so and then reassembled our little caravan and moved cautiously forward.

Even from a distance we saw what we had hoped not to see: two men sitting in a jeep. They had bogged down in gotch, had tried to pile stones under the wheels, had probably burned out their clutch.

We hiked across the soft gypsum and reached the uncanny sight: two men fully dressed for desert travel, resting in their jeep, their eyes wide open but completely dried out. They had been dead for eight or nine days, but rarely had the hand of death been placed so gently upon two human beings, for the desiccating wind, blowing constantly through the day with a hundred and twenty or thirty degrees of heat, had completely mummified the bodies.

"We'll leave them here," Nazrullah said finally. "Nothing'll harm them now."

I studied the bodies for clues, but there were none. The jeep contained ample food, some gasoline, but no water. Nazrullah said, "Shift him over, Miller. I'll see if the clutch works." With some apprehension I lifted the driver away from the wheel, while Nazrullah slipped in and started the car. The dead man weighed little. The engine choked, coughed, started. There was no clutch. "Poor bastards," Nazrullah said. "Put him back."

When we were back at our jeeps he said, "They may have lived two days . . . no more. Miller, if you leave a jeep even for twenty yards in this climate, you're dead."

Nur asked in Pashto, "I wonder who blamed the other?"

The idea was so unexpected that we all stared at Nur, but we were also forced to look back at the dead men, and whatever hideous recriminations may have passed between them were now silenced. The younger of the two had been driving.

When we stopped to recover our flag Nazrullah said with real sadness, "Foolish, foolish men, to take one jeep across this desert. Miller, why don't you ride with me on this leg?"

After we had taken the lead I asked, "Did you know them?"

"Fortunately no. I'd hate to think my friends were so idiotic." We drove for some time, then he chuckled. "It's rather fun riding with Stiglitz. He's so German."

"Is it true that he's a Muslim? Or is he just kidding?"

"Why not? He has to live here the rest of his life."

"How do you know that?" I asked.

"The minute he steps across our boundary, the English will arrest him, or the Russians."

"Nazi crimes?"

"Naturally."

"Guilty . . . or just charges?"

"We've seen the legal papers. That is, the government has." He said carefully, "I'd say the charges weren't hypothetical."

I pondered this for some minutes and wondered to myself: If the Afghan government has the dossier, why hasn't it been shared with our ambassador, who's obviously looking Stiglitz over as a possible doctor? I didn't want to ask Nazrullah about this directly, but I did hit upon what I considered a neat alternative: "Surely the British must know about him, if they've threatened to arrest him."

"They do," Nazrullah laughed, for he had guessed the purpose of my question. On his own he added, "As a government, they know his record, and if they could catch him in India, they'd arrest him. But if he gets clearance for Kabul, which I'm sure he will, the embassy people as individuals would consult him medically." Dryly he added, "I'm sure your ambassador would behave the same way—arrest him in New York but use him in Kabul."

"You're probably right," I said noncommittally.

We dropped the matter there, but later Nazrullah observed, "You expressed surprise that Dr. Stiglitz had become a Muslim. Surely, if I'd stayed permanently in Dorset, Pennsylvania, with Ellen's people I'd have become a Presbyterian."

The fact that he had mentioned Ellen of his own volition startled me, but his casual attitude toward abandoning Islam seemed even more striking, for I was then in the days when I believed that Muslims, Christians and Jews were destined not to shift back and forth, so I argued, "Could you really have become a Christian?"

"For six years in Germany and America I was a

Christian in everything but formal conversion. Suppose you lived in Afghanistan permanently, wouldn't you pray as a Muslim?"

I thought: Wouldn't he be amused if he knew whom he was asking this question of. That conceit produced my next question: "But if you were to work in Palestine with the British, could you become a Jew?"

"Why not? If the facts were known, probably half our Afghan heritage is Jewish. For hundreds of years we boasted of being one of the Lost Tribes of Israel. Then Hitler decreed us to be Aryans, which gave us certain advantages."

"What's your own opinion?" I asked bluntly.

"I think we're a delightful hodgepodge. Have you heard our marvelous myth? In the valleys west of Kabul we have a concentration of the Hazara people. Know what we believe about them? We claim that every Mongol who ever settled in Afghanistan—and there must have been millions—settled in those particular valleys and never once intermarried with any of us. A thousand years of racial purity. If the truth were known, I'm probably descended from the bastards who plastered up that pillar."

"You mean you could become a Jew?" I repeated seriously.

"I probably am a Jew," he insisted. "And a Mongol, and a Hindu, and a Tajik. But I'm also a hundred percent Aryan, because I have a certificate from Göttingen University to prove it."

We lapsed again into the deep silence of the desert and the faint stirrings of a brotherhood that was developing between us. Then I asked what I know Nazrullah intended me to ask when he suggested that I ride in his jeep: "Where's Ellen?"

"She ran away."

"You know where?"

"Not exactly."

"You think she's alive?"

"I know she is," he said, clenching his hands on the

steering wheel. "I'm morally sure she is." From his actions and manner of speech I had to conclude that he was still in love with his wife, hungrily, deeply; yet I found it almost comical that I should worry about a man, no matter how much I respected him, who was worried about his second wife when he had a perfectly good wife waiting for him in Kandahar. It all seemed so Muslim. I was then too young to know at first hand any of those average American men who deeply loved their wives but who could at the same time become agonized if something untoward happened to their mistresses. It was the same problem in two different guises, but at the time I didn't know it.

"She hasn't written to her parents in thirteen months," I said.

With a certain grim humor he asked, "Have you met her parents?"

"No, but I've read their reports."

"Then you know." He smiled as he recalled them, then added, "They're like this, Miller. If they'd seen that pillar at the caravanserai they'd have cried, 'Goodness, something ought to be done about that,' but they'd never have understood if you replied, 'About Genghis Khan you can't do anything.' " He grew painfully intense and said, "There wasn't a thing they could have done about Ellen. They were fated to lose her. I was fated to lose her. And there wasn't a goddamned thing that any of us could have done to prevent it."

I waited till the signs of his bitterness vanished, then asked, "Is she still in Afghanistan?"

I remember distinctly, and at the time I remarked upon it to myself, that before Nazrullah answered he leaned out to look at the stars, both west and east, then said quietly, "I'm sure she is. Yes, she's in Afghanistan."

I wanted to pursue the matter further, but at this moment I saw to the west, where Nazrullah had peered in search of his wife, a star that seemed brighter than the others and pointed it out to my guide. "Good," he said, halting the jeep till the others could overtake us. When they did he pointed to the star and said, "The City."

I looked again at the star and none of us except Nazrullah knew that it was a light and not a star. "It's a light at The City," Nazrullah said. "We'll camp here."

"If it's so close, why don't we finish the drive?"

"It's sixty miles away," Nazrullah replied.

"Impossible," I protested, but Nur supported his friend.

"When you first see something like this, you can't believe it. The light may well be sixty miles away."

"It is," Nazrullah assured us. "Let's get out the sleeping bags."

I looked for low ground that would give me some protection from the wind that was rising, but Nazrullah led us to the highest part of a small hill and when we were prepared for bed he explained, "Tonight we saw two men who died in the desert from sun and heat. For everyone who dies that way, a hundred die from floods."

Stiglitz and I looked at each other in the white moonlight and Nazrullah continued, "Once every three or four years it rains over some part of this desert. In a way you never saw before. Terrible, shattering. A wall of water builds up thirty feet high and destroys everything before it. Moves whole dunes from one place to another, and anything caught in a low spot is crushed."

We looked at the gullies with new respect as he finished, "Probably hasn't been any water down there in five hundred years. But just south of here—due south, as a matter of fact—Alexander the Great was marching his troops home from their conquest of India. They camped in the desert and in four minutes a wall of water swept over them, killing two men in three. This is a tough country, Miller. Don't sleep in gullies."

At dawn we rose and headed west, and when I saw the last sixty miles of terrain I appreciated why Nazrullah had left Qala Bist in a hurry, for we could not have traversed at night what now faced us, and if we had tried to drive through the heart of the desert at midday, the heat would have been unbearable. In these last sixty miles the sand had largely disappeared and we were forced to pick our way through heaps of shale which thundered the day's heat right back at us. The humidity was down to nearly zero and a strong wind dried us out as we moved across the blazing dasht. Nur Muhammad warned me, "Be careful not to bump your nose. The mucus dries up into little needles which puncture the skin. Bad infection." Warily I touched my nose, and he was right. The thirsty air had sucked away all moisture, and my nose was lined with needles.

At one period I thought I would collapse if we didn't stop for a drink, but Nazrullah fell back to warn us, "We've plenty of water and cans of fruit juice, but we're not going to touch it until we're sure we'll reach The City today." He must have seen my disappointment, for he added, "You can discipline yourself, Miller."

So we pressed on, parched with heat. In the States I had never known anything like this, a heat so forceful that it seemed to fight with you for all body moisture. I could feel water evaporating from my skin, and my thoughts constantly returned to the soldiers who had perished in the jeep: This damned wind sucked them dry as they sat there.

Slowly I began to exercise the discipline of which Nazrullah spoke, and I began to find ways to adjust. I wasn't as thirsty as I thought, nor as near dead as I feared. I was on an ugly mission across inhospitable terrain that would kill me if I gave it a chance, but there were many ways to survive, and Nazrullah now taught us one. "We'd better put on the turbans," he suggested, and when we had done so he produced a canister of river water, not for drinking, and from it poured water directly onto the turbans until they were dripping down our necks. We then drove on.

The turban, about eight yards of cloth, held a lot of water and released it slowly, lowering the temperature of our heads as it evaporated. I thought: This is the way to lick the heat. But within twelve minutes the voracious wind had sucked all moisture from the cloth. So we stopped again and sloshed on more river water, and for a while we were cool, but after ten or twelve minutes the turbans were again dry.

At last we reached a narrow pass that dropped down between rocks, and having descended this canyon for about a mile, we reached a low plain and saw ahead of us trees and signs of life and a village, beyond which lay an ancient city and a large body of water. We cheered and blew our horns, for the transit of the desert was completed.

A few Afghans in dirty desert dress straggled out to greet us, but we did not stop. "Tell the sharif we'll be back!" Nazrullah called, and we sped for the lake, where we quickly undressed and lay in the water, so that our bodies could absorb the liquid they had lost.

"Look at him!" Stiglitz said after a while, and I saw Nazrullah far out from shore, where the water came only to his knees. When I caught up with him he said, "You can walk completely across, if you care to."

It was here, in this vast shallow lake, that the great Helmand River ended, for the desert sun and wind evaporated the water as fast as the mountains near Kabul delivered it. The powerful Helmand simply flowed into the desert and died. I hadn't believed it when Nur told me, but here it was, the death of a river. In late summer even this lake might be gone.

When we dressed, the sharif joined us. His title was pronounced *sha-reef,* with the accent on the second syllable, and he brought us melons and fruit, which in their richness, dripped juice from our chins. He listened impassively as Nazrullah explained the location of the missing jeep, and said that he'd dispatch a scouting party. No one was much perturbed about the deaths; if men crossed the desert often enough, some were bound to die, and many from that area had done so.

Talk then turned to the American engineer Pritchard, and we were all brought into the conversation. The sharif reported that twenty-two days ago the American, who worked at Chahar, seventy miles to the south, had broken his leg while taking water levels. It was originally intended to haul him to this village on a stretcher for a trip across the desert, but the sharif at Chahar had felt that local practitioners could heal the leg, and no stretcher was dispatched. A week ago news came to the village that an infection had set in.

"Did the broken bones puncture the skin?" Dr. Stiglitz asked.

"We were told so," the sharif replied.

"And they tried to treat a case like that?"

"They've been doing it for three thousand years," the sharif grunted. He sent a servant to fetch a man who hobbled in on a leg that had been broken three weeks ago. "We fixed his."

Dr. Stiglitz examined the leg and said in Pashto, "It's as good as I'd have done."

Nazrullah asked, "You'll send a guide with us?"

"Of course," the sharif said, and he ordered servants to refill our water bottles. "But I wouldn't travel in this heat."

"We have to," Nazrullah replied. And we were off.

I have said that when we dropped down off the desert we saw a city by the lake. What we actually saw was one of the marvels of Asia, The City, and we were about to explore a fair portion of its incredible length. For more than seventy miles this nameless metropolis stretched along the lake, the marshes and the river that formed the western boundary between Afghanistan and Persia. At the dawn of history it had been a stupendous settlement. In the age of Alexander it had been one of the world's major concentrations, and he had camped near its bazaars. For a millennium after his departure it flourished to become one of the prime targets of the Mongols, and Genghis Khan had once slaughtered most of the people in the area. Tamerlane . . . all the others had ravaged the treasure, and now it stood in majestic silence, mile after mile after mile.

I thought: We're probably in error, calling this a city. It must have been like Route One between New York and Richmond. At intersections there were towns, and some were sizable, but much of the distance must have been interurban, so that city merged into town and town into rural area, with always the roadway itself hemmed in by buildings of some sort. Here the roadway had been the Helmand River, and now as we traversed it we saw the relics of The City.

At times there would be walls of substantial height running for miles, broken by majestic gates and marked with niches in which, before the Muslims outlawed human statuary, depictions of local heroes had stood. At other times we saw municipal buildings which might have sent emissaries to Jerusalem a thousand years before the time of Herod. And everything we saw was withering in the dry air, an inch or two eroding every hundred years.

There were rugged forts, obviously built by the Muslims: against unorganized shepherds from Persia they must have been impressive; against the skilled troops of Genghis Khan they probably lasted a day or two, at most, after which all the defenders were slaughtered.

We drove along the entire length of The City, and I cannot recall many moments when we were out of sight of really noble monuments. The architecture was solid and secure, wholly fitted to the bleak terrain, and the impression was one of dignity and organization. Qala Bist, at the eastern edge of the Desert of Death, had stunned me with its magnificence. The City, on the western edge, left no such impression. It was so huge, so beyond normal comprehension, and yet so intimate—I felt that men had actually walked these streets and collected taxes in these buildings—that no reaction was required. There it was. Damn it all, there the stupendous thing was, abandoned in the desert the way Route One, two thousand years from now, might reach in shadowy grandeur from what used to be New York to what used to be Richmond.

If the early morning heat on the desert had been oppressive, the heat we experienced at noonday along The City was almost unbearable. Of it I will say only this: Whenever we came upon an irrigation ditch or an arm of the river, we jumped from our jeeps, held our watches and wallets over our heads, and plunged fully dressed into the water, soaking in the moisture through aching pores. We then took with us large cans of dirty water, which we poured over our turbans as we rode, but as before, any relief was temporary, for within a few minutes we were once more completely dry. At least ten times we jumped into the ditches, and if we had not been able to do so, we could not have continued our journey. We would have been forced to seek protection in one of the vast, vacant buildings and wait for nightfall.

After one such dunking Nazrullah again asked me to ride with him, but he would not speak of his marriage. He wished to discuss the old days, when The City flourished. "It probably had trade with areas as far removed as Moscow, Peking, Delhi and Arabia. It was never the superb city that Balkh was, but it must have been impressive. What do you suppose killed it?"

"Genghis Khan," I replied with confidence. "In school I read about him, as a name, but never appreciated what a devastating force he was. He stood before your city and shouted, 'Here I am!' and pretty soon there was no city."

"No," Nazrullah laughed, "you give good old Genghis too much credit. Now Balkh, the best city we ever had . . . He did destroy that. But not this place. Nor Herat. He wiped out the population, but people are easy to replace and Herat still exists. He didn't wipe out The City. Something else did that."

"Plague?" I hazarded, for my mind was not yet geared to Central Asia.

"Three hypotheses are predominant, not mutually exclusive," he said slowly. This was the kind of talk he liked, arguing in Germanic patterns, like most learned Afghans.

I interrupted him, laughing. "It just occurred to me, Nazrullah. I've been with you and Moheb Khan and Nur Muhammad for some time now, and none of you ever says, 'By the beard of the Prophet,' or 'By the blood of the infidel,' or 'Allah shall be revenged.' I don't believe you're real Muslims."

"I have the same complaint against you," he replied seriously. "Not once do you or the ambassador say 'By cracky' or 'Gee whillikens.' We're living in a denatured age."

"Proceed, Son of the Prophet."

"That reminds me of something amusing," he said. "For a while I dated a Penn coed whose sole knowledge of Asia was that fine ballad 'Abdul Abulbul Amir.' Funny thing was, she made about as much sense as any of the others."

"What did wreck The City?"

"First, this used to be the world's foremost example of irrigation. I think Alexander commented on that. You can see relics of the old system everywhere. Over there, for example. Probably a reservoir. But people got lazy. They didn't keep working on it. They felt that what had worked for a hundred years was good enough for the next hundred years. They stopped cleaning the ditches . . . built no new dams. They guessed right. For a hundred years, no trouble. But the death warrant had been signed. Genghis Khan can't be blamed for that. The people had grown fat and lazy.

"Second, and I place much emphasis on this, there was salt. If you irrigate a piece of land long enough, the constant flow of water must deposit salt, so that each year you raise a crop, you deteriorate the land that made the crop possible. Therefore I don't blame the lazy people entirely. Maybe the salt was just too big a problem to handle. In some future century, perhaps, all of Colorado and Utah will be useless because the men of this century were such good farmers. Your salt levels are rising ominously. Behold, Denver, Colorado!" And he pointed to the ruins.

"The third reason is the most tantalizing of all. Goats. Those damned goats are the curse of Asia. God gave us a fertile land, covered with magnificent trees and soil rich enough to feed all men. But the Devil got even by giving us just one thing. Goats. And they took care of the forests. Ate all the young trees. And the rich fields. Ate the cover off and turned them to deserts. Probably the most destructive animal ever created. Much more dangerous than the cobra."

"But how would goats affect The City?" I asked.

"When this was a metropolis," Nazrullah explained, "the hills you see must have been covered with trees. Brisk business in timber and charcoal. Excessive cutting killed some forests, but goats took care of the rest. So today in Afghanistan we have almost no forests. Do you suppose we live in mud houses on purpose? They're miserable, but we have no wood. All the time I was in America I wondered, 'What is the goat in America?' I found out. It's the man who destroys your forests." He paused, then observed, "You defeated Germany in this war, but in the future Germany's bound to win. Because Germans plant trees."

I tried to lead the conversation back to Ellen Jaspar but was forestalled when our guide, perched on the spare tires behind my ear, sang out that we were approaching Chahar, where Pritchard lay. We looked for a ditch and plunged in to refresh ourselves, then stood on the bank as the monstrous wind sucked us dry, and when our turbans were no longer wet we replaced them with karakul caps. We straightened our clothes to make ourselves as presentable as possible, and while we were doing this I asked, "Why all the falderal?"

Nazrullah replied, "Down here you impress the sharif, or you get nothing." As we drove into the village he added, "We're so far from Kabul that government doesn't actually exist, except in the person of this brigand who rules as he wishes. Who's going to drive across that desert to correct him?"

It was an attractive village with an oversized caravanserai and cool pomegranate trees whose blossoms sent me an unfamiliar fragrance. The sharif came out to greet us, a huge fellow well over six feet in height, and I thought: How often we choose tall men to govern us.

And this sharif governed, that was obvious. As absolute monarch of a tiny kingdom, he had his own army, his own judges, his own treasury. Since he lived so close to Persia and so far from Kabul, his little kingdom used mainly Persian coins and Persian stamps. "Dozens of these principalities remain in Afghanistan," Nazrullah explained, and I understood why, in Chahar, the evacuation of an American with a broken leg was impossible. When you got sick here, the local medicine man cured you, or you died.

The sharif led us to a low, stifling hut tucked away in a corner of the caravanserai, and there on a straw mattress laid over a rope bed we found the gaunt, gray-faced American engineer John Pritchard, a wiry man in his late forties. Nazrullah held out his hand and said, "Hello, Professor. The American embassy's sent a man to get you out of here."

"I'm willing to go . . . right now," the sick man replied. The sharif's servants had kept him clean, fed and shaved, but he was in pitiful shape and I sensed at once that he was close to dying, for his left leg, exposed to dry air to speed the healing, had been punctured by two fractures and was now clearly gangrenous. The skin was taut and greenish.

Dr. Stiglitz hurried to the bed and studied the leg for some minutes, smelling his fingers as he did so. He then probed the man's groin and armpits. When he was done he placed his right hand on Pritchard's shoulder and said quietly, "Herr Professor Pritchard, the leg must come off." The engineer groaned and his face went even whiter than it had been.

Stiglitz continued, as if to convince the rest of us, "In my opinion there's no chance on earth to save this leg. I'm positive other doctors would agree. I'm sorry, Herr Professor, but you must know." Pritchard made no further sound; he must have expected such a decision.

Stiglitz added in a dispassionate professional voice, "We face a difficult choice, for which we are all responsible—Pritchard, Nazrullah, Miller. I can take the leg off here, but where would you recuperate? Tell me that. Or I can medicate the leg now, then rush you back to Kandahar, where the operation could be performed much better and where you could recuperate at ease. In that case the question is, Could you stand the trip across the desert?"

Each waited for the other to speak, then Pritchard said firmly, "If I stay here, I will surely die."

Stiglitz asked, "Then you want to go back to Kandahar?"

"Yes! Yes!" Pritchard cried.

"What do you think, Nazrullah Sahib?" Stiglitz continued.

"I'd like to ask one question," Nazrullah countered. "Professor Pritchard, you remember what the desert was like. Do you feel strong enough to cross it now?"

"Yes!" Pritchard repeated. "If I stay here I'll die."

"We'll take you to Kandahar," Nazrullah said

firmly, and when the decision was reached he became once more his efficient self. Looking at his watch, he said crisply, "We must get back to The City before darkness. We'll sleep there. Start across the desert at dawn. You fellows up to it?" Nur and Stiglitz said they were. Then he addressed Pritchard directly: "This is the last chance. You're sure you can cross the desert?"

"Right now," the engineer replied.

"We go," Nazrullah announced.

But I was appalled, both at the decision itself and at the hasty manner in which it had been reached. "Wait a minute!" I protested. "Dr. Stiglitz, is Professor Pritchard qualified to make a decision like this?"

"I am," Pritchard interrupted. "I've waited here too damned long. If I stay here, I'm going to die."

"Have you ever crossed the desert?" I asked, betraying my nervousness at intervening in such a matter, for I was the youngest present.

"I'm here, aren't I?" Pritchard asked contemptuously.

"You remember the heat?"

"Look, Miller, I refuse to stay here. Let's get going."

"The heat?" I shouted. "Have you ever crossed in daytime?"

"Yes!" the sick man shouted back. "I can take it."

I appealed to Dr. Stiglitz. "You know very well, Doctor, that intense heat and movement will increase the danger from that leg." The German was silent and I shouted, "Don't you?"

"Yes," Stiglitz grudgingly assented. "And every minute we don't operate increases the risk."

"That's what I thought," I said weakly. I felt as if I were going to burst into tears. Very quietly I said, "We'll operate here—right now."

Stiglitz spoke solemnly: "But the risk to his life is just as great here, Herr Miller."

"For God's sake!" I cried. "Give me an answer, yes or no."

"There is no answer, yes or no," the German replied stubbornly. "There is risk. There is risk here and risk there. I cannot decide." He turned to Pritchard and asked gently, "You know you're in grave danger, don't you Herr Professor?"

"Three days ago I thought I was dead," Pritchard said. "I'm not afraid any longer. In your opinion, Doctor, which way gives me the best mathematical chance?"

"That I cannot answer," Stiglitz insisted. "You and your American adviser must decide."

The sick man looked up at me, and I almost had to turn away, death seemed so close. "Young fellow," he said quietly, "I calculate my own chances as being best if we go to Kandahar."

I was so certain that once we got that leg on the desert it would insure his death, pumping poison constantly throughout his body, that I could not accept either his answer, or Nazrullah's assent, or the doctor's impartiality. I knew we must take the leg off at once. In my anguish I looked at Nazrullah and said, "Could we walk in the garden a moment?"

"You're wasting time," Nazrullah warned me.

"I need your advice," I said.

"You have my advice . . . Kandahar."

"Please," I begged.

Against his will I led him out beneath the pomegranate trees, sweet in the spring, where I had a chance to confront the hard quality of his mind. "You're the American in charge," he said harshly. "You must decide . . . in fifteen minutes."

"But, Nazrullah, you're a scientist. You know that a leg like that is pumping poison right through that man's blood. He can't possibly get to Kandahar."

"The doctor thinks he can. I think he can. We should leave."

"But if we do decide to operate here, will you arrange things for us?"

"Absolutely, Miller. I'll stay here a month if necessary. You make the decision and I'll abide by it. But make the decision."

"Help me do what's best," I pleaded. "There's a man dying in there."

"I can't do your job for you," he said coldly.

"Could I see the doctor again? For just a minute?"

"Stiglitz? He's incapable of a moral decision. He said clearly: The facts are these. You decide."

"What did he say the facts were?" I asked, sweating nervously. "I want to hear them from him again before we decide."

"No!" Nazrullah cried. "You can't evade your responsibility."

"Please, review with me what he said. I don't have it clear."

"He said," Nazrullah repeated impatiently, "that Pritchard would probably die, whether we amputated his leg here or hauled him across the desert to do it."

"He never said that!" I protested in real confusion.

"He implied it. He believes it. And if that's true, which I'm sure it is, the problem becomes simple. What's best for your country and mine?"

"That's a hell of a way to talk about a man who may be dying."

"Miller, he is dying. What's best for you and me to do? Speak up or we're leaving."

"Wait a minute. Let me think," I pleaded. "Nazrullah, we know he wants to get out of here. How much weight should I put on that fact?"

"The whole weight, Miller. If he stays here he knows he'll die."

I hesitated, then said firmly, "All right. We take him to Kandahar."

"That's your decision?"

"Yes. Let's get started. Right now."

"Please put it in writing."

"What are you trying to do?" I cried.

"Things like this often end badly," Nazrullah said cautiously. "Americans like to blame Afghans . . .

make us look stupid. If a stupid decision is being made, you'll make it, and you'll put it in writing."

"I'm not afraid," I said bravely, feeling much older than twenty-six. "But in that case I've got to talk with Stiglitz and Pritchard."

"You have ten minutes," Nazrullah said. "After that we stay here . . . for many weeks."

We returned to the sick room and I asked Dr. Stiglitz to join me in the garden. He protested but Nazrullah said in German, "Go ahead."

"Your honest judgment, Stiglitz, and you can't evade now. What's best for this man?"

"This is a decision I cannot make," Stiglitz insisted stubbornly.

"That's a hell of a position for a doctor to take."

"It's the only one under the circumstances," he said defensively.

"What are the circumstances?" I shouted, losing control of my patience under the hammering I was undergoing.

"Pritchard is going to die," he replied bluntly.

"I say that if we take the leg off right now he'd have a chance."

"You're right."

"And if you haul him through the desert death is almost inevitable."

"You're right."

"Then for God's sake, let's go in there and operate."

"I warned you, Herr Miller, that this is not a decision I can make. Pritchard is convinced that if he stays here any longer he will die. His spirit is worn out . . . can you understand that at your age? Worn out. It might be wiser for him to risk the journey to Kandahar if it restores his hope."

"Who can decide this?"

"Pritchard."

I returned to the room and told Nazrullah, "I'll write out the order in five minutes."

"You'd better," he said.

I went to the sickbed and before I spoke to Pritchard I looked at the bleak walls of the caravanserai and smelled the stale, baked air. I would not have wanted to live in that room, even in health. But to have lain in that stifling heat for three weeks while local practitioners ruined my leg, to have watched it swell and grow green, would have been intolerable, and now to face the prospect of six more weeks would kill my spirit.

I sat on the bed and told Pritchard, "I guess it's up to you and me. Here or Kandahar?"

"I know I'm in bad shape. But if I stay here . . . what'd you say your name was?"

"Miller. I'm from the embassy." Then I had an idea. "You know, Professor Pritchard, the ambassador himself sent me here. He's deeply worried about you."

"I didn't know anybody gave a damn." He turned his head, unable to control his tears. "Jesus, Miller, this is the end of the world."

"I can see that," I agreed.

"How the hell did I get here?" he mumbled. "Making a water study for a nation that just don't give a damn."

"Don't say that. You wrote to us about Nazrullah. He's a fine engineer."

"The guy with the beard?"

"Trained in Germany," I assured him.

"Some of the best come from Germany," he said in the approving manner of practical men who recognize excellence wherever developed.

"You're determined to make the run to Kandahar?"

"If I stay here I'll die."

"You appreciate the risk?"

His spirit cracked. Rising on one elbow he shouted, "If you're afraid of your lousy job, I'll put it in writing. I want to get the hell out of here."

"I'll do the writing," I said, feeling miserable, for I knew I was condemning him to death. I called Nur

Muhammad to bring my brief case, and on official paper I wrote:

> Chahar, Afghanistan
> April 12, 1946
>
> I have this day ordered the American irrigation engineer John Pritchard to be transported to the hospital in Kandahar, so that medical attention unavailable here may be given his badly infected left leg.
>
> Mark Miller
> United States Embassy
> Kabul, Afghanistan

Feeling sick at what I had done, I handed Nazrullah the directive. He read it twice, showed it to Stiglitz and Nur Muhammad, and folded it carefully. "We'll leave in ten minutes, sleep at the edge of the desert and start our crossing as soon as we can negotiate that bad approach."

He had overlooked one fact. John Pritchard refused to leave his post until his water-level records were collected. "That's why I came here," he said. "If they want to build that dam, they'll need these records." To my surprise, Dr. Stiglitz supported him.

"A scientist should keep records," the German said.

So I was led by a guide to a spot two miles down the Helmand, where John Pritchard had been collecting the data on which Nazrullah would build his dam. More significantly, perhaps, Pritchard's word would form the basis for riparian treaties between Afghanistan and Persia, who had threatened war over the river. We found a small shed, boiling hot, some water gauges, a sheaf of irreplaceable records. The guide warned me in Pashto to watch the steps leading to the shed, for it was here that Pritchard had broken his leg; and as I stood in this lonely shack, this veritable end of the world where the temperature was daily above a hundred and thirty, I thought of all the careless speeches made in Congress about the cookie-pushers of the State Department, those striped-pants boys who haunt afternoon teas, and I wished that some of the arrogant speakers could have seen the work that John Pritchard had accomplished for our nation and for Afghanistan.

"Was Pritchard a good man?" I asked the guide. It was a kind of judgment he had not previously been asked to make, and he was confused. Finally he said brightly, "Yes, he could handle a gun with skill."

I was to ride with Nazrullah in his jeep, while Nur and Stiglitz supervised loading Pritchard in the back of theirs. As they did so the German said heartily, "If I ever saw a man with a good chance to get across the desert, it's this one."

"We'll make it!" the engineer called as we set forth, and it became my duty when we stopped to pour as much water as possible over the stricken man, thus keeping his temperature down, but before we had traveled far he became partially delirious and asked that I ride with him, as he wished to speak of America.

Thus we rode past the brooding, empty buildings of The City, and in the cooler evening his fever abated and we talked. He was from Fort Collins, Colorado, and had spent each autumn hunting in the Rockies. He was, he admitted, a fairly good rifle shot and had bagged elk, bear and mountain goats. He had a low opinion of the latter and felt they did more harm than good. He was optimistic about one thing: said he knew a one-legged man in Loveland who had no trouble hunting.

"I'm the kind of man," he said, "who won't give up till I learn how to walk with a wooden leg." But at the next stop Dr. Stiglitz decided to give Pritchard a knock-out pill, and the engineer fell asleep.

10

As soon as morning light permitted, we negotiated the canyon, and when the sun was well ablaze we were on the desert, stopping frequently to pour water on our turbans. At first I rode with Nur and the sick man, keeping his body under wet compresses, but he grew constantly worse, and at one of the water stops Stiglitz insisted upon changing places with me so that he might supervise the invalid. The more drastic steps he took to keep Pritchard alive worked. At the start of our trip I had given the engineer no chance to live, but apparently I was going to be proved wrong.

I now rode with Nazrullah, and after we had discussed Pritchard's leg, he asked me bluntly, "What else do you need to know about my wife?"

The question startled me, for I had been devising stratagems whereby I could trick him into comment, and for a moment I could not think clearly, so I repeated lamely, "She ran away?"

"Yes. Last September."

"That's eight months ago," I stammered.

"Seems longer," he reflected, rubbing his beard. In his soggy, formless turban he looked quite Asiatic.

"Why did she run away?"

"You wouldn't understand," he replied with a nervous laugh. He wanted to be helpful, but the facts were so preposterous that he was unable to evaluate them, so he kept silent, reminding me of the worried Afghan husband who had hustled back and forth between his sick wife and Dr. Stiglitz: he would report only what he himself understood.

I appreciated his efforts at good will, for the conditions under which we rode made conversation difficult. The desert was intolerably hot and we were both gasping for air. "This must be hell on Pritchard," he observed.

"It's what I was worried about yesterday," I reminded him.

"We've been through that!" he cautioned. "I have your order, in writing."

"Did you warn Ellen Jaspar that . . ."

"That I was married? Yes."

"The other day in Kandahar I met your wife, your Afghan wife, that is."

"I know. Karima told me about it in her letter."

"How could she send a letter?" I asked, like a movie detective trapping a suspect. "I saw her only a short time before I left."

"The messenger who brought Dr. Stiglitz also brought her letter," he explained, and I had to laugh at my own suspicions.

"I'm sorry," I apologized. "This whole thing seems so shadowy."

"To me it's even more so," he confessed.

"Then what Karima said was true? You did tell Ellen?"

"Whatever Karima says is apt to be true."

"Is she a beautiful girl?" I asked for no obvious reason.

"Very. It was stupid of her to wear the chaderi. I don't require it."

"I suspect she was afraid of Nur Muhammad."

Inappropriately, Nazrullah began to laugh and I must have looked at him with censure, for he said, "I'm sorry, but when you mentioned the chaderi I remembered something which explains Ellen rather better than anything else I could tell you. I sympathize with your suspicions. You're sure that I mistreated her and that my family kept her prisoner and that she's walled up somewhere pining for freedom. Miller, when she arrived in Kabul, all of us . . . everybody . . . tried to make her feel at ease. You know what she did? On the morning after the marriage she came down to breakfast wearing a chaderi."

"What?"

"Yes, at breakfast. A very expensive silk chaderi which she had asked a dressmaker in London to make from a picture in a book. She was going to be more Afghan than the Afghans. My family tried not to laugh, and I had tears in my eyes to think that she was such a good sport. We explained that you don't wear a chaderi at breakfast. But I had one hell of a time keeping her from wearing it on the street."

He laughed in memory of that bizarre event as a father laughs during a business lunch when he recollects his child's mistakes. "You may have heard that one day in Kandahar the mullahs spat at her. When it was all over, she started to cry, not at the mullahs but at me. 'If you'd let me wear the chaderi,' she whimpered, 'this wouldn't have happened.' "

"I don't understand."

"None of you Americans understand what an extraordinary woman Ellen is. Obviously her parents didn't. Nor her professors. Don't call her a girl any more. She is a woman. I doubt that she was ever a girl. She is a rare human being who sees through to the essence of God. I suppose you know that on one of our first dates she told me all about the atomic bomb."

"You met her in 1944," I checked. "At that time there wasn't such a bomb."

"She invented it," he said cryptically.

I looked at him askance and he was about to elaborate when the rear jeep signaled us to stop, and in the moments we waited for them to overtake us he added, "Ellen foresaw that if the nations continued their madness, they would be forced to invent some super-terrible weapon. She even described it rather accurately. 'It's the age of air, so they'll deliver it by air, and it'll wipe out whole cities.' She added that there was no way to prevent it and probably no way to escape. She said, 'I hope I can get to Afghanistan before they destroy us all.' At first I thought she was using us as a refuge . . . because we would be the last place bombed, but that wasn't her idea. She told me, 'There isn't going to be any refuge, and if I'm to die, I want to die in Afghanistan, which is as far away from our pitiful civilization as any place I know. Let's live and die close to primitive things.' I suppose that's what she had in mind when she protested my building the dam."

Dr. Stiglitz walked gloomily to our jeep and said frankly, "He won't make it, Nazrullah. He wants Miller to ride with him."

But I was so close to probing Nazrullah's secret that I protested, selfishly: "I want to talk with Nazrullah . . . just a little longer."

Stiglitz said without expression, "Pritchard wants to talk, too. To an American."

"Forgive me," I said, and when I took my seat, close to the engineer's fevered head, I started applying towels, but he merely gasped and rolled his eyes at me. He was very close to death.

Finally he whispered, "I can't breathe." Nur was weeping.

"I can't breathe either," I assured the dying man. "This heat."

"With you the cause is different," he replied lucidly. "You don't carry a leg that's beating like a drum. I can feel it pumping poison."

I bit my tongue to keep from reminding him that he was repeating my words. I said, "We're better than halfway through the desert."

"I want you to give my wife a message," he said with

painful effort. "She lives in Fort Collins. Damned good woman. Tell her . . ." He winced, as an almost visible pain streaked across his face, driving him to incoherency.

I soaked his turban and applied wet rags to his leg. The river water was used up and I proposed to Nur, "We've got to use some of our drinking water." Nur looked at me in dismay, studied the desert ahead, then listened to Pritchard moan. I saw tears start down his cheek and dry to salt in the desperate air.

"If he needs water, give it to him," he said in Pashto.

I poured some of the drinking water over Pritchard's head and he regained consciousness long enough to dictate jumbled phrases to his wife. She was to consult with a Mr. Forgraves in Denver. The kids must graduate from college, both of them. Then, for some reason I didn't understand, he went into a long discourse about a new kind of paint he had seen described in a technical journal. It would cure their cellar problems once and for all. Be worth two hundred dollars but he thought she might get it for less.

"Pritchard," I broke in after the paint monologue, "I think I'd better get Dr. Stiglitz."

"Don't. If I'm gonna die, let me die with my kind, not some goddamned Nazi." He started shivering. Then a dreadful sweat broke out across his face and little rivulets of perspiration accumulated, to be evaporated instantly in the swirling heat.

"I'm burning up!" he shouted. Nur Muhammad, who heard the conversation, began to cry openly and finally stopped the jeep.

"I will not drive a man to meet death," he sobbed as he stood bareheaded in the sun. "If death wants this man, death must come . . . here."

In a kind of frenzy I saw the jeep ahead pulling away, so I blew the horn repeatedly. "Knock off the noise, you kids," Pritchard cried.

Nazrullah caught my signal and whirled about on

the blazing dasht. "What the hell's the matter with you?" he stormed at Nur.

"I will not drive a man to meet death," Nur stubbornly repeated. Taking a small rug from his gear, he spread it on the sand and, kneeling westward to Mecca, prayed.

"He looks awful," Nazrullah said, and Dr. Stiglitz hurried over to check the delirious engineer.

A strange, desert prayer came to my lips, silently: "Oh, God, spare my countryman." At the mumbling of these words, John Pritchard died.

I looked distractedly at Nazrullah, who shrugged his shoulders and said, "It was a chance. Nobody thought it was a good chance." The callousness of this remark made me want to storm at the incompetents who had permitted this disgraceful suicide, but that obligation was taken from me by Nur Muhammad, who wept, "You're all criminals. Bringing this doomed man onto the desert."

This was too much. I shouted, "If you thought that, why didn't you say so?"

"Nobody asked me," he sobbed, and it occurred to me that if he had once supported my argument, we never would have left Chahar and Pritchard would now be alive. But I knew why he had remained silent: he had been afraid to contradict his social superior, Nazrullah, so now we were on the desert with a dead body to deliver . . . remorselessly assaulted by the noonday heat.

Nur Muhammad was quite incapable of driving, so I took charge of the second jeep, the one with the corpse, and we headed for Kandahar, but when we reached about forty miles an hour on the shale I suddenly saw looming ahead a field of gotch, which I swerved sharply to avoid, recalling the soldiers who were dead for not having done so, and I threw the jeep against a series of jolting rocks which snapped the front axle.

Nur Muhammad went to pieces, berating himself

for the fact that he was not at the wheel in this difficult terrain and cursing fate because the corpse had been thrown out of the jeep and now lay in horrible contortion on the dasht. Nazrullah, in contrast, was superb. He quieted Nur, absolved me of blame, and helped Dr. Stiglitz load the corpse into the workable jeep. He then quietly studied his map and informed us, "The Caravanserai of the Tongues must be a little distance to the north. We'll tow the broken jeep there and decide what to do."

But while we were attaching two ropes Dr. Stiglitz said, "Why don't we drive back and take the front axle from the jeep of the two soldiers?"

Nazrullah stopped sharp, dropped the ropes and stood in the blazing sun considering the alternatives the German had suggested. Clutching his beard he mumbled, "Why didn't I think of that? Stupid. Stupid." He walked away from us, positioning his opened hands as if they were two jeeps. For a long time he strode back and forth across the desert, then returned to us.

"For three reasons we must go directly to the caravanserai," he said. "First, I'm not sure we could find the other jeep if we wanted to."

"It's right back there." I pointed.

"It's more than forty miles," he corrected, "and sometimes you can't find things a second time in the desert. Second, we don't have enough water to double back and forth. But most important, suppose the sharif's scouting party has already been there? Suppose we go back and find that the jeep is gone?"

Saying no more, he completed tying the ropes, then hauled us up to the Caravanserai of the Tongues, into which we limped at four that afternoon. His note was still fastened to the door.

We pushed the jeep into one of the honeycomb rooms, then held a council in which Nazrullah explored the alternatives available to us. We decided that two men in the good jeep must try to get back to Qala Bist, taking Pritchard's body along. It was no use risking four lives. The other two men, with what food could be spared, must remain at the caravanserai with the damaged jeep until such time as a rescue party could return. "There's only one question," Nazrullah concluded. "How shall we pair up?"

Learning from the past, I responded quickly: "I'll write an order and accept full responsibility. Stiglitz and Nur will stay here. Nazrullah and I will drive to Qala Bist."

"Reasonable," Stiglitz grunted.

Nur Muhammad, still shaken, wrecked that plan. He sniffled, "It's my duty to stay with Miller Sahib."

"Your duty is discharged," I replied in Pashto.

"No! You are in my care," Nur insisted.

"The whole argument's irrelevant," Nazrullah said. "If anyone must cross the desert it's got to be the Afghans. Miller and Stiglitz, stay here. Nur, jump in the jeep." Nur started to voice some new objection, but Nazrullah shouted a phrase remembered from his American education. "For Christ sake, scram!" When Nur was settled, Nazrullah and I hiked with the water jugs to the stagnant pool that provided a meager supply for the caravanserai. "Can you live on this stuff for three or four days?" he asked.

"You get back here before then," I joked, but I remembered the terror that Nazrullah felt about being on the desert with only one jeep, so I took all the jugs of sweet water and gave them to him. As I did so I said, "Keep this crate away from the gotch."

As he drove off he assured me, "When I come back to get you, Miller, I'll answer all your questions about Ellen. That's a promise." He headed the jeep back toward the desert he dreaded, and I last saw him speeding eastward, his lone flag whipping in the furnace-like air.

At dusk Dr. Stiglitz and I ate a frugal meal and drank a little of the brackish water. We could exist on it, but the prospect was not attractive. We then went out to watch the blazing sun sink behind the dunes and sat together in the refreshing coolness until the great stars appeared, and the white moon. We were about to retire when Stiglitz whispered, "What's that?" And we heard a soft sound, as if a human being were creeping upon us.

We remained very silent, and then saw moving into the moonlight a small group of gazelles, more graceful now, perhaps, than they had been in sunlight. They had been feeding somewhere to the north and were returning to the safety of the desert, where none of their predators could surprise them. They formed such a contrast to the ugly death we had witnessed, that both Stiglitz and I watched them for many minutes. Then, with an unexpected clap of his hands, he startled the little beasts and they leaped and spun in the moonlight, vanishing at last over the dunes.

"Exquisite," Stiglitz whispered, and for the first time I felt some kind of identification with the German. I still wanted to know why he had made the incredible decision of hauling Pritchard onto the desert, and I was about to question him on this when he said, "It's after nine. Let's get ready for bed." We entered the vast caravanserai and lit our Coleman lamp, studiously avoiding the ghostly pillar at the far end of the fort. But it was there.

I said, "You surprised me at Chahar when you refused to make a medical decision . . . when the facts were so clear. Once Pritchard carried that leg into the desert . . . he was doomed. Why didn't you support me?"

"Was he doomed?" Stiglitz asked cautiously.

"Of course he was. Even I saw that." Something in the way I spoke shattered the empathy we had felt while watching the gazelles. Perhaps Stiglitz suspected that when I returned to Kabul I would use Pritchard as an excuse for not recommending him to our ambassador.

A darkness came over his face and he asked contemptuously, "So even you could make that diagnosis, eh? Well, let me tell you, my young friend, I couldn't make it. And I've been a doctor damned near as long as you've been alive. There are many diagnoses you're not qualified to make, Herr Miller."

Without warning he rose and stamped off to the pillar, taking with him our only carving knife, which he scraped vigorously against the plaster, as if driven by some harsh compulsion.

"Nazrullah said it's a national monument," I warned from the opposite end of the room.

"It's a universal monument," he corrected me, "and I'm going to see what's inside." He spoke with determination, then called, "Come here, Miller. It's a human skull."

Against my better judgment I walked slowly down the room, lugging the Coleman lamp, which Dr. Stiglitz grabbed from my hand to hold against the pillar. Behind the inch of plaster I could see a rounded bone. "Is that a skull?" I asked.

"Yes. How many bodies would you estimate are in this pillar?" Before I could answer he did a most ghoulish thing. He planted the lantern in the middle of an open space and said, "This will be the central pole." Then he lay flat on the earth, his toes near the lantern, and commanded me: "Mark where my shoulders come." When the scratches were in the earth, he shifted his body so that I could mark off a new shoulder, and so on around the imaginary pillar.

"Well," he concluded with some satisfaction, "that makes thirty bodies jammed into one layer. Now how many layers?" He stepped back to calculate the number of tiers required to reach the roof. "Perhaps forty-five layers." He paused and a slow look of horror crossed his face. "My God! There's over thirteen hundred people in that pillar."

We sat on the floor, surveying the grisly monument, and I was struck by the grip it had on Stiglitz. Finally

I asked, "When Pritchard died, did I see you crossing yourself?"

"Yes."

"You were a Catholic?"

"In Munich, yes."

"Yet you turned apostate?"

"Of course. Since I'm to live here the rest of my life."

"Why?" I asked bluntly.

"Surely you've been told, Herr Miller," he said with contempt. "That's why this pillar fascinates me. Gives me hope."

"What do you mean by that?" I asked.

"It proves what I've always suspected. The things we did in Germany . . . the really dreadful things, are what men have always done." Before I could express my disgust at excusing the civilized man Adolf Hitler by citing the barbarian Genghis Khan, he added, "In each civilization some men run wild. If we're lucky, we control them early. If not . . ." He pointed to the pillar.

We spent the hours before midnight discussing this theory, and he marshaled strong support for his idea that what he had seen in Germany was a recurring sickness which might strike any nation at any time. I argued against this theory of inevitability, but he was adamant in extending it.

"To be specific," he said, "I haven't been to America but I've seen your films and read your books. I'm positive that in your country there would be no difficulty in finding S.S. volunteers for the job of collecting Negroes and throwing them into concentration camps."

"Wait a minute!" I cried, condescendingly.

"Herr Miller!" he replied, pulling my face close to his. "Don't you know in your heart that you could do to the Negroes what we did to the Jews?"

I said quietly, "Don't judge us by the fact that we have a few sick people."

"You have an endless supply," he assured me. "We turned ours loose on Jews. Some day you'll turn yours loose on Negroes."

"But never Buchenwald," I resisted.

"In the beginning, never," he agreed. "Your sensibilities would not permit it. Your Bill of Rights . . . But after two or three years of total propaganda . . . the president, churches, newspapers, cinema, labor unions . . . don't you understand that you would find many Americans eager to shoot down Negroes with machine guns?"

"No," I announced confidently.

"Herr Miller, you're an idiot," he stormed. To my surprise he leaped to his feet and rushed to the pillar, which he banged with his fist. "Do you think that Genghis Khan started with this pillar? No. He marched step by step until this pillar was nothing. I could find in any American city you care to mention men who would be glad—joyous, shall we say—to be led step by step until they were building this pillar with living bodies. Do you think we Germans started out one day by building pillars? No, Herr Miller, no! Do you think I started with this?" He beat the pillar until I expected his knuckles to come away bleeding.

Breathing hard, he came and sat beside me. It was now past midnight and we were both worn by the tragic day on the desert, but the pillar kept us awake, and Stiglitz said softly, "Do you really think, Herr Miller, that the reports the Allied governments have on me started with a pillar like that grisly thing? Oh, no! I was a fine, respectable doctor in Munich, married to the daughter of an important businessman . . . a member of the church. My wife and I saw certain promotions available through the Nazi party and we joined. Many prudent men and women did. It was easy at first. The Jews, whom we all despised"—he told me this in a confidential voice, as if I would appreciate why any reasonable man would despise Jews; indeed, as if our hating them together made us brothers—

"were merely to be sequestered. That was all, sequestered.

"One day they asked me to check the health of the Jews they rounded up, and I did so, very carefully. Believe me, Herr Miller, if I found a Jew who needed an expensive medicine, I said so, and there are many Jews alive today solely because I prescribed expensive medicine for them." He nodded in confirmation of his own plea, and I judged that he had often conducted this dialogue with himself. There were Jews living today because of what Dr. Stiglitz had done for them, of that I was sure.

"If I were ever brought to trial," he assured me with great confidence, "the health records of the City of Munich would show case after case where I saved the lives of Jews. It's all there . . . in the reports."

He looked at me beseechingly, a tired, pudgy man with turbaned head, wrinkled brow and worried eyes. I thought, perhaps, that he was perspiring, but he was sitting with his back to the lantern, and all I could see was shadow. Persuasively, cautiously, his words resumed: "Unexpectedly other problems arose. A Jew was to be certified mentally deficient so he could be sterilized. The government wanted me to designate a complete stranger as three-quarters Jewish so his property could be confiscated. I'd never seen him before, but he was obviously Jewish . . . you can always tell a Jew. So step by step my soul was corrupted."

He was driven by some deep hatred back to the pillar, which he hammered with his open hands. "Miller," he cried in a hoarse shout, "do you suppose that the man who applied this plaster over living, breathing mouths started with this job? Do you believe that you're immune?"

"To killing Jews, yes!"

"Ah, but the Negro is your Jew. Are you immune there?"

"Of course!" I shouted in disgust.

"Herr Miller, you're a liar! You're a self-deceiving

liar!" He beat the pillar again. "This is your pillar, too. This is the pillar of Americans and Englishmen and Germans alike. I couldn't have built this alone, you know."

To my embarrassment his voice began to choke, as if he were going to burst into tears of confession. Then, thank heavens, he gained control of himself and rejoined me on the floor. It was now about two in the morning and in the flickering light of our Coleman lamp I could see his drawn face, weary yet driven to further revelation, and in some strange way he looked as he had that night in the square at Kandahar when he was condemning the dancers. I could hear his voice speaking the words but this time applying them somehow to his own history: *They're cruel little sodomites. When they come to town they create a great evil.* What ugly passage in his own life among the Nazis did that repeated phrase illuminate?

Toward four he got to the heart of his chronicle: "Finally, when we were winning the war on all fronts —it was 1941—they came to me and said, 'We're looking for a director of research. Military problems of the gravest significance. Involved is the final destruction of England.' What could I say? I was flattered.

"They gave me a fine laboratory in Munich. I could live at home." He seemed to savor, here in the Afghan desert, those bright visions of a happy German home life in Munich. "I could live at home," he explained persuasively, as if eager to convince me. "I had to take the job, you can see that. At first it was routine experiments on colds . . . very sensible, very productive. I believe they're selling in America now a cold remedy that came from my researches. I convinced myself that I was helping win the war.

"I enjoyed other successes and then one day in 1943 they asked me to explore a purely theoretical question: How much cold can a human being tolerate? Now that's a nice question. A very important one, militarily speaking." He paused a long time to stare at the pillar, then laughed in a high-pitched giggle. "Without my knowing it, we were about to conduct pragmatic experiments on the same subject . . . at Stalingrad." He laughed openly. Undoubtedly he had used the joke before.

"A fascinating medical question, Herr Miller," he said reflectively. "How much cold can a human being tolerate? Yesterday, for example. You were very hot . . . thought you couldn't take any more. But Nazrullah said, 'You can discipline yourself,' and the thermometer rose fourteen degrees and you did discipline yourself. How much heat could you have stood? That's a nice question. How much cold . . . I remember the exact phrasing because I wrote it down the day they posed it. You see, Herr Miller, I have a love for keeping records. Yesterday I could sympathize with John Pritchard when he said, 'I must have the records.' Because it is only from careful records that science can . . ." His voice broke and he dropped his head in his hands. His turban fell off and I could see the gray hairs on his stubbly head; I could see his shoulders moving up and down, silently. Finally he put his hand on my knee and said, "The English captured my records. I was meticulous. I was meticulous."

For some minutes we said nothing, then he rose, overcome by a terrible emotion which I did not try to specify, and walked about the pillar several times, his mouth moving as if he were making a speech. The flickering light—the Coleman lamp gives a very white light and throws facial shadows in deep relief—made him look old. Suddenly he leaned against the pillar and issued a flood of words: "In the cage there was this Jew. About fifty years old, a fine human being. His name . . . you can check this in the records . . . was Sem Levin. I had tried all sorts of experiments and had proved what required to be proved, but I had not applied my findings to an average, healthy man like the older soldiers in our army. So I chose Sem Levin. I chose him right from a nondescript group in the cage. I told my aide, 'That's the man! Now we'll see what's what.' "

He hesitated. He could look from the pillar to where I sat and he must have seen the horror and revulsion rising in my face, but he could not silence himself. "Each morning we put Sem Levin completely naked into a room whose temperature could be exactly controlled. We dropped it lower and lower. After eight hours' exposure we discharged him and he returned to the cage filled with nondescript Jews. At first he merely dressed and talked with them. Later, when he joined them blue with cold, two fat middle-aged Jewish women began caring for him. They took his frozen body and held it between them, as if he were a baby. Everyone in the cage who had clothes to spare piled them over the three Jews, the two fat women and shivering Sem Levin.

"I grew to hate this tough little Jew, because each time he entered that room he announced quietly, 'I am still alive.' And when he said this, the Jews cheered, no matter what we had done to them that day. 'I am still alive.' Now it became with them a matter of honor to keep him alive. They saved food for him. Massaged him. Stole medicine for him. And from their resolve he too became determined not to die.

"No man could have withstood what he withstood. He'd come back to the cage with his dirty little penis shriveled up and blue, and he'd say, 'I am still alive.' And the fat women, remembering their husbands dead somewhere in Germany, would take him in their arms.

"It was at this point, when pneumonia was about to begin, that he started greeting me each morning with the same statement. Very polite. 'Good morning, Herr Professor. I am still alive.' "

Stiglitz leaned against the pillar, weak with horror. Then he said in a ghost-like voice well suited to the silent room, "And all the time my filthy wife was going to bed with anyone who had a little authority." He looked at me with the beseeching face a man uses when he is beyond personal salvation and asks help of a priest or a rabbi. In a kind of wail he protested, "But I was honest about the experiment. I could have killed Sem Levin any time I wished, and silenced that speech: 'I am still alive.' No, I held rigorously to the schedule as planned. We lowered the degrees day by day. My records will show that . . . exactly as planned.

"Much later than anyone would have dared predict, this dirty little Jew"—ten minutes ago he had been a *fine human being*—"contracted pneumonia. He should have died. By all human precedent he should have died. But those fat women somehow infused life into him. All that I took away they gave back. On the last three days he could scarcely make his voice heard, but he rasped, 'Good morning, Herr Professor. I am still alive.'

"Finally we broke him. Would you believe it, Miller, he spent three days stark naked in a room two degrees above zero, your system."

Neither of us spoke. Then, in a wild rage, he shouted, "That's why, you stupid American, I could not make the decision yesterday. John Pritchard would have refused to live if we had left him there. If Sem Levin could refuse to die, why couldn't Pritchard refuse to live? Tell me that, Mr. Know-it-all."

"What happened?" I asked in unconcealed horror.

"He died. Two full weeks after we had predicted . . . fourteen days . . . he died. The man in charge was so infuriated with the fat women that he sent the whole cage full of Jews away."

"Away?" I shouted. "Say it. Where?"

"Away," he repeated dully. Then quickly: "I don't know where he sent them. He signed the order . . . the other man."

"Stiglitz," I said quietly, trying to keep control of myself, "you're lying."

"No, no, Herr Miller. It was he who signed the order."

"You're lying," I repeated, not moving.

"No, before God, he signed the order. For Sem Levin I was responsible. That I admit. The records will prove my guilt regarding him. But the others . . ."

"Stiglitz!" I screamed, driven to my feet by an impulse outside me. "I am a Jew!"

He stared at me in awful disbelief, then drew back against the pillar. He tried to laugh, as if I were joking. He moved his mouth to speak but could say nothing, and failing, ran behind the pillar for protection. "Herr Miller . . ." he gasped weakly.

"I'm going to kill you," I threatened, making a lunge at him, but he used the pillar adroitly to protect himself, and I did not touch him.

In the large room there was no furniture, no weapon of any kind except the knife he had used for scraping away the plaster. It had been left lying on the earth near where I stood, but I didn't see it. To my surprise, Stiglitz left the protection of the pillar and made a lunge at me. I felt I could handle him, although he was heavier than I, and I got set to tackle him head on, but my preparation was useless, because he had no interest in me. With a swoop, he fell on the knife and leaped to his feet, jubilant.

"I'm going to kill you," I repeated slowly. "For Sem Levin and the others in the cage." He grinned at me, holding the knife awkwardly with both hands before his chest, and I made a strong feint to the right, then a drive to the left, aiming a kick at his groin. I caught him well and sent him down in a screaming heap, with the useless knife still held before his chest. Had there been a chair in the room, I would have killed him then, beating him to death, but since I had only my hands, I refrained from leaping on him. Instead, I started kicking at him savagely as he lay huddled on the floor. Then, with a second feint at his head, I drove in with a powerful kick at his stomach, straightening him out and sending the knife softly into the dust. I made a football lunge at him and caught his throat in my hands.

I was about to strangle him when the great door of the serai creaked open, admitting daylight and a tall Afghan. With a deep voice he asked in Pashto, "Who would fight in a serai?" I looked up and saw above me a dark-faced man with mustaches and a flowing turban. Across his chest were bandoleers and in his belt a silver-handled dagger.

"Who would fight in a serai?" he repeated.

"There was no reason," I replied in Pashto, scrambling to my feet.

"Good," he cried, and with a deft kick of his booted foot spun our knife against the wall, where it fell quietly to earth. Recovering it, he jammed it into his belt beside his own and said, "The knife I will keep."

As he spoke, other men began filing into the fort and finally a woman, tall and stalwart, with bangles in her nose and no chaderi. Then I recognized who the intruders were: the Povindahs I had seen at Ghazni, and this tall man with the two daggers was the one whom Nur and I had met that day on horseback.

He seemed to recognize me too, for he turned away and strode to the door, where he issued commands which I could not hear. When he returned, additional men appeared bearing bits of wood and utensils, which they carried to the center of the room, where a substantial fire was started.

When it was well ablaze, with smoke drifting out a hole in the ceiling, three Povindah women marched in with that wild, matchless gait I had admired in Ghazni. They were dressed in good gray blouses and black skirts, and since they passed close to me and wore no chaderies, I stared at them and found them handsome . . . not beautiful in any way but handsome.

After they had taken their places about the fire another Povindah entered, and she was not only handsome; she was bewitching, a saucy pigtailed girl of seventeen or eighteen, dressed in red skirt and pink blouse. We looked at each other, and I recognized her as the girl chasing the goat at Ghazni, and I saw that in her nose she wore no bangles and that her face was extremely clean and sensitive. She kept looking at me as she moved toward the fire and seemed to smile, as if she recognized me, and the grace of her movement reminded me of the gazelles, who could twist and turn at any moment, and so we stared at each other until the man with the bandoleers cried roughly, "Mira!" And the girl went to him for instructions which I did not hear.

She either did not understand what the leader directed or she thought his words unwise, for she stood perplexed, whereupon he gave her a shove and cried, "Mira, do as I say." He propelled her from the serai and I had to assume that he was angry with her for having paraded before me, but I was wrong.

For soon she appeared at the door bringing with her a most beautiful young woman with blond hair, fair complexion and sparkling blue eyes. She was obviously not a Povindah, even though she was dressed as one in black skirt and bracelets. It had to be Ellen Jaspar —tanned from long hours of marching in the sun, slim, vibrant, more challenging even than her photographs.

I can't recall now what I had expected Ellen to look like: vaguely, I had supposed she would be brittle, or obviously neurotic, or reticent with an overt fear of sex, or generally odd-ball like the typical college girl who reacts negatively to the world. She was none of these. Not a single cliché of the sterile revolutionary was visible in this unmarked, wonderful face, and I could hear Richardson of Intelligence saying in the embassy: *I'd date that one. She's stunning.*

Then I understood why her husband, when I had asked him on the desert if she were in Afghanistan, had looked first to the eastern and western stars, judging from them that it was the season when his wife would return to this country with the march of the nomads. Any man who had ever known Ellen Jaspar would keep in his mind a schedule of her movements. It was to this band of Povindahs that she had run away, and I stepped forward to introduce myself and to tell her that I had come to rescue her. But before I could speak, she nodded slightly, as if she already knew who I was, and hurried past me to where Dr. Stiglitz remained in a dazed condition on the ground.

I remember clearly that her lips started to form a word, then stopped. On her second attempt she cried, "Dr. Stiglitz!" He looked up, saw who it was, and more or less collapsed, hiding his face from what he could scarcely believe.

She knelt beside him, took his hands and gently pulled him from the ground. "Are you all right?" she asked.

"Madame Nazrullah, I can't believe . . ."

Having restored him to his feet, she left him abruptly and came to me, her blond hair peeking from beneath an embroidered Asian cap. Standing before me she said graciously, "I'm Ellen Jaspar, and you must be Mark Miller from the American embassy."

"How did you know?" I asked in some confusion.

"Our people followed you at the execution in Ghazni," she explained.

In some strange way her composure made me feel out of place, and I didn't know what to say. "I'm glad to find you alive," I fumbled.

She suppressed a smile and said, "The savages have treated me rather well." Then she moved to the side of the tall leader and linked her arm with his in one of those automatic gestures which cannot be explained but which betray everything . . . only a woman who is living with a man ever makes that particular movement. Ellen Jaspar had run off with the leader of a nomad caravan, and it must have been this improbable rumor that had reached Shah Khan in Kabul. Little wonder that he had refused to repeat it or have it attributed to him in our embassy records.

"This is Zulfiqar," Ellen announced.

"Is the feud ended?" the big nomad asked Stiglitz and me. When we nodded he cried, "Then let us eat!" And I had my first meal with the nomads.

11

We had not finished breakfast when two Povindah boys with darting eyes and quick gestures—the kind who steal you blind in a bazaar—came yelling that a jeep was hidden in one of the rooms. The Povindahs piled out to see the vehicle and Zulfiqar demanded, "Whose is it?"

"Mine,"I said.

"Why is it here?"

I pointed to the broken axle and explained, "I hit rocks on the dasht."

"What were you doing on the dasht?"

The Povindahs gathered round, and since Dr. Stiglitz was still unnerved by the unforeseen consequences of the pillar, I had to explain Pritchard's death in Pashto. Having done so, I began translating into English for Ellen, but she interrupted, in good Pashto, "I learned the language."

When we returned to our breakfast, Zulfiqar surprised me by inquiring bluntly, "Now what do you want to ask us about Ellen?" He pronounced her name gently, in two careful syllables: *El-len*.

I turned to Ellen and asked, "When you first saw me . . . how did you know who I was?"

Zulfiqar replied. "They told us in Ghazni."

"No one in Ghazni knew what I was doing," I protested.

At this Zulfiqar laughed and indicated with his thumb that Ellen was to speak. She brushed back her blond hair and chuckled. "Two minutes after you arrived in Ghazni, Mira saw you in the bazaar."

"There were no women in the bazaar at Ghazni."

"Mira is everywhere."

"Is that true of all Povindahs?"

The indulgent smile on Zulfiqar's face disappeared and he banged his extended fingertips onto the rug from which we were eating. "We're not Povindahs!" he exploded. "That's an ugly name given us by the British. It means that we're permitted"—his voice assumed much scorn—"permitted, if you will, to cross into their lands. We are the Kochis, the Wanderers, and we ask no nation's permission to cross boundaries. It was we who established the boundaries, centuries ago!" He subsided, but warned me quietly, "We are the Kochis."

Ellen resumed: "Mira saw you in the bazaar and sprinted back to camp to warn us that a ferangi was in town. She already knew that you were from the embassy, had a jeep, traveled with an Afghan driver who worked for the government, and that you were headed for Kandahar. Don't ask me how she knew."

I looked at Mira, whose dark eyes were flashing satisfaction. She smiled, but said nothing.

"When you attended the stoning of the woman, three of our men were spying on you. Later they talked with your armed guards. They found you were headed for Qala Bist, and when you hiked out to our camp at the edge of Ghazni, I watched you from the tents."

Zulfiqar smiled again and said, "She wanted to speak then, but I argued, 'No. Don't spoil his fun. He's a young man. Let him go to Qala Bist. Find out for himself. Let him follow us across the desert. He'll talk about it the rest of his life.'"

I was struck by his shrewdness and recalled the things I would have missed: Kandahar, the arch at Qala Bist, The City, and this caravanserai. In some way I must have betrayed my thoughts, for with a twist of his hand he imitated a man fighting with a knife and observed, "A caravanserai at dawn . . . who would steal this from a young man?"

I looked at Zulfiqar with new respect and reminded him, "You offered to answer my questions. Why is Miss Jaspar here?"

With no resentment he explained. "Last September we camped for three days at Qala Bist. On our way to winter quarters at Jhelum. And this American woman came out from the fort to visit with our children . . . with our women. She spoke some Pashto and our people talked. She asked them where we were going, and they said, the Jhelum. She asked by what route, and they told her Spin Baldak, Dera Ismail Khan, Bannu, Nowshera, Rawalpindi. As we were leaving she came to me and said, 'I'd like to travel with your caravan!' I asked her why, and she replied . . ."

"I said," Ellen interrupted in Pashto, "that I would like to march with the free people."

I turned to Ellen and asked in English, "Is he married?"

In Pashto she replied, so that all the nomads could hear, "It seems I can love only married men." Then she pointed to one of the handsome older women and said, "That's Racha, Mira's mother." It was thus made obvious to all what my English question had been, and thus I began my acquaintance with Ellen Jaspar in irritation and embarrassment.

The older woman, with a golden bangle in her nose, bowed gracefully, and I felt like a reproved child. I thought: I'm two years older than Ellen Jaspar, but she makes me feel like an infant. I remember that as I finished this thought, I happened to look across the rug and saw that Mira was smiling at my confusion.

When we finished eating, Zulfiqar asked Ellen in Pashto, "Is the fat one a doctor?" Ellen replied that he was, and Zulfiqar said, "Ask him if he'd look at some of our people." Ellen said, "Ask him yourself. He speaks Pashto."

"I'd be happy to help," Stiglitz volunteered, eager to reestablish himself after the fight at the pillar.

Zulfiqar announced, "The doctor will look at your sores," and the Kochis lined up to show him torn fingers, scarred legs and teeth that should have been yanked earlier. As I watched Stiglitz work, I was again impressed by his skill in handling sick people and I was torn between admiring him as a doctor and hating him for what he had once done as a doctor; while on his part he began to revive his hope that in spite of last night I might still recommend his employment by our embassy. Once he looked at me with a half-smile and asked in English, "For a people without doctors, the Kochis are quite healthy, aren't they? They get along very well without doctors."

I felt it unnecessary for me to put him completely at ease, so I ignored the question and had started toward the door when I was met by a travesty of a nomad, one of the funniest-looking men I ever saw. He was about five feet three, scrawny, unshaved, dirty, and clothed in the grimiest rags imaginable. He wore his filthy turban with one end almost to his knees and grinned through broken teeth and a left eye that had a scar dropping three inches from the corner to his jawbone. He shuffled along in sandals that almost fell from his feet and nodded obsequiously to all.

He had been bitten by something, and showed his left arm to Dr. Stiglitz, who asked, "What happened?"

"That damned camel!" the man railed, spitting between his black teeth.

"Looks like you've been chewed," Stiglitz mused, looking at the ugly, extended wound.

"This is Maftoon," Ellen explained. "He tends the camels. What happened, Maftoon?"

"That damned camel!" the little man repeated.

"He has great trouble with the beasts," Ellen laughed. She spoke rapidly with Maftoon and he nodded. "One of the camels gummed his arm," she said.

"Don't you mean bit?" I asked.

"No, I mean gummed. Camels have no upper teeth, you know. At least not in front. When they get mad at you, and Maftoon's are always mad at him, they gum you."

"What are you talking about?" I asked.

"Come along," she volunteered, and she took me out to the camels, where she threw bits of nan at them, so that they opened their mouths wide to catch the food and I could see that she was right. In front the beasts had strong lower teeth but no uppers, only a broad plate of hard gum against which they bit to chew off grass or other fodder. In back, of course, they had grinding teeth.

"I never heard of this," I said, looking for a baby camel that I could inspect more closely.

"Try this one," Ellen suggested, and she called an enormous brute some nine feet tall at the hump, the female with a bad disposition who had attacked Maftoon and sent him to the doctor. "This old devil hates Maftoon but gets along well with me. Hey, hey!" she called, and the huge beast came close, lowered her head, and muzzled Ellen for a piece of nan. The split upper lip opened and Ellen pressed her thumb against the hard flat gum, then threw a chunk of nan, which the camel caught. "You try it," she said, and I took the nan and got the old camel to open her mouth. The plate against which her lower teeth hit was hard as bone.

"Extraordinary," I said as the big beast ambled away, but as she did so she caught sight of little Maftoon coming from the doctor, and she began to make noises, showing her irritation. I say "make noises" but I'm sure that isn't the right phrase: the camel uttered a sound that was a combination groan, growl, gurgle and grunt. And it was clear that whereas Ellen and I could inspect her teeth, Maftoon had better stand clear.

"Watch!" Ellen whispered, as the little camel driver took off his turban and threw it on the ground. He took off his long shirt, his tattered pants, his sandals, everything until he stood quite naked. Then he moved back and waited while the embittered camel shuffled up, smelled the clothes and began kicking them violently. She bit them, stamped on them, spit at them and then pushed them about the sand with her head. When she had vented her spleen she stalked majestically away, gurgling and grunting.

When she was gone, Maftoon recovered his clothes, dressed and went in pursuit of the placated camel. When he reached her head he scratched her neck, she gurgled amiably, and the two walked off toward the meager pasture.

"What's it all about?" I asked.

"The old camel drivers believe . . . and it seems to work . . . that a camel bears terrible grudges. Maftoon and the old lady had a fight, and even though she gummed his arm, she'd attack him again and again unless he allowed her to fight his clothes. She's satisfied and tomorrow he'll be able to load her again."

We followed the little man and his camel for some distance, then sat on rocks to watch the animals graze over land where I could see nothing. Ellen said, "I never tire of watching camels. I suppose it goes back to my Sunday school in Dorset, Pennsylvania. At Christmas we traced camels on the wall. Goodness, that seems years ago."

My interrogation of Nazrullah had been so constantly postponed that I was determined to learn as much as possible in my one day with the Kochis, so I launched right in: "Why won't you write to your parents?"

She was expecting some opening attack like this and replied easily, "What could I tell them?" She looked at me pleasantly as the bright sun illuminated her well-scrubbed face. "If they couldn't understand a simple problem like Nazrullah, how could they possibly understand this?" She pointed to Maftoon, the camels and the caravanserai.

"Perhaps I could understand."

"Not likely." She spoke with a contempt which erased the pleasantness I had observed before.

"Nazrullah is still very much in love with you. What happened?"

"He's very kind. He's very tedious," she replied.

I was irritated by her assumed superiority and was about to comment on it when I saw at the caravanserai gate the tall figure of Zulfiqar, spying on us, but after a while I had to conclude that he was not spying, for he seemed neither jealous nor suspicious; he looked as if he were glad that Ellen had found a chance to talk with an American. I thought: Wonder what they talk about when they're alone. Aloud I asked, "Can Zulfiqar read and write?"

"Books, no. Figures . . . better than either of us."

She said this in a bored manner implying that no further comment from me would be welcomed, so I observed, "Nazrullah seemed one of the ablest men in the country."

"He is," she said with equal finality and equal boredom. Then with a show of real warmth she added, "His wife Karima's even better."

"I met her . . . in chaderi."

"Karima! She never wears chaderi if she can help it."

"I had a government official with me."

"That's how it works," she observed, reverting to a monotone. "Karima observes the custom to protect Nazrullah, and he assures the government that he approves in order to protect Karima."

It was a neatly phrased summary, but I remembered what Nazrullah had said on the desert: *On the morning after the marriage Ellen came to breakfast wearing a chaderi.* Probably I should have kept my mouth shut, but she had gone out of her way to irritate and embarrass me, so I remarked, "Nazrullah told me that when you first came to Afghanistan you wore the chaderi."

She blushed angrily, blood coursing across her beautiful face. "Nazrullah talks a lot," she said.

"Karima talked a lot, too," I continued. "She told me that while you were still in America you learned that Nazrullah already had a wife."

She laughed uneasily. "Why are you American men so preoccupied with such trivialities? Of course I knew he was married. This proves, Mr. Miller, why you could never understand my reasons for leaving Dorset, Pennsylvania."

"Any chance of my understanding why you left Nazrullah?"

She looked at me steadily, almost insultingly, with deep blue eyes, then laughed. "No one who works for the American embassy could possibly understand."

That did it. "If you were a man," I said coldly, "I'd bust you in the nose. Why don't you have the decency to tell your parents where you are?"

My bluntness shocked her and she bit her knuckles, then toyed nervously with the embroidery on her blouse. "Your question is a sensible one, Mr. Miller, and it hurts. My parents are good, decent people and I'm sure they mean well. But what can I possibly write to them?" She looked at me with the first compassion I had seen since we started talking, but it quickly faded. "Would you suggest something like this?" she asked brightly, as she began reciting an imaginary letter.

"Dear Mumsy and Dadsy,

I have run away from Mr. Nazrullah because he's one of the most boring men on earth, and I'm sure his other wife thinks so too. He could move right into Dorset without causing a ripple, because he believes like you, Mumsy-wumsy, that God wants men to have big cars, that electricity makes people happy, and that if you sell enough canned goods, tensions will cease. You were deadly afraid of him, Dadsy-wadsy, but you shouldn't have been. He's your twin brother and if you'd recognized a good thing when you saw it, you'd have fought to keep him, not me. Because he could sell insurance ten times better than you ever did.

Your loving daughter,
Ellen
Bryn Mawr 1945, busted out

P.S. I am now living with a man who has no home, no nation and no responsibility except ninety-one camels. His wife made me the most adorable gray blouse you ever saw in your life, and I'm wearing it as I hike over the Lower Himalayas. I'll write to you next from Jhelum when we get there eleven months from now.
Your Ellie"

She looked at me bitterly and said, "If you think that would put them at ease, send it to them. Frankly, I haven't the guts."

I was disgusted with her. She sounded like a freshman I knew at Mount Holyoke, except for two things: the other girl's father sold stocks and bonds in Omaha, and in her sophomore year she got some sense. This Jaspar girl was irritating, and I said something which must have made me sound foolish: "When the years pass, you'll be old. What will you do in a Kochi caravan then?"

"What will Senator Vandenberg do? He'll be old. And you . . . what's your first name, Miller?"

"Mark. Groton and Yale."

"That's just dandy. If there's anyone I like to meet in the middle of the Afghan desert it's a Yale man. Tell me, do you honestly believe that in my home town of Dorset, Pennsylvania, there's a basic good, while here in Afghanistan there's a basic evil?"

"I believe that anyone does best when he clings to

his own nation, his own people . . . and his own religion. I understand you gave yours up."

"Presbyterianism is not difficult to give up," she replied.

"A moment ago I said to myself, She sounds like a Mount Holyoke freshman. I put you about four years too high. You sound like a high-school freshman."

"Damn you!" she snapped. "I'm sitting here among the camels thinking: That poor dear boy, Mark Miller. Groton and Yale. The years will pass and he'll be stuck in some pothole like the embassy in Brussels. And he'll be old. And he'll have missed the whole meaning . . . the whole goddamned meaning." She looked at me sadly and said, "You're a young jerk and you're already prematurely middle-aged and I'm terribly sorry for you."

I stared at her. I said nothing for at least four minutes, just stared at her. Finally she shrugged her shoulders and said, "I surrender. Get me some paper. I'll write the letter."

I asked her if she would come inside, but she replied, "I never get enough of this free air," and as I entered the caravanserai to get some paper from my brief case I met Zulfiqar and told him, "She's going to write to her parents," and he replied, "I asked her to, months ago."

I handed her the paper and she sat scrunched up on the rocks, biting my pen. Then, as she started writing freely and easily, I had a second chance to study her. If I hadn't just heard her bitter comments, I would have sworn that she was exactly what I had guessed when I first saw her in the caravanserai: a lovelier, more beautiful, more delightful person than we had seen in the embassy photographs. She simply did not look like a disgruntled post-adolescent. She was a mature, sensible-looking woman with a plenitude of charm, and if I could have erased her recent conversation I could easily have agreed with her enthusiastic roommate, whose report I now recalled so clearly:

Ellen Jaspar was a dear, sweet kid. She was loyal, responsive, and trustworthy. It sounded like the Girl Scout oath, but now Ellen came to a difficult part of her letter and a scowl crossed her face—a harsh, belligerent scowl—and I could not possibly kid myself into thinking that I was dealing with any Girl Scout.

"Will that do?" she asked, thrusting the finished letter at me. I took it, turned away from the bright sunlight, and read:

Dear Folks,

I'm terribly sorry I haven't written sooner, but some rather dramatic things have been happening and frankly, I found it almost impossible to explain them to you in a letter. Let me say quickly that they leave me happier than I have ever been, in better spirits, secure in all things. I love you very much.

My marriage to Nazrullah didn't work out too well, but it was not because of his unkindness. He was an even better man than I told you, and I am terribly sorry to have hurt him, but there was no escape. I am now with some wonderful people whom you would like, and I'll tell you all about them later.

To show you how crazy this world can be, I am now sitting with a herd of camels on the edge of the desert talking to a perfectly delightful Yale man, Mark Miller, who will send you a fuller letter of his own explaining all that has happened. He will tell you that I am happy, healthy and alive.

Your loving daughter . . .

Thinking of my own close-knit family in Boston, I could have wept at her inability to communicate with her people. I returned the letter and said, "Sign it, and I'll airmail it from Kandahar."

But before writing her signature she let the pen hang idly and mused, "God knows, Miller, I told them the truth. I am happy, healthy and alive. And if I were to grow old as pleasantly as Racha has done, I'd be content."

She signed the letter, addressed the envelope carefully, then bit the pen for some moments. Extending the sealed letter provocatively toward me, she waved it twice, then studiously tore it into minute bits, which she scattered among the camels. "I cannot send such evasions," she said hoarsely.

We stared at each other for some time and I saw in her eyes hatred, bitterness and confusion. But as I continued to look at her, these ugly attributes vanished and I saw merely the appealing gaze of an attractive, perplexed young woman. I said, "I'll write to them."

"Please do," she replied.

I returned to the caravanserai, where I faced one of the more difficult decisions of my mission: on the one hand I was dead tired from the long, tragic day on the desert followed by the sleepless night at the pillar, so that my whole autonomic system demanded that I fall asleep; but on the other I awaited the momentary arrival of a rescue mission led by either Nazrullah or troops from Kandahar, so that before the rescue party took me away I wanted to see as much of Kochi life as possible. I forced myself to stay awake, watching the children and the older women working at their jobs. I thought constantly: I'm probably the only person from the American embassy who ever saw the Kochis close-up. I can sleep tomorrow.

But when I looked at Dr. Stiglitz, spread out on the floor by the pillar, it became impossible to fight sleep any longer. I dropped on the hard-packed earth and almost immediately lost consciousness. My last memory was of Racha throwing a shawl over me.

I awoke in darkness and my first thought was: Good! If the rescue party hasn't made it by now, they won't come till tomorrow. I can stay with the Kochis tonight. The big room was filled with the smell of cooking, for Zulfiqar had ordered a substantial fire, around which many were working. Then I became aware of someone sitting beside me, and it was Mira in her red skirt, and when I stirred she said in Pashto, "Zulfiqar told me to keep the children away." Then in broken English she said, "Ellen tell me English few words." She spoke in a lilting, pleasant voice that sounded as if it belonged to a younger girl, and she had a gamin smile. When I reached out to inspect her attractive pigtails, which no other Kochis wore, she smiled with pride and explained, "Ellen fix my hair American way." She pronounced Ellen's name as her father did, in two gentle syllables.

In Pashto I asked, "Does Ellen work in the camp?"

"All work," she replied in English, followed by Pashto: "Have you come to take Ellen away?"

"I wanted to, but she won't come."

"I am so glad."

"Who told you I was going to take her away?"

"We've always known she would leave some day," Mira replied. "Look how she works."

Ellen, not knowing that I was awake, was busy at the fire, the antagonisms of her letter lost in work. Zulfiqar had killed a sheep in honor of the ferangi and it was roasting, with Ellen in charge to see that it didn't burn. From time to time she stuck a long fork into the flanks and tasted it, smacking her lips as she did so. Children stayed close to the fire, begging her for stray pieces of mutton, as if she were their mother, while against the wall lounged Kochi men, waiting silently for the unscheduled feast. Other women were preparing pilau in stone vessels, while Dr. Stiglitz and Zulfiqar were opening K-rations, whose tops were promptly licked clean by other children. Except for the American cans, it was a scene that dated back to the beginning of man on the plains of Central Asia.

"We eat!" Zulfiqar announced, and it was exciting to watch Ellen, relaxed and motherly, standing by the roasted sheep and passing out portions as if she had done so all her life. From time to time, with greasy hands, she brushed her blond hair back from her moist face, appearing as feminine as any woman I had ever seen, and I recalled her words from the destroyed letter: *I am happy, healthy and alive*. Clearly she was, and when it came time to serve me she smiled as she gave me a chunk of well-browned meat.

"Be sure to try the nan," she advised, as I helped myself to pilau.

Mira led me to a rug where the leaders were sitting, and I found a place across from Dr. Stiglitz, beside whom Ellen would sit. Later, when I tasted the nan Ellen asked, "Delicious, eh?" I replied that it had a nut-like flavor and she explained in English that it had been baked directly over dried camel dung. "Can't you taste it?" she pressed, and I could. In Pashto she said, "It is of the earth. It is of our life."

Zulfiqar nodded and said, "The sheep you're eating . . . we raised."

Later I told Zulfiqar, "Ellen wrote the letter to her parents, but tore it up." Ellen added, "Zulfiqar understands. I can't explain Dorset to him, nor him to Dorset."

The big Kochi chieftain said, "You write, Mil-lair."

"I will . . . tomorrow."

My mention of this word evoked a sadness, and at our rug nothing was said; each looked at the other with a sense of strangeness. Mira broke the spell: "What will you tell her parents?"

"What should I tell them?" I asked the group, and to my surprise it was Racha who spoke.

"Tell them," Zulfiqar's wife said, "that now we head for the Oxus and in the winter back to the Jhelum. We live between the rivers."

"But don't call it the Oxus in your letter," Ellen warned. "They'll go crazy looking for it on their maps. Correct name's the Amu Darya . . . about a thousand miles from the Jhelum . . . and we make the round trip each year."

"Two thousand miles?"

"Each year."

"You ride the camels?" I asked.

This occasioned great laughter and Ellen explained, "Only the babies ride camels. The rest of us . . . we walk." She indicated Zulfiqar: "He has a horse, of course, but he must ride back and forth watching the animals."

"Do you mind the walking?" I asked.

Ellen indicated her legs tucked beneath the black skirt. "They get very strong," she assured me.

"How long has your clan been making this trip to the Jhelum?" I asked, and Ellen consulted Zulfiqar.

"There is no memory," he replied.

"Where exactly is the Jhelum?" I asked.

"Far over the border in India," was Zulfiqar's answer, which caused me to burst into laughter.

The big Kochi looked at me quizzically and I explained, "At a meeting in the American embassy we were trying to guess where she might be." I indicated Ellen, who said in English, "I'll bet you were." Quickly she translated the joke into Pashto, and the group laughed.

"And this important officer said"—I imitated Richardson's pipe-puffing, self-assured style—" 'The chances of an American girl's entering India without being noticed are just not measurable.' "

Zulfiqar chuckled. "The British! A million of us pass back and forth each year and no one knows where we go or how we feed ourselves."

Ellen added, "We're the wanderers who make fools of petty nations."

"Where are you headed now?" I asked.

"Musa Darul, Daulat Deh . . . in twenty-five days, Kabul. Bamian, Qabir . . ." Then he added a name that excited my imagination, for I had known it from boyhood days: Balkh, in ages past the greatest name in Central Asia.

"Balkh!" I said, and for a moment I daydreamed of how it would be to visit Balkh, but my fantasy was broken by Ellen, whose unpredictable behavior I was about to witness for the first time. Because our argument over the letter had become acrimonious, I expected her to be resentful, but to my surprise, and for reasons I could not decipher, she said quietly, "We go right to Kabul." Zulfiqar nodded, and from something in the way he acted or from some nuance in Ellen's speech, I received the impression that I might be welcomed on the march to Kabul. I leaned forward to broach the matter and Mira did the same, as if she were anticipating hopefully my reaction to one of the most tenuous invitations ever extended.

"You go right to Kabul?" I repeated. No one spoke.

Then Zulfiqar said quietly, "You're young. They'll send soldiers to fetch the broken jeep."

I turned to consult Dr. Stiglitz, whom I had continued to rebuff, and he said in English, hoping to win back my approval, "He's right, Herr Miller. You should see the mountain passes. I'll stay with the jeep."

Ellen contradicted: "You must come too, Doctor. We could use you in the caravan."

Zulfiqar leaned back and surveyed the ceiling, then asked Racha, "Could we use such a doctor at Qabir?" Racha studied the German and nodded, whereupon Zulfiqar warned, "We won't reach Qabir for many weeks. Will you join us?"

Dr. Stiglitz licked his lips and replied weakly, "Yes."

At this, Zulfiqar ended consultation with the women. "You two," he demanded of the ferangi, "how much money can you share with us?" I had two hundred dollars Afghan and Stiglitz much less, but he pointed out, "The Americans owe me money. When you pass Kandahar on the way back this autumn . . ." Zulfiqar reached out and gripped the doctor's hand.

But before the agreement was sealed I felt, for some reason I could not have explained, that it was my duty to warn Stiglitz of the risk he was taking. I led him away from the table and said, "With me it's simple. If Verbruggen gets mad, I'm sent home. I'll gamble, because from something he said I think he'll understand. But with you, Doctor, if you antagonize the Afghan government . . ."

"I'm a sick man, Herr Miller," he said weakly. "You know how sick I am. Unless I can find a rebirth . . ."

"You could be thrown out of the country," I warned. "You know what that would mean."

"Unless I can purify myself . . ."

"You're placing a great burden on the Kochis," I pointed out.

"Zulfiqar knows that," he argued. "He will use me as I will use him."

"I wonder what he meant, Could we use him at Qabir?"

"I don't know," the German replied. "But I must make this trip. It will be my salvation." And we rejoined the others.

As we did so, Mira came to me and said, in the dying light of the fire, "The Kochis would like you to join us, Miller." Then in English she added, "I like it too."

"I'm going to," I said.

We sat as a group by the embers and I repeated the story of the pillar, to which Ellen responded, "That's no surprise. One more outrage in a long series." Zulfiqar inspected the exposed skull and others satisfied themselves that bodies were immured in the pillar, but no one seemed perturbed.

At bedtime I had my first doubts: Suppose Nazrullah arrives with the rescue party? I'd have to go with them. Suppose the ambassador blows his stack when he gets back from Hong Kong? This could finish me with the State Department. Suppose Shah Khan makes an official protest? I'd be packed out like the two Marines. Then I heard Zulfiqar's powerful voice announcing, "We will move forward at four in the morning." Somehow this set my mind at rest. Nazrullah was not going to intercept me, and once I started north with the Kochis, it didn't matter what the ambassador and Shah Khan thought. They couldn't do a damned thing about it till I reached Kabul.

I was awakened by the fearful clatter of Kochis preparing to launch their caravan for another day. Protesting camels were loaded with trade stuffs. Black tents were struck and folded. Animals in the courtyard were herded onto the trail, and children were assigned tasks to which they attended promptly to avoid stout blows from Zulfiqar. If I had ever thought of nomads as lazy, such ideas were dispelled that morning.

As we were about to leave the serai I recalled how careful Nazrullah had been to post messages which would explain to others where he had been and what he had accomplished, and it occurred to me that I ought to extend him the same courtesy, so I scribbled a brief note stating simply that I had found his wife in good health and that I was hiking to Kabul with a caravan of Kochis. Would he advise our ambassador? "That'll give the old man something to chew on when he gets back," I chuckled, but when I told Zulfiqar what I was about to do he went suddenly pale—I mean he turned almost white—and ordered me to stay where I was while he went to consult the leaders. Sometime later he returned, badly shaken, and asked me to redraft the note omitting any reference to Kochis. I did so, and he asked Ellen to read it, but she could scarcely keep from laughing. She said cryptically, "It's accomplished its purpose," but he asked for further minor changes and at last I carried it with a bit of string to the jeep, where I tied it to the steering wheel.

In darkness we started our journey north, an ageless caravan heading across an ageless land. In the lead, with checkered vest and French overcoat, rode Zulfiqar on his brown horse, complete with dagger, German rifle and leather bandoleer. On the camels rode several infants and one sick woman in her late fifties. The rest walked, slowly, comfortably, tending the sheep or keeping the ninety-one camels in line.

Donkeys burdened with panniers chugged along, and behind them marched Ellen Jaspar, wearing stout army-type shoes, and Mira, in sandals.

The busiest person in line was jagged-eyed Maftoon, flapping back and forth along his string of camels, checking the ugly beasts to be sure their burdens were riding properly. I was to discover that during each day's hike, some one of the camels was outraged at Maftoon and made his frenzied life miserable: the ugly beast would not rise, would not lie down, would stray from the caravan, would fight and gurgle and protest. It was amusing to watch Maftoon as he tried to keep his camels in line.

At dawn the sun made Ellen's blond hair shine like gold, and she knew she was a beauty among the dark Kochis, for she carried herself with dignity. She had developed a healthy stride and her broad shoulders swung in the morning sunlight; but she was not alone in her beauty, for beside her with matching stride and jet-black hair hiked Mira, daughter of the chief and a notable person in her own right. She sensed instinctively when I watched her, and this pleased her, for occasionally I would catch her whispering to Ellen and pointing at me.

A day's trip was about fourteen miles. Except in the desert, where all travel had to be at night, we walked from pre-dawn till about noon, stopping at predetermined spots to which the Kochis had been returning for years, and this pitching and striking of tents became the dominant beat of the day's rhythm. I volunteered to help with the camels, for the preposterous brown beasts continued to fascinate me, and I often sat for hours watching them chew, with flopping jaws that seemed to lack all terminal attachments.

Once, when I was observing the frowsy old female who had attacked Maftoon, it occurred to me that the forlorn beast with the droopy eyes looked exactly like my Aunt Rebecca in Boston. I could hear her whining as I left for Afghanistan, "Mark, be careful. Find yourself a nice Jewish girl." Like the camel, Aunt Rebecca uncovered an endless supply of things to complain about, her eyes were jaundiced, and she chewed sideways. If she had had a coat of hair, I'm sure it would have been as bedraggled as the camel's. It was uncanny how much alike they were, and I was fond of them both. I started calling the camel "Aunt Becky," and she responded in a way that infuriated Maftoon. She would nip at him, bump him, cry bitterly when he approached her, then turn to me and be as docile as an indulgent old woman. I made her my special charge and often hiked beside her during the long marches.

My legs grew strong. I acquired a good tan and my sleep was unbroken. My appetite was unbelievable and I had never felt better. I thought: No wonder Ellen joined the Kochis.

But any illusions I had about the nomads as noble savages were dispelled on the sixth day, when we reached the outskirts of the little bazaar town of Musa Darul, for as soon as we struck camp six Kochis and four camels, including Aunt Becky, headed for town and in due course returned with an unprecedented supply of melons, meats, shoes and other necessities. That day we had a choice lunch and all would have been well, except that in mid-afternoon Dr. Stiglitz approached me while I was talking with Mira, and pleaded in a begging manner: "I'm hungry for tobacco. This empty pipe drives me crazy. When you mail your report to Kabul, could you get me a little at the bazaar? I have no money." I replied that after my nap I would see what could be done.

I mailed my report to the embassy, then wandered through the bazaar, seeking parcels of tobacco, and an old Afghan said, "I know I had some right here, but I must have misplaced it," and I was about to leave empty-handed when I was overtaken by a thin, ingratiating Afghan who spoke a little English.

"Sahib, you got car?"

In Pashto I replied that I did not, whereupon the salesman assured me, "I have a bargain you can't resist, sahib. You owe it to yourself."

"What is it?"

"Wait till you see," he whispered, taking my arm and leading me to the stall of an accomplice. There, amid karakul caps and fabrics from India, were six relatively new automobile tires. "Quite something, eh?" he asked admiringly.

I was startled by the tires. How could they have reached Musa Darul? Then off to one side I spotted a jeep carburetor, an oil filter, a jack, a complete set of tools and practically everything else that could be removed from a jeep frame. There was even a steering wheel, to which was attached my letter to Nazrullah.

"Where'd you get these?" I asked.

"Just came in this afternoon," he said happily. "From Russia."

"You've got a bargain here," I assured him, as I ticked off some twenty separate items which I knew were going to be charged against my salary in Kabul. "But you may have to wait some time for a customer," I warned him.

He laughed and said, "Five weeks, six weeks. If nobody wants them, we'll ship it all to Kabul." I winced as I thought of myself wandering through that bazaar, buying back these useful items.

"You send them to Kabul," I said with resignation. "Somebody'll be sure to need them."

I stormed back to camp and the first person I met was Ellen Jaspar. "These damned crooks!" I bellowed. "They invited me on this trip solely to steal my jeep . . . piece by piece."

Ellen tried to control her laughter but couldn't. "What did you think they wanted, your charm?" she chided.

"Did you know what they were up to?" I asked in outrage.

"Didn't you?" she countered. "Remember the panic you caused when you said you were tying the note to the steering wheel? Didn't you see me laughing at Zulfiqar, who tricked you to stay inside? Miller, when you started for the jeep, the steering wheel was already packed . . . on Aunt Becky."

I felt humiliated. "You mean they stole my jeep and hid it on my own camel?"

"Miller, you should have seen those Kochis unpacking the wheels off Aunt Becky and propping them back onto the jeep until you tied the letter to the wheel."

"It's going to cost me a month's salary," I said ruefully.

"That's cheap, for a trip like this. And don't protest to Zulfiqar. Strictly speaking, what he did was a breach of honor and he's ashamed. No man should be robbed in a caravanserai."

I was about to raise hell when Mira came in to hand me something. It was three packs of smoking tobacco. "I got them at the bazaar . . . for doctor."

I looked at Ellen and asked, "How did she get them at the bazaar? She has no money."

Ellen replied, "Mira is very quick."

12

I was deflated by my discovery that the Kochis had invited me to Kabul merely to steal the wheels off my jeep, but I soon forgot my irritation. For one thing, after Musa Darul the terrain became more interesting, since we were heading up the Helmand valley, which would ultimately deposit us near Kabul, a valley that few foreigners had seen. It lay west of the barren plains of Ghazni and east of the towering Koh-i-Baba mountains. No roads traversed it and for days we saw no villages and often only the barest of trails.

As we hiked, I grew to appreciate Nazrullah's complaint about the goats of Asia, for weeks passed and we saw not a single tree in what seemed otherwise almost virgin territory. Once great forests had covered these hills; there were historical records of that fact; but slowly the goats and the greed of men had denuded even the remote plateaus, leaving only rocky bleakness. I often wondered how our sheep existed as they plodded from one barren pasture to the next, but like the hungry camels, they usually found something.

In our caravan there were about two hundred Kochis, and on the march we were strung out over several miles, with camels and sheep predominant, so it was Zulfiqar's responsibility, as inheritor of this clan, to ride constantly back and forth, supervising our progress. He offered a striking appearance: tall and dark, with heavy mustaches, and a rifle to maintain his authority. On the trail he wore a white turban, but his conspicuous traits were his taciturnity and his smile. He smiled because he knew that keeping his people contented was half the battle; he kept his mouth shut to cultivate the legend that he knew more than his followers.

When the Kochis had served me roast sheep at the caravanserai, I did not appreciate how special the meal was, for the nomads ate poorly. At breakfast we had hot tea and a slab of nan, on which we hiked for twelve or fourteen miles, after which we had a meager helping of pilau lacking meat. In the evening we had curds and a little nan with some shreds of meat, if any was available. We lived close to the poverty level and seemed to thrive on it, but the children were perpetually hungry. I worried about this until Ellen pointed out, "They don't have protruding bellies. They're wonderful specimens," and I had to agree that what little they got nourished them, but I also noticed they were starved for fat and would avidly lick up any scraps, even if they had fallen to the ground.

Three aspects of nomad life distressed me: the Kochis were dirty; they were unkempt; and they made no attempt to develop intellectual interests. The wild free life of the wanderer left much to be desired.

The baggy trousers and flapping white shirts of the Kochi men were rarely clean, while the felt skirts of the women were apt to be streaked with dirt and tangled with briars, which they ignored. They washed infrequently, but I must admit that the extreme dryness of the air prevented offensive odors from accumulating. In my own case, with the humidity at two or three I could wear a shirt for more than a week because nothing could happen to it except a downright accident: there was no soot to soil the cloth and it was anatomically impossible for perspiration to collect. The minute it appeared it evaporated. I suspected that many Kochi garments were worn for months at a time without washing; only thus could they have become as dirty as they did.

The slovenliness of the Kochis was principally shown in the way they managed their hair. Women rarely combed theirs and men wore shoulder-length bobs which flapped with any vigorous movement. Their heads, men's and women's alike, were actually matted and probably worse. I often thought how much fun it would be to run the whole clan through a barber shop some afternoon to see what surprises would turn up.

As for the life of the mind, the speculation about good and evil, the judgment of past and future, there was none. Since they could neither read nor write, and since there was no radio, conversation was limited to the chance events of the caravan: the birth of sheep, the straying of a camel, the long march, outwitting the border guards and who stole what at the last bazaar. Days sped into months and months into years without any extension of the group intellect. It may be that the Kochis were supremely happy in their rough adaptation to nature; I often found them boring, and I had the ungenerous suspicion that Ellen Jaspar found comfort in the caravan partly because against their illiteracy she could stand out as a person with desirable skills. In any event, I noticed how often she came to Stiglitz or me to escape the dullness of the Kochis and to talk philosophically with an educated person.

There were two exceptions to this tradition of dirtiness, slovenliness and apathy: Zulfiqar and his daughter Mira were alert mentally and far above average in cleanliness, largely due to Ellen, who cut Zulfiqar's hair and tended his clothes. As to Mira, she kept herself well groomed partly because Ellen gave her instruction and partly because she mimicked whatever Ellen did in the way of cleanliness or personal adornment.

She owned several changes of costume: red dress, blue dress, gray felt dress; blue, red, white, green blouses; filmy gray, brown and white turbans; and an extra pair of sandals that she wore only when heading for some village bazaar off the caravan trail. Best of all, she had acquired a stout comb with which she managed her black hair and a washrag which she applied to her clear and even skin. Her face was brown and she wore no makeup, but her eyes and brows were so black that in comparison her face looked more creamy white than brown.

On the trail I often walked with Mira, whose job it was to help mind the sheep, which represented a large proportion of the Kochi wealth, and to swing along beside her as she chattered in Pashto or broken English was delightful. I tried repeatedly to fathom her narrow world and soon discovered that she knew nothing of history or other school subjects and had no desire to learn. But she did not share the apathy of the other Kochis, for she knew much about Central Asia and in all matters affecting the Kochis was an expert. Skilled in trading, witty in negotiation, and a master in the care of animals, she confessed a major sorrow: her clan had but one horse, and it was assigned to Zulfiqar.

"A man like you should not walk with the rest of us," she told me. "In your own country you would be a chief." I asked her not to feel sorry for me and reminded her that I did have a jeep, which in some ways was better than a horse. She considered this for a moment, then concluded, "Where we go a horse is better."

"Don't worry. I like to walk."

"A chief ought to have his own horse. Look at my father! Would he be so powerful without a horse?"

But if there were disappointments in nomad life there were also congenial surprises and none was more appealing than Maftoon, the cockeyed cameleer. We had marched five days toward Musa Darul when I happened to see a camel halted for no reason that I could ascertain. I therefore started across the meadowland to retrieve the beast when I saw, crouched down between her hind legs, Maftoon, with turban awry, mouth open, and on his face an expression of almost heavenly bliss. With his right hand on the camel's teat, he was squirting a flow of milk directly from the udder into his mouth, drinking at the rate of about a quart a minute.

"What the hell are you doing, Maftoon?" I shouted.

"Hungry," he said, halting the flow of milk and looking at me with his good eye.

"Get up! That milk's for the babies." He made no effort to leave his lunch, so I added, "And by the way, Maftoon, I've found out why Aunt Becky tries to bite you so much. You abuse her."

The little man stayed crouched between the camel's legs and looked at me with an expression of sorrow and disgust. "I abuse that beast?" he stammered.

"Yes!" I insisted. "I've listened to you the last three mornings. It's a wonder she didn't gum your arm again."

"You listened . . . to what?"

"To Aunt Becky, complaining of the way you overload her, mistreat her. Damn it all, Maftoon, get away from that camel and listen to me."

Reluctantly the little Kochi left his meal, stood up with his turban reaching his knees, and to my surprise laughed at me. "Tomorrow," he said, "you'll load Aunt Becky." With that he left.

Next morning I was routed out of bed by the little cameleer and taken to where his beasts were being loaded. Aunt Becky, one of the largest animals we had, still rested on the thick callus built up on her chest, her pedestal it was called, and she was loath to leave it, but when she saw that I was to load her, and not her enemy Maftoon, she seemed as happy as a mournful, droopy-eyed, coat-shedding camel could; but as soon as I placed the first blanket on her—it must have weighed about three-quarters of a pound—she let out a sob that would have broken the heart of Nero. It was almost human, a wail of protest against the harshness of the world. I slapped her muzzle, and placed on the blanket a few items that she could hardly have felt, and her groans increased to the point of despair. She really sounded like my own Aunt Becky back in Boston, complaining of the Irish politicians, the Italian grocers, the Jewish merchants, and the ingratitude of her family. "How can I possibly bear this awful burden?" Becky the camel sobbed. No matter what I put on her back, the groans increased, and when she was burdened much more lightly than she had been when running over the desert with my jeep, she struggled to her ungainly feet as if this were her last day on earth; for me she would make that extra little effort and then collapse in a heap before my eyes. I gave her a slap and felt more kindly toward Maftoon. At eleven that morning Aunt Becky was striding along the trail with as much joy as a camel ever exhibits and gave me a pleasant nuzzle as I went past.

The next morning Maftoon summoned me again, and this time as soon as I approached Aunt Becky she became apprehensive that I was about to torture her once more, so I placed on her broad, hairy back a handkerchief. It had barely touched her when she began to rage in protest: "Oh, this is more than a poor camel can bear!" she seemed to say. A stranger listening from a distance would have sworn that I was pushing hot swords into her great bulk, and this kept up all during the loading; so on the third morning I said to Maftoon, "Let's see how much this ugly beast can carry." And this day we loaded her down with well over eight hundred pounds. Her protests were exactly the same; her reluctance to rise identical; and her loping, carefree performance on the trail no different from before. In fact, once we got her started, it was hard to stop her. She loved the heft of the burden and again nuzzled me as I went by. After this indoctrination I decided to leave the camels to Maftoon, and it was well that I did, for when it came time to unload Aunt Becky her dim brain remembered that today she had been mistreated, and she started mauling Maftoon. Luckily he escaped, but soon I saw him naked before the camel while she attacked his clothes. When he was dressed he warned me, "Miller Sahib! You better undress!"

I laughed at the suggestion, but as I approached the huge camel she started for me. Maftoon interceded and, since he had made his peace, saved me. Prudently I undressed and stood by while Aunt Becky kicked the very devil out of my clothes. She bit them, spat on them, and even urinated a little. The next morning we were friends again.

Caravan life provided moments of pride and arrogance: as dawn was breaking we would reach some rise in the trail from which we could look down upon a sleeping village, where dogs would spot us and begin to bark. A few men would appear to see what had agitated the dogs and, seeing the Kochis coming to town, would signal their neighbors, whereupon the villagers would rush about in a frenzy, moving indoors anything that might be stolen. Women in their chaderies would dash out to grab their children lest they be kidnaped, and families would remain cautiously by doorways as women stared through veils waiting for the approaching nomads. An excited hush would fall over the village, at whose outskirts the first Kochi camels were already sniffing.

At such entries Zulfiqar rode at the head of the column, a handsome figure with his rifle slung insolently across his pommel. He affected not to see the frightened families and ignored the pestilent dogs. Behind him came the lumbering camels, with Aunt Becky thrusting her big, inquisitive face from side to side, followed by a large group of Kochi men; then the sheep and most of the women; finally the donkeys, the children, and the rear guard of armed men. It was an impressive caravan when seen in the close confines of a village street, but what outraged the villagers, men and women alike, was the brazen manner in which our nomad women marched handsomely forward with no chaderi.

When Zulfiqar's clan moved through a village we had with us three additional elements for arousing suspicion and disgust: there was Ellen Jaspar, obviously not a Kochi; there was Dr. Stiglitz, and what was he doing in such a motley group; and there was the young American who marched with the beautiful nomad girl in the red dress.

Several times infuriated mountain mullahs dashed among us to spit at Ellen as they had done at Kandahar, but she had since learned to ward them off indulgently. She understood the moral and mental pressures these fanatics were experiencing in a changing world and she wished to do nothing that would exasperate them, but if Zulfiqar saw them coming, he patiently cut them off with his horse, whereupon the long-robed mullahs would back against some mud-walled house and curse our passing.

When the villagers tried to abuse Stiglitz or me they got a sharp surprise: we swore at them in Pashto, claimed to be light-skinned Kochis, and warned them to mind their own business. Sometimes they stopped dead and stared at us, whereupon we laughed and they laughed. Braver men among them would run beside us, asking if we were ferangi, and at such times we would confess that we were German and American, and the animosity would vanish. Occasionally some young man in the village who wanted to comprehend his world would march with us for miles, even to our camp, asking a hundred questions. Such men became our friends, and even if I had not mailed my report to Kabul, these inquisitive men would have got the message to our ambassador, by word of mouth from one village to the next until it crossed Afghanistan. It was such a rumor that had reached Shah Khan in Kabul: "Traveling with the Kochis is a blond ferangi."

We had reached the halfway spot on our march to Kabul when we came upon an especially pathetic village, where I had a chance to see for myself the gentler side of Ellen Jaspar's honest concern with human problems. It was not yet dawn as we moved down the main street, glaring back at frightened faces which peered at us through darkness, and Ellen whispered, "It does my heart good to compare these suspicious villagers with our free nomads."

"I agree. I get a positive bang out of marching through a village like this."

"Just think!" she cried with real intellectual excitement. "In a few years Afghanistan will destroy prisons like this"—she indicated the tight-barred houses—"and the country will go back to the ancient freedom of the caravan."

I should have allowed the subject to drop, but I was struck by a fundamental contradiction in her thinking: the idea that freedom could be preserved only by turning back the clock. I could hear her arguing with Nazrullah at the site of the future dam: *It's a shame that the river must lose its freedom,* refusing to realize that only when the river was harnessed and used could Afghanistan know the real freedom of release from poverty. Therefore I said, "I'm afraid you have it backwards, Ellen. Afghanistan will never gain a single freedom by reverting to the caravan. It will save itself by generating true freedom in the villages."

"How?" she asked with some contempt.

"Roads, books, Nazrullah's electricity."

"Oh, Miller!" she cried passionately. "You misunderstand history and the nature of man. We are born free, like the nomads. But step by step we insist upon crawling into little prisons on little streets in mean little villages. We must destroy these prisons and restore the nomad spirit."

"I'm sorry, Ellen. What you want is impossible. What we must do is go into the villages and rebuild them on a basis of freedom. We must go forward. We can't go back."

"But in Pennsylvania, my father is the village. In Afghanistan these surly people are the village. Will books and electricity cure my father . . . or these clods?"

"Only books and electricity can do it."

She stopped in the middle of the road, pressed her right hand to her mouth, and weighed my arguments. Light from one of the houses, reflecting on her bracelets, flashed across her lovely face. "Miller," she whispered generously, "in part you're right, but you forget that men like my father . . ."

I was not allowed to hear her rebuttal, for out of the shadows darted a pretty little girl of nine or ten, less fearful than her elders. Running through the darkness, she caught Ellen's hand and cried in Pashto, "Your bracelets are beautiful." With a gesture of instinctive warmth, Ellen caught the child, swung her in the air, kissed her, and held her in her left arm while she took off one of her bracelets to give the child.

It was a moment I cannot forget. There in an alien street, beset by enmity, Ellen cradled the child in timeless pose: a lovely young mother holding in the darkness a child who intuitively trusted her; and I was forced to recall Karima as she said: *Ellen knew that I could have children and apparently she couldn't. Dr. Stiglitz will confirm that.* I wondered if this were true, and if so, did it account for her essential barrenness of spirit?

My reflections were shattered by the agonizing shriek of the child's mother, who burst upon us screaming, "The Kochis have stolen my child!"

This was a signal for villagers, long trained to repulse such thefts, to rush at us from many sides, and there was fighting. But what stunned me was the arrival of six or eight determined women in chaderies, moving swiftly through the darkness like avenging furies. Their shadowy forms engulfed Ellen as they tore at her hair, her clothes, her face. One thin figure in a gray chaderi swept in like a ferret and grabbed the child. Seeing that the little girl held a contaminated bracelet, the thin figure tore it from the child's hands and threw it back at Ellen.

"Don't steal our children!" a voice of passion warned. The avengers withdrew, but from the shadows came a gaunt, bearded man rushing belatedly to the brawl and hissing hatred.

"Whores! Whores!" he shouted, maneuvering like a robed ghost in his efforts to spit at Ellen.

Zulfiqar had seen the mullah coming and had deftly swung his horse across the man's trajectory to drive him away. The mullah followed at a distance, screaming impotently; and thus we left the frightened villagers, who remained in excited groups, congratulating each other on having once more thwarted the Kochi kidnapers.

Zulfiqar, concerned over Ellen's welfare, dismounted to assure himself that all was well, and she buried her head in his shoulder, sniffling, "All I wanted to do was give the little girl a bracelet."

"How did it start?" the big Kochi asked indulgently.

"Miller and I were having a peaceful argument . . ."

"About what?"

"I claimed that originally Afghanistan knew the freedom of the caravan, but that willfully the people put themselves in these village prisons under the rule of mullahs."

"You're right about the past."

"Miller claimed that we can never go back to the caravan. That we will know freedom only when the villages have books and roads and electricity."

"He's right about the future," and before Ellen

could protest the decision, he leaped upon his horse to lead our caravan from the niggardly village, but then he galloped back to us and cried, "Some day all of us will live in villages like this. But they will be better villages." And he was gone.

The very next morning I had poetic confirmation that Zulfiqar's vision of the future was more likely than Ellen's, for in the early hours when light was just beginning to break across the peaks of the Koh-i-Baba, we sighted a village where dogs were silent, and we crept upon it unawares and were well inside the confines before we were discovered—great camels lumbering down the main road, peering into windows as the villagers were rising—and at one corner I saw a house lit with candles, and it seemed, there in the shadow of the mountains, like all the warm, homely refuges of the world. It was a small segment of space, walled in against the wandering nomads and the camels. It was one man's home. Not even the soaring freedom of the Kochi tents, pitched beside torrents in the mountain passes, could equal the security of that chance home we saw in the half-darkness of dawn. The village people knew something the nomads would never know, a kind of spiritual freedom, and if they were forced to pay a terrible price for it, perhaps that was their choice.

To my surprise, as I brooded on these matters I looked up to see Zulfiqar, on his brown horse, staring at me and the house, and I think he was remembering our discussion of the morning before, and deciding anew that he and I were right; but a dog began barking, the villagers poured out, and the old antagonism between nomad and villager was resumed.

At first I hadn't realized why the villagers were so apprehensive about locking things up as our caravan approached, but after I had seen flashing Mira at work I understood their antagonism. Whenever we made camp after transiting a village I found that she had acquired some new piece of clothing, or a farm tool, or a kitchen utensil. Ellen once said, "The only thing that child hasn't stolen is a bed. You watch! If somebody leaves a door open some day . . ."

At one camp I caught Mira with a new saw and asked her, "Why do you steal from the villagers?"

"When we march through," she replied, "they look at me with hate and I look right back at them the same way." Then she added, "But do you notice how the men follow me so hungrily with their eyes? They'd like to join the Kochis . . . for one night. I could spit at them!"

Our clan had ten large black tents, but many of the Kochis preferred sleeping on blankets in the open. Zulfiqar, his wife Racha, Ellen and Mira occupied one of the smaller tents, notable because it had an awning held up by two additional poles forming a kind of porch where rugs were thrown and where the camp's social life took place. In the late afternoons, when the animals were at ease, Zulfiqar would sit cross-legged between Racha and Ellen, discussing matters with his people. I often joined them and thus formed the foundation for the friendship which developed between the Kochi leader and me.

He asked me many questions, but I learned more than I taught. The Kochis were Muslims who ignored the tyranny of the mullahs but who held Mecca in as deep regard as any Sunni. As we discussed Islam, with its strong reliance upon nature and a powerful God who motivated all natural things, I better understood how Ellen and Dr. Stiglitz had been able to embrace this religion. One afternoon as we sat under the awning, Ellen said, "I could never explain my apostasy to my parents, and that's the real reason why I can't write to them. You see, I was raised to believe that God personally hovered like an unseen helicopter just above the steeple of the Presbyterian Church on Adams Street in Dorset, Pennsylvania"—I had remarked earlier how she loved to reel off that rubric, as if names alone symbolized the focus of her rebellion

—"and although He was free to keep a weather eye on the Lutheran church down the street, His real responsibility was our congregation. We were the true religion. All else was delusion. I think that if my parents had only once, while I was growing up, intimated that God might also be personally worried about the Jews, I would still be in Dorset. For that would have made sense."

At the end of this rather protracted speech Zulfiqar asked, "Do all American women talk so much?" I said yes and he shrugged his shoulders the way scar-eyed Maftoon did when he couldn't comprehend the behavior of a camel.

The figure of speech Ellen had used disturbed me. Had she spoken with spurious concern for the Jews because Stiglitz had warned her that I was one? In English I asked, "Did Stiglitz tell you I was a Jew?"

"You are?" she shouted in real delight. "Zulfiqar! Miller is a Jew!"

The big leader, his bandoleer and rifle beside him on the rug, leaned forward to inspect me. "You Jewish?" I nodded and he burst into laughter.

Ellen said in Pashto, "You should hear what this big fool believes about Jews!"

Again Zulfiqar laughed, attracting other nomads, who gathered to see what was happening. He stood beside me and compared his large Semitic nose to my small Nordic one. "I'm the real Jew!" he shouted, and other Kochis stepped up to compare their faces with mine. A long discussion followed, at the end of which Zulfiqar asked, "Millair, are Jews really as avaricious as we say?"

I thought a moment, smiled at Ellen and replied, "Let me put it this way. Zulfiqar, if you parked your jeep near a bunch of Jews . . . they'd steal the tires while you weren't looking."

It took some moments for the boldness of my reply to sink in, and some of the lesser Kochis caught on before Zulfiqar. They were loath to react until he had set the pattern, but they obviously relished my gall. Then he exploded in rollicking laughter and imitated a steering wheel. "Millair," he laughed, "you scared us when you started for the jeep. We had most of it packed on camels." Then he stopped laughing and looked suspiciously at Ellen. "How did you know about the jeep?"

"In the bazaar at Musa Darul . . . they tried to sell it back to me." My discovery of their duplicity pleased the Kochis, and from that moment Miller the Jew became blood brother to the Aryan nomads.

But to one obligatory aspect of Kochi life I never did become adjusted. As we marched week after week through the treeless valleys a detail of four women worked at the rear of the caravan, moving back and forth across the landscape, and it was their duty to gather the fresh droppings of the camels, the sheep and the donkeys and with their bare hands to mold the manure into briquettes which were carefully hoarded in the panniers carried by the donkeys; for in a land where there were few trees other fuel had to be found, and dried dung was excellent. It burned slowly, like punk, had a pleasing odor which imparted flavor to food cooked over it, and was light in transportation.

The Kochi children delighted in coming upon dried dung which the sharp-eyed women of some former caravan had overlooked, and it was a kind of game for them to see who would spot the next camel dropping. One day Mira and I were following Aunt Becky, who as usual was straying, when the camel dropped a large deposit which the women would probably miss; so I gritted my teeth, turned my nose away, and scooped up the precious stuff, running it to the panniers, where the women tending the caravan cheered. I was blushing when I returned to Mira, who, when she satisfied herself that no one was spying, threw her arms about me and kissed me for the first time. "You're a real Kochi!" she teased, and thereafter when

I went to her father's awning-porch it was to see her and not to talk with him; and we took long walks among the deserted hills.

Two days after our first kiss, we were hiking up a narrow valley where flowers were in bloom and I thought: The Kochis know only two seasons, the best of spring and the best of autumn. I looked at Mira and asked, "You never know winter, do you?"

She surprised me by pointing to the mountains overhead and saying, "It's always ready to pounce on us." And there it hung, the snowline of the Koh-i-Baba, an ominous threat which reminded me of our impending arrival at Kabul, when I would have to leave the caravan.

I think Mira must have sensed my sadness, for she kissed me ardently, but the moment was spoiled by the sharp voice of Ellen, who said, "You'd better join the others, Mira."

When the little nomad left the valley, Ellen said with some asperity, "You be careful what you do with that girl. One day in India a camel attacked her and in rage she nearly killed it. She takes nothing lightly, and remember . . . she is the chieftain's daughter." Then she added, "She's also much smarter than most of the girls I knew in college."

"Why don't you teach her to read?"

"You be careful what you teach her," she warned.

It was after this intrusion that I first began to notice that Ellen was also becoming involved in matters which could lead to dangerous conclusions, and that when she warned me about Mira she was perhaps thinking not of me but of herself. For example, on the trail she most often walked with Dr. Stiglitz, ahead of the camels; and under the canopy, when we gathered in the afternoons, she took her seat beside him. One of the reasons why Ellen sought out Stiglitz was that at Bryn Mawr she had studied German and French and could thus converse with him in four different languages, and they maintained long discussions on philosophical matters.

I wondered if Zulfiqar took umbrage at this, for I had read in many books that men of the desert were subject to ungovernable passions where their women were concerned, and certainly in normal Afghan life the chaderi and the high wall topped by broken glass proved that the books were right; and I began to fear that my affection for Mira might get me involved in these nomad rages; but the more I watched Zulfiqar the more confused I became, for he certainly did not act like the vengeful, romanticized sheik of fiction. On the contrary, when Ellen and Stiglitz were hiking together, Zulfiqar often rode by on his brown horse, kicking its ribs expertly, and he would occasionally stop to talk but more often he continued past, according them his professional smile, and I got the clear impression that instead of being jealous of Stiglitz, he was somewhat relieved to have in the caravan a man who had spare time for arguing with his second woman.

With me the problem was somewhat different, for Mira was his daughter. I was sure that once or twice he had seen us kissing, and he must have noticed how we always sat together at the tent or at meals, yet he treated Mira and me much as he did the others: infrequent conversation, inevitable smile.

On the night before we reached Kabul, the Kochis prepared a farewell feast for me. Maftoon impressed some men who formed a noisy orchestra for nomad dancing and songs from many trails in Asia. I tried to keep away from Mira, for leaving her was proving to be extremely difficult, and several times I caught myself staring at Stiglitz and Ellen, thinking: They're the lucky ones. Together all the way to Balkh.

That night as I crept into my sleeping bag I asked Stiglitz, "Have you told Ellen what you told me . . . at the pillar?"

"I've told her I can't leave Afghanistan."

"Have you told her why?"

"Sooner or later everyone knows everything," he replied. "The timetable of discovery is not significant."

"That's not true. When I discovered your history . . . in the caravanserai . . . I might have killed you."

"It would have been of no consequence," he said fatalistically.

"How do you feel about me now . . . as a Jew?" I asked.

He considered this for some minutes, while the camels moved about behind us, and at first I thought he had fallen asleep. Then he replied in evasive fashion, "I've given up my home, my family . . ."

"You called her your filthy wife," I reminded him.

"I was speaking of my children," he corrected. "They were different. I surrendered everything . . . profession, opera, a city I loved . . . so in a sense, Herr Miller, I'm a dead man, and dead men have no further responsibility for passing judgments."

I made no comment to this and he continued, "To the Jews I did terrible things. You're a Jew. Believe it or not, Herr Miller, the two facts are completely unrelated. Toward you as a Jew I have no feeling whatsoever. Toward you as a man . . . I'd like to be your friend, Herr Miller."

"Would you stop calling me Herr Miller?" I asked.

"I'm very thoughtless," he said, reaching out from his sleeping bag to grasp my arm. "Please forgive me," he begged, and a cesspool of bitterness began to drain away.

After a long silence he asked, "Do you remember how our discussion at the pillar started? No, I thought not. You were berating me for not having amputated Pritchard's leg at Chahar. I tried to tell you that there are factors in life which go beyond medical comprehension, and I equated Pritchard's determination to die with Sem Levin's determination to live. The point is this, I'm sick with shame and grief over what I did to Sem Levin, because I acted against his will, but I haven't the slightest regret over the case of John Pritchard, because I acted in furtherance of his will. One way or other he had commanded himself to die."

"I'm beginning to see what you're talking about," I admitted.

"With me it's the same way," he added. "I'm dead. If the Russians hang me it's no matter. They're hanging a dead man. But if I'm allowed to live, I have willed myself to be reborn. When you saw me in Kandahar I was a walking corpse, concerned only with my bottle of beer. Now I shall be a human being."

I asked, "Has Ellen accomplished this?"

"Yes," he confessed. "But don't forget, Miller, when you leave us in Kabul you'll be a living man too." He allowed this to sink in, then asked, "Have you ever made love to a woman?"

"Certainly," I lied, counting some frenzied moments in war as qualifiers.

"Well, leaving this nomad girl is going to be a different experience from what you imagine. I am wondering what you will do after Mira vanishes. What will you do, Miller?"

"I'll go back to the embassy," I said brashly. "Pick up where I left off."

"With the smell of camels haunting you? Don't be stupid." He turned over and went to sleep.

From the caravanserai to Kabul had been a distance of some three hundred and fifty miles, which required twenty-five days of marching, but since we occasionally held camp for two or three days at sites with adequate forage, it was not until the middle of May that we came over a pass and saw below us the sprawling capital whose center was filled by the low mountain. I stood with Mira and explained, "My house is over there . . . to the north of that mountain. Tomorrow I'll be sleeping there."

The nomad girl rejected my prediction and took my face in her hands. She kissed me warmly and whispered, "Oh, no, Miller! Tomorrow night you won't be sleeping there."

Few Kochi caravans ever entered Kabul with the advance excitement caused by ours, and as soon as we pitched our black tents in the traditional nomad area some miles west and south of the British embassy, we were visited by three important emissaries. First Moheb Khan, trim and polished in a new Chevrolet, drove out to investigate my report that Ellen Jaspar was traveling with the Kochis, and he consulted lengthily with Zulfiqar and Ellen while Mira and I lingered outside the tent trying to eavesdrop. I remember her asking me, "Who is this Moheb Khan?" I explained that he was an important official who could do her father much harm if he was made angry and she agreed: "He does look very important."

I avoided seeing Moheb, because I did not want to talk with him at that moment, dressed as I was in Afghan clothes; but after he had gone, a lesser official reported to see Dr. Stiglitz, and they sat in a corner of our tent conversing in German, so I did not understand what they were saying, but the upshot was that Stiglitz was not to be arrested or sent back to Kandahar.

Now came my turn, for Richardson of Intelligence drove out after lunch at the British embassy, lit his pipe with infuriating care, stroked his mustache and said in his deep voice, "Miller, I'm afraid there's hell to pay over that jeep." He watched the effect on me and added, "Going to cost you . . . say . . . six hundred dollars. Miller, they stole everything but the name in front. Nazrullah had to make two trips across that desert."

I threw myself on his mercy: "It was stupid, and I know it. But I did feel that Verbruggen would understand."

"The ambassador is raising hell," Richardson confided, and I could feel the boom being lowered.

"What's the bad word?" I asked.

"Well, you saved your neck by that report from Musa Darul. We notified Washington and at least the senator from Pennsylvania's mollified. But the girl's parents! Why doesn't she write to them?"

"She has written . . . several times. I sat over her while she did the last one. But there's so much to explain she tears the letters up. I've drafted this letter, which we can send them, and this complete report."

"Good, and I don't think you need worry too much about the ambassador. Washington's rather pleased that you rescued Miss Jaspar."

"Rescued her? She's never been happier in her life."

"You mean she's staying with the Kochis?" Richardson gasped.

I thought: If I try to explain everything . . . Zulfiqar, Stiglitz, Islam . . . he'll get all balled up. So I said, "I didn't rescue her. She rescued me."

"Now what the hell do you mean by that?" he asked huffily, drawing on his pipe.

"I'll explain in the office tomorrow."

"Now wait a minute," he protested. Then he changed his mind and asked quietly, "Could we take a walk?"

"Why not? I've just walked three hundred and fifty miles."

"Don't you ride the camels?" he asked, and I looked at him with scorn.

When we were far from the tents he said, "Maybe you won't be in the office tomorrow."

"They sending me home?" I asked with a sort of sick feeling.

"No. Washington's come up with a peculiar idea." He paused to let the drama sink in, then sucked his pipe and studied me. "You ever heard of Qabir?"

"No." Then I reflected. Where had I heard that name? I corrected myself: "I've heard the name but I forget where."

"It's an important meeting place of the nomads," he said. "Somewhere in the Hindu Kush."

"Where?"

"Doesn't show on the map."

"Did you ask the British? They know these areas."

"They know it only as a name," he said. "Qabir. Qabir. Does it mean anything at all to you?"

Then I remembered. "One night the chief was ticking off the route of the caravan. Musa Darul, Balkh. And he said he'd be able to use Dr. Stiglitz at Qabir."

"In what capacity?"

"He didn't say."

Richardson walked away from me and kicked pebbles for some time. Then he asked bluntly, "Miller, could you manage some way to stay with the Kochis till they get to Qabir?"

"Why?"

"It's damned important that our side have someone who's been there. We've no information about it except that every summer the nomads gather there, and we think that Russians, Chinese, Tajiks, Uzbeks . . . the lot . . ."

"Supposing I could get there, what do you want me to do?"

"Just look. Find out who the Russians send and how they get across the Oxus."

"I'd stand out like a sore thumb," I protested.

"That may be an advantage," he said. "Think you can arrange to stay with the caravan?"

"Possibly," I evaded, trying not to show the joy I felt at the reprieve.

"If you could," he said cautiously, "I think we'd forget about the jeep."

I said, "I'm not keen on Qabir. Sounds dull. But I've always wanted to see Balkh. Can I come in tonight for some fresh gear?"

"No. We don't want you around the embassy. Tell me what you need and I'll get it."

"Some money, a few vitamin pills, some nose drops . . . boy, your nose dries out . . . and some note pads."

"Don't take any notes on Qabir," he warned.

"I haven't said I could get there," I cautioned. "If there is such a place."

Late that afternoon, while Mira was scrounging the Kabul bazaars, Richardson returned with my gear and a batch of mail, and in a gesture unprecedented for him shook my hand warmly and said with feeling, "Miller, do you even dimly comprehend the opportunity you have? For seven years we've been trying to get to Qabir. So have the British. For God's sake, keep your eyes open."

"What did the ambassador say?"

"He said, 'Imagine such a job going to such a squirt.' " Richardson left, and I swore to myself: Somehow or other, I'm getting to Qabir.

I sat at the edge of my tent in the twilight and wondered what trick I could use for staying with the Kochis, and as I pondered the problem I realized that I wasn't much interested in Richardson's Russians but I was keenly concerned about continuing with Mira. With no plans at all, I felt: Something's bound to work out.

I turned to my mail. Girls had replied to my letters, but now I couldn't even remember their faces. A letter from my father sounded as if Mr. Jaspar were arguing incomprehensibly with Ellen, and provincial Boston matters which had once been of significance were now tedious. How could a group of Kochi women gathering camel dung seem more important than my aunts in Boston? How could my adventures with a gang of nomads and a mixed-up girl from Pennsylvania preoccupy my thoughts? More particularly, how could I manage to stay with Mira?

My problem was unexpectedly solved by Zulfiqar. Accompanied by Dr. Stiglitz he came to my tent and said half apologetically, "The doctor has official permission to stay with us. He's coming to Qabir."

"Where's that?" I asked, trying to appear nonchalant.

"Where the nomads meet each summer. In the Hindu Kush."

"Hope you have a good trip," I said to Stiglitz. "Sounds a long way off."

"It is," the German agreed. "But what we wanted to discuss with you . . . we need a lot of medicine."

I put on a serious face and said, "I suppose you could buy what you need in the bazaar."

"Yes . . ." Zulfiqar said, "if we had the money."

"This time I have no jeep," I reminded him.

"But the American officer . . . when he came, did he give you any money?"

"Yes," I replied, and waited.

"We were wondering," Stiglitz proposed. "Would you buy us the medicine if . . ."

"If what?" I asked cautiously.

"If we took you to Balkh with us?" Zulfiqar suggested.

I wasted time so that it would look as if I were judging the proposal, then asked suspiciously, "How much money would you need?"

"About two hundred dollars," Zulfiqar replied.

"I have a hundred and fifty," I offered, unable to control my excitement at having tricked him into doing what I wanted.

"Good!" he cried, and four hours later he and Stiglitz returned to camp with a cache of drugs and medical implements that would have done justice to a small pharmacy. They had been blackmarketed from as far away as Paris and Manila, and in the areas where we would be heading they'd be worth a fortune.

"You got a lot with my dollars," I observed.

"For what we want to do we'll need a lot," Zulfiqar said briefly. He advised us to get to sleep promptly, for we were off to the high mountains next morning at four.

Stiglitz, tired from the bargaining at the bazaar, followed his advice, but apparently Zulfiqar himself did not, for before I could fall asleep I heard the clatter of horses' hoofs, and since no one was permitted to ride the brown horse but the leader of the clan, it must have been Zulfiqar. There came a scratching at my tent and a boy of eight or nine slipped in to advise me that I was wanted. Throwing a shawl about me, I went out expecting to meet the Kochi but saw instead the stars and a beautiful white horse that Mira was holding for me.

"It isn't right that you should walk, Miller," she said.

"Where'd you get this?" I asked, dumfounded.

"In Kabul," she said softly. "My present to you."

"But, Mira! Where'd you find the money?"

"I was afraid that if you had to walk all the way to Balkh you might leave us," she whispered. "You require a horse, Miller. An important man like you deserves one."

I was about to protest her extravagance when I looked at the right flank of the beast, and there emblazoned deep was the letter W. I was being handed a white horse branded with a memento of the Wharton School in Philadelphia, and when Moheb Khan discovered the theft I could be arrested. I started to upbraid her for having the horse, but I was halted by a powerful doubt as to just how she might have acquired it. I recalled her keen interest in Moheb Khan. Weakly I asked, "How did you know I was staying with the caravan?"

She replied gently, "For days my father and I have been trying to think of some trick that would keep you with us. Last night he told me, 'Go to sleep, Mira. I'll think of something.' "

I thought of my lost hundred and fifty dollars and asked, "You mean that Zulfiqar was trying to get me to stay with the caravan?"

"Yes," she whispered. "How did he manage it?"

"In a very interesting way," I replied.

Slowly, gently she took my hand and told the little boy that it was now time for him to leave us, and she led me and the white horse far from camp to a spot where that afternoon she had cached a blanket and I noticed for the first time that from somewhere—probably the bazaar in Kabul—she had stolen a bottle of perfume, and in a wild embrace we found each other. For each of us, I discovered, it was the introduction to love, under a full moon on the high plateau of Asia; so that when toward four the next morning we headed back toward camp, I had the most persuasive reason in the world for accompanying the Kochis to Balkh.

13

For many centuries there had been a circuitous highway leading from Kabul to the historic Vale of Bamian, where Buddhism had flourished centuries before the birth of Muhammad, and gifted travelers from the age of Alexander to the present had described the rugged beauties of this road; but Kochis avoided it, for they knew a caravan route which climbed directly into the Koh-i-Baba, a route so spectacular, passing as it did through gorges and along cliffs, that its grandeur was reserved for those who traveled in the ancient caravan manner. So far as I know, this road has never been described in books, because only Kochis used it, and they did not write.

The mountains were fifteen and sixteen thousand feet high, forbidding bulwarks whose peaks no man had climbed, and wherever we looked they dominated the view; it seemed unlikely that anyone could penetrate them, let alone a caravan of camels. But under Zulfiqar's experienced guidance we headed for one apparently solid wall after another and somehow each barrier provided us with one lucky escape: sometimes a gorge, sometimes a green valley that opened dramatically to the north.

Now the animals grew fat on abundant grass and on some days even the camels modified their grumbling. I spent hours watching our fat-tailed sheep, those preposterous beasts that looked not like sheep but like small-headed beetles stuck onto very long legs. They derived their name from an enormous tail, perhaps two feet across and shaped like a thick country frying pan covered with wool and rich with accumulated lanolin. The tail bumped up and down when the sheep walked, a grotesque afterpiece that served the same function as a camel's hump: in good times it stored food which in bad times it fed back to the animal. I was told that the lanolin was not solid but could be moved about with the hands; certainly it could be eaten, as we proved in our pilaus, but now that the tails were at their maximum they made the ugly sheep seem like something an ungifted schoolboy had scratched on a tablet, and as I sat watching the huge bustles bounce up and down I used to speculate on how the beasts managed to copulate. To this day I don't know.

Our fat-tails were made to look even more farcical by the fact that we occasionally overtook the caravan of some mountain tribe with a flock of karakul sheep, those superbly built patricians with long necks, expressive faces, deep-set eyes and soft ears. They were the finest animals in Afghanistan and were extremely valuable, since karakul skins were a major item in the nation's trade with the outside world. Whenever one examined the fortunes of men like Shah Khan in Kabul, it was usually found that their wealth derived in some way from karakul. The wool of the older animals was not impressive and had, so far as I know, no particular value, but newborn lambs were covered with the silky, close-matted, curly fur that is treasured in all countries; and to compare these aristocratic sheep with the ungainly fat-tailed clowns of our caravan was all to our disadvantage. I asked Zulfiqar why we had no karakuls and he explained, "I'd like to, but the desert marches would kill them."

Because the mountains of the Koh-i-Baba grew increasingly difficult for the caravan—camels growled at rocky areas—we made shorter journeys than before and were inclined, when we found good pasture, to halt for three or four days. It was in these periods of rest, these peaceful days in the high mountains, that Mira and I had our good times. We would leave my white horse in camp for the children to ride and with a chunk of nan would hike to some higher plateau where we would lie in the cold sun, talk and make love.

To be with Mira was a primitive joy. By now I was able to share her concern with matters of the caravan: "Where should we stop?" "When will the ewes throw their lambs?" "Could you live in a village like the one we saw yesterday?" It was her opinion that six weeks of village life beneath a chaderi would kill her, a judgment that I was prepared to accept.

She was like an elf, old enough to be married but young enough to run after a herd of camels with a stick. She had shown no inclination to accept any of the nomad men as her mate, nor did she think of me as a potential solution. On the fifth day north of Kabul she said, "It would be pleasant if you could ride with us forever, Miller. On the trail you're a strong man."

When I asked her how Kochis organized their marriages she said, "We don't usually consult mullahs. A young man goes to an older man like my father and says, 'I want your daughter Mira. How many sheep do I get if I take her?' Or he may demand some camels. Of course, if they do get married he stays with the clan. That way the animals don't leave. Neither does the daughter."

"Is there a feast?" I asked, still uncertain as to what the ceremony consisted of.

"Drums, flutes, a roasted sheep. The children get colored candies and the bride two new sets of clothing. When I marry I'll get a black skirt."

"Ellen wears a black skirt. Is she married to your father?"

"Oh, no! He didn't give her the black skirt. Racha did, out of kindness, because Ellen's were wearing out."

"Did Racha give her the bracelets, too?" I asked idly as we lay looking at the white clouds seeping over the edge of the Koh-i-Baba as its peaks watched us from the north. Mira explained that Zulfiqar had given Ellen the bracelets, but I did not hear her full reply, for I was thinking: I've been with them eight weeks and not a moment of rain. Not even a cloud. What an amazing world, drifting along like this year after year. Then an irritating thought oppressed me: What's so amazing about it? They probably have the same kind of days in Arizona. But I found consolation in one fact: In Arizona they don't have Mira.

As I ended my soliloquy, she ended her explanation of the bracelets, then asked pertly, "If somebody asks you, 'How did you join the Kochis, Miller?' what will you say?"

"I'll say, 'For the first part of the trip, I had to join because somebody stole my jeep.' "

"Did you know that I helped take off the wheels? When we sold them at Musa Darul I got some of the money."

"For the second part of the trip . . . that's more difficult to explain. Maybe I'll say, 'A beautiful Kochi girl bought me with a white horse.' "

Mira kissed me and ran to a brook to catch a drink of fresh mountain water, bringing me some in her felt cap. "How did you get that horse?" I asked, with a nagging memory of Moheb Khan and the possessive way he had taken the arm of the Swedish girl Ingrid.

"With the money I got from stealing the jeep, I bought the horse. Isn't that fair? Lose a jeep, find a horse?"

My recollection of Moheb Khan reminded me of

Nazrullah and I asked, "Did you ever meet Ellen's husband, Nazrullah?"

"I saw him. He has a beard."

"Did your father meet him?"

"Why should he? As my father told you in the caravanserai, we made a three-day camp at Qala Bist . . . because of the desert ahead. At the end of the three days Ellen asked Zulfiqar if she could come with us. Up to then she had never spoken to him, so he had nothing to do with her running away. It was us she loved, the caravan and the camels and the children. It was much later that he allowed her to sleep in his tent."

"Was Racha angry?"

"Why should she be? He allowed her to stay in the tent, too."

"Are Ellen and your father . . ." I didn't know the Kochi words and started again. "Is she his woman?"

"Of course," Mira laughed, using the vulgar Kochi gesture for sexual intercourse. "But not like you and me. Not for great fun under the stars."

"Does she love your father?" I persisted.

"Everybody loves my father," she said simply. "In some clans men try to kill each other. Not in ours. But she doesn't love him the way I love you, Miller." To demonstrate the difference, she grabbed me and we ended up rolling on the ground, then seeking a protected crevice in the rocky walls.

It was tacitly understood that Mira and I would not embarrass Zulfiqar by sleeping together in the camp, since he chose to ignore his daughter's misalliance. We were therefore driven to sleep in the open and it became customary for Mira to make a show of going to bed in Zulfiqar's tent, while I did the same in mine, and then later for her to throw pebbles against the black felt, whereupon I would drag out my sleeping gear and lug it beyond the camels, where we would sleep till just before the break of camp.

Strangely, it was in daylight on the trail that I experienced my deepest sense of love for Mira, and I find it difficult to explain why; but when I was riding the white horse, moving up and down the column like Zulfiqar, I would occasionally overtake Mira when she did not see me, and for some minutes I would watch her, swinging along the road in her loose sandals, her shawl falling across her shoulders and her black pigtails bobbing in the sun, and I would recognize her as the freest human being I would ever know. She envied no one, loved whom she wished, took what she needed, concerned herself only with the immediate problems at hand, and lived on the high plateaus where nature was superb or on the edges of the desert where life was as clearly outlined as man ever sees it. Then she would hear me, and she would look over her shoulder at her man on the horse she had acquired for him, and in her look was both equality and pride, and it was sharing that look which made me feel so much a man. I had survived the war as a courageous boy; on the caravan trails, riding through the Koh-i-Baba on a white horse, I discovered what it was to be a man.

We had been traveling like this for five or six days when I began to detect a marked change in Dr. Stiglitz. The apprehension I had noticed in Kandahar and Musa Darul, when he worried about his tobacco and his beer, had left him, and the strong sense of guilt that had characterized him at the caravanserai was gone. He strode briskly along the trail without turban or karakul, his steel-gray hair close-cropped for sun and wind to play upon. At times he looked even happy, in a studied Germanic manner, and made overtures to extend the mutual respect which had begun to develop on that last night before we reached Kabul.

One day he left his position at the head of the camels and fell back to talk with me. Ignoring Mira in his German manner, he said, "A man could march on like this forever."

I suggested, "Maybe it's because your health is better . . . the open air."

"I place no great reliance on exercise," he assured me professionally. "In Munich I lived perfectly happily walking a few blocks from my home to my office." He lost himself in contemplation of those good, gone days before the war, then added significantly, "I think what accounts for the difference is the confession I made to you at the caravanserai. To be able to tell those things to a Jew . . ."

"You feel you've purged yourself?" I asked coldly.

"No, Miller! Remember, when we spoke I didn't know you were a Jew. Of what I did I can never purge myself. But I can learn to live with history . . . to accept its full burden. That I'm doing."

"Why was the release deferred until this trip? The evil occurred years ago."

"Ah, so!" he agreed. "But always before I was preoccupied with myself. Could I get out of Germany? Could I enter Persia? Would I be caught and hanged?" He shuddered. "I was pathetic, involved only with myself and my tobacco and my beer."

I asked him what specifically had led him beyond himself, and he said, "Fighting with you in the serai. For years Sem Levin had been a ghost hanging upon my throat. But fighting with you by the pillar made Jews real again . . . quit them from being ghosts. I killed a man . . . a living man, but I've paid the penalty. The caravan moves on."

I said bluntly, "I hate to think I enabled you to exorcise your ghosts."

"You did. The caravan moves on. Germany moves on. In a few years America will be begging Germany for friendship. Strange, isn't it?"

"You think this erases the past? A fist fight with a Jew?"

"In a sense, yes. We can bear terror only so long. Then it goes away, either because one fights with a Jew, or because one makes a trip with Kochis, or because the calendar reads 1946 instead of 1943. The pillar remains standing in the serai, with the bodies sealed inside, but in the sunlight the nomads graze their flocks." He looked at me in triumph as he cried to the encroaching mountains, "The terror goes away."

Then, still ignoring Mira, he stopped on the rocky trail and asked, "Miller, as a final act of contrition, may I kiss the hand of Sem Levin?"

I was repelled, but when I saw how much he needed this act of absolution, I had to say, "Yes." As the animals moved past us he knelt on the rocks and kissed my hand. When he rose I clasped his shoulder and said, "What you say is true, Dr. Stiglitz. The terror does go away. I no longer look at you as a depraved animal. You're one of us . . . one of us."

He nodded and walked on to resume his customary place with Maftoon and the camels; but when he was gone, shrewd Mira, to whom he had not once spoken, said in Pashto, "He talks a lot, but his real trouble is . . . he's in love with Ellen. Pretty soon . . ." and she made the Kochi sign for sex.

I asked, "What will happen if they do?"

"You mean?" and she made the sign again.

"Yes."

"Maybe my father kill him," she said without emotion. She told me of the time Maftoon's wife had fallen in love with a bazaar man in the Indian town of Rawalpindi, and Zulfiqar had beaten her savagely, so that she had crawled away from the caravan and gone to hide with the townsman. But Maftoon had followed her and knifed the bazaar man to death. "That's his wife over there," Mira said placidly, and I looked at one of the four women gathering camel dung, a woman somewhat older than Racha, vibrant, laughing, handsome, with a gold medallion piercing the right side of her nose. She suspected that Mira was speaking of her and she came to us in great peasant strides.

"What's that one telling you?" she demanded.

"That Maftoon killed a man . . . for you."

"He did," she laughed. "He broke off this tooth, too," and she showed me the stump. "I'd never have been happy in the city." Then she winked at me and warned, "You go away from Mira, Mira kill you, too."

When she returned to the camel droppings Mira laughed and said, "I'm not so foolish. When the time comes, you go. When the time comes, I go."

For two days I studied Stiglitz and Ellen as carefully as possible, and I had to admit that Mira was right. They were in love and Zulfiqar knew it. So far he had kept the German from the tent and of course Ellen was not free to leave her bed at night as Mira did, but I looked for an opportunity to warn her of the danger she was inviting, for in spite of his seeming acquiescence I was convinced that Zulfiqar would kill Stiglitz if honor required.

I had never seen Ellen looking so radiant. We were now in cold country, well above ten thousand feet, with snow only a short distance above us and occasionally in some high pass actually nipping at our ears, and Ellen had acquired a long gray burnoose like those worn by Tajik mountaineers. It was made of raw wool and reached to her ankles; so that even in very cold weather it was comfortable. Into its attached hood Racha had worked gold and silver threads, showing Ellen's lovely blond head to good advantage, and when she rode my white horse, as she sometimes did when I wished to walk with Mira, she created the image of a fair young goddess leading her Aryans to some mountain fortress. I understood why Dr. Stiglitz had fallen in love with her.

Well before dawn on the ninth day out of Kabul I was lugging my sleeping gear back to the camels for loading when I saw that Ellen was standing in the darkness, watching for a chance to talk with me, so I wandered over to her and asked, "You need some help?"

"Not in packing," she replied. "But could we talk?"

I threw my gear to Maftoon and told him, "You can ride the white horse," whereupon Ellen and I started down the trail.

It was a matchless time for the discussion of ideas, since we were about to enter one of the noblest areas of Asia, the great Vale of Bamian. Because we were approaching it in darkness from the west, we would be hiking toward the sunrise, and the silvery cliffs on the north would loom out of the shadowy world just as our bodies and our incorporate thoughts came into being from their own universe of shadow. But it was the vale itself that lured us on: a lush, irrigated valley of historic richness from which Buddhism had spread to China and Japan, a vale crowded with trees and cool brooks and pasture lands. It was lined with poplars like a formal Italian garden, and to come upon it in the darkness, when each step revealed new beauties, when the approach of the still-distant sun brought more and more illumination both to the vale and to the problems we carried to it, was an experience not to be forgotten.

In the darkness Ellen cried, "Miller, I've fallen in love!" and the anguish of her cry, the honest perplexity it echoed, had to be respected.

"Mira told me . . . some time ago."

"We've tried to keep it secret . . . even from ourselves."

"Mira says you could invite great danger," I warned.

"I'm not concerned with danger," she said boldly. "I left Bryn Mawr seeking something like this. I left Qala Bist for the same reason. Now that I've found it . . ."

We hiked in darkness, with now and then a fugitive ray of light streaking across the sky like a scout sent forward by some Mongol army. In the gloom Ellen cried, "Miller! What shall I do?"

The pleading in her voice enlisted my sympathy and I tried to be as helpful as possible. "Let me ask your question another way," I suggested. "What are you already doing . . . hiking along a caravan trail at four-thirty in the morning in Central Asia? Ellen, what are you doing?"

She became defensive and countered, "I might ask you the same question."

"With me it's easy. I was sent here. By the government. To find you."

In the darkness she laughed. "Oh, no! The government didn't send you here. It sent you to Qala Bist, but you came here on your own account." Something of the gentleness that had marked her beginning observations now vanished and she added with some asperity, "You're here because for the first time in your circumscribed little life you're sleeping with a wonderful girl, and I don't blame you a bit. But please don't try to convince Aunt Ellen that the United States government told you, 'Go out and sleep under the stars.' "

"That takes care of me. Now what about you?"

Her gentleness returned, and as new streaks of light appeared in the east she explained, "I was driven here. It wasn't Nazrullah, who was a most considerate husband, and it wasn't Zulfiqar, whom any girl could admire. It had nothing to do with love or men. I suppose I was driven here by what I saw happening in the world . . . I was driven by something I was powerless to fight."

I listened, tried to understand, walked for some time in silence, then said, "Ellen, I've done my damnedest to analyze your behavior, and I've failed. When we were in Kabul I turned in my official report, so this discussion concerns only you and me. Can you please explain in simple words?"

"I don't think so," she replied thoughtfully. "Either the words I've already used trigger your intellect or they don't. Either you intuitively feel that America is making terrible mistakes, or you don't."

"Well, I don't feel it. America's doing a damned good job."

"I'm talking to an idiot," she groaned in the darkness. "Dear God! I need help so desperately, and You send me an idiot."

"Try it again," I said with resignation. "In the simplest words you can muster."

"I will," she said softly. "Miller, don't you see that we're bound to build bigger bombs and then bigger bombs and finally bombs so big that we can destroy the whole world?"

"What you say could be true, but I take consolation in the fact that America is building those bombs and not somebody else."

"Miller!" she screamed. "Do you think no one else can build them?"

"Of course they can't. Russia? China? They'll never have the technical skill."

"Miller!" she shouted. "Don't be an idiot! We're talking about your soul and mine. Don't you see that . . ."

"Who's been feeding you this line? Stiglitz?"

"Yes, he says . . ."

"Does he also say that he was a Nazi . . . in charge of killing Jews?"

"Yes," she replied softly. "And that's why I must live with him . . . the rest of my life."

I was so infuriated with her garbled nonsense that I raised my hand to slap her, but in the half-light she saw it and drew back. "Talk sense," I growled.

The sun, as if eager to provide an illumination which we could not find for ourselves, crept toward the eastern horizon and sent shafts of light high across the heavens. Ellen, happy that the night was ending, shook the gold and silver cowl from her head and allowed the twilight to play upon her shimmering hair. Looking at me in deep confusion of spirit she said, "I am talking sense. Promise me that no matter what I say in the next few minutes . . . no matter how I outrage your logic, you'll listen and try to understand."

"Out of sheer curiosity, I will."

"Let's say I was a girl growing up in a normal family, in a normal church, with a normal group of friends. Boys liked me, and teachers too. I went to dances, gave parties, did well in college. But one day when I was about fifteen . . . long before the war . . . I saw that everything my family did was irrelevant. We were keeping score . . . I can't call it anything else . . . in a game that simply didn't exist except in our imagination. Did that idea ever occur to you?"

"No."

"I'm sure it didn't," she replied, without rancor. "Well, World War II came and I listened to such nonsense as men rarely display in public. I kept my mouth shut, primarily because Father took it so seriously. He was home safe . . . too old to fight. So he could be pretty heroic. As chairman of the draft board he gave a rousing speech to all the young men he sent away. It would have moved you deeply, Miller. Some of the boys my age told me, 'Your old man makes you want to march right out and do your job . . . and his.' Some of my classmates weren't so dumb."

"Some of my classmates weren't so dumb either," I snapped. "I remember a philosophy major named Krakowitz. He said, 'There's only one thing worse than winning a war. That's losing it.' It was his opinion that when you were fighting Hitler, Mussolini and Tojo it might be true that nobody could win, but it was also true that if you lost, it could be real hell. Krakowitz. He died at Iwo Jima."

"I'm deeply touched," she said, bowing in the morning twilight. "So in college I met this gang of kept professors. What else can you call them? Their moral responsibility was to dissect the world, but they were paid to defend it. I suppose they had a job to do . . . learn, earn; pray, stay; live, give. They had one hell of a system going for them, those professors.

"But there was one who used to drop hints that he

knew the world needed dissecting, and he caught on to me very fast. Taught music and wrote to my parents that I was rejecting the world. Boy, was he right! Father bullied him in his best draft-board manner and pointed out that I was doing all right in my 'real' classes. Reminded me of the passage in Plato where citizens looked so long in the mirror they confused image with reality. It never occurred to Father that this befuddled music master was looking at the real world while the others were marking me on attributes that would never matter . . . not even when Gabriel blows his horn."

She paused, leaving me space to confute her if I wished, but I was so befuddled by her succession of comment—as compared to the ease with which Mira accepted the life of the caravan, and to hell with what was bothering London or Tokyo—that I refrained from entering the argument. I had asked for an explanation, and I was getting it, whether I understood it or not. She continued, "When the worst part of the war arrived, my vision was confirmed. I don't know why I wanted to marry Nazrullah. For one thing, in those days I hadn't discovered that he was exactly like my father. Dear Nazrullah! He'll have paved roads in Afghanistan yet. I suppose I came here because Afghanistan was as far from American values as I could get." She paused, then added a curious comment: "The fact that Nazrullah already had a wife made the decision easier. Do you follow me?"

"I'm lost," I confessed.

"What I mean is, my father described anything out of the ordinary as ridiculous, and I wanted to outrage his whole petty scale of judgment. What was the most ridiculous thing I could do? Run off with an Afghan who had a turban and another wife." She laughed a little, then added, "Do you know what started my disillusionment with Nazrullah? That turban. He wore it in Philadelphia for show. He'd never think of wearing it in Kabul."

"I still don't understand," I replied.

"Lots of young people in America will," she assured me. "They're beginning to reject any society built by men like my father."

"Then God help America," I said bitterly.

"It's the young people like me who will save America," she responded. "They'll understand what's happening, and they'll change things."

I was pondering this chicanery of mind and thinking: I have to respect the passion of her thought and the sincerity with which she advances it, but I certainly distrust the logic—when the sun burst above the horizon and poured some much-needed light into the Vale of Bamian, illuminating the series of white limestone cliffs that rimmed the northern boundary. They rose high above the vale and were deeply eroded, so that shadows played across them in fascinating variety. The green poplars that grew so plentifully elsewhere stopped at the cliffs, alowing them to stand forth in sharp relief. Then, as the sun grew brighter, Ellen called, "Miller! Look!"

At first I did not see what had startled her, since I was looking for some ordinary thing. Then, looming from a gigantic niche cut in the face of the tallest cliff, appeared a towering statue of a man, many scores of feet high, wonderfully carved from the living rock. It was apparently a religious figure of heroic proportions, but what gave it an eerie quality was the fact that its enormous face had been chopped away: lips and chin remained, big as human beings themselves, but all above was a flat expanse of limestone.

While we stood in awe before the towering statue, the rest of the caravan drew up, permitting Zulfiqar to point with his gun at the faceless figure and announce, laconically, "Buddha."

The caravan moved on to its accustomed tenting space, but Ellen and I remained staring at the hypnotic figure. I asked her to stand for comparison by the mammoth feet while I stood back to calculate how tall the statue was: my rough guesswork yielded about a hundred and fifty feet. Who had carved it here in the heart of a Muslim country? Who had chopped away the benign face?

I was not to find an answer to these questions, but as we studied the gigantic statue I became aware that the cliff beside it was honeycombed with caves, whose windows were literally peppered across the limestone. "What are they?" I asked, and Ellen suggested this might at one time have been a monastery. We looked some more and found an opening which seemed to lead to the caves, and Ellen indicated that she would like to explore them.

We entered a dark shaft that led upward through solid rock and after much climbing and skirting of precipitous ledges came to a small wooden bridge that carried us to the top of Buddha's head. We were now far above the earth and a fall would have been disastrous, but we perched safely on the god's head, surveying the vale that opened out before us. In the distance, in bright sunlight, we could see our tents going up.

From the head we found another passageway leading eastward to an interlocking nest of larger caves, which in the old days must have been lecture halls seating hundreds of monks. We found one especially lovely room whose windows, a hundred feet above the earth, framed a view of the Koh-i-Baba, and it was here that Ellen sat cross-legged on the rocky floor, her burnoose covering her body, as she resumed her argument with me.

"When you see the world for the pathetic thing it is"—at the moment I was at the window, inspecting one of the most glorious views in Asia—"my mother used to tremble with gratification when we bought a bigger car than the one before or a college missing the whole point of education but congratulating itself on a million-dollar dormitory . . ." She was trapped in a sentence from which there was no escape and laughed nervously. "You decide to turn your back on the whole thing and find some simpler base. I thought Nazrullah was simpler than Dorset. Zulfiqar was simpler than Nazrullah. And now Otto Stiglitz is simpler than all."

"How can you say that? The man's an M.D. from a good university."

"He's simpler because he's a non-man. In Munich he descended into hell. He's carried the memory of it halfway around the world. He's fought free of the world and its burden. He's a non-man . . . the thing from which we begin all over."

"Do you really believe this nonsense?" I pleaded.

"You're the way I used to be, Miller," she said condescendingly. "You honestly think that someone up there is keeping score on your life. If you learn fifteen new birds, you get a merit badge. If you study calculus, you make the junior honor role. If you keep your nose clean in the navy, the old man signs a favorable letter. If you obey the ambassador, he may sign another favorable letter. All these little credits are entered in a big book by what some sportswriter called the Divine Scorekeeper. It's a comforting theory . . . made my father very happy. He built up points and got a bigger car. Because he had the big car he was entitled to a bigger house. He won the house, so he was voted into the country club. And because he was in the country club his daughter was welcomed at Bryn Mawr. See where it leads? If his daughter does well at Bryn Mawr she's entitled to marry Mark Miller, who by the same series of tricks earned the points to enter Yale. Now see what happens? His daughter and Mark Miller have got to start collecting their points, and if they don't, the old folks will be scared stiff.

"No, Miller, you're betting on the wrong game. There's no scorekeeper. Nobody really gave a damn whether or not you kept your nose clean in the navy. And when we reach Balkh and you walk out on Mira, the Divine Scorekeeper ought to kick the living bejeezus out of you and set your score back to zero for having been such a swine. But He won't. Because the Scorekeeper, supposing there is one, will be laughing at what's happened and observing to His cronies, 'That boy Miller's a damned sight better kid than when he joined the caravan.' And at Balkh, when you leave Mira, I too shall leave . . . but I'll go with Otto Stiglitz."

I looked at the old lecture hall in which we sat; from here wisdom had been poured to the ends of the nations, as they then existed, and I felt morally certain that every lesson propounded in this classroom, this curious cell in the beehive of the monastery where men spent years surrounded by rock, out of touch with the earth until their passions were burned away and their vision clarified—almost every lesson had refuted what Ellen was saying. The wisdom of the world, whether Buddhist, Muslim, Christian or Jewish, insisted that there were desirable ends, that society was worth preserving no matter how badly scarred at a given moment in time, and that there was a Divine Scorekeeper, man himself perhaps, who did judge some deeds as better than others. To the ancient lessons which came to us from this lecture hall in the cliffs of Bamian I was committed, and if Ellen Jaspar was not, the more pity I felt for her.

"Have you slept with Stiglitz?" I asked bluntly.

"No, but I shall when he asks me."

"I suppose you know that Mira's afraid Zulfiqar might kill Stiglitz . . . or you."

"That's of no consequence to either of us."

"It is to me," I countered.

"But you tried to kill Stiglitz yourself."

"I've grown beyond that."

"Miller! That's what I mean. That's the first sensible thing you've said on this trip. Now can you understand me when I say that Stiglitz and I have grown beyond your prejudices? We have, Miller. We are cleansed of this world, and whether Zulfiqar kills us or not is of no significance."

"Might it be of significance to Zulfiqar?" I asked.

Ellen grew grave and said, "That's a difficult question. I had no moral right to intrude on Nazrullah, but I excused myself by remembering that he had a wife and a daughter."

"He now has a son, too."

"Oh, Karima must be so happy!" she cried spontaneously. "He wanted a son so much. Well, I also admit I had no right to intrude on Zulfiqar, but he can stand it. He has a good family and a caravan which couldn't exist without him. But Otto Stiglitz has nothing . . . hardly even a job. It's through his regeneration and mine that the world has a fighting chance. Frankly, Miller, with men like you and Nazrullah and Zulfiqar the world neither gains nor loses. You're of no moral significance whatever."

I asked, "You know that Stiglitz could be extradited . . . and hanged?"

"Yes. For that very reason he needs me most. But one of the good aspects of living in a non-nation like Afghanistan is that they don't extradite non-men who have already died."

"At Balkh we're only a few miles from Russia. He could be kidnaped."

"Civilized nations don't kidnap," she argued, and I thought it indicative that she rejected civilization when it suited her philosophy to do so, but fled to it for protection of her desires.

"You forget—or did he tell you?—that he kept day-by-day records of his experiments. 'I'm a real scientist,' he boasted, 'I keep records.' The English have those records, you know. He's a prime war criminal."

"You've stated my case for me, Miller. He's already convicted and dead. I've rejected all the lives I've known, so I'm dead too. I can live only at the bottom . . . at the bottom dregs of an insane world. Where hope is being reborn. Does this at last make sense?"

"No," I said.

"It's strange you're so obtuse," she reflected sorrowfully. She rose and went to the far end of the cave, drawing her burnoose about her as if it were an academic robe. "Every honest teacher who stood on this spot lecturing to his students is listening now to what I'm saying. They're applauding. They know that society becomes corrupt and that men must reject it if they are to remain free. They know that life, to replenish itself, must sometimes return to the dregs, to the primitive slime. The men who stood here know that I am right, even if I can't make you listen."

As she left the cave, she waved to the unseen docents who had instructed generations of Buddhist monks in this rock-girt university, those savants who were already dead and buried centuries before America and Dorset, Pennsylvania, were known. "They'll understand," she whispered, and smiling left them.

❁

14

On the second day north of Bamian I had finished checking the caravan on my white horse and had ridden off casually to explore a lateral valley, when I saw two figures climbing over the rocks above me. I was about to hail them but stopped, for when I rode closer I saw that they were Ellen Jaspar and Dr. Stiglitz, and I sensed intuitively that this day they did not wish either companionship or surveillance. I became sure of this when they turned a corner which would hide them from the caravan and ran to each other in hungry embrace. In a moment the German started undressing Ellen, and I withdrew unseen.

I would have returned to the caravan, except that as I rode away a pebble fell from the rocks and struck me, and then another, and I realized that someone perched on the high ledges overlooking the lovers was trying to signal me. I reined in the horse, scanned the rocks above me, and spotted a figure in red dress and pigtails. It was Mira, who, having anticipated the intentions of the lovers, had gone into the valley before them to sequester herself at a vantage point from which she could observe the proceedings.

I waved to her angrily: Get off that ledge! But she pressed her fingers against her lips, cautioning silence; then, after watching the lovers for some minutes, she raised her hands triumphantly above her head and made the Kochi sign for successful sexual intercourse. And so the four of us remained gripped in the mountains, Ellen and Stiglitz in their long-delayed passion, Mira spying on them from the overhanging ledge, and I watching her gestures from the valley below. It was one of the most erotic moments I had ever known, but it was colored by a sense of tragedy, for I was convinced that if Zulfiqar discovered their passion, Ellen and her German doctor were self-committed to disaster.

After the lovers rejoined the caravan, I signaled Mira to scramble down from her ledge and join me on the white horse. "You mustn't mention this to the others," I warned.

"They know," she laughed, gripping me about the waist as we galloped back to the caravan.

"How could they know unless you tell them?" I demanded.

"Anybody can look at those two and know," she insisted.

And she was right. By noon, when Zulfiqar halted the caravan, it was known throughout the clan that the long-predicted encounter had taken place and we awaited the consequences. Since Zulfiqar was much larger than Dr. Stiglitz and could presumably strangle him if he wished—I thought it incredible that any woman should trade in the great Kochi for the insignificant German—I supposed there would be a savage beating if not a murder, but to my surprise nothing happened. In the succeeding days Ellen became an increasingly beautiful woman, lovelier even than her high-school photographs or my first sight of her in the caravanserai. Her smile grew more warm. Her freedom of movement was enhanced. Even the manner in which she wore her long gray burnoose became more feminine and alluring, but I remember best the way her blue eyes sparkled during the long uphill hikes.

When Zulfiqar failed to react to their affair, the lovers grew more bold. They began sleeping in the doctor's gear under the stars, along the edge of camp, and in the afternoons Stiglitz no longer went to sit with Zulfiqar and Racha beneath the tent awning. The effect of this upon the German was profound and with one exception good. He was no longer so obviously preoccupied with himself, and often when he fumbled with matches while lighting his pipe, he smiled. His nervousness disappeared and he would sometimes lean against the pole in our tent and actually relax.

The only ill effect occurred on the march, for whenever Zulfiqar rode by on his brown horse, Stiglitz tensed himself in case the big Kochi should leap upon him with dagger unsheathed. No amount of inner glow could halt this involuntary reflex, and I thought: They started this mountain-top love affair as nonpeople indifferent to Zulfiqar, but the deeper they fall in love, the more scared they become.

The march from Bamian to Qabir required eleven days along the most spectacular portion of the caravan route: we were penetrating the heart of the Hindu Kush, and while there were taller mountains in Asia—indeed, the Pamirs, the Karakorams and the Himalayas were all higher—none surpassed these mountains of Afghanistan for their combination of rocky grandeur and valley charm. Sometimes we would swing around the end of a ridge and see before us ten or fifteen miles of green valley without a single indication that men had ever been there before. At other times the trail would narrow to an ugly defile down which a river tumbled, and the trail would halt abruptly against the face of a cliff, but a rickety bridge built years ago by nomads would carry it across the river and send it onto higher land. It was exciting, fresh, magnificent.

One aspect of the Hindu Kush reminded me of the desert. On the fifth day north of Bamian we rounded a corner on the trail to see before us a valley of some magnitude. At the far end, say four miles away, rose a striking mountain, and I thought: We'll probably camp under that mountain at noon. But when noon came, the near-at-hand mountain was a few miles away. On the next day we resumed march and at noon the elusive peak was still a few miles distant. So on the following day we plugged along until the mountain was almost near enough to touch, but when another day arrived, the damned mountain was still ahead of us! It finally took us four full days and fifty miles of marching to reach a spot which at first had looked as if we would overrun it before lunch.

During the days when we were trying to reach the mountain I saw little of Ellen Jaspar, for she and Stiglitz were so preoccupied with their burgeoning affair that I had no wish to intrude, and we spoke only occasionally when we met lugging our sleeping gear to and from the tents. Then on the day we finally reached the mountain, Ellen came to me as we were unpacking and made the comment which first set me wondering about her basic sincerity. She said, half in earnest, half in jest, something which I could have taken as an honest concern in my future but which for some reason, I didn't: "Miller, this caravan is bound to end one day. Don't injure yourself by taking Mira too seriously." This seemed a most inappropriate comment from a girl whose own love affair with Stiglitz was so intemperate that it could incur even murder, and most contradictory to the things she had said about Mira and me during the trip to Bamian. I was about to question her on these incongruities when Mira came to help me, and Ellen moved on.

"I think Ellen likes you," Mira observed casually, but I was so captivated with Mira herself that I forgot her words.

It was no wonder. For each night we slept under the stars in a series of the most spectacular boudoirs two lovers had ever known: the mountains hovered aloft to protect us, the rivers brought us music, the moon was our night lamp, while not far away the sounds of the caravan reassured us. When we finally went to bed beneath the elusive mountain, Mira was especially adorable, a crazy, elfin thing with an unpredictable insight into human affairs, and the majesty of our surroundings and the knowledge that soon we would leave the Hindu Kush and perhaps the loveliest weeks of our lives forced me to consider what might happen to both of us at the end of the caravan trail. I say forced me to consider because a young man who lives with a girl like Mira slips unconsciously, day by day, from first rapture to deepening realization to the gnawing suspicion that she has become an inescapable part of his life, not to be dismissed easily nor forgotten ever, and he does not willingly explore the future. To my surprise, Mira was willing to do so and with frightening accuracy anticipated each problem that disturbed me. The nimble fingers of her thought ransacked my mind to uncover my most sensitive apprehensions.

When I asked what Zulfiqar might do to her when I left: "He can't do anything. Who would inherit his camels?"

When I asked if she would be able to find a husband within the caravan since all the men knew of her love for me: "If I have the camels, I have a husband."

When I asked what might happen if she had a baby: "What happened to those children over there? Some mothers are dead. Some fathers are unknown."

When I asked what she wanted in life: "In winter Jhelum. In summer Hindu Kush. Any better in America?"

And when I asked her if she loved me: "I bought you a white horse, didn't I? She kissed me and added, "Go to sleep. It is the woman's job to worry about these matters. After all, we have the babies, not you."

But it was when I had asked no question that I sometimes learned most about this delectable young nomad: I was hiking with Mira, having turned the horse over to Maftoon, who galloped up and down the file like a Kazak, when without preparation she observed, "Ellen is the prettiest woman I've ever seen. I would like to look like Ellen. But I would like to be like Racha." When I asked why, she replied, "All the people Racha touches are made stronger. That is not so with Ellen."

I objected and pointed to Dr. Stiglitz, whom Ellen had transformed. At this Mira chuckled: "He was a dying man. Any woman with a good pair of legs could have saved him. I don't count Dr. Stiglitz at all."

"What's going to happen to him . . . when Zulfiqar gets mad, I mean?"

"My father may kill him," she speculated as before. "On the other hand, my father may be grateful that Ellen has been taken off his hands."

"That's an astonishing thing to say," I exploded.

She ignored my question by saying of Racha, "She helps women in childbirth, and handles the camels well, and knows how to care for sick sheep. You know, Miller, Racha is the only one able to argue with my father in the councils, and he trusts her to put the caravan money in the bank at Jhelum." She paused, thinking of her mother, and added, "Racha wears gold in her nose and does not comb her hair, but she is the heart of our caravan, and Zulfiqar would be stupid to trade her for Ellen. He knows that."

"Did he ever love Ellen?" I asked.

Again she evaded my question. "If you stayed with us, Miller," she promised, "I would be like Racha for you." At this point Maftoon rode up on the white horse and asked, "Would the sahib like to have it back?" and Mira snapped, "Yes, you dirty loafer. It's improper for you to ride while he walks." She cupped her hands to make a stirrup for me, and with a quick heft of her tiny body tossed me onto the horse.

As I left Mira, Zulfiqar rode up flashing excitement. "Follow me, Millair!" he cried, and for several miles

I trailed him until he reached the crest of the ridge, where he reined in his brown horse to wait for me.

Pointing to an extensive plateau unfolding below us, he said, "That's Qabir."

Richardson had told me that this was a place of much importance, but even so I had not guessed its magnitude. Across the great plain two rivers came from different ranges of the Hindu Kush and met to form a stately Y. As far as I could see, along both the tributaries and the main river, nomads had erected clusters of black tents. Estimating roughly, I judged there were at least four hundred caravans like ours, which at two hundred persons per caravan meant . . .

Startled by my own figures, I asked, "How many people?"

"Who cares?" he asked in boyish excitement. "Sixty thousand? Maybe more."

It was difficult to believe that for more than a thousand years the nomads had been convening in this remote spot at the confluence of rivers and that no national government was yet sure where the meeting place was, nor who attended, nor how the camp was composed. Now that the war was over, airplanes would soon penetrate the secret, but for the time being this was the last outpost of free men.

"Here we go!" Zulfiqar shouted, and he spurred his horse into a gallop that carried him down onto the plateau and among the gathering caravans. I followed as boldly as I dared, but it was some time before I caught up with my Kochi. When I did, I found him hurrying from one caravan to the next, shouting to old friends, reporting on his winter in India and making plans for trading sessions. It was obvious that he was one of the unifying forces of the encampment.

Finally he remembered that I was with him and crying, "Millair! Follow me!" he galloped along the left bank of the nearest tributary until he found an attractive area as yet unoccupied. "We'll camp here," he shouted. "You wait and tell the others." With this he dug his heels into his horse and sped off to new greetings, but he had gone only a short distance when he reared his horse handsomely, spun him around and came dashing back to me: "As soon as they arrive, tell Maftoon to roast four fat sheep." The horse reared again and he was gone.

It would be an hour before the Kochis could reach us, and the waiting became one of the most poignant times of my life, for around me swirled the enigmatic caravans from the heartland of Asia. I saw beside me men and women from tribes I had never known existed, camels that had crossed the Oxus from areas a thousand miles away, children with round red faces, and women wearing fur boots and wonderful tanned smiles derived from months spent in sunlight. In the distance, at some caravan up the river, a man played a flute and it was like an evocation of the Arabian Nights or the music of Borodin that I had heard at the symphony in Boston. As a stranger on a white horse I attracted attention, and some of the nomads even tried to speak to me in strange tongues, but to all I made it clear that this choice spot by the river was reserved for Zulfiqar and I found that people respected his name.

The poignancy grew more intense when I happened to look toward the Hindu Kush and saw the Kochis coming out of the mountains on their way to the camp ground, and for the first time I saw our caravan in its entirety and realized what an impressive aggregation it was: two hundred people, nearly a hundred camels laden with costly goods, several score of donkeys, some goats and more than five hundred choice sheep. This was my caravan, these were my people; and when I remembered the warm family life I had enjoyed in Boston, I felt grateful that I had been allowed to know this larger family.

And then I saw, marching together, dark little Mira in her red skirt and pigtails and shining Ellen, the hood of her burnoose thrown back, so that her beauty flashed in sunlight, and I was unable to move or think or speak. I merely sat on the white horse and looked at these two persons as they came toward me, the nomad whom I loved so much and the strange, fair woman whom I wanted to help and whom I found so difficult to understand, and as I looked at them the thought came from outside me: They are your life, the essence of your caravan.

In a kind of repose—quiet and unfathomed and undisturbed by the men of Asia moving around me—I watched as the Kochis approached, until three of our men spotted me and shouted, "Here we are!"

"This is the place," I called back, and with a whip of the bridle I sent the white horse speeding toward the caravan, where I leaped to the ground, kissed Mira in front of everyone and whispered, "I was afraid . . ."

"Of what?" she asked quietly.

"That . . . well, that you might not come."

She did not laugh, nor did Ellen, but she plunged her quick hand into my pocket and asked, "Miller, you got any afghanis?"

I came up with a few local coins and when I handed them to her she smiled like a little child, and rounded up all the youngsters of our caravan and led them across the plateau toward the sound of music. I followowed my pigtailed Pied Piper until she brought her charges to a traditional spot where some Russian Uzbeks had erected a primitive merry-go-round: a wooden socket had been sunk in the ground and into it was fitted a strong, upright pillar, from whose top branched out ten arms. At the end of each arm hung a free-swinging iron pole, which ended in a rudely carved wooden horse. In half a dozen different languages the Uzbeks shouted, "The wildest rearing horses in the world!"

"Give them all a ride," Mira told the Uzbeks, and our Kochi children were piled on the rough horses, quivering with apprehension and joy. Then two burly Uzbeks, pressing their chests against poles that projected from the pillar, began moving slowly in a tight circle, which made the pillar and the horses revolve, and everything was so neatly balanced that soon the Uzbeks had their contraption spinning smoothly, whereupon they ran faster and faster until at last they had to spend little effort, while the squealing children on the horses spun at great speed, their little bodies almost parallel to earth.

"These horses are the first exciting thing I can remember," Mira shouted, as children from scores of different tribes cheered the flying Kochis. "When I was young, Zulfiqar always gave me a ride." Her face was radiant, as if she were again one of the wild and happy children. Then without warning, she turned and pressed her head against my shoulder and whispered, "Oh, Miller! I am again so happy."

It was in this manner—from Mira's spontaneous turning to me while mothers from many caravans watched—that the nomads of Qabir discovered that we were in love, and if there was any one thing that made my mission at the encampment easier it was this fact: as a strange American set down on the high plateau I was bound to be conspicuous and ineffective; but as a young man in love with a spirited Kochi girl I was so obvious that the nomads felt sorry for me and I was accorded freedoms that no other stranger would have been permitted.

Then, as the Uzbeks halted their merry-go-round and Mira recovered her children, I saw that on the other side of the circle Ellen had gathered a group of nondescript children whose mothers were not present with coins, and she brought these round-faced youngsters to the Uzbeks and there was some haggling in Pashto. Finally Ellen took off two of her bracelets and gave them to the Uzbek, who tried to bend them in his fingers. He accepted them, and Ellen's children were placed on the horses and again the burly Uzbeks groaned against the poles to get the pillar spinning; and as the children rose higher and higher, speeding through the air, Ellen stood in the afternoon sunlight, biting her knuckles and watching.

At dusk, when the four sheep were well roasted and Ellen had taken her accustomed place to serve the portions, we heard a shout at the edge of our caravan and Zulfiqar appeared, bringing with him some thirty leaders of other caravans plus an orchestra of Tajik musicians, who found a place by the fire and started banging their drums. "Ellen!" Zulfiqar shouted. "Leave the cooking!" And with a sweep of his arm he brought the American girl into the center of the crowd and danced with her vigorously. The visitors watched, then reached out for Kochi women and launched a hilarious celebration. Soon Zulfiqar passed Ellen along to one of the Russians and came to me, out of breath. "Millair," he laughed, "I want you to meet one of the leaders," and he took me through the gyrating dancers to where a tall, heavy, baldheaded man in his late forties stood in fur boots, rough wool jacket and brass-studded belt. His big face was round and clean-shaven, while the slant of his eyes indicated Mongolian ancestry. Grasping him by the shoulder, Zulfiqar said, "This is Shakkur the Kirghiz. He smuggles guns and sells most of the German rifles on the high plateau. He sold me mine."

The big Kirghiz nodded pleasantly, showing large white teeth with a prominent space in the middle. "You English?" he asked in broken Pashto.

"American," I replied.

He burst into a generous laugh and made a machine gun with his arms. "Ah-ah-ah-ah-ah, Chicago!" he cried. "I see cinema."

I respected the man's vitality, but was irritated by his view of Americans, and on the spur of the moment I dropped so that I was sitting on my ankles, and with my arms folded I did a poor imitation of a Russian dance. "I see cinema too," I laughed.

"No!" he protested boisterously. He shouted at the Tajik musicians and they began a new selection to which he danced a passage of real Kirghiz violence. Here there was no mock clicking of the heels but rather the heavy-booted stamp and whirl of the steppes. Seeing Ellen standing near the roast sheep, he leaped at her, grabbed her by the waist, and swung her into a sweeping, dipping step which made her burnoose swirl over the earth. They were a handsome couple, and although she could not follow the intricate steps, the Kirghiz kept her moving so easily that it looked as if she were indeed dancing with him. The Tajik orchestra brought its music to a climax and the big dancer swept his partner high in the air, turned her about, and put her down gently beside the waiting sheep.

"Time to eat!" he shouted, and Ellen started handing out chunks of mutton to the hungry visitors.

When the feasting ended, Zulfiqar asked Dr. Stiglitz to stand beside him while he announced, "This is a German doctor. He has many medicines." Turning toward one of the tents he shouted, "Maftoon! Bring the box of medicine," and when the impressive collection was displayed Zulfiqar said, "If you have any sick, bring them here tomorrow."

"What charge?" Shakkur the Kirghiz asked.

"No charge," Zulfiqar assured him, and next morning outside our tent a line of men and women, dressed in many different tribal costumes, sought aid. In caring for them Stiglitz was assisted by Ellen, who acted as his nurse, and once while she talked with patients in Pashto the doctor wandered over to me to observe, "You've no idea, Miller, how refreshing it is to treat a woman patient who takes off her clothes and says, 'It hurts here.' Believe me, if I ever get to Kabul the men will turn their wives over to me and leave. No more chaderies in my office."

I had not been at the sick line long when Zulfiqar appeared, leading my white horse. After noticing the patients approvingly, he said, "Come along," and we rode to the other end of the encampment, where he began a systematic visit to all the caravans. At each he did two things; he advised the traders in that caravan how to earn more profit from their goods, and he invited each group to send its sick to his German doctor.

I was impressed with Zulfiqar as he moved among the caravans: a smile, a joke, a reference to me . . . It all made commercial bargaining something more than a mere business occupation. I found that I was in the presence of a real political talent, a man who knew that his simple smile and transparent honesty could win him rewards that another might miss. He was politicking like mad, but I didn't know what for.

Thus I made my way into the yurts of the north, those brown hide-walled circular tents where men with Oriental eyes laughed easily while their buxom wives served yak cheese and roast mutton. Casually I shared hospitality with nomads who had come from all parts of Central Asia and I learned how they made their pilgrimages, what goods they traded, the condition of life in their valleys. I was satisfied that no Russian soldiers accompanied the nomads and probably no political commissars, but of this latter I could not be certain. The great gathering at Qabir seemed to be just that: one of the largest commercial fairs in the world, rivaling Nizhni Novgorod and Leipzig. But there was one thing I was not allowed to learn, perhaps the most important of all, and my defeat on this score was a disappointment. I never did find out where these Russian migrants crossed the Oxus.

Richardson had ordered me not to take notes, but at night I memorized the various tribes and subdivisions I had been with that day. From India came the true Povindahs, the Baluchis, and the stocky men from the kingdoms of Chitral, Dir and Swat.

From southern Afghanistan came the Pashtuns, the Brahuis and the Kochis.

From central Afghanistan came the Durani tribe of the Pashtuns, who now ruled the kingdom, the Ghilzais, who used to rule it, and the curious Kizilbash, a Persian tribe of gifted traders.

From northern Afghanistan came the Tajiks, Uzbeks and Kirghizes, all of whom had related tribes north of the Oxus in Russia, the Karakalpaks, the Nuristanis, who were supposed to be of Greek origin, and the Hazaras, who were the descendants of Genghis Khan's troops.

From western Afghanistan came the Jamshedis, the Firuzkuhis, the Taimuris and the Arabs.

From Persia came the nomads of Meshed and Nishapur, the Sakars, the Salors, and additional tribes of Kizilbash.

From Russia came its segments of the Tajik, Uzbek, Sart and Kirghiz tribes, plus the Kazaks and traders from the old market city of Samarkand.

From remote areas came the nameless tribes of the Pamirs, the Chinese from Kashgar and Yarkand, and the handsome mountaineers of Gilgit and Hunza.

And from everywhere—Persia, Afghanistan, Russia, China—came members of that mysterious and omnipresent group, the Turkomans, a people not clearly defined but brave and canny traders.

When I had spent some time in the tents and yurts of all these tribes, I began to feel a certain smugness that I, of all the foreigners in Afghanistan, should have been the one to penetrate Qabir, but so far I had seen only the externals. On the fifth day Zulfiqar saddled up the horses and said, "Today you will see Qabir," and he led me to the confluence of the rivers where an area had been marked inside of which only men were allowed, and only the leaders of the men. We pulled up before a large Russian-style yurt, whose primitive sides were made of skins and whose spacious interior was decorated with guns, daggers, sabers and three handsome red-and-blue Persian rugs. This was the center from which the encampment was governed.

At the far end a small, low table stood on a white rug brought down from Samarkand, and on this rug, cross-legged, were seated the two sharifs who controlled Qabir. The first was Shakkur, the Kirghiz gunrunner who had danced at our feast, and as he sat in the place of honor he was impressive indeed, a big hulk of man with shining head and penetrating eyes. The humor that had marked him at our feast was gone, for ruling this large encampment was a serious business.

The other sharif was an elderly Hazara, a man whose Mongol ancestry would have placed him beneath contempt in Kabul, but who had built a substantial trade in karakul, so that a fair portion of the skins bartered that year at Qabir would come under his jurisdiction. He wore the tattered clothes of a peasant and often listened to argument with his eyes closed, but he was known as a shrewd trader. "He was sharif when my father first brought me here," Zulfiqar explained, and I asked if I might speak with the old man.

He spoke good Pashto and told me, "You're the first westerner ever to see this yurt." I asked him if Russians from Moscow had attended the camp and he smiled indulgently, saying, "No Communists." Then he added, "This year we have a special event which will make the bazaar exciting for you." I replied that it already was.

Almost every man I met in that yurt was an authentic epic, but my favorite was an old Mongol in his seventies wearing a Gilgit cap. He had come from far beyond the Karakorams with two donkeys and a horse. Of the men who frequented the yurt he wore the filthiest clothes, yet his white beard and toothless mouth were constantly flapping in negotiation. He had been alone on the highest road in the world for eight weeks, starting as soon as snow melted in the high passes, and he carried a considerable quantity of gold, one of the few nomads who did. He told me,

"I've been traveling this route sixty-six years. Everyone knows me as the old man with the gold."

"Ever run into any trouble?"

"Never shot a bandit in my life."

Later Zulfiqar told me, "He's telling the truth. All he shot were honest people. For the first forty years on the trail he was a robber in the Karakorams."

Toward the end of the fourth week a Tajik was caught stealing goods from an Uzbek and the culprit was dragged to the big yurt, where the two sharifs were discussing other business. The Tajik had no defense. Witnesses had apprehended him with the goods and he had to confess.

We gathered about the white rug as the two sharifs discussed the matter, and I realized that no nation exercised any sovereignty over this congregation of seventy or eighty thousand people. By consent these two sharifs, one a gunrunner and the other an outcast, enjoyed absolute control. If they now decided to execute the trembling Tajik, they could, but after a short consultation Shakkur the Kirghiz announced the verdict: the right hand to be cut off.

I gasped at the severity of the judgment and impulsively stepped forward. In Pashto I offered to pay the value of the goods stolen, but the old Hazara pointed out that my gesture made no sense. "The goods have already been recovered. What we try to accomplish is not punishment of this poor thief but prevention of further stealing. Carry out the order."

The Tajik began to whimper, but attendants whom I had often seen in the yurt and had taken as mere loungers grabbed the thief and whisked him outside. There was a pitiful scream, after which an Uzbek returned with a red dagger and the man's right hand.

The Hazara sharif, seeing that I was shaken to the point of sickness, took me aside and said, "We must be harsh. I've been sharif here for many years and this is the last cruel judgment I shall make. Don't think unkindly of me."

"Are you retiring?" I asked.

"Tomorrow," he replied with no regrets, "and there are many who think that your friend Zulfiqar should be the next sharif."

Then it became clear! Zulfiqar, having shrewdly guessed the old Hazara's intention to step down, had been conniving for twelve months to be his successor. He had used Ellen, Stiglitz and me exactly as he would have used us had he been bucking for a promotion at the General Motors office in Pontiac, Michigan. In a perverse way I was delighted with my discovery of Zulfiqar's frailty, for it proved that my view of the world was correct and not Ellen Jaspar's. Men everywhere behaved pretty much like her father in Pennsylvania; they had the same banal ambitions, which they expressed in the same banal phrases. But no sooner had I reached this conclusion than a chilling thought possessed me: This isn't Pennsylvania, and there are differences. If Zulfiqar tolerated Ellen's common-law adultery only because he wanted to achieve a goal here in Qabir, what will he do to Ellen and Stiglitz when he's through using them? Then an even more disturbing thought: For that matter, what will he do to me? Because as sharif of the camp he could order anyone destroyed, and who would halt him?

In this gloomy frame of mind I returned to our tents and hurried to see Dr. Stiglitz. "A dreadful thing happened at the yurt," I began, but my news was unnecessary, for in the glow of a lamp Ellen stood holding the right arm of the Tajik thief while Dr. Stiglitz cauterized the wound.

"How did this occur?" Stiglitz asked.

"In this camp two sharifs hold absolute power. Half an hour ago this Tajik was caught stealing; his trial took about four minutes. This is the clean-cut primitive life you wanted, Ellen."

The sight of the bloody stump, plus my news of how the camp was run, became too much for Ellen, and she started to faint, but the Tajik, sensing that she was about to fall, tried instinctively to catch her, and his bloody right arm tore across her burnoose, lacerating the nerve ends so that he screamed with pain. His cries brought Ellen to her senses and she gripped the table. The sight of her ashen face dispelled any sense of triumph I might have had. Afghanistan was much different from Pennsylvania and I wondered how this beautiful woman was going to extricate herself from the complications into which she had so willingly marched.

The next day Zulfiqar shaved with special care and asked me to accompany him to the yurt, where I entered a formal meeting in time to hear the old Hazara karakul merchant announce that he wished to relinquish his duty as sharif. He said, "You must choose a younger man, who can be depended upon to serve you for many years."

I never knew whether Zulfiqar had the meeting rigged or not, but as soon as the old Hazara sat down, a young Kirghiz who had frequented our tent rose and said, "Since one of our sharifs is my clansman Shakkur from north of the Oxus, I think it proper that the new man come from the south." I considered this a rather nice tactic, for the retiring Hazara did not come from the south; as a matter of fact, he came from about as far north in Afghanistan as one could and still remain in the country.

But the trick worked, and an Uzbek who had frequently shared our hospitality asked, "Why should we not select the Kochi, Zulfiqar? He's reliable."

There were no cheers, but there was quiet discussion, and by a process which I did not understand, my caravan leader Zulfiqar was elected sharif of the great encampment. It was a moment of triumph. Those who could speak Pashto told me, "We supported your friend because we were impressed with the way he shared his medical services . . . free." When I left, Zulfiqar was surrounded by the leaders he had been so assiduously wooing in the preceding weeks.

I rode out to camp and broke in upon Stiglitz and Ellen. "Heard the news?" I cried.

"What?" the German asked, as he tended an elderly Uzbek woman.

"Zulfiqar's been elected sharif of the encampment."

"What does it mean?" Ellen asked.

"You saw the Tajik thief . . . no right hand. It means power." She blanched.

It was Stiglitz who first acknowledged the implications of this election. Slowly he pieced together his conclusions: "Zulfiqar's been plotting this for months . . . must have guessed there'd be an election . . . knew he could impress the caravans with me as a doctor . . . Ellen for entertaining . . . Miller for the money. Damn! He used every one of us."

Ellen protested. "You're making it sound too pat."

Stiglitz continued, "So as long as he needed us for the election . . ." He looked at me and I nodded approval of his analysis.

"I'd leave camp," I added. "Right now."

"No!" Ellen cried. "Miller, you must not spread panic. We will not run away. Otto and I believe what I told you in the caves at Bamian. If this is the way it's to end, it's better than anything I ever anticipated."

She kissed Stiglitz and the two lovers renewed their determination to act as planned. I should have been impressed by Ellen's noble sentiment, but I wasn't; for in recent weeks whenever she had made one of her high-sounding speeches I had remembered my conclusion on the road to Bamian: *I have to respect Ellen's sincerity, but not her logic.* Now, for some subtle reason which I could not explain—perhaps because of her casual dismissal of Mira or her willingness to hurt Nazrullah and Zulfiqar—I was beginning to doubt not only her logic but also her sincerity.

In the days that followed, Zulfiqar treated me as a son-in-law. I cannot believe that he knew I had been commissioned by our embassy to spy out Qabir, but he could not have been more helpful had he been my assistant. He said, "In the camp we hear many rumors that this is the last year the Russians will permit their nomads to cross the Oxus, and that was one reason why I wanted the job of sharif. If next year Shakkur the Kirghiz cannot return . . ."

Thus he exposed his final tactic. He suspected that Shakkur might have to relinquish his job as sharif, which would leave him, Zulfiqar, as leading sharif if not the only one. I asked him why the Russians were threatening to close the border and he replied, "When India becomes a free nation, she'll close her borders, too. The day is coming when Kochis will have to stay home."

"What will you do then?" I asked.

"That's why Racha banks our money in Jhelum," he confided. "We're collecting what funds we can and in a few years we'll buy land." He hesitated, then spoke to me as he would have to a son: "I was discussing this with Moheb Khan when we met in Kabul. When the new irrigation dam is built, there will be much new land available at the edge of the desert."

"And you applied for some—to settle down?"

"A winter base," he replied. "We'll go to India no longer. In the spring, of course, we'll bring our goods to Qabir, but only a few of us. The rest will stay home to tend the fields."

"Do the others know?"

"They wouldn't believe it," he laughed, "but Racha and I have about decided. Soon it will happen."

It was a moment when the sweep of time stood exposed, and I thought of the arguments Ellen and I had conducted on this very problem. "Remember the morning when the villagers thought we were kidnapers?" I asked. "Ellen argued that Afghanistan must go back to the caravan and I argued that the caravan must go forward to the village?" I stopped. It was a hollow triumph. "God," I cried, "how exciting it was to march through those dreary villages at your side. Will your village be any better?"

"When you have known freedom," Zulfiqar said, "there's always a chance."

"Why are you stopping now?" I asked.

"Because the old freedom is slipping away from us. They're sending troops to check us at the borders . . . tax collectors. Next they'll inspect our tents. Qabir . . . how many more years will we assemble here?"

I looked at the sprawling tents where I had been so happy and said, "They'll be here when you and I are forgotten."

"No," he corrected. "The black tents are doomed."

"Does Ellen know you think this way?"

"She may have guessed. Perhaps that's why . . ." He didn't finish his sentence. Instead he gave me his professional laugh and said, "People like Ellen always have fixed ideas about how nomads should live . . . and think. We aren't like that, and I'm sorry if we are disappointing."

"But you worked so hard to become sharif. If the black tents are doomed, why did you do it?"

"The tents will go, but the trade will continue."

"And you want to become a trader? An important man like the old Hazara?"

"In ten years few of the tents we see today will be here. Just a handful of men like me and the Hazara and Shakkur . . . bringing camels and a few servants to load them. We'll trade twice the goods—five times as much. It's clear, Millair, that four-fifths of this camp is unnecessary. The women and children accomplish nothing."

"Do the others agree?"

"All of us in the big yurt . . . especially the Russians." Then he surprised me by using the phrase that Stiglitz had spoken: "The caravans move on. They move to a distant horizon."

The time had now come for disbanding the camp

and I discovered that this event was traditionally marked by a game of Afghan polo. Early one morning Zulfiqar sent Maftoon to find me and the cameleer asked, "You like to play polo?"

I said, "Tell Zulfiqar I know nothing about polo," but Mira clapped her hands and cried, "Tell Zulfiqar he'll play." But when I saddled up she checked the lashings and warned, "Better tie everything twice. This game can get rough."

I joined Zulfiqar and we rode to a field east of the confluence, where children waited, chattering with excitement, and the women of the camp, who made a place for Ellen and Mira. The field was crowded with horsemen clustering about the old Hazara, who was trying to establish some rough-and-ready rules. He did not ride his horse well, for under his left arm he held a white goat who struggled to get free, but the old man did succeed in showing us the two goal lines, about two hundred yards apart. Then he cried, "Shakkur, have your men pass out the arm bands," and the big Kirghiz gave the signal.

Shakkur gave me a white arm band and said, "Fight well."

It was to be south-of-the-Oxus versus north-of-the-Oxus, for Shakkur kept on his team the Uzbeks, Tajiks, Kazaks and Kirghizes, while Zulfiqar had riders from Afghanistan, India, China and Persia. There were about forty to a side, but for reasons which became apparent to me later on, no one bothered to insure that we were evenly matched.

Zulfiqar's White team lined up to defend the eastern goal and the Russians opposed us. In the center the old Hazara held aloft the goat by his rear legs while an Uzbek whipped out a knife and cut off the animal's head. With a savage cry the umpire threw the goat's body high in the air and left the field, not to interfere again. Before the goat, spurting blood, could land, a Tajik horseman swept in, caught the animal and raised it over his head in a mad gallop toward our goal line. He had covered only a few yards when he was hit from three sides by our riders, who tackled, grabbed, gouged and beat him. Finally one of our Turkomans leaped almost clear of his horse, grabbed the goat and wrenched it away from the battered Tajik, who was now bleeding from the mouth.

Our Turkoman set off boldly for the Russian goal, but a force of shouting Uzbeks and Kirghizes slammed into him and not only stole the goat but also knocked down his horse, so that he catapulted across the rocky playing field. No one stopped to see if he was hurt, and after a while he recovered his horse and rejoined the game. Meanwhile, one of our Afghans drew even with the Uzbek who had captured the goat and literally threw himself at his opponent, knocking the Russian rider right out of the saddle, but before the goat touched earth, Shakkur the Kirghiz sped in, caught it by one leg and fought his way through the mob to find himself with a clear path to our goal. The polo game was over, for no White rider could possibly catch him.

At this point the essential feature of Afghan polo was made clear. When the victorious Russian team saw that their captain was about to score they regretted that the game was ending, so one of their own men, a fiery Uzbek, set forth in hot pursuit and just as the baldheaded sharif was about to cross our line, this Uzbek teammate came up from behind, gave him a wallop across the back of his neck, grabbed the goat and brought it back into play. Both sides applauded, and the game continued. Thereafter, when any player threatened to score, his own teammates slugged him, gouged him and tried to knock him from his horse. It was always one rider fighting forty of the enemy plus thirty-nine of his friends, and sometimes it was the latter who did the worst damage.

For nearly sixty bruising minutes we played without my distinguishing myself—it seemed that half the other riders were bleeding from the mouth—when I happened to gallop past the children of our caravan and heard them shout, "Get in the game." I saw Ellen, and she looked a bit stunned by the brutality of the sport, but little Mira was furious. "Why did I get you the horse?" she shouted. "Do something!"

So I dashed into the middle of the fracas, where I accomplished nothing until a north-of-the-Oxus Kazak broke loose with what was left of the goat and headed in my general direction. It was apparent that unless I stopped him, the game was over, so I tried to turn him back into the mob, but the Russian decided that he could scare me into yielding ground, so he drove directly at me, and so far as I was concerned his strategy would have worked, for I was willing to withdraw, but Moheb's horse had been trained for just this kind of challenge and, ignoring my reins, leaped ahead seeking contact. We struck the Kazak with stunning force, spun him around and caused him to drop the goat, which to my surprise I caught.

But before I got started for the Russian goal, I caught a glimpse of Shakkur bearing down on me and in order to escape him tried evasive action. He anticipated my move and with his left arm clubbed me across the back so violently that I nearly pitched over my horse's head. In attempting to regain control I exposed the goat, which Shakkur grabbed, literally tearing it from me. He rode off with the body; I was left with one leg.

Dazed from his blow, I started in pursuit, but the chase was fruitless, for Shakkur had a clear run for the goal, and even though one of his own Kazaks tried to knock him from his horse, the big sharif defended himself by clubbing the Kazak in the face with the bloody goat. Thus ended our game of polo, the sport of gentlemen.

Of the eighty players, more than half had substantial contusions and cuts, and of these, twenty-two were injured seriously enough to require help from Dr. Stiglitz, who set broken bones, pulled broken teeth and applied antiseptic to several square yards of flesh from which the skin had been abraded in sliding falls across the rocky field. This year, however, there had been no deaths.

As we finished treating the last of the cripples and listened to the sounds of festivity in the tents, where the game was being celebrated, I could not resist observing to Ellen, "Sort of like Saturday night after the Yale-Harvard game, isn't it? Or the country club in Dorset after a golf match?"

She had a good answer for this, I'm sure, but she was prevented from giving it by the arrival of the old Hazara, who had come by to congratulate me: "Your play was a credit to Zulfiqar and he should be pleased. A year ago I warned him, 'In 1946 I shall retire. If you act wisely you could be my successor.' Well, everything he's done this year has been correct and your presence and the young lady's"—he smiled at Ellen approvingly —"has helped him very much." He bade me farewell and rode back to the yurt.

When he was gone I saw that Ellen was trembling, partly from outrage, partly from apprehension. "He's been plotting this for a whole year," she muttered, her composure gone. "He's used us most shamefully. I wonder what he'll do now?"

I should have been sympathetic with her, but for some reason I wasn't, and an irreverent thought possessed me, which I ungallantly shared: "Rather neat trick he pulled, picking you up at Qala Bist and keeping you on ice for ten months."

She glared at me, but ignored the joke. "What do you think he'll do?" she asked nervously.

Toward me, at least, his friendship increased. The day after the polo we rode to see the Russians dismantling the administration yurt and watched as a colorful procession of Uzbek, Tajik and Hunza caravans wound slowly to the east, heading for the crevices of the Hindu Kush. A visible sadness seized the Kochi leader and he turned on his horse to say, "If they do die, these caravans . . ." He paused, then said quietly, "Who could believe Qabir if he had not seen it? Son"—he had never called me this before—"I wanted you to see this plain with four hundred caravans. I saw it when I was a boy . . . no, when I was an infant too young to see anything. This is how men should live."

But each day we became more lonely. The Nuristanis next to us had departed and so had the Tajiks to the west, and a very real sense of doom enveloped our camp. I was constantly expecting retribution to overtake Ellen and Dr. Stiglitz, and I am sure they were too. In fact, I became so jittery that I began spotting where the guns were, and the knives, in case I was myself attacked, for it seemed to me that the brooding figure of Zulfiqar was everywhere.

Finally even Shakkur the Kirghiz departed with his eighty camels, and our caravan was alone on the high plateau. I overheard little Maftoon complaining to the other cameleers, "If we don't start soon for Balkh, on the return trip the snows will trap us."

"Zulfiqar will tell us when to move," they assured him.

"He's not thinking of the snows," Maftoon lamented.

The next morning I heard a shouting at Zulfiqar's tent and I rushed over to find him standing with dagger in hand, towering over Dr. Stiglitz, who was unarmed and terrified. In his baggy Afghan trousers and dirty turban Stiglitz made a pitiful contrast to the powerful Kochi.

"Give him a dagger," Zulfiqar commanded, and when there was hesitation he shouted at Maftoon, "Give him yours. It killed a man in Rawalpindi."

Fumbling, Maftoon placed his dagger into the trembling hands of the doctor, who knew no more how to use it now than he had that morning in the caravanserai: he held it in both hands, pointed out from his chest.

I fought my way to the front of the circle and shouted, "Zulfiqar! No!"

"You be still!" the huge Kochi roared, and men grabbed my arms.

At the doorway to the tent Racha and some women held Ellen Jaspar, and I looked beseechingly at Mira, who refused to look back at me. Then Ellen screamed and I saw Zulfiqar, with a quick lunge, dive at Stiglitz, who, in a response born of despair, managed to escape the flashing blade but took no steps to attack his adversary.

Zulfiqar whirled expertly and drove at Stiglitz from the opposite direction, but again Ellen screamed and the doctor jumped aside just in time. He was terrified and was obviously about to be killed, except that Ellen, who had convinced him that death was of no consequence, now shouted, "Otto! Protect yourself!" And with this cry the insignificant man wanted to live. He became wary.

What followed occurred with dreadful swiftness, but each motion was etched on my mind. I shall never forget. I thought: I hope Stiglitz wins. I despised him, both for what he had done and for what he represented, but now that he was close to death at the very moment he had found Ellen Jaspar to restore his life, I wanted him to survive. Dear God, I prayed, let the German live.

A roar went up as Zulfiqar made a savage lunge at Stiglitz, who drew himself in so that the Kochi dagger missed, then stabbed at Zulfiqar as the latter flashed by. Stiglitz had drawn blood and the crowd murmured in astonishment.

I never knew whether Zulfiqar realized he was hit or not, but with a roaring leap he struck his opponent with both boots and knocked him to the ground. Like a cat he pounced upon him and wrenched away his dagger. Applying his knees to the doctor's arms, he stared down at the terrified face.

Ellen screamed as Zulfiqar's dagger flashed in the air and I was caught with horror as I watched it speed downward. I heard the crowd sigh. Then I heard voices.

Zulfiqar had driven his dagger into the soft earth, less than an inch from the pudgy doctor's neck. The powerful Kochi left it there as he pushed himself up, loomed over the fallen man and carefully spat in his face.

"Leave the caravan!" he cried in a terrifying voice.

He then stalked to the doorway of his tent and grabbed Ellen away from the women. With a cruel swipe of his hand he knocked her off her feet. Contemptuously he spat in her face and repeated his order: "Leave the caravan!"

Then he stepped across the two stupefied westerners and grabbed me by the throat with his left hand. With his right he gave me a blow that sent me staggering backward in the dust. "Get out!" he roared. "Get out!"

Finally he grabbed little Maftoon and lifted him off the ground. "They're your friends," he shouted scornfully. "Take them to Balkh. Now! Now!"

In a storming rage he tore into his tent and began throwing out all the possessions that Ellen had accumulated. This done, he rushed to my tent, where he did the same with everything belonging to Stiglitz and me. The doctor's bag landed on one corner and popped open, spilling medicine which the silent Kochis began greedily grabbing.

"Put it back!" Zulfiqar shouted. "We want nothing of theirs."

In this manner he continued, with blood reddening his back, until he saw us packed, the white horse saddled, and Maftoon ready with the camel Becky, who carried a tent for us, and a donkey whose panniers contained some food.

"Get out!" he bellowed, and as we crept away down the river trail toward the confluence where he had gained glory in the yurt, I saw him rip off his shirt to inspect his wound. It was not deep and he yelled for Racha to wash it. That was the last I ever saw of Zulfiqar or his wife Racha.

15

We formed a pathetic caravan as we moved out of the Hindu Kush. Stiglitz, shaken by his approach to death, was allowed to ride the white horse, which he did in silence. Ellen was in a state of unbelief: her jaw was sore and her vanity abused. Confusion was increased by the effect of her gray burnoose, which made her look soft and feminine while her words made her harsh and unlovely.

"How dare he strike me?" she asked several times. "And spit at me? He's no better than an ignorant mullah. I should have killed him myself." She was shaken with anger at the memory of her humiliation, and as I studied these bedraggled lovers I was willing to concede that they had converted themselves into non-people, those rejected dregs on which the world rebuilds, and I was sure they felt confirmed in this claim.

Little Maftoon was equally disturbed, because when he got rid of us at Balkh there was no escape: he would have to rejoin the caravan, and it had been his knife that had wounded Zulfiqar, his friendship for me that accounted for his being with us. The scar-eyed cameleer found no pleasure in this caravan, nor did his enemy Aunt Becky, who like all camels protested any trail that descended, since it threw unaccustomed burdens on her awkward front legs. She growled and gurgled so much that pretty soon somebody in the caravan had better undress and let her fight his clothes or there would be serious trouble.

Nor was I exempt from the sense of melancholy which had been closing in on me for days. I had lost Mira, the elfin spirit of the caravan, and I could imagine her trapped in the mountains by her father's hatred of me. In my loneliness I was forced to admit, for the first time, that I loved her without reservation. On the high plateaus she had laughed and teased her way into my heart, and she would remain a part of me as long as I lived. To have lost her without even a farewell was intolerable. But I had also been abused by her father, who during the preceding weeks had been treating me as his predilected son, sharing with me thoughts he would not confide to others. He had gone out of his way to help me with my mission, introducing me to the Kirghiz sharif, and from watching him at work I had grown to admire his cool calculations and mastery of politics; yet our friendship had ended with his knocking me down, cursing me and throwing me out of his camp. Frankly, I couldn't understand what had happened.

In fact, if one considered the entire complement of our cut-rate caravan, the only member not spiritually wounded was the donkey. He plodded along with panniers banging his sides, content to know that if he didn't work for us, on this trail, he would have to work for someone else, on some other trail.

We had proceeded thus for two silent hours when I heard Maftoon cry, "Miller Sahib! Look!"

I turned to see what new misfortune had befallen us, half expecting to find that Aunt Becky had broken a leg, but instead I saw Maftoon pointing back along the trail we had traveled, and there came Mira, in red skirt and pink blouse, running to overtake us.

"Her father will kill her," Maftoon lamented.

She was more than a mile away, a marvelous little

hummingbird skipping across the meadowland, and I started running back to meet her. "Take the horse," Stiglitz offered, but I was already on my way.

Out of breath we met on the trail and rushed into a long kiss, which convinced me of how desperately I needed her, how ashamed I had been at being forced to leave the caravan without speaking to her. I think that as we finished our embrace she was weeping, but I do not know, for in these matters she was proud and she buried her face in my shoulder as I lifted her and carried her along the trail.

The others came back to meet us, all except Aunt Becky, who, when she started downhill, turned back for nothing. We looked at her gaunt brown figure plopping across rocks and began to laugh. It was so joyful to be with Mira, and cockeyed Maftoon, and the lovers and the beat-up old camel.

As I put Mira down, Ellen ran to embrace her as if they were schoolgirl roommates, and the affection between the girls was real, for to Ellen Mira owed her dress, her manner of doing her hair and her few English sentences; and it was obvious that she was pleased to be with the American girl again.

But Maftoon warned in a doom-laden voice, "You should not have done this, Mira. Your father will kill you."

To our astonishment Mira replied, "He told me to come."

"He what?"

"Of course. I told him, 'I'd like to go to Balkh with Miller,' and he said, 'Why not?' "

"You mean that Zulfiqar . . ."

"He's not mad at anybody," Mira assured us, expressing surprise that we should think so.

"He knocked me down," Ellen protested. "He spat at me."

Again Mira embraced her friend. "He had to do that, Ellen. The others were looking, waiting—the whole caravan."

"He almost killed me," Stiglitz added, rubbing his neck.

Mira looked almost condescendingly at the German and asked proudly, "If my father had been truly angry, do you think he would have missed with his dagger? His honor demanded that he do something about you, Doctor. But he wasn't angry. It was only make-believe . . . in front of the others."

I caught Mira by the shoulders and shook her: "Are you telling the truth?"

She laughed at me as she broke free. "Miller! When my father said good-by just now he was chuckling. He told me, 'Tell that damned German he put up a good fight.' And he sent you this, Dr. Stiglitz." From her pink blouse she produced the Damascus dagger Zulfiqar had used in the duel. Handing the silver sheath gravely to the German, she said, "His wedding present to you. My father said, 'It will remind the wife that her husband was once willing to fight for her . . . with daggers.' "

Then she took me aside and explained softly, "When you left, Miller, my father went to our tent and threw himself on the rugs. Again and again he said, 'He was like my son. He was my son. Why did I strike him?' For a while at Qabir I think he hoped that by some miracle you would stay with us and help him run the caravan." There was a moment of intense silence, broken by her sharp cry, "There goes Becky!"

The willful old camel had spotted, off to one side of the trail, some grass that she fancied and, having eaten it, now continued straight ahead in the new direction even though it was taking her into dangerous rocky areas. Nothing would stop her, dumb beast that she was, for she would continue plodding ahead until she destroyed herself, unless some human teased her into returning to the trail. By those who know them best, camels are considered the stupidest of animals, and Aunt Becky was out to prove her claim to the title, but she was forestalled by Mira, who dashed after the lumbering beast, cursing her madly, and we fell to laughing as the determined little nomad pursued the huge camel, scrambling over rock and shale until she had maneuvered Aunt Becky back to safety.

This was the tonic our bedraggled group needed, and without fully appreciating what I was doing or its consequences I took Ellen by the hands and teased her in a schoolboy's way. "Ellen and her men!" I chanted, waving her arms up and down. "She wants to reject the world, so she runs off with Nazrullah, whose only ambition is to build a big dam. So she drops him for wild free Zulfiqar, who wants to settle down beside the dam. Then she chooses Dr. Stiglitz. Look at him up there grinning on that horse. He's planning to build a hospital on Zulfiqar's land beside Nazrullah's dam."

"Ring-around-a-rosy," Ellen cried, joining in the joke. And with a sudden lilt of her body she began dancing me over the trail, her gray burnoose swinging free in haunting beauty. Then I felt the pulsating throb of life in her hands as they gripped mine and realized that this was the first time I had touched Ellen. She was vibrant and her eyes flashed, making her irresistible and quite different from the troubled young college girl we had discussed that wintry day at the American embassy in Kabul. I was caught by an embarrassment which sprang from reasons I did not then fully comprehend, and I let her hands fall, so that the force of her dancing spun her away in lovely gyrations until she collapsed in laughter on a grassy bank.

Dr. Stiglitz leaped from his horse to lift her to her feet, but Mira reached her first and asked with real concern, "Are you hurt, Ellen?"

"I could dance right out of the mountains," she told the little nomad. Then she reached up and kissed Dr. Stiglitz as he helped her back onto the trail.

In this manner we re-formed our little caravan and, with Mira restoring the levity we had lost, began one of the loveliest journeys any of us would ever know. From Qabir to Balkh was only eighty miles, which we should have covered in about five days, but we were in no hurry and our patient progress through the mountains became an extended joy. It had been one thing to carry on a light love affair with a bright-eyed nomad girl, built of hasty meetings in rocky enclaves; it was quite another to live with that girl twenty-four hours a day, helping her prepare pilau, watching her as she loaded the donkey and sharing her life as if we intended never to part. Once she said, "We should find mountains where it never snows and get us a flock of karakuls," and she laughed when Ellen teased, "Can't you imagine Mark Miller herding karakul sheep on Boston Common?" But her easy laughter did not hide the fact that we were falling deeper and deeper in love, so that our final parting was bound to be a matter of anguish.

At the same time I had a chance to observe Ellen and her doctor as they started their new life freed from the presence of Zulfiqar, and as I watched them I had to admit that there was some substance to Ellen's confused thesis about the non-people. She and Stiglitz worried about nothing. For them there was no past, no future, no responsibility. The days came and went, and the two lovers existed. They were non-people who on a high plateau in Afghanistan had found each other after a series of improbable adventures, and the days of their rebirth from nothingness were brilliant to watch.

Yet as soon as I have said this, I must confess that it was also now that I became aware for the first time of a dark presence when they were with us in the tent, an element of strangeness, almost of tangible foreboding. It was Mira who pointed this out to me. For us, love had been a relaxed and easily accepted experience. To be sure, the little nomad girl reveled in an exquisite passion, which she found joy in sharing, and I, although I am no expert in these matters, felt sure at the time that my response was adequate. But on the first night out of Qabir, when the bunks were made and all four of us had gone to bed in the black tent, Mira and I were astonished at the sounds which came from the opposite side of our quarters. It was as if those other lovers feared that nights were numbered and that at Balkh some tragedy would envelop them. Mira whispered, "We better leave the tent for them," but as we crept away I had the curious feeling that this extraordinary performance in the other bed had somehow been directed at me.

Mira and I walked in the gray light of the full moon, passing the nook where Maftoon slept with the animals, while the white horse, that symbol of leadership and manliness that Mira had brought me, grazed on the hillside. In Pashto Mira said, "I am convinced now that my father was relieved when Ellen started sleeping with Dr. Stiglitz."

"That's still an astonishing thing to say."

"I think he'd had enough of lovemaking," she suggested.

"With a girl like Ellen? You must be crazy."

"Do you remember that first morning?" she asked. "At the caravanserai? My father found you fighting and ran out to warn us, 'Hide Ellen. The American is here looking for her.' So we hid her in one of the little rooms. But only a few minutes later he ordered me to bring her before you."

I tried to recall the scene. Zulfiqar had taken our knife and the Kochis had entered, including Mira, whose saucy pigtails I could still see. Yes, Mira was right. Zulfiqar had sent her out specifically to fetch Ellen, and had he not done so, we need never have known that she was with the Kochis. He had intended me to find her.

Mira and I walked for some hours through the great mountains of Afghanistan, then crept quietly back to the tent where Ellen and Stiglitz were asleep, but on the second night the performance in the other bed was repeated and again Mira suggested that we leave, and in this manner my ambivalent feeling toward the other couple developed: in the day they were persons of feeling and judgment with whom I found an increasing sense of identification; but at night they became something strange. One curious facet of this ambivalence concerned Dr. Stiglitz, for I had gradually been forced to concede that he had transformed himself from a Nazi criminal into a man determined to serve humanity. My hatred for what he had done to the Jews in Munich was exorcised; our weeks together, our long discussions, had made him like a brother. I therefore had to conclude that whatever uneasiness I felt about the couple must stem not from Stiglitz but from Ellen.

For example, on the third evening out we pitched our camp in a rocky gorge that would lead us out of the Hindu Kush, and at the end of day Maftoon spread his little prayer rug on the rocks. Estimating where Mecca stood, he knelt to pray, but he had uttered only a few words when Dr. Stiglitz, impressed by the gravity of the mountains at dusk, joined him, and they knelt as the Koran directed, shoulder to shoulder in that brotherhood which Islam fosters and which is unknown to most other religions.

Women were not allowed to pray with men, so well to the rear Mira knelt and after a while Ellen joined her and I was left standing alone within the circle of rocks, wondering how there could be any connection between that spot and Mecca. I respected Islam, but I had never felt either a part of it or capable of ever becoming a part; but at this moment I remembered Nazrullah's question: *If you lived in Afghanistan permanently, wouldn't you pray as a Muslim?* Impulsively I knelt beside Dr. Stiglitz and felt his shoulder touching mine, and for some minutes the five of us prayed and I heard illiterate Maftoon chanting, "God is great. God is great. I am witness that there is no God but the one God, and I am His servant. For God is great. God is great." At that moment of fellowship I could believe that this strange religion, so difficult for a Jew like me to comprehend, had been specially ordained for deserts and high plateaus, and it had been sent by God Himself to make men in these lonely areas act as brothers. At that moment I experienced an intense sensation of Otto Stiglitz as my brother.

"God is great. God is good. We are the servants of God," Maftoon chanted, and it occurred to me: In all the Muslim prayers I have actually heard recited as compared to those one reads in books, I've heard only of God, never of Muhammad. Maftoon, as if he had overheard my thoughts, ended his prayer, "God is great, and I am witness that Muhammad is His Prophet." When we rose I looked back at the girls, and there was dark little Mira in pigtails still kneeling beside blond Ellen, whose burnoose fell about her stately figure like the robes of some saint in prayer, and there was a sense of beauty hovering above the worshipers so harmonious with the setting that for a long time we stayed in the shadow of the mountains saying little.

On the next day we penetrated the last range of hills separating the Hindu Kush from the arid plains leading to Balkh, and as Aunt Becky stumbled out of the mountains and saw flat ground again, she gave a series of joyful gurgles and started loping across the dusty fields, as if here at last was the true Afghanistan.

The heat became considerable, for this was mid-July, and we had to exercise caution in our use of water. We also reverted to the desert practice of traveling at night, but since the moon was nearly full this added to the beauty of our trip. During the day we slept, Stiglitz and Ellen in the tent, Maftoon with the camel, and Mira and I wherever we could find shade.

"I thought Ellen was your dearest friend," I chided Mira as we hiked through the heat looking for a place to sleep.

"She is," the little nomad replied, "but it will be safer if you sleep away from her."

"Why do you say a thing like that?" I demanded.

At first she refused to speak, then added simply, "It was while she was sleeping with my father that I discovered she was in love with Dr. Stiglitz."

"How could anybody know a thing like that?" I asked with some irritation, for we were finding no shade.

"I told you at the time, didn't I?" she reminded me.

"How did you know?" I snapped.

"I knew, that's all."

Toward midnight of our fourth day on the plains I was riding the white horse at the head of the caravan when I spotted, in the silvery moonlight ahead, an extensive area denuded of trees but marked by solitary mounds on which grass seemed to be growing in scanty spots. In the semidarkness it looked like a burial ground for giants, but when Maftoon overtook me in the moonlight he said, "That is Balkh," and I rode on to inspect the meaningless sweep of empty earth.

So this was Balkh, mother of cities, fair Balkh where Alexander had married Roxane, the learned city at the crossroads of the world, the leading metropolis of Central Asia! As a boy I had been fascinated by this city, ancient and famous even before the days of Darius. All the remembered travelers of Asia had recorded their impressions of this dazzling treasure house: Ibn Batuta, Hsuan Tsang, Genghis, Marco Polo, Tamerlane, Baber. Its history was resplendent. Its memory was obscured. And now even its outlines were destroyed.

Could this be Balkh, this empty field of arid mounds where herd boys tended goats and wandering Kochis came to camp? This expanse of buried rubble with no plaques, no banners, not even a line of brick indicating where the great libraries had once stood . . . could this be the end of the city?

I felt inconsolably lonely, as if I were lost in the paralyzing sweep of history, a shard left by time. I felt like crying out in protest, and when I saw our faltering caravan approaching—one camel, one donkey, for Balkh—I could not find solace even in the thought that Mira would soon be with me.

At Rome the imperial ruins had also depressed me, but only for a moment, because it required no great imagination to believe that something of that grandeur persisted. But in Afghanistan my depression not only affected me; it also permeated the land and the culture and the people. It was difficult to believe that civilization had ever graced this arid waste or that it could return. At miserable Ghazni, at silent Qala Bist, at The City, at faceless Bamian and here at Balkh nothing remained. Were the generations indifferent to history, allowing their finest monuments to disappear while Rome retained hers? Or was it simply that Asia was different, its conquerors so terrible that western man could not visualize their cargoes of horror?

Many times I had crossed the path of Genghis Khan, merely one of the scourges and not necessarily the worst, and each time I had stood where he had erased a population. Perhaps a society cannot absorb such repeated punishments. Perhaps the scourging does something to the minds of men, converting citizens into frightened nomads who feel safe only when carrying their goods with them under their own surveillance. Perhaps it was Genghis Khan who explained why the Kochis and the Kizilbash and the Tajiks remained wanderers with no fixed civilization to sustain them.

Brooding in the moonlight at Balkh, I found increased respect for men like Moheb Khan, Nazrullah, and my preceptor Zulfiqar, who were determined to build a new Afghanistan that would conserve the memories of Ghazni and Balkh yet build upon the newer ideas of Russia and America. Had I been an

Afghan, I would have allied myself to these impatient men.

As I reached this conclusion Maftoon brought his little caravan to the ruins, where for the past centuries the Kochis had camped, and while he and Stiglitz unrolled the tent Ellen came to me in the moonlight and said generously, "I'm sorry, Miller, that we quarreled so much on this trip. I've been struggling to find understanding."

"Found any?"

"Some. When it looked as if Otto might die in the duel, I did learn one important fact. That life of itself is good. I found myself praying that he would live."

"It's lucky he did," I replied. "You and he are bound to accomplish some great thing in Afghanistan."

"The non-people don't accomplish," she corrected gently. "They exist, and from them the world takes hope."

"One thing makes me feel better, Ellen. At last I have a glimmer of what you're talking about. But I'm like Nazrullah . . . committed to working for the civilization I'm caught in."

She smiled warmly and grasped my hands, and the effect was as electrifying as before. "How adorable of you, Miller, how predictable! To say a thing like that at Balkh."

"Why Balkh?" I asked.

"Don't you know that at the apex of their history the people here talked just like you? The mullahs proclaimed, 'Allah has this city in His special care. No harm can befall it.' And the generals boasted, 'Our forts are impregnable. No enemy can reach us.' And the bankers were especially reassuring: 'Last year our gross city product rose four percent. We can all afford two slaves in every kitchen.' And here is Balkh. And here is New York."

"Do you honestly believe that the same thing will

happen to New York?" I asked, and immediately I was irritated with myself, for I had to recall my own thoughts when traveling down the ruins of The City: *This is Route One between New York and Richmond.*

"I believe that this is the future," Ellen replied. "But you mustn't. Because you're young. You're destined to go back to Boston and work there the way Nazrullah will work in Kandahar. I shall pray for you both, but I will never believe in what you're doing. It's really of no consequence . . . none whatever."

I told her, "I'll try to explain to your parents," and she was on the verge of speaking about them contemptuously when she changed her mind and kissed me, not politely on the cheeks but full on the lips with that abundance of love which had marked her life, and for a moment I comprehended the passion which had carried her so chaotically to Balkh. The impact of her kiss was like the touch of her hand at the dancing: it conveyed the sense of a woman with tremendous vital power and against my better judgment I was driven to wonder: What might have happened had I met her in the States? In reply I heard the Haverford College boy telling the F.B.I. agent: *I always felt that somebody else might have kept Ellen on the track. But I will admit this. I wasn't the man to do it.*

I was about to break away when, to my surprise, she gripped my shoulders and kissed me again, desperately. "I wish I'd met you in America. After you'd learned what you have in Afghanistan." She brushed the hair from her forehead and looked at the ruins of Balkh. "No, I'd have been horrid for you. These ruins were in my bones." Laughing nervously she added, "Besides, you're so young and hopeful. And I've always been so very old."

As she said this the moonlight played upon her lovely face. Her body swayed backward in the gray blouse that Racha had embroidered, and her bare legs showed beneath the black skirt of the Kochis. Her ankles were caught by thongs from her sandals and she was beyond comparison the most vital and attractive woman I had ever seen. This time it was I who kissed her, and with a violence of consent she pressed her beauty into my arms and against my face and through my being. I was astonished by the overwhelming power of her response and betrayed my fear that the others might see us, but with a practiced eye she calculated that the men would be occupied for some time with the tent while little Mira would remain engaged in unloading the camel.

"They won't miss us," she assured me as she sought a hiding place among the mounds. She found one and beckoned.

"What are you doing?" I asked in astonishment.

She had kicked off her sandals and was untying the cord that held her skirt. "Didn't we just agree that life of itself was good? Let's enjoy it." When I hesitated she argued, "What difference would it make if they did find us?"

The idea stunned me and I remained where I was. "Mira would make the difference," I stammered.

"Don't you want to?" she asked provocatively, as the skirt fell about her ankles.

"You know I do."

"Then come on," and with ravishing grace she stepped from the fallen garment.

I knew that any man who hesitated at such a moment was bound to look pathetic, both to the girl and to himself, and I longed to join those slim, inviting legs. Instead I heard myself making the most improbable reply: "You shouldn't do this to Stiglitz."

With a kind of disgust—whether at me or Stiglitz or Mira I did not know—she recovered her skirt and refastened the cord. "I've done everything for Stiglitz I could," she said. Barefooted she came to me and whispered, "Besides, sooner or later the Russians are bound to get him."

Her callousness seemed as bleak as the desert and now I was glad that I had not followed her deeper into the dunes. "What happened to your idealism about Stiglitz?" I asked. "A few minutes ago you said you had prayed for him to live."

"He lived."

I thought: I'll bet she used the same kind of argument with Stiglitz when she was inviting him to move in on Zulfiqar. *But Otto, Zulfiqar's busy with other things. He won't care.* And she had been right. "Your flowery ideas about the non-people?" I asked. "You give them up? For a couple of days back there you had me convinced."

"Ideas come and go," she replied. Recovering her sandals, she said, "You know very well what we ought to do. Get us a sleeping bag and leave that tent right now."

"With Mira there?"

"I warned you on the trail that you were taking Mira too seriously. Besides, in a couple of days she'll be back with her father."

I drew away, appalled. "At Bamian you made fun of men who play what you called the point game. Right now I appreciate how important that game is. I honestly believe that if I treat Mira decently I get a point in my favor. And whether you like it or not, if you kick Stiglitz around, you lose points."

"With whom?" she asked contemptuously. "The Divine Scorekeeper?"

"No, damn it all. With me." She started to laugh and I got angry. "You reject religion. I don't. Millions of Jews are dead because they took religion seriously. So do I."

"Miller!" she cried, almost loud enough for the others to hear. "You don't take being a Jew seriously, do you?"

"Skip it," I said impatiently, sorry that I had raised the subject. "But the way you reject religion—what were you, Presbyterian?" She laughed and I added, "You know, Ellen, if you took Islam seriously . . ."

"I might be saved?" she asked mockingly.

"It wouldn't take much to save you. The more I hear you bleat about Dorset, Pennsylvania, the more convinced I become that it must be a pretty fair place. You ought to try it some time."

She laughed again and I became embarrassed with my prosaic philosophy and inept performance as a lover. I started back to camp but had moved only a few steps when she overtook me and grasped my arm. Again I could feel the lovely urgency of her body as she made an honest effort to conciliate our quarrel. Without rancor she asked, "Seriously, Miller, doesn't it make you self-conscious? Sentimental speeches like this . . . at Balkh, of all places?"

Her words were forceful and they made me stop. I looked at the undulating graveyard of the great city and saw, in my imagination, the rise and fall of Balkh —Balkh of the Flying Pennants it had been called, as if the city were proud to advertise its accomplishments, temporary though they proved to be—and I sensed some of the meaning behind my mission. I said, "I don't accept your view of Balkh. Cities crumble and civilizations vanish, but people go on. And damn it all, they eat and make love and go to war and die according to certain hopeful rules. I accept those rules."

"The rules?" she asked quietly. "They don't permit you to make love?" She moved close to me and I saw her in the moonlight, as beautiful a girl as I would ever know, more provocative a dozen times than Mira. "The rules won't permit you?" she repeated.

"Not with Mira over there," I fumbled.

"In the morning? Won't you feel like an idiot?"

"How do you suppose I feel now." I grasped her hands and said, "You're marvelously beautiful, Ellen."

She was pleased that I had done this, and returned to her former imaginings. "Why didn't we meet two years ago?" she asked softly. Then, more desperately, she cried, "Miller! Why didn't you come to Bryn Mawr that spring? In your clean white uniform? With your courage and your hopes?" She dropped my hands and asked quietly, "Why weren't you there?"

I left her and dodged among the mounds until I could present myself casually among the others. Improbably, they had not missed us and soon Ellen slipped inconspicuously back into the group she had been prepared to abuse. Once I caught sight of her unpacking the donkey, and as the night wind tugged at her hair she looked as if she had always been a part of these harsh, impersonal steppes.

It was now about three in the morning, and we made a little tea and pilau before going to bed, and as we sat about the fire Ellen said, through either accident or perversity, "Only a few miles up there is Russia."

A visible chill came over Stiglitz, but no one remarked upon his fear, so Ellen added, "Wouldn't you love to see what Samarkand looks like? They say its public square is the most exciting in the world." No one responded to this, so after a while she said languidly, "I think I'll go to bed," and Stiglitz dutifully followed her.

To share the tent with her that night would have been impossible, so I dragged out my sleeping gear and Mira lugged along a pillow, but before we had left the camp Maftoon took me aside and like a conspirator slipped me his dagger: "You must keep this, Miller."

"Why?"

"Because the German . . ."

"What about him?"

"When you and Ellen were in the dunes, he crept over to listen." The little cameleer sucked his teeth, then added, "And remember, he has Zulfiqar's dagger."

I felt dizzy. "Does Mira know?" I asked.

"It was she who asked me to give you my dagger,"

he explained. "She watched Stiglitz following you." And he was off.

When I rejoined Mira she said nothing, but ran her hands across my clothes till she felt Maftoon's dagger. "It's safer," she said.

There was nothing I could reply, so we looked for a sleeping place and after a while she observed quietly, "You and Ellen are the best friends I have. All I know about being pretty she taught me. She's a wonderful girl . . . like a sister. I told you, Miller, that she was hungry to sleep with you, but you laughed. After I go back with my father, why don't you and Ellen . . ."

I took her brown hands and kissed them. "I'm here because it's you I love," and I told her of the discovery I made while being expelled from the Hindu Kush without her: "You will be part of my life forever."

"Go to sleep," she said. "We have not many more nights."

The sun was well up when scraggly-bearded Maftoon hurried to where we slept and warned me. "Important government car from Kabul. Man to see you, Miller!"

I assumed this must be Richardson of Intelligence, so I dressed hastily in order that he should not see me with Mira, but when I reached the tent area I found that it was Moheb Khan looking very official in a tan sharkskin suit and silver karakul cap. He was patting his stolen white horse, behind which, to my surprise, I saw Nazrullah, come north to reclaim his lawful wife. Instinctively I felt sorry for him, and because I had not seen him since his forced trip across the Dasht-i-Margo I hurried first to him, embraced him warmly and asked, "How was the desert?"

"As always, hateful."

"We kept our fingers crossed."

Now Moheb Khan interrupted, speaking with severity: "How'd you get my horse?"

I couldn't tell whether he was truly angry or merely joking, so I temporized: "Mira bought him in Kabul."

Moheb brushed dust from his suit and asked, "You certainly knew it was mine. Didn't you guess it was stolen?"

"Was it?" I bluffed.

Moheb was unable to continue the pose and began laughing. "You know how it is. You find a pretty girl. You roll over thinking, 'This is going to be a night of passion.' And you find that your white horse has been stolen."

"Don't punish her."

"Did she steal it for you?"

"Yes."

"Then it's you I curse. For eight weeks you ride and I walk."

I replied, "You know how love is. Roll over again. There's your white horse, well fed and cared for."

Now Mira appeared on one of the mounds lugging our sleeping gear, which told its own story, and when she saw Moheb Khan, from whom she had stolen the horse, she dropped the bedclothes and started running for the tent, but I caught her by the wrist.

"Little thief!" Moheb snarled.

Mira was like me. She didn't know whether Moheb was joking or not, but her irrepressible nature asserted itself—or perhaps she remembered Moheb in some earlier pose—for she broke out laughing and pointed with derision at the handsome Afghan. Making involved gestures, which could only be interpreted as the pantomime of her escape through a bedroom window to steal the white horse, she soon had Moheb laughing with her.

But then Mira saw Nazrullah and recognized him by his beard. "You're Ellen's husband!" she cried in dismay, and the involuntary manner in which she moved protectively before the tent proved that Nazrullah's wife must be inside. Slowly, step by step, Mira retreated, bowed ceremoniously and ducked into the tent.

"Is Ellen there?" the engineer asked me.

"Yes."

He started for the tent but I stopped him. "Is the big Kochi with her?" he asked suspiciously.

And suddenly I realized that whole new cycles of adventure had engulfed his wife, none of which I fully understood but some of which I was myself involved in. At any rate, I couldn't explain these new developments to Nazrullah, so I stammered, "Look, this is going to be difficult to get into focus. But that big Kochi . . ."

I was spared by the appearance of Ellen and Stiglitz. What kind of hateful truce they had patched up during the night I couldn't guess, but in the morning sunlight Ellen Jaspar was dazzling, and if her husband was still determined to win her back, I could sympathize, for when I saw her in daylight I had to say, against my own conscience: It's you she wants to leave with, you idiot. Move in. Move in fast.

Nazrullah was bewildered by the facts before him and refused to accept their implications. As if nothing had happened, he stepped forward to greet his wife. "I've come to fetch you," he said. "You remember Moheb Khan. Moheb, this is Dr. Otto Stiglitz."

The tall diplomat bowed gracefully and shook hands. "We'll drive you back to Qala Bist," he said to Ellen with a studied air which seemed to say: We're going to give you one chance. Don't mess it up.

"I'm not going," she said firmly, whereupon Moheb Khan shrugged his shoulders and withdrew from the conversation. He had made a conciliatory offer and it had been rejected.

It was Nazrullah who took over. "Please, Ellen. We have the car waiting."

Stiglitz gave the answer: "She's to stay with me. I'm sorry, Nazrullah."

The engineer was determined not to surrender his wife and appealed to Moheb for support, but the diplomat ignored him and asked me, "Is this what happened? Stiglitz?" My nod triggered a dramatic barrage of decisions announced by Moheb.

First he blew a whistle, which was answered by a group of soldiers who had followed him in a truck. "I want that horse taken back to Kabul," he ordered. "This man," he snapped, indicating Stiglitz, "is to be kept here under arrest. The American woman is not to leave this tent. You, Miller, get in the car. I want to interrogate you at headquarters in Mazar-i-Sharif. Nazrullah, come along." And while the soldiers moved quickly in response to his commands, he led Nazrullah and me to the car.

We sped toward Mazar-i-Sharif, which lay some twenty miles east of Balkh, but as we reached the city our car was impeded by an extensive camel caravan which was setting forth to central Russia, and we had to wait while some eighty lumbering beasts went by, poking their ungainly heads toward our car and grunting at us as they adjusted to the heavy burdens which they were to carry north. The camel drivers, an unusually dirty and unkempt gang, stared at us like their camels and Moheb remarked with some irritation, "Of all the people you meet in our country, ninety-four percent are illiterate. Are we crazy, trying to build a modern state from such rabble?"

I looked at the camel drivers, barely out of the bronze age, and said to the two impatient men beside me, "If I were an Afghan, I'd certainly make the effort."

"I wish we had a million Afghans like you," Moheb replied, as the last camel went by, leering at us. And then I saw, riding a sturdy black horse, the master of this nondescript caravan and I understood why his cameleers had looked so filthy. Their owner had wanted them to look that way lest his camels give the impression of carrying some unusual wealth which might attract brigands.

For this was the caravan of Shakkur, the Kirghiz gunrunner from Russia. He had loaded his camels at

Mazar-i-Sharif, and was now on his way to cross the Oxus and the great Pamirs and the steppes of Central Asia. Since his was the most dangerous route followed by any of the major caravans attending Qabir—perhaps this was the last time a caravan of such magnitude would make the trip—he sought to avoid attention.

As he rode by I called to him and he remembered me from the encampment. Stopping his horse near our car, he poked his huge bald head our way and, after studying Moheb with suspicion, asked, "Government man?" When I nodded, he said, "So you were a government spy? I warned Zulfiqar."

"No," Moheb laughed. "We've just arrested him."

The big Kirghiz put his left hand over his forehead and cried, "My sympathy to all prisoners," and he spurred his horse so that he might overtake his eighty camels.

At the government offices Moheb ordered tea and biscuits with honey, reminding me of how primitively we had been eating for the past seventeen weeks; but I was dragged back to present problems when he summoned a secretary—a man, of course—and started arranging papers as he asked, "Now what shall the official report state regarding that horse?"

"Is this for the record?"

"That's why I'm here. The horse and the American woman . . . both stolen."

"Mira told me she bought the horse."

"Where would a Kochi girl get the money?"

"She said she got it from the jeep they stole."

"Jeep?" Moheb repeated.

"Could I strike that from the record?"

"You'd better," Moheb nodded to the secretary.

Nazrullah interrupted. "What did happen to that jeep?"

"Can I speak confidentially?"

"Of course," Moheb agreed, nodding again to the secretary.

"While I stood not twenty feet away, those damned Kochis stole every movable part."

Abruptly Moheb asked, "Who exactly is Mira?"

"Daughter of Zulfiqar," I explained.

"The same Zulfiqar?" he asked, indicating Nazrullah.

"Yes."

"Now as to the new developments regarding Ellen Jaspar."

"It's difficult to explain," I fumbled.

"We have plenty of time," Moheb assured me, pouring some more tea.

"Well, as you know, she ran away from Qala Bist last September. It wasn't love. It wasn't sex. Nazrullah wasn't at fault. Neither was Zulfiqar. When she joined the caravan she didn't even know who Zulfiqar was."

"Is that what you're going to say in your report to the American government?"

"I've already said it."

"Where did she spend the winter?"

"Jhelum."

"All the way to Jhelum? On foot?" Apparently Moheb knew less about some of his country's customs than I did.

"Was she ever in love with the big Kochi?" Nazrullah asked.

"Never."

"Miller," Moheb asked carefully, "if this secretary has to record one simple reason for Ellen's behavior, what shall he write?"

I pondered this question for some minutes, reviewing Ellen Jaspar's motivation as I understood it. It wasn't sex, because her behavior with Nazrullah, Zulfiqar and Stiglitz had an almost sexless quality; she was neither driven by desire nor faithful to anyone who fulfilled it. I wondered if she might be suffering from some kind of schizophrenia, but I could find no evidence that she was; no one was persecuting her; she persecuted herself. At one point I had thought she might be a victim of nostalgia for a past age, but she would have been the same in Renaissance Florence or Victorian England; history was replete with people like her, and although she despised this age, no other would have satisfied her better. It was true that like many sentimentalists she indulged in an infantile primitivism; if bread was baked over camel dung it was automatically better than bread baked in a General Electric range, but many people were afflicted with this heresy and they didn't wind up in a caravan at Balkh. There remained the possibility that she suffered from pure jaundice of the spirit, a vision which perverted reality and made it unpalatable; but with Ellen this was not the case. She saw reality rather clearly, I thought. It was her reaction to it that was faulty. And then I heard the dry, emotionless voice of Nexler reading from the music professor's report: *I saw her as a girl of good intention who was determined to disaffiliate herself from our society.* This didn't explain why she acted as she did, but it certainly described what her actions were. I looked at Moheb and suggested, "Put it down as rejection."

"Name one man she ever rejected," he demanded.

I preferred to ignore his condemnation and replied, "She rejected the forms and structures of our society . . . yours as well as mine."

"It's about time somebody rejected her," Moheb snapped. "And I'm the man to do it."

"Don't abuse her," Nazrullah pleaded.

"Would you still take her back?" Moheb asked incredulously.

"Yes," Nazrullah replied. "She's my wife."

"He's right," I told Moheb. "You'd both better get used to Ellen Jaspar," I warned. "Because once you let your women out of chaderi, Afghanistan's going to have a lot of girls like her."

Moheb groaned. "Do you believe that?"

"It's inevitable," I assured him. Then to protect Ellen, who in so many ways merited help, I added,

"Give her the benefit of one thing, Moheb. She loves your country. In fact, she plans to live here the rest of her life."

"With Stiglitz?"

I started to say yes, but hesitated, and from the way Moheb Khan looked at me I knew he suspected something between Ellen and me. I was another of the men she had not rejected, but Nazrullah, still fighting to get her back, missed the interplay, so I finished my sentence. "Yes, she's staying with Stiglitz."

"Tell me about him," Moheb said.

"She knew him in Kandahar, but I'm sure nothing romantic happened." Then I was forced again to pause, for I saw before me the caravanserai and my first meeting with Ellen Jaspar, and she was sweeping past me on her way to greet Stiglitz. I heard her clear voice crying, *Dr. Stiglitz! Are you all right?* Now what had really happened became clear to me. When she unexpectedly saw Stiglitz against the wall that morning her lips had begun to form a word, which she suppressed instantly. The discarded word was *Otto,* and I could now see it on her lips. Had they known each other that well in Kandahar? Had her blond, Germanic beauty so deeply affected him there at the edge of the desert?

"Something romantic did happen?" Moheb pressed.

"No," I said firmly. "Now about Stiglitz. On our trip north . . ."

"Who suggested that he come north?"

I had not previously considered this matter, but now I tried to reconstruct additional events from that first day with the nomads, and after a long pause I had to say, "I think it was her idea. I think she planned it all . . . that evening."

"I thought so, too," Moheb replied.

"At any rate, on the trip north they fell in love. At Qabir there was the dagger fight. Stiglitz handled himself capably and even wounded Zulfiqar. After which we were all thrown out."

"Is she determined to live with him?" Nazrullah asked quietly.

"Absolutely," I lied, as Moheb smiled.

"Could I possibly win her back?" Nazrullah pleaded.

"Never," I said with some assurance.

"Suppose we deported Stiglitz?" Moheb suggested.

I thought I was listening to Ellen's insidious suggestion: *Sooner or later the Russians are bound to get him.* I hesitated, and Moheb continued, "When Stiglitz left Kandahar for this . . . this stupid caravan, he broke our law. We've the right to throw him out. Shall we?" The two Afghans leaned forward to catch my reply.

I hesitated. Here, in a strange room in a drowsy provincial capital, my whole mission in Afghanistan was coming to focus. To calm myself I took a drink of tea and thought: These men want me to recommend his deportation. If I really wanted revenge on Stiglitz, I could get it now. The possibilities were gruesomely fascinating, particularly if I recalled the cage full of Jews he had destroyed; but I could feel against my shoulder, as if it were a real force in that room, the pressure of the German's body against mine as we prayed at evening, and I heard myself diverting Moheb with the question, "Does your intelligence report on me cover the fact that I'm a Jew?"

"It does not," Moheb replied, masking any surprise he might have felt.

"I am. That night at the caravanserai, Stiglitz betrayed the horrible things he had done in Munich. More than a thousand Jews sent to death."

"We know," Moheb observed, indicating his papers.

"I tried to kill him. Would have done it, but Zulfiqar arrived with his caravan. I despise Stiglitz. He's a criminal and he ought to hang. But on this trip I've come to know him. He'll serve your country well, Moheb. You just said you needed men like me. He's much stronger than I would ever be. Don't deport him."

"Why not?" Moheb asked cynically. "His going would solve Nazrullah's problem."

"Don't do it!" I warned.

"Why not?" he repeated.

"Because it would be wrong . . . morally wrong."

Nazrullah broke in: "Is there nothing I can do to bring her back?"

"Nothing," I said with great finality. "Even if you were to hang Stiglitz, you'll never get her back."

The force of my words struck the bearded engineer, and to my surprise he dropped into a chair and buried his head in his arms. For some moments his shoulders twitched while we watched in embarrassment. Then Moheb coughed and said, "Dear friend, Miller's right. You've lost her and there's nothing to do about it."

I remember thinking: It's really ridiculous, carrying on like this over a second wife, but then I recalled Ellen as she had been among the ruins, as she was in bed with Stiglitz in the black tent, and I admitted to myself: He's no fool. No wonder he wants to keep her.

Moheb took my arm and said, "Leave him alone," and he led me to another room, where he dismissed the two government clerks and checked doors to be sure no one was listening. When all was secure he moved close and stared into my eyes. "What did you discover at Qabir?" he asked.

"Nothing," I replied with as much simplicity as I could muster.

"Don't lie to me," he snapped. "Don't you suppose I know why you were sent north?"

"I don't know what you're talking about," I bluffed.

"Miller, for heaven's sake! Richardson drove out to the Kochi camp in Kabul and personally handed you orders: Go to Qabir and see what the Russians are up to."

"He did not!"

"Damn it all, we know he did. How else do you suppose he got Shah Khan's permission?"

The reasoning was logical and I was almost ready

to come clean when I thought: What if he's bluffing? I replied with some impatience, "If that's what he was supposed to tell me, he certainly forgot. All he did was raise hell about that stolen jeep."

He had been bluffing. "What'd he say about the jeep?" he asked lamely.

"That they were docking my pay six hundred dollars."

Seeking to catch me off guard, Moheb whipped his long forefinger into my face and shouted, "Miller! You know damned well the American embassy would never let you wander off to Qabir without orders. What were they?"

"Richardson didn't give me orders. I asked to go."

"Why?"

"Because I'd fallen in love with Mira."

"You mean that you told the American ambassador you wanted leave for ten weeks because," and here his voice dripped with contempt, "you'd fallen in love with a little nomad girl?"

"I didn't tell Richardson about her."

"What did you tell him?"

"I reminded him that Washington wanted me to stay on the Ellen Jaspar case until it was settled."

Moheb dropped his truculence and asked casually, "So what did happen at Qabir?"

"Like I said. Zulfiqar damned near killed Stiglitz."

He slammed his fist on the table. "The Russians?"

"I don't know anything about the Russians," I protested. Then I changed my voice. "I did discover one thing. That big Kirghiz we just saw was the leading sharif at the camp."

"How does he get into Afghanistan?"

"I wouldn't know about that."

"What the hell do you know about?"

"That the other sharif was this old Hazara who trades in karakul."

"We know about him."

"But this year he retired."

"He did?"

"And to take his place they elected Zulfiqar."

"Indeed?"

"And since Zulfiqar is eager to settle down on some of that new irrigated land near Qala Bist, you might do a good thing for Afghanistan if you settled his clan on five or six thousand acres."

Moheb tried to mask his irritation over the fact that I knew of this confidential matter and asked quietly, "Miller, if we offered Zulfiqar the land, would he take it . . . and stay put?"

"Positively."

"How can you be so sure?"

"We discussed it."

"Why would he confide in a ferangi? On such a matter?"

I wanted to say something that would help Zulfiqar, so I lied, "One day I mentioned that I knew you, and he said, 'Moheb has power of life and death over those lands.' He didn't ask me to intercede, but I know he hoped that I would."

"Well, at least you found out something."

"Then you'll give him the land?"

"We have many applications," he evaded.

"But none like Zulfiqar. He's a man like you and Nazrullah. He needs the land and you need him."

Moheb looked at me with compassion and said, "Why are you Americans so hopelessly stupid? I'll bet there were a dozen Russian agents in that camp, but you saw nothing except a nomad girl."

"I wasn't worrying about Russians," I laughed. He shook his head in amiable disgust and we returned to where Nazrullah was staring at the wall.

"What must I do?" the engineer asked us, no further in his solutions than when we left.

"I know what I must do," Moheb replied briskly. He summoned the secretary and asked, "Did you check my portfolio to be sure the alternative papers are in order? Good . . . Nazrullah, Miller, come along."

"To do what?" Nazrullah asked.

"To find three white pebbles."

"No!" Nazrullah cried. "I won't."

"Then I will," Moheb replied matter-of-factly. Then he stopped, reflected and said, "There is another way out for you."

"What?" Nazrullah asked eagerly.

"We'll turn your wife over to a bunch of mountain mullahs. A woman taken in adultery." He laughed at his grisly joke, then added gently, "Old friend, take my advice. Find the white pebbles."

As we left the office the secretary stopped us: "Don't forget your call to the English embassy."

"Of course!" Moheb agreed, sending us ahead, and before we left the building we could hear him shouting into the fragile Afghan telephone, "Hello, hello, hello! Is that you, Your Excellency? Here is Moheb Khan. Your Excellency, I want the British government to be alerted . . ." We did not hear the rest.

On our trip back to the barren fields of Balkh, Moheb consoled Nazrullah by reciting verses from the Persian poets, but when the car stopped at our capsule caravan it was Moheb who started hunting for the three white pebbles. When they had satisfied themselves, Nazrullah walked boldly to the black tent and called, "Ellen."

The soldiers brought her forth dressed in black skirt with gray blouse and three gold bracelets on her left wrist. Her tanned face was radiant in the sunlight, her marvelous blond hair framing it in windblown lines. As her legal husband approached, she looked solemnly at him and waited for his question: "Wife, will you come back with me to Qala Bist?"

"No," she replied in an icy voice, whereupon he raised his right hand and threw one of the pebbles to the ground.

"I divorce thee," he announced. Again he looked at her, beseeching her to rejoin him, but again he had to raise his arm and throw a second pebble to the ground.

"I divorce thee," he announced as Ellen listened without emotion. For the third time he pleaded with her, and for the third time she rejected him. Looking at her with eyes that had filled with tears, he hesitated in hopes she might reconsider, but she remained impassive, and he dropped the last pebble.

"I divorce thee," he said in a ghostly whisper. Unable to look further at the beautiful woman he had wooed in a strange land, he turned and walked with dignity to the car.

As he went, I watched Ellen Jaspar, now legally divorced, standing immobile by the tent. A smile of quiet satisfaction marked her lips, for now she was free, and from the right side of her body she lifted her hand ever so slightly so that she could form with her thumb and forefinger a circle, which she flashed at me, signifying: "All's well."

"Bring out Stiglitz," Moheb ordered, and the German was led forth, blinking in the sunlight. He must have guessed that Ellen intended to desert him, for he ignored her and looked only at Moheb.

"Otto Stiglitz," Moheb began, "we've informed the British government that you're being surrendered to them at Peshawar, in India. You're a criminal of war, and we have no place for you in Afghanistan." He blew his whistle and other soldiers appeared. "Take him to Peshawar," he announced, and an officer started clapping handcuffs about the German's wrists.

But this was to be no easy arrest, for Stiglitz broke loose and threw himself at me. "Jew! Jew!" he screamed. "You've done this to me." He scratched at my face until one of the soldiers tore him away.

Then he lunged at Moheb Khan, pleading, "Excellency, don't believe him. He's a filthy Jew and he told you lies. Why did he lie to you? Because he wants the girl himself. Yes! Yes!"

The commotion brought Nazrullah back in time to

hear Stiglitz cry, "Yes, Excellency! Last night this Jew took the girl over there. They committed indecencies. And while they were doing it they plotted my death."

He left Moheb and threw himself at Ellen, who drew back in disgust. "This one made love with the Jew behind that mound. And she told him, Hand the German over to the Russians, they'll hang him. Excellency, the Jew has poisoned your mind."

Moheb ordered the soldiers to pinion the doctor's arms, and when this was done he stood before the German and said, "The Jew you condemn has just spent an hour with us, pleading for your life. At your trial, I'm sure he'll testify for you."

Snapping his fingers, Moheb ordered the soldiers to drag the prisoner off, but as he went he tried to grab my arm. "You will tell the judges what I said at the pillar? There are many Jews in Munich alive today because . . . You will testify for me?"

"I will," I said, and he was dragged away. The truck engine sputtered. The wheels spun in the sand, and the soldiers were gone.

"Take the girl to the car," Moheb ordered Maftoon, and the unshaved cameleer led Ellen away. Since I had assumed that I was to remain in Balkh until Zulfiqar arrived, I supposed that this was the last time I would see Ellen Jaspar, and it was with real confusion that I saw her go. Her fair head was as provocative as ever, her lithe body beneath the gray blouse and black skirt as exciting, and her long legs ending in the leather sandals were as alluring. The clever rationalizations I had given at the interrogation seemed irrelevant when confronted by the girl herself.

I broke the spell by turning away and going to Mira, but I was unexpectedly halted by Moheb, who grabbed my arm and said, "You, too, Miller. We start for Kabul . . . now."

"I'm not leaving."

"Shah Khan's orders."

"I've got to say good-by," I protested, bringing Mira to my side.

"Say it. In five minutes we go."

"What about my gear?"

"You," he shouted at Maftoon, "pack his stuff. Hers too."

I led Mira away from the tent to one of the mounds of Balkh, from which we could see the foothills of the Hindu Kush, where we had been so happy. "I hoped we'd be here for a week," I began.

"You will look after Ellen," she replied. "She talks strong but she needs help." She was about to speak further when her nomad boisterousness took command and she cried, "Look at that crazy camel."

We left the mound and walked to where Aunt Becky was searching for grass. Her droopy eyes, ungainly feet and preposterous lower jaw kept her a comedian, even at this painful moment, and in gratitude for her having brought us so far I reached out to pat her in farewell, but she was not one to be tricked by sentiment. She interpreted my gesture only as a preamble to being loaded with burdens and withdrew uttering loud protests, and we were left alone.

"Mira, Mira," was all I could say, for in these last precious minutes there was so much we should have said and so little capacity for speech. Our parting had come so suddenly and was accompanied by so much ugliness that any chance for a decent farewell had been destroyed.

"Qabir, Bamian, Musa Darul," she recited. "When we are at those places . . ." She looked at me, deeply ashamed of the tears forming in her eyes. She blinked them away, laughed, and said, "Without you the caravan will be a marching of ghosts. You were very handsome on your white horse."

At the car Moheb was blowing the horn.

Then I remembered the warning which Stiglitz had sounded in the black tent: *Leaving this nomad girl is going to be a different experience from what you imagine*. But to leave her in this manner . . . a part of my conscience, of my growing up, was being torn away.

"Inshallah," I mumbled.

"Inshallah," she replied.

Unable to look back, I hurried to the car where Moheb sat at the wheel with Ellen beside him and Nazrullah in the rear. The engineer, ignoring his former wife, sat gazing through field glasses at the foothills of the Hindu Kush.

"It's uncanny," he mused. "How could she have seen such a distance?"

He handed me the glasses and I saw that Mira had left the ruins and was striding purposefully toward the mountains, out of which her father's caravan had appeared, following those ancient trails which soon the nomads would travel no more.

On the drive back to Mazar-i-Sharif no one spoke. Ellen's presence, following the charges against her that Stiglitz had broadcast, was more than we could cope with at the moment. Besides, I was affected by real suspense concerning her future, for I could not guess Moheb's plans, and he drove in imperious silence, his firm jaw locked in self-counsel. I supposed that when we reached Mazar we would deposit her at the government building, but we did not.

To my surprise we drove straight through the city and picked up an ancient road, thousands of years old, leading to the northeast. Along it plodded a camel caravan, insensitive to our intrusion, and as I looked ahead I saw on his black horse Shakkur, the Kirghiz gunrunner.

"Ho, sharif!" Moheb called from the car, and the Russian galloped up and dismounted.

He saw me sitting gloomily in the rear seat and asked seriously, in broken Pashto, "You taking the criminal out to shoot him?"

"No," Moheb laughed. "We have a passenger for your caravan."

Now the big Kirghiz saw Ellen, with whom he had danced that night at Qabir, and intuitively he grasped the situation. "This one?" he asked.

"Yes."

"She have papers?"

"Yes." From his portfolio Moheb took Ellen's green passport and handed it to the sharif. In Arabic, Cyrillic and Roman writing, signed jointly by Shah Khan and the Russian ambassador, it was stated that the bearer had permission to transit Russia on her way home to America. On a special page, for me to see, was the official notice that Ellen Jaspar, having been legally divorced from her Afghan husband, was free to exit the country. Ceremoniously Moheb Khan handed Ellen the precious document and announced, "Madam, you are being kicked out of Afghanistan."

To the Kirghiz he explained these matters, handing him a substantial number of Afghan gold coins. "This will pay her passage to Moscow. We'll cable her parents, and they'll have the rest waiting there."

"Christ Almighty," I exploded, jumping from the car. "You can't do this."

"I'm not doing it," Moheb protested. "She's doing it herself."

"What do you mean?"

"I came to Balkh with two sets of papers for this girl. One would have restored everything as it was. The other set kicks her out of the country. I gave her the choice. She made it."

"She didn't know what was involved!" I protested, trying to get Ellen to appeal for a second chance.

The tall Afghan turned his back on us and explained to Shakkur, "The poor boy's in love with her."

The big Kirghiz smiled indulgently, then asked with caution, "Does my friend Zulfiqar know of this?"

"He kicked her out of his caravan," Moheb reported. "We're doing the same."

Apparently the young leaders of Afghanistan were not afraid of making difficult decisions, but in the case of Ellen Jaspar their decisions were wrong, so I went to Moheb and warned him in rapid French, "This could cause serious trouble between our governments. How do you know what will happen to this girl?"

At that moment Moheb was helping Ellen from the car and he replied thoughtfully, "This girl? Nothing will ever happen to this girl." And he escorted her graciously to the Kirghiz, to whom he also delivered her pitifully small bundle of clothes.

At this point I had to interrupt. I took Ellen and Shakkur away from the others and asked, "Ellen, do you appreciate what's happening?"

With infuriating equanimity she ignored me and asked the sharif, "Where are we going?"

Pointing northeast he replied, "We cross the Oxus at Rushan, cut through the Pamirs, then Garm, Samarkand, Tashkent." It was a trip I would have given a year to take, and Ellen appreciated this, for when Samarkand was mentioned she smiled at me with deep satisfaction.

"Will we get there safely?" she asked.

"That's my job," the sharif replied, and I reflected: For ten weeks I tried every trick in the book to find out how the Russian nomads cross the Oxus. Now the top man tells me.

I said, "Ellen, I could force the Afghan government . . ."

"I'm not afraid," she answered, and she looked at me as if she were free and I the prisoner.

I summoned the others and announced, "I want everyone to hear that in the name of the United States government I do protest most vigorously this incredible act."

Ellen laughed and replied, "You heard him, gentlemen. If he catches hell, we'll all have to testify for him." She held out her hands, took mine and kissed me. "I do wish we'd met in America," she said.

With this speech she intended to leave, but decency

would not permit her to go without acknowledging Nazrullah, so at last she stepped before him and said, "Dear friend, I am most sorry." They looked at each other without moving and I thought again of how, on the desert, he had consulted the stars before assuring me that Ellen was safe once more in Afghanistan. Now he would follow those same stars till he knew that she was safe in America.

Finally she turned away and swung easily into the rhythm of her new caravan, as if she had been traveling with it for many months. I watched as the big Kirghiz galloped back to the head of his camels, spurring them on; for this caravan, excused from the encumbrance of either sheep or families, did not intend to cover a mere fourteen miles a day. It was headed for towering passes that must be cleared before the fall of snow, and for these travelers to Russia there would be no restful halting at noon.

The last camel passed us and we stood alone on the ancient road, watching the caravan as it lost itself in dust. I last saw Ellen Jaspar with her blond hair and black skirt swirling among the camels, marching east toward the greatest of the mountains.

"It's barbaric," I protested weakly, and Nazrullah agreed.

"She would have destroyed you both," Moheb Khan replied.

NOTE TO THE READER

The scene of this novel is the Kingdom of Afghanistan in 1946. Conditions are described as they existed in that year and as truthfully as research and memory will permit.

The reader may be curious about what has been happening in the intervening seventeen years, and a brief note covering recent developments may prove helpful.

Few nations have experienced a more spectacular growth and change during this period than Afghanistan. Kabul has paved streets (Russian money). Kandahar has an airport (American money). The city of Kabul has a fine public bakery (Russian). And many towns have good schools (American).

Foreigners have been visiting the country with ease and frequency. President Eisenhower was there in 1959, and many Russian leaders arrived both before and after that date. The vigorous struggle between America and Russia for Afghanistan's affection, referred to in this novel, goes on unceasingly with ultimate victory uncertain. An overriding fact is this: Russia abuts on the northern border for nearly seven hundred unguarded miles, while the United States is nearly eight thousand miles away. Under these circumstances it is remarkable that our side has done as well as it has.

Our victories have been the result of selfless work by dedicated men and women like John Pritchard, the fictional engineer of Chapters Nine and Ten. Apparently, when our country needs such men, there is an endless supply, but we rarely call upon them or find a worthy place for them when they are called.

The battle between old and new which is a feature of this

novel has produced some interesting skirmishes. In 1959 women were allowed, even encouraged, to dispense with the chaderi in public. A few did; many preferred the isolation and protection of the shroud . . . or more likely, their husbands did. Symptomatic of the future, however, was the plebiscite held in neighboring Iran in 1963 on similar matters of civil freedom and relaxation of mullah rule. In Iran, which is about fifty years ahead of Afghanistan in social change, the vote was on the order of 4,000 to 1 in favor of modernism. Young women wearing no chaderi stormed the streets on election day, begging people to go to the polls. Old-fashioned mullahs interpreted the vote as the end of organized religion, which of course it was not.

The bright young men represented in this novel by foreign-trained Moheb Khan and Nazrullah and by locally trained Nur Muhammad have brought their nation improved administration. They have by no means achieved victory, but they have won a position from which victory is possible. Many such young men find themselves inclining toward Russia; others, thank heavens, see promise in continued links with the West.

The patterns of social life depicted in the novel have changed radically in the past seventeen years. Kabul now has a good hotel, newspapers, radio, a public cinema to which westerners can go, stores other than bazaars, and several restaurants. Amenities in the cities like Kandahar and Mazar-i-Sharif are also better, but Ghazni remains pretty much as described.

The public punishments described in the novel are no longer common. Since the reader may wonder, I witnessed the first execution, but not in Ghazni; as for the second, I arrived in Kandahar only a few days after it occurred and was given a series of photographs taken by an enterprising man who told me that he had prevailed upon the father to work from the other side because the sunlight was better. Afghan polo, properly called buzkashi (goat dragging), still flourishes and is both rougher and more fun than I describe.

The great dam on whose preliminaries Nazrullah worked in 1946 is in being—one of the marvels of Asia—and its electricity is eagerly sought. The land opposite Qala Bist which was to have been irrigated was found, alas, to be too full of residual salts to be productive. In a sense, this failure of one aspect of the Helmand Project had unfortunate overtones not dissimilar to those that grew out of the German bridges: Afghans looked at the mighty dam, at the cost, at the partial failure and asked, "Why bother?" The German bridges, when I traveled the road from Kabul to Kandahar, were exactly as described; but the Afghan bridge built by Shah Khan and Nazrullah's father stood on a different road.

As for the Kochis, restrictions have been placed on them at every turn. They cannot enter Russia. Traders from China can no longer penetrate the Pamirs with goods. Pakistan, the western portion of old India, conducts a running fight with Afghanistan over the nationality of Pashtuns and halts many of the nomads at that arbitrary border. The tents are still black; the women are still superb in their freedom; the fat-tailed sheep are still among the most preposterous of animals; and the camels still protest at everything.

The reader may also wish to check my credentials for writing this novel. My first acquaintance with Afghanistan came in 1952, when I was living in the Khyber Pass and had a chance to scout the Afghan border for many miles north and south of that historic area. It was then that I conceived my determination to visit Afghanistan. It was then also that I came to know several Kochi tribes fairly well—Povindahs, we called them, for I did not hear the name Kochi until later—and decided that one day I might try to write about them.

In 1955 I was able to enter Afghanistan itself and made these journeys: First, Khyber Pass to Kabul; second, Kabul to Qala Bist; third, across the Dasht-i-Margo to the Chakhansur, called in this novel The City, which is perhaps a more appropriate name; fourth, down to Chahar Burjak, one of the worst trips I have ever made; fifth, up to Herat and back down to Girishk; sixth, Kabul to Istalif and the lower Koh-i-Baba; seventh, Kabul to Bamian and on to Balkh; eighth, Kandahar to Spin Baldak and Quetta. And there was a ninth trip, perhaps the most memorable I have ever taken, from Qala Bist along the untraveled left bank of the Helmand River to Rudbar. This took us across the Registan desert in a caravan that camped at night in sand dunes with little water and less food. It was from the experiences on this trip, not referred to in this novel, that I developed my love of desert life.

On one of these trips I was visited by friends of a European woman who sought my help. Some years before she had married an Afghan and had passed into the limbo described in parts of this novel. I asked to see her and was taken to a pathetic hovel where I talked with her for the better part of an hour, but I was unable to help. Later I heard of similar cases and met with people actively concerned in liberating wives of foreign origin. However, in fairness I must add that I also met several European women married to enlightened Afghans, and these wives led normal, happy lives; they wore no chaderi, visited Europe when they wished, and were pleased that they had come to live in Afghanistan. Today, of course, quite a few American girls have been marrying Afghans without encountering difficulties with citizenship or the right to travel.

Qabir is an invented name, but the facts associated with it are not. The massive nomad convocation met at no regular place, and where it did meet bore no proper name, for the land is unbelievably wild, empty and unknown. It was called merely The Abul Camp and was probably larger than I suggest. Also, the subsidiary camps for attendant families seem to have been farther from the trading center than I have indicated. The Abul Camp was for men only. Until 1954 no known outsider had ever visited the camp, so that events depicted in this novel are anachronistic by eight years. As for a foreign woman's visiting the camp, there is no record of its having happened.

The archaeological sites referred to—Qala Bist, The City, Bamian, Balkh—are faithfully described. Bamian remains one of the compelling sights of Asia. My notes, penciled hurriedly as we approached from the east, tell the story:

> Bamian: at eastern approach the Red City (name Zak?) high on hill and cliffs several hundred feet high. Note

little castles guarding trail all the way up. City 4 main levels. It was here Genghis Khan lost his son. Destruction of Bamian followed. Red City on right bank of Bamian River. City at Bamian named Ghulghulah and stood back of present hostel. KOCHI is Farsi word (those who move).

Cliffs 350 feet high, reddish tan. Probably over 500 cave entrances visible, each leading to 4 or 5 rooms. Some caves 300 feet high, sheer drop. Magnificent corridors. Frescoes. All faces routed out. Located foot of soaring sepia and purple-brown mountains facing Koh-i-Baba.

From one room in the highest level of caves I counted 61 snow-covered peaks in midsummer, all over 15,000 feet high.

The Caravanserai of the Tongues, its location and its pillar are inventions, but each is true to the spirit of Afghanistan. I camped in many of these deserted caravanserais, great lonely structures scattered over the land, and never failed to be impressed with their mood and their function. It was at one that I met my first Kochis in Afghanistan and jotted down the outline of a novel much different from this one. As for the pillar, I forget where I heard about an event of similar import; possibly it was at Herat, where Genghis Khan is reliably reported to have slain a million people. One contemporary authority wrote that it was a million and a half.

My contacts with Islam have been consistent and varied: Indonesia, Borneo, Malaya, Pakistan, Afghanistan, the Near East, Turkey. I have written favorably of the religion, have known many of its leaders, and hold it in both respect and affection. My experiences, as the reader may guess, place me in opposition to the rural mullahs.

Practically every Afghan word, when transliterated into the Roman alphabet, can be spelled in alternate ways (Kabul, Caboul; Helmand, Helmund) and consistency in orthography seems at this point impossible. The editors of this book and I drew up lists of many variant spellings. We consulted numerous experts, some with rather exalted credentials, and in the end found ourselves repeating the lament of Omar, the poet from nearby Persia:

Myself when young did eagerly frequent
  Doctor and Saint, and heard great argument
  About it and about: but evermore
Came out by the same door wherein I went.

It will be some years before the Roman spelling of essential Afghan words is standardized. Those which offered the most interesting variants include:

chaderi, choudhry, shaddry, chadhri, charderi
ferangi, farangi, faranji, ferengi, feringhee
Tajik, Tadjik, Tadzhik
Pashtun, Pushtun, Pushtoon, Pakhtoon, Pathan
Kandahar, Qandahar
Koran, Qur'an
Bamian, Bamyan, Bamiyan
Kochi, Kuchi
Pashto, Pushto, Pushtu, Pukhto
Povindah, Powindeh

I must make it clear that our decision to spell a given word in a given way was never taken without extensive study, but I must also confess that the final decision was usually arbitrary and that consistency from one decision to the next did not seem possible in view of the conflicts existing among the experts.

For two usages I am alone responsible. In 1946 in this part of the world Iran was known as Persia, the Amu Darya river as the Oxus. If I were writing about today, I would of course use the contemporary forms.

In recent years whenever I have been asked which of the countries I have seen I would most prefer to visit again, I have invariably said Afghanistan. I remember it as an exciting, violent, provocative place. Almost every American or European who worked there in the old days says the same. It was, in the years I knew it, what Mark Miller says: "One of the world's great cauldrons."

Now! The World's Greatest give you an Electrifying

BUTTERWORTHS E-COMMERCE AND IT LAW HANDBOOK

Fourth edition

CONSULTANT EDITOR

JEREMY PHILLIPS BA (Cantab), PhD

Intellectual Property Consultant, Slaughter and May
Research Director, Intellectual Property Institute
Visiting Professor, Faculty of Laws, University College London
Co-blogmeister, IPKat weblog

Members of the LexisNexis Group Worldwide

United Kingdom	LexisNexis Butterworths, a Division of Reed Elsevier (UK) Ltd, Halsbury House, 35 Chancery Lane, London, WC2A 1EL, and RSH, London House, 20–22 East London Street, Edinburgh EH7 4BQ
Argentina	LexisNexis Argentina, Buenos Aires
Australia	LexisNexis Butterworths, Chatswood, New South Wales
Austria	LexisNexis Verlag ARD Orac GmbH & Co KG, Vienna
Benelux	LexisNexis Benelux, Amsterdam
Canada	LexisNexis Canada, Markham, Ontario
Chile	LexisNexis Chile Ltda, Santiago
China	LexisNexis China, Beijing and Shanghai
France	LexisNexis SA, Paris
Germany	LexisNexis Deutschland GmbH, Munster
Hong Kong	LexisNexis Hong Kong, Hong Kong
India	LexisNexis India, New Delhi
Italy	Giuffrè Editore, Milan
Japan	LexisNexis Japan, Tokyo
Malaysia	Malayan Law Journal Sdn Bhd, Kuala Lumpur
Mexico	LexisNexis Mexico, Mexico
New Zealand	LexisNexis NZ Ltd, Wellington
Poland	Wydawnictwo Prawnicze LexisNexis Sp, Warsaw
Singapore	LexisNexis Singapore, Singapore
South Africa	LexisNexis Butterworths, Durban
USA	LexisNexis, Dayton, Ohio

Published by LexisNexis Butterworths

A CIP Catalogue record for this book is available from the British Library.

ISBN 978 14057 1582 9

Typeset by Columns Design Ltd, Reading, UK
Printed and bound in Great Britain by CPI Bath Press, Bath

Visit LexisNexis Butterworths at www.lexisnexis.co.uk

PREFACE

In the two and a half years since the Third Edition, e-commerce and the information technologies have quietly but firmly displaced the ancient regime as the driving force of the twenty-first century economy. Chip-and-pin transactions, electronic banking, the online purchase of groceries, disposing of unwanted presents and filling gaps in a precious stamp collection via eBay – these are no longer activities that raise an eyebrow, for they have become the norm, the commonplace. Our dependence on advanced communications concepts has increased as dial-up yields to broadband, Bluetooth and wi-fi. Music is increasingly downloaded via digital rights management systems if it is not ripped and burned on to MP3 players, while our telephones have become cameras, videos and much more besides. We march to the beat of the Tom-Tom.

The past few years, in legal terms, have displayed two principal features. One is the relative consolidation of legislation, after a decade or so of constant reform. The other is the shift of focus from legislation to litigation, as uses of the new technologies increasingly generate disputes that require judicial intervention and clarification, with some surprising results. While data protection law remains stable and predictable, the European Court of Justice has all but destroyed the Commission's attempts to establish a sui generis form of protection for databases comprised of factual information. Computer software remains both patentable and unpatentable, often unpredictably so. Evidential issues relating to computers and telecommunications are now gradually being resolved and the uncertainty that existed just a few years ago is now giving way to a gentle incremental tide of precedent.

The period since the publication of the Third Edition has also seen the coming of age of the long-cherished .eu top level domain. The legal framework for this has met with fierce criticism, both on account of its alleged deficiencies over the ICANN-based scheme for dispute resolution and on account of what many accusers see as a partial reinvention of the wheel at a time when perfectly adequate systems for the allocation and administration of domain names already existed. Time will tell whether these criticisms are well-founded.

It is, as ever, my pleasure as Consultant Editor to thank and to congratulate the LexisNexis Butterworths team for the painless manner in which this edition has emerged, grey and Phoenix-like, from the ashes of its predecessor. Their efforts are proof positive that the desirable goals of speed and accuracy are not mutually exclusive.

Finally I should like to express my gratitude to my colleagues in Slaughter and May's Intellectual Property and Information Technology Group for their support and encouragement, which I have enjoyed in such liberal proportions that I feel myself to be in danger of taking it for granted. Particular thanks are due to Susie Middlemiss, Cathy Connolly and Rob Sumroy for the interest that they continue to show in all my publishing activities, with a special mention for the tireless and resourceful Julia Adams for her constructive suggestions and her continued ability to identify lacunae in the Handbook's content.

Jeremy Phillips
Temple Fortune

February 2007

CONTENTS

PART III INTERNET AND DOMAIN NAMES

PART IV INTELLECTUAL PROPERTY

PART V BROADCASTING AND TRANSMISSION

PART VII MISCELLANEOUS

PART I
ELECTRONIC COMMERCE

ELECTRONIC COMMUNICATIONS ACT 2000

(2000 c 7)

ARRANGEMENT OF SECTIONS

PART II
FACILITATION OF ELECTRONIC COMMERCE, DATA STORAGE, ETC

PART III
MISCELLANEOUS AND SUPPLEMENTAL

Supplemental

An Act to make provision to facilitate the use of electronic communications and electronic data storage; to make provision about the modification of licences granted under section 7 of the Telecommunications Act 1984; and for connected purposes

[25 May 2000]

1–6 (*Pt I repealed by virtue of s 16(4) of this Act at* **[8]**.)

PART II
FACILITATION OF ELECTRONIC COMMERCE, DATA STORAGE, ETC

7 Electronic signatures and related certificates

(1) In any legal proceedings—

(a) an electronic signature incorporated into or logically associated with a particular electronic communication or particular electronic data; and

(b) the certification by any person of such a signature,

shall each be admissible in evidence in relation to any question as to the authenticity of the communication or data or as to the integrity of the communication or data.

(2) For the purposes of this section an electronic signature is so much of anything in electronic form as—

(a) is incorporated into or otherwise logically associated with any electronic communication or electronic data; and

(b) purports to be so incorporated or associated for the purpose of being used in establishing the authenticity of the communication or data, the integrity of the communication or data, or both.

(3) For the purposes of this section an electronic signature incorporated into or associated with a particular electronic communication or particular electronic data is certified by any person if that person (whether before or after the making of the communication) has made a statement confirming that—

(a) the signature,

(b) a means of producing, communicating or verifying the signature, or

(c) a procedure applied to the signature,

is (either alone or in combination with other factors) a valid means of establishing the authenticity of the communication or data, the integrity of the communication or data, or both.

[1]

8 Power to modify legislation

(1) Subject to subsection (3), the appropriate Minister may by order made by statutory instrument modify the provisions of—

(a) any enactment or subordinate legislation, or

(b) any scheme, licence, authorisation or approval issued, granted or given by or under any enactment or subordinate legislation,

in such manner as he may think fit for the purpose of authorising or facilitating the use of electronic communications or electronic storage (instead of other forms of communication or storage) for any purpose mentioned in subsection (2).

(2) Those purposes are—

(a) the doing of anything which under any such provisions is required to be or may be done or evidenced in writing or otherwise using a document, notice or instrument;

(b) the doing of anything which under any such provisions is required to be or may be done by post or other specified means of delivery;

(c) the doing of anything which under any such provisions is required to be or may be authorised by a person's signature or seal, or is required to be delivered as a deed or witnessed;

(d) the making of any statement or declaration which under any such provisions is required to be made under oath or to be contained in a statutory declaration;

(e) the keeping, maintenance or preservation, for the purposes or in pursuance of any such provisions, of any account, record, notice, instrument or other document;

(f) the provision, production or publication under any such provisions of any information or other matter;

(g) the making of any payment that is required to be or may be made under any such provisions.

(3) The appropriate Minister shall not make an order under this section authorising the use of electronic communications or electronic storage for any purpose, unless he considers that the authorisation is such that the extent (if any) to which records of things done for that purpose will be available will be no less satisfactory in cases where use is made of electronic communications or electronic storage than in other cases.

(4) Without prejudice to the generality of subsection (1), the power to make an order under this section shall include power to make an order containing any of the following provisions—

(a) provision as to the electronic form to be taken by any electronic communications or electronic storage the use of which is authorised by an order under this section;

(b) provision imposing conditions subject to which the use of electronic communications or electronic storage is so authorised;

(c) provision, in relation to cases in which any such conditions are not satisfied, for treating anything for the purposes of which the use of such communications or storage is so authorised as not having been done;

(d) provision, in connection with anything so authorised, for a person to be able to refuse to accept receipt of something in electronic form except in such circumstances as may be specified in or determined under the order;

(e) provision, in connection with any use of electronic communications so authorised, for intermediaries to be used, or to be capable of being used, for the transmission of any data or for establishing the authenticity or integrity of any data;

(f) provision, in connection with any use of electronic storage so authorised, for persons satisfying such conditions as may be specified in or determined under the regulations to carry out functions in relation to the storage;

(g) provision, in relation to cases in which the use of electronic communications or electronic storage is so authorised, for the determination of any of the matters mentioned in subsection (5), or as to the manner in which they may be proved in legal proceedings;

(h) provision, in relation to cases in which fees or charges are or may be imposed in connection with anything for the purposes of which the use of electronic communications or electronic storage is so authorised, for different fees or charges to apply where use is made of such communications or storage;

(i) provision, in relation to any criminal or other liabilities that may arise (in respect of the making of false or misleading statements or otherwise) in connection with anything for the purposes of which the use of electronic communications or electronic storage is so authorised, for corresponding liabilities to arise in corresponding circumstances where use is made of such communications or storage;

(j) provision requiring persons to prepare and keep records in connection with any use of electronic communications or electronic storage which is so authorised;

(k) provision requiring the production of the contents of any records kept in accordance with an order under this section;

(l) provision for a requirement imposed by virtue of paragraph (j) or (k) to be enforceable at the suit or instance of such person as may be specified in or determined in accordance with the order;

(m) any such provision, in relation to electronic communications or electronic storage the use of which is authorised otherwise than by an order under this section, as corresponds to any provision falling within any of the preceding paragraphs that may be made where it is such an order that authorises the use of the communications or storage.

(5) The matters referred to in subsection (4)(g) are—

(a) whether a thing has been done using an electronic communication or electronic storage;

(b) the time at which, or date on which, a thing done using any such communication or storage was done;

(c) the place where a thing done using such communication or storage was done;

(d) the person by whom such a thing was done; and

(e) the contents, authenticity or integrity of any electronic data.

(6) An order under this section—

(a) shall not (subject to paragraph (b)) require the use of electronic communications or electronic storage for any purpose; but

(b) may make provision that a period of notice specified in the order must expire before effect is given to a variation or withdrawal of an election or other decision which—

(i) has been made for the purposes of such an order; and

(ii) is an election or decision to make use of electronic communications or electronic storage.

(7) The matters in relation to which provision may be made by an order under this section do not include any matter under the care and management of the Commissioners of Inland Revenue or any matter under the care and management of the Commissioners of Customs and Excise.

(8) In this section references to doing anything under the provisions of any enactment include references to doing it under the provisions of any subordinate legislation the power to make which is conferred by that enactment.

[2]

NOTES

Orders: the Local Government and Housing Act 1989 (Electronic Communications) (England) Order 2000, SI 2000/3056; the Companies Act 1985 (Electronic Communications) Order 2000, SI 2000/3373; the Local Government and Housing Act 1989 (Electronic Communications) (Wales) Order 2001, SI 2001/605; the Unsolicited Goods and Services Act 1971 (Electronic Communications) Order 2001, SI 2001/2778; the National Health Service (Charges for Drugs and Appliances) (Electronic Communications) Order 2001, SI 2001/2887; the National Health Service (Pharmaceutical Services) and (Misuse of Drugs) (Electronic Communications) Order 2001, SI 2001/2888; the Prescription Only Medicines (Human Use) (Electronic Communications) Order 2001, SI 2001/2889; the Housing (Right to Acquire) (Electronic Communications) (England) Order 2001, SI 2001/3257; the Public Records Act 1958 (Admissibility of Electronic Copies of Public Records) Order 2001, SI 2001/4058; the Building Societies Act 1986 (Electronic Communications) Order 2003, SI 2003/404; the Patents Act 1977 (Electronic Communications) Order 2003, SI 2003/512; the Town and Country Planning (Electronic Communications) (England) Order 2003, SI 2003/956; the Council Tax and Non-Domestic Rating (Electronic Communications) (England) Order 2003, SI 2003/2604; the Social Security (Electronic Communications) (Carer's Allowance) Order 2003, SI 2003/2800; the Council Tax and Non-Domestic Rating (Electronic Communications) (England) (No 2) Order 2003, SI 2003/3052; the Town and Country Planning (Electronic Communications) (Scotland) Order 2004, SSI 2004/332; the Education Act (Electronic Communications) Order 2004, SI 2004/2521; the Town and Country Planning (Electronic Communications) (Wales) (No 1) Order 2004, SI 2004/3156; the Town and Country Planning (Electronic Communications) (Wales) (No 2) Order 2004, SI 2004/3157; the Town and Country Planning (Electronic Communications) (Wales) (No 3) Order 2004, SI 2004/3172; the Consumer Credit Act 1974 (Electronic Communications) Order 2004, SI 2004/3236; the Social Security (Electronic Communications) (Miscellaneous Benefits) Order 2005, SI 2005/3321; the Council Tax (Electronic Communications)

(Scotland) Order 2006, SSI 2006/67; the Non-Domestic Rating (Electronic Communications) (Scotland) Order 2006, SSI 2006/201; the Non-Domestic Rating and Council Tax (Electronic Communications) (England) Order 2006, SI 2006/237; the Electronic Communications (Scotland) Order 2006, SSI 2006/367; the Automated Registration of Title to Land (Electronic Communications) (Scotland) Order 2006, SSI 2006/491; the Registered Designs Act 1949 and Patents Act 1977 (Electronic Communications) Order 2006, SI 2006/1229; the Transport Security (Electronic Communications) Order 2006, SI 2006/2190; the Registration of Births and Deaths (Electronic Communications and Electronic Storage) Order 2006, SI 2006/2809; the Housing Benefit and Council Tax Benefit (Electronic Communications) Order 2006, SI 2006/2968.

9 Section 8 orders

(1) In this Part "the appropriate Minister" means (subject to subsections (2) and (7) and section 10(1))—

(a) in relation to any matter with which a department of the Secretary of State is concerned, the Secretary of State;

(b) in relation to any matter with which the Treasury is concerned, the Treasury; and

(c) in relation to any matter with which any Government department other than a department of the Secretary of State or the Treasury is concerned, the Minister in charge of the other department.

(2) Where in the case of any matter—

(a) that matter falls within more than one paragraph of subsection (1),

(b) there is more than one such department as is mentioned in paragraph (c) of that subsection that is concerned with that matter, or

(c) both paragraphs (a) and (b) of this subsection apply,

references, in relation to that matter, to the appropriate Minister are references to any one or more of the appropriate Ministers acting (in the case of more than one) jointly.

(3) Subject to subsection (4) and section 10(6), a statutory instrument containing an order under section 8 shall be subject to annulment in pursuance of a resolution of either House of Parliament.

(4) Subsection (3) does not apply in the case of an order a draft of which has been laid before Parliament and approved by a resolution of each House.

(5) An order under section 8 may—

(a) provide for any conditions or requirements imposed by such an order to be framed by reference to the directions of such persons as may be specified in or determined in accordance with the order;

(b) provide that any such condition or requirement is to be satisfied only where a person so specified or determined is satisfied as to specified matters.

(6) The provision made by such an order may include—

(a) different provision for different cases;

(b) such exceptions and exclusions as the person making the order may think fit; and

(c) any such incidental, supplemental, consequential and transitional provision as he may think fit;

and the provision that may be made by virtue of paragraph (c) includes provision modifying any enactment or subordinate legislation or any scheme, licence, authorisation or approval issued, granted or given by or under any enactment or subordinate legislation.

(7) In the case of any matter which is not one of the reserved matters within the meaning of the Scotland Act 1998 or in respect of which functions are, by virtue of section 63 of that Act, exercisable by the Scottish Ministers instead of by or concurrently with a Minister of the Crown, this section and section 8 shall apply to Scotland subject to the following modifications—

(a) subsections (1) and (2) of this section are omitted;

(b) any reference to the appropriate Minister is to be read as a reference to the Secretary of State;

(c) any power of the Secretary of State, by virtue of paragraph (b), to make an order under section 8 may also be exercised by the Scottish Ministers with the consent of the Secretary of State; and

(d) where the Scottish Ministers make an order under section 8—

(i) any reference to the Secretary of State (other than a reference in this subsection) shall be construed as a reference to the Scottish Ministers; and

(ii) any reference to Parliament or to a House of Parliament shall be construed as a reference to the Scottish Parliament.

[3]

10 Modifications in relation to Welsh matters

(1) For the purposes of the exercise of the powers conferred by section 8 in relation to any matter the functions in respect of which are exercisable by the National Assembly for Wales, the appropriate Minister is the Secretary of State.

(2) Subject to the following provisions of this section, the powers conferred by section 8, so far as they fall within subsection (3), shall be exercisable by the National Assembly for Wales, as well as by the appropriate Minister.

(3) The powers conferred by section 8 fall within this subsection to the extent that they are exercisable in relation to—

(a) the provisions of any subordinate legislation made by the National Assembly for Wales;

(b) so much of any other subordinate legislation as makes provision the power to make which is exercisable by that Assembly;

(c) any power under any enactment to make provision the power to make which is so exercisable;

(d) the giving, sending or production of any notice, account, record or other document or of any information to or by a body mentioned in subsection (4); or

(e) the publication of anything by a body mentioned in subsection (4).

(4) Those bodies are—

(a) the National Assembly for Wales;

(b) any body specified in Schedule 4 to the Government of Wales Act 1998 (Welsh public bodies subject to reform by that Assembly);

(c) any other such body as may be specified for the purposes of this section by an order made by the Secretary of State with the consent of that Assembly.

(5) The National Assembly for Wales shall not make an order under section 8 except with the consent of the Secretary of State.

(6) Section 9(3) shall not apply to any order made under section 8 by the National Assembly for Wales.

(7) Nothing in this section shall confer any power on the National Assembly for Wales to modify any provision of the Government of Wales Act 1998.

(8) The power of the Secretary of State to make an order under subsection (4)(c)—

(a) shall include power to make any such incidental, supplemental, consequential and transitional provision as he may think fit; and

(b) shall be exercisable by statutory instrument subject to annulment in pursuance of a resolution of either House of Parliament.

[4]

PART III
MISCELLANEOUS AND SUPPLEMENTAL

11, 12 (*Repealed by the Communications Act 2003, s 406(7), Sch 19(1).*)

Supplemental

13 Ministerial expenditure etc

There shall be paid out of money provided by Parliament—

(a) any expenditure incurred by the Secretary of State for or in connection with the carrying out of his functions under this Act; and

(b) any increase attributable to this Act in the sums which are payable out of money so provided under any other Act.

[5]

14 Prohibition on key escrow requirements

(1) Subject to subsection (2), nothing in this Act shall confer any power on any Minister of the Crown, on the Scottish Ministers, on the National Assembly for Wales or on any person appointed under section 3—

(a) by conditions of an approval under Part I, or

(b) by any regulations or order under this Act,

to impose a requirement on any person to deposit a key for electronic data with another person.

(2) Subsection (1) shall not prohibit the imposition by an order under section 8 of—

(a) a requirement to deposit a key for electronic data with the intended recipient of electronic communications comprising the data; or

(b) a requirement for arrangements to be made, in cases where a key for data is not deposited with another person, which otherwise secure that the loss of a key, or its becoming unusable, does not have the effect that the information contained in a record kept in pursuance of any provision made by or under any enactment or subordinate legislation becomes inaccessible or incapable of being put into an intelligible form.

(3) In this section "key", in relation to electronic data, means any code, password, algorithm, key or other data the use of which (with or without other keys)—

(a) allows access to the electronic data, or

(b) facilitates the putting of the electronic data into an intelligible form;

and references in this section to depositing a key for electronic data with a person include references to doing anything that has the effect of making the key available to that person. **[6]**

15 General interpretation

(1) In this Act, except in so far as the context otherwise requires—

"document" includes a map, plan, design, drawing, picture or other image;

"communication" includes a communication comprising sounds or images or both and a communication effecting a payment;

"electronic communication" means a communication transmitted (whether from one person to another, from one device to another or from a person to a device or vice versa)—

(a) by means of [an electronic communications network]; or

(b) by other means but while in an electronic form;

"enactment" includes—

(a) an enactment passed after the passing of this Act,

(b) an enactment comprised in an Act of the Scottish Parliament; and

(c) an enactment contained in Northern Ireland legislation,

but does not include an enactment contained in Part I or II of this Act;

"modification" includes any alteration, addition or omission, and cognate expressions shall be construed accordingly;

"record" includes an electronic record; and

"subordinate legislation" means—

(a) any subordinate legislation (within the meaning of the Interpretation Act 1978);

(b) any instrument made under an Act of the Scottish Parliament; or

(c) any statutory rules (within the meaning of the Statutory Rules (Northern Ireland) Order 1979).

(2) In this Act—

(a) references to the authenticity of any communication or data are references to any one or more of the following—

(i) whether the communication or data comes from a particular person or other source;

(ii) whether it is accurately timed and dated;

(iii) whether it is intended to have legal effect; and

(b) references to the integrity of any communication or data are references to whether there has been any tampering with or other modification of the communication or data.

(3) References in this Act to something's being put into an intelligible form include references to its being restored to the condition in which it was before any encryption or similar process was applied to it.

[7]

NOTES

Sub-s (1): in definition "electronic communication" words in square brackets substituted by the Communications Act 2003, s 406(1), Sch 17, para 158.

16 Short title, commencement, extent

(1) This Act may be cited as the Electronic Communications Act 2000.

(2) Part I of this Act and sections 7, 11 and 12 shall come into force on such day as the Secretary of State may by order made by statutory instrument appoint; and different days may be appointed under this subsection for different purposes.

(3) An order shall not be made for bringing any of Part I of this Act into force for any purpose unless a draft of the order has been laid before Parliament and approved by a resolution of each House.

(4) If no order for bringing Part I of this Act into force has been made under subsection (2) by the end of the period of five years beginning with the day on which this Act is passed, that Part shall, by virtue of this subsection, be repealed at the end of that period.

(5) This Act extends to Northern Ireland.

[8]

NOTES

Orders: the Electronic Communications Act 2000 (Commencement No 1) Order 2000, SI 2000/1798.

CONSUMER PROTECTION (DISTANCE SELLING) REGULATIONS 2000

(SI 2000/2334)

NOTES

Made: 31 August 2000.
Authority: European Communities Act 1972, s 2(2).
Commencement: 31 October 2000.

ARRANGEMENT OF REGULATIONS

1 Title, commencement and extent

(1) These Regulations may be cited as the Consumer Protection (Distance Selling) Regulations 2000 and shall come into force on 31st October 2000.

(2) These Regulations extend to Northern Ireland.

[9]

2 (*Revokes the Mail Order Transactions (Information) Order 1976, SI 1976/1812.*)

3 Interpretation

(1) In these Regulations—

["the 2000 Act" means the Financial Services and Markets Act 2000;

"appointed representative" has the same meaning as in section 39(2) of the 2000 Act;

"authorised person" has the same meaning as in section 31(2) of the 2000 Act;]

"breach" means contravention by a supplier of a prohibition in, or failure to comply with a requirement of, these Regulations;

"business" includes a trade or profession;

"consumer" means any natural person who, in contracts to which these Regulations apply, is acting for purposes which are outside his business;

"court" in relation to England and Wales and Northern Ireland means a county court or the High Court, and in relation to Scotland means the Sheriff Court or the Court of Session;

"credit" includes a cash loan and any other form of financial accommodation, and for this purpose "cash" includes money in any form;

"[OFT]" means the [Office of Fair Trading];

"distance contract" means any contract concerning goods or services concluded between a supplier and a consumer under an organised distance sales or service provision scheme run by the supplier who, for the purpose of the contract, makes exclusive use of one or more means of distance communication up to and including the moment at which the contract is concluded;

"EEA Agreement" means the Agreement on the European Economic Area signed at Oporto on 2 May 1992 as adjusted by the Protocol signed at Brussels on 17 March 1993;

"enactment" includes an enactment comprised in, or in an instrument made under, an Act of the Scottish Parliament;

"enforcement authority" means the [OFT], every weights and measures authority in Great Britain, and the Department of Enterprise, Trade and Investment in Northern Ireland;

"excepted contract" means a contract such as is mentioned in regulation 5(1);

["financial service" means any service of a banking, credit, insurance, personal pension, investment or payment nature;]

"means of distance communication" means any means which, without the simultaneous physical presence of the supplier and the consumer, may be used for the conclusion of a contract between those parties; and an indicative list of such means is contained in Schedule 1;

"Member State" means a State which is a contracting party to the EEA Agreement;

"operator of a means of communication" means any public or private person whose business involves making one or more means of distance communication available to suppliers;

"period for performance" has the meaning given by regulation 19(2);

"personal credit agreement" has the meaning given by regulation 14(8);

["regulated activity" has the same meaning as in section 22 of the 2000 Act;]

"related credit agreement" has the meaning given by regulation 15(5);

"supplier" means any person who, in contracts to which these Regulations apply, is acting in his commercial or professional capacity; and

"working days" means all days other than Saturdays, Sundays and public holidays.

(2) In the application of these Regulations to Scotland, for references to an "injunction" or an "interim injunction" there shall be substituted references to an "interdict" or an "interim interdict" respectively.

[10]

NOTES

Para (1): definitions "the 2000 Act", "appointed representative", "authorised person", "financial service" and "regulated activity" inserted by the Financial Services (Distance Marketing) Regulations 2004, SI 2004/2095, reg 25(1), (2); in definitions "OFT" and "enforcement authority" references to "OFT" in square brackets substituted, for word "Director" as originally enacted, and other words in square brackets substituted by virtue of the Enterprise Act 2002, s 2 (for transitional and transitory provisions and savings see s 276 to, and Sch 24, paras 2–6 of, that Act).

4 Contracts to which these Regulations apply

These Regulations apply, subject to regulation 6, to distance contracts other than excepted contracts.

[11]

5 Excepted contracts

(1) The following are excepted contracts, namely any contract—

(a) for the sale or other disposition of an interest in land except for a rental agreement;

(b) for the construction of a building where the contract also provides for a sale or other disposition of an interest in land on which the building is constructed, except for a rental agreement;

(c) relating to financial services . . . ;

(d) concluded by means of an automated vending machine or automated commercial premises;

(e) concluded with a telecommunications operator through the use of a public pay-phone;

(f) concluded at an auction.

(2) References in paragraph (1) to a rental agreement—

(a) if the land is situated in England and Wales, are references to any agreement which does not have to be made in writing (whether or not in fact made in writing) because of section 2(5)(a) of the Law of Property (Miscellaneous Provisions) Act 1989;

(b) if the land is situated in Scotland, are references to any agreement for the creation, transfer, variation or extinction of an interest in land, which does not have to be made in writing (whether or not in fact made in writing) as provided for in section 1(2) and (7) of the Requirements of Writing (Scotland) Act 1995; and

(c) if the land is situated in Northern Ireland, are references to any agreement which is not one to which section II of the Statute of Frauds, (Ireland) 1695 applies.

(3) Paragraph (2) shall not be taken to mean that a rental agreement in respect of land situated outside the United Kingdom is not capable of being a distance contract to which these Regulations apply.

[12]

NOTES

Para (1): words omitted from sub-para (c) revoked by the Financial Services (Distance Marketing) Regulations 2004, SI 2004/2095, reg 25(1), (3).

6 Contracts to which only part of these Regulations apply

(1) Regulations 7 to 20 shall not apply to a contract which is a "timeshare agreement" within the meaning of the Timeshare Act 1992 and to which that Act applies.

(2) Regulations 7 to 19(1) shall not apply to—

(a) contracts for the supply of food, beverages or other goods intended for everyday consumption supplied to the consumer's residence or to his workplace by regular roundsmen; or

(b) contracts for the provision of accommodation, transport, catering or leisure services, where the supplier undertakes, when the contract is concluded, to provide these services on a specific date or within a specific period.

(3) Regulations 19(2) to (8) and 20 do not apply to a contract for a "package" within the meaning of the Package Travel, Package Holidays and Package Tours Regulations 1992 which is sold or offered for sale in the territory of the Member States.

[(4) Regulations 7 to 14, 17 to 20 and 25 do not apply to any contract which is made, and regulation 24 does not apply to any unsolicited services which are supplied, by an authorised person where the making or performance of that contract or the supply of those services, as the case may be, constitutes or is part of a regulated activity carried on by him.

(5) Regulations 7 to 9, 17 to 20 and 25 do not apply to any contract which is made, and regulation 24 does not apply to any unsolicited services which are supplied, by an appointed representative where the making or performance of that contract or the supply of those services, as the case may be, constitutes or is part of a regulated activity carried on by him.]

[13]

NOTES

Paras (4), (5): added by the Financial Services (Distance Marketing) Regulations 2004, SI 2004/2095, reg 25(1), (4).

7 Information required prior to the conclusion of the contract

(1) Subject to paragraph (4), in good time prior to the conclusion of the contract the supplier shall—

(a) provide to the consumer the following information—

(i) the identity of the supplier and, where the contract requires payment in advance, the supplier's address;

(ii) a description of the main characteristics of the goods or services;

(iii) the price of the goods or services including all taxes;

(iv) delivery costs where appropriate;

(v) the arrangements for payment, delivery or performance;

(vi) the existence of a right of cancellation except in the cases referred to in regulation 13;

(vii) the cost of using the means of distance communication where it is calculated other than at the basic rate;

(viii) the period for which the offer or the price remains valid; and

(ix) where appropriate, the minimum duration of the contract, in the case of contracts for the supply of goods or services to be performed permanently or recurrently;

(b) inform the consumer if he proposes, in the event of the goods or services ordered by the consumer being unavailable, to provide substitute goods or services (as the case may be) of equivalent quality and price; and

(c) inform the consumer that the cost of returning any such substitute goods to the supplier in the event of cancellation by the consumer would be met by the supplier.

(2) The supplier shall ensure that the information required by paragraph (1) is provided in a clear and comprehensible manner appropriate to the means of distance communication used, with due regard in particular to the principles of good faith in commercial transactions and the principles governing the protection of those who are unable to give their consent such as minors.

(3) Subject to paragraph (4), the supplier shall ensure that his commercial purpose is made clear when providing the information required by paragraph (1).

(4) In the case of a telephone communication, the identity of the supplier and the commercial purpose of the call shall be made clear at the beginning of the conversation with the consumer.

[14]

8 Written and additional information

(1) Subject to regulation 9, the supplier shall provide to the consumer in writing, or in another durable medium which is available and accessible to the consumer, the information referred to in paragraph (2), either—

(a) prior to the conclusion of the contract, or
(b) thereafter, in good time and in any event—
  (i) during the performance of the contract, in the case of services; and
  (ii) at the latest at the time of delivery where goods not for delivery to third parties are concerned.

(2) The information required to be provided by paragraph (1) is—

(a) the information set out in paragraphs (i) to (vi) of Regulation 7(1)(a);
(b) information about the conditions and procedures for exercising the right to cancel under regulation 10, including—
  (i) where a term of the contract requires (or the supplier intends that it will require) that the consumer shall return the goods to the supplier in the event of cancellation, notification of that requirement; …
  (ii) information as to whether the consumer or the supplier would be responsible under these Regulations for the cost of returning any goods to the supplier, or the cost of his recovering them, if the consumer cancels the contract under regulation 10;
  [(iii) in the case of a contract for the supply of services, information as to how the right to cancel may be affected by the consumer agreeing to performance of the services beginning before the end of the seven working day period referred to in regulation 12;]
(c) the geographical address of the place of business of the supplier to which the consumer may address any complaints;
(d) information about any after-sales services and guarantees; and
(e) the conditions for exercising any contractual right to cancel the contract, where the contract is of an unspecified duration or a duration exceeding one year.

(3) …

[15]

NOTES

Para (2): word omitted from sub-para (b)(i) revoked and sub-para (b)(iii) inserted by the Consumer Protection (Distance Selling) (Amendment) Regulations 2005, SI 2005/689, reg 2, Schedule, para 1(1), (2).

Para (3): revoked by SI 2005/689, reg 2, Schedule, para 1(1), (3).

9 Services performed through the use of a means of distance communication

(1) Regulation 8 shall not apply to a contract for the supply of services which are performed through the use of a means of distance communication, where those services are supplied on only one occasion and are invoiced by the operator of the means of distance communication.

(2) But the supplier shall take all necessary steps to ensure that a consumer who is a party to a contract to which paragraph (1) applies is able to obtain the supplier's geographical address and the place of business to which the consumer may address any complaints.

[16]

10 Right to cancel

(1) Subject to regulation 13, if within the cancellation period set out in regulations 11 and 12, the consumer gives a notice of cancellation to the supplier, or any other person previously notified by the supplier to the consumer as a person to whom notice of cancellation may be given, the notice of cancellation shall operate to cancel the contract.

(2) Except as otherwise provided by these Regulations, the effect of a notice of cancellation is that the contract shall be treated as if it had not been made.

(3) For the purposes of these Regulations, a notice of cancellation is a notice in writing or in another durable medium available and accessible to the supplier (or to the other person to whom it is given) which, however expressed, indicates the intention of the consumer to cancel the contract.

(4) A notice of cancellation given under this regulation by a consumer to a supplier or other person is to be treated as having been properly given if the consumer—

(a) leaves it at the address last known to the consumer and addressed to the supplier or other person by name (in which case it is to be taken to have been given on the day on which it was left);

(b) sends it by post to the address last known to the consumer and addressed to the supplier or other person by name (in which case, it is to be taken to have been given on the day on which it was posted);

(c) sends it by facsimile to the business facsimile number last known to the consumer (in which case it is to be taken to have been given on the day on which it is sent); or

(d) sends it by electronic mail, to the business electronic mail address last known to the consumer (in which case it is to be taken to have been given on the day on which it is sent).

(5) Where a consumer gives a notice in accordance with paragraph (4)(a) or (b) to a supplier who is a body corporate or a partnership, the notice is to be treated as having been properly given if—

(a) in the case of a body corporate, it is left at the address of, or sent to, the secretary or clerk of that body; or

(b) in the case of a partnership, it is left with or sent to a partner or a person having control or management of the partnership business.

[17]

11 Cancellation period in the case of contracts for the supply of goods

(1) For the purposes of regulation 10, the cancellation period in the case of contracts for the supply of goods begins with the day on which the contract is concluded and ends as provided in paragraphs (2) to (5).

(2) Where the supplier complies with regulation 8, the cancellation period ends on the expiry of the period of seven working days beginning with the day after the day on which the consumer receives the goods.

(3) Where a supplier who has not complied with regulation 8 provides to the consumer the information referred to in regulation 8(2), and does so in writing or in another durable medium available and accessible to the consumer, within the period of three months beginning with the day after the day on which the consumer receives the goods, the cancellation period ends on the expiry of the period of seven working days beginning with the day after the day on which the consumer receives the information.

(4) Where neither paragraph (2) nor (3) applies, the cancellation period ends on the expiry of the period of three months and seven working days beginning with the day after the day on which the consumer receives the goods.

(5) In the case of contracts for goods for delivery to third parties, paragraphs (2) to (4) shall apply as if the consumer had received the goods on the day on which they were received by the third party.

[18]

12 Cancellation period in the case of contracts for the supply of services

(1) For the purposes of regulation 10, the cancellation period in the case of contracts for the supply of services begins with the day on which the contract is concluded and ends as provided in paragraphs (2) to (4).

(2) Where the supplier complies with regulation 8 on or before the day on which the contract is concluded, the cancellation period ends on the expiry of the period of seven working days beginning with the day after the day on which the contract is concluded.

(3) [Subject to paragraph (3A)] where a supplier who has not complied with regulation 8 on or before the day on which the contract is concluded provides to the consumer the information referred to in regulation 8(2) … , and does so in writing or in another durable medium available and accessible to the consumer, within the period of three months beginning with the day after the day on which the contract is concluded, the cancellation period ends on the expiry of the period of seven working days beginning with the day after the day on which the consumer receives the information.

[(3A) Where the performance of the contract has begun with the consumer's agreement before the expiry of the period of seven working days beginning with the day after the day on which the contract was concluded and the supplier has not complied with regulation 8 on or before the day on which performance began, but provides to the consumer the information referred to in regulation 8(2) in good time during the performance of the contract, the cancellation period ends—

(a) on the expiry of the period of seven working days beginning with the day after the day on which the consumer receives the information; or

(b) if the performance of the contract is completed before the expiry of the period referred to in sub-paragraph (a), on the day when the performance of the contract is completed.]

(4) Where [none of paragraphs (2) to (3A) applies], the cancellation period ends on the expiry of the period of three months and seven working days beginning with the day after the day on which the contract is concluded.

[19]

NOTES

Para (3): words in square brackets inserted and words omitted revoked by the Consumer Protection (Distance Selling) (Amendment) Regulations 2005, SI 2005/689, reg 2, Schedule, para 2(1), (2).

Para (3A): inserted by SI 2005/689, reg 2, Schedule, para 2(1), (3).

Para (4): words in square brackets substituted by SI 2005/689, reg 2, Schedule, para 2(1), (4).

13 Exceptions to the right to cancel

(1) Unless the parties have agreed otherwise, the consumer will not have the right to cancel the contract by giving notice of cancellation pursuant to regulation 10 in respect of contracts—

[(a) for the supply of services if the performance of the contract has begun with the consumer's agreement—

(i) before the end of the cancellation period applicable under regulation 12(2); and

(ii) after the supplier has provided the information referred to in regulation 8(2)];

(b) for the supply of goods or services the price of which is dependent on fluctuations in the financial market which cannot be controlled by the supplier;

(c) for the supply of goods made to the consumer's specifications or clearly personalised or which by reason of their nature cannot be returned or are liable to deteriorate or expire rapidly;

(d) for the supply of audio or video recordings or computer software if they are unsealed by the consumer;

(e) for the supply of newspapers, periodicals or magazines; or

(f) for gaming, betting or lottery services.

[20]

NOTES

Para (1): sub-para (a) substituted by the Consumer Protection (Distance Selling) (Amendment) Regulations 2005, SI 2005/689, reg 2, Schedule, para 3.

14 Recovery of sums paid by or on behalf of the consumer on cancellation, and return of security

(1) On the cancellation of a contract under regulation 10, the supplier shall reimburse any sum paid by or on behalf of the consumer under or in relation to the contract to the person by whom it was made free of any charge, less any charge made in accordance with paragraph (5).

(2) The reference in paragraph (1) to any sum paid on behalf of the consumer includes any sum paid by a creditor who is not the same person as the supplier under a personal credit agreement with the consumer.

(3) The supplier shall make the reimbursement referred to in paragraph (1) as soon as possible and in any case within a period not exceeding 30 days beginning with the day on which the notice of cancellation was given.

(4) Where any security has been provided in relation to the contract, the security (so far as it is so provided) shall, on cancellation under regulation 10, be treated as never having had effect and any property lodged with the supplier solely for the purposes of the security as so provided shall be returned by him forthwith.

(5) Subject to paragraphs (6) and (7), the supplier may make a charge, not exceeding the direct costs of recovering any goods supplied under the contract, where a term of the contract provides that the consumer must return any goods supplied if he cancels the contract under regulation 10 but the consumer does not comply with this provision or returns the goods at the expense of the supplier.

(6) Paragraph (5) shall not apply where—

(a) the consumer cancels in circumstances where he has the right to reject the goods under a term of the contract, including a term implied by virtue of any enactment, or

(b) the term requiring the consumer to return any goods supplied if he cancels the contract is an "unfair term" within the meaning of the Unfair Terms in Consumer Contracts Regulations 1999.

(7) Paragraph (5) shall not apply to the cost of recovering any goods which were supplied as substitutes for the goods ordered by the consumer.

(8) For the purposes of these Regulations, a personal credit agreement is an agreement between the consumer and any other person ("the creditor") by which the creditor provides the consumer with credit of any amount.

[21]

15 Automatic cancellation of a related credit agreement

(1) Where a notice of cancellation is given under regulation 10 which has the effect of cancelling the contract, the giving of the notice shall also have the effect of cancelling any related credit agreement.

(2) Where a related credit agreement is cancelled by virtue of paragraph (1), the supplier shall, if he is not the same person as the creditor under that agreement, forthwith on receipt of the notice of cancellation inform the creditor that the notice has been given.

(3) Where a related credit agreement is cancelled by virtue of paragraph (1)—

(a) any sum paid by or on behalf of the consumer under, or in relation to, the credit agreement which the supplier is not obliged to reimburse under regulation 14(1) shall be reimbursed, except for any sum which, if it had not already been paid, would have to be paid under subparagraph (b);

(b) the agreement shall continue in force so far as it relates to repayment of the credit and payment of interest, subject to regulation 16; and

(c) subject to subparagraph (b), the agreement shall cease to be enforceable.

(4) Where any security has been provided under a related credit agreement, the security, so far as it is so provided, shall be treated as never having had effect and any property lodged with the creditor solely for the purposes of the security as so provided shall be returned by him forthwith.

(5) For the purposes of this regulation and regulation 16, a "related credit agreement" means an agreement under which fixed sum credit which fully or partly covers the price under a contract cancelled under regulation 10 is granted—

(a) by the supplier, or

(b) by another person, under an arrangement between that person and the supplier.

(6) For the purposes of this regulation and regulation 16—

(a) "creditor" is a person who grants credit under a related credit agreement;

(b) "fixed sum credit" has the same meaning as in section 10 of the Consumer Credit Act 1974;

(c) "repayment" in relation to credit means repayment of money received by the consumer, and cognate expressions shall be construed accordingly; and

(d) "interest" means interest on money so received.

[22]

16 Repayment of credit and interest after cancellation of a related credit agreement

(1) This regulation applies following the cancellation of a related credit agreement by virtue of regulation 15(1).

(2) If the consumer repays the whole or a portion of the credit—

(a) before the expiry of one month following the cancellation of the credit agreement, or

(b) in the case of a credit repayable by instalments, before the date on which the first instalment is due,

no interest shall be payable on the amount repaid.

(3) If the whole of a credit repayable by instalments is not repaid on or before the date referred to in paragraph (2)(b), the consumer shall not be liable to repay any of the credit except on receipt of a request in writing, signed by the creditor, stating the amounts of the remaining instalments (recalculated by the creditor as nearly as may be in accordance with the agreement and without extending the repayment period), but excluding any sum other than principal and interest.

(4) Where any security has been provided under a related credit agreement the duty imposed on the consumer to repay credit and to pay interest shall not be enforceable before the creditor has discharged any duty imposed on him by regulation 15(4) to return any property lodged with him as security on cancellation.

[23]

17 Restoration of goods by consumer after cancellation

(1) This regulation applies where a contract is cancelled under regulation 10 after the consumer has acquired possession of any goods under the contract other than any goods mentioned in regulation 13(1)(b) to (e).

(2) The consumer shall be treated as having been under a duty throughout the period prior to cancellation—

(a) to retain possession of the goods; and
(b) to take reasonable care of them.

(3) On cancellation, the consumer shall be under a duty to restore the goods to the supplier in accordance with this regulation, and in the meanwhile to retain possession of the goods and take reasonable care of them.

(4) The consumer shall not be under any duty to deliver the goods except at his own premises and in pursuance of a request in writing, or in another durable medium available and accessible to the consumer, from the supplier and given to the consumer either before, or at the time when, the goods are collected from those premises.

(5) If the consumer—

(a) delivers the goods (whether at his own premises or elsewhere) to any person to whom, under regulation 10(1), a notice of cancellation could have been given; or
(b) sends the goods at his own expense to such a person,

he shall be discharged from any duty to retain possession of the goods or restore them to the supplier.

(6) Where the consumer delivers the goods in accordance with paragraph (5)(a), his obligation to take care of the goods shall cease; and if he sends the goods in accordance with paragraph (5)(b), he shall be under a duty to take reasonable care to see that they are received by the supplier and not damaged in transit, but in other respects his duty to take care of the goods shall cease when he sends them.

(7) Where, at any time during the period of 21 days beginning with the day notice of cancellation was given, the consumer receives such a request as is mentioned in paragraph (4), and unreasonably refuses or unreasonably fails to comply with it, his duty to retain possession and take reasonable care of the goods shall continue until he delivers or sends the goods as mentioned in paragraph (5), but if within that period he does not receive such a request his duty to take reasonable care of the goods shall cease at the end of that period.

(8) Where—

(a) a term of the contract provides that if the consumer cancels the contract, he must return the goods to the supplier, and
(b) the consumer is not otherwise entitled to reject the goods under the terms of the contract or by virtue of any enactment,

paragraph (7) shall apply as if for the period of 21 days there were substituted the period of 6 months.

(9) Where any security has been provided in relation to the cancelled contract, the duty to restore goods imposed on the consumer by this regulation shall not be enforceable before the supplier has discharged any duty imposed on him by regulation 14(4) to return any property lodged with him as security on cancellation.

(10) Breach of a duty imposed by this regulation on a consumer is actionable as a breach of statutory duty.

[24]

18 Goods given in part-exchange

(1) This regulation applies on the cancellation of a contract under regulation 10 where the supplier agreed to take goods in part-exchange (the "part-exchange goods") and those goods have been delivered to him.

(2) Unless, before the end of the period of 10 days beginning with the date of cancellation, the part-exchange goods are returned to the consumer in a condition substantially as good as when they were delivered to the supplier, the consumer shall be entitled to recover from the supplier a sum equal to the part-exchange allowance.

(3) In this regulation the part-exchange allowance means the sum agreed as such in the cancelled contract, or if no such sum was agreed, such sum as it would have been reasonable to allow in respect of the part-exchange goods if no notice of cancellation had been served.

(4) Where the consumer recovers from the supplier a sum equal to the part-exchange allowance, the title of the consumer to the part-exchange goods shall vest in the supplier (if it has not already done so) on recovery of that sum.

[25]

19 Performance

(1) Unless the parties agree otherwise, the supplier shall perform the contract within a maximum of 30 days beginning with the day after the day the consumer sent his order to the supplier.

(2) Subject to paragraphs (7) and (8), where the supplier is unable to perform the contract because the goods or services ordered are not available, within the period for performance referred to in paragraph (1) or such other period as the parties agree ("the period for performance"), he shall—

(a) inform the consumer; and
(b) reimburse any sum paid by or on behalf of the consumer under or in relation to the contract to the person by whom it was made.

(3) The reference in paragraph (2)(b) to any sum paid on behalf of the consumer includes any sum paid by a creditor who is not the same person as the supplier under a personal credit agreement with the consumer.

(4) The supplier shall make the reimbursement referred to in paragraph (2)(b) as soon as possible and in any event within a period of 30 days beginning with the day after the day on which the period for performance expired.

(5) A contract which has not been performed within the period for performance shall be treated as if it had not been made, save for any rights or remedies which the consumer has under it as a result of the non-performance.

(6) Where any security has been provided in relation to the contract, the security (so far as it is so provided) shall, where the supplier is unable to perform the contract within the period for performance, be treated as never having had any effect and any property lodged with the supplier solely for the purposes of the security as so provided shall be returned by him forthwith.

(7) Where the supplier is unable to supply the goods or services ordered by the consumer, the supplier may perform the contract for the purposes of these Regulations by providing substitute goods or services (as the case may be) of equivalent quality and price provided that—

(a) this possibility was provided for in the contract;
(b) prior to the conclusion of the contract the supplier gave the consumer the information required by regulation 7(1)(b) and (c) in the manner required by regulation 7(2).

(8) In the case of outdoor leisure events which by their nature cannot be rescheduled, paragraph 2(b) shall not apply where the consumer and the supplier so agree.

[26]

20 Effect of non-performance on related credit agreement

Where a supplier is unable to perform the contract within the period for performance—

(a) regulations 15 and 16 shall apply to any related credit agreement as if the consumer had given a valid notice of cancellation under regulation 10 on the expiry of the period for performance; and

(b) the reference in regulation 15(3)(a) to regulation 14(1) shall be read, for the purposes of this regulation, as a reference to regulation 19(2).

[27]

21 Payment by card

(1) Subject to paragraph (4), the consumer shall be entitled to cancel a payment where fraudulent use has been made of his payment card in connection with a contract to which this regulation applies by another person not acting, or to be treated as acting, as his agent.

(2) Subject to paragraph (4), the consumer shall be entitled to be recredited, or to have all sums returned by the card issuer, in the event of fraudulent use of his payment card in connection with a contract to which this regulation applies by another person not acting, or to be treated as acting, as the consumer's agent.

(3) Where paragraphs (1) and (2) apply, in any proceedings if the consumer alleges that any use made of the payment card was not authorised by him it is for the card issuer to prove that the use was so authorised.

(4) Paragraphs (1) and (2) shall not apply to an agreement to which section 83(1) of the Consumer Credit Act 1974 applies.

(5) …

(6) For the purposes of this regulation—

"card issuer" means the owner of the card; and

"payment card" includes credit cards, charge cards, debit cards and store cards.

[28]

NOTES

Para (5): amends the Consumer Credit Act 1974, s 84.

22, 23 (*Reg 22 repeals the Unsolicited Goods and Services Act 1971, s 1 and amends s 2 to that Act; reg 23 repeals the Unsolicited Goods and Services (Northern Ireland) Order 1976, art 3 and amends art 4 of that Order.*)

24 Inertia Selling

(1) Paragraphs (2) and (3) apply if—

(a) unsolicited goods are sent to a person ("the recipient") with a view to his acquiring them;

(b) the recipient has no reasonable cause to believe that they were sent with a view to their being acquired for the purposes of a business; and

(c) the recipient has neither agreed to acquire nor agreed to return them.

(2) The recipient may, as between himself and the sender, use, deal with or dispose of the goods as if they were an unconditional gift to him.

(3) The rights of the sender to the goods are extinguished.

(4) A person who, not having reasonable cause to believe there is a right to payment, in the course of any business makes a demand for payment, or asserts a present or prospective right to payment, for what he knows are—

(a) unsolicited goods sent to another person with a view to his acquiring them for purposes other than those of his business, or

(b) unsolicited services supplied to another person for purposes other than those of his business,

is guilty of an offence and liable, on summary conviction, to a fine not exceeding level 4 on the standard scale.

(5) A person who, not having reasonable cause to believe there is a right to payment, in the course of any business and with a view to obtaining payment for what he knows are unsolicited goods sent or services supplied as mentioned in paragraph (4)—

(a) threatens to bring any legal proceedings, or

(b) places or causes to be placed the name of any person on a list of defaulters or debtors or threatens to do so, or

(c) invokes or causes to be invoked any other collection procedure or threatens to do so,

is guilty of an offence and liable, on summary conviction, to a fine not exceeding level 5 on the standard scale.

(6) In this regulation—

"acquire" includes hire;

"send" includes deliver;

"sender", in relation to any goods, includes—

(a) any person on whose behalf or with whose consent the goods are sent;

(b) any other person claiming through or under the sender or any person mentioned in paragraph (a); and

(c) any person who delivers the goods; and

"unsolicited" means, in relation to goods sent or services supplied to any person, that they are sent or supplied without any prior request made by or on behalf of the recipient.

(7) For the purposes of this regulation, an invoice or similar document which—

(a) states the amount of a payment; and

(b) fails to comply with [the conditions set out in Part 2 of the Schedule to the Regulatory Reform (Unsolicited Goods and Services Act 1971) (Directory Entries and Demands for Payment) Order 2005] or, as the case may be, [the requirements of regulations made under] Article 6 of the Unsolicited Goods and Services (Northern Ireland) Order 1976 applicable to it,

is to be regarded as asserting a right to the payment.

(8) Section 3A of the Unsolicited Goods and Services Act 1971 applies for the purposes of this regulation in its application to England, Wales and Scotland as it applies for the purposes of that Act.

(9) Article 6 of the Unsolicited Goods and Services (Northern Ireland) Order 1976 applies for the purposes of this regulation in its application to Northern Ireland as it applies for the purposes of that Order.

(10) This regulation applies only to goods sent and services supplied after the date on which it comes into force.

[29]

NOTES

Para (7): in sub-para (b), words in first pair of square brackets substituted and words in second pair of square brackets inserted by the Regulatory Reform (Unsolicited Goods and Services Act 1971) (Directory Entries and Demands for Payment) Order 2005, SI 2005/55, art 4.

---

25 No contracting-out

(1) A term contained in any contract to which these Regulations apply is void if, and to the extent that, it is inconsistent with a provision for the protection of the consumer contained in these Regulations.

(2) Where a provision of these Regulations specifies a duty or liability of the consumer in certain circumstances, a term contained in a contract to which these Regulations apply, other than a term to which paragraph (3) applies, is inconsistent with that provision if it purports to impose, directly or indirectly, an additional duty or liability on him in those circumstances.

(3) This paragraph applies to a term which requires the consumer to return any goods supplied to him under the contract if he cancels it under regulation 10.

(4) A term to which paragraph (3) applies shall, in the event of cancellation by the consumer under regulation 10, have effect only for the purposes of regulation 14(5) and 17(8).

(5) These Regulations shall apply notwithstanding any contract term which applies or purports to apply the law of a non-Member State if the contract has a close connection with the territory of a Member State.

[30]

26 Consideration of complaints

(1) It shall be the duty of an enforcement authority to consider any complaint made to it about a breach unless—

(a) the complaint appears to the authority to be frivolous or vexatious; or

(b) another enforcement authority has notified the [OFT] that it agrees to consider the complaint.

(2) If an enforcement authority notifies the [OFT] that it agrees to consider a complaint made to another enforcement authority, the first mentioned authority shall be under a duty to consider the complaint.

(3) An enforcement authority which is under a duty to consider a complaint shall give reasons for its decision to apply or not to apply, as the case may be, for an injunction under regulation 27.

(4) In deciding whether or not to apply for an injunction in respect of a breach an enforcement authority may, if it considers it appropriate to do so, have regard to any undertaking given to it or another enforcement authority by or on behalf of any person as to compliance with these Regulations.

[31]

NOTES

Paras (1), (2): references to "OFT" in square brackets substituted, for word "Director" as originally enacted, by virtue of the Enterprise Act 2002, s 2 (for transitional and transitory provisions and savings see s 276 to, and Sch 24, paras 2–6 of, that Act).

27 Injunctions to secure compliance with these Regulations

(1) The [OFT] or, subject to paragraph (2), any other enforcement authority may apply for a injunction (including an interim injunction) against any person who appears to the [OFT] or that authority to be responsible for a breach.

(2) An enforcement authority other than the [OFT] may apply for an injunction only where—

(a) it has notified the [OFT] of its intention to apply at least fourteen days before the date on which the application is to be made, beginning with the date on which the notification was given; or

(b) the [OFT] consents to the application being made within a shorter period.

(3) The court on an application under this regulation may grant an injunction on such terms as it thinks fit to secure compliance with these Regulations.

[32]

NOTES

Paras (1), (2): references to "OFT" in square brackets substituted, for word "Director" as originally enacted, by virtue of the Enterprise Act 2002, s 2 (for transitional and transitory provisions and savings see s 276 to, and Sch 24, paras 2–6 of, that Act).

28 Notification of undertakings and orders to the [OFT]

An enforcement authority other than the [OFT] shall notify the [OFT]—

(a) of any undertaking given to it by or on behalf of any person who appears to it to be responsible for a breach;

(b) of the outcome of any application made by it under regulation 27 and of the terms of any undertaking given to or order made by the court;

(c) of the outcome of any application made by it to enforce a previous order of the court.

[33]

NOTES

References to "OFT" in square brackets substituted, for word "Director" as originally enacted, by virtue of the Enterprise Act 2002, s 2 (for transitional and transitory provisions and savings see s 276 to, and Sch 24, paras 2–6 of, that Act).

29 Publication, information and advice

(1) The [OFT] shall arrange for the publication in such form and manner as [it] considers appropriate of—

(a) details of any undertaking or order notified to [it] under regulation 28;

(b) details of any undertaking given to [it] by or on behalf of any person as to compliance with these Regulations;

(c) details of any application made by [it] under regulation 27, and of the terms of any undertaking given to, or order made by, the court;

(d) details of any application made by the [OFT] to enforce a previous order of the court.

(2) The [OFT] may arrange for the dissemination in such form and manner as [it] considers appropriate of such information and advice concerning the operation of these Regulations as it may appear to [it] to be expedient to give to the public and to all persons likely to be affected by these Regulations.

[34]

NOTES

Paras (1), (2): references to "OFT" in square brackets substituted, for word "Director" as originally enacted, and other words in square brackets substituted, by virtue of the Enterprise Act 2002, s 2 (for transitional and transitory provisions and savings see s 276 to, and Sch 24, paras 2–6 of, that Act).

SCHEDULE 1
INDICATIVE LIST OF MEANS OF DISTANCE COMMUNICATION

Regulation 3

1. Unaddressed printed matter.
2. Addressed printed matter.
3. Letter.
4. Press advertising with order form.
5. Catalogue.
6. Telephone with human intervention.
7. Telephone without human intervention (automatic calling machine, audiotext).
8. Radio.
9. Videophone (telephone with screen).
10. Videotext (microcomputer and television screen) with keyboard or touch screen.
11. Electronic mail.
12. Facsimile machine (fax).
13. Television (teleshopping).

[35]

(Sch 2 revoked by the Financial Services (Distance Marketing) Regulations 2004, SI 2004/2095, reg 25(1), (5).)

ELECTRONIC SIGNATURES REGULATIONS 2002

(SI 2002/318)

NOTES

Made: 13 February 2002.
Authority: European Communities Act 1972, s 2(2).
Commencement: 8 March 2002.

ARRANGEMENT OF REGULATIONS

1 Citation and commencement

These Regulations may be cited as the Electronic Signatures Regulations 2002 and shall come into force on 8th March 2002.

[36]

NOTES

Commencement: 8 March 2002.

2 Interpretation

In these Regulations—

"advanced electronic signature" means an electronic signature—

(a) which is uniquely linked to the signatory;

(b) which is capable of identifying the signatory;

(c) which is created using means that the signatory can maintain under his sole control; and

(d) which is linked to the data to which it relates in such a manner that any subsequent change of the data is detectable;

"certificate" means an electronic attestation which links signature-verification data to a person and confirms the identity of that person;

"certification-service-provider" means a person who issues certificates or provides other services related to electronic signatures;

"Directive" means Directive 1999/93/EC of the European Parliament and of the Council on a Community framework for electronic signatures;

"electronic signature" means data in electronic form which are attached to or logically associated with other electronic data and which serve as a method of authentication;

"qualified certificate" means a certificate which meets the requirements in Schedule 1 and is provided by a certification-service-provider who fulfils the requirements in Schedule 2;

"signatory" means a person who holds a signature-creation device and acts either on his own behalf or on behalf of the person he represents;

"signature-creation data" means unique data (including, but not limited to, codes or private cryptographic keys) which are used by the signatory to create an electronic signature;

"signature-creation device" means configured software or hardware used to implement the signature-creation data;

"signature-verification data" means data (including, but not limited to, codes or public cryptographic keys) which are used for the purpose of verifying an electronic signature;

"signature-verification device" means configured software or hardware used to implement the signature-verification data;

"voluntary accreditation" means any permission, setting out rights and obligations specific to the provision of certification services, to be granted upon request by the certification-service-provider concerned by the person charged with the elaboration of, and supervision of compliance with, such rights and obligations, where the certification-service-provider is not entitled to exercise the rights stemming from the permission until he has received the decision of that person.

[37]

NOTES

Commencement: 8 March 2002.

3 Supervision of certification-service-providers

(1) It shall be the duty of the Secretary of State to keep under review the carrying on of activities of certification-service-providers who are established in the United Kingdom and who issue qualified certificates to the public and the persons by whom they are carried on with a view to her becoming aware of the identity of those persons and the circumstances relating to the carrying on of those activities.

(2) It shall also be the duty of the Secretary of State to establish and maintain a register of certification-service-providers who are established in the United Kingdom and who issue qualified certificates to the public.

(3) The Secretary of State shall record in the register the names and addresses of those certification-service-providers of whom she is aware who are established in the United Kingdom and who issue qualified certificates to the public.

(4) The Secretary of State shall publish the register in such manner as she considers appropriate.

(5) The Secretary of State shall have regard to evidence becoming available to her with respect to any course of conduct of a certification-service-provider who is established in the United Kingdom and who issues qualified certificates to the public and which appears to her to be conduct detrimental to the interests of those persons who use or rely on those certificates with a view to making any of this evidence as she considers expedient available to the public in such manner as she considers appropriate.

[38]

NOTES

Commencement: 8 March 2002.

4 Liability of certification-service-providers

(1) Where—

(a) a certification-service-provider either—
  (i) issues a certificate as a qualified certificate to the public, or
  (ii) guarantees a qualified certificate to the public,

(b) a person reasonably relies on that certificate for any of the following matters—
  (i) the accuracy of any of the information contained in the qualified certificate at the time of issue,
  (ii) the inclusion in the qualified certificate of all the details referred to in Schedule 1,
  (iii) the holding by the signatory identified in the qualified certificate at the time of its issue of the signature-creation data corresponding to the signature-verification data given or identified in the certificate, or
  (iv) the ability of the signature-creation data and the signature-verification data to be used in a complementary manner in cases where the certification-service-provider generates them both,

(c) that person suffers loss as a result of such reliance, and

(d) the certification-service-provider would be liable in damages in respect of any extent of the loss—
  (i) had a duty of care existed between him and the person referred to in sub-paragraph (b) above, and
  (ii) had the certification-service-provider been negligent,

then that certification-service-provider shall be so liable to the same extent notwithstanding that there is no proof that the certification-service-provider was negligent unless the certification-service-provider proves that he was not negligent.

(2) For the purposes of the certification-service-provider's liability under paragraph (1) above there shall be a duty of care between that certification-service-provider and the person referred to in paragraph (1)(b) above.

(3) Where—

(a) a certification-service-provider issues a certificate as a qualified certificate to the public,

(b) a person reasonably relies on that certificate,

(c) that person suffers loss as a result of any failure by the certification-service-provider to register revocation of the certificate, and

(d) the certification-service-provider would be liable in damages in respect of any extent of the loss—
  (i) had a duty of care existed between him and the person referred to in sub-paragraph (b) above, and
  (ii) had the certification-service-provider been negligent,

then that certification-service-provider shall be so liable to the same extent notwithstanding that there is no proof that the certification-service-provider was negligent unless the certification-service-provider proves that he was not negligent.

(4) For the purposes of the certification-service-provider's liability under paragraph (3) above there shall be a duty of care between that certification-service-provider and the person referred to in paragraph (3)(b) above.

[39]

NOTES

Commencement: 8 March 2002.

5 Data Protection

(1) A certification-service-provider who issues a certificate to the public and to whom this paragraph applies in accordance with paragraph (6) below—
(a) shall not obtain personal data for the purpose of issuing or maintaining that certificate otherwise than directly from the data subject or after the explicit consent of the data subject, and
(b) shall not process the personal data referred to in sub-paragraph (a) above—
  (i) to a greater extent than is necessary for the purpose of issuing or maintaining that certificate, or
  (ii) to a greater extent than is necessary for any other purpose to which the data subject has explicitly consented,

unless the processing is necessary for compliance with any legal obligation, to which the certification-service-provider is subject, other than an obligation imposed by contract.

(2) The obligation to comply with paragraph (1) above shall be a duty owed to any data subject who may be affected by a contravention of paragraph (1).

(3) Where a duty is owed by virtue of paragraph (2) above to any data subject, any breach of that duty which causes that data subject to sustain loss or damage shall be actionable by him.

(4) Compliance with paragraph (1) above shall also be enforceable by civil proceedings brought by the Crown for an injunction or for an interdict or for any other appropriate relief or remedy.

(5) Paragraph (4) above shall not prejudice any right that a data subject may have by virtue of paragraph (3) above to bring civil proceedings for the contravention or apprehended contravention of paragraph (1) above.

(6) Paragraph (1) above applies to a certification-service-provider in respect of personal data only if the certification-service-provider is established in the United Kingdom and the personal data are processed in the context of that establishment.

(7) For the purposes of paragraph (6) above, each of the following is to be treated as established in the United Kingdom—
(a) an individual who is ordinarily resident in the United Kingdom,
(b) a body incorporated under the law of, or in any part of, the United Kingdom,
(c) a partnership or other unincorporated association formed under the law of any part of the United Kingdom, and
(d) any person who does not fall within sub-paragraph (a), (b) or (c) above but maintains in the United Kingdom—
  (i) an office, branch or agency through which he carries on any activity, or
  (ii) a regular practice.

(8) In this regulation—

"data subject" and "personal data" and "processing" shall have the same meanings as in section 1(1) of the Data Protection Act 1998, and

"obtain" shall bear the same interpretation as "obtaining" in section 1(2) of the Data Protection Act 1998.

[40]

NOTES

Commencement: 8 March 2002.

SCHEDULES

SCHEDULE 1

Regulation 2

(ANNEX I TO THE DIRECTIVE)

REQUIREMENTS FOR QUALIFIED CERTIFICATES

Qualified certificates must contain:

(a) an indication that the certificate is issued as a qualified certificate;

(b) the identification of the certification-service-provider and the State in which it is established;

(c) the name of the signatory or a pseudonym, which shall be identified as such;

(d) provision for a specific attribute of the signatory to be included if relevant, depending on the purpose for which the certificate is intended;

(e) signature-verification data which correspond to signature-creation data under the control of the signatory;

(f) an indication of the beginning and end of the period of validity of the certificate;

(g) the identity code of the certificate;

(h) the advanced electronic signature of the certification-service-provider issuing it;

(i) limitations on the scope of use of the certificate, if applicable; and

(j) limits on the value of transactions for which the certificate can be used, if applicable.

[41]

NOTES

Commencement: 8 March 2002.

SCHEDULE 2

Regulation 2

(ANNEX II TO THE DIRECTIVE)

REQUIREMENTS FOR CERTIFICATION-SERVICE-PROVIDERS ISSUING QUALIFIED CERTIFICATES

Certification-service-providers must:

(a) demonstrate the reliability necessary for providing certification services;

(b) ensure the operation of a prompt and secure directory and a secure and immediate revocation service;

(c) ensure that the date and time when a certificate is issued or revoked can be determined precisely;

(d) verify, by appropriate means in accordance with national law, the identity and, if applicable, any specific attributes of the person to which a qualified certificate is issued;

(e) employ personnel who possess the expert knowledge, experience, and qualifications necessary for the services provided, in particular competence at managerial level, expertise in electronic signature technology and familiarity with proper security procedures; they must also apply administrative and management procedures which are adequate and correspond to recognised standards;

(f) use trustworthy systems and products which are protected against modification and ensure the technical and cryptographic security of the process supported by them;

(g) take measures against forgery of certificates, and, in cases where the certification-service-provider generates signature-creation data, guarantee confidentiality during the process of generating such data;

(h) maintain sufficient financial resources to operate in conformity with the requirements laid down in the Directive, in particular to bear the risk of liability for damages, for example, by obtaining appropriate insurance;

(i) record all relevant information concerning a qualified certificate for an appropriate period of time, in particular for the purpose of providing evidence of certification for the purposes of legal proceedings. Such recording may be done electronically;

(j) not store or copy signature-creation data of the person to whom the certification-service-provider provided key management services;

(k) before entering into a contractual relationship with a person seeking a certificate to support his electronic signature inform that person by a durable means of communication of the precise terms and conditions regarding the use of the certificate, including any limitations on its use, the existence of a voluntary accreditation scheme and procedures for complaints and dispute settlement. Such information, which may be transmitted electronically, must be in writing and in readily understandable language. Relevant parts of this information must also be made available on request to third parties relying on the certificate;

(l) use trustworthy systems to store certificates in a verifiable form so that:
- — only authorised persons can make entries and changes,
- — information can be checked for authenticity,
- — certificates are publicly available for retrieval in only those cases for which the certificate-holder's consent has been obtained, and
- — any technical changes compromising these security requirements are apparent to the operator.

[42]

NOTES

Commencement: 8 March 2002.

ELECTRONIC COMMERCE (EC DIRECTIVE) REGULATIONS 2002

(SI 2002/2013)

ARRANGEMENT OF REGULATIONS

NOTES

Made: 30 July 2002.
Authority: European Communities Act 1972, s 2(2).
Commencement: 21 August 2002 (regs 1–15, 17–22, Schedule); 23 October 2002 (reg 16).

1 Citation and commencement

(1) These Regulations may be cited as the Electronic Commerce (EC Directive) Regulations 2002 and except for regulation 16 shall come into force on 21st August 2002.

(2) Regulation 16 shall come into force on 23rd October 2002.

[43]

NOTES

Commencement: 21 August 2002.

2 Interpretation

(1) In these Regulations and in the Schedule—

"commercial communication" means a communication, in any form, designed to promote, directly or indirectly, the goods, services or image of any person pursuing a commercial, industrial or craft activity or exercising a regulated profession, other than a communication—

(a) consisting only of information allowing direct access to the activity of that person including a geographic address, a domain name or an electronic mail address; or

(b) relating to the goods, services or image of that person provided that the communication has been prepared independently of the person making it (and for this purpose, a communication prepared without financial consideration is to be taken to have been prepared independently unless the contrary is shown);

"the Commission" means the Commission of the European Communities;

"consumer" means any natural person who is acting for purposes other than those of his trade, business or profession;

"coordinated field" means requirements applicable to information society service providers or information society services, regardless of whether they are of a general nature or specifically designed for them, and covers requirements with which the service provider has to comply in respect of—

(a) the taking up of the activity of an information society service, such as requirements concerning qualifications, authorisation or notification, and

(b) the pursuit of the activity of an information society service, such as requirements concerning the behaviour of the service provider, requirements regarding the quality or content of the service including those applicable to advertising and contracts, or requirements concerning the liability of the service provider,

but does not cover requirements such as those applicable to goods as such, to the delivery of goods or to services not provided by electronic means;

"the Directive" means Directive 2000/31/EC of the European Parliament and of the Council of 8 June 2000 on certain legal aspects of information society services, in particular electronic commerce, in the Internal Market (Directive on electronic commerce);

"EEA Agreement" means the Agreement on the European Economic Area signed at Oporto on 2 May 1992 as adjusted by the Protocol signed at Brussels on 17 March 1993;

"enactment" includes an enactment comprised in Northern Ireland legislation and comprised in, or an instrument made under, an Act of the Scottish Parliament;

"enforcement action" means any form of enforcement action including, in particular—

(a) in relation to any legal requirement imposed by or under any enactment, any action taken with a view to or in connection with imposing any sanction (whether criminal or otherwise) for failure to observe or comply with it; and

(b) in relation to a permission or authorisation, anything done with a view to removing or restricting that permission or authorisation;

"enforcement authority" does not include courts but, subject to that, means any person who is authorised, whether by or under an enactment or otherwise, to take enforcement action;

"established service provider" means a service provider who is a national of a member State or a company or firm as mentioned in Article 48 of the Treaty and who effectively pursues an economic activity by virtue of which he is a service provider using a fixed establishment in a member State for an indefinite period, but the presence and use of the technical means and technologies required to provide the information society service do not, in themselves, constitute an establishment of the provider; in cases where it cannot be determined from which of a number of places of establishment a given service is provided, that service is to be regarded as provided from the place of establishment where the provider has the centre of his activities relating to that service; references to a service provider being established or to the establishment of a service provider shall be construed accordingly;

"information society services" (which is summarised in recital 17 of the Directive as covering "any service normally provided for remuneration, at a distance, by means of electronic equipment for the processing (including digital compression) and storage of data, and at the individual request of a recipient of a service") has the meaning set out in Article 2(a) of the Directive, (which refers to Article 1(2) of Directive 98/34/EC of the European Parliament and of the Council of 22 June 1998 laying down a procedure for the provision of information in the field of technical standards and regulations, as amended by Directive 98/48/EC of 20 July 1998);

"member State" includes a State which is a contracting party to the EEA Agreement;

"recipient of the service" means any person who, for professional ends or otherwise, uses an information society service, in particular for the purposes of seeking information or making it accessible;

"regulated profession" means any profession within the meaning of either Article 1(d) of Council Directive 89/48/EEC of 21 December 1988 on a general system for the recognition of higher-education diplomas awarded on completion of professional education and training of at least three years' duration or of Article 1(f) of Council Directive 92/51/EEC of 18 June 1992 on a second general system for the recognition of professional education and training to supplement Directive 89/48/EEC;

"service provider" means any person providing an information society service;

"the Treaty" means the treaty establishing the European Community.

(2) In regulation 4 and 5, "requirement" means any legal requirement under the law of the United Kingdom, or any part of it, imposed by or under any enactment or otherwise.

(3) Terms used in the Directive other than those in paragraph (1) above shall have the same meaning as in the Directive.

[44]

NOTES

Commencement: 21 August 2002.

3 Exclusions

(1) Nothing in these Regulations shall apply in respect of—

(a) the field of taxation;

(b) questions relating to information society services covered by the Data Protection Directive and the Telecommunications Data Protection Directive and Directive 2002/58/EC of the European Parliament and of the Council of 12th July 2002 concerning the processing of personal data and the protection of privacy in the electronic communications sector (Directive on privacy and electronic communications);

(c) questions relating to agreements or practices governed by cartel law; and

(d) the following activities of information society services—

(i) the activities of a public notary or equivalent professions to the extent that they involve a direct and specific connection with the exercise of public authority,

(ii) the representation of a client and defence of his interests before the courts, and

(iii) betting, gaming or lotteries which involve wagering a stake with monetary value.

[(2) These Regulations shall not apply in relation to any Act passed on or after the date these Regulations are made or in relation to the exercise of a power to legislate after that date.]

(3) In this regulation—

"cartel law" means so much of the law relating to agreements between undertakings, decisions by associations of undertakings or concerted practices as relates to agreements to divide the market or fix prices;

"Data Protection Directive" means Directive 95/46/EC of the European Parliament and of the Council of 24 October 1995 on the protection of individuals with regard to the processing of personal data and on the free movement of such data; and

"Telecommunications Data Protection Directive" means Directive 97/66/EC of the European Parliament and of the Council of 15 December 1997 concerning the processing of personal data and the protection of privacy in the telecommunications sector.

[45]

NOTES

Commencement: 21 August 2002.

Para (2): substituted by the Electronic Commerce (EC Directive) (Extension) Regulations 2004, SI 2004/1178, reg 3.

Notwithstanding para (2), these regulations apply to certain Acts passed after 30 July 2002: see the Electronic Commerce (EC Directive) (Extension) Regulations 2003, SI 2003/115 at **[65]**, the Electronic Commerce (EC Directive) (Extension) (No 2) Regulations 2003, SI 2003/2500 at **[68]**, the Price Marking Order 2004, SI 2004/102, art 3(2) and the Electronic Commerce (EC Directive) (Extension) Regulations 2004, SI 2004/1178 at **[72]**.

4 Internal market

(1) Subject to paragraph (4) below, any requirement which falls within the coordinated field shall apply to the provision of an information society service by a service provider established in the United Kingdom irrespective of whether that information society service is provided in the United Kingdom or another member State.

(2) Subject to paragraph (4) below, an enforcement authority with responsibility in relation to any requirement in paragraph (1) shall ensure that the provision of an information society service by a service provider established in the United Kingdom complies with that requirement irrespective of whether that service is provided in the United Kingdom or another member State and any power, remedy or procedure for taking enforcement action shall be available to secure compliance.

(3) Subject to paragraphs (4), (5) and (6) below, any requirement shall not be applied to the provision of an information society service by a service provider established in a member State other than the United Kingdom for reasons which fall within the coordinated field where its application would restrict the freedom to provide information society services to a person in the United Kingdom from that member State.

(4) Paragraphs (1), (2) and (3) shall not apply to those fields in the annex to the Directive set out in the Schedule.

(5) The reference to any requirements the application of which would restrict the freedom to provide information society services from another member State in paragraph (3) above does not include any requirement maintaining the level of protection for public health and consumer interests established by Community acts.

(6) To the extent that anything in these Regulations creates any new criminal offence, it shall not be punishable with imprisonment for more than two years or punishable on summary conviction with imprisonment for more than three months or with a fine of more than level 5 on the standard scale (if not calculated on a daily basis) or with a fine of more than £100 a day.

[46]

NOTES

Commencement: 21 August 2002.

5 Derogations from Regulation 4

(1) Notwithstanding regulation 4(3), an enforcement authority may take measures, including applying any requirement which would otherwise not apply by virtue of regulation 4(3) in respect of a given information society service, where those measures are necessary for reasons of—

(a) public policy, in particular the prevention, investigation, detection and prosecution of criminal offences, including the protection of minors and the fight against any incitement to hatred on grounds of race, sex, religion or nationality, and violations of human dignity concerning individual persons;

(b) the protection of public health;
(c) public security, including the safeguarding of national security and defence, or
(d) the protection of consumers, including investors,

and proportionate to those objectives.

(2) Notwithstanding regulation 4(3), in any case where an enforcement authority with responsibility in relation to the requirement in question is not party to the proceedings, a court may, on the application of any person or of its own motion, apply any requirement which would otherwise not apply by virtue of regulation 4(3) in respect of a given information society service, if the application of that enactment or requirement is necessary for and proportionate to any of the objectives set out in paragraph (1) above.

(3) Paragraphs (1) and (2) shall only apply where the information society service prejudices or presents a serious and grave risk of prejudice to an objective in paragraph (1)(a) to (d).

(4) Subject to paragraphs (5) and (6), an enforcement authority shall not take the measures in paragraph (1) above, unless it—

(a) asks the member State in which the service provider is established to take measures and the member State does not take such measures or they are inadequate; and
(b) notifies the Commission and the member State in which the service provider is established of its intention to take such measures.

(5) Paragraph (4) shall not apply to court proceedings, including preliminary proceedings and acts carried out in the course of a criminal investigation.

(6) If it appears to the enforcement authority that the matter is one of urgency, it may take the measures under paragraph (1) without first asking the member State in which the service provider is established to take measures and notifying the Commission and the member State in derogation from paragraph (4).

(7) In a case where a measure is taken pursuant to paragraph (6) above, the enforcement authority shall notify the measures taken to the Commission and to the member State concerned in the shortest possible time thereafter and indicate the reasons for urgency.

(8) In paragraph (2), "court" means any court or tribunal.

[47]

NOTES

Commencement: 21 August 2002.

6 General information to be provided by a person providing an information society service

(1) A person providing an information society service shall make available to the recipient of the service and any relevant enforcement authority, in a form and manner which is easily, directly and permanently accessible, the following information—

(a) the name of the service provider;
(b) the geographic address at which the service provider is established;
(c) the details of the service provider, including his electronic mail address, which make it possible to contact him rapidly and communicate with him in a direct and effective manner;
(d) where the service provider is registered in a trade or similar register available to the public, details of the register in which the service provider is entered and his registration number, or equivalent means of identification in that register;
(e) where the provision of the service is subject to an authorisation scheme, the particulars of the relevant supervisory authority;
(f) where the service provider exercises a regulated profession—
  (i) the details of any professional body or similar institution with which the service provider is registered;
  (ii) his professional title and the member State where that title has been granted;
  (iii) a reference to the professional rules applicable to the service provider in the member State of establishment and the means to access them; and
(g) where the service provider undertakes an activity that is subject to value added tax, the identification number referred to in Article 22(1) of the sixth Council

Directive 77/388/EEC of 17 May 1977 on the harmonisation of the laws of the member States relating to turnover taxes—Common system of value added tax: uniform basis of assessment.

(2) Where a person providing an information society service refers to prices, these shall be indicated clearly and unambiguously and, in particular, shall indicate whether they are inclusive of tax and delivery costs.

[48]

NOTES

Commencement: 21 August 2002.

7 Commercial communications

A service provider shall ensure that any commercial communication provided by him and which constitutes or forms part of an information society service shall—

(a) be clearly identifiable as a commercial communication;

(b) clearly identify the person on whose behalf the commercial communication is made;

(c) clearly identify as such any promotional offer (including any discount, premium or gift) and ensure that any conditions which must be met to qualify for it are easily accessible, and presented clearly and unambiguously; and

(d) clearly identify as such any promotional competition or game and ensure that any conditions for participation are easily accessible and presented clearly and unambiguously.

[49]

NOTES

Commencement: 21 August 2002.

8 Unsolicited commercial communications

A service provider shall ensure that any unsolicited commercial communication sent by him by electronic mail is clearly and unambiguously identifiable as such as soon as it is received.

[50]

NOTES

Commencement: 21 August 2002.

9 Information to be provided where contracts are concluded by electronic means

(1) Unless parties who are not consumers have agreed otherwise, where a contract is to be concluded by electronic means a service provider shall, prior to an order being placed by the recipient of a service, provide to that recipient in a clear, comprehensible and unambiguous manner the information set out in (a) to (d) below—

(a) the different technical steps to follow to conclude the contract;

(b) whether or not the concluded contract will be filed by the service provider and whether it will be accessible;

(c) the technical means for identifying and correcting input errors prior to the placing of the order; and

(d) the languages offered for the conclusion of the contract.

(2) Unless parties who are not consumers have agreed otherwise, a service provider shall indicate which relevant codes of conduct he subscribes to and give information on how those codes can be consulted electronically.

(3) Where the service provider provides terms and conditions applicable to the contract to the recipient, the service provider shall make them available to him in a way that allows him to store and reproduce them.

(4) The requirements of paragraphs (1) and (2) above shall not apply to contracts concluded exclusively by exchange of electronic mail or by equivalent individual communications.

[51]

NOTES

Commencement: 21 August 2002.

10 Other information requirements

Regulations 6, 7, 8 and 9(1) have effect in addition to any other information requirements in legislation giving effect to Community law.

[52]

NOTES

Commencement: 21 August 2002.

11 Placing of the order

(1) Unless parties who are not consumers have agreed otherwise, where the recipient of the service places his order through technological means, a service provider shall–

(a) acknowledge receipt of the order to the recipient of the service without undue delay and by electronic means; and

(b) make available to the recipient of the service appropriate, effective and accessible technical means allowing him to identify and correct input errors prior to the placing of the order.

(2) For the purposes of paragraph (1)(a) above—

(a) the order and the acknowledgement of receipt will be deemed to be received when the parties to whom they are addressed are able to access them; and

(b) the acknowledgement of receipt may take the form of the provision of the service paid for where that service is an information society service.

(3) The requirements of paragraph (1) above shall not apply to contracts concluded exclusively by exchange of electronic mail or by equivalent individual communications.

[53]

NOTES

Commencement: 21 August 2002.

12 Meaning of the term "order"

Except in relation to regulation 9(1)(c) and regulation 11(1)(b) where "order" shall be the contractual offer, "order" may be but need not be the contractual offer for the purposes of regulations 9 and 11.

[54]

NOTES

Commencement: 21 August 2002.

13 Liability of the service provider

The duties imposed by regulations 6, 7, 8, 9(1) and 11(1)(a) shall be enforceable, at the suit of any recipient of a service, by an action against the service provider for damages for breach of statutory duty.

[55]

NOTES

Commencement: 21 August 2002.

14 Compliance with Regulation 9(3)

Where on request a service provider has failed to comply with the requirement in regulation 9(3), the recipient may seek an order from any court having jurisdiction in relation to the contract requiring that service provider to comply with that requirement.

[56]

NOTES

Commencement: 21 August 2002.

15 Right to rescind contract

Where a person—

(a) has entered into a contract to which these Regulations apply, and

(b) the service provider has not made available means of allowing him to identify and correct input errors in compliance with regulation 11(1)(b),

he shall be entitled to rescind the contract unless any court having jurisdiction in relation to the contract in question orders otherwise on the application of the service provider.

[57]

NOTES

Commencement: 21 August 2002.

16 (*Amends the Stop Now Orders (EC Directive) Regulations 2001, SI 2001/1422, reg 2, Sch 1.*)

17 Mere conduit

(1) Where an information society service is provided which consists of the transmission in a communication network of information provided by a recipient of the service or the provision of access to a communication network, the service provider (if he otherwise would) shall not be liable for damages or for any other pecuniary remedy or for any criminal sanction as a result of that transmission where the service provider—

(a) did not initiate the transmission;

(b) did not select the receiver of the transmission; and

(c) did not select or modify the information contained in the transmission.

(2) The acts of transmission and of provision of access referred to in paragraph (1) include the automatic, intermediate and transient storage of the information transmitted where—

(a) this takes place for the sole purpose of carrying out the transmission in the communication network, and

(b) the information is not stored for any period longer than is reasonably necessary for the transmission.

[58]

NOTES

Commencement: 21 August 2002.

18 Caching

Where an information society service is provided which consists of the transmission in a communication network of information provided by a recipient of the service, the service provider (if he otherwise would) shall not be liable for damages or for any other pecuniary remedy or for any criminal sanction as a result of that transmission where—

(a) the information is the subject of automatic, intermediate and temporary storage where that storage is for the sole purpose of making more efficient onward transmission of the information to other recipients of the service upon their request, and

(b) the service provider—

(i) does not modify the information;

(ii) complies with conditions on access to the information;

(iii) complies with any rules regarding the updating of the information, specified in a manner widely recognised and used by industry;

(iv) does not interfere with the lawful use of technology, widely recognised and used by industry, to obtain data on the use of the information; and

(v) acts expeditiously to remove or to disable access to the information he has stored upon obtaining actual knowledge of the fact that the information at the initial source of the transmission has been removed from the network, or access to it has been disabled, or that a court or an administrative authority has ordered such removal or disablement.

[59]

NOTES

Commencement: 21 August 2002.

19 Hosting

Where an information society service is provided which consists of the storage of information provided by a recipient of the service, the service provider (if he otherwise would) shall not be liable for damages or for any other pecuniary remedy or for any criminal sanction as a result of that storage where—

(a) the service provider—

(i) does not have actual knowledge of unlawful activity or information and, where a claim for damages is made, is not aware of facts or circumstances from which it would have been apparent to the service provider that the activity or information was unlawful; or

(ii) upon obtaining such knowledge or awareness, acts expeditiously to remove or to disable access to the information, and

(b) the recipient of the service was not acting under the authority or the control of the service provider.

[60]

NOTES

Commencement: 21 August 2002.

20 Protection of rights

(1) Nothing in regulations 17, 18 and 19 shall—

(a) prevent a person agreeing different contractual terms; or

(b) affect the rights of any party to apply to a court for relief to prevent or stop infringement of any rights.

(2) Any power of an administrative authority to prevent or stop infringement of any rights shall continue to apply notwithstanding regulations 17, 18 and 19.

[61]

NOTES

Commencement: 21 August 2002.

21 Defence in Criminal Proceedings: burden of proof

(1) This regulation applies where a service provider charged with an offence in criminal proceedings arising out of any transmission, provision of access or storage falling within regulation 17, 18 or 19 relies on a defence under any of regulations 17, 18 and 19.

(2) Where evidence is adduced which is sufficient to raise an issue with respect to that defence, the court or jury shall assume that the defence is satisfied unless the prosecution proves beyond reasonable doubt that it is not.

[62]

NOTES

Commencement: 21 August 2002.

22 Notice for the purposes of actual knowledge

In determining whether a service provider has actual knowledge for the purposes of regulations 18(b)(v) and 19(a)(i), a court shall take into account all matters which appear to it in the particular circumstances to be relevant and, among other things, shall have regard to—

(a) whether a service provider has received a notice through a means of contact made available in accordance with regulation 6(1)(c), and

(b) the extent to which any notice includes—

(i) the full name and address of the sender of the notice;
(ii) details of the location of the information in question; and
(iii) details of the unlawful nature of the activity or information in question.

[63]

NOTES

Commencement: 21 August 2002.

SCHEDULE

Regulation 4(4)

1. Copyright, neighbouring rights, rights referred to in Directive 87/54/EEC and Directive 96/9/EC and industrial property rights.

2. The freedom of the parties to a contract to choose the applicable law.

3. Contractual obligations concerning consumer contracts.

4. Formal validity of contracts creating or transferring rights in real estate where such contracts are subject to mandatory formal requirements of the law of the member State where the real estate is situated.

5. The permissibility of unsolicited commercial communications by electronic mail.

[64]

NOTES

Commencement: 21 August 2002.

ELECTRONIC COMMERCE (EC DIRECTIVE) (EXTENSION) REGULATIONS 2003

(SI 2003/115)

NOTES

Made: 24 January 2003.
Authority: European Communities Act 1972, s 2(2).
Commencement: 14 February 2003.

1 Citation and commencement

(1) These Regulations may be cited as the Electronic Commerce (EC Directive) (Extension) Regulations 2003.

(2) These Regulations shall come into force on 14th February 2003.

[65]

NOTES

Commencement: 14 February 2003.

2 Application of the E-Commerce Regulations

The Electronic Commerce (EC Directive) Regulations 2002 shall apply to the enactments listed in the Schedule notwithstanding Regulation 3(2) of those Regulations.

[66]

NOTES

Commencement: 14 February 2003.

SCHEDULE

Regulation 2

1. The Copyright (Visually Impaired Persons) Act 2002.

2. …

[67]

NOTES

Commencement: 14 February 2003.

Para 2: revoked by the Tobacco Advertising and Promotion Act 2002 etc (Amendment) Regulations 2006, SI 2006/2369, reg 10.

ELECTRONIC COMMERCE (EC DIRECTIVE) (EXTENSION) (NO 2) REGULATIONS 2003

(SI 2003/2500)

NOTES

Made: 29 September 2003.
Authority: European Communities Act 1972, s 2(2).
Commencement: 31 October 2003.

1 Citation and commencement

(1) These Regulations may be cited as the Electronic Commerce (EC Directive) (Extension) (No 2) Regulations 2003.

(2) These Regulations shall come into force on 31st October 2003 immediately after the Copyright (Visually Impaired Persons) Act 2002 (Commencement) Order 2003 has come into force.

[68]

NOTES

Commencement: 31 October 2003.

2 Application of the E-Commerce Regulations

The Electronic Commerce (EC Directive) Regulations 2002 ("the E-Commerce Regulations") shall apply to—

(a) the enactments listed in Part 1 of the Schedule, as amended by the Copyright and Related Rights Regulations 2003; and

(b) the enactments listed in Part 2 of the Schedule,

notwithstanding regulation 3(2) of the E-Commerce Regulations.

[69]

NOTES

Commencement: 31 October 2003.

SCHEDULE

Regulation 2

PART 1
ENACTMENTS AMENDED BY THE COPYRIGHT AND RELATED RIGHTS REGULATIONS 2003

Acts

Copyright, Designs and Patents Act 1988 (c 48)

Olympic Symbol etc (Protection) Act 1995 (c 32)

Copyright (Visually Impaired Persons) Act 2002 (c 33)

Instruments

Copyright (Recording of Folksongs for Archives) (Designated Bodies) Order 1989 (SI 1989/1012)

Copyright (Application of Provisions relating to Educational Establishments to Teachers) (No 2) Order 1989 (SI 1989/1067)

Copyright Tribunal Rules 1989 (SI 1989/1129)

Copyright (Librarians and Archivists) (Copying of Copyright Material) Regulations 1989 (SI 1989/1212)

Copyright (Certification of Licensing Scheme for Educational Recording of Broadcasts and Cable Programmes) (Educational Recording Agency Limited) Order 1990 (SI 1990/879)

Copyright (Recording for Archives of Designated Class of Broadcasts and Cable Programmes) (Designated Bodies) Order 1993 (SI 1993/74)

Copyright and Related Rights Regulations 1996 (SI 1996/2967)

Copyright (Certification of Licensing Scheme for Educational Recording of Broadcasts) (Open University) Order 2003 (SI 2003/187)

[70]

NOTES

Commencement: 31 October 2003.

PART 2
OTHER ENACTMENTS

Performances (Reciprocal Protection) (Convention Countries and Isle of Man) Order 2003 (SI 2003/773)

Copyright (Application to Other Countries) (Amendment) Order 2003 (SI 2003/774)

[71]

NOTES

Commencement: 31 October 2003.

ELECTRONIC COMMERCE (EC DIRECTIVE) (EXTENSION) REGULATIONS 2004

(SI 2004/1178)

NOTES

Made: 19 April 2004.
Authority: European Communities Act 1972, s 2(2).
Commencement: 14 May 2004.

1 Citation and commencement

These Regulations may be cited as the Electronic Commerce (EC Directive) (Extension) Regulations 2004 and shall come into force on 14th May 2004.

[72]

NOTES

Commencement: 14 May 2004.

2 Application of the E-Commerce Regulations

The Electronic Commerce (EC Directive) Regulations 2002 shall apply to the Sexual Offences Act 2003 notwithstanding regulation 3(2) of those Regulations.

[73]–[300]

NOTES

Commencement: 14 May 2004.

3 (*Amends the Electronic Commerce (EC Directive) Regulations 2002, SI 2002/2013, reg 3 at* **[45]**.)

DIRECTIVE OF THE EUROPEAN PARLIAMENT AND OF THE COUNCIL

of 20 May 1997

on the protection of consumers in respect of distance contracts

(97/7/EC)

NOTES

Date of publication in OJ: OJ L144, 4.6.1997, p 19.

THE EUROPEAN PARLIAMENT AND THE COUNCIL OF THE EUROPEAN UNION,

Having regard to the Treaty establishing the European Community, and in particular Article 100a thereof,

Having regard to the proposal from the Commission,[1]

Having regard to the opinion of the Economic and Social Committee,[2]

Acting in accordance with the procedure laid down in Article 189b of the Treaty,[3] in the light of the joint text approved by the Conciliation Committee on 27 November 1996,

(1) Whereas, in connection with the attainment of the aims of the internal market, measures must be taken for the gradual consolidation of that market;

(2) Whereas the free movement of goods and services affects not only the business sector but also private individuals; whereas it means that consumers should be able to have access to the goods and services of another Member State on the same terms as the population of that State;

(3) Whereas, for consumers, cross-border distance selling could be one of the main tangible results of the completion of the internal market, as noted, inter alia, in the communication from the Commission to the Council entitled "Towards a single market in distribution"; whereas it is essential to the smooth operation of the internal market for consumers to be able to have dealings with a business outside their country, even if it has a subsidiary in the consumer's country of residence;

(4) Whereas the introduction of new technologies is increasing the number of ways for consumers to obtain information about offers anywhere in the Community and to place orders; whereas some Member States have already taken different or diverging measures to protect consumers in respect of distance selling, which has had a detrimental effect on competition between businesses in the internal market; whereas it is therefore necessary to introduce at Community level a minimum set of common rules in this area;

(5) Whereas paragraphs 18 and 19 of the Annex to the Council resolution of 14 April 1975 on a preliminary programme of the European Economic Community for a consumer protection and information policy[4] point to the need to protect the purchasers of goods or services from demands for payment for unsolicited goods and from high-pressure selling methods;

(6) Whereas paragraph 33 of the communication from the Commission to the Council entitled "A new impetus for consumer protection policy", which was approved by the Council resolution of 23 June 1986,[5] states that the Commission will submit proposals regarding the use of new information technologies enabling consumers to place orders with suppliers from their homes;

(7) Whereas the Council resolution of 9 November 1989 on future priorities for relaunching consumer protection policy[6] calls upon the Commission to give priority to the areas referred to in the Annex to that resolution; whereas that Annex refers to new technologies involving teleshopping; whereas the Commission has responded to that resolution by adopting a three-year action plan for consumer protection policy in the European Economic Community (1990–1992); whereas that plan provides for the adoption of a Directive;

(8) Whereas the languages used for distance contracts are a matter for the Member States;

(9) Whereas contracts negotiated at a distance involve the use of one or more means of distance communication; whereas the various means of communication are used as part of an

organised distance sales or service-provision scheme not involving the simultaneous presence of the supplier and the consumer; whereas the constant development of those means of communication does not allow an exhaustive list to be compiled but does require principles to be defined which are valid even for those which are not as yet in widespread use;

(10) Whereas the same transaction comprising successive operations or a series of separate operations over a period of time may give rise to different legal descriptions depending on the law of the Member States; whereas the provisions of this Directive cannot be applied differently according to the law of the Member States, subject to their recourse to Article 14; whereas, to that end, there is therefore reason to consider that there must at least be compliance with the provisions of this Directive at the time of the first of a series of successive operations or the first of a series of separate operations over a period of time which may be considered as forming a whole, whether that operation or series of operations are the subject of a single contract or successive, separate contracts;

(11) Whereas the use of means of distance communication must not lead to a reduction in the information provided to the consumer; whereas the information that is required to be sent to the consumer should therefore be determined, whatever the means of communication used; whereas the information supplied must also comply with the other relevant Community rules, in particular those in Council Directive 84/450/EEC of 10 September 1984 relating to the approximation of the laws, regulations and administrative provisions of the Member States concerning misleading advertising;[7] whereas, if exceptions are made to the obligation to provide information, it is up to the consumer, on a discretionary basis, to request certain basic information such as the identity of the supplier, the main characteristics of the goods or services and their price;

(12) Whereas in the case of communication by telephone it is appropriate that the consumer receive enough information at the beginning of the conversation to decide whether or not to continue;

(13) Whereas information disseminated by certain electronic technologies is often ephemeral in nature insofar as it is not received on a permanent medium; whereas the consumer must therefore receive written notice in good time of the information necessary for proper performance of the contract;

(14) Whereas the consumer is not able actually to see the product or ascertain the nature of the service provided before concluding the contract; whereas provision should be made, unless otherwise specified in this Directive, for a right of withdrawal from the contract; whereas, if this right is to be more than formal, the costs, if any, borne by the consumer when exercising the right of withdrawal must be limited to the direct costs for returning the goods; whereas this right of withdrawal shall be without prejudice to the consumer's rights under national laws, with particular regard to the receipt of damaged products and services or of products and services not corresponding to the description given in the offer of such products or services; whereas it is for the Member States to determine the other conditions and arrangements following exercise of the right of withdrawal;

(15) Whereas it is also necessary to prescribe a time limit for performance of the contract if this is not specified at the time of ordering;

(16) Whereas the promotional technique involving the dispatch of a product or the provision of a service to the consumer in return for payment without a prior request from, or the explicit agreement of, the consumer cannot be permitted, unless a substitute product or service is involved;

(17) Whereas the principles set out in Articles 8 and 10 of the European Convention for the Protection of Human Rights and Fundamental Freedoms of 4 November 1950 apply; whereas the consumer's right to privacy, particularly as regards freedom from certain particularly intrusive means of communication, should be recognised; whereas specific limits on the use of such means should therefore be stipulated; whereas Member States should take appropriate measures to protect effectively those consumers, who do not wish to be contacted through certain means of communication, against such contacts, without prejudice to the particular safeguards available to the consumer under Community legislation concerning the protection of personal data and privacy;

(18) Whereas it is important for the minimum binding rules contained in this Directive to be supplemented where appropriate by voluntary arrangements among the traders concerned, in line with Commission recommendation 92/295/EEC of 7 April 1992 on codes of practice for the protection of consumers in respect of contracts negotiated at a distance;[8]

(19) Whereas in the interest of optimum consumer protection it is important for consumers to be satisfactorily informed of the provisions of this Directive and of codes of practice that may exist in this field;

(20) Whereas non-compliance with this Directive may harm not only consumers but also competitors; whereas provisions may therefore be laid down enabling public bodies or their representatives, or consumer organisations which, under national legislation, have a legitimate

interest in consumer protection, or professional organisations which have a legitimate interest in taking action, to monitor the application thereof;

(21) Whereas it is important, with a view to consumer protection, to address the question of cross-border complaints as soon as this is feasible; whereas the Commission published on 14 February 1996 a plan of action on consumer access to justice and the settlement of consumer disputes in the internal market; whereas that plan of action includes specific initiatives to promote out-of-court procedures; whereas objective criteria (Annex II) are suggested to ensure the reliability of those procedures and provision is made for the use of standardised claims forms (Annex III);

(22) Whereas in the use of new technologies the consumer is not in control of the means of communication used; whereas it is therefore necessary to provide that the burden of proof may be on the supplier;

(23) Whereas there is a risk that, in certain cases, the consumer may be deprived of protection under this Directive through the designation of the law of a non-member country as the law applicable to the contract; whereas provisions should therefore be included in this Directive to avert that risk;

(24) Whereas a Member State may ban, in the general interest, the marketing on its territory of certain goods and services through distance contracts; whereas that ban must comply with Community rules; whereas there is already provision for such bans, notably with regard to medicinal products, under Council Directive 89/552/EEC of 3 October 1989 on the coordination of certain provisions laid down by law, regulation or administrative action in Member States concerning the pursuit of television broadcasting activities[9] and Council Directive 92/28/EEC of 31 March 1992 on the advertising of medicinal products for human use,[10]

NOTES

1 OJ C156, 23.6.1992, p 14 and OJ C308, 15.11.1993, p 18.
2 OJ C19, 25.1.1993, p 111.
3 Opinion of the European Parliament of 26 May 1993 (OJ C176, 28.6.1993, p 95), Council common position of 29 June 1995 (OJ C288, 30.10.1995, p 1) and Decision of the European Parliament of 13 December 1995 (OJ C17, 22.1.1996, p 51). Decision of the European Parliament of 16 January 1997 and Council Decision of 20 January 1997.
4 OJ C92, 25.4.1975, p 1.
5 OJ C167, 5.7.1986, p 1.
6 OJ C294, 22.11.1989, p 1.
7 OJ L250, 19.9.1984, p 17.
8 OJ L156, 10.6.1992, p 21.
9 OJ L298, 17.10.1989, p 23.
10 OJ L113, 30.4.1992, p 13.

HAVE ADOPTED THIS DIRECTIVE—

Article 1

Object

The object of this Directive is to approximate the laws, regulations and administrative provisions of the Member States concerning distance contracts between consumers and suppliers.

[301]

Article 2

Definitions

For the purposes of this Directive—

(1) "distance contract" means any contract concerning goods or services concluded between a supplier and a consumer under an organised distance sales or service-provision scheme run by the supplier, who, for the purpose of the contract, makes exclusive use of one or more means of distance communication up to and including the moment at which the contract is concluded;

(2) "consumer" means any natural person who, in contracts covered by this Directive, is acting for purposes which are outside his trade, business or profession;

(3) "supplier" means any natural or legal person who, in contracts covered by this Directive, is acting in his commercial or professional capacity;

(4) "means of distance communication" means any means which, without the

simultaneous physical presence of the supplier and the consumer, may be used for the conclusion of a contract between those parties. An indicative list of the means covered by this Directive is contained in Annex I;

(5) "operator of a means of communication" means any public or private natural or legal person whose trade, business or profession involves making one or more means of distance communication available to suppliers.

[302]

Article 3

Exemptions

1. This Directive shall not apply to contracts—

[— relating to any financial service to which Directive 2002/65/EC[1] of the European Parliament and of the Council of 23 September 2002 concerning the distance marketing of consumer financial services and amending Council Directive 90/619/EEC[2] and Directives 97/7/EC and 98/27/EC[3] applies,]

— concluded by means of automatic vending machines or automated commercial premises,

— concluded with telecommunications operators through the use of public payphones,

— concluded for the construction and sale of immovable property or relating to other immovable property rights, except for rental,

— concluded at an auction.

2. Articles 4, 5, 6 and 7(1) shall not apply—

— to contracts for the supply of foodstuffs, beverages or other goods intended for everyday consumption supplied to the home of the consumer, to his residence or to his workplace by regular roundsmen,

— to contracts for the provision of accommodation, transport, catering or leisure services, where the supplier undertakes, when the contract is concluded, to provide these services on a specific date or within a specific period; exceptionally, in the case of outdoor leisure events, the supplier can reserve the right not to apply Article 7(2) in specific circumstances.

[303]

NOTES

Para 1: words in square brackets substituted by European Parliament and Council Directive 2002/65/EC, Art 18(1).

1 OJ L271, 9.10.02, p 16–24.
2 OJ L330, 29.11.90, p 50–61.
3 OJ L166, 11.6.98, p 51–55.

Article 4

Prior information

1. In good time prior to the conclusion of any distance contract, the consumer shall be provided with the following information—

(a) the identity of the supplier and, in the case of contracts requiring payment in advance, his address;
(b) the main characteristics of the goods or services;
(c) the price of the goods or services including all taxes;
(d) delivery costs, where appropriate;
(e) the arrangements for payment, delivery or performance;
(f) the existence of a right of withdrawal, except in the cases referred to in Article 6(3);
(g) the cost of using the means of distance communication, where it is calculated other than at the basic rate;
(h) the period for which the offer or the price remains valid;
(i) where appropriate, the minimum duration of the contract in the case of contracts for the supply of products or services to be performed permanently or recurrently.

2. The information referred to in paragraph 1, the commercial purpose of which must be made clear, shall be provided in a clear and comprehensible manner in any way appropriate to the means of distance communication used, with due regard, in particular, to the principles of

good faith in commercial transactions, and the principles governing the protection of those who are unable, pursuant to the legislation of the Member States, to give their consent, such as minors.

3. Moreover, in the case of telephone communications, the identity of the supplier and the commercial purpose of the call shall be made explicitly clear at the beginning of any conversation with the consumer.

[304]

Article 5

Written confirmation of information

1. The consumer must receive written confirmation or confirmation in another durable medium available and accessible to him of the information referred to in Article 4(1)(a) to (f), in good time during the performance of the contract, and at the latest at the time of delivery where goods not for delivery to third parties are concerned, unless the information has already been given to the consumer prior to conclusion of the contract in writing or on another durable medium available and accessible to him.

In any event the following must be provided—

— written information on the conditions and procedures for exercising the right of withdrawal, within the meaning of Article 6, including the cases referred to in the first indent of Article 6(3),
— the geographical address of the place of business of the supplier to which the consumer may address any complaints,
— information on after-sales services and guarantees which exist,
— the conclusion for cancelling the contract, where it is of unspecified duration or a duration exceeding one year.

2. Paragraph 1 shall not apply to services which are performed through the use of a means of distance communication, where they are supplied on only one occasion and are invoiced by the operator of the means of distance communication. Nevertheless, the consumer must in all cases be able to obtain the geographical address of the place of business of the supplier to which he may address any complaints.

[305]

Article 6

Right of withdrawal

1. For any distance contract the consumer shall have a period of at least seven working days in which to withdraw from the contract without penalty and without giving any reason. The only charge that may be made to the consumer because of the exercise of his right of withdrawal is the direct cost of returning the goods. The period for exercise of this right shall begin—

— in the case of goods, from the day of receipt by the consumer where the obligations laid down in Article 5 have been fulfilled,
— in the case of services, from the day of conclusion of the contract or from the day on which the obligations laid down in Article 5 were fulfilled if they are fulfilled after conclusion of the contract, provided that this period does not exceed the three-month period referred to in the following subparagraph.

If the supplier has failed to fulfil the obligations laid down in Article 5, the period shall be three months. The period shall begin—

— in the case of goods, from the day of receipt by the consumer,
— in the case of services, from the day of conclusion of the contract.

If the information referred to in Article 5 is supplied within this three-month period, the seven working day period referred to in the first subparagraph shall begin as from that moment.

2. Where the right of withdrawal has been exercised by the consumer pursuant to this Article, the supplier shall be obliged to reimburse the sums paid by the consumer free of charge. The only charge that may be made to the consumer because of the exercise of his right of withdrawal is the direct cost of returning the goods. Such reimbursement must be carried out as soon as possible and in any case within 30 days.

3. Unless the parties have agreed otherwise, the consumer may not exercise the right of withdrawal provided for in paragraph 1 in respect of contracts—

— for the provision of services if performance has begun, with the consumer's agreement, before the end of the seven working day period referred to in paragraph 1,
— for the supply of goods or services the price of which is dependent on fluctuations in the financial market which cannot be controlled by the supplier,
— for the supply of goods made to the consumer's specifications or clearly personalised or which, by reason of their nature, cannot be returned or are liable to deteriorate or expire rapidly,
— for the supply of audio or video recordings or computer software which were unsealed by the consumer,
— for the supply of newspapers, periodicals and magazines,
— for gaming and lottery services.

4. The Member States shall make provision in their legislation to ensure that—

— if the price of goods or services is fully or partly covered by credit granted by the supplier, or
— if that price is fully or partly covered by credit granted to the consumer by a third party on the basis of an agreement between the third party and the supplier, the credit agreement shall be cancelled, without any penalty, if the consumer exercises his right to withdraw from the contract in accordance with paragraph 1.

Member States shall determine the detailed rules for cancellation of the credit agreement.

[306]

Article 7

Performance

1. Unless the parties have agreed otherwise, the supplier must execute the order within a maximum of 30 days from the day following that on which the consumer forwarded his order to the supplier.

2. Where a supplier fails to perform his side of the contract on the grounds that the goods or services ordered are unavailable, the consumer must be informed of this situation and must be able to obtain a refund of any sums he has paid as soon as possible and in any case within 30 days.

3. Nevertheless, Member States may lay down that the supplier may provide the consumer with goods or services of equivalent quality and price provided that this possibility was provided for prior to the conclusion of the contract or in the contract. The consumer shall be informed of this possibility in a clear and comprehensible manner. The cost of returning the goods following exercise of the right of withdrawal shall, in this case, be borne by the supplier, and the consumer must be informed of this. In such cases the supply of goods or services may not be deemed to constitute inertia selling within the meaning of Article 9.

[307]

Article 8

Payment by card

Member States shall ensure that appropriate measures exist to allow a consumer—

— to request cancellation of a payment where fraudulent use has been made of his payment card in connection with distance contracts covered by this Directive,
— in the event of fraudulent use, to be recredited with the sums paid or have them returned.

[308]

[Article 9

Inertia selling

Given the prohibition of inertia selling practices laid down in Directive 2005/29/EC of 11 May 2005 of the European Parliament and of the Council concerning unfair business-to-consumer commercial practices in the internal market,[1] Member States shall take the measures necessary to exempt the consumer from the provision of any consideration in cases of unsolicited supply, the absence of a response not constituting consent.]

[309]

NOTES

Substituted by European Parliament and Council Directive 2005/29/EC, Art 15(1).

[1] OJ L149, 11.6.05, p 22.

Article 10

Restrictions on the use of certain means of distance communication

1. Use by a supplier of the following means requires the prior consent of the consumer—
— automated calling system without human intervention (automatic calling machine),
— facsimile machine (fax).

2. Member States shall ensure that means of distance communication, other than those referred to in paragraph 1, which allow individual communications may be used only where there is no clear objection from the consumer.

[310]

Article 11

Judicial or administrative redress

1. Member States shall ensure that adequate and effective means exist to ensure compliance with this Directive in the interests of consumers.

2. The means referred to in paragraph 1 shall include provisions whereby one or more of the following bodies, as determined by national law, may take action under national law before the courts or before the competent administrative bodies to ensure that the national provisions for the implementation of this Directive are applied—
(a) public bodies or their representatives;
(b) consumer organisations having a legitimate interest in protecting consumers;
(c) professional organisations having a legitimate interest in acting.

3.
(a) Member States may stipulate that the burden of proof concerning the existence of prior information, written confirmation, compliance with time-limits or consumer consent can be placed on the supplier.
(b) Member States shall take the measures needed to ensure that suppliers and operators of means of communication, where they are able to do so, cease practices which do not comply with measures adopted pursuant to this Directive.

4. Member States may provide that voluntary supervision by self-regulatory bodies of compliance with the provisions of this Directive and recourse to such bodies for the settlement of disputes be added to the means which Member States must provide to ensure compliance with the provisions of this Directive.

[311]

Article 12

Binding nature

1. The consumer may not waive the rights conferred on him by the transposition of this Directive into national law.

2. Member States shall take the measures needed to ensure that the consumer does not lose the protection granted by this Directive by virtue of the choice of the law of a non-member country as the law applicable to the contract if the latter has close connection with the territory of one or more Member States.

[312]

Article 13

Community rules

1. The provisions of this Directive shall apply insofar as there are no particular provisions in rules of Community law governing certain types of distance contracts in their entirety.

2. Where specific Community rules contain provisions governing only certain aspects of the supply of goods or provision of services, those provisions, rather than the provisions of this Directive, shall apply to these specific aspects of the distance contracts.

[313]

Article 14

Minimal clause

Member States may introduce or maintain, in the area covered by this Directive, more stringent provisions compatible with the Treaty, to ensure a higher level of consumer protection. Such provisions shall, where appropriate, include a ban, in the general interest, on the marketing of certain goods or services, particularly medicinal products, within their territory by means of distance contracts, with due regard for the Treaty.

[314]

Article 15

Implementation

1. Member States shall bring into force the laws, regulations and administrative provisions necessary to comply with this Directive no later than three years after it enters into force. They shall forthwith inform the Commission thereof.

2. When Member States adopt the measures referred to in paragraph 1, these shall contain a reference to this Directive or shall be accompanied by such reference on the occasion of their official publication. The procedure for such reference shall be laid down by Member States.

3. Member States shall communicate to the Commission the text of the provisions of national law which they adopt in the field governed by this Directive.

4. No later than four years after the entry into force of this Directive the Commission shall submit a report to the European Parliament and the Council on the implementation of this Directive, accompanied if appropriate by a proposal for the revision thereof.

[315]

Article 16

Consumer information

Member States shall take appropriate measures to inform the consumer of the national law transposing this Directive and shall encourage, where appropriate, professional organisations to inform consumers of their codes of practice.

[316]

Article 17

Complaints systems

The Commission shall study the feasibility of establishing effective means to deal with consumers' complaints in respect of distance selling. Within two years after the entry into force of this Directive the Commission shall submit a report to the European Parliament and the Council on the results of the studies, accompanied if appropriate by proposals.

[317]

Article 18

This Directive shall enter into force on the day of its publication in the Official Journal of the European Communities.

[318]

Article 19

This Directive is addressed to the Member States.

[319]

Done at Brussels, 20 May 1997.

ANNEX I

Means of communication covered by Article 2(4)

— Unaddressed printed matter
— Addressed printed matter
— Standard letter
— Press advertising with order form
— Catalogue
— Telephone with human intervention
— Telephone without human intervention (automatic calling machine, audiotext)
— Radio
— Videophone (telephone with screen)
— Videotex (microcomputer and television screen) with keyboard or touch screen
— Electronic mail
— Facsimile machine (fax)
— Television (teleshopping).

[320]

(*Annex II repealed by European Parliament and Council Directive 2002/65/EC, Art 18(2)*)

Statement by the Council and the Parliament re Article 6(1)

The Council and the Parliament note that the Commission will examine the possibility and desirability of harmonising the method of calculating the cooling-off period under existing consumer-protection legislation, notably Directive 85/577/EEC of 20 December 1985 on the protection of consumers in respect of contracts negotiated away from commercial establishments ("door-to-door sales").[1]

Statement by the Commission re Article 3(1), first indent

The Commission recognizes the importance of protecting consumers in respect of distance contracts concerning financial services and has published a Green Paper entitled "Financial services: meeting consumers' expectations". In the light of reactions to the Green Paper the Commission will examine ways of incorporating consumer protection into the policy on financial services and the possible legislative implications and, if need be, will submit appropriate proposals.

[321]

NOTES

[1] OJ L372, 31.12.1985, p 31.

DIRECTIVE OF THE EUROPEAN PARLIAMENT AND OF THE COUNCIL

of 20 November 1998

on the legal protection of services based on, or consisting of, conditional access

(98/84/EC)

NOTES

Date of publication in OJ: OJ L320, 28.11.1998, p 54.

THE EUROPEAN PARLIAMENT AND THE COUNCIL OF THE EUROPEAN UNION,

Having regard to the Treaty establishing the European Community, and in particular Articles 57(2), 66 and 100a thereof,

Having regard to the proposal from the Commission,[1]

Having regard to the opinion of the Economic and Social Committee,[2]

Acting in accordance with the procedure laid down in Article 189b of the Treaty,[3]

(1) Whereas the objectives of the Community as laid down in the Treaty include creating an ever closer union among the peoples of Europe and ensuring economic and social progress, by eliminating the barriers which divide them;

(2) Whereas the cross-border provision of broadcasting and information society services may contribute, from the individual point of view, to the full effectiveness of freedom of expression as a fundamental right and, from the collective point of view, to the achievement of the objectives laid down in the Treaty;

(3) Whereas the Treaty provides for the free movement of all services which are normally provided for remuneration; whereas this right, as applied to broadcasting and information society services, is also a specific manifestation in Community law of a more general principle, namely freedom of expression as enshrined in Article 10 of the European Convention for the Protection of Human Rights and Fundamental Freedoms; whereas that Article explicitly recognizes the right of citizens to receive and impart information regardless of frontiers and whereas any restriction of that right must be based on due consideration of other legitimate interests deserving of legal protection;

(4) Whereas the Commission undertook a wide-ranging consultation based on the Green Paper "Legal Protection of Encrypted Services in the Internal Market"; whereas the results of that consultation confirmed the need for a Community legal instrument ensuring the legal protection of all those services whose remuneration relies on conditional access;

(5) Whereas the European Parliament, in its Resolution of 13 May 1997 on the Green Paper,[4] called on the Commission to present a proposal for a Directive covering all encoded services in respect of which encoding is used to ensure payment of a fee, and agreed that this should include information society services provided at a distance by electronic means and at the individual request of a service receiver, as well as broadcasting services;

(6) Whereas the opportunities offered by digital technologies provide the potential for increasing consumer choice and contributing to cultural pluralism, by developing an even wider range of services within the meaning of Articles 59 and 60 of the Treaty; whereas the viability of those services will often depend on the use of conditional access in order to obtain the remuneration of the service provider; whereas, accordingly, the legal protection of service providers against illicit devices which allow access to these services free of charge seems necessary in order to ensure the economic viability of the services;

(7) Whereas the importance of this issue was recognized by the Commission Communication on "A European Initiative in Electronic Commerce";

(8) Whereas, in accordance with Article 7a of the Treaty, the internal market is to comprise an area without internal frontiers in which the free movement of services and goods is ensured; whereas Article 128(4) of the Treaty requires the Community to take cultural aspects into account in its action under other provisions of the Treaty; whereas by virtue of Article 130(3) of the Treaty, the Community must, through the policies and activities it pursues, contribute to creating the conditions necessary for the competitiveness of its industry;

(9) Whereas this Directive is without prejudice to possible future Community or national provisions meant to ensure that a number of broadcasting services, recognized as being of public interest, are not based on conditional access;

(10) Whereas this Directive is without prejudice to the cultural aspects of any further Community action concerning new services;

(11) Whereas the disparity between national rules concerning the legal protection of services based on, or consisting of, conditional access is liable to create obstacles to the free movement of services and goods;

(12) Whereas the application of the Treaty is not sufficient to remove these internal market obstacles; whereas those obstacles should therefore be removed by providing for an equivalent level of protection between Member States; whereas this implies an approximation of the national rules relating to the commercial activities which concern illicit devices;

(13) Whereas it seems necessary to ensure that Member States provide appropriate legal protection against the placing on the market, for direct or indirect financial gain, of an illicit device which enables or facilitates without authority the circumvention of any technological measures designed to protect the remuneration of a legally provided service;

(14) Whereas those commercial activities which concern illicit devices include commercial communications covering all forms of advertising, direct marketing, sponsorship, sales promotion and public relations promoting such products and services;

(15) Whereas those commercial activities are detrimental to consumers who are misled about the origin of illicit devices; whereas a high level of consumer protection is needed in order to fight against this kind of consumer fraud; whereas Article 129a(1) of the Treaty provides that the Community should contribute to the achievement of a high level of consumer protection by the measures it adopts pursuant to Article 100a thereof;

(16) Whereas, therefore, the legal framework for the creation of a single audiovisual area laid down in Council Directive 89/552/EEC of 3 October 1989 on the coordination of certain provisions laid down by law, regulation or administrative action in Member States concerning the pursuit of television broadcasting activities[5] should be supplemented with reference to

conditional access techniques as laid down in this Directive, in order, not least, to ensure equal treatment of the suppliers of cross-border broadcasts, regardless of their place of establishment;

(17) Whereas, in accordance with the Council Resolution of 29 June 1995 on the effective uniform application of Community law and on the penalties applicable for breaches of Community law in the internal market,[6] Member States are required to take action to ensure that Community law is duly applied with the same effectiveness and thoroughness as national law;

(18) Whereas, in accordance with Article 5 of the Treaty, Member States are required to take all appropriate measures to guarantee the application and effectiveness of Community law, in particular by ensuring that the sanctions chosen are effective, dissuasive and proportionate and the remedies appropriate;

(19) Whereas the approximation of the laws, regulations and administrative provisions of the Member States should be limited to what is needed in order to achieve the objectives of the internal market, in accordance with the principle of proportionality as set out in the third paragraph of Article 3b of the Treaty;

(20) Whereas the distribution of illicit devices includes transfer by any means and putting such devices on the market for circulation inside or outside the Community;

(21) Whereas this Directive is without prejudice to the application of any national provisions which may prohibit the private possession of illicit devices, to the application of Community competition rules and to the application of Community rules concerning intellectual property rights;

(22) Whereas national law concerning sanctions and remedies for infringing commercial activities may provide that the activities have to be carried out in the knowledge or with reasonable grounds for knowing that the devices in question were illicit;

(23) Whereas the sanctions and remedies provided for under this Directive are without prejudice to any other sanction or remedy for which provision may be made under national law, such as preventive measures in general or seizure of illicit devices; whereas Member States are not obliged to provide criminal sanctions for infringing activities covered by this Directive; whereas Member States' provisions for actions for damages are to be in conformity with their national legislative and judicial systems;

(24) Whereas this Directive is without prejudice to the application of national rules which do not fall within the field herein coordinated, such as those adopted for the protection of minors, including those in compliance with Directive 89/552/EEC, or national provisions concerned with public policy or public security,

NOTES

1 OJ C314, 16.10.1997, p 7 and OJ C 203, 30.6.1998, p 12.
2 OJ C129, 27.4.1998, p 16.
3 Opinion of the European Parliament of 30 April 1998 (OJ C152, 18.5.1998, p 59), Council Common Position of 29 June 1998 (OJ C262, 19.8.1998, p 34) and Decision of the European Parliament of 8 October 1998 (OJ C328, 26.10.1998). Council Decision of 9 November 1998.
4 OJ C167, 2.6.1997, p 31.
5 OJ L298, 17.10.1989, p 23. Directive as amended by Directive 97/36/EC of the European Parliament and of the Council (OJ L202, 30.7.1997, p 60).
6 OJ C188, 22.7.1995, p 1.

HAVE ADOPTED THIS DIRECTIVE—

Article 1

Scope

The objective of this Directive is to approximate provisions in the Member States concerning measures against illicit devices which give unauthorised access to protected services.

[322]

Article 2

Definitions

For the purposes of this Directive—

(a) protected service shall mean any of the following services, where provided against remuneration and on the basis of conditional access—
— television broadcasting, as defined in Article 1(a) of Directive 89/552/EEC,

— radio broadcasting, meaning any transmission by wire or over the air, including by satellite, of radio programmes intended for reception by the public,

— information society services within the meaning of Article 1(2) of Directive 98/34/EC of the European Parliament and of the Council of 22 June 1998 laying down a procedure for the provision of information in the field of technical standards and regulations and of rules on information society services,[1] or the provision of conditional access to the above services considered as a service in its own right;

(b) conditional access shall mean any technical measure and/or arrangement whereby access to the protected service in an intelligible form is made conditional upon prior individual authorisation;

(c) conditional access device shall mean any equipment or software designed or adapted to give access to a protected service in an intelligible form;

(d) associated service shall mean the installation, maintenance or replacement of conditional access devices, as well as the provision of commercial communication services in relation to them or to protected services;

(e) illicit device shall mean any equipment or software designed or adapted to give access to a protected service in an intelligible form without the authorisation of the service provider;

(f) field coordinated by this Directive shall mean any provision relating to the infringing activities specified in Article 4.

[323]

NOTES

[1] OJ L 204, 21.7.1998, p 37. Directive as amended by Directive 98/48/EC (OJ L217, 5.8.1998, p 18).

Article 3

Internal market principles

1. Each Member State shall take the measures necessary to prohibit on its territory the activities listed in Article 4, and to provide for the sanctions and remedies laid down in Article 5.

2. Without prejudice to paragraph 1, Member States may not—

(a) restrict the provision of protected services, or associated services, which originate in another Member State; or

(b) restrict the free movement of conditional access devices; for reasons falling within the field coordinated by this Directive.

[324]

Article 4

Infringing activities

Member States shall prohibit on their territory all of the following activities—

(a) the manufacture, import, distribution, sale, rental or possession for commercial purposes of illicit devices;

(b) the installation, maintenance or replacement for commercial purposes of an illicit device;

(c) the use of commercial communications to promote illicit devices.

[325]

Article 5

Sanctions and remedies

1. The sanctions shall be effective, dissuasive and proportionate to the potential impact of the infringing activity.

2. Member States shall take the necessary measures to ensure that providers of protected services whose interests are affected by an infringing activity as specified in Article 4, carried out on their territory, have access to appropriate remedies, including bringing an action for

damages and obtaining an injunction or other preventive measure, and where appropriate, applying for disposal outside commercial channels of illicit devices.

[326]

Article 6

Implementation

1. Member States shall bring into force the laws, regulations and administrative provisions necessary to comply with this Directive by 28 May 2000. They shall notify them to the Commission forthwith.

When Member States adopt such measures, they shall contain a reference to this Directive or shall be accompanied by such reference at the time of their official publication. The methods of making such reference shall be laid down by Member States.

2. Member States shall communicate to the Commission the text of the provisions of national law which they adopt in the field coordinated by this Directive.

[327]

Article 7

Reports

Not later than three years after the entry into force of this Directive, and every two years thereafter, the Commission shall present a report to the European Parliament, the Council and the Economic and Social Committee concerning the implementation of this Directive accompanied, where appropriate, by proposals, in particular as regards the definitions under Article 2, for adapting it in light of technical and economic developments and of the consultations carried out by the Commission.

[328]

Article 8

Entry into force

This Directive shall enter into force on the day of its publication in the *Official Journal of the European Communities.*

[329]

Article 9

Addressees

This Directive is addressed to the Member States.

[330]

Done at Brussels, 20 November 1998.

DIRECTIVE OF THE EUROPEAN PARLIAMENT AND OF THE COUNCIL

of 13 December 1999

on a Community framework for electronic signatures

(1999/93/EC)

NOTES

Date of publication in OJ: OJ L13, 19.1.2000, p 12.

THE EUROPEAN PARLIAMENT AND THE COUNCIL OF THE EUROPEAN UNION,

Having regard to the Treaty establishing the European Community, and in particular Articles 47(2), 55 and 95 thereof,

Having regard to the proposal from the Commission,[1]
Having regard to the opinion of the Economic and Social Committee,[2]
Having regard to the opinion of the Committee of the Regions,[3]
Acting in accordance with the procedure laid down in Article 251 of the Treaty,[4]
Whereas—

(1) On 16 April 1997 the Commission presented to the European Parliament, the Council, the Economic and Social Committee and the Committee of the Regions a Communication on a European Initiative in Electronic Commerce;

(2) On 8 October 1997 the Commission presented to the European Parliament, the Council, the Economic and Social Committee and the Committee of the Regions a Communication on ensuring security and trust in electronic communication—towards a European framework for digital signatures and encryption;

(3) On 1 December 1997 the Council invited the Commission to submit as soon as possible a proposal for a Directive of the European Parliament and of the Council on digital signatures;

(4) Electronic communication and commerce necessitate "electronic signatures" and related services allowing data authentication; divergent rules with respect to legal recognition of electronic signatures and the accreditation of certification-service providers in the Member States may create a significant barrier to the use of electronic communications and electronic commerce; on the other hand, a clear Community framework regarding the conditions applying to electronic signatures will strengthen confidence in, and general acceptance of, the new technologies; legislation in the Member States should not hinder the free movement of goods and services in the internal market;

(5) The interoperability of electronic-signature products should be promoted; in accordance with Article 14 of the Treaty, the internal market comprises an area without internal frontiers in which the free movement of goods is ensured; essential requirements specific to electronic-signature products must be met in order to ensure free movement within the internal market and to build trust in electronic signatures, without prejudice to Council Regulation (EC) No 3381/94 of 19 December 1994 setting up a Community regime for the control of exports of dual-use goods[5] and Council Decision 94/942/CFSP of 19 December 1994 on the joint action adopted by the Council concerning the control of exports of dual-use goods;[6]

(6) This Directive does not harmonise the provision of services with respect to the confidentiality of information where they are covered by national provisions concerned with public policy or public security;

(7) The internal market ensures the free movement of persons, as a result of which citizens and residents of the European Union increasingly need to deal with authorities in Member States other than the one in which they reside; the availability of electronic communication could be of great service in this respect;

(8) Rapid technological development and the global character of the Internet necessitate an approach which is open to various technologies and services capable of authenticating data electronically;

(9) Electronic signatures will be used in a large variety of circumstances and applications, resulting in a wide range of new services and products related to or using electronic signatures; the definition of such products and services should not be limited to the issuance and management of certificates, but should also encompass any other service and product using, or ancillary to, electronic signatures, such as registration services, time-stamping services, directory services, computing services or consultancy services related to electronic signatures;

(10) The internal market enables certification-service-providers to develop their cross-border activities with a view to increasing their competitiveness, and thus to offer consumers and businesses new opportunities to exchange information and trade electronically in a secure way, regardless of frontiers; in order to stimulate the Community-wide provision of certification services over open networks, certification-service-providers should be free to provide their services without prior authorisation; prior authorisation means not only any permission whereby the certification-service-provider concerned has to obtain a decision by national authorities before being allowed to provide its certification services, but also any other measures having the same effect;

(11) Voluntary accreditation schemes aiming at an enhanced level of service-provision may offer certification-service-providers the appropriate framework for developing further their services towards the levels of trust, security and quality demanded by the evolving market; such schemes should encourage the development of best practice among certification-service-providers; certification-service-providers should be left free to adhere to and benefit from such accreditation schemes;

(12) Certification services can be offered either by a public entity or a legal or natural person, when it is established in accordance with the national law; whereas Member States should not prohibit certification-service-providers from operating outside voluntary accreditation schemes; it should be ensured that such accreditation schemes do not reduce competition for certification services;

(13) Member States may decide how they ensure the supervision of compliance with the provisions laid down in this Directive; this Directive does not preclude the establishment of private-sector-based supervision systems; this Directive does not oblige certification-service-providers to apply to be supervised under any applicable accreditation scheme;

(14) It is important to strike a balance between consumer and business needs;

(15) Annex III covers requirements for secure signature-creation devices to ensure the functionality of advanced electronic signatures; it does not cover the entire system environment in which such devices operate; the functioning of the internal market requires the Commission and the Member States to act swiftly to enable the bodies charged with the conformity assessment of secure signature devices with Annex III to be designated; in order to meet market needs conformity assessment must be timely and efficient;

(16) This Directive contributes to the use and legal recognition of electronic signatures within the Community; a regulatory framework is not needed for electronic signatures exclusively used within systems, which are based on voluntary agreements under private law between a specified number of participants; the freedom of parties to agree among themselves the terms and conditions under which they accept electronically signed data should be respected to the extent allowed by national law; the legal effectiveness of electronic signatures used in such systems and their admissibility as evidence in legal proceedings should be recognised;

(17) This Directive does not seek to harmonise national rules concerning contract law, particularly the formation and performance of contracts, or other formalities of a non-contractual nature concerning signatures; for this reason the provisions concerning the legal effect of electronic signatures should be without prejudice to requirements regarding form laid down in national law with regard to the conclusion of contracts or the rules determining where a contract is concluded;

(18) The storage and copying of signature-creation data could cause a threat to the legal validity of electronic signatures;

(19) Electronic signatures will be used in the public sector within national and Community administrations and in communications between such administrations and with citizens and economic operators, for example in the public procurement, taxation, social security, health and justice systems;

(20) Harmonised criteria relating to the legal effects of electronic signatures will preserve a coherent legal framework across the Community; national law lays down different requirements for the legal validity of hand-written signatures; whereas certificates can be used to confirm the identity of a person signing electronically; advanced electronic signatures based on qualified certificates aim at a higher level of security; advanced electronic signatures which are based on a qualified certificate and which are created by a secure-signature-creation device can be regarded as legally equivalent to hand-written signatures only if the requirements for hand-written signatures are fulfilled;

(21) In order to contribute to the general acceptance of electronic authentication methods it has to be ensured that electronic signatures can be used as evidence in legal proceedings in all Member States; the legal recognition of electronic signatures should be based upon objective criteria and not be linked to authorisation of the certification-service-provider involved; national law governs the legal spheres in which electronic documents and electronic signatures may be used; this Directive is without prejudice to the power of a national court to make a ruling regarding conformity with the requirements of this Directive and does not affect national rules regarding the unfettered judicial consideration of evidence;

(22) Certification-service-providers providing certification-services to the public are subject to national rules regarding liability;

(23) The development of international electronic commerce requires cross-border arrangements involving third countries; in order to ensure interoperability at a global level, agreements on multilateral rules with third countries on mutual recognition of certification services could be beneficial;

(24) In order to increase user confidence in electronic communication and electronic commerce, certification-service-providers must observe data protection legislation and individual privacy;

(25) Provisions on the use of pseudonyms in certificates should not prevent Member States from requiring identification of persons pursuant to Community or national law;

(26) The measures necessary for the implementation of this Directive are to be adopted in accordance with Council Decision 1999/468/EC of 28 June 1999 laying down the procedures for the exercise of implementing powers conferred on the Commission;[7]

(27) Two years after its implementation the Commission will carry out a review of this Directive so as, inter alia, to ensure that the advance of technology or changes in the legal environment have not created barriers to achieving the aims stated in this Directive; it should examine the implications of associated technical areas and submit a report to the European Parliament and the Council on this subject;

(28) In accordance with the principles of subsidiarity and proportionality as set out in Article 5 of the Treaty, the objective of creating a harmonised legal framework for the provision of electronic signatures and related services cannot be sufficiently achieved by the Member States and can therefore be better achieved by the Community; this Directive does not go beyond what is necessary to achieve that objective,

NOTES

1 OJ C325, 23.10.1998, p 5.

2 OJ C40, 15.2.1999, p 29.

3 OJ C93, 6.4.1999, p 33.

4 Opinion of the European Parliament of 13 January 1999 (OJ C104, 14.4.1999, p 49), Council Common Position of 28 June 1999 (OJ C243, 27.8.1999, p 33) and Decision of the European Parliament of 27 October 1999 (not yet published in the Official Journal). Council Decision of 30 November 1999.

5 OJ L367, 31.12.1994, p 1. Regulation as amended by Regulation (EC) No 837/95 (OJ L90, 21.4.1995, p 1).

6 OJ L367, 31.12.1994, p 8. Decision as last amended by Decision 99/193/CFSP (OJ L73, 19.3.1999, p 1).

7 OJ L184, 17.7.1999, p 23.

HAVE ADOPTED THIS DIRECTIVE—

Article 1

Scope

The purpose of this Directive is to facilitate the use of electronic signatures and to contribute to their legal recognition. It establishes a legal framework for electronic signatures and certain certification-services in order to ensure the proper functioning of the internal market.

It does not cover aspects related to the conclusion and validity of contracts or other legal obligations where there are requirements as regards form prescribed by national or Community law nor does it affect rules and limits, contained in national or Community law, governing the use of documents.

[331]

Article 2

Definitions

For the purpose of this Directive—

1. "electronic signature" means data in electronic form which are attached to or logically associated with other electronic data and which serve as a method of authentication;

2. "advanced electronic signature" means an electronic signature which meets the following requirements—
   (a) it is uniquely linked to the signatory;
   (b) it is capable of identifying the signatory;
   (c) it is created using means that the signatory can maintain under his sole control; and
   (d) it is linked to the data to which it relates in such a manner that any subsequent change of the data is detectable;

3. "signatory" means a person who holds a signature-creation device and acts either on his own behalf or on behalf of the natural or legal person or entity he represents;

4. "signature-creation data" means unique data, such as codes or private cryptographic keys, which are used by the signatory to create an electronic signature;

5. "signature-creation device" means configured software or hardware used to implement the signature-creation data;

6. "secure-signature-creation device" means a signature-creation device which meets the requirements laid down in Annex III;

7. "signature-verification-data" means data, such as codes or public cryptographic keys, which are used for the purpose of verifying an electronic signature;

8. "signature-verification device" means configured software or hardware used to implement the signature-verification-data;

9. "certificate" means an electronic attestation which links signature-verification data to a person and confirms the identity of that person;

10. "qualified certificate" means a certificate which meets the requirements laid down in Annex I and is provided by a certification-service-provider who fulfils the requirements laid down in Annex II;

11. "certification-service-provider" means an entity or a legal or natural person who issues certificates or provides other services related to electronic signatures;

12. "electronic-signature product" means hardware or software, or relevant components thereof, which are intended to be used by a certification-service-provider for the provision of electronic-signature services or are intended to be used for the creation or verification of electronic signatures;

13. "voluntary accreditation" means any permission, setting out rights and obligations specific to the provision of certification services, to be granted upon request by the certification-service-provider concerned, by the public or private body charged with the elaboration of, and supervision of compliance with, such rights and obligations, where the certification-service-provider is not entitled to exercise the rights stemming from the permission until it has received the decision by the body.

[332]

Article 3

Market access

1. Member States shall not make the provision of certification services subject to prior authorisation.

2. Without prejudice to the provisions of paragraph 1, Member States may introduce or maintain voluntary accreditation schemes aiming at enhanced levels of certification-service provision. All conditions related to such schemes must be objective, transparent, proportionate and non-discriminatory. Member States may not limit the number of accredited certification-service-providers for reasons which fall within the scope of this Directive.

3. Each Member State shall ensure the establishment of an appropriate system that allows for supervision of certification-service-providers which are established on its territory and issue qualified certificates to the public.

4. The conformity of secure signature-creation-devices with the requirements laid down in Annex III shall be determined by appropriate public or private bodies designated by Member States. The Commission shall, pursuant to the procedure laid down in Article 9, establish criteria for Member States to determine whether a body should be designated.

A determination of conformity with the requirements laid down in Annex III made by the bodies referred to in the first subparagraph shall be recognised by all Member States.

5. The Commission may, in accordance with the procedure laid down in Article 9, establish and publish reference numbers of generally recognised standards for electronic-signature products in the Official Journal of the European Communities. Member States shall presume that there is compliance with the requirements laid down in Annex II, point (f), and Annex III when an electronic signature product meets those standards.

6. Member States and the Commission shall work together to promote the development and use of signature-verification devices in the light of the recommendations for secure signature-verification laid down in Annex IV and in the interests of the consumer.

7. Member States may make the use of electronic signatures in the public sector subject to possible additional requirements. Such requirements shall be objective, transparent, proportionate and non-discriminatory and shall relate only to the specific characteristics of the application concerned. Such requirements may not constitute an obstacle to cross-border services for citizens.

[333]

Article 4

Internal market principles

1. Each Member State shall apply the national provisions which it adopts pursuant to this Directive to certification-service-providers established on its territory and to the services which they provide. Member States may not restrict the provision of certification-services originating in another Member State in the fields covered by this Directive.

2. Member States shall ensure that electronic-signature products which comply with this Directive are permitted to circulate freely in the internal market.

[334]

Article 5

Legal effects of electronic signatures

1. Member States shall ensure that advanced electronic signatures which are based on a qualified certificate and which are created by a secure-signature-creation device—

(a) satisfy the legal requirements of a signature in relation to data in electronic form in the same manner as a handwritten signature satisfies those requirements in relation to paper-based data; and

(b) are admissible as evidence in legal proceedings.

2. Member States shall ensure that an electronic signature is not denied legal effectiveness and admissibility as evidence in legal proceedings solely on the grounds that it is—

— in electronic form, or

— not based upon a qualified certificate, or

— not based upon a qualified certificate issued by an accredited certification-service-provider, or

— not created by a secure signature-creation device.

[335]

Article 6

Liability

1. As a minimum, Member States shall ensure that by issuing a certificate as a qualified certificate to the public or by guaranteeing such a certificate to the public a certification-service-provider is liable for damage caused to any entity or legal or natural person who reasonably relies on that certificate—

(a) as regards the accuracy at the time of issuance of all information contained in the qualified certificate and as regards the fact that the certificate contains all the details prescribed for a qualified certificate;

(b) for assurance that at the time of the issuance of the certificate, the signatory identified in the qualified certificate held the signature-creation data corresponding to the signature-verification data given or identified in the certificate;

(c) for assurance that the signature-creation data and the signature-verification data can be used in a complementary manner in cases where the certification-service-provider generates them both;

unless the certification-service-provider proves that he has not acted negligently.

2. As a minimum Member States shall ensure that a certification-service-provider who has issued a certificate as a qualified certificate to the public is liable for damage caused to any entity or legal or natural person who reasonably relies on the certificate for failure to register revocation of the certificate unless the certification-service-provider proves that he has not acted negligently.

3. Member States shall ensure that a certification-service-provider may indicate in a qualified certificate limitations on the use of that certificate, provided that the limitations are recognisable to third parties. The certification-service-provider shall not be liable for damage arising from use of a qualified certificate which exceeds the limitations placed on it.

4. Member States shall ensure that a certification-service-provider may indicate in the qualified certificate a limit on the value of transactions for which the certificate can be used, provided that the limit is recognisable to third parties.

The certification-service-provider shall not be liable for damage resulting from this maximum limit being exceeded.

5. The provisions of paragraphs 1 to 4 shall be without prejudice to Council Directive 93/13/EEC of 5 April 1993 on unfair terms in consumer contracts.[1]

[336]

NOTES

[1] OJ L95, 21.4.1993, p 29.

Article 7

International aspects

1. Member States shall ensure that certificates which are issued as qualified certificates to the public by a certification-service-provider established in a third country are recognised as legally equivalent to certificates issued by a certification-service-provider established within the Community if—

(a) the certification-service-provider fulfils the requirements laid down in this Directive and has been accredited under a voluntary accreditation scheme established in a Member State; or

(b) a certification-service-provider established within the Community which fulfils the requirements laid down in this Directive guarantees the certificate; or

(c) the certificate or the certification-service-provider is recognised under a bilateral or multilateral agreement between the Community and third countries or international organisations.

2. In order to facilitate cross-border certification services with third countries and legal recognition of advanced electronic signatures originating in third countries, the Commission shall make proposals, where appropriate, to achieve the effective implementation of standards and international agreements applicable to certification services. In particular, and where necessary, it shall submit proposals to the Council for appropriate mandates for the negotiation of bilateral and multilateral agreements with third countries and international organisations. The Council shall decide by qualified majority.

3. Whenever the Commission is informed of any difficulties encountered by Community undertakings with respect to market access in third countries, it may, if necessary, submit proposals to the Council for an appropriate mandate for the negotiation of comparable rights for Community undertakings in these third countries. The Council shall decide by qualified majority.

Measures taken pursuant to this paragraph shall be without prejudice to the obligations of the Community and of the Member States under relevant international agreements.

[337]

Article 8

Data protection

1. Member States shall ensure that certification-service-providers and national bodies responsible for accreditation or supervision comply with the requirements laid down in Directive 95/46/EC of the European Parliament and of the Council of 24 October 1995 on the protection of individuals with regard to the processing of personal data and on the free movement of such data.[1]

2. Member States shall ensure that a certification-service-provider which issues certificates to the public may collect personal data only directly from the data subject, or after the explicit consent of the data subject, and only insofar as it is necessary for the purposes of issuing and maintaining the certificate. The data may not be collected or processed for any other purposes without the explicit consent of the data subject.

3. Without prejudice to the legal effect given to pseudonyms under national law, Member States shall not prevent certification-service-providers from indicating in the certificate a pseudonym instead of the signatory's name.

[338]

NOTES

[1] OJ L281, 23.11.1995, p 31.

Article 9

Committee

1. The Commission shall be assisted by an "Electronic-Signature Committee", hereinafter referred to as "the committee".

2. Where reference is made to this paragraph, Articles 4 and 7 of Decision 1999/468/EC shall apply, having regard to the provisions of Article 8 thereof.

The period laid down in Article 4(3) of Decision 1999/468/EC shall be set at three months.

3. The Committee shall adopt its own rules of procedure.

[339]

Article 10

Tasks of the committee

The committee shall clarify the requirements laid down in the Annexes of this Directive, the criteria referred to in Article 3(4) and the generally recognised standards for electronic signature products established and published pursuant to Article 3(5), in accordance with the procedure laid down in Article 9(2).

[340]

Article 11

Notification

1. Member States shall notify to the Commission and the other Member States the following—

(a) information on national voluntary accreditation schemes, including any additional requirements pursuant to Article 3(7);

(b) the names and addresses of the national bodies responsible for accreditation and supervision as well as of the bodies referred to in Article 3(4);

(c) the names and addresses of all accredited national certification service providers.

2. Any information supplied under paragraph 1 and changes in respect of that information shall be notified by the Member States as soon as possible.

[341]

Article 12

Review

1. The Commission shall review the operation of this Directive and report thereon to the European Parliament and to the Council by 19 July 2003 at the latest.

2. The review shall inter alia assess whether the scope of this Directive should be modified, taking account of technological, market and legal developments. The report shall in particular include an assessment, on the basis of experience gained, of aspects of harmonisation. The report shall be accompanied, where appropriate, by legislative proposals.

[342]

Article 13

Implementation

1. Member States shall bring into force the laws, regulations and administrative provisions necessary to comply with this Directive before 19 July 2001. They shall forthwith inform the Commission thereof.

When Member States adopt these measures, they shall contain a reference to this Directive or shall be accompanied by such a reference on the occasion of their official publication. The methods of making such reference shall be laid down by the Member States.

2. Member States shall communicate to the Commission the text of the main provisions of domestic law which they adopt in the field governed by this Directive.

[343]

Article 14

Entry into force

This Directive shall enter into force on the day of its publication in the Official Journal of the European Communities.

[344]

Article 15

Addressees

This Directive is addressed to the Member States.

[345]

Done at Brussels, 13 December 1999.

ANNEX I
REQUIREMENTS FOR QUALIFIED CERTIFICATES

Qualified certificates must contain—

(a) an indication that the certificate is issued as a qualified certificate;
(b) the identification of the certification-service-provider and the State in which it is established;
(c) the name of the signatory or a pseudonym, which shall be identified as such;
(d) provision for a specific attribute of the signatory to be included if relevant, depending on the purpose for which the certificate is intended;
(e) signature-verification data which correspond to signature-creation data under the control of the signatory;
(f) an indication of the beginning and end of the period of validity of the certificate;
(g) the identity code of the certificate;
(h) the advanced electronic signature of the certification-service-provider issuing it;
(i) limitations on the scope of use of the certificate, if applicable; and
(j) limits on the value of transactions for which the certificate can be used, if applicable.

[346]

ANNEX II
REQUIREMENTS FOR CERTIFICATION-SERVICE-PROVIDERS ISSUING QUALIFIED CERTIFICATES

Certification-service-providers must—

(a) demonstrate the reliability necessary for providing certification services;
(b) ensure the operation of a prompt and secure directory and a secure and immediate revocation service;
(c) ensure that the date and time when a certificate is issued or revoked can be determined precisely;
(d) verify, by appropriate means in accordance with national law, the identity and, if applicable, any specific attributes of the person to which a qualified certificate is issued;
(e) employ personnel who possess the expert knowledge, experience, and qualifications necessary for the services provided, in particular competence at managerial level, expertise in electronic signature technology and familiarity with proper security procedures; they must also apply administrative and management procedures which are adequate and correspond to recognised standards;
(f) use trustworthy systems and products which are protected against modification and ensure the technical and cryptographic security of the process supported by them;
(g) take measures against forgery of certificates, and, in cases where the certification-service-provider generates signature-creation data, guarantee confidentiality during the process of generating such data;
(h) maintain sufficient financial resources to operate in conformity with the requirements laid down in the Directive, in particular to bear the risk of liability for damages, for example, by obtaining appropriate insurance;
(i) record all relevant information concerning a qualified certificate for an appropriate period of time, in particular for the purpose of providing evidence of certification for the purposes of legal proceedings. Such recording may be done electronically;

(j) not store or copy signature-creation data of the person to whom the certification-service-provider provided key management services;

(k) before entering into a contractual relationship with a person seeking a certificate to support his electronic signature inform that person by a durable means of communication of the precise terms and conditions regarding the use of the certificate, including any limitations on its use, the existence of a voluntary accreditation scheme and procedures for complaints and dispute settlement. Such information, which may be transmitted electronically, must be in writing and in readily understandable language. Relevant parts of this information must also be made available on request to third-parties relying on the certificate;

(l) use trustworthy systems to store certificates in a verifiable form so that—

- only authorised persons can make entries and changes,
- information can be checked for authenticity,
- certificates are publicly available for retrieval in only those cases for which the certificate-holder's consent has been obtained, and
- any technical changes compromising these security requirements are apparent to the operator.

[347]

ANNEX III
REQUIREMENTS FOR SECURE SIGNATURE-CREATION DEVICES

1. Secure signature-creation devices must, by appropriate technical and procedural means, ensure at the least that—

(a) the signature-creation-data used for signature generation can practically occur only once, and that their secrecy is reasonably assured;

(b) the signature-creation-data used for signature generation cannot, with reasonable assurance, be derived and the signature is protected against forgery using currently available technology;

(c) the signature-creation-data used for signature generation can be reliably protected by the legitimate signatory against the use of others.

2. Secure signature-creation devices must not alter the data to be signed or prevent such data from being presented to the signatory prior to the signature process.

[348]

ANNEX IV
RECOMMENDATIONS FOR SECURE SIGNATURE VERIFICATION

During the signature-verification process it should be ensured with reasonable certainty that—

(a) the data used for verifying the signature correspond to the data displayed to the verifier;

(b) the signature is reliably verified and the result of that verification is correctly displayed;

(c) the verifier can, as necessary, reliably establish the contents of the signed data;

(d) the authenticity and validity of the certificate required at the time of signature verification are reliably verified;

(e) the result of verification and the signatory's identity are correctly displayed;

(f) the use of a pseudonym is clearly indicated; and

(g) any security-relevant changes can be detected.

[349]

DIRECTIVE OF THE EUROPEAN PARLIAMENT AND OF THE COUNCIL

of 8 June 2000

on certain legal aspects of information society services, in particular electronic commerce, in the Internal Market (Directive on electronic commerce)

(2000/31/EC)

NOTES

Date of publication in OJ: OJ L178, 17.7.2000, p 1.

THE EUROPEAN PARLIAMENT AND THE COUNCIL OF THE EUROPEAN UNION,

Having regard to the Treaty establishing the European Community, and in particular Articles 47(2), 55 and 95 thereof,

Having regard to the proposal from the Commission,[1]

Having regard to the opinion of the Economic and Social Committee,[2]

Acting in accordance with the procedure laid down in Article 251 of the Treaty,[3]

Whereas—

(1) The European Union is seeking to forge ever closer links between the States and peoples of Europe, to ensure economic and social progress; in accordance with Article 14(2) of the Treaty, the internal market comprises an area without internal frontiers in which the free movements of goods, services and the freedom of establishment are ensured; the development of information society services within the area without internal frontiers is vital to eliminating the barriers which divide the European peoples.

(2) The development of electronic commerce within the information society offers significant employment opportunities in the Community, particularly in small and medium-sized enterprises, and will stimulate economic growth and investment in innovation by European companies, and can also enhance the competitiveness of European industry, provided that everyone has access to the Internet.

(3) Community law and the characteristics of the Community legal order are a vital asset to enable European citizens and operators to take full advantage, without consideration of borders, of the opportunities afforded by electronic commerce; this Directive therefore has the purpose of ensuring a high level of Community legal integration in order to establish a real area without internal borders for information society services.

(4) It is important to ensure that electronic commerce could fully benefit from the internal market and therefore that, as with Council Directive 89/552/EEC of 3 October 1989 on the coordination of certain provisions laid down by law, regulation or administrative action in Member States concerning the pursuit of television broadcasting activities,[4] a high level of Community integration is achieved.

(5) The development of information society services within the Community is hampered by a number of legal obstacles to the proper functioning of the internal market which make less attractive the exercise of the freedom of establishment and the freedom to provide services; these obstacles arise from divergences in legislation and from the legal uncertainty as to which national rules apply to such services; in the absence of coordination and adjustment of legislation in the relevant areas, obstacles might be justified in the light of the case-law of the Court of Justice of the European Communities; legal uncertainty exists with regard to the extent to which Member States may control services originating from another Member State.

(6) In the light of Community objectives, of Articles 43 and 49 of the Treaty and of secondary Community law, these obstacles should be eliminated by coordinating certain national laws and by clarifying certain legal concepts at Community level to the extent necessary for the proper functioning of the internal market; by dealing only with certain specific matters which give rise to problems for the internal market, this Directive is fully consistent with the need to respect the principle of subsidiarity as set out in Article 5 of the Treaty.

(7) In order to ensure legal certainty and consumer confidence, this Directive must lay down a clear and general framework to cover certain legal aspects of electronic commerce in the internal market.

(8) The objective of this Directive is to create a legal framework to ensure the free movement of information society services between Member States and not to harmonise the field of criminal law as such.

(9) The free movement of information society services can in many cases be a specific reflection in Community law of a more general principle, namely freedom of expression as enshrined in Article 10(1) of the Convention for the Protection of Human Rights and Fundamental Freedoms, which has been ratified by all the Member States; for this reason, directives covering the supply of information society services must ensure that this activity may be engaged in freely in the light of that Article, subject only to the restrictions laid down in paragraph 2 of that Article and in Article 46(1) of the Treaty; this Directive is not intended to affect national fundamental rules and principles relating to freedom of expression.

(10) In accordance with the principle of proportionality, the measures provided for in this Directive are strictly limited to the minimum needed to achieve the objective of the proper functioning of the internal market; where action at Community level is necessary, and in order to guarantee an area which is truly without internal frontiers as far as electronic commerce is concerned, the Directive must ensure a high level of protection of objectives of general interest, in particular the protection of minors and human dignity, consumer protection and the

protection of public health; according to Article 152 of the Treaty, the protection of public health is an essential component of other Community policies.

(11) This Directive is without prejudice to the level of protection for, in particular, public health and consumer interests, as established by Community acts; amongst others, Council Directive 93/13/EEC of 5 April 1993 on unfair terms in consumer contracts[5] and Directive 97/7/EC of the European Parliament and of the Council of 20 May 1997 on the protection of consumers in respect of distance contracts[6] form a vital element for protecting consumers in contractual matters; those Directives also apply in their entirety to information society services; that same Community acquis, which is fully applicable to information society services, also embraces in particular Council Directive 84/450/EEC of 10 September 1984 concerning misleading and comparative advertising,[7] Council Directive 87/102/EEC of 22 December 1986 for the approximation of the laws, regulations and administrative provisions of the Member States concerning consumer credit,[8] Council Directive 93/22/EEC of 10 May 1993 on investment services in the securities field,[9] Council Directive 90/314/EEC of 13 June 1990 on package travel, package holidays and package tours,[10] Directive 98/6/EC of the European Parliament and of the Council of 16 February 1998 on consumer production in the indication of prices of products offered to consumers,[11] Council Directive 92/59/EEC of 29 June 1992 on general product safety,[12] Directive 94/47/EC of the European Parliament and of the Council of 26 October 1994 on the protection of purchasers in respect of certain aspects on contracts relating to the purchase of the right to use immovable properties on a timeshare basis,[13] Directive 98/27/EC of the European Parliament and of the Council of 19 May 1998 on injunctions for the protection of consumers' interests,[14] Council Directive 85/374/EEC of 25 July 1985 on the approximation of the laws, regulations and administrative provisions concerning liability for defective products,[15] Directive 1999/44/EC of the European Parliament and of the Council of 25 May 1999 on certain aspects of the sale of consumer goods and associated guarantees,[16] the future Directive of the European Parliament and of the Council concerning the distance marketing of consumer financial services and Council Directive 92/28/EEC of 31 March 1992 on the advertising of medicinal products;[17] this Directive should be without prejudice to Directive 98/43/EC of the European Parliament and of the Council of 6 July 1998 on the approximation of the laws, regulations and administrative provisions of the Member States relating to the advertising and sponsorship of tobacco products[18] adopted within the framework of the internal market, or to directives on the protection of public health; this Directive complements information requirements established by the abovementioned Directives and in particular Directive 97/7/EC.

(12) It is necessary to exclude certain activities from the scope of this Directive, on the grounds that the freedom to provide services in these fields cannot, at this stage, be guaranteed under the Treaty or existing secondary legislation; excluding these activities does not preclude any instruments which might prove necessary for the proper functioning of the internal market; taxation, particularly value added tax imposed on a large number of the services covered by this Directive, must be excluded from the scope of this Directive.

(13) This Directive does not aim to establish rules on fiscal obligations nor does it pre-empt the drawing up of Community instruments concerning fiscal aspects of electronic commerce.

(14) The protection of individuals with regard to the processing of personal data is solely governed by Directive 95/46/EC of the European Parliament and of the Council of 24 October 1995 on the protection of individuals with regard to the processing of personal data and on the free movement of such data[19] and Directive 97/66/EC of the European Parliament and of the Council of 15 December 1997 concerning the processing of personal data and the protection of privacy in the telecommunications sector[20] which are fully applicable to information society services; these Directives already establish a Community legal framework in the field of personal data and therefore it is not necessary to cover this issue in this Directive in order to ensure the smooth functioning of the internal market, in particular the free movement of personal data between Member States; the implementation and application of this Directive should be made in full compliance with the principles relating to the protection of personal data, in particular as regards unsolicited commercial communication and the liability of intermediaries; this Directive cannot prevent the anonymous use of open networks such as the Internet.

(15) The confidentiality of communications is guaranteed by Article 5 Directive 97/66/EC; in accordance with that Directive, Member States must prohibit any kind of interception or surveillance of such communications by others than the senders and receivers, except when legally authorised.

(16) The exclusion of gambling activities from the scope of application of this Directive covers only games of chance, lotteries and betting transactions, which involve wagering a stake with monetary value; this does not cover promotional competitions or games where the

purpose is to encourage the sale of goods or services and where payments, if they arise, serve only to acquire the promoted goods or services.

(17) The definition of information society services already exists in Community law in Directive 98/34/EC of the European Parliament and of the Council of 22 June 1998 laying down a procedure for the provision of information in the field of technical standards and regulations and of rules on information society services[21] and in Directive 98/84/EC of the European Parliament and of the Council of 20 November 1998 on the legal protection of services based on, or consisting of, conditional access;[22] this definition covers any service normally provided for remuneration, at a distance, by means of electronic equipment for the processing (including digital compression) and storage of data, and at the individual request of a recipient of a service; those services referred to in the indicative list in Annex V to Directive 98/34/EC which do not imply data processing and storage are not covered by this definition.

(18) Information society services span a wide range of economic activities which take place on-line; these activities can, in particular, consist of selling goods on-line; activities such as the delivery of goods as such or the provision of services off-line are not covered; information society services are not solely restricted to services giving rise to on-line contracting but also, in so far as they represent an economic activity, extend to services which are not remunerated by those who receive them, such as those offering non-line information or commercial communications, or those providing tools allowing for search, access and retrieval of data; information society services also include services consisting of the transmission of information via a communication network, in providing access to a communication network or in hosting information provided by a recipient of the service; television broadcasting within the meaning of Directive EEC/89/552 and radio broadcasting are not information society services because they are not provided at individual request; by contrast, services which are transmitted point to point, such as video-on-demand or the provision of commercial communications by electronic mail are information society services; the use of electronic mail or equivalent individual communications for instance by natural persons acting outside their trade, business or profession including their use for the conclusion of contracts between such persons is not an information society service; the contractual relationship between an employee and his employer is not an information society service; activities which by their very nature cannot be carried out at a distance and by electronic means, such as the statutory auditing of company accounts or medical advice requiring the physical examination of a patient are not information society services.

(19) The place at which a service provider is established should be determined in conformity with the case-law of the Court of Justice according to which the concept of establishment involves the actual pursuit of an economic activity through a fixed establishment for an indefinite period; this requirement is also fulfilled where a company is constituted for a given period; the place of establishment of a company providing services via an Internet website is not the place at which the technology supporting its website is located or the place at which its website is accessible but the place where it pursues its economic activity; in cases where a provider has several places of establishment it is important to determine from which place of establishment the service concerned is provided; in cases where it is difficult to determine from which of several places of establishment a given service is provided, this is the place where the provider has the centre of his activities relating to this particular service.

(20) The definition of "recipient of a service" covers all types of usage of information society services, both by persons who provide information on open networks such as the Internet and by persons who seek information on the Internet for private or professional reasons.

(21) The scope of the coordinated field is without prejudice to future Community harmonisation relating to information society services and to future legislation adopted at national level in accordance with Community law; the coordinated field covers only requirements relating to on-line activities such as on-line information, on-line advertising, on-line shopping, on-line contracting and does not concern Member States' legal requirements relating to goods such as safety standards, labelling obligations, or liability for goods, or Member States' requirements relating to the delivery or the transport of goods, including the distribution of medicinal products; the coordinated field does not cover the exercise of rights of pre-emption by public authorities concerning certain goods such as works of art.

(22) Information society services should be supervised at the source of the activity, in order to ensure an effective protection of public interest objectives; to that end, it is necessary to ensure that the competent authority provides such protection not only for the citizens of its own country but for all Community citizens; in order to improve mutual trust between Member States, it is essential to state clearly this responsibility on the part of the Member

State where the services originate; moreover, in order to effectively guarantee freedom to provide services and legal certainty for suppliers and recipients of services, such information society services should in principle be subject to the law of the Member State in which the service provider is established.

(23) This Directive neither aims to establish additional rules on private international law relating to conflicts of law nor does it deal with the jurisdiction of Courts; provisions of the applicable law designated by rules of private international law must not restrict the freedom to provide information society services as established in this Directive.

(24) In the context of this Directive, notwithstanding the rule on the control at source of information society services, it is legitimate under the conditions established in this Directive for Member States to take measures to restrict the free movement of information society services.

(25) National courts, including civil courts, dealing with private law disputes can take measures to derogate from the freedom to provide information society services in conformity with conditions established in this Directive.

(26) Member States, in conformity with conditions established in this Directive, may apply their national rules on criminal law and criminal proceedings with a view to taking all investigative and other measures necessary for the detection and prosecution of criminal offences, without there being a need to notify such measures to the Commission.

(27) This Directive, together with the future Directive of the European Parliament and of the Council concerning the distance marketing of consumer financial services, contributes to the creating of a legal framework for the on-line provision of financial services; this Directive does not pre-empt future initiatives in the area of financial services in particular with regard to the harmonisation of rules of conduct in this field; the possibility for Member States, established in this Directive, under certain circumstances of restricting the freedom to provide information society services in order to protect consumers also covers measures in the area of financial services in particular measures aiming at protecting investors.

(28) The Member States' obligation not to subject access to the activity of an information society service provider to prior authorisation does not concern postal services covered by Directive 97/67/EC of the European Parliament and of the Council of 15 December 1997 on common rules for the development of the internal market of Community postal services and the improvement of quality of service[23] consisting of the physical delivery of a printed electronic mail message and does not affect voluntary accreditation systems, in particular for providers of electronic signature certification service.

(29) Commercial communications are essential for the financing of information society services and for developing a wide variety of new, charge-free services; in the interests of consumer protection and fair trading, commercial communications, including discounts, promotional offers and promotional competitions or games, must meet a number of transparency requirements; these requirements are without prejudice to Directive 97/7/EC; this Directive should not affect existing Directives on commercial communications, in particular Directive 98/43/EC.

(30) The sending of unsolicited commercial communications by electronic mail may be undesirable for consumers and information society service providers and may disrupt the smooth functioning of interactive networks; the question of consent by recipient of certain forms of unsolicited commercial communications is not addressed by this Directive, but has already been addressed, in particular, by Directive 97/7/EC and by Directive 97/66/EC; in Member States which authorise unsolicited commercial communications by electronic mail, the setting up of appropriate industry filtering initiatives should be encouraged and facilitated; in addition it is necessary that in any event unsolicited commercial communities are clearly identifiable as such in order to improve transparency and to facilitate the functioning of such industry initiatives; unsolicited commercial communications by electronic mail should not result in additional communication costs for the recipient.

(31) Member States which allow the sending of unsolicited commercial communications by electronic mail without prior consent of the recipient by service providers established in their territory have to ensure that the service providers consult regularly and respect the opt-out registers in which natural persons not wishing to receive such commercial communications can register themselves.

(32) In order to remove barriers to the development of cross-border services within the Community which members of the regulated professions might offer on the Internet, it is necessary that compliance be guaranteed at Community level with professional rules aiming, in particular, to protect consumers or public health; codes of conduct at Community level would be the best means of determining the rules on professional ethics applicable to commercial communication; the drawing-up or, where appropriate, the adaptation of such rules should be encouraged without prejudice to the autonomy of professional bodies and associations.

(33) This Directive complements Community law and national law relating to regulated professions maintaining a coherent set of applicable rules in this field.

(34) Each Member State is to amend its legislation containing requirements, and in particular requirements as to form, which are likely to curb the use of contracts by electronic means; the examination of the legislation requiring such adjustment should be systematic and should cover all the necessary stages and acts of the contractual process, including the filing of the contract; the result of this amendment should be to make contracts concluded electronically workable; the legal effect of electronic signatures is dealt with by Directive 1999/93/EC of the European Parliament and of the Council of 13 December 1999 on a Community framework for electronic signatures;[24] the acknowledgement of receipt by a service provider may take the form of the on-line provision of the service paid for.

(35) This Directive does not affect Member States' possibility of maintaining or establishing general or specific legal requirements for contracts which can be fulfilled by electronic means, in particular requirements concerning secure electronic signatures.

(36) Member States may maintain restrictions for the use of electronic contracts with regard to contracts requiring by law the involvement of courts, public authorities, or professions exercising public authority; this possibility also covers contracts which require the involvement of courts, public authorities, or professions exercising public authority in order to have an effect with regard to third parties as well as contracts requiring by law certification or attestation by a notary.

(37) Member States' obligation to remove obstacles to the use of electronic contracts concerns only obstacles resulting from legal requirements and not practical obstacles resulting from the impossibility of using electronic means in certain cases.

(38) Member States' obligation to remove obstacles to the use of electronic contracts is to be implemented in conformity with legal requirements for contracts enshrined in Community law.

(39) The exceptions to the provisions concerning the contracts concluded exclusively by electronic mail or by equivalent individual communications provided for by this Directive, in relation to information to be provided and the placing of orders, should not enable, as a result, the by-passing of those provisions by providers of information society services.

(40) Both existing and emerging disparities in Member States' legislation and case-law concerning liability of service providers acting as intermediaries prevent the smooth functioning of the internal market, in particular by impairing the development of cross-border services and producing distortions of competition; service providers have a duty to act, under certain circumstances, with a view to preventing or stopping illegal activities; this Directive should constitute the appropriate basis for the development of rapid and reliable procedures for removing and disabling access to illegal information; such mechanisms could be developed on the basis of voluntary agreements between all parties concerned and should be encouraged by Member States; it is in the interest of all parties involved in the provision of information society services to adopt and implement such procedures; the provisions of this Directive relating to liability should not preclude the development and effective operation, by the different interested parties, of technical systems of protection and identification and of technical surveillance instruments made possible by digital technology within the limits laid down by Directives 95/46/EC and 97/66/EC.

(41) This Directive strikes a balance between the different interests at stake and establishes principles upon which industry agreements and standards can be based.

(42) The exemptions from liability established in this Directive cover only cases where the activity of the information society service provider is limited to the technical process of operating and giving access to a communication network over which information made available by third parties is transmitted or temporarily stored, for the sole purpose of making the transmission more efficient; this activity is of a mere technical, automatic and passive nature, which implies that the information society service provider has neither knowledge of nor control over the information which is transmitted or stored.

(43) A service provider can benefit from the exemptions for "mere conduit" and for "caching" when he is in no way involved with the information transmitted; this requires among other things that he does not modify the information that he transmits; this requirement does not cover manipulations of a technical nature which take place in the course of the transmission as they do not alter the integrity of the information contained in the transmission.

(44) A service provider who deliberately collaborates with one of the recipients of his service in order to undertake illegal acts goes beyond the activities of "mere conduit" or "caching" and as a result cannot benefit from the liability exemptions established for these activities.

(45) The limitations of the liability of intermediary service providers established in this Directive do not affect the possibility of injunctions of different kinds; such injunctions can in

particular consist of orders by courts or administrative authorities requiring the termination or prevention of any infringement, including the removal of illegal information or the disabling of access to it.

(46) In order to benefit from a limitation of liability, the provider of an information society service, consisting of the storage of information, upon obtaining actual knowledge or awareness of illegal activities has to act expeditiously to remove or to disable access to the information concerned; the removal or disabling of access has to be undertaken in the observance of the principle of freedom of expression and of procedures established for this purpose at national level; this Directive does not affect Member States' possibility of establishing specific requirements which must be fulfilled expeditiously prior to the removal or disabling of information.

(47) Member States are prevented from imposing a monitoring obligation on service providers only with respect to obligations of a general nature; this does not concern monitoring obligations in a specific case and, in particular, does not affect orders by national authorities in accordance with national legislation.

(48) This Directive does not affect the possibility for Member States of requiring service providers, who host information provided by recipients of their service, to apply duties of care, which can reasonably be expected from them and which are specified by national law, in order to detect and prevent certain types of illegal activities.

(49) Member States and the Commission are to encourage the drawing-up of codes of conduct; this is not to impair the voluntary nature of such codes and the possibility for interested parties of deciding freely whether to adhere to such codes.

(50) It is important that the proposed directive on the harmonisation of certain aspects of copyright and related rights in the information society and this Directive come into force within a similar time scale with a view to establishing a clear framework of rules relevant to the issue of liability of intermediaries for copyright and relating rights infringements at Community level.

(51) Each Member State should be required, where necessary, to amend any legislation which is liable to hamper the use of schemes for the out-of-court settlement of disputes through electronic channels; the result of this amendment must be to make the functioning of such schemes genuinely and effectively possible in law and in practice, even across borders.

(52) The effective exercise of the freedoms of the internal market makes it necessary to guarantee victims effective access to means of settling disputes; damage which may arise in connection with information society services is characterised both by its rapidity and by its geographical extent; in view of this specific character and the need to ensure that national authorities do not endanger the mutual confidence which they should have in one another, this Directive requests Member States to ensure that appropriate court actions are available; Member States should examine the need to provide access to judicial procedures by appropriate electronic means.

(53) Directive 98/27/EC, which is applicable to information society services, provides a mechanism relating to actions for an injunction aimed at the protection of the collective interests of consumers; this mechanism will contribute to the free movement of information society services by ensuring a high level of consumer protection.

(54) The sanctions provided for under this Directive are without prejudice to any other sanction or remedy provided under national law; Member States are not obliged to provide criminal sanctions for infringement of national provisions adopted pursuant to this Directive.

(55) This Directive does not affect the law applicable to contractual obligations relating to consumer contracts; accordingly, this Directive cannot have the result of depriving the consumer of the protection afforded to him by the mandatory rules relating to contractual obligations of the law of the Member State in which he has his habitual residence.

(56) As regards the derogation contained in this Directive regarding contractual obligations concerning contracts concluded by consumers, those obligations should be interpreted as including information on the essential elements of the content of the contract, including consumer rights, which have a determining influence on the decision to contract.

(57) The Court of Justice has consistently held that a Member State retains the right to take measures against a service provider that is established in another Member State but directs all or most of his activity to the territory of the first Member State if the choice of establishment was made with a view to evading the legislation that would have applied to the provider had he been established on the territory of the first Member State.

(58) This Directive should not apply to services supplied by service providers established in a third country; in view of the global dimension of electronic commerce, it is, however, appropriate to ensure that the Community rules are consistent with international rules; this Directive is without prejudice to the results of discussions within international organisations (amongst others WTO, OECD, UNCITRAL) on legal issues.

(59) Despite the global nature of electronic communications, coordination of national regulatory measures at European Union level is necessary in order to avoid fragmentation of the internal market, and for the establishment of an appropriate European regulatory framework; such coordination should also contribute to the establishment of a common and strong negotiating position in international forums.

(60) In order to allow the unhampered development of electronic commerce, the legal framework must be clear and simple, predictable and consistent with the rules applicable at international level so that it does not adversely affect the competitiveness of European industry or impede innovation in that sector.

(61) If the market is actually to operate by electronic means in the context of globalisation, the European Union and the major non-European areas need to consult each other with a view to making laws and procedures compatible.

(62) Cooperation with third countries should be strengthened in the area of electronic commerce, in particular with applicant countries, the developing countries and the European Union's other trading partners.

(63) The adoption of this Directive will not prevent the Member States from taking into account the various social, societal and cultural implications which are inherent in the advent of the information society; in particular it should not hinder measures which Member States might adopt in conformity with Community law to achieve social, cultural and democratic goals taking into account their linguistic diversity, national and regional specificities as well as their cultural heritage, and to ensure and maintain public access to the widest possible range of information society services; in any case, the development of the information society is to ensure that Community citizens can have access to the cultural European heritage provided in the digital environment.

(64) Electronic communication offers the Member States an excellent means of providing public services in the cultural, educational and linguistic fields.

(65) The Council, in its resolution of 19 January 1999 on the consumer dimension of the information society,[25] stressed that the protection of consumers deserved special attention in this field; the Commission will examine the degree to which existing consumer protection rules provide insufficient protection in the context of the information society and will identify, where necessary, the deficiencies of this legislation and those issues which could require additional measures; if need be, the Commission should make specific additional proposals to resolve such deficiencies that will thereby have been identified,

NOTES

1 OJ C30, 5.2.1999, p 4.
2 OJ C169, 16.6.1999, p 36.
3 Opinion of the European Parliament of 6 May 1999 (OJ C279, 1.10.1999, p 389), Council common position of 28 February 2000 (OJ C128, 8.5.2000, p 32) and Decision of the European Parliament of 4 May 2000 (not yet published in the Official Journal).
4 OJ L298, 17.10.1989, p 23. Directive as amended by Directive 97/36/EC of the European Parliament and of the Council (OJ L202, 30.7.1997, p 60).
5 OJ L95, 21.4.1993, p 29.
6 OJ L144, 4.6.1999, p 19.
7 OJ L250, 19.9.1984, p 17. Directive as amended by Directive 97/55/EC of the European Parliament and of the Council (OJ L290, 23.10.1997, p 18).
8 OJ L42, 12.2.1987, p 48. Directive as last amended by Directive 98/7/EC of the European Parliament and of the Council (OJ L101, 1.4.1998, p 17).
9 OJ L141, 11.6.1993, p 27. Directive as last amended by Directive 97/9/EC of the European Parliament and of the Council (OJ L84, 26.3.1997, p 22).
10 OJ L158, 23.6.1990, p 59.
11 OJ L80, 18.3.1998, p 27.
12 OJ L228, 11.8.1992, p 24.
13 OJ L280, 29.10.1994, p 83.
14 OJ L166, 11.6.1998, p 51. Directive as amended by Directive 1999/44/EC (OJ L171, 7.7.1999, p 12).
15 OJ L210, 7.8.1985, p 29. Directive as amended by Directive 1999/34/EC (OJ L141, 4.6.1999, p 20).
16 OJ L171, 7.7.1999, p 12.
17 OJ L113, 30.4.1992, p 13.
18 OJ L213, 30.7.1998, p 9.
19 OJ L281, 23.11.1995, p 31.
20 OJ L24, 30.1.1998, p 1.
21 OJ L204, 21.7.1998, p 37. Directive as amended by Directive 98/48/EC (OJ L217, 5.8.1998, p 18).
22 OJ L320, 28.11.1998, p 54.
23 OJ L15, 21.1.1998, p 14.
24 OJ L13, 19.1.2000, p 12.
25 OJ C23, 28.1.1999, p 1.

HAVE ADOPTED THIS DIRECTIVE—

CHAPTER I
GENERAL PROVISIONS

Article 1

Objective and scope

1. This Directive seeks to contribute to the proper functioning of the internal market by ensuring the free movement of information society services between the Member States.

2. This Directive approximates, to the extent necessary for the achievement of the objective set out in paragraph 1, certain national provisions on information society services relating to the internal market, the establishment of service providers, commercial communications, electronic contracts, the liability of intermediaries, codes of conduct, out-of-court dispute settlements, court actions and cooperation between Member States.

3. This Directive complements Community law applicable to information society services without prejudice to the level of protection for, in particular, public health and consumer interests, as established by Community acts and national legislation implementing them in so far as this does not restrict the freedom to provide information society services.

4. This Directive does not establish additional rules on private international law nor does it deal with the jurisdiction of Courts.

5. This Directive shall not apply to—

(a) the field of taxation;

(b) questions relating to information society services covered by Directives 95/46/EC and 97/66/EC;

(c) questions relating to agreements or practices governed by cartel law;

(d) the following activities of information society services—

— the activities of notaries or equivalent professions to the extent that they involve a direct and specific connection with the exercise of public authority,

— the representation of a client and defence of his interests before the courts,

— gambling activities which involve wagering a stake with monetary value in games of chance, including lotteries and betting transactions.

6. This Directive does not affect measures taken at Community or national level, in the respect of Community law, in order to promote cultural and linguistic diversity and to ensure the defence of pluralism.

[350]

Article 2

Definitions

For the purpose of this Directive, the following terms shall bear the following meanings—

(a) "information society services": services within the meaning of Article 1(2) of Directive 98/34/EC as amended by Directive 98/48/EC;

(b) "service provider": any natural or legal person providing an information society service;

(c) "established service provider": a service provider who effectively pursues an economic activity using a fixed establishment for an indefinite period. The presence and use of the technical means and technologies required to provide the service do not, in themselves, constitute an establishment of the provider;

(d) "recipient of the service": any natural or legal person who, for professional ends or otherwise, uses an information society service, in particular for the purposes of seeking information or making it accessible;

(e) "consumer": any natural person who is acting for purposes which are outside his or her trade, business or profession;

(f) "commercial communication": any form of communication designed to promote, directly or indirectly, the goods, services or image of a company, organisation or person pursuing a commercial, industrial or craft activity or exercising a regulated profession. The following do not in themselves constitute commercial communications—

— information allowing direct access to the activity of the company, organisation or person, in particular a domain name or an electronic-mail address,

— communications relating to the goods, services or image of the company, organisation or person compiled in an independent manner, particularly when this is without financial consideration;

(g) "regulated profession": any profession within the meaning of either Article 1(d) of Council Directive 89/48/EEC of 21 December 1988 on a general system for the recognition of higher-education diplomas awarded on completion of professional education and training of at least three-years duration[1] or of Article 1(f) of Council Directive 92/51/EEC of 18 June 1992 on a second general system for the recognition of professional education and training to supplement Directive 89/48/EEC;[2]

(h) "coordinated field": requirements laid down in Member States' legal systems applicable to information society service providers or information society services, regardless of whether they are of a general nature or specifically designed for them.

(i) The coordinated field concerns requirements with which the service provider has to comply in respect of—

— the taking up of the activity of an information society service, such as requirements concerning qualifications, authorisation or notification,

— the pursuit of the activity of an information society service, such as requirements concerning the behaviour of the service provider, requirements regarding the quality or content of the service including those applicable to advertising and contracts, or requirements concerning the liability of the service provider;

(ii) The coordinated field does not cover requirements such as—

— requirements applicable to goods as such,

— requirements applicable to the delivery of goods,

— requirements applicable to services not provided by electronic means.

[351]

NOTES

1 OJ L19, 24.1.1989, p 16.

2 OJ L209, 24.7.1992, p 25. Directive as last amended by Commission Directive 97/38/EC (OJ L184, 12.7.1997, p 31).

Article 3

Internal market

1. Each Member State shall ensure that the information society services provided by a service provider established on its territory comply with the national provisions applicable in the Member State in question which fall within the coordinated field.

2. Member States may not, for reasons falling within the coordinated field, restrict the freedom to provide information society services from another Member State.

3. Paragraphs 1 and 2 shall not apply to the fields referred to in the Annex.

4. Member States may take measures to derogate from paragraph 2 in respect of a given information society service if the following conditions are fulfilled—

(a) the measures shall be—

(i) necessary for one of the following reasons—

— public policy, in particular the prevention, investigation, detection and prosecution of criminal offences, including the protection of minors and the fight against any incitement to hatred on grounds of race, sex, religion or nationality, and violations of human dignity concerning individual persons,

— the protection of public health,

— public security, including the safeguarding of national security and defence,

— the protection of consumers, including investors;

(ii) taken against a given information society service which prejudices the objectives referred to in point (i) or which presents a serious and grave risk of prejudice to those objectives;

(iii) proportionate to those objectives;

(b) before taking the measures in question and without prejudice to court proceedings, including preliminary proceedings and acts carried out in the framework of a criminal investigation, the Member State has—

— asked the Member State referred to in paragraph 1 to take measures and the latter did not take such measures, or they were inadequate,

— notified the Commission and the Member State referred to in paragraph 1 of its intention to take such measures.

5. Member States may, in the case of urgency, derogate from the conditions stipulated in paragraph 4(b). Where this is the case, the measures shall be notified in the shortest possible time to the Commission and to the Member State referred to in paragraph 1, indicating the reasons for which the Member State considers that there is urgency.

6. Without prejudice to the Member State's possibility of proceeding with the measures in question, the Commission shall examine the compatibility of the notified measures with Community law in the shortest possible time; where it comes to the conclusion that the measure is incompatible with Community law, the Commission shall ask the Member State in question to refrain from taking any proposed measures or urgently to put an end to the measures in question.

[352]

CHAPTER II
PRINCIPLES

Section 1: Establishment and information requirements

Article 4

Principle excluding prior authorisation

1. Member States shall ensure that the taking up and pursuit of the activity of an information society service provider may not be made subject to prior authorisation or any other requirement having equivalent effect.

2. Paragraph 1 shall be without prejudice to authorisation schemes which are not specifically and exclusively targeted at information society services, or which are covered by Directive 97/13/EC of the European Parliament and of the Council of 10 April 1997 on a common framework for general authorisations and individual licences in the field of telecommunications services.[1]

[353]

NOTES

[1] OJ L117, 7.5.1997, p 15.

Article 5

General information to be provided

1. In addition to other information requirements established by Community law, Member States shall ensure that the service provider shall render easily, directly and permanently accessible to the recipients of the service and competent authorities, at least the following information—

(a) the name of the service provider;

(b) the geographic address at which the service provider is established;

(c) the details of the service provider, including his electronic mail address, which allow him to be contacted rapidly and communicated with in a direct and effective manner;

(d) where the service provider is registered in a trade or similar public register, the trade register in which the service provider is entered and his registration number, or equivalent means of identification in that register;

(e) where the activity is subject to an authorisation scheme, the particulars of the relevant supervisory authority;

(f) as concerns the regulated professions—

— any professional body or similar institution with which the service provider is registered,

— the professional title and the Member State where it has been granted,

— a reference to the applicable professional rules in the Member State of establishment and the means to access them;

(g) where the service provider undertakes an activity that is subject to VAT, the identification number referred to in Article 22(1) of the sixth Council Directive 77/388/EEC of 17 May 1977 on the harmonisation of the laws of the Member States relating to turnover taxes—Common system of value added tax: uniform basis of assessment.[1]

2. In addition to other information requirements established by Community law, Member States shall at least ensure that, where information society services refer to prices, these are to be indicated clearly and unambiguously and, in particular, must indicate whether they are inclusive of tax and delivery costs.

[354]

NOTES

[1] OJ L145, 13.6.1977, p 1. Directive as last amended by Directive 1999/85/EC (OJ L277, 28.10.1999, p 34).

Section 2: Commercial communications

Article 6

Information to be provided

In addition to other information requirements established by Community law, Member States shall ensure that commercial communications which are part of, or constitute, an information society service comply at least with the following conditions—

(a) the commercial communication shall be clearly identifiable as such;

(b) the natural or legal person on whose behalf the commercial communication is made shall be clearly identifiable;

(c) promotional offers, such as discounts, premiums and gifts, where permitted in the Member State where the service provider is established, shall be clearly identifiable as such, and the conditions which are to be met to qualify for them shall be easily accessible and be presented clearly and unambiguously;

(d) promotional competitions or games, where permitted in the Member State where the service provider is established, shall be clearly identifiable as such, and the conditions for participation shall be easily accessible and be presented clearly and unambiguously.

[355]

Article 7

Unsolicited commercial communication

1. In addition to other requirements established by Community law, Member States which permit unsolicited commercial communication by electronic mail shall ensure that such commercial communication by a service provider established in their territory shall be identifiable clearly and unambiguously as such as soon as it is received by the recipient.

2. Without prejudice to Directive 97/7/EC and Directive 97/66/EC, Member States shall take measures to ensure that service providers undertaking unsolicited commercial communications by electronic mail consult regularly and respect the opt-out registers in which natural persons not wishing to receive such commercial communications can register themselves.

[356]

Article 8

Regulated professions

1. Member States shall ensure that the use of commercial communications which are part of, or constitute, an information society service provided by a member of a regulated

profession is permitted subject to compliance with the professional rules regarding, in particular, the independence, dignity and honour of the profession, professional secrecy and fairness towards clients and other members of the profession.

2. Without prejudice to the autonomy of professional bodies and associations, Member States and the Commission shall encourage professional associations and bodies to establish codes of conduct at Community level in order to determine the types of information that can be given for the purposes of commercial communication in conformity with the rules referred to in paragraph 1.

3. When drawing up proposals for Community initiatives which may become necessary to ensure the proper functioning of the Internal Market with regard to the information referred to in paragraph 2, the Commission shall take due account of codes of conduct applicable at Community level and shall act in close cooperation with the relevant professional associations and bodies.

4. This Directive shall apply in addition to Community Directives concerning access to, and the exercise of, activities of the regulated professions.

[357]

Section 3: Contracts concluded by electronic means

Article 9

Treatment of contracts

1. Member States shall ensure that their legal system allows contracts to be concluded by electronic means. Member States shall in particular ensure that the legal requirements applicable to the contractual process neither create obstacles for the use of electronic contracts nor result in such contracts being deprived of legal effectiveness and validity on account of their having been made by electronic means.

2. Member States may lay down that paragraph 1 shall not apply to all or certain contracts falling into one of the following categories—

(a) contracts that create or transfer rights in real estate, except for rental rights;

(b) contracts requiring by law the involvement of courts, public authorities or professions exercising public authority;

(c) contracts of suretyship granted and on collateral securities furnished by persons acting for purposes outside their trade, business or profession;

(d) contracts governed by family law or by the law of succession.

3. Member States shall indicate to the Commission the categories referred to in paragraph 2 to which they do not apply paragraph 1. Member States shall submit to the Commission every five years a report on the application of paragraph 2 explaining the reasons why they consider it necessary to maintain the category referred to in paragraph 2(b) to which they do not apply paragraph 1.

[358]

Article 10

Information to be provided

1. In addition to other information requirements established by Community law, Member States shall ensure, except when otherwise agreed by parties who are not consumers, that at least the following information is given by the service provider clearly, comprehensibly and unambiguously and prior to the order being placed by the recipient of the service—

(a) the different technical steps to follow to conclude the contract;

(b) whether or not the concluded contract will be filed by the service provider and whether it will be accessible;

(c) the technical means for identifying and correcting input errors prior to the placing of the order;

(d) the languages offered for the conclusion of the contract.

2. Member States shall ensure that, except when otherwise agreed by parties who are not consumers, the service provider indicates any relevant codes of conduct to which he subscribes and information on how those codes can be consulted electronically.

3. Contract terms and general conditions provided to the recipient must be made available in a way that allows him to store and reproduce them.

4. Paragraphs 1 and 2 shall not apply to contracts concluded exclusively by exchange of electronic mail or by equivalent individual communications.

[359]

Article 11

Placing of the order

1. Member States shall ensure, except when otherwise agreed by parties who are not consumers, that in cases where the recipient of the service places his order through technological means, the following principles apply—

— the service provider has to acknowledge the receipt of the recipient's order without undue delay and by electronic means,

— the order and the acknowledgement of receipt are deemed to be received when the parties to whom they are addressed are able to access them.

2. Member States shall ensure that, except when otherwise agreed by parties who are not consumers, the service provider makes available to the recipient of the service appropriate, effective and accessible technical means allowing him to identify and correct input errors, prior to the placing of the order.

3. Paragraph 1, first indent, and paragraph 2 shall not apply to contracts concluded exclusively by exchange of electronic mail or by equivalent individual communications.

[360]

Section 4: Liability of intermediary service providers

Article 12

"Mere conduit"

1. Where an information society service is provided that consists of the transmission in a communication network of information provided by a recipient of the service, or the provision of access to a communication network, Member States shall ensure that the service provider is not liable for the information transmitted, on condition that the provider—

(a) does not initiate the transmission;

(b) does not select the receiver of the transmission; and

(c) does not select or modify the information contained in the transmission.

2. The acts of transmission and of provision of access referred to in paragraph 1 include the automatic, intermediate and transient storage of the information transmitted in so far as this takes place for the sole purpose of carrying out the transmission in the communication network, and provided that the information is not stored for any period longer than is reasonably necessary for the transmission.

3. This Article shall not affect the possibility for a court or administrative authority, in accordance with Member States' legal systems, of requiring the service provider to terminate or prevent an infringement.

[361]

Article 13

"Caching"

1. Where an information society service is provided that consists of the transmission in a communication network of information provided by a recipient of the service, Member States shall ensure that the service provider is not liable for the automatic, intermediate and temporary storage of that information, performed for the sole purpose of making more efficient the information's onward transmission to other recipients of the service upon their request, on condition that—

(a) the provider does not modify the information;

(b) the provider complies with conditions on access to the information;

(c) the provider complies with rules regarding the updating of the information, specified in a manner widely recognised and used by industry;

(d) the provider does not interfere with the lawful use of technology, widely recognised and used by industry, to obtain data on the use of the information; and

(e) the provider acts expeditiously to remove or to disable access to the information it has stored upon obtaining actual knowledge of the fact that the information at the initial source of the transmission has been removed from the network, or access to it has been disabled, or that a court or an administrative authority has ordered such removal or disablement.

2. This Article shall not affect the possibility for a court or administrative authority, in accordance with Member States' legal systems, of requiring the service provider to terminate or prevent an infringement.

[362]

Article 14

Hosting

1. Where an information society service is provided that consists of the storage of information provided by a recipient of the service, Member States shall ensure that the service provider is not liable for the information stored at the request of a recipient of the service, on condition that—

(a) the provider does not have actual knowledge of illegal activity or information and, as regards claims for damages, is not aware of facts or circumstances from which the illegal activity or information is apparent; or

(b) the provider, upon obtaining such knowledge or awareness, acts expeditiously to remove or to disable access to the information.

2. Paragraph 1 shall not apply when the recipient of the service is acting under the authority or the control of the provider.

3. This Article shall not affect the possibility for a court or administrative authority, in accordance with Member States' legal systems, of requiring the service provider to terminate or prevent an infringement, nor does it affect the possibility for Member States of establishing procedures governing the removal or disabling of access to information.

[363]

Article 15

No general obligation to monitor

1. Member States shall not impose a general obligation on providers, when providing the services covered by Articles 12, 13 and 14, to monitor the information which they transmit or store, nor a general obligation actively to seek facts or circumstances indicating illegal activity.

2. Member States may establish obligations for information society service providers promptly to inform the competent public authorities of alleged illegal activities undertaken or information provided by recipients of their service or obligations to communicate to the competent authorities, at their request, information enabling the identification of recipients of their service with whom they have storage agreements.

[364]

CHAPTER III
IMPLEMENTATION

Article 16

Codes of conduct

1. Member States and the Commission shall encourage—

(a) the drawing up of codes of conduct at Community level, by trade, professional and consumer associations or organisations, designed to contribute to the proper implementation of Articles 5 to 15;

(b) the voluntary transmission of draft codes of conduct at national or Community level to the Commission;

(c) the accessibility of these codes of conduct in the Community languages by electronic means;

(d) the communication to the Member States and the Commission, by trade, professional and consumer associations or organisations, of their assessment of the application of their codes of conduct and their impact upon practices, habits or customs relating to electronic commerce;

(e) the drawing up of codes of conduct regarding the protection of minors and human dignity.

2. Member States and the Commission shall encourage the involvement of associations or organisations representing consumers in the drafting and implementation of codes of conduct affecting their interests and drawn up in accordance with paragraph 1(a). Where appropriate, to take account of their specific needs, associations representing the visually impaired and disabled should be consulted.

[365]

Article 17

Out-of-court dispute settlement

1. Member States shall ensure that, in the event of disagreement between an information society service provider and the recipient of the service, their legislation does not hamper the use of out-of-court schemes, available under national law, for dispute settlement, including appropriate electronic means.

2. Member States shall encourage bodies responsible for the out-of-court settlement of, in particular, consumer disputes to operate in a way which provides adequate procedural guarantees for the parties concerned.

3. Member States shall encourage bodies responsible for out-of-court dispute settlement to inform the Commission of the significant decisions they take regarding information society services and to transmit any other information on the practices, usages or customs relating to electronic commerce.

[366]

Article 18

Court actions

1. Member States shall ensure that court actions available under national law concerning information society services' activities allow for the rapid adoption of measures, including interim measures, designed to terminate any alleged infringement and to prevent any further impairment of the interests involved.

2. …

[367]

NOTES

Para 2: amends Directive 98/27/EC, Annex.

Article 19

Cooperation

1. Member States shall have adequate means of supervision and investigation necessary to implement this Directive effectively and shall ensure that service providers supply them with the requisite information.

2. Member States shall cooperate with other Member States; they shall, to that end, appoint one or several contact points, whose details they shall communicate to the other Member States and to the Commission.

3. Member States shall, as quickly as possible, and in conformity with national law, provide the assistance and information requested by other Member States or by the Commission, including by appropriate electronic means.

4. Member States shall establish contact points which shall be accessible at least by electronic means and from which recipients and service providers may—

(a) obtain general information on contractual rights and obligations as well as on the complaint and redress mechanisms available in the event of disputes, including practical aspects involved in the use of such mechanisms;

(b) obtain the details of authorities, associations or organisations from which they may obtain further information or practical assistance.

5. Member States shall encourage the communication to the Commission of any significant administrative or judicial decisions taken in their territory regarding disputes relating to information society services and practices, usages and customs relating to electronic commerce. The Commission shall communicate these decisions to the other Member States.

[368]

Article 20

Sanctions

Member States shall determine the sanctions applicable to infringements of national provisions adopted pursuant to this Directive and shall take all measures necessary to ensure that they are enforced. The sanctions they provide for shall be effective, proportionate and dissuasive.

[369]

CHAPTER IV
FINAL PROVISIONS

Article 21
Re-examination

1. Before 17 July 2003, and thereafter every two years, the Commission shall submit to the European Parliament, the Council and the Economic and Social Committee a report on the application of this Directive, accompanied, where necessary, by proposals for adapting it to legal, technical and economic developments in the field of information society services, in particular with respect to crime prevention, the protection of minors, consumer protection and to the proper functioning of the internal market.

2. In examining the need for an adaptation of this Directive, the report shall in particular analyse the need for proposals concerning the liability of providers of hyperlinks and location tool services, "notice and take down" procedures and the attribution of liability following the taking down of content. The report shall also analyse the need for additional conditions for the exemption from liability, provided for in Articles 12 and 13, in the light of technical developments, and the possibility of applying the internal market principles to unsolicited commercial communications by electronic mail.

[370]

Article 22
Transposition

1. Member States shall bring into force the laws, regulations and administrative provisions necessary to comply with this Directive before 17 January 2002. They shall forthwith inform the Commission thereof.

2. When Member States adopt the measures referred to in paragraph 1, these shall contain a reference to this Directive or shall be accompanied by such reference at the time of their official publication. The methods of making such reference shall be laid down by Member States.

[371]

Article 23

Entry into force

This Directive shall enter into force on the day of its publication in the *Official Journal of the European* Communities.

[372]

Article 24

Addressees

This Directive is addressed to the Member States.

[373]

Done at Luxembourg, 8 June 2000.

ANNEX
DEROGATIONS FROM ARTICLE 3

As provided for in Article 3(3), Article 3(1) and (2) do not apply to—

- copyright, neighbouring rights, rights referred to in Directive 87/54/EEC[1] and Directive 96/9/EC[2] as well as industrial property rights,
- the emission of electronic money by institutions in respect of which Member States have applied one of the derogations provided for in Article 8(1) of Directive 2000/46/EC,[3]
- Article 44(2) of Directive 85/611/EEC,[4]
- Article 30 and Title IV of Directive 92/49/EEC,[5] Title IV of Directive 92/96/EEC,[6] Articles 7 and 8 of Directive 88/357/EEC[7] and Article 4 of Directive 90/619/EEC,[8]
- the freedom of the parties to choose the law applicable to their contract,
- contractual obligations concerning consumer contacts,
- formal validity of contracts creating or transferring rights in real estate where such contracts are subject to mandatory formal requirements of the law of the Member State where the real estate is situated,
- the permissibility of unsolicited commercial communications by electronic mail.

[374]–[500]

NOTES

1 OJ L24, 27.1.1987, p 36.
2 OJ L77, 27.3.1996, p 20.
3 Not yet published in the Official Journal.
4 OJ L375, 31.12.1985, p 3. Directive as last amended by Directive 95/26/EC (OJ L168, 18.7.1995, p 7).
5 OJ L228, 11.8.1992, p 1. Directive as last amended by Directive 95/26/EC.
6 OJ L360, 9.12.1992, p 2. Directive as last amended by Directive 95/26/EC.
7 OJ L172, 4.7.1988, p 1. Directive as last amended by Directive 92/49/EC.
8 OJ L330, 29.11.1990, p 50. Directive as last amended by Directive 92/96/EC.

PART II
DATA PROTECTION, ACCESS TO DATA AND HUMAN RIGHTS

DATA PROTECTION ACT 1998

(1998 c 29)

ARRANGEMENT OF SECTIONS

PART I
PRELIMINARY

PART II
RIGHTS OF DATA SUBJECTS AND OTHERS

PART III
NOTIFICATION BY DATA CONTROLLERS

PART IV
EXEMPTIONS

PART V
ENFORCEMENT

PART VI
MISCELLANEOUS AND GENERAL

Functions of Commissioner

Unlawful obtaining etc of personal data

Records obtained under data subject's right of access

Information provided to Commissioner or Tribunal

General provisions relating to offences

General

An Act to make new provision for the regulation of the processing of information relating to individuals, including the obtaining, holding, use or disclosure of such information

[16 July 1998]

PART I
PRELIMINARY

1 Basic interpretative provisions

(1) In this Act, unless the context otherwise requires—

"data" means information which—

(a) is being processed by means of equipment operating automatically in response to instructions given for that purpose,

(b) is recorded with the intention that it should be processed by means of such equipment,

(c) is recorded as part of a relevant filing system or with the intention that it should form part of a relevant filing system, …

(d) does not fall within paragraph (a), (b) or (c) but forms part of an accessible record as defined by section 68, [or

(e) is recorded information held by a public authority and does not fall within any of paragraphs (a) to (d);]

"data controller" means, subject to subsection (4), a person who (either alone or jointly or in common with other persons) determines the purposes for which and the manner in which any personal data are, or are to be, processed;

"data processor", in relation to personal data, means any person (other than an employee of the data controller) who processes the data on behalf of the data controller;

"data subject" means an individual who is the subject of personal data;

"personal data" means data which relate to a living individual who can be identified—

(a) from those data, or

(b) from those data and other information which is in the possession of, or is likely to come into the possession of, the data controller,

and includes any expression of opinion about the individual and any indication of the intentions of the data controller or any other person in respect of the individual;

"processing", in relation to information or data, means obtaining, recording or holding the information or data or carrying out any operation or set of operations on the information or data, including—

(a) organisation, adaptation or alteration of the information or data,

(b) retrieval, consultation or use of the information or data,

(c) disclosure of the information or data by transmission, dissemination or otherwise making available, or

(d) alignment, combination, blocking, erasure or destruction of the information or data;

["public authority" means a public authority as defined by the Freedom of Information Act 2000 or a Scottish public authority as defined by the Freedom of Information (Scotland) Act 2002;]

"relevant filing system" means any set of information relating to individuals to the extent that, although the information is not processed by means of equipment operating automatically in response to instructions given for that purpose, the set is structured, either by reference to individuals or by reference to criteria relating to individuals, in such a way that specific information relating to a particular individual is readily accessible.

(2) In this Act, unless the context otherwise requires—

(a) "obtaining" or "recording", in relation to personal data, includes obtaining or recording the information to be contained in the data, and

(b) "using" or "disclosing", in relation to personal data, includes using or disclosing the information contained in the data.

(3) In determining for the purposes of this Act whether any information is recorded with the intention—

(a) that it should be processed by means of equipment operating automatically in response to instructions given for that purpose, or

(b) that it should form part of a relevant filing system,

it is immaterial that it is intended to be so processed or to form part of such a system only after being transferred to a country or territory outside the European Economic Area.

(4) Where personal data are processed only for purposes for which they are required by or under any enactment to be processed, the person on whom the obligation to process the data is imposed by or under that enactment is for the purposes of this Act the data controller.

[(5) In paragraph (e) of the definition of "data" in subsection (1), the reference to information "held" by a public authority shall be construed in accordance with section 3(2) of the Freedom of Information Act 2000 [or section 3(2), (4) and (5) of the Freedom of Information (Scotland) Act 2002].

(6) Where

[(a)] section 7 of the Freedom of Information Act 2000 prevents Parts I to V of that Act [or

(b) section 7(1) of the Freedom of Information (Scotland) Act 2002 prevents that Act,]

from applying to certain information held by a public authority, that information is not to be treated for the purposes of paragraph (e) of the definition of "data" in subsection (1) as held by a public authority.]

[501]–[505]

NOTES

Sub-s (1): in definition "data" word omitted from para (c) repealed, and para (e) and word immediately preceding it inserted by the Freedom of Information Act 2000, ss 68(1), (2)(a), 86, Sch 8, Pt III; definition "public authority" (originally inserted by the Freedom of Information Act 2000, s 68(1), (2)(b)) substituted by the Freedom of Information (Scotland) Act 2002 (Consequential Modifications) Order 2004, SI 2004/3089, art 2(1), (2)(a).

Sub-s (5): added by the Freedom of Information Act 2000, s 68(1), (3); words in square brackets inserted by SI 2004/3089, art 2(1), (2)(b).

Sub-s (6): added by the Freedom of Information Act 2000, s 68(1), (3); para (a) numbered as such and para (b) and the word immediately preceding it inserted by SI 2004/3089, art 2(1), (2)(c).

2 Sensitive personal data

In this Act "sensitive personal data" means personal data consisting of information as to—

(a) the racial or ethnic origin of the data subject,

(b) his political opinions,

(c) his religious beliefs or other beliefs of a similar nature,

(d) whether he is a member of a trade union (within the meaning of the Trade Union and Labour Relations (Consolidation) Act 1992,

(e) his physical or mental health or condition,

(f) his sexual life,

(g) the commission or alleged commission by him of any offence, or

(h) any proceedings for any offence committed or alleged to have been committed by him, the disposal of such proceedings or the sentence of any court in such proceedings.

[506]

3 The special purposes

In this Act "the special purposes" means any one or more of the following—

(a) the purposes of journalism,

(b) artistic purposes, and

(c) literary purposes.

[507]

4 The data protection principles

(1) References in this Act to the data protection principles are to the principles set out in Part I of Schedule 1.

(2) Those principles are to be interpreted in accordance with Part II of Schedule 1.

(3) Schedule 2 (which applies to all personal data) and Schedule 3 (which applies only to sensitive personal data) set out conditions applying for the purposes of the first principle; and Schedule 4 sets out cases in which the eighth principle does not apply.

(4) Subject to section 27(1), it shall be the duty of a data controller to comply with the data protection principles in relation to all personal data with respect to which he is the data controller.

[508]

5 Application of Act

(1) Except as otherwise provided by or under section 54, this Act applies to a data controller in respect of any data only if—

(a) the data controller is established in the United Kingdom and the data are processed in the context of that establishment, or

(b) the data controller is established neither in the United Kingdom nor in any other EEA State but uses equipment in the United Kingdom for processing the data otherwise than for the purposes of transit through the United Kingdom.

(2) A data controller falling within subsection (1)(b) must nominate for the purposes of this Act a representative established in the United Kingdom.

(3) For the purposes of subsections (1) and (2), each of the following is to be treated as established in the United Kingdom—

(a) an individual who is ordinarily resident in the United Kingdom,

(b) a body incorporated under the law of, or of any part of, the United Kingdom,

(c) a partnership or other unincorporated association formed under the law of any part of the United Kingdom, and

(d) any person who does not fall within paragraph (a), (b) or (c) but maintains in the United Kingdom—

  (i) an office, branch or agency through which he carries on any activity, or

  (ii) a regular practice;

and the reference to establishment in any other EEA State has a corresponding meaning.

[509]

PART II DATA PROTECTION

6 The Commissioner and the Tribunal

[(1) For the purposes of this Act and of the Freedom of Information Act 2000 there shall be an officer known as the Information Commissioner (in this Act referred to as "the Commissioner").]

(2) The Commissioner shall be appointed by Her Majesty by Letters Patent.

[(3) For the purposes of this Act and of the Freedom of Information Act 2000 there shall be a tribunal known as the Information Tribunal (in this Act referred to as "the Tribunal").]

(4) The Tribunal shall consist of—

(a) a chairman appointed by the Lord Chancellor after consultation with the [Secretary of State],

(b) such number of deputy chairmen so appointed as the Lord Chancellor may determine, and

(c) such number of other members appointed by the [Secretary of State] as he may determine.

(5) The members of the Tribunal appointed under subsection (4)(a) and (b) shall be—

(a) persons who have a 7 year general qualification, within the meaning of section 71 of the Courts and Legal Services Act 1990,

(b) advocates or solicitors in Scotland of at least 7 years' standing, or

(c) members of the bar of Northern Ireland or *solicitors of the Supreme Court of Northern Ireland* of at least 7 years' standing.

(6) The members of the Tribunal appointed under subsection (4)(c) shall be—

(a) persons to represent the interests of data subjects,

[(aa) persons to represent the interests of those who make requests for information under the Freedom of Information Act 2000,]

(b) persons to represent the interests of data controllers [and

(bb) persons to represent the interests of public authorities].

(7) Schedule 5 has effect in relation to the Commissioner and the Tribunal.

[510]

NOTES

Sub-ss (1), (3): substituted by the Freedom of Information Act 2000, s 18(4), Sch 2, Pt 1, para 13.

Sub-s (4): words in square brackets in para (a) substituted by virtue of the Transfer of Functions (Lord Advocate and Secretary of State) Order 1999, SI 1999/678, art 2(1), Schedule; words in square brackets in para (c) substituted by the Secretary of State for Constitutional Affairs Order 2003, SI 2003/1887, art 9, Sch 2, para 9(1)(a).

Sub-s (5): for the words in italics there are substituted the words "solicitors of the Court of Judicature of Northern Ireland" by the Constitutional Reform Act 2005, s 59(5), Sch 11, Pt 3, para 5, as from a day to be appointed.

Sub-s (6): para (aa) substituted for original word "and" at the end of para (a), and para (bb) and word immediately preceding it inserted, by the Freedom of Information Act 2000, s 18(4), Sch 2, Pt II, para 16.

PART II
RIGHTS OF DATA SUBJECTS AND OTHERS

7 Right of access to personal data

(1) Subject to the following provisions of this section and to [sections 8, 9 and 9A], an individual is entitled—

(a) to be informed by any data controller whether personal data of which that individual is the data subject are being processed by or on behalf of that data controller,

(b) if that is the case, to be given by the data controller a description of—

(i) the personal data of which that individual is the data subject,

(ii) the purposes for which they are being or are to be processed, and

(iii) the recipients or classes of recipients to whom they are or may be disclosed,

(c) to have communicated to him in an intelligible form—

(i) the information constituting any personal data of which that individual is the data subject, and

(ii) any information available to the data controller as to the source of those data, and

(d) where the processing by automatic means of personal data of which that individual is the data subject for the purpose of evaluating matters relating to him such as, for example, his performance at work, his creditworthiness, his reliability or his conduct, has constituted or is likely to constitute the sole basis for any decision significantly affecting him, to be informed by the data controller of the logic involved in that decision-taking.

(2) A data controller is not obliged to supply any information under subsection (1) unless he has received—

(a) a request in writing, and

(b) except in prescribed cases, such fee (not exceeding the prescribed maximum) as he may require.

[(3) Where a data controller—

(a) reasonably requires further information in order to satisfy himself as to the identity of the person making a request under this section and to locate the information which that person seeks, and

(b) has informed him of that requirement,

the data controller is not obliged to comply with the request unless he is supplied with that further information.]

(4) Where a data controller cannot comply with the request without disclosing information relating to another individual who can be identified from that information, he is not obliged to comply with the request unless—

(a) the other individual has consented to the disclosure of the information to the person making the request, or

(b) it is reasonable in all the circumstances to comply with the request without the consent of the other individual.

(5) In subsection (4) the reference to information relating to another individual includes a reference to information identifying that individual as the source of the information sought by the request; and that subsection is not to be construed as excusing a data controller from communicating so much of the information sought by the request as can be communicated without disclosing the identity of the other individual concerned, whether by the omission of names or other identifying particulars or otherwise.

(6) In determining for the purposes of subsection (4)(b) whether it is reasonable in all the circumstances to comply with the request without the consent of the other individual concerned, regard shall be had, in particular, to—

(a) any duty of confidentiality owed to the other individual,

(b) any steps taken by the data controller with a view to seeking the consent of the other individual,

(c) whether the other individual is capable of giving consent, and

(d) any express refusal of consent by the other individual.

(7) An individual making a request under this section may, in such cases as may be prescribed, specify that his request is limited to personal data of any prescribed description.

(8) Subject to subsection (4), a data controller shall comply with a request under this section promptly and in any event before the end of the prescribed period beginning with the relevant day.

(9) If a court is satisfied on the application of any person who has made a request under the foregoing provisions of this section that the data controller in question has failed to comply with the request in contravention of those provisions, the court may order him to comply with the request.

(10) In this section—

"prescribed" means prescribed by the [Secretary of State] by regulations;

"the prescribed maximum" means such amount as may be prescribed;

"the prescribed period" means forty days or such other period as may be prescribed;

"the relevant day", in relation to a request under this section, means the day on which the data controller receives the request or, if later, the first day on which the data controller has both the required fee and the information referred to in subsection (3).

(11) Different amounts or periods may be prescribed under this section in relation to different cases.

[511]

PART II
DATA PROTECTION

NOTES

Sub-s (1): words in square brackets substituted by the Freedom of Information Act 2000, s 69(1).

Sub-s (3): substituted by the Freedom of Information Act 2000, s 73, Sch 6, para 1.

Sub-s (10): words in square brackets substituted by the Secretary of State for Constitutional Affairs Order 2003, SI 2003/1887, art 9, Sch 2, para 9(1)(a).

Regulations: the Data Protection (Subject Access) (Fees and Miscellaneous Provisions) Regulations 2000, SI 2000/191 at **[878]**.

8 Provisions supplementary to section 7

(1) The [Secretary of State] may by regulations provide that, in such cases as may be prescribed, a request for information under any provision of subsection (1) of section 7 is to be treated as extending also to information under other provisions of that subsection.

(2) The obligation imposed by section 7(1)(c)(i) must be complied with by supplying the data subject with a copy of the information in permanent form unless—

(a) the supply of such a copy is not possible or would involve disproportionate effort, or

(b) the data subject agrees otherwise;

and where any of the information referred to in section 7(1)(c)(i) is expressed in terms which are not intelligible without explanation the copy must be accompanied by an explanation of those terms.

(3) Where a data controller has previously complied with a request made under section 7 by an individual, the data controller is not obliged to comply with a subsequent identical or similar request under that section by that individual unless a reasonable interval has elapsed between compliance with the previous request and the making of the current request.

(4) In determining for the purposes of subsection (3) whether requests under section 7 are made at reasonable intervals, regard shall be had to the nature of the data, the purpose for which the data are processed and the frequency with which the data are altered.

(5) Section 7(1)(d) is not to be regarded as requiring the provision of information as to the logic involved in any decision-taking if, and to the extent that, the information constitutes a trade secret.

(6) The information to be supplied pursuant to a request under section 7 must be supplied by reference to the data in question at the time when the request is received, except that it may take account of any amendment or deletion made between that time and the time when the information is supplied, being an amendment or deletion that would have been made regardless of the receipt of the request.

(7) For the purposes of section 7(4) and (5) another individual can be identified from the information being disclosed if he can be identified from that information, or from that and any other information which, in the reasonable belief of the data controller, is likely to be in, or to come into, the possession of the data subject making the request.

[512]

NOTES

Sub-s (1): words in square brackets substituted by the Secretary of State for Constitutional Affairs Order 2003, SI 2003/1887, art 9, Sch 2, para 9(1)(a).

Regulations: the Data Protection (Subject Access) (Fees and Miscellaneous Provisions) Regulations 2000, SI 2000/191 at **[878]**.

9 Application of section 7 where data controller is credit reference agency

(1) Where the data controller is a credit reference agency, section 7 has effect subject to the provisions of this section.

(2) An individual making a request under section 7 may limit his request to personal data relevant to his financial standing, and shall be taken to have so limited his request unless the request shows a contrary intention.

(3) Where the data controller receives a request under section 7 in a case where personal data of which the individual making the request is the data subject are being processed by or on behalf of the data controller, the obligation to supply information under that section includes an obligation to give the individual making the request a statement, in such form as may be prescribed by the [Secretary of State] by regulations, of the individual's rights—

(a) under section 159 of the Consumer Credit Act 1974, and
(b) to the extent required by the prescribed form, under this Act.

[513]

NOTES

Sub-s (3): words in square brackets substituted by the Secretary of State for Constitutional Affairs Order 2003, SI 2003/1887, art 9, Sch 2, para 9(1)(a).

Regulations: the Consumer Credit (Credit Reference Agency) Regulations 2000, SI 2000/290 at **[5229]**.

[9A Unstructured personal data held by public authorities

(1) In this section "unstructured personal data" means any personal data falling within paragraph (e) of the definition of "data" in section 1(1), other than information which is recorded as part of, or with the intention that it should form part of, any set of information relating to individuals to the extent that the set is structured by reference to individuals or by reference to criteria relating to individuals.

(2) A public authority is not obliged to comply with subsection (1) of section 7 in relation to any unstructured personal data unless the request under that section contains a description of the data.

(3) Even if the data are described by the data subject in his request, a public authority is not obliged to comply with paragraph (a) of section 7(1) in relation to the unstructured personal data if the authority estimates that the cost of complying with the request so far as relating to those data would exceed the appropriate limit.

(4) Subsection (3) does not exempt the public authority from its obligation to comply with paragraph (a) of section 7(1) in relation to the unstructured personal data unless the estimated cost of complying with that paragraph alone in relation to those data would exceed the appropriate limit.

(5) In subsections (3) and (4) "the appropriate limit" means such amount as may be prescribed by the [Secretary of State] by regulations, and different amounts may be prescribed in relation to different cases.

(6) Any estimate for the purposes of this section must be made in accordance with regulations under s 12(5) of the Freedom of Information Act 2000.]

[514]

NOTES

Commencement: 30 November 2000 (for the purpose of making regulations); 1 January 2005 (otherwise).

Inserted by the Freedom of Information Act 2000, s 69(2).

Sub-s (5): words in square brackets substituted by the Secretary of State for Constitutional Affairs Order 2003, SI 2003/1887, art 9, Sch 2, paras 9(1)(a), 12(1)(b).

Regulations: the Freedom of Information and Data Protection (Appropriate Limit and Fees) Regulations 2004, SI 2004/3244.

10 Right to prevent processing likely to cause damage or distress

(1) Subject to subsection (2), an individual is entitled at any time by notice in writing to a data controller to require the data controller at the end of such period as is reasonable in the circumstances to cease, or not to begin, processing, or processing for a specified purpose or in a specified manner, any personal data in respect of which he is the data subject, on the ground that, for specified reasons—

(a) the processing of those data or their processing for that purpose or in that manner is causing or is likely to cause substantial damage or substantial distress to him or to another, and
(b) that damage or distress is or would be unwarranted.

(2) Subsection (1) does not apply—

(a) in a case where any of the conditions in paragraphs 1 to 4 of Schedule 2 is met, or
(b) in such other cases as may be prescribed by the [Secretary of State] by order.

(3) The data controller must within twenty-one days of receiving a notice under subsection (1) ("the data subject notice") give the individual who gave it a written notice—

(a) stating that he has complied or intends to comply with the data subject notice, or

(b) stating his reasons for regarding the data subject notice as to any extent unjustified and the extent (if any) to which he has complied or intends to comply with it.

(4) If a court is satisfied, on the application of any person who has given a notice under subsection (1) which appears to the court to be justified (or to be justified to any extent), that the data controller in question has failed to comply with the notice, the court may order him to take such steps for complying with the notice (or for complying with it to that extent) as the court thinks fit.

(5) The failure by a data subject to exercise the right conferred by subsection (1) or section 11(1) does not affect any other right conferred on him by this Part.

[515]

NOTES

Sub-s (2): words in square brackets in para (b) substituted by the Secretary of State for Constitutional Affairs Order 2003, SI 2003/1887, art 9, Sch 2, para 9(1)(a).

11 Right to prevent processing for purposes of direct marketing

(1) An individual is entitled at any time by notice in writing to a data controller to require the data controller at the end of such period as is reasonable in the circumstances to cease, or not to begin, processing for the purposes of direct marketing personal data in respect of which he is the data subject.

(2) If the court is satisfied, on the application of any person who has given a notice under subsection (1), that the data controller has failed to comply with the notice, the court may order him to take such steps for complying with the notice as the court thinks fit.

[(2A) This section shall not apply in relation to the processing of such data as are mentioned in paragraph (1) of regulation 8 of the Telecommunications (Data Protection and Privacy) Regulations 1999 (processing of telecommunications billing data for certain marketing purposes) for the purposes mentioned in paragraph (2) of that regulation.]

(3) In this section "direct marketing" means the communication (by whatever means) of any advertising or marketing material which is directed to particular individuals.

[516]

NOTES

Sub-s (2A): inserted by the Telecommunications (Data Protection and Privacy) Regulations 1999, SI 1999/2093, reg 3(3), Sch 1, Pt II, para 3.

12 Rights in relation to automated decision-taking

(1) An individual is entitled at any time, by notice in writing to any data controller, to require the data controller to ensure that no decision taken by or on behalf of the data controller which significantly affects that individual is based solely on the processing by automatic means of personal data in respect of which that individual is the data subject for the purpose of evaluating matters relating to him such as, for example, his performance at work, his creditworthiness, his reliability or his conduct.

(2) Where, in a case where no notice under subsection (1) has effect, a decision which significantly affects an individual is based solely on such processing as is mentioned in subsection (1)—

(a) the data controller must as soon as reasonably practicable notify the individual that the decision was taken on that basis, and
(b) the individual is entitled, within twenty-one days of receiving that notification from the data controller, by notice in writing to require the data controller to reconsider the decision or to take a new decision otherwise than on that basis.

(3) The data controller must, within twenty-one days of receiving a notice under subsection (2)(b) ("the data subject notice") give the individual a written notice specifying the steps that he intends to take to comply with the data subject notice.

(4) A notice under subsection (1) does not have effect in relation to an exempt decision; and nothing in subsection (2) applies to an exempt decision.

(5) In subsection (4) "exempt decision" means any decision—

(a) in respect of which the condition in subsection (6) and the condition in subsection (7) are met, or

(b) which is made in such other circumstances as may be prescribed by the [Secretary of State] by order.

(6) The condition in this subsection is that the decision—

(a) is taken in the course of steps taken—
(i) for the purpose of considering whether to enter into a contract with the data subject,
(ii) with a view to entering into such a contract, or
(iii) in the course of performing such a contract, or

(b) is authorised or required by or under any enactment.

(7) The condition in this subsection is that either—

(a) the effect of the decision is to grant a request of the data subject, or

(b) steps have been taken to safeguard the legitimate interests of the data subject (for example, by allowing him to make representations).

(8) If a court is satisfied on the application of a data subject that a person taking a decision in respect of him ("the responsible person") has failed to comply with subsection (1) or (2)(b), the court may order the responsible person to reconsider the decision, or to take a new decision which is not based solely on such processing as is mentioned in subsection (1).

(9) An order under subsection (8) shall not affect the rights of any person other than the data subject and the responsible person.

[517]

NOTES

Sub-s (5): words in square brackets in para (b) substituted by the Secretary of State for Constitutional Affairs Order 2003, SI 2003/1887, art 9, Sch 2, para 9(1)(a).

[12A Rights of data subjects in relation to exempt manual data

(1) A data subject is entitled at any time by notice in writing—

(a) to require the data controller to rectify, block, erase or destroy exempt manual data which are inaccurate or incomplete, or

(b) to require the data controller to cease holding exempt manual data in a way incompatible with the legitimate purposes pursued by the data controller.

(2) A notice under subsection (1)(a) or (b) must state the data subject's reasons for believing that the data are inaccurate or incomplete or, as the case may be, his reasons for believing that they are held in a way incompatible with the legitimate purposes pursued by the data controller.

(3) If the court is satisfied, on the application of any person who has given a notice under subsection (1) which appears to the court to be justified (or to be justified to any extent) that the data controller in question has failed to comply with the notice, the court may order him to take such steps for complying with the notice (or for complying with it to that extent) as the court thinks fit.

(4) In this section "exempt manual data" means—

(a) in relation to the first transitional period, as defined by paragraph 1(2) of Schedule 8, data to which paragraph 3 or 4 of that Schedule applies, and

(b) in relation to the second transitional period, as so defined, data to which paragraph 14 [or 14A] of that Schedule applies.

(5) For the purposes of this section personal data are incomplete if, and only if, the data, although not inaccurate, are such that their incompleteness would constitute a contravention of the third or fourth data protection principles, if those principles applied to the data.]

[518]

NOTES

Inserted by s 72, Sch 13, para 1 of this Act, to have effect during the period beginning with the commencement of s 72 (1 March 2000) and ending 23 October 2007; see s 72 at **[580]**.

Sub-s (4): words in square brackets in para (b) inserted by the Freedom of Information Act 2000, s 70(4).

13 Compensation for failure to comply with certain requirements

(1) An individual who suffers damage by reason of any contravention by a data controller of any of the requirements of this Act is entitled to compensation from the data controller for that damage.

(2) An individual who suffers distress by reason of any contravention by a data controller of any of the requirements of this Act is entitled to compensation from the data controller for that distress if—

(a) the individual also suffers damage by reason of the contravention, or
(b) the contravention relates to the processing of personal data for the special purposes.

(3) In proceedings brought against a person by virtue of this section it is a defence to prove that he had taken such care as in all the circumstances was reasonably required to comply with the requirement concerned.

[519]

14 Rectification, blocking, erasure and destruction

(1) If a court is satisfied on the application of a data subject that personal data of which the applicant is the subject are inaccurate, the court may order the data controller to rectify, block, erase or destroy those data and any other personal data in respect of which he is the data controller and which contain an expression of opinion which appears to the court to be based on the inaccurate data.

(2) Subsection (1) applies whether or not the data accurately record information received or obtained by the data controller from the data subject or a third party but where the data accurately record such information, then—

(a) if the requirements mentioned in paragraph 7 of Part II of Schedule 1 have been complied with, the court may, instead of making an order under subsection (1), make an order requiring the data to be supplemented by such statement of the true facts relating to the matters dealt with by the data as the court may approve, and
(b) if all or any of those requirements have not been complied with, the court may, instead of making an order under that subsection, make such order as it thinks fit for securing compliance with those requirements with or without a further order requiring the data to be supplemented by such a statement as is mentioned in paragraph (a).

(3) Where the court

(a) makes an order under subsection (1), or
(b) is satisfied on the application of a data subject that personal data of which he was the data subject and which have been rectified, blocked, erased or destroyed were inaccurate,

it may, where it considers it reasonably practicable, order the data controller to notify third parties to whom the data have been disclosed of the rectification, blocking, erasure or destruction.

(4) If a court is satisfied on the application of a data subject—

(a) that he has suffered damage by reason of any contravention by a data controller of any of the requirements of this Act in respect of any personal data, in circumstances entitling him to compensation under section 13, and
(b) that there is a substantial risk of further contravention in respect of those data in such circumstances,

the court may order the rectification, blocking, erasure or destruction of any of those data.

(5) Where the court makes an order under subsection (4) it may, where it considers it reasonably practicable, order the data controller to notify third parties to whom the data have been disclosed of the rectification, blocking, erasure or destruction.

(6) In determining whether it is reasonably practicable to require such notification as is mentioned in subsection (3) or (5) the court shall have regard, in particular, to the number of persons who would have to be notified.

[520]

15 Jurisdiction and procedure

(1) The jurisdiction conferred by sections 7 to 14 is exercisable by the High Court or a county court or, in Scotland, by the Court of Session or the sheriff.

(2) For the purpose of determining any question whether an applicant under subsection (9) of section 7 is entitled to the information which he seeks (including any question whether any relevant data are exempt from that section by virtue of Part IV) a court may require the information constituting any data processed by or on behalf of the data controller and any information as to the logic involved in any decision-taking as mentioned in section 7(1)(d) to be made available for its own inspection but shall not, pending the determination of that question in the applicant's favour, require the information sought by the applicant to be disclosed to him or his representatives whether by discovery (or, in Scotland, recovery) or otherwise.

[521]

PART III
NOTIFICATION BY DATA CONTROLLERS

16 Preliminary

(1) In this Part "the registrable particulars", in relation to a data controller, means—

(a) his name and address,

(b) if he has nominated a representative for the purposes of this Act, the name and address of the representative,

(c) a description of the personal data being or to be processed by or on behalf of the data controller and of the category or categories of data subject to which they relate,

(d) a description of the purpose or purposes for which the data are being or are to be processed,

(e) a description of any recipient or recipients to whom the data controller intends or may wish to disclose the data,

(f) the names, or a description of, any countries or territories outside the European Economic Area to which the data controller directly or indirectly transfers, or intends or may wish directly or indirectly to transfer, the data,

[(ff) where the data controller is a public authority, a statement of that fact,] and

(g) in any case where—

(i) personal data are being, or are intended to be, processed in circumstances in which the prohibition in subsection (1) of section 17 is excluded by subsection (2) or (3) of that section, and

(ii) the notification does not extend to those data,

a statement of that fact.

(2) In this Part—

"fees regulations" means regulations made by the [Secretary of State] under section 18(5) or 19(4) or (7);

"notification regulations" means regulations made by the [Secretary of State] under the other provisions of this Part;

"prescribed", except where used in relation to fees regulations, means prescribed by notification regulations.

(3) For the purposes of this Part, so far as it relates to the addresses of data controllers—

(a) the address of a registered company is that of its registered office, and

(b) the address of a person (other than a registered company) carrying on a business is that of his principal place of business in the United Kingdom.

[522]

NOTES

Sub-s (1): para (ff) inserted by the Freedom of Information Act 2000, s 71.

Sub-s (2): words in square brackets substituted by the Secretary of State for Constitutional Affairs Order 2003, SI 2003/1887, art 9, Sch 2, para 9(1)(a).

17 Prohibition on processing without registration

(1) Subject to the following provisions of this section, personal data must not be processed unless an entry in respect of the data controller is included in the register maintained by the Commissioner under section 19 (or is treated by notification regulations made by virtue of section 19(3) as being so included).

(2) Except where the processing is assessable processing for the purposes of section 22, subsection (1) does not apply in relation to personal data consisting of information which falls neither within paragraph (a) of the definition of "data" in section 1(1) nor within paragraph (b) of that definition.

(3) If it appears to the [Secretary of State] that processing of a particular description is unlikely to prejudice the rights and freedoms of data subjects, notification regulations may provide that, in such cases as may be prescribed, subsection (1) is not to apply in relation to processing of that description.

(4) Subsection (1) does not apply in relation to any processing whose sole purpose is the maintenance of a public register.

[523]

NOTES

Sub-s (3): words in square brackets substituted by the Secretary of State for Constitutional Affairs Order 2003, SI 2003/1887, art 9, Sch 2, para 9(1)(a).

Regulations: the Data Protection (Notification and Notification Fees) Regulations 2000, SI 2000/188 at **[828]**.

18 Notification by data controllers

(1) Any data controller who wishes to be included in the register maintained under section 19 shall give a notification to the Commissioner under this section.

(2) A notification under this section must specify in accordance with notification regulations—

(a) the registrable particulars, and

(b) a general description of measures to be taken for the purpose of complying with the seventh data protection principle.

(3) Notification regulations made by virtue of subsection (2) may provide for the determination by the Commissioner, in accordance with any requirements of the regulations, of the form in which the registrable particulars and the description mentioned in subsection (2)(b) are to be specified, including in particular the detail required for the purposes of section 16(1)(c), (d), (e) and (f) and subsection (2)(b).

(4) Notification regulations may make provision as to the giving of notification—

(a) by partnerships, or

(b) in other cases where two or more persons are the data controllers in respect of any personal data.

(5) The notification must be accompanied by such fee as may be prescribed by fees regulations.

(6) Notification regulations may provide for any fee paid under subsection (5) or section 19(4) to be refunded in prescribed circumstances.

[524]

NOTES

Regulations: the Data Protection (Notification and Notification Fees) Regulations 2000, SI 2000/188 at **[828]**.

19 Register of notifications

(1) The Commissioner shall—

(a) maintain a register of persons who have given notification under section 18, and

(b) make an entry in the register in pursuance of each notification received by him under that section from a person in respect of whom no entry as data controller was for the time being included in the register.

(2) Each entry in the register shall consist of—

(a) the registrable particulars notified under section 18 or, as the case requires, those particulars as amended in pursuance of section 20(4), and

(b) such other information as the Commissioner may be authorised or required by notification regulations to include in the register.

(3) Notification regulations may make provision as to the time as from which any entry in respect of a data controller is to be treated for the purposes of section 17 as having been made in the register.

(4) No entry shall be retained in the register for more than the relevant time except on payment of such fee as may be prescribed by fees regulations.

(5) In subsection (4) "the relevant time" means twelve months or such other period as may be prescribed by notification regulations; and different periods may be prescribed in relation to different cases.

(6) The Commissioner—

(a) shall provide facilities for making the information contained in the entries in the register available for inspection (in visible and legible form) by members of the public at all reasonable hours and free of charge, and

(b) may provide such other facilities for making the information contained in those entries available to the public free of charge as he considers appropriate.

(7) The Commissioner shall, on payment of such fee, if any, as may be prescribed by fees regulations, supply any member of the public with a duly certified copy in writing of the particulars contained in any entry made in the register.

[525]

NOTES

Regulations: the Data Protection (Fees under section 19(7)) Regulations 2000, SI 2000/187 at **[826]**; the Data Protection (Notification and Notification Fees) Regulations 2000, SI 2000/188 at **[828]**.

20 Duty to notify changes

(1) For the purpose specified in subsection (2), notification regulations shall include provision imposing on every person in respect of whom an entry as a data controller is for the time being included in the register maintained under section 19 a duty to notify to the Commissioner, in such circumstances and at such time or times and in such form as may be prescribed, such matters relating to the registrable particulars and measures taken as mentioned in section 18(2)(b) as may be prescribed.

(2) The purpose referred to in subsection (1) is that of ensuring, so far as practicable, that at any time—

(a) the entries in the register maintained under section 19 contain current names and addresses and describe the current practice or intentions of the data controller with respect to the processing of personal data, and

(b) the Commissioner is provided with a general description of measures currently being taken as mentioned in section 18(2)(b).

(3) Subsection (3) of section 18 has effect in relation to notification regulations made by virtue of subsection (1) as it has effect in relation to notification regulations made by virtue of subsection (2) of that section.

(4) On receiving any notification under notification regulations made by virtue of subsection (1), the Commissioner shall make such amendments of the relevant entry in the register maintained under section 19 as are necessary to take account of the notification.

[526]

NOTES

Regulations: the Data Protection (Notification and Notification Fees) Regulations 2000, SI 2000/188 at **[828]**.

21 Offences

(1) If section 17(1) is contravened, the data controller is guilty of an offence.

(2) Any person who fails to comply with the duty imposed by notification regulations made by virtue of section 20(1) is guilty of an offence.

(3) It shall be a defence for a person charged with an offence under subsection (2) to show that he exercised all due diligence to comply with the duty.

[527]

PART II DATA PROTECTION

22 Preliminary assessment by Commissioner

(1) In this section "assessable processing" means processing which is of a description specified in an order made by the [Secretary of State] as appearing to him to be particularly likely—

(a) to cause substantial damage or substantial distress to data subjects, or
(b) otherwise significantly to prejudice the rights and freedoms of data subjects.

(2) On receiving notification from any data controller under section 18 or under notification regulations made by virtue of section 20 the Commissioner shall consider—

(a) whether any of the processing to which the notification relates is assessable processing, and
(b) if so, whether the assessable processing is likely to comply with the provisions of this Act.

(3) Subject to subsection (4), the Commissioner shall, within the period of twenty-eight days beginning with the day on which he receives a notification which relates to assessable processing, give a notice to the data controller stating the extent to which the Commissioner is of the opinion that the processing is likely or unlikely to comply with the provisions of this Act.

(4) Before the end of the period referred to in subsection (3) the Commissioner may, by reason of special circumstances, extend that period on one occasion only by notice to the data controller by such further period not exceeding fourteen days as the Commissioner may specify in the notice.

(5) No assessable processing in respect of which a notification has been given the Commissioner as mentioned in subsection (2) shall be carried on unless either—

(a) the period of twenty-eight days beginning with the day on which the notification is received by the Commissioner (or, in a case falling within subsection (4), that period as extended under that subsection) has elapsed, or
(b) before the end of that period (or that period as so extended) the data controller has received a notice from the Commissioner under subsection (3) in respect of the processing.

(6) Where subsection (5) is contravened, the data controller is guilty of an offence.

(7) The [Secretary of State] may by order amend subsections (3), (4) and (5) by substituting for the number of days for the time being specified there a different number specified in the order.

[528]

NOTES

Sub-ss (1), (7): words in square brackets substituted by the Secretary of State for Constitutional Affairs Order 2003, SI 2003/1887, art 9, Sch 2, para 9(1)(a).

23 Power to make provision for appointment of data protection supervisors

(1) The [Secretary of State] may by order—

(a) make provision under which a data controller may appoint a person to act as a data protection supervisor responsible in particular for monitoring in an independent manner the data controller's compliance with the provisions of this Act, and
(b) provide that, in relation to any data controller who has appointed a data protection supervisor in accordance with the provisions of the order and who complies with such conditions as may be specified in the order, the provisions of this Part are to have effect subject to such exemptions or other modifications as may be specified in the order.

(2) An order under this section may—

(a) impose duties on data protection supervisors in relation to the Commissioner, and
(b) confer functions on the Commissioner in relation to data protection supervisors.

[529]

NOTES

Sub-s (1): words in square brackets substituted by the Secretary of State for Constitutional Affairs Order 2003, SI 2003/1887, art 9, Sch 2, para 9(1)(a).

24 Duty of certain data controllers to make certain information available

(1) Subject to subsection (3), where personal data are processed in a case where—

(a) by virtue of subsection (2) or (3) of section 17, subsection (1) of that section does not apply to the processing, and

(b) the data controller has not notified the relevant particulars in respect of that processing under section 18,

the data controller must, within twenty-one days of receiving a written request from any person, make the relevant particulars available to that person in writing free of charge.

(2) In this section "the relevant particulars" means the particulars referred to in paragraphs (a) to (f) of section 16(1).

(3) This section has effect subject to any exemption conferred for the purposes of this section by notification regulations.

(4) Any data controller who fails to comply with the duty imposed by subsection (1) is guilty of an offence.

(5) It shall be a defence for a person charged with an offence under subsection (4) to show that he exercised all due diligence to comply with the duty.

[530]

25 Functions of Commissioner in relation to making of notification regulations

(1) As soon as practicable after the passing of this Act, the Commissioner shall submit to the Secretary of State proposals as to the provisions to be included in the first notification regulations.

(2) The Commissioner shall keep under review the working of notification regulations and may from time to time submit to the [Secretary of State] proposals as to amendments to be made to the regulations.

(3) The [Secretary of State] may from time to time require the Commissioner to consider any matter relating to notification regulations and to submit to him proposals as to amendments to be made to the regulations in connection with that matter.

(4) Before making any notification regulations, the [Secretary of State] shall—

(a) consider any proposals made to him by the Commissioner under [subsection (2) or (3)], and

(b) consult the Commissioner.

[531]

NOTES

Sub-ss (2), (3): words in square brackets substituted by the Secretary of State for Constitutional Affairs Order 2003, SI 2003/1887, art 9, Sch 2, para 9(1)(a).

Sub-s (4): words in first pair of square brackets substituted by SI 2003/1887, art 9, Sch 2, para 9(1)(a); words in second pair of square brackets substituted by the Transfer of Functions (Miscellaneous) Order 2001, SI 2001/3500, art 8, Sch 2, Pt I, para 6(2).

26 Fees regulations

(1) Fees regulations prescribing fees for the purposes of any provision of this Part may provide for different fees to be payable in different cases.

(2) In making any fees regulations, the [Secretary of State] shall have regard to the desirability of securing that the fees payable to the Commissioner are sufficient to offset—

(a) the expenses incurred by the Commissioner and the Tribunal in discharging their functions [under this Act] and any expenses of the [Secretary of State] in respect of the Commissioner or the Tribunal [so far as attributable to their functions under this Act], and

(b) to the extent that the [Secretary of State] considers appropriate—

(i) any deficit previously incurred (whether before or after the passing of this Act) in respect of the expenses mentioned in paragraph (a), and

(ii) expenses incurred or to be incurred by the [Secretary of State] in respect of the inclusion of any officers or staff of the Commissioner in any scheme under section 1 of the Superannuation Act 1972.

[532]

NOTES

Sub-s (2): words in first, third, fifth and sixth pair of square brackets substituted by the Secretary of State for Constitutional Affairs Order 2003, SI 2003/1887, art 9, Sch 2, para 9(1)(a); words in second and fourth pairs of square brackets inserted by the Freedom of Information Act 2000, s 18(4), Sch 2, Pt II, para 17.

Regulations: the Data Protection (Notification and Notification Fees) Regulations 2000, SI 2000/188 at **[828]**.

PART IV
EXEMPTIONS

27 Preliminary

(1) References in any of the data protection principles or any provision of Parts II and III to personal data or to the processing of personal data do not include references to data or processing which by virtue of this Part are exempt from that principle or other provision.

(2) In this Part "the subject information provisions" means—

(a) the first data protection principle to the extent to which it requires compliance with paragraph 2 of Part II of Schedule 1, and

(b) section 7.

(3) In this Part "the non-disclosure provisions" means the provisions specified in subsection (4) to the extent to which they are inconsistent with the disclosure in question.

(4) The provisions referred to in subsection (3) are—

(a) the first data protection principle, except to the extent to which it requires compliance with the conditions in Schedules 2 and 3,

(b) the second, third, fourth and fifth data protection principles, and

(c) sections 10 and 14(1) to (3).

(5) Except as provided by this Part, the subject information provisions shall have effect notwithstanding any enactment or rule of law prohibiting or restricting the disclosure, or authorising the withholding, of information.

[533]

28 National security

(1) Personal data are exempt from any of the provisions of—

(a) the data protection principles,

(b) Parts II, III and V, and

(c) [sections 54A and] 55,

if the exemption from that provision is required for the purpose of safeguarding national security.

(2) Subject to subsection (4), a certificate signed by a Minister of the Crown certifying that exemption from all or any of the provisions mentioned in subsection (1) is or at any time was required for the purpose there mentioned in respect of any personal data shall be conclusive evidence of that fact.

(3) A certificate under subsection (2) may identify the personal data to which it applies by means of a general description and may be expressed to have prospective effect.

(4) Any person directly affected by the issuing of a certificate under subsection (2) may appeal to the Tribunal against the certificate.

(5) If on an appeal under subsection (4), the Tribunal finds that, applying the principles applied by the court on an application for judicial review, the Minister did not have reasonable grounds for issuing the certificate, the Tribunal may allow the appeal and quash the certificate.

(6) Where in any proceedings under or by virtue of this Act it is claimed by a data controller that a certificate under subsection (2) which identifies the personal data to which it applies by means of a general description applies to any personal data, any other party to the proceedings may appeal to the Tribunal on the ground that the certificate does not apply to the personal data in question and, subject to any determination under subsection (7), the certificate shall be conclusively presumed so to apply.

(7) On any appeal under subsection (6), the Tribunal may determine that the certificate does not so apply.

(8) A document purporting to be a certificate under subsection (2) shall be received in evidence and deemed to be such a certificate unless the contrary is proved.

(9) A document which purports to be certified by or on behalf of a Minister of the Crown as a true copy of a certificate issued by that Minister under subsection (2) shall in any legal proceedings be evidence (or, in Scotland, sufficient evidence) of that certificate.

(10) The power conferred by subsection (2) on a Minister of the Crown shall not be exercisable except by a Minister who is a member of the Cabinet or by the Attorney General or the [Advocate General for Scotland].

(11) No power conferred by any provision of Part V may be exercised in relation to personal data which by virtue of this section are exempt from that provision.

(12) Schedule 6 shall have effect in relation to appeals under subsection (4) or (6) and the proceedings of the Tribunal in respect of any such appeal.

[534]

NOTES

Sub-s (1): words in square brackets substituted by the Crime (International Co-operation) Act 2003, s 91(1), Sch 5, paras 68, 69.

Sub-s (10): words in square brackets substituted by the Transfer of Functions (Lord Advocate and Advocate General for Scotland) Order 1999, SI 1999/679, art 2, Schedule.

29 Crime and taxation

(1) Personal data processed for any of the following purposes—

(a) the prevention or detection of crime,

(b) the apprehension or prosecution of offenders, or

(c) the assessment or collection of any tax or duty or of any imposition of a similar nature,

are exempt from the first data protection principle (except to the extent to which it requires compliance with the conditions in Schedules 2 and 3) and section 7 in any case to the extent to which the application of those provisions to the data would be likely to prejudice any of the matters mentioned in this subsection.

(2) Personal data which—

(a) are processed for the purpose of discharging statutory functions, and

(b) consist of information obtained for such a purpose from a person who had it in his possession for any of the purposes mentioned in subsection (1),

are exempt from the subject information provisions to the same extent as personal data processed for any of the purposes mentioned in that subsection.

(3) Personal data are exempt from the non-disclosure provisions in any case in which—

(a) the disclosure is for any of the purposes mentioned in subsection (1), and

(b) the application of those provisions in relation to the disclosure would be likely to prejudice any of the matters mentioned in that subsection.

(4) Personal data in respect of which the data controller is a relevant authority and which—

(a) consist of a classification applied to the data subject as part of a system of risk assessment which is operated by that authority for either of the following purposes—

(i) the assessment or collection of any tax or duty or any imposition of a similar nature, or

(ii) the prevention or detection of crime, or apprehension or prosecution of offenders, where the offence concerned involves any unlawful claim for any payment out of, or any unlawful application of, public funds, and

(b) are processed for either of those purposes,

are exempt from section 7 to the extent to which the exemption is required in the interests of the operation of the system.

(5) In subsection (4)—

"public funds" includes funds provided by any Community institution;

"relevant authority" means—

(a) a government department,
(b) a local authority, or
(c) any other authority administering housing benefit or council tax benefit.

[535]

30 Health, education and social work

(1) The [Secretary of State] may by order exempt from the subject information provisions, or modify those provisions in relation to, personal data consisting of information as to the physical or mental health or condition of the data subject.

(2) The [Secretary of State] may by order exempt from the subject information provisions, or modify those provisions in relation to—

(a) personal data in respect of which the data controller is the proprietor of, or a teacher at, a school, and which consist of information relating to persons who are or have been pupils at the school, or
(b) personal data in respect of which the data controller is an education authority in Scotland, and which consist of information relating to persons who are receiving, or have received, further education provided by the authority.

(3) The [Secretary of State] may by order exempt from the subject information provisions, or modify those provisions in relation to, personal data of such other descriptions as may be specified in the order, being information—

(a) processed by government departments or local authorities or by voluntary organisations or other bodies designated by or under the order, and
(b) appearing to him to be processed in the course of, or for the purposes of, carrying out social work in relation to the data subject or other individuals;

but the [Secretary of State] shall not under this subsection confer any exemption or make any modification except so far as he considers that the application to the data of those provisions (or of those provisions without modification) would be likely to prejudice the carrying out of social work.

(4) An order under this section may make different provision in relation to data consisting of information of different descriptions.

(5) In this section—

"education authority" and "further education" have the same meaning as in the Education (Scotland) Act 1980 ("the 1980 Act"), and

"proprietor"—

(a) in relation to a school in England or Wales, has the same meaning as in the Education Act 1996,
(b) in relation to a school in Scotland, means—
    (i) …
    (ii) in the case of an independent school, the proprietor within the meaning of the 1980 Act,
    (iii) in the case of a grant-aided school, the managers within the meaning of the 1980 Act, and
    (iv) in the case of a public school, the education authority within the meaning of the 1980 Act, and
(c) in relation to a school in Northern Ireland, has the same meaning as in the Education and Libraries (Northern Ireland) Order 1986 and includes, in the case of a controlled school, the Board of Governors of the school.

[536]

NOTES

Sub-ss (1)–(3): words in square brackets substituted by the Secretary of State for Constitutional Affairs Order 2003, SI 2003/1887, art 9, Sch 2, para 9(1)(a).

Sub-s (5): in definition "proprietor" para (b)(i) repealed by the Standards in Scotland's Schools etc Act 2000, s 60(2), Sch 3.

Transfer of functions: the National Assembly for Wales (Transfer of Functions) Order 1999, SI 1999/672, art 2(a), Sch 1 provided that, subject to art 2(b)–(f), all functions of a Minister of the Crown under this section were, in so far as exercisable in relation to Wales, transferred to the National Assembly for Wales. As a consequence of the amendment of Sch 1 to the 1999 Order by the National Assembly for Wales (Transfer of Functions) Order 2000, SI 2000/253, art 4, Sch 3(g), the functions transferred to the Assembly by the 1999 Order ceased to be exercisable by the Assembly and instead (by virtue of art 5 of the 2000 Order) became exercisable by the Minister of the Crown by whom they were exercisable, in relation to Wales, immediately before 1 July 1999.

Orders: the Data Protection (Subject Access Modification) (Health) Order 2000, SI 2000/413 at **[915]**; the Data Protection (Subject Access Modification) (Education) Order 2000, SI 2000/414 at **[923]**; the Data Protection (Subject Access Modification) (Social Work) Order 2000, SI 2000/415 at **[930]**.

31 Regulatory activity

(1) Personal data processed for the purposes of discharging functions to which this subsection applies are exempt from the subject information provisions in any case to the extent to which the application of those provisions to the data would be likely to prejudice the proper discharge of those functions.

(2) Subsection (1) applies to any relevant function which is designed—
- (a) for protecting members of the public against—
  - (i) financial loss due to dishonesty, malpractice or other seriously improper conduct by, or the unfitness or incompetence of, persons concerned in the provision of banking, insurance, investment or other financial services or in the management of bodies corporate,
  - (ii) financial loss due to the conduct of discharged or undischarged bankrupts, or
  - (iii) dishonesty, malpractice or other seriously improper conduct by, or the unfitness or incompetence of, persons authorised to carry on any profession or other activity,
- (b) for protecting charities [or community interest companies] against misconduct or mismanagement (whether by trustees[, directors] or other persons) in their administration,
- (c) for protecting the property of charities [or community interest companies] from loss or misapplication,
- (d) for the recovery of the property of charities [or community interest companies],
- (e) for securing the health, safety and welfare of persons at work, or
- (f) for protecting persons other than persons at work against risk to health or safety arising out of or in connection with the actions of persons at work.

(3) In subsection (2) "relevant function" means—
- (a) any function conferred on any person by or under any enactment,
- (b) any function of the Crown, a Minister of the Crown or a government department, or
- (c) any other function which is of a public nature and is exercised in the public interest.

(4) Personal data processed for the purpose of discharging any function which—
- (a) is conferred by or under any enactment on—
  - (i) the Parliamentary Commissioner for Administration,
  - (ii) the Commission for Local Administration in England […] … ,
  - (iii) the Health Service Commissioner for England […] …,
  - [(iv) the Public Services Ombudsman for Wales,]
  - (v) the Assembly Ombudsman for Northern Ireland, …
  - (vi) the Northern Ireland Commissioner for Complaints, [or]
  - [(vii) the Scottish Public Services Ombudsman, and]
- (b) is designed for protecting members of the public against—
  - (i) maladministration by public bodies,
  - (ii) failures in services provided by public bodies, or
  - (iii) a failure of a public body to provide a service which it was a function of the body to provide,

are exempt from the subject information provisions in any case to the extent to which the application of those provisions to the data would be likely to prejudice the proper discharge of that function.

[(4A) Personal data processed for the purpose of discharging any function which is conferred by or under Part XVI of the Financial Services and Markets Act 2000 on the body established by the Financial Services Authority for the purposes of that Part are exempt from the subject information provisions in any case to the extent to which the application of those provisions to the data would be likely to prejudice the proper discharge of the function.]

(5) Personal data processed for the purpose of discharging any function which—
- (a) is conferred by or under any enactment on [the Office of Fair Trading], and
- (b) is designed—

(i) for protecting members of the public against conduct which may adversely affect their interests by persons carrying on a business,

(ii) for regulating agreements or conduct which have as their object or effect the prevention, restriction or distortion of competition in connection with any commercial activity, or

(iii) for regulating conduct on the part of one or more undertakings which amounts to the abuse of a dominant position in a market,

are exempt from the subject information provisions in any case to the extent to which the application of those provisions to the data would be likely to prejudice the proper discharge of that function.

[(6) Personal data processed for the purpose of the function of considering a complaint under [section 14 of the NHS Redress Act 2006,] section 113(1) or (2) or 114(1) or (3) of the Health and Social Care (Community Health and Standards) Act 2003, or section 24D, 26, *26ZA* or 26ZB of the Children Act 1989, are exempt from the subject information provisions in any case to the extent to which the application of those provisions to the data would be likely to prejudice the proper discharge of that function.] **[537]**

NOTES

Sub-s (2): words in square brackets inserted by the Companies (Audit, Investigations and Community Enterprise) Act 2004, s 59(3).

Sub-s (4): in para (a)(ii), word omitted from square brackets (as inserted by the Scottish Public Services Ombudsman Act 2002 (Consequential Provisions and Modifications) Order 2004, SI 2004/1823, art 19(a)(i)) repealed by the Public Services Ombudsman (Wales) Act 2005, s 39, Sch 6, para 60(a), Sch 7, and other words omitted repealed by SI 2004/1823, art 19(a)(ii) and the Public Services Ombudsman (Wales) Act 2005, s 39, Sch 6, para 60(a), Sch 7; in para (a)(iii), word omitted from square brackets (as inserted by SI 2004/1823, art 19(b)(i)) repealed by the Public Services Ombudsman (Wales) Act 2005, s 39, Sch 6, para 60(b), Sch 7, and other words omitted repealed by SI 2004/1823, art 19(b)(ii) and the Public Services Ombudsman (Wales) Act 2005, s 39, Sch 6, para 60(b), Sch 7; para (a)(iv) substituted by the Public Services Ombudsman (Wales) Act 2005, s 39(1), Sch 6, para 60(c); word omitted from para (a)(v) repealed, word in square brackets in para (a)(vi) substituted and para (a)(vii) inserted by SI 2004/1823, art 19(c)–(e).

Sub-s (4A): inserted by the Financial Services and Markets Act 2000, s 233.

Sub-s (5): words in square brackets substituted by the Enterprise Act 2002, s 278(1), Sch 25, para 37.

Sub-s (6): inserted by the Health and Social Care (Community Health and Standards) Act 2003, s 119; words in square brackets inserted by the NHS Redress Act 2006, s 14(10), as from a day to be appointed; figure in italics repealed by the Education and Inspections Act 2006, ss 157, 184, Sch 14, para 32, Sch 18, Pt 5, as from a day to be appointed.

32 Journalism, literature and art

(1) Personal data which are processed only for the special purposes are exempt from any provision to which this subsection relates if—

(a) the processing is undertaken with a view to the publication by any person of any journalistic, literary or artistic material,

(b) the data controller reasonably believes that, having regard in particular to the special importance of the public interest in freedom of expression, publication would be in the public interest, and

(c) the data controller reasonably believes that, in all the circumstances, compliance with that provision is incompatible with the special purposes.

(2) Subsection (1) relates to the provisions of—

(a) the data protection principles except the seventh data protection principle,

(b) section 7,

(c) section 10,

(d) section 12, and

(e) section 14(1) to (3).

(3) In considering for the purposes of subsection (1)(b) whether the belief of a data controller that publication would be in the public interest was or is a reasonable one, regard may be had to his compliance with any code of practice which—

(a) is relevant to the publication in question, and

(b) is designated by the [Secretary of State] by order for the purposes of this subsection.

(4) Where at any time ("the relevant time") in any proceedings against a data controller under section 7(9), 10(4), 12(8) or 14 or by virtue of section 13 the data controller claims, or it appears to the court, that any personal data to which the proceedings relate are being processed—

(a) only for the special purposes, and

(b) with a view to the publication by any person of any journalistic, literary or artistic material which, at the time twenty-four hours immediately before the relevant time, had not previously been published by the data controller,

the court shall stay the proceedings until either of the conditions in subsection (5) is met.

(5) Those conditions are—

(a) that a determination of the Commissioner under section 45 with respect to the data in question takes effect, or

(b) in a case where the proceedings were stayed on the making of a claim, that the claim is withdrawn.

(6) For the purposes of this Act "publish", in relation to journalistic, literary or artistic material, means make available to the public or any section of the public.

[538]

NOTES

Sub-s (3): words in square brackets in para (b) substituted by the Secretary of State for Constitutional Affairs Order 2003, SI 2003/1887, art 9, Sch 2, para 9(1)(a).

Modifications: by virtue of s 72 of, and Sch 13, para 2 to, this Act at **[580]**, **[602]**, for the period beginning with the commencement of s 72 of this Act (1 March 2000) and ending 23 October 2007, sub-s (2) above has effect with the following added after para (d)—

"(dd) section 12A,"

and sub-s (4) above has effect with the figure ", 12A(3)" inserted after "12(8)".

Orders: the Data Protection (Designated Codes of Practice) (No 2) Order 2000, SI 2000/1864 at **[980]**.

33 Research, history and statistics

(1) In this section—

"research purposes" includes statistical or historical purposes;

"the relevant conditions", in relation to any processing of personal data, means the conditions—

(a) that the data are not processed to support measures or decisions with respect to particular individuals, and

(b) that the data are not processed in such a way that substantial damage or substantial distress is, or is likely to be, caused to any data subject.

(2) For the purposes of the second data protection principle, the further processing of personal data only for research purposes in compliance with the relevant conditions is not to be regarded as incompatible with the purposes for which they were obtained.

(3) Personal data which are processed only for research purposes in compliance with the relevant conditions may, notwithstanding the fifth data protection principle, be kept indefinitely.

(4) Personal data which are processed only for research purposes are exempt from section 7 if—

(a) they are processed in compliance with the relevant conditions, and

(b) the results of the research or any resulting statistics are not made available in a form which identifies data subjects or any of them.

(5) For the purposes of subsections (2) to (4) personal data are not to be treated as processed otherwise than for research purposes merely because the data are disclosed—

(a) to any person, for research purposes only,

(b) to the data subject or a person acting on his behalf,

(c) at the request, or with the consent, of the data subject or a person acting on his behalf, or

(d) in circumstances in which the person making the disclosure has reasonable grounds for believing that the disclosure falls within paragraph (a), (b) or (c).

[539]

[33A Manual data held by authorities

(1) Personal data falling within paragraph (e) of the definition of "data" in section 1(1) are exempt from—

(a) the first, second, third, fifth, seventh and eighth data protection principles,

(b) the sixth data protection principle except so far as it relates to the rights conferred on data subjects by sections 7 and 14,

(c) sections 10 to 12,

(d) section 13, except so far as it relates to damage caused by a contravention of section 7 or of the fourth data protection principle and to any distress which is also suffered by reason of that contravention,

(e) Part III, and

(f) section 55.

(2) Personal data which fall within paragraph (e) of the definition of "data" in section 1(1) and relate to appointments or removals, pay, discipline, superannuation or other personnel matters, in relation to—

(a) service in any of the armed forces of the Crown,

(b) service in any office or employment under the Crown or under any public authority, or

(c) service in any office or employment, or under any contract for services, in respect of which power to take action, or to determine or approve the action taken, in such matters is vested in Her Majesty, any Minister of the Crown, the National Assembly for Wales, any Northern Ireland Minister (within the meaning of the Freedom of Information Act 2000) or any public authority,

are also exempt from the remaining data protection principles and the remaining provisions of Part II.]

[540]

NOTES

Commencement: 1 January 2005.
Inserted by the Freedom of Information Act 2000, s 70(1).

34 Information available to the public by or under enactment

Personal data are exempt from—

(a) the subject information provisions,

(b) the fourth data protection principle and section 14(1) to (3), and

(c) the non-disclosure provisions,

if the data consist of information which the data controller is obliged by or under any enactment [other than an enactment contained in the Freedom of Information Act 2000] to make available to the public, whether by publishing it, by making it available for inspection, or otherwise and whether gratuitously or on payment of a fee.

[541]

NOTES

Words in square brackets inserted by the Freedom of Information Act 2000, s 72.

Modifications: by virtue of s 72 of, and Sch 13, para 3 to, this Act at **[580]**, **[602]**, for the period beginning with the commencement of s 72 (1 March 2000) of this Act and ending 23 October 2007, this section has effect with the words "sections 12A and 14(1) to (3)" substituted for the words "section 14(1) to (3)".

35 Disclosures required by law or made in connection with legal proceedings etc

(1) Personal data are exempt from the non-disclosure provisions where the disclosure is required by or under any enactment, by any rule of law or by the order of a court.

(2) Personal data are exempt from the non-disclosure provisions where the disclosure is necessary—

(a) for the purpose of, or in connection with, any legal proceedings (including prospective legal proceedings), or

(b) for the purpose of obtaining legal advice,

or is otherwise necessary for the purposes of establishing, exercising or defending legal rights.

[542]

[35A Parliamentary Privilege

Personal data are exempt from—

(a) the first data protection principle, except to the extent to which it requires compliance with the conditions in Schedules 2 and 3,

(b) the second, third, fourth and fifth data protection principles,

(c) second 7, and

(d) sections 10 and 14(1) to (3),

if the exemption is required for the purpose of avoiding an infringement of the privileges of either House of Parliament.]

[543]

NOTES

Commencement: 1 January 2005.

Inserted by the Freedom of Information Act 2000, s 73, Sch 6, para 2.

36 Domestic purposes

Personal data processed by an individual only for the purposes of that individual's personal, family or household affairs (including recreational purposes) are exempt from the data protection principles and the provisions of Parts II and III.

[544]

37 Miscellaneous exemptions

Schedule 7 (which confers further miscellaneous exemptions) has effect.

[545]

38 Powers to make further exemptions by order

(1) The [Secretary of State] may by order exempt from the subject information provisions personal data consisting of information the disclosure of which is prohibited or restricted by or under any enactment if and to the extent that he considers it necessary for the safeguarding of the interests of the data subject or the rights and freedoms of any other individual that the prohibition or restriction ought to prevail over those provisions.

(2) The [Secretary of State] may by order exempt from the non-disclosure provisions any disclosures of personal data made in circumstances specified in the order, if he considers the exemption is necessary for the safeguarding of the interests of the data subject or the rights and freedoms of any other individual.

[546]

NOTES

Sub-ss (1), (2): words in square brackets substituted by the Secretary of State for Constitutional Affairs Order 2003, SI 2003/1887, art 9, Sch 2, para 9(1)(a).

Orders: the Data Protection (Miscellaneous Subject Access Exemptions) Order 2000, SI 2000/419 at **[944]**.

39 Transitional relief

Schedule 8 (which confers transitional exemptions) has effect.

[547]

PART V
ENFORCEMENT

40 Enforcement notices

(1) If the Commissioner is satisfied that a data controller has contravened or is contravening any of the data protection principles, the Commissioner may serve him with a notice (in this Act referred to as "an enforcement notice") requiring him, for complying with the principle or principles in question, to do either or both of the following—

(a) to take within such time as may be specified in the notice, or to refrain from taking after such time as may be so specified, such steps as are so specified, or

(b) to refrain from processing any personal data, or any personal data of a description specified in the notice, or to refrain from processing them for a purpose so specified or in a manner so specified, after such time as may be so specified.

(2) In deciding whether to serve an enforcement notice, the Commissioner shall consider whether the contravention has caused or is likely to cause any person damage or distress.

(3) An enforcement notice in respect of a contravention of the fourth data protection principle which requires the data controller to rectify, block, erase or destroy any inaccurate data may also require the data controller to rectify, block, erase or destroy any other data held by him and containing an expression of opinion which appears to the Commissioner to be based on the inaccurate data.

(4) An enforcement notice in respect of a contravention of the fourth data protection principle, in the case of data which accurately record information received or obtained by the data controller from the data subject or a third party, may require the data controller either—

(a) to rectify, block, erase or destroy any inaccurate data and any other data held by him and containing an expression of opinion as mentioned in subsection (3), or

(b) to take such steps as are specified in the notice for securing compliance with the requirements specified in paragraph 7 of Part II of Schedule 1 and, if the Commissioner thinks fit, for supplementing the data with such statement of the true facts relating to the matters dealt with by the data as the Commissioner may approve.

(5) Where—

(a) an enforcement notice requires the data controller to rectify, block, erase or destroy any personal data, or

(b) the Commissioner is satisfied that personal data which have been rectified, blocked, erased or destroyed had been processed in contravention of any of the data protection principles,

an enforcement notice may, if reasonably practicable, require the data controller to notify third parties to whom the data have been disclosed of the rectification, blocking, erasure or destruction; and in determining whether it is reasonably practicable to require such notification regard shall be had, in particular, to the number of persons who would have to be notified.

(6) An enforcement notice must contain—

(a) a statement of the data protection principle or principles which the Commissioner is satisfied have been or are being contravened and his reasons for reaching that conclusion, and

(b) particulars of the rights of appeal conferred by section 48.

(7) Subject to subsection (8), an enforcement notice must not require any of the provisions of the notice to be complied with before the end of the period within which an appeal can be brought against the notice and, if such an appeal is brought, the notice need not be complied with pending the determination or withdrawal of the appeal.

(8) If by reason of special circumstances the Commissioner considers that an enforcement notice should be complied with as a matter of urgency he may include in the notice a statement to that effect and a statement of his reasons for reaching that conclusion; and in that event subsection (7) shall not apply but the notice must not require the provisions of the notice to be complied with before the end of the period of seven days beginning with the day on which the notice is served.

(9) Notification regulations (as defined by section 16(2)) may make provision as to the effect of the service of an enforcement notice on any entry in the register maintained under section 19 which relates to the person on whom the notice is served.

(10) This section has effect subject to section 46(1).

[548]

41 Cancellation of an enforcement notice

(1) If the Commissioner considers that all or any of the provisions of an enforcement notice need not be complied with in order to ensure compliance with the data protection principle or principles to which it relates, he may cancel or vary the notice by written notice to the person on whom it was served.

(2) A person on whom an enforcement notice has been served may, at any time after the expiry of the period during which an appeal can be brought against that notice, apply in

writing to the Commissioner for the cancellation or variation of that notice on the ground that, by reason of a change of circumstances, all or any of the provisions of that notice need not be complied with in order to ensure compliance with the data protection principle or principles to which that notice relates.

[549]

42 Request for assessment

(1) A request may be made to the Commissioner by or on behalf of any person who is, or believes himself to be, directly affected by any processing of personal data for an assessment as to whether it is likely or unlikely that the processing has been or is being carried out in compliance with the provisions of this Act.

(2) On receiving a request under this section, the Commissioner shall make an assessment in such manner as appears to him to be appropriate, unless he has not been supplied with such information as he may reasonably require in order to—

(a) satisfy himself as to the identity of the person making the request, and

(b) enable him to identify the processing in question.

(3) The matters to which the Commissioner may have regard in determining in what manner it is appropriate to make an assessment include—

(a) the extent to which the request appears to him to raise a matter of substance,

(b) any undue delay in making the request, and

(c) whether or not the person making the request is entitled to make an application under section 7 in respect of the personal data in question.

(4) Where the Commissioner has received a request under this section he shall notify the person who made the request—

(a) whether he has made an assessment as a result of the request, and

(b) to the extent that he considers appropriate, having regard in particular to any exemption from section 7 applying in relation to the personal data concerned, of any view formed or action taken as a result of the request.

[550]

43 Information notices

(1) If the Commissioner—

(a) has received a request under section 42 in respect of any processing of personal data, or

(b) reasonably requires any information for the purpose of determining whether the data controller has complied or is complying with the data protection principles,

he may serve the data controller with a notice (in this Act referred to as "an information notice") requiring the data controller, within such time as is specified in the notice, to furnish the Commissioner, in such form as may be so specified, with such information relating to the request or to compliance with the principles as is so specified.

(2) An information notice must contain—

(a) in a case falling within subsection (1)(a), a statement that the Commissioner has received a request under section 42 in relation to the specified processing, or

(b) in a case falling within subsection (1)(b), a statement that the Commissioner regards the specified information as relevant for the purpose of determining whether the data controller has complied, or is complying, with the data protection principles and his reasons for regarding it as relevant for that purpose.

(3) An information notice must also contain particulars of the rights of appeal conferred by section 48.

(4) Subject to subsection (5), the time specified in an information notice shall not expire before the end of the period within which an appeal can be brought against the notice and, if such an appeal is brought, the information need not be furnished pending the determination or withdrawal of the appeal.

(5) If by reason of special circumstances the Commissioner considers that the information is required as a matter of urgency, he may include in the notice a statement to that effect and a statement of his reasons for reaching that conclusion; and in that event subsection (4) shall not apply, but the notice shall not require the information to be furnished before the end of the period of seven days beginning with the day on which the notice is served.

(6) A person shall not be required by virtue of this section to furnish the Commissioner with any information in respect of—

(a) any communication between a professional legal adviser and his client in connection with the giving of legal advice to the client with respect to his obligations, liabilities or rights under this Act, or

(b) any communication between a professional legal adviser and his client, or between such an adviser or his client and any other person, made in connection with or in contemplation of proceedings under or arising out of this Act (including proceedings before the Tribunal) and for the purposes of such proceedings.

(7) In subsection (6) references to the client of a professional legal adviser include references to any person representing such a client.

(8) A person shall not be required by virtue of this section to furnish the Commissioner with any information if the furnishing of that information would, by revealing evidence of the commission of any offence other than an offence under this Act, expose him to proceedings for that offence.

(9) The Commissioner may cancel an information notice by written notice to the person on whom it was served.

(10) This section has effect subject to section 46(3). **[551]**

44 Special information notices

If the Commissioner—

(a) has received a request under section 42 in respect of any processing of personal data, or

(b) has reasonable grounds for suspecting that, in a case in which proceedings have been stayed under section 32, the personal data to which the proceedings relate—

(i) are not being processed only for the special purposes, or

(ii) are not being processed with a view to the publication by any person of any journalistic, literary or artistic material which has not previously been published by the data controller,

he may serve the data controller with a notice (in this Act referred to as a "special information notice") requiring the data controller, within such time as is specified in the notice, to furnish the Commissioner, in such form as may be so specified, with such information as is so specified for the purpose specified in subsection (2).

(2) That purpose is the purpose of ascertaining—

(a) whether the personal data are being processed only for the special purposes, or

(b) whether they are being processed with a view to the publication by any person of any journalistic, literary or artistic material which has not previously been published by the data controller.

(3) A special information notice must contain—

(a) in a case falling within paragraph (a) of subsection (1), a statement that the Commissioner has received a request under section 42 in relation to the specified processing, or

(b) in a case falling within paragraph (b) of that subsection, a statement of the Commissioner's grounds for suspecting that the personal data are not being processed as mentioned in that paragraph.

(4) A special information notice must also contain particulars of the rights of appeal conferred by section 48.

(5) Subject to subsection (6), the time specified in a special information notice shall not expire before the end of the period within which an appeal can be brought against the notice and, if such an appeal is brought, the information need not be furnished pending the determination or withdrawal of the appeal.

(6) If by reason of special circumstances the Commissioner considers that the information is required as a matter of urgency, he may include in the notice a statement to that effect and a statement of his reasons for reaching that conclusion; and in that event subsection (5) shall not apply, but the notice shall not require the information to be furnished before the end of the period of seven days beginning with the day on which the notice is served.

(7) A person shall not be required by virtue of this section to furnish the Commissioner with any information in respect of—

(a) any communication between a professional legal adviser and his client in connection with the giving of legal advice to the client with respect to his obligations, liabilities or rights under this Act, or

(b) any communication between a professional legal adviser and his client, or between such an adviser or his client and any other person, made in connection with or in contemplation of proceedings under or arising out of this Act (including proceedings before the Tribunal) and for the purposes of such proceedings.

(8) In subsection (7) references to the client of a professional legal adviser include references to any person representing such a client.

(9) A person shall not be required by virtue of this section to furnish the Commissioner with any information if the furnishing of that information would, by revealing evidence of the commission of any offence other than an offence under this Act, expose him to proceedings for that offence.

(10) The Commissioner may cancel a special information notice by written notice to the person on whom it was served.

[552]

45 Determination by Commissioner as to the special purposes

(1) Where at any time it appears to the Commissioner (whether as a result of the service of a special information notice or otherwise) that any personal data—

(a) are not being processed only for the special purposes, or

(b) are not being processed with a view to the publication by any person of any journalistic, literary or artistic material which has not previously been published by the data controller,

he may make a determination in writing to that effect.

(2) Notice of the determination shall be given to the data controller; and the notice must contain particulars of the right of appeal conferred by section 48.

(3) A determination under subsection (1) shall not take effect until the end of the period within which an appeal can be brought and, where an appeal is brought, shall not take effect pending the determination or withdrawal of the appeal.

[553]

46 Restriction on enforcement in case of processing for the special purposes

(1) The Commissioner may not at any time serve an enforcement notice on a data controller with respect to the processing of personal data for the special purposes unless—

(a) a determination under section 45(1) with respect to those data has taken effect, and

(b) the court has granted leave for the notice to be served.

(2) The court shall not grant leave for the purposes of subsection (1)(b) unless it is satisfied—

(a) that the Commissioner has reason to suspect a contravention of the data protection principles which is of substantial public importance, and

(b) except where the case is one of urgency, that the data controller has been given notice, in accordance with rules of court, of the application for leave.

(3) The Commissioner may not serve an information notice on a data controller with respect to the processing of personal data for the special purposes unless a determination under section 45(1) with respect to those data has taken effect.

[554]

47 Failure to comply with notice

(1) A person who fails to comply with an enforcement notice, an information notice or a special information notice is guilty of an offence.

(2) A person who, in purported compliance with an information notice or a special information notice—

(a) makes a statement which he knows to be false in a material respect, or

(b) recklessly makes a statement which is false in a material respect, is guilty of an offence.

(3) It is a defence for a person charged with an offence under subsection (1) to prove that he exercised all due diligence to comply with the notice in question.

[555]

48 Rights of appeal

(1) A person on whom an enforcement notice, an information notice or a special information notice has been served may appeal to the Tribunal against the notice.

(2) A person on whom an enforcement notice has been served may appeal to the Tribunal against the refusal of an application under section 41(2) for cancellation or variation of the notice.

(3) Where an enforcement notice, an information notice or a special information notice contains a statement by the Commissioner in accordance with section 40(8), 43(5) or 44(6) then, whether or not the person appeals against the notice, he may appeal against—

(a) the Commissioner's decision to include the statement in the notice, or

(b) the effect of the inclusion of the statement as respects any part of the notice.

(4) A data controller in respect of whom a determination has been made under section 45 may appeal to the Tribunal against the determination.

(5) Schedule 6 has effect in relation to appeals under this section and the proceedings of the Tribunal in respect of any such appeal.

[556]

49 Determination of appeals

(1) If on an appeal under section 48(1) the Tribunal considers—

(a) that the notice against which the appeal is brought is not in accordance with the law, or

(b) to the extent that the notice involved an exercise of discretion by the Commissioner, that he ought to have exercised his discretion differently,

the Tribunal shall allow the appeal or substitute such other notice or decision as could have been served or made by the Commissioner; and in any other case the Tribunal shall dismiss the appeal.

(2) On such an appeal, the Tribunal may review any determination of fact on which the notice in question was based.

(3) If on an appeal under section 48(2) the Tribunal considers that the enforcement notice ought to be cancelled or varied by reason of a change in circumstances, the Tribunal shall cancel or vary the notice.

(4) On an appeal under subsection (3) of section 48 the Tribunal may direct—

(a) that the notice in question shall have effect as if it did not contain any such statement as is mentioned in that subsection, or

(b) that the inclusion of the statement shall not have effect in relation to any part of the notice,

and may make such modifications in the notice as may be required for giving effect to the direction.

(5) On an appeal under section 48(4), the Tribunal may cancel the determination of the Commissioner.

(6) Any party to an appeal to the Tribunal under section 48 may appeal from the decision of the Tribunal on a point of law to the appropriate court; and that court shall be—

(a) the High Court of Justice in England if the address of the person who was the appellant before the Tribunal is in England or Wales,

(b) the Court of Session if that address is in Scotland, and

(c) the High Court of Justice in Northern Ireland if that address is in Northern Ireland.

(7) For the purposes of subsection (6)—

(a) the address of a registered company is that of its registered office, and

(b) the address of a person (other than a registered company) carrying on a business is that of his principal place of business in the United Kingdom.

[557]

50 Powers of entry and inspection

Schedule 9 (powers of entry and inspection) has effect.

[558]

PART VI
MISCELLANEOUS AND GENERAL

Functions of Commissioner

51 General duties of Commissioner

(1) It shall be the duty of the Commissioner to promote the following of good practice by data controllers and, in particular, so to perform his functions under this Act as to promote the observance of the requirements of this Act by data controllers.

(2) The Commissioner shall arrange for the dissemination in such form and manner as he considers appropriate of such information as it may appear to him expedient to give to the public about the operation of this Act, about good practice, and about other matters within the scope of his functions under this Act, and may give advice to any person as to any of those matters.

(3) Where—

(a) the [Secretary of State] so directs by order, or

(b) the Commissioner considers it appropriate to do so,

the Commissioner shall, after such consultation with trade associations, data subjects or persons representing data subjects as appears to him to be appropriate, prepare and disseminate to such persons as he considers appropriate codes of practice for guidance as to good practice.

(4) The Commissioner shall also—

(a) where he considers it appropriate to do so, encourage trade associations to prepare, and to disseminate to their members, such codes of practice, and

(b) where any trade association submits a code of practice to him for his consideration, consider the code and, after such consultation with data subjects or persons representing data subjects as appears to him to be appropriate, notify the trade association whether in his opinion the code promotes the following of good practice.

(5) An order under subsection (3) shall describe the personal data or processing to which the code of practice is to relate, and may also describe the persons or classes of persons to whom it is to relate.

(6) The Commissioner shall arrange for the dissemination in such form and manner as he considers appropriate of—

(a) any Community finding as defined by paragraph 15(2) of Part II of Schedule 1,

(b) any decision of the European Commission, under the procedure provided for in Article 31(2) of the Data Protection Directive, which is made for the purposes of Article 26(3) or (4) of the Directive, and

(c) such other information as it may appear to him to be expedient to give to data controllers in relation to any personal data about the protection of the rights and freedoms of data subjects in relation to the processing of personal data in countries and territories outside the European Economic Area.

(7) The Commissioner may, with the consent of the data controller, assess any processing of personal data for the following of good practice and shall inform the data controller of the results of the assessment.

(8) The Commissioner may charge such sums as he may with the consent of the [Secretary of State] determine for any services provided by the Commissioner by virtue of this Part.

(9) In this section—

"good practice" means such practice in the processing of personal data as appears to the Commissioner to be desirable having regard to the interests of data subjects and others, and includes (but is not limited to) compliance with the requirements of this Act;

"trade association" includes any body representing data controllers.

[559]

NOTES

Sub-ss (3), (8): words in square brackets substituted by the Secretary of State for Constitutional Affairs Order 2003, SI 2003/1887, art 9, Sch 2, para 9(1)(a).

52 Reports and codes of practice to be laid before Parliament

(1) The Commissioner shall lay annually before each House of Parliament a general report on the exercise of his functions under this Act.

(2) The Commissioner may from time to time lay before each House of Parliament such other reports with respect to those functions as he thinks fit.

(3) The Commissioner shall lay before each House of Parliament any code of practice prepared under section 51(3) for complying with a direction of the [Secretary of State], unless the code is included in any report laid under subsection (1) or (2).

[560]

NOTES

Sub-s (3): words in square brackets substituted by the Secretary of State for Constitutional Affairs Order 2003, SI 2003/1887, art 9, Sch 2, para 9(1)(a).

53 Assistance by Commissioner in cases involving processing for the special purposes

(1) An individual who is an actual or prospective party to any proceedings under section 7(9), 10(4), 12(8) or 14 or by virtue of section 13 which relate to personal data processed for the special purposes may apply to the Commissioner for assistance in relation to those proceedings.

(2) The Commissioner shall, as soon as reasonably practicable after receiving an application under subsection (1), consider it and decide whether and to what extent to grant it, but he shall not grant the application unless, in his opinion, the case involves a matter of substantial public importance.

(3) If the Commissioner decides to provide assistance, he shall, as soon as reasonably practicable after making the decision, notify the applicant, stating the extent of the assistance to be provided.

(4) If the Commissioner decides not to provide assistance, he shall, as soon as reasonably practicable after making the decision, notify the applicant of his decision and, if he thinks fit, the reasons for it.

(5) In this section—

(a) references to "proceedings" include references to prospective proceedings, and

(b) "applicant", in relation to assistance under this section, means an individual who applies for assistance.

(6) Schedule 10 has effect for supplementing this section.

[561]

NOTES

Modification: by virtue of s 72 of, and Sch 13, para 4 to, this Act at **[580]**, **[602]**, for the period beginning with the commencement of s 72 of this Act (1 March 2000) and ending 23 October 2007, sub-s (1) above has effect with the figure ", 12A(3)" inserted after the figure "12(8)".

54 International co-operation

(1) The Commissioner—

(a) shall continue to be the designated authority in the United Kingdom for the purposes of Article 13 of the Convention, and

(b) shall be the supervisory authority in the United Kingdom for the purposes of the Data Protection Directive.

(2) The [Secretary of State] may by order make provision as to the functions to be discharged by the Commissioner as the designated authority in the United Kingdom for the purposes of Article 13 of the Convention.

(3) The [Secretary of State] may by order make provision as to co-operation by the Commissioner with the European Commission and with supervisory authorities in other EEA States in connection with the performance of their respective duties and, in particular, as to—

(a) the exchange of information with supervisory authorities in other EEA States or with the European Commission, and

(b) the exercise within the United Kingdom at the request of a supervisory authority in another EEA State, in cases excluded by section 5 from the application of the other provisions of this Act, of functions of the Commissioner specified in the order.

(4) The Commissioner shall also carry out any data protection functions which the [Secretary of State] may by order direct him to carry out for the purpose of enabling Her Majesty's Government in the United Kingdom to give effect to any international obligations of the United Kingdom.

(5) The Commissioner shall, if so directed by the [Secretary of State], provide any authority exercising data protection functions under the law of a colony specified in the direction with such assistance in connection with the discharge of those functions as the [Secretary of State] may direct or approve, on such terms (including terms as to payment) as the [Secretary of State] may direct or approve.

(6) Where the European Commission makes a decision for the purposes of Article 26(3) or (4) of the Data Protection Directive under the procedure provided for in Article 31(2) of the Directive, the Commissioner shall comply with that decision in exercising his functions under paragraph 9 of Schedule 4 or, as the case may be, paragraph 8 of that Schedule.

(7) The Commissioner shall inform the European Commission and the supervisory authorities in other EEA States—

(a) of any approvals granted for the purposes of paragraph 8 of Schedule 4, and

(b) of any authorisations granted for the purposes of paragraph 9 of that Schedule.

(8) In this section—

"the Convention" means the Convention for the Protection of Individuals with regard to Automatic Processing of Personal Data which was opened for signature on 28th January 1981;

"data protection functions" means functions relating to the protection of individuals with respect to the processing of personal information.

[562]

NOTES

Sub-ss (2)–(5): words in square brackets substituted by the Secretary of State for Constitutional Affairs Order 2003, SI 2003/1887, art 9, Sch 2, para 9(1)(a).

Orders: the Data Protection (Functions of Designated Authority) Order 2000, SI 2000/186 at **[820]**; the Data Protection (International Co-operation) Order 2000, SI 2000/190 at **[871]**.

[54A Inspection of overseas information systems

(1) The Commissioner may inspect any personal data recorded in—

(a) the Schengen information system,

(b) the Europol information system,

(c) the Customs information system.

(2) The power conferred by subsection (1) is exercisable only for the purpose of assessing whether or not any processing of the data has been or is being carried out in compliance with this Act.

(3) The power includes power to inspect, operate and test equipment which is used for the processing of personal data.

(4) Before exercising the power, the Commissioner must give notice in writing of his intention to do so to the data controller.

(5) But subsection (4) does not apply if the Commissioner considers that the case is one of urgency.

(6) Any person who—

(a) intentionally obstructs a person exercising the power conferred by subsection (1), or

(b) fails without reasonable excuse to give any person exercising the power any assistance he may reasonably require,

is guilty of an offence.

(7) In this section—

"the Customs information system" means the information system established under Chapter II of the Convention on the Use of Information Technology for Customs Purposes,

"the Europol information system" means the information system established under Title II of the Convention on the Establishment of a European Police Office,

"the Schengen information system" means the information system established under Title IV of the Convention implementing the Schengen Agreement of 14th June 1985, or any system established in its place in pursuance of any Community obligation.]

[562A]

NOTES

Commencement: 26 April 2004.

Inserted by the Crime (International Co-operation) Act 2003, s 81.

Unlawful obtaining etc of personal data

55 Unlawful obtaining etc of personal data

(1) A person must not knowingly or recklessly, without the consent of the data controller—

(a) obtain or disclose personal data or the information contained in personal data, or

(b) procure the disclosure to another person of the information contained in personal data.

(2) Subsection (1) does not apply to a person who shows—

(a) that the obtaining, disclosing or procuring—

(i) was necessary for the purpose of preventing or detecting crime, or

(ii) was required or authorised by or under any enactment, by any rule of law or by the order of a court,

(b) that he acted in the reasonable belief that he had in law the right to obtain or disclose the data or information or, as the case may be, to procure the disclosure of the information to the other person,

(c) that he acted in the reasonable belief that he would have had the consent of the data controller if the data controller had known of the obtaining, disclosing or procuring and the circumstances of it, or

(d) that in the particular circumstances the obtaining, disclosing or procuring was justified as being in the public interest.

(3) A person who contravenes subsection (1) is guilty of an offence.

(4) A person who sells personal data is guilty of an offence if he has obtained the data in contravention of subsection (1).

(5) A person who offers to sell personal data is guilty of an offence if—

(a) he has obtained the data in contravention of subsection (1), or

(b) he subsequently obtains the data in contravention of that subsection.

(6) For the purposes of subsection (5), an advertisement indicating that personal data are or may be for sale is an offer to sell the data.

(7) Section 1(2) does not apply for the purposes of this section; and for the purposes of subsections (4) to (6), "personal data" includes information extracted from personal data.

(8) References in this section to personal data do not include references to personal data which by virtue of section 28 [or 33A] are exempt from this section.

[563]

NOTES

Sub-s (8): words in square brackets inserted by the Freedom of Information Act 2000, s 70(2).

Records obtained under data subject's right of access

56 Prohibition of requirement as to production of certain records

(1) A person must not, in connection with—

(a) the recruitment of another person as an employee,

(b) the continued employment of another person, or

(c) any contract for the provision of services to him by another person,

require that other person or a third party to supply him with a relevant record or to produce a relevant record to him.

(2) A person concerned with the provision (for payment or not) of goods, facilities or services to the public or a section of the public must not, as a condition of providing or offering to provide any goods, facilities or services to another person, require that other person or a third party to supply him with a relevant record or to produce a relevant record to him.

(3) Subsections (1) and (2) do not apply to a person who shows—

(a) that the imposition of the requirement was required or authorised by or under any enactment, by any rule of law or by the order of a court, or

(b) that in the particular circumstances the imposition of the requirement was justified as being in the public interest.

(4) Having regard to the provisions of Part V of the Police Act 1997 (certificates of criminal records etc), the imposition of the requirement referred to in subsection (1) or (2) is not to be regarded as being justified as being in the public interest on the ground that it would assist in the prevention or detection of crime.

(5) A person who contravenes subsection (1) or (2) is guilty of an offence.

(6) In this section "a relevant record" means any record which—

(a) has been or is to be obtained by a data subject from any data controller specified in the first column of the Table below in the exercise of the right conferred by section 7, and

(b) contains information relating to any matter specified in relation to that data controller in the second column,

and includes a copy of such a record or a part of such a record.

TABLE

Data controller	*Subject-matter*
1. Any of the following persons—	(a) Convictions.
(a) a chief officer of police of a police force in England and Wales.	(b) Cautions.
(b) a chief constable of a police force in Scotland.	
(c) the [Chief Constable of the Police Service of Northern Ireland].	
[(d) the Director General of the Serious Organised Crime Agency.]	
2. The Secretary of State.	(a) Convictions.
	(b) Cautions.

PART II DATA PROTECTION

Data controller	*Subject-matter*
	(c) His functions under [section 92 of the Powers of Criminal Courts (Sentencing) Act 2000], section 205(2) or 208 of the Criminal Procedure (Scotland) Act 1995 or section 73 of the Children and Young Persons Act (Northern Ireland) 1968 in relation to any person sentenced to detention.
	(d) His functions under the Prison Act 1952, the Prisons (Scotland) Act 1989 or the Prison Act (Northern Ireland) 1953 in relation to any person imprisoned or detained.
	(e) His functions under the Social Security Contributions and Benefits Act 1992, the Social Security Administration Act 1992 or the Jobseekers Act 1995.
	(f) His functions under Part V of the Police Act 1997.
	[(g) His functions under the Safeguarding Vulnerable Groups Act 2006.]
3. The Department of Health and Social Services for Northern Ireland.	Its functions under the Social Security Contributions and Benefits (Northern Ireland) Act 1992, the Social Security Administration (Northern Ireland) Act 1992 or the Jobseekers (Northern Ireland) Order 1995.
[4. The Independent Barring Board	Its functions under the Safeguarding Vulnerable Groups Act 2006.]

[(6A) A record is not a relevant record to the extent that it relates, or is to relate, only to personal data falling within paragraph (e) of the definition of "data" in section 1(1).]

(7) In the Table in subsection (6)—

"caution" means a caution given to any person in England and Wales or Northern Ireland in respect of an offence which, at the time when the caution is given, is admitted;

"conviction" has the same meaning as in the Rehabilitation of Offenders Act 1974 or the Rehabilitation of Offenders (Northern Ireland) Order 1978.

(8) The [Secretary of State] may by order amend—

(a) the Table in subsection (6), and

(b) subsection (7).

(9) For the purposes of this section a record which states that a data controller is not processing any personal data relating to a particular matter shall be taken to be a record containing information relating to that matter.

(10) In this section "employee" means an individual who—

(a) works under a contract of employment, as defined by section 230(2) of the Employment Rights Act 1996, or

(b) holds any office,

whether or not he is entitled to remuneration; and "employment" shall be construed accordingly.

[564]

NOTES

Sub-s (6): words in square brackets in entry 1(c) of the Table substituted by the Police (Northern Ireland) Act 2000, s 78(2)(a); entry 1(d) of the Table substituted for original entry 1(d), (e) by the Serious Organised Crime and Police Act 2005, s 59, Sch 4, para 112; words in square brackets in entry 2(c) of the Table substituted by the Powers of Criminal Courts (Sentencing) Act 2000, s 165(1), Sch 9, para 191; entries 2(g), 4 of the Table inserted by the Safeguarding Vulnerable Groups Act 2006, s 63(1), Sch 9, Pt 2, para 15(1), (2), as from a day to be appointed.

Sub-s (6A): inserted by the Freedom of Information Act 2000, s 68(4).

Sub-s (8): words in square brackets substituted by the Secretary of State for Constitutional Affairs Order 2003, SI 2003/1887, art 9, Sch 2, para 9(1)(a).

57 Avoidance of certain contractual terms relating to health records

(1) Any term or condition of a contract is void in so far as it purports to require an individual—

(a) to supply any other person with a record to which this section applies, or with a copy of such a record or a part of such a record, or

(b) to produce to any other person such a record, copy or part.

(2) This section applies to any record which—

(a) has been or is to be obtained by a data subject in the exercise of the right conferred by section 7, and

(b) consists of the information contained in any health record as defined by section 68(2).

[565]

Information provided to Commissioner or Tribunal

58 Disclosure of information

No enactment or rule of law prohibiting or restricting the disclosure of information shall preclude a person from furnishing the Commissioner or the Tribunal with any information necessary for the discharge of their functions under this Act [or the Freedom of Information Act].

[566]

NOTES

Words in square brackets added by the Freedom of Information Act 2000, s 18(4), Sch 2, Pt II, para 18.

59 Confidentiality of information

(1) No person who is or has been the Commissioner, a member of the Commissioner's staff or an agent of the Commissioner shall disclose any information which—

(a) has been obtained by, or furnished to, the Commissioner under or for the purposes of [the information Acts],

(b) relates to an identified or identifiable individual or business, and

(c) is not at the time of the disclosure, and has not previously been, available to the public from other sources,

unless the disclosure is made with lawful authority.

(2) For the purposes of subsection (1) a disclosure of information is made with lawful authority only if, and to the extent that—

(a) the disclosure is made with the consent of the individual or of the person for the time being carrying on the business,

(b) the information was provided for the purpose of its being made available to the public (in whatever manner) under any provision of [the information Acts],

(c) the disclosure is made for the purposes of, and is necessary for, the discharge of—

(i) any functions under [the information Acts], or

(ii) any Community obligation,

(d) the disclosure is made for the purposes of any proceedings, whether criminal or civil and whether arising under, or by virtue of, [the information Acts] or otherwise, or

(e) having regard to the rights and freedoms or legitimate interests of any person, the disclosure is necessary in the public interest.

(3) Any person who knowingly or recklessly discloses information in contravention of subsection (1) is guilty of an offence.

[(4) In this section "the information Acts" means this Act and the Freedom of Information Act 2000.]

[567]

NOTES

Sub-ss (1), (2): words in square brackets substituted by the Freedom of Information Act 2000, s 18(4), Sch 2, Pt II, para 19(1), (2).

Sub-s (4): added by the Freedom of Information Act 2000, s 18(4), Sch 2, Pt II, para 19(1), (3).

General provisions relating to offences

60 Prosecutions and penalties

(1) No proceedings for an offence under this Act shall be instituted—

(a) in England or Wales, except by the Commissioner or by or with the consent of the Director of Public Prosecutions;

(b) in Northern Ireland, except by the Commissioner or by or with the consent of the Director of Public Prosecutions for Northern Ireland.

(2) A person guilty of an offence under any provision of this Act other than [section 54A and] paragraph 12 of Schedule 9 is liable—

(a) on summary conviction, to a fine not exceeding the statutory maximum, or

(b) on conviction on indictment, to a fine.

(3) A person guilty of an offence under [section 54A and] paragraph 12 of Schedule 9 is liable on summary conviction to a fine not exceeding level 5 on the standard scale.

(4) Subject to subsection (5), the court by or before which a person is convicted of—

(a) an offence under section 21(1), 22(6), 55 or 56,

(b) an offence under section 21(2) relating to processing which is assessable processing for the purposes of section 22, or

(c) an offence under section 47(1) relating to an enforcement notice,

may order any document or other material used in connection with the processing of personal data and appearing to the court to be connected with the commission of the offence to be forfeited, destroyed or erased.

(5) The court shall not make an order under subsection (4) in relation to any material where a person (other than the offender) claiming to be the owner of or otherwise interested in the material applies to be heard by the court, unless an opportunity is given to him to show cause why the order should not be made.

[568]

NOTES

Sub-ss (2), (3): words in square brackets inserted by the Crime (International Co-operation) Act 2003, s 91(1), Sch 5, paras 68, 70.

61 Liability of directors etc

(1) Where an offence under this Act has been committed by a body corporate and is proved to have been committed with the consent or connivance of or to be attributable to any neglect on the part of any director, manager, secretary or similar officer of the body corporate or any person who was purporting to act in any such capacity, he as well as the body corporate shall be guilty of that offence and be liable to be proceeded against and punished accordingly.

(2) Where the affairs of a body corporate are managed by its members subsection (1) shall apply in relation to the acts and defaults of a member in connection with his functions of management as if he were a director of the body corporate.

(3) Where an offence under this Act has been committed by a Scottish partnership and the contravention in question is proved to have occurred with the consent or connivance of, or to be attributable to any neglect on the part of, a partner, he as well as the partnership shall be guilty of that offence and shall be liable to be proceeded against and punished accordingly.

[569]

62 (*Amends the Consumer Credit Act 1974, ss 158–160.*)

General

63 Application to Crown

(1) This Act binds the Crown.

(2) For the purposes of this Act each government department shall be treated as a person separate from any other government department.

(3) Where the purposes for which and the manner in which any personal data are, or are to be, processed are determined by any person acting on behalf of the Royal Household, the Duchy of Lancaster or the Duchy of Cornwall, the data controller in respect of those data for the purposes of this Act shall be—

(a) in relation to the Royal Household, the Keeper of the Privy Purse,

(b) in relation to the Duchy of Lancaster, such person as the Chancellor of the Duchy appoints, and

(c) in relation to the Duchy of Cornwall, such person as the Duke of Cornwall, or the possessor for the time being of the Duchy of Cornwall, appoints.

(4) Different persons may be appointed under subsection (3)(b) or (c) for different purposes.

(5) Neither a government department nor a person who is a data controller by virtue of subsection (3) shall be liable to prosecution under this Act, but [sections 54A and] 55 and paragraph 12 of Schedule 9 shall apply to a person in the service of the Crown as they apply to any other person.

[570]

NOTES

Sub-s (5): words in square brackets substituted by the Crime (International Co-operation) Act 2003, s 91(1), Sch 5, paras 68, 71.

[63A Application to Parliament

(1) Subject to the following provisions of this section and to section 35A, this Act applies to the processing of personal data by or on behalf of either House of Parliament as it applies to the processing of personal data by other persons.

(2) Where the purposes for which and the manner in which any personal data are, or are to be, processed are determined by or on behalf of the House of Commons, the data controller in respect of those data for the purposes of this Act shall be the Corporate Officer of that House.

(3) Where the purposes for which and the manner in which any personal data are, or are to be, processed are determined by or on behalf of the House of Lords, the data controller in respect of those data for the purposes of this Act shall be the Corporate Officer of that House.

(4) Nothing in subsection (2) or (3) is to be taken to render the Corporate Officer of the House of Commons or the Corporate Officer of the House of Lords liable to prosecution under this Act, but section 55 and paragraph 12 of Schedule 9 shall apply to a person acting on behalf of either House as they apply to any other person.]

[571]

NOTES

Commencement: 1 January 2005.
Inserted by the Freedom of Information Act 2000, s 73, Sch 6, para 3.

64 Transmission of notices etc by electronic or other means

(1) This section applies to—

(a) a notice or request under any provision of Part II,

(b) a notice under subsection (1) of section 24 or particulars made available under that subsection, or

(c) an application under section 41(2),

PART II
DATA PROTECTION

but does not apply to anything which is required to be served in accordance with rules of court.

(2) The requirement that any notice, request, particulars or application to which this section applies should be in writing is satisfied where the text of the notice, request, particulars or application—

(a) is transmitted by electronic means,
(b) is received in legible form, and
(c) is capable of being used for subsequent reference.

(3) The [Secretary of State] may by regulations provide that any requirement that any notice, request, particulars or application to which this section applies should be in writing is not to apply in such circumstances as may be prescribed by the regulations.

[572]

NOTES

Sub-s (3): words in square brackets substituted by the Secretary of State for Constitutional Affairs Order 2003, SI 2003/1887, art 9, Sch 2, para 9(1)(a).

65 Service of notices by Commissioner

(1) Any notice authorised or required by this Act to be served on or given to any person by the Commissioner may—

(a) if that person is an individual, be served on him—
  (i) by delivering it to him, or
  (ii) by sending it to him by post addressed to him at his usual or last-known place of residence or business, or
  (iii) by leaving it for him at that place;
(b) if that person is a body corporate or unincorporate, be served on that body—
  (i) by sending it by post to the proper officer of the body at its principal office, or
  (ii) by addressing it to the proper officer of the body and leaving it at that office;
(c) if that person is a partnership in Scotland, be served on that partnership—
  (i) by sending it by post to the principal office of the partnership, or
  (ii) by addressing it to that partnership and leaving it at that office.

(2) In subsection (1)(b) "principal office", in relation to a registered company, means its registered office and "proper officer", in relation to any body, means the secretary or other executive officer charged with the conduct of its general affairs.

(3) This section is without prejudice to any other lawful method of serving or giving a notice.

[573]

66 Exercise of rights in Scotland by children

(1) Where a question falls to be determined in Scotland as to the legal capacity of a person under the age of sixteen years to exercise any right conferred by any provision of this Act, that person shall be taken to have that capacity where he has a general understanding of what it means to exercise that right.

(2) Without prejudice to the generality of subsection (1), a person of twelve years of age or more shall be presumed to be of sufficient age and maturity to have such understanding as is mentioned in that subsection.

[574]

67 Orders, regulations and rules

(1) Any power conferred by this Act on the [Secretary of State] to make an order, regulations or rules shall be exercisable by statutory instrument.

(2) Any order, regulations or rules made by the [Secretary of State] under this Act may—

(a) make different provision for different cases, and
(b) make such supplemental, incidental, consequential or transitional provision or savings as the [Secretary of State] considers appropriate;

and nothing in section 7(11), 19(5), 26(1) or 30(4) limits the generality of paragraph (a).

(3) Before making—

(a) an order under any provision of this Act other than section 75(3),

(b) any regulations under this Act other than notification regulations (as defined by section 16(2)),

the [Secretary of State] shall consult the Commissioner.

(4) A statutory instrument containing (whether alone or with other provisions) an order under—

section 10(2)(b),
section 12(5)(b),
section 22(1),
section 30, section 32(3),
section 38,
section 56(8),
paragraph 10 of Schedule 3, or
paragraph 4 of Schedule 7,

shall not be made unless a draft of the instrument has been laid before and approved by a resolution of each House of Parliament.

(5) A statutory instrument which contains (whether alone or with other provisions)—

(a) an order under—
section 22(7),
section 23,
section 51(3),
section 54(2), (3) or (4),
paragraph 3, 4 or 14 of Part II of Schedule 1,
paragraph 6 of Schedule 2,
paragraph 2, 7 or 9 of Schedule 3,
paragraph 4 of Schedule 4,
paragraph 6 of Schedule 7,

(b) regulations under section 7 which—
(i) prescribe cases for the purposes of subsection (2)(b),
(ii) are made by virtue of subsection (7), or
(iii) relate to the definition of "the prescribed period",

(c) regulations under section 8(1)[, 9(3) or 9A(5)],

(d) regulations under section 64,

(e) notification regulations (as defined by section 16(2)), or

(f) rules under paragraph 7 of Schedule 6,

and which is not subject to the requirement in subsection (4) that a draft of the instrument be laid before and approved by a resolution of each House of Parliament, shall be subject to annulment in pursuance of a resolution of either House of Parliament.

(6) A statutory instrument which contains only—

(a) regulations prescribing fees for the purposes of any provision of this Act, or

(b) regulations under section 7 prescribing fees for the purposes of any other enactment,

shall be laid before Parliament after being made.

[575]

NOTES

Sub-ss (1)–(3): words in square brackets substituted by the Secretary of State for Constitutional Affairs Order 2003, SI 2003/1887, art 9, Sch 2, para 9(1)(a).

Sub-s (5): words in square brackets in para (c) substituted by the Freedom of Information Act 2000, s 69(3).

Orders: the Data Protection (Processing of Sensitive Personal Data) (Elected Representatives) Order 2002, SI 2002/2905 at **[1050]**; the Information Tribunal (National Security Appeals) Rules 2005, SI 2005/13 at **[1123]**; the Information Tribunal (Enforcement Appeals) Rules 2005, SI 2005/14 at **[1153]**; the Data Protection (Processing of Sensitive Personal Data) Order 2006, SI 2006/2068 at **[1183]**.

Regulations: the Freedom of Information and Data Protection (Appropriate Limit and Fees) Regulations 2004, SI 2004/3244.

68 Meaning of "accessible record"

(1) In this Act "accessible record" means—

(a) a health record as defined by subsection (2),

(b) an educational record as defined by Schedule 11, or

(c) an accessible public record as defined by Schedule 12.

(2) In subsection (1)(a) "health record" means any record which—

(a) consists of information relating to the physical or mental health or condition of an individual, and

(b) has been made by or on behalf of a health professional in connection with the care of that individual.

[576]

69 Meaning of "health professional"

(1) In this Act "health professional" means any of the following—

(a) a registered medical practitioner,

(b) a registered dentist as defined by section 53(1) of the Dentists Act 1984,

[(c) a registered dispensing optician or a registered optometrist within the meaning of the Opticians Act 1989,]

(d) a registered pharmaceutical chemist as defined by section 24(1) of the Pharmacy Act 1954 or a registered person as defined by Article 2(2) of the Pharmacy (Northern Ireland) Order 1976,

[(e) a registered nurse or midwife]

(f) a registered osteopath as defined by section 41 of the Osteopaths Act 1993,

(g) a registered chiropractor as defined by section 43 of the Chiropractors Act 1994,

(h) any person who is registered as a member of a profession to which [the Health Professions Order 2001] for the time being extends,

(i) a clinical psychologist [or child psychotherapist],

(j) … and

(k) a scientist employed by such a body as head of a department.

(2) In subsection (1)(a) "registered medical practitioner" includes any person who is provisionally registered under section 15 or 21 of the Medical Act 1983 and is engaged in such employment as is mentioned in subsection (3) of that section.

(3) In subsection (1) "health service body" means—

(a) a [Strategic Health Authority *or a] Health Authority established under section 8 of the National Health Service Act 1977*,

(b) a Special Health Authority established under *section 11 of that Act*,

[(bb) a Primary Care Trust established under *section 16A of that Act*,]

[(bbb) a Local Health Board established under *section 16BA of that Act*,]

(c) a Health Board within the meaning of the National Health Service (Scotland) Act 1978,

(d) a Special Health Board within the meaning of that Act,

(e) the managers of a State Hospital provided under section 102 of that Act,

(f) a National Health Service trust first established under section 5 of the National Health Service and Community Care Act 1990[, section 25 of the National Health Service Act 2006, section 18 of the National Health Service (Wales) Act 2006] or section 12A of the National Health Service (Scotland) Act 1978,

[(fa) an NHS foundation trust,]

(g) a Health and Social Services Board established under Article 16 of the Health and Personal Social Services (Northern Ireland) Order 1972,

(h) a special health and social services agency established under the Health and Personal Social Services (Special Agencies) (Northern Ireland) Order 1990, or

(i) a Health and Social Services trust established under Article 10 of the Health and Personal Social Services (Northern Ireland) Order 1991.

[577]

NOTES

Sub-s (1): para (c) substituted by the Opticians Act 1989 (Amendment) Order 2005, SI 2005/848, art 28, Sch 1, Pt 2, para 12; para (e) substituted by the Nursery and Midwifery Order 2001, SI 2000/253, art 54(3), Sch 5, para 14; words in square brackets in para (h) substituted by the Health Professions Order 2001, SI 2000/254, art 48(3), Sch 4, para 7; words in square brackets in para (i) substituted, and para (j) repealed, by the Health Professions Order 2001 (Consequential Amendments) Order 2003, SI 2003/1590, art 3, Schedule, Pt 1, para 1.

Sub-s (3): in para (a) words in square brackets inserted by the National Health Service Reform and Health Care Professions Act 2002 (Supplementary, Consequential etc Provisions) Regulations 2002, SI 2002/2469, reg 4, Sch 1, para 24; for the words in italics in para (a) there are substituted the words "established under section 13 of the National Health Service Act 2006", for the words in italics in para (b) there are substituted the words "section 28 of that Act, or section 22 of the National Health Service (Wales) Act 2006", for the words in italics in para (bb) there are substituted the words "section 18 of the

National Health Service Act 2006", for the words in italics in para (bbb) there are substituted the words "section 11 of the National Health Service (Wales) Act 2006", and words in square brackets in para (f) inserted by the National Health Service (Consequential Provisions) Act 2006, s 2, Sch 1, paras 190, 191, as from a day to be appointed; para (bb) inserted by the Health Act 1999 (Supplementary, Consequential etc Provisions) Order 2000, SI 2000/90, art 3(1), Sch 1, para 33; para (bbb) inserted by the National Health Service Reform and Health Care Professions Act 2002, s 6(2), Sch 5, para 41; para (fa) inserted by the Health and Social Care (Community Health and Standards) Act 2003, s 34, Sch 4, paras 106, 107.

70 Supplementary definitions

(1) In this Act, unless the context otherwise requires—

"business" includes any trade or profession;

"the Commissioner" means [the Information Commissioner];

"credit reference agency" has the same meaning as in the Consumer Credit Act 1974;

"the Data Protection Directive" means Directive 95/46/EC on the protection of individuals with regard to the processing of personal data and on the free movement of such data;

"EEA State" means a State which is a contracting party to the Agreement on the European Economic Area signed at Oporto on 2nd May 1992 as adjusted by the Protocol signed at Brussels on 17th March 1993;

"enactment" includes an enactment passed after this Act [and any enactment comprised in, or in any instrument made under, an Act of the Scottish Parliament];

"government department" includes a Northern Ireland department and any body or authority exercising statutory functions on behalf of the Crown;

"Minister of the Crown" has the same meaning as in the Ministers of the Crown Act 1975;

"public register" means any register which pursuant to a requirement imposed—

(a) by or under any enactment, or

(b) in pursuance of any international agreement,

is open to public inspection or open to inspection by any person having a legitimate interest;

"pupil"—

(a) in relation to a school in England and Wales, means a registered pupil within the meaning of the Education Act 1996,

(b) in relation to a school in Scotland, means a pupil within the meaning of the Education (Scotland) Act 1980, and

(c) in relation to a school in Northern Ireland, means a registered pupil within the meaning of the Education and Libraries (Northern Ireland) Order 1986;

"recipient", in relation to any personal data, means any person to whom the data are disclosed, including any person (such as an employee or agent of the data controller, a data processor or an employee or agent of a data processor) to whom they are disclosed in the course of processing the data for the data controller, but does not include any person to whom disclosure is or may be made as a result of, or with a view to, a particular inquiry by or on behalf of that person made in the exercise of any power conferred by law;

"registered company" means a company registered under the enactments relating to companies for the time being in force in the United Kingdom;

"school"—

(a) in relation to England and Wales, has the same meaning as in the Education Act 1996,

(b) in relation to Scotland, has the same meaning as in the Education (Scotland) Act 1980, and

(c) in relation to Northern Ireland, has the same meaning as in the Education and Libraries (Northern Ireland) Order 1986;

"teacher" includes—

(a) in Great Britain, head teacher, and

(b) in Northern Ireland, the principal of a school;

"third party", in relation to personal data, means any person other than—

(a) the data subject,

(b) the data controller, or

(c) any data processor or other person authorised to process data for the data controller or processor;

"the Tribunal" means [the Information Tribunal].

(2) For the purposes of this Act data are inaccurate if they are incorrect or misleading as to any matter of fact.

[578]

NOTES

Sub-s (1): in definitions "the Commissioner" and "the Tribunal" words in square brackets substituted by the Freedom of Information Act 2000, s 18(4), Sch 2, Pt I, para 14; in definition "enactment" words in square brackets added by the Scotland Act 1999 (Consequential Modifications) (No 2) Order 1999, SI 1999/1820, art 4, Sch 2, Pt I, para 133.

Directive 95/46/EC: OJ L281, 23.11.95, p 31.

71 Index of defined expressions

The following Table shows provisions defining or otherwise explaining expressions used in this Act (other than provisions defining or explaining an expression only used in the same section or Schedule)—

accessible record	section 68
address (in Part III)	section 16(3)
business	section 70(1)
the Commissioner	section 70(1)
credit reference agency	section 70(1)
data	section 1(1)
data controller	sections 1(1) and (4) and 63(3)
data processor	section 1(1)
the Data Protection Directive	section 70(1)
data protection principles	section 4 and Schedule 1
data subject	section 1(1)
disclosing (of personal data)	section 1(2)(b)
EEA State	section 70(1)
enactment	section 70(1)
enforcement notice	section 40(1)
fees regulations (in Part III)	section 16(2)
government department	section 70(1)
health professional	section 69
inaccurate (in relation to data)	section 70(2)
information notice	section 43(1)
Minister of the Crown	section 70(1)
the non-disclosure provisions (in Part IV)	section 27(3)
notification regulations (in Part III)	section 16(2)
obtaining (of personal data)	section 1(2)(a)
personal data	section 1(1)
prescribed (in Part III)	section 16(2)
processing (of information or data)	section 1(1) and paragraph 5 of Schedule 8
[public authority	section 1(1)]
public register	section 70(1)
publish (in relation to journalistic, literary or artistic material)	section 32(6)
pupil (in relation to a school)	section 70(1)

recipient (in relation to personal data)	section 70(1)
recording (of personal data)	section 1(2)(a)
registered company	section 70(1)
registrable particulars (in Part III)	section 16(1)
relevant filing system	section 1(1)
school	section 70(1)
sensitive personal data	section 2
special information notice	section 44(1)
the special purposes	section 3
the subject information provisions (in Part IV)	section 27(2)
teacher	section 70(1)
third party (in relation to processing of personal data)	section 70(1)
the Tribunal	section 70(1)
using (of personal data)	section 1(2)(b).

[579]

NOTES

Table: entry "public authority" inserted by the Freedom of Information Act 2000, s 68(5).

72 Modifications of Act

During the period beginning with the commencement of this section and ending with 23rd October 2007, the provisions of this Act shall have effect subject to the modifications set out in Schedule 13.

[580]

73 Transitional provisions and savings

Schedule 14 (which contains transitional provisions and savings) has effect.

[581]

74 Minor and consequential amendments and repeals and revocations

(1) Schedule 15 (which contains minor and consequential amendments) has effect.

(2) The enactments and instruments specified in Schedule 16 are repealed or revoked to the extent specified.

[582]

75 Short title, commencement and extent

(1) This Act may be cited as the Data Protection Act 1998.

(2) The following provisions of this Act—

(a) sections 1 to 3,
(b) section 25(1) and (4),
(c) section 26,
(d) sections 67 to 71,
(e) this section,
(f) paragraph 17 of Schedule 5,
(g) Schedule 11,
(h) Schedule 12, and
(i) so much of any other provision of this Act as confers any power to make subordinate legislation,

shall come into force on the day on which this Act is passed.

(3) The remaining provisions of this Act shall come into force on such day as the [Secretary of State] may by order appoint; and different days may be appointed for different purposes.

(4) The day appointed under subsection (3) for the coming into force of section 56 must not be earlier than the first day on which sections 112, 113 and 115 of the Police Act 1997 (which provide for the issue by the Secretary of State of criminal conviction certificates, criminal record certificates and enhanced criminal record certificates) are all in force.

[(4A) Subsection (4) does not apply to section 56 so far as that section relates to a record containing information relating to—

(a) the Secretary of State's functions under the Safeguarding Vulnerable Groups Act 2006, or

(b) the Independent Barring Board's functions under that Act.]

(5) Subject to subsection (6), this Act extends to Northern Ireland.

(6) Any amendment, repeal or revocation made by Schedule 15 or 16 has the same extent as that of the enactment or instrument to which it relates.

[583]

NOTES

Sub-s (3): words in square brackets substituted by the Secretary of State for Constitutional Affairs Order 2003, SI 2003/1887, art 9, Sch 2, para 9(1)(a).

Sub-s (4A): inserted by the Safeguarding Vulnerable Groups Act 2006, s 63(1), Sch 9, Pt 2, para 15(1), (3), as from a day to be appointed.

Orders: the Data Protection Act 1998 (Commencement) Order 2000, SI 2000/183.

SCHEDULES

SCHEDULE 1
THE DATA PROTECTION PRINCIPLES

Section 4(1) and (2)

PART I
THE PRINCIPLES

1. Personal data shall be processed fairly and lawfully and, in particular, shall not be processed unless—

(a) at least one of the conditions in Schedule 2 is met, and

(b) in the case of sensitive personal data, at least one of the conditions in Schedule 3 is also met.

2. Personal data shall be obtained only for one or more specified and lawful purposes, and shall not be further processed in any manner incompatible with that purpose or those purposes.

3. Personal data shall be adequate, relevant and not excessive in relation to the purpose or purposes for which they are processed.

4. Personal data shall be accurate and, where necessary, kept up to date.

5. Personal data processed for any purpose or purposes shall not be kept for longer than is necessary for that purpose or those purposes.

6. Personal data shall be processed in accordance with the rights of data subjects under this Act.

7. Appropriate technical and organisational measures shall be taken against unauthorised or unlawful processing of personal data and against accidental loss or destruction of, or damage to, personal data.

8. Personal data shall not be transferred to a country or territory outside the European Economic Area unless that country or territory ensures an adequate level of protection for the rights and freedoms of data subjects in relation to the processing of personal data.

[584]

PART II
INTERPRETATION OF THE PRINCIPLES IN PART I

The first principle

1.—(1) In determining for the purposes of the first principle whether personal data are processed fairly, regard is to be had to the method by which they are obtained, including in particular whether any person from whom they are obtained is deceived or misled as to the purpose or purposes for which they are to be processed.

(2) Subject to paragraph 2, for the purposes of the first principle data are to be treated as obtained fairly if they consist of information obtained from a person who—

(a) is authorised by or under any enactment to supply it, or

(b) is required to supply it by or under any enactment or by any convention or other instrument imposing an international obligation on the United Kingdom.

2.—(1) Subject to paragraph 3, for the purposes of the first principle personal data are not to be treated as processed fairly unless—

(a) in the case of data obtained from the data subject, the data controller ensures so far as practicable that the data subject has, is provided with, or has made readily available to him, the information specified in sub-paragraph (3), and

(b) in any other case, the data controller ensures so far as practicable that, before the relevant time or as soon as practicable after that time, the data subject has, is provided with, or has made readily available to him, the information specified in sub-paragraph (3).

(2) In sub-paragraph (1)(b) "the relevant time" means—

(a) the time when the data controller first processes the data, or

(b) in a case where at that time disclosure to a third party within a reasonable period is envisaged—

(i) if the data are in fact disclosed to such a person within that period, the time when the data are first disclosed,

(ii) if within that period the data controller becomes, or ought to become, aware that the data are unlikely to be disclosed to such a person within that period, the time when the data controller does become, or ought to become, so aware, or

(iii) in any other case, the end of that period.

(3) The information referred to in sub-paragraph (1) is as follows, namely—

(a) the identity of the data controller,

(b) if he has nominated a representative for the purposes of this Act, the identity of that representative,

(c) the purpose or purposes for which the data are intended to be processed, and

(d) any further information which is necessary, having regard to the specific circumstances in which the data are or are to be processed, to enable processing in respect of the data subject to be fair.

3.—(1) Paragraph 2(1)(b) does not apply where either of the primary conditions in subparagraph (2), together with such further conditions as may be prescribed by the [Secretary of State] by order, are met.

(2) The primary conditions referred to in sub-paragraph (1) are—

(a) that the provision of that information would involve a disproportionate effort, or

(b) that the recording of the information to be contained in the data by, or the disclosure of the data by, the data controller is necessary for compliance with any legal obligation to which the data controller is subject, other than an obligation imposed by contract.

4.—(1) Personal data which contain a general identifier falling within a description prescribed by the [Secretary of State] by order are not to be treated as processed fairly and lawfully unless they are processed in compliance with any conditions so prescribed in relation to general identifiers of that description.

(2) In sub-paragraph (1) "a general identifier" means any identifier (such as, for example, a number or code used for identification purposes) which—

(a) relates to an individual, and

(b) forms part of a set of similar identifiers which is of general application.

The second principle

5. The purpose or purposes for which personal data are obtained may in particular be specified—

(a) in a notice given for the purposes of paragraph 2 by the data controller to the data subject, or

(b) in a notification given to the Commissioner under Part III of this Act.

6. In determining whether any disclosure of personal data is compatible with the purpose or purposes for which the data were obtained, regard is to be had to the purpose or purposes for which the personal data are intended to be processed by any person to whom they are disclosed.

The fourth principle

7. The fourth principle is not to be regarded as being contravened by reason of any inaccuracy in personal data which accurately record information obtained by the data controller from the data subject or a third party in a case where—

(a) having regard to the purpose or purposes for which the data were obtained and further processed, the data controller has taken reasonable steps to ensure the accuracy of the data, and

(b) if the data subject has notified the data controller of the data subject's view that the data are inaccurate, the data indicate that fact.

The sixth principle

8. A person is to be regarded as contravening the sixth principle if, but only if—

(a) he contravenes section 7 by failing to supply information in accordance with that section,

(b) he contravenes section 10 by failing to comply with a notice given under subsection (1) of that section to the extent that the notice is justified or by failing to give a notice under subsection (3) of that section,

(c) he contravenes section 11 by failing to comply with a notice given under subsection (1) of that section, or

(d) he contravenes section 12 by failing to comply with a notice given under subsection (1) or (2)(b) of that section or by failing to give a notification under subsection (2)(a) of that section or a notice under subsection (3) of that section.

The seventh principle

9. Having regard to the state of technological development and the cost of implementing any measures, the measures must ensure a level of security appropriate to—

(a) the harm that might result from such unauthorised or unlawful processing or accidental loss, destruction or damage as are mentioned in the seventh principle, and

(b) the nature of the data to be protected.

10. The data controller must take reasonable steps to ensure the reliability of any employees of his who have access to the personal data.

11. Where processing of personal data is carried out by a data processor on behalf of a data controller, the data controller must in order to comply with the seventh principle—

(a) choose a data processor providing sufficient guarantees in respect of the technical and organisational security measures governing the processing to be carried out, and

(b) take reasonable steps to ensure compliance with those measures.

12. Where processing of personal data is carried out by a data processor on behalf of a data controller, the data controller is not to be regarded as complying with the seventh principle unless—

(a) the processing is carried out under a contract—

(i) which is made or evidenced in writing, and

(ii) under which the data processor is to act only on instructions from the data controller, and

(b) the contract requires the data processor to comply with obligations equivalent to those imposed on a data controller by the seventh principle.

The eighth principle

13. An adequate level of protection is one which is adequate in all the circumstances of the case, having regard in particular to—

(a) the nature of the personal data,
(b) the country or territory of origin of the information contained in the data,
(c) the country or territory of final destination of that information,
(d) the purposes for which and period during which the data are intended to be processed,
(e) the law in force in the country or territory in question,
(f) the international obligations of that country or territory,
(g) any relevant codes of conduct or other rules which are enforceable in that country or territory (whether generally or by arrangement in particular cases), and
(h) any security measures taken in respect of the data in that country or territory.

14. The eighth principle does not apply to a transfer falling within any paragraph of Schedule 4, except in such circumstances and to such extent as the [Secretary of State] may by order provide.

15.—(1) Where—

(a) in any proceedings under this Act any question arises as to whether the requirement of the eighth principle as to an adequate level of protection is met in relation to the transfer of any personal data to a country or territory outside the European Economic Area, and
(b) a Community finding has been made in relation to transfers of the kind in question,

that question is to be determined in accordance with that finding.

(2) In sub-paragraph (1) "Community finding" means a finding of the European Commission, under the procedure provided for in Article 31(2) of the Data Protection Directive, that a country or territory outside the European Economic Area does, or does not, ensure an adequate level of protection within the meaning of Article 25(2) of the Directive.

[585]

NOTES

Paras 3, 4, 14: words in square brackets substituted by the Secretary of State for Constitutional Affairs Order 2003, SI 2003/1887, art 9, Sch 2, para 9(1)(b).

Modification: by virtue of s 72 of, and Sch 13, para 5 to, this Act, for the period beginning with the commencement of s 72 (1 March 2000) and ending 23 October 2007, para 8 above has effect with the omission of the word "or" at the end of sub-para (c) and with the following added after sub-para (d)—

"or

(e) he contravenes section 12A by failing to comply with a notice given under subsection (1) of that section to the extent that the notice is justified.".

Orders: the Data Protection (Conditions under Paragraph 3 of Part II of Schedule 1) Order 2000, SI 2000/185 at **[815]**.

SCHEDULE 2
CONDITIONS RELEVANT FOR PURPOSES OF THE FIRST PRINCIPLE: PROCESSING OF ANY PERSONAL DATA

Section 4(3)

1. The data subject has given his consent to the processing.

2. The processing is necessary—

(a) for the performance of a contract to which the data subject is a party, or
(b) for the taking of steps at the request of the data subject with a view to entering into a contract.

3. The processing is necessary for compliance with any legal obligation to which the data controller is subject, other than an obligation imposed by contract.

4. The processing is necessary in order to protect the vital interests of the data subject.

5. The processing is necessary—
(a) for the administration of justice,
[(aa) for the exercise of any functions of either House of Parliament,]
(b) for the exercise of any functions conferred on any person by or under any enactment,
(c) for the exercise of any functions of the Crown, a Minister of the Crown or a government department, or
(d) for the exercise of any other functions of a public nature exercised in the public interest by any person.

6.—(1) The processing is necessary for the purposes of legitimate interests pursued by the data controller or by the third party or parties to whom the data are disclosed, except where the processing is unwarranted in any particular case by reason of prejudice to the rights and freedoms or legitimate interests of the data subject.

(2) The [Secretary of State] may by order specify particular circumstances in which this condition is, or is not, to be taken to be satisfied.

[586]

NOTES

Para 5: sub-para (aa) inserted by the Freedom of Information Act, s 73, Sch 6, para 4.

Para 6: words in square brackets in sub-para (2) substituted by the Secretary of State for Constitutional Affairs Order 2003, SI 2003/1887, art 9, Sch 2, para 9(1)(b).

SCHEDULE 3
CONDITIONS RELEVANT FOR PURPOSES OF THE FIRST PRINCIPLE: PROCESSING OF SENSITIVE PERSONAL DATA

Section 4(3)

1. The data subject has given his explicit consent to the processing of the personal data.

2.—(1) The processing is necessary for the purposes of exercising or performing any right or obligation which is conferred or imposed by law on the data controller in connection with employment.

(2) The [Secretary of State] may by order—
(a) exclude the application of sub-paragraph (1) in such cases as may be specified, or
(b) provide that, in such cases as may be specified, the condition in subparagraph (1) is not to be regarded as satisfied unless such further conditions as may be specified in the order are also satisfied.

3. The processing is necessary—
(a) in order to protect the vital interests of the data subject or another person, in a case where—
(i) consent cannot be given by or on behalf of the data subject, or
(ii) the data controller cannot reasonably be expected to obtain the consent of the data subject, or
(b) in order to protect the vital interests of another person, in a case where consent by or on behalf of the data subject has been unreasonably withheld.

4. The processing—
(a) is carried out in the course of its legitimate activities by any body or association which—
(i) is not established or conducted for profit, and
(ii) exists for political, philosophical religious or trade-union purposes,
(b) is carried out with appropriate safeguards for the rights and freedoms of data subjects,
(c) relates only to individuals who either are members of the body or association or have regular contact with it in connection with its purposes, and

(d) does not involve disclosure of the personal data to a third party without the consent of the data subject.

5. The information contained in the personal data has been made public as a result of steps deliberately taken by the data subject.

6. The processing—
(a) is necessary for the purpose of, or in connection with, any legal proceedings (including prospective legal proceedings),
(b) is necessary for the purpose of obtaining legal advice, or
(c) is otherwise necessary for the purposes of establishing, exercising or defending legal rights.

7.—(1) The processing is necessary—
(a) for the administration of justice,
[(aa) for the exercise of any functions of either House of Parliament,]
(b) for the exercise of any functions conferred on any person by or under an enactment, or
(c) for the exercise of any functions of the Crown, a Minister of the Crown or a government department.

(2) The [Secretary of State] may by order—
(a) exclude the application of sub-paragraph (1) in such cases as may be specified, or
(b) provide that, in such cases as may be specified, the condition in subparagraph (1) is not to be regarded as satisfied unless such further conditions as may be specified in the order are also satisfied.

8.—(1) The processing is necessary for medical purposes and is undertaken by—
(a) a health professional, or
(b) a person who in the circumstances owes a duty of confidentiality which is equivalent to that which would arise if that person were a health professional.

(2) In this paragraph "medical purposes" includes the purposes of preventative medicine, medical diagnosis, medical research, the provision of care and treatment and the management of healthcare services.

9.—(1) The processing—
(a) is of sensitive personal data consisting of information as to racial or ethnic origin,
(b) is necessary for the purpose of identifying or keeping under review the existence or absence of equality of opportunity or treatment between persons of different racial or ethnic origins, with a view to enabling such equality to be promoted or maintained, and
(c) is carried out with appropriate safeguards for the rights and freedoms of data subjects.

(2) The [Secretary of State] may by order specify circumstances in which processing falling within sub-paragraph (1)(a) and (b) is, or is not, to be taken for the purposes of subparagraph (1)(c) to be carried out with appropriate safeguards for the rights and freedoms of data subjects.

10. The personal data are processed in circumstances specified in an order made by the [Secretary of State] for the purposes of this paragraph.

[587]

NOTES

Paras 2, 9, 10: words in square brackets substituted by the Secretary of State for Constitutional Affairs Order 2003, SI 2003/1887, art 9, Sch 2, para 9(1)(b).

Para 7: sub-para (1)(aa) inserted by the Freedom of Information Act 2000, s 73, Sch 6, para 5; words in square brackets in sub-para (2) substituted by SI 2003/1887, art 9, Sch 2, para 9(1)(b).

Orders: the Data Protection (Processing of Sensitive Personal Data) Order 2000, SI 2000/417 at **[941]**; the Data Protection (Processing of Sensitive Personal Data) (Elected Representatives) Order 2002, SI 2002/2905 at **[1050]**; the Data Protection (Processing of Sensitive Personal Data) Order 2006, SI 2006/2068 at **[1183]**.

SCHEDULE 4
CASES WHERE THE EIGHTH PRINCIPLE DOES NOT APPLY

Section 4(3)

1. The data subject has given his consent to the transfer.

2. The transfer is necessary—
   (a) for the performance of a contract between the data subject and the data controller, or
   (b) for the taking of steps at the request of the data subject with a view to his entering into a contract with the data controller.

3. The transfer is necessary—
   (a) for the conclusion of a contract between the data controller and a person other than the data subject which—
      (i) is entered into at the request of the data subject, or
      (ii) is in the interests of the data subject, or
   (b) for the performance of such a contract.

4.—(1) The transfer is necessary for reasons of substantial public interest.

(2) The [Secretary of State] may by order specify—
   (a) circumstances in which a transfer is to be taken for the purposes of subparagraph (1) to be necessary for reasons of substantial public interest, and
   (b) circumstances in which a transfer which is not required by or under an enactment is not to be taken for the purpose of sub-paragraph (1) to be necessary for reasons of substantial public interest.

5. The transfer—
   (a) is necessary for the purpose of, or in connection with, any legal proceedings (including prospective legal proceedings),
   (b) is necessary for the purpose of obtaining legal advice, or
   (c) is otherwise necessary for the purposes of establishing, exercising or defending legal rights.

6. The transfer is necessary in order to protect the vital interests of the data subject.

7. The transfer is of part of the personal data on a public register and any conditions subject to which the register is open to inspection are complied with by any person to whom the data are or may be disclosed after the transfer.

8. The transfer is made on terms which are of a kind approved by the Commissioner as ensuring adequate safeguards for the rights and freedoms of data subjects.

9. The transfer has been authorised by the Commissioner as being made in such a manner as to ensure adequate safeguards for the rights and freedoms of data subjects.

[588]

NOTES

Para 4: words in square brackets in sub-para (2) substituted by the Secretary of State for Constitutional Affairs Order 2003, SI 2003/1887, art 9, Sch 2, para 9(1)(b).

SCHEDULE 5
THE [INFORMATION COMMISSIONER] AND THE [INFORMATION TRIBUNAL]

Section 6(7)

PART I
THE COMMISSIONER

Status and capacity

1.—(1) The corporation sole by the name of the Data Protection Registrar established by the Data Protection Act 1984 shall continue in existence by the name of the [Information Commissioner].

(2) The Commissioner and his officers and staff are not to be regarded as servants or agents of the Crown.

Tenure of office

2.—(1) Subject to the provisions of this paragraph, the Commissioner shall hold office for such term not exceeding five years as may be determined at the time of his appointment.

(2) The Commissioner may be relieved of his office by Her Majesty at his own request.

(3) The Commissioner may be removed from office by Her Majesty in pursuance of an Address from both Houses of Parliament.

(4) The Commissioner shall in any case vacate his office—
- (a) on completing the year of service in which he attains the age of sixty-five years, or
- (b) if earlier, on completing his fifteenth year of service.

(5) Subject to sub-paragraph (4), a person who ceases to be Commissioner on the expiration of his term of office shall be eligible for re-appointment, but a person may not be re-appointed for a third or subsequent term as Commissioner unless, by reason of special circumstances, the person's re-appointment for such a term is desirable in the public interest.

Salary etc

3.—(1) There shall be paid—
- (a) to the Commissioner such salary, and
- (b) to or in respect of the Commissioner such pension,

as may be specified by a resolution of the House of Commons.

(2) A resolution for the purposes of this paragraph may—
- (a) specify the salary or pension,
- (b) provide that the salary or pension is to be the same as, or calculated on the same basis as, that payable to, or to or in respect of, a person employed in a specified office under, or in a specified capacity in the service of, the Crown, or
- (c) specify the salary or pension and provide for it to be increased by reference to such variables as may be specified in the resolution.

(3) A resolution for the purposes of this paragraph may take effect from the date on which it is passed or from any earlier or later date specified in the resolution.

(4) A resolution for the purposes of this paragraph may make different provision in relation to the pension payable to or in respect of different holders of the office of Commissioner.

(5) Any salary or pension payable under this paragraph shall be charged on and issued out of the Consolidated Fund.

(6) In this paragraph "pension" includes an allowance or gratuity and any reference to the payment of a pension includes a reference to the making of payments towards the provision of a pension.

Officers and staff

4.—(1) The Commissioner—

(a) shall appoint a deputy commissioner [or two deputy commissioners], and

(b) may appoint such number of other officers and staff as he may determine.

[(1A) The Commissioner shall, when appointing any second deputy commissioner, specify which of the Commissioner's functions are to be performed, in the circumstances referred to in paragraph 5(1), by each of the deputy commissioners.]

(2) The remuneration and other conditions of service of the persons appointed under this paragraph shall be determined by the Commissioner.

(3) The Commissioner may pay such pensions, allowances or gratuities to or in respect of the persons appointed under this paragraph, or make such payments towards the provision of such pensions, allowances or gratuities, as he may determine.

(4) The references in sub-paragraph (3) to pensions, allowances or gratuities to or in respect of the persons appointed under this paragraph include references to pensions, allowances or gratuities by way of compensation to or in respect of any of those persons who suffer loss of office or employment.

(5) Any determination under sub-paragraph (1)(b), (2) or (3) shall require the approval of the [Secretary of State].

(6) The Employers' Liability (Compulsory Insurance) Act 1969 shall not require insurance to be effected by the Commissioner.

5.—(1) The deputy commissioner [or deputy commissioners] shall perform the functions conferred by this Act on the Commissioner during any vacancy in that office or at any time when the Commissioner is for any reason unable to act.

(2) Without prejudice to sub-paragraph (1), any functions of the Commissioner under this Act [or the Freedom of Information Act 2000] may, to the extent authorised by him, be performed by any of his officers or staff.

Authentication of seal of the Commissioner

6. The application of the seal of the Commissioner shall be authenticated by his signature or by the signature of some other person authorised for the purpose.

Presumption of authenticity of documents issued by the Commissioner

7. Any document purporting to be an instrument issued by the Commissioner and to be duly executed under the Commissioner's seal or to be signed by or on behalf of the Commissioner shall be received in evidence and shall be deemed to be such an instrument unless the contrary is shown.

Money

8. The [Secretary of State] may make payments to the Commissioner out of money provided by Parliament.

9.—(1) All fees and other sums received by the Commissioner in the exercise of his functions under this Act[, under section 159 of the Consumer Credit Act 1974 or under the Freedom of Information Act 2000] shall be paid by him to the [Secretary of State].

(2) Sub-paragraph (1) shall not apply where the [Secretary of State], with the consent of the Treasury, otherwise directs.

(3) Any sums received by the [Secretary of State] under sub-paragraph (1) shall be paid into the Consolidated Fund.

Accounts

10.—(1) It shall be the duty of the Commissioner—

(a) to keep proper accounts and other records in relation to the accounts,

(b) to prepare in respect of each financial year a statement of account in such form as the [Secretary of State] may direct, and

(c) to send copies of that statement to the Comptroller and Auditor General on or before 31st August next following the end of the year to which the statement relates or on or before such earlier date after the end of that year as the Treasury may direct.

(2) The Comptroller and Auditor General shall examine and certify any statement sent to him under this paragraph and lay copies of it together with his report thereon before each House of Parliament.

(3) In this paragraph "financial year" means a period of twelve months beginning with 1st April.

Application of Part I in Scotland

11. Paragraphs 1(1), 6 and 7 do not extend to Scotland.

[589]

NOTES

Schedule heading: words in square brackets substituted by the Freedom of Information Act 2000, s 18(4), Sch 2, Pt I, para 1.

Para 1: words in square brackets in sub-para (1) substituted by the Freedom of Information Act 2000, s 18(4), Sch 2, Pt I, para 15(1), (2).

Para 4: words in square brackets in sub-para (1)(a), and the whole of sub-para (1A), inserted by the Freedom of Information Act 2000, s 18(4), Sch 2, Pt II, para 20; words in square brackets in sub-para (5) substituted by the Secretary of State for Constitutional Affairs Order 2003, SI 2003/1887, art 9, Sch 2, para 9(1)(c).

Para 5: words in square brackets inserted by the Freedom of Information Act 2000, s 18(4), Sch 2, Pt II, para 21.

Paras 8, 10: words in square brackets substituted by SI 2003/1887, art 9, Sch 2, para 9(1)(c).

Para 9: words in first pair of square brackets substituted by the Freedom of Information Act 2000, s 18(4), Sch 2, Pt II, para 22; words in second, third and fourth pairs of square brackets substituted by SI 2003/1887, art 9, Sch 2, para 9(1)(c).

PART II
THE TRIBUNAL

Tenure of office

12.—(1) Subject to the following provisions of this paragraph, a member of the Tribunal shall hold and vacate his office in accordance with the terms of his appointment and shall, on ceasing to hold office, be eligible for re-appointment.

(2) Any member of the Tribunal may at any time resign his office by notice in writing to the Lord Chancellor … [(in the case of the chairman or a deputy chairman) or to the Secretary of State (in the case of any other member)].

(3) A person who is the chairman or deputy chairman of the Tribunal shall vacate his office on the day on which he attains the age of seventy years; but this sub-paragraph is subject to section 26(4) to (6) of the Judicial Pensions and Retirement Act 1993 (power to authorise continuance in office up to the age of seventy-five years).

Salary etc

13. The [Secretary of State] shall pay to the members of the Tribunal out of money provided by Parliament such remuneration and allowances as he may determine.

Officers and staff

14. The [Secretary of State] may provide the Tribunal with such officers and staff as he thinks necessary for the proper discharge of its functions.

Expenses

15. Such expenses of the Tribunal as the [Secretary of State] may determine shall be defrayed by the [Secretary of State] out of money provided by Parliament.

[590]

NOTES

Para 12: in sub-para (2), words omitted repealed by the Transfer of Functions (Miscellaneous) Order 2001, SI 2001/3500, art 8, Sch 2, Pt I, para 6(3); words in square brackets added by the Secretary of State for Constitutional Affairs Order 2003, SI 2003/1887, art 9, Sch 2, para 9(2).

Paras 13–15: words in square brackets substituted by SI 2003/1887, art 9, Sch 2, para 9(1)(c).

(*Pt III repealed by the Freedom of Information Act 2000, ss 18(4), 86, Sch 2, Pt I, para 15(1), (3), Sch 8, Pt II.*)

SCHEDULE 6
APPEAL PROCEEDINGS

Sections 28(12), 48(5)

Hearing of appeals

1. For the purpose of hearing and determining appeals or any matter preliminary or incidental to an appeal the Tribunal shall sit at such times and in such places as the chairman or a deputy chairman may direct and may sit in two or more divisions.

Constitution of Tribunal in national security cases

2.—(1) The Lord Chancellor shall from time to time designate, from among the chairman and deputy chairmen appointed by him under section 6(4)(a) and (b), those persons who are to be capable of hearing appeals under section 28(4) or (6) [or under section 60(1) or (4) of the Freedom of Information Act 2000].

(2) A designation under sub-paragraph (1) may at any time be revoked by the Lord Chancellor.

[(3) The Lord Chancellor may make, or revoke, a designation under this paragraph only with the concurrence of all of the following—

(a) the Lord Chief Justice;
(b) the Lord President of the Court of Session;
(c) the Lord Chief Justice of Northern Ireland.

(4) The Lord Chief Justice of England and Wales may nominate a judicial office holder (as defined in section 109(4) of the Constitutional Reform Act 2005) to exercise his functions under sub-paragraph (3) so far as they relate to a designation under this paragraph.

(5) The Lord President of the Court of Session may nominate a judge of the Court of Session who is a member of the First or Second Division of the Inner House of that Court to exercise his functions under sub-paragraph (3) so far as they relate to a designation under this paragraph.

(6) The Lord Chief Justice of Northern Ireland may nominate any of the following to exercise his functions under sub-paragraph (3) so far as they relate to a designation under this paragraph—

(a) the holder of one of the offices listed in Schedule 1 to the Justice (Northern Ireland) Act 2002;
(b) a Lord Justice of Appeal (as defined in section 88 of that Act).]

[3.—[(1)] The Tribunal shall be duly constituted—

(a) for an appeal under section 28(4) or (6) in any case where the application of paragraph 6(1) is excluded by rules under paragraph 7, or

(b) for an appeal under section 60(1) or (4) of the Freedom of Information Act 2000,

if it consists of three of the persons designated under paragraph 2(1), of whom one shall be designated by the Lord Chancellor to preside.

[(2) The Lord Chancellor may designate a person to preside under this paragraph only with the concurrence of all of the following—

(a) the Lord Chief Justice of England and Wales;

(b) the Lord President of the Court of Session;

(c) the Lord Chief Justice of Northern Ireland.

(3) The Lord Chief Justice of England and Wales may nominate a judicial office holder (as defined in section 109(4) of the Constitutional Reform Act 2005) to exercise his functions under this paragraph.

(4) The Lord President of the Court of Session may nominate a judge of the Court of Session who is a member of the First or Second Division of the Inner House of that Court to exercise his functions under this paragraph.

(5) The Lord Chief Justice of Northern Ireland may nominate any of the following to exercise his functions under this paragraph—

(a) the holder of one of the offices listed in Schedule 1 to the Justice (Northern Ireland) Act 2002;

(b) a Lord Justice of Appeal (as defined in section 88 of that Act).]]

Constitution of Tribunal in other cases

4.—(1) Subject to any rules made under paragraph 7, the Tribunal shall be duly constituted for an appeal under section 48(1), (2) or (4) if it consists of—

(a) the chairman or a deputy chairman (who shall preside), and

(b) an equal number of the members appointed respectively in accordance with paragraphs (a) and (b) of section 6(6).

[(1A) Subject to any rules made under paragraph 7, the Tribunal shall be duly constituted for an appeal under section 57(1) or (2) of the Freedom of Information Act 2000 if it consists of—

(a) the chairman or a deputy chairman (who shall preside), and

(b) an equal number of the members appointed respectively in accordance with paragraphs (aa) and (bb) of section 6(6).]

(2) The members who are to constitute the Tribunal in accordance with subparagraph (1) [or (1A)] shall be nominated by the chairman or, if he is for any reason unable to act, by a deputy chairman.

Determination of questions by full Tribunal

5. The determination of any question before the Tribunal when constituted in accordance with paragraph 3 or 4 shall be according to the opinion of the majority of the members hearing the appeal.

Ex parte proceedings

6.—(1) Subject to any rules made under paragraph 7, the jurisdiction of the Tribunal in respect of an appeal under section 28(4) or (6) shall be exercised ex parte by one or more persons designated under paragraph 2(1).

(2) Subject to any rules made under paragraph 7, the jurisdiction of the Tribunal in respect of an appeal under section 48(3) shall be exercised ex parte by the chairman or a deputy chairman sitting alone.

Rules of procedure

7.—(1) The [Secretary of State] may make rules for [regulating—

PART II DATA PROTECTION

(a) the exercise of the rights of appeal conferred—
   (i) by sections 28(4) and (6) and 48, and
   (ii) by sections 57(1) and (2) and section 60(1) and (4) of the Freedom of Information Act 2000, and
(b) the practice and procedure of the Tribunal.]

(2) Rules under this paragraph may in particular make provision—
(a) with respect to the period within which an appeal can be brought and the burden of proof on an appeal,
[(aa) for the joinder of any person as a party to any proceedings on an appeal under the Freedom of Information Act 2000,
(ab) for the hearing of an appeal under this Act with an appeal under the Freedom of Information Act 2000,]
(b) for the summoning (or, in Scotland, citation) of witnesses and the administration of oaths,
(c) for securing the production of documents and material used for the processing of personal data,
(d) for the inspection, examination, operation and testing of any equipment or material used in connection with the processing of personal data,
(e) for the hearing of an appeal wholly or partly in camera,
(f) for hearing an appeal in the absence of the appellant or for determining an appeal without a hearing,
(g) for enabling an appeal under section 48(1) against an information notice to be determined by the chairman or a deputy chairman,
(h) for enabling any matter preliminary or incidental to an appeal to be dealt with by the chairman or a deputy chairman,
(i) for the awarding of costs or, in Scotland, expenses,
(j) for the publication of reports of the Tribunal's decisions, and
(k) for conferring on the Tribunal such ancillary powers as the [Secretary of State] thinks necessary for the proper discharge of its functions.

(3) In making rules under this paragraph which relate to appeals under section 28(4) or (6) the [Secretary of State] shall have regard, in particular, to the need to secure that information is not disclosed contrary to the public interest.

Obstruction etc

8.—(1) If any person is guilty of any act or omission in relation to proceedings before the Tribunal which, if those proceedings were proceedings before a court having power to commit for contempt, would constitute contempt of court, the Tribunal may certify the offence to the High Court or, in Scotland, the Court of Session.

(2) Where an offence is so certified, the court may inquire into the matter and, after hearing any witness who may be produced against or on behalf of the person charged with the offence, and after hearing any statement that may be offered in defence, deal with him in any manner in which it could deal with him if he had committed the like offence in relation to the court.

[591]

NOTES

Para 2: words in square brackets in sub-para (1) inserted by the Freedom of Information Act 2000, s 61(1), Sch 4, para 1; sub-paras (3)–(6) added by the Constitutional Reform Act 2005, s 15(1), Sch 4, Pt 1, para 275(1), (2).

Para 3: substituted by the Freedom of Information Act 2000, s 61(1), Sch 4, para 2; sub-para (1) numbered as such and sub-paras (2)–(5) added by the Constitutional Reform Act 2005, s 15(1), Sch 4, Pt 1, para 275(1), (3).

Para 4: sub-para (1A) and words in square brackets in sub-para (2) inserted by the Freedom of Information Act 2000, s 61(1), Sch 4, para 3.

Para 7: words in second pair of square brackets substituted, and sub-para (2)(aa), (ab) inserted, by the Freedom of Information Act 2000, s 61(1), Sch 4, para 4; other words in square brackets substituted by the Secretary of State for Constitutional Affairs Order 2003, SI 2003/1887, art 9, Sch 2, para 9(1)(d).

Rules: the [Information Tribunal] (National Security Appeals) (Telecommunications) Rules 2000, SI 2000/731 at **[950]**; the Information Tribunal (National Security Appeals) Rules 2005, SI 2005/13 at **[1123]**; the Information Tribunal (Enforcement Appeals) Rules 2005, SI 2005/14 at **[1153]**.

SCHEDULE 7
MISCELLANEOUS EXEMPTIONS

Section 37

Confidential references given by the data controller

1. Personal data are exempt from section 7 if they consist of a reference given or to be given in confidence by the data controller for the purposes of—
   (a) the education, training or employment, or prospective education, training or employment, of the data subject,
   (b) the appointment, or prospective appointment, of the data subject to any office, or
   (c) the provision, or prospective provision, by the data subject of any service.

Armed forces

2. Personal data are exempt from the subject information provisions in any case to the extent to which the application of those provisions would be likely to prejudice the combat effectiveness of any of the armed forces of the Crown.

Judicial appointments and honours

3. Personal data processed for the purposes of—
   (a) assessing any person's suitability for judicial office or the office of Queen's Counsel, or
   (b) the conferring by the Crown of any honour [or dignity],

are exempt from the subject information provisions.

Crown employment and Crown or Ministerial appointments

4.—[(1)] The [Secretary of State] may by order exempt from the subject information provisions personal data processed for the purposes of assessing any person's suitability for—
   (a) employment by or under the Crown, or
   (b) any office to which appointments are made by Her Majesty, by a Minister of the Crown or by a [Northern Ireland authority].

[(2) In this paragraph "Northern Ireland authority" means the First Minister, the deputy First Minister, a Northern Ireland Minister or a Northern Ireland department.]

Management forecasts etc

5. Personal data processed for the purposes of management forecasting or management planning to assist the data controller in the conduct of any business or other activity are exempt from the subject information provisions in any case to the extent to which the application of those provisions would be likely to prejudice the conduct of that business or other activity.

Corporate finance

6.—(1) Where personal data are processed for the purposes of, or in connection with, a corporate finance service provided by a relevant person—
   (a) the data are exempt from the subject information provisions in any case to the extent to which either—
      (i) the application of those provisions to the data could affect the price of any instrument which is already in existence or is to be or may be created, or
      (ii) the data controller reasonably believes that the application of those provisions to the data could affect the price of any such instrument, and
   (b) to the extent that the data are not exempt from the subject information provisions

PART II DATA PROTECTION

by virtue of paragraph (a), they are exempt from those provisions if the exemption is required for the purpose of safeguarding an important economic or financial interest of the United Kingdom.

(2) For the purposes of sub-paragraph (1)(b) the [Secretary of State] may by order specify—

(a) matters to be taken into account in determining whether exemption from the subject information provisions is required for the purpose of safeguarding an important economic or financial interest of the United Kingdom, or

(b) circumstances in which exemption from those provisions is, or is not, to be taken to be required for that purpose.

(3) In this paragraph—

"corporate finance service" means a service consisting in—

(a) underwriting in respect of issues of, or the placing of issues of, any instrument,

(b) advice to undertakings on capital structure, industrial strategy and related matters and advice and service relating to mergers and the purchase of undertakings, or

(c) services relating to such underwriting as is mentioned in paragraph (a);

"instrument" means any instrument listed in section B of the Annex to the Council Directive on investment services in the securities field (93/22/EEC) … ;

"price" includes value;

"relevant person" means—

[(a) any person who, by reason of any permission he has under Part IV of the Financial Services and Markets Act 2000, is able to carry on a corporate finance service without contravening the general prohibition, within the meaning of section 19 of that Act,

(b) an EEA firm of the kind mentioned in paragraph 5(a) or (b) of Schedule 3 to that Act which has qualified for authorisation under paragraph 12 of that Schedule, and may lawfully carry on a corporate finance service,

(c) any person who is exempt from the general prohibition in respect of any corporate finance service—

(i) as a result of an exemption order made under section 38(1) of that Act, or

(ii) by reason of section 39(1) of that Act (appointed representatives),

(cc) any person, not falling within paragraph (a), (b) or (c) who may lawfully carry on a corporate finance service without contravening the general prohibition,]

(d) any person who, in the course of his employment, provides to his employer a service falling within paragraph (b) or (c) of the definition of "corporate finance service", or

(e) any partner who provides to other partners in the partnership a service falling within either of those paragraphs.

Negotiations

7. Personal data which consist of records of the intentions of the data controller in relation to any negotiations with the data subject are exempt from the subject information provisions in any case to the extent to which the application of those provisions would be likely to prejudice those negotiations.

Examination marks

8.—(1) Section 7 shall have effect subject to the provisions of sub-paragraphs (2) to (4) in the case of personal data consisting of marks or other information processed by a data controller—

(a) for the purpose of determining the results of an academic, professional or other examination or of enabling the results of any such examination to be determined, or

(b) in consequence of the determination of any such results.

(2) Where the relevant day falls before the day on which the results of the examination are announced, the period mentioned in section 7(8) shall be extended until—

(a) the end of five months beginning with the relevant day, or

(b) the end of forty days beginning with the date of the announcement,

whichever is the earlier.

(3) Where by virtue of sub-paragraph (2) a period longer than the prescribed period elapses after the relevant day before the request is complied with, the information to be supplied pursuant to the request shall be supplied both by reference to the data in question at the time when the request is received and (if different) by reference to the data as from time to time held in the period beginning when the request is received and ending when it is complied with.

(4) For the purposes of this paragraph the results of an examination shall be treated as announced when they are first published or (if not published) when they are first made available or communicated to the candidate in question.

(5) In this paragraph—

"examination" includes any process for determining the knowledge, intelligence, skill or ability of a candidate by reference to his performance in any test, work or other activity;

"the prescribed period" means forty days or such other period as is for the time being prescribed under section 7 in relation to the personal data in question;

"relevant day" has the same meaning as in section 7.

Examination scripts etc

9.—(1) Personal data consisting of information recorded by candidates during an academic, professional or other examination are exempt from section 7.

(2) In this paragraph "examination" has the same meaning as in paragraph 8.

Legal professional privilege

10. Personal data are exempt from the subject information provisions if the data consist of information in respect of which a claim to legal professional privilege [or, in Scotland, to confidentiality of communications] could be maintained in legal proceedings.

Self-incrimination

11.—(1) A person need not comply with any request or order under section 7 to the extent that compliance would, by revealing evidence of the commission of any offence other than an offence under this Act, expose him to proceedings for that offence.

(2) Information disclosed by any person in compliance with any request or order under section 7 shall not be admissible against him in proceedings for an offence under this Act.

[592]

NOTES

Para 3: words in square brackets in sub-para (b) inserted by the Freedom of Information Act 2000, s 73, Sch 6, para 6.

Para 4: sub-para (1) numbered as such, words in square brackets in sub-para (1)(b) substituted, and sub-para (2) added, by the Northern Ireland Act 1998, s 99, Sch 13, para 21; words in first pair of square brackets substituted by the Secretary of State for Constitutional Affairs Order 2003, SI 2003/1887, art 9, Sch 2, para 9(1)(e).

Para 6: words in square brackets in sub-para (2) substituted by SI 2003/1887, art 9, Sch 2, para 9(1)(e); in sub-para (3), words omitted from definition "instrument" repealed, and in definition "relevant person" paras (a)–(c), (cc) substituted, for paras (a)–(c) as originally enacted, by the Financial Services and Markets Act 2000 (Consequential Amendments) Order 2002, SI 2002/1555, art 25.

Para 10: words in square brackets substituted by the Freedom of Information Act 2000, s 73, Sch 6, para 7.

Orders: the Data Protection (Corporate Finance Exemption) Order 2000, SI 2000/184 at **[813]**; the Data Protection (Crown Appointments) Order 2000, SI 2000/416 at **[938]**.

SCHEDULE 8
TRANSITIONAL RELIEF

Section 39

PART I
INTERPRETATION OF SCHEDULE

1.—(1) For the purposes of this Schedule, personal data are "eligible data" at any time if, and to the extent that, they are at that time subject to processing which was already under way immediately before 24th October 1998.

(2) In this Schedule—

"eligible automated data" means eligible data which fall within paragraph (a) or (b) of the definition of "data" in section 1(1);

"eligible manual data" means eligible data which are not eligible automated data;

"the first transitional period" means the period beginning with the commencement of this Schedule and ending with 23rd October 2001;

"the second transitional period" means the period beginning with 24th October 2001 and ending with 23rd October 2007.

[593]

PART II
EXEMPTIONS AVAILABLE BEFORE 24TH OCTOBER 2001

Manual data

2.—(1) Eligible manual data, other than data forming part of an accessible record, are exempt from the data protection principles and Parts II and III of this Act during the first transitional period.

(2) This paragraph does not apply to eligible manual data to which paragraph 4 applies.

3.—(1) This paragraph applies to—

(a) eligible manual data forming part of an accessible record, and

(b) personal data which fall within paragraph (d) of the definition of "data" in section 1(1) but which, because they are not subject to processing which was already under way immediately before 24th October 1998, are not eligible data for the purposes of this Schedule.

(2) During the first transitional period, data to which this paragraph applies are exempt from—

(a) the data protection principles, except the sixth principle so far as relating to sections 7 and 12A,

(b) Part II of this Act, except—

(i) section 7 (as it has effect subject to section 8) and section 12A, and

(ii) section 15 so far as relating to those sections, and

(c) Part III of this Act.

4.—(1) This paragraph applies to eligible manual data which consist of information relevant to the financial standing of the data subject and in respect of which the data controller is a credit reference agency.

(2) During the first transitional period, data to which this paragraph applies are exempt from—

(a) the data protection principles, except the sixth principle so far as relating to sections 7 and 12A,

(b) Part II of this Act, except—

(i) section 7 (as it has effect subject to sections 8 and 9) and section 12A, and

(ii) section 15 so far as relating to those sections, and

(c) Part III of this Act.

Processing otherwise than by reference to the data subject

5. During the first transitional period, for the purposes of this Act (apart from paragraph 1), eligible automated data are not to be regarded as being "processed" unless the processing is by reference to the data subject.

Payrolls and accounts

6.—(1) Subject to sub-paragraph (2), eligible automated data processed by a data controller for one or more of the following purposes—

(a) calculating amounts payable by way of remuneration or pensions in respect of service in any employment or office or making payments of, or of sums deducted from, such remuneration or pensions, or

(b) keeping accounts relating to any business or other activity carried on by the data controller or keeping records of purchases, sales or other transactions for the purpose of ensuring that the requisite payments are made by or to him in respect of those transactions or for the purpose of making financial or management forecasts to assist him in the conduct of any such business or activity,

are exempt from the data protection principles and Parts II and III of this Act during the first transitional period.

(2) It shall be a condition of the exemption of any eligible automated data under this paragraph that the data are not processed for any other purpose, but the exemption is not lost by any processing of the eligible data for any other purpose if the data controller shows that he had taken such care to prevent it as in all the circumstances was reasonably required.

(3) Data processed only for one or more of the purposes mentioned in subparagraph (1)(a) may be disclosed—

(a) to any person, other than the data controller, by whom the remuneration or pensions in question are payable,

(b) for the purpose of obtaining actuarial advice,

(c) for the purpose of giving information as to the persons in any employment or office for use in medical research into the health of, or injuries suffered by, persons engaged in particular occupations or working in particular places or areas,

(d) if the data subject (or a person acting on his behalf) has requested or consented to the disclosure of the data either generally or in the circumstances in which the disclosure in question is made, or

(e) if the person making the disclosure has reasonable grounds for believing that the disclosure falls within paragraph (d).

(4) Data processed for any of the purposes mentioned in sub-paragraph (1) may be disclosed—

(a) for the purpose of audit or where the disclosure is for the purpose only of giving information about the data controller's financial affairs, or

(b) in any case in which disclosure would be permitted by any other provision of this Part of this Act if sub-paragraph (2) were included among the non-disclosure provisions.

(5) In this paragraph "remuneration" includes remuneration in kind and "pensions" includes gratuities or similar benefits.

Unincorporated members' clubs and mailing lists

7. Eligible automated data processed by an unincorporated members' club and relating only to the members of the club are exempt from the data protection principles and Parts II and III of this Act during the first transitional period.

8. Eligible automated data processed by a data controller only for the purposes of distributing, or recording the distribution of, articles or information to the data subjects and consisting only of their names, addresses or other particulars necessary for effecting the distribution, are exempt from the data protection principles and Parts II and III of this Act during the first transitional period.

PART II DATA PROTECTION

9. Neither paragraph 7 nor paragraph 8 applies to personal data relating to any data subject unless he has been asked by the club or data controller whether he objects to the data relating to him being processed as mentioned in that paragraph and has not objected.

10. It shall be a condition of the exemption of any data under paragraph 7 that the data are not disclosed except as permitted by paragraph 11 and of the exemption under paragraph 8 that the data are not processed for any purpose other than that mentioned in that paragraph or as permitted by paragraph 11, but—

- (a) the exemption under paragraph 7 shall not be lost by any disclosure in breach of that condition, and
- (b) the exemption under paragraph 8 shall not be lost by any processing in breach of that condition,

if the data controller shows that he had taken such care to prevent it as in all the circumstances was reasonably required.

11. Data to which paragraph 10 applies may be disclosed—

- (a) if the data subject (or a person acting on his behalf) has requested or consented to the disclosure of the data either generally or in the circumstances in which the disclosure in question is made,
- (b) if the person making the disclosure has reasonable grounds for believing that the disclosure falls within paragraph (a), or
- (c) in any case in which disclosure would be permitted by any other provision of this Part of this Act if paragraph 8 were included among the non-disclosure provisions.

Back-up data

12. Eligible automated data which are processed only for the purpose of replacing other data in the event of the latter being lost, destroyed or impaired are exempt from section 7 during the first transitional period.

Exemption of all eligible automated data from certain requirements

13.—(1) During the first transitional period, eligible automated data are exempt from the following provisions—

- (a) the first data protection principle to the extent to which it requires compliance with—
  - (i) paragraph 2 of Part II of Schedule 1,
  - (ii) the conditions in Schedule 2, and
  - (iii) the conditions in Schedule 3,
- (b) the seventh data protection principle to the extent to which it requires compliance with paragraph 12 of Part II of Schedule 1;
- (c) the eighth data protection principle,
- (d) in section 7(1), paragraphs (b), (c)(ii) and (d),
- (e) sections 10 and 11,
- (f) section 12, and
- (g) section 13, except so far as relating to—
  - (i) any contravention of the fourth data protection principle,
  - (ii) any disclosure without the consent of the data controller,
  - (iii) loss or destruction of data without the consent of the data controller, or
  - (iv) processing for the special purposes.

(2) The specific exemptions conferred by sub-paragraph (1)(a), (c) and (e) do not limit the data controller's general duty under the first data protection principle to ensure that processing is fair.

[594]

PART III
EXEMPTIONS AVAILABLE AFTER 23RD OCTOBER 2001 BUT BEFORE 24TH OCTOBER 2007

14.—(1) This paragraph applies to—

- (a) eligible manual data which were held immediately before 24th October 1998, and

(b) personal data which fall within paragraph (d) of the definition of "data" in section 1(1) but do not fall within paragraph (a) of this subparagraph,

but does not apply to eligible manual data to which the exemption in paragraph 16 applies.

(2) During the second transitional period, data to which this paragraph applies are exempt from the following provisions—

(a) the first data protection principle except to the extent to which it requires compliance with paragraph 2 of Part II of Schedule 1,
(b) the second, third, fourth and fifth data protection principles, and
(c) section 14(1) to (3).

[14A.—(1) This paragraph applies to personal data which fall within paragraph (e) of the definition of "data" in section 1(1) and do not fall within paragraph 14(1)(a), but does not apply to eligible manual data to which the exemption in paragraph 16 applies.

(2) During the second transitional period, data to which this paragraph applies are exempt from—

(a) the fourth data protection principle, and
(b) section 14(1) to (3).]

[595]

NOTES

Para 14A: inserted by the Freedom of Information Act 2000, s 70(3).

PART IV
EXEMPTIONS AFTER 23RD OCTOBER 2001 FOR HISTORICAL RESEARCH

15. In this Part of this Schedule "the relevant conditions" has the same meaning as in section 33.

16.—(1) Eligible manual data which are processed only for the purpose of historical research in compliance with the relevant conditions are exempt from the provisions specified in sub-paragraph (2) after 23rd October 2001.

(2) The provisions referred to in sub-paragraph (1) are—

(a) the first data protection principle except in so far as it requires compliance with paragraph 2 of Part II of Schedule 1,
(b) the second, third, fourth and fifth data protection principles, and
(c) section 14(1) to (3).

17.—(1) After 23rd October 2001 eligible automated data which are processed only for the purpose of historical research in compliance with the relevant conditions are exempt from the first data protection principle to the extent to which it requires compliance with the conditions in Schedules 2 and 3.

(2) Eligible automated data which are processed—

(a) only for the purpose of historical research,
(b) in compliance with the relevant conditions, and
(c) otherwise than by reference to the data subject,

are also exempt from the provisions referred to in sub-paragraph (3) after 23rd October 2001.

(3) The provisions referred to in sub-paragraph (2) are—

(a) the first data protection principle except in so far as it requires compliance with paragraph 2 of Part II of Schedule 1,
(b) the second, third, fourth and fifth data protection principles, and
(c) section 14(1) to (3).

18. For the purposes of this Part of this Schedule personal data are not to be treated as processed otherwise than for the purpose of historical research merely because the data are disclosed—

(a) to any person, for the purpose of historical research only,
(b) to the data subject or a person acting on his behalf,
(c) at the request, or with the consent, of the data subject or a person acting on his behalf, or

(d) in circumstances in which the person making the disclosure has reasonable grounds for believing that the disclosure falls within paragraph (a), (b) or (c).

[596]

PART V
EXEMPTION FROM SECTION 22

19. Processing which was already under way immediately before 24th October 1998 is not assessable processing for the purposes of section 22.

[597]

SCHEDULE 9
POWERS OF ENTRY AND INSPECTION

Section 50

Issue of warrants

1.—(1) If a circuit judge [or a District Judge (Magistrates' Courts)] is satisfied by information on oath supplied by the Commissioner that there are reasonable grounds for suspecting—

(a) that a data controller has contravened or is contravening any of the data protection principles, or

(b) that an offence under this Act has been or is being committed,

and that evidence of the contravention or of the commission of the offence is to be found on any premises specified in the information, he may, subject to subparagraph (2) and paragraph 2, grant a warrant to the Commissioner.

(2) A judge shall not issue a warrant under this Schedule in respect of any personal data processed for the special purposes unless a determination by the Commissioner under section 45 with respect to those data has taken effect.

(3) A warrant issued under sub-paragraph (1) shall authorise the Commissioner or any of his officers or staff at any time within seven days of the date of the warrant to enter the premises, to search them, to inspect, examine, operate and test any equipment found there which is used or intended to be used for the processing of personal data and to inspect and seize any documents or other material found there which may be such evidence as is mentioned in that sub-paragraph.

2.—(1) A judge shall not issue a warrant under this Schedule unless he is satisfied—

(a) that the Commissioner has given seven days' notice in writing to the occupier of the premises in question demanding access to the premises, and

(b) that either—

(i) access was demanded at a reasonable hour and was unreasonably refused, or

(ii) although entry to the premises was granted, the occupier unreasonably refused to comply with a request by the Commissioner or any of the Commissioner's officers or staff to permit the Commissioner or the officer or member of staff to do any of the things referred to in paragraph 1(3), and

(c) that the occupier, has, after the refusal, been notified by the Commissioner of the application for the warrant and has had an opportunity of being heard by the judge on the question whether or not it should be issued.

(2) Sub-paragraph (1) shall not apply if the judge is satisfied that the case is one of urgency or that compliance with those provisions would defeat the object of the entry.

3. A judge who issues a warrant under this Schedule shall also issue two copies of it and certify them clearly as copies.

Execution of warrants

4. A person executing a warrant issued under this Schedule may use such reasonable force as may be necessary.

5. A warrant issued under this Schedule shall be executed at a reasonable hour unless it appears to the person executing it that there are grounds for suspecting that the evidence in question would not be found if it were so executed.

6. If the person who occupies the premises in respect of which a warrant is issued under this Schedule is present when the warrant is executed, he shall be shown the warrant and supplied with a copy of it; and if that person is not present a copy of the warrant shall be left in a prominent place on the premises.

7.—(1) A person seizing anything in pursuance of a warrant under this Schedule shall give a receipt for it if asked to do so.

(2) Anything so seized may be retained for so long as is necessary in all the circumstances but the person in occupation of the premises in question shall be given a copy of anything that is seized if he so requests and the person executing the warrant considers that it can be done without undue delay.

Matters exempt from inspection and seizure

8. The powers of inspection and seizure conferred by a warrant issued under this Schedule shall not be exercisable in respect of personal data which by virtue of section 28 are exempt from any of the provisions of this Act.

9.—(1) Subject to the provisions of this paragraph, the powers of inspection and seizure conferred by a warrant issued under this Schedule shall not be exercisable in respect of—

(a) any communication between a professional legal adviser and his client in connection with the giving of legal advice to the client with respect to his obligations, liabilities or rights under this Act, or

(b) any communication between a professional legal adviser and his client, or between such an adviser or his client and any other person, made in connection with or in contemplation of proceedings under or arising out of this Act (including proceedings before the Tribunal) and for the purposes of such proceedings.

(2) Sub-paragraph (1) applies also to—

(a) any copy or other record of any such communication as is there mentioned, and

(b) any document or article enclosed with or referred to in any such communication if made in connection with the giving of any advice or, as the case may be, in connection with or in contemplation of and for the purposes of such proceedings as are there mentioned.

(3) This paragraph does not apply to anything in the possession of any person other than the professional legal adviser or his client or to anything held with the intention of furthering a criminal purpose.

(4) In this paragraph references to the client of a professional legal adviser include references to any person representing such a client.

10. If the person in occupation of any premises in respect of which a warrant is issued under this Schedule objects to the inspection or seizure under the warrant of any material on the grounds that it consists partly of matters in respect of which those powers are not exercisable, he shall, if the person executing the warrant so requests, furnish that person with a copy of so much of the material as is not exempt from those powers.

Return of warrants

11. A warrant issued under this Schedule shall be returned to the court from which it was issued—

(a) after being executed, or

(b) if not executed within the time authorised for its execution;

and the person by whom any such warrant is executed shall make an endorsement on it stating what powers have been exercised by him under the warrant.

Offences

12. Any person who—
   (a) intentionally obstructs a person in the execution of a warrant issued under this Schedule, or
   (b) fails without reasonable excuse to give any person executing such a warrant such assistance as he may reasonably require for the execution of the warrant,

is guilty of an offence.

Vessels, vehicles etc

13. In this Schedule "premises" includes any vessel, vehicle, aircraft or hovercraft, and references to the occupier of any premises include references to the person in charge of any vessel, vehicle, aircraft or hovercraft.

Scotland and Northern Ireland

14. In the application of this Schedule to Scotland—
   (a) for any reference to a circuit judge there is substituted a reference to the sheriff,
   (b) for any reference to information on oath there is substituted a reference to evidence on oath, and
   (c) for the reference to the court from which the warrant was issued there is substituted a reference to the sheriff clerk.

15. In the application of this Schedule to Northern Ireland—
   (a) for any reference to a circuit judge there is substituted a reference to a county court judge, and
   (b) for any reference to information on oath there is substituted a reference to a complaint on oath.

[598]

NOTES

Para 1: words in square brackets inserted by the Courts Act 2003, s 65, Sch 4, para 8, as from a day to be appointed.

As to the power of seizure under para 1 of this Schedule, see the Criminal Justice and Police Act 2001, s 50, Sch 1, Pt 1, para 65 (additional powers of seizure of material from premises).

SCHEDULE 10

FURTHER PROVISIONS RELATING TO ASSISTANCE UNDER SECTION 53

Section 53(6)

1. In this Schedule "applicant" and "proceedings" have the same meaning as in section 53.

2. The assistance provided under section 53 may include the making of arrangements for, or for the Commissioner to bear the costs of—
   (a) the giving of advice or assistance by a solicitor or counsel, and
   (b) the representation of the applicant, or the provision to him of such assistance as is usually given by a solicitor or counsel—
      (i) in steps preliminary or incidental to the proceedings, or
      (ii) in arriving at or giving effect to a compromise to avoid or bring an end to the proceedings.

3. Where assistance is provided with respect to the conduct of proceedings—
   (a) it shall include an agreement by the Commissioner to indemnify the applicant (subject only to any exceptions specified in the notification) in respect of any liability to pay costs or expenses arising by virtue of any judgment or order of the court in the proceedings,
   (b) it may include an agreement by the Commissioner to indemnify the applicant in respect of any liability to pay costs or expenses arising by virtue of any compromise or settlement arrived at in order to avoid the proceedings or bring the proceedings to an end, and
   (c) it may include an agreement by the Commissioner to indemnify the applicant in

respect of any liability to pay damages pursuant to an undertaking given on the grant of interlocutory relief (in Scotland, an interim order) to the applicant.

4. Where the Commissioner provides assistance in relation to any proceedings, he shall do so on such terms, or make such other arrangements, as will secure that a person against whom the proceedings have been or are commenced is informed that assistance has been or is being provided by the Commissioner in relation to them.

5. In England and Wales or Northern Ireland, the recovery of expenses incurred by the Commissioner in providing an applicant with assistance (as taxed or assessed in such manner as may be prescribed by rules of court) shall constitute a first charge for the benefit of the Commissioner—

(a) on any costs which, by virtue of any judgment or order of the court, are payable to the applicant by any other person in respect of the matter in connection with which the assistance is provided, and

(b) on any sum payable to the applicant under a compromise or settlement arrived at in connection with that matter to avoid or bring to an end any proceedings.

6. In Scotland, the recovery of such expenses (as taxed or assessed in such manner as may be prescribed by rules of court) shall be paid to the Commissioner, in priority to other debts—

(a) out of any expenses which, by virtue of any judgment or order of the court, are payable to the applicant by any other person in respect of the matter in connection with which the assistance is provided, and

(b) out of any sum payable to the applicant under a compromise or settlement arrived at in connection with that matter to avoid or bring to an end any proceedings.

[599]

SCHEDULE 11
EDUCATIONAL RECORDS

Section 68(1), (6)

Meaning of "educational record"

1. For the purposes of section 68 "educational record" means any record to which paragraph 2, 5 or 7 applies.

England and Wales

2. This paragraph applies to any record of information which—

(a) is processed by or on behalf of the governing body of, or a teacher at, any school in England and Wales specified in paragraph 3,

(b) relates to any person who is or has been a pupil at the school, and

(c) originated from or was supplied by or on behalf of any of the persons specified in paragraph 4,

other than information which is processed by a teacher solely for the teacher's own use.

3. The schools referred to in paragraph 2(a) are—

(a) a school maintained by a local education authority, and

(b) a special school, as defined by section 6(2) of the Education Act 1996, which is not so maintained.

4. The persons referred to in paragraph 2(c) are—

(a) an employee of the local education authority which maintains the school,

(b) in the case of—

(i) a voluntary aided, foundation or foundation special school (within the meaning of the School Standards and Framework Act 1998), or

(ii) a special school which is not maintained by a local education authority,

a teacher or other employee at the school (including an educational psychologist engaged by the governing body under a contract for services),

(c) the pupil to whom the record relates, and

(d) a parent, as defined by section 576(1) of the Education Act 1996, of that pupil.

5. This paragraph applies to any record of information which is processed—

(a) by an education authority in Scotland, and
(b) for the purpose of the relevant function of the authority,

other than information which is processed by a teacher solely for the teacher's own use.

6. For the purposes of paragraph 5—
(a) "education authority" means an education authority within the meaning of the Education (Scotland) Act 1980 ("the 1980 Act") . . . ,
(b) "the relevant function" means, in relation to each of those authorities, their function under section 1 of the 1980 Act and section 7(1) of the 1989 Act, and
(c) information processed by an education authority is processed for the purpose of the relevant function of the authority if the processing relates to the discharge of that function in respect of a person—
(i) who is or has been a pupil in a school provided by the authority, or
(ii) who receives, or has received, further education (within the meaning of the 1980 Act) so provided.

Northern Ireland

7.—(1) This paragraph applies to any record of information which—
(a) is processed by or on behalf of the Board of Governors of, or a teacher at, any grant-aided school in Northern Ireland,
(b) relates to any person who is or has been a pupil at the school, and
(c) originated from or was supplied by or on behalf of any of the persons specified in paragraph 8,

other than information which is processed by a teacher solely for the teacher's own use.

(2) In sub-paragraph (1) "grant-aided school" has the same meaning as in the Education and Libraries (Northern Ireland) Order 1986.

8. The persons referred to in paragraph 7(1) are—
(a) a teacher at the school,
(b) an employee of an education and library board, other than such a teacher,
(c) the pupil to whom the record relates, and
(d) a parent (as defined by Article 2(2) of the Education and Libraries (Northern Ireland) Order 1986) of that pupil.

England and Wales: transitory provisions

9.—(1) Until the appointed day within the meaning of section 20 of the School Standards and Framework Act 1998, this Schedule shall have effect subject to the following modifications.

(2) Paragraph 3 shall have effect as if for paragraph (b) and the "and" immediately preceding it there were substituted—
"(aa) a grant-maintained school, as defined by section 183(1) of the Education Act 1996,
(ab) a grant-maintained special school, as defined by section 337(4) of that Act, and
(b) a special school, as defined by section 6(2) of that Act, which is neither a maintained special school, as defined by section 337(3) of that Act, nor a grant-maintained special school.".

(3) Paragraph 4(b)(i) shall have effect as if for the words from "foundation", in the first place where it occurs, to "1998)" there were substituted "or grant-maintained school".

[600]

NOTES

Para 6: words omitted from sub-para (a) repealed by the Standards in Scotland's Schools etc Act 2000, s 60(2), Sch 3.

SCHEDULE 12
ACCESSIBLE PUBLIC RECORDS

Section 68(1)(c)

Meaning of "accessible public record"

1. For the purposes of section 68 "accessible public record" means any record which is kept by an authority specified—
   (a) as respects England and Wales, in the Table in paragraph 2,
   (b) as respects Scotland, in the Table in paragraph 4, or
   (c) as respects Northern Ireland, in the Table in paragraph 6,

and is a record of information of a description specified in that Table in relation to that authority.

Housing and social services records: England and Wales

2. The following is the Table referred to in paragraph 1(a).

TABLE OF AUTHORITIES AND INFORMATION

The authorities	*The accessible information*
Housing Act local authority.	Information held for the purpose of any of the authority's tenancies.
Local social services authority.	Information held for any purpose of the authority's social services functions.

3.—(1) The following provisions apply for the interpretation of the Table in paragraph 2.

(2) Any authority which, by virtue of section 4(e) of the Housing Act 1985, is a local authority for the purpose of any provision of that Act is a "Housing Act local authority" for the purposes of this Schedule, and so is any housing action trust established under Part III of the Housing Act 1988.

(3) Information contained in records kept by a Housing Act local authority is "held for the purpose of any of the authority's tenancies" if it is held for any purpose of the relationship of landlord and tenant of a dwelling which subsists, has subsisted or may subsist between the authority and any individual who is, has been or, as the case may be, has applied to be, a tenant of the authority.

(4) Any authority which, by virtue of section 1 or 12 of the Local Authority Social Services Act 1970, is or is treated as a local authority for the purposes of that Act is a "local social services authority" for the purposes of this Schedule; and information contained in records kept by such an authority is "held for any purpose of the authority's social services functions" if it is held for the purpose of any past, current or proposed exercise of such a function in any case.

(5) Any expression used in paragraph 2 or this paragraph and in Part II of the Housing Act 1985 or the Local Authority Social Services Act 1970 has the same meaning as in that Act.

Housing and social services records: Scotland

4. The following is the Table referred to in paragraph 1(b).

TABLE OF AUTHORITIES AND INFORMATION

The authorities	*The accessible information*
Local authority.	Information held for any purpose of any of the body's tenancies.
Scottish Homes.	
Social work authority.	Information held for any purpose of the authority's functions under the Social Work (Scotland) Act 1968 and the enactments referred to in section 5(1B) of that Act.

5.—(1) The following provisions apply for the interpretation of the Table in paragraph 4.

(2) "Local authority" means—

(a) a council constituted under section 2 of the Local Government etc (Scotland) Act 1994,

(b) a joint board or joint committee of two or more of those councils, or

(c) any trust under the control of such a council.

(3) Information contained in records kept by a local authority *or Scottish Homes* is held for the purpose of any of their tenancies if it is held for any purpose of the relationship of landlord and tenant of a dwelling-house which subsists, has subsisted or may subsist between the authority *or, as the case may be, Scottish Homes* and any individual who is, has been or, as the case may be, has applied to be a tenant of theirs.

(4) "Social work authority" means a local authority for the purposes of the Social Work (Scotland) Act 1968; and information contained in records kept by such an authority is held for any purpose of their functions if it is held for the purpose of any past, current or proposed exercise of such a function in any case.

Housing and social services records: Northern Ireland

6. The following is the Table referred to in paragraph 1(c).

TABLE OF AUTHORITIES AND INFORMATION

The authorities	*The accessible information*
The Northern Ireland Housing Executive.	Information held for the purpose of any of the Executive's tenancies.
A Health and Social Services Board.	Information held for the purpose of any past, current or proposed exercise by the Board of any function exercisable, by virtue of directions under Article 17(1) of the Health and Personal Social Services (Northern Ireland) Order 1972, by the Board on behalf of the Department of Health and Social Services with respect to the administration of personal social services under— (a) the Children and Young Persons Act (Northern Ireland) 1968; (b) the Health and Personal Social Services (Northern Ireland) Order 1972; (c) Article 47 of the Matrimonial Causes (Northern Ireland) Order 1978;

The authorities	*The accessible information*
	(d) Article 11 of the Domestic Proceedings (Northern Ireland) Order 1980;
	(e) the Adoption (Northern Ireland) Order 1987; or
	(f) the Children (Northern Ireland) Order 1995.
An HSS trust.	Information held for the purpose of any past, current or proposed exercise by the trust of any function exercisable, by virtue of an authorisation under Article 3(1) of the Health and Personal Social Services (Northern Ireland) Order 1994, by the trust on behalf of a Health and Social Services Board with respect to the administration of personal social services under any statutory provision mentioned in the last preceding entry.

7.—(1) This paragraph applies for the interpretation of the Table in paragraph 6.

(2) Information contained in records kept by the Northern Ireland Housing Executive is "held for the purpose of any of the Executive's tenancies" if it is held for any purpose of the relationship of landlord and tenant of a dwelling which subsists, has subsisted or may subsist between the Executive and any individual who is, has been or, as the case may be, has applied to be, a tenant of the Executive.

[601]

NOTES

Para 4: entry "Scottish Homes" repealed by the Housing (Scotland) Act 2001, s 112, Sch 10, para 26(a), as from a day to be appointed.

Para 5: words in italics repealed by the Housing (Scotland) Act 2001, s 112, Sch 10, para 26(b), as from a day to be appointed.

SCHEDULE 13

MODIFICATIONS OF ACT HAVING EFFECT BEFORE 24TH OCTOBER 2007

Section 72

1. After section 12 there is inserted—

"12A Rights of data subjects in relation to exempt manual data

(1) A data subject is entitled at any time by notice in writing—

(a) to require the data controller to rectify, block, erase or destroy exempt manual data which are inaccurate or incomplete, or

(b) to require the data controller to cease holding exempt manual data in a way incompatible with the legitimate purposes pursued by the data controller.

(2) A notice under subsection (1)(a) or (b) must state the data subject's reasons for believing that the data are inaccurate or incomplete or, as the case may be, his reasons for believing that they are held in a way incompatible with the legitimate purposes pursued by the data controller.

(3) If the court is satisfied, on the application of any person who has given a notice under subsection (1) which appears to the court to be justified (or to be justified to any extent) that the data controller in question has failed to comply with the notice, the court may order him to take such steps for complying with the notice (or for complying with it to that extent) as the court thinks fit.

(4) In this section "exempt manual data" means—

(a) in relation to the first transitional period, as defined by paragraph 1(2) of Schedule 8, data to which paragraph 3 or 4 of that Schedule applies, and

(b) in relation to the second transitional period, as so defined, data to which paragraph 14 [or 14A] of that Schedule applies.

PART II DATA PROTECTION

(5) For the purposes of this section personal data are incomplete if, and only if, the data, although not inaccurate, are such that their incompleteness would constitute a contravention of the third or fourth data protection principles, if those principles applied to the data.".

2. In section 32—
(a) in subsection (2) after "section 12" there is inserted—
"(dd) section 12A,", and
(b) in subsection (4) after "12(8)" there is inserted ", 12A(3)".

3. In section 34 for "section 14(1) to (3)" there is substituted "sections 12A and 14(1) to (3)."

4. In section 53(1) after "12(8)" there is inserted ", 12A(3)".

5. In paragraph 8 of Part II of Schedule 1, the word "or" at the end of paragraph (c) is omitted and after paragraph (d) there is inserted
"or
(e) he contravenes section 12A by failing to comply with a notice given under subsection (1) of that section to the extent that the notice is justified.".

[602]

NOTES

Para 1: words in square brackets in s 12A(4)(b) (as set out above) inserted by the Freedom of Information Act 2000, s 70(4).

SCHEDULE 14
TRANSITIONAL PROVISIONS AND SAVINGS

Section 73

Interpretation

1. In this Schedule—
"the 1984 Act" means the Data Protection Act 1984;
"the old principles" means the data protection principles within the meaning of the 1984 Act;
"the new principles" means the data protection principles within the meaning of this Act.

Effect of registration under Part II of 1984 Act

2.—(1) Subject to sub-paragraphs (4) and (5) any person who, immediately before the commencement of Part III of this Act—
(a) is registered as a data user under Part II of the 1984 Act, or
(b) is treated by virtue of section 7(6) of the 1984 Act as so registered,
is exempt from section 17(1) of this Act until the end of the registration period …

(2) In sub-paragraph (1) "the registration period", in relation to a person, means—
(a) where there is a single entry in respect of that person as a data user, the period at the end of which, if section 8 of the 1984 Act had remained in force, that entry would have fallen to be removed unless renewed, and
(b) where there are two or more entries in respect of that person as a data user, the period at the end of which, if that section had remained in force, the last of those entries to expire would have fallen to be removed unless renewed.

(3) Any application for registration as a data user under Part II of the 1984 Act which is received by the Commissioner before the commencement of Part III of this Act (including any appeal against a refusal of registration) shall be determined in accordance with the old principles and the provisions of the 1984 Act.

(4) If a person falling within paragraph (b) of sub-paragraph (1) receives a notification under section 7(1) of the 1984 Act of the refusal of his application, sub-paragraph (1) shall cease to apply to him—
(a) if no appeal is brought, at the end of the period within which an appeal can be brought against the refusal, or

(b) on the withdrawal or dismissal of the appeal.

(5) If a data controller gives a notification under section 18(1) at a time when he is exempt from section 17(1) by virtue of sub-paragraph (1), he shall cease to be so exempt.

(6) The Commissioner shall include in the register maintained under section 19 an entry in respect of each person who is exempt from section 17(1) by virtue of sub-paragraph (1); and each entry shall consist of the particulars which, immediately before the commencement of Part III of this Act, were included (or treated as included) in respect of that person in the register maintained under section 4 of the 1984 Act.

(7) Notification regulations under Part III of this Act may make provision modifying the duty referred to in section 20(1) in its application to any person in respect of whom an entry in the register maintained under section 19 has been made under sub-paragraph (6).

(8) Notification regulations under Part III of this Act may make further transitional provision in connection with the substitution of Part III of this Act for Part II of the 1984 Act (registration), including provision modifying the application of provisions of Part III in transitional cases.

Rights of data subjects

3.—(1) The repeal of section 21 of the 1984 Act (right of access to personal data) does not affect the application of that section in any case in which the request (together with the information referred to in paragraph (a) of subsection (4) of that section and, in a case where it is required, the consent referred to in paragraph (b) of that subsection) was received before the day on which the repeal comes into force.

(2) Sub-paragraph (1) does not apply where the request is made by reference to this Act.

(3) Any fee paid for the purposes of section 21 of the 1984 Act before the commencement of section 7 in a case not falling within sub-paragraph (1) shall be taken to have been paid for the purposes of section 7.

4. The repeal of section 22 of the 1984 Act (compensation for inaccuracy) and the repeal of section 23 of that Act (compensation for loss or unauthorised disclosure) do not affect the application of those sections in relation to damage or distress suffered at any time by reason of anything done or omitted to be done before the commencement of the repeals.

5. The repeal of section 24 of the 1984 Act (rectification and erasure) does not affect any case in which the application to the court was made before the day on which the repeal comes into force.

6. Subsection (3)(b) of section 14 does not apply where the rectification, blocking, erasure or destruction occurred before the commencement of that section.

Enforcement and transfer prohibition notices served under Part V of 1984 Act

7.—(1) If, immediately before the commencement of section 40—

(a) an enforcement notice under section 10 of the 1984 Act has effect, and

(b) either the time for appealing against the notice has expired or any appeal has been determined,

then, after that commencement, to the extent mentioned in sub-paragraph (3), the notice shall have effect for the purposes of sections 41 and 47 as if it were an enforcement notice under section 40.

(2) Where an enforcement notice has been served under section 10 of the 1984 Act before the commencement of section 40 and immediately before that commencement either—

(a) the time for appealing against the notice has not expired, or

(b) an appeal has not been determined,

the appeal shall be determined in accordance with the provisions of the 1984 Act and the old principles and, unless the notice is quashed on appeal, to the extent mentioned in sub-paragraph (3) the notice shall have effect for the purposes of sections 41 and 47 as if it were an enforcement notice under section 40.

(3) An enforcement notice under section 10 of the 1984 Act has the effect described in sub-paragraph (1) or (2) only to the extent that the steps specified in the notice for complying with the old principle or principles in question are steps which the data controller could be required by an enforcement notice under section 40 to take for complying with the new principles or any of them.

8.—(1) If, immediately before the commencement of section 40—

(a) a transfer prohibition notice under section 12 of the 1984 Act has effect, and

(b) either the time for appealing against the notice has expired or any appeal has been determined,

then, on and after that commencement, to the extent specified in sub-paragraph (3), the notice shall have effect for the purposes of sections 41 and 47 as if it were an enforcement notice under section 40.

(2) Where a transfer prohibition notice has been served under section 12 of the 1984 Act and immediately before the commencement of section 40 either—

(a) the time for appealing against the notice has not expired, or

(b) an appeal has not been determined,

the appeal shall be determined in accordance with the provisions of the 1984 Act and the old principles and, unless the notice is quashed on appeal, to the extent mentioned in sub-paragraph (3) the notice shall have effect for the purposes of sections 41 and 47 as if it were an enforcement notice under section 40.

(3) A transfer prohibition notice under section 12 of the 1984 Act has the effect described in sub-paragraph (1) or (2) only to the extent that the prohibition imposed by the notice is one which could be imposed by an enforcement notice under section 40 for complying with the new principles or any of them.

Notices under new law relating to matters in relation to which 1984 Act had effect

9. The Commissioner may serve an enforcement notice under section 40 on or after the day on which that section comes into force if he is satisfied that, before that day, the data controller contravened the old principles by reason of any act or omission which would also have constituted a contravention of the new principles if they had applied before that day.

10. Subsection (5)(b) of section 40 does not apply where the rectification, blocking, erasure or destruction occurred before the commencement of that section.

11. The Commissioner may serve an information notice under section 43 on or after the day on which that section comes into force if he has reasonable grounds for suspecting that, before that day, the data controller contravened the old principles by reason of any act or omission which would also have constituted a contravention of the new principles if they had applied before that day.

12. Where by virtue of paragraph 11 an information notice is served on the basis of anything done or omitted to be done before the day on which section 43 comes into force, subsection (2)(b) of that section shall have effect as if the reference to the data controller having complied, or complying, with the new principles were a reference to the data controller having contravened the old principles by reason of any such act or omission as is mentioned in paragraph 11.

Self-incrimination, etc

13.—(1) In section 43(8), section 44(9) and paragraph 11 of Schedule 7, any reference to an offence under this Act includes a reference to an offence under the 1984 Act.

(2) In section 34(9) of the 1984 Act, any reference to an offence under that Act includes a reference to an offence under this Act.

Warrants issued under 1984 Act

14. The repeal of Schedule 4 to the 1984 Act does not affect the application of that Schedule in any case where a warrant was issued under that Schedule before the commencement of the repeal.

Complaints under section 36(2) of 1984 Act and requests for assessment under section 42

15. The repeal of section 36(2) of the 1984 Act does not affect the application of that provision in any case where the complaint was received by the Commissioner before the commencement of the repeal.

16. In dealing with a complaint under section 36(2) of the 1984 Act or a request for an assessment under section 42 of this Act, the Commissioner shall have regard to the provisions from time to time applicable to the processing, and accordingly—

(a) in section 36(2) of the 1984 Act, the reference to the old principles and the provisions of that Act includes, in relation to any time when the new principles and the provisions of this Act have effect, those principles and provisions, and

(b) in section 42 of this Act, the reference to the provisions of this Act includes, in relation to any time when the old principles and the provisions of the 1984 Act had effect, those principles and provisions.

Applications under Access to Health Records Act 1990 or corresponding Northern Ireland legislation

17.—(1) The repeal of any provision of the Access to Health Records Act 1990 does not affect—

(a) the application of section 3 or 6 of that Act in any case in which the application under that section was received before the day on which the repeal comes into force, or

(b) the application of section 8 of that Act in any case in which the application to the court was made before the day on which the repeal comes into force.

(2) Sub-paragraph (1)(a) does not apply in relation to an application for access to information which was made by reference to this Act.

18.—(1) The revocation of any provision of the Access to Health Records (Northern Ireland) Order 1993 does not affect—

(a) the application of Article 5 or 8 of that Order in any case in which the application under that Article was received before the day on which the repeal comes into force, or

(b) the application of Article 10 of that Order in any case in which the application to the court was made before the day on which the repeal comes into force.

(2) Sub-paragraph (1)(a) does not apply in relation to an application for access to information which was made by reference to this Act.

Applications under regulations under Access to Personal Files Act 1987 or corresponding Northern Ireland legislation

19.—(1) The repeal of the personal files enactments does not affect the application of regulations under those enactments in relation to—

(a) any request for information,

(b) any application for rectification or erasure, or

(c) any application for review of a decision,

which was made before the day on which the repeal comes into force.

(2) Sub-paragraph (1)(a) does not apply in relation to a request for information which was made by reference to this Act.

(3) In sub-paragraph (1) "the personal files enactments" means—

(a) in relation to Great Britain, the Access to Personal Files Act 1987, and

(b) in relation to Northern Ireland, Part II of the Access to Personal Files and Medical Reports (Northern Ireland) Order 1991.

Applications under section 158 of Consumer Credit Act 1974

20. Section 62 does not affect the application of section 158 of the Consumer Credit Act 1974 in any case where the request was received before the commencement of section 62, unless the request is made by reference to this Act.

[603]

NOTES

Para 2: words omitted from sub-para (1) repealed by the Freedom of Information Act 2000, ss 73, 86, Sch 6, para 8, Sch 8, Pt I.

Regulations: the Data Protection (Notification and Notification Fees) Regulations 2000, SI 2000/188 at **[828]**.

(*Sch 15 contains minor and consequential amendments.*)

SCHEDULE 16
REPEALS AND REVOCATIONS

Section 74(2)

PART I
REPEALS

Chapter	*Short title*	*Extent of repeal*
1984 c 35.	The Data Protection Act 1984.	The whole Act.
1986 c 60.	The Financial Services Act 1986.	Section 190.
1987 c 37.	The Access to Personal Files Act 1987.	The whole Act.
1988 c 40.	The Education Reform Act 1988.	Section 223.
1988 c 50.	The Housing Act 1988.	In Schedule 17, paragraph 80.
1990 c 23.	The Access to Health Records Act 1990.	In section 1(1), the words from "but does not" to the end.
		In section 3, subsection (1)(a) to (e) and, in subsection (6)(a), the words "in the case of an application made otherwise than by the patient".
		Section 4(1) and (2).
		In section 5(1)(a)(i), the words "of the patient or" and the word "other".
		In section 10, in subsection (2) the words "or orders" and in subsection (3) the words "or an order under section 2(3) above".
		In section 11, the definitions of "child" and "parental responsibility".
1990 c 37.	The Human Fertilisation and Embryology Act 1990.	Section 33(8).
1990 c 41.	The Courts and Legal Services Act 1990.	In Schedule 10, paragraph 58.
1992 c 13.	The Further and Higher Education Act 1992.	Section 86.
1992 c 37.	The Further and Higher Education (Scotland) Act 1992.	Section 59.

Chapter	*Short title*	*Extent of repeal*
1993 c 8.	The Judicial Pensions and Retirement Act 1993.	In Schedule 6, paragraph 50.
1993 c 10.	The Charities Act 1993.	Section 12.
1993 c 21.	The Osteopaths Act 1993.	Section 38.
1994 c 17.	The Chiropractors Act 1994.	Section 38.
1994 c 19.	The Local Government (Wales) Act 1994.	In Schedule 13, paragraph 30.
1994 c 33.	The Criminal Justice and Public Order Act 1994.	Section 161.
1994 c 39.	The Local Government etc (Scotland) Act 1994.	In Schedule 13, paragraph 154.

[604]

PART II
REVOCATIONS

Number	Title	Extent of revocation
SI 1991/1142	The Data Protection Registration Fee Order 1991	The Whole Order.
SI 1991/1707 (NI 14)	The Access to Personal Files and Medical Reports (Northern Ireland) Order 1991	Part II. The Schedule.
SI 1992/3218	The Banking Co-ordination (Second Council Directive) Regulations 1992	In Schedule 10, paragraphs 15 and 40.
SI 1993/1250 (NI 4)	The Access to Health Records (Northern Ireland) Order 1993	In Article 2(2), the definitions of "child" and "parental responsibility".
		In Article 3(1), the words from "but does not include" to the end.
		In Article 5, paragraph (1)(a) to (d) and, in paragraph (6)(a), the words "in the case of an application made otherwise than by the patient".
		Article 6(1) and (2).
		In Article 7(1)(a)(i), the words "of the patient or" and the word "other".
SI 1994/429 (NI 2)	The Health and Personal Social Services (Northern Ireland) Order 1994	In Schedule 1, the entries relating to the Access to Personal Files and Medical Reports (Northern Ireland) Order 1991.
SI 1994/1696	The Insurance Companies (Third Insurance Directives) Regulations 1994	In Schedule 8, paragraph 8.
SI 1995/755 (NI 2)	The Children (Northern Ireland) Order 1995	In Schedule 9, paragraphs 177 and 191.
SI 1995/3275	The Investment Services Regulations 1995	In Schedule 10, paragraphs 3 and 15.

Number	Title	Extent of revocation
SI 1996/2827	The Open-Ended Investment Companies (Investment Companies with Variable Capital) Regulations 1996	In Schedule 8, paragraphs 3 and 26.

[605]

HUMAN RIGHTS ACT 1998

(1998 c 42)

An Act to give further effect to rights and freedoms guaranteed under the European Convention on Human Rights; to make provision with respect to holders of certain judicial offices who become judges of the European Court of Human Rights; and for connected purposes

[9 November 1998]

ARRANGEMENT OF SECTIONS

Introduction

Judges of the European Court of Human Rights

Parliamentary procedure

Supplemental

Introduction

1 The Convention Rights

(1) In this Act "the Convention rights" means the rights and fundamental freedoms set out in—
- (a) Articles 2 to 12 and 14 of the Convention,
- (b) Articles 1 to 3 of the First Protocol, and
- (c) [Article 1 of the Thirteenth Protocol],

as read with Articles 16 to 18 of the Convention.

(2) Those Articles are to have effect for the purposes of this Act subject to any designated derogation or reservation (as to which see sections 14 and 15).

(3) The Articles are set out in Schedule 1.

(4) The [Secretary of State] may by order make such amendments to this Act as he considers appropriate to reflect the effect, in relation to the United Kingdom, of a protocol.

(5) In subsection (4) "protocol" means a protocol to the Convention—
- (a) which the United Kingdom has ratified; or
- (b) which the United Kingdom has signed with a view to ratification.

(6) No amendment may be made by an order under subsection (4) so as to come into force before the protocol concerned is in force in relation to the United Kingdom.

[606]

NOTES

Sub-s (1): words in square brackets substituted by the Human Rights Act 1998 (Amendment) Order 2004, SI 2004/1574, art 2(1).

Sub-s (4): words in square brackets substituted by the Secretary of State for Constitutional Affairs Order 2003, SI 2003/1887, art 9, Sch 2, para 10(1).

2 Interpretation of Convention rights

(1) A court or tribunal determining a question which has arisen in connection with a Convention right must take into account any—
- (a) judgment, decision, declaration or advisory opinion of the European Court of Human Rights,
- (b) opinion of the Commission given in a report adopted under Article 31 of the Convention,

(c) decision of the Commission in connection with Article 26 or 27(2) of the Convention, or

(d) decision of the Committee of Ministers taken under Article 46 of the Convention,

whenever made or given, so far as, in the opinion of the court or tribunal, it is relevant to the proceedings in which that question has arisen.

(2) Evidence of any judgment, decision, declaration or opinion of which account may have to be taken under this section is to be given in proceedings before any court or tribunal in such manner as may be provided by rules.

(3) In this section "rules" means rules of court or, in the case of proceedings before a tribunal, rules made for the purposes of this section—

(a) by … [the Lord Chancellor or] the Secretary of State, in relation to any proceedings outside Scotland;

(b) by the Secretary of State, in relation to proceedings in Scotland; or

(c) by a Northern Ireland department, in relation to proceedings before a tribunal in Northern Ireland—

(i) which deals with transferred matters; and

(ii) for which no rules made under paragraph (a) are in force.

[607]

NOTES

Sub-s (3): words omitted repealed by the Secretary of State for Constitutional Affairs Order 2003, SI 2003/1887, art 9, Sch 2, para 10(2); words in square brackets inserted by the Transfer of Functions (Lord Chancellor and Secretary of State) Order 2005, SI 2005/3429, art 8, Schedule, para 3.

Legislation

3 Interpretation of legislation

(1) So far as it is possible to do so, primary legislation and subordinate legislation must be read and given effect in a way which is compatible with the Convention rights.

(2) This section—

(a) applies to primary legislation and subordinate legislation whenever enacted;

(b) does not affect the validity, continuing operation or enforcement of any incompatible primary legislation; and

(c) does not affect the validity, continuing operation or enforcement of any incompatible subordinate legislation if (disregarding any possibility of revocation) primary legislation prevents removal of the incompatibility.

[608]

4 Declaration of incompatibility

(1) Subsection (2) applies in any proceedings in which a court determines whether a provision of primary legislation is compatible with a Convention right.

(2) If the court is satisfied that the provision is incompatible with a Convention right, it may make a declaration of that incompatibility.

(3) Subsection (4) applies in any proceedings in which a court determines whether a provision of subordinate legislation, made in the exercise of a power conferred by primary legislation, is compatible with a Convention right.

(4) If the court is satisfied—

(a) that the provision is incompatible with a Convention right, and

(b) that (disregarding any possibility of revocation) the primary legislation concerned prevents removal of the incompatibility,

it may make a declaration of that incompatibility.

(5) In this section "court" means—

(a) the House of Lords;

(b) the Judicial Committee of the Privy Council;

(c) the *Courts-Martial Appeal Court*;

(d) in Scotland, the High Court of Justiciary sitting otherwise than as a trial court or the Court of Session;

(e) in England and Wales or Northern Ireland, the High Court or the Court of Appeal.

[(f) the Court of Protection, in any matter being dealt with by the President of the Family Division, the Vice-Chancellor or a puisne judge of the High Court].

(6) A declaration under this section ("a declaration of incompatibility")—

(a) does not affect the validity, continuing operation or enforcement of the provision in respect of which it is given; and

(b) is not binding on the parties to the proceedings in which it is made.

[609]

NOTES

Sub-s (5): para (a) substituted by the Constitutional Reform Act 2005, s 40(4), Sch 9, Pt 1, para 66(1), (2), as from a day to be appointed, as follows:

"(a) the Supreme Court;";

for the words in italics in para (c) there are substituted the words "Court Martial Appeal Court" by the Armed Forces Act 2006, s 378(1), Sch 16, para 156, as from a day to be appointed; para (f) inserted by the Mental Capacity Act 2005, s 67(1), Sch 6, para 43, as from a day to be appointed.

5 Right of Crown to intervene

(1) Where a court is considering whether to make a declaration of incompatibility, the Crown is entitled to notice in accordance with rules of court.

(2) In any case to which subsection (1) applies—

(a) a Minister of the Crown (or a person nominated by him),

(b) a member of the Scottish Executive,

(c) a Northern Ireland Minister,

(d) a Northern Ireland department,

is entitled, on giving notice in accordance with rules of court, to be joined as a party to the proceedings.

(3) Notice under subsection (2) may be given at any time during the proceedings.

(4) A person who has been made a party to criminal proceedings (other than in Scotland) as the result of a notice under subsection (2) may, with leave, appeal to the *House of Lords* against any declaration of incompatibility made in the proceedings.

(5) In subsection (4)—

"criminal proceedings" includes all proceedings before the *Courts-Martial Appeal Court*; and

"leave" means leave granted by the court making the declaration of incompatibility or by the *House of Lords*.

[610]

NOTES

Sub-s (4): for the words in italics there are substituted the words "Supreme Court" by the Constitutional Reform Act 2005, s 40(4), Sch 9, Pt 1, para 66(1), (3), as from a day to be appointed.

Sub-s (5): for the first words in italics there are substituted the words "Court Martial Appeal Court" by the Armed Forces Act 2006, s 378(1), Sch 16, para 157, as from a day to be appointed; for the second words in italics there are substituted the words "Supreme Court" by the Constitutional Reform Act 2005, s 40(4), Sch 9, Pt 1, para 66(1), (3), as from a day to be appointed.

Transfer of functions: the function under sub-s (2) shall be exercisable by the National Assembly for Wales concurrently with any Minister of the Crown by whom it is exercisable, in so far as it relates to any proceedings in which a court is considering whether to make a declaration of incompatibility within the meaning of s 4 of this Act, in respect of subordinate legislation made by the National Assembly, and subordinate legislation made, in relation to Wales, by a Minister of the Crown in the exercise of a function which is exercisable by the National Assembly: see the National Assembly for Wales (Transfer of Functions) (No 2) Order 2000, SI 2000/1830, art 2.

Public authorities

6 Acts of public authorities

(1) It is unlawful for a public authority to act in a way which is incompatible with a Convention right.

(2) Subsection (1) does not apply to an act if—

(a) as the result of one or more provisions of primary legislation, the authority could not have acted differently; or

(b) in the case of one or more provisions of, or made under, primary legislation which cannot be read or given effect in a way which is compatible with the Convention rights, the authority was acting so as to give effect to or enforce those provisions.

(3) In this section "public authority" includes—

(a) a court or tribunal; and

(b) any person certain of whose functions are functions of a public nature,

but does not include either House of Parliament or a person exercising functions in connection with proceedings in Parliament.

(4) In subsection (3) "Parliament" does not include the House of Lords in its judicial capacity.

(5) In relation to a particular act, a person is not a public authority by virtue only of subsection (3)(b) if the nature of the act is private.

(6) "An act" includes a failure to act but does not include a failure to—

(a) introduce in, or lay before, Parliament a proposal for legislation; or

(b) make any primary legislation or remedial order.

[611]

NOTES

Sub-s (4): repealed by the Constitutional Reform Act 2005, ss 40(4), 146, Sch 9, Pt 1, para 66(1), (4), Sch 18, Pt 5, as from a day to be appointed.

For the circumstances in which a public authority, as construed in accordance with this section, is permitted to disclose information that it has obtained under the Enterprise Act 2002, see Pt 9 of that Act.

7 Proceedings

(1) A person who claims that a public authority has acted (or proposes to act) in a way which is made unlawful by section 6(1) may—

(a) bring proceedings against the authority under this Act in the appropriate court or tribunal, or

(b) rely on the Convention right or rights concerned in any legal proceedings,

but only if he is (or would be) a victim of the unlawful act.

(2) In subsection (1)(a) "appropriate court or tribunal" means such court or tribunal as may be determined in accordance with rules; and proceedings against an authority include a counterclaim or similar proceeding.

(3) If the proceedings are brought on an application for judicial review, the applicant is to be taken to have a sufficient interest in relation to the unlawful act only if he is, or would be, a victim of that act.

(4) If the proceedings are made by way of a petition for judicial review in Scotland, the applicant shall be taken to have title and interest to sue in relation to the unlawful act only if he is, or would be, a victim of that act.

(5) Proceedings under subsection (1)(a) must be brought before the end of—

(a) the period of one year beginning with the date on which the act complained of took place; or

(b) such longer period as the court or tribunal considers equitable having regard to all the circumstances,

but that is subject to any rule imposing a stricter time limit in relation to the procedure in question.

(6) In subsection (1)(b) "legal proceedings" includes—

(a) proceedings brought by or at the instigation of a public authority; and

(b) an appeal against the decision of a court or tribunal.

(7) For the purposes of this section, a person is a victim of an unlawful act only if he would be a victim for the purposes of Article 34 of the Convention if proceedings were brought in the European Court of Human Rights in respect of that act.

(8) Nothing in this Act creates a criminal offence.

(9) In this section "rules" means—

(a) in relation to proceedings before a court or tribunal outside Scotland, rules made by … [the Lord Chancellor or] the Secretary of State for the purposes of this section or rules of court,

(b) in relation to proceedings before a court or tribunal in Scotland, rules made by the Secretary of State for those purposes,

(c) in relation to proceedings before a tribunal in Northern Ireland—

(i) which deals with transferred matters; and

(ii) for which no rules made under paragraph (a) are in force,

rules made by a Northern Ireland department for those purposes,

and includes provision made by order under section 1 of the Courts and Legal Services Act 1990.

(10) In making rules, regard must be had to section 9.

(11) The Minister who has power to make rules in relation to a particular tribunal may, to the extent he considers it necessary to ensure that the tribunal can provide an appropriate remedy in relation to an act (or proposed act) of a public authority which is (or would be) unlawful as a result of section 6(1), by order add to—

(a) the relief or remedies which the tribunal may grant; or

(b) the grounds on which it may grant any of them.

(12) An order made under subsection (11) may contain such incidental, supplemental, consequential or transitional provision as the Minister making it considers appropriate.

(13) "The Minister" includes the Northern Ireland department concerned.

[612]

NOTES

Sub-s (9): words omitted repealed by the Secretary of State for Constitutional Affairs Order 2003, SI 2003/1887, art 9, Sch 2, para 10(2); words in square brackets inserted by the Transfer of Functions (Lord Chancellor and Secretary of State) Order 2005, SI 2005/3429, art 8, Schedule, para 3.

Rules: the Human Rights Act 1998 (Jurisdiction) (Scotland) Rules 2000, SSI 2000/301; the Proscribed Organisations Appeal Commission (Human Rights Act 1998 Proceedings) Rules 2006, SI 2006/2290.

8 Judicial remedies

(1) In relation to any act (or proposed act) of a public authority which the court finds is (or would be) unlawful, it may grant such relief or remedy, or make such order, within its powers as it considers just and appropriate.

(2) But damages may be awarded only by a court which has power to award damages, or to order the payment of compensation, in civil proceedings.

(3) No award of damages is to be made unless, taking account of all the circumstances of the case, including—

(a) any other relief or remedy granted, or order made, in relation to the act in question (by that or any other court), and

(b) the consequences of any decision (of that or any other court) in respect of that act,

the court is satisfied that the award is necessary to afford just satisfaction to the person in whose favour it is made.

(4) In determining—

(a) whether to award damages, or

(b) the amount of an award,

the court must take into account the principles applied by the European Court of Human Rights in relation to the award of compensation under Article 41 of the Convention.

(5) A public authority against which damages are awarded is to be treated—

(a) in Scotland, for the purposes of section 3 of the Law Reform (Miscellaneous Provisions) (Scotland) Act 1940 as if the award were made in an action of damages in which the authority has been found liable in respect of loss or damage to the person to whom the award is made;

(b) for the purposes of the Civil Liability (Contribution) Act 1978 as liable in respect of damage suffered by the person to whom the award is made.

(6) In this section—

"court" includes a tribunal;

PART II DATA PROTECTION

"damages" means damages for an unlawful act of a public authority; and
"unlawful" means unlawful under section 6(1).

[613]

9 Judicial acts

(1) Proceedings under section 7(1)(a) in respect of a judicial act may be brought only—
- (a) by exercising a right of appeal;
- (b) on an application (in Scotland a petition) for judicial review; or
- (c) in such other forum as may be prescribed by rules.

(2) That does not affect any rule of law which prevents a court from being the subject of judicial review.

(3) In proceedings under this Act in respect of a judicial act done in good faith, damages may not be awarded otherwise than to compensate a person to the extent required by Article 5(5) of the Convention.

(4) An award of damages permitted by subsection (3) is to be made against the Crown; but no award may be made unless the appropriate person, if not a party to the proceedings, is joined.

(5) In this section—

"appropriate person" means the Minister responsible for the court concerned, or a person or government department nominated by him;

"court" includes a tribunal;

"judge" includes a member of a tribunal, a justice of the peace [(or, in Northern Ireland, a lay magistrate)] and a clerk or other officer entitled to exercise the jurisdiction of a court;

"judicial act" means a judicial act of a court and includes an act done on the instructions, or on behalf, of a judge; and

"rules" has the same meaning as in section 7(9).

[614]

NOTES

Sub-s (5): words in square brackets in definition "judge" inserted by the Justice (Northern Ireland) Act 2002, s 10(6), Sch 4, para 39.

Rules: the Human Rights Act 1998 (Jurisdiction) (Scotland) Rules 2000, SSI 2000/301.

Remedial action

10 Power to take remedial action

(1) This section applies if—
- (a) a provision of legislation has been declared under section 4 to be incompatible with a Convention right and, if an appeal lies—
  - (i) all persons who may appeal have stated in writing that they do not intend to do so;
  - (ii) the time for bringing an appeal has expired and no appeal has been brought within that time; or
  - (iii) an appeal brought within that time has been determined or abandoned; or
- (b) it appears to a Minister of the Crown or Her Majesty in Council that, having regard to a finding of the European Court of Human Rights made after the coming into force of this section in proceedings against the United Kingdom, a provision of legislation is incompatible with an obligation of the United Kingdom arising from the Convention.

(2) If a Minister of the Crown considers that there are compelling reasons for proceeding under this section, he may by order make such amendments to the legislation as he considers necessary to remove the incompatibility.

(3) If, in the case of subordinate legislation, a Minister of the Crown considers—
- (a) that it is necessary to amend the primary legislation under which the subordinate legislation in question was made, in order to enable the incompatibility to be removed, and
- (b) that there are compelling reasons for proceeding under this section,

he may by order make such amendments to the primary legislation as he considers necessary.

(4) This section also applies where the provision in question is in subordinate legislation and has been quashed, or declared invalid, by reason of incompatibility with a Convention right and the Minister proposes to proceed under paragraph 2(b) of Schedule 2.

(5) If the legislation is an Order in Council, the power conferred by subsection (2) or (3) is exercisable by Her Majesty in Council.

(6) In this section "legislation" does not include a Measure of the Church Assembly or of the General Synod of the Church of England.

(7) Schedule 2 makes further provision about remedial orders.

[615]

NOTES

Orders: the Mental Health Act 1983 (Remedial) Order 2001, SI 2001/3712; the Naval Discipline Act 1957 (Remedial) Order 2004, SI 2004/66.

Other rights and proceedings

11 Safeguard for existing human rights

A person's reliance on a Convention right does not restrict—

(a) any other right or freedom conferred on him by or under any law having effect in any part of the United Kingdom; or

(b) his right to make any claim or bring any proceedings which he could make or bring apart from sections 7 to 9.

[616]

12 Freedom of expression

(1) This section applies if a court is considering whether to grant any relief which, if granted, might affect the exercise of the Convention right to freedom of expression.

(2) If the person against whom the application for relief is made ("the respondent") is neither present nor represented, no such relief is to be granted unless the court is satisfied—

(a) that the applicant has taken all practicable steps to notify the respondent; or

(b) that there are compelling reasons why the respondent should not be notified.

(3) No such relief is to be granted so as to restrain publication before trial unless the court is satisfied that the applicant is likely to establish that publication should not be allowed.

(4) The court must have particular regard to the importance of the Convention right to freedom of expression and, where the proceedings relate to material which the respondent claims, or which appears to the court, to be journalistic, literary or artistic material (or to conduct connected with such material), to—

(a) the extent to which—

(i) the material has, or is about to, become available to the public; or

(ii) it is, or would be, in the public interest for the material to be published;

(b) any relevant privacy code.

(5) In this section—

"court" includes a tribunal; and

"relief" includes any remedy or order (other than in criminal proceedings).

[617]

13 Freedom of thought, conscience and religion

(1) If a court's determination of any question arising under this Act might affect the exercise by a religious organisation (itself or its members collectively) of the Convention right to freedom of thought, conscience and religion, it must have particular regard to the importance of that right.

(2) In this section "court" includes a tribunal.

[618]

Derogations and reservations

14 Derogations

(1) In this Act "designated derogation" means—

...

any derogation by the United Kingdom from an Article of the Convention, or of any protocol to the Convention, which is designated for the purposes of this Act in an order made by the [Secretary of State].

(2) ...

(3) If a designated derogation is amended or replaced it ceases to be a designated derogation.

(4) But subsection (3) does not prevent the [Secretary of State] from exercising his power under subsection (1) ... to make a fresh designation order in respect of the Article concerned.

(5) The [Secretary of State] must by order make such amendments to Schedule 3 as he considers appropriate to reflect—

(a) any designation order; or
(b) the effect of subsection (3).

(6) A designation order may be made in anticipation of the making by the United Kingdom of a proposed derogation.

[619]

NOTES

Sub-s (1): words omitted repealed by the Human Rights Act (Amendment) Order 2001, SI 2001/1216, art 2(a); words in square brackets substituted by the Secretary of State for Constitutional Affairs Order 2003, SI 2003/1887, art 9, Sch 2, para 10(1).

Sub-s (2): repealed by SI 2001/1216, art 2(b).

Sub-s (4): words in square brackets substituted by SI 2003/1887, art 9, Sch 2, para 10(1); word omitted repealed by SI 2001/1216, art 2(c).

Sub-s (5): words in square brackets substituted by SI 2003/1887, art 9, Sch 2, para 10(1).

Orders: the Human Rights Act 1998 (Designated Derogation) Order 2001, SI 2001/3644.

15 Reservations

(1) In this Act "designated reservation" means—

(a) the United Kingdom's reservation to Article 2 of the First Protocol to the Convention; and
(b) any other reservation by the United Kingdom to an Article of the Convention, or of any protocol to the Convention, which is designated for the purposes of this Act in an order made by the [Secretary of State].

(2) The text of the reservation referred to in subsection (1)(a) is set out in Part II of Schedule 3.

(3) If a designated reservation is withdrawn wholly or in part it ceases to be a designated reservation.

(4) But subsection (3) does not prevent the [Secretary of State] from exercising his power under subsection (1)(b) to make a fresh designation order in respect of the Article concerned.

(5) The [Secretary of State] must by order make such amendments to this Act as he considers appropriate to reflect—

(a) any designation order; or
(b) the effect of subsection (3).

[620]

NOTES

Sub-ss (1), (4), (5): words in square brackets substituted by the Secretary of State for Constitutional Affairs Order 2003, SI 2003/1887, art 9, Sch 2, para 10(1).

16 Period for which designated derogations have effect

(1) If it has not already been withdrawn by the United Kingdom, a designated derogation ceases to have effect for the purposes of this Act—

…

at the end of the period of five years beginning with the date on which the order designating it was made.

(2) At any time before the period—

(a) fixed by subsection (1) … , or

(b) extended by an order under this subsection,

comes to an end, the [Secretary of State] may by order extend it by a further period of five years.

(3) An order under section 14(1) … ceases to have effect at the end of the period for consideration, unless a resolution has been passed by each House approving the order.

(4) Subsection (3) does not affect—

(a) anything done in reliance on the order; or

(b) the power to make a fresh order under section 14(1) …

(5) In subsection (3) "period for consideration" means the period of forty days beginning with the day on which the order was made.

(6) In calculating the period for consideration, no account is to be taken of any time during which—

(a) Parliament is dissolved or prorogued; or

(b) both Houses are adjourned for more than four days.

(7) If a designated derogation is withdrawn by the United Kingdom, the [Secretary of State] must by order make such amendments to this Act as he considers are required to reflect that withdrawal.

[621]

NOTES

Sub-ss (1), (3), (4): words omitted repealed by the Human Rights Act (Amendment) Order 2001, SI 2001/1216, art 3(a), (c), (d).

Sub-s (2): words omitted repealed by SI 2001/1216, art 3(b); words in square brackets substituted by the Secretary of State for Constitutional Affairs Order 2003, SI 2003/1887, art 9, Sch 2, para 10(1).

Sub-s (7): words in square brackets substituted by SI 2003/1887, art 9, Sch 2, para 10(1).

17 Periodic review of designated reservations

(1) The appropriate Minister must review the designated reservation referred to in section 15(1)(a)—

(a) before the end of the period of five years beginning with the date on which section 1(2) came into force; and

(b) if that designation is still in force, before the end of the period of five years beginning with the date on which the last report relating to it was laid under subsection (3).

(2) The appropriate Minister must review each of the other designated reservations (if any)—

(a) before the end of the period of five years beginning with the date on which the order designating the reservation first came into force; and

(b) if the designation is still in force, before the end of the period of five years beginning with the date on which the last report relating to it was laid under subsection (3).

(3) The Minister conducting a review under this section must prepare a report on the result of the review and lay a copy of it before each House of Parliament.

[622]

Judges of the European Court of Human Rights

18 Appointment to European Court of Human Rights

(1) In this section "judicial office" means the office of—

(a) Lord Justice of Appeal, Justice of the High Court or Circuit judge, in England and Wales;

(b) judge of the Court of Session or sheriff, in Scotland;

(c) Lord Justice of Appeal, judge of the High Court or county court judge, in Northern Ireland.

(2) The holder of a judicial office may become a judge of the European Court of Human Rights ("the Court") without being required to relinquish his office.

(3) But he is not required to perform the duties of his judicial office while he is a judge of the Court.

(4) In respect of any period during which he is a judge of the Court—

(a) a Lord Justice of Appeal or Justice of the High Court is not to count as a judge of the relevant court for the purposes of section 2(1) or 4(1) of the *Supreme Court Act 1981* (maximum number of judges) nor as a judge of the *Supreme Court* for the purposes of section 12(1) to (6) of that Act (salaries etc);

(b) a judge of the Court of Session is not to count as a judge of that court for the purposes of section 1(1) of the Court of Session Act 1988 (maximum number of judges) or of section 9(1)(c) of the Administration of Justice Act 1973 ("the 1973 Act") (salaries etc);

(c) a Lord Justice of Appeal or judge of the High Court in Northern Ireland is not to count as a judge of the relevant court for the purposes of section 2(1) or 3(1) of the Judicature (Northern Ireland) Act 1978 (maximum number of judges) nor as a judge of the *Supreme Court* of Northern Ireland for the purposes of section 9(1)(d) of the 1973 Act (salaries etc);

(d) a Circuit judge is not to count as such for the purposes of section 18 of the Courts Act 1971 (salaries etc);

(e) a sheriff is not to count as such for the purposes of section 14 of the Sheriff Courts (Scotland) Act 1907 (salaries etc);

(f) a county court judge of Northern Ireland is not to count as such for the purposes of section 106 of the County Courts Act (Northern Ireland) 1959 (salaries etc).

(5) If a sheriff principal is appointed a judge of the Court, section 11(1) of the Sheriff Courts (Scotland) Act 1971 (temporary appointment of sheriff principal) applies, while he holds that appointment, as if his office is vacant.

(6) Schedule 4 makes provision about judicial pensions in relation to the holder of a judicial office who serves as a judge of the Court.

(7) The Lord Chancellor or the Secretary of State may by order make such transitional provision (including, in particular, provision for a temporary increase in the maximum number of judges) as he considers appropriate in relation to any holder of a judicial office who has completed his service as a judge of the Court.

[(7A) The following paragraphs apply to the making of an order under subsection (7) in relation to any holder of a judicial office listed in subsection (1)(a)—

(a) before deciding what transitional provision it is appropriate to make, the person making the order must consult the Lord Chief Justice of England and Wales;

(b) before making the order, that person must consult the Lord Chief Justice of England and Wales.

(7B) The following paragraphs apply to the making of an order under subsection (7) in relation to any holder of a judicial office listed in subsection (1)(c)—

(a) before deciding what transitional provision it is appropriate to make, the person making the order must consult the Lord Chief Justice of Northern Ireland;

(b) before making the order, that person must consult the Lord Chief Justice of Northern Ireland.

(7C) The Lord Chief Justice of England and Wales may nominate a judicial office holder (within the meaning of section 109(4) of the Constitutional Reform Act 2005) to exercise his functions under this section.

(7D) The Lord Chief Justice of Northern Ireland may nominate any of the following to exercise his functions under this section—

(a) the holder of one of the offices listed in Schedule 1 to the Justice (Northern Ireland) Act 2002;

(b) a Lord Justice of Appeal (as defined in section 88 of that Act).]

[623]

NOTES

Sub-s (4): in para (a) for the first words in italics there are substituted the words "Senior Courts Act 1981", for the second words in italics there are substituted the words "Senior Courts", and for the words in italics in para (c) there are substituted the words "Court of Judicature" by the Constitutional Reform Act 2005, s 59(5), Sch 11, Pt 1, para 1(2), Pt 2, para 4(1), (3), Pt 3, para 6(1), (3), as from a day to be appointed.

Sub-ss (7A)–(7D): added by the Constitutional Reform Act 2005, s 15(1), Sch 4, Pt 1, para 278.

Orders: the Judicial Pensions (European Court of Human Rights) Order 1998, SI 1998/2768.

Parliamentary procedure

19 Statements of compatibility

(1) A Minister of the Crown in charge of a Bill in either House of Parliament must, before Second Reading of the Bill—

(a) make a statement to the effect that in his view the provisions of the Bill are compatible with the Convention rights ("a statement of compatibility"); or

(b) make a statement to the effect that although he is unable to make a statement of compatibility the government nevertheless wishes the House to proceed with the Bill.

(2) The statement must be in writing and be published in such manner as the Minister making it considers appropriate.

[624]

Supplemental

20 Orders etc under this Act

(1) Any power of a Minister of the Crown to make an order under this Act is exercisable by statutory instrument.

(2) The power of … [the Lord Chancellor or] the Secretary of State to make rules (other than rules of court) under section 2(3) or 7(9) is exercisable by statutory instrument.

(3) Any statutory instrument made under section 14, 15 or 16(7) must be laid before Parliament.

(4) No order may be made by … [the Lord Chancellor or] the Secretary of State under section 1(4), 7(11) or 16(2) unless a draft of the order has been laid before, and approved by, each House of Parliament.

(5) Any statutory instrument made under section 18(7) or Schedule 4, or to which subsection (2) applies, shall be subject to annulment in pursuance of a resolution of either House of Parliament.

(6) The power of a Northern Ireland department to make—

(a) rules under section 2(3)(c) or 7(9)(c), or

(b) an order under section 7(11),

is exercisable by statutory rule for the purposes of the Statutory Rules (Northern Ireland) Order 1979.

(7) Any rules made under section 2(3)(c) or 7(9)(c) shall be subject to negative resolution; and section 41(6) of the Interpretation Act (Northern Ireland) 1954 (meaning of "subject to negative resolution") shall apply as if the power to make the rules were conferred by an Act of the Northern Ireland Assembly.

(8) No order may be made by a Northern Ireland department under section 7(11) unless a draft of the order has been laid before, and approved by, the Northern Ireland Assembly.

[625]

NOTES

Sub-s (2): words omitted repealed by the Secretary of State for Constitutional Affairs Order 2003, SI 2003/1887, art 9, Sch 2, para 10(2); words in square brackets inserted by the Transfer of Functions (Lord Chancellor and Secretary of State) Order 2005, SI 2005/3429, art 8, Schedule, para 3.

Sub-s (4): words omitted repealed by SI 2003/1887, art 9, Sch 2, para 10(2); words in square brackets inserted by SI 2005/3429, art 8, Schedule, para 3.

21 Interpretation, etc

(1) In this Act—

"amend" includes repeal and apply (with or without modifications);

"the appropriate Minister" means the Minister of the Crown having charge of the appropriate authorised government department (within the meaning of the Crown Proceedings Act 1947);

"the Commission" means the European Commission of Human Rights;

"the Convention" means the Convention for the Protection of Human Rights and Fundamental Freedoms, agreed by the Council of Europe at Rome on 4th November 1950 as it has effect for the time being in relation to the United Kingdom;

"declaration of incompatibility" means a declaration under section 4;

"Minister of the Crown" has the same meaning as in the Ministers of the Crown Act 1975;

"Northern Ireland Minister" includes the First Minister and the deputy First Minister in Northern Ireland;

"primary legislation" means any—

(a) public general Act;
(b) local and personal Act;
(c) private Act;
(d) Measure of the Church Assembly;
(e) Measure of the General Synod of the Church of England;
(f) Order in Council—
  (i) made in exercise of Her Majesty's Royal Prerogative;
  (ii) made under section 38(1)(a) of the Northern Ireland Constitution Act 1973 or the corresponding provision of the Northern Ireland Act 1998; or
  (iii) amending an Act of a kind mentioned in paragraph (a), (b) or (c);

and includes an order or other instrument made under primary legislation (otherwise than by the *National Assembly for Wales*, a member of the Scottish Executive, a Northern Ireland Minister or a Northern Ireland department) to the extent to which it operates to bring one or more provisions of that legislation into force or amends any primary legislation;

"the First Protocol" means the protocol to the Convention agreed at Paris on 20th March 1952;

. . . . .

"the Eleventh Protocol" means the protocol to the Convention (restructuring the control machinery established by the Convention) agreed at Strasbourg on 11th May 1994;

["the Thirteenth Protocol" means the protocol to the Convention (concerning the abolition of the death penalty in all circumstances) agreed at Vilnius on 3rd May 2002;]

"remedial order" means an order under section 10;

"subordinate legislation" means any—

(a) Order in Council other than one—
  (i) made in exercise of Her Majesty's Royal Prerogative;
  (ii) made under section 38(1)(a) of the Northern Ireland Constitution Act 1973 or the corresponding provision of the Northern Ireland Act 1998; or
  (iii) amending an Act of a kind mentioned in the definition of primary legislation;
(b) Act of the Scottish Parliament;
[(ba) Measure of the National Assembly for Wales;
(bb) Act of the National Assembly for Wales;]
(c) Act of the Parliament of Northern Ireland;
(d) Measure of the Assembly established under section 1 of the Northern Ireland Assembly Act 1973;
(e) Act of the Northern Ireland Assembly;
(f) order, rules, regulations, scheme, warrant, byelaw or other instrument made under primary legislation (except to the extent to which it operates to bring one or more provisions of that legislation into force or amends any primary legislation);
(g) order, rules, regulations, scheme, warrant, byelaw or other instrument made under legislation mentioned in paragraph (b), (c), (d) or (e) or made under an Order in Council applying only to Northern Ireland;
(h) order, rules, regulations, scheme, warrant, byelaw or other instrument made

by a member of the Scottish Executive[, Welsh Ministers, the First Minister for Wales, the Counsel General to the Welsh Assembly Government], a Northern Ireland Minister or a Northern Ireland department in exercise of prerogative or other executive functions of Her Majesty which are exercisable by such a person on behalf of Her Majesty;

"transferred matters" has the same meaning as in the Northern Ireland Act 1998; and

"tribunal" means any tribunal in which legal proceedings may be brought.

(2) The references in paragraphs (b) and (c) of section 2(1) to Articles are to Articles of the Convention as they had effect immediately before the coming into force of the Eleventh Protocol.

(3) The reference in paragraph (d) of section 2(1) to Article 46 includes a reference to Articles 32 and 54 of the Convention as they had effect immediately before the coming into force of the Eleventh Protocol.

(4) The references in section 2(1) to a report or decision of the Commission or a decision of the Committee of Ministers include references to a report or decision made as provided by paragraphs 3, 4 and 6 of Article 5 of the Eleventh Protocol (transitional provisions).

(5) Any liability under the Army Act 1955, the Air Force Act 1955 or the Naval Discipline Act 1957 to suffer death for an offence is replaced by a liability to imprisonment for life or any less punishment authorised by those Acts; and those Acts shall accordingly have effect with the necessary modifications.

[626]

NOTES

Sub-s (1): definition omitted repealed, and definition "the Thirteenth Protocol" inserted, by the Human Rights Act 1998 (Amendment) Order 2004, SI 2004/1574, art 2(2); for the words in italics in definition "primary legislation" there are substituted the words "Welsh Ministers, the First Minister for Wales, the Counsel General to the Welsh Assembly Government", in definition "subordinate legislation" paras (ba), (bb) and words in square brackets in para (h) inserted by the Government of Wales Act 2006, s 160(1), Sch 10, para 56, with effect immediately after the ordinary election (under the Government of Wales Act 1998, s 3) to be held in 2007; see the Government of Wales Act 2006, s 161(1), (4), (5).

Sub-s (5): repealed by the Armed Forces Act 2006, s 378(2), Sch 17, as from a day to be appointed.

22 Short title, commencement, application and extent

(1) This Act may be cited as the Human Rights Act 1998.

(2) Sections 18, 20 and 21(5) and this section come into force on the passing of this Act.

(3) The other provisions of this Act come into force on such day as the Secretary of State may by order appoint; and different days may be appointed for different purposes.

(4) Paragraph (b) of subsection (1) of section 7 applies to proceedings brought by or at the instigation of a public authority whenever the act in question took place; but otherwise that subsection does not apply to an act taking place before the coming into force of that section.

(5) This Act binds the Crown.

(6) This Act extends to Northern Ireland.

(7) Section 21(5), so far as it relates to any provision contained in the Army Act 1955, the Air Force Act 1955 or the Naval Discipline Act 1957, extends to any place to which that provision extends.

[627]

NOTES

Sub-s (7): repealed by the Armed Forces Act 2006, s 378(2), Sch 17, as from a day to be appointed.

Orders: the Human Rights Act 1998 (Commencement) Order 1998, SI 1998/2882; the Human Rights Act 1998 (Commencement No 2) Order 2000, SI 2000/1851.

SCHEDULES

SCHEDULE 1
THE ARTICLES

Section 1(3)

PART I
THE CONVENTION

RIGHTS AND FREEDOMS

Article 2
Right to life

1. Everyone's right to life shall be protected by law. No one shall be deprived of his life intentionally save in the execution of a sentence of a court following his conviction of a crime for which this penalty is provided by law.

2. Deprivation of life shall not be regarded as inflicted in contravention of this Article when it results from the use of force which is no more than absolutely necessary—

(a) in defence of any person from unlawful violence;
(b) in order to effect a lawful arrest or to prevent the escape of a person lawfully detained;
(c) in action lawfully taken for the purpose of quelling a riot or insurrection.

Article 3
Prohibition of torture

No one shall be subjected to torture or to inhuman or degrading treatment or punishment.

Article 4
Prohibition of slavery and forced labour

1. No one shall be held in slavery or servitude.

2. No one shall be required to perform forced or compulsory labour.

3. For the purpose of this Article the term "forced or compulsory labour" shall not include—

(a) any work required to be done in the ordinary course of detention imposed according to the provisions of Article 5 of this Convention or during conditional release from such detention;
(b) any service of a military character or, in case of conscientious objectors in countries where they are recognised, service exacted instead of compulsory military service;
(c) any service exacted in case of an emergency or calamity threatening the life or well-being of the community;
(d) any work or service which forms part of normal civic obligations.

Article 5
Right to liberty and security

1. Everyone has the right to liberty and security of person. No one shall be deprived of his liberty save in the following cases and in accordance with a procedure prescribed by law—

(a) the lawful detention of a person after conviction by a competent court;
(b) the lawful arrest or detention of a person for non-compliance with the lawful order of a court or in order to secure the fulfilment of any obligation prescribed by law;
(c) the lawful arrest or detention of a person effected for the purpose of bringing him before the competent legal authority on reasonable suspicion of having committed an offence or when it is reasonably considered necessary to prevent his committing an offence or fleeing after having done so;
(d) the detention of a minor by lawful order for the purpose of educational supervision or his lawful detention for the purpose of bringing him before the competent legal authority;

(e) the lawful detention of persons for the prevention of the spreading of infectious diseases, of persons of unsound mind, alcoholics or drug addicts or vagrants;
(f) the lawful arrest or detention of a person to prevent his effecting an unauthorised entry into the country or of a person against whom action is being taken with a view to deportation or extradition.

2. Everyone who is arrested shall be informed promptly, in a language which he understands, of the reasons for his arrest and of any charge against him.

3. Everyone arrested or detained in accordance with the provisions of paragraph 1(c) of this Article shall be brought promptly before a judge or other officer authorised by law to exercise judicial power and shall be entitled to trial within a reasonable time or to release pending trial. Release may be conditioned by guarantees to appear for trial.

4. Everyone who is deprived of his liberty by arrest or detention shall be entitled to take proceedings by which the lawfulness of his detention shall be decided speedily by a court and his release ordered if the detention is not lawful.

5. Everyone who has been the victim of arrest or detention in contravention of the provisions of this Article shall have an enforceable right to compensation.

Article 6
Right to a fair trial

1. In the determination of his civil rights and obligations or of any criminal charge against him, everyone is entitled to a fair and public hearing within a reasonable time by an independent and impartial tribunal established by law. Judgment shall be pronounced publicly but the press and public may be excluded from all or part of the trial in the interest of morals, public order or national security in a democratic society, where the interests of juveniles or the protection of the private life of the parties so require, or to the extent strictly necessary in the opinion of the court in special circumstances where publicity would prejudice the interests of justice.

2. Everyone charged with a criminal offence shall be presumed innocent until proved guilty according to law.

3. Everyone charged with a criminal offence has the following minimum rights—
(a) to be informed promptly, in a language which he understands and in detail, of the nature and cause of the accusation against him;
(b) to have adequate time and facilities for the preparation of his defence;
(c) to defend himself in person or through legal assistance of his own choosing or, if he has not sufficient means to pay for legal assistance, to be given it free when the interests of justice so require;
(d) to examine or have examined witnesses against him and to obtain the attendance and examination of witnesses on his behalf under the same conditions as witnesses against him;
(e) to have the free assistance of an interpreter if he cannot understand or speak the language used in court.

Article 7
No punishment without law

1. No one shall be held guilty of any criminal offence on account of any act or omission which did not constitute a criminal offence under national or international law at the time when it was committed. Nor shall a heavier penalty be imposed than the one that was applicable at the time the criminal offence was committed.

2. This Article shall not prejudice the trial and punishment of any person for any act or omission which, at the time when it was committed, was criminal according to the general principles of law recognised by civilised nations.

Article 8
Right to respect for private and family life

1. Everyone has the right to respect for his private and family life, his home and his correspondence.

2. There shall be no interference by a public authority with the exercise of this right except such as is in accordance with the law and is necessary in a democratic society in the interests of national security, public safety or the economic well-being of the country, for the prevention of disorder or crime, for the protection of health or morals, or for the protection of the rights and freedoms of others.

Article 9
Freedom of thought, conscience and religion

1. Everyone has the right to freedom of thought, conscience and religion; this right includes freedom to change his religion or belief and freedom, either alone or in community with others and in public or private, to manifest his religion or belief, in worship, teaching, practice and observance.

2. Freedom to manifest one's religion or beliefs shall be subject only to such limitations as are prescribed by law and are necessary in a democratic society in the interests of public safety, for the protection of public order, health or morals, or for the protection of the rights and freedoms of others.

Article 10
Freedom of expression

1. Everyone has the right to freedom of expression. This right shall include freedom to hold opinions and to receive and impart information and ideas without interference by public authority and regardless of frontiers. This Article shall not prevent States from requiring the licensing of broadcasting, television or cinema enterprises.

2. The exercise of these freedoms, since it carries with it duties and responsibilities, may be subject to such formalities, conditions, restrictions or penalties as are prescribed by law and are necessary in a democratic society, in the interests of national security, territorial integrity or public safety, for the prevention of disorder or crime, for the protection of health or morals, for the protection of the reputation or rights of others, for preventing the disclosure of information received in confidence, or for maintaining the authority and impartiality of the judiciary.

Article 11
Freedom of assembly and association

1. Everyone has the right to freedom of peaceful assembly and to freedom of association with others, including the right to form and to join trade unions for the protection of his interests.

2. No restrictions shall be placed on the exercise of these rights other than such as are prescribed by law and are necessary in a democratic society in the interests of national security or public safety, for the prevention of disorder or crime, for the protection of health or morals or for the protection of the rights and freedoms of others. This Article shall not prevent the imposition of lawful restrictions on the exercise of these rights by members of the armed forces, of the police or of the administration of the State.

Article 12
Right to marry

Men and women of marriageable age have the right to marry and to found a family, according to the national laws governing the exercise of this right.

Article 14
Prohibition of discrimination

The enjoyment of the rights and freedoms set forth in this Convention shall be secured without discrimination on any ground such as sex, race, colour, language, religion, political or other opinion, national or social origin, association with a national minority, property, birth or other status.

Article 16
Restrictions on political activity of aliens

Nothing in Articles 10, 11 and 14 shall be regarded as preventing the High Contracting Parties from imposing restrictions on the political activity of aliens.

Article 17
Prohibition of abuse of rights

Nothing in this Convention may be interpreted as implying for any State, group or person any right to engage in any activity or perform any act aimed at the destruction of any of the rights and freedoms set forth herein or at their limitation to a greater extent than is provided for in the Convention.

Article 18
Limitation on use of restrictions on rights

The restrictions permitted under this Convention to the said rights and freedoms shall not be applied for any purpose other than those for which they have been prescribed.

[628]

PART II
THE FIRST PROTOCOL

Article 1
Protection of property

Every natural or legal person is entitled to the peaceful enjoyment of his possessions. No one shall be deprived of his possessions except in the public interest and subject to the conditions provided for by law and by the general principles of international law.

The preceding provisions shall not, however, in any way impair the right of a State to enforce such laws as it deems necessary to control the use of property in accordance with the general interest or to secure the payment of taxes or other contributions or penalties.

Article 2
Right to education

No person shall be denied the right to education. In the exercise of any functions which it assumes in relation to education and to teaching, the State shall respect the right of parents to ensure such education and teaching in conformity with their own religious and philosophical convictions.

Article 3
Right to free elections

The High Contracting Parties undertake to hold free elections at reasonable intervals by secret ballot, under conditions which will ensure the free expression of the opinion of the people in the choice of the legislature.

[629]

[PART III
ARTICLE 1 OF THE THIRTEENTH PROTOCOL

Abolition of the death penalty

The death penalty shall be abolished. No one shall be condemned to such penalty or executed.]

[630]

NOTES

Commencement: 22 June 2004.
Substituted by the Human Rights Act 1998 (Amendment) Order 2004, SI 2004/1574, art 2(3).

SCHEDULE 2
REMEDIAL ORDERS

Section 10

Orders

1.—(1) A remedial order may—
- (a) contain such incidental, supplemental, consequential or transitional provision as the person making it considers appropriate,
- (b) be made so as to have effect from a date earlier than that on which it is made,
- (c) make provision for the delegation of specific functions,
- (d) make different provision for different cases.

(2) The power conferred by sub-paragraph (1)(a) includes—
- (a) power to amend primary legislation (including primary legislation other than that which contains the incompatible provision), and
- (b) power to amend or revoke subordinate legislation (including subordinate legislation other than that which contains the incompatible provision).

(3) A remedial order may be made so as to have the same extent as the legislation which it affects.

(4) No person is to be guilty of an offence solely as a result of the retrospective effect of a remedial order.

Procedure

2. No remedial order may be made unless—
- (a) a draft of the order has been approved by a resolution of each House of Parliament made after the end of the period of 60 days beginning with the day on which the draft was laid, or
- (b) it is declared in the order that it appears to the person making it that, because of the urgency of the matter, it is necessary to make the order without a draft being so approved.

Orders laid in draft

3.—(1) No draft may be laid under paragraph 2(a) unless—
- (a) the person proposing to make the order has laid before Parliament a document which contains a draft of the proposed order and the required information, and
- (b) the period of 60 days, beginning with the day on which the document required by this sub-paragraph was laid, has ended.

(2) If representations have been made during that period, the draft laid under paragraph 2(a) must be accompanied by a statement containing—
- (a) a summary of the representations, and
- (b) if, as a result of the representations, the proposed order has been changed, details of the changes.

Urgent cases

4.—(1) If a remedial order ("the original order") is made without being approved in draft, the person making it must lay it before Parliament, accompanied by the required information, after it is made.

(2) If representations have been made during the period of 60 days beginning with the day on which the original order was made, the person making it must (after the end of that period) lay before Parliament a statement containing—
- (a) a summary of the representations, and
- (b) if, as a result of the representations, he considers it appropriate to make changes to the original order, details of the changes.

(3) If sub-paragraph (2)(b) applies, the person making the statement must—
- (a) make a further remedial order replacing the original order, and

(b) lay the replacement order before Parliament.

(4) If, at the end of the period of 120 days beginning with the day on which the original order was made, a resolution has not been passed by each House approving the original or replacement order, the order ceases to have effect (but without that affecting anything previously done under either order or the power to make a fresh remedial order).

Definitions

5. In this Schedule—

"representations" means representations about a remedial order (or proposed remedial order) made to the person making (or proposing to make) it and includes any relevant Parliamentary report or resolution, and

"required information" means—

(a) an explanation of the incompatibility which the order (or proposed order) seeks to remove, including particulars of the relevant declaration, finding or order, and

(b) a statement of the reasons for proceeding under section 10 and for making an order in those terms.

Calculating periods

6. In calculating any period for the purposes of this Schedule, no account is to be taken of any time during which—

(a) Parliament is dissolved or prorogued, or

(b) both Houses are adjourned for more than four days.

[7.—(1) This paragraph applies in relation to—

(a) any remedial order made, and any draft of such an order proposed to be made—

(i) by the Scottish Ministers, or

(ii) within devolved competence (within the meaning of the Scotland Act 1998) by Her Majesty in Council, and

(b) any document or statement to be laid in connection with such an order (or proposed order).

(2) This Schedule has effect in relation to any such order (or proposed order), document or statement subject to the following modifications.

(3) Any reference to Parliament, each House of Parliament or both Houses of Parliament shall be construed as a reference to the Scottish Parliament.

(4) Paragraph 6 does not apply and instead, in calculating any period for the purposes of this Schedule, no account is to be taken of any time during which the Scottish Parliament is dissolved or is in recess for more than four days.]

[631]–[632]

NOTES

Para 7: added by the Scotland Act 1998 (Consequential Modifications) Order 2000, SI 2000/2040, art 2, Schedule, Pt I, para 21.

Orders: the Mental Health Act 1983 (Remedial) Order 2001, SI 2001/3712; the Naval Discipline Act 1957 (Remedial) Order 2004, SI 2004/66.

SCHEDULE 3
DEROGATION AND RESERVATION

Sections 14 and 15

(Original Sch 3, Pt I repealed by the Human Rights Act (Amendment) Order 2001, SI 2001/1216, art 4; a new Pt I inserted by the Human Rights Act 1998 (Amendment No 2) Order 2001, SI 2001/4032, art 2, Schedule, and repealed by the Human Rights Act 1998 (Amendment) Order 2005, SI 2005/1071, art 2.)

PART II
RESERVATION

At the time of signing the present (First) Protocol, I declare that, in view of certain provisions of the Education Acts in the United Kingdom, the principle affirmed in the second sentence of

PART II DATA PROTECTION

Article 2 is accepted by the United Kingdom only so far as it is compatible with the provision of efficient instruction and training, and the avoidance of unreasonable public expenditure.

Dated 20 March 1952. Made by the United Kingdom Permanent Representative to the Council of Europe.

[633]

SCHEDULE 4
JUDICIAL PENSIONS

Section 18(6)

Duty to make orders about pensions

1.—(1) The appropriate Minister must by order make provision with respect to pensions payable to or in respect of any holder of a judicial office who serves as an ECHR judge.

(2) A pensions order must include such provision as the Minister making it considers is necessary to secure that—

(a) an ECHR judge who was, immediately before his appointment as an ECHR judge, a member of a judicial pension scheme is entitled to remain as a member of that scheme;

(b) the terms on which he remains a member of the scheme are those which would have been applicable had he not been appointed as an ECHR judge; and

(c) entitlement to benefits payable in accordance with the scheme continues to be determined as if, while serving as an ECHR judge, his salary was that which would (but for section 18(4)) have been payable to him in respect of his continuing service as the holder of his judicial office.

Contributions

2. A pensions order may, in particular, make provision—

(a) for any contributions which are payable by a person who remains a member of a scheme as a result of the order, and which would otherwise be payable by deduction from his salary, to be made otherwise than by deduction from his salary as an ECHR judge; and

(b) for such contributions to be collected in such manner as may be determined by the administrators of the scheme.

Amendments of other enactments

3. A pensions order may amend any provision of, or made under, a pensions Act in such manner and to such extent as the Minister making the order considers necessary or expedient to ensure the proper administration of any scheme to which it relates.

Definitions

4. In this Schedule—

"appropriate Minister" means—

(a) in relation to any judicial office whose jurisdiction is exercisable exclusively in relation to Scotland, the Secretary of State; and

(b) otherwise, the Lord Chancellor;

"ECHR judge" means the holder of a judicial office who is serving as a judge of the Court;

"judicial pension scheme" means a scheme established by and in accordance with a pensions Act;

"pensions Act" means—

(a) the County Courts Act (Northern Ireland) 1959;

(b) the Sheriffs' Pensions (Scotland) Act 1961;

(c) the Judicial Pensions Act 1981; or

(d) the Judicial Pensions and Retirement Act 1993; and

"pensions order" means an order made under paragraph 1.

[634]

NOTES

Orders: the Judicial Pensions (European Court of Human Rights) Order 1998, SI 1998/2768.

REGULATION OF INVESTIGATORY POWERS ACT 2000

(2000 c 23)

An Act to make provision for and about the interception of communications, the acquisition and disclosure of data relating to communications, the carrying out of surveillance, the use of covert human intelligence sources and the acquisition of the means by which electronic data protected by encryption or passwords may be decrypted or accessed; to provide for Commissioners and a tribunal with functions and jurisdiction in relation to those matters, to entries on and interferences with property or with wireless telegraphy and to the carrying out of their functions by the Security Service, the Secret Intelligence Service and the Government Communications Headquarters; and for connected purposes

[28 July 2000]

ARRANGEMENT OF SECTIONS

PART I
COMMUNICATIONS

CHAPTER I
INTERCEPTION

Unlawful and authorised interception

Interception warrants

Interception capability and costs

Restrictions on use of intercepted material etc

Interpretation of Chapter I

CHAPTER II
ACQUISITION AND DISCLOSURE OF COMMUNICATIONS DATA

PART II
SURVEILLANCE AND COVERT HUMAN INTELLIGENCE SOURCES

Introductory

Authorisation of surveillance and human intelligence sources

Police and customs authorisations

Other authorisations

Grant, renewal and duration of authorisations

Scotland

Supplemental provision for Part II

PART III
INVESTIGATION OF ELECTRONIC DATA PROTECTED BY ENCRYPTION ETC

Power to require disclosure

Contributions to costs

Offences

Safeguards

Interpretation of Part III

PART IV
SCRUTINY ETC OF INVESTIGATORY POWERS AND OF THE FUNCTIONS OF THE INTELLIGENCE SERVICES

Commissioners

The Tribunal

Codes of practice

PART V
MISCELLANEOUS AND SUPPLEMENTAL

Supplemental

NOTES

Transfer of functions: as to the transfer of certain functions under this Act to the Scottish Ministers, in so far as they are exercisable in or as regards Scotland, see the Scotland Act 1998 (Transfer of Functions to the Scottish Ministers etc) (No 2) Order 2000, SI 2000/3253, and the Scotland Act 1998 (Transfer of Functions to the Scottish Ministers etc) (No 2) Order 2003, SI 2003/2617.

PART I
COMMUNICATIONS

CHAPTER I
INTERCEPTION

Unlawful and authorised interception

1 Unlawful interception

(1) It shall be an offence for a person intentionally and without lawful authority to intercept, at any place in the United Kingdom, any communication in the course of its transmission by means of—

(a) a public postal service; or

(b) a public telecommunication system.

(2) It shall be an offence for a person—

(a) intentionally and without lawful authority, and

(b) otherwise than in circumstances in which his conduct is excluded by subsection (6) from criminal liability under this subsection,

to intercept, at any place in the United Kingdom, any communication in the course of its transmission by means of a private telecommunication system.

(3) Any interception of a communication which is carried out at any place in the United Kingdom by, or with the express or implied consent of, a person having the right to control the operation or the use of a private telecommunication system shall be actionable at the suit or instance of the sender or recipient, or intended recipient, of the communication if it is without lawful authority and is either—

(a) an interception of that communication in the course of its transmission by means of that private system; or

(b) an interception of that communication in the course of its transmission, by means of a public telecommunication system, to or from apparatus comprised in that private telecommunication system.

(4) Where the United Kingdom is a party to an international agreement which—

(a) relates to the provision of mutual assistance in connection with, or in the form of, the interception of communications,
(b) requires the issue of a warrant, order or equivalent instrument in cases in which assistance is given, and
(c) is designated for the purposes of this subsection by an order made by the Secretary of State,

it shall be the duty of the Secretary of State to secure that no request for assistance in accordance with the agreement is made on behalf of a person in the United Kingdom to the competent authorities of a country or territory outside the United Kingdom except with lawful authority.

(5) Conduct has lawful authority for the purposes of this section if, and only if—
(a) it is authorised by or under section 3 or 4;
(b) it takes place in accordance with a warrant under section 5 ("an interception warrant"); or
(c) it is in exercise, in relation to any stored communication, of any statutory power that is exercised (apart from this section) for the purpose of obtaining information or of taking possession of any document or other property;

and conduct (whether or not prohibited by this section) which has lawful authority for the purposes of this section by virtue of paragraph (a) or (b) shall also be taken to be lawful for all other purposes.

(6) The circumstances in which a person makes an interception of a communication in the course of its transmission by means of a private telecommunication system are such that his conduct is excluded from criminal liability under subsection (2) if—
(a) he is a person with a right to control the operation or the use of the system; or
(b) he has the express or implied consent of such a person to make the interception.

(7) A person who is guilty of an offence under subsection (1) or (2) shall be liable—
(a) on conviction on indictment, to imprisonment for a term not exceeding two years or to a fine, or to both;
(b) on summary conviction, to a fine not exceeding the statutory maximum.

(8) No proceedings for any offence which is an offence by virtue of this section shall be instituted—
(a) in England and Wales, except by or with the consent of the Director of Public Prosecutions;
(b) in Northern Ireland, except by or with the consent of the Director of Public Prosecutions for Northern Ireland.

[635]

NOTES

Orders: the Regulation of Investigatory Powers (Designation of an International Agreement) Order 2004, SI 2004/158 at **[1121]**.

2 Meaning and location of "interception" etc

(1) In this Act—

"postal service" means any service which—
(a) consists in the following, or in any one or more of them, namely, the collection, sorting, conveyance, distribution and delivery (whether in the United Kingdom or elsewhere) of postal items; and
(b) is offered or provided as a service the main purpose of which, or one of the main purposes of which, is to make available, or to facilitate, a means of transmission from place to place of postal items containing communications;

"private telecommunication system" means any telecommunication system which, without itself being a public telecommunication system, is a system in relation to which the following conditions are satisfied—
(a) it is attached, directly or indirectly and whether or not for the purposes of the communication in question, to a public telecommunication system; and
(b) there is apparatus comprised in the system which is both located in the United Kingdom and used (with or without other apparatus) for making the attachment to the public telecommunication system;

"public postal service" means any postal service which is offered or provided to, or to a substantial section of, the public in any one or more parts of the United Kingdom;

PART II DATA PROTECTION

"public telecommunications service" means any telecommunications service which is offered or provided to, or to a substantial section of, the public in any one or more parts of the United Kingdom;

"public telecommunication system" means any such parts of a telecommunication system by means of which any public telecommunications service is provided as are located in the United Kingdom;

"telecommunications service" means any service that consists in the provision of access to, and of facilities for making use of, any telecommunication system (whether or not one provided by the person providing the service); and

"telecommunication system" means any system (including the apparatus comprised in it) which exists (whether wholly or partly in the United Kingdom or elsewhere) for the purpose of facilitating the transmission of communications by any means involving the use of electrical or electromagnetic energy.

(2) For the purposes of this Act, but subject to the following provisions of this section, a person intercepts a communication in the course of its transmission by means of a telecommunication system if, and only if, he—

(a) so modifies or interferes with the system, or its operation,
(b) so monitors transmissions made by means of the system, or
(c) so monitors transmissions made by wireless telegraphy to or from apparatus comprised in the system,

as to make some or all of the contents of the communication available, while being transmitted, to a person other than the sender or intended recipient of the communication.

(3) References in this Act to the interception of a communication do not include references to the interception of any communication broadcast for general reception.

(4) For the purposes of this Act the interception of a communication takes place in the United Kingdom if, and only if, the modification, interference or monitoring or, in the case of a postal item, the interception is effected by conduct within the United Kingdom and the communication is either—

(a) intercepted in the course of its transmission by means of a public postal service or public telecommunication system; or
(b) intercepted in the course of its transmission by means of a private telecommunication system in a case in which the sender or intended recipient of the communication is in the United Kingdom.

(5) References in this Act to the interception of a communication in the course of its transmission by means of a postal service or telecommunication system do not include references to—

(a) any conduct that takes place in relation only to so much of the communication as consists in any traffic data comprised in or attached to a communication (whether by the sender or otherwise) for the purposes of any postal service or telecommunication system by means of which it is being or may be transmitted; or
(b) any such conduct, in connection with conduct falling within paragraph (a), as gives a person who is neither the sender nor the intended recipient only so much access to a communication as is necessary for the purpose of identifying traffic data so comprised or attached.

(6) For the purposes of this section references to the modification of a telecommunication system include references to the attachment of any apparatus to, or other modification of or interference with—

(a) any part of the system; or
(b) any wireless telegraphy apparatus used for making transmissions to or from apparatus comprised in the system.

(7) For the purposes of this section the times while a communication is being transmitted by means of a telecommunication system shall be taken to include any time when the system by means of which the communication is being, or has been, transmitted is used for storing it in a manner that enables the intended recipient to collect it or otherwise to have access to it.

(8) For the purposes of this section the cases in which any contents of a communication are to be taken to be made available to a person while being transmitted shall include any case in which any of the contents of the communication, while being transmitted, are diverted or recorded so as to be available to a person subsequently.

(9) In this section "traffic data", in relation to any communication, means—

(a) any data identifying, or purporting to identify, any person, apparatus or location to or from which the communication is or may be transmitted,

(b) any data identifying or selecting, or purporting to identify or select, apparatus through which, or by means of which, the communication is or may be transmitted,

(c) any data comprising signals for the actuation of apparatus used for the purposes of a telecommunication system for effecting (in whole or in part) the transmission of any communication, and

(d) any data identifying the data or other data as data comprised in or attached to a particular communication,

but that expression includes data identifying a computer file or computer program access to which is obtained, or which is run, by means of the communication to the extent only that the file or program is identified by reference to the apparatus in which it is stored.

(10) In this section—

(a) references, in relation to traffic data comprising signals for the actuation of apparatus, to a telecommunication system by means of which a communication is being or may be transmitted include references to any telecommunication system in which that apparatus is comprised; and

(b) references to traffic data being attached to a communication include references to the data and the communication being logically associated with each other;

and in this section "data", in relation to a postal item, means anything written on the outside of the item.

(11) In this section "postal item" means any letter, postcard or other such thing in writing as may be used by the sender for imparting information to the recipient, or any packet or parcel.

[636]

3 Lawful interception without an interception warrant

(1) Conduct by any person consisting in the interception of a communication is authorised by this section if the communication is one which, or which that person has reasonable grounds for believing, is both—

(a) a communication sent by a person who has consented to the interception; and

(b) a communication the intended recipient of which has so consented.

(2) Conduct by any person consisting in the interception of a communication is authorised by this section if—

(a) the communication is one sent by, or intended for, a person who has consented to the interception; and

(b) surveillance by means of that interception has been authorised under Part II.

(3) Conduct consisting in the interception of a communication is authorised by this section if—

(a) it is conduct by or on behalf of a person who provides a postal service or a telecommunications service; and

(b) it takes place for purposes connected with the provision or operation of that service or with the enforcement, in relation to that service, of any enactment relating to the use of postal services or telecommunications services.

(4) Conduct by any person consisting in the interception of a communication in the course of its transmission by means of wireless telegraphy is authorised by this section if it takes place—

(a) with the authority of a designated person under [section 48 of the Wireless Telegraphy Act 2006 (interception and disclosure of wireless telegraphy messages)]; and

(b) for purposes connected with anything falling within subsection (5).

(5) Each of the following falls within this subsection—

[(a) the grant of wireless telegraphy licences under the Wireless Telegraphy Act 2006;]

(b) the prevention or detection of anything which constitutes interference with wireless telegraphy; and

(c) the enforcement of[—

(i) any provision of Part 2 (other than Chapter 2 and sections 27 to 31) or Part 3 of that Act, or

(ii) any enactment not falling within sub-paragraph (i)]
that relates to such interference.

[637]

NOTES

Sub-s (4): words in square brackets in para (a) substituted by the Wireless Telegraphy Act 2006, s 123, Sch 7, paras 21, 22(1), (2).

Sub-s (5): para (a), and words in square brackets in para (c) substituted by the Wireless Telegraphy Act 2006, s 123, Sch 7, paras 21, 22(1), (3).

4 Power to provide for lawful interception

(1) Conduct by any person ("the interceptor") consisting in the interception of a communication in the course of its transmission by means of a telecommunication system is authorised by this section if—

(a) the interception is carried out for the purpose of obtaining information about the communications of a person who, or who the interceptor has reasonable grounds for believing, is in a country or territory outside the United Kingdom;

(b) the interception relates to the use of a telecommunications service provided to persons in that country or territory which is either—

(i) a public telecommunications service; or

(ii) a telecommunications service that would be a public telecommunications service if the persons to whom it is offered or provided were members of the public in a part of the United Kingdom;

(c) the person who provides that service (whether the interceptor or another person) is required by the law of that country or territory to carry out, secure or facilitate the interception in question;

(d) the situation is one in relation to which such further conditions as may be prescribed by regulations made by the Secretary of State are required to be satisfied before conduct may be treated as authorised by virtue of this subsection; and

(e) the conditions so prescribed are satisfied in relation to that situation.

(2) Subject to subsection (3), the Secretary of State may by regulations authorise any such conduct described in the regulations as appears to him to constitute a legitimate practice reasonably required for the purpose, in connection with the carrying on of any business, of monitoring or keeping a record of—

(a) communications by means of which transactions are entered into in the course of that business; or

(b) other communications relating to that business or taking place in the course of its being carried on.

(3) Nothing in any regulations under subsection (2) shall authorise the interception of any communication except in the course of its transmission using apparatus or services provided by or to the person carrying on the business for use wholly or partly in connection with that business.

(4) Conduct taking place in a prison is authorised by this section if it is conduct in exercise of any power conferred by or under any rules made under section 47 of the Prison Act 1952, section 39 of the Prisons (Scotland) Act 1989 or section 13 of the Prison Act (Northern Ireland) 1953 (prison rules).

(5) Conduct taking place in any hospital premises where high security psychiatric services are provided is authorised by this section if it is conduct in pursuance of, and in accordance with, any direction given under *section 17 of the National Health Service Act 1977* (directions as to the carrying out of their functions by health bodies) to the body providing those services at those premises.

(6) Conduct taking place in a state hospital is authorised by this section if it is conduct in pursuance of, and in accordance with, any direction given to the State Hospitals Board for Scotland under section 2(5) of the National Health Service (Scotland) Act 1978 (regulations and directions as to the exercise of their functions by health boards) as applied by Article 5(1) of and the Schedule to The State Hospitals Board for Scotland Order 1995 (which applies certain provisions of that Act of 1978 to the State Hospitals Board).

(7) In this section references to a business include references to any activities of a government department, of any public authority or of any person or office holder on whom functions are conferred by or under any enactment.

(8) In this section—
"government department" includes any part of the Scottish Administration, a Northern Ireland department and the National Assembly for Wales;
"high security psychiatric services" has the same meaning as in *the National Health Service Act 1977*;
"hospital premises" has the same meaning as in section 4(3) of that Act; and
"state hospital" has the same meaning as in the National Health Service (Scotland) Act 1978.

(9) In this section "prison" means—
(a) any prison, young offender institution, young offenders centre or remand centre which is under the general superintendence of, or is provided by, the Secretary of State under the Prison Act 1952 or the Prison Act (Northern Ireland) 1953, or
(b) any prison, young offenders institution or remand centre which is under the general superintendence of the Scottish Ministers under the Prisons (Scotland) Act 1989,

and includes any contracted out prison, within the meaning of Part IV of the Criminal Justice Act 1991 or section 106(4) of the Criminal Justice and Public Order Act 1994, and any legalised police cells within the meaning of section 14 of the Prisons (Scotland) Act 1989.
[638]

NOTES

Sub-s (5): for the words in italics there are substituted the words "section 8 of the National Health Service Act 2006, or section 19 or 23 of the National Health Service (Wales) Act 2006", by the National Health Service (Consequential Provisions) Act 2006, s 2, Sch 1, paras 207, 208(a), as from a day to be appointed.

Sub-s (8): for the words in italics there are substituted the words "section 4 of the National Health Service Act 2006", by the National Health Service (Consequential Provisions) Act 2006, s 2, Sch 1, paras 207, 208(b), as from a day to be appointed.

Regulations: the Telecommunications (Lawful Business Practice) (Interception of Communications) Regulations 2000, SI 2000/2699 at **[1010]**; the Regulation of Investigatory Powers (Conditions for the Lawful Interception of Persons outside the United Kingdom) Regulations 2004, SI 2004/157 at **[1118]**.

PART II
DATA PROTECTION

5 Interception with a warrant

(1) Subject to the following provisions of this Chapter, the Secretary of State may issue a warrant authorising or requiring the person to whom it is addressed, by any such conduct as may be described in the warrant, to secure any one or more of the following—
(a) the interception in the course of their transmission by means of a postal service or telecommunication system of the communications described in the warrant;
(b) the making, in accordance with an international mutual assistance agreement, of a request for the provision of such assistance in connection with, or in the form of, an interception of communications as may be so described;
(c) the provision, in accordance with an international mutual assistance agreement, to the competent authorities of a country or territory outside the United Kingdom of any such assistance in connection with, or in the form of, an interception of communications as may be so described;
(d) the disclosure, in such manner as may be so described, of intercepted material obtained by any interception authorised or required by the warrant, and of related communications data.

(2) The Secretary of State shall not issue an interception warrant unless he believes—
(a) that the warrant is necessary on grounds falling within subsection (3); and
(b) that the conduct authorised by the warrant is proportionate to what is sought to be achieved by that conduct.

(3) Subject to the following provisions of this section, a warrant is necessary on grounds falling within this subsection if it is necessary—
(a) in the interests of national security;
(b) for the purpose of preventing or detecting serious crime;
(c) for the purpose of safeguarding the economic well-being of the United Kingdom; or
(d) for the purpose, in circumstances appearing to the Secretary of State to be equivalent to those in which he would issue a warrant by virtue of paragraph (b), of giving effect to the provisions of any international mutual assistance agreement.

(4) The matters to be taken into account in considering whether the requirements of subsection (2) are satisfied in the case of any warrant shall include whether the information which it is thought necessary to obtain under the warrant could reasonably be obtained by other means.

(5) A warrant shall not be considered necessary on the ground falling within subsection (3)(c) unless the information which it is thought necessary to obtain is information relating to the acts or intentions of persons outside the British Islands.

(6) The conduct authorised by an interception warrant shall be taken to include—

(a) all such conduct (including the interception of communications not identified by the warrant) as it is necessary to undertake in order to do what is expressly authorised or required by the warrant;

(b) conduct for obtaining related communications data; and

(c) conduct by any person which is conduct in pursuance of a requirement imposed by or on behalf of the person to whom the warrant is addressed to be provided with assistance with giving effect to the warrant.

[639]

Interception warrants

6 Application for issue of an interception warrant

(1) An interception warrant shall not be issued except on an application made by or on behalf of a person specified in subsection (2).

(2) Those persons are—

(a) the Director-General of the Security Service;

(b) the Chief of the Secret Intelligence Service;

(c) the Director of GCHQ;

(d) the Director General of the [Serious Organised Crime Agency];

(e) the Commissioner of Police of the Metropolis;

(f) the [Chief Constable of the Police Service of Northern Ireland];

(g) the chief constable of any police force maintained under or by virtue of section 1 of the Police (Scotland) Act 1967;

(h) the Commissioners of Customs and Excise;

(i) the Chief of Defence Intelligence;

(j) a person who, for the purposes of any international mutual assistance agreement, is the competent authority of a country or territory outside the United Kingdom.

(3) An application for the issue of an interception warrant shall not be made on behalf of a person specified in [paragraph (a), (b), (c), (e), (f), (g), (h), (i) or (j) of] subsection (2) except by a person holding office under the Crown.

[640]

NOTES

Sub-s (2): words in square brackets in para (d) substituted by the Serious Organised Crime and Police Act 2005, s 59, Sch 4, paras 131, 132(1), (2), subject to transitional provisions in SI 2006/378, art 4(4), (8); words in square brackets in para (f) substituted by the Police (Northern Ireland) Act 2000, s 78(2)(a).

Sub-s (3): words in square brackets inserted by the Serious Organised Crime and Police Act 2005, s 59, Sch 4, paras 131, 132(1), (3), subject to transitional provisions in SI 2006/378, art 4(4), (8).

7 Issue of warrants

(1) An interception warrant shall not be issued except—

(a) under the hand of the Secretary of State [or, in the case of a warrant issued by the Scottish Ministers (by virtue of provision made under section 63 of the Scotland Act 1998), a member of the Scottish Executive]; or

(b) in a case falling within subsection (2)[(a) or (b)], under the hand of a senior official[; or

(c) in a case falling within subsection (2)(aa), under the hand of a member of the staff of the Scottish Administration who is a member of the Senior Civil Service and who is designated by the Scottish Ministers as a person under whose hand a warrant may be issued in such a case].

(2) Those cases are—

(a) an urgent case in which the Secretary of State has himself expressly authorised the issue of the warrant in that case; and

[(aa) an urgent case in which the Scottish Ministers have themselves (by virtue of provision made under section 63 of the Scotland Act 1998) expressly authorised the use of the warrant in that case and a statement of that fact is endorsed on the warrant; and]

(b) a case in which the warrant is for the purposes of a request for assistance made under an international mutual assistance agreement by the competent authorities of a country or territory outside the United Kingdom and either—

(i) it appears that the interception subject is outside the United Kingdom; or

(ii) the interception to which the warrant relates is to take place in relation only to premises outside the United Kingdom.

(3) An interception warrant—

(a) must be addressed to the person falling within section 6(2) by whom, or on whose behalf, the application for the warrant was made; and

(b) in the case of a warrant issued under the hand of a senior official, must contain, according to whatever is applicable—

(i) one of the statements set out in subsection (4); and

(ii) if it contains the statement set out in subsection (4)(b), one of the statements set out in subsection (5).

(4) The statements referred to in subsection (3)(b)(i) are—

(a) a statement that the case is an urgent case in which the Secretary of State has himself expressly authorised the issue of the warrant;

(b) a statement that the warrant is issued for the purposes of a request for assistance made under an international mutual assistance agreement by the competent authorities of a country or territory outside the United Kingdom.

(5) The statements referred to in subsection (3)(b)(ii) are—

(a) a statement that the interception subject appears to be outside the United Kingdom;

(b) a statement that the interception to which the warrant relates is to take place in relation only to premises outside the United Kingdom.

[641]

PART II
DATA PROTECTION

NOTES

Sub-ss (1), (2): words in square brackets inserted by the Scotland Act 1998 (Transfer of Functions to the Scottish Ministers etc) (No 2) Order 2000, SI 2000/3253, art 4(1), Sch 3, Pt II, paras 3, 4.

8 Contents of warrants

(1) An interception warrant must name or describe either—

(a) one person as the interception subject; or

(b) a single set of premises as the premises in relation to which the interception to which the warrant relates is to take place.

(2) The provisions of an interception warrant describing communications the interception of which is authorised or required by the warrant must comprise one or more schedules setting out the addresses, numbers, apparatus or other factors, or combination of factors, that are to be used for identifying the communications that may be or are to be intercepted.

(3) Any factor or combination of factors set out in accordance with subsection (2) must be one that identifies communications which are likely to be or to include—

(a) communications from, or intended for, the person named or described in the warrant in accordance with subsection (1); or

(b) communications originating on, or intended for transmission to, the premises so named or described.

(4) Subsections (1) and (2) shall not apply to an interception warrant if—

(a) the description of communications to which the warrant relates confines the conduct authorised or required by the warrant to conduct falling within subsection (5); and

(b) at the time of the issue of the warrant, a certificate applicable to the warrant has been issued by the Secretary of State certifying—

(i) the descriptions of intercepted material the examination of which he considers necessary; and

(ii) that he considers the examination of material of those descriptions necessary as mentioned in section 5(3)(a), (b) or (c).

(5) Conduct falls within this subsection if it consists in—

(a) the interception of external communications in the course of their transmission by means of a telecommunication system; and

(b) any conduct authorised in relation to any such interception by section 5(6).

(6) A certificate for the purposes of subsection (4) shall not be issued except under the hand of the Secretary of State.

[642]

9 Duration, cancellation and renewal of warrants

(1) An interception warrant—

(a) shall cease to have effect at the end of the relevant period; but

(b) may be renewed, at any time before the end of that period, by an instrument under the hand of the Secretary of State [or, in the case of a warrant issued by the Scottish Ministers (by virtue of provision made under section 63 of the Scotland Act 1998), a member of the Scottish Executive] or, in a case falling within section 7(2)(b), under the hand of a senior official.

(2) An interception warrant shall not be renewed under subsection (1) unless the Secretary of State believes that the warrant continues to be necessary on grounds falling within section 5(3).

(3) The Secretary of State shall cancel an interception warrant if he is satisfied that the warrant is no longer necessary on grounds falling within section 5(3).

(4) The Secretary of State shall cancel an interception warrant if, at any time before the end of the relevant period, he is satisfied in a case in which—

(a) the warrant is one which was issued containing the statement set out in section 7(5)(a) or has been renewed by an instrument containing the statement set out in subsection (5)(b)(i) of this section, and

(b) the latest renewal (if any) of the warrant is not a renewal by an instrument under the hand of the Secretary of State,

that the person named or described in the warrant as the interception subject is in the United Kingdom.

(5) An instrument under the hand of a senior official that renews an interception warrant must contain—

(a) a statement that the renewal is for the purposes of a request for assistance made under an international mutual assistance agreement by the competent authorities of a country or territory outside the United Kingdom; and

(b) whichever of the following statements is applicable—

(i) a statement that the interception subject appears to be outside the United Kingdom;

(ii) a statement that the interception to which the warrant relates is to take place in relation only to premises outside the United Kingdom.

(6) In this section "the relevant period"—

(a) in relation to an unrenewed warrant issued in a case falling within section 7(2)(a) under the hand of a senior official, means the period ending with the fifth working day following the day of the warrant's issue;

[(ab) in relation to an unrenewed warrant which is endorsed under the hand of the Secretary of State with a statement that the issue of the warrant is believed to be necessary on grounds falling within section 5(3)(a) or (c), means the period of six months beginning with the day of the warrant's issue;]

(b) in relation to a renewed warrant the latest renewal of which was by an instrument endorsed under the hand of the Secretary of State with a statement that the renewal is believed to be necessary on grounds falling within section 5(3)(a) or (c), means the period of six months beginning with the day of the warrant's renewal; and

(c) in all other cases, means the period of three months beginning with the day of the warrant's issue or, in the case of a warrant that has been renewed, of its latest renewal.

[643]

NOTES

Sub-s (1): words in square brackets inserted by the Scotland Act 1998 (Transfer of Functions to the Scottish Ministers etc) (No 2) Order 2000, SI 2000/3253, art 4(1), Sch 3, Pt II, paras 3, 5.

Sub-s (6): para (ab) inserted by the Terrorism Act 2006, s 32(1), (2).

10 Modification of warrants and certificates

(1) The Secretary of State may at any time—

(a) modify the provisions of an interception warrant; or

(b) modify a section 8(4) certificate so as to include in the certified material any material the examination of which he considers to be necessary as mentioned in section 5(3)(a), (b) or (c).

(2) If at any time the Secretary of State considers that any factor set out in a schedule to an interception warrant is no longer relevant for identifying communications which, in the case of that warrant, are likely to be or to include communications falling within section 8(3)(a) or (b), it shall be his duty to modify the warrant by the deletion of that factor.

(3) If at any time the Secretary of State considers that the material certified by a section 8(4) certificate includes any material the examination of which is no longer necessary as mentioned in any of paragraphs (a) to (c) of section 5(3), he shall modify the certificate so as to exclude that material from the certified material.

(4) Subject to subsections (5) to (8), a warrant or certificate shall not be modified under this section except by an instrument under the hand of the Secretary of State or of a senior official.

[(4A) Subject to subsections (5A), (6) and (8), a warrant issued by the Scottish Ministers (by virtue of provision made under section 63 of the Scotland Act 1998) shall not be modified under this section except by an instrument under the hand of a member of the Scottish Executive or a member of the staff of the Scottish Administration who is a member of the Senior Civil Service and is designated by the Scottish Ministers as a person under whose hand an instrument may be issued in such a case (in this section referred to as "a designated official").]

(5) Unscheduled parts of an interception warrant shall not be modified under the hand of a senior official except in an urgent case in which—

(a) the Secretary of State has himself expressly authorised the modification; and

(b) a statement of that fact is endorsed on the modifying instrument.

[(5A) Unscheduled parts of an interception warrant issued by the Scottish Ministers shall not be modified under the hand of a designated official except in an urgent case in which—

(a) they have themselves (by virtue of provision made under section 63 of the Scotland Act 1998) expressly authorised the modification; and

(b) a statement of that fact is endorsed on the modifying instrument.]

[(6) Subsection (4) authorises the modification of the scheduled parts of an interception warrant under the hand of a senior official who is either—

(a) the person to whom the warrant is addressed, or

(b) a person holding a position subordinate to that person,

only if the applicable condition specified in subsection (6A) is satisfied and a statement that the condition is satisfied is endorsed on the modifying instrument.

(6A) The applicable condition is—

(a) in the case of an unrenewed warrant, that the warrant is endorsed with a statement that the issue of the warrant is believed to be necessary in the interests of national security; and

(b) in the case of a renewed warrant, that the instrument by which it was last renewed is endorsed with a statement that the renewal is believed to be necessary in the interests of national security.]

(7) A section 8(4) certificate shall not be modified under the hand of a senior official except in an urgent case in which—

(a) the official in question holds a position in respect of which he is expressly authorised by provisions contained in the certificate to modify the certificate on the Secretary of State's behalf; or

(b) the Secretary of State has himself expressly authorised the modification and a statement of that fact is endorsed on the modifying instrument.

(8) Where modifications in accordance with this subsection are expressly authorised by provision contained in the warrant, the scheduled parts of an interception warrant may, in an urgent case, be modified by an instrument under the hand of—

(a) the person to whom the warrant is addressed; or

(b) a person holding any such position subordinate to that person as may be identified in the provisions of the warrant.

(9) Where—

(a) a warrant or certificate is modified by an instrument under the hand of a person other than the Secretary of State [or, as the case may be, the Scottish Ministers (by virtue of provision made under section 63 of the Scotland Act 1998)]; and

(b) a statement for the purposes of subsection (5)(b)[, (5A)(b)][, (6)] or (7)(b) is endorsed on the instrument, or the modification is made under subsection (8),

that modification shall cease to have effect at the end of the fifth working day following the day of the instrument's issue.

(10) For the purposes of this section—

(a) the scheduled parts of an interception warrant are any provisions of the warrant that are contained in a schedule of identifying factors comprised in the warrant for the purposes of section 8(2); and

(b) the modifications that are modifications of the scheduled parts of an interception warrant include the insertion of an additional such schedule in the warrant;

and references in this section to unscheduled parts of an interception warrant, and to their modification, shall be construed accordingly.

[644]

NOTES

Sub-ss (4A), (5A): inserted by the Scotland Act 1998 (Transfer of Functions to the Scottish Ministers etc) (No 2) Order 2000, SI 2000/3253, art 4(1), Sch 3, Pt II, paras 3, 6(a), (b).

Sub-ss (6), (6A): substituted for original sub-s (6) by the Terrorism Act 2006, s 32(1), (3).

Sub-s (9): words in square brackets in para (a), and figure in first pair of square brackets in para (b) inserted by SI 2000/3253, art 4(1), Sch 3, Pt II, paras 3, 6(d); figure in second pair of square brackets in para (b) inserted by the Terrorism Act 2006, s 32(1), (4).

11 Implementation of warrants

(1) Effect may be given to an interception warrant either—

(a) by the person to whom it is addressed; or

(b) by that person acting through, or together with, such other persons as he may require (whether under subsection (2) or otherwise) to provide him with assistance with giving effect to the warrant.

(2) For the purpose of requiring any person to provide assistance in relation to an interception warrant the person to whom it is addressed may—

(a) serve a copy of the warrant on such persons as he considers may be able to provide such assistance; or

(b) make arrangements under which a copy of it is to be or may be so served.

(3) The copy of an interception warrant that is served on any person under subsection (2) may, to the extent authorised—

(a) by the person to whom the warrant is addressed, or

(b) by the arrangements made by him for the purposes of that subsection,

omit any one or more of the schedules to the warrant.

(4) Where a copy of an interception warrant has been served by or on behalf of the person to whom it is addressed on—

(a) a person who provides a postal service,

(b) a person who provides a public telecommunications service, or

(c) a person not falling within paragraph (b) who has control of the whole or any part of a telecommunication system located wholly or partly in the United Kingdom,

it shall (subject to subsection (5)) be the duty of that person to take all such steps for giving effect to the warrant as are notified to him by or on behalf of the person to whom the warrant is addressed.

(5) A person who is under a duty by virtue of subsection (4) to take steps for giving effect to a warrant shall not be required to take any steps which it is not reasonably practicable for him to take.

(6) For the purposes of subsection (5) the steps which it is reasonably practicable for a person to take in a case in which obligations have been imposed on him by or under section 12 shall include every step which it would have been reasonably practicable for him to take had he complied with all the obligations so imposed on him.

(7) A person who knowingly fails to comply with his duty under subsection (4) shall be guilty of an offence and liable—

(a) on conviction on indictment, to imprisonment for a term not exceeding two years or to a fine, or to both;

(b) on summary conviction, to imprisonment for a term not exceeding six months or to a fine not exceeding the statutory maximum, or to both.

(8) A person's duty under subsection (4) to take steps for giving effect to a warrant shall be enforceable by civil proceedings by the Secretary of State for an injunction, or for specific performance of a statutory duty under section 45 of the Court of Session Act 1988, or for any other appropriate relief.

(9) For the purposes of this Act the provision of assistance with giving effect to an interception warrant includes any disclosure to the person to whom the warrant is addressed, or to persons acting on his behalf, of intercepted material obtained by any interception authorised or required by the warrant, and of any related communications data.

[645]

Interception capability and costs

12 Maintenance of interception capability

(1) The Secretary of State may by order provide for the imposition by him on persons who—

(a) are providing public postal services or public telecommunications services, or

(b) are proposing to do so,

of such obligations as it appears to him reasonable to impose for the purpose of securing that it is and remains practicable for requirements to provide assistance in relation to interception warrants to be imposed and complied with.

(2) The Secretary of State's power to impose the obligations provided for by an order under this section shall be exercisable by the giving, in accordance with the order, of a notice requiring the person who is to be subject to the obligations to take all such steps as may be specified or described in the notice.

(3) Subject to subsection (11), the only steps that may be specified or described in a notice given to a person under subsection (2) are steps appearing to the Secretary of State to be necessary for securing that that person has the practical capability of providing any assistance which he may be required to provide in relation to relevant interception warrants.

(4) A person shall not be liable to have an obligation imposed on him in accordance with an order under this section by reason only that he provides, or is proposing to provide, to members of the public a telecommunications service the provision of which is or, as the case may be, will be no more than—

(a) the means by which he provides a service which is not a telecommunications service; or

(b) necessarily incidental to the provision by him of a service which is not a telecommunications service.

(5) Where a notice is given to any person under subsection (2) and otherwise than by virtue of subsection (6)(c), that person may, before the end of such period as may be specified in an order under this section, refer the notice to the Technical Advisory Board.

(6) Where a notice given to any person under subsection (2) is referred to the Technical Advisory Board under subsection (5)—

(a) there shall be no requirement for that person to comply, except in pursuance of a notice under paragraph (c)(ii), with any obligations imposed by the notice;

(b) the Board shall consider the technical requirements and the financial consequences, for the person making the reference, of the notice referred to them and shall report their conclusions on those matters to that person and to the Secretary of State; and

(c) the Secretary of State, after considering any report of the Board relating to the notice, may either—
  (i) withdraw the notice; or
  (ii) give a further notice under subsection (2) confirming its effect, with or without modifications.

(7) It shall be the duty of a person to whom a notice is given under subsection (2) to comply with the notice; and that duty shall be enforceable by civil proceedings by the Secretary of State for an injunction, or for specific performance of a statutory duty under section 45 of the Court of Session Act 1988, or for any other appropriate relief.

(8) A notice for the purposes of subsection (2) must specify such period as appears to the Secretary of State to be reasonable as the period within which the steps specified or described in the notice are to be taken.

(9) Before making an order under this section the Secretary of State shall consult with—

(a) such persons appearing to him to be likely to be subject to the obligations for which it provides,
(b) the Technical Advisory Board,
(c) such persons representing persons falling within paragraph (a), and
(d) such persons with statutory functions in relation to persons falling within that paragraph,

as he considers appropriate.

(10) The Secretary of State shall not make an order under this section unless a draft of the order has been laid before Parliament and approved by a resolution of each House.

(11) For the purposes of this section the question whether a person has the practical capability of providing assistance in relation to relevant interception warrants shall include the question whether all such arrangements have been made as the Secretary of State considers necessary—

(a) with respect to the disclosure of intercepted material;
(b) for the purpose of ensuring that security and confidentiality are maintained in relation to, and to matters connected with, the provision of any such assistance; and
(c) for the purpose of facilitating the carrying out of any functions in relation to this Chapter of the Interception of Communications Commissioner;

but before determining for the purposes of the making of any order, or the imposition of any obligation, under this section what arrangements he considers necessary for the purpose mentioned in paragraph (c) the Secretary of State shall consult that Commissioner.

(12) In this section "relevant interception warrant"—

(a) in relation to a person providing a public postal service, means an interception warrant relating to the interception of communications in the course of their transmission by means of that service; and
(b) in relation to a person providing a public telecommunications service, means an interception warrant relating to the interception of communications in the course of their transmission by means of a telecommunication system used for the purposes of that service.

[646]

NOTES

Orders: the Regulation of Investigatory Powers (Maintenance of Interception Capability) Order 2002, SI 2002/1931 at **[1044]**.

13 Technical Advisory Board

(1) There shall be a Technical Advisory Board consisting of such number of persons appointed by the Secretary of State as he may by order provide.

(2) The order providing for the membership of the Technical Advisory Board must also make provision which is calculated to ensure—

(a) that the membership of the Technical Advisory Board includes persons likely effectively to represent the interests of the persons on whom obligations may be imposed under section 12;

(b) that the membership of the Board includes persons likely effectively to represent the interests of the persons by or on whose behalf applications for interception warrants may be made;

(c) that such other persons (if any) as the Secretary of State thinks fit may be appointed to be members of the Board; and

(d) that the Board is so constituted as to produce a balance between the representation of the interests mentioned in paragraph (a) and the representation of those mentioned in paragraph (b).

(3) The Secretary of State shall not make an order under this section unless a draft of the order has been laid before Parliament and approved by a resolution of each House.

[647]

NOTES

Orders: the Regulation of Investigatory Powers (Technical Advisory Board) Order 2001, SI 2001/3734 at **[1042]**.

14 Grants for interception costs

(1) It shall be the duty of the Secretary of State to ensure that such arrangements are in force as are necessary for securing that a person who provides—

(a) a postal service, or

(b) a telecommunications service,

receives such contribution as is, in the circumstances of that person's case, a fair contribution towards the costs incurred, or likely to be incurred, by that person in consequence of the matters mentioned in subsection (2).

(2) Those matters are—

(a) in relation to a person providing a postal service, the issue of interception warrants relating to communications transmitted by means of that postal service;

(b) in relation to a person providing a telecommunications service, the issue of interception warrants relating to communications transmitted by means of a telecommunication system used for the purposes of that service;

(c) in relation to each description of person, the imposition on that person of obligations provided for by an order under section 12.

(3) For the purpose of complying with his duty under this section, the Secretary of State may make arrangements for payments to be made out of money provided by Parliament.

[648]

Restrictions on use of intercepted material etc

15 General safeguards

(1) Subject to subsection (6), it shall be the duty of the Secretary of State to ensure, in relation to all interception warrants, that such arrangements are in force as he considers necessary for securing—

(a) that the requirements of subsections (2) and (3) are satisfied in relation to the intercepted material and any related communications data; and

(b) in the case of warrants in relation to which there are section 8(4) certificates, that the requirements of section 16 are also satisfied.

(2) The requirements of this subsection are satisfied in relation to the intercepted material and any related communications data if each of the following—

(a) the number of persons to whom any of the material or data is disclosed or otherwise made available,

(b) the extent to which any of the material or data is disclosed or otherwise made available,

(c) the extent to which any of the material or data is copied, and

(d) the number of copies that are made,

is limited to the minimum that is necessary for the authorised purposes.

(3) The requirements of this subsection are satisfied in relation to the intercepted material and any related communications data if each copy made of any of the material or data (if not destroyed earlier) is destroyed as soon as there are no longer any grounds for retaining it as necessary for any of the authorised purposes.

PART II
DATA PROTECTION

(4) For the purposes of this section something is necessary for the authorised purposes if, and only if—

(a) it continues to be, or is likely to become, necessary as mentioned in section 5(3);

(b) it is necessary for facilitating the carrying out of any of the functions under this Chapter of the Secretary of State;

(c) it is necessary for facilitating the carrying out of any functions in relation to this Part of the Interception of Communications Commissioner or of the Tribunal;

(d) it is necessary to ensure that a person conducting a criminal prosecution has the information he needs to determine what is required of him by his duty to secure the fairness of the prosecution; or

(e) it is necessary for the performance of any duty imposed on any person by the Public Records Act 1958 or the Public Records Act (Northern Ireland) 1923.

(5) The arrangements for the time being in force under this section for securing that the requirements of subsection (2) are satisfied in relation to the intercepted material or any related communications data must include such arrangements as the Secretary of State considers necessary for securing that every copy of the material or data that is made is stored, for so long as it is retained, in a secure manner.

(6) Arrangements in relation to interception warrants which are made for the purposes of subsection (1)—

(a) shall not be required to secure that the requirements of subsections (2) and (3) are satisfied in so far as they relate to any of the intercepted material or related communications data, or any copy of any such material or data, possession of which has been surrendered to any authorities of a country or territory outside the United Kingdom; but

(b) shall be required to secure, in the case of every such warrant, that possession of the intercepted material and data and of copies of the material or data is surrendered to authorities of a country or territory outside the United Kingdom only if the requirements of subsection (7) are satisfied.

(7) The requirements of this subsection are satisfied in the case of a warrant if it appears to the Secretary of State—

(a) that requirements corresponding to those of subsections (2) and (3) will apply, to such extent (if any) as the Secretary of State thinks fit, in relation to any of the intercepted material or related communications data possession of which, or of any copy of which, is surrendered to the authorities in question; and

(b) that restrictions are in force which would prevent, to such extent (if any) as the Secretary of State thinks fit, the doing of anything in, for the purposes of or in connection with any proceedings outside the United Kingdom which would result in such a disclosure as, by virtue of section 17, could not be made in the United Kingdom.

(8) In this section "copy", in relation to intercepted material or related communications data, means any of the following (whether or not in documentary form)—

(a) any copy, extract or summary of the material or data which identifies itself as the product of an interception, and

(b) any record referring to an interception which is a record of the identities of the persons to or by whom the intercepted material was sent, or to whom the communications data relates,

and "copied" shall be construed accordingly.

[649]

16 Extra safeguards in the case of certificated warrants

(1) For the purposes of section 15 the requirements of this section, in the case of a warrant in relation to which there is a section 8(4) certificate, are that the intercepted material is read, looked at or listened to by the persons to whom it becomes available by virtue of the warrant to the extent only that it—

(a) has been certified as material the examination of which is necessary as mentioned in section 5(3)(a), (b) or (c); and

(b) falls within subsection (2).

(2) Subject to subsections (3) and (4), intercepted material falls within this subsection so far only as it is selected to be read, looked at or listened to otherwise than according to a factor which—

(a) is referable to an individual who is known to be for the time being in the British Islands; and

(b) has as its purpose, or one of its purposes, the identification of material contained in communications sent by him, or intended for him.

(3) Intercepted material falls within subsection (2), notwithstanding that it is selected by reference to any such factor as is mentioned in paragraph (a) and (b) of that subsection, if—

(a) it is certified by the Secretary of State for the purposes of section 8(4) that the examination of material selected according to factors referable to the individual in question is necessary as mentioned in subsection 5(3)(a), (b) or (c); and

(b) the material relates only to communications sent during [a period specified in the certificate that is no longer than the permitted maximum].

[(3A) In subsection (3)(b) 'the permitted maximum' means—

(a) in the case of material the examination of which is certified for the purposes of section 8(4) as necessary in the interests of national security, six months; and

(b) in any other case, three months.]

(4) Intercepted material also falls within subsection (2), notwithstanding that it is selected by reference to any such factor as is mentioned in paragraph (a) and (b) of that subsection, if—

(a) the person to whom the warrant is addressed believes, on reasonable grounds, that the circumstances are such that the material would fall within that subsection; or

(b) the conditions set out in subsection (5) below are satisfied in relation to the selection of the material.

(5) Those conditions are satisfied in relation to the selection of intercepted material if—

(a) it has appeared to the person to whom the warrant is addressed that there has been such a relevant change of circumstances as, but for subsection (4)(b), would prevent the intercepted material from falling within subsection (2);

(b) since it first so appeared, a written authorisation to read, look at or listen to the material has been given by a senior official; and

(c) the selection is made before the end of [the permitted period].

[(5A) In subsection (5)(c) 'the permitted period' means—

(a) in the case of material the examination of which is certified for the purposes of section 8(4) as necessary in the interests of national security, the period ending with the end of the fifth working day after it first appeared as mentioned in subsection (5)(a) to the person to whom the warrant is addressed; and

(b) in any other case, the period ending with the end of the first working day after it first so appeared to that person.]

(6) References in this section to its appearing that there has been a relevant change of circumstances are references to its appearing either—

(a) that the individual in question has entered the British Islands; or

(b) that a belief by the person to whom the warrant is addressed in the individual's presence outside the British Islands was in fact mistaken.

[650]

NOTES

Sub-s (3): words in square brackets substituted by the Terrorism Act 2006, s 32(1), (5)(a).
Sub-ss (3A), (5A): inserted by the Terrorism Act 2006, s 32(1), (6), (7).
Sub-s (5): words in square brackets substituted by the Terrorism Act 2006, s 32(1), (5)(b).

17 Exclusion of matters from legal proceedings

(1) Subject to section 18, no evidence shall be adduced, question asked, assertion or disclosure made or other thing done in, for the purposes of or in connection with any legal proceedings [or Inquiries Act proceedings] which (in any manner)—

(a) discloses, in circumstances from which its origin in anything falling within subsection (2) may be inferred, any of the contents of an intercepted communication or any related communications data; or

(b) tends (apart from any such disclosure) to suggest that anything falling within subsection (2) has or may have occurred or be going to occur.

(2) The following fall within this subsection—

(a) conduct by a person falling within subsection (3) that was or would be an offence under section 1(1) or (2) of this Act or under section 1 of the Interception of Communications Act 1985,

(b) a breach by the Secretary of State of his duty under section 1(4) of this Act,

PART II DATA PROTECTION

(c) the issue of an interception warrant or of a warrant under the Interception of Communications Act 1985,
(d) the making of an application by any person for an interception warrant, or for a warrant under that Act,
(e) the imposition of any requirement on any person to provide assistance with giving effect to an interception warrant.

(3) The persons referred to in subsection (2)(a) are—
(a) any person to whom a warrant under this Chapter may be addressed;
(b) any person holding office under the Crown;
[(c) any member of the staff of the Serious Organised Crime Agency;]
(e) any person employed by or for the purposes of a police force;
(f) any person providing a postal service or employed for the purposes of any business of providing such a service; and
(g) any person providing a public telecommunications service or employed for the purposes of any business of providing such a service.

(4) [In this section—
"Inquiries Act proceedings" means proceedings of an inquiry under the Inquiries Act 2005;
"intercepted communications" means] any communication intercepted in the course of its transmission by means of a postal service or telecommunication system.

[651]

NOTES

Sub-s (1): words in square brackets inserted by the Inquiries Act 2005, s 48(1), Sch 2, Pt 1, para 20(1), (2).

Sub-s (3): para (c) substituted for original paras (c), (d) by the Serious Organised Crime and Police Act 2005, s 59, Sch 4, paras 131, 133, subject to transitional provisions in SI 2006/378, art 4(4), (8).

Sub-s (4): words in square brackets substituted by the Inquiries Act 2005, s 48(1), Sch 2, Pt 1, para 20(1), (3).

18 Exceptions to section 17

(1) Section 17(1) shall not apply in relation to—
(a) any proceedings for a relevant offence;
(b) any civil proceedings under section 11(8);
(c) any proceedings before the Tribunal;
(d) any proceedings on an appeal or review for which provision is made by an order under section 67(8);
[(da) any control order proceedings (within the meaning of the Prevention of Terrorism Act 2005) or any proceedings arising out of such proceedings;]
(e) any proceedings before the Special Immigration Appeals Commission or any proceedings arising out of proceedings before that Commission; or
(f) any proceedings before the Proscribed Organisations Appeal Commission or any proceedings arising out of proceedings before that Commission.

(2) Subsection (1) shall not, by virtue of [paragraphs (da) to (f)], authorise the disclosure of anything—
[(za) in the case of any proceedings falling within paragraph (da) to—
(i) a person who, within the meaning of the Schedule to the Prevention of Terrorism Act 2005, is or was a relevant party to the control order proceedings; or
(ii) any person who for the purposes of any proceedings so falling (but otherwise than by virtue of an appointment under paragraph 7 of that Schedule) represents a person falling within sub-paragraph (i);]
(a) in the case of any proceedings falling within paragraph (e), to—
(i) the appellant to the Special Immigration Appeals Commission; or
(ii) any person who for the purposes of any proceedings so falling (but otherwise than by virtue of an appointment under section 6 of the Special Immigration Appeals Commission Act 1997) represents that appellant;
or
(b) in the case of proceedings falling within paragraph (f), to—
(i) the applicant to the Proscribed Organisations Appeal Commission;
(ii) the organisation concerned (if different);

(iii) any person designated under paragraph 6 of Schedule 3 to the Terrorism Act 2000 to conduct proceedings so falling on behalf of that organisation; or

(iv) any person who for the purposes of any proceedings so falling (but otherwise than by virtue of an appointment under paragraph 7 of that Schedule) represents that applicant or that organisation.

(3) Section 17(1) shall not prohibit anything done in, for the purposes of, or in connection with, so much of any legal proceedings as relates to the fairness or unfairness of a dismissal on the grounds of any conduct constituting an offence under section 1(1) or (2), 11(7) or 19 of this Act, or section 1 of the Interception of Communications Act 1985.

(4) Section 17(1)(a) shall not prohibit the disclosure of any of the contents of a communication if the interception of that communication was lawful by virtue of section 1(5)(c), 3 or 4.

(5) Where any disclosure is proposed to be or has been made on the grounds that it is authorised by subsection (4), section 17(1) shall not prohibit the doing of anything in, or for the purposes of, so much of any … proceedings as relates to the question whether that disclosure is or was so authorised.

(6) Section 17(1)(b) shall not prohibit the doing of anything that discloses any conduct of a person for which he has been convicted of an offence under section 1(1) or (2), 11(7) or 19 of this Act, or section 1 of the Interception of Communications Act 1985.

(7) Nothing in section 17(1) shall prohibit any such disclosure of any information that continues to be available for disclosure as is confined to—

(a) a disclosure to a person conducting a criminal prosecution for the purpose only of enabling that person to determine what is required of him by his duty to secure the fairness of the prosecution; …

(b) a disclosure to a relevant judge in a case in which that judge has ordered the disclosure to be made to him alone[; or

(c) a disclosure to the panel of an inquiry held under the Inquiries Act 2005 in the course of which the panel has ordered the disclosure to be made to the panel alone.]

(8) A relevant judge shall not order a disclosure under subsection (7)(b) except where he is satisfied that the exceptional circumstances of the case make the disclosure essential in the interests of justice.

[(8A) The panel of an inquiry shall not order a disclosure under subsection (7)(c) except where it is satisfied that the exceptional circumstances of the case make the disclosure essential to enable the inquiry to fulfil its terms of reference.]

(9) Subject to subsection (10), where in any criminal proceedings—

(a) a relevant judge does order a disclosure under subsection (7)(b), and

(b) in consequence of that disclosure he is of the opinion that there are exceptional circumstances requiring him to do so,

he may direct the person conducting the prosecution to make for the purposes of the proceedings any such admission of fact as that judge thinks essential in the interests of justice.

(10) Nothing in any direction under subsection (9) shall authorise or require anything to be done in contravention of section 17(1).

(11) In this section "a relevant judge" means—

(a) any judge of the High Court or of the Crown Court or any Circuit judge;

(b) any judge of the High Court of Justiciary or any sheriff;

(c) *in relation to a court-martial, the judge advocate appointed in relation to that court-martial under section 84B of the Army Act 1955, section 84B of the Air Force Act 1955 or section 53B of the Naval Discipline Act 1957; or*

(d) any person holding any such judicial office as entitles him to exercise the jurisdiction of a judge falling within paragraph (a) or (b).

(12) In this section "relevant offence" means—

(a) an offence under any provision of this Act;

(b) an offence under section 1 of the Interception of Communications Act 1985;

(c) an offence under [section 47 or 48 of the Wireless Telegraphy Act 2006];

(d) an offence under … [section 83 or 84 of the Postal Services Act 2000];

(e) …

PART II
DATA PROTECTION

(f) an offence under section 4 of the Official Secrets Act 1989 relating to any such information, document or article as is mentioned in subsection (3)(a) of that section;
(g) an offence under section 1 or 2 of the Official Secrets Act 1911 relating to any sketch, plan, model, article, note, document or information which incorporates or relates to the contents of any intercepted communication or any related communications data or tends to suggest as mentioned in section 17(1)(b) of this Act;
(h) perjury committed in the course of any proceedings mentioned in subsection (1) or (3) of this section;
(i) attempting or conspiring to commit, or aiding, abetting, counselling or procuring the commission of, an offence falling within any of the preceding paragraphs; and
(j) contempt of court committed in the course of, or in relation to, any proceedings mentioned in subsection (1) or (3) of this section.

(13) In subsection (12) "intercepted communication" has the same meaning as in section 17.

[652]

NOTES

Sub-s (1): para (da) inserted by the Prevention of Terrorism Act 2005, s 11(5), Schedule, para 9(1), (2).
Sub-s (2): words in first pair of square brackets substituted and para (za) inserted by the Prevention of Terrorism Act 2005, s 11(5), Schedule, para 9(1), (3), (4).
Sub-s (5): word omitted repealed by the Inquiries Act 2005, ss 48(1), 49(2), Sch 2, Pt 1, para 21(1), (2), Sch 3.
Sub-s (7): word omitted from para (a) repealed, and para (c) and the word immediately preceding it inserted by the Inquiries Act 2005, ss 48(1), 49(2), Sch 2, Pt 1, para 21(1), (3), Sch 3, subject to transitional provisions in s 44(5) of the 2005 Act.
Sub-s (8A): inserted by the Inquiries Act 2005, s 48(1), Sch 2, Pt 1, para 21(1), (4).
Sub-s (11): para (c) substituted by the Armed Forces Act 2006, s 378(1), Sch 16, para 169, as from a day to be appointed, as follows:

"(c) in relation to proceedings before the Court Martial, the judge advocate for those proceedings; or".

Sub-s (12): words in square brackets in para (c) substituted by the Wireless Telegraphy Act 2006, s 123, Sch 7, paras 21, 23; in para (d) words omitted repealed, and words in square brackets substituted, by the Postal Services Act 2000 (Consequential Modifications No 1) Order 2001, SI 2001/1149, art 3, Sch 1, para 135(1), (2), Sch 2, subject to transitional provisions and savings, in art 4(8), (11) thereof; para (e) repealed by the Communications Act 2003, s 406(7), Sch 19(1).

19 Offence for unauthorised disclosures

(1) Where an interception warrant has been issued or renewed, it shall be the duty of every person falling within subsection (2) to keep secret all the matters mentioned in subsection (3).

(2) The persons falling within this subsection are—
(a) the persons specified in section 6(2);
(b) every person holding office under the Crown;
[(c) every member of the staff of the Serious Organised Crime Agency;]
(e) every person employed by or for the purposes of a police force;
(f) persons providing postal services or employed for the purposes of any business of providing such a service;
(g) persons providing public telecommunications services or employed for the purposes of any business of providing such a service;
(h) persons having control of the whole or any part of a telecommunication system located wholly or partly in the United Kingdom.

(3) Those matters are—
(a) the existence and contents of the warrant and of any section 8(4) certificate in relation to the warrant;
(b) the details of the issue of the warrant and of any renewal or modification of the warrant or of any such certificate;
(c) the existence and contents of any requirement to provide assistance with giving effect to the warrant;
(d) the steps taken in pursuance of the warrant or of any such requirement; and
(e) everything in the intercepted material, together with any related communications data.

(4) A person who makes a disclosure to another of anything that he is required to keep secret under this section shall be guilty of an offence and liable—

(a) on conviction on indictment, to imprisonment for a term not exceeding five years or to a fine, or to both;

(b) on summary conviction, to imprisonment for a term not exceeding six months or to a fine not exceeding the statutory maximum, or to both.

(5) In proceedings against any person for an offence under this section in respect of any disclosure, it shall be a defence for that person to show that he could not reasonably have been expected, after first becoming aware of the matter disclosed, to take steps to prevent the disclosure.

(6) In proceedings against any person for an offence under this section in respect of any disclosure, it shall be a defence for that person to show that—

(a) the disclosure was made by or to a professional legal adviser in connection with the giving, by the adviser to any client of his, of advice about the effect of provisions of this Chapter; and

(b) the person to whom or, as the case may be, by whom it was made was the client or a representative of the client.

(7) In proceedings against any person for an offence under this section in respect of any disclosure, it shall be a defence for that person to show that the disclosure was made by a legal adviser—

(a) in contemplation of, or in connection with, any legal proceedings; and

(b) for the purposes of those proceedings.

(8) Neither subsection (6) nor subsection (7) applies in the case of a disclosure made with a view to furthering any criminal purpose.

(9) In proceedings against any person for an offence under this section in respect of any disclosure, it shall be a defence for that person to show that the disclosure was confined to a disclosure made to the Interception of Communications Commissioner or authorised—

(a) by that Commissioner;

(b) by the warrant or the person to whom the warrant is or was addressed;

(c) by the terms of the requirement to provide assistance; or

(d) by section 11(9).

[653]

NOTES

Sub-s (2): para (c) substituted for original paras (c), (d) by the Serious Organised Crime and Police Act 2005, s 59, Sch 4, paras 131, 134, subject to transitional provisions in SI 2006/378, art 4(4), (8).

Interpretation of Chapter I

20 Interpretation of Chapter I

In this Chapter—

"certified", in relation to a section 8(4) certificate, means of a description certified by the certificate as a description of material the examination of which the Secretary of State considers necessary;

"external communication" means a communication sent or received outside the British Islands;

"intercepted material", in relation to an interception warrant, means the contents of any communications intercepted by an interception to which the warrant relates;

"the interception subject", in relation to an interception warrant, means the person about whose communications information is sought by the interception to which the warrant relates;

"international mutual assistance agreement" means an international agreement designated for the purposes of section 1(4);

"related communications data", in relation to a communication intercepted in the course of its transmission by means of a postal service or telecommunication system, means so much of any communications data (within the meaning of Chapter II of this Part) as—

(a) is obtained by, or in connection with, the interception; and

(b) relates to the communication or to the sender or recipient, or intended recipient, of the communication;

PART II DATA PROTECTION

"section 8(4) certificate" means any certificate issued for the purposes of section 8(4). **[654]**

CHAPTER II
ACQUISITION AND DISCLOSURE OF COMMUNICATIONS DATA

21 Lawful acquisition and disclosure of communications data

(1) This Chapter applies to—

(a) any conduct in relation to a postal service or telecommunication system for obtaining communications data, other than conduct consisting in the interception of communications in the course of their transmission by means of such a service or system; and

(b) the disclosure to any person of communications data.

(2) Conduct to which this Chapter applies shall be lawful for all purposes if—

(a) it is conduct in which any person is authorised or required to engage by an authorisation or notice granted or given under this Chapter; and

(b) the conduct is in accordance with, or in pursuance of, the authorisation or requirement.

(3) A person shall not be subject to any civil liability in respect of any conduct of his which—

(a) is incidental to any conduct that is lawful by virtue of subsection (2); and

(b) is not itself conduct an authorisation or warrant for which is capable of being granted under a relevant enactment and might reasonably have been expected to have been sought in the case in question.

(4) In this Chapter "communications data" means any of the following—

(a) any traffic data comprised in or attached to a communication (whether by the sender or otherwise) for the purposes of any postal service or telecommunication system by means of which it is being or may be transmitted;

(b) any information which includes none of the contents of a communication (apart from any information falling within paragraph (a)) and is about the use made by any person—

(i) of any postal service or telecommunications service; or

(ii) in connection with the provision to or use by any person of any telecommunications service, of any part of a telecommunication system;

(c) any information not falling within paragraph (a) or (b) that is held or obtained, in relation to persons to whom he provides the service, by a person providing a postal service or telecommunications service.

(5) In this section "relevant enactment" means—

(a) an enactment contained in this Act;

(b) section 5 of the Intelligence Services Act 1994 (warrants for the intelligence services); or

(c) an enactment contained in Part III of the Police Act 1997 (powers of the police and of customs officers).

(6) In this section "traffic data", in relation to any communication, means—

(a) any data identifying, or purporting to identify, any person, apparatus or location to or from which the communication is or may be transmitted,

(b) any data identifying or selecting, or purporting to identify or select, apparatus through which, or by means of which, the communication is or may be transmitted,

(c) any data comprising signals for the actuation of apparatus used for the purposes of a telecommunication system for effecting (in whole or in part) the transmission of any communication, and

(d) any data identifying the data or other data as data comprised in or attached to a particular communication,

but that expression includes data identifying a computer file or computer program access to which is obtained, or which is run, by means of the communication to the extent only that the file or program is identified by reference to the apparatus in which it is stored.

(7) In this section—

(a) references, in relation to traffic data comprising signals for the actuation of apparatus, to a telecommunication system by means of which a communication is being or may be transmitted include references to any telecommunication system in which that apparatus is comprised; and

(b) references to traffic data being attached to a communication include references to the data and the communication being logically associated with each other;

and in this section "data", in relation to a postal item, means anything written on the outside of the item.

[655]

NOTES

Commencement: 2 October 2000 (sub-s (4), for the purpose of giving effect to the definition of "related communications data" in s 20); 5 January 2004 (otherwise).

22 Obtaining and disclosing communications data

(1) This section applies where a person designated for the purposes of this Chapter believes that it is necessary on grounds falling within subsection (2) to obtain any communications data.

(2) It is necessary on grounds falling within this subsection to obtain communications data if it is necessary—

(a) in the interests of national security;

(b) for the purpose of preventing or detecting crime or of preventing disorder;

(c) in the interests of the economic well-being of the United Kingdom;

(d) in the interests of public safety;

(e) for the purpose of protecting public health;

(f) for the purpose of assessing or collecting any tax, duty, levy or other imposition, contribution or charge payable to a government department;

(g) for the purpose, in an emergency, of preventing death or injury or any damage to a person's physical or mental health, or of mitigating any injury or damage to a person's physical or mental health; or

(h) for any purpose (not falling within paragraphs (a) to (g)) which is specified for the purposes of this subsection by an order made by the Secretary of State.

(3) Subject to subsection (5), the designated person may grant an authorisation for persons holding offices, ranks or positions with the same relevant public authority as the designated person to engage in any conduct to which this Chapter applies.

(4) Subject to subsection (5), where it appears to the designated person that a postal or telecommunications operator is or may be in possession of, or be capable of obtaining, any communications data, the designated person may, by notice to the postal or telecommunications operator, require the operator—

(a) if the operator is not already in possession of the data, to obtain the data; and

(b) in any case, to disclose all of the data in his possession or subsequently obtained by him.

(5) The designated person shall not grant an authorisation under subsection (3), or give a notice under subsection (4), unless he believes that obtaining the data in question by the conduct authorised or required by the authorisation or notice is proportionate to what is sought to be achieved by so obtaining the data.

(6) It shall be the duty of the postal or telecommunications operator to comply with the requirements of any notice given to him under subsection (4).

(7) A person who is under a duty by virtue of subsection (6) shall not be required to do anything in pursuance of that duty which it is not reasonably practicable for him to do.

(8) The duty imposed by subsection (6) shall be enforceable by civil proceedings by the Secretary of State for an injunction, or for specific performance of a statutory duty under section 45 of the Court of Session Act 1988, or for any other appropriate relief.

(9) The Secretary of State shall not make an order under subsection (2)(h) unless a draft of the order has been laid before Parliament and approved by a resolution of each House.

[656]

NOTES

Commencement: 5 January 2004.

PART II DATA PROTECTION

23 Form and duration of authorisations and notices

(1) An authorisation under section 22(3)—

(a) must be granted in writing or (if not in writing) in a manner that produces a record of its having been granted;

(b) must describe the conduct to which this Chapter applies that is authorised and the communications data in relation to which it is authorised;

(c) must specify the matters falling within section 22(2) by reference to which it is granted; and

(d) must specify the office, rank or position held by the person granting the authorisation.

(2) A notice under section 22(4) requiring communications data to be disclosed or to be obtained and disclosed—

(a) must be given in writing or (if not in writing) must be given in a manner that produces a record of its having been given;

(b) must describe the communications data to be obtained or disclosed under the notice;

(c) must specify the matters falling within section 22(2) by reference to which the notice is given;

(d) must specify the office, rank or position held by the person giving it; and

(e) must specify the manner in which any disclosure required by the notice is to be made.

(3) A notice under section 22(4) shall not require the disclosure of data to any person other than—

(a) the person giving the notice; or

(b) such other person as may be specified in or otherwise identified by, or in accordance with, the provisions of the notice;

but the provisions of the notice shall not specify or otherwise identify a person for the purposes of paragraph (b) unless he holds an office, rank or position with the same relevant public authority as the person giving the notice.

(4) An authorisation under section 22(3) or notice under section 22(4)—

(a) shall not authorise or require any data to be obtained after the end of the period of one month beginning with the date on which the authorisation is granted or the notice given; and

(b) in the case of a notice, shall not authorise or require any disclosure after the end of that period of any data not in the possession of, or obtained by, the postal or telecommunications operator at a time during that period.

(5) An authorisation under section 22(3) or notice under section 22(4) may be renewed at any time before the end of the period of one month applying (in accordance with subsection (4) or subsection (7)) to that authorisation or notice.

(6) A renewal of an authorisation under section 22(3) or of a notice under section 22(4) shall be by the grant or giving, in accordance with this section, of a further authorisation or notice.

(7) Subsection (4) shall have effect in relation to a renewed authorisation or renewal notice as if the period of one month mentioned in that subsection did not begin until the end of the period of one month applicable to the authorisation or notice that is current at the time of the renewal.

(8) Where a person who has given a notice under subsection (4) of section 22 is satisfied—

(a) that it is no longer necessary on grounds falling within subsection (2) of that section for the requirements of the notice to be complied with, or

(b) that the conduct required by the notice is no longer proportionate to what is sought to be achieved by obtaining communications data to which the notice relates,

he shall cancel the notice.

(9) The Secretary of State may by regulations provide for the person by whom any duty imposed by subsection (8) is to be performed in a case in which it would otherwise fall on a person who is no longer available to perform it; and regulations under this subsection may provide for the person on whom the duty is to fall to be a person appointed in accordance with the regulations.

[657]

NOTES
Commencement: 5 January 2004.

24 Arrangements for payments

(1) It shall be the duty of the Secretary of State to ensure that such arrangements are in force as he thinks appropriate for requiring or authorising, in such cases as he thinks fit, the making to postal and telecommunications operators of appropriate contributions towards the costs incurred by them in complying with notices under section 22(4).

(2) For the purpose of complying with his duty under this section, the Secretary of State may make arrangements for payments to be made out of money provided by Parliament.

[658]

NOTES
Commencement: 5 January 2004.

25 Interpretation of Chapter II

(1) In this Chapter—

"communications data" has the meaning given by section 21(4);

"designated" shall be construed in accordance with subsection (2);

"postal or telecommunications operator" means a person who provides a postal service or telecommunications service;

"relevant public authority" means (subject to subsection (4)) any of the following—

(a) a police force;
[(b) the Serious Organised Crime Agency;]
(d) the Commissioners of Customs and Excise;
(e) the Commissioners of Inland Revenue;
(f) any of the intelligence services;
(g) any such public authority not falling within paragraphs (a) to (f) as may be specified for the purposes of this subsection by an order made by the Secretary of State.

(2) Subject to subsection (3), the persons designated for the purposes of this Chapter are the individuals holding such offices, ranks or positions with relevant public authorities as are prescribed for the purposes of this subsection by an order made by the Secretary of State.

(3) The Secretary of State may by order impose restrictions—

(a) on the authorisations and notices under this Chapter that may be granted or given by any individual holding an office, rank or position with a specified public authority; and
(b) on the circumstances in which, or the purposes for which, such authorisations may be granted or notices given by any such individual.

[(3A) References in this Chapter to an individual holding an office or position with the Serious Organised Crime Agency include references to any member of the staff of that Agency.]

[(4) The Secretary of State may by order—

(a) remove any person from the list of persons who are for the time being relevant public authorities for the purposes of this Chapter; and
(b) make such consequential amendments, repeals or revocations in this or any other enactment as appear to him to be necessary or expedient.

(5) The Secretary of State shall not make an order under this section—

(a) that adds any person to the list of persons who are for the time being relevant public authorities for the purposes of this Chapter, or
(b) that by virtue of subsection (4)(b) amends or repeals any provision of an Act,

unless a draft of the order has been laid before Parliament and approved by a resolution of each House.]

[659]

NOTES
Commencement: 5 January 2004.

Sub-s (1): in definition "relevant public authority", para (b) substituted for original paras (b), (c) by the Serious Organised Crime and Police Act 2005, s 59, Sch 4, paras 131, 135(1), (2).

Sub-s (3A): inserted by the Serious Organised Crime and Police Act 2005, s 59, Sch 4, paras 131, 135(1), (3).

Sub-ss (4), (5): substituted by the Serious Organised Crime and Police Act 2005, s 59, Sch 4, paras 131, 135(1), (4).

Regulations: the Regulation of Investigatory Powers (Communications Data) Order 2003, SI 2003/3172 at **[1099]**.

PART II
SURVEILLANCE AND COVERT HUMAN INTELLIGENCE SOURCES

NOTES

Application and modification in relation to the detection of television receivers: as to the application of, and modifications to, this Act, see the Regulation of Investigatory Powers (British Broadcasting Corporation) Order 2001, SI 2001/1057 at **[1034]**.

Introductory

26 Conduct to which Part II applies

(1) This Part applies to the following conduct—

(a) directed surveillance;

(b) intrusive surveillance; and

(c) the conduct and use of covert human intelligence sources.

(2) Subject to subsection (6), surveillance is directed for the purposes of this Part if it is covert but not intrusive and is undertaken—

(a) for the purposes of a specific investigation or a specific operation;

(b) in such a manner as is likely to result in the obtaining of private information about a person (whether or not one specifically identified for the purposes of the investigation or operation); and

(c) otherwise than by way of an immediate response to events or circumstances the nature of which is such that it would not be reasonably practicable for an authorisation under this Part to be sought for the carrying out of the surveillance.

(3) Subject to subsections (4) to (6), surveillance is intrusive for the purposes of this Part if, and only if, it is covert surveillance that—

(a) is carried out in relation to anything taking place on any residential premises or in any private vehicle; and

(b) involves the presence of an individual on the premises or in the vehicle or is carried out by means of a surveillance device.

(4) For the purposes of this Part surveillance is not intrusive to the extent that—

(a) it is carried out by means only of a surveillance device designed or adapted principally for the purpose of providing information about the location of a vehicle; or

(b) it is surveillance consisting in any such interception of a communication as falls within section 48(4).

(5) For the purposes of this Part surveillance which—

(a) is carried out by means of a surveillance device in relation to anything taking place on any residential premises or in any private vehicle, but

(b) is carried out without that device being present on the premises or in the vehicle,

is not intrusive unless the device is such that it consistently provides information of the same quality and detail as might be expected to be obtained from a device actually present on the premises or in the vehicle.

(6) For the purposes of this Part surveillance which—

(a) is carried out by means of apparatus designed or adapted for the purpose of detecting the installation or use in any residential or other premises of a television receiver (within the meaning of [Part 4 of the Communications Act 2003)], and

(b) is carried out from outside those premises exclusively for that purpose,

is neither directed nor intrusive.

(7) In this Part—

(a) references to the conduct of a covert human intelligence source are references to any conduct of such a source which falls within any of paragraphs (a) to (c) of subsection (8), or is incidental to anything falling within any of those paragraphs; and

(b) references to the use of a covert human intelligence source are references to inducing, asking or assisting a person to engage in the conduct of such a source, or to obtain information by means of the conduct of such a source.

(8) For the purposes of this Part a person is a covert human intelligence source if—

(a) he establishes or maintains a personal or other relationship with a person for the covert purpose of facilitating the doing of anything falling within paragraph (b) or (c);

(b) he covertly uses such a relationship to obtain information or to provide access to any information to another person; or

(c) he covertly discloses information obtained by the use of such a relationship, or as a consequence of the existence of such a relationship.

(9) For the purposes of this section—

(a) surveillance is covert if, and only if, it is carried out in a manner that is calculated to ensure that persons who are subject to the surveillance are unaware that it is or may be taking place;

(b) a purpose is covert, in relation to the establishment or maintenance of a personal or other relationship, if and only if the relationship is conducted in a manner that is calculated to ensure that one of the parties to the relationship is unaware of the purpose; and

(c) a relationship is used covertly, and information obtained as mentioned in subsection (8)(c) is disclosed covertly, if and only if it is used or, as the case may be, disclosed in a manner that is calculated to ensure that one of the parties to the relationship is unaware of the use or disclosure in question.

(10) In this section "private information", in relation to a person, includes any information relating to his private or family life.

(11) References in this section, in relation to a vehicle, to the presence of a surveillance device in the vehicle include references to its being located on or under the vehicle and also include references to its being attached to it.

[660]

PART II DATA PROTECTION

NOTES

Sub-s (6): words in square brackets substituted by the Communications Act 2003, s 406(1), Sch 17, para 161(1), (2).

Authorisation of surveillance and human intelligence sources

27 Lawful surveillance etc

(1) Conduct to which this Part applies shall be lawful for all purposes if—

(a) an authorisation under this Part confers an entitlement to engage in that conduct on the person whose conduct it is; and

(b) his conduct is in accordance with the authorisation.

(2) A person shall not be subject to any civil liability in respect of any conduct of his which—

(a) is incidental to any conduct that is lawful by virtue of subsection (1); and

(b) is not itself conduct an authorisation or warrant for which is capable of being granted under a relevant enactment and might reasonably have been expected to have been sought in the case in question.

(3) The conduct that may be authorised under this Part includes conduct outside the United Kingdom.

(4) In this section "relevant enactment" means—

(a) an enactment contained in this Act;

(b) section 5 of the Intelligence Services Act 1994 (warrants for the intelligence services); or

(c) an enactment contained in Part III of the Police Act 1997 (powers of the police and of customs officers).

[661]

28 Authorisation of directed surveillance

(1) Subject to the following provisions of this Part, the persons designated for the purposes of this section shall each have power to grant authorisations for the carrying out of directed surveillance.

(2) A person shall not grant an authorisation for the carrying out of directed surveillance unless he believes—

(a) that the authorisation is necessary on grounds falling within subsection (3); and
(b) that the authorised surveillance is proportionate to what is sought to be achieved by carrying it out.

(3) An authorisation is necessary on grounds falling within this subsection if it is necessary—

(a) in the interests of national security;
(b) for the purpose of preventing or detecting crime or of preventing disorder;
(c) in the interests of the economic well-being of the United Kingdom;
(d) in the interests of public safety;
(e) for the purpose of protecting public health;
(f) for the purpose of assessing or collecting any tax, duty, levy or other imposition, contribution or charge payable to a government department; or
(g) for any purpose (not falling within paragraphs (a) to (f)) which is specified for the purposes of this subsection by an order made by the Secretary of State.

(4) The conduct that is authorised by an authorisation for the carrying out of directed surveillance is any conduct that—

(a) consists in the carrying out of directed surveillance of any such description as is specified in the authorisation; and
(b) is carried out in the circumstances described in the authorisation and for the purposes of the investigation or operation specified or described in the authorisation.

(5) The Secretary of State shall not make an order under subsection (3)(g) unless a draft of the order has been laid before Parliament and approved by a resolution of each House.

[662]

29 Authorisation of covert human intelligence sources

(1) Subject to the following provisions of this Part, the persons designated for the purposes of this section shall each have power to grant authorisations for the conduct or the use of a covert human intelligence source.

(2) A person shall not grant an authorisation for the conduct or the use of a covert human intelligence source unless he believes—

(a) that the authorisation is necessary on grounds falling within subsection (3);
(b) that the authorised conduct or use is proportionate to what is sought to be achieved by that conduct or use; and
(c) that arrangements exist for the source's case that satisfy the requirements of subsection (5) and such other requirements as may be imposed by order made by the Secretary of State.

(3) An authorisation is necessary on grounds falling within this subsection if it is necessary—

(a) in the interests of national security;
(b) for the purpose of preventing or detecting crime or of preventing disorder;
(c) in the interests of the economic well-being of the United Kingdom;
(d) in the interests of public safety;
(e) for the purpose of protecting public health;
(f) for the purpose of assessing or collecting any tax, duty, levy or other imposition, contribution or charge payable to a government department; or
(g) for any purpose (not falling within paragraphs (a) to (f)) which is specified for the purposes of this subsection by an order made by the Secretary of State.

(4) The conduct that is authorised by an authorisation for the conduct or the use of a covert human intelligence source is any conduct that—

(a) is comprised in any such activities involving conduct of a covert human intelligence source, or the use of a covert human intelligence source, as are specified or described in the authorisation;
(b) consists in conduct by or in relation to the person who is so specified or described as the person to whose actions as a covert human intelligence source the authorisation relates; and
(c) is carried out for the purposes of, or in connection with, the investigation or operation so specified or described.

(5) For the purposes of this Part there are arrangements for the source's case that satisfy the requirements of this subsection if such arrangements are in force as are necessary for ensuring—
(a) that there will at all times be a person holding an office, rank or position with the relevant investigating authority who will have day-to-day responsibility for dealing with the source on behalf of that authority, and for the source's security and welfare;
(b) that there will at all times be another person holding an office, rank or position with the relevant investigating authority who will have general oversight of the use made of the source;
(c) that there will at all times be a person holding an office, rank or position with the relevant investigating authority who will have responsibility for maintaining a record of the use made of the source;
(d) that the records relating to the source that are maintained by the relevant investigating authority will always contain particulars of all such matters (if any) as may be specified for the purposes of this paragraph in regulations made by the Secretary of State; and
(e) that records maintained by the relevant investigating authority that disclose the identity of the source will not be available to persons except to the extent that there is a need for access to them to be made available to those persons.

(6) The Secretary of State shall not make an order under subsection (3)(g) unless a draft of the order has been laid before Parliament and approved by a resolution of each House.

(7) The Secretary of State may by order—
(a) prohibit the authorisation under this section of any such conduct or uses of covert human intelligence sources as may be described in the order; and
(b) impose requirements, in addition to those provided for by subsection (2), that must be satisfied before an authorisation is granted under this section for any such conduct or uses of covert human intelligence sources as may be so described.

(8) In this section "relevant investigating authority", in relation to an authorisation for the conduct or the use of an individual as a covert human intelligence source, means (subject to subsection (9)) the public authority for whose benefit the activities of that individual as such a source are to take place.

(9) In the case of any authorisation for the conduct or the use of a covert human intelligence source whose activities are to be for the benefit of more than one public authority, the references in subsection (5) to the relevant investigating authority are references to one of them (whether or not the same one in the case of each reference).

[663]

NOTES

Regulations: the Regulation of Investigatory Powers (Source Records) Regulations 2000, SI 2000/2725 at **[1013]**.

Orders: the Regulation of Investigatory Powers (Juveniles) Order 2000, SI 2000/2793 at **[1016]**.

30 Persons entitled to grant authorisations under ss 28 and 29

(1) Subject to subsection (3), the persons designated for the purposes of sections 28 and 29 are the individuals holding such offices, ranks or positions with relevant public authorities as are prescribed for the purposes of this subsection by an order under this section.

(2) For the purposes of the grant of an authorisation that combines—
(a) an authorisation under section 28 or 29; and
(b) an authorisation by the Secretary of State for the carrying out of intrusive surveillance,

the Secretary of State himself shall be a person designated for the purposes of that section.

(3) An order under this section may impose restrictions—
- (a) on the authorisations under sections 28 and 29 that may be granted by any individual holding an office, rank or position with a specified public authority; and
- (b) on the circumstances in which, or the purposes for which, such authorisations may be granted by any such individual.

(4) A public authority is a relevant public authority for the purposes of this section—
- (a) in relation to section 28 if it is specified in Part I or II of Schedule 1; and
- (b) in relation to section 29 if it is specified in Part I of that Schedule.

(5) An order under this section may amend Schedule 1 by—
- (a) adding a public authority to Part I or II of that Schedule;
- (b) removing a public authority from that Schedule;
- (c) moving a public authority from one Part of that Schedule to the other;
- (d) making any change consequential on any change in the name of a public authority specified in that Schedule.

(6) Without prejudice to section 31, the power to make an order under this section shall be exercisable by the Secretary of State.

(7) The Secretary of State shall not make an order under subsection (5) containing any provision for—
- (a) adding any public authority to Part I or II of that Schedule, or
- (b) moving any public authority from Part II to Part I of that Schedule,

unless a draft of the order has been laid before Parliament and approved by a resolution of each House.

[664]

NOTES

Orders: the Regulation of Investigatory Powers (Directed Surveillance and Covert Human Intelligence Sources) Order 2003, SI 2003/3171 at **[1089]**.

31 Orders under s 30 for Northern Ireland

(1) Subject to subsections (2) and (3), the power to make an order under section 30 for the purposes of the grant of authorisations for conduct in Northern Ireland shall be exercisable by the Office of the First Minister and deputy First Minister in Northern Ireland (concurrently with being exercisable by the Secretary of State).

(2) The power of the Office of the First Minister and deputy First Minister to make an order under section 30 by virtue of subsection (1) or (3) of that section shall not be exercisable in relation to any public authority other than—
- (a) the Food Standards Agency;
- (b) …
- (c) an authority added to Schedule 1 by an order made by that Office;
- (d) an authority added to that Schedule by an order made by the Secretary of State which it would (apart from that order) have been within the powers of that Office to add to that Schedule for the purposes mentioned in subsection (1) of this section.

(3) The power of the Office of the First Minister and deputy First Minister to make an order under section 30—
- (a) shall not include power to make any provision dealing with an excepted matter;
- (b) shall not include power, except with the consent of the Secretary of State, to make any provision dealing with a reserved matter.

(4) The power of the Office of the First Minister and deputy First Minister to make an order under section 30 shall be exercisable by statutory rule for the purposes of the Statutory Rules (Northern Ireland) Order 1979.

(5) A statutory rule containing an order under section 30 which makes provision by virtue of subsection (5) of that section for—
- (a) adding any public authority to Part I or II of Schedule 1, or
- (b) moving any public authority from Part II to Part I of that Schedule,

shall be subject to affirmative resolution (within the meaning of section 41(4) of the Interpretation Act (Northern Ireland) 1954).

(6) A statutory rule containing an order under section 30 (other than one to which subsection (5) of this section applies) shall be subject to negative resolution (within the meaning of section 41(6) of the Interpretation Act (Northern Ireland) 1954).

(7) An order under section 30 made by the Office of the First Minister and deputy First Minister may—

(a) make different provision for different cases;

(b) contain such incidental, supplemental, consequential and transitional provision as that Office thinks fit.

(8) The reference in subsection (2) to an addition to Schedule 1 being within the powers of the Office of the First Minister and deputy First Minister includes a reference to its being within the powers exercisable by that Office with the consent for the purposes of subsection (3)(b) of the Secretary of State.

(9) In this section "excepted matter" and "reserved matter" have the same meanings as in the Northern Ireland Act 1998; and, in relation to those matters, section 98(2) of that Act (meaning of "deals with") applies for the purposes of this section as it applies for the purposes of that Act.

[665]

NOTES

Sub-s (2): para (b) repealed by the Intervention Board for Agricultural for Agricultural Produce (Abolition) Regulations 2001, SI 2001/3686, reg 6(17)(a).

32 Authorisation of intrusive surveillance

(1) Subject to the following provisions of this Part, the Secretary of State and each of the senior authorising officers shall have power to grant authorisations for the carrying out of intrusive surveillance.

(2) Neither the Secretary of State nor any senior authorising officer shall grant an authorisation for the carrying out of intrusive surveillance unless he believes—

(a) that the authorisation is necessary on grounds falling within subsection (3); and

(b) that the authorised surveillance is proportionate to what is sought to be achieved by carrying it out.

(3) Subject to the following provisions of this section, an authorisation is necessary on grounds falling within this subsection if it is necessary—

(a) in the interests of national security;

(b) for the purpose of preventing or detecting serious crime; or

(c) in the interests of the economic well-being of the United Kingdom.

[(3A) In the case of an authorisation granted by the chairman of the OFT, the authorisation is necessary on grounds falling within subsection (3) only if it is necessary for the purpose of preventing or detecting an offence under section 188 of the Enterprise Act 2002 (cartel offence).]

(4) The matters to be taken into account in considering whether the requirements of subsection (2) are satisfied in the case of any authorisation shall include whether the information which it is thought necessary to obtain by the authorised conduct could reasonably be obtained by other means.

(5) The conduct that is authorised by an authorisation for the carrying out of intrusive surveillance is any conduct that—

(a) consists in the carrying out of intrusive surveillance of any such description as is specified in the authorisation;

(b) is carried out in relation to the residential premises specified or described in the authorisation or in relation to the private vehicle so specified or described; and

(c) is carried out for the purposes of, or in connection with, the investigation or operation so specified or described.

(6) For the purposes of this section the senior authorising officers are—

(a) the chief constable of every police force maintained under section 2 of the Police Act 1996 (police forces in England and Wales outside London);

(b) the Commissioner of Police of the Metropolis and every Assistant Commissioner of Police of the Metropolis;

(c) the Commissioner of Police for the City of London;

(d) the chief constable of every police force maintained under or by virtue of section 1 of the Police (Scotland) Act 1967 (police forces for areas in Scotland);

(e) the [Chief Constable of the Police Service of Northern Ireland] and the Deputy Chief Constable of the [Police Service of Northern Ireland];

(f) the Chief Constable of the Ministry of Defence Police;

(g) the Provost Marshal of the *Royal Navy Regulating Branch*;

(h) the Provost Marshal of the Royal Military Police;

(i) the Provost Marshal of the Royal Air Force Police;

(j) the Chief Constable of the British Transport Police;

[(k) the Director General of the Serious Organised Crime Agency and any member of the staff of that Agency who is designated for the purposes of this paragraph by that Director General;]

(m) any customs officer designated for the purposes of this paragraph by the Commissioners of Customs and Excise[; and

(n) the chairman of the OFT.]

[666]

NOTES

Sub-s (3A): inserted by the Enterprise Act 2002, s 199(1), (2)(a).

Sub-s (6): words in square brackets in para (e) substituted by the Police (Northern Ireland) Act 2000, s 78(2)(a), (b); for the words in italics in para (g) there are substituted the words "Royal Navy Police" by the Armed Forces Act 2006, s 378(1), Sch 16, para 170, as from a day to be appointed; para (k) substituted for original paras (k), (l) by the Serious Organised Crime and Police Act 2005, s 59, Sch 4, paras 131, 136, subject to transitional provisions in SI 2006/378, art 4(5), (8); para (n) and word immediately preceding it inserted by the Enterprise Act 2002, s 199(1), (2)(b).

Modification: for the purposes of carrying out the functions of the Independent Police Complaints Commission, sub-s (6) is modified by the Independent Police Complaints Commission (Investigatory Powers) Order 2004, SI 2004/815, art 3(1), (2).

Police and customs authorisations

33 Rules for grant of authorisations

(1) A person who is a designated person for the purposes of section 28 or 29 by reference to his office, rank or position with a police force … shall not grant an authorisation under that section except on an application made by a member of the same force …

[(1A) A person who is a designated person for the purposes of section 28 or 29 by reference to his office or position with the Serious Organised Crime Agency shall not grant an authorisation under that section except on an application made by a member of the staff of the Agency.]

(2) A person who is designated for the purposes of section 28 or 29 by reference to his office, rank or position with the Commissioners of Customs and Excise shall not grant an authorisation under that section except on an application made by a customs officer.

(3) A person who is a senior authorising officer by reference to a police force … shall not grant an authorisation for the carrying out of intrusive surveillance except—

(a) on an application made by a member of the same force … ; and

(b) in the case of an authorisation for the carrying out of intrusive surveillance in relation to any residential premises, where those premises are in the area of operation of that force …

[(3A) The Director General of the Serious Organised Crime Agency or a person designated for the purposes of section 32(6)(k) by that Director General shall not grant an authorisation for the carrying out of intrusive surveillance except on an application made by a member of the staff of the Agency.]

(4) A person who is a senior authorising officer by virtue of a designation by the Commissioners of Customs and Excise shall not grant an authorisation for the carrying out of intrusive surveillance except on an application made by a customs officer.

[(4A) The chairman of the OFT shall not grant an authorisation for the carrying out of intrusive surveillance except on an application made by an officer of the OFT.]

(5) A single authorisation may combine both—

(a) an authorisation granted under this Part by, or on the application of, an individual who is a member of a police force, [a member of the staff of the Serious Organised Crime Agency,] or who is a customs officer [or the chairman or an officer of the OFT]; and

(b) an authorisation given by, or on the application of, that individual under Part III of the Police Act 1997;

but the provisions of this Act or that Act that are applicable in the case of each of the authorisations shall apply separately in relation to the part of the combined authorisation to which they are applicable.

(6) For the purposes of this section—

(a) the area of operation of a police force maintained under section 2 of the Police Act 1996, of the metropolitan police force, of the City of London police force or of a police force maintained under or by virtue of section 1 of the Police (Scotland) Act 1967 is the area for which that force is maintained;

(b) the area of operation of the [Police Service of Northern Ireland] is Northern Ireland;

(c) residential premises are in the area of operation of the Ministry of Defence Police if they are premises where the members of that police force, under section 2 of the Ministry of Defence Police Act 1987, have the powers and privileges of a constable;

(d) residential premises are in the area of operation of the *Royal Navy Regulating Branch*, the Royal Military Police or the Royal Air Force Police if they are premises owned or occupied by, or used for residential purposes by, a *person subject to service discipline*;

(e) the area of operation of the British Transport Police … is the United Kingdom;

(f) …

and references in this section to the United Kingdom or to any part or area of the United Kingdom include any adjacent waters within the seaward limits of the territorial waters of the United Kingdom.

(7) For the purposes of this section a person is subject to service discipline—

(a) in relation to the Royal Navy Regulating Branch, if he is subject to the Naval Discipline Act 1957 or is a civilian to whom Parts I and II of that Act for the time being apply by virtue of section 118 of that Act;

(b) in relation to the Royal Military Police, if he is subject to military law or is a civilian to whom Part II of the Army Act 1955 for the time being applies by virtue of section 209 of that Act; and

(c) in relation to the Royal Air Force Police, if he is subject to air-force law or is a civilian to whom Part II of the Air Force Act 1955 for the time being applies by virtue of section 209 of that Act.

[667]

NOTES

Sub-s (1): words omitted repealed by the Serious Organised Crime and Police Act 2005, ss 59, 174(2), Sch 4, paras 131, 137(1), (2), Sch 17, Pt 2, subject to transitional provisions in SI 2006/378, art 4(5), (6), (8).

Sub-ss (1A), (3A): inserted by the Serious Organised Crime and Police Act 2005, s 59, Sch 4, paras 131, 137(1), (3), (5), subject to transitional provisions in SI 2006/378, art 4(5), (6), (8).

Sub-s (3): words omitted repealed by the Serious Organised Crime and Police Act 2005, ss 59, 174(2), Sch 4, paras 131, 137(1), (4), Sch 17, Pt 2, subject to transitional provisions in SI 2006/378, art 4(5), (6), (8).

Sub-s (4A): inserted by the Enterprise Act 2002, s 199(1), (3).

Sub-s (5): in para (a), words in first pair of square brackets substituted by the Serious Organised Crime and Police Act 2005, s 59, Sch 4, paras 131, 137(1), (6), subject to transitional provisions in SI 2006/378, art 4(5), (6), (8); words in second pair of square brackets inserted by the Enterprise Act 2002, s 199(1), (4).

Sub-s (6): words in square brackets in para (b) substituted by the Police (Northern Ireland) Act 2000, s 78(2)(f); in para (d), for the first words in italics there are substituted the words "Royal Navy Police" and for the second words in italics there are substituted the words "person subject to service law or a civilian subject to service discipline" by the Armed Forces Act 2006, s 378(1), Sch 16, para 171(1), (2), as from a day to be appointed; words omitted from para (e), and the whole of para (f) repealed by Serious Organised Crime and Police Act 2005, ss 59, 174(2), Sch 4, paras 131, 137(1), (7), Sch 17, Pt 2, subject to transitional provisions in SI 2006/378, art 4(5), (6), (8).

Sub-s (7): substituted by the Armed Forces Act 2006, s 378(1), Sch 16, para 171(1), (3), as from a day to be appointed, as follows:

"(7) In subsection (6) "subject to service law" and "civilian subject to service discipline" have the same meanings as in the Armed Forces Act 2006.".

Modification: for the purposes of carrying out the functions of the Independent Police Complaints Commission, this section is modified by the Independent Police Complaints Commission (Investigatory Powers) Order 2004, SI 2004/815, art 3(1), (3).

34 Grant of authorisations in the senior officer's absence

(1) This section applies in the case of an application for an authorisation for the carrying out of intrusive surveillance where—

(a) the application is one made by a member of a police force, [a member of the staff of the Serious Organised Crime Agency] or by [an officer of the OFT or] a customs officer; and

(b) the case is urgent.

(2) If—

(a) it is not reasonably practicable, having regard to the urgency of the case, for the application to be considered by any person who is a senior authorising officer by reference to the force [or Agency] in question or, as the case may be, [as chairman of the OFT or] by virtue of a designation by the Commissioners of Customs and Excise, and

(b) it also not reasonably practicable, having regard to the urgency of the case, for the application to be considered by a person (if there is one) who is entitled, as a designated deputy of a senior authorising officer, to exercise the functions in relation to that application of such an officer,

the application may be made to and considered by any person who is entitled under subsection (4) to act for any senior authorising officer who would have been entitled to consider the application.

(3) A person who considers an application under subsection (1) shall have the same power to grant an authorisation as the person for whom he is entitled to act.

(4) For the purposes of this section—

(a) a person is entitled to act for the chief constable of a police force maintained under section 2 of the Police Act 1996 if he holds the rank of assistant chief constable in that force;

(b) a person is entitled to act for the Commissioner of Police of the Metropolis, or for an Assistant Commissioner of Police of the Metropolis, if he holds the rank of commander in the metropolitan police force;

(c) a person is entitled to act for the Commissioner of Police for the City of London if he holds the rank of commander in the City of London police force;

(d) a person is entitled to act for the chief constable of a police force maintained under or by virtue of section 1 of the Police (Scotland) Act 1967 if he holds the rank of assistant chief constable in that force;

(e) a person is entitled to act for the [Chief Constable of the Police Service of Northern Ireland], or for the Deputy Chief Constable of the [Police Service of Northern Ireland], if he holds the rank of assistant chief constable in the Royal Ulster Constabulary;

(f) a person is entitled to act for the Chief Constable of the Ministry of Defence Police if he holds the rank of deputy or assistant chief constable in that force;

(g) a person is entitled to act for the Provost Marshal of the *Royal Navy Regulating Branch* if he holds the position of assistant Provost Marshal in *that Branch*;

(h) a person is entitled to act for the Provost Marshal of the Royal Military Police or the Provost Marshal of the Royal Air Force Police if he holds the position of deputy Provost Marshal in the police force in question;

(i) a person is entitled to act for the Chief Constable of the British Transport Police if he holds the rank of deputy or assistant chief constable in that force;

[(j) a person is entitled to act for the Director General of the Serious Organised Crime Agency if he is a person designated for the purposes of this paragraph by that Director General as a person entitled so to act in an urgent case;]

(l) a person is entitled to act for a person who is a senior authorising officer by virtue of a designation by the Commissioners of Customs and Excise, if he is designated for the purposes of this paragraph by those Commissioners as a person entitled so to act in an urgent case;

[(m) a person is entitled to act for the chairman of the OFT if he is an officer of the OFT designated by it for the purposes of this paragraph as a person entitled so to act in an urgent case].

(5) …

(6) In this section "designated deputy"—

[(a) in relation to the chief constable for a police force in England and Wales, means—

(i) the person who is the appropriate deputy chief constable for the purposes of section 12A(1) of the Police Act 1996, or

(ii) a person holding the rank of assistant chief constable who is designated to act under section 12A(2) of that Act;

(aa) in relation to the chief constable for a police force in Scotland, means—

(i) a person holding the rank of deputy chief constable and, where there is more than one person in the police force who holds that rank, who is designated as the officer having the powers and duties conferred on a deputy chief constable by section 5A(1) of the Police (Scotland) Act 1967, or

(ii) a person holding the rank of assistant chief constable who is designated to act under section 5A(2) of that Act;]

(b) in relation to the Commissioner of Police for the City of London, means a person authorised to act under section 25 of the City of London Police Act 1839;

(c) …

[668]

NOTES

Sub-s (1): words in first pair of square brackets substituted by the Serious Organised Crime and Police Act 2005, s 59, Sch 4, paras 131, 138(1), (2), subject to transitional provisions in SI 2006/378, art 4(6), (8); words in second pair of square brackets inserted by the Enterprise Act 2002, s 199(1), (5)(a).

Sub-s (2): words in first pair of square brackets substituted by the Serious Organised Crime and Police Act 2005, s 59, Sch 4, paras 131, 138(1), (3), subject to transitional provisions in SI 2006/378, art 4(6), (8); words in second pair of square brackets inserted by the Enterprise Act 2002, s 199(1), (5)(b).

Sub-s (4): words in square brackets in para (e) substituted by the Police (Northern Ireland) Act 2000, s 78(2)(a), (b); in para (g), for the first words in italics there are substituted the words "Royal Navy Police" and for the second words in italics there are substituted the words "that force" by the Armed Forces Act 2006, s 378(1), Sch 16, para 172, as from a day to be appointed; para (j) substituted for original paras (j), (k) by the Serious Organised Crime and Police Act 2005, s 59, Sch 4, paras 131, 138(1), (4), subject to transitional provisions in SI 2006/378, art 4(6), (8); para (m) added by the Enterprise Act 2002, s 199(1), (5)(c).

Sub-s (5): repealed by Serious Organised Crime and Police Act 2005, ss 59, 174(2), Sch 4, paras 131, 138(1), (5), Sch 17, Pt 2, subject to transitional provisions in SI 2006/378, art 4(6), (8).

Sub-s (6): paras (a), (aa) substituted for original para (a) by the Police and Justice Act 2006, s 52, Sch 14, para 39; para (c) repealed by Serious Organised Crime and Police Act 2005, ss 59, 174(2), Sch 4, paras 131, 138(1), (6), Sch 17, Pt 2, subject to transitional provisions in SI 2006/378, art 4(6), (8).

Modification: for the purposes of carrying out the functions of the Independent Police Complaints Commission, this section is modified by the Independent Police Complaints Commission (Investigatory Powers) Order 2004, SI 2004/815, art 3(1), (4).

35 Notification of authorisations for intrusive surveillance

(1) Where a person grants or cancels a [police, SOCA, customs] [or OFT] authorisation for the carrying out of intrusive surveillance, he shall give notice that he has done so to an ordinary Surveillance Commissioner.

(2) A notice given for the purposes of subsection (1)—

(a) must be given in writing as soon as reasonably practicable after the grant or, as the case may be, cancellation of the authorisation to which it relates;

(b) must be given in accordance with any such arrangements made for the purposes of this paragraph by the Chief Surveillance Commissioner as are for the time being in force; and

(c) must specify such matters as the Secretary of State may by order prescribe.

(3) A notice under this section of the grant of an authorisation shall, as the case may be, either—

(a) state that the approval of a Surveillance Commissioner is required by section 36 before the grant of the authorisation will take effect; or

(b) state that the case is one of urgency and set out the grounds on which the case is believed to be one of urgency.

(4) Where a notice for the purposes of subsection (1) of the grant of an authorisation has been received by an ordinary Surveillance Commissioner, he shall, as soon as practicable—

(a) scrutinise the authorisation; and

(b) in a case where notice has been given in accordance with subsection (3)(a), decide whether or not to approve the authorisation.

(5) Subject to subsection (6), the Secretary of State shall not make an order under subsection (2)(c) unless a draft of the order has been laid before Parliament and approved by a resolution of each House.

(6) Subsection (5) does not apply in the case of the order made on the first occasion on which the Secretary of State exercises his power to make an order under subsection (2)(c).

(7) The order made on that occasion shall cease to have effect at the end of the period of forty days beginning with the day on which it was made unless, before the end of that period, it has been approved by a resolution of each House of Parliament.

(8) For the purposes of subsection (7)—

(a) the order's ceasing to have effect shall be without prejudice to anything previously done or to the making of a new order; and

(b) in reckoning the period of forty days no account shall be taken of any period during which Parliament is dissolved or prorogued or during which both Houses are adjourned for more than four days.

(9) Any notice that is required by any provision of this section to be given in writing may be given, instead, by being transmitted by electronic means.

(10) In this section references to a [police, SOCA, customs] [or OFT] authorisation are references to an authorisation granted by—

(a) a person who is a senior authorising officer by reference to a police force [or the Serious Organised Crime Agency];

(b) a person who is a senior authorising officer by virtue of a designation by the Commissioners of Customs and Excise; …

[(ba) the chairman of the OFT; or]

(c) a person who for the purposes of section 34 is entitled to act for a person falling within paragraph (a) or for a person falling within paragraph (b) [or for a person falling within paragraph (ba)].

[669]

NOTES

Sub-s (1): words in first pair of square brackets substituted by the Serious Organised Crime and Police Act 2005, s 59, Sch 4, paras 131, 139(1), (2), subject to transitional provisions in SI 2006/378, art 4(5), (6), (8); words in second pair of square brackets substituted by the Enterprise Act 2002, s 199(1), (6)(a).

Sub-s (10): words in first pair of square brackets, and words in square brackets in para (a) substituted by the Serious Organised Crime and Police Act 2005, s 59, Sch 4, paras 131, 139(1), (3), subject to transitional provisions in SI 2006/378, art 4(5), (6), (8); words in second pair of square brackets substituted, word omitted from para (b) repealed, and para (ba) and the words in square brackets in para (c) inserted, by the Enterprise Act 2002, ss 199(1), (6)(a)–(c), 278(2), Sch 26.

Modification: for the purposes of carrying out the functions of the Independent Police Complaints Commission, this section is modified by the Independent Police Complaints Commission (Investigatory Powers) Order 2004, SI 2004/815, art 3(1), (5).

Orders: the Regulation of Investigatory Powers (Notification of Authorisations etc) Order 2000, SI 2000/2563 at **[992]**.

36 Approval required for authorisations to take effect

(1) This section applies where an authorisation for the carrying out of intrusive surveillance has been granted on the application of—

(a) a member of a police force;

[(b) a member of the staff of the Serious Organised Crime Agency;]

(d) a customs officer[; or

(e) an officer of the OFT].

(2) Subject to subsection (3), the authorisation shall not take effect until such time (if any) as—

(a) the grant of the authorisation has been approved by an ordinary Surveillance Commissioner; and

(b) written notice of the Commissioner's decision to approve the grant of the authorisation has been given, in accordance with subsection (4), to the person who granted the authorisation.

(3) Where the person who grants the authorisation—

(a) believes that the case is one of urgency, and
(b) gives notice in accordance with section 35(3)(b),

subsection (2) shall not apply to the authorisation, and the authorisation shall have effect from the time of its grant.

(4) Where subsection (2) applies to the authorisation—

(a) a Surveillance Commissioner shall give his approval under this section to the authorisation if, and only if, he is satisfied that there are reasonable grounds for believing that the requirements of section 32(2)(a) and (b) are satisfied in the case of the authorisation; and
(b) a Surveillance Commissioner who makes a decision as to whether or not the authorisation should be approved shall, as soon as reasonably practicable after making that decision, give written notice of his decision to the person who granted the authorisation.

(5) If an ordinary Surveillance Commissioner decides not to approve an authorisation to which subsection (2) applies, he shall make a report of his findings to the most senior relevant person.

(6) In this section "the most senior relevant person" means—

(a) where the authorisation was granted by the senior authorising officer with any police force who is not someone's deputy, that senior authorising officer;
(b) where the authorisation was granted by the Director General of the [Serious Organised Crime Agency,] that Director General;
(c) where the authorisation was granted by a senior authorising officer with a police force who is someone's deputy, the senior authorising officer whose deputy granted the authorisation;
[(d) where the authorisation was granted by a person designated for the purposes of section 32(6)(k), or by a person entitled to act for the Director General of the Serious Organised Crime Agency by virtue of section 34(4)(j), that Director General;]
(f) where the authorisation was granted by a person entitled to act for a senior authorising officer under section 34(4)(a) to (i), the senior authorising officer in the force in question who is not someone's deputy; …
(g) where the authorisation was granted by a customs officer, the customs officer for the time being designated for the purposes of this paragraph by a written notice given to the Chief Surveillance Commissioner by the Commissioners of Customs and Excise[; and
(h) where the authorisation was granted by the chairman of the OFT or a person entitled to act for him by virtue of section 34(4)(m), that chairman].

(7) The references in subsection (6) to a person's deputy are references to the following—

(a) in relation to—
  (i) a chief constable of a police force maintained under section 2 of the Police Act 1996,
  (ii) the Commissioner of Police for the City of London, or
  (iii) a chief constable of a police force maintained under or by virtue of section 1 of the Police (Scotland) Act 1967,

  to his designated deputy;
(b) in relation to the Commissioner of Police of the Metropolis, to an Assistant Commissioner of Police of the Metropolis; and
(c) in relation to the [Chief Constable of the Police Service of Northern Ireland], to the Deputy Chief Constable of the [Police Service of Northern Ireland];

and in this subsection and that subsection "designated deputy" has the same meaning as in section 34.

(8) Any notice that is required by any provision of this section to be given in writing may be given, instead, by being transmitted by electronic means.

[670]

NOTES

Sub-s (1): para (b) substituted for original paras (b), (c) by the Serious Organised Crime and Police Act 2005, s 59, Sch 4, paras 131, 140(1), (2), subject to transitional provisions in SI 2006/378, art 4(5), (6), (8); para (e) and the word immediately preceding it added by the Enterprise Act 2002, s 199(1), (7)(a).

PART II
DATA PROTECTION

Sub-s (6): words in square brackets in para (b) substituted and para (d) substituted for original paras (d), (e), by the Serious Organised Crime and Police Act 2005, s 59, Sch 4, paras 131, 140(1), (3), subject to transitional provisions in SI 2006/378, art 4(5), (6), (8); word omitted from para (f) repealed, and para (h) and the word immediately preceding it added, by the Enterprise Act 2002, ss 199(1), (7)(b), 278(2), Sch 26.

Sub-s (7): words in square brackets in para (c) substituted by the Police (Northern Ireland) Act 2000, s 78(2)(a), (b).

Modification: for the purposes of carrying out the functions of the Independent Police Complaints Commission, this section is modified by the Independent Police Complaints Commission (Investigatory Powers) Order 2004, SI 2004/815, art 3(1), (6).

37 Quashing of police and customs authorisations etc

(1) This section applies where an authorisation for the carrying out of intrusive surveillance has been granted on the application of—

(a) a member of a police force;

[(b) a member of the staff of the Serious Organised Crime Agency;]

(d) a customs officer[; or

(e) an officer of the OFT].

(2) Where an ordinary Surveillance Commissioner is at any time satisfied that, at the time when the authorisation was granted or at any time when it was renewed, there were no reasonable grounds for believing that the requirements of section 32(2)(a) and (b) were satisfied, he may quash the authorisation with effect, as he thinks fit, from the time of the grant of the authorisation or from the time of any renewal of the authorisation.

(3) If an ordinary Surveillance Commissioner is satisfied at any time while the authorisation is in force that there are no longer any reasonable grounds for believing that the requirements of section 32(2)(a) and (b) are satisfied in relation to the authorisation, he may cancel the authorisation with effect from such time as appears to him to be the time from which those requirements ceased to be so satisfied.

(4) Where, in the case of any authorisation of which notice has been given in accordance with section 35(3)(b), an ordinary Surveillance Commissioner is at any time satisfied that, at the time of the grant or renewal of the authorisation to which that notice related, there were no reasonable grounds for believing that the case was one of urgency, he may quash the authorisation with effect, as he thinks fit, from the time of the grant of the authorisation or from the time of any renewal of the authorisation.

(5) Subject to subsection (7), where an ordinary Surveillance Commissioner quashes an authorisation under this section, he may order the destruction of any records relating wholly or partly to information obtained by the authorised conduct after the time from which his decision takes effect.

(6) Subject to subsection (7), where—

(a) an authorisation has ceased to have effect (otherwise than by virtue of subsection (2) or (4)), and

(b) an ordinary Surveillance Commissioner is satisfied that there was a time while the authorisation was in force when there were no reasonable grounds for believing that the requirements of section 32(2)(a) and (b) continued to be satisfied in relation to the authorisation,

he may order the destruction of any records relating, wholly or partly, to information obtained at such a time by the authorised conduct.

(7) No order shall be made under this section for the destruction of any records required for pending criminal or civil proceedings.

(8) Where an ordinary Surveillance Commissioner exercises a power conferred by this section, he shall, as soon as reasonably practicable, make a report of his exercise of that power, and of his reasons for doing so—

(a) to the most senior relevant person (within the meaning of section 36); and

(b) to the Chief Surveillance Commissioner.

(9) Where an order for the destruction of records is made under this section, the order shall not become operative until such time (if any) as—

(a) the period for appealing against the decision to make the order has expired; and

(b) any appeal brought within that period has been dismissed by the Chief Surveillance Commissioner.

(10) No notice shall be required to be given under section 35(1) in the case of a cancellation under subsection (3) of this section.

[671]

NOTES

Sub-s (1): para (b) substituted for original paras (b), (c), by the Serious Organised Crime and Police Act 2005, s 59, Sch 4, paras 131, 141, subject to transitional provisions in SI 2006/378, art 4(5), (6), (8); para (e) and the word immediately preceding it inserted, by the Enterprise Act 2002, s 199(1), (8).

Modification: for the purposes of carrying out the functions of the Independent Police Complaints Commission, this section is modified by the Independent Police Complaints Commission (Investigatory Powers) Order 2004, SI 2004/815, art 3(1), (7).

38 Appeals against decisions by Surveillance Commissioners

(1) Any senior authorising officer may appeal to the Chief Surveillance Commissioner against any of the following—

- (a) any refusal of an ordinary Surveillance Commissioner to approve an authorisation for the carrying out of intrusive surveillance;
- (b) any decision of such a Commissioner to quash or cancel such an authorisation;
- (c) any decision of such a Commissioner to make an order under section 37 for the destruction of records.

(2) In the case of an authorisation granted by the designated deputy of a senior authorising office or by a person who for the purposes of section 34 is entitled to act for a senior authorising officer, that designated deputy or person shall also be entitled to appeal under this section.

(3) An appeal under this section must be brought within the period of seven days beginning with the day on which the refusal or decision appealed against is reported to the appellant.

(4) Subject to subsection (5), the Chief Surveillance Commissioner, on an appeal under this section, shall allow the appeal if—

- (a) he is satisfied that there were reasonable grounds for believing that the requirements of section 32(2)(a) and (b) were satisfied in relation to the authorisation at the time in question; and
- (b) he is not satisfied that the authorisation is one of which notice was given in accordance with section 35(3)(b) without there being any reasonable grounds for believing that the case was one of urgency.

(5) If, on an appeal falling within subsection (1)(b), the Chief Surveillance Commissioner—

- (a) is satisfied that grounds exist which justify the quashing or cancellation under section 37 of the authorisation in question, but
- (b) considers that the authorisation should have been quashed or cancelled from a different time from that from which it was quashed or cancelled by the ordinary Surveillance Commissioner against whose decision the appeal is brought,

he may modify that Commissioner's decision to quash or cancel the authorisation, and any related decision for the destruction of records, so as to give effect to the decision under section 37 that he considers should have been made.

(6) Where, on an appeal under this section against a decision to quash or cancel an authorisation, the Chief Surveillance Commissioner allows the appeal he shall also quash any related order for the destruction of records relating to information obtained by the authorised conduct.

(7) In this section "designated deputy" has the same meaning as in section 34.

[672]

39 Appeals to the Chief Surveillance Commissioner: supplementary

(1) Where the Chief Surveillance Commissioner has determined an appeal under section 38, he shall give notice of his determination to both—

- (a) the person by whom the appeal was brought; and
- (b) the ordinary Surveillance Commissioner whose decision was appealed against.

(2) Where the determination of the Chief Surveillance Commissioner on an appeal under section 38 is a determination to dismiss the appeal, the Chief Surveillance Commissioner shall make a report of his findings—

PART II DATA PROTECTION

(a) to the persons mentioned in subsection (1); and
(b) to the Prime Minister.

(3) Subsections (3) and (4) of section 107 of the Police Act 1997 (reports to be laid before Parliament and exclusion of matters from the report) apply in relation to any report to the Prime Minister under subsection (2) of this section as they apply in relation to any report under subsection (2) of that section.

(4) Subject to subsection (2) of this section, the Chief Surveillance Commissioner shall not give any reasons for any determination of his on an appeal under section 38.

[673]

40 Information to be provided to Surveillance Commissioners

It shall be the duty of—

(a) every member of a police force,
[(b) every member of the staff of the Serious Organised Crime Agency,]
(d) every customs officer[, and
(e) every officer of the OFT,]

to comply with any request of a Surveillance Commissioner for documents or information required by that Commissioner for the purpose of enabling him to carry out the functions of such a Commissioner under sections 35 to 39.

[674]

NOTES

Para (b) substituted for original paras (b), (c), by the Serious Organised Crime and Police Act 2005, s 59, Sch 4, paras 131, 142, subject to transitional provisions in SI 2006/378, art 4(5), (6), (8); para (e) and the word immediately preceding it inserted by the Enterprise Act 2002, s 199(1), (9).

Modification: for the purposes of carrying out the functions of the Independent Police Complaints Commission, this section is modified by the Independent Police Complaints Commission (Investigatory Powers) Order 2004, SI 2004/815, art 3(1), (8).

Other authorisations

41 Secretary of State authorisations

(1) The Secretary of State shall not grant an authorisation for the carrying out of intrusive surveillance except on an application made by—

(a) a member of any of the intelligence services;
(b) an official of the Ministry of Defence;
(c) a member of Her Majesty's forces;
(d) an individual holding an office, rank or position with any such public authority as may be designated for the purposes of this section as an authority whose activities may require the carrying out of intrusive surveillance.

(2) Section 32 shall have effect in relation to the grant of an authorisation by the Secretary of State on the application of an official of the Ministry of Defence, or of a member of Her Majesty's forces, as if the only matters mentioned in subsection (3) of that section were—

(a) the interests of national security; and
(b) the purpose of preventing or detecting serious crime.

(3) The designation of any public authority for the purposes of this section shall be by order made by the Secretary of State.

(4) The Secretary of State may by order provide, in relation to any public authority, that an application for an authorisation for the carrying out of intrusive surveillance may be made by an individual holding an office, rank or position with that authority only where his office, rank or position is one prescribed by the order.

(5) The Secretary of State may by order impose restrictions—

(a) on the authorisations for the carrying out of intrusive surveillance that may be granted on the application of an individual holding an office, rank or position with any public authority designated for the purposes of this section; and
(b) on the circumstances in which, or the purposes for which, such authorisations may be granted on such an application.

(6) The Secretary of State shall not make a designation under subsection (3) unless a draft of the order containing the designation has been laid before Parliament and approved by a resolution of each House.

(7) References in this section to a member of Her Majesty's forces do not include references to any member of Her Majesty's forces who is a member of a police force by virtue of his service with the *Royal Navy Regulating Branch*, the Royal Military Police or the Royal Air Force Police.

[675]

NOTES

Sub-s (7): for the words in italics there are substituted the words "Royal Navy Police" by the Armed Forces Act 2006, s 378(1), Sch 16, para 173, as from a day to be appointed.

Orders: the Regulation of Investigatory Powers (Designation of Public Authorities for the Purposes of Intrusive Surveillance) Order 2001, SI 2001/1126 at **[1039]**; the Regulation of Investigatory Powers (Intrusive Surveillance) Order 2003, SI 2003/3174 at **[1115]**.

42 Intelligence services authorisations

(1) The grant by the Secretary of State [or, the Scottish Ministers (by virtue of provision under section 63 of the Scotland Act 1998)] on the application of a member of one of the intelligence services of any authorisation under this Part must be made by the issue of a warrant.

(2) A single warrant issued by the Secretary of State [or, the Scottish Ministers (by virtue of provision under section 63 of the Scotland Act 1998)] may combine both—

(a) an authorisation under this Part; and

(b) an intelligence services warrant;

but the provisions of this Act or the Intelligence Services Act 1994 that are applicable in the case of the authorisation under this Part or the intelligence services warrant shall apply separately in relation to the part of the combined warrant to which they are applicable.

(3) Intrusive surveillance in relation to any premises or vehicle in the British Islands shall be capable of being authorised by a warrant issued under this Part on the application of a member of the Secret Intelligence Service or GCHQ only if the authorisation contained in the warrant is one satisfying the requirements of section 32(2)(a) otherwise than in connection with any functions of that intelligence service in support of the prevention or detection of serious crime.

(4) Subject to subsection (5), the functions of the Security Service shall include acting on behalf of the Secret Intelligence Service or GCHQ in relation to—

(a) the application for and grant of any authorisation under this Part in connection with any matter within the functions of the Secret Intelligence Service or GCHQ; and

(b) the carrying out, in connection with any such matter, of any conduct authorised by such an authorisation.

(5) Nothing in subsection (4) shall authorise the doing of anything by one intelligence service on behalf of another unless—

(a) it is something which either the other service or a member of the other service has power to do; and

(b) it is done otherwise than in connection with functions of the other service in support of the prevention or detection of serious crime.

(6) In this section "intelligence services warrant" means a warrant under section 5 of the Intelligence Services Act 1994.

[676]

NOTES

Sub-ss (1), (2): words in square brackets inserted by the Scotland Act 1998 (Transfer of Functions to the Scottish Ministers etc) (No 2) Order 2000, SI 2000/3253, art 4(1), Sch 3, Pt II, paras 3, 7.

Grant, renewal and duration of authorisations

43 General rules about grant, renewal and duration

(1) An authorisation under this Part—

(a) may be granted or renewed orally in any urgent case in which the entitlement to act of the person granting or renewing it is not confined to urgent cases; and
(b) in any other case, must be in writing.

(2) A single authorisation may combine two or more different authorisations under this Part; but the provisions of this Act that are applicable in the case of each of the authorisations shall apply separately in relation to the part of the combined authorisation to which they are applicable.

(3) Subject to subsections (4) and (8), an authorisation under this Part shall cease to have effect at the end of the following period—

(a) in the case of an authorisation which—
  (i) has not been renewed and was granted either orally or by a person whose entitlement to act is confined to urgent cases, or
  (ii) was last renewed either orally or by such a person,

the period of seventy-two hours beginning with the time when the grant of the authorisation or, as the case may be, its latest renewal takes effect;

(b) in a case not falling within paragraph (a) in which the authorisation is for the conduct or the use of a covert human intelligence source, the period of twelve months beginning with the day on which the grant of the authorisation or, as the case may be, its latest renewal takes effect; and
(c) in any case not falling within paragraph (a) or (b), the period of three months beginning with the day on which the grant of the authorisation or, as the case may be, its latest renewal takes effect.

(4) Subject to subsection (6), an authorisation under this Part may be renewed, at any time before the time at which it ceases to have effect, by any person who would be entitled to grant a new authorisation in the same terms.

(5) Sections 28 to 41 shall have effect in relation to the renewal of an authorisation under this Part as if references to the grant of an authorisation included references to its renewal.

(6) A person shall not renew an authorisation for the conduct or the use of a covert human intelligence source, unless he—

(a) is satisfied that a review has been carried out of the matters mentioned in subsection (7); and
(b) has, for the purpose of deciding whether he should renew the authorisation, considered the results of that review.

(7) The matters mentioned in subsection (6) are—

(a) the use made of the source in the period since the grant or, as the case may be, latest renewal of the authorisation; and
(b) the tasks given to the source during that period and the information obtained from the conduct or the use of the source.

(8) The Secretary of State may by order provide in relation to authorisations of such descriptions as may be specified in the order that subsection (3) is to have effect as if the period at the end of which an authorisation of a description so specified is to cease to have effect were such period shorter than that provided for by that subsection as may be fixed by or determined in accordance with that order.

(9) References in this section to the time at which, or the day on which, the grant or renewal of an authorisation takes effect are references—

(a) in the case of the grant of an authorisation to which paragraph (c) does not apply, to the time at which or, as the case may be, day on which the authorisation is granted;
(b) in the case of the renewal of an authorisation to which paragraph (c) does not apply, to the time at which or, as the case may be, day on which the authorisation would have ceased to have effect but for the renewal; and
(c) in the case of any grant or renewal that takes effect under subsection (2) of section 36 at a time or on a day later than that given by paragraph (a) or (b), to the time at which or, as the case may be, day on which the grant or renewal takes effect in accordance with that subsection.

(10) In relation to any authorisation granted by a member of any of the intelligence services, and in relation to any authorisation contained in a warrant issued by the Secretary of State on the application of a member of any of the intelligence services, this section has effect subject to the provisions of section 44.

[677]

NOTES

Orders: the Regulation of Investigatory Powers (Juveniles) Order 2000, SI 2000/2793 at **[1016]**.

44 Special rules for intelligence services authorisations

(1) Subject to subsection (2), a warrant containing an authorisation for the carrying out of intrusive surveillance—

- (a) shall not be issued on the application of a member of any of the intelligence services, and
- (b) if so issued shall not be renewed,

except under the hand of the Secretary of State [or, in the case of a warrant issued by the Scottish Ministers (by virtue of provision made under section 63 of the Scotland Act 1998), a member of the Scottish Executive].

(2) In an urgent case in which—

- (a) an application for a warrant containing an authorisation for the carrying out of intrusive surveillance has been made by a member of any of the intelligence services, and
- (b) the Secretary of State has himself [or the Scottish Ministers (by virtue of provision made under section 63 of the Scotland Act 1998) have themselves] expressly authorised the issue of the warrant in that case,

the warrant may be issued (but not renewed) under the hand of a senior official [or, as the case may be, a member of the staff of the Scottish Administration who is a member of the Senior Civil Service and is designated by the Scottish Ministers as a person under whose hand a warrant may be issued in such a case (in this section referred to as "a designated official")].

(3) Subject to subsection (6), a warrant containing an authorisation for the carrying out of intrusive surveillance which—

- (a) was issued, on the application of a member of any of the intelligence services, under the hand of a senior official [or, as the case may be, a designated official], and
- (b) has not been renewed under the hand of the Secretary of State [or, in the case of a warrant issued by the Scottish Ministers (by virtue of provision made under section 63 of the Scotland Act 1998), a member of the Scottish Executive],

shall cease to have effect at the end of the second working day following the day of the issue of the warrant, instead of at the time provided for by section 43(3).

(4) Subject to subsections (3) and (6), where any warrant for the carrying out of intrusive surveillance which is issued or was last renewed on the application of a member of any of the intelligence services, the warrant (unless renewed or, as the case may be, renewed again) shall cease to have effect at the following time, instead of at the time provided for by section 43(3), namely—

- (a) in the case of a warrant that has not been renewed, at the end of the period of six months beginning with the day on which it was issued; and
- (b) in any other case, at the end of the period of six months beginning with the day on which it would have ceased to have effect if not renewed again.

(5) Subject to subsection (6), where—

- (a) an authorisation for the carrying out of directed surveillance is granted by a member of any of the intelligence services, and
- (b) the authorisation is renewed by an instrument endorsed under the hand of the person renewing the authorisation with a statement that the renewal is believed to be necessary on grounds falling within section 32(3)(a) or (c),

the authorisation (unless renewed again) shall cease to have effect at the end of the period of six months beginning with the day on which it would have ceased to have effect but for the renewal, instead of at the time provided for by section 43(3).

(6) The Secretary of State may by order provide in relation to authorisations of such descriptions as may be specified in the order that subsection (3), (4) or (5) is to have effect as if the period at the end of which an authorisation of a description so specified is to cease to have effect were such period shorter than that provided for by that subsection as may be fixed by or determined in accordance with that order.

(7) Notwithstanding anything in section 43(2), in a case in which there is a combined warrant containing both—

(a) an authorisation for the carrying out of intrusive surveillance, and

(b) an authorisation for the carrying out of directed surveillance,

the reference in subsection (4) of this section to a warrant for the carrying out of intrusive surveillance is a reference to the warrant so far as it confers both authorisations.

[678]

NOTES

Sub-ss (1)–(3): words in square brackets inserted by the Scotland Act 1998 (Transfer of Functions to the Scottish Ministers etc) (No 2) Order 2000, SI 2000/3253, art 4(1), Sch 3, Pt II, paras 3, 8.

45 Cancellation of authorisations

(1) The person who granted or, as the case may be, last renewed an authorisation under this Part shall cancel it if—

(a) he is satisfied that the authorisation is one in relation to which the requirements of section 28(2)(a) and (b), 29(2)(a) and (b) or, as the case may be, 32(2)(a) and (b) are no longer satisfied; or

(b) in the case of an authorisation under section 29, he is satisfied that arrangements for the source's case that satisfy the requirements mentioned in subsection (2)(c) of that section no longer exist.

(2) Where an authorisation under this Part was granted or, as the case may be, last renewed—

(a) by a person entitled to act for any other person, or

(b) by the deputy of any other person,

that other person shall cancel the authorisation if he is satisfied as to either of the matters mentioned in subsection (1).

(3) Where an authorisation under this Part was granted or, as the case may be, last renewed by a person whose deputy had power to grant it, that deputy shall cancel the authorisation if he is satisfied as to either of the matters mentioned in subsection (1).

(4) The Secretary of State may by regulations provide for the person by whom any duty imposed by this section is to be performed in a case in which it would otherwise fall on a person who is no longer available to perform it.

(5) Regulations under subsection (4) may provide for the person on whom the duty is to fall to be a person appointed in accordance with the regulations.

(6) The references in this section to a person's deputy are references to the following—

(a) in relation to—

(i) a chief constable of a police force maintained under section 2 of the Police Act 1996,

(ii) the Commissioner of Police for the City of London, or

(iii) a chief constable of a police force maintained under or by virtue of section 1 of the Police (Scotland) Act 1967,

to his designated deputy;

(b) in relation to the Commissioner of Police of the Metropolis, to an Assistant Commissioner of Police of the Metropolis; [and]

(c) in relation to the [Chief Constable of the Police Service of Northern Ireland], to the Deputy Chief Constable of the [Police Service of Northern Ireland].

(d), (e) …

(7) In this section "designated deputy" has the same meaning as in section 34.

[679]

NOTES

Sub-s (6): word in square brackets in para (b) inserted and paras (d), (e) repealed by the Serious Organised Crime and Police Act 2005, ss 59, 174(2), Sch 4, paras 131, 143, Sch 17, Pt 2; words in square brackets in para (c) substituted by the Police (Northern Ireland) Act 2000, s 78(2)(a), (b).

Modification: for the purposes of carrying out the functions of the Independent Police Complaints Commission, this section is modified by the Independent Police Complaints Commission (Investigatory Powers) Order 2004, SI 2004/815, art 3(1), (9).

Regulations: the Regulation of Investigatory Powers (Cancellation of Authorisations) Regulations 2000, SI 2000/2794 at **[1022]**.

Scotland

46 Restrictions on authorisations extending to Scotland

(1) No person shall grant or renew an authorisation under this Part for the carrying out of any conduct if it appears to him—

(a) that the authorisation is not one for which this Part is the relevant statutory provision for all parts of the United Kingdom; and

(b) that all the conduct authorised by the grant or, as the case may be, renewal of the authorisation is likely to take place in Scotland.

(2) In relation to any authorisation, this Part is the relevant statutory provision for all parts of the United Kingdom in so far as it—

(a) is granted or renewed on the grounds that it is necessary in the interests of national security or in the interests of the economic well-being of the United Kingdom;

(b) is granted or renewed by or on the application of a person holding any office, rank or position with any of the public authorities specified in subsection (3);

(c) authorises conduct of a person holding an office, rank or position with any of the public authorities so specified;

(d) authorises conduct of an individual acting as a covert human intelligence source for the benefit of any of the public authorities so specified; or

(e) authorises conduct that is surveillance by virtue of section 48(4).

(3) The public authorities mentioned in subsection (2) are—

(a) each of the intelligence services;

(b) Her Majesty's forces;

(c) the Ministry of Defence;

(d) the Ministry of Defence Police;

[(dza) the Civil Nuclear Constabulary;]

[(da) the OFT;]

[(db) the Serious Organised Crime Agency;]

(e) the Commissioners of Customs and Excise; and

(f) the British Transport Police.

(4) For the purposes of so much of this Part as has effect in relation to any other public authority by virtue of—

(a) the fact that it is a public authority for the time being specified in Schedule 1, or

(b) an order under subsection (1)(d) of section 41 designating that authority for the purposes of that section,

the authorities specified in subsection (3) of this section shall be treated as including that authority to the extent that the Secretary of State by order directs that the authority is a relevant public authority or, as the case may be, is a designated authority for all parts of the United Kingdom.

[680]

NOTES

Sub-s (3): para (dza) inserted by the Energy Act 2004, s 69(1), Sch 14, para 8(1); para (da) inserted by the Enterprise Act 2002, s 199(1), (10); para (db) inserted by the Serious Organised Crime and Police Act 2005, s 59, Sch 4, paras 131, 144.

Orders: the Regulation of Investigatory Powers (Authorisations Extending to Scotland) Order 2000, SI 2000/2418 at **[989]**.

Supplemental provision for Part II

47 Power to extend or modify authorisation provisions

(1) The Secretary of State may by order do one or both of the following—

(a) apply this Part, with such modifications as he thinks fit, to any such surveillance that is neither directed nor intrusive as may be described in the order;

(b) provide for any description of directed surveillance to be treated for the purposes of this Part as intrusive surveillance.

(2) No order shall be made under this section unless a draft of it has been laid before Parliament and approved by a resolution of each House.

[681]

NOTES

Orders: the Regulation of Investigatory Powers (British Broadcasting Corporation) Order 2001, SI 2001/1057 at **[1034]**.

48 Interpretation of Part II

(1) In this Part—

"covert human intelligence source" shall be construed in accordance with section 26(8);

"directed" and "intrusive", in relation to surveillance, shall be construed in accordance with section 26(2) to (6);

["OFT" means the Office of Fair Trading;]

"private vehicle" means (subject to subsection (7)(a)) any vehicle which is used primarily for the private purposes of the person who owns it or of a person otherwise having the right to use it;

"residential premises" means (subject to subsection (7)(b)) so much of any premises as is for the time being occupied or used by any person, however temporarily, for residential purposes or otherwise as living accommodation (including hotel or prison accommodation that is so occupied or used);

"senior authorising officer" means a person who by virtue of subsection (6) of section 32 is a senior authorising officer for the purposes of that section;

"surveillance" shall be construed in accordance with subsections (2) to (4);

"surveillance device" means any apparatus designed or adapted for use in surveillance.

(2) Subject to subsection (3), in this Part "surveillance" includes—

(a) monitoring, observing or listening to persons, their movements, their conversations or their other activities or communications;

(b) recording anything monitored, observed or listened to in the course of surveillance; and

(c) surveillance by or with the assistance of a surveillance device.

(3) References in this Part to surveillance do not include references to—

(a) any conduct of a covert human intelligence source for obtaining or recording (whether or not using a surveillance device) any information which is disclosed in the presence of the source;

(b) the use of a covert human intelligence source for so obtaining or recording information; or

(c) any such entry on or interference with property or with wireless telegraphy as would be unlawful unless authorised under—

(i) section 5 of the Intelligence Services Act 1994 (warrants for the intelligence services); or

(ii) Part III of the Police Act 1997 (powers of the police and of customs officers).

(4) References in this Part to surveillance include references to the interception of a communication in the course of its transmission by means of a postal service or telecommunication system if, and only if—

(a) the communication is one sent by or intended for a person who has consented to the interception of communications sent by or to him; and

(b) there is no interception warrant authorising the interception.

(5) References in this Part to an individual holding an office or position with a public authority include references to any member, official or employee of that authority.

(6) For the purposes of this Part the activities of a covert human intelligence source which are to be taken as activities for the benefit of a particular public authority include any conduct of his as such a source which is in response to inducements or requests made by or on behalf of that authority.

(7) In subsection (1)—

(a) the reference to a person having the right to use a vehicle does not, in relation to a motor vehicle, include a reference to a person whose right to use the vehicle derives only from his having paid, or undertaken to pay, for the use of the vehicle and its driver for a particular journey; and

(b) the reference to premises occupied or used by any person for residential purposes or otherwise as living accommodation does not include a reference to so much of any premises as constitutes any common area to which he has or is allowed access in connection with his use or occupation of any accommodation.

(8) In this section—

"premises" includes any vehicle or moveable structure and any other place whatever, whether or not occupied as land;

"vehicle" includes any vessel, aircraft or hovercraft.

[682]

NOTES

Sub-s (1): definition "OFT" inserted by the Enterprise Act 2002, s 199(1), (11).

PART III
INVESTIGATION OF ELECTRONIC DATA PROTECTED BY ENCRYPTION ETC

Power to require disclosure

49 Notices requiring disclosure

(1) This section applies where any protected information—

(a) has come into the possession of any person by means of the exercise of a statutory power to seize, detain, inspect, search or otherwise to interfere with documents or other property, or is likely to do so;

(b) has come into the possession of any person by means of the exercise of any statutory power to intercept communications, or is likely to do so;

(c) has come into the possession of any person by means of the exercise of any power conferred by an authorisation under section 22(3) or under Part II, or as a result of the giving of a notice under section 22(4), or is likely to do so;

(d) has come into the possession of any person as a result of having been provided or disclosed in pursuance of any statutory duty (whether or not one arising as a result of a request for information), or is likely to do so; or

(e) has, by any other lawful means not involving the exercise of statutory powers, come into the possession of any of the intelligence services, the police[, SOCA] or the customs and excise, or is likely so to come into the possession of any of those services, the police[, SOCA] or the customs and excise.

(2) If any person with the appropriate permission under Schedule 2 believes, on reasonable grounds—

(a) that a key to the protected information is in the possession of any person,

(b) that the imposition of a disclosure requirement in respect of the protected information is—

(i) necessary on grounds falling within subsection (3), or

(ii) necessary for the purpose of securing the effective exercise or proper performance by any public authority of any statutory power or statutory duty,

(c) that the imposition of such a requirement is proportionate to what is sought to be achieved by its imposition, and

(d) that it is not reasonably practicable for the person with the appropriate permission to obtain possession of the protected information in an intelligible form without the giving of a notice under this section,

the person with that permission may, by notice to the person whom he believes to have possession of the key, impose a disclosure requirement in respect of the protected information.

(3) A disclosure requirement in respect of any protected information is necessary on grounds falling within this subsection if it is necessary—

(a) in the interests of national security;

(b) for the purpose of preventing or detecting crime; or

(c) in the interests of the economic well-being of the United Kingdom.

(4) A notice under this section imposing a disclosure requirement in respect of any protected information—

(a) must be given in writing or (if not in writing) must be given in a manner that produces a record of its having been given;

(b) must describe the protected information to which the notice relates;

(c) must specify the matters falling within subsection (2)(b)(i) or (ii) by reference to which the notice is given;

(d) must specify the office, rank or position held by the person giving it;

(e) must specify the office, rank or position of the person who for the purposes of Schedule 2 granted permission for the giving of the notice or (if the person giving the notice was entitled to give it without another person's permission) must set out the circumstances in which that entitlement arose;

(f) must specify the time by which the notice is to be complied with; and

(g) must set out the disclosure that is required by the notice and the form and manner in which it is to be made;

and the time specified for the purposes of paragraph (f) must allow a period for compliance which is reasonable in all the circumstances.

(5) Where it appears to a person with the appropriate permission—

(a) that more than one person is in possession of the key to any protected information,

(b) that any of those persons is in possession of that key in his capacity as an officer or employee of any body corporate, and

(c) that another of those persons is the body corporate itself or another officer or employee of the body corporate,

a notice under this section shall not be given, by reference to his possession of the key, to any officer or employee of the body corporate unless he is a senior officer of the body corporate or it appears to the person giving the notice that there is no senior officer of the body corporate and (in the case of an employee) no more senior employee of the body corporate to whom it is reasonably practicable to give the notice.

(6) Where it appears to a person with the appropriate permission—

(a) that more than one person is in possession of the key to any protected information,

(b) that any of those persons is in possession of that key in his capacity as an employee of a firm, and

(c) that another of those persons is the firm itself or a partner of the firm,

a notice under this section shall not be given, by reference to his possession of the key, to any employee of the firm unless it appears to the person giving the notice that there is neither a partner of the firm nor a more senior employee of the firm to whom it is reasonably practicable to give the notice.

(7) Subsections (5) and (6) shall not apply to the extent that there are special circumstances of the case that mean that the purposes for which the notice is given would be defeated, in whole or in part, if the notice were given to the person to whom it would otherwise be required to be given by those subsections.

(8) A notice under this section shall not require the making of any disclosure to any person other than—

(a) the person giving the notice; or

(b) such other person as may be specified in or otherwise identified by, or in accordance with, the provisions of the notice.

(9) A notice under this section shall not require the disclosure of any key which—

(a) is intended to be used for the purpose only of generating electronic signatures; and

(b) has not in fact been used for any other purpose.

(10) In this section "senior officer", in relation to a body corporate, means a director, manager, secretary or other similar officer of the body corporate; and for this purpose "director", in relation to a body corporate whose affairs are managed by its members, means a member of the body corporate.

(11) Schedule 2 (definition of the appropriate permission) shall have effect.

[683]

NOTES

Commencement: to be appointed.

Sub-s (1): words in square brackets in para (e) inserted by the Serious Organised Crime and Police Act 2005, s 59, Sch 4, paras 131, 145.

50 Effect of notice imposing disclosure requirement

(1) Subject to the following provisions of this section, the effect of a section 49 notice imposing a disclosure requirement in respect of any protected information on a person who is in possession at a relevant time of both the protected information and a means of obtaining access to the information and of disclosing it in an intelligible form is that he—

(a) shall be entitled to use any key in his possession to obtain access to the information or to put it into an intelligible form; and

(b) shall be required, in accordance with the notice imposing the requirement, to make a disclosure of the information in an intelligible form.

(2) A person subject to a requirement under subsection (1)(b) to make a disclosure of any information in an intelligible form shall be taken to have complied with that requirement if—

(a) he makes, instead, a disclosure of any key to the protected information that is in his possession; and

(b) that disclosure is made, in accordance with the notice imposing the requirement, to the person to whom, and by the time by which, he was required to provide the information in that form.

(3) Where, in a case in which a disclosure requirement in respect of any protected information is imposed on any person by a section 49 notice—

(a) that person is not in possession of the information,

(b) that person is incapable, without the use of a key that is not in his possession, of obtaining access to the information and of disclosing it in an intelligible form, or

(c) the notice states, in pursuance of a direction under section 51, that it can be complied with only by the disclosure of a key to the information,

the effect of imposing that disclosure requirement on that person is that he shall be required, in accordance with the notice imposing the requirement, to make a disclosure of any key to the protected information that is in his possession at a relevant time.

(4) Subsections (5) to (7) apply where a person ("the person given notice")—

(a) is entitled or obliged to disclose a key to protected information for the purpose of complying with any disclosure requirement imposed by a section 49 notice; and

(b) is in possession of more than one key to that information.

(5) It shall not be necessary, for the purpose of complying with the requirement, for the person given notice to make a disclosure of any keys in addition to those the disclosure of which is, alone, sufficient to enable the person to whom they are disclosed to obtain access to the information and to put it into an intelligible form.

(6) Where—

(a) subsection (5) allows the person given notice to comply with a requirement without disclosing all of the keys in his possession, and

(b) there are different keys, or combinations of keys, in the possession of that person the disclosure of which would, under that subsection, constitute compliance,

the person given notice may select which of the keys, or combination of keys, to disclose for the purpose of complying with that requirement in accordance with that subsection.

(7) Subject to subsections (5) and (6), the person given notice shall not be taken to have complied with the disclosure requirement by the disclosure of a key unless he has disclosed every key to the protected information that is in his possession at a relevant time.

(8) Where, in a case in which a disclosure requirement in respect of any protected information is imposed on any person by a section 49 notice—

(a) that person has been in possession of the key to that information but is no longer in possession of it,

(b) if he had continued to have the key in his possession, he would have been required by virtue of the giving of the notice to disclose it, and

(c) he is in possession, at a relevant time, of information to which subsection (9) applies,

the effect of imposing that disclosure requirement on that person is that he shall be required, in accordance with the notice imposing the requirement, to disclose all such information to which subsection (9) applies as is in his possession and as he may be required, in accordance with that notice, to disclose by the person to whom he would have been required to disclose the key.

(9) This subsection applies to any information that would facilitate the obtaining or discovery of the key or the putting of the protected information into an intelligible form.

(10) In this section "relevant time", in relation to a disclosure requirement imposed by a section 49 notice, means the time of the giving of the notice or any subsequent time before the time by which the requirement falls to be complied with.

[684]

NOTES

Commencement: to be appointed.

51 Cases in which key required

(1) A section 49 notice imposing a disclosure requirement in respect of any protected information shall not contain a statement for the purposes of section 50(3)(c) unless—

(a) the person who for the purposes of Schedule 2 granted the permission for the giving of the notice in relation to that information, or

(b) any person whose permission for the giving of a such a notice in relation to that information would constitute the appropriate permission under that Schedule,

has given a direction that the requirement can be complied with only by the disclosure of the key itself.

(2) A direction for the purposes of subsection (1) by [the police, SOCA, the customs] and excise or a member of Her Majesty's forces shall not be given—

(a) in the case of a direction by the police or by a member of Her Majesty's forces who is a member of a police force, except by or with the permission of a chief officer of police;

[(aa) in the case of a direction by SOCA, except by or with the permission of the Director General of the Serious Organised Crime Agency;]

(b) in the case of a direction by the customs and excise, except by or with the permission of the Commissioners of Customs and Excise; or

(c) in the case of a direction by a member of Her Majesty's forces who is not a member of a police force, except by or with the permission of a person of or above the rank of brigadier or its equivalent.

(3) A permission given for the purposes of subsection (2) by a chief officer of police, [the Director General of the Serious Organised Crime Agency,] the Commissioners of Customs and Excise or a person of or above any such rank as is mentioned in paragraph (c) of that subsection must be given expressly in relation to the direction in question.

(4) A person shall not give a direction for the purposes of subsection (1) unless he believes—

(a) that there are special circumstances of the case which mean that the purposes for which it was believed necessary to impose the requirement in question would be defeated, in whole or in part, if the direction were not given; and

(b) that the giving of the direction is proportionate to what is sought to be achieved by prohibiting any compliance with the requirement in question otherwise than by the disclosure of the key itself.

(5) The matters to be taken into account in considering whether the requirement of subsection (4)(b) is satisfied in the case of any direction shall include—

(a) the extent and nature of any protected information, in addition to the protected information in respect of which the disclosure requirement is imposed, to which the key is also a key; and

(b) any adverse effect that the giving of the direction might have on a business carried on by the person on whom the disclosure requirement is imposed.

(6) Where a direction for the purposes of subsection (1) is given by a chief officer of police, [by the Director General of the Serious Organised Crime Agency,] by the Commissioners of Customs and Excise or by a member of Her Majesty's forces, the person giving the direction shall give a notification that he has done so—

(a) in a case where the direction is given—

(i) by a member of Her Majesty's forces who is not a member of a police force, and

(ii) otherwise than in connection with activities of members of Her Majesty's forces in Northern Ireland,

to the Intelligences Services Commissioner; and

(b) in any other case, to the Chief Surveillance Commissioner.

(7) A notification under subsection (6)—

(a) must be given not more than seven days after the day of the giving of the direction to which it relates; and

(b) may be given either in writing or by being transmitted to the Commissioner in question by electronic means.

[685]

NOTES

Commencement: to be appointed.

Sub-s (2): words in square brackets substituted and para (aa) inserted by the Serious Organised Crime and Police Act 2005, s 59, Sch 4, paras 131, 146(1), (2).

Sub-ss (3), (6): words in square brackets inserted by the Serious Organised Crime and Police Act 2005, s 59, Sch 4, paras 131, 146(1), (3), (4).

Contributions to costs

52 Arrangements for payments for disclosure

(1) It shall be the duty of the Secretary of State to ensure that such arrangements are in force as he thinks appropriate for requiring or authorising, in such cases as he thinks fit, the making to persons to whom section 49 notices are given of appropriate contributions towards the costs incurred by them in complying with such notices.

(2) For the purpose of complying with his duty under this section, the Secretary of State may make arrangements for payments to be made out of money provided by Parliament.

[686]

NOTES

Commencement: to be appointed.

Offences

53 Failure to comply with a notice

(1) A person to whom a section 49 notice has been given is guilty of an offence if he knowingly fails, in accordance with the notice, to make the disclosure required by virtue of the giving of the notice.

(2) In proceedings against any person for an offence under this section, if it is shown that that person was in possession of a key to any protected information at any time before the time of the giving of the section 49 notice, that person shall be taken for the purposes of those proceedings to have continued to be in possession of that key at all subsequent times, unless it is shown that the key was not in his possession after the giving of the notice and before the time by which he was required to disclose it.

(3) For the purposes of this section a person shall be taken to have shown that he was not in possession of a key to protected information at a particular time if—

(a) sufficient evidence of that fact is adduced to raise an issue with respect to it; and

(b) the contrary is not proved beyond a reasonable doubt.

(4) In proceedings against any person for an offence under this section it shall be a defence for that person to show—

(a) that it was not reasonably practicable for him to make the disclosure required by virtue of the giving of the section 49 notice before the time by which he was required, in accordance with that notice, to make it; but

(b) that he did make that disclosure as soon after that time as it was reasonably practicable for him to do so.

(5) A person guilty of an offence under this section shall be liable—

(a) on conviction on indictment, to imprisonment for a term not exceeding [the appropriate maximum term] or to a fine, or to both;

(b) on summary conviction, to imprisonment for a term not exceeding six months or to a fine not exceeding the statutory maximum, or to both.

[(5A) In subsection (5) 'the appropriate maximum term' means—

(a) in a national security case, five years; and

(b) in any other case, two years.

(5B) In subsection (5A) 'a national security case' means a case in which the grounds specified in the notice to which the offence relates as the grounds for imposing a disclosure requirement were or included a belief that the imposition of the requirement was necessary in the interests of national security.]

[687]

NOTES

Commencement: to be appointed.

Sub-s (5): words in square brackets in para (a) substituted for original words "two years" by the Terrorism Act 2006, s 15(1)(a), except in relation to offences committed before 13 April 2006.

Sub-ss (5A), (5B): added by the Terrorism Act 2006, s 15(1)(b), (2), except in relation to offences committed before 13 April 2006.

54 Tipping-off

(1) This section applies where a section 49 notice contains a provision requiring—

(a) the person to whom the notice is given, and

(b) every other person who becomes aware of it or of its contents,

to keep secret the giving of the notice, its contents and the things done in pursuance of it.

(2) A requirement to keep anything secret shall not be included in a section 49 notice except where—

(a) it is included with the consent of the person who for the purposes of Schedule 2 granted the permission for the giving of the notice; or

(b) the person who gives the notice is himself a person whose permission for the giving of such a notice in relation to the information in question would have constituted appropriate permission under that Schedule.

(3) A section 49 notice shall not contain a requirement to keep anything secret except where the protected information to which it relates—

(a) has come into the possession of the police, [SOCA,] the customs and excise or any of the intelligence services, or

(b) is likely to come into the possession of the police, [SOCA,] the customs and excise or any of the intelligence services,

by means which it is reasonable, in order to maintain the effectiveness of any investigation or operation or of investigatory techniques generally, or in the interests of the safety or well-being of any person, to keep secret from a particular person.

(4) A person who makes a disclosure to any other person of anything that he is required by a section 49 notice to keep secret shall be guilty of an offence and liable—

(a) on conviction on indictment, to imprisonment for a term not exceeding five years or to a fine, or to both;

(b) on summary conviction, to imprisonment for a term not exceeding six months or to a fine not exceeding the statutory maximum, or to both.

(5) In proceedings against any person for an offence under this section in respect of any disclosure, it shall be a defence for that person to show that—

(a) the disclosure was effected entirely by the operation of software designed to indicate when a key to protected information has ceased to be secure; and

(b) that person could not reasonably have been expected to take steps, after being given the notice or (as the case may be) becoming aware of it or of its contents, to prevent the disclosure.

(6) In proceedings against any person for an offence under this section in respect of any disclosure, it shall be a defence for that person to show that—

(a) the disclosure was made by or to a professional legal adviser in connection with the giving, by the adviser to any client of his, of advice about the effect of provisions of this Part; and

(b) the person to whom or, as the case may be, by whom it was made was the client or a representative of the client.

(7) In proceedings against any person for an offence under this section in respect of any disclosure, it shall be a defence for that person to show that the disclosure was made by a legal adviser—

(a) in contemplation of, or in connection with, any legal proceedings; and

(b) for the purposes of those proceedings.

(8) Neither subsection (6) nor subsection (7) applies in the case of a disclosure made with a view to furthering any criminal purpose.

(9) In proceedings against any person for an offence under this section in respect of any disclosure, it shall be a defence for that person to show that the disclosure was confined to a disclosure made to a relevant Commissioner or authorised—

(a) by such a Commissioner;
(b) by the terms of the notice;
(c) by or on behalf of the person who gave the notice; or
(d) by or on behalf of a person who—
 (i) is in lawful possession of the protected information to which the notice relates; and
 (ii) came into possession of that information as mentioned in section 49(1).

(10) In proceedings for an offence under this section against a person other than the person to whom the notice was given, it shall be a defence for the person against whom the proceedings are brought to show that he neither knew nor had reasonable grounds for suspecting that the notice contained a requirement to keep secret what was disclosed.

(11) In this section "relevant Commissioner" means the Interception of Communications Commissioner, the Intelligence Services Commissioner or any Surveillance Commissioner or Assistant Surveillance Commissioner.

[688]

NOTES

Commencement: to be appointed.

Sub-s (3): words in square brackets inserted by the Serious Organised Crime and Police Act 2005, s 59, Sch 4, paras 131, 147.

Safeguards

55 General duties of specified authorities

(1) This section applies to—

(a) the Secretary of State and every other Minister of the Crown in charge of a government department;
(b) every chief officer of police;
[(ba) the Director General of the Serious Organised Crime Agency;]
(c) the Commissioners of Customs and Excise; and
(d) every person whose officers or employees include persons with duties that involve the giving of section 49 notices.

(2) It shall be the duty of each of the persons to whom this section applies to ensure that such arrangements are in force, in relation to persons under his control who by virtue of this Part obtain possession of keys to protected information, as he considers necessary for securing—

(a) that a key disclosed in pursuance of a section 49 notice is used for obtaining access to, or putting into an intelligible form, only protected information in relation to which power to give such a notice was exercised or could have been exercised if the key had not already been disclosed;
(b) that the uses to which a key so disclosed is put are reasonable having regard both to the uses to which the person using the key is entitled to put any protected information to which it relates and to the other circumstances of the case;
(c) that, having regard to those matters, the use and any retention of the key are proportionate to what is sought to be achieved by its use or retention;
(d) that the requirements of subsection (3) are satisfied in relation to any key disclosed in pursuance of a section 49 notice;
(e) that, for the purpose of ensuring that those requirements are satisfied, any key so disclosed is stored, for so long as it is retained, in a secure manner;
(f) that all records of a key so disclosed (if not destroyed earlier) are destroyed as soon as the key is no longer needed for the purpose of enabling protected information to be put into an intelligible form.

(3) The requirements of this subsection are satisfied in relation to any key disclosed in pursuance of a section 49 notice if—

(a) the number of persons to whom the key is disclosed or otherwise made available, and

(b) the number of copies made of the key,

are each limited to the minimum that is necessary for the purpose of enabling protected information to be put into an intelligible form.

[(3A) Paragraph 11 of Schedule 1 to the Serious Organised Crime and Police Act 2005 does not apply in relation to the duties of the Director General of the Serious Organised Crime Agency under this section.]

(4) Subject to subsection (5), where any relevant person incurs any loss or damage in consequence of—

(a) any breach by a person to whom this section applies of the duty imposed on him by subsection (2), or

(b) any contravention by any person whatever of arrangements made in pursuance of that subsection in relation to persons under the control of a person to whom this section applies,

the breach or contravention shall be actionable against the person to whom this section applies at the suit or instance of the relevant person.

(5) A person is a relevant person for the purposes of subsection (4) if he is—

(a) a person who has made a disclosure in pursuance of a section 49 notice; or

(b) a person whose protected information or key has been disclosed in pursuance of such a notice;

and loss or damage shall be taken into account for the purposes of that subsection to the extent only that it relates to the disclosure of particular protected information or a particular key which, in the case of a person falling with paragraph (b), must be his information or key.

(6) For the purposes of subsection (5)—

(a) information belongs to a person if he has any right that would be infringed by an unauthorised disclosure of the information; and

(b) a key belongs to a person if it is a key to information that belongs to him or he has any right that would be infringed by an unauthorised disclosure of the key.

(7) In any proceedings brought by virtue of subsection (4), it shall be the duty of the court to have regard to any opinion with respect to the matters to which the proceedings relate that is or has been given by a relevant Commissioner.

(8) In this section "relevant Commissioner" means the Interception of Communications Commissioner, the Intelligence Services Commissioner, the Investigatory Powers Commissioner for Northern Ireland or any Surveillance Commissioner or Assistant Surveillance Commissioner.

[689]

NOTES

Commencement: to be appointed.

Sub-s (1): para (ba) inserted by the Serious Organised Crime and Police Act 2005, s 59, Sch 4, paras 131, 148(1), (2).

Sub-s (3A): inserted by the Serious Organised Crime and Police Act 2005, s 59, Sch 4, paras 131, 148(1), (3).

Interpretation of Part III

56 Interpretation of Part III

(1) In this Part—

"chief officer of police" means any of the following—

(a) the chief constable of a police force maintained under or by virtue of section 2 of the Police Act 1996 or section 1 of the Police (Scotland) Act 1967;

(b) the Commissioner of Police of the Metropolis;

(c) the Commissioner of Police for the City of London;

(d) the [Chief Constable of the Police Service of Northern Ireland];

(e) the Chief Constable of the Ministry of Defence Police;

(f) the Provost Marshal of the *Royal Navy Regulating Branch*;
(g) the Provost Marshal of the Royal Military Police;
(h) the Provost Marshal of the Royal Air Force Police;
(i) the Chief Constable of the British Transport Police;
(j), (k) …

"the customs and excise" means the Commissioners of Customs and Excise or any customs officer;

"electronic signature" means anything in electronic form which—

(a) is incorporated into, or otherwise logically associated with, any electronic communication or other electronic data;
(b) is generated by the signatory or other source of the communication or data; and
(c) is used for the purpose of facilitating, by means of a link between the signatory or other source and the communication or data, the establishment of the authenticity of the communication or data, the establishment of its integrity, or both;

"key", in relation to any electronic data, means any key, code, password, algorithm or other data the use of which (with or without other keys)—

(a) allows access to the electronic data, or
(b) facilitates the putting of the data into an intelligible form;

"the police" means—

(a) any constable [(except a constable who is a member of the staff of the Serious Organised Crime Agency)];
(b) the Commissioner of Police of the Metropolis or any Assistant Commissioner of Police of the Metropolis; or
(c) the Commissioner of Police for the City of London;

"protected information" means any electronic data which, without the key to the data—

(a) cannot, or cannot readily, be accessed, or
(b) cannot, or cannot readily, be put into an intelligible form;

"section 49 notice" means a notice under section 49;

["SOCA" means the Serious Organised Crime Agency or any member of the staff of the Serious Organised Crime Agency;]

"warrant" includes any authorisation, notice or other instrument (however described) conferring a power of the same description as may, in other cases, be conferred by a warrant.

(2) References in this Part to a person's having information (including a key to protected information) in his possession include references—

(a) to its being in the possession of a person who is under his control so far as that information is concerned;
(b) to his having an immediate right of access to it, or an immediate right to have it transmitted or otherwise supplied to him; and
(c) to its being, or being contained in, anything which he or a person under his control is entitled, in exercise of any statutory power and without otherwise taking possession of it, to detain, inspect or search.

(3) References in this Part to something's being intelligible or being put into an intelligible form include references to its being in the condition in which it was before an encryption or similar process was applied to it or, as the case may be, to its being restored to that condition.

(4) In this section—

(a) references to the authenticity of any communication or data are references to any one or more of the following—
  (i) whether the communication or data comes from a particular person or other source;
  (ii) whether it is accurately timed and dated;
  (iii) whether it is intended to have legal effect; and
(b) references to the integrity of any communication or data are references to whether there has been any tampering with or other modification of the communication or data.

[690]

NOTES

Commencement: to be appointed.

Sub-s (1): in definition "chief officer of police", words in square brackets in para (d) substituted by the Police (Northern Ireland) Act 2000, s 78(2)(a); in definition "chief officer of police", for the words in italics in para (f) there are substituted the words "Royal Navy Police" by the Armed Forces Act 2006, s 378(1), Sch 16, para 174, as from a day to be appointed; paras (j), (k) in definition "chief officer of police" repealed, words in square brackets in definition "the police" inserted, and definition "SOCA" inserted by the Serious Organised Crime and Police Act 2005, ss 59, 174(2), Sch 4, paras 131, 149, Sch 17, Pt 2.

PART IV
SCRUTINY ETC OF INVESTIGATORY POWERS AND OF THE FUNCTIONS OF THE INTELLIGENCE SERVICES

Commissioners

57 Interception of Communications Commissioner

(1) The Prime Minister shall appoint a Commissioner to be known as the Interception of Communications Commissioner.

(2) Subject to subsection (4), the Interception of Communications Commissioner shall keep under review—

(a) the exercise and performance by the Secretary of State of the powers and duties conferred or imposed on him by or under sections 1 to 11;

[(aa) the exercise and performance by the Scottish Ministers (by virtue of provision made under section 63 of the Scotland Act 1998) of the powers and duties conferred or imposed on them by or under sections 5, 9 and 10;]

(b) the exercise and performance, by the persons on whom they are conferred or imposed, of the powers and duties conferred or imposed by or under Chapter II of Part I;

(c) the exercise and performance by the Secretary of State in relation to information obtained under Part I of the powers and duties conferred or imposed on him by or under Part III; and

(d) the adequacy of the arrangements by virtue of which—

(i) the duty which is imposed on the Secretary of State[, or the Scottish Ministers (by virtue of provision under section 63 of the Scotland Act 1998),] by section 15, and

(ii) so far as applicable to information obtained under Part I, the duties imposed by section 55,

are sought to be discharged.

(3) The Interception of Communications Commissioner shall give the Tribunal all such assistance (including his opinion as to any issue falling to be determined by the Tribunal) as the Tribunal may require—

(a) in connection with the investigation of any matter by the Tribunal; or

(b) otherwise for the purposes of the Tribunal's consideration or determination of any matter.

(4) It shall not be the function of the Interception of Communications Commissioner to keep under review the exercise of any power of the Secretary of State to make, amend or revoke any subordinate legislation.

(5) A person shall not be appointed under this section as the Interception of Communications Commissioner unless he holds or has held a high judicial office (within the meaning of *the Appellate Jurisdiction Act 1876*).

(6) The Interception of Communications Commissioner shall hold office in accordance with the terms of his appointment; and there shall be paid to him out of money provided by Parliament such allowances as the Treasury may determine.

(7) The Secretary of State, after consultation with the Interception of Communications Commissioner, shall—

(a) make such technical facilities available to the Commissioner, and

(b) subject to the approval of the Treasury as to numbers, provide the Commissioner with such staff,

as are sufficient to secure that the Commissioner is able properly to carry out his functions.

(8) On the coming into force of this section the Commissioner holding office as the Commissioner under section 8 of the Interception of Communications Act 1985 shall take and hold office as the Interception of Communications Commissioner as if appointed under this Act—

(a) for the unexpired period of his term of office under that Act; and
(b) otherwise, on the terms of his appointment under that Act.

[691]

NOTES

Commencement: 2 October 2000 (sub-ss (1), (2)(a), (d)(i), (3)–(8)); 5 January 2004 (sub-s (2)(b)); to be appointed (otherwise).

Sub-s (2): para (aa) and words in square brackets in para (d) inserted by the Scotland Act 1998 (Transfer of Functions to the Scottish Ministers etc) (No 2) Order 2000, SI 2000/3253, art 4(1), Sch 3, Pt II, paras 3, 9.

Sub-s (5): for the words in italics there are substituted the words "Part 3 of the Constitutional Reform Act 2005) or is or has been a member of the Judicial Committee of the Privy Council" by the Constitutional Reform Act 2005, s 145, Sch 17, Pt 2, para 30(1), (2)(a), as from a day to be appointed.

58 Co-operation with and reports by s 57 Commissioner

(1) It shall be the duty of—

(a) every person holding office under the Crown,
[(b) every member of the staff of the Serious Organised Crime Agency,]
(d) every person employed by or for the purposes of a police force,
(e) every person required for the purposes of section 11 to provide assistance with giving effect to an interception warrant,
(f) every person on whom an obligation to take any steps has been imposed under section 12,
(g) every person by or to whom an authorisation under section 22(3) has been granted,
(h) every person to whom a notice under section 22(4) has been given,
(i) every person to whom a notice under section 49 has been given in relation to any information obtained under Part I, and
(j) every person who is or has been employed for the purposes of any business of a person falling within paragraph (e), (f), (h) or (i),

to disclose or provide to the Interception of Communications Commissioner all such documents and information as he may require for the purpose of enabling him to carry out his functions under section 57.

(2) If it at any time appears to the Interception of Communications Commissioner—

(a) that there has been a contravention of the provisions of this Act in relation to any matter with which that Commissioner is concerned, and
(b) that the contravention has not been the subject of a report made to the Prime Minister by the Tribunal,

he shall make a report to the Prime Minister with respect to that contravention.

(3) If it at any time appears to the Interception of Communications Commissioner that any arrangements by reference to which the duties imposed by sections 15 and 55 have sought to be discharged have proved inadequate in relation to any matter with which the Commissioner is concerned, he shall make a report to the Prime Minister with respect to those arrangements.

(4) As soon as practicable after the end of each calendar year, the Interception of Communications Commissioner shall make a report to the Prime Minister with respect to the carrying out of that Commissioner's functions.

(5) The Interception of Communications Commissioner may also, at any time, make any such other report to the Prime Minister on any matter relating to the carrying out of the Commissioner's functions as the Commissioner thinks fit.

[(5A) The Interception of Communications Commissioner may also, at any time, make any such other report to the First Minister on any matter relating to the carrying out of the Commissioner's functions so far as they relate to the exercise by the Scottish Ministers (by virtue of provision made under section 63 of the Scotland Act 1998) of their powers under sections 5, 9(1)(b) and (3), 10(1)(a) and (2) and 15(1) of this Act, as the Commissioner thinks fit.]

(6) The Prime Minister shall lay before each House of Parliament a copy of every annual report made by the Interception of Communications Commissioner under subsection (4), together with a statement as to whether any matter has been excluded from that copy in pursuance of subsection (7).

[(6A) The Prime Minister shall send a copy of every annual report made by the Interception of Communications Commissioner under subsection (4) which he lays in terms of subsection (6), together with a copy of the statement referred to in subsection (6), to the First Minister who shall forthwith lay that copy report and statement before the Scottish Parliament.]

(7) If it appears to the Prime Minister, after consultation with the Interception of Communications Commissioner [and, if it appears relevant to do so, with the First Minister], that the publication of any matter in an annual report would be contrary to the public interest or prejudicial to—

- (a) national security,
- (b) the prevention or detection of serious crime,
- (c) the economic well-being of the United Kingdom, or
- (d) the continued discharge of the functions of any public authority whose activities include activities that are subject to review by that Commissioner,

the Prime Minister may exclude that matter from the copy of the report as laid before each House of Parliament.

[692]

NOTES

Commencement: 2 October 2000 (sub-ss (1)(a)–(f), (2)–(7), sub-s (1)(j) (certain purposes)); 5 January 2004 (sub-s (1)(g), (h), (j) (remaining purposes)); to be appointed (otherwise).

Sub-s (1): para (b) substituted for original paras (b), (c) by the Serious Organised Crime and Police Act 2005, s 59, Sch 4, paras 131, 150.

Sub-ss (5A), (6A): inserted by the Scotland Act 1998 (Transfer of Functions to the Scottish Ministers etc) (No 2) Order 2000, SI 2000/3253, art 4(1), Sch 3, Pt II, paras 3, 10(a), (b).

Sub-s (7): words in square brackets inserted by SI 2000/3253, art 4(1), Sch 3, Pt II, paras 3, 10(c).

59 Intelligence Services Commissioner

(1) The Prime Minister shall appoint a Commissioner to be known as the Intelligence Services Commissioner.

(2) Subject to subsection (4), the Intelligence Services Commissioner shall keep under review, so far as they are not required to be kept under review by the Interception of Communications Commissioner—

- (a) the exercise by the Secretary of State of his powers under sections 5 to 7 of[, or the Scottish Ministers (by virtue of provision made under section 63 of the Scotland Act 1998) of their powers under sections 5 and 6(3) and (4) of,] the Intelligence Services Act 1994 (warrants for interference with wireless telegraphy, entry and interference with property etc);
- (b) the exercise and performance by the Secretary of State, [or the Scottish Ministers (by virtue of provision made under section 63 of the Scotland Act 1998),] in connection with or in relation to—
  - (i) the activities of the intelligence services, and
  - (ii) the activities in places other than Northern Ireland of the officials of the Ministry of Defence and of members of Her Majesty's forces, of

  the powers and duties conferred or imposed on him by Parts II and III of this Act [or on them by Part II of this Act];
- (c) the exercise and performance by members of the intelligence services of the powers and duties conferred or imposed on them by or under Parts II and III of this Act;
- (d) the exercise and performance in places other than Northern Ireland, by officials of the Ministry of Defence and by members of Her Majesty's forces, of the powers and duties conferred or imposed on such officials or members of Her Majesty's forces by or under Parts II and III; and
- (e) the adequacy of the arrangements by virtue of which the duty imposed by section 55 is sought to be discharged—
  - (i) in relation to the members of the intelligence services; and
  - (ii) in connection with any of their activities in places other than Northern Ireland, in relation to officials of the Ministry of Defence and members of Her Majesty's forces.

[(2A) The Intelligence Services Commissioner shall also keep under review—
- (a) the acquisition, storage and use by the intelligence services of information recorded in the National Identity Register;
- (b) the provision of such information to members of the intelligence services in accordance with any provision made by or under the Identity Cards Act 2006;
- (c) arrangements made by the Secretary of State or any of the intelligence services for the purposes of anything mentioned in paragraph (a) or (b).]

(3) The Intelligence Services Commissioner shall give the Tribunal all such assistance (including his opinion as to any issue falling to be determined by the Tribunal) as the Tribunal may require—
- (a) in connection with the investigation of any matter by the Tribunal; or
- (b) otherwise for the purposes of the Tribunal's consideration or determination of any matter.

(4) It shall not be the function of the Intelligence Services Commissioner to keep under review the exercise of any power of the Secretary of State to make, amend or revoke any subordinate legislation.

(5) A person shall not be appointed under this section as the Intelligence Services Commissioner unless he holds or has held a high judicial office (within the meaning of *the Appellate Jurisdiction Act 1876*).

(6) The Intelligence Services Commissioner shall hold office in accordance with the terms of his appointment; and there shall be paid to him out of money provided by Parliament such allowances as the Treasury may determine.

(7) The Secretary of State shall, after consultation with the Intelligence Services Commissioner and subject to the approval of the Treasury as to numbers, provide him with such staff as the Secretary of State considers necessary for the carrying out of the Commissioner's functions.

(8) …

(9) On the coming into force of this section the Commissioner holding office as the Commissioner under section 8 of the Intelligence Services Act 1994 shall take and hold office as the Intelligence Services Commissioner as if appointed under this Act—
- (a) for the unexpired period of his term of office under that Act; and
- (b) otherwise, on the terms of his appointment under that Act.

(10) Subsection (7) of section 41 shall apply for the purposes of this section as it applies for the purposes of that section.

[693]

NOTES

Commencement: 2 October 2000 (sub-ss (1), (2)(a), (3)–(10), sub-s (2)(b)–(e) in so far as relating to ss 26–48 of this Act); to be appointed (otherwise).

Sub-s (2): words in square brackets inserted by the Scotland Act 1998 (Transfer of Functions to the Scottish Ministers etc) (No 2) Order 2000, SI 2000/3253, art 4(1), Sch 3, Pt II, paras 3, 11.

Sub-s (2A): inserted by the Identity Cards Act 2006, s 24(1), (2), as from a day to be appointed.

Sub-s (5): for the words in italics there are substituted the words "Part 3 of the Constitutional Reform Act 2005) or is or has been a member of the Judicial Committee of the Privy Council" by the Constitutional Reform Act 2005, s 145, Sch 17, Pt 2, para 30(1), (2)(b), as from a day to be appointed.

Sub-s (8): repeals the Security Service Act 1989, s 4, and the Intelligence Services Act 1994, s 8.

60 Co-operation with and reports by s 59 Commissioner

(1) It shall be the duty of—
- (a) every member of an intelligence service,
- (b) every official of the department of the Secretary of State [and every member of staff of the Scottish Administration (by virtue of provision under section 63 of the Scotland Act 1998)], and
- (c) every member of Her Majesty's forces,

to disclose or provide to the Intelligence Services Commissioner all such documents and information as he may require for the purpose of enabling him to carry out his functions under section 59.

(2) As soon as practicable after the end of each calendar year, the Intelligence Services Commissioner shall make a report to the Prime Minister with respect to the carrying out of that Commissioner's functions.

PART II DATA PROTECTION

(3) The Intelligence Services Commissioner may also, at any time, make any such other report to the Prime Minister on any matter relating to the carrying out of the Commissioner's functions as the Commissioner thinks fit.

[(3A) The Intelligence Services Commissioner may also, at any time, make any such other report to the First Minister on any matter relating to the carrying out of the Commissioner's functions so far as they relate to the exercise by the Scottish Ministers (by virtue of provision made under section 63 of the Scotland Act 1998) of their powers under sections 5 and 6(3) and (4) of the Intelligence Services Act 1994 or under Parts I and II of this Act, as the Commissioner thinks fit.]

(4) The Prime Minister shall lay before each House of Parliament a copy of every annual report made by the Intelligence Services Commissioner under subsection (2), together with a statement as to whether any matter has been excluded from that copy in pursuance of subsection (5).

[(4A) The Prime Minister shall send a copy of every annual report made by the Intelligence Services Commissioner under subsection (2) which he lays in terms of subsection (4), together with a copy of the statement referred to in subsection (4), to the First Minister who shall forthwith lay that copy report and statement before the Scottish Parliament.]

(5) If it appears to the Prime Minister, after consultation with the Intelligence Services Commissioner [and, if it appears relevant to do so, with the First Minister], that the publication of any matter in an annual report would be contrary to the public interest or prejudicial to—

- (a) national security,
- (b) the prevention or detection of serious crime,
- (c) the economic well-being of the United Kingdom, or
- (d) the continued discharge of the functions of any public authority whose activities include activities that are subject to review by that Commissioner,

the Prime Minister may exclude that matter from the copy of the report as laid before each House of Parliament.

(6) Subsection (7) of section 41 shall apply for the purposes of this section as it applies for the purposes of that section.

[694]

NOTES

Sub-ss (1), (5): words in square brackets inserted by the Scotland Act 1998 (Transfer of Functions to the Scottish Ministers etc) (No 2) Order 2000, SI 2000/3253, art 4(1), Sch 3, Pt II, paras 3, 12(a), (d).

Sub-ss (3A), (4A): inserted by SI 2000/3253, art 4(1), Sch 3, Pt II, paras 3, 12(b), (c).

61 Investigatory Powers Commissioner for Northern Ireland

(1) The Prime Minister, after consultation with the First Minister and deputy First Minister in Northern Ireland, shall appoint a Commissioner to be known as the Investigatory Powers Commissioner for Northern Ireland.

(2) The Investigatory Powers Commissioner for Northern Ireland shall keep under review the exercise and performance in Northern Ireland, by the persons on whom they are conferred or imposed, of any powers or duties under Part II which are conferred or imposed by virtue of an order under section 30 made by the Office of the First Minister and deputy First Minister in Northern Ireland.

(3) The Investigatory Powers Commissioner for Northern Ireland shall give the Tribunal all such assistance (including his opinion as to any issue falling to be determined by the Tribunal) as the Tribunal may require—

- (a) in connection with the investigation of any matter by the Tribunal; or
- (b) otherwise for the purposes of the Tribunal's consideration or determination of any matter.

(4) It shall be the duty of—

- (a) every person by whom, or on whose application, there has been given or granted any authorisation the function of giving or granting which is subject to review by the Investigatory Powers Commissioner for Northern Ireland,
- (b) every person who has engaged in conduct with the authority of such an authorisation,

(c) every person who holds or has held any office, rank or position with the same public authority as a person falling within paragraph (a), and

(d) every person who holds or has held any office, rank or position with any public authority for whose benefit (within the meaning of Part II) activities which are or may be subject to any such review have been or may be carried out,

to disclose or provide to that Commissioner all such documents and information as he may require for the purpose of enabling him to carry out his functions.

(5) As soon as practicable after the end of each calendar year, the Investigatory Powers Commissioner for Northern Ireland shall make a report to the First Minister and deputy First Minister in Northern Ireland with respect to the carrying out of that Commissioner's functions.

(6) The First Minister and deputy First Minister in Northern Ireland shall lay before the Northern Ireland Assembly a copy of every annual report made by the Investigatory Powers Commissioner for Northern Ireland under subsection (5), together with a statement as to whether any matter has been excluded from that copy in pursuance of subsection (7).

(7) If it appears to the First Minister and deputy First Minister in Northern Ireland, after consultation with the Investigatory Powers Commissioner for Northern Ireland, that the publication of any matter in an annual report would be contrary to the public interest or prejudicial to—

(a) the prevention or detection of serious crime, or

(b) the continued discharge of the functions of any public authority whose activities include activities that are subject to review by that Commissioner,

they may exclude that matter from the copy of the report as laid before the Northern Ireland Assembly.

(8) A person shall not be appointed under this section as the Investigatory Powers Commissioner for Northern Ireland unless he holds or has held office in Northern Ireland—

(a) in any capacity in which he is or was the holder of a high judicial office (within the meaning of *the Appellate Jurisdiction Act 1876*); or

(b) as a county court judge.

(9) The Investigatory Powers Commissioner for Northern Ireland shall hold office in accordance with the terms of his appointment; and there shall be paid to him out of the Consolidated Fund of Northern Ireland such allowances as the Department of Finance and Personnel may determine.

(10) The First Minister and deputy First Minister in Northern Ireland shall, after consultation with the Investigatory Powers Commissioner for Northern Ireland, provide him with such staff as they consider necessary for the carrying out of his functions.

[695]

NOTES

Sub-s (8): for the words in italics there are substituted the words "Part 3 of the Constitutional Reform Act 2005" by the Constitutional Reform Act 2005, s 145, Sch 17, Pt 2, para 30(1), (3), as from a day to be appointed.

62 Additional functions of Chief Surveillance Commissioner

(1) The Chief Surveillance Commissioner shall (in addition to his functions under the Police Act 1997) keep under review, so far as they are not required to be kept under review by the Interception of Communications Commissioner, the Intelligence Services Commissioner or the Investigatory Powers Commissioner for Northern Ireland—

(a) the exercise and performance, by the persons on whom they are conferred or imposed, of the powers and duties conferred or imposed by or under Part II;

(b) the exercise and performance, by any person other than a judicial authority, of the powers and duties conferred or imposed, otherwise than with the permission of such an authority, by or under Part III; and

(c) the adequacy of the arrangements by virtue of which the duties imposed by section 55 are sought to be discharged in relation to persons whose conduct is subject to review under paragraph (b).

(2) It shall not by virtue of this section be the function of the Chief Surveillance Commissioner to keep under review the exercise of any power of the Secretary of State to make, amend or revoke any subordinate legislation.

(3) In this section "judicial authority" means—
- (a) any judge of the High Court or of the Crown Court or any Circuit Judge;
- (b) any judge of the High Court of Justiciary or any sheriff;
- (c) any justice of the peace;
- (d) any county court judge or resident magistrate in Northern Ireland;
- (e) any person holding any such judicial office as entitles him to exercise the jurisdiction of a judge of the Crown Court or of a justice of the peace.

[696]

NOTES

Commencement: 25 September 2000 (sub-ss (1)(a), (2), (3)); to be appointed (otherwise).

63 Assistant Surveillance Commissioners

(1) The Prime Minister may, after consultation with the Chief Surveillance Commissioner as to numbers, appoint as Assistant Surveillance Commissioners such number of persons as the Prime Minister considers necessary (in addition to the ordinary Surveillance Commissioners) for the purpose of providing the Chief Surveillance Commissioner with assistance under this section.

(2) A person shall not be appointed as an Assistant Surveillance Commissioner unless he holds or has held office as—
- (a) a judge of the Crown Court or a Circuit judge;
- (b) a sheriff in Scotland; or
- (c) a county court judge in Northern Ireland.

(3) The Chief Surveillance Commissioner may—
- (a) require any ordinary Surveillance Commissioner or any Assistant Surveillance Commissioner to provide him with assistance in carrying out his functions under section 62(1); or
- (b) require any Assistant Surveillance Commissioner to provide him with assistance in carrying out his equivalent functions under any Act of the Scottish Parliament in relation to any provisions of such an Act that are equivalent to those of Part II of this Act.

(4) The assistance that may be provided under this section includes—
- (a) the conduct on behalf of the Chief Surveillance Commissioner of the review of any matter; and
- (b) the making of a report to the Chief Surveillance Commissioner about the matter reviewed.

(5) Subsections (3) to (8) of section 91 of the Police Act 1997 (Commissioners) apply in relation to a person appointed under this section as they apply in relation to a person appointed under that section.

[697]

64 Delegation of Commissioners' functions

(1) Anything authorised or required by or under any enactment or any provision of an Act of the Scottish Parliament to be done by a relevant Commissioner may be done by any member of the staff of that Commissioner who is authorised for the purpose (whether generally or specifically) by that Commissioner.

(2) In this section "relevant Commissioner" means the Interception of Communications Commissioner, the Intelligence Services Commissioner, the Investigatory Powers Commissioner for Northern Ireland or any Surveillance Commissioner or Assistant Surveillance Commissioner.

[698]

The Tribunal

65 The Tribunal

(1) There shall, for the purpose of exercising the jurisdiction conferred on them by this section, be a tribunal consisting of such number of members as Her Majesty may by Letters Patent appoint.

(2) The jurisdiction of the Tribunal shall be—

(a) to be the only appropriate tribunal for the purposes of section 7 of the Human Rights Act 1998 in relation to any proceedings under subsection (1)(a) of that section (proceedings for actions incompatible with Convention rights) which fall within subsection (3) of this section;

(b) to consider and determine any complaints made to them which, in accordance with subsection (4) [or (4A)], are complaints for which the Tribunal is the appropriate forum;

(c) to consider and determine any reference to them by any person that he has suffered detriment as a consequence of any prohibition or restriction, by virtue of section 17, on his relying in, or for the purposes of, any civil proceedings on any matter; and

(d) to hear and determine any other such proceedings falling within subsection (3) as may be allocated to them in accordance with provision made by the Secretary of State by order.

(3) Proceedings fall within this subsection if—

(a) they are proceedings against any of the intelligence services;

(b) they are proceedings against any other person in respect of any conduct, or proposed conduct, by or on behalf of any of those services;

(c) they are proceedings brought by virtue of section 55(4); *or*

[(ca) they are proceedings relating to the provision to a member of any of the intelligence services of information recorded in an individual's entry in the National Identity Register;

(cb) they are proceedings relating to the acquisition, storage or use of such information by any of the intelligence services; or]

(d) they are proceedings relating to the taking place in any challengeable circumstances of any conduct falling within subsection (5).

(4) The Tribunal is the appropriate forum for any complaint if it is a complaint by a person who is aggrieved by any conduct falling within subsection (5) which he believes—

(a) to have taken place in relation to him, to any of his property, to any communications sent by or to him, or intended for him, or to his use of any postal service, telecommunications service or telecommunication system; and

(b) to have taken place in challengeable circumstances or to have been carried out by or on behalf of any of the intelligence services.

[(4A) The Tribunal is also the appropriate forum for a complaint if it is a complaint by an individual about what he believes to be—

(a) the provision to a member of any of the intelligence services of information recorded in that individual's entry in the National Identity Register; or

(b) the acquisition, storage or use of such information by any of the intelligence services.]

(5) Subject to subsection (6), conduct falls within this subsection if (whenever it occurred) it is—

(a) conduct by or on behalf of any of the intelligence services;

(b) conduct for or in connection with the interception of communications in the course of their transmission by means of a postal service or telecommunication system;

(c) conduct to which Chapter II of Part I applies;

[(ca) the carrying out of surveillance by a foreign police or customs officer (within the meaning of section 76A);]

(d) [other] conduct to which Part II applies;

(e) the giving of a notice under section 49 or any disclosure or use of a key to protected information;

(f) any entry on or interference with property or any interference with wireless telegraphy.

(6) For the purposes only of subsection (3), nothing mentioned in paragraph (d) or (f) of subsection (5) shall be treated as falling within that subsection unless it is conduct by or on behalf of a person holding any office, rank or position with—

(a) any of the intelligence services;

(b) any of Her Majesty's forces;

(c) any police force;

[(d) the Serious Organised Crime Agency; or]

(f) the Commissioners of Customs and Excise;

and section 48(5) applies for the purposes of this subsection as it applies for the purposes of Part II.

(7) For the purposes of this section conduct takes place in challengeable circumstances if—

(a) it takes place with the authority, or purported authority, of anything falling within subsection (8); or

(b) the circumstances are such that (whether or not there is such authority) it would not have been appropriate for the conduct to take place without it, or at least without proper consideration having been given to whether such authority should be sought;

but conduct does not take place in challengeable circumstances to the extent that it is authorised by, or takes place with the permission of, a judicial authority.

[(7A) For the purposes of this section conduct also takes place in challengeable circumstances if it takes place, or purports to take place, under section 76A.]

(8) The following fall within this subsection—

(a) an interception warrant or a warrant under the Interception of Communications Act 1985;

(b) an authorisation or notice under Chapter II of Part I of this Act;

(c) an authorisation under Part II of this Act or under any enactment contained in or made under an Act of the Scottish Parliament which makes provision equivalent to that made by that Part;

(d) a permission for the purposes of Schedule 2 to this Act;

(e) a notice under section 49 of this Act; or

(f) an authorisation under section 93 of the Police Act 1997.

(9) Schedule 3 (which makes further provision in relation to the Tribunal) shall have effect.

(10) In this section—

(a) references to a key and to protected information shall be construed in accordance with section 56;

(b) references to the disclosure or use of a key to protected information taking place in relation to a person are references to such a disclosure or use taking place in a case in which that person has had possession of the key or of the protected information; and

(c) references to the disclosure of a key to protected information include references to the making of any disclosure in an intelligible form (within the meaning of section 56) of protected information by a person who is or has been in possession of the key to that information;

and the reference in paragraph (b) to a person's having possession of a key or of protected information shall be construed in accordance with section 56.

(11) In this section "judicial authority" means—

(a) any judge of the High Court or of the Crown Court or any Circuit Judge;

(b) any judge of the High Court of Justiciary or any sheriff;

(c) any justice of the peace;

(d) any county court judge or resident magistrate in Northern Ireland;

(e) any person holding any such judicial office as entitles him to exercise the jurisdiction of a judge of the Crown Court or of a justice of the peace.

[699]

NOTES

Commencement: 2 October 2000 (sub-ss (1), (2)(a), (b), (3)(a), (b), (d), (4), (5)(a), (b), (d), (f), (6), (7), (8)(a), (c), (f), (9), (11)); 5 January 2004 (sub-ss (5)(c), (8)(b)); to be appointed (otherwise).

Sub-s (2): words in square brackets in para (b) inserted by the Identity Cards Act 2006, s 24(1), (3), as from a day to be appointed.

Sub-s (3): for the word in italics in para (c), there are substituted paras (ca), (cb) by the Identity Cards Act 2006, s 24(1), (4), as from a day to be appointed.

Sub-s (4A): inserted by the Identity Cards Act 2006, s 24(1), (5), as from a day to be appointed.

Sub-s (5): para (ca) and word in square brackets in para (d) inserted by the Crime (International Co-operation) Act 2003, s 91(1), Sch 5, paras 78, 79(a).

Sub-s (6): para (d) substituted for original paras (d), (e) by the Serious Organised Crime and Police Act 2005, s 59, Sch 4, paras 131, 151.

Sub-s (7A): inserted by the Crime (International Co-operation) Act 2003, s 91(1), Sch 5, paras 78, 79(b).

Modification: for the purposes of carrying out the functions of the Independent Police Complaints Commission, this section is modified by the Independent Police Complaints Commission (Investigatory Powers) Order 2004, SI 2004/815, art 3(1), (10).

66 Orders allocating proceedings to the Tribunal

(1) An order under section 65(2)(d) allocating proceedings to the Tribunal—

(a) may provide for the Tribunal to exercise jurisdiction in relation to that matter to the exclusion of the jurisdiction of any court or tribunal; but

(b) if it does so provide, must contain provision conferring a power on the Tribunal, in the circumstances provided for in the order, to remit the proceedings to the court or tribunal which would have had jurisdiction apart from the order.

(2) In making any provision by an order under section 65(2)(d) the Secretary of State shall have regard, in particular, to—

(a) the need to secure that proceedings allocated to the Tribunal are properly heard and considered; and

(b) the need to secure that information is not disclosed to an extent, or in a manner, that is contrary to the public interest or prejudicial to national security, the prevention or detection of serious crime, the economic well-being of the United Kingdom or the continued discharge of the functions of any of the intelligence services.

(3) The Secretary of State shall not make an order under section 65(2)(d) unless a draft of the order has been laid before Parliament and approved by a resolution of each House.
[700]

NOTES

Commencement: to be appointed.

67 Exercise of the Tribunal's jurisdiction

(1) Subject to subsections (4) and (5), it shall be the duty of the Tribunal—

(a) to hear and determine any proceedings brought before them by virtue of section 65(2)(a) or (d); and

(b) to consider and determine any complaint or reference made to them by virtue of section 65(2)(b) or (c).

(2) Where the Tribunal hear any proceedings by virtue of section 65(2)(a), they shall apply the same principles for making their determination in those proceedings as would be applied by a court on an application for judicial review.

(3) Where the Tribunal consider a complaint made to them by virtue of section 65(2)(b), it shall be the duty of the Tribunal—

(a) to investigate whether the persons against whom any allegations are made in the complaint have engaged in relation to—

(i) the complainant,

(ii) any of his property,

(iii) any communications sent by or to him, or intended for him, or

(iv) his use of any postal service, telecommunications service or telecommunication system,

in any conduct falling within section 65(5);

(b) to investigate the authority (if any) for any conduct falling within section 65(5) which they find has been so engaged in; and

(c) in relation to the Tribunal's findings from their investigations, to determine the complaint by applying the same principles as would be applied by a court on an application for judicial review.

(4) The Tribunal shall not be under any duty to hear, consider or determine any proceedings, complaint or reference if it appears to them that the bringing of the proceedings or the making of the complaint or reference is frivolous or vexatious.

(5) Except where the Tribunal, having regard to all the circumstances, are satisfied that it is equitable to do so, they shall not consider or determine any complaint made by virtue of section 65(2)(b) if it is made more than one year after the taking place of the conduct to which it relates.

(6) Subject to any provision made by rules under section 69, where any proceedings have been brought before the Tribunal or any reference made to the Tribunal, they shall have power to make such interim orders, pending their final determination, as they think fit.

(7) Subject to any provision made by rules under section 69, the Tribunal on determining any proceedings, complaint or reference shall have power to make any such award of compensation or other order as they think fit; and, without prejudice to the power to make rules under section 69(2)(h), the other orders that may be made by the Tribunal include—

(a) an order quashing or cancelling any warrant or authorisation; and

(b) an order requiring the destruction of any records of information which—

(i) has been obtained in exercise of any power conferred by a warrant or authorisation; or

(ii) is held by any public authority in relation to any person.

(8) Except to such extent as the Secretary of State may by order otherwise provide, determinations, awards, orders and other decisions of the Tribunal (including decisions as to whether they have jurisdiction) shall not be subject to appeal or be liable to be questioned in any court.

(9) It shall be the duty of the Secretary of State to secure that there is at all times an order under subsection (8) in force allowing for an appeal to a court against any exercise by the Tribunal of their jurisdiction under section 65(2)(c) or (d).

(10) The provision that may be contained in an order under subsection (8) may include—

(a) provision for the establishment and membership of a tribunal or body to hear appeals;

(b) the appointment of persons to that tribunal or body and provision about the remuneration and allowances to be payable to such persons and the expenses of the tribunal;

(c) the conferring of jurisdiction to hear appeals on any existing court or tribunal; and

(d) any such provision in relation to an appeal under the order as corresponds to provision that may be made by rules under section 69 in relation to proceedings before the Tribunal, or to complaints or references made to the Tribunal.

(11) The Secretary of State shall not make an order under subsection (8) unless a draft of the order has been laid before Parliament and approved by a resolution of each House.

(12) The Secretary of State shall consult the Scottish Ministers before making any order under subsection (8); and any such order shall be laid before the Scottish Parliament.

[701]

NOTES

Commencement: 2 October 2000 (sub-s (1), to the extent that it relates to s 65(2)(a), (b), sub-ss (2)–(8), (10)–(12)); to be appointed (otherwise).

68 Tribunal procedure

(1) Subject to any rules made under section 69, the Tribunal shall be entitled to determine their own procedure in relation to any proceedings, complaint or reference brought before or made to them.

(2) The Tribunal shall have power—

(a) in connection with the investigation of any matter, or

(b) otherwise for the purposes of the Tribunal's consideration or determination of any matter,

to require a relevant Commissioner appearing to the Tribunal to have functions in relation to the matter in question to provide the Tribunal with all such assistance (including that Commissioner's opinion as to any issue falling to be determined by the Tribunal) as the Tribunal think fit.

(3) Where the Tribunal hear or consider any proceedings, complaint or reference relating to any matter, they shall secure that every relevant Commissioner appearing to them to have functions in relation to that matter—

(a) is aware that the matter is the subject of proceedings, a complaint or a reference brought before or made to the Tribunal; and

(b) is kept informed of any determination, award, order or other decision made by the Tribunal with respect to that matter.

(4) Where the Tribunal determine any proceedings, complaint or reference brought before or made to them, they shall give notice to the complainant which (subject to any rules made by virtue of section 69(2)(i)) shall be confined, as the case may be, to either—

(a) a statement that they have made a determination in his favour; or

(b) a statement that no determination has been made in his favour.

(5) Where—

(a) the Tribunal make a determination in favour of any person by whom any proceedings have been brought before the Tribunal or by whom any complaint or reference has been made to the Tribunal, and

(b) the determination relates to any act or omission by or on behalf of the Secretary of State or to conduct for which any warrant, authorisation or permission was issued, granted or given by the Secretary of State,

they shall make a report of their findings to the Prime Minister.

(6) It shall be the duty of the persons specified in subsection (7) to disclose or provide to the Tribunal all such documents and information as the Tribunal may require for the purpose of enabling them—

(a) to exercise the jurisdiction conferred on them by or under section 65; or

(b) otherwise to exercise or perform any power or duty conferred or imposed on them by or under this Act.

(7) Those persons are—

(a) every person holding office under the Crown;

[(b) every member of the staff of the Serious Organised Crime Agency;]

(d) every person employed by or for the purposes of a police force;

(e) every person required for the purposes of section 11 to provide assistance with giving effect to an interception warrant;

(f) every person on whom an obligation to take any steps has been imposed under section 12;

(g) every person by or to whom an authorisation under section 22(3) has been granted;

(h) every person to whom a notice under section 22(4) has been given;

(i) every person by whom, or on whose application, there has been granted or given any authorisation under Part II of this Act or under Part III of the Police Act 1997;

(j) every person who holds or has held any office, rank or position with the same public authority as a person falling within paragraph (i);

(k) every person who has engaged in any conduct with the authority of an authorisation under section 22 or Part II of this Act or under Part III of the Police Act 1997;

(l) every person who holds or has held any office, rank or position with a public authority for whose benefit any such authorisation has been or may be given;

(m) every person to whom a notice under section 49 has been given; and

(n) every person who is or has been employed for the purposes of any business of a person falling within paragraph (e), (f), (h) or (m).

(8) In this section "relevant Commissioner" means the Interception of Communications Commissioner, the Intelligence Services Commissioner, the Investigatory Powers Commissioner for Northern Ireland or any Surveillance Commissioner or Assistant Surveillance Commissioner.

[702]

NOTES

Commencement: 2 October 2000 (sub-ss (1)–(6), (7)(a)–(f), (i)–(l), (n) except in respect of para (m), (8)); 5 January 2004 (sub-s (7)(g), (h)); to be appointed (otherwise).

Sub-s (7): para (b) substituted for original paras (b), (c) by the Serious Organised Crime and Police Act 2005, s 59, Sch 4, paras 131, 152.

Modification: for the purposes of carrying out the functions of the Independent Police Complaints Commission, this section is modified by the Independent Police Complaints Commission (Investigatory Powers) Order 2004, SI 2004/815, art 3(1), (11).

69 Tribunal rules

(1) The Secretary of State may make rules regulating—

(a) the exercise by the Tribunal of the jurisdiction conferred on them by or under section 65; and

(b) any matters preliminary or incidental to, or arising out of, the hearing or consideration of any proceedings, complaint or reference brought before or made to the Tribunal.

(2) Without prejudice to the generality of subsection (1), rules under this section may—

(a) enable the jurisdiction of the Tribunal to be exercised at any place in the United Kingdom by any two or more members of the Tribunal designated for the purpose by the President of the Tribunal;

(b) enable different members of the Tribunal to carry out functions in relation to different complaints at the same time;

(c) prescribe the form and manner in which proceedings are to be brought before the Tribunal or a complaint or reference is to be made to the Tribunal;

(d) require persons bringing proceedings or making complaints or references to take such preliminary steps, and to make such disclosures, as may be specified in the rules for the purpose of facilitating a determination of whether—

(i) the bringing of the proceedings, or

(ii) the making of the complaint or reference,

is frivolous or vexatious;

(e) make provision about the determination of any question as to whether a person by whom—

(i) any proceedings have been brought before the Tribunal, or

(ii) any complaint or reference has been made to the Tribunal,

is a person with a right to bring those proceedings or make that complaint or reference;

(f) prescribe the forms of hearing or consideration to be adopted by the Tribunal in relation to particular proceedings, complaints or references (including a form that requires any proceedings brought before the Tribunal to be disposed of as if they were a complaint or reference made to the Tribunal);

(g) prescribe the practice and procedure to be followed on, or in connection with, the hearing or consideration of any proceedings, complaint or reference (including, where applicable, the mode and burden of proof and the admissibility of evidence);

(h) prescribe orders that may be made by the Tribunal under section 67(6) or (7);

(i) require information about any determination, award, order or other decision made by the Tribunal in relation to any proceedings, complaint or reference to be provided (in addition to any statement under section 68(4)) to the person who brought the proceedings or made the complaint or reference, or to the person representing his interests.

(3) Rules under this section in relation to the hearing or consideration of any matter by the Tribunal may provide—

(a) for a person who has brought any proceedings before or made any complaint or reference to the Tribunal to have the right to be legally represented;

(b) for the manner in which the interests of a person who has brought any proceedings before or made any complaint or reference to the Tribunal are otherwise to be represented;

(c) for the appointment in accordance with the rules, by such person as may be determined in accordance with the rules, of a person to represent those interests in the case of any proceedings, complaint or reference.

(4) The power to make rules under this section includes power to make rules—

(a) enabling or requiring the Tribunal to hear or consider any proceedings, complaint or reference without the person who brought the proceedings or made the complaint or reference having been given full particulars of the reasons for any conduct which is the subject of the proceedings, complaint or reference;

(b) enabling or requiring the Tribunal to take any steps in exercise of their jurisdiction in the absence of any person (including the person bringing the proceedings or making the complaint or reference and any legal representative of his);

(c) enabling or requiring the Tribunal to give a summary of any evidence taken in his absence to the person by whom the proceedings were brought or, as the case may be, to the person who made the complaint or reference;

(d) enabling or requiring the Tribunal to exercise their jurisdiction, and to exercise and perform the powers and duties conferred or imposed on them (including, in particular, in relation to the giving of reasons), in such manner provided for in the rules as prevents or limits the disclosure of particular matters.

(5) Rules under this section may also include provision—

(a) enabling powers or duties of the Tribunal that relate to matters preliminary or incidental to the hearing or consideration of any proceedings, complaint or reference to be exercised or performed by a single member of the Tribunal; and

(b) conferring on the Tribunal such ancillary powers as the Secretary of State thinks necessary for the purposes of, or in connection with, the exercise of the Tribunal's jurisdiction, or the exercise or performance of any power or duty conferred or imposed on them.

(6) In making rules under this section the Secretary of State shall have regard, in particular, to—

(a) the need to secure that matters which are the subject of proceedings, complaints or references brought before or made to the Tribunal are properly heard and considered; and

(b) the need to secure that information is not disclosed to an extent, or in a manner, that is contrary to the public interest or prejudicial to national security, the prevention or detection of serious crime, the economic wellbeing of the United Kingdom or the continued discharge of the functions of any of the intelligence services.

(7) Rules under this section may make provision by the application, with or without modification, of the provision from time to time contained in specified rules of court.

(8) Subject to subsection (9), no rules shall be made under this section unless a draft of them has first been laid before Parliament and approved by a resolution of each House.

(9) Subsection (8) does not apply in the case of the rules made on the first occasion on which the Secretary of State exercises his power to make rules under this section.

(10) The rules made on that occasion shall cease to have effect at the end of the period of forty days beginning with the day on which they were made unless, before the end of that period, they have been approved by a resolution of each House of Parliament.

(11) For the purposes of subsection (10)—

(a) the rules' ceasing to have effect shall be without prejudice to anything previously done or to the making of new rules; and

(b) in reckoning the period of forty days no account shall be taken of any period during which Parliament is dissolved or prorogued or during which both Houses are adjourned for more than four days.

(12) The Secretary of State shall consult the Scottish Ministers before making any rules under this section; and any rules so made shall be laid before the Scottish Parliament.

[703]

NOTES

Rules: the Investigatory Powers Tribunal Rules 2000, SI 2000/2665 at **[997]**.

70 Abolition of jurisdiction in relation to complaints

(1) The provisions set out in subsection (2) (which provide for the investigation etc of certain complaints) shall not apply in relation to any complaint made after the coming into force of this section.

(2) Those provisions are—

(a) section 5 of, and Schedules 1 and 2 to, the Security Service Act 1989 (investigation of complaints about the Security Service made to the Tribunal established under that Act);

(b) section 9 of, and Schedules 1 and 2 to, the Intelligence Services Act 1994 (investigation of complaints about the Secret Intelligence Service or GCHQ made to the Tribunal established under that Act); and

(c) section 102 of, and Schedule 7 to, the Police Act 1997 (investigation of complaints made to the Surveillance Commissioners).

[704]

Codes of practice

71 Issue and revision of codes of practice

(1) The Secretary of State shall issue one or more codes of practice relating to the exercise and performance of the powers and duties mentioned in subsection (2).

(2) Those powers and duties are those (excluding any power to make subordinate legislation) that are conferred or imposed otherwise than on the Surveillance Commissioners by or under—

- (a) Parts I to III of this Act;
- (b) section 5 of the Intelligence Services Act 1994 (warrants for interference with property or wireless telegraphy for the purposes of the intelligence services); and
- (c) Part III of the Police Act 1997 (authorisation by the police or customs and excise of interference with property or wireless telegraphy).

(3) Before issuing a code of practice under subsection (1), the Secretary of State shall—

- (a) prepare and publish a draft of that code; and
- (b) consider any representations made to him about the draft; and the Secretary of State may incorporate in the code finally issued any modifications made by him to the draft after its publication.

(4) The Secretary of State shall lay before both Houses of Parliament every draft code of practice prepared and published by him under this section.

(5) A code of practice issued by the Secretary of State under this section shall not be brought into force except in accordance with an order made by the Secretary of State.

(6) An order under subsection (5) may contain such transitional provisions and savings as appear to the Secretary of State to be necessary or expedient in connection with the bringing into force of the code brought into force by that order.

(7) The Secretary of State may from time to time—

- (a) revise the whole or any part of a code issued under this section; and
- (b) issue the revised code.

(8) Subsections (3) to (6) shall apply (with appropriate modifications) in relation to the issue of any revised code under this section as they apply in relation to the first issue of such a code.

(9) The Secretary of State shall not make an order containing provision for any of the purposes of this section unless a draft of the order has been laid before Parliament and approved by a resolution of each House.

[705]

NOTES

Commencement: 25 September 2000 (in so far as relating to ss 26–48 of this Act, the Intelligence Services Act 1994, s 5 or the Police Act 1997, Pt III); 2 October 2000 (in so far as relating to ss 1–20 of this Act); 13 August 2001 (in so far as relating to ss 21–25 of this Act); to be appointed (otherwise).

Orders: the Regulation of Investigatory Powers (Interception of Communications: Code of Practice) Order 2002, SI 2002/1693; the Regulation of Investigatory Powers (Covert Human Intelligence Sources: Code of Practice) Order 2002, SI 2002/1932; the Regulation of Investigatory Powers (Covert Surveillance: Code of Practice) Order 2002, SI 2002/1933.

72 Effect of codes of practice

(1) A person exercising or performing any power or duty in relation to which provision may be made by a code of practice under section 71 shall, in doing so, have regard to the provisions (so far as they are applicable) of every code of practice for the time being in force under that section.

(2) A failure on the part of any person to comply with any provision of a code of practice for the time being in force under section 71 shall not of itself render him liable to any criminal or civil proceedings.

(3) A code of practice in force at any time under section 71 shall be admissible in evidence in any criminal or civil proceedings.

(4) If any provision of a code of practice issued or revised under section 71 appears to—

- (a) the court or tribunal conducting any civil or criminal proceedings,

(b) the Tribunal,
(c) a relevant Commissioner carrying out any of his functions under this Act,
(d) a Surveillance Commissioner carrying out his functions under this Act or the Police Act 1997, or
(e) any Assistant Surveillance Commissioner carrying out any functions of his under section 63 of this Act,

to be relevant to any question arising in the proceedings, or in connection with the exercise of that jurisdiction or the carrying out of those functions, in relation to a time when it was in force, that provision of the code shall be taken into account in determining that question.

(5) In this section "relevant Commissioner" means the Interception of Communications Commissioner, the Intelligence Services Commissioner or the Investigatory Powers Commissioner for Northern Ireland.

[706]

NOTES

Commencement: 25 September 2000 (in so far as relating to ss 26–48 of this Act, the Intelligence Services Act 1994, s 5 or the Police Act 1997, Pt III); 2 October 2000 (in so far as relating to ss 1–20 of this Act); 13 August 2001 (in so far as relating to ss 21–25 of this Act); to be appointed (otherwise).

PART V
MISCELLANEOUS AND SUPPLEMENTAL

Miscellaneous

73–75 (*S 73 repealed by the Wireless Telegraphy Act 2006, s 125(1), Sch 9, Pt 1, subject to transitional provisions and savings in s 124 of, Sch 8, Pt 1, paras 1–8, 24 to, that Act at* **[4230]**, **[4239]**; *s 74 amends the Intelligence Services Act 1994, ss 5–7, 11; s 75 amends the Police Act 1997, s 93.*)

76 Surveillance etc operations beginning in Scotland

(1) Subject to subsection (2), where—
(a) an authorisation under the relevant Scottish legislation has the effect of authorising the carrying out in Scotland of the conduct described in the authorisation,
(b) the conduct so described is or includes conduct to which Part II of this Act applies, and
(c) circumstances arise by virtue of which some or all of the conduct so described can for the time being be carried out only outwith Scotland,

section 27 of this Act shall have effect for the purpose of making lawful the carrying out outwith Scotland of the conduct so described as if the authorisation, so far as is it relates to conduct to which that Part applies, were an authorisation duly granted under that Part.

(2) Where any such circumstances as are mentioned in paragraph (c) of subsection (1) so arise as to give effect outwith Scotland to any authorisation granted under the relevant Scottish legislation, that authorisation shall not authorise any conduct outwith Scotland at any time after the end of the period of three weeks beginning with the time when the circumstances arose.

(3) Subsection (2) is without prejudice to the operation of subsection (1) in relation to any authorisation on the second or any subsequent occasion on which any such circumstances as are mentioned in subsection (1)(c) arise while the authorisation remains in force.

(4) In this section "the relevant Scottish legislation" means an enactment contained in or made under an Act of the Scottish Parliament which makes provision, corresponding to that made by Part II, for the authorisation of conduct to which that Part applies.

[707]

[76A Foreign surveillance operations

(1) This section applies where—
(a) a foreign police or customs officer is carrying out relevant surveillance outside the United Kingdom which is lawful under the law of the country or territory in which it is being carried out;

(b) circumstances arise by virtue of which the surveillance can for the time being be carried out only in the United Kingdom; and

(c) it is not reasonably practicable in those circumstances for a United Kingdom officer to carry out the surveillance in the United Kingdom in accordance with an authorisation under Part 2 or the Regulation of Investigatory Powers (Scotland) Act 2000.

(2) "Relevant surveillance" means surveillance which—

(a) is carried out in relation to a person who is suspected of having committed a relevant crime; and

(b) is, for the purposes of Part 2, directed surveillance or intrusive surveillance.

(3) "Relevant crime" means crime which—

(a) falls within Article 40(7) of the Schengen Convention; or

(b) is crime for the purposes of any other international agreement to which the United Kingdom is a party and which is specified for the purposes of this section in an order made by the Secretary of State with the consent of the Scottish Ministers.

(4) Relevant surveillance carried out by the foreign police or customs officer in the United Kingdom during the permitted period is to be lawful for all purposes if—

(a) the condition mentioned in subsection (6) is satisfied;

(b) the officer carries out the surveillance only in places to which members of the public have or are permitted to have access, whether on payment or otherwise; and

(c) conditions specified in any order made by the Secretary of State with the consent of the Scottish Ministers are satisfied in relation to its carrying out;

but no surveillance is lawful by virtue of this subsection if the officer subsequently seeks to stop and question the person in the United Kingdom in relation to the relevant crime.

(5) The officer is not to be subject to any civil liability in respect of any conduct of his which is incidental to any surveillance that is lawful by virtue of subsection (4).

(6) The condition in this subsection is satisfied if, immediately after the officer enters the United Kingdom—

(a) he notifies a person designated by the Director General of the [Serious Organised Crime Agency] of that fact; and

(b) (if the officer has not done so before) he requests an application to be made for an authorisation under Part 2, or the Regulation of Investigatory Powers (Scotland) Act 2000, for the carrying out of the surveillance.

(7) "The permitted period" means the period of five hours beginning with the time when the officer enters the United Kingdom.

(8) But a person designated by an order made by the Secretary of State may notify the officer that the surveillance is to cease being lawful by virtue of subsection (4) when he gives the notification.

(9) The Secretary of State is not to make an order under subsection (4) unless a draft of the order has been laid before Parliament and approved by a resolution of each House.

(10) In this section references to a foreign police or customs officer are to a police or customs officer who, in relation to a country or territory other than the United Kingdom, is an officer for the purposes of—

(a) Article 40 of the Schengen Convention; or

(b) any other international agreement to which the United Kingdom is a party and which is specified for the purposes of this section in an order made by the Secretary of State with the consent of the Scottish Ministers.

(11) In this section—

"the Schengen Convention" means the Convention implementing the Schengen Agreement of 14th June 1985;

"United Kingdom officer" means—

(a) a member of a police force;

(b) a member of the [staff of the Serious Organised Crime Agency];

(c) *a member of … the Scottish Crime Squad (within the meaning of the Regulation of Investigatory Powers (Scotland) Act 2000);*

(d) a customs officer.]

[707A]

NOTES

Commencement: 26 April 2004.

Inserted by the Crime (International Co-operation) Act 2003, s 83.

Sub-s (6): words in square brackets substituted by the Serious Organised Crime and Police Act 2005, s 59, Sch 4, paras 131, 154(1), (2).

Sub-s (11): in the definition "United Kingdom officer" words in square brackets in para (b) substituted and words omitted from para (c) repealed by the Serious Organised Crime and Police Act 2005, ss 59, 174(2), Sch 4, paras 131, 154(1), (3), Sch 17, Pt 2; para (c) substituted by the Police, Public Order and Criminal Justice (Scotland) Act 2006, s 101, Sch 6, Pt 1, para 8, as from a day to be appointed, as follows:

"(c) a police member of the Scottish Crime and Drug Enforcement Agency appointed in accordance with paragraph 7 of schedule 2 to the Police, Public Order and Criminal Justice (Scotland) Act 2006 (asp 10);".

Orders: the Regulation of Investigatory Powers (Foreign Surveillance Operations) Order 2004, SI 2004/1128.

Supplemental

77 Ministerial expenditure etc

There shall be paid out of money provided by Parliament—

(a) any expenditure incurred by the Secretary of State for or in connection with the carrying out of his functions under this Act; and

(b) any increase attributable to this Act in the sums which are payable out of money so provided under any other Act.

[708]

78 Orders, regulations and rules

(1) This section applies to any power of the Secretary of State to make any order, regulations or rules under any provision of this Act.

(2) The powers to which this section applies shall be exercisable by statutory instrument.

(3) A statutory instrument which contains any order made in exercise of a power to which this section applies (other than the power to appoint a day under section 83(2)) but which contains neither—

(a) an order a draft of which has been approved for the purposes of section 12(10), 13(3), 22(9), 25(5), 28(5), 29(6), 30(7), 35(5), 41(6), 47(2), 66(3), 67(11)[, 71(9) or 76A(9)], nor

(b) the order to which section 35(7) applies,

shall be subject to annulment in pursuance of a resolution of either House of Parliament.

(4) A statutory instrument containing any regulations made in exercise of a power to which this section applies shall be subject to annulment in pursuance of a resolution of either House of Parliament.

(5) Any order, regulations or rules made in exercise of a power to which this section applies may—

(a) make different provisions for different cases;

(b) contain such incidental, supplemental, consequential and transitional provision as the Secretary of State thinks fit.

[709]

NOTES

Sub-s (3): words in square brackets substituted by the Crime (International Co-operation) Act 2003, s 91(1), Sch 5, paras 78, 80.

Orders: the Regulation of Investigatory Powers (Directed Surveillance and Covert Human Intelligence Sources) Order 2003, SI 2003/3171 at **[1089]**; the Regulation of Investigatory Powers (Communications Data) Order 2003, SI 2003/3172 at **[1099]**.

79 Criminal liability of directors etc

(1) Where an offence under any provision of this Act other than a provision of Part III is committed by a body corporate and is proved to have been committed with the consent or connivance of, or to be attributable to any neglect on the part of—

(a) a director, manager, secretary or other similar officer of the body corporate, or
(b) any person who was purporting to act in any such capacity,

he (as well as the body corporate) shall be guilty of that offence and liable to be proceeded against and punished accordingly.

(2) Where an offence under any provision of this Act other than a provision of Part III—
(a) is committed by a Scottish firm, and
(b) is proved to have been committed with the consent or connivance of, or to be attributable to any neglect on the part of, a partner of the firm,

he (as well as the firm) shall be guilty of that offence and liable to be proceeded against and punished accordingly.

(3) In this section "director", in relation to a body corporate whose affairs are managed by its members, means a member of the body corporate.

[710]

80 General saving for lawful conduct

Nothing in any of the provisions of this Act by virtue of which conduct of any description is or may be authorised by any warrant, authorisation or notice, or by virtue of which information may be obtained in any manner, shall be construed—
(a) as making it unlawful to engage in any conduct of that description which is not otherwise unlawful under this Act and would not be unlawful apart from this Act;
(b) as otherwise requiring—
(i) the issue, grant or giving of such a warrant, authorisation or notice, or
(ii) the taking of any step for or towards obtaining the authority of such a warrant, authorisation or notice,

before any such conduct of that description is engaged in; or
(c) as prejudicing any power to obtain information by any means not involving conduct that may be authorised under this Act.

[711]

81 General interpretation

(1) In this Act—

"apparatus" includes any equipment, machinery or device and any wire or cable;

"Assistant Commissioner of Police of the Metropolis" includes the Deputy Commissioner of Police of the Metropolis;

"Assistant Surveillance Commissioner" means any person holding office under section 63;

"civil proceedings" means any proceedings in or before any court or tribunal that are not criminal proceedings;

"communication" includes—
(a) (except in the definition of "postal service" in section 2(1)) anything transmitted by means of a postal service;
(b) anything comprising speech, music, sounds, visual images or data of any description; and
(c) signals serving either for the impartation of anything between persons, between a person and a thing or between things or for the actuation or control of any apparatus;

"criminal", in relation to any proceedings or prosecution, shall be construed in accordance with subsection (4);

"customs officer" means an officer commissioned by the Commissioners of Customs and Excise under section 6(3) of the Customs and Excise Management Act 1979;

"document" includes a map, plan, design, drawing, picture or other image;

"enactment" includes—
(a) an enactment passed after the passing of this Act; and
(b) an enactment contained in Northern Ireland legislation;

"GCHQ" has the same meaning as in the Intelligence Services Act 1994;

"Her Majesty's forces" has the same meaning as in the *Army Act 1955*;

"intelligence service" means the Security Service, the Secret Intelligence Service or GCHQ;

"interception" and cognate expressions shall be construed (so far as it is applicable) in accordance with section 2;

"interception warrant" means a warrant under section 5;

["justice of the peace" does not include a justice of the peace in Northern Ireland;]

"legal proceedings" means civil or criminal proceedings in or before any court or tribunal [or proceedings before an officer in respect of a service offence within the meaning of the Armed Forces Act 2006];

"modification" includes alterations, additions and omissions, and cognate expressions shall be construed accordingly;

"ordinary Surveillance Commissioner" means a Surveillance Commissioner other than the Chief Surveillance Commissioner;

"person" includes any organisation and any association or combination of persons;

"police force" means any of the following—

(a) any police force maintained under section 2 of the Police Act 1996 (police forces in England and Wales outside London);

(b) the metropolitan police force;

(c) the City of London police force;

(d) any police force maintained under or by virtue of section 1 of the Police (Scotland) Act 1967;

(e) the [Police Service of Northern Ireland];

(f) the Ministry of Defence Police;

(g) the *Royal Navy Regulating Branch*;

(h) the Royal Military Police;

(i) the Royal Air Force Police;

(j) the British Transport Police;

"postal service" and "public postal service" have the meanings given by section 2(1);

"private telecommunication system", "public telecommunications service" and "public telecommunication system" have the meanings given by section 2(1);

"public authority" means any public authority within the meaning of section 6 of the Human Rights Act 1998 (acts of public authorities) other than a court or tribunal;

"senior official" means, subject to subsection (7), a member of the Senior Civil Service or a member of the Senior Management Structure of Her Majesty's Diplomatic Service;

"statutory", in relation to any power or duty, means conferred or imposed by or under any enactment or subordinate legislation;

"subordinate legislation" means any subordinate legislation (within the meaning of the Interpretation Act 1978) or any statutory rules (within the meaning of the Statutory Rules (Northern Ireland) Order 1979);

"Surveillance Commissioner" means a Commissioner holding office under section 91 of the Police Act 1997 and "Chief Surveillance Commissioner" shall be construed accordingly;

"telecommunication system" and "telecommunications service" have the meanings given by section 2(1);

"the Tribunal" means the tribunal established under section 65;

"wireless telegraphy" has the same meaning as in [the Wireless Telegraphy Act 2006] and, in relation to wireless telegraphy, "interfere" has the same meaning as in that Act;

"working day" means any day other than a Saturday, a Sunday, Christmas Day, Good Friday or a day which is a bank holiday under the Banking and Financial Dealings Act 1971 in any part of the United Kingdom.

(2) In this Act—

(a) references to crime are references to conduct which constitutes one or more criminal offences or is, or corresponds to, any conduct which, if it all took place in any one part of the United Kingdom would constitute one or more criminal offences; and

(b) references to serious crime are references to crime that satisfies the test in subsection (3)(a) or (b).

(3) Those tests are—

(a) that the offence or one of the offences that is or would be constituted by the conduct is an offence for which a person who has attained the age of twenty-one [(eighteen in relation to England and Wales)] and has no previous convictions could reasonably be expected to be sentenced to imprisonment for a term of three years or more;

(b) that the conduct involves the use of violence, results in substantial financial gain or is conduct by a large number of persons in pursuit of a common purpose.

(4) In this Act "criminal proceedings" includes—

(*a*) *proceedings in the United Kingdom or elsewhere before—*

PART II DATA PROTECTION

(i) *a court-martial constituted under the Army Act 1955, the Air Force Act 1955 or the Naval Discipline Act 1957; ...*

(ii) ... ;

(b) *proceedings before the Courts-Martial Appeal Court; and*

(c) *proceedings before a Standing Civilian Court;*

and references in this Act to criminal prosecutions shall be construed accordingly.

(5) For the purposes of this Act detecting crime shall be taken to include—

(a) establishing by whom, for what purpose, by what means and generally in what circumstances any crime was committed; and

(b) the apprehension of the person by whom any crime was committed;

and any reference in this Act to preventing or detecting serious crime shall be construed accordingly, except that, in Chapter I of Part I, it shall not include a reference to gathering evidence for use in any legal proceedings.

(6) In this Act—

(a) references to a person holding office under the Crown include references to any servant of the Crown and to any member of Her Majesty's forces; and

(b) references to a member of a police force, in relation to the *Royal Navy Regulating Branch*, the Royal Military Police or the Royal Air Force Police, do not include references to any member of *that Branch or Force who is not for the time being attached to or serving either with the Branch or Force of which he is a member or with another of those police forces.*

(7) If it appears to the Secretary of State that it is necessary to do so in consequence of any changes to the structure or grading of the home civil service or diplomatic service, he may by order make such amendments of the definition of "senior official" in subsection (1) as appear to him appropriate to preserve, so far as practicable, the effect of that definition.

[712]

NOTES

Sub-s (1): for the words in italics in definition "Her Majesty's forces" there are substituted the words "Armed Forces Act 2006", words in square brackets in definition "legal proceedings" inserted and in definition "police force" for the words in italics in para (g) there are substituted the words "Royal Navy Police", by the Armed Forces Act 2006, s 378(1), Sch 16, para 175(1), (2), as from a day to be appointed; definition "justice of the peace" inserted by the Justice (Northern Ireland) Act 2002, s 10(6), Sch 4, para 40; in definition "police force" words in square brackets in para (e) substituted by the Police (Northern Ireland) Act 2000, s 78(2)(f); words in square brackets in definition "wireless telegraphy" substituted by the Wireless Telegraphy Act 2006, s 123, Sch 7, paras 21, 24.

Sub-s (3): words in square brackets in para (a) inserted by the Criminal Justice and Court Services Act 2000, s 74, Sch 7, Pt II, para 211, as from a day to be appointed.

Sub-s (4): para (a)(ii) and the word immediately preceding it repealed by the Armed Forces Act 2001, s 38, Sch 7, Pt 1; for paras (a)–(c) there are substituted the words "proceedings before a court in respect of a service offence within the meaning of the Armed Forces Act 2006," by the Armed Forces Act 2006, s 378(1), Sch 16, para 175(1), (3), as from a day to be appointed.

Sub-s (6): in para (b), for the first words in italics there are substituted the words "Royal Navy Police" and for the second words in italics there are substituted the words "that force who is not for the time being attached to or serving either with that force or with another of those police forces" by the Armed Forces Act 2006, s 378(1), Sch 16, para 175(1), (4), as from a day to be appointed.

82 Amendments, repeals and savings etc

(1) The enactments specified in Schedule 4 (amendments consequential on the provisions of this Act) shall have effect with the amendments set out in that Schedule.

(2) The enactments mentioned in Schedule 5 are hereby repealed to the extent specified in the third column of that Schedule.

(3) For the avoidance of doubt it is hereby declared that nothing in this Act ... affects any power conferred on [a postal operator (within the meaning of the Postal Services Act 2000)] by or under any enactment to open, detain or delay any postal packet or to deliver any such packet to a person other than the person to whom it is addressed.

(4) Where any warrant under the Interception of Communications Act 1985 is in force under that Act at the time when the repeal by this Act of section 2 of that Act comes into force, the conduct authorised by that warrant shall be deemed for the period which—

(a) begins with that time, and

(b) ends with the time when that warrant would (without being renewed) have ceased to have effect under that Act, as if it were conduct authorised by an interception warrant issued in accordance with the requirements of Chapter I of Part I of this Act.

(5) In relation to any such warrant, any certificate issued for the purposes of section 3(2) of the Interception of Communications Act 1985 shall have effect in relation to that period as if it were a certificate issued for the purposes of section 8(4) of this Act.

(6) Sections 15 and 16 of this Act shall have effect as if references to interception warrants and to section 8(4) certificates included references, respectively, to warrants under section 2 of the Interception of Communications Act 1985 and to certificates under section 3(2) of that Act; and references in sections 15 and 16 of this Act to intercepted or certified material shall be construed accordingly.

[713]

NOTES

Sub-s (3): words omitted repealed, and words in square brackets substituted, by the Postal Services Act 2000 (Consequential Modifications No 1) Order 2001, SI 2001/1149, art 3, Sch 1, para 135(1), (3), Sch 2.

83 Short title, commencement and extent

(1) This Act may be cited as the Regulation of Investigatory Powers Act 2000.

(2) The provisions of this Act, other than this section, shall come into force on such day as the Secretary of State may by order appoint; and different days may be appointed under this subsection for different purposes.

(3) This Act extends to Northern Ireland.

[714]

NOTES

Regulations: the Regulation of Investigatory Powers (Commencement No 1 and Transitional Provisions) Order 2000, SI 2000/2543; the Regulation of Investigatory Powers Act 2000 (Commencement No 2) Order 2001, SI 2001/2727; the Regulation of Investigatory Powers Act 2000 (Commencement No 3) Order 2003, SI 2003/3140.

SCHEDULES

SCHEDULE 1
RELEVANT PUBLIC AUTHORITIES

Section 30

PART I
RELEVANT AUTHORITIES FOR THE PURPOSES OF SS 28 AND 29

Police forces etc

1. Any police force.

[1A. The Civil Nuclear Constabulary.]

[2. The Serious Organised Crime Agency.]

4. The Serious Fraud Office.

[4A. The force comprising the special constables appointed under section 79 of the Harbours, Docks and Piers Clauses Act 1847 on the nomination of the Dover Harbour Board.

4B. The force comprising the constables appointed under article 3 of the Mersey Docks and Harbour (Police) Order 1975 on the nomination of the Mersey Docks and Harbour Company.]

The intelligence services

5. Any of the intelligence services.

The armed forces

6. Any of Her Majesty's forces.

The revenue departments

7. The Commissioners of Customs and Excise.

8. The Commissioners of Inland Revenue.

Government departments

9. …

[9A. The Department for Communities and Local Government.]

10. The Ministry of Defence.

[10ZA. The Office of the Deputy Prime Minister.]

[10A. The Department for Environment, Food and Rural Affairs.]

11. …

12. The Department of Health.

13. The Home Office.

[13A. The Northern Ireland Office.]

14. …

15. The Department of Trade and Industry.

[15A. The Department for Transport.]

[15B. The Department for Work and Pensions.]

The National Assembly for Wales

16. The National Assembly for Wales.

Local authorities

[17. Any county council or district council in England, a London borough council, the Common Council of the City of London in its capacity as a local authority, the Council of the Isles of Scilly, and any county council or county borough council in Wales.]

[17A. Any fire authority within the meaning of the Fire Services Act 1947 (read with paragraph 2 of Schedule 11 to the Local Government Act 1985).]

Other bodies

[17B. The Charity Commission.]

18. The Environment Agency.

19. The Financial Services Authority.

20. The Food Standards Agency.

[20A. The [Gambling Commission].

20B. The Office of Fair Trading.

20C. The Office of the Police Ombudsman for Northern Ireland.

20D. The Postal Services Commission.]

[20E. The Gangmasters Licensing Authority.

20F. The Commission for Healthcare Audit and Inspection.]

21, 22. …

23. [A universal service provider (within the meaning of the Postal Services Act 2000) acting in connection with the provision of a universal postal service (within the meaning of that Act)].

[23A. The Office of Communications.]

[Northern Ireland authorities

23A. The Department of Agriculture and Rural Development.

23B. The Department of Enterprise, Trade and Investment.

23C. The Department of the Environment.

23D. Any district council (within the meaning of section 44 of the Interpretation Act (Northern Ireland) 1954).]

[715]

NOTES

Para 1A: originally inserted by the Regulation of Investigatory Powers (Directed Surveillance and Covert Human Intelligence Sources) Order 2003, SI 2003/3171, art 2(1), (2); substituted by the Energy Act 2004, s 69(1), Sch 14, para 8(2).

Para 2: substituted for original paras 2, 3, by the Serious Organised Crime and Police Act 2005, s 59, Sch 4, paras 131, 155.

Paras 4A, 4B: inserted by the Regulation of Investigatory Powers (Directed Surveillance and Covert Human Intelligence Sources) (Amendment) Order 2005, SI 2005/1084, art 2(1).

Para 9: repealed by the Ministry of Agriculture, Fisheries and Food (Dissolution) Order 2002, SI 2002/794, art 5(2), Sch 2.

Para 9A: inserted by the Secretary of State for Communities and Local Government Order 2006, SI 2006/1926, art 9, Schedule, para 7.

Para 10ZA: inserted by the Transfer of Functions (Transport, Local Government and the Regions) Order 2002, SI 2002/2626, art 20, Sch 2, para 24(b).

Para 10A: inserted by SI 2002/794, art 5(1), Sch 1, para 39.

Para 11: repealed by the Secretaries of State for Transport, Local Government and the Regions and for Environment, Food and Rural Affairs Order 2001, SI 2001/2568, art 16, Schedule, para 18(a).

Paras 13A, 17A, 17B, 20B–20D: inserted by SI 2003/3171, art 2(1), (3), (5)–(7).

Para 14: repealed by the Secretaries of State for Education and Skills and for Work and Pensions Order 2002, SI 2002/1397, art 12, Schedule, Pt I, para 16(a).

Para 15A: originally inserted by SI 2001/2568, art 16, Schedule, para 18(b); substituted by virtue of SI 2002/2626, art 20, Sch 2, para 24.

Para 15B: inserted by SI 2002/1397, art 12, Schedule, Pt I, para 16(b).

Para 17: substituted by SI 2003/3171, art 2(1), (4).

Para 20A: inserted by SI 2003/3171, art 2(1), (7); words in square brackets substituted by the Gambling Act 2005, s 356(1), Sch 16, Pt 2, para 14.

Paras 20E, 20F: inserted by the Regulation of Investigatory Powers (Directed Surveillance and Covert Human Intelligence Sources) (Amendment) Order 2006, SI 2006/1874, art 2.

Para 21: repealed by the Intervention Board for Agricultural Produce (Abolition) Regulations 2001, SI 2001/3686, reg 6(17)(b).

Para 22: repealed by the Financial Services and Markets Act 2000 (Consequential Amendments) Order 2002, SI 2002/1555, art 26.

Para 23: substituted by the Postal Services Act 2000 (Consequential Modifications No 1) Order 2001, SI 2001/1149, art 3(1), Sch 1, para 135(1), (4).

First para 23A: added by the Communications Act 2003, s 406(1), Sch 17, para 161(1), (3).

Second para 23A, paras 23B–23D: added by the Regulation of Investigatory Powers Act 2000 (Amendment) Order (Northern Ireland) 2002, SR 2002/183, arts 2, 3.

Modification: for the purposes of carrying out the functions of the Independent Police Complaints Commission, this Schedule is modified by the Independent Police Complaints Commission (Investigatory Powers) Order 2004, SI 2004/815, art 3(1), (12).

PART II
RELEVANT AUTHORITIES FOR THE PURPOSES ONLY OF S 28

The Health and Safety Executive

24. The Health and Safety Executive.

NHS bodies in England and Wales

25. …

26. A Special Health Authority established under *section 11 of the National Health Service Act 1977*.

27. …

[27A. …

Her Majesty's Chief Inspector of Schools in England

27B. Her Majesty's Chief Inspector of Schools in England.

The Information Commissioner

27C. The Information Commissioner.

…

27D. …]

The Royal Pharmaceutical Society of Great Britain

28. The Royal Pharmaceutical Society of Great Britain.

[Northern Ireland authorities

29. The Department of Health, Social Services and Public Safety.

30. The Department for Regional Development.

31. The Department for Social Development.

32. The Department of Culture, Arts and Leisure.

33. The Foyle, Carlingford and Irish Lights Commission.

34. The Fisheries Conservancy Board for Northern Ireland.

35. A Health and Social Services trust established under Article 10 of the Health and Personal Social Services (Northern Ireland) Order 1991.

36. A Health and Social Services Board established under Article 16 of the Health and Personal Social Services (Northern Ireland) Order 1972.

37. The Health and Safety Executive for Northern Ireland.

38. The Northern Ireland Central Services Agency for the Health and Social Services.

39. The Fire Authority for Northern Ireland.

40. The Northern Ireland Housing Executive.]

[716]

NOTES

Para 25: repealed by the Regulation of Investigatory Powers (Directed Surveillance and Covert Human Intelligence Sources) (Amendment) Order 2005, SI 2005/1084, art 2(2).

Para 26: for the words in italics there are substituted the words "section 28 of the National Health Service Act 2006 or section 22 of the National Health Service (Wales) Act 2006" by the National Health Service (Consequential Provisions) Act 2006, s 2, Sch 1, paras 207, 209(a), as from a day to be appointed.

Para 27: repealed by the Regulation of Investigatory Powers (Directed Surveillance and Covert Human Intelligence Sources) (Amendment) Order 2006, SI 2006/1874, art 3(a).

Para 27A: inserted by the Regulation of Investigatory Powers (Directed Surveillance and Covert Human Intelligence Sources) Order 2003, SI 2003/3171, art 3; repealed by SI 2006/1874, art 3(b).

Para 27B: inserted, together with preceding cross-heading, by SI 2003/3171, art 3; substituted, together with preceding cross-heading, by the Education and Inspections Act 2006, s 157, Sch 14, para 68, as from a day to be appointed, as follows:

"HM Chief Inspector of Education, Children's Services and Skills

27B. Her Majesty's Chief Inspector of Education, Children's Services and Skills.".

Para 27C: inserted, together with preceding cross-heading, by SI 2003/3171, art 3.

Para 27D: inserted, together with preceding cross-heading, by SI 2003/3171, art 3; repealed, together with preceding cross-heading, by the Serious Organised Crime and Police Act 2005, ss 161(5), 174(2), Sch 13, Pt 2, para 10, Sch 17, Pt 2.

Paras 29–40: added by the Regulation of Investigatory Powers Act 2000 (Amendment) Order (Northern Ireland) 2002, SR 2002/183, arts 2, 4.

SCHEDULE 2
PERSONS HAVING THE APPROPRIATE PERMISSION

Section 49

Requirement that appropriate permission is granted by a judge

1.—(1) Subject to the following provisions of this Schedule, a person has the appropriate permission in relation to any protected information if, and only if, written permission for the giving of section 49 notices in relation to that information has been granted—

(a) in England and Wales, by a Circuit judge [or a District Judge (Magistrates' Courts)];
(b) in Scotland, by a sheriff; or
(c) in Northern Ireland, by a county court judge.

(2) Nothing in paragraphs 2 to 5 of this Schedule providing for the manner in which a person may be granted the appropriate permission in relation to any protected information without a grant under this paragraph shall be construed as requiring any further permission to be obtained in a case in which permission has been granted under this paragraph.

Data obtained under warrant etc

2.—(1) This paragraph applies in the case of protected information falling within section 49(1)(a), (b) or (c) where the statutory power in question is one exercised, or to be exercised, in accordance with—

(a) a warrant issued by the Secretary of State or a person holding judicial office; or
(b) an authorisation under Part III of the Police Act 1997 (authorisation of otherwise unlawful action in respect of property).

(2) Subject to sub-paragraphs (3) to (5) and paragraph 6(1), a person has the appropriate permission in relation to that protected information (without any grant of permission under paragraph 1) if—

(a) the warrant or, as the case may be, the authorisation contained the relevant authority's permission for the giving of section 49 notices in relation to protected information to be obtained under the warrant or authorisation; or
(b) since the issue of the warrant or authorisation, written permission has been granted by the relevant authority for the giving of such notices in relation to protected information obtained under the warrant or authorisation.

(3) Only persons holding office under the Crown, the police[, SOCA] and customs and excise shall be capable of having the appropriate permission in relation to protected information obtained, or to be obtained, under a warrant issued by the Secretary of State.

(4) Only a person who—

(a) was entitled to exercise the power conferred by the warrant, or
(b) is of the description of persons on whom the power conferred by the warrant was, or could have been, conferred,

shall be capable of having the appropriate permission in relation to protected information obtained, or to be obtained, under a warrant issued by a person holding judicial office.

(5) Only the police[, SOCA] and the customs and excise shall be capable of having the appropriate permission in relation to protected information obtained, or to be obtained, under an authorisation under Part III of the Police Act 1997.

(6) In this paragraph "the relevant authority"—

(a) in relation to a warrant issued by the Secretary of State, means the Secretary of State;
(b) in relation to a warrant issued by a person holding judicial office, means any person holding any judicial office that would have entitled him to issue the warrant; and
(c) in relation to protected information obtained under an authorisation under Part III of the Police Act 1997, means (subject to sub-paragraph (7)) an authorising officer within the meaning of section 93 of that Act.

(7) Section 94 of the Police Act 1997 (power of other persons to grant authorisations in urgent cases) shall apply in relation to—

(a) an application for permission for the giving of section 49 notices in relation to protected information obtained, or to be obtained, under an authorisation under Part III of that Act, and

(b) the powers of any authorising officer (within the meaning of section 93 of that Act) to grant such a permission,

as it applies in relation to an application for an authorisation under section 93 of that Act and the powers of such an officer under that section.

(8) References in this paragraph to a person holding judicial office are references to—

(a) any judge of the Crown Court or of the High Court of Justiciary;

(b) any sheriff;

(c) any justice of the peace;

(d) any resident magistrate in Northern Ireland; or

(e) any person holding any such judicial office as entitles him to exercise the jurisdiction of a judge of the Crown Court or of a justice of the peace.

(9) Protected information that comes into a person's possession by means of the exercise of any statutory power which—

(a) is exercisable without a warrant, but

(b) is so exercisable in the course of, or in connection with, the exercise of another statutory power for which a warrant is required,

shall not be taken, by reason only of the warrant required for the exercise of the power mentioned in paragraph (b), to be information in the case of which this paragraph applies.

Data obtained by the intelligence services under statute but without a warrant

3.—(1) This paragraph applies in the case of protected information falling within section 49(1)(a), (b) or (c) which—

(a) has come into the possession of any of the intelligence services or is likely to do so; and

(b) is not information in the case of which paragraph 2 applies.

(2) Subject to paragraph 6(1), a person has the appropriate permission in relation to that protected information (without any grant of permission under paragraph 1) if written permission for the giving of section 49 notices in relation to that information has been granted by the Secretary of State.

(3) Sub-paragraph (2) applies where the protected information is in the possession, or (as the case may be) is likely to come into the possession, of both—

(a) one or more of the intelligence services, and

(b) a public authority which is not one of the intelligence services,

as if a grant of permission under paragraph 1 were unnecessary only where the application to the Secretary of State for permission under that sub-paragraph is made by or on behalf of a member of one of the intelligence services.

Data obtained under statute by other persons but without a warrant

4.—(1) This paragraph applies—

(a) in the case of protected information falling within section 49(1)(a), (b) or (c) which is not information in the case of which paragraph 2 or 3 applies; and

(b) in the case of protected information falling within section 49(1)(d) which is not information also falling within section 49(1)(a), (b) or (c) in the case of which paragraph 3 applies.

(2) Subject to paragraph 6, where—

(a) the statutory power was exercised, or is likely to be exercised, by the police, [SOCA,] the customs and excise or a member of Her Majesty's forces, or

(b) the information was provided or disclosed, or is likely to be provided or disclosed, to the police, [SOCA,] the customs and excise or a member of Her Majesty's forces, or

(c) the information is in the possession of, or is likely to come into the possession of, the police, [SOCA,] the customs and excise or a member of Her Majesty's forces, the police, [SOCA,] the customs and excise or, as the case may be, members of Her Majesty's forces have the appropriate permission in relation to the protected information, without any grant of permission under paragraph 1.

(3) In any other case a person shall not have the appropriate permission by virtue of a grant of permission under paragraph 1 unless he is a person falling within sub-paragraph (4).

(4) A person falls within this sub-paragraph if, as the case may be—

(a) he is the person who exercised the statutory power or is of the description of persons who would have been entitled to exercise it;

(b) he is the person to whom the protected information was provided or disclosed, or is of a description of person the provision or disclosure of the information to whom would have discharged the statutory duty; or

(c) he is a person who is likely to be a person falling within paragraph (a) or (b) when the power is exercised or the protected information provided or disclosed.

Data obtained without the exercise of statutory powers

5.—(1) This paragraph applies in the case of protected information falling within section 49(1)(e).

(2) Subject to paragraph 6, a person has the appropriate permission in relation to that protected information (without any grant of permission under paragraph 1) if—

(a) the information is in the possession of any of the intelligence services, or is likely to come into the possession of any of those services; and

(b) written permission for the giving of section 49 notices in relation to that information has been granted by the Secretary of State.

(3) Sub-paragraph (2) applies where the protected information is in the possession, or (as the case may be) is likely to come into the possession, of both—

(a) one or more of the intelligence services, and

(b) the police[, SOCA] or the customs and excise,

as if a grant of permission under paragraph 1 were unnecessary only where the application to the Secretary of State for permission under that sub-paragraph is made by or on behalf of a member of one of the intelligence services.

General requirements relating to the appropriate permission

6.—(1) A person does not have the appropriate permission in relation to any protected information unless he is either—

(a) a person who has the protected information in his possession or is likely to obtain possession of it; or

(b) a person who is authorised (apart from this Act) to act on behalf of such a person.

(2) Subject to sub-paragraph (3), a constable does not by virtue of paragraph 1, 4 or 5 have the appropriate permission in relation to any protected information unless—

(a) he is of or above the rank of superintendent; or

(b) permission to give a section 49 notice in relation to that information has been granted by a person holding the rank of superintendent, or any higher rank.

(3) In the case of protected information that has come into the police's possession by means of the exercise of powers conferred by—

(a) section 44 of the Terrorism Act 2000 (power to stop and search), or

(b) section 13A or 13B of the Prevention of Terrorism (Temporary Provisions) Act 1989 (which had effect for similar purposes before the coming into force of section 44 of the Terrorism Act 2000),

the permission required by sub-paragraph (2) shall not be granted by any person below the rank mentioned in section 44(4) of that Act of 2000 or, as the case may be, section 13A(1) of that Act of 1989.

[(3A) A member of the staff of the Serious Organised Crime Agency does not by virtue of paragraph 1, 4 or 5 have the appropriate permission in relation to any protected information unless permission to give a section 49 notice in relation to that information has been granted—

(a) by the Director General; or

(b) by a member of the staff of the Agency of or above such level as the Director General may designate for the purposes of this sub-paragraph.]

(4) A person commissioned by the Commissioners of Customs and Excise does not by virtue of paragraph 1, 4 or 5 have the appropriate permission in relation to any protected information unless permission to give a section 49 notice in relation to that information has been granted—

(a) by those Commissioners themselves; or
(b) by an officer of their department of or above such level as they may designate for the purposes of this sub-paragraph.

(5) A member of Her Majesty's forces does not by virtue of paragraph 1, 4 or 5 have the appropriate permission in relation to any protected information unless—

(a) he is of or above the rank of lieutenant colonel or its equivalent; or
(b) permission to give a section 49 notice in relation to that information has been granted by a person holding the rank of lieutenant colonel or its equivalent, or by a person holding a rank higher than lieutenant colonel or its equivalent.

[(6) In sub-paragraph (2) "constable" does not include a constable who is a member of the staff of the Serious Organised Crime Agency.]

Duration of permission

7.—(1) A permission granted by any person under any provision of this Schedule shall not entitle any person to give a section 49 notice at any time after the permission has ceased to have effect.

(2) Such a permission, once granted, shall continue to have effect (notwithstanding the cancellation, expiry or other discharge of any warrant or authorisation in which it is contained or to which it relates) until such time (if any) as it—

(a) expires in accordance with any limitation on its duration that was contained in its terms; or
(b) is withdrawn by the person who granted it or by a person holding any office or other position that would have entitled him to grant it.

Formalities for permissions granted by the Secretary of State

8. A permission for the purposes of any provision of this Schedule shall not be granted by the Secretary of State except—

(a) under his hand; or
(b) in an urgent case in which the Secretary of State has expressly authorised the grant of the permission, under the hand of a senior official.

[717]

NOTES

Commencement: to be appointed.

Para 1: words in square brackets inserted by the Courts Act 2003, s 65, Sch 4, para 12, as from a day to be appointed.

Paras 2, 4, 5: words in square brackets inserted by the Serious Organised Crime and Police Act 2005, s 59, Sch 4, paras 131, 156(1)–(4).

Para 6: sub-paras (3A), (6) inserted by the Serious Organised Crime and Police Act 2005, s 59, Sch 4, paras 131, 156(1), (5).

SCHEDULE 3
THE TRIBUNAL

Section 65

Membership of the Tribunal

1.—(1) A person shall not be appointed as a member of the Tribunal unless he is—

(a) a person who holds or has held a high judicial office (within the meaning of *the Appellate Jurisdiction Act 1876*);
(b) a person who has a ten year general qualification, within the meaning of section 71 of the Courts and Legal Services Act 1990;

(c) an advocate or solicitor in Scotland of at least ten years' standing; or
(d) a member of the Bar of Northern Ireland or *solicitor of the Supreme Court of Northern Ireland* of at least ten years' standing.

(2) Subject to the following provisions of this paragraph, the members of the Tribunal shall hold office during good behaviour.

(3) A member of the Tribunal shall vacate office at the end of the period of five years beginning with the day of his appointment, but shall be eligible for reappointment.

(4) A member of the Tribunal may be relieved of office by Her Majesty at his own request.

(5) A member of the Tribunal may be removed from office by Her Majesty on an Address presented to Her by both Houses of Parliament.

(6) If the Scottish Parliament passes a resolution calling for the removal of a member of the Tribunal, it shall be the duty of the Secretary of State to secure that a motion for the presentation of an Address to Her Majesty for the removal of that member, and the resolution of the Scottish Parliament, are considered by each House of Parliament.

President and Vice-President

2.—(1) Her Majesty may by Letters Patent appoint as President or Vice-President of the Tribunal a person who is, or by virtue of those Letters will be, a member of the Tribunal.

(2) A person shall not be appointed President of the Tribunal unless he holds or has held a high judicial office (within the meaning of *the Appellate Jurisdiction Act 1876*).

(3) If at any time—
(a) the President of the Tribunal is temporarily unable to carry out any functions conferred on him by this Schedule or any rules under section 69, or
(b) the office of President of the Tribunal is for the time being vacant,

the Vice-President shall carry out those functions.

(4) A person shall cease to be President or Vice-President of the Tribunal if he ceases to be a member of the Tribunal.

Members of the Tribunal with special responsibilities

3.—(1) The President of the Tribunal shall designate one or more members of the Tribunal as the member or members having responsibilities in relation to matters involving the intelligence services.

(2) It shall be the duty of the President of the Tribunal, in exercising any power conferred on him by rules under section 69 to allocate the members of the Tribunal who are to consider or hear any complaint, proceedings, reference or preliminary or incidental matter, to exercise that power in a case in which the complaint, proceedings or reference relates to, or to a matter involving—
(a) an allegation against any of the intelligence services or any member of any of those services, or
(b) conduct by or on behalf of any of those services or any member of any of those services,

in such manner as secures that the allocated members consist of, or include, one or more of the members for the time being designated under sub-paragraph (1).

Salaries and expenses

4.—(1) The Secretary of State shall pay to the members of the Tribunal out of money provided by Parliament such remuneration and allowances as he may with the approval of the Treasury determine.

(2) Such expenses of the Tribunal as the Secretary of State may with the approval of the Treasury determine shall be defrayed by him out of money provided by Parliament.

Officers

5.—(1) The Secretary of State may, after consultation with the Tribunal and with the approval of the Treasury as to numbers, provide the Tribunal with such officers as he thinks necessary for the proper discharge of their functions.

(2) The Tribunal may authorise any officer provided under this paragraph to obtain any documents or information on the Tribunal's behalf.

6. …

[718]

NOTES

Para 1: for the words in italics in sub-para (1)(a) there are substituted the words "Part 3 of the Constitutional Reform Act 2005) or is or has been a member of the Judicial Committee of the Privy Council", and for the words in italics in sub-para (1)(d) there are substituted the words "solicitor of the Court of Judicature of Northern Ireland" by the Constitutional Reform Act 2005, ss 59(5), 145, Sch 11, Pt 3, para 5, Sch 17, Pt 2, para 30(1), (2)(c), as from a day to be appointed.

Para 2: for the words in italics in sub-para (2) there are substituted the words "Part 3 of the Constitutional Reform Act 2005) or is or has been a member of the Judicial Committee of the Privy Council" by the Constitutional Reform Act 2005, s 145, Sch 17, Pt 2, para 30(1), (2)(c), as from a day to be appointed.

Para 6: amends the House of Commons Disqualification Act 1975, Sch 1, Pt II and the Northern Ireland Assembly Disqualification Act 1975, Sch 1, Pt II.

(*Sch 4 repealed in part; remainder contains amendments outside the scope of this work.*)

SCHEDULE 5
REPEALS

Section 82

Chapter	*Short title*	*Extent of repeal*
1975 c 24	The House of Commons Disqualification Act 1975.	In Part II of Schedule 1, the words "The Tribunal established under the Interception of Communications Act 1985", "The Tribunal established under the Security Service Act 1989", and "The Tribunal established under section 9 of the Intelligence Services Act 1994".
1975 c 25	The Northern Ireland Assembly Disqualification Act 1975.	In Part II of Schedule 1, the words "The Tribunal established under the Interception of Communications Act 1985", "The Tribunal established under the Security Service Act 1989", and "The Tribunal established under section 9 of the Intelligence Services Act 1994".
1985 c 56	The Interception of Communications Act 1985.	Sections 1 to 10.
		Section 11(3) to (5).
		Schedule 1.
1989 c 5	The Security Service Act 1989.	Sections 4 and 5.
		Schedules 1 and 2.
1989 c 6	The Official Secrets Act 1989.	In Schedule 1, paragraph 3.
1990 c 41	The Courts and Legal Services Act 1990.	In Schedule 10, paragraphs 62 and 74.

Chapter	*Short title*	*Extent of repeal*
1994 c 13	The Intelligence Services Act 1994.	In section 6(1)(b), the words "of his department". In section 7(5)(b), the words "of his department". Sections 8 and 9. In section 11(1), paragraph (b). Schedules 1 and 2.
1997 c 50	The Police Act 1997.	In section 93(6), paragraph (f) and the word "and" immediately preceding it. In section 94(1), the word "or" at the end of paragraph (a). In section 94(2)(e), the words "or (g)" and "or, as the case may be, of the National Crime Squad". In section 94(4)— (a) the words "in his absence", in each place where they occur; and (b) paragraph (d) and the word "and" immediately preceding it. In section 97(6), the words from "(and paragraph 7" onwards. Sections 101 and 102. In section 104— (a) in subsection (1), paragraph (g); (b) in each of subsections (4), (5) and (6), paragraph (b) and the word "or" immediately preceding it; (c) in subsection (8), paragraph (b) and the word "and" immediately preceding it. In section 105(1)(a), sub-paragraph (iii) and the word "and" immediately preceding it. Section 106. Section 107(6). Schedule 7.
1997 c 68	The Special Immigration Appeals Commission Act 1997.	Section 5(7).
1998 c 37	The Crime and Disorder Act 1998.	Section 113(1) and (3).
2000 c 11	The Terrorism Act 2000.	In Schedule 3, paragraph 8.

[719]

FREEDOM OF INFORMATION ACT 2000

(2000 c 36)

ARRANGEMENT OF SECTIONS

PART I
ACCESS TO INFORMATION HELD BY PUBLIC AUTHORITIES

Right to information

Refusal of request

The Information Commissioner and the Information Tribunal

Publication schemes

PART II
EXEMPT INFORMATION

PART III
GENERAL FUNCTIONS OF LORD CHANCELLOR AND INFORMATION COMMISSIONER

PART IV
ENFORCEMENT

PART V
APPEALS

PART VI
HISTORICAL RECORDS AND RECORDS IN PUBLIC RECORD OFFICE OR PUBLIC RECORD OFFICE OF NORTHERN IRELAND

PART VIII
MISCELLANEOUS AND SUPPLEMENTAL

PART I
ACCESS TO INFORMATION HELD BY PUBLIC AUTHORITIES

Right to information

1 General right of access to information held by public authorities

(1) Any person making a request for information to a public authority is entitled—

(a) to be informed in writing by the public authority whether it holds information of the description specified in the request, and

(b) if that is the case, to have that information communicated to him.

(2) Subsection (1) has effect subject to the following provisions of this section and to the provisions of sections 2, 9, 12 and 14.

(3) Where a public authority—

(a) reasonably requires further information in order to identify and locate the information requested, and

(b) has informed the applicant of that requirement,

the authority is not obliged to comply with subsection (1) unless it is supplied with that further information.

(4) The information—

(a) in respect of which the applicant is to be informed under subsection (1)(a), or

(b) which is to be communicated under subsection (1)(b),

is the information in question held at the time when the request is received, except that account may be taken of any amendment or deletion made between that time and the time when the information is to be communicated under subsection (1)(b), being an amendment or deletion that would have been made regardless of the receipt of the request.

(5) A public authority is to be taken to have complied with subsection (1)(a) in relation to any information if it has communicated the information to the applicant in accordance with subsection (1)(b).

(6) In this Act, the duty of a public authority to comply with subsection (1)(a) is referred to as "the duty to confirm or deny".

[720]

NOTES

Commencement: 1 January 2005.

2 Effect of the exemptions in Part II

(1) Where any provision of Part II states that the duty to confirm or deny does not arise in relation to any information, the effect of the provision is that where either—

(a) the provision confers absolute exemption, or

(b) in all the circumstances of the case, the public interest in maintaining the exclusion of the duty to confirm or deny outweighs the public interest in disclosing whether the public authority holds the information,

section 1(1)(a) does not apply.

(2) In respect of any information which is exempt information by virtue of any provision of Part II, section 1(1)(b) does not apply if or to the extent that—

(a) the information is exempt information by virtue of a provision conferring absolute exemption, or

(b) in all the circumstances of the case, the public interest in maintaining the exemption outweighs the public interest in disclosing the information.

(3) For the purposes of this section, the following provisions of Part II (and no others) are to be regarded as conferring absolute exemption—

(a) section 21,

(b) section 23,

(c) section 32,

(d) section 34,

(e) section 36 so far as relating to information held by the House of Commons or the House of Lords,

(f) in section 40—

(i) subsection (1), and

(ii) subsection (2) so far as relating to cases where the first condition referred to in that subsection is satisfied by virtue of subsection (3)(a)(i) or (b) of that section,

(g) section 41, and

(h) section 44.

[721]

NOTES

Commencement: 1 January 2005.

3 Public authorities

(1) In this Act "public authority" means—

(a) subject to section 4(4), any body which, any other person who, or the holder of any office which—

(i) is listed in Schedule 1, or

(ii) is designated by order under section 5, or

(b) a publicly-owned company as defined by section 6.

(2) For the purposes of this Act, information is held by a public authority if—

(a) it is held by the authority, otherwise than on behalf of another person, or

(b) it is held by another person on behalf of the authority.

[722]

4 Amendment of Schedule 1

(1) The [Secretary of State] may by order amend Schedule 1 by adding to that Schedule a reference to any body or the holder of any office which (in either case) is not for the time being listed in that Schedule but as respects which both the first and the second conditions below are satisfied.

(2) The first condition is that the body or office—

(a) is established by virtue of Her Majesty's prerogative or by an enactment or by subordinate legislation, or

(b) is established in any other way by a Minister of the Crown in his capacity as Minister, by a government department or by the National Assembly for Wales.

(3) The second condition is—

(a) in the case of a body, that the body is wholly or partly constituted by appointment made by the Crown, by a Minister of the Crown, by a government department or by the National Assembly for Wales, or

(b) in the case of an office, that appointments to the office are made by the Crown, by a Minister of the Crown, by a government department or by the National Assembly for Wales.

(4) If either the first or the second condition above ceases to be satisfied as respects any body or office which is listed in Part VI or VII of Schedule 1, that body or the holder of that office shall cease to be a public authority by virtue of the entry in question.

(5) The [Secretary of State] may by order amend Schedule 1 by removing from Part VI or VII of that Schedule an entry relating to any body or office—

(a) which has ceased to exist, or

(b) as respects which either the first or the second condition above has ceased to be satisfied.

(6) An order under subsection (1) may relate to a specified person or office or to persons or offices falling within a specified description.

(7) Before making an order under subsection (1), the [Secretary of State] shall—

(a) if the order adds to Part II, III, IV or VI of Schedule 1 a reference to—

(i) a body whose functions are exercisable only or mainly in or as regards Wales, or

(ii) the holder of an office whose functions are exercisable only or mainly in or as regards Wales, consult the National Assembly for Wales, and

(b) if the order relates to a body which, or the holder of any office who, if the order were made, would be a Northern Ireland public authority, consult the First Minister and deputy First Minister in Northern Ireland.

(8) This section has effect subject to section 80.

(9) In this section "Minister of the Crown" includes a Northern Ireland Minister.

[723]

NOTES

Sub-ss (1), (5), (7): words in square brackets substituted by the Secretary of State for Constitutional Affairs Order 2003, SI 2003/1887, art 9, Sch 2, para 12(1)(a).

Orders: the Freedom of Information (Additional Public Authorities) Order 2002, SI 2002/2623; the Freedom of Information (Additional Public Authorities) Order 2003, SI 2003/1882; the Freedom of Information (Removal of References to Public Authorities) Order 2003, SI 2003/1883; the Freedom of Information (Additional Public Authorities) Order 2004, SI 2004/938; the Freedom of Information (Removal of References to Public Authorities) Order 2004, SI 2004/1641; the Freedom of Information (Additional Public Authorities) Order 2005, SI 2005/3593; the Freedom of Information (Removal of References to Public Authorities) Order 2005, SI 2005/3594.

5 Further power to designate public authorities

(1) The [Secretary of State] may by order designate as a public authority for the purposes of this Act any person who is neither listed in Schedule 1 nor capable of being added to that Schedule by an order under section 4(1), but who—

(a) appears to the [Secretary of State] to exercise functions of a public nature, or

(b) is providing under a contract made with a public authority any service whose provision is a function of that authority.

(2) An order under this section may designate a specified person or office or persons or offices falling within a specified description.

(3) Before making an order under this section, the [Secretary of State] shall consult every person to whom the order relates, or persons appearing to him to represent such persons.

(4) This section has effect subject to section 80.

[724]

NOTES

Sub-ss (1), (3): words in square brackets substituted by the Secretary of State for Constitutional Affairs Order 2003, SI 2003/1887, art 9, Sch 2, para 12(1)(a).

6 Publicly-owned companies

(1) A company is a "publicly-owned company" for the purposes of section 3(1)(b) if—
- (a) it is wholly owned by the Crown, or
- (b) it is wholly owned by any public authority listed in Schedule 1 other than—
  - (i) a government department, or
  - (ii) any authority which is listed only in relation to particular information.

(2) For the purposes of this section—
- (a) a company is wholly owned by the Crown if it has no members except—
  - (i) Ministers of the Crown, government departments or companies wholly owned by the Crown, or
  - (ii) persons acting on behalf of Ministers of the Crown, government departments or companies wholly owned by the Crown, and
- (b) a company is wholly owned by a public authority other than a government department if it has no members except—
  - (i) that public authority or companies wholly owned by that public authority, or
  - (ii) persons acting on behalf of that public authority or of companies wholly owned by that public authority.

(3) In this section—

"company" includes any body corporate;

"Minister of the Crown" includes a Northern Ireland Minister.

[725]

7 Public authorities to which Act has limited application

(1) Where a public authority is listed in Schedule 1 only in relation to information of a specified description, nothing in Parts I to V of this Act applies to any other information held by the authority.

(2) An order under section 4(1) may, in adding an entry to Schedule 1, list the public authority only in relation to information of a specified description.

(3) The [Secretary of State] may by order amend Schedule 1—
- (a) by limiting to information of a specified description the entry relating to any public authority, or
- (b) by removing or amending any limitation to information of a specified description which is for the time being contained in any entry.

(4) Before making an order under subsection (3), the [Secretary of State] shall—
- (a) if the order relates to the National Assembly for Wales or a Welsh public authority, consult the National Assembly for Wales,
- (b) if the order relates to the Northern Ireland Assembly, consult the Presiding Officer of that Assembly, and
- (c) if the order relates to a Northern Ireland department or a Northern Ireland public authority, consult the First Minister and deputy First Minister in Northern Ireland.

(5) An order under section 5(1)(a) must specify the functions of the public authority designated by the order with respect to which the designation is to have effect; and nothing in Parts I to V of this Act applies to information which is held by the authority but does not relate to the exercise of those functions.

(6) An order under section 5(1)(b) must specify the services provided under contract with respect to which the designation is to have effect; and nothing in Parts I to V of this Act applies to information which is held by the public authority designated by the order but does not relate to the provision of those services.

(7) Nothing in Parts I to V of this Act applies in relation to any information held by a publicly-owned company which is excluded information in relation to that company.

(8) In subsection (7) "excluded information", in relation to a publicly-owned company, means information which is of a description specified in relation to that company in an order made by the [Secretary of State] for the purposes of this subsection.

(9) In this section "publicly-owned company" has the meaning given by section 6.

[726]

NOTES

Sub-ss (3), (4), (8): words in square brackets substituted by the Secretary of State for Constitutional Affairs Order 2003, SI 2003/1887, art 9, Sch 2, para 12(1)(a).

Orders: the Freedom of Information (Additional Public Authorities) Order 2002, SI 2002/2623; the Freedom of Information (Additional Public Authorities) Order 2003, SI 2003/1882; the Freedom of Information (Additional Public Authorities) Order 2005, SI 2005/3593.

8 Request for information

(1) In this Act any reference to a "request for information" is a reference to such a request which—

(a) is in writing,
(b) states the name of the applicant and an address for correspondence, and
(c) describes the information requested.

(2) For the purposes of subsection (1)(a), a request is to be treated as made in writing where the text of the request—

(a) is transmitted by electronic means,
(b) is received in legible form, and
(c) is capable of being used for subsequent reference.

[727]

9 Fees

(1) A public authority to whom a request for information is made may, within the period for complying with section 1(1), give the applicant a notice in writing (in this Act referred to as a "fees notice") stating that a fee of an amount specified in the notice is to be charged by the authority for complying with section 1(1).

(2) Where a fees notice has been given to the applicant, the public authority is not obliged to comply with section 1(1) unless the fee is paid within the period of three months beginning with the day on which the fees notice is given to the applicant.

(3) Subject to subsection (5), any fee under this section must be determined by the public authority in accordance with regulations made by the [Secretary of State].

(4) Regulations under subsection (3) may, in particular, provide—

(a) that no fee is to be payable in prescribed cases,
(b) that any fee is not to exceed such maximum as may be specified in, or determined in accordance with, the regulations, and
(c) that any fee is to be calculated in such manner as may be prescribed by the regulations.

(5) Subsection (3) does not apply where provision is made by or under any enactment as to the fee that may be charged by the public authority for the disclosure of the information.

[728]

NOTES

Commencement: 30 November 2000 (in so far as confers powers to make any order, regulations or code of practice); 1 January 2005 (otherwise).

Sub-s (3): words in square brackets substituted by the Secretary of State for Constitutional Affairs Order 2003, SI 2003/1887, art 9, Sch 2, para 12(1)(a).

Regulations: the Freedom of Information and Data Protection (Appropriate Limit and Fees) Regulations 2004, SI 2004/3244.

10 Time for compliance with request

(1) Subject to subsections (2) and (3), a public authority must comply with section 1(1) promptly and in any event not later than the twentieth working day following the date of receipt.

(2) Where the authority has given a fees notice to the applicant and the fee is paid in accordance with section 9(2), the working days in the period beginning with the day on which the fees notice is given to the applicant and ending with the day on which the fee is received by the authority are to be disregarded in calculating for the purposes of subsection (1) the twentieth working day following the date of receipt.

(3) If, and to the extent that—

(a) section 1(1)(a) would not apply if the condition in section 2(1)(b) were satisfied, or

(b) section 1(1)(b) would not apply if the condition in section 2(2)(b) were satisfied,

the public authority need not comply with section 1(1)(a) or (b) until such time as is reasonable in the circumstances; but this subsection does not affect the time by which any notice under section 17(1) must be given.

(4) The [Secretary of State] may by regulations provide that subsections (1) and (2) are to have effect as if any reference to the twentieth working day following the date of receipt were a reference to such other day, not later than the sixtieth working day following the date of receipt, as may be specified in, or determined in accordance with, the regulations.

(5) Regulations under subsection (4) may—

(a) prescribe different days in relation to different cases, and

(b) confer a discretion on the Commissioner.

(6) In this section—

"the date of receipt" means—

(a) the day on which the public authority receives the request for information, or

(b) if later, the day on which it receives the information referred to in section 1(3);

"working day" means any day other than a Saturday, a Sunday, Christmas Day, Good Friday or a day which is a bank holiday under the Banking and Financial Dealings Act 1971 in any part of the United Kingdom.

[729]

NOTES

Commencement: 30 November 2000 (in so far as confers powers to make any order, regulations or code of practice); 1 January 2005 (otherwise).

Sub-s (4): words in square brackets substituted by the Secretary of State for Constitutional Affairs Order 2003, SI 2003/1887, art 9, Sch 2, para 12(1)(a).

Regulations: the Freedom of Information (Time for Compliance with Request) Regulations 2004, SI 2004/3364.

11 Means by which communication to be made

(1) Where, on making his request for information, the applicant expresses a preference for communication by any one or more of the following means, namely—

(a) the provision to the applicant of a copy of the information in permanent form or in another form acceptable to the applicant,

(b) the provision to the applicant of a reasonable opportunity to inspect a record containing the information, and

(c) the provision to the applicant of a digest or summary of the information in permanent form or in another form acceptable to the applicant,

the public authority shall so far as reasonably practicable give effect to that preference.

(2) In determining for the purposes of this section whether it is reasonably practicable to communicate information by particular means, the public authority may have regard to all the circumstances, including the cost of doing so.

(3) Where the public authority determines that it is not reasonably practicable to comply with any preference expressed by the applicant in making his request, the authority shall notify the applicant of the reasons for its determination.

(4) Subject to subsection (1), a public authority may comply with a request by communicating information by any means which are reasonable in the circumstances.

[730]

NOTES

Commencement: 1 January 2005.

12 Exemption where cost of compliance exceeds appropriate limit

(1) Section 1(1) does not oblige a public authority to comply with a request for information if the authority estimates that the cost of complying with the request would exceed the appropriate limit.

PART II DATA PROTECTION

(2) Subsection (1) does not exempt the public authority from its obligation to comply with paragraph (a) of section 1(1) unless the estimated cost of complying with that paragraph alone would exceed the appropriate limit.

(3) In subsections (1) and (2) "the appropriate limit" means such amount as may be prescribed, and different amounts may be prescribed in relation to different cases.

(4) The [Secretary of State] may by regulations provide that, in such circumstances as may be prescribed, where two or more requests for information are made to a public authority—

(a) by one person, or
(b) by different persons who appear to the public authority to be acting in concert or in pursuance of a campaign,

the estimated cost of complying with any of the requests is to be taken to be the estimated total cost of complying with all of them.

(5) The [Secretary of State] may by regulations make provision for the purposes of this section as to the costs to be estimated and as to the manner in which they are to be estimated.
[731]

NOTES

Commencement: 30 November 2000 (in so far as confers powers to make any order, regulations or code of practice); 1 January 2005 (otherwise).

Sub-ss (4), (5): words in square brackets substituted by the Secretary of State for Constitutional Affairs Order 2003, SI 2003/1887, art 9, Sch 2, para 12(1)(a).

Regulations: the Freedom of Information and Data Protection (Appropriate Limit and Fees) Regulations 2004, SI 2004/3244.

13 Fees for disclosure where cost of compliance exceeds appropriate limit

(1) A public authority may charge for the communication of any information whose communication—

(a) is not required by section 1(1) because the cost of complying with the request for information exceeds the amount which is the appropriate limit for the purposes of section 12(1) and (2), and
(b) is not otherwise required by law,

such fee as may be determined by the public authority in accordance with regulations made by the [Secretary of State].

(2) Regulations under this section may, in particular, provide—

(a) that any fee is not to exceed such maximum as may be specified in, or determined in accordance with, the regulations, and
(b) that any fee is to be calculated in such manner as may be prescribed by the regulations.

(3) Subsection (1) does not apply where provision is made by or under any enactment as to the fee that may be charged by the public authority for the disclosure of the information.
[732]

NOTES

Commencement: 30 November 2000 (in so far as confers powers to make any order, regulations or code of practice); 1 January 2005 (otherwise).

Sub-s (1): words in square brackets substituted by the Secretary of State for Constitutional Affairs Order 2003, SI 2003/1887, art 9, Sch 2, para 12(1)(a).

Regulations: the Freedom of Information and Data Protection (Appropriate Limit and Fees) Regulations 2004, SI 2004/3244.

14 Vexatious or repeated requests

(1) Section 1(1) does not oblige a public authority to comply with a request for information if the request is vexatious.

(2) Where a public authority has previously complied with a request for information which was made by any person, it is not obliged to comply with a subsequent identical or substantially similar request from that person unless a reasonable interval has elapsed between compliance with the previous request and the making of the current request.
[733]

NOTES

Commencement: 1 January 2005.

15 Special provisions relating to public records transferred to Public Record Office, etc

(1) Where—

(a) the appropriate records authority receives a request for information which relates to information which is, or if it existed would be, contained in a transferred public record, and

(b) either of the conditions in subsection (2) is satisfied in relation to any of that information,

that authority shall, within the period for complying with section 1(1), send a copy of the request to the responsible authority.

(2) The conditions referred to in subsection (1)(b) are—

(a) that the duty to confirm or deny is expressed to be excluded only by a provision of Part II not specified in subsection (3) of section 2, and

(b) that the information is exempt information only by virtue of a provision of Part II not specified in that subsection.

(3) On receiving the copy, the responsible authority shall, within such time as is reasonable in all the circumstances, inform the appropriate records authority of the determination required by virtue of subsection (3) or (4) of section 66.

(4) In this Act "transferred public record" means a public record which has been transferred—

(a) to the Public Record Office,

(b) to another place of deposit appointed by the Lord Chancellor under the Public Records Act 1958, or

(c) to the Public Record Office of Northern Ireland.

(5) In this Act—

"appropriate records authority", in relation to a transferred public record, means—

(a) in a case falling within subsection (4)(a), the Public Record Office,

(b) in a case falling within subsection (4)(b), the Lord Chancellor, and

(c) in a case falling within subsection (4)(c), the Public Record Office of Northern Ireland;

"responsible authority", in relation to a transferred public record, means—

(a) in the case of a record transferred as mentioned in subsection (4)(a) or (b) from a government department in the charge of a Minister of the Crown, the Minister of the Crown who appears to the Lord Chancellor to be primarily concerned,

(b) in the case of a record transferred as mentioned in subsection (4)(a) or (b) from any other person, the person who appears to the Lord Chancellor to be primarily concerned,

(c) in the case of a record transferred to the Public Record Office of Northern Ireland from a government department in the charge of a Minister of the Crown, the Minister of the Crown who appears to the appropriate Northern Ireland Minister to be primarily concerned,

(d) in the case of a record transferred to the Public Record Office of Northern Ireland from a Northern Ireland department, the Northern Ireland Minister who appears to the appropriate Northern Ireland Minister to be primarily concerned, or

(e) in the case of a record transferred to the Public Record Office of Northern Ireland from any other person, the person who appears to the appropriate Northern Ireland Minister to be primarily concerned.

[734]

NOTES

Commencement: 1 January 2005.

16 Duty to provide advice and assistance

(1) It shall be the duty of a public authority to provide advice and assistance, so far as it would be reasonable to expect the authority to do so, to persons who propose to make, or have made, requests for information to it.

(2) Any public authority which, in relation to the provision of advice or assistance in any case, conforms with the code of practice under section 45 is to be taken to comply with the duty imposed by subsection (1) in relation to that case.

[735]

NOTES

Commencement: 1 January 2005.

Refusal of request

17 Refusal of request

(1) A public authority which, in relation to any request for information, is to any extent relying on a claim that any provision of Part II relating to the duty to confirm or deny is relevant to the request or on a claim that information is exempt information must, within the time for complying with section 1(1), give the applicant a notice which—

(a) states that fact,
(b) specifies the exemption in question, and
(c) states (if that would not otherwise be apparent) why the exemption applies.

(2) Where—

(a) in relation to any request for information, a public authority is, as respects any information, relying on a claim—
 (i) that any provision of Part II which relates to the duty to confirm or deny and is not specified in section 2(3) is relevant to the request, or
 (ii) that the information is exempt information only by virtue of a provision not specified in section 2(3), and
(b) at the time when the notice under subsection (1) is given to the applicant, the public authority (or, in a case falling within section 66(3) or (4), the responsible authority) has not yet reached a decision as to the application of subsection (1)(b) or (2)(b) of section 2,

the notice under subsection (1) must indicate that no decision as to the application of that provision has yet been reached and must contain an estimate of the date by which the authority expects that such a decision will have been reached.

(3) A public authority which, in relation to any request for information, is to any extent relying on a claim that subsection (1)(b) or (2)(b) of section 2 applies must, either in the notice under subsection (1) or in a separate notice given within such time as is reasonable in the circumstances, state the reasons for claiming—

(a) that, in all the circumstances of the case, the public interest in maintaining the exclusion of the duty to confirm or deny outweighs the public interest in disclosing whether the authority holds the information, or
(b) that, in all the circumstances of the case, the public interest in maintaining the exemption outweighs the public interest in disclosing the information.

(4) A public authority is not obliged to make a statement under subsection (1)(c) or (3) if, or to the extent that, the statement would involve the disclosure of information which would itself be exempt information.

(5) A public authority which, in relation to any request for information, is relying on a claim that section 12 or 14 applies must, within the time for complying with section 1(1), give the applicant a notice stating that fact.

(6) Subsection (5) does not apply where—

(a) the public authority is relying on a claim that section 14 applies,
(b) the authority has given the applicant a notice, in relation to a previous request for information, stating that it is relying on such a claim, and
(c) it would in all the circumstances be unreasonable to expect the authority to serve a further notice under subsection (5) in relation to the current request.

(7) A notice under subsection (1), (3) or (5) must—

(a) contain particulars of any procedure provided by the public authority for dealing with complaints about the handling of requests for information or state that the authority does not provide such a procedure, and

(b) contain particulars of the right conferred by section 50.

[736]

NOTES

Commencement: 1 January 2005.

The Information Commissioner and the Information Tribunal

18 The Information Commissioner and the Information Tribunal

(1) The Data Protection Commissioner shall be known instead as the Information Commissioner.

(2) The Data Protection Tribunal shall be known instead as the Information Tribunal.

(3) In this Act—

(a) the Information Commissioner is referred to as "the Commissioner", and

(b) the Information Tribunal is referred to as "the Tribunal".

(4) Schedule 2 (which makes provision consequential on subsections (1) and (2) and amendments of the Data Protection Act 1998 relating to the extension by this Act of the functions of the Commissioner and the Tribunal) has effect.

(5) If the person who held office as Data Protection Commissioner immediately before the day on which this Act is passed remains in office as Information Commissioner at the end of the period of two years beginning with that day, he shall vacate his office at the end of that period.

(6) Subsection (5) does not prevent the re-appointment of a person whose appointment is terminated by that subsection.

(7) In the application of paragraph 2(4)(b) and (5) of Schedule 5 to the Data Protection Act 1998 (Commissioner not to serve for more than fifteen years and not to be appointed, except in special circumstances, for a third or subsequent term) to anything done after the passing of this Act, there shall be left out of account any term of office served by virtue of an appointment made before the passing of this Act.

[737]

NOTES

Commencement: 30 November 2000 (sub-s (4) certain purposes); 30 January 2001 (sub-s (1), sub-s (4) certain purposes); 14 May 2001 (sub-ss (2), (3), (5)–(7), sub-s (4) certain purposes); 30 November 2002 (otherwise).

Publication schemes

19 Publication schemes

(1) It shall be the duty of every public authority—

(a) to adopt and maintain a scheme which relates to the publication of information by the authority and is approved by the Commissioner (in this Act referred to as a "publication scheme"),

(b) to publish information in accordance with its publication scheme, and

(c) from time to time to review its publication scheme.

(2) A publication scheme must—

(a) specify classes of information which the public authority publishes or intends to publish,

(b) specify the manner in which information of each class is, or is intended to be, published, and

(c) specify whether the material is, or is intended to be, available to the public free of charge or on payment.

PART II
DATA PROTECTION

(3) In adopting or reviewing a publication scheme, a public authority shall have regard to the public interest—

(a) in allowing public access to information held by the authority, and
(b) in the publication of reasons for decisions made by the authority.

(4) A public authority shall publish its publication scheme in such manner as it thinks fit.

(5) The Commissioner may, when approving a scheme, provide that his approval is to expire at the end of a specified period.

(6) Where the Commissioner has approved the publication scheme of any public authority, he may at any time give notice to the public authority revoking his approval of the scheme as from the end of the period of six months beginning with the day on which the notice is given.

(7) Where the Commissioner—

(a) refuses to approve a proposed publication scheme, or
(b) revokes his approval of a publication scheme,

he must give the public authority a statement of his reasons for doing so.

[738]

NOTES

Commencement (sub-ss (1)–(4)): 30 November 2000 (in so far as relating to the approval of publication schemes); 30 November 2002 (in so far as relating to public authorities listed in Sch 1, paras 1 (except the Crown Prosecution Service and the Serious Fraud Office), 2, 3, 5 to the Act and SI 2002/2812, Sch 1); 28 February 2003 (in so far as relating to the Common Council of the City of London, in respect of information held in its capacity as a local authority or port health authority and public authorities listed in Sch 1, paras 7, 8, 10–16, 18–36 to the Act and SI 2002/2812, Sch 2); 30 June 2003 (in so far as relating to the Crown Prosecution Service and the Serious Fraud Office, the Common Council of the City of London, in respect of information held in its capacity as a police authority, and public authorities listed in Sch 1, paras 6, 57–64 to the Act and SI 2002/2812, Sch 3); 31 October 2003 (in so far as relating to the public authorities listed in Sch 1, Pt III to the Act, the Distinction and Meritorious Service Awards Committee, Invest Northern Ireland and The Northern Ireland Council for Postgraduate Medical and Dental Education); 29 February 2004 (in so far as relating to the public authorities listed in Sch 1, Pt IV to the Act (except for those specified in para 52(b)) and SI 2003/2603, Sch 1 and any publicly-owned company as defined in s 6 of the Act); 30 June 2004 (in so far as relating to all public authorities in respect of which these provisions have not been commenced elsewhere, except for the public authority listed in Sch 1, para 17 to the Act and the consultative Civic Forum referred to in the Northern Ireland Act 1998, s 56(4)); 30 November 2005 (otherwise).

Commencement (sub-ss (5)–(7)): 30 November 2000 (in so far as relating to the approval of publication schemes); 30 November 2002 (otherwise).

20 Model publication schemes

(1) The Commissioner may from time to time approve, in relation to public authorities falling within particular classes, model publication schemes prepared by him or by other persons.

(2) Where a public authority falling within the class to which an approved model scheme relates adopts such a scheme without modification, no further approval of the Commissioner is required so long as the model scheme remains approved; and where such an authority adopts such a scheme with modifications, the approval of the Commissioner is required only in relation to the modifications.

(3) The Commissioner may, when approving a model publication scheme, provide that his approval is to expire at the end of a specified period.

(4) Where the Commissioner has approved a model publication scheme, he may at any time publish, in such manner as he thinks fit, a notice revoking his approval of the scheme as from the end of the period of six months beginning with the day on which the notice is published.

(5) Where the Commissioner refuses to approve a proposed model publication scheme on the application of any person, he must give the person who applied for approval of the scheme a statement of the reasons for his refusal.

(6) Where the Commissioner refuses to approve any modifications under subsection (2), he must give the public authority a statement of the reasons for his refusal.

(7) Where the Commissioner revokes his approval of a model publication scheme, he must include in the notice under subsection (4) a statement of his reasons for doing so.

[739]

NOTES

Commencement: 30 November 2000 (so far as relating to the approval and preparation by the Commissioner of model publication schemes); 30 November 2002 (otherwise).

PART II
EXEMPT INFORMATION

21 Information accessible to applicant by other means

(1) Information which is reasonably accessible to the applicant otherwise than under section 1 is exempt information.

(2) For the purposes of subsection (1)—

(a) information may be reasonably accessible to the applicant even though it is accessible only on payment, and

(b) information is to be taken to be reasonably accessible to the applicant if it is information which the public authority or any other person is obliged by or under any enactment to communicate (otherwise than by making the information available for inspection) to members of the public on request, whether free of charge or on payment.

(3) For the purposes of subsection (1), information which is held by a public authority and does not fall within subsection (2)(b) is not to be regarded as reasonably accessible to the applicant merely because the information is available from the public authority itself on request, unless the information is made available in accordance with the authority's publication scheme and any payment required is specified in, or determined in accordance with, the scheme.

[740]

NOTES

Commencement: 1 January 2005.

22 Information intended for future publication

(1) Information is exempt information if—

(a) the information is held by the public authority with a view to its publication, by the authority or any other person, at some future date (whether determined or not),

(b) the information was already held with a view to such publication at the time when the request for information was made, and

(c) it is reasonable in all the circumstances that the information should be withheld from disclosure until the date referred to in paragraph (a).

(2) The duty to confirm or deny does not arise if, or to the extent that, compliance with section 1(1)(a) would involve the disclosure of any information (whether or not already recorded) which falls within subsection (1).

[741]

NOTES

Commencement: 1 January 2005.

23 Information supplied by, or relating to, bodies dealing with security matters

(1) Information held by a public authority is exempt information if it was directly or indirectly supplied to the public authority by, or relates to, any of the bodies specified in subsection (3).

(2) A certificate signed by a Minister of the Crown certifying that the information to which it applies was directly or indirectly supplied by, or relates to, any of the bodies specified in subsection (3) shall, subject to section 60, be conclusive evidence of that fact.

(3) The bodies referred to in subsections (1) and (2) are—

(a) the Security Service,
(b) the Secret Intelligence Service,
(c) the Government Communications Headquarters,
(d) the special forces,
(e) the Tribunal established under section 65 of the Regulation of Investigatory Powers Act 2000,
(f) the Tribunal established under section 7 of the Interception of Communications Act 1985,
(g) the Tribunal established under section 5 of the Security Service Act 1989,
(h) the Tribunal established under section 9 of the Intelligence Services Act 1994,
(i) the Security Vetting Appeals Panel,
(j) the Security Commission,
(k) the National Criminal Intelligence Service, …
(l) the Service Authority for the National Criminal Intelligence Service,
[(m) the Serious Organised Crime Agency]

(4) In subsection (3)(c) "the Government Communications Headquarters" includes any unit or part of a unit of the armed forces of the Crown which is for the time being required by the Secretary of State to assist the Government Communications Headquarters in carrying out its functions.

(5) The duty to confirm or deny does not arise if, or to the extent that, compliance with section 1(1)(a) would involve the disclosure of any information (whether or not already recorded) which was directly or indirectly supplied to the public authority by, or relates to, any of the bodies specified in subsection (3).

[742]

NOTES

Commencement: 1 January 2005.

Sub-s (3): word omitted from para (k) repealed and para (m) inserted by the Serious Organised Crime and Police Act 2005, ss 59, 174(2), Sch 4, paras 158, 159, Sch 17, Pt 2.

24 National security

(1) Information which does not fall within section 23(1) is exempt information if exemption from section 1(1)(b) is required for the purpose of safeguarding national security.

(2) The duty to confirm or deny does not arise if, or to the extent that, exemption from section 1(1)(a) is required for the purpose of safeguarding national security.

(3) A certificate signed by a Minister of the Crown certifying that exemption from section 1(1)(b), or from section 1(1)(a) and (b), is, or at any time was, required for the purpose of safeguarding national security shall, subject to section 60, be conclusive evidence of that fact.

(4) A certificate under subsection (3) may identify the information to which it applies by means of a general description and may be expressed to have prospective effect.

[743]

NOTES

Commencement: 1 January 2005.

25 Certificates under ss 23 and 24: supplementary provisions

(1) A document purporting to be a certificate under section 23(2) or 24(3) shall be received in evidence and deemed to be such a certificate unless the contrary is proved.

(2) A document which purports to be certified by or on behalf of a Minister of the Crown as a true copy of a certificate issued by that Minister under section 23(2) or 24(3) shall in any legal proceedings be evidence (or, in Scotland, sufficient evidence) of that certificate.

(3) The power conferred by section 23(2) or 24(3) on a Minister of the Crown shall not be exercisable except by a Minister who is a member of the Cabinet or by the Attorney General, the Advocate General for Scotland or the Attorney General for Northern Ireland.

[744]

NOTES

Commencement: 1 January 2005.

26 Defence

(1) Information is exempt information if its disclosure under this Act would, or would be likely to, prejudice—

(a) the defence of the British Islands or of any colony, or

(b) the capability, effectiveness or security of any relevant forces.

(2) In subsection (1)(b) "relevant forces" means—

(a) the armed forces of the Crown, and

(b) any forces co-operating with those forces,

or any part of any of those forces.

(3) The duty to confirm or deny does not arise if, or to the extent that, compliance with section 1(1)(a) would, or would be likely to, prejudice any of the matters mentioned in subsection (1).

[745]

NOTES

Commencement: 1 January 2005.

27 International relations

(1) Information is exempt information if its disclosure under this Act would, or would be likely to, prejudice—

(a) relations between the United Kingdom and any other State,

(b) relations between the United Kingdom and any international organisation or international court,

(c) the interests of the United Kingdom abroad, or

(d) the promotion or protection by the United Kingdom of its interests abroad.

(2) Information is also exempt information if it is confidential information obtained from a State other than the United Kingdom or from an international organisation or international court.

(3) For the purposes of this section, any information obtained from a State, organisation or court is confidential at any time while the terms on which it was obtained require it to be held in confidence or while the circumstances in which it was obtained make it reasonable for the State, organisation or court to expect that it will be so held.

(4) The duty to confirm or deny does not arise if, or to the extent that, compliance with section 1(1)(a)—

(a) would, or would be likely to, prejudice any of the matters mentioned in subsection (1), or

(b) would involve the disclosure of any information (whether or not already recorded) which is confidential information obtained from a State other than the United Kingdom or from an international organisation or international court.

(5) In this section—

"international court" means any international court which is not an international organisation and which is established—

(a) by a resolution of an international organisation of which the United Kingdom is a member, or

(b) by an international agreement to which the United Kingdom is a party;

"international organisation" means any international organisation whose members include any two or more States, or any organ of such an organisation;

"State" includes the government of any State and any organ of its government, and references to a State other than the United Kingdom include references to any territory outside the United Kingdom.

[746]

NOTES

Commencement: 1 January 2005.

28 Relations within the United Kingdom

(1) Information is exempt information if its disclosure under this Act would, or would be likely to, prejudice relations between any administration in the United Kingdom and any other such administration.

(2) In subsection (1) "administration in the United Kingdom" means—
(a) the government of the United Kingdom,
(b) the Scottish Administration,
(c) the Executive Committee of the Northern Ireland Assembly, or
(d) the National Assembly for Wales.

(3) The duty to confirm or deny does not arise if, or to the extent that, compliance with section 1(1)(a) would, or would be likely to, prejudice any of the matters mentioned in subsection (1).

[747]

NOTES
Commencement: 1 January 2005.

29 The economy

(1) Information is exempt information if its disclosure under this Act would, or would be likely to, prejudice—
(a) the economic interests of the United Kingdom or of any part of the United Kingdom, or
(b) the financial interests of any administration in the United Kingdom, as defined by section 28(2).

(2) The duty to confirm or deny does not arise if, or to the extent that, compliance with section 1(1)(a) would, or would be likely to, prejudice any of the matters mentioned in subsection (1).

[748]

NOTES
Commencement: 1 January 2005.

30 Investigations and proceedings conducted by public authorities

(1) Information held by a public authority is exempt information if it has at any time been held by the authority for the purposes of—
(a) any investigation which the public authority has a duty to conduct with a view to it being ascertained—
(i) whether a person should be charged with an offence, or
(ii) whether a person charged with an offence is guilty of it,
(b) any investigation which is conducted by the authority and in the circumstances may lead to a decision by the authority to institute criminal proceedings which the authority has power to conduct, or
(c) any criminal proceedings which the authority has power to conduct.

(2) Information held by a public authority is exempt information if—
(a) it was obtained or recorded by the authority for the purposes of its functions relating to—
(i) investigations falling within subsection (1)(a) or (b),
(ii) criminal proceedings which the authority has power to conduct,
(iii) investigations (other than investigations falling within subsection (1)(a) or (b)) which are conducted by the authority for any of the purposes specified in section 31(2) and either by virtue of Her Majesty's prerogative or by virtue of powers conferred by or under any enactment, or
(iv) civil proceedings which are brought by or on behalf of the authority and arise out of such investigations, and
(b) it relates to the obtaining of information from confidential sources.

(3) The duty to confirm or deny does not arise in relation to information which is (or if it were held by the public authority would be) exempt information by virtue of subsection (1) or (2).

(4) In relation to the institution or conduct of criminal proceedings or the power to conduct them, references in subsection (1)(b) or (c) and subsection (2)(a) to the public authority include references—

(a) to any officer of the authority,

(b) in the case of a government department other than a Northern Ireland department, to the Minister of the Crown in charge of the department, and

(c) in the case of a Northern Ireland department, to the Northern Ireland Minister in charge of the department.

(5) In this section—

"criminal proceedings" includes—

(a) proceedings before a court-martial constituted under the Army Act 1955, the Air Force Act 1955 or the Naval Discipline Act 1957... ,

(b) proceedings on dealing summarily with a charge under the Army Act 1955 or the Air Force Act 1955 or on summary trial under the Naval Discipline Act 1957,

(c) proceedings before a court established by section 83ZA of the Army Act 1955, section 83ZA of the Air Force Act 1955 or section 52FF of the Naval Discipline Act 1957 (summary appeal courts),

(d) proceedings before the Courts-Martial Appeal Court, and

(e) proceedings before a Standing Civilian Court;

"offence" includes any offence under the Army Act 1955, the Air Force Act 1955 or the Naval Discipline Act 1957.

(6) In the application of this section to Scotland—

(a) in subsection (1)(b), for the words from "a decision" to the end there is substituted "a decision by the authority to make a report to the procurator fiscal for the purpose of enabling him to determine whether criminal proceedings should be instituted",

(b) in subsections (1)(c) and (2)(a)(ii) for "which the authority has power to conduct" there is substituted "which have been instituted in consequence of a report made by the authority to the procurator fiscal", and

(c) for any reference to a person being charged with an offence there is substituted a reference to the person being prosecuted for the offence.

[749]

NOTES

Commencement: 1 January 2005.

Sub-s (5): in definition "criminal proceedings" words omitted from para (a) repealed by the Armed Forces Act 2001, s 38, Sch 7, Pt 1 (note that the Queen's Printer's copy of the 2001 Act erroneously purports to make this amendment to s 29(5) of this Act); substituted by the Armed Forces Act 2006, s 378(1), Sch 16, para 176, as from a day to be appointed, as follows:

"(5) In this section—

"criminal proceedings" includes service law proceedings (as defined by section 324(5) of the Armed Forces Act 2006);

"offence" includes a service offence (as defined by section 50 of that Act).".

31 Law enforcement

(1) Information which is not exempt information by virtue of section 30 is exempt information if its disclosure under this Act would, or would be likely to, prejudice—

(a) the prevention or detection of crime,

(b) the apprehension or prosecution of offenders,

(c) the administration of justice,

(d) the assessment or collection of any tax or duty or of any imposition of a similar nature,

(e) the operation of the immigration controls,

(f) the maintenance of security and good order in prisons or in other institutions where persons are lawfully detained,

(g) the exercise by any public authority of its functions for any of the purposes specified in subsection (2),

(h) any civil proceedings which are brought by or on behalf of a public authority and arise out of an investigation conducted, for any of the purposes specified in subsection (2), by or on behalf of the authority by virtue of Her Majesty's prerogative or by virtue of powers conferred by or under an enactment, or

(i) any inquiry held under the Fatal Accidents and Sudden Deaths Inquiries

(Scotland) Act 1976 to the extent that the inquiry arises out of an investigation conducted, for any of the purposes specified in subsection (2), by or on behalf of the authority by virtue of Her Majesty's prerogative or by virtue of powers conferred by or under an enactment.

(2) The purposes referred to in subsection (1)(g) to (i) are—

(a) the purpose of ascertaining whether any person has failed to comply with the law,

(b) the purpose of ascertaining whether any person is responsible for any conduct which is improper,

(c) the purpose of ascertaining whether circumstances which would justify regulatory action in pursuance of any enactment exist or may arise,

(d) the purpose of ascertaining a person's fitness or competence in relation to the management of bodies corporate or in relation to any profession or other activity which he is, or seeks to become, authorised to carry on,

(e) the purpose of ascertaining the cause of an accident,

(f) the purpose of protecting charities against misconduct or mismanagement (whether by trustees or other persons) in their administration,

(g) the purpose of protecting the property of charities from loss or misapplication,

(h) the purpose of recovering the property of charities,

(i) the purpose of securing the health, safety and welfare of persons at work, and

(j) the purpose of protecting persons other than persons at work against risk to health or safety arising out of or in connection with the actions of persons at work.

(3) The duty to confirm or deny does not arise if, or to the extent that, compliance with section 1(1)(a) would, or would be likely to, prejudice any of the matters mentioned in subsection (1).

[750]

NOTES

Commencement: 1 January 2005.

32 Court records, etc

(1) Information held by a public authority is exempt information if it is held only by virtue of being contained in—

(a) any document filed with, or otherwise placed in the custody of, a court for the purposes of proceedings in a particular cause or matter,

(b) any document served upon, or by, a public authority for the purposes of proceedings in a particular cause or matter, or

(c) any document created by—

(i) a court, or

(ii) a member of the administrative staff of a court,

for the purposes of proceedings in a particular cause or matter.

(2) Information held by a public authority is exempt information if it is held only by virtue of being contained in—

(a) any document placed in the custody of a person conducting an inquiry or arbitration, for the purposes of the inquiry or arbitration, or

(b) any document created by a person conducting an inquiry or arbitration, for the purposes of the inquiry or arbitration.

(3) The duty to confirm or deny does not arise in relation to information which is (or if it were held by the public authority would be) exempt information by virtue of this section.

(4) In this section—

(a) "court" includes any tribunal or body exercising the judicial power of the State,

(b) "proceedings in a particular cause or matter" includes any inquest or post-mortem examination,

(c) "inquiry" means any inquiry or hearing held under any provision contained in, or made under, an enactment, and

(d) except in relation to Scotland, "arbitration" means any arbitration to which Part I of the Arbitration Act 1996 applies.

[751]

NOTES

Commencement: 1 January 2005.

Disapplication: sub-s (2) is disapplied in relation to information contained in documents that, in pursuance of rules under the Inquiries Act 2005, s 41(1)(b), have been passed to and are held by a public authority, by the Inquiries Act 2005, s 18(3).

33 Audit functions

(1) This section applies to any public authority which has functions in relation to—

(a) the audit of the accounts of other public authorities, or

(b) the examination of the economy, efficiency and effectiveness with which other public authorities use their resources in discharging their functions.

(2) Information held by a public authority to which this section applies is exempt information if its disclosure would, or would be likely to, prejudice the exercise of any of the authority's functions in relation to any of the matters referred to in subsection (1).

(3) The duty to confirm or deny does not arise in relation to a public authority to which this section applies if, or to the extent that, compliance with section 1(1)(a) would, or would be likely to, prejudice the exercise of any of the authority's functions in relation to any of the matters referred to in subsection (1).

[752]

NOTES

Commencement: 1 January 2005.

34 Parliamentary privilege

(1) Information is exempt information if exemption from section 1(1)(b) is required for the purpose of avoiding an infringement of the privileges of either House of Parliament.

(2) The duty to confirm or deny does not apply if, or to the extent that, exemption from section 1(1)(a) is required for the purpose of avoiding an infringement of the privileges of either House of Parliament.

(3) A certificate signed by the appropriate authority certifying that exemption from section 1(1)(b), or from section 1(1)(a) and (b), is, or at any time was, required for the purpose of avoiding an infringement of the privileges of either House of Parliament shall be conclusive evidence of that fact.

(4) In subsection (3) "the appropriate authority" means—

(a) in relation to the House of Commons, the Speaker of that House, and

(b) in relation to the House of Lords, the Clerk of the Parliaments.

[753]

NOTES

Commencement: 1 January 2005.

35 Formulation of government policy, etc

(1) Information held by a government department or by the National Assembly for Wales is exempt information if it relates to—

(a) the formulation or development of government policy,

(b) Ministerial communications,

(c) the provision of advice by any of the Law Officers or any request for the provision of such advice, or

(d) the operation of any Ministerial private office.

(2) Once a decision as to government policy has been taken, any statistical information used to provide an informed background to the taking of the decision is not to be regarded—

(a) for the purposes of subsection (1)(a), as relating to the formulation or development of government policy, or

(b) for the purposes of subsection (1)(b), as relating to Ministerial communications.

(3) The duty to confirm or deny does not arise in relation to information which is (or if it were held by the public authority would be) exempt information by virtue of subsection (1).

(4) In making any determination required by section 2(1)(b) or (2)(b) in relation to information which is exempt information by virtue of subsection (1)(a), regard shall be had to

the particular public interest in the disclosure of factual information which has been used, or is intended to be used, to provide an informed background to decision-taking.

(5) In this section—

"government policy" includes the policy of the Executive Committee of the Northern Ireland Assembly and the policy of the National Assembly for Wales;

"the Law Officers" means the Attorney General, the Solicitor General, the Advocate General for Scotland, the Lord Advocate, the Solicitor General for Scotland and the Attorney General for Northern Ireland;

"Ministerial communications" means any communications—

(a) between Ministers of the Crown,

(b) between Northern Ireland Ministers, including Northern Ireland junior Ministers, or

(c) between Assembly Secretaries, including the Assembly First Secretary,

and includes, in particular, proceedings of the Cabinet or of any committee of the Cabinet, proceedings of the Executive Committee of the Northern Ireland Assembly, and proceedings of the executive committee of the National Assembly for Wales;

"Ministerial private office" means any part of a government department which provides personal administrative support to a Minister of the Crown, to a Northern Ireland Minister or a Northern Ireland junior Minister or any part of the administration of the National Assembly for Wales providing personal administrative support to the Assembly First Secretary or an Assembly Secretary;

"Northern Ireland junior Minister" means a member of the Northern Ireland Assembly appointed as a junior Minister under section 19 of the Northern Ireland Act 1998.

[754]

NOTES

Commencement: 1 January 2005.

36 Prejudice to effective conduct of public affairs

(1) This section applies to—

(a) information which is held by a government department or by the National Assembly for Wales and is not exempt information by virtue of section 35, and

(b) information which is held by any other public authority.

(2) Information to which this section applies is exempt information if, in the reasonable opinion of a qualified person, disclosure of the information under this Act—

(a) would, or would be likely to, prejudice—

(i) the maintenance of the convention of the collective responsibility of Ministers of the Crown, or

(ii) the work of the Executive Committee of the Northern Ireland Assembly, or

(iii) the work of the executive committee of the National Assembly for Wales,

(b) would, or would be likely to, inhibit—

(i) the free and frank provision of advice, or

(ii) the free and frank exchange of views for the purposes of deliberation, or

(c) would otherwise prejudice, or would be likely otherwise to prejudice, the effective conduct of public affairs.

(3) The duty to confirm or deny does not arise in relation to information to which this section applies (or would apply if held by the public authority) if, or to the extent that, in the reasonable opinion of a qualified person, compliance with section 1(1)(a) would, or would be likely to, have any of the effects mentioned in subsection (2).

(4) In relation to statistical information, subsections (2) and (3) shall have effect with the omission of the words "in the reasonable opinion of a qualified person".

(5) In subsections (2) and (3) "qualified person"—

(a) in relation to information held by a government department in the charge of a Minister of the Crown, means any Minister of the Crown,

(b) in relation to information held by a Northern Ireland department, means the Northern Ireland Minister in charge of the department,

(c) in relation to information held by any other government department, means the commissioners or other person in charge of that department,

(d) in relation to information held by the House of Commons, means the Speaker of that House,

(e) in relation to information held by the House of Lords, means the Clerk of the Parliaments,

(f) in relation to information held by the Northern Ireland Assembly, means the Presiding Officer,

(g) in relation to information held by the National Assembly for Wales, means the Assembly First Secretary,

(h) in relation to information held by any Welsh public authority other than the Auditor General for Wales, means—

(i) the public authority, or

(ii) any officer or employee of the authority authorised by the Assembly First Secretary,

(i) in relation to information held by the National Audit Office, means the Comptroller and Auditor General,

(j) in relation to information held by the Northern Ireland Audit Office, means the Comptroller and Auditor General for Northern Ireland,

(k) in relation to information held by the Auditor General for Wales, means the Auditor General for Wales,

(l) in relation to information held by any Northern Ireland public authority other than the Northern Ireland Audit Office, means—

(i) the public authority, or

(ii) any officer or employee of the authority authorised by the First Minister and deputy First Minister in Northern Ireland acting jointly,

(m) in relation to information held by the Greater London Authority, means the Mayor of London,

(n) in relation to information held by a functional body within the meaning of the Greater London Authority Act 1999, means the chairman of that functional body, and

(o) in relation to information held by any public authority not falling within any of paragraphs (a) to (n), means—

(i) a Minister of the Crown,

(ii) the public authority, if authorised for the purposes of this section by a Minister of the Crown, or

(iii) any officer or employee of the public authority who is authorised for the purposes of this section by a Minister of the Crown.

(6) Any authorisation for the purposes of this section—

(a) may relate to a specified person or to persons falling within a specified class,

(b) may be general or limited to particular classes of case, and

(c) may be granted subject to conditions.

(7) A certificate signed by the qualified person referred to in subsection (5)(d) or (e) above certifying that in his reasonable opinion—

(a) disclosure of information held by either House of Parliament, or

(b) compliance with section 1(1)(a) by either House,

would, or would be likely to, have any of the effects mentioned in subsection (2) shall be conclusive evidence of that fact.

[755]

NOTES

Commencement: 1 January 2005.

37 Communications with Her Majesty, etc and honours

(1) Information is exempt information if it relates to—

(a) communications with Her Majesty, with other members of the Royal Family or with the Royal Household, or

(b) the conferring by the Crown of any honour or dignity.

(2) The duty to confirm or deny does not arise in relation to information which is (or if it were held by the public authority would be) exempt information by virtue of subsection (1).

[756]

NOTES

Commencement: 1 January 2005.

PART II
DATA PROTECTION

38 Health and safety

(1) Information is exempt information if its disclosure under this Act would, or would be likely to—

(a) endanger the physical or mental health of any individual, or
(b) endanger the safety of any individual.

(2) The duty to confirm or deny does not arise if, or to the extent that, compliance with section 1(1)(a) would, or would be likely to, have either of the effects mentioned in subsection (1).

[757]

NOTES

Commencement: 1 January 2005.

39 Environmental information

(1) Information is exempt information if the public authority holding it—

(a) is obliged by [environmental information regulations] to make the information available to the public in accordance with the regulations, or
(b) would be so obliged but for any exemption contained in the regulations.

[(1A) In subsection (1) "environmental information regulations" means—

(a) regulations made under section 74, or
(b) regulations made under section 2(2) of the European Communities Act 1972 for the purpose of implementing any Community obligation relating to public access to, and the dissemination of, information on the environment.]

(2) The duty to confirm or deny does not arise in relation to information which is (or if it were held by the public authority would be) exempt information by virtue of subsection (1).

(3) Subsection (1)(a) does not limit the generality of section 21(1).

[758]

NOTES

Commencement: 1 January 2005.
Sub-s (1): words in square brackets substituted by the Environmental Information Regulations 2004, SI 2004/3391, reg 20(1), (2).
Sub-s (1A): inserted by SI 2004/3391, reg 20(1), (3).

40 Personal information

(1) Any information to which a request for information relates is exempt information if it constitutes personal data of which the applicant is the data subject.

(2) Any information to which a request for information relates is also exempt information if—

(a) it constitutes personal data which do not fall within subsection (1), and
(b) either the first or the second condition below is satisfied.

(3) The first condition is—

(a) in a case where the information falls within any of paragraphs (a) to (d) of the definition of "data" in section 1(1) of the Data Protection Act 1998, that the disclosure of the information to a member of the public otherwise than under this Act would contravene—
 (i) any of the data protection principles, or
 (ii) section 10 of that Act (right to prevent processing likely to cause damage or distress), and
(b) in any other case, that the disclosure of the information to a member of the public otherwise than under this Act would contravene any of the data protection principles if the exemptions in section 33A(1) of the Data Protection Act 1998 (which relate to manual data held by public authorities) were disregarded.

(4) The second condition is that by virtue of any provision of Part IV of the Data Protection Act 1998 the information is exempt from section 7(1)(c) of that Act (data subject's right of access to personal data).

(5) The duty to confirm or deny—

(a) does not arise in relation to information which is (or if it were held by the public authority would be) exempt information by virtue of subsection (1), and

(b) does not arise in relation to other information if or to the extent that either—

(i) the giving to a member of the public of the confirmation or denial that would have to be given to comply with section 1(1)(a) would (apart from this Act) contravene any of the data protection principles or section 10 of the Data Protection Act 1998 or would do so if the exemptions in section 33A(1) of that Act were disregarded, or

(ii) by virtue of any provision of Part IV of the Data Protection Act 1998 the information is exempt from section 7(1)(a) of that Act (data subject's right to be informed whether personal data being processed).

(6) In determining for the purposes of this section whether anything done before 24th October 2007 would contravene any of the data protection principles, the exemptions in Part III of Schedule 8 to the Data Protection Act 1998 shall be disregarded.

(7) In this section—

"the data protection principles" means the principles set out in Part I of Schedule 1 to the Data Protection Act 1998, as read subject to Part II of that Schedule and section 27(1) of that Act;

"data subject" has the same meaning as in section 1(1) of that Act;

"personal data" has the same meaning as in section 1(1) of that Act.

[759]

NOTES

Commencement: 1 January 2005.

41 Information provided in confidence

(1) Information is exempt information if—

(a) it was obtained by the public authority from any other person (including another public authority), and

(b) the disclosure of the information to the public (otherwise than under this Act) by the public authority holding it would constitute a breach of confidence actionable by that or any other person.

(2) The duty to confirm or deny does not arise if, or to the extent that, the confirmation or denial that would have to be given to comply with section 1(1)(a) would (apart from this Act) constitute an actionable breach of confidence.

[760]

NOTES

Commencement: 1 January 2005.

42 Legal professional privilege

(1) Information in respect of which a claim to legal professional privilege or, in Scotland, to confidentiality of communications could be maintained in legal proceedings is exempt information.

(2) The duty to confirm or deny does not arise if, or to the extent that, compliance with section 1(1)(a) would involve the disclosure of any information (whether or not already recorded) in respect of which such a claim could be maintained in legal proceedings.

[761]

NOTES

Commencement: 1 January 2005.

43 Commercial interests

(1) Information is exempt information if it constitutes a trade secret.

(2) Information is exempt information if its disclosure under this Act would, or would be likely to, prejudice the commercial interests of any person (including the public authority holding it).

(3) The duty to confirm or deny does not arise if, or to the extent that, compliance with section 1(1)(a) would, or would be likely to, prejudice the interests mentioned in subsection (2).

[762]

NOTES

Commencement: 1 January 2005.

44 Prohibitions on disclosure

(1) Information is exempt information if its disclosure (otherwise than under this Act) by the public authority holding it—

(a) is prohibited by or under any enactment,

(b) is incompatible with any Community obligation, or

(c) would constitute or be punishable as a contempt of court.

(2) The duty to confirm or deny does not arise if the confirmation or denial that would have to be given to comply with section 1(1)(a) would (apart from this Act) fall within any of paragraphs (a) to (c) of subsection (1).

[763]

NOTES

Commencement: 1 January 2005.

PART III
GENERAL FUNCTIONS OF … LORD CHANCELLOR AND INFORMATION COMMISSIONER

45 Issue of code of practice …

(1) The [Secretary of State] shall issue, and may from time to time revise, a code of practice providing guidance to public authorities as to the practice which it would, in his opinion, be desirable for them to follow in connection with the discharge of the authorities' functions under Part I.

(2) The code of practice must, in particular, include provision relating to—

(a) the provision of advice and assistance by public authorities to persons who propose to make, or have made, requests for information to them,

(b) the transfer of requests by one public authority to another public authority by which the information requested is or may be held,

(c) consultation with persons to whom the information requested relates or persons whose interests are likely to be affected by the disclosure of information,

(d) the inclusion in contracts entered into by public authorities of terms relating to the disclosure of information, and

(e) the provision by public authorities of procedures for dealing with complaints about the handling by them of requests for information.

(3) The code may make different provision for different public authorities.

(4) Before issuing or revising any code under this section, the [Secretary of State] shall consult the Commissioner.

(5) The [Secretary of State] shall lay before each House of Parliament any code or revised code made under this section.

[764]

NOTES

Commencement: 30 November 2000 (for the purpose of exercising the power to make codes of practice); 30 November 2002 (otherwise).

Part heading, section heading: words omitted repealed by the Transfer of Functions (Miscellaneous) Order 2001, SI 2001/3500, art 8, Sch 2, Pt I, para 8(1)(h).

Sub-ss (1), (4), (5): words in square brackets substituted by the Secretary of State for Constitutional Affairs Order 2003, SI 2003/1887, art 9, Sch 2, para 12(1)(a).

46 Issue of code of practice by Lord Chancellor

(1) The Lord Chancellor shall issue, and may from time to time revise, a code of practice providing guidance to relevant authorities as to the practice which it would, in his opinion, be desirable for them to follow in connection with the keeping, management and destruction of their records.

(2) For the purpose of facilitating the performance by the Public Record Office, the Public Record Office of Northern Ireland and other public authorities of their functions under this Act in relation to records which are public records for the purposes of the Public Records Act 1958 or the Public Records Act (Northern Ireland) 1923, the code may also include guidance as to—

(a) the practice to be adopted in relation to the transfer of records under section 3(4) of the Public Records Act 1958 or section 3 of the Public Records Act (Northern Ireland) 1923, and
(b) the practice of reviewing records before they are transferred under those provisions.

(3) In exercising his functions under this section, the Lord Chancellor shall have regard to the public interest in allowing public access to information held by relevant authorities.

(4) The code may make different provision for different relevant authorities.

(5) Before issuing or revising any code under this section the Lord Chancellor shall consult—

(a) …
[(a) the Secretary of State,]
(b) the Commissioner, and
(c) in relation to Northern Ireland, the appropriate Northern Ireland Minister.

(6) The Lord Chancellor shall lay before each House of Parliament any code or revised code made under this section.

(7) In this section "relevant authority" means—

(a) any public authority, and
(b) any office or body which is not a public authority but whose administrative and departmental records are public records for the purposes of the Public Records Act 1958 or the Public Records Act (Northern Ireland) 1923.

[765]

NOTES

Commencement: 30 November 2000 (for the purpose of exercising the power to make codes of practice); 30 November 2002 (otherwise).

Sub-s (5): original para (a) repealed by the Transfer of Functions (Miscellaneous) Order 2001, SI 2001/3500, art 8, Sch 2, Pt I, para 8(2); new para (a) inserted by the Secretary of State for Constitutional Affairs Order 2003, SI 2003/1887, art 9, Sch 2, para 12(2).

47 General functions of Commissioner

(1) It shall be the duty of the Commissioner to promote the following of good practice by public authorities and, in particular, so to perform his functions under this Act as to promote the observance by public authorities of—

(a) the requirements of this Act, and
(b) the provisions of the codes of practice under sections 45 and 46.

(2) The Commissioner shall arrange for the dissemination in such form and manner as he considers appropriate of such information as it may appear to him expedient to give to the public—

(a) about the operation of this Act,
(b) about good practice, and
(c) about other matters within the scope of his functions under this Act,

and may give advice to any person as to any of those matters.

(3) The Commissioner may, with the consent of any public authority, assess whether that authority is following good practice.

(4) The Commissioner may charge such sums as he may with the consent of the [Secretary of State] determine for any services provided by the Commissioner under this section.

(5) The Commissioner shall from time to time as he considers appropriate—

(a) consult the Keeper of Public Records about the promotion by the Commissioner of the observance by public authorities of the provisions of the code of practice under section 46 in relation to records which are public records for the purposes of the Public Records Act 1958, and

(b) consult the Deputy Keeper of the Records of Northern Ireland about the promotion by the Commissioner of the observance by public authorities of those provisions in relation to records which are public records for the purposes of the Public Records Act (Northern Ireland) 1923.

(6) In this section "good practice", in relation to a public authority, means such practice in the discharge of its functions under this Act as appears to the Commissioner to be desirable, and includes (but is not limited to) compliance with the requirements of this Act and the provisions of the codes of practice under sections 45 and 46.

[766]

NOTES

Commencement: 30 November 2000 (sub-ss (2)–(6)); 30 November 2002 (otherwise).

Sub-s (4): words in square brackets substituted by the Secretary of State for Constitutional Affairs Order 2003, SI 2003/1887, art 9, Sch 2, para 12(1)(a).

48 Recommendations as to good practice

(1) If it appears to the Commissioner that the practice of a public authority in relation to the exercise of its functions under this Act does not conform with that proposed in the codes of practice under sections 45 and 46, he may give to the authority a recommendation (in this section referred to as a "practice recommendation") specifying the steps which ought in his opinion to be taken for promoting such conformity.

(2) A practice recommendation must be given in writing and must refer to the particular provisions of the code of practice with which, in the Commissioner's opinion, the public authority's practice does not conform.

(3) Before giving to a public authority other than the Public Record Office a practice recommendation which relates to conformity with the code of practice under section 46 in respect of records which are public records for the purposes of the Public Records Act 1958, the Commissioner shall consult the Keeper of Public Records.

(4) Before giving to a public authority other than the Public Record Office of Northern Ireland a practice recommendation which relates to conformity with the code of practice under section 46 in respect of records which are public records for the purposes of the Public Records Act (Northern Ireland) 1923, the Commissioner shall consult the Deputy Keeper of the Records of Northern Ireland.

[767]

NOTES

Commencement: 30 November 2002 (sub-ss (1), (2), in relation to the issue of practice recommendations relating to the conformity with the code of practice under s 45 hereof of the practice of public authorities in relation to the exercise of their functions under the publication scheme provisions); 1 January 2005 (otherwise).

49 Reports to be laid before Parliament

(1) The Commissioner shall lay annually before each House of Parliament a general report on the exercise of his functions under this Act.

(2) The Commissioner may from time to time lay before each House of Parliament such other reports with respect to those functions as he thinks fit.

[768]

PART IV
ENFORCEMENT

50 Application for decision by Commissioner

(1) Any person (in this section referred to as "the complainant") may apply to the Commissioner for a decision whether, in any specified respect, a request for information made by the complainant to a public authority has been dealt with in accordance with the requirements of Part I.

(2) On receiving an application under this section, the Commissioner shall make a decision unless it appears to him—
- (a) that the complainant has not exhausted any complaints procedure which is provided by the public authority in conformity with the code of practice under section 45,
- (b) that there has been undue delay in making the application,
- (c) that the application is frivolous or vexatious, or
- (d) that the application has been withdrawn or abandoned.

(3) Where the Commissioner has received an application under this section, he shall either—
- (a) notify the complainant that he has not made any decision under this section as a result of the application and of his grounds for not doing so, or
- (b) serve notice of his decision (in this Act referred to as a "decision notice") on the complainant and the public authority.

(4) Where the Commissioner decides that a public authority—
- (a) has failed to communicate information, or to provide confirmation or denial, in a case where it is required to do so by section 1(1), or
- (b) has failed to comply with any of the requirements of sections 11 and 17,

the decision notice must specify the steps which must be taken by the authority for complying with that requirement and the period within which they must be taken.

(5) A decision notice must contain particulars of the right of appeal conferred by section 57.

(6) Where a decision notice requires steps to be taken by the public authority within a specified period, the time specified in the notice must not expire before the end of the period within which an appeal can be brought against the notice and, if such an appeal is brought, no step which is affected by the appeal need be taken pending the determination or withdrawal of the appeal.

(7) This section has effect subject to section 53.

[769]

NOTES

Commencement: 1 January 2005.

51 Information notices

(1) If the Commissioner—
- (a) has received an application under section 50, or
- (b) reasonably requires any information—
  - (i) for the purpose of determining whether a public authority has complied or is complying with any of the requirements of Part I, or
  - (ii) for the purpose of determining whether the practice of a public authority in relation to the exercise of its functions under this Act conforms with that proposed in the codes of practice under sections 45 and 46,

he may serve the authority with a notice (in this Act referred to as "an information notice") requiring it, within such time as is specified in the notice, to furnish the Commissioner, in such form as may be so specified, with such information relating to the application, to compliance with Part I or to conformity with the code of practice as is so specified.

(2) An information notice must contain—
- (a) in a case falling within subsection (1)(a), a statement that the Commissioner has received an application under section 50, or
- (b) in a case falling within subsection (1)(b), a statement—

PART II
DATA PROTECTION

(i) that the Commissioner regards the specified information as relevant for either of the purposes referred to in subsection (1)(b), and

(ii) of his reasons for regarding that information as relevant for that purpose.

(3) An information notice must also contain particulars of the right of appeal conferred by section 57.

(4) The time specified in an information notice must not expire before the end of the period within which an appeal can be brought against the notice and, if such an appeal is brought, the information need not be furnished pending the determination or withdrawal of the appeal.

(5) An authority shall not be required by virtue of this section to furnish the Commissioner with any information in respect of—

(a) any communication between a professional legal adviser and his client in connection with the giving of legal advice to the client with respect to his obligations, liabilities or rights under this Act, or

(b) any communication between a professional legal adviser and his client, or between such an adviser or his client and any other person, made in connection with or in contemplation of proceedings under or arising out of this Act (including proceedings before the Tribunal) and for the purposes of such proceedings.

(6) In subsection (5) references to the client of a professional legal adviser include references to any person representing such a client.

(7) The Commissioner may cancel an information notice by written notice to the authority on which it was served.

(8) In this section "information" includes unrecorded information.

[770]

NOTES

Commencement: 30 November 2002 (in relation to the issue and enforcement of information notices relating to the conformity with the code of practice under s 45 hereof of the practice of public authorities in relation to the exercise of their functions under the publication scheme provisions); 1 January 2005 (otherwise).

52 Enforcement notices

(1) If the Commissioner is satisfied that a public authority has failed to comply with any of the requirements of Part I, the Commissioner may serve the authority with a notice (in this Act referred to as "an enforcement notice") requiring the authority to take, within such time as may be specified in the notice, such steps as may be so specified for complying with those requirements.

(2) An enforcement notice must contain—

(a) a statement of the requirement or requirements of Part I with which the Commissioner is satisfied that the public authority has failed to comply and his reasons for reaching that conclusion, and

(b) particulars of the right of appeal conferred by section 57.

(3) An enforcement notice must not require any of the provisions of the notice to be complied with before the end of the period within which an appeal can be brought against the notice and, if such an appeal is brought, the notice need not be complied with pending the determination or withdrawal of the appeal.

(4) The Commissioner may cancel an enforcement notice by written notice to the authority on which it was served.

(5) This section has effect subject to section 53.

[771]

NOTES

Commencement: 30 November 2002 (in relation to the enforcement of the requirements on public authorities under the publication scheme provisions); 1 January 2005 (otherwise).

53 Exception from duty to comply with decision notice or enforcement notice

(1) This section applies to a decision notice or enforcement notice which—

(a) is served on—
   (i) a government department,
   (ii) the National Assembly for Wales, or
   (iii) any public authority designated for the purposes of this section by an order made by the [Secretary of State], and
(b) relates to a failure, in respect of one or more requests for information—
   (i) to comply with section 1(1)(a) in respect of information which falls within any provision of Part II stating that the duty to confirm or deny does not arise, or
   (ii) to comply with section 1(1)(b) in respect of exempt information.

(2) A decision notice or enforcement notice to which this section applies shall cease to have effect if, not later than the twentieth working day following the effective date, the accountable person in relation to that authority gives the Commissioner a certificate signed by him stating that he has on reasonable grounds formed the opinion that, in respect of the request or requests concerned, there was no failure falling within subsection (1)(b).

(3) Where the accountable person gives a certificate to the Commissioner under subsection (2) he shall as soon as practicable thereafter lay a copy of the certificate before—
(a) each House of Parliament,
(b) the Northern Ireland Assembly, in any case where the certificate relates to a decision notice or enforcement notice which has been served on a Northern Ireland department or any Northern Ireland public authority, or
(c) the National Assembly for Wales, in any case where the certificate relates to a decision notice or enforcement notice which has been served on the National Assembly for Wales or any Welsh public authority.

(4) In subsection (2) "the effective date", in relation to a decision notice or enforcement notice, means—
(a) the day on which the notice was given to the public authority, or
(b) where an appeal under section 57 is brought, the day on which that appeal (or any further appeal arising out of it) is determined or withdrawn.

(5) Before making an order under subsection (1)(a)(iii), the [Secretary of State] shall—
(a) if the order relates to a Welsh public authority, consult the National Assembly for Wales,
(b) if the order relates to the Northern Ireland Assembly, consult the Presiding Officer of that Assembly, and
(c) if the order relates to a Northern Ireland public authority, consult the First Minister and deputy First Minister in Northern Ireland.

(6) Where the accountable person gives a certificate to the Commissioner under subsection (2) in relation to a decision notice, the accountable person shall, on doing so or as soon as reasonably practicable after doing so, inform the person who is the complainant for the purposes of section 50 of the reasons for his opinion.

(7) The accountable person is not obliged to provide information under subsection (6) if, or to the extent that, compliance with that subsection would involve the disclosure of exempt information.

(8) In this section "the accountable person"—
(a) in relation to a Northern Ireland department or any Northern Ireland public authority, means the First Minister and deputy First Minister in Northern Ireland acting jointly,
(b) in relation to the National Assembly for Wales or any Welsh public authority, means the Assembly First Secretary, and
(c) in relation to any other public authority, means—
   (i) a Minister of the Crown who is a member of the Cabinet, or
   (ii) the Attorney General, the Advocate General for Scotland or the Attorney General for Northern Ireland.

(9) In this section "working day" has the same meaning as in section 10.

[772]

NOTES

Commencement: 30 November 2000 (so far as confers powers to make any order, regulations or code of practice): 1 January 2005 (otherwise).

Sub-ss (1), (5): words in square brackets substituted by the Secretary of State for Constitutional Affairs Order 2003, SI 2003/1887, art 9, Sch 2, para 12(1)(a).

54 Failure to comply with notice

(1) If a public authority has failed to comply with—

(a) so much of a decision notice as requires steps to be taken,

(b) an information notice, or

(c) an enforcement notice,

the Commissioner may certify in writing to the court that the public authority has failed to comply with that notice.

(2) For the purposes of this section, a public authority which, in purported compliance with an information notice—

(a) makes a statement which it knows to be false in a material respect, or

(b) recklessly makes a statement which is false in a material respect,

is to be taken to have failed to comply with the notice.

(3) Where a failure to comply is certified under subsection (1), the court may inquire into the matter and, after hearing any witness who may be produced against or on behalf of the public authority, and after hearing any statement that may be offered in defence, deal with the authority as if it had committed a contempt of court.

(4) In this section "the court" means the High Court or, in Scotland, the Court of Session. **[773]**

NOTES

Commencement: 30 November 2002 (in so far as it relates to the enforcement of the requirements on public authorities under the publication scheme provisions and so far as relates to: (i) the issue of practice recommendations, and (ii) the issue and enforcement of information notices, relating to the conformity with the code of practice under s 45 of the practice of public authorities in relation to the exercise of their functions under the publication scheme provisions); 1 January 2005 (otherwise).

55 Powers of entry and inspection

Schedule 3 (powers of entry and inspection) has effect. **[774]**

NOTES

Commencement: 30 November 2002 (certain purposes); 1 January 2005 (otherwise).

56 No action against public authority

(1) This Act does not confer any right of action in civil proceedings in respect of any failure to comply with any duty imposed by or under this Act.

(2) Subsection (1) does not affect the powers of the Commissioner under section 54. **[775]**

NOTES

Commencement: 30 November 2002.

PART V
APPEALS

57 Appeal against notices served under Part IV

(1) Where a decision notice has been served, the complainant or the public authority may appeal to the Tribunal against the notice.

(2) A public authority on which an information notice or an enforcement notice has been served by the Commissioner may appeal to the Tribunal against the notice.

(3) In relation to a decision notice or enforcement notice which relates—

(a) to information to which section 66 applies, and

(b) to a matter which by virtue of subsection (3) or (4) of that section falls to be determined by the responsible authority instead of the appropriate records authority,

subsections (1) and (2) shall have effect as if the reference to the public authority were a reference to the public authority or the responsible authority.

[776]

NOTES

Commencement: 30 November 2002 (sub-s (2)); 1 January 2005 (otherwise).

58 Determination of appeals

(1) If on an appeal under section 57 the Tribunal considers—

(a) that the notice against which the appeal is brought is not in accordance with the law, or

(b) to the extent that the notice involved an exercise of discretion by the Commissioner, that he ought to have exercised his discretion differently,

the Tribunal shall allow the appeal or substitute such other notice as could have been served by the Commissioner; and in any other case the Tribunal shall dismiss the appeal.

(2) On such an appeal, the Tribunal may review any finding of fact on which the notice in question was based.

[777]

NOTES

Commencement: 30 November 2002.

59 Appeals from decision of Tribunal

Any party to an appeal to the Tribunal under section 57 may appeal from the decision of the Tribunal on a point of law to the appropriate court; and that court shall be—

(a) the High Court of Justice in England if the address of the public authority is in England or Wales,

(b) the Court of Session if that address is in Scotland, and

(c) the High Court of Justice in Northern Ireland if that address is in Northern Ireland.

[778]

NOTES

Commencement: 30 November 2002.

60 Appeals against national security certificate

(1) Where a certificate under section 23(2) or 24(3) has been issued—

(a) the Commissioner, or

(b) any applicant whose request for information is affected by the issue of the certificate,

may appeal to the Tribunal against the certificate.

(2) If on an appeal under subsection (1) relating to a certificate under section 23(2), the Tribunal finds that the information referred to in the certificate was not exempt information by virtue of section 23(1), the Tribunal may allow the appeal and quash the certificate.

(3) If on an appeal under subsection (1) relating to a certificate under section 24(3), the Tribunal finds that, applying the principles applied by the court on an application for judicial review, the Minister did not have reasonable grounds for issuing the certificate, the Tribunal may allow the appeal and quash the certificate.

(4) Where in any proceedings under this Act it is claimed by a public authority that a certificate under section 24(3) which identifies the information to which it applies by means of a general description applies to particular information, any other party to the proceedings may appeal to the Tribunal on the ground that the certificate does not apply to the information in question and, subject to any determination under subsection (5), the certificate shall be conclusively presumed so to apply.

(5) On any appeal under subsection (4), the Tribunal may determine that the certificate does not so apply.

[779]

NOTES

Commencement: 1 January 2005.

61 Appeal proceedings

(1) Schedule 4 (which contains amendments of Schedule 6 to the Data Protection Act 1998 relating to appeal proceedings) has effect.

(2) Accordingly, the provisions of Schedule 6 to the Data Protection Act 1998 have effect (so far as applicable) in relation to appeals under this Part.

[780]

NOTES

Commencement: 14 May 2001 (sub-s (1), certain purposes); 30 November 2002 (sub-s (1) certain purposes, sub-s (2)); 1 January 2005 (otherwise).

PART VI
HISTORICAL RECORDS AND RECORDS IN PUBLIC RECORD OFFICE OR PUBLIC RECORD OFFICE OF NORTHERN IRELAND

62 Interpretation of Part VI

(1) For the purposes of this Part, a record becomes a "historical record" at the end of the period of thirty years beginning with the year following that in which it was created.

(2) Where records created at different dates are for administrative purposes kept together in one file or other assembly, all the records in that file or other assembly are to be treated for the purposes of this Part as having been created when the latest of those records was created.

(3) In this Part "year" means a calendar year.

[781]

NOTES

Commencement: 1 January 2005.

63 Removal of exemptions: historical records generally

(1) Information contained in a historical record cannot be exempt information by virtue of section 28, 30(1), 32, 33, 35, 36, 37(1)(a), 42 or 43.

(2) Compliance with section 1(1)(a) in relation to a historical record is not to be taken to be capable of having any of the effects referred to in section 28(3), 33(3), 36(3), 42(2) or 43(3).

(3) Information cannot be exempt information by virtue of section 37(1)(b) after the end of the period of sixty years beginning with the year following that in which the record containing the information was created.

(4) Information cannot be exempt information by virtue of section 31 after the end of the period of one hundred years beginning with the year following that in which the record containing the information was created.

(5) Compliance with section 1(1)(a) in relation to any record is not to be taken, at any time after the end of the period of one hundred years beginning with the year following that in which the record was created, to be capable of prejudicing any of the matters referred to in section 31(1).

[782]

NOTES

Commencement: 1 January 2005.

64 Removal of exemptions: historical records in public record offices

(1) Information contained in a historical record in the Public Record Office or the Public Record Office of Northern Ireland cannot be exempt information by virtue of section 21 or 22.

(2) In relation to any information falling within section 23(1) which is contained in a historical record in the Public Record Office or the Public Record Office of Northern Ireland, section 2(3) shall have effect with the omission of the reference to section 23.

[783]

NOTES

Commencement: 1 January 2005.

65 Decisions as to refusal of discretionary disclosure of historical records

(1) Before refusing a request for information relating to information which is contained in a historical record and is exempt information only by virtue of a provision not specified in section 2(3), a public authority shall—

(a) if the historical record is a public record within the meaning of the Public Records Act 1958, consult the Lord Chancellor, or

(b) if the historical record is a public record to which the Public Records Act (Northern Ireland) 1923 applies, consult the appropriate Northern Ireland Minister.

(2) This section does not apply to information to which section 66 applies.

[784]

NOTES

Commencement: 1 January 2005.

66 Decisions relating to certain transferred public records

(1) This section applies to any information which is (or, if it existed, would be) contained in a transferred public record, other than information which the responsible authority has designated as open information for the purposes of this section.

(2) Before determining whether—

(a) information to which this section applies falls within any provision of Part II relating to the duty to confirm or deny, or

(b) information to which this section applies is exempt information,

the appropriate records authority shall consult the responsible authority.

(3) Where information to which this section applies falls within a provision of Part II relating to the duty to confirm or deny but does not fall within any of the provisions of that Part relating to that duty which are specified in subsection (3) of section 2, any question as to the application of subsection (1)(b) of that section is to be determined by the responsible authority instead of the appropriate records authority.

(4) Where any information to which this section applies is exempt information only by virtue of any provision of Part II not specified in subsection (3) of section 2, any question as to the application of subsection (2)(b) of that section is to be determined by the responsible authority instead of the appropriate records authority.

(5) Before making by virtue of subsection (3) or (4) any determination that subsection (1)(b) or (2)(b) of section 2 applies, the responsible authority shall consult—

(a) where the transferred public record is a public record within the meaning of the Public Records Act 1958, the Lord Chancellor, and

(b) where the transferred public record is a public record to which the Public Records Act (Northern Ireland) 1923 applies, the appropriate Northern Ireland Minister.

(6) Where the responsible authority in relation to information to which this section applies is not (apart from this subsection) a public authority, it shall be treated as being a public authority for the purposes of Parts III, IV and V of this Act so far as relating to—

(a) the duty imposed by section 15(3), and

(b) the imposition of any requirement to furnish information relating to compliance with Part I in connection with the information to which this section applies.

[785]

NOTES
Commencement: 1 January 2005.

67–73 (*S 67 introduces Sch 5 to this Act (amendments to the Public Records Act 1958 and the Public Records Act (Northern Ireland) 1923) outside the scope of this work; ss 68–72 amend the Data Protection Act 1998, ss 1, 7, 16, 34, 55, 56, 67, 71, Sch 8, Pt III, Sch 13 at* **[505]**, **[511]**, **[522]**, **[541]**, **[563]**, **[564]**, **[575]**, **[579]**, **[595]**, **[602]**, *and insert ss 9A, 33A of that Act at* **[514]**, **[540]**; *s 73 introduces Sch 6 to this Act (further amendments to the Data Protection Act 1998).*)

PART VIII
MISCELLANEOUS AND SUPPLEMENTAL

74 Power to make provision relating to environmental information

(1) In this section "the Aarhus Convention" means the Convention on Access to Information, Public Participation in Decision-making and Access to Justice in Environmental Matters signed at Aarhus on 25th June 1998.

(2) For the purposes of this section "the information provisions" of the Aarhus Convention are Article 4, together with Articles 3 and 9 so far as relating to that Article.

(3) The Secretary of State may by regulations make such provision as he considers appropriate—

(a) for the purpose of implementing the information provisions of the Aarhus Convention or any amendment of those provisions made in accordance with Article 14 of the Convention, and

(b) for the purpose of dealing with matters arising out of or related to the implementation of those provisions or of any such amendment.

(4) Regulations under subsection (3) may in particular—

(a) enable charges to be made for making information available in accordance with the regulations,

(b) provide that any obligation imposed by the regulations in relation to the disclosure of information is to have effect notwithstanding any enactment or rule of law,

(c) make provision for the issue by the Secretary of State of a code of practice,

(d) provide for sections 47 and 48 to apply in relation to such a code with such modifications as may be specified,

(e) provide for any of the provisions of Parts IV and V to apply, with such modifications as may be specified in the regulations, in relation to compliance with any requirement of the regulations, and

(f) contain such transitional or consequential provision (including provision modifying any enactment) as the Secretary of State considers appropriate.

(5) This section has effect subject to section 80.

[786]

75 Power to amend or repeal enactments prohibiting disclosure of information

(1) If, with respect to any enactment which prohibits the disclosure of information held by a public authority, it appears to the [Secretary of State] that by virtue of section 44(1)(a) the enactment is capable of preventing the disclosure of information under section 1, he may by order repeal or amend the enactment for the purpose of removing or relaxing the prohibition.

(2) In subsection (1)—

"enactment" means—

(a) any enactment contained in an Act passed before or in the same Session as this Act, or

(b) any enactment contained in Northern Ireland legislation or subordinate legislation passed or made before the passing of this Act;

"information" includes unrecorded information.

(3) An order under this section may do all or any of the following—

(a) make such modifications of enactments as, in the opinion of the [Secretary of State], are consequential upon, or incidental to, the amendment or repeal of the enactment containing the prohibition;

(b) contain such transitional provisions and savings as appear to the [Secretary of State] to be appropriate;

(c) make different provision for different cases.

[787]

NOTES

Sub-ss (1), (3): words in square brackets substituted by the Secretary of State for Constitutional Affairs Order 2003, SI 2003/1887, art 9, Sch 2, para 12(1)(c).

Orders: the Freedom of Information (Removal and Relaxation of Statutory Prohibitions on Disclosure of Information) Order 2004, SI 2004/3363.

76 Disclosure of information between Commissioner and ombudsmen

(1) The Commissioner may disclose to a person specified in the first column of the Table below any information obtained by, or furnished to, the Commissioner under or for the purposes of this Act or the Data Protection Act 1998 if it appears to the Commissioner that the information relates to a matter which could be the subject of an investigation by that person under the enactment specified in relation to that person in the second column of that Table.

TABLE

Ombudsman	*Enactment*
The Parliamentary Commissioner for Administration	The Parliamentary Commissioner Act 1967 (c 13).
The Health Service Commissioner for England	The Health Service Commissioners Act 1993 (c 46).
…	…
…	…
A Local Commissioner as defined by section 23(3) of the Local Government Act 1974	Part III of the Local Government Act 1974 (c 7).
[The Scottish Public Services Ombudsman	The Scottish Public Services Ombudsman Act 2002 (asp 11)]
…	…
…	…
[The Public Services Ombudsman for Wales	Part 2 of the Public Services Ombudsman (Wales) Act 2005.]
[…	…]
The Northern Ireland Commissioner for Complaints	The Commissioner for Complaints (Northern Ireland) Order 1996 (SI 1996/1297 (NI 7)).
The Assembly Ombudsman for Northern Ireland	The Ombudsman (Northern Ireland) Order 1996 (SI 1996/1298 (NI 8)).
[The Commissioner for Older People in Wales	The Commissioner for Older People (Wales) Act 2006.]

(2) Schedule 7 (which contains amendments relating to information disclosed to ombudsmen under subsection (1) and to the disclosure of information by ombudsmen to the Commissioner) has effect.

[788]

NOTES

Sub-s (1), Table: entry relating to "The Health Service Commissioner for Wales" (omitted) repealed and entry relating to "The Public Services Ombudsman for Wales" substituted for original entry "The

Welsh Administration Ombudsman" by the Public Services Ombudsman (Wales) Act 2005, s 39, Sch 6, paras 70, 71, Sch 7, subject to transitional provisions in SI 2005/2800, arts 6, 7; entries relating to "The Health Service Commissioner for Scotland", "The Commissioner for Local Administration in Scotland" and "The Scottish Parliamentary Commissioner for Administration" (omitted) repealed and entry relating to "The Scottish Public Services Ombudsman" inserted by the Scottish Public Services Ombudsman Act 2002, s 25(1), Sch 6, para 23(1), (2); entry relating to "The Social Housing Ombudsman for Wales" (omitted) inserted by the Housing Act 2004, s 265(1), Sch 15, para 46, and repealed by the Public Services Ombudsman (Wales) Act 2005, s 39, Sch 6, paras 70, 71(a), Sch 7, subject to transitional provisions in SI 2005/2800, arts 6, 7; entry relating to "The Commissioner for Older People in Wales" inserted by the Commissioner for Older People (Wales) Act 2006, s 1(2), Sch 1, para 21(a).

[76A Disclosure between Commissioner and Scottish Information Commissioner

The Commissioner may disclose to the Scottish Information Commissioner any information obtained or furnished as mentioned in section 76(1) of this Act if it appears to the Commissioner that the information is of the same type that could be obtained by, or furnished to, the Scottish Information Commissioner under or for the purposes of the Freedom of Information (Scotland) Act 2002.]

[788A]

NOTES

Commencement: 1 January 2005.

Inserted by the Freedom of Information (Scotland) Act 2002 (Consequential Modifications) Order 2004, SI 2004/3089, art 3(1), (2).

77 Offence of altering etc records with intent to prevent disclosure

(1) Where—

(a) a request for information has been made to a public authority, and

(b) under section 1 of this Act or section 7 of the Data Protection Act 1998, the applicant would have been entitled (subject to payment of any fee) to communication of any information in accordance with that section,

any person to whom this subsection applies is guilty of an offence if he alters, defaces, blocks, erases, destroys or conceals any record held by the public authority, with the intention of preventing the disclosure by that authority of all, or any part, of the information to the communication of which the applicant would have been entitled.

(2) Subsection (1) applies to the public authority and to any person who is employed by, is an officer of, or is subject to the direction of, the public authority.

(3) A person guilty of an offence under this section is liable on summary conviction to a fine not exceeding level 5 on the standard scale.

(4) No proceedings for an offence under this section shall be instituted—

(a) in England or Wales, except by the Commissioner or by or with the consent of the Director of Public Prosecutions;

(b) in Northern Ireland, except by the Commissioner or by or with the consent of the Director of Public Prosecutions for Northern Ireland.

[789]

NOTES

Commencement: 1 January 2005.

78 Saving for existing powers

Nothing in this Act is to be taken to limit the powers of a public authority to disclose information held by it.

[790]

79 Defamation

Where any information communicated by a public authority to a person ("the applicant") under section 1 was supplied to the public authority by a third person, the publication to the applicant of any defamatory matter contained in the information shall be privileged unless the publication is shown to have been made with malice.

[791]

80 Scotland

(1) No order may be made under section 4(1) or 5 in relation to any of the bodies specified in subsection (2); and the power conferred by section 74(3) does not include power to make provision in relation to information held by any of those bodies.

(2) The bodies referred to in subsection (1) are—

(a) the Scottish Parliament,

(b) any part of the Scottish Administration,

(c) the Scottish Parliamentary Corporate Body, or

(d) any Scottish public authority with mixed functions or no reserved functions (within the meaning of the Scotland Act 1998).

[(3) Section 50 of the Copyright, Designs and Patents Act 1988 and paragraph 6 of Schedule 1 to the Copyright and Rights in Databases Regulations 1997 apply in relation to the Freedom of Information (Scotland) Act 2002 as they apply in relation to this Act.]

[792]

NOTES

Sub-s (3): added by the Freedom of Information (Scotland) Act 2002 (Consequential Modifications) Order 2004, SI 2004/3089, art 3(1), (3).

81 Application to government departments, etc

(1) For the purposes of this Act each government department is to be treated as a person separate from any other government department.

(2) Subsection (1) does not enable—

(a) a government department which is not a Northern Ireland department to claim for the purposes of section 41(1)(b) that the disclosure of any information by it would constitute a breach of confidence actionable by any other government department (not being a Northern Ireland department), or

(b) a Northern Ireland department to claim for those purposes that the disclosure of information by it would constitute a breach of confidence actionable by any other Northern Ireland department.

(3) A government department is not liable to prosecution under this Act, but section 77 and paragraph 12 of Schedule 3 apply to a person in the public service of the Crown as they apply to any other person.

(4) The provisions specified in subsection (3) also apply to a person acting on behalf of either House of Parliament or on behalf of the Northern Ireland Assembly as they apply to any other person.

[793]

82 Orders and regulations

(1) Any power of the […] Secretary of State to make an order or regulations under this Act shall be exercisable by statutory instrument.

(2) A statutory instrument containing (whether alone or with other provisions)—

(a) an order under section 5, 7(3) or (8), 53(1)(a)(iii) or 75, or

(b) regulations under section 10(4) or 74(3),

shall not be made unless a draft of the instrument has been laid before, and approved by a resolution of, each House of Parliament.

(3) A statutory instrument which contains (whether alone or with other provisions)—

(a) an order under section 4(1), or

(b) regulations under any provision of this Act not specified in subsection (2)(b),

and which is not subject to the requirement in subsection (2) that a draft of the instrument be laid before and approved by a resolution of each House of Parliament, shall be subject to annulment in pursuance of a resolution of either House of Parliament.

(4) An order under section 4(5) shall be laid before Parliament after being made.

(5) If a draft of an order under section 5 or 7(8) would, apart from this subsection, be treated for the purposes of the Standing Orders of either House of Parliament as a hybrid instrument, it shall proceed in that House as if it were not such an instrument.

[794]

NOTES

Sub-s (1): words omitted from square brackets inserted by the Transfer of Functions (Miscellaneous) Order 2001, SI 2001/3500, art 8, Sch 2, Pt I, para 8(3), and repealed by the Secretary of State for Constitutional Affairs Order 2003, SI 2003/1887, art 9, Sch 2, para 12(3).

83 Meaning of "Welsh public authority"

(1) In this Act "Welsh public authority" means—

(a) any public authority which is listed in Part II, III, IV or VI of Schedule 1 and whose functions are exercisable only or mainly in or as regards Wales, other than an excluded authority, or

(b) any public authority which is an Assembly subsidiary as defined by section 99(4) of the Government of Wales Act 1998.

(2) In paragraph (a) of subsection (1) "excluded authority" means a public authority which is designated by the [Secretary of State] by order as an excluded authority for the purposes of that paragraph.

(3) Before making an order under subsection (2), the [Secretary of State] shall consult the National Assembly for Wales.

[795]

NOTES

Sub-ss (2), (3): words in square brackets substituted by the Secretary of State for Constitutional Affairs Order 2003, SI 2003/1887, art 9, Sch 2, para 12(1)(c).

Orders: the Freedom of Information (Excluded Welsh Authorities) Order 2002, SI 2002/2832.

84 Interpretation

In this Act, unless the context otherwise requires—

"applicant", in relation to a request for information, means the person who made the request;

"appropriate Northern Ireland Minister" means the Northern Ireland Minister in charge of the Department of Culture, Arts and Leisure in Northern Ireland;

"appropriate records authority", in relation to a transferred public record, has the meaning given by section 15(5);

"body" includes an unincorporated association;

"the Commissioner" means the Information Commissioner;

"decision notice" has the meaning given by section 50;

"the duty to confirm or deny" has the meaning given by section 1(6);

"enactment" includes an enactment contained in Northern Ireland legislation;

"enforcement notice" has the meaning given by section 52;

"executive committee", in relation to the National Assembly for Wales, has the same meaning as in the Government of Wales Act 1998;

"exempt information" means information which is exempt information by virtue of any provision of Part II;

"fees notice" has the meaning given by section 9(1);

"government department" includes a Northern Ireland department, the Northern Ireland Court Service and any other body or authority exercising statutory functions on behalf of the Crown, but does not include—

(a) any of the bodies specified in section 80(2),

(b) the Security Service, the Secret Intelligence Service or the Government Communications Headquarters, or

(c) the National Assembly for Wales;

"information" (subject to sections 51(8) and 75(2)) means information recorded in any form;

"information notice" has the meaning given by section 51;

"Minister of the Crown" has the same meaning as in the Ministers of the Crown Act 1975;

"Northern Ireland Minister" includes the First Minister and deputy First Minister in Northern Ireland;

"Northern Ireland public authority" means any public authority, other than the Northern Ireland Assembly or a Northern Ireland department, whose functions are exercisable only or mainly in or as regards Northern Ireland and relate only or mainly to transferred matters;

"prescribed" means prescribed by regulations made by the [Secretary of State];

"public authority" has the meaning given by section 3(1);

"public record" means a public record within the meaning of the Public Records Act 1958 or a public record to which the Public Records Act (Northern Ireland) 1923 applies;

"publication scheme" has the meaning given by section 19;

"request for information" has the meaning given by section 8;

"responsible authority", in relation to a transferred public record, has the meaning given by section 15(5);

"the special forces" means those units of the armed forces of the Crown the maintenance of whose capabilities is the responsibility of the Director of Special Forces or which are for the time being subject to the operational command of that Director;

"subordinate legislation" has the meaning given by subsection (1) of section 21 of the Interpretation Act 1978, except that the definition of that term in that subsection shall have effect as if "Act" included Northern Ireland legislation;

"transferred matter", in relation to Northern Ireland, has the meaning given by section 4(1) of the Northern Ireland Act 1998;

"transferred public record" has the meaning given by section 15(4);

"the Tribunal" means the Information Tribunal;

"Welsh public authority" has the meaning given by section 83.

[796]

NOTES

Words in square brackets in definition "prescribed" substituted by the Secretary of State for Constitutional Affairs Order 2003, SI 2003/1887, art 9, Sch 2, para 12(1)(c).

85 Expenses

There shall be paid out of money provided by Parliament—

(a) any increase attributable to this Act in the expenses of the [Secretary of State] in respect of the Commissioner, the Tribunal or the members of the Tribunal,

(b) any administrative expenses of the [Secretary of State] attributable to this Act,

(c) any other expenses incurred in consequence of this Act by a Minister of the Crown or government department or by either House of Parliament, and

(d) any increase attributable to this Act in the sums which under any other Act are payable out of money so provided.

[797]

NOTES

Words in square brackets in paras (a), (b) substituted by the Secretary of State for Constitutional Affairs Order 2003, SI 2003/1887, art 9, Sch 2, para 12(1)(c).

86 Repeals

Schedule 8 (repeals) has effect.

[798]

NOTES

Commencement: 30 November 2000 (certain purposes); 30 January 2001 (certain purposes); 1 January 2005 (otherwise).

87 Commencement

(1) The following provisions of this Act shall come into force on the day on which this Act is passed—

(a) sections 3 to 8 and Schedule 1,

(b) section 19 so far as relating to the approval of publication schemes,

(c) section 20 so far as relating to the approval and preparation by the Commissioner of model publication schemes,

(d) section 47(2) to (6),

(e) section 49,

(f) section 74,

(g) section 75,

(h) sections 78 to 85 and this section,

(i) paragraphs 2 and 17 to 22 of Schedule 2 (and section 18(4) so far as relating to those paragraphs),

(j) paragraph 4 of Schedule 5 (and section 67 so far as relating to that paragraph),

(k) paragraph 8 of Schedule 6 (and section 73 so far as relating to that paragraph),

(l) Part I of Schedule 8 (and section 86 so far as relating to that Part), and

(m) so much of any other provision of this Act as confers power to make any order, regulations or code of practice.

(2) The following provisions of this Act shall come into force at the end of the period of two months beginning with the day on which this Act is passed—

(a) section 18(1),

(b) section 76 and Schedule 7,

(c) paragraphs 1(1), 3(1), 4, 6, 7, 8(2), 9(2), 10(a), 13(1) and (2), 14(a) and 15(1) and (2) of Schedule 2 (and section 18(4) so far as relating to those provisions), and

(d) Part II of Schedule 8 (and section 86 so far as relating to that Part).

(3) Except as provided by subsections (1) and (2), this Act shall come into force at the end of the period of five years beginning with the day on which this Act is passed or on such day before the end of that period as the [Secretary of State] may by order appoint; and different days may be appointed for different purposes.

(4) An order under subsection (3) may contain such transitional provisions and savings (including provisions capable of having effect after the end of the period referred to in that subsection) as the [Secretary of State] considers appropriate.

(5) During the twelve months beginning with the day on which this Act is passed, and during each subsequent complete period of twelve months in the period beginning with that day and ending with the first day on which all the provisions of this Act are fully in force, the [Secretary of State] shall—

(a) prepare a report on his proposals for bringing fully into force those provisions of this Act which are not yet fully in force, and

(b) lay a copy of the report before each House of Parliament.

[799]

NOTES

Sub-ss (3)–(5): words in square brackets substituted by the Secretary of State for Constitutional Affairs Order 2003, SI 2003/1887, art 9, Sch 2, para 12(1)(c).

Orders: the Freedom of Information Act 2000 (Commencement No 1) Order 2001, SI 2001/1637; the Freedom of Information Act 2002 (Commencement No 2) Order 2002, SI 2002/2812; the Freedom of Information Act 2000 (Commencement No 3) Order 2003, SI 2003/2603; the Freedom of Information Act 2000 (Commencement No 4) Order 2004, SI 2004/1909; the Freedom of Information Act 2000 (Commencement No 5) Order 2004, SI 2004/3122.

88 Short title and extent

(1) This Act may be cited as the Freedom of Information Act 2000.

(2) Subject to subsection (3), this Act extends to Northern Ireland.

(3) The amendment or repeal of any enactment by this Act has the same extent as that enactment.

[800]

NOTES

Commencement: 30 November 2002.

SCHEDULES

SCHEDULE 1
PUBLIC AUTHORITIES

Section 3(1)(a)(i)

PART I
GENERAL

1. Any government department [other than the Office for Standards in Education, Children's Services and Skills].

[1A. The Office for Standards in Education, Children's Services and Skills, in respect of information held for purposes other than those of the functions exercisable by Her Majesty's Chief Inspector of Education, Children's Services and Skills by virtue of section 5(1)(a)(iii) of the Care Standards Act 2000.]

2. The House of Commons.

3. The House of Lords.

4. The Northern Ireland Assembly.

5. The National Assembly for Wales.

6. The armed forces of the Crown, except—
   (a) the special forces, and
   (b) any unit or part of a unit which is for the time being required by the Secretary of State to assist the Government Communications Headquarters in the exercise of its functions.

[801]

NOTES

Para 1: words in square brackets inserted by the Education and Inspections Act 2006, s 157, Sch 14, para 69(1), (2)(a), as from a day to be appointed.

Para 1A: inserted by the Education and Inspections Act 2006, s 157, Sch 14, para 69(1), (2)(b), as from a day to be appointed.

PART II
LOCAL GOVERNMENT

England and Wales

7. A local authority within the meaning of the Local Government Act 1972, namely—
   (a) in England, a county council, a London borough council, a district council or a parish council,
   (b) in Wales, a county council, a county borough council or a community council.

8. The Greater London Authority.

9. The Common Council of the City of London, in respect of information held in its capacity as a local authority, police authority or port health authority.

10. The Sub-Treasurer of the Inner Temple or the Under-Treasurer of the Middle Temple, in respect of information held in his capacity as a local authority.

11. The Council of the Isles of Scilly.

12. A parish meeting constituted under section 13 of the Local Government Act 1972.

13. Any charter trustees constituted under section 246 of the Local Government Act 1972.

[14. A fire and rescue authority constituted by a scheme under section 2 of the Fire and Rescue Services Act 2004 or a scheme to which section 4 of that Act applies.]

15. A waste disposal authority established by virtue of an order under section 10(1) of the Local Government Act 1985.

16. A port health authority constituted by an order under section 2 of the Public Health (Control of Disease) Act 1984.

17. …

18. An internal drainage board which is continued in being by virtue of section 1 of the Land Drainage Act 1991.

19. A joint authority established under Part IV of the Local Government Act 1985 [(fire and rescue services and transport)].

20. The London Fire and Emergency Planning Authority.

21. A joint fire authority established by virtue of an order under section 42(2) of the Local Government Act 1985 (reorganisation of functions).

22. A body corporate established pursuant to an order under section 67 of the Local Government Act 1985 (transfer of functions to successors of residuary bodies, etc).

23. A body corporate established pursuant to an order under section 22 of the Local Government Act 1992 (residuary bodies).

24. The Broads Authority established by section 1 of the Norfolk and Suffolk Broads Act 1988.

25. A joint committee constituted in accordance with section 102(1)(b) of the Local Government Act 1972.

26. A joint board which is continued in being by virtue of section 263(1) of the Local Government Act 1972.

27. A joint authority established under section 21 of the Local Government Act 1992.

28. A Passenger Transport Executive for a passenger transport area within the meaning of Part II of the Transport Act 1968.

29. Transport for London.

30. The London Transport Users Committee.

31. A joint board the constituent members of which consist of any of the public authorities described in paragraphs 8, 9, 10, 12, 15, 16, 20 to 31, 57 and 58.

32. A National Park authority established by an order under section 63 of the Environment Act 1995.

33. A joint planning board constituted for an area in Wales outside a National Park by an order under section 2(1B) of the Town and Country Planning Act 1990.

34. …

35. The London Development Agency.

[35A. A local fisheries committee for a sea fisheries district established under section 1 of the Sea Fisheries Regulation Act 1966.]

Northern Ireland

36. A district council within the meaning of the Local Government Act (Northern Ireland) 1972.

[802]

NOTES

Para 14: substituted by the Fire and Rescue Services Act 2004, s 53(1), Sch 1, para 95.

Para 17: repealed by the Licensing Act 2003, s 199, Sch 7, subject to savings in SI 2005/3056, art 4.

Para 19: words in square brackets substituted by the Civil Contingencies Act 2004, s 32(1), Sch 2, Pt 1, para 10(3)(d).

Para 34: repealed by the Courts Act 2003, s 109(1), (3), Sch 8, para 392, Sch 10, subject to transitional provisions in SI 2005/911, arts 2–5.

Para 35A: inserted by virtue of the Freedom of Information (Additional Public Authorities) Order 2004, SI 2004/938, art 2, Sch 1 (as amended by the Freedom of Information (Additional Public Authorities) (Amendment) Order 2004, SI 2004/1870, art 2).

PART III
THE NATIONAL HEALTH SERVICE

England and Wales

[36A. A strategic Health Authority established under *section 8 of the National Health Service Act 1977*.]

37. A Health Authority established under section 8 of the National Health Service Act 1977.

38. A special health authority established under *section 11 of the National Health Service Act 1977*.

39. A primary care trust established under *section 16A of the National Health Service Act 1977*.

[39A. A Local Health Board established under *section 16BA of the National Health Service Act 1977*.]

40. A National Health Service trust established under *section 5 of the National Health Service and Community Care Act 1990*.

[40A. An NHS foundation trust.]

41. A Community Health Council *[continued in existence by or established under section 20A] of the National Health Service Act 1977*.

[41A. A Patients' Forum established under *section 15 of the National Health Service Reform and Health Care Professions Act 2002*.]

42. …

43. …

[43A. Any person providing primary medical services *or primary dental services*—

(a) in accordance with arrangements made under *section 28C of the National Health Service Act 1977*; or

(b) under a contract under *section 28K or 28Q of that Act*;

in respect of information relating to the provision of those services.]

44. Any person providing *general medical services, general dental services,* general ophthalmic services or pharmaceutical services under *Part II of the National Health Service Act 1977*, in respect of information relating to the provision of those services.

PART II
DATA PROTECTION

45. *Any person providing personal medical services or personal dental services under arrangements made under section 28C of the National Health Service Act 1977, in respect of information relating to the provision of those services.*

[45A. Any person providing local pharmaceutical services under—

(a) a pilot scheme established under *section 28 of the Health and Social Care Act 2001*; or

(b) an LPS scheme established under *Schedule 8A to the National Health Service Act 1977 (c 49)*,

in respect of information relating to the provision of those services.]

[45B. The Commission for Patient and Public Involvement in Health.]

Northern Ireland

46. A Health and Social Services Board established under Article 16 of the Health and Personal Social Services (Northern Ireland) Order 1972.

47. A Health and Social Services Council established under Article 4 of the Health and Personal Social Services (Northern Ireland) Order 1991.

48. A Health and Social Services Trust established under Article 10 of the Health and Personal Social Services (Northern Ireland) Order 1991.

49. A special agency established under Article 3 of the Health and Personal Social Services (Special Agencies) (Northern Ireland) Order 1990.

50. The Northern Ireland Central Services Agency for the Health and Social Services established under Article 26 of the Health and Personal Social Services (Northern Ireland) Order 1972.

51. Any person providing [primary medical services], general dental services, general ophthalmic services or pharmaceutical services under Part VI of the Health and Personal Social Services (Northern Ireland) Order 1972, in respect of information relating to the provision of those services.

[803]

NOTES

Para 36A: inserted by the National Health Service Reform and Health Care Professions Act 2002 (Supplementary, Consequential etc Provisions) Regulations 2002, SI 2002/2649, reg 4, Sch 1, para 29; for the words in italics there are substituted the words "section 13 of the National Health Service Act 2006" by the National Health Service (Consequential Provisions) Act 2006, s 2, Sch 1, para 210(a), as from a day to be appointed.

Para 37: repealed by the National Health Service (Consequential Provisions) Act 2006, ss 2, 6, Sch 1, para 210(b), Sch 4, as from a day to be appointed.

Para 38: for the words in italics there are substituted the words "section 28 of the National Health Service Act 2006 or section 22 of the National Health Service (Wales) Act 2006", by the National Health Service (Consequential Provisions) Act 2006, s 2, Sch 1, para 210(c), as from a day to be appointed.

Para 39: for the words in italics there are substituted the words "section 18 of the National Health Service Act 2006", by the National Health Service (Consequential Provisions) Act 2006, s 2, Sch 1, para 210(d), as from a day to be appointed.

Para 39A: inserted by the National Health Service Reform and Health Care Professions Act 2002, ss 6(2), 19(7), Sch 5, para 48; for the words in italics there are substituted the words "section 11 of the National Health Service (Wales) Act 2006", by the National Health Service (Consequential Provisions) Act 2006, s 2, Sch 1, para 210(e), as from a day to be appointed.

Para 40: for the words in italics there are substituted the words "section 25 of the National Health Service Act 2006 or section 18 of the National Health Service (Wales) Act 2006", by the National Health Service (Consequential Provisions) Act 2006, s 2, Sch 1, para 210(f), as from a day to be appointed.

Para 40A: inserted by the Health and Social Care (Community Health and Standards) Act 2003, s 34, Sch 4, paras 113, 114.

Para 41: words in square brackets substituted by the Health (Wales) Act 2003, s 7(1), Sch 3, para 14; for the words in italics there are substituted the words "established under section 182 of the National Health Service (Wales) Act 2006", by the National Health Service (Consequential Provisions) Act 2006, s 2, Sch 1, para 210(g), as from a day to be appointed.

Para 41A: inserted by the National Health Service Reform and Health Care Professions Act 2002, ss 6(2), 19(7), Sch 5, para 48; for the words in italics there are substituted the words "section 237 of the

National Health Service Act 2006", by the National Health Service (Consequential Provisions) Act 2006, s 2, Sch 1, para 210(h), as from a day to be appointed.

Paras 42, 43: repealed by the Health and Social Care (Community Health and Standards) Act 2003, ss 190(2), 196, Sch 13, para 10, Sch 14, Pts 4, 7.

Para 43A: inserted by the Health and Social Care (Community Health and Standards) Act 2003, s 184, Sch 11, para 68, partly as from a day to be appointed in relation to Wales; for the first words in italics there are substituted the words ", primary dental services or primary ophthalmic services" and for the words "or 28Q" in italics in para (b) there are substituted the words ", 28Q or 28WA" by the Health Act 2006, s 80(1), Sch 8, para 45(1), (2), as from a day to be appointed; for the words in italics in para (a) there are substituted the words "section 92 or 107 of the National Health Service Act 2006, or section 50 or 64 of the National Health Service (Wales) Act 2006", and for the words "section 28K or 28Q of that Act" in italics in para (b) there are substituted the words "section 84 or 100 of the National Health Service Act 2006 or section 42 or 57 of the National Health Service (Wales) Act 2006" by the National Health Service (Consequential Provisions) Act 2006, s 2, Sch 1, para 210(i), (j), as from a day to be appointed.

Para 44: first words in italics repealed by the Health and Social Care (Community Health and Standards) Act 2003, s 196, Sch 14, Pt 4, partly as from a day to be appointed in relation to Wales; for the second words in italics there are substituted the words "the National Health Service Act 2006 or the National Health Service (Wales) Act 2006" by the National Health Service (Consequential Provisions) Act 2006, s 2, Sch 1, para 210(k), as from a day to be appointed.

Para 45: repealed by the Health and Social Care (Community Health and Standards) Act 2003, s 196, Sch 14, Pt 4, partly as from a day to be appointed in relation to Wales.

Para 45A: inserted by the Health and Social Care Act 2001, s 67(1), Sch 5, Pt 1, para 14(1); for the words in italics in para (a) there are substituted the words "section 134 of the National Health Service Act 2006 or section 92 of the National Health Service (Wales) Act 2006", and for the words in italics in para (b) there are substituted the words "Schedule 12 to the National Health Service Act 2006 or Schedule 7 to the National Health Service (Wales) Act 2006", by the National Health Service (Consequential Provisions) Act 2006, s 2, Sch 1, para 210(l), (m), as from a day to be appointed.

Para 45B: inserted by the National Health Service Reform and Health Care Professions Act 2002, s 20(11), Sch 6, para 19.

Para 51: words in square brackets substituted by the Primary Medical Services (Northern Ireland) Order 2004, SI 2004/311, art 10, Sch 1, para 18.

PART IV
MAINTAINED SCHOOLS AND OTHER EDUCATIONAL INSTITUTIONS

England and Wales

[52. The governing body of—

(a) a maintained school, as defined by section 20(7) of the School Standards and Framework Act 1998, or

(b) a maintained nursery school, as defined by section 22(9) of that Act.]

53.—(1) The governing body of—

(a) an institution within the further education sector,

(b) a university receiving financial support under section 65 of the Further and Higher Education Act 1992,

(c) an institution conducted by a higher education corporation,

(d) a designated institution for the purposes of Part II of the Further and Higher Education Act 1992 as defined by section 72(3) of that Act, or

(e) any college, school, hall or other institution of a university which falls within paragraph (b).

(2) In sub-paragraph (1)—

(a) "governing body" is to be interpreted in accordance with subsection (1) of section 90 of the Further and Higher Education Act 1992 but without regard to subsection (2) of that section,

(b) in paragraph (a), the reference to an institution within the further education sector is to be construed in accordance with section 91(3) of the Further and Higher Education Act 1992,

(c) in paragraph (c), "higher education corporation" has the meaning given by section 90(1) of that Act, and

(d) in paragraph (e) "college" includes any institution in the nature of a college.

Northern Ireland

54.—(1) The managers of—

(a) a controlled school, voluntary school or grant-maintained integrated school within the meaning of Article 2(2) of the Education and Libraries (Northern Ireland) Order 1986, or

(b) a pupil referral unit as defined by Article 87(1) of the Education (Northern Ireland) Order 1998.

(2) In sub-paragraph (1) "managers" has the meaning given by Article 2(2) of the Education and Libraries (Northern Ireland) Order 1986.

55.—(1) The governing body of—

(a) a university receiving financial support under Article 30 of the Education and Libraries (Northern Ireland) Order 1993,

(b) a college of education … in respect of which grants are paid under Article 66(2) or (3) of the Education and Libraries (Northern Ireland) Order 1986, or

(c) an institution of further education within the meaning of the Further Education (Northern Ireland) Order 1997.

(2) In sub-paragraph (1) "governing body" has the meaning given by Article 30(3) of the Education and Libraries (Northern Ireland) Order 1993.

56. Any person providing further education to whom grants, loans or other payments are made under Article 5(1)(b) of the Further Education (Northern Ireland) Order 1997.

[804]

NOTES

Para 52: substituted by the Education Act 2002, s 215(1), Sch 21, para 127.

Para 55: words omitted from sub-para (1)(b) repealed by the Colleges of Education (Northern Ireland) Order 2005, SI 2005/1963, art 14, Sch 3, para 4, Sch 4.

PART V
POLICE

England and Wales

57. A police authority established under section 3 of the Police Act 1996.

58. The Metropolitan Police Authority established under section 5B of the Police Act 1996.

59. A chief officer of police of a police force in England or Wales.

Northern Ireland

60. The [Northern Ireland Policing Board].

61. The Chief Constable of the [Police Service of Northern Ireland].

Miscellaneous

62. The British Transport Police.

63. The Ministry of Defence Police established by section 1 of the Ministry of Defence Police Act 1987.

[63A. The Civil Nuclear Police Authority.

63B. The chief constable of the Civil Nuclear Constabulary.]

64. Any person who—

(a) by virtue of any enactment has the function of nominating individuals who may be appointed as special constables by justices of the peace, and

(b) is not a public authority by virtue of any other provision of this Act, in respect of information relating to the exercise by any person appointed on his nomination of the functions of a special constable.

[805]

NOTES

Paras 60, 61: words in square brackets substituted by the Police (Northern Ireland) Act 2000, s 78(1), Sch 6, para 25(1), (2).

Paras 63A, 63B: inserted by the Energy Act 2004, s 51(2), Sch 10, para 18.

PART VI
OTHER PUBLIC BODIES AND OFFICES: GENERAL

[The Adjudication Panel for Wales.]

The Adjudicator for the Inland Revenue and Customs and Excise.

The Administration of Radioactive Substances Advisory Committee.

[*The Adult Learning Inspectorate*.]

…

The Advisory Board on Restricted Patients.

The Advisory Board on the Registration of Homoeopathic Products.

…

The Advisory Committee for Disabled People in Employment and Training.

The Advisory Committee for the Public Lending Right.

…

The Advisory Committee on Advertising.

The Advisory Committee on Animal Feedingstuffs.

The Advisory Committee on Borderline Substances.

The Advisory Committee on Business and the Environment.

The Advisory Committee on Business Appointments.

The Advisory Committee on Conscientious Objectors.

The Advisory Committee on Consumer Products and the Environment.

The Advisory Committee on Dangerous Pathogens.

The Advisory Committee on Distinction Awards.

An Advisory Committee on General Commissioners of Income Tax.

The Advisory Committee on the Government Art Collection.

The Advisory Committee on Hazardous Substances.

The Advisory Committee on Historic Wreck Sites.

An Advisory Committee on Justices of the Peace in England and Wales.

The Advisory Committee on the Microbiological Safety of Food.

…

The Advisory Committee on Novel Foods and Processes.

[The Advisory Committee on Organic Standards.]

The Advisory Committee on Overseas Economic and Social Research.

The Advisory Committee on Packaging.

The Advisory Committee on Pesticides.

The Advisory Committee on Releases to the Environment.

[The Advisory Committee on Statute Law.]

[The Advisory Committee on Telecommunications for the Disabled and Elderly.]

[The Advisory Council on Historical Manuscripts.]

The Advisory Council on Libraries.

The Advisory Council on the Misuse of Drugs.

[The Advisory Council on National Records and Archives.]

The Advisory Council on Public Records.

The Advisory Group on Hepatitis.

[The Advisory Group on Medical Countermeasures.]

[The Advisory Panel on Beacon Councils.]

[The Advisory Panel on Public Sector Information.]

The Advisory Panel on Standards for the Planning Inspectorate.

The Aerospace Committee.

An Agricultural Dwelling House Advisory Committee.

An Agricultural Wages Board for England and Wales.

An Agricultural Wages Committee.

The Agriculture and Environment Biotechnology Commission.

[The Air Quality Expert Group.]

The Airborne Particles Expert Group.

The Alcohol Education and Research Council.

[The All-Wales Medicines Strategy Group.]

…

The Animal Procedures Committee.

The Animal Welfare Advisory Committee.

…

[The Appointments Commission.]

[The Architects Registration Board.]

The Armed Forces Pay Review Body.

[The Arts and Humanities Research Council.]

The Arts Council of England.

The Arts Council of Wales.

The Audit Commission for Local Authorities and the National Health Service in England and Wales.

The Auditor General for Wales.

The Authorised Conveyancing Practitioners Board.

The Bank of England, in respect of information held for purposes other than those of its functions with respect to—

(a) monetary policy,
(b) financial operations intended to support financial institutions for the purposes of maintaining stability, and
(c) the provision of private banking services and related services.

The Better Regulation Task Force.

The Biotechnology and Biological Sciences Research Council.

[The Board of the Pension Protection Fund.]

Any Board of Visitors established under section 6(2) of the Prison Act 1952.

The Britain-Russia Centre and East-West Centre.

The British Association for Central and Eastern Europe.

The British Broadcasting Corporation, in respect of information held for purposes other than those of journalism, art or literature.

The British Coal Corporation.

The British Council.

The British Educational Communications and Technology Agency.

The British Hallmarking Council.

The British Library.

The British Museum.

The British Pharmacopoeia Commission.

The British Potato Council.

The British Railways Board.

British Shipbuilders.

The British Tourist Authority.

[The British Transport Police Authority.]

The British Waterways Board.

The British Wool Marketing Board.

The Broadcasting Standards Commission.

The Building Regulations Advisory Committee.

[…]

[The Care Council for Wales.]

The Central Advisory Committee on War Pensions.

…

[*The Central Police Training and Development Authority.*]

The Central Rail Users' Consultative Committee.

[The Certification Officer.]

The Channel Four Television Corporation, in respect of information held for purposes other than those of journalism, art or literature.

[The Chemical Weapons Convention National Authority Advisory Committee.]

The Children and Family Court Advisory and Support Service.

[The Children's Commissioner.]

[The Children's Commissioner for Wales.]

The Civil Aviation Authority.

The Civil Justice Council.

The Civil Procedure Rule Committee.

The Civil Service Appeal Board.

The Civil Service Commissioners.

The Coal Authority.

The Commission for Architecture and the Built Environment.

…

[The Commission for Equality and Human Rights]

[The Commission for Healthcare Audit and Inspection, in respect of information held for purposes other than those of its functions exercisable by virtue of paragraph 5(a)(i) of the Care Standards Act 2000.]

[The Commission for Integrated Transport.]

The Commission for Local Administration in England.

…

The Commission for Racial Equality.

[Commission for Rural Communities.]

[The Commission for Social Care Inspection, in respect of information held for purposes other than those of its functions exercisable by virtue of paragraph 5(a)(ii) of the Care Standards Act 2000.]

The Commission for the New Towns.

…

[The Commissioner for Older People in Wales.]

The Commissioner for Public Appointments.

[The Commissioners of Northern Lighthouses.]

The Committee for Monitoring Agreements on Tobacco Advertising and Sponsorship.

…

The Committee on Agricultural Valuation.

The Committee on Carcinogenicity of Chemicals in Food, Consumer Products and the Environment.

The Committee on Chemicals and Materials of Construction For Use in Public Water Supply and Swimming Pools.

The Committee on Medical Aspects of Food and Nutrition Policy.

The Committee on Medical Aspects of Radiation in the Environment.

The Committee on Mutagenicity of Chemicals in Food, Consumer Products and the Environment.

[The Committee on Radioactive Waste Management.]

[The Committee on Safety of Devices.]

The Committee on Standards in Public Life.

The Committee on Toxicity of Chemicals in Food, Consumer Products and the Environment.

The Committee on the Medical Effects of Air Pollutants.

The Committee on the Safety of Medicines.

The Commonwealth Scholarship Commission in the United Kingdom.

[Communications for Business.]

The Community Development Foundation.

The Competition Commission, in relation to information held by it otherwise than as a tribunal.

[The Competition Service.]

[A conservation board established under section 86 of the Countryside and Rights of Way Act 2000.]

The Construction Industry Training Board.

Consumer Communications for England.

[The Consumer Council for Postal Services.]

…

[The Consumer Panel established under section 16 of the Communications Act 2003.]

…

…

[The Council for the Regulation of Health Care Professionals.]

The Council for the Central Laboratory of the Research Councils.

The Council for Science and Technology.

The Council on Tribunals.

…

The Countryside Council for Wales.

[A courts board established under section 4 of the Courts Act 2003.]

The Covent Garden Market Authority.

The Criminal Cases Review Commission.

[The Criminal Injuries Compensation Appeals Panel, in relation to information held by it otherwise than as a tribunal.]

[The Criminal Injuries Compensation Authority.]

The Criminal Justice Consultative Council.

[The Criminal Procedure Rule Committee.]

The Crown Court Rule Committee.

The Dartmoor Steering Group and Working Party.

The Darwin Advisory Committee.

The Defence Nuclear Safety Committee.

The Defence Scientific Advisory Council.

The Design Council.

…

The Diplomatic Service Appeal Board.

[The Director of Fair Access to Higher Education.]

[The Disability Employment Advisory Committee.]

The Disability Living Allowance Advisory Board.

The Disability Rights Commission.

The Disabled Persons Transport Advisory Committee.

[The Distributed Generation Co-Ordinating Group.]

[The East of England Industrial Development Board.]

The Economic and Social Research Council.

…

[The Electoral Commission.]

…

The Engineering Construction Industry Training Board.

The Engineering and Physical Sciences Research Council.

…

…

The English Sports Council.

The English Tourist Board.

The Environment Agency.

The Equal Opportunities Commission.

[The Ethnic Minority Business Forum.]

The Expert Advisory Group on AIDS.

The Expert Group on Cryptosporidium in Water Supplies.

An Expert Panel on Air Quality Standards.

The Export Guarantees Advisory Council.

[The Family Justice Council.]

[The Family Procedure Rule Committee.]

The Family Proceedings Rules Committee.

The Farm Animal Welfare Council.

[The Financial Reporting Advisory Board.]

[The Financial Services Authority.]

The Fire Services Examination Board.

The Firearms Consultative Committee.

The Food Advisory Committee.

Food from Britain.

The Football Licensing Authority.

The Fuel Cell Advisory Panel.

[The Fuel Poverty Advisory Group.]

…

[The Gaelic Media Service, in respect of information held for purposes other than those of journalism, art or literature.]

[The Gambling Commission.]

[Gangmasters Licensing Authority.]

…

[The Gas and Electricity Consumer Council.]

The Gene Therapy Advisory Committee.

The General Chiropractic Council.

The General Dental Council.

The General Medical Council.

[The General Optical Council.]

The General Osteopathic Council.

[The General Social Care Council.]

[The General Teaching Council for England.]

[The General Teaching Council for Wales.]

The Genetic Testing and Insurance Committee.

The Government Hospitality Advisory Committee for the Purchase of Wine.

[The Government–Industry Forum on Non-Food Use of Crops.]

The Government Chemist.

The Great Britain-China Centre.

[The Health Professions Council.]

[The Health Protection Agency.]

The Health and Safety Commission.

The Health and Safety Executive.

The Health Service Commissioner for England.

…

[The Hearing Aid Council.]

[Her Majesty's Chief Inspector of Education and Training in Wales or Prif Arolygydd Ei Mawrhydi dros Addysg a Hyfforddiant yng Nghymru].

[Her Majesty's Commissioners for Judicial Appointments.]

The Higher Education Funding Council for England.

The Higher Education Funding Council for Wales.

…

…

The Historic Buildings and Monuments Commission for England.

The Historic Royal Palaces Trust.

The Home-Grown Cereals Authority.

…

The Horserace Betting Levy Board.

The Horserace Totalisator Board.

The Horticultural Development Council.

Horticulture Research International.

The House of Lords Appointments Commission.

Any housing action trust established under Part III of the Housing Act 1988.

The Housing Corporation.

The Human Fertilisation and Embryology Authority.

[The Human Tissue Authority.]

The Human Genetics Commission.

The Immigration Services Commissioner.

The Imperial War Museum.

[The Independent Advisory Group on Teenage Pregnancy.]

The Independent Board of Visitors for Military Corrective Training Centres.

The Independent Case Examiner for the Child Support Agency.

[The Independent Groundwater Complaints Administrator.]

The Independent Living Funds.

[The Independent Police Complaints Commission.]

[The Independent Regulator of NHS Foundation Trusts.]

[The Independent Review Panel for Advertising.]

[The Independent Review Panel for Borderline Products.]

[The Independent Scientific Group on Cattle Tuberculosis.]

The Independent Television Commission.

…

The Industrial Development Advisory Board.

The Industrial Injuries Advisory Council.

The Information Commissioner.

The *Inland Waterways Amenity Advisory Council.*

The Insolvency Rules Committee.

…

[The Integrated Administration and Controls System Appeals Panel.]

[The Intellectual Property Advisory Committee.]

Investors in People UK.

The Joint Committee on Vaccination and Immunisation.

The Joint Nature Conservation Committee.

The Joint Prison/Probation Accreditation Panel.

[The Judicial Appointments and Conduct Ombudsman.]

[The Judicial Appointments Commission.]

The Judicial Studies Board.

The Know-How Fund Advisory Board.

The Land Registration Rule Committee.

The Law Commission.

[The Learning and Skills Council for England.]

The Legal Services Commission.

[The Legal Services Complaints Commissioner.]

The Legal Services Consultative Panel.

The Legal Services Ombudsman.

…

The Local Government Boundary Commission for Wales.

The Local Government Commission for England.

A local probation board established under section 4 of the Criminal Justice and Court Services Act 2000.

[The London and South East Industrial Development Board.]

The London Pensions Fund Authority.

The Low Pay Commission.

The Magistrates' Courts Rules Committee.

The Marshall Aid Commemoration Commission.

The Measurement Advisory Committee.

The Meat and Livestock Commission.

…

The Medical Research Council.

…

The Medicines Commission.

The Milk Development Council.

…

The Museum of London.

The National Army Museum.

The National Audit Office.

The National Biological Standards Board (UK).

[The National Care Standards Commission.]

The National Consumer Council.

[…]

…

The National Employers' Liaison Committee.

[The National Employment Panel.]

The National Endowment for Science, Technology and the Arts.

…

[The National Forest Company.]

The National Gallery.

The National Heritage Memorial Fund.

[The National Identity Scheme Commissioner.]

The National Library of Wales.

…

The National Lottery Commission.

The National Maritime Museum.

The National Museum of Science and Industry.

The National Museums and Galleries of Wales.

The National Museums and Galleries on Merseyside.

[The National Policing Improvement Agency.]

The National Portrait Gallery.

…

[Natural England.]

The Natural Environment Research Council.

The Natural History Museum.

The New Deal Task Force.

…

[The North East Industrial Development Board.]

[The North West Industrial Development Board.]

[The Northern Ireland Judicial Appointments Ombudsman.]

[The Nuclear Decommissioning Authority.]

[The Nuclear Research Advisory Council.]

[The Nursing and Midwifery Council.]

…

[The Office of Communications.]

[The Office of Government Commerce.]

[The Office of Manpower Economics.]

The Oil and Pipelines Agency.

[The Olympic Delivery Authority.]

[The Ombudsman for the Board of the Pension Protection Fund.]

The OSO Board.

The Overseas Service Pensions Scheme Advisory Board.

The Panel on Standards for the Planning Inspectorate.

The Parliamentary Boundary Commission for England.

The Parliamentary Boundary Commission for Scotland.

The Parliamentary Boundary Commission for Wales.

The Parliamentary Commissioner for Administration.

The Parole Board.

The Particle Physics and Astronomy Research Council.

[The Patient Information Advisory Group.]

…

The Pensions Ombudsman.

[The Pensions Regulator.]

[The Pesticide Residues Committee.]

[The Pesticides Forum.]

…

…

The Poisons Board.

[The Police Advisory Board for England and Wales.]

…

The Police Information Technology Organisation.

The Police Negotiating Board.

The Political Honours Scrutiny Committee.

[The Postgraduate Medical Education and Training Board.]

The Post Office.

…

…

[The Prison Service Pay Review Body.]

…

[The Public Private Partnership Agreement Arbiter.]

[The Public Service Ombudsman for Wales.]

…

The Qualifications Curriculum Authority.

The Race Education and Employment Forum.

The Race Relations Forum.

The Radio Authority.

The Radioactive Waste Management Advisory Committee.

[…]

A Regional Cultural Consortium.

Any regional development agency established under the Regional Development Agencies Act 1998, other than the London Development Agency.

Any regional flood defence committee.

…

[The Registrar General for England and Wales.]

The Registrar of Public Lending Right.

Remploy Ltd.

The Renewable Energy Advisory Committee.

[The Renewables Advisory Board.]

Resource: The Council for Museums, Archives and Libraries.

The Review Board for Government Contracts.

The Review Body for Nursing Staff, Midwives, Health Visitors and Professions Allied to Medicine.

The Review Body on Doctors and Dentists Remuneration.

The Reviewing Committee on the Export of Works of Art.

The Royal Air Force Museum.

The Royal Armouries.

The Royal Botanic Gardens, Kew.

[The Royal College of Veterinary Surgeons, in respect of information held by it otherwise than as a tribunal.]

The Royal Commission on Ancient and Historical Monuments of Wales.

The Royal Commission on Environmental Pollution.

The Royal Commission on Historical Manuscripts.

[The Royal Hospital at Chelsea.]

…

The Royal Mint Advisory Committee on the Design of Coins, Medals, Seals and Decorations.

[The Royal Pharmaceutical Society of Great Britain, in respect of information held by it otherwise than as a tribunal.]

The School Teachers' Review Body.

[The Scientific Advisory Committee on Nutrition.]

The Scientific Committee on Tobacco and Health.

…

The Scottish Committee of the Council on Tribunals.

The Sea Fish Industry Authority.

[The Security Industry Authority].

The Senior Salaries Review Body.

The Sentencing Advisory Panel.

[The Sentencing Guidelines Council.]

…

Sianel Pedwar Cymru, in respect of information held for purposes other than those of journalism, art or literature.

Sir John Soane's Museum.

…

[The Small Business Council.]

[The Small Business Investment Task Force.]

[The Social Care Institute for Excellence.]

The social fund Commissioner appointed under section 65 of the Social Security Administration Act 1992.

PART II
DATA PROTECTION

The Social Security Advisory Committee.

The Social Services Inspectorate for Wales Advisory Group.

[The South West Industrial Development Board.]

[The Specialist Advisory Committee on Antimicrobial Research.]

The Spongiform Encephalopathy Advisory Committee.

The Sports Council for Wales.

[The Standards Board for England.]

The Standing Advisory Committee on Industrial Property.

The Standing Advisory Committee on Trunk Road Assessment.

The Standing Dental Advisory Committee.

…

…

…

[The Statistics Commission.]

The Steering Committee on Pharmacy Postgraduate Education.

[The Strategic Investment Board.]

[…]

The subsidence adviser appointed under section 46 of the Coal Industry Act 1994.

The Substance Misuse Advisory Panel.

The Sustainable Development Commission.

…

[The Sustainable Energy Policy Advisory Board.]

The Tate Gallery.

The Teacher Training Agency.

[The Technical Advisory Board.]

The Theatres Trust.

The Traffic Commissioners, in respect of information held by them otherwise than as a tribunal.

[The Training and Development Agency for Schools.]

The Treasure Valuation Committee.

The UK Advisory Panel for Health Care Workers Infected with Bloodborne Viruses.

[The UK Chemicals Stakeholder Forum.]

The UK Sports Council.

The United Kingdom Atomic Energy Authority.

…

…

The United Kingdom Xenotransplantation Interim Regulatory Authority.

[The University for Industry.]

The Unlinked Anonymous Serosurveys Steering Group.

The Unrelated Live Transplant Regulatory Authority.

The Urban Regeneration Agency.

[The Valuation Tribunal Service.]

[The verderers of the New Forest, in respect of information held by them otherwise than as a tribunal.]

The Veterinary Products Committee.

[The Veterinary Residues Committee.]

The Victoria and Albert Museum.

[The Wales Centre for Health.]

…

…

The Wallace Collection.

The War Pensions Committees.

The Water Regulations Advisory Committee.

…

…

The Welsh Committee for Professional Development of Pharmacy.

The Welsh Dental Committee.

…

The Welsh Industrial Development Advisory Board.

The Welsh Language Board.

The Welsh Medical Committee.

…

The Welsh Nursing and Midwifery Committee.

The Welsh Optometric Committee.

The Welsh Pharmaceutical Committee.

The Welsh Scientific Advisory Committee.

[The West Midlands Industrial Development Board.]

The Westminster Foundation for Democracy.

The Wilton Park Academic Council.

The Wine Standards Board of the Vintners' Company.

The Women's National Commission.

[The Yorkshire and the Humber and the East Midlands Industrial Development Board.]

The Youth Justice Board for England and Wales.

The Zoos Forum.

[806]

NOTES

Entries "The Adjudication Panel for Wales", "The All-Wales Medicines Strategy Group", "The Care Council for Wales", "The Certification Officer", "The Children's Commissioner for Wales", "The Commissioners of Northern Lighthouses", "The Consumer Council for Postal Services", "The Criminal Injuries Compensation Appeals Panel", "The Criminal Injuries Compensation Authority", "The Electoral Commission", "The Gas and Electricity Consumer Council", "The General Social Care Council", "The General Teaching Council for Wales", "The National Care Standards Commission", and "The Standards Board for England" inserted by the Freedom of Information (Additional Public Authorities) Order 2002, SI 2002/2623, art 2, Sch 1.

Entries "The Adult Learning Inspectorate", "The Advisory Committee on Telecommunications for the Disabled and Elderly", "The Advisory Council on Historical Manuscripts", "The Advisory Council on National Records and Archives", "The Advisory Group on Medical Countermeasures", "The Advisory Panel on Beacon Councils", "The Air Quality Expert Group", "The Business Incubation Fund Investment Panel", "The Committee on Safety of Devices", "Communications for Business", "The Competition Service", "The Disability Employment Advisory Committee", "The Ethnic Minority Business Forum", "The Financial Reporting Advisory Board", "The Financial Services Authority", "The General Teaching

Council for England", "The Government–Industry Forum on Non-Food Use of Crops", "The Hearing Aid Council", "The Independent Advisory Group on Teenage Pregnancy", "The Independent Scientific Group on Cattle Tuberculosis", "The Integrated Administration and Controls System Appeals Panel", "The Intellectual Property Advisory Committee", "The Learning and Skills Council for England", "The National Employment Panel", "The National Forest Company", "The Nuclear Research Advisory Council", "The Office of Government Commerce", "The Office of Manpower Economics", "The Pesticide Residues Committee", "The Scientific Advisory Committee on Nutrition", "The Small Business Council", "The Small Business Investment Task Force", "The Social Care Institute for Excellence", "The Specialist Advisory Committee on Antimicrobial Research", "The Statistics Commission", "The Strategic Investment Board", "The Technical Advisory Board", "The UK Chemicals Stakeholder Forum" and "The Veterinary Residues Committee" inserted by the Freedom of Information (Additional Public Authorities) Order 2003, SI 2003/1882, art 2, Sch 1.

Entry "The Adult Learning Inspectorate" repealed by the Education and Inspections Act 2006, ss 157, 184, Sch 14, para 69(1), (3), Sch 18, Pt 5, as from a day to be appointed.

Entries "The Advisory Board on Family Law", "The Advisory Committee for Wales, (in relation to the Environment Agency)", "The Advisory Committee on NHS Drugs", "The Apple and Pear Research Council", "The Consumer Panel", "The Development Awareness Working Group", "The Education Transfer Council", "The Energy Advisory Panel", "The Further Education Funding Council for Wales", "The Gas Consumers' Council", "The Honorary Investment Advisory Council", "The Indian Family Pensions Funds Body of Commissioners", "The Medical Practices Committee", "The Medical Workforce Standing Advisory Committee", "The Place Names Advisory Committee", "The Post Office Users' Councils for Scotland, Wales and Northern Ireland", "The Post Office Users' National Council", "The Sustainable Development Education Panel" and "The Wales New Deal Advisory Task Force", (all omitted) repealed by the Freedom of Information (Removal of References to Public Authorities) Order 2003, SI 2003/1883, art 2, Sch 1.

Entries "The Advisory Committee for Cleaner Coal Technology", "The Hill Farming Advisory Committee", "The Hill Farming Advisory Sub-committee for Wales", "The Property Advisory Group", "The Royal Military College of Science Advisory Council", "The Skills Task Force" and "The United Kingdom Register of Organic Food Standards" (all omitted) repealed by the Freedom of Information (Removal of References to Public Authorities) Order 2004, SI 2004/1641, art 2, Sch 1.

Entries "The Advisory Committee on Organic Standards", "The Advisory Committee on Statute Law", "The Architects Registration Board", "The Chemical Weapons Convention National Authority Advisory Committee", "The Committee on Radioactive Waste Management", "The Distributed Generation Co-Ordinating Group", "The East of England Industrial Development Board", "The Fuel Poverty Advisory Group", "Her Majesty's Commissioners for Judicial Appointments", "The Independent Review Panel for Advertising", "The Independent Review Panel for Borderline Products", "The Legal Services Complaints Commissioner", "The London and South East Industrial Development Board", "The North East Industrial Development Board", "The North West Industrial Development Board", "The Pesticides Forum", "The Police Advisory Board for England and Wales", "The Postgraduate Medical Education and Training Board", "The Prison Service Pay Review Body", "The Public Private Partnership Agreement Arbiter", "The Renewables Advisory Board", "The Royal Hospital at Chelsea", "The South West Industrial Development Board", "The Sustainable Energy Policy Advisory Board", "The West Midlands Industrial Development Board", and "The Yorkshire and the Humber and the East Midlands Industrial Development Board" inserted by the Freedom of Information (Additional Public Authorities) Order 2004, SI 2004/938, art 3, Sch 2.

Entries "The Advisory Panel on Public Sector Information", "The British Transport Police Authority", "The Children's Commissioner", "A conservation board", "A courts board", "The Commission for Integrated Transport", "The Criminal Procedure Rule Committee", "The Family Justice Council", "The Family Procedure Rule Committee", "The Gaelic Media Service", "The General Optical Council", "The Independent Groundwater Complaints Administrator", "The Independent Regulator of NHS Foundation Trusts", "The Registrar General for England and Wales", "The Royal College of Veterinary Surgeons", "The Royal Pharmaceutical Society of Great Britain", "The Sentencing Guidelines Council", "The University for Industry", and "The verderers of the New Forest" inserted by the Freedom of Information (Additional Public Authorities) Order 2005, SI 2005/3593, arts 2, 3, Schs 1, 2.

Entry "The Ancient Monuments Board for Wales" (omitted) repealed by the Ancient Monuments Board for Wales (Abolition) Order 2006, SI 2006/64, art 3(1)(b)(iii).

Entry "The Appointments Commission" inserted by the Health Act 2006, s 80(1), Sch 8, para 45(1), (3).

Entries "The Arts and Humanities Research Council" and "The Director of Fair Access to Higher Education" inserted by the Higher Education Act 2004, s 49, Sch 6, para 10.

Entries "The Board of the Pension Protection Fund", "The Ombudsman for the Board of the Pension Protection Fund" and "The Pensions Regulator" inserted, and entries "The Occupational Pensions Regulatory Authority", "The Pensions Compensation Board", "The Registrar of Occupational and Personal Pension Schemes" (all omitted) repealed, by the Pensions Act 2004, ss 319(1), 320, Sch 12, para 79, Sch 13, Pt 1.

Entry "The British Railways Board" repealed by the Transport Act 2000, s 274, Sch 31, Pt IV, as from a day to be appointed.

Entries "The Broadcasting Standards Commission", "The Independent Television Commission" and "The Radio Authority" repealed as from a day to be appointed, entries "The Scottish Advisory Committee on Telecommunications" and "The Welsh Advisory Committee on Telecommunications" (both omitted) repealed, and entry "The Consumer Panel established under section 16 of the Communications Act 2003" inserted, by the Communications Act 2003, s 406(1), (7), Sch 17, para 164, Sch 19(1).

Entries "The Business Incubation Fund Investment Panel" (as inserted by SI 2003/1882), "The Commissioner for Integrated Transport", "The National Expert Group", "The Pharmacists' Review Panel", "The Standing Medical Advisory Committee", "The Standing Nursing and Midwifery Advisory

Committee", and "The Standing Pharmaceutical Advisory Committee" (all omitted) repealed by the Freedom of Information (Removal of References to Public Authorities) Order 2005, SI 2005/3594, art 2, Sch 1.

Entry "The Central Council for Education and Training in Social Work (UK)" (omitted) repealed by the Abolition of the Central Council for Education and Training in Social Work Order 2002, SI 2002/797, art 2(c).

Entry "The Central Police Training and Development Authority" inserted by the Criminal Justice and Police Act 2001, s 102, Sch 4, para 8; repealed by the Police and Justice Act 2006, s 52, Sch 15, Pt 1, as from a day to be appointed.

Entry "The Commission for Equality and Human Rights" inserted by the Equality Act 2006, s 2, Sch 1, Pt 4, para 48.

Entry "The Commission for Health Improvement" (omitted) repealed, and entries "The Commission for Healthcare Audit and Inspection" and "The Commission for Social Care Inspection" inserted, by the Health and Social Care (Community Health and Standards) Act 2003, ss 147, 196, Sch 9, para 31, Sch 14, Pt 2.

Entries "The Commission for Local Administration in Wales", "The Health Service Commissioner for Wales" and "The Welsh Administration Ombudsman" (all omitted) repealed and entry "The Public Services Ombudsman for Wales" inserted by the Public Services Ombudsman Act 2005, s 39, Sch 6, paras 70, 72, Sch 7.

Entries "The Commission for Racial Equality", "The Disability Rights Commission", and "The Equal Opportunities Commission" repealed by the Equality Act 2006, ss 40, 91, Sch 3, para 60, Sch 4, as from a day to be appointed.

Entries "Commission for Rural Communities" and "Natural England" inserted, and entries "The Committee of Investigation for Great Britain", "The consumers' committee for Great Britain", "The Countryside Agency", "English Nature" (all omitted) repealed by the Natural Environment and Rural Communities Act 2006, s 105, Sch 11, Pt 1, para 153, Sch 12.

Entry "The Commissioner for Older People in Wales" inserted by the Commissioner for Older People (Wales) Act 2006, s 1(2), Sch 1, para 21(b).

Entry "The Council for Professions Supplementary to Medicine" (omitted) repealed, and entry "The Health Professions Council" inserted, by the Health Professions Order 2001, SI 2002/254, art 48(3), Sch 4, para 9; for transitional provisions see Sch 2 to that Order.

Entry "The Council for the Regulation of Health Care Professionals" inserted by the National Health Service Reform and Health Care Professions Act 2002, s 25(4), Sch 7, para 24.

Entries "The English National Board for Nursing, Midwifery and Health Visiting", "The United Kingdom Central Council for Nursing, Midwifery and Health Visiting" and "The Welsh National Board for Nursing, Midwifery and Health Visiting" (all omitted) repealed, and entry "The Nursing and Midwifery Council" inserted, by the Nursing and Midwifery Order 2001, SI 2002/253, art 54(3), Sch 5, para 17; for transitional provisions see Sch 2 to that Order.

Entry "The Gambling Commission" substituted for original entry "The Gaming Board for Great Britain" by the Gambling Act 2005, s 356(1), Sch 16, Pt 2, para 16.

Entry "Gangmasters Licensing Authority" inserted by the Gangmasters (Licensing) Act 2004, s 1(6), Sch 1, para 6.

Entry "The Health Protection Agency" inserted and entry "The National Radiological Protection Board" (omitted) repealed, by the Health Protection Agency Act 2004, s 11(1), (2), Sch 3, para 15, Sch 4.

Entry "Her Majesty's Chief Inspector of Education and Training in Wales" substituted by the Learning and Skills Act 2000, s 73(1), (3)(a).

Entry "The Historic Buildings Council for Wales" (omitted) repealed by the Historic Buildings Council for Wales (Abolition) Order 2006, SI 2006/63, art 3(1)(c)(iii).

Entries "The Horserace Betting Levy Board" and "The Horserace Totaliser Board" repealed by the Horserace Betting and Olympic Lottery Act 2004, ss 13, 17(2), 38, Sch 2, para 22, Sch 4, para 9, Sch 6, as from a day to be appointed.

Entry "The Human Tissue Authority" inserted by the Human Tissue Act 2004, s 13(2), Sch 2, para 27.

Entry "The Independent Police Complaints Commission" inserted, and entry "The Police Complaints Authority" (omitted) repealed, by the Police Reform Act 2002, s 107, Sch 7, para 23, Sch 8.

In entry "The Inland Waterways Amenity Advisory Council" for the words in italics there are substituted the words "Inland Waterways Advisory Council" by the Natural Environment and Rural Communities Act 2006, s 105(1), Sch 11, Pt 2, para 175(1)(a), (2), as from a day to be appointed.

Entry "The Insurance Brokers Registration Council" (omitted) repealed by the Financial Services and Markets Act 2000 (Dissolution of the Insurance Brokers Registration Council) (Consequential Provisions) Order 2001, SI 2001/1283, art 3(7).

Entries "The Judicial Appointments Commission" and "The Judicial Appointments and Conduct Ombudsman" inserted by the Constitutional Reform Act 2005, ss 61(2), 62(2), Sch 12, Pt 2, para 36(3), Sch 13, para 17(3).

Entry "The Library and Information Services Council (Wales)" (omitted) repealed by the Library Advisory Council for Wales Abolition and Consequential Amendments Order 2004, SI 2004/803, art 3(3).

Entries "The Millennium Commission", "The National Lottery Charities Board", and "The New Opportunities Fund" (omitted) repealed by the National Lottery Act 2006, s 21, Sch 3.

Entry "The National Council for Education and Training for Wales" (omitted) inserted by SI 2002/2623, art 2, Sch 1; repealed by the National Council for Education and Training for Wales (Transfer of Functions to the National Assembly for Wales and Abolition) Order 2005, SI 2005/3238, art 9(1), Sch 1, para 85.

Entries "The National Crime Squad" and "The Service Authority for the National Crime Squad" (omitted) repealed by the Serious Organised Crime and Police Act 2005, ss 59, 174(2), Sch 4, paras 158, 160, Sch 17, Pt 2.

Entry "The National Identity Scheme Commissioner" inserted by the Identity Cards Act 2006, s 22(8), as from a day to be appointed.

Entry "The Northern Ireland Judicial Appointments Ombudsman" inserted by the Justice (Northern Ireland) Act 2002, s 9A(3), Sch 3A, para 17(3) (as inserted by the Constitutional Reform Act 2005, s 124(3), Sch 15).

Entry "The Nuclear Decommissioning Authority" inserted by the Energy Act 2004, s 2(10), Sch 1, para 18.

Entry "The Office of Communications" inserted by the Office of Communications Act 2002, s 1(10), Schedule, para 22.

Entry "The Olympic Delivery Authority" inserted by the London Olympic Games and Paralympic Games Act 2006, s 3(2), Sch 1, Pt 2, para 23.

Entry "The Patient Information Advisory Group" inserted by the Health and Social Care Act 2001, s 67(1), Sch 5, Pt 3, para 18.

Entry "The Police Information Technology Organisation" repealed and entry "The National Policing Improvement Agency" inserted, by the Police and Justice Act 2006, ss 1(3), 52, Sch 1, Pt 7, para 74, Sch 15, Pt 1, as from a day to be appointed.

Entry "The Qualifications, Curriculum and Assessment Authority for Wales" (omitted) repealed by the Qualifications, Curriculum and Assessment Authority for Wales (Transfer of Functions to the National Assembly for Wales and Abolition) Order 2005, SI 2005/3239, art 9(1), Sch 1, para 31, subject to transitional provisions in art 7 thereof.

Entry "Any Rail Passengers' Committee" (omitted) inserted by SI 2002/2623, art 2, Sch 1; repealed by the Railways Act 2005, s 59(6), Sch 13, Pt 1.

Entry "The Security Industry Authority" inserted by the Private Security Industry Act 2001, s 1, Sch 1, para 23.

Entry "Strategic Rail Authority" (omitted) inserted by the Transport Act 2000, s 204, Sch 14, Pt V, para 30; repealed by the Railways Act 2005, s 59(6), Sch 13, Pt 1.

Entry "The Training and Development Agency for Schools" inserted by the Education Act 2005, s 98, Sch 14, para 22.

Entry "The Valuation Tribunal Service" inserted by the Local Government Act 2003, s 105(9), Sch 4, para 24.

Entry "The Wales Centre for Health" inserted by the Health (Wales) Act 2003, s 7(1), Sch 3, para 15.

Entry "The Wales Tourist Board" (omitted) repealed by the Wales Tourist Board (Transfer of Functions to the National Assembly for Wales and Abolition) Order 2005, SI 2005/3225, art 6(2), Sch 2, Pt 1, para 5, subject to transitional provisions in art 3 thereof.

Entry "The Welsh Development Agency" (omitted) repealed by the Welsh Development Agency (Transfer of Functions to the National Assembly for Wales and Abolition) Order 2005, SI 2005/3226, art 7(1)(b), Sch 2, Pt 1, para 13, subject to transitional provisions in art 3 thereof.

PART VII
OTHER PUBLIC BODIES AND OFFICES: NORTHERN IRELAND

[An advisory committee established under paragraph 25 of the Health and Personal Social Services (Northern Ireland) Order 1972.]

An Advisory Committee on General Commissioners of Income Tax (Northern Ireland).

The Advisory Committee on Justices of the Peace in Northern Ireland.

…

The Advisory Committee on Pesticides for Northern Ireland.

[The Agri-food and Biosciences Institute.]

…

The Agricultural Wages Board for Northern Ireland.

The Arts Council of Northern Ireland.

The Assembly Ombudsman for Northern Ireland.

[The Attorney General for Northern Ireland.]

[The Belfast Harbour Commissioners.]

The Board of Trustees of National Museums and Galleries of Northern Ireland.

…

The Boundary Commission for Northern Ireland.

[A central advisory committee established under paragraph 24 of the Health and Personal Social Services (Northern Ireland) Order 1972.]

[The Certification Officer for Northern Ireland.]

The Charities Advisory Committee.

The Chief Electoral Officer for Northern Ireland.

[The Chief Inspector of Criminal Justice in Northern Ireland.]

The Civil Service Commissioners for Northern Ireland.

[Comhairle na Gaelscolaíochta.]

[Commissioner for Children and Young People for Northern Ireland.]

The Commissioner for Public Appointments for Northern Ireland.

[The Commissioner for Victims and Survivors for Northern Ireland.]

The Construction Industry Training Board.

The consultative Civic Forum referred to in section 56(4) of the Northern Ireland Act 1998.

The Council for Catholic Maintained Schools.

The Council for Nature Conservation and the Countryside.

The County Court Rules Committee (Northern Ireland).

[The Criminal Injuries Compensation Appeals Panel for Northern Ireland, in relation to information held by it otherwise than as a tribunal.]

[A development corporation established under Part III of the Strategic Investment and Regeneration of Sites (Northern Ireland) Order 2003.]

The Disability Living Allowance Advisory Board for Northern Ireland.

The Distinction and Meritorious Service Awards Committee.

[A district policing partnership.]

The Drainage Council for Northern Ireland.

An Education and Library Board established under Article 3 of the Education and Libraries (Northern Ireland) Order 1986.

Enterprise Ulster.

The Equality Commission for Northern Ireland.

The Family Proceedings Rules Committee (Northern Ireland).

…

The Fisheries Conservancy Board for Northern Ireland.

The General Consumer Council for Northern Ireland.

[The General Teaching Council for Northern Ireland.]

[The Governors of the Armargh Observatory and Planetarium.]

[The Harbour of Donaghadee Commissioners.]

The Health and Safety Agency for Northern Ireland.

The Historic Buildings Council.

The Historic Monuments Council.

The Independent Assessor of Military Complaints Procedures in Northern Ireland.

[An independent monitoring board appointed under section 10 of the Prison Act (Northern Ireland) 1953.]

The Independent Reviewer of the Northern Ireland (Emergency Provisions) Act.

The Independent Commissioner for Holding Centres.

…

…

[Invest Northern Ireland.]

…

The Labour Relations Agency.

The Laganside Corporation.

The Law Reform Advisory Committee for Northern Ireland.

The Lay Observer for Northern Ireland.

[…]

The Legal Aid Advisory Committee (Northern Ireland).

[The Life Sentence Review Commissioners appointed under Article 3 of the Life Sentences (Northern Ireland) Order 2001.]

The Livestock & Meat Commission for Northern Ireland.

…

The Local Government Staff Commission.

[The Londonderry Port and Harbour Commissioners.]

The Magistrates' Courts Rules Committee (Northern Ireland).

The Mental Health Commission for Northern Ireland.

…

The Northern Ireland Audit Office.

The Northern Ireland Building Regulations Advisory Committee.

The Northern Ireland Civil Service Appeal Board.

The Northern Ireland Commissioner for Complaints.

The Northern Ireland Community Relations Council.

…

The Northern Ireland Council for the Curriculum, Examinations and Assessment.

…

[The Northern Ireland Court of Judicature Rules Committee.]

The Northern Ireland Crown Court Rules Committee.

…

[The Northern Ireland Events Company.]

[The Northern Ireland Fire and Rescue Service Board.]

The Northern Ireland Fishery Harbour Authority.

[The Northern Ireland Health and Personal Social Services Regulation and Improvement Authority.]

The Northern Ireland Higher Education Council.

The Northern Ireland Housing Executive.

The Northern Ireland Human Rights Commission.

The Northern Ireland Insolvency Rules Committee.

[The Northern Ireland Judicial Appointments Commission.]

[The Northern Ireland Law Commission.]

[The Northern Ireland Legal Services Commission.]

The Northern Ireland Local Government Officers' Superannuation Committee.

The Northern Ireland Museums Council.

The Northern Ireland Pig Production Development Committee.

[The Northern Ireland Practice and Education Council for Nursing and Midwifery.]

[The Northern Ireland Social Care Council.]

The Northern Ireland Supreme Court Rules Committee.

The Northern Ireland Tourist Board.

The Northern Ireland Transport Holding Company.

The Northern Ireland Water Council.

[…]

The Parades Commission.

[The Pharmaceutical Society of Northern Ireland, in respect of information held by it otherwise than as a tribunal.]

[The Poisons Board (Northern Ireland).]

The Police Ombudsman for Northern Ireland.

The Probation Board for Northern Ireland.

The Rural Development Council for Northern Ireland.

The Sentence Review Commissioners appointed under section 1 of the Northern Ireland (Sentences) Act 1998.

The social fund Commissioner appointed under Article 37 of the Social Security (Northern Ireland) Order 1998.

The Sports Council for Northern Ireland.

The Staff Commission for Education and Library Boards.

The Statistics Advisory Committee.

The Statute Law Committee for Northern Ireland.

[A sub-group established under section 21 of the Police (Northern Ireland) Act 2000.]

…

Ulster Supported Employment Ltd.

[The Warrenpoint Harbour Authority.]

[The Waste Management Advisory Board.]

The Youth Council for Northern Ireland.

[807]

NOTES

Entry "Advisory Committee on Juvenile Court Lay Panel (Northern Ireland)" (omitted) repealed by the Justice (Northern Ireland) Act 2002, s 86, Sch 13.

Entry "The Agri-food and Biosciences Institute" inserted, and entry "The Agricultural Research Institute of Northern Ireland" (omitted) repealed by the Agriculture (Northern Ireland) Order 2004, SI 2004/3327, arts 3(5), 13, Sch 1, para 21, Sch 4.

Entries "The Belfast Harbour Commissioners", "The Certification Officer for Northern Ireland", "The Londonderry Port and Harbour Commissioners", and "The Warrenpoint Harbour Authority" inserted by the Freedom of Information (Additional Public Authorities) Order 2002, SI 2002/2623, art 3, Sch 2.

Entry "Boards of Visitors and Visiting Committees" (omitted) repealed and entry "An independent monitoring board appointed under section 10 of the Prison Act (Northern Ireland) 1953" inserted by the Criminal Justice (Northern Ireland) Order 2005, SI 2005/1965, art 10(2), Sch 1, para 10.

Entries "A central advisory committee established under paragraph 24 of the Health and Personal Social Services (Northern Ireland) Order 1972" and "An advisory committee established under paragraph 25 of the Health and Personal Social Services (Northern Ireland) Order 1972" inserted by the Freedom of Information (Additional Public Authorities) Order 2004, SI 2004/938, art 4, Sch 3.

Entry "The Chief Inspector of Criminal Justice in Northern Ireland" inserted by the Justice (Northern Ireland) Act 2002, s 45(3), Sch 8, para 16.

Entries "Comhairle na Gaelscolaíochta", "The Criminal Injuries Compensation Appeals Panel for Northern Ireland", "The General Teaching Council for Northern Ireland", "The Governors of the Armargh Observatory and Planetarium", "The Harbour of Donaghadee Commissioners", "The Northern Ireland Practice and Education Council for Nursing and Midwifery", "The Northern Ireland Social Care Council" and "The Waste Management Advisory Board" inserted by the Freedom of Information (Additional Public Authorities) Order 2003, SI 2003/1882, art 3, Sch 2.

Entry "Commissioner for Children and Young People for Northern Ireland" inserted by the Commissioner for Children and Young People (Northern Ireland) Order 2003, SI 2003/439, art 5(3), Sch 2, para 15.

PART II DATA PROTECTION

Entry "The Commissioner for Victims and Survivors for Northern Ireland" inserted by the Victims and Survivors (Northern Ireland) Order 2006, SI 2006/2953, art 4(3), Schedule, para 15, as from a day to be appointed.

Entry beginning "A development corporation" inserted by the Strategic Investment and Regeneration of Sites (Northern Ireland) Order 2003, SI 2003/410, art 15(3), Sch 1, para 23.

Entry "A district policing partnership" inserted by the Police (Northern Ireland) Act 2000, s 78(1), Sch 6, para 25(1), (3).

Entry "The Fire Authority for Northern Ireland" (omitted) repealed and entry "The Northern Ireland Fire and Rescue Service Board" inserted by the Fire and Rescue Services (Northern Ireland) Order 2006, SI 2006/1254, arts 3(3), 62(2), Sch 1, para 19, Sch 4.

Entries "Industrial Development Board for Northern Ireland", "Industrial Research and Technology Unit" and "Local Enterprise Development Unit" (all omitted) repealed, and entry "Invest Northern Ireland" inserted, by the Industrial Development Act (Northern Ireland) 2002, ss 1(2), 5(4), Sch 1, para 21, Sch 4.

Entries "The Juvenile Justice Board", "The Northern Ireland Consumer Committee for Electricity", "The Northern Ireland Council for Postgraduate Medical and Dental Education" and "The Training and Employment Agency" (all omitted) repealed by the Freedom of Information (Removal of References to Public Authorities) Order 2004, SI 2004/1641, art 3, Sch 2.

Entry "Law Reform Advisory Committee for Northern Ireland" repealed, and entries "The Attorney General for Northern Ireland" and "The Northern Ireland Law Commission" inserted, by the Justice (Northern Ireland) Act 2002, ss 23(9), 50(7), 86, Sch 9, para 15, Sch 13, as from a day to be appointed.

Entry "The Learning and Skills Advisory Board" inserted by SI 2003/1882, art 3, Sch 2; repealed by SI 2004/1641, art 3, Sch 2.

Entry "The Life Sentence Review Commissioners" inserted by the Life Sentences (Northern Ireland Consequential Amendments) Order 2001, SI 2001/2565, art 4.

Entry "The Northern Ireland Advisory Committee on Telecommunications" repealed by the Communications Act 2003, s 406(7), Sch 19(1).

Entry "The Northern Ireland Court of Judicature Rules Committee" inserted and entry "The Northern Ireland Supreme Court Rules Committee" repealed by the Constitutional Reform Act 2005, ss 59(5), 146, Sch 11, Pt 4, para 34, Sch 18, Pt 5, as from a day to be appointed.

Entries "The Northern Ireland Economic Council" and "Obstetrics Committee" (as inserted by SI 2004/938, art 4, Sch 3) (omitted) repealed by the Freedom of Information (Removal of References to Public Authorities) Order 2005, SI 2005/3594, art 2, Sch 1.

Entries "The Northern Ireland Events Company", "The Northern Ireland Health and Personal Social Services Regulation and Improvement Authority", "The Pharmaceutical Society of Northern Ireland", and "The Poisons Board (Northern Ireland)" inserted by the Freedom of Information (Additional Public Authorities) Order 2005, SI 2005/3593, arts 4, 5, Schs 3, 4.

Entry "The Northern Ireland Judicial Appointments Commission" inserted by the Justice (Northern Ireland) Act 2002, s 3(3), Sch 2, para 20.

Entry "The Northern Ireland Legal Services Commission" inserted by the Access to Justice (Northern Ireland) Order 2003, SI 2003/435, art 49(1), Sch 4, para 15.

Entry relating to "section 21 of the Police (Northern Ireland) Act 2000" inserted by the Police (Northern Ireland) Act 2003, s 19(1), Sch 1, paras 1, 15, as from a day to be appointed.

SCHEDULE 2
THE COMMISSIONER AND THE TRIBUNAL

Section 18(4)

PART I
PROVISION CONSEQUENTIAL ON S 18(1) AND (2)

General

1.—(1) Any reference in any enactment, instrument or document to the Data Protection Commissioner or the Data Protection Registrar shall be construed, in relation to any time after the commencement of section 18(1), as a reference to the Information Commissioner.

(2) Any reference in any enactment, instrument or document to the Data Protection Tribunal shall be construed, in relation to any time after the commencement of section 18(2), as a reference to the Information Tribunal.

2.—(1) Any reference in this Act or in any instrument under this Act to the Commissioner shall be construed, in relation to any time before the commencement of section 18(1), as a reference to the Data Protection Commissioner.

(2) Any reference in this Act or in any instrument under this Act to the Tribunal shall be construed, in relation to any time before the commencement of section 18(2), as a reference to the Data Protection Tribunal.

3–15. …

[808]

NOTES

Paras 3–15: amend the Data Protection Act 1998, ss 6, 70, Sch 5 at **[510]**, **[578]**, **[589]**, and contain other amendments outside the scope of this work.

(*Pt II amends the Data Protection Act 1998, ss 6, 26, 58, 59, Sch 5 at* **[510]**, **[532]**, **[566]**, **[567]**, **[589]**.)

SCHEDULE 3
POWERS OF ENTRY AND INSPECTION

Section 55

Issue of warrants

1.—(1) If a circuit judge [or a District Judge (Magistrates' Courts)] is satisfied by information on oath supplied by the Commissioner that there are reasonable grounds for suspecting—

- (a) that a public authority has failed or is failing to comply with—
  - (i) any of the requirements of Part I of this Act,
  - (ii) so much of a decision notice as requires steps to be taken, or
  - (iii) an information notice or an enforcement notice, or
- (b) that an offence under section 77 has been or is being committed,

and that evidence of such a failure to comply or of the commission of the offence is to be found on any premises specified in the information, he may, subject to paragraph 2, grant a warrant to the Commissioner.

(2) A warrant issued under sub-paragraph (1) shall authorise the Commissioner or any of his officers or staff at any time within seven days of the date of the warrant—

- (a) to enter and search the premises,
- (b) to inspect and seize any documents or other material found there which may be such evidence as is mentioned in that sub-paragraph, and
- (c) to inspect, examine, operate and test any equipment found there in which information held by the public authority may be recorded.

2.—(1) A judge shall not issue a warrant under this Schedule unless he is satisfied—

- (a) that the Commissioner has given seven days' notice in writing to the occupier of the premises in question demanding access to the premises, and
- (b) that either—
  - (i) access was demanded at a reasonable hour and was unreasonably refused, or
  - (ii) although entry to the premises was granted, the occupier unreasonably refused to comply with a request by the Commissioner or any of the Commissioner's officers or staff to permit the Commissioner or the officer or member of staff to do any of the things referred to in paragraph 1(2), and
- (c) that the occupier, has, after the refusal, been notified by the Commissioner of the application for the warrant and has had an opportunity of being heard by the judge on the question whether or not it should be issued.

(2) Sub-paragraph (1) shall not apply if the judge is satisfied that the case is one of urgency or that compliance with those provisions would defeat the object of the entry.

3. A judge who issues a warrant under this Schedule shall also issue two copies of it and certify them clearly as copies.

Execution of warrants

4. A person executing a warrant issued under this Schedule may use such reasonable force as may be necessary.

PART II
DATA PROTECTION

5. A warrant issued under this Schedule shall be executed at a reasonable hour unless it appears to the person executing it that there are grounds for suspecting that the evidence in question would not be found if it were so executed.

6.—(1) If the premises in respect of which a warrant is issued under this Schedule are occupied by a public authority and any officer or employee of the authority is present when the warrant is executed, he shall be shown the warrant and supplied with a copy of it; and if no such officer or employee is present a copy of the warrant shall be left in a prominent place on the premises.

(2) If the premises in respect of which a warrant is issued under this Schedule are occupied by a person other than a public authority and he is present when the warrant is executed, he shall be shown the warrant and supplied with a copy of it; and if that person is not present a copy of the warrant shall be left in a prominent place on the premises.

7.—(1) A person seizing anything in pursuance of a warrant under this Schedule shall give a receipt for it if asked to do so.

(2) Anything so seized may be retained for so long as is necessary in all the circumstances but the person in occupation of the premises in question shall be given a copy of anything that is seized if he so requests and the person executing the warrant considers that it can be done without undue delay.

Matters exempt from inspection and seizure

8. The powers of inspection and seizure conferred by a warrant issued under this Schedule shall not be exercisable in respect of information which is exempt information by virtue of section 23(1) or 24(1).

9.—(1) Subject to the provisions of this paragraph, the powers of inspection and seizure conferred by a warrant issued under this Schedule shall not be exercisable in respect of—

(a) any communication between a professional legal adviser and his client in connection with the giving of legal advice to the client with respect to his obligations, liabilities or rights under this Act, or

(b) any communication between a professional legal adviser and his client, or between such an adviser or his client and any other person, made in connection with or in contemplation of proceedings under or arising out of this Act (including proceedings before the Tribunal) and for the purposes of such proceedings.

(2) Sub-paragraph (1) applies also to—

(a) any copy or other record of any such communication as is there mentioned, and

(b) any document or article enclosed with or referred to in any such communication if made in connection with the giving of any advice or, as the case may be, in connection with or in contemplation of and for the purposes of such proceedings as are there mentioned.

(3) This paragraph does not apply to anything in the possession of any person other than the professional legal adviser or his client or to anything held with the intention of furthering a criminal purpose.

(4) In this paragraph references to the client of a professional legal adviser include references to any person representing such a client.

10. If the person in occupation of any premises in respect of which a warrant is issued under this Schedule objects to the inspection or seizure under the warrant of any material on the grounds that it consists partly of matters in respect of which those powers are not exercisable, he shall, if the person executing the warrant so requests, furnish that person with a copy of so much of the material in relation to which the powers are exercisable.

Return of warrants

11. A warrant issued under this Schedule shall be returned to the court from which it was issued—

(a) after being executed, or

(b) if not executed within the time authorised for its execution;

and the person by whom any such warrant is executed shall make an endorsement on it stating what powers have been exercised by him under the warrant.

Offences

12. Any person who—
   (a) intentionally obstructs a person in the execution of a warrant issued under this Schedule, or
   (b) fails without reasonable excuse to give any person executing such a warrant such assistance as he may reasonably require for the execution of the warrant,

is guilty of an offence.

Vessels, vehicles etc

13. In this Schedule "premises" includes any vessel, vehicle, aircraft or hovercraft, and references to the occupier of any premises include references to the person in charge of any vessel, vehicle, aircraft or hovercraft.

Scotland and Northern Ireland

14. In the application of this Schedule to Scotland—
   (a) for any reference to a circuit judge there is substituted a reference to the sheriff, and
   (b) for any reference to information on oath there is substituted a reference to evidence on oath.

15. In the application of this Schedule to Northern Ireland—
   (a) for any reference to a circuit judge there is substituted a reference to a county court judge, and
   (b) or any reference to information on oath there is substituted a reference to a complaint on oath.

[809]

NOTES

Commencement: 30 November 2002 (in so far as it relates to the enforcement of the requirements on public authorities under the publication scheme provisions and in so far as relates to: (i) the issue of practice recommendations, and (ii) the issue and enforcement of information notices, relating to the conformity with the code of practice under s 45 of the practice of public authorities in relation to the exercise of their functions under the publication scheme provisions); 1 January 2005 (otherwise).

Para 1: words in square brackets in sub-para (1) inserted by the Courts Act 2003, s 65, Sch 4, para 13, as from a day to be appointed.

See further, in relation to additional powers of seizure from premises: the Criminal Justice and Police Act 2001, s 50, Sch 1, Pt 1, para 73.

(*Sch 4 amends the Data Protection Act 1998, Sch 6 at* **[591]***; Sch 5 (amendments of public records legislation) outside the scope of this work; Sch 6 amends s 7 of, Schs 2, 3, 7, 14 to, the 1998 Act at* **[511]**, **[586]**, **[587]**, **[592]**, **[603]**, *and inserts ss 35A, 63A of that Act at* **[543]**, **[571]***; Sch 7 (amendments relating to disclosure of information by Ombudsmen) outside the scope of this work.*)

SCHEDULE 8
REPEALS

Section 86

PART I
REPEAL COMING INTO FORCE ON PASSING OF ACT

Chapter	*Short title*	*Extent of repeal*
1998 c 29	The Data Protection Act 1998	In Schedule 14, in paragraph 2(1), the words "or, if earlier, 24th October 2001".

[810]

PART II
REPEALS COMING INTO FORCE IN ACCORDANCE WITH SECTION 87(2)

Chapter	*Short title*	*Extent of repeal*
1958 c 51	The Public Records Act 1958	In Schedule 1, in Part II of the Table in paragraph 3, the entry relating to the Data Protection Commissioner.
1967 c 13	The Parliamentary Commissioner Act 1967	In Schedule 2, the entry relating to the Data Protection Commissioner.
1975 c 24	The House of Commons Disqualification Act 1975	In Schedule 1, in Part III, the entry relating to the Data Protection Commissioner.
1975 c 25	The Northern Ireland Assembly Disqualification Act 1975	In Schedule 1, in Part III, the entry relating to the Data Protection Commissioner.
1998 c 29	The Data Protection Act 1998	In Schedule 5, Part III.
		In Schedule 15, paragraphs 1(1), 2, 4, 5(2) and 6(2).

[811]

PART III
REPEALS COMING INTO FORCE IN ACCORDANCE WITH SECTION 87(3)

Chapter	*Short title*	*Extent of repeal*
1958 c 51	The Public Records Act 1958	In section 5, subsections (1), (2) and (4) and, in subsection (5), the words from "and subject to" to the end.
		Schedule 2.
1975 c 24	The House of Commons Disqualification Act 1975	In Schedule 1, in Part II, the entry relating to the Data Protection Tribunal.
1975 c 25	The Northern Ireland Assembly Disqualification Act 1975'	In Schedule 1, in Part II, the entry relating to the Data Protection Tribunal.

Chapter	*Short title*	*Extent of repeal*
1998 c 29	The Data Protection Act 1998	In section 1(1), in the definition of "data", the word "or" at the end of paragraph (c). In Schedule 15, paragraphs 1(2) and (3), 3, 5(1) and 6(1).

[812]

NOTES

Commencement: 1 January 2005.

DATA PROTECTION (CORPORATE FINANCE EXEMPTION) ORDER 2000

(SI 2000/184)

NOTES

Made: 31 January 2000.
Authority: Data Protection Act 1998, s 67(2), Sch 7, para 6(2).
Commencement: 1 March 2000.

PART II DATA PROTECTION

1 Citation and commencement

(1) This Order may be cited as the Data Protection (Corporate Finance Exemption) Order 2000 and shall come into force on 1st March 2000.

(2) In this Order, "the Act" means the Data Protection Act 1998.

[813]

2 Matters to be taken into account

(1) The matter set out in paragraph (2) below is hereby specified for the purposes of paragraph 6(1)(b) of Schedule 7 to the Act (matters to be taken into account in determining whether exemption from the subject information provisions is required for the purpose of safeguarding an important economic or financial interest of the United Kingdom).

(2) The matter referred to in paragraph (1) above is the inevitable prejudicial effect on—
(a) the orderly functioning of financial markets, or
(b) the efficient allocation of capital within the economy,
which will result from the application (whether on an occasional or regular basis) of the subject information provisions to data to which paragraph (3) below applies.

(3) This paragraph applies to any personal data to which the application of the subject information provisions could, in the reasonable belief of the relevant person within the meaning of paragraph 6 of Schedule 7 to the Act, affect—
(a) any decision of any person whether or not to—
(i) deal in,
(ii) subscribe for, or
(iii) issue,
any instrument which is already in existence or is to be, or may be, created; or
(b) any decision of any person to act or not to act in a way that is likely to have an effect on any business activity including, in particular, an effect on—
(i) the industrial strategy of any person (whether the strategy is, or is to be, pursued independently or in association with others),
(ii) the capital structure of an undertaking, or
(iii) the legal or beneficial ownership of a business or asset.

[814]

DATA PROTECTION (CONDITIONS UNDER PARAGRAPH 3 OF PART II OF SCHEDULE 1) ORDER 2000

(SI 2000/185)

NOTES

Made: 31 January 2000.
Authority: Data Protection Act 1998, s 67(2), Sch 1, Pt II, para 3(1).
Commencement: 1 March 2000.

1 Citation and commencement

This Order may be cited as the Data Protection (Conditions under Paragraph 3 of Part II of Schedule 1) Order 2000 and shall come into force on 1st March 2000.

[815]

2 Interpretation

In this Order, "Part II" means Part II of Schedule 1 to the Data Protection Act 1998.

[816]

3 General provisions

(1) In cases where the primary condition referred to in paragraph 3(2)(a) of Part II is met, the provisions of articles 4 and 5 apply.

(2) In cases where the primary condition referred to in paragraph 3(2)(b) of that Part is met by virtue of the fact that the recording of the information to be contained in the data by, or the disclosure of the data by, the data controller is not a function conferred on him by or under any enactment or an obligation imposed on him by order of a court, but is necessary for compliance with any legal obligation to which the data controller is subject, other than an obligation imposed by contract, the provisions of article 4 apply.

[817]

4 Notices in writing

(1) One of the further conditions prescribed in paragraph (2) must be met if paragraph 2(1)(b) of Part II is to be disapplied in respect of any particular data subject.

(2) The conditions referred to in paragraph (1) are that—

(a) no notice in writing has been received at any time by the data controller from an individual, requiring that data controller to provide the information set out in paragraph 2(3) of that Part before the relevant time (as defined in paragraph 2(2) of that Part) or as soon as practicable after that time; or

(b) where such notice in writing has been received but the data controller does not have sufficient information about the individual in order readily to determine whether he is processing personal data about that individual, the data controller shall send to the individual a written notice stating that he cannot provide the information set out in paragraph 2(3) of that Part because of his inability to make that determination, and explaining the reasons for that inability.

(3) The requirement in paragraph (2) that notice should be in writing is satisfied where the text of the notice—

(a) is transmitted by electronic means,
(b) is received in legible form, and
(c) is capable of being used for subsequent reference.

[818]

5 Further condition in cases of disproportionate effort

(1) The further condition prescribed in paragraph (2) must be met for paragraph 2(1)(b) of Part II to be disapplied in respect of any data.

(2) The condition referred to in paragraph (1) is that the data controller shall record the reasons for his view that the primary condition referred to in article 3(1) is met in respect of the data.

[819]

DATA PROTECTION (FUNCTIONS OF DESIGNATED AUTHORITY) ORDER 2000

(SI 2000/186)

NOTES

Made: 31 January 2000.
Authority: Data Protection Act 1998, ss 54(2), 67(2).
Commencement: 1 March 2000.

ARRANGEMENT OF ARTICLES

1 Citation and commencement

This Order may be cited as the Data Protection (Functions of Designated Authority) Order 2000 and shall come into force on 1st March 2000.

[820]

2 Interpretation

(1) In this Order—

"the Act" means the Data Protection Act 1998;

"foreign designated authority" means an authority designated for the purposes of Article 13 of the Convention by a party (other than the United Kingdom) which is bound by that Convention;

"register" means the register maintained under section 19(1) of the Act;

"request", except in article 3, means a request for assistance under Article 14 of the Convention which states—

(a) the name and address of the person making the request;
(b) particulars which identify the personal data to which the request relates;
(c) the rights under Article 8 of the Convention to which the request relates;
(d) the reasons why the request has been made;

and "requesting person" means a person making such a request.

(2) In this Order, references to the Commissioner are to the Commissioner as the designated authority in the United Kingdom for the purposes of Article 13 of the Convention.

[821]

3 Co-operation between the Commissioner and foreign designated authorities

(1) The Commissioner shall, at the request of a foreign designated authority, furnish to that foreign designated authority such information referred to in Article 13(3)(a) of the Convention, and in particular the data protection legislation in force in the United Kingdom at the time the request is made, as is the subject of the request.

(2) The Commissioner shall, at the request of a foreign designated authority, take appropriate measures in accordance with Article 13(3)(b) of the Convention, for furnishing to that foreign designated authority information relating to the processing of personal data in the United Kingdom.

(3) The Commissioner may request a foreign designated authority to furnish to him or, as the case may be, to take appropriate measures for furnishing to him, the information referred to in Article 13(3) of the Convention.

[822]

4 Persons resident outside the United Kingdom

(1) This article applies where a person resident outside the United Kingdom makes a request to the Commissioner under Article 14 of the Convention, including a request

PART II DATA PROTECTION

forwarded to the Commissioner through the Secretary of State or a foreign designated authority, seeking assistance in exercising any of the rights under Article 8 of the Convention.

(2) If the request—

(a) seeks assistance in exercising the rights under section 7 of the Act; and

(b) does not indicate that the data controller has failed, contrary to section 7 of the Act, to comply with the same request on a previous occasion,

the Commissioner shall notify the requesting person of the data controller's address for the receipt of notices from data subjects exercising their rights under that section and of such other information as the Commissioner considers necessary to enable that person to exercise his rights under that section.

(3) If the request indicates that a data protection principle has been contravened by a data controller the Commissioner shall either—

(a) notify the requesting person of the rights of data subjects and the remedies available to them under Part II of the Act together with such particulars as are contained in the data controller's entry in the register as are necessary to enable the requesting person to avail himself of those remedies; or

(b) if the Commissioner considers that notification in accordance with sub-paragraph (a) would not assist the requesting person or would, for any other reason, be inappropriate, treat the request as if it were a request for an assessment which falls to be dealt with under section 42 of the Act.

(4) The Commissioner shall not be required, in response to any request referred to in paragraphs (2) and (3) above, to supply to the requesting person a duly certified copy in writing of the particulars contained in any entry made in the register other than on payment of such fee as is prescribed for the purposes of section 19(7) of the Act.

[823]

5 Persons resident in the United Kingdom

(1) Where a request for assistance in exercising any of the rights referred to in Article 8 of the Convention in a country or territory (other than the United Kingdom) specified in the request is made by a person resident in the United Kingdom and submitted through the Commissioner under Article 14(2) of the Convention, the Commissioner shall, if he is satisfied that the request contains all necessary particulars referred to in Article 14(3) of the Convention, send it to the foreign designated authority in the specified country or territory.

(2) If the Commissioner decides that he is not required by paragraph (1) above to render assistance to the requesting person he shall, where practicable, notify that person of the reasons for his decision.

[824]

6 Restrictions on use of information

Where the Commissioner receives information from a foreign designated authority as a result of either—

(a) a request made by him under article 3(3) above; or

(b) a request received by him under articles 3(2) or 4 above,

the Commissioner shall use that information only for the purposes specified in the request.

[825]

DATA PROTECTION (FEES UNDER SECTION 19(7)) REGULATIONS 2000

(SI 2000/187)

NOTES

Made: 31 January 2000.
Authority: Data Protection Act 1998, s 19(7).
[Co]mmencement: 1 March 2000.

1 These Regulations may be cited as the Data Protection (Fees under section 19(7)) Regulations 2000 and shall come into force on 1st March 2000.

[826]

2 The fee payable by a member of the public for the supply by [the Information Commissioner] under section 19(7) of the Data Protection Act 1998 of a duly certified written copy of the particulars contained in any entry made in the register maintained under section 19(1) of that Act shall be £2.

[827]

NOTES

Words in square brackets substituted by virtue of the Freedom of Information Act 2000, s 18(4), Sch 2, Pt I, para 1(1).

DATA PROTECTION (NOTIFICATION AND NOTIFICATION FEES) REGULATIONS 2000

(SI 2000/188)

NOTES

Made: 31 January 2000.

Authority: Data Protection Act 1998, ss 17(3), 18(2), (4), (5), 19(2), (3), (4), (5), 20(1), 26(1), 67(2), Sch 14, para 2(7), (8).

Commencement: 1 March 2000.

ARRANGEMENT OF REGULATIONS

1 Citation and commencement

These Regulations may be cited as the Data Protection (Notification and Notification Fees) Regulations 2000 and shall come into force on 1st March 2000.

[828]

2 Interpretation

In these Regulations–

"the Act" means the Data Protection Act 1998;

"the register" means the register maintained by the Commissioner under section 19 of the Act.

[829]

3 Exemptions from notification

Except where the processing is assessable processing for the purposes of section 22 of the Act, section 17(1) of the Act shall not apply in relation to processing—

(a) falling within one or more of the descriptions of processing set out in paragraphs 2 to 5 of the Schedule to these Regulations (being processing appearing to the Secretary of State to be unlikely to prejudice the rights and freedoms of data subjects); or

(b) which does not fall within one or more of those descriptions solely by virtue of the fact that disclosure of the personal data to a person other than those specified in the descriptions—

(i) is required by or under any enactment, by any rule of law or by the order of a court, or

(ii) may be made by virtue of an exemption from the non-disclosure provisions (as defined in section 27(3) of the Act).

[830]

4 Form of giving notification

(1) Subject to regulations 5 and 6 below, the Commissioner shall determine the form in which the registrable particulars (within the meaning of section 16(1) of the Act) and the description mentioned in section 18(2)(b) of the Act are to be specified, including in particular the detail required for the purposes of that description and section 16(1)(c), (d), (e) and (f) of the Act.

(2) Subject to regulations 5 and 6 below, the Commissioner shall determine the form in which a notification under regulation 12 (including that regulation as modified by regulation 13) is to be specified.

[831]

5 Notification in respect of partnerships

(1) In any case in which two or more persons carrying on a business in partnership are the data controllers in respect of any personal data for the purposes of that business, a notification under section 18 of the Act or under regulation 12 below may be given in respect of those persons in the name of the firm.

(2) Where a notification is given in the name of a firm under paragraph (1) above—

(a) the name to be specified for the purposes of section 16(1)(a) of the Act is the name of the firm, and

(b) the address to be specified for the purposes of section 16(1)(a) of the Act is the address of the firm's principal place of business.

[832]

6 Notification in respect of the governing body of, and head teacher at, any school

(1) In any case in which a governing body of, and a head teacher at, any school are, in those capacities, the data controllers in respect of any personal data, a notification under section 18 of the Act or under regulation 12 below may be given in respect of that governing body and head teacher in the name of the school.

(2) Where a notification is given in the name of a school under paragraph (1) above, the name and address to be specified for the purposes of section 16(1)(a) of the Act are those of the school.

(3) In this regulation, "head teacher" includes in Northern Ireland the principal of a school.

[833]

7 Fees to accompany notification under section 18 of the Act

(1) This regulation applies to any notification under section 18 of the Act, including a notification which, by virtue of regulation 5 or 6 above, is given in respect of more than one data controller.

(2) A notification to which this regulation applies must be accompanied by a fee of £35.

[834]

8 Date of entry in the register

(1) The time from which an entry in respect of a data controller who has given a notification under section 18 of the Act in accordance with these Regulations is to be treated for the purposes of section 17 of the Act as having been made in the register shall be determined as follows.

(2) In the case of a data controller who has given the notification by sending it by registered post or the recorded delivery service, that time is the day after the day on which it is received for dispatch by the [postal operator (within the meaning of the Postal Services Act 2000) concerned].

(3) In the case of a data controller who has given a notification by some other means, that time is the day on which it is received by the Commissioner.

[835]

NOTES

Para (2): words in square brackets substituted by the Postal Services Act 2000 (Consequential Modifications No 1) Order 2001, SI 2001/1149, art 3(1), Sch 1, para 137.

9 Acknowledgment of receipt of notification in the case of assessable processing

(1) In any case in which the Commissioner considers under section 22(2)(a) of the Act that any of the processing to which a notification relates is assessable processing within the meaning of that section he shall, within 10 days of receipt of the notification, give a written notice to the data controller who has given the notification, acknowledging its receipt.

(2) A notice under paragraph (1) above shall indicate—

(a) the date on which the Commissioner received the notification, and

(b) the processing which the Commissioner considers to be assessable processing.

[836]

10 Confirmation of register entries

(1) The Commissioner shall, as soon as practicable and in any event within a period of 28 days after making an entry in the register under section 19(1)(b) of the Act or amending an entry in the register under section 20(4) of the Act, give the data controller to whom the register entry relates notice confirming the register entry.

(2) A notice under paragraph (1) above shall include a statement of—

(a) the date on which—

(i) in the case of an entry made under section 19(1)(b) of the Act, the entry is treated as having been included by virtue of regulation 8 above, or

(ii) in the case of an entry made under section 20(4) of the Act, the notification was received by the Commissioner;

(b) the particulars entered in the register, or the amendment made, in pursuance of the notification; and

(c) in the case of a notification under section 18 of the Act, the date by which the fee payable under regulation 14 below must be paid in order for the entry to be retained in the register as provided by section 19(4) of the Act.

[837]

11 Additional information in register entries

In addition to the matters mentioned in section 19(2)(a) of the Act, the Commissioner may include in a register entry—

(a) a registration number issued by the Commissioner in respect of that entry;

(b) the date on which the entry is treated, by virtue of regulation 8 above, as having been included in pursuance of a notification under section 18 of the Act;

(c) the date on which the entry falls or may fall to be removed by virtue of regulation 14 or 15 below; and

(d) information additional to the registrable particulars for the purpose of assisting persons consulting the register to communicate with any data controller to whom the entry relates concerning matters relating to the processing of personal data.

[838]

12 Duty to notify changes to matters previously notified

(1) Subject to regulation 13 below, every person in respect of whom an entry is for the time being included in the register is under a duty to give the Commissioner a notification specifying any respect in which—

(a) that entry becomes inaccurate or incomplete as a statement of his current registrable particulars, or

(b) the general description of measures notified under section 18(2)(b) of the Act or, as the case may be, that description as amended in pursuance of a notification under this regulation, becomes inaccurate or incomplete,

and setting out the changes which need to be made to that entry or general description in order to make it accurate and complete.

(2) Such a notification must be given as soon as practicable and in any event within a period of 28 days from the date on which the entry or, as the case may be, the general description, becomes inaccurate or incomplete.

(3) References in this regulation to an entry being included in the register include any entry being treated under regulation 8 above as being so included.

[839]

13 Duty to notify changes—transitional modifications

(1) This regulation applies to persons in respect of whom an entry in the register has been made under paragraph 2(6) of Schedule 14 to the Act.

(2) In the case of a person to whom this regulation applies, the duty imposed by regulation 12 above shall be modified so as to have effect as follows.

(3) Every person in respect of whom an entry is for the time being included in the register is under a duty to give the Commissioner a notification specifying—

- (a) his name and address, in any case in which a change to his name or address results in the entry in respect of him no longer including his current name and address;
- (b) to the extent to which the entry relates to eligible data—
  - (i) a description of any eligible data being or to be processed by him or on his behalf, in any case in which such processing is of personal data of a description not included in that entry;
  - (ii) a description of the category or categories of data subject to which eligible data relate, in any case in which such category or categories are of a description not included in that entry;
  - (iii) a description of the purpose or purposes for which eligible data are being or are to be processed in any case in which such processing is for a purpose or purposes of a description not included in that entry;
  - (iv) a description of the source or sources from which he intends or may wish to obtain eligible data, in any case in which such obtaining is from a source of a description not included in that entry;
  - (v) a description of any recipient or recipients to whom he intends or may wish to disclose eligible data, in any case in which such disclosure is to a recipient or recipients of a description not included in that entry; and
  - (vi) the names, or a description of, any countries or territories outside the United Kingdom to which he directly or indirectly transfers, or intends or may wish directly or indirectly to transfer, eligible data, in any case in which such transfer would be to a country or territory not named or described in that entry; and
- (c) to the extent to which sub-paragraph (b) above does not apply, any respect in which the entry is or becomes inaccurate or incomplete as—
  - (i) a statement of his current registrable particulars to the extent mentioned in section 16(1)(c), (d) and (e) of the Act;
  - (ii) a description of the source or sources from which he currently intends or may wish to obtain personal data; and
  - (iii) the names or a description of any countries or territories outside the United Kingdom to which he currently intends or may wish directly or indirectly to transfer personal data;

and setting out the changes which need to be made to that entry in order to make it accurate and complete in those respects.

(4) Such a notification must be given as soon as practicable and in any event within a period of 28 days from the date on which—

- (a) in the case of a notification under paragraph (3)(a) above, the entry no longer includes the current name and address;
- (b) in the case of a notification under paragraph (3)(b) above, the specified practice or intentions are in the particulars there mentioned of a description not included in the entry; and
- (c) in the case of a notification under paragraph (3)(c) above, the entry becomes inaccurate or incomplete in the particulars there mentioned.

(5) For the purposes of this regulation, personal data are "eligible data" at any time if, and to the extent that, they are at that time subject to processing which was already under way immediately before 24th October 1998.

[840]

14 Retention of register entries

(1) This regulation applies to any entry in respect of a person which is for the time being included, or by virtue of regulation 8 is treated as being included, in the register, other than an entry to which regulation 15 below applies.

(2) In relation to an entry to which this regulation applies, the fee referred to in section 19(4) of the Act is £35.

[841]

15 Retention of register entries—transitional provisions

(1) This regulation applies to any entry in respect of a person which is for the time being included in the register under paragraph 2(6) of Schedule 14 to the Act or, as the case may be, such an entry as amended in pursuance of regulation 12 (including that regulation as modified by regulation 13).

(2) Section 19(4) and (5) of the Act applies to entries to which this regulation applies subject to the modifications in paragraph (3) below.

(3) Section 19(4) and (5) of the Act shall be modified so as to have effect as follows—

"(4) No entry shall be retained in the register after—

(a) the end of the registration period, or

(b) ...

[(b)] the date on which the data controller gives a notification under section 18 of the Act,

whichever occurs first.

(5) In subsection (4) "the registration period" has the same meaning as in paragraph 2(2) of Schedule 14.".

[842]

NOTES

Para (3): sub-para (b) revoked, and original sub-para (c) lettered as sub-para (b), by the Data Protection (Notification and Notification Fees) (Amendment) Regulations 2001, SI 2001/3214, reg 2.

SCHEDULE
PROCESSING TO WHICH SECTION 17(1) DOES NOT APPLY

Regulation 3

1 Interpretation

In this Schedule–

"exempt purposes" in paragraphs 2 to 4 shall mean the purposes specified in sub-paragraph (a) of those paragraphs and in paragraph 5 shall mean the purposes specified in sub-paragraph (b) of that paragraph;

"staff" includes employees or office holders, workers within the meaning given in section 296 of the Trade Union and Labour Relations (Consolidation) Act 1992, persons working under any contract for services, and volunteers.

2 Staff administration exemption

The processing—

(a) is for the purposes of appointments or removals, pay, discipline, superannuation, work management or other personnel matters in relation to the staff of the data controller;

(b) is of personal data in respect of which the data subject is—

(i) a past, existing or prospective member of staff of the data controller; or

(ii) any person the processing of whose personal data is necessary for the exempt purposes;

(c) is of personal data consisting of the name, address and other identifiers of the data subject or information as to—

(i) qualifications, work experience or pay; or
(ii) other matters the processing of which is necessary for the exempt purposes;

(d) does not involve disclosure of the personal data to any third party other than—
(i) with the consent of the data subject; or
(ii) where it is necessary to make such disclosure for the exempt purposes; and

(e) does not involve keeping the personal data after the relationship between the data controller and staff member ends, unless and for so long as it is necessary to do so for the exempt purposes.

3 Advertising, marketing and public relations exemption

The processing—

(a) is for the purposes of advertising or marketing the data controller's business, activity, goods or services and promoting public relations in connection with that business or activity, or those goods or services;

(b) is of personal data in respect of which the data subject is—
(i) a past, existing or prospective customer or supplier; or
(ii) any person the processing of whose personal data is necessary for the exempt purposes;

(c) is of personal data consisting of the name, address and other identifiers of the data subject or information as to other matters the processing of which is necessary for the exempt purposes;

(d) does not involve disclosure of the personal data to any third party other than—
(i) with the consent of the data subject; or
(ii) where it is necessary to make such disclosure for the exempt purposes; and

(e) does not involve keeping the personal data after the relationship between the data controller and customer or supplier ends, unless and for so long as it is necessary to do so for the exempt purposes.

4 Accounts and records exemption

(1) The processing—

(a) is for the purposes of keeping accounts relating to any business or other activity carried on by the data controller, or deciding whether to accept any person as a customer or supplier, or keeping records of purchases, sales or other transactions for the purpose of ensuring that the requisite payments and deliveries are made or services provided by or to the data controller in respect of those transactions, or for the purpose of making financial or management forecasts to assist him in the conduct of any such business or activity;

(b) is of personal data in respect of which the data subject is—
(i) a past, existing or prospective customer or supplier; or
(ii) any person the processing of whose personal data is necessary for the exempt purposes;

(c) is of personal data consisting of the name, address and other identifiers of the data subject or information as to—
(i) financial standing; or
(ii) other matters the processing of which is necessary for the exempt purposes;

(d) does not involve disclosure of the personal data to any third party other than—
(i) with the consent of the data subject; or
(ii) where it is necessary to make such disclosure for the exempt purposes; and

(e) does not involve keeping the personal data after the relationship between the data controller and customer or supplier ends, unless and for so long as it is necessary to do so for the exempt purposes.

(2) Sub-paragraph (1)(c) shall not be taken as including personal data processed by or obtained from a credit reference agency.

5 Non profit-making organisations exemptions

The processing—

(a) is carried out by a data controller which is a body or association which is not established or conducted for profit;

(b) is for the purposes of establishing or maintaining membership of or support for the body or association, or providing or administering activities for individuals who are either members of the body or association or have regular contact with it;

(c) is of personal data in respect of which the data subject is—
(i) a past, existing or prospective member of the body or organisation;

(ii) any person who has regular contact with the body or organisation in connection with the exempt purposes; or
(iii) any person the processing of whose personal data is necessary for the exempt purposes;

(d) is of personal data consisting of the name, address and other identifiers of the data subject or information as to—
(i) eligibility for membership of the body or association; or
(ii) other matters the processing of which is necessary for the exempt purposes;

(e) does not involve disclosure of the personal data to any third party other than—
(i) with the consent of the data subject; or
(ii) where it is necessary to make such disclosure for the exempt purposes; and

(f) does not involve keeping the personal data after the relationship between the data controller and data subject ends, unless and for so long as it is necessary to do so for the exempt purposes.

[843]–[870]

DATA PROTECTION (INTERNATIONAL CO-OPERATION) ORDER 2000

(SI 2000/190)

NOTES

Made: 31 January 2000.
Authority: Data Protection Act 1998, ss 54(3), 67(2).
Commencement: 1 March 2000.

ARRANGEMENT OF ARTICLES

1 Citation and commencement

This Order may be cited as the Data Protection (International Co-operation) Order 2000 and shall come into force on 1st March 2000.

[871]

2 Interpretation

In this Order—

"the Act" means the Data Protection Act 1998;

"supervisory authority" means a supervisory authority in an EEA State other than the United Kingdom for the purposes of the Data Protection Directive;

"transfer" means a transfer of personal data to a country or territory outside the European Economic Area.

[872]

3 Information relating to adequacy

(1) Subject to paragraph (2), this article applies in any case where the Commissioner is satisfied that any transfer or proposed transfer by a data controller has involved or would involve a contravention of the eighth principle.

(2) In cases where an enforcement notice has been served in respect of a contravention of the eighth principle, this article shall not apply unless—

(a) the period within which an appeal can be brought under section 48(1) of the Act has expired without an appeal being brought; or

(b) where an appeal has been brought under section 48(1), either—

(i) the decision of the Tribunal is to the effect that there has been a breach of that eighth principle, or

(ii) where any decision of the Tribunal is to the effect that there has not been a breach of that eighth principle, the Commissioner has appealed successfully against that finding.

(3) In cases to which this article applies, the Commissioner shall inform the European Commission and the supervisory authorities of the reasons why he is satisfied that any transfer or proposed transfer has involved or would involve a contravention of the eighth principle.

(4) In this article, "the eighth principle" means the eighth principle set out in paragraph 8 of Part I of Schedule 1 to the Act, having regard to paragraphs 13, 14 and 15 of Part II of that Schedule.

[873]

4 Objections to authorisations

(1) This article applies where—

(a) a transfer has been authorised by another Member State in purported compliance with Article 26(2) of the Data Protection Directive, and

(b) the Commissioner is satisfied that such authorisation is not in compliance with that Article.

(2) The Commissioner may inform the European Commission of the particulars of the authorisation together with the reasons for his view that the authorisation is not in compliance with Article 26(2) of the Directive.

[874]

5 Requests from supervisory authorities in relation to certain data controllers

(1) This article applies in any case where a data controller is processing data in the United Kingdom—

(a) in circumstances other than those described in section 5(1) of the Act, and

(b) within the scope of the functions of a supervisory authority in another EEA State.

(2) The Commissioner may, at the request of a supervisory authority referred to in paragraph (1)(b), exercise his functions under Part V of the Act in relation to the processing referred to in paragraph (1) as if the data controller were processing those data in the circumstances described in section 5(1)(a) of the Act.

(3) Where the Commissioner has received a request from a supervisory authority under paragraph (2), he shall—

(a) in any case where he decides to exercise his functions under Part V of the Act, send to the supervisory authority as soon as reasonably practicable after exercising those functions such statement of the extent of the action that he has taken as he thinks fit; and

(b) in any case where he decides not to exercise those functions, send to the supervisory authority as soon as reasonably practicable after making the decision the reasons for that decision.

[875]

6 Requests by Commissioner in relation to certain data controllers

(1) This article applies in any case where a data controller is processing data in another EEA State in circumstances described in section 5(1) of the Act.

(2) The Commissioner may request the supervisory authority of the EEA State referred to in paragraph (1) to exercise the functions conferred on it by that EEA State pursuant to Article 28(3) of the Data Protection Directive in relation to the processing in question.

(3) Any request made under paragraph (2) must specify—

(a) the name and address in the EEA State, in so far as they are known by the Commissioner, of the data controller; and

(b) such details of the circumstances of the case as the Commissioner thinks fit to enable the supervisory authority to exercise those functions.

[876]

7 General exchange of information

The Commissioner may supply to the European Commission or any supervisory authority information to the extent to which, in the opinion of the Commissioner, the supply of that information is necessary for the performance of the data protection functions of the recipient.

[877]

DATA PROTECTION (SUBJECT ACCESS) (FEES AND MISCELLANEOUS PROVISIONS) REGULATIONS 2000

(SI 2000/191)

NOTES

Made: 31 January 2000.
Authority: Data Protection Act 1998, ss 7(2), (7), (8), (11).
Commencement: 1 March 2000.

ARRANGEMENT OF REGULATIONS

1 Citation, commencement and interpretation

(1) These Regulations may be cited as the Data Protection (Subject Access) (Fees and Miscellaneous Provisions) Regulations 2000 and shall come into force on 1st March 2000.

(2) In these Regulations "the Act" means the Data Protection Act 1998.

[878]

2 Extent of subject access requests

(1) A request for information under any provision of section 7(1)(a), (b) or (c) of the Act is to be treated as extending also to information under all other provisions of section 7(1)(a), (b) and (c).

(2) A request for information under any provision of section 7(1) of the Act is to be treated as extending to information under the provisions of section 7(1)(d) only where the request shows an express intention to that effect.

(3) A request for information under the provisions of section 7(1)(d) of the Act is to be treated as extending also to information under any other provision of section 7(1) only where the request shows an express intention to that effect.

[879]

3 Maximum subject access fee

Except as otherwise provided by regulations 4, 5 and 6 below, the maximum fee which may be required by a data controller under section 7(2)(b) of the Act is £10.

[880]

4 Limited requests for subject access where data controller is credit reference agency

(1) In any case in which a request under section 7 of the Act has been made to a data controller who is a credit reference agency, and has been limited, or by virtue of section 9(2) of the Act is taken to have been limited, to personal data relevant to an individual's financial standing—

(a) the maximum fee which may be required by a data controller under section 7(2)(b) of the Act is £2, and

(b) the prescribed period for the purposes of section 7(8) of the Act is seven working days.

(2) In this regulation "working day" means any day other than—

(a) Saturday or Sunday,

(b) Christmas Day or Good Friday,

(c) a bank holiday, within the meaning of section 1 of the Banking and Financial Dealings Act 1971, in the part of the United Kingdom in which the data controller's address is situated.

(3) For the purposes of paragraph (2)(c) above—

(a) the address of a registered company is that of its registered office, and

(b) the address of a person (other than a registered company) carrying on a business is that of his principal place of business in the United Kingdom.

[881]

5 Subject access requests in respect of educational records

(1) This regulation applies to any case in which a request made under section 7 of the Act relates wholly or partly to personal data forming part of an accessible record which is an educational record within the meaning of Schedule 11 to the Act.

(2) Except as provided by paragraph (3) below, a data controller may not require a fee under section 7(2)(b) of the Act in any case to which this regulation applies.

(3) Where, in a case to which this regulation applies, the obligation imposed by section 7(1)(c)(i) of the Act is to be complied with by supplying the data subject with a copy of information in permanent form, the maximum fee which may be required by a data controller under section 7(2)(b) of the Act is that applicable to the case under the Schedule to these Regulations.

(4) In any case to which this regulation applies, and in which the address of the data controller to whom the request is made is situated in England and Wales, the prescribed period for the purposes of section 7(8) of the Act is fifteen school days within the meaning of section 579(1) of the Education Act 1996.

[882]

6 Certain subject access requests in respect of health records …

(1) This regulation applies only to cases in which a request made under section 7 of the Act—

(a) relates wholly or partly to personal data forming part of an accessible record which is a health record within the meaning of section 68(2) of the Act [and],

(b) does not relate exclusively to data within paragraphs (a) and (b) of the definition of "data" in section 1(1) of the Act …

(c) …

(2) Where in a case to which this regulation applies, the obligation imposed by section 7(1)(c)(i) of the Act is to be complied with by supplying the data subject with a copy of information in permanent form, the maximum fee which may be required by a data controller under section 7(2)(b) of the Act is £50.

(3) Except in a case to which paragraph (2) above applies, a data controller may not require a fee under section 7(2)(b) of the Act where, in a case to which this regulation applies, the request relates solely to personal data which—

(a) form part of an accessible record—

(i) which is a health record within the meaning of section 68(2) of the Act, and

(ii) at least some of which was made after the beginning of the period of 40 days immediately preceding the date of the request; and

(b) do not fall within paragraph (a) or (b) of the definition of "data" in section 1(1) of the Act.

(4) For the purposes of paragraph (3) above, an individual making a request in any case to which this regulation applies may specify that his request is limited to personal data of the description set out in that paragraph.

[883]

NOTES

Provision heading: words omitted revoked by the Data Protection (Subject Access (Fees and Miscellaneous Provisions) (Amendment) Regulations 2001, SI 2001/3223, reg 2(1), (2).

Para (1): word in square brackets in sub-para (a) added, and sub-para (c) and the word immediately preceding it revoked, by SI 2001/3223, reg 2(1), (3).

SCHEDULE
MAXIMUM SUBJECT ACCESS FEES WHERE A COPY OF INFORMATION CONTAINED IN AN EDUCATIONAL RECORD IS SUPPLIED IN PERMANENT FORM

Regulation 5(3)

1. In any case in which the copy referred to in regulation 5(3) includes material in any form other than a record in writing on paper, the maximum fee applicable for the purposes of regulation 5(3) is £50.

2. In any case in which the copy referred to in regulation 5(3) consists solely of a record in writing on paper, the maximum fee applicable for the purposes of regulation 5(3) is set out in the table below.

TABLE

number of pages of information comprising the copy	*maximum fee*
fewer than 20	£1
20–29	£2
30–39	£3
40–49	£4
50–59	£5
60–69	£6
70–79	£7
80–89	£8
90–99	£9
100–149	£10
150–199	£15
200–249	£20
250–299	£25
300–349	£30
350–399	£35
400–449	£40
450–499	£45
500 or more	£50

[884]–[914]

DATA PROTECTION (SUBJECT ACCESS MODIFICATION) (HEALTH) ORDER 2000

(SI 2000/413)

NOTES

Made: 17 February 2000.
Authority: Data Protection Act 1998, ss 30(1), (4), 67(2).
Commencement: 1 March 2000.

PART II DATA PROTECTION

ARRANGEMENT OF ARTICLES

1 Citation and commencement

This Order may be cited as the Data Protection (Subject Access Modification) (Health) Order 2000 and shall come into force on 1st March 2000.

[915]

2 Interpretation

In this Order—

"the Act" means the Data Protection Act 1998;

"the appropriate health professional" means—

(a) the health professional who is currently or was most recently responsible for the clinical care of the data subject in connection with the matters to which the information which is the subject of the request relates; or

(b) where there is more than one such health professional, the health professional who is the most suitable to advise on the matters to which the information which is the subject of the request relates; or

(c) where—

(i) there is no health professional available falling within paragraph (a) or (b), or

(ii) the data controller is the Secretary of State and data to which this Order applies are processed in connection with the exercise of the functions conferred on him by or under the Child Support Act 1991 and the Child Support Act 1995 or his functions in relation to social security or war pensions,

a health professional who has the necessary experience and qualifications to advise on the matters to which the information which is the subject of the request relates;

"care" includes examination, investigation, diagnosis and treatment;

"request" means a request made under section 7;

"section 7" means section 7 of the Act; and

"war pension" has the same meaning as in section 25 of the Social Security Act 1989 (establishment and functions of war pensions committees).

[916]

3 Personal data to which Order applies

(1) Subject to paragraph (2), this Order applies to personal data consisting of information as to the physical or mental health or condition of the data subject.

(2) This Order does not apply to any data which are exempted from section 7 by an order made under section 38(1) of the Act.

[917]

4 Exemption from the subject information provisions

(1) Personal data falling within paragraph (2) and to which this Order applies are exempt from the subject information provisions.

(2) This paragraph applies to personal data processed by a court and consisting of information supplied in a report or other evidence given to the court by a local authority, Health and Social Services Board, Health and Social Services Trust, probation officer or other person in the course of any proceedings to which the Family Proceedings Courts (Children Act 1989) Rules 1991, the Magistrates' Courts (Children and Young Persons) Rules 1992, the Magistrates' Courts (Criminal Justice (Children)) Rules (Northern Ireland) 1999, the Act of

Sederunt (Child Care and Maintenance Rules) 1997 or the Children's Hearings (Scotland) Rules 1996 apply where, in accordance with a provision of any of those Rules, the information may be withheld by the court in whole or in part from the data subject.

[918]

5 Exemptions from section 7

(1) Personal data to which this Order applies are exempt from section 7 in any case to the extent to which the application of that section would be likely to cause serious harm to the physical or mental health or condition of the data subject or any other person.

(2) Subject to article 7(1), a data controller who is not a health professional shall not withhold information constituting data to which this Order applies on the ground that the exemption in paragraph (1) applies with respect to the information unless the data controller has first consulted the person who appears to the data controller to be the appropriate health professional on the question whether or not the exemption in paragraph (1) applies with respect to the information.

(3) Where any person falling within paragraph (4) is enabled by or under any enactment or rule of law to make a request on behalf of a data subject and has made such a request, personal data to which this Order applies are exempt from section 7 in any case to the extent to which the application of that section would disclose information—

- (a) provided by the data subject in the expectation that it would not be disclosed to the person making the request;
- (b) obtained as a result of any examination or investigation to which the data subject consented in the expectation that the information would not be so disclosed; or
- (c) which the data subject has expressly indicated should not be so disclosed,

provided that sub-paragraphs (a) and (b) shall not prevent disclosure where the data subject has expressly indicated that he no longer has the expectation referred to therein.

(4) A person falls within this paragraph if—

- (a) except in relation to Scotland, the data subject is a child, and that person has parental responsibility for that data subject;
- (b) in relation to Scotland, the data subject is a person under the age of sixteen, and that person has parental responsibilities for that data subject; or
- (c) the data subject is incapable of managing his own affairs and that person has been appointed by a court to manage those affairs.

[919]

6 Modification of section 7 relating to data controllers who are not health professionals

(1) Subject to paragraph (2) and article 7(3), section 7 of the Act is modified so that a data controller who is not a health professional shall not communicate information constituting data to which this Order applies in response to a request unless the data controller has first consulted the person who appears to the data controller to be the appropriate health professional on the question whether or not the exemption in article 5(1) applies with respect to the information.

(2) Paragraph (1) shall not apply to the extent that the request relates to information which the data controller is satisfied has previously been seen by the data subject or is already within the knowledge of the data subject.

[920]

7 Additional provision relating to data controllers who are not health professionals

(1) Subject to paragraph (2), article 5(2) shall not apply in relation to any request where the data controller has consulted the appropriate health professional prior to receiving the request and obtained in writing from that appropriate health professional an opinion that the exemption in article 5(1) applies with respect to all of the information which is the subject of the request.

(2) Paragraph (1) does not apply where the opinion either—

- (a) was obtained before the period beginning six months before the relevant day (as defined by section 7(10) of the Act) and ending on that relevant day, or
- (b) was obtained within that period and it is reasonable in all the circumstances to re-consult the appropriate health professional.

(3) Article 6(1) shall not apply in relation to any request where the data controller has consulted the appropriate health professional prior to receiving the request and obtained in

PART II DATA PROTECTION

writing from that appropriate health professional an opinion that the exemption in article 5(1) does not apply with respect to all of the information which is the subject of the request.

[921]

8 Further modifications of section 7

In relation to data to which this Order applies—

(a) section 7(4) of the Act shall have effect as if there were inserted after paragraph (b) of that subsection "or, (c) the information is contained in a health record and the other individual is a health professional who has compiled or contributed to the health record or has been involved in the care of the data subject in his capacity as a health professional";

(b) section 7(9) shall have effect as if—

(i) there was substituted—

"(9) If a court is satisfied on the application of—

(a) any person who has made a request under the foregoing provisions of this section, or

(b) any other person to whom serious harm to his physical or mental health or condition would be likely to be caused by compliance with any such request in contravention of those provisions,

that the data controller in question is about to comply with or has failed to comply with the request in contravention of those provisions, the court may order him not to comply or, as the case may be, to comply with the request."; and

(ii) the reference therein to a contravention of the foregoing provisions of that section included a reference to a contravention of the provisions contained in this Order.

[922]

DATA PROTECTION (SUBJECT ACCESS MODIFICATION) (EDUCATION) ORDER 2000

(SI 2000/414)

NOTES

Made: 17 February 2000.
Authority: Data Protection Act 1998, ss 30(2), (4), 67(2).
Commencement: 1 March 2000.

ARRANGEMENT OF ARTICLES

1 Citation and commencement

This Order may be cited as the Data Protection (Subject Access Modification) (Education) Order 2000 and shall come into force on 1st March 2000.

[923]

2 Interpretation

In this Order—

"the Act" means the Data Protection Act 1998;

"education authority" in article 6 has the same meaning as in paragraph 6 of Schedule 11 to the Act;

"Principal Reporter" means the Principal Reporter appointed under section 127 of the Local Government etc (Scotland) Act 1994 or any officer of the Scottish Children's Reporter Administration to whom there is delegated under section 131(1) of that Act any function of the Principal Reporter;

"request" means a request made under section 7; and

"section 7" means section 7 of the Act.

[924]

3 Personal data to which the Order applies

(1) Subject to paragraph (2), this Order applies to personal data consisting of information constituting an educational record as defined in paragraph 1 of Schedule 11 to the Act.

(2) This Order does not apply—

(a) to any data consisting of information as to the physical or mental health or condition of the data subject to which the Data Protection (Subject Access Modification) (Health) Order 2000 applies; or

(b) to any data which are exempted from section 7 by an order made under section 38(1) of the Act.

[925]

4 Exemption from the subject information provisions

(1) Personal data falling within paragraph (2) and to which this Order applies are exempt from the subject information provisions.

(2) This paragraph applies to personal data processed by a court and consisting of information supplied in a report or other evidence given to the court in the course of proceedings to which the Magistrates' Courts (Children and Young Persons) Rules 1992, the Magistrates' Courts (Criminal Justice (Children)) Rules (Northern Ireland) 1999, the Act of Sederunt (Child Care and Maintenance Rules) 1997 or the Children's Hearings (Scotland) Rules 1996 apply where, in accordance with a provision of any of those Rules, the information may be withheld by the court in whole or in part from the data subject.

[926]

5 Exemptions from section 7

(1) Personal data to which this Order applies are exempt from section 7 in any case to the extent to which the application of that section would be likely to cause serious harm to the physical or mental health or condition of the data subject or any other person.

(2) In circumstances where the exemption in paragraph (1) does not apply, where any person falling within paragraph (3) is enabled by or under any enactment or rule of law to make a request on behalf of a data subject and has made such a request, personal data consisting of information as to whether the data subject is or has been the subject of or may be at risk of child abuse are exempt from section 7 in any case to the extent to which the application of that section would not be in the best interests of that data subject.

(3) A person falls within this paragraph if—

(a) the data subject is a child, and that person has parental responsibility for that data subject; or

(b) the data subject is incapable of managing his own affairs and that person has been appointed by a court to manage those affairs.

(4) For the purposes of paragraph (2), "child abuse" includes physical injury (other than accidental injury) to, and physical and emotional neglect, ill-treatment and sexual abuse of, a child.

(5) Paragraph (2) shall not apply in Scotland.

[927]

6 Modification of section 7 relating to Principal Reporter

Where in Scotland a data controller who is an education authority receives a request relating to information constituting data to which this Order applies and which the education authority believes to have originated from or to have been supplied by or on behalf of the Principal Reporter acting in pursuance of his statutory duties, other than information which the data subject is entitled to receive from the Principal Reporter, section 7 shall be modified so that—

(a) the data controller shall, within fourteen days of the relevant day (as defined by section 7(10) of the Act), inform the Principal Reporter that a request has been made; and

(b) the data controller shall not communicate information to the data subject pursuant to that section unless the Principal Reporter has informed that data controller that, in his opinion, the exemption specified in article 5(1) does not apply with respect to the information.

[928]

7 Further modifications of section 7

(1) In relation to data to which this Order applies—

(a) section 7(4) of the Act shall have effect as if there were inserted after paragraph (b) of that subsection "or (c) the other individual is a relevant person";

(b) section 7(9) shall have effect as if—

(i) there was substituted—

"(9) If a court is satisfied on the application of—

(a) any person who has made a request under the foregoing provisions of this section, or

(b) any person to whom serious harm to his physical or mental health or condition would be likely to be caused by compliance with any such request in contravention of those provisions,

that the data controller in question is about to comply with or has failed to comply with the request in contravention of those provisions, the court may order him not to comply or, as the case may be, to comply with the request."; and

(ii) the reference to a contravention of the foregoing provisions of that section included a reference to a contravention of the provisions contained in this Order.

(2) After section 7(ii) of the Act insert—

"(12) A person is a relevant person for the purposes of subsection (4)(c) if he—

(a) is a person referred to in paragraph 4(a) or (b) or paragraph 8(a) or (b) of Schedule 11;

(b) is employed by an education authority (within the meaning of paragraph 6 of Schedule 11) in pursuance of its functions relating to education and the information relates to him, or he supplied the information in his capacity as such an employee; or

(c) is the person making the request.".

[929]

DATA PROTECTION (SUBJECT ACCESS MODIFICATION) (SOCIAL WORK) ORDER 2000

(SI 2000/415)

NOTES

Made: 17 February 2000.
Authority: Data Protection Act 1998, s 30(3), (4), 67(2).
Commencement: 1 March 2000.

ARRANGEMENT OF ARTICLES

1 Citation and commencement

This Order may be cited as the Data Protection (Subject Access Modification) (Social Work) Order 2000 and shall come into force on 1st March 2000.

[930]

2 Interpretation

(1) In this Order—

"the Act" means the Data Protection Act 1998;

"compulsory school age" in paragraph 1(f) of the Schedule has the same meaning as in section 8 of the Education Act 1996, and in paragraph 1(g) of the Schedule has the same meaning as in Article 46 of the Education and Libraries (Northern Ireland) Order 1986;

"Health and Social Services Board" means a Health and Social Services Board established under Article 16 of the Health and Personal Social Services (Northern Ireland) Order 1972;

"Health and Social Services Trust" means a Health and Social Services Trust established under the Health and Personal Social Services (Northern Ireland) Order 1991;

"Principal Reporter" means the Principal Reporter appointed under section 127 of the Local Government etc (Scotland) Act 1994 or any officer of the Scottish Children's Reporter Administration to whom there is delegated under section 131(1) of that Act any function of the Principal Reporter;

"request" means a request made under section 7;

"school age" in paragraph 1(h) of the Schedule has the same meaning as in section 31 of the Education (Scotland) Act 1980;

"section 7" means section 7 of the Act; and

"social work authority" in article 6 means a local authority for the purposes of the Social Work (Scotland) Act 1968.

(2) Any reference in this Order to a local authority in relation to data processed or formerly processed by it includes a reference to the Council of the Isles of Scilly in relation to data processed or formerly processed by the Council in connection with any functions mentioned in paragraph 1(a)(ii) of the Schedule which are or have been conferred upon the Council by or under any enactment.

[931]

3 Personal data to which Order applies

(1) Subject to paragraph (2), this Order applies to personal data falling within any of the descriptions set out in paragraphs 1 and 2 of the Schedule.

(2) This Order does not apply—

(a) to any data consisting of information as to the physical or mental health or condition of the data subject to which the Data Protection (Subject Access Modification) (Health) Order 2000 or the Data Protection (Subject Access Modification) (Education) Order 2000 applies; or

(b) to any data which are exempted from section 7 by an order made under section 38(1) of the Act.

[932]

4 Exemption from subject information provisions

Personal data to which this Order applies by virtue of paragraph 2 of the Schedule are exempt from the subject information provisions.

[933]

5 Exemption from section 7

(1) Personal data to which this Order applies by virtue of paragraph 1 of the Schedule are exempt from the obligations in section 7(1)(b) to (d) of the Act in any case to the extent to which the application of those provisions would be likely to prejudice the carrying out of social work by reason of the fact that serious harm to the physical or mental health or condition of the data subject or any other person would be likely to be caused.

(2) In paragraph (1) the "carrying out of social work" shall be construed as including—

(a) the exercise of any functions mentioned in paragraph 1(a)(i), (d), (f) to (j), (m)[, (o), (r), (s) or (t)] of the Schedule;

PART II DATA PROTECTION

(b) the provision of any service mentioned in paragraph 1(b), (c) or (k) of the Schedule; and

(c) the exercise of the functions of any body mentioned in paragraph 1(e) of the Schedule or any person mentioned in paragraph 1(p) or (q) of the Schedule.

(3) Where any person falling within paragraph (4) is enabled by or under any enactment or rule of law to make a request on behalf of a data subject and has made such a request, personal data to which this Order applies are exempt from section 7 in any case to the extent to which the application of that section would disclose information—

(a) provided by the data subject in the expectation that it would not be disclosed to the person making the request;

(b) obtained as a result of any examination or investigation to which the data subject consented in the expectation that the information would not be so disclosed; or

(c) which the data subject has expressly indicated should not be so disclosed,

provided that sub-paragraphs (a) and (b) shall not prevent disclosure where the data subject has expressly indicated that he no longer has the expectation referred to therein.

(4) A person falls within this paragraph if—

(a) except in relation to Scotland, the data subject is a child, and that person has parental responsibility for that data subject;

(b) in relation to Scotland, the data subject is a person under the age of sixteen, and that person has parental responsibilities for that data subject; or

(c) the data subject is incapable of managing his own affairs and that person has been appointed by a court to manage those affairs.

[934]

NOTES

Sub-s (2): words in square brackets substituted by the Data Protection (Subject Access Modification) (Social Work) (Amendment) Order 2005, SI 2005/467, art 3.

6 Modification of section 7 relating to Principal Reporter

Where in Scotland a data controller who is a social work authority receives a request relating to information constituting data to which this Order applies and which originated from or was supplied by the Principal Reporter acting in pursuance of his statutory duties, other than information which the data subject is entitled to receive from the Principal Reporter, section 7 shall be modified so that—

(a) the data controller shall, within fourteen days of the relevant day (within the meaning of section 7(10) of the Act), inform the Principal Reporter that a request has been made; and

(b) the data controller shall not communicate information to the data subject pursuant to that section unless the Principal Reporter has informed that data controller that, in his opinion, the exemption specified in article 5(1) does not apply with respect to the information.

[935]

7 Further modifications of section 7

(1) In relation to data to which this Order applies by virtue of paragraph 1 of the Schedule—

(a) section 7(4) shall have effect as if there were inserted after paragraph (b) of that subsection "or, (c) the other individual is a relevant person";

(b) section 7(9) shall have effect as if—

(i) there was substituted—

"(9) If a court is satisfied on the application of—

(a) any person who has made a request under the foregoing provisions of this section, or

(b) any person to whom serious harm to his physical or mental health or condition would be likely to be caused by compliance with any such request in contravention of those provisions,

that the data controller in question is about to comply with or has failed to comply with the request in contravention of those provisions, the court may order him not to comply or, as the case may be, to comply with the request."; and

(ii) the reference to a contravention of the foregoing provisions of that section included a reference to a contravention of the provisions contained in this Order.

(2) [In relation to data to which this Order applies by virtue of paragraph 1 of the Schedule, section 7 shall have effect as if after subsection (11) there were inserted—]

"(12) A person is a relevant person for the purposes of subsection (4)(c) if he—

(a) is a person referred to in paragraph [1(p), (q), (r), (s) or (t)] of the Schedule to the Data Protection (Subject Access Modification) (Social Work) Order 2000; or

(b) is or has been employed by any person or body referred to in paragraph 1 of that Schedule in connection with functions which are or have been exercised in relation to the data consisting of the information; or

(c) has provided for reward a service similar to a service provided in the exercise of any functions specified in paragraph 1(a)(i), (b), (c) or (d) of that Schedule,

and the information relates to him or he supplied the information in his official capacity or, as the case may be, in connection with the provision of that service.".

[936]

NOTES

Sub-s (2): words in square brackets substituted by the Data Protection (Subject Access Modification) (Social Work) (Amendment) Order 2005, SI 2005/467, art 4.

SCHEDULE
PERSONAL DATA TO WHICH THIS ORDER APPLIES

Article 3

1. This paragraph applies to personal data falling within any of the following descriptions—

(a) data processed by a local authority—

(i) in connection with its social services functions within the meaning of the Local Authority Social Services Act 1970 or any functions exercised by local authorities under the Social Work (Scotland) Act 1968 or referred to in section 5(1B) of that Act, or

(ii) in the exercise of other functions but obtained or consisting of information obtained in connection with any of those functions;

(b) data processed by a Health and Social Services Board in connection with the provision of personal social services within the meaning of the Health and Personal Social Services (Northern Ireland) Order 1972 or processed by the Health and Social Services Board in the exercise of other functions but obtained or consisting of information obtained in connection with the provision of those services;

(c) data processed by a Health and Social Services Trust in connection with the provision of personal social services within the meaning of the Health and Personal Social Services (Northern Ireland) Order 1972 on behalf of a Health and Social Services Board by virtue of an authorisation made under Article 3(1) of the Health and Personal Social Services (Northern Ireland) Order 1994 or processed by the Health and Social Services Trust in the exercise of other functions but obtained or consisting of information obtained in connection with the provision of those services;

(d) data processed by a council in the exercise of its functions under Part II of Schedule 9 to the Health and Social Services and Social Security Adjudications Act 1983;

(e) data processed by a probation committee established by section 3 of the Probation Service Act 1993 or the Probation Board for Northern Ireland established by the Probation Board (Northern Ireland) Order 1982;

(f) data processed by a local education authority in the exercise of its functions under section 36 of the Children Act 1989 or Chapter II of Part VI of the Education Act 1996 so far as those functions relate to ensuring that children of compulsory school age receive suitable education whether by attendance at school or otherwise;

(g) data processed by an education and library board in the exercise of its functions under article 55 of the Children (Northern Ireland) Order 1995 or article 45 of, and Schedule 13 to, the Education and Libraries (Northern Ireland) Order 1986 so far as those functions relate to ensuring that children of compulsory school age receive efficient full-time education suitable to their age, ability and aptitude and to any special educational needs they may have, either by regular attendance at school or otherwise;

(h) data processed by an education authority in the exercise of its functions under sections 35 to 42 of the Education (Scotland) Act 1980 so far as those functions relate to ensuring that children of school age receive efficient education suitable to their age, ability and aptitude, whether by attendance at school or otherwise;

(i) data relating to persons detained in a special hospital provided under section 4 of the National Health Service Act 1977 and processed by a special health authority established under section 11 of that Act in the exercise of any functions similar to any social services functions of a local authority;

(j) data relating to persons detained in special accommodation provided under article 110 of the Mental Health (Northern Ireland) Order 1986 and processed by a Health and Social Services Trust in the exercise of any functions similar to any social services functions of a local authority;

(k) data processed by the National Society for the Prevention of Cruelty to Children or by any other voluntary organisation or other body designated under this sub-paragraph by the Secretary of State or the Department of Health, Social Services and Public Safety and appearing to the Secretary of State or the Department, as the case may be, to be processed for the purposes of the provision of any service similar to a service provided in the exercise of any functions specified in sub-paragraphs (a)(i), (b), (c) or (d) above;

(l) data processed by—

[(zi) a Strategic Health Authority established under section 8 of the National Health Service Act 1977;]

(i) a Health Authority established under section 8 of the National Health Service Act 1977;

(ii) an NHS Trust established under section 5 of the National Health Service and Community Care Act 1990; …

[(iiza) an NHS foundation trust within the meaning of section 1(1) of the Health and Social Care (Community Health and Standards) Act 2003;]

[(iia) a Primary Care Trust established under section 16A of the National Health Service Act 1977; or]

(iii) a Health Board established under section 2 of the National Health Service (Scotland) Act 1978,

which were obtained or consisted of information which was obtained from any authority or body mentioned above or government department and which, whilst processed by that authority or body or government department, fell within any sub-paragraph of this paragraph;

(m) data processed by an NHS Trust as referred to in sub-paragraph (l)(ii) above in the exercise of any functions similar to any social services functions of a local authority;

[(mm) data processed by an NHS foundation trust as referred to in sub-paragraph (l)(iiza) above in the exercise of any functions similar to any social services functions of a local authority;]

(n) data processed by a government department and obtained or consisting of information obtained from any authority or body mentioned above and which, whilst processed by that authority or body, fell within any of the preceding sub-paragraphs of this paragraph;

(o) data processed for the purposes of the functions of the Secretary of State pursuant to section 82(5) of the Children Act 1989;

[(p) data processed by any children's guardian appointed under [rule 4.10 of the Family Proceedings Rules 1991 or rule 10 of the Family Proceedings Courts (Children Act 1989) Rules 1991], by any guardian ad litem appointed under Article 60 of the Children (Northern Ireland) Order 1995 or Article 66 of the Adoption (Northern Ireland) Order 1987 or by a safeguarder appointed under section 41 of the Children (Scotland) Act 1995;]

(q) data processed by the Principal Reporter;

[(r) data processed by any officer of the Children and Family Court Advisory and Support Service for the purpose of his functions under section 7 of the Children Act 1989, rules 4.11 and 4.11B of the Family Proceedings Rules 1991, and rules 11 and 11B of the Family Proceedings Courts (Children Act 1989) Rules 1991;

(s) data processed by any officer of the service appointed as guardian ad litem under rule 9.5(1) of the Family Proceedings Rules 1991;

(t) data processed by the Children and Family Court Advisory and Support Service for the purpose of its functions under section 12(1) and (2) and section 13(1), (2) and (4) of the Criminal Justice and Court Services Act 2000];

[(u) data processed for the purposes of the functions of the appropriate Minister pursuant to section 12 of the Adoption and Children Act 2002 (independent review of determinations)].

2. This paragraph applies to personal data processed by a court and consisting of information supplied in a report or other evidence given to the court by a local authority, Health and Social Services Board, Health and Social Services Trust, probation officer[, officer of the Children and Family Court Advisory and Support Service] or other person in the course of any proceedings to which the Family Proceedings Courts (Children Act 1989) Rules 1991, the Magistrates' Courts (Children and Young Persons) Rules 1992, the Magistrates' Courts (Criminal Justice (Children)) Rules (Northern Ireland) 1999, the Act of Sederunt (Child Care and Maintenance Rules) 1997[, the Children's Hearings (Scotland) Rules 1996 or the Family Proceedings Rules 1991] apply where, in accordance with a provision of any of those Rules, the information may be withheld by the court in whole or in part from the data subject.

[937]

NOTES

Para 1: sub-para (l)(zi), (iia) inserted, and the word omitted from sub-para (l)(ii) revoked, by the National Health Service Reform and Health Care Professions Act 2002 (Supplementary, Consequential etc Provisions) Regulations 2002, SI 2002/2469, reg 4, Sch 1, Pt 2, para 88; sub-paras (l)(iiza), (mm) inserted by the Health and Social Care (Community Health and Standards) Act 2003 (Supplementary and Consequential Provision) (NHS Foundation Trusts) Order 2004, SI 2004/696, art 3(1), Sch 1, para 34; sub-para (p) substituted by the Children and Family Court Advisory Support Service (Miscellaneous Amendments) Order 2002, SI 2002/3220, art 3; words in square brackets in sub-para (p) substituted and sub-paras (r), (s), (t) inserted by the Data Protection (Subject Access Modification) (Social Work) (Amendment) Order 2005, SI 2005/467, art 5(1)–(3); sub-para (u) inserted by the Adoption and Children Act 2002 (Consequential Amendments) Order 2005, SI 2005/3504, art 2(2).

Para 2: words in first pair of square brackets inserted and words in second pair of square brackets substituted by SI 2005/467, art 5(1), (4).

DATA PROTECTION (CROWN APPOINTMENTS) ORDER 2000

(SI 2000/416)

NOTES

Made: 17 February 2000.
Authority: Data Protection Act 1998, Sch 7, para 4.
Commencement: 1 March 2000.

1 This Order may be cited as the Data Protection (Crown Appointments) Order 2000 and shall come into force on 1st March 2000.

[938]

2 There shall be exempted from the subject information provisions of the Data Protection Act 1998 (as defined by section 27(2) of that Act) personal data processed for the purposes of assessing any person's suitability for any of the offices listed in the Schedule to this Order.

[939]

SCHEDULE
EXEMPTIONS FROM SUBJECT INFORMATION PROVISIONS

Article 2

Offices to which appointments are made by Her Majesty:—

(a) Archbishops, diocesan and suffragan bishops in the Church of England
(b) Deans of cathedrals of the Church of England
(c) Deans and Canons of the two Royal Peculiars
(d) The First and Second Church Estates Commissioners
(e) Lord-Lieutenants
(f) Masters of Trinity College and Churchill College, Cambridge
(g) The Provost of Eton
(h) The Poet Laureate

(i) The Astronomer Royal

[940]

DATA PROTECTION (PROCESSING OF SENSITIVE PERSONAL DATA) ORDER 2000

(SI 2000/417)

NOTES

Made: 17 February 2000.
Authority: Data Protection Act 1998, s 67(2), Sch 3, para 10.
Commencement: 1 March 2000.

1—(1) This Order may be cited as the Data Protection (Processing of Sensitive Personal Data) Order 2000 and shall come into force on 1st March 2000.

(2) In this Order, "the Act" means the Data Protection Act 1998.

[941]

2 For the purposes of paragraph 10 of Schedule 3 to the Act, the circumstances specified in any of the paragraphs in the Schedule to this Order are circumstances in which sensitive personal data may be processed.

[942]

SCHEDULE
CIRCUMSTANCES IN WHICH SENSITIVE PERSONAL DATA MAY BE PROCESSED

Article 2

1.—(1) The processing—

(a) is in the substantial public interest;
(b) is necessary for the purposes of the prevention or detection of any unlawful act; and
(c) must necessarily be carried out without the explicit consent of the data subject being sought so as not to prejudice those purposes.

(2) In this paragraph, "act" includes a failure to act.

2. The processing—

(a) is in the substantial public interest;
(b) is necessary for the discharge of any function which is designed for protecting members of the public against—
   (i) dishonesty, malpractice, or other seriously improper conduct by, or the unfitness or incompetence of, any person, or
   (ii) mismanagement in the administration of, or failures in services provided by, any body or association; and
(c) must necessarily be carried out without the explicit consent of the data subject being sought so as not to prejudice the discharge of that function.

3.—(1) The disclosure of personal data—

(a) is in the substantial public interest;
(b) is in connection with—
   (i) the commission by any person of any unlawful act (whether alleged or established),
   (ii) dishonesty, malpractice, or other seriously improper conduct by, or the unfitness or incompetence of, any person (whether alleged or established), or
   (iii) mismanagement in the administration of, or failures in services provided by, any body or association (whether alleged or established);
(c) is for the special purposes as defined in section 3 of the Act; and
(d) is made with a view to the publication of those data by any person and the data controller reasonably believes that such publication would be in the public interest.

(2) In this paragraph, "act" includes a failure to act.

4. The processing—
   (a) is in the substantial public interest;
   (b) is necessary for the discharge of any function which is designed for the provision of confidential counselling, advice, support or any other service; and
   (c) is carried out without the explicit consent of the data subject because the processing—
      (i) is necessary in a case where consent cannot be given by the data subject,
      (ii) is necessary in a case where the data controller cannot reasonably be expected to obtain the explicit consent of the data subject, or
      (iii) must necessarily be carried out without the explicit consent of the data subject being sought so as not to prejudice the provision of that counselling, advice, support or other service.

5.—(1) The processing—
   (a) is necessary for the purpose of—
      (i) carrying on insurance business, or
      (ii) making determinations in connection with eligibility for, and benefits payable under, an occupational pension scheme as defined in section 1 of the Pension Schemes Act 1993;
   (b) is of sensitive personal data consisting of information falling within section 2(e) of the Act relating to a data subject who is the parent, grandparent, great grandparent or sibling of—
      (i) in the case of paragraph (a)(i), the insured person, or
      (ii) in the case of paragraph (a)(ii), the member of the scheme;
   (c) is necessary in a case where the data controller cannot reasonably be expected to obtain the explicit consent of that data subject and the data controller is not aware of the data subject withholding his consent; and
   (d) does not support measures or decisions with respect to that data subject.

(2) In this paragraph—
   [(a) "insurance business" means business which consists of effecting or carrying out contracts of insurance of the following kind—
      (i) life and annuity,
      (ii) linked long term,
      (iii) permanent health,
      (iv) accident, or
      (v) sickness; and]
   (b) "insured" and "member" includes an individual who is seeking to become an insured person or member of the scheme respectively.

[(2A) The definition of "insurance business" in sub-paragraph (2) above must be read with—
   (a) section 22 of the Financial Services and Markets Act 2000;
   (b) any relevant order under that section; and
   (c) Schedule 2 to that Act.]

6. The processing—
   (a) is of sensitive personal data in relation to any particular data subject that are subject to processing which was already under way immediately before the coming into force of this Order;
   (b) is necessary for the purpose of—
      [(i) effecting or carrying out contracts of long-term insurance of the kind mentioned in sub-paragraph (2)(a)(i), (ii) or (iii) of paragraph 5 above;]
      (ii) establishing or administering an occupational pension scheme as defined in section 1 of the Pension Schemes Act 1993; and
   (c) either—
      (i) is necessary in a case where the data controller cannot reasonably be expected to obtain the explicit consent of the data subject and that data subject has not informed the data controller that he does not so consent, or
      (ii) must necessarily be carried out even without the explicit consent of the data subject so as not to prejudice those purposes.

7.—(1) Subject to the provisions of sub-paragraph (2), the processing—
   (a) is of sensitive personal data consisting of information falling within section 2(c) or (e) of the Act;

(b) is necessary for the purpose of identifying or keeping under review the existence or absence of equality of opportunity or treatment between persons—
(i) holding different beliefs as described in section 2(c) of the Act, or
(ii) of different states of physical or mental health or different physical or mental conditions as described in section 2(e) of the Act,

with a view to enabling such equality to be promoted or maintained;
(c) does not support measures or decisions with respect to any particular data subject otherwise than with the explicit consent of that data subject; and
(d) does not cause, nor is likely to cause, substantial damage or substantial distress to the data subject or any other person.

(2) Where any individual has given notice in writing to any data controller who is processing personal data under the provisions of sub-paragraph (1) requiring that data controller to cease processing personal data in respect of which that individual is the data subject at the end of such period as is reasonable in the circumstances, that data controller must have ceased processing those personal data at the end of that period.

8.—(1) Subject to the provisions of sub-paragraph (2), the processing—
(a) is of sensitive personal data consisting of information falling within section 2(b) of the Act;
(b) is carried out by any person or organisation included in the register maintained pursuant to section 1 of the Registration of Political Parties Act 1998 in the course of his or its legitimate political activities; and
(c) does not cause, nor is likely to cause, substantial damage or substantial distress to the data subject or any other person.

(2) Where any individual has given notice in writing to any data controller who is processing personal data under the provisions of sub-paragraph (1) requiring that data controller to cease processing personal data in respect of which that individual is the data subject at the end of such period as is reasonable in the circumstances, that data controller must have ceased processing those personal data at the end of that period.

9. The processing—
(a) is in the substantial public interest;
(b) is necessary for research purposes (which expression shall have the same meaning as in section 33 of the Act);
(c) does not support measures or decisions with respect to any particular data subject otherwise than with the explicit consent of that data subject; and
(d) does not cause, nor is likely to cause, substantial damage or substantial distress to the data subject or any other person.

10. The processing is necessary for the exercise of any functions conferred on a constable by any rule of law.

[943]

NOTES

Para 5: sub-para (2)(a) substituted, and sub-para (2A) inserted, by the Financial Services and Markets Act 2000 (Consequential Amendments and Repeals) Order 2001, SI 2001/3649, art 587(1)–(3).

Para 6: sub-para (b)(i) substituted by SI 2001/3649, art 587(1), (4).

DATA PROTECTION (MISCELLANEOUS SUBJECT ACCESS EXEMPTIONS) ORDER 2000

(SI 2000/419)

NOTES

Made: 17 February 2000.
Authority: Data Protection Act 1998, s 38(1), 67(2).
Commencement: 1 March 2000.

1 This Order may be cited as the Data Protection (Miscellaneous Subject Access Exemptions) Order 2000 and shall come into force on 1st March 2000.

[944]

2 Personal data consisting of information the disclosure of which is prohibited or restricted by the enactments and instruments listed in the Schedule to this Order are exempt from section 7 of the Data Protection Act 1998.

[945]

SCHEDULE
EXEMPTIONS FROM SECTION 7

Article 2

PART I
ENACTMENTS AND INSTRUMENTS EXTENDING TO THE UNITED KINGDOM

Human fertilisation and embryology: information about the provision of treatment services, the keeping or use of gametes or embryos and whether identifiable individuals were born in consequence of treatment services.

Sections 31 and 33 of the Human Fertilisation and Embryology Act 1990.

[946]

PART II
ENACTMENTS AND INSTRUMENTS EXTENDING TO ENGLAND AND WALES

[(a) *Adoption records and reports*
Sections 57 to 62, 77 and 79 of, and Schedule 2 to, the Adoption and Children Act 2002.
Regulation 14 of the Adoption Agencies Regulations 1983.
Regulation 41 of the Adoption Agencies Regulations 2005.
Regulation 42 of the Adoption Agencies (Wales) Regulations 2005.
Rules 5, 6, 9, 17, 18, 21, 22 and 53 of the Adoption Rules 1984.
Rules 5, 6, 9, 17, 18, 21, 22 and 32 of the Magistrates' Courts (Adoption) Rules 1984.
Rules 24, 29, 30, 65, 72, 73, 77, 78 and 83 of the Family Procedure (Adoption) Rules 2005.]

(b) *Statement of child's special educational needs*
Regulation 19 of the Education (Special Educational Needs) Regulations 1994.

(c) *Parental order records and reports*
Sections 50 and 51 of the Adoption Act 1976 as modified by paragraphs 4(a) and (b) of Schedule 1 to the Parental Orders (Human Fertilisation and Embryology) Regulations 1994 in relation to parental orders made under section 30 of the Human Fertilisation and Embryology Act 1990.
Rules 4A.5 and 4A.9 of the Family Proceedings Rules 1991.
Rules 21E and 21I of the Family Proceedings Courts (Children Act 1989) Rules 1991.

[947]

NOTES

Para (a): substituted by the Adoption and Children Act 2002 (Consequential Amendments) Order 2005, SI 2005/3504, art 2(1).

PART III
ENACTMENTS AND INSTRUMENTS EXTENDING TO SCOTLAND

(a) *Adoption records and reports*
Section 45 of the Adoption (Scotland) Act 1978.
Regulation 23 of the Adoption Agencies (Scotland) Regulations 1996 …
Rule 67.3 of the Act of Sederunt (Rules of the Court of Session 1994) 1994.
Rules 2.12, 2.14, 2.30 and 2.33 of the Act of Sederunt (Child Care and Maintenance Rules)1997.
Regulation 8 of the Adoption Allowance (Scotland) Regulations 1996.

(b) *Information provided by principal reporter for children's hearing*
Rules 5 and 21 of the Children's Hearings (Scotland) Rules 1996.

(c) *Record of child or young person's special educational needs*
Section 60(4) of the Education (Scotland) Act 1980.
Proviso (bb) to regulation 7(2) of the Education (Record of Needs) (Scotland) Regulations 1982.

(d) *Parental order records and reports*
Section 45 of the Adoption (Scotland) Act 1978 as modified by paragraph 10 of Schedule 1 to the Parental Orders (Human Fertilisation and Embryology) (Scotland) Regulations 1994 in relation to parental orders made under section 30 of the Human Fertilisation and Embryology Act 1990.
Rules 2.47 and 2.59 of the Act of Sederunt (Child Care and Maintenance Rules) 1997.
Rules 81.3 and 81.18 of the Act of Sederunt (Rules of the Court of Session 1994) 1994.

[948]

NOTES

Words omitted revoked by the Data Protection (Miscellaneous Subject Access Exemptions) (Amendment) Order 2000, SI 2000/1865, art 2(1), (3).

PART IV
ENACTMENTS AND INSTRUMENTS EXTENDING TO NORTHERN IRELAND

(a) *Adoption records and reports*
Articles 50 and 54 of the Adoption (Northern Ireland) Act 1987.
Rule 53 of Order 84 of the *Rules of the Supreme Court (Northern Ireland) 1980.*
Rule 22 of the County Court (Adoption) Rules (Northern Ireland) 1980.
Rule 32 of Order 50 of the County Court Rules (Northern Ireland) 1981.

(b) *Statement of child's special educational needs*
Regulation 17 of the Education (Special Educational Needs) Regulations (Northern Ireland) 1997.

(c) *Parental order records and reports*
Articles 50 and 54 of the Adoption (Northern Ireland) Order 1987 as modified by paragraph 5(a) and (e) of Schedule 2 to the Parental Orders (Human Fertilisation and Embryology) Regulations 1994 in respect of parental orders made under section 30 of the Human Fertilisation and Embryology Act 1990.
Rules 4, 5 and 16 of Order 84A of the *Rules of the Supreme Court (Northern Ireland) 1980.*
Rules 3, 4 and 15 of Order 50A of the County Court Rules (Northern Ireland) 1981.

[949]

NOTES

For the words "Rules of the Supreme Court (Northern Ireland) 1980" in italics in paras (a), (c) there are substituted the words "Rules of the Court of Judicature (Northern Ireland) 1980" by the Constitutional Reform Act 2005, s 59(5), Sch 11, Pt 1, para 3(4), as from a day to be appointed.

[INFORMATION TRIBUNAL] (NATIONAL SECURITY APPEALS) (TELECOMMUNICATIONS) RULES 2000

(SI 2000/731)

NOTES

Made: 9 March 2000.
Authority: Data Protection Act 1998, s 67(2), Sch 6, para 7.
Commencement: 5 April 2000.
Words in square brackets substituted by virtue of the Freedom of Information Act 2000, s 18(4), Sch 2, Pt I, para 1(2).

ARRANGEMENT OF RULES

PART II
DATA PROTECTION

1 Citation and commencement

These Rules may be cited as the [Information Tribunal] (National Security Appeals) (Telecommunications) Rules 2000 and shall come into force on 5th April 2000.

[950]

NOTES

Words in square brackets substituted by virtue of the Freedom of Information Act 2000, s 18(4), Sch 2, Pt I, para 1(2).

2 Application and interpretation

(1) These Rules apply to appeals under regulation 32(4) and (6) of the Regulations, and the provisions of these Rules are to be construed accordingly.

(2) In these Rules—

"the Act" means the Data Protection Act 1998;

"appeal" means an appeal under regulation 32 of the Regulations;

"appellant" means a person who brings or intends to bring an appeal under regulation 32 of the Regulations;

"costs"—

(a) except in Scotland, includes fees, charges, disbursements, expenses and remuneration;

(b) in Scotland means expenses, and includes fees, charges, disbursements and remuneration;

"disputed certification" means—

(a) in relation to an appeal under regulation 32(4) of the Regulations, the certificate against which the appeal is brought or intended to be brought, and

(b) in relation to an appeal under regulation 32(6) of the Regulations, the claim by the telecommunications provider, against which the appeal is brought or intended to be brought, that a certificate applies to the circumstance in question;

"party" has the meaning given in paragraph (3) below;

"president" means the person designated by the Lord Chancellor under paragraph 3 of Schedule 6 to the Act to preside when the Tribunal is constituted under that paragraph;

"proper officer" in relation to a rule means an officer or member of staff provided to the Tribunal under paragraph 14 of Schedule 5 to the Act and appointed by the chairman to perform the duties of a proper officer under that rule;

"the Regulations" means the Telecommunications (Data Protection and Privacy) Regulations 1999;

"relevant Minister" means the Minister of the Crown who is responsible for the signing of the certificate under regulation 32(2) of the Regulations to which the appeal relates, and except where the context otherwise requires, references in these Rules to the relevant Minister include a person appointed under rule 21 below to represent his interests;

"respondent telecommunications provider" in relation to an appeal under regulation 32(6) of the Regulations means the telecommunications provider making the claim which constitutes the disputed certification; and

"telecommunications provider" means a telecommunications service or network provider as defined in the Regulations.

(3) In these Rules, except where the context otherwise requires, "party" means the appellant or—

(a) in relation to an appeal under section 32(4) of the Regulations, the relevant Minister, and

(b) in relation to an appeal under section 32(6) of the Regulations, the respondent telecommunications provider,

and except where the context otherwise requires, references in these Rules to a party include a person appointed under rule 21 below to represent his interests.

(4) In relation to proceedings before the Tribunal in Scotland, for the words "on the trial of an action" in rules 15(6) and 26(2) below there is substituted "in a proof".

[951]

3 Constitution and general duty of the Tribunal

(1) When exercising its functions under these Rules, the Tribunal shall secure that information is not disclosed contrary to the interests of national security.

(2) Paragraph 6(1) of Schedule 6 to the Act applies only to the exercise of the jurisdiction of the Tribunal in accordance with rule 11 below.

(3) For the purposes of paragraph (1) above, but without prejudice to the application of that paragraph, the disclosure of information is to be regarded as contrary to the interests of national security if it would indicate the existence or otherwise of any material.

[952]

4 Method of appealing

(1) An appeal must be brought by a written notice of appeal served on the Tribunal.

(2) The notice of appeal shall—

(a) identify the disputed certification; and

(b) state—

(i) the name and address of the appellant;

(ii) the grounds of the appeal; and

(iii) an address for service of notices and other documents on the appellant.

(3) In the case of an appeal under regulation 32(6) of the Regulations, the notice of appeal shall also state—

(a) the date on which the respondent telecommunications provider made the claim constituting the disputed certification;

(b) an address for service of notices and other documents on the respondent telecommunications provider; and

(c) where applicable, the special circumstances which the appellant considers justify the Tribunal's accepting jurisdiction under rule 5(3) below.

[953]

5 Time limit for appealing

(1) In the case of an appeal under regulation 32(4) of the Regulations, a notice of appeal may be served on the Tribunal at any time during the currency of the disputed certification to which it relates.

(2) In the case of an appeal under regulation 32(6) of the Regulations, subject to paragraph (3) below, a notice of appeal must be served on the Tribunal within 28 days of the date on which the claim constituting the disputed certification was made.

(3) The Tribunal may accept a notice of appeal served after the expiry of the period permitted by paragraph (2) above if it is of the opinion that, by reason of special circumstances, it is just and right to do so.

(4) A notice of appeal shall if sent by post in accordance with rule 30(1) below be treated as having been served on the date on which it is received for dispatch by the [postal operator (within the meaning of the Postal Services Act 2000) concerned].

[954]

NOTES

Para (4): words in square brackets substituted by the Postal Services Act 2000 (Consequential Modifications No 1) Order 2001, SI 2001/1149, art 3(1), Sch 1, para 140(1), (2).

6 Acknowledgment of notice of appeal and notification by the Tribunal

(1) Upon receipt of a notice of appeal, the proper officer shall send—

(a) an acknowledgment of the service of a notice of appeal to the appellant, and

(b) a copy of the notice of appeal to—

(i) the relevant Minister,

(ii) the Commissioner, and

(iii) in the case of an appeal under regulation 32(6) of the Regulations, the respondent telecommunications provider.

(2) An acknowledgment of service under paragraph (1)(a) above shall be accompanied by a statement of the Tribunal's powers to award costs against the appellant under rule 28 below.

[955]

7 Relevant Minister's notice in reply

(1) No later than 42 days after receipt of a copy of a notice of appeal under rule 6(1)(b) above, the relevant Minister shall send to the Tribunal—

(a) a copy of the certificate to which the appeal relates, and

(b) a written notice in accordance with paragraph (2) below.

(2) The notice shall state—

(a) with regard to an appeal under regulation 32(4) of the Regulations, whether or not he intends to oppose the appeal and, if so—

(i) a summary of the circumstances relating to the issue of the certificate, and the reasons for the issue of the certificate;

(ii) the grounds upon which he relies in opposing the appeal; and

(iii) a statement of the evidence upon which he relies in support of those grounds; and

(b) with regard to an appeal under regulation 32(6) of the Regulations, whether or not he wishes to make representations in relation to the appeal and, if so—

(i) the extent to which he intends to support or oppose the appeal;

(ii) the grounds upon which he relies in supporting or opposing the appeal; and

(iii) a statement of the evidence upon which he relies in support of those grounds.

(3) Except where the Tribunal proposes to determine the appeal in accordance with rule 11 below, and subject to rule 12 below, the proper officer shall send a copy of the notice to—

(a) the appellant,

(b) the Commissioner, and

(c) in the case of an appeal under regulation 32(6) of the Regulations, the respondent telecommunications provider.

[956]

8 Reply by respondent telecommunications provider

(1) A respondent telecommunications provider shall, within 42 days of the date on which he receives a copy of a notice of appeal under rule 6(1)(b) above, send to the Tribunal a written reply acknowledging service upon him of the notice of appeal, and stating—

(a) whether or not he intends to oppose the appeal and, if so,

(b) the grounds upon which he relies in opposing the appeal.

(2) Before the expiry of the period of 42 days referred to in paragraph (1) above, the respondent telecommunications provider may apply to the Tribunal for an extension of that period, showing cause why, by reason of special circumstances, it would be just and right to do so, and the Tribunal may grant such extension as it considers appropriate.

(3) Except where the Tribunal proposes to determine the appeal in accordance with rule 11 below, the proper officer shall send a copy of the reply to—

(a) the relevant Minister; and

(b) subject to paragraph (4) and rule 12 below, the appellant and the Commissioner.

(4) No copy may be sent under paragraph (3)(b) above before the period of 42 days referred to in rule 12(2)(b) below has expired, otherwise than in accordance with rule 12, unless the relevant Minister has indicated that he does not object.

[957]

9 Amendment and supplementary grounds

(1) With the leave of the Tribunal, the appellant may amend his notice of appeal or deliver supplementary grounds of appeal.

(2) Rule 6(1) above and rule 11(1)(a) below apply to an amended notice of appeal and to supplementary grounds of appeal provided under paragraph (1) above as they do to a notice of appeal.

(3) Upon receipt of a copy of an amended notice of appeal or amended grounds of appeal under rule 6(1) above, the relevant Minister may amend his notice in reply and, in the case of an appeal under regulation 32(6) of the Regulations, the respondent telecommunications provider, may amend his reply to the notice of appeal.

(4) An amended notice or reply under paragraph (3) above must be sent to the Tribunal within 28 days of the date on which the copy referred to in that paragraph is received.

(5) Without prejudice to paragraph (3) above, and with the leave of the Tribunal—

(a) the relevant Minister may amend a notice in reply, and

(b) the respondent telecommunications provider may amend a reply to the notice of appeal.

(6) Rule 7(3) above and rules 11(1)(b) and 12(1)(a) below apply to an amended notice in reply by the relevant Minister provided under paragraph (3) or (5) above as they do to a notice in reply.

(7) Rule 8(3) and (4) above and rules 11(1)(c) and 12(1)(b) below apply to an amended reply by the respondent telecommunications provider provided under paragraph (3) or (5) above as they do to a reply.

[958]

10 Application for striking out

(1) Where the relevant Minister or, in the case of an appeal under regulation 32(6) of the Regulations, the respondent telecommunications provider is of the opinion that an appeal does not lie to, or cannot be entertained by, the Tribunal, or that the notice of appeal discloses no reasonable grounds of appeal, he may include in his notice under rule 7 or, as the case may be, his reply under rule 8 above a notice to that effect stating the grounds for such contention and applying for the appeal to be struck out.

(2) An application under this rule may be heard as a preliminary issue or at the beginning of the hearing of the substantive appeal.

[959]

11 Summary disposal of appeals

(1) Where, having considered—

(a) the notice of appeal,

(b) the relevant Minister's notice under rule 7 above, and
(c) in the case of an appeal under regulation 32(6) of the Regulations, the respondent telecommunication provider's reply,

the Tribunal is of the opinion that the appeal is of such a nature that it can properly be determined by dismissing it forthwith, it may, subject to the provisions of this rule, so determine the appeal.

(2) Where the Tribunal proposes to determine an appeal under paragraph (1) above, it must first notify the appellant and the relevant Minister of the proposal.

(3) A notification to the appellant under paragraph (2) above must contain particulars of the appellant's entitlements set out in paragraph (4) below.

(4) An appellant notified in accordance with paragraph (2) above is entitled, within such time as the Tribunal may reasonably allow—
(a) to make written representations, and
(b) to request the Tribunal to hear oral representations

against the proposal to determine the appeal under paragraph (1) above.

(5) Where an appellant requests a hearing under paragraph (4)(b) above, the Tribunal shall, as soon as practicable and with due regard to the convenience of the appellant, appoint a time and place for a hearing accordingly.

(6) The proper officer shall send to the appellant a notice informing him of—
(a) the time and place of any hearing under paragraph (5) above, which, unless the appellant otherwise agrees, shall not be earlier than 14 days after the date on which the notice is sent, and
(b) the effect of rule 22 below.

(7) The Tribunal must as soon as practicable notify the appellant and the relevant Minister if, having given a notification under paragraph (2) above, it ceases to propose to determine the appeal under paragraph (1) above.

[960]

12 Relevant Minister's objection to disclosure

(1) Where the relevant Minister objects, on grounds of the need to secure that information is not disclosed contrary to the interests of national security, to the disclosure of—
(a) his notice in reply to the appellant, the Commissioner or, in the case of an appeal under regulation 32(6) of the Regulations, the respondent telecommunications provider; or
(b) the reply of a respondent telecommunications provider to the appellant or the Commissioner,

he may send a notice of objection to the Tribunal.

(2) A notice of objection under paragraph (1) above must be sent—
(a) where paragraph (1)(a) above applies, with the notice in reply; and
(b) where paragraph (1)(b) above applies, within 42 days of the date on which he receives the copy mentioned in rule 8(3) above.

(3) A notice of objection under paragraph (1) above shall—
(a) state the reasons for the objection; and
(b) where paragraph (1)(a) above applies, if and to the extent it is possible to do so without disclosing information contrary to the interests of national security, be accompanied by a version of the relevant Minister's notice in a form which can be shown to the appellant, the Commissioner or, as the case may be, the respondent telecommunications provider.

(4) Where the relevant Minister sends a notice of objection under paragraph (1) above, the Tribunal must not disclose the material in question otherwise than in accordance with rule 17 below.

[961]

13 Withdrawal of appeal

(1) The appellant may at any time withdraw his appeal by sending to the Tribunal a notice of withdrawal signed by him or on his behalf, and the proper officer shall send a copy of that notice to—

PART II DATA PROTECTION

(a) the relevant Minister,
(b) the Commissioner, and
(c) in the case of an appeal under regulation 32(6) of the Regulations, the respondent telecommunications provider.

(2) A notice of withdrawal shall if sent by post in accordance with rule 30(1) below have effect on the date on which it is received for dispatch by the [postal operator (within the meaning of the Postal Services Act 2000) concerned].

(3) Where an appeal is withdrawn under this rule a fresh appeal may not be brought by the same appellant in relation to the same disputed certification except with the leave of the Tribunal.

[962]

NOTES

Para (2): words in square brackets substituted by the Postal Services Act 2000 (Consequential Modifications No 1) Order 2001, SI 2001/1149, art 3(1), Sch 1, para 140(1), (3).

14 Consolidation of appeals

(1) Subject to paragraph (2) below, where in the case of two or more appeals to which these Rules apply it appears to the Tribunal—
(a) that some common question of law or fact arises in both or all of them, or
(b) that for some other reason it is desirable to proceed with the appeals under this rule,

the Tribunal may order that the appeals be consolidated or heard together.

(2) The Tribunal shall not make an order under this rule without giving the parties and the relevant Minister an opportunity to show cause why such an order should not be made.

[963]

15 Directions

(1) This rule is subject to rule 16 below.

(2) In this rule, references to a "party" include the relevant Minister notwithstanding that he may not be a party to an appeal under regulation 32(6) of the Regulations.

(3) Subject to paragraphs (6) and (7) below, the Tribunal may at any time of its own motion or on the application of any party give such directions as it thinks proper to enable the parties to prepare for the hearing of the appeal or to assist the Tribunal to determine the issues.

(4) Such directions may in particular—
(a) provide for a particular matter to be dealt with as a preliminary issue and for a pre-hearing review to be held;
(b) provide for—
 (i) the exchange between the parties of lists of documents held by them which are relevant to the appeal,
 (ii) the inspection by the parties of the documents so listed,
 (iii) the exchange between the parties of statements of evidence, and
 (iv) the provision by the parties to the Tribunal of statements or lists of agreed matters;
(c) require any party to send to the Tribunal and to the other parties—
 (i) statements of facts and statements of the evidence which will be adduced, including such statements provided in a modified or edited form;
 (ii) a skeleton argument which summarises the submissions which will be made and cites the authorities which will be relied upon, identifying any particular passages to be relied upon;
 (iii) a chronology of events;
 (iv) any other particulars or supplementary statements which may reasonably be required for the determination of the appeal;
 (v) any document or other material which the Tribunal may require and which it is in the power of that party to deliver;
 (vi) an estimate of the time which will be needed for any hearing; and
 (vii) a list of the witnesses he intends to call to give evidence at any hearing;
(d) limit the length of oral submissions and the time allowed for the examination and cross-examination of witnesses; and

(e) limit the number of expert witnesses to be heard on either side.

(5) The Tribunal may, subject to any specific provisions of these Rules, specify time limits for steps to be taken in the proceedings and may extend any time limit.

(6) Nothing in this rule may require the production of any document or other material which the party could not be compelled to produce on the trial of an action in a court of law in that part of the United Kingdom where the appeal is to be determined.

(7) It shall be a condition of the supply of any information or material provided under this rule that any recipient of that information or material may use it only for the purposes of the appeal.

(8) The power to give directions may be exercised in the absence of the parties.

(9) Notice of any directions given under this rule shall be served on all the parties, and the Tribunal may, on the application of any party, set aside or vary such directions.

[964]

16 Applications by relevant Minister

(1) This rule applies in any case where the Tribunal proposes to—

(a) give or vary any direction under rule 15 above or rule 18(2) below,

(b) issue a summons under rule 20 below, or

(c) certify or publish a determination under rule 27 below.

(2) Before the Tribunal proceeds as proposed in any case to which this rule applies, it must first notify the relevant Minister of the proposal.

(3) If the relevant Minister considers that proceeding as proposed by the Tribunal would cause information to be disclosed contrary to the interests of national security, he may make an application to the Tribunal requesting it to reconsider the proposal or reconsider it to any extent.

(4) An application by the relevant Minister under paragraph (3) above must be made within 14 days of receipt of notification under paragraph (2), and the Tribunal must not proceed as proposed in any case to which this rule applies before that period has expired, otherwise than in accordance with rule 17 below, unless the relevant Minister has indicated that he does not object.

(5) Where the relevant Minister makes an application under this rule, the Tribunal must not proceed as proposed otherwise than in accordance with rule 17 below.

[965]

17 Determinations on relevant Minister's objections and applications

(1) Except where rule 11 above applies, the Tribunal shall determine whether to uphold any objection of the relevant Minister under rule 12 above, and any application under rule 16 above, in accordance with this rule.

(2) Subject to paragraph (3) below, proceedings under this rule shall take place in the absence of the parties.

(3) The relevant Minister (or a person authorised to act on his behalf), may attend any proceedings under this rule, whether or not he is a party to the appeal in question.

(4) An objection under rule 12 above must be considered under this rule as a preliminary issue, and an application under rule 16 above may be considered as a preliminary issue or at the hearing of the substantive appeal.

(5) Where, in the case of an objection under rule 12 above, the Tribunal is minded to overrule the relevant Minister's objection, or to require him to provide a version of his notice in a form other than that in which he provided it under rule 12(3)(b) above, the Tribunal must invite the relevant Minister to make oral representations.

(6) Where the Tribunal under paragraph (5) above overrules an objection by the relevant Minister under rule 12 above, or requires him to provide a version of his notice in a form other than that in which he provided it under rule 12(3)(b) above, the Tribunal shall not disclose, and the relevant Minister shall not be required to disclose, any material which was the subject of the unsuccessful objection if the relevant Minister chooses not to rely upon it in opposing the appeal.

(7) Where, in the case of an objection under rule 12 above, the Tribunal upholds the relevant Minister's objection and either—

(a) approves the version of his notice provided under rule 12(3)(b); or

(b) requires him to provide a version of his notice in a form other than that in which he provided it under rule 12(3)(b),

rule 7(3) above applies to that version of the notice.

[966]

18 Power to determine without a hearing

(1) Without prejudice to rule 11 above, where either—

(a) the parties so agree in writing, or

(b) it appears to the Tribunal that the issues raised on the appeal have been determined on a previous appeal brought by the appellant on the basis of facts which did not materially differ from those to which the appeal relates and the Tribunal has given the parties an opportunity of making representations to the effect that the appeal ought not to be determined without a hearing,

the Tribunal may determine an appeal, or any particular issue, without a hearing.

(2) Before determining any matter under this rule, the Tribunal may, subject to rule 16 above, if it thinks fit direct any party to provide in writing further information about any matter relevant to the appeal within such time as the Tribunal may allow.

[967]

19 Time and place of hearings

(1) Except where rule 11 or 18 above applies, as soon as practicable after notice of appeal has been given, and with due regard to the convenience of the parties, the Tribunal shall appoint a time and place for a hearing of the appeal.

(2) Except in relation to a hearing under rule 11(5) above, the proper officer shall send to each party, the Commissioner and the relevant Minister a notice informing him of the time and place of any hearing, which, unless the parties otherwise agree, shall not be earlier than 14 days after the date on which the notice is sent.

(3) A notice to a party under this rule shall inform him of the effect of rule 22 below.

(4) The Tribunal may—

(a) postpone the time appointed for any hearing;

(b) adjourn a hearing to such time as the Tribunal may determine; or

(c) alter the place appointed for any hearing;

and, if it exercises any of the above powers, it shall notify each person previously notified of that hearing under this rule or rule 11(6) above, and any person summoned under rule 20 below to attend as a witness at that hearing, of the revised arrangements.

[968]

20 Summoning of witnesses

(1) This rule is subject to rule 16 above.

(2) Subject to paragraph (3) below, the Tribunal may by summons require any person in the United Kingdom to attend as a witness at a hearing of an appeal at such time and place as may be specified in the summons and, subject to rule 26(2) and (3) below, at the hearing to answer any questions or produce any documents in his custody or under his control which relate to any matter in question in the appeal.

(3) No person shall be required to attend in obedience to a summons under paragraph (2) above unless he has been given at least 7 days' notice of the hearing or, if less than 7 days, he has informed the Tribunal that he accepts such notice as he has been given.

(4) The Tribunal may upon the application of a person summoned under this rule set the summons aside.

(5) A person who has attended a hearing as a witness in obedience to a summons shall be entitled to such sum as the Tribunal considers reasonable in respect of his attendance at, and his travelling to and from, the hearing; and where the summons was issued at the request of a party such sum shall be paid or tendered to him by that party.

(6) In relation to proceedings before the Tribunal in Scotland, in this rule "summons" means citation and the provisions of this rule are to be construed accordingly.

[969]

21 Representation at a hearing

(1) At any hearing by the Tribunal, other than a hearing under rule 11 above—

(a) a party may, subject to rules 17(2) above and 23(3) below, conduct his case himself or may appear and be represented by any person whom he may appoint for the purpose, and

(b) the relevant Minister may appear and be represented by any person whom he may appoint for the purpose.

(2) At any hearing by the Tribunal under rule 11(5) above, the appellant may conduct his case himself or may appear and be represented by any person whom he may appoint for the purpose.

[970]

22 Default of appearance at hearing

If, without furnishing the Tribunal with sufficient reason for his absence, a party fails to appear at a hearing, having been duly notified of the hearing, the Tribunal may, if that party is the appellant, dismiss the appeal or, in any case, hear and determine the appeal, or any particular issue, in the party's absence and may make such order as to costs as it thinks fit.

[971]

23 Hearings to be in private

(1) All hearings by the Tribunal (including preliminary hearings) shall be in private unless the Tribunal, with the consent of the parties and the relevant Minister, directs that the hearing or any part of the hearing shall take place in public.

(2) Where the Tribunal sits in private it may, with the consent of the parties and the relevant Minister, admit to a hearing such persons on such terms and conditions as it considers appropriate.

(3) Where the Tribunal considers it necessary for any party other than the relevant Minister to be excluded from proceedings or any part of them in order to secure that information is not disclosed contrary to the interests of national security, it must—

(a) direct accordingly,

(b) inform the person excluded of its reasons, to the extent that it is possible to do so without disclosing information contrary to the interests of national security, and record those reasons in writing, and

(c) inform the relevant Minister.

(4) The relevant Minister, or a person authorised to act on his behalf, may attend any hearing, other than a hearing under rule 11 above, notwithstanding that it is in private.

[972]

24 Conduct of proceedings at hearing

(1) Subject to rules 22 and 23(3) above, the Tribunal shall at the hearing of an appeal give to each party and the relevant Minister an opportunity—

(a) to address the Tribunal and to amplify orally written statements previously furnished under these Rules, to give evidence and to call witnesses, and to put questions to any person giving evidence before the Tribunal, and

(b) to make representations on the evidence (if any) and on the subject matter of the appeal generally but, where evidence is taken, such opportunity shall not be given before the completion of the taking of evidence.

(2) Except as provided by these Rules, the Tribunal shall conduct the proceedings in such manner as it considers appropriate in the circumstances for discharging its functions and shall so far as appears to it appropriate seek to avoid formality in its proceedings.

[973]

25 Preliminary and incidental matters

As regards matters preliminary or incidental to an appeal the president may act for the Tribunal under rules 5(3), 8(2), 9, 13 to 15, 19(1) and (4)(a) and (c) and 20.

[974]

26 Evidence

(1) The Tribunal may receive in evidence any document or information notwithstanding that such document or information would be inadmissible in a court of law.

(2) No person shall be compelled to give any evidence or produce any document which he could not be compelled to give or produce on the trial of an action in a court of law in that part of the United Kingdom where the appeal is to be determined.

(3) The Tribunal may require oral evidence of a witness (including a party) to be given on oath or affirmation and for that purpose the president or the proper officer shall have power to administer oaths or take affirmations.

[975]

27 Determination of appeal

(1) As soon as practicable after the Tribunal has determined an appeal, the president shall certify in writing that determination and sign and date the certificate.

(2) If and to the extent that it is possible to do so without disclosing information contrary to the interests of national security, and subject to rule 16 above, the certificate shall include—

(a) any material finding of fact, and
(b) the reasons for the decision.

(3) The proper officer shall send a copy of the certificate to—

(a) the parties,
(b) the relevant Minister, and
(c) the Commissioner.

(4) Subject to rule 16 above, the Tribunal shall make arrangements for the publication of its determination but in doing so shall have regard to—

(a) the desirability of safeguarding the privacy of data subjects and commercially sensitive information, and
(b) the need to secure that information is not disclosed contrary to the interests of national security,

and for those purposes may make any necessary amendments to the text of the certificate.

(5) For the purposes of this rule (but without prejudice to it generally), the disclosure of information is to be regarded as contrary to the interests of national security if it would indicate the existence or otherwise of any material.

[976]

28 Costs

(1) In any appeal before the Tribunal, including one withdrawn under rule 13 above, the Tribunal may make an order awarding costs—

(a) in the case of an appeal under regulation 32(4) of the Regulations—
  (i) against the appellant and in favour of the relevant Minister where it considers that the appeal was manifestly unreasonable;
  (ii) against the relevant Minister and in favour of the appellant where it allows the appeal and quashes the disputed certification, or does so to any extent;
(b) in the case of an appeal under regulation 32(6) of the Regulations—
  (i) against the appellant and in favour of any other party where it dismisses the appeal or dismisses it to any extent;
  (ii) in favour of the appellant and against any other party where it allows the appeal or allows it to any extent; and
(c) where it considers that a party has been responsible for frivolous, vexatious, improper or unreasonable action, or for any failure to comply with a direction or any delay which with diligence could have been avoided, against that party and in favour of the other.

(2) The Tribunal shall not make an order under paragraph (1) above awarding costs against a party without first giving that party an opportunity of making representations against the making of the order.

(3) An order under paragraph (1) above may be to the party or parties in question to pay to the other party or parties either a specified sum in respect of the costs incurred by that other party or parties in connection with the proceedings or the whole or part of such costs as taxed (if not otherwise agreed).

(4) Any costs required by an order under this rule to be taxed may be taxed in the county court according to such of the scales prescribed by the county court rules for proceedings in the county court as shall be directed by the order.

(5) In relation to proceedings before the Tribunal in Scotland, for the purposes of the application of paragraph (4) above, for the reference to the county court and the county court rules there shall be substituted references to the sheriff court and the sheriff court rules and for the reference to proceedings there shall be substituted a reference to civil proceedings.

[977]

29 Irregularities

(1) Any irregularity resulting from failure to comply with any provision of these Rules or of any direction of the Tribunal before the Tribunal has reached its decision shall not of itself render the proceedings void, but the Tribunal may, and shall if it considers that any person may have been prejudiced by that irregularity, give such directions or take such steps as it thinks fit before reaching its decision to cure or waive the irregularity, whether by amendment of any document, the giving of notice or otherwise.

(2) Clerical mistakes in any document recording or certifying a direction, decision or determination of the Tribunal or president, or errors arising in such a document from an accidental slip or omission, may at any time be corrected by the president by certificate signed by him.

[978]

30 Notices etc

(1) Any notice or other document required or authorised by these Rules to be served on or sent to any person or authority may be sent by post in a registered letter or by the recorded delivery service—

(a) in the case of the Tribunal, to the proper officer of the Tribunal;

(b) in the case of an appellant or a respondent telecommunications provider, to him at his address for service under these Rules;

(c) in the case of the relevant Minister or the Commissioner, to him at his office.

(2) An appellant or respondent telecommunications provider may at any time by notice to the Tribunal change his address for service under these Rules.

[979]

DATA PROTECTION (DESIGNATED CODES OF PRACTICE) (NO 2) ORDER 2000

(SI 2000/1864)

NOTES

Made: 13 July 2000.
Authority: Data Protection Act 1998, s 32(3).
Commencement: 27 July 2000.

1 This Order may be cited as the Data Protection (Designated Codes of Practice) (No 2) Order 2000 and shall come into force on the fourteenth day after the day on which it is made.

[980]

2 The codes of practice listed in the Schedule to this Order shall be designated for the purposes of section 32(3) of the Data Protection Act 1998.

[981]

3 (*Revokes the Data Protection* (*Designated Codes of Practice*) *Order 2000, SI 2000/418.*)

SCHEDULE
DESIGNATED CODES OF PRACTICE

1. The code published by the Broadcasting Standards Commission under section 107 of the Broadcasting Act 1996.

2. The code published by the Independent Television Commission under section 7 of the Broadcasting Act 1990.

3. The Code of Practice published by the Press Complaints Commission.

4. The Producers' Guidelines published by the British Broadcasting Corporation.

5. The code published by the Radio Authority under section 91 of the Broadcasting Act 1990.

[982]–[988]

NOTES

The Communications Act 2003, s 31(4)(b) provides that, on such day as the Secretary of State may by order appoint, the Broadcasting Standards Commission, the Independent Television Commission and the Radio Authority shall cease to exist. Accordingly, references to those bodies and other related expressions are revoked. For transitional provisions until an order is made under that section see the Office of Communications Act 2002 (Commencement No 3) and Communications Act 2003 (Commencement No 2) Order 2003, SI 2003/3142, art 6(1), (2) at **[3595]**.

REGULATION OF INVESTIGATORY POWERS (AUTHORISATIONS EXTENDING TO SCOTLAND) ORDER 2000

(SI 2000/2418)

NOTES

Made: 7 September 2000.
Authority: Regulation of Investigatory Powers Act 2000, s 46(4).
Commencement: 2 October 2000.

1 Citation and commencement

This Order may be cited as the Regulation of Investigatory Powers (Authorisations Extending to Scotland) Order 2000 and shall come into force on 2nd October 2000.

[989]

2 Relevant public authorities for all parts of the United Kingdom

(1) Subject to paragraph (2), the public authorities listed in column 1 of the Schedule to this Order (being public authorities for the time being specified in Schedule 1 to the Regulation of Investigatory Powers Act 2000) are relevant public authorities for all parts of the United Kingdom.

(2) Where there is an entry in column 2 against a particular authority, that authority is a relevant public authority for all parts of the United Kingdom only to the extent specified in that column.

[990]

SCHEDULE

Article 2

(1)	(2)
[The Serious Organised Crime Agency]	
The Commissioners of Inland Revenue	
The Department of the Environment, Transport and the Regions	
The Department of Health	
The Home Office	The Immigration Service
The Department of Social Security	
The Department of Trade and Industry	

(1)	(2)
The Environment Agency	
The Financial Services Authority	
…	
[A universal service provider (within the meaning of the Postal Services Act 2000) acting in connection with the provision of a universal postal service (within the meaning of that Act)]	
The Health and Safety Executive	
The Royal Pharmaceutical Society of Great Britain	

[991]

NOTES

Entry relating to "The Serious Organised Crime Agency" substituted for original entry relating to "The National Criminal Intelligence Service" by the Serious Organised Crime and Police Act 2005 (Consequential and Supplementary Amendments to Secondary Legislation) Order 2006, SI 2006/594, art 2, Schedule, para 22.

Entry relating to "The Personal Investment Authority" (omitted) revoked by the Financial Services and Markets Act 2000 (Consequential Amendments) Order 2002, SI 2002/1555, art 42.

Entry relating to "A universal service provider" substituted by the Postal Services Act 2000 (Consequential Modifications No 1) Order 2001, SI 2001/1149, art 3(1), Sch 1, para 144.

REGULATION OF INVESTIGATORY POWERS (NOTIFICATION OF AUTHORISATIONS ETC) ORDER 2000

(SI 2000/2563)

NOTES

Made: 20 September 2000.
Authority: Regulation of Investigatory Powers Act 2000, s 35(2)(c).
Commencement: 25 September 2000.

1 Citation and commencement

This Order may be cited as the Regulation of Investigatory Powers (Notification of Authorisations etc) Order 2000 and shall come into force on 25th September 2000.

[992]

2 Interpretation

In this Order—

"the 2000 Act" means the Regulation of Investigatory Powers Act 2000;

"authorisation" means a police or customs authorisation for the carrying out of intrusive surveillance;

"Commissioner" means an ordinary Surveillance Commissioner; and

"notice to a Commissioner" means the notice required to be given under section 35(1) of the 2000 Act.

[993]

3 Notice of authorisation

Where a person grants an authorisation, the notice to a Commissioner shall, in addition to the statement required by section 35(3) of the 2000 Act, specify the following matters—

(a) the grounds on which he believes the matters specified in section 32(2)(a) and (b) of the 2000 Act;

(b) the nature of the authorised conduct including the residential premises or private vehicle in relation to which the conduct is authorised and the identity, where known, of persons to be the subject of the authorised conduct; and

(c) whether the conduct to be authorised is likely to lead to intrusion on the privacy of persons other than any person who is to be the subject of that conduct.

[994]

4 Notice of renewal of authorisation

Where a person renews an authorisation, the notice to a Commissioner shall, in addition to the statement required by section 35(3) of the 2000 Act, specify the following matters—

(a) whether the authorisation is being renewed for the first time, or, where it has been previously renewed, each occasion on which it has been renewed;

(b) the matters required by article 3, as they apply at the time of notice of renewal;

(c) every respect in which the information provided in the previous notice has changed;

(d) the reason why it is considered to be necessary to renew the authorisation;

(e) the content, and value to the investigation, of the information obtained to date by the conduct authorised;

(f) the results of any reviews of the authorisation and

(g) the period for which the authorisation is considered likely to continue to be necessary.

[995]

5 Notice of cancellation of authorisation

Where a person cancels an authorisation, the notice to a Commissioner shall specify the following matters—

(a) the date and time when he gave the instructions to cease the conduct authorised;

(b) the reasons for cancelling the authorisation;

(c) the outcome of the investigation to which the authorisation related, and details of any criminal proceedings instituted or intended to be instituted; and

(d) what arrangements have been made for the storage of material obtained as a result of the conduct authorised, for its review and its destruction when its retention is no longer required, and for the immediate destruction of any material unrelated to the purposes for which the conduct was authorised.

[996]

INVESTIGATORY POWERS TRIBUNAL RULES 2000

(SI 2000/2665)

NOTES

Made: 28 September 2000.
Authority: Regulation of Investigatory Powers Act 2000, s 69.
Commencement: 2 October 2000.

ARRANGEMENT OF RULES

PART I
GENERAL PROVISIONS

PART II
PROCEEDINGS AND COMPLAINTS

PART I
GENERAL PROVISIONS

1 Citation and commencement

These Rules may be cited as the Investigatory Powers Tribunal Rules 2000, and shall come into force on 2nd October 2000.

[997]

2 Interpretation

In these Rules—

"the Act" means the Regulation of Investigatory Powers Act 2000;

"Commissioner" means the Interception of Communications Commissioner, the Intelligence Services Commissioner, the Investigatory Powers Commissioner for Northern Ireland or any Surveillance Commissioner or Assistant Surveillance Commissioner;

"complainant" means a person who brings section 7 proceedings or, as the case may be, makes a complaint;

"complaint" means a complaint for which the Tribunal is the appropriate forum by virtue of section 65(2)(b) and section 65(4) of the Act;

"Convention right" has the same meaning as in the Human Rights Act 1998;

"section 7 proceedings" means proceedings under section 7(1)(a) of the Human Rights Act 1998 in relation to which the Tribunal is the only appropriate tribunal by virtue of section 65(2)(a) of the Act;

"the Tribunal" means the tribunal established under section 65(1) of the Act.

[998]

3 Application of Rules

These Rules apply to section 7 proceedings, and to complaints.

[999]

4 Exercise of Tribunal's jurisdiction

(1) The jurisdiction of the Tribunal may be exercised at any place in the United Kingdom, by any two or more members of the Tribunal designated for the purpose by the President; and different members of the Tribunal may carry out functions in relation to different complaints at the same time.

(2) This rule is subject to paragraph 3 of Schedule 3 to the Act (members of the Tribunal with special responsibilities).

[1000]

5 Functions exercisable by single member

(1) Subject to paragraph (2), the following powers and duties may be exercised or performed by a single member of the Tribunal—

(a) the power under rule 7(4) or rule 8(4) to invite the complainant to supply information or make representations;

(b) the power under section 68(2) of the Act to require a Commissioner to provide assistance;

(c) the power under section 68(6) of the Act to require the disclosure or provision of documents or information;

(d) the power under paragraph 5(2) of Schedule 3 to the Act to authorise an officer to obtain documents or information on the Tribunal's behalf;

(e) the power under section 7(5)(b) of the Human Rights Act 1998 to extend the time limit for section 7 proceedings;

(f) the power under section 67(5) of the Act to extend the time limit for complaints;

(g) the duty under rule 13 to notify the complainant of any of the determinations described in that rule;
(h) the duty, in considering a complaint, to investigate the matters described in paragraphs (a) and (b) of section 67(3) of the Act.

(2) In relation to a case falling within paragraph 3(2) of Schedule 3 to the Act, a single member discharging any of these functions must be a member designated under paragraph 3(1) of that Schedule.

[1001]

6 Disclosure of Information

(1) The Tribunal shall carry out their functions in such a way as to secure that information is not disclosed to an extent, or in a manner, that is contrary to the public interest or prejudicial to national security, the prevention or detection of serious crime, the economic well-being of the United Kingdom or the continued discharge of the functions of any of the intelligence services.

(2) Without prejudice to this general duty, but subject to paragraphs (3) and (4), the Tribunal may not disclose to the complainant or to any other person—
(a) the fact that the Tribunal have held, or propose to hold, an oral hearing under rule 9(4);
(b) any information or document disclosed or provided to the Tribunal in the course of that hearing, or the identity of any witness at that hearing;
(c) any information or document otherwise disclosed or provided to the Tribunal by any person pursuant to section 68(6) of the Act (or provided voluntarily by a person specified in section 68(7));
(d) any information or opinion provided to the Tribunal by a Commissioner pursuant to section 68(2) of the Act;
(e) the fact that any information, document, identity or opinion has been disclosed or provided in the circumstances mentioned in subparagraphs (b) to (d).

(3) The Tribunal may disclose anything described in paragraph (2) with the consent of—
(a) in the case of sub-paragraph (a), the person required to attend the hearing;
(b) in the case of sub-paragraphs (b) and (c), the witness in question or the person who disclosed or provided the information or document;
(c) in the case of sub-paragraph (d), the Commissioner in question and, to the extent that the information or opinion includes information provided to the Commissioner by another person, that other person;
(d) in the case of sub-paragraph (e), the person whose consent is required under this rule for disclosure of the information, document or opinion in question.

(4) The Tribunal may also disclose anything described in paragraph (2) as part of the information provided to the complainant under rule 13(2), subject to the restrictions contained in rule 13(4) and (5).

(5) The Tribunal may not order any person to disclose any information or document which the Tribunal themselves would be prohibited from disclosing by virtue of this rule, had the information or document been disclosed or provided to them by that person.

(6) The Tribunal may not, without the consent of the complainant, disclose to any person holding office under the Crown (except a Commissioner) or to any other person anything to which paragraph (7) applies.

(7) This paragraph applies to any information or document disclosed or provided to the Tribunal by or on behalf of the complainant, except for the statements described in rule 7(2)(a) and (b) or, as the case may be, rule 8(2)(a) and (b).

[1002]

PART II
PROCEEDINGS AND COMPLAINTS

7 Bringing section 7 proceedings

(1) Section 7 proceedings are brought by a complainant sending to the Tribunal a form and other information in accordance with this rule.

(2) The form must be signed by the complainant and must—

(a) state the name, address and date of birth of the complainant;
(b) state each public authority against which the proceedings are brought;
(c) describe the nature of the claim (including details of the Convention right which it is alleged has been infringed) and of the complainant's interest; and
(d) specify the remedy which the complainant seeks.

(3) The complainant must also supply, either in or with the form, a summary of the information on which the claim is based.

(4) At any time, the Tribunal may invite the complainant to supply further information or to make written representations on any matter.

[1003]

8 Making a complaint

(1) A complaint is brought by a complainant sending to the Tribunal a form in accordance with this rule.

(2) The form must be signed by the complainant and must—
(a) state the name, address and date of birth of the complainant;
(b) state the person or authority whose conduct, to the best of the complainant's knowledge or belief, is the subject of the complaint; and
(c) describe, to the best of the complainant's knowledge or belief, that conduct.

(3) The complainant must also supply, either in or with the form, a summary of the information on which the claim is based.

(4) At any time, the Tribunal may invite the complainant to supply further information or to make written representations on any matter.

[1004]

9 Forms of hearing and consideration

(1) The Tribunal's power to determine their own procedure in relation to section 7 proceedings and complaints shall be subject to this rule.

(2) The Tribunal shall be under no duty to hold oral hearings, but they may do so in accordance with this rule (and not otherwise).

(3) The Tribunal may hold, at any stage of their consideration, oral hearings at which the complainant may make representations, give evidence and call witnesses.

(4) The Tribunal may hold separate oral hearings which—
(a) the person whose conduct is the subject of the complaint,
(b) the public authority against which the section 7 proceedings are brought, or
(c) any other person specified in section 68(7) of the Act,
may be required to attend and at which that person or authority may make representations, give evidence and call witnesses.

(5) Within a period notified by the Tribunal for the purpose of this rule, the complainant, person or authority in question must inform the Tribunal of any witnesses he or it intends to call; and no other witnesses may be called without the leave of the Tribunal.

(6) The Tribunal's proceedings, including any oral hearings, shall be conducted in private.

[1005]

10 Representation

(1) A person entitled to make representations at an oral hearing may appear in person or may be represented by any person he may appoint for that purpose, subject to paragraph (2).

(2) The leave of the Tribunal is required except where the representative is—
(a) a member of the Bar of England and Wales or of Northern Ireland,
(b) a solicitor of the Supreme Court in England and Wales or in Northern Ireland,
(c) a member of the Faculty of Advocates, or
(d) a solicitor within the meaning of the Solicitors (Scotland) Act 1980.

[1006]

11 Evidence

(1) The Tribunal may receive evidence in any form, and may receive evidence that would not be admissible in a court of law.

(2) The Tribunal may require a witness to give evidence on oath.

(3) No person shall be compelled to give evidence at an oral hearing under rule 9(3).

[1007]

12 Remedies

(1) Before exercising their power under section 67(7) of the Act, the Tribunal shall invite representations in accordance with this rule.

(2) Where they propose to make an award of compensation, the Tribunal shall give the complainant and the person who would be required to pay the compensation an opportunity to make representations as to the amount of the award.

(3) Where they propose to make any other order (including an interim order) affecting the public authority against whom the section 7 proceedings are brought, or the person whose conduct is the subject of the complaint, the Tribunal shall give that authority or person an opportunity to make representations on the proposed order.

[1008]

13 Notification to the complainant

(1) In addition to any statement under section 68(4) of the Act, the Tribunal shall provide information to the complainant in accordance with this rule.

(2) Where they make a determination in favour of the complainant, the Tribunal shall provide him with a summary of that determination including any findings of fact.

(3) Where they make a determination—

(a) that the bringing of the section 7 proceedings or the making of the complaint is frivolous or vexatious;

(b) that the section 7 proceedings have been brought, or the complaint made, out of time and that the time limit should not be extended; or

(c) that the complainant does not have the right to bring the section 7 proceedings or make the complaint;

the Tribunal shall notify the complainant of that fact.

(4) The duty to provide information under this rule is in all cases subject to the general duty imposed on the Tribunal by rule 6(1).

(5) No information may be provided under this rule whose disclosure would be restricted under rule 6(2) unless the person whose consent would be needed for disclosure under that rule has been given the opportunity to make representations to the Tribunal.

[1009]

TELECOMMUNICATIONS (LAWFUL BUSINESS PRACTICE) (INTERCEPTION OF COMMUNICATIONS) REGULATIONS 2000

(SI 2000/2699)

NOTES

Made: 2 October 2000.
Authority: Regulation of Investigatory Powers Act 2000, ss 4(2), 78(5).
Commencement: 24 October 2000.

1 Citation and commencement

These Regulations may be cited as the Telecommunications (Lawful Business Practice) (Interception of Communications) Regulations 2000 and shall come into force on 24th October 2000.

[1010]

2 Interpretation

In these Regulations—

(a) references to a business include references to activities of a government department, of any public authority or of any person or office holder on whom functions are conferred by or under any enactment;

(b) a reference to a communication as relevant to a business is a reference to—

(i) a communication—

(aa) by means of which a transaction is entered into in the course of that business, or

(bb) which otherwise relates to that business, or

(ii) a communication which otherwise takes place in the course of the carrying on of that business;

(c) "regulatory or self-regulatory practices or procedures" means practices or procedures—

(i) compliance with which is required or recommended by, under or by virtue of—

(aa) any provision of the law of a member state or other state within the European Economic Area, or

(bb) any standard or code of practice published by or on behalf of a body established in a member state or other state within the European Economic Area which includes amongst its objectives the publication of standards or codes of practice for the conduct of business, or

(ii) which are otherwise applied for the purpose of ensuring compliance with anything so required or recommended;

(d) "system controller" means, in relation to a particular telecommunication system, a person with a right to control its operation or use.

[1011]

3 Lawful interception of a communication

(1) For the purpose of section 1(5)(a) of the Act, conduct is authorised, subject to paragraphs (2) and (3) below, if it consists of interception of a communication, in the course of its transmission by means of a telecommunication system, which is effected by or with the express or implied consent of the system controller for the purpose of—

(a) monitoring or keeping a record of communications—

(i) in order to—

(aa) establish the existence of facts, or

(bb) ascertain compliance with regulatory or self-regulatory practices or procedures which are—

applicable to the system controller in the carrying on of his business or

applicable to another person in the carrying on of his business where that person is supervised by the system controller in respect of those practices or procedures, or

(cc) ascertain or demonstrate the standards which are achieved or ought to be achieved by persons using the system in the course of their duties, or

(ii) in the interests of national security, or

(iii) for the purpose of preventing or detecting crime, or

(iv) for the purpose of investigating or detecting the unauthorised use of that or any other telecommunication system, or

(v) where that is undertaken—

(aa) in order to secure, or

(bb) as an inherent part of,

the effective operation of the system (including any monitoring or keeping of a record which would be authorised by section 3(3) of the Act if the conditions in paragraphs (a) and (b) thereof were satisfied); or

(b) monitoring communications for the purpose of determining whether they are communications relevant to the system controller's business which fall within regulation 2(b)(i) above; or

(c) monitoring communications made to a confidential voice-telephony counselling or support service which is free of charge (other than the cost, if any, of making a telephone call) and operated in such a way that users may remain anonymous if they so choose.

(2) Conduct is authorised by paragraph (1) of this regulation only if—

(a) the interception in question is effected solely for the purpose of monitoring or (where appropriate) keeping a record of communications relevant to the system controller's business;

(b) the telecommunication system in question is provided for use wholly or partly in connection with that business;

(c) the system controller has made all reasonable efforts to inform every person who may use the telecommunication system in question that communications transmitted by means thereof may be intercepted; and

(d) in a case falling within—

(i) paragraph (1)(a)(ii) above, the person by or on whose behalf the interception is effected is a person specified in section 6(2)(a) to (i) of the Act;

(ii) paragraph (1)(b) above, the communication is one which is intended to be received (whether or not it has been actually received) by a person using the telecommunication system in question.

[(3) Conduct falling within paragraph (1)(a)(i) above is authorised only to the extent that Article 5 of Directive 2002/58/EC of the European Parliament and of the Council of 12 July 2002 concerning the processing of personal data and the protection of privacy in the electronic communications sector so permits.]

[1012]

NOTES

Para (3): substituted by the Privacy and Electronic Communications (EC Directive) Regulations 2003, SI 2003/2426, reg 34.

REGULATION OF INVESTIGATORY POWERS (SOURCE RECORDS) REGULATIONS 2000

(SI 2000/2725)

NOTES

Made: 4 October 2000.
Authority: Regulation of Investigatory Powers Act 2000, s 29(5)(d).
Commencement: 1 November 2000.

1 Citation and commencement

These Regulations may be cited as the Regulation of Investigatory Powers (Source Records) Regulations 2000 and shall come into force on 1st November 2000.

[1013]

2 Interpretation

In these Regulations—

"the 2000 Act" means the Regulation of Investigatory Powers Act 2000;

"relevant investigating authority" has the meaning given by section 29(8) of the 2000 Act, but the qualification in section 29(9) does not apply;

"source" means a covert human intelligence source; and

"undercover operative" means a source who holds an office, rank or position with a relevant investigating authority.

[1014]

3 Particulars to be contained in records

The following matters are specified for the purposes of paragraph (d) of section 29(5) of the 2000 Act (as being matters particulars of which must be included in the records relating to each source)—

(a) the identity of the source;

(b) the identity, where known, used by the source;

(c) any relevant investigating authority other than the authority maintaining the records;

(d) the means by which the source is referred to within each relevant investigating authority;
(e) any other significant information connected with the security and welfare of the source;
(f) any confirmation made by a person granting or renewing an authorisation for the conduct or use of a source that the information in paragraph (d) has been considered and that any identified risks to the security and welfare of the source have where appropriate been properly explained to and understood by the source;
(g) the date when, and the circumstances in which, the source was recruited;
(h) the identities of the persons who, in relation to the source, are discharging or have discharged the functions mentioned in section 29(5)(a) to (c) of the 2000 Act or in any order made by the Secretary of State under section 29(2)(c);
(i) the periods during which those persons have discharged those responsibilities;
(j) the tasks given to the source and the demands made of him in relation to his activities as a source;
(k) all contacts or communications between the source and a person acting on behalf of any relevant investigating authority;
(l) the information obtained by each relevant investigating authority by the conduct or use of the source;
(m) any dissemination by that authority of information obtained in that way; and
(n) in the case of a source who is not an undercover operative, every payment, benefit or reward and every offer of a payment, benefit or reward that is made or provided by or on behalf of any relevant investigating authority in respect of the source's activities for the benefit of that or any other relevant investigating authority.

[1015]

REGULATION OF INVESTIGATORY POWERS (JUVENILES) ORDER 2000

(SI 2000/2793)

NOTES

Made: 10 October 2000.
Authority: Regulation of Investigatory Powers Act 2000, ss 29(2)(c), 29(7)(a), (b), 43(8).
Commencement: 6 November 2000.

ARRANGEMENT OF ARTICLES

1 Citation and commencement

This Order may be cited as the Regulation of Investigatory Powers (Juveniles) Order 2000 and shall come into force on 6th November 2000.

[1016]

2 Interpretation

In this Order—

"the 2000 Act" means the Regulation of Investigatory Powers Act 2000;
"guardian", in relation to a source, has the same meaning as is given to "guardian of a child" by section 105 of the Children Act 1989;
"relative" has the same meaning as it is given by section 105 of the Children Act 1989;
"relevant investigating authority" has the meaning given by section 29(8) of the 2000 Act, and where the activities of a source are to be for the benefit of more than one public authority, each of these authorities is a relevant investigating authority;

"source" means covert human intelligence source.

[1017]

3 Sources under 16: prohibition

No authorisation may be granted for the conduct or use of a source if—

(a) the source is under the age of sixteen; and

(b) the relationship to which the conduct or use would relate is between the source and his parent or any person who has parental responsibility for him.

[1018]

4 Sources under 16: arrangements for meetings

(1) Where a source is under the age of sixteen, the arrangements referred to in section 29(2)(c) of the 2000 Act must be such that there is at all times a person holding an office, rank or position with a relevant investigating authority who has responsibility for ensuring that an appropriate adult is present at meetings to which this article applies.

(2) This article applies to all meetings between the source and a person representing any relevant investigating authority that take place while the source remains under the age of sixteen.

(3) In paragraph (1), "appropriate adult" means—

(a) the parent or guardian of the source;

(b) any other person who has for the time being assumed responsibility for his welfare; or

(c) where no person falling within paragraph (a) or (b) is available, any responsible person aged eighteen or over who is neither a member of nor employed by any relevant investigating authority.

[1019]

5 Sources under 18: risk assessments etc

An authorisation for the conduct or use of a source may not be granted or renewed in any case where the source is under the age of eighteen at the time of the grant or renewal, unless—

(a) a person holding an office, rank or position with a relevant investigating authority has made and, in the case of a renewal, updated a risk assessment sufficient to demonstrate that—

(i) the nature and magnitude of any risk of physical injury to the source arising in the course of, or as a result of, carrying out the conduct described in the authorisation have been identified and evaluated; and

(ii) the nature and magnitude of any risk of psychological distress to the source arising in the course of, or as a result of, carrying out the conduct described in the authorisation have been identified and evaluated;

(b) the person granting or renewing the authorisation has considered the risk assessment and has satisfied himself that any risks identified in it are justified and, if they are, that they have been properly explained to and understood by the source; and

(c) the person granting or renewing the authorisation knows whether the relationship to which the conduct or use would relate is between the source and a relative, guardian or person who has for the time being assumed responsibility for the source's welfare, and, if it is, has given particular consideration to whether the authorisation is justified in the light of that fact.

[1020]

6 Sources under 18: duration of authorisations

In relation to an authorisation for the conduct or the use of a source who is under the age of eighteen at the time the authorisation is granted or renewed, section 43(3) of the 2000 Act shall have effect as if the period specified in paragraph (b) of that subsection were one month instead of twelve months.

[1021]

REGULATION OF INVESTIGATORY POWERS (CANCELLATION OF AUTHORISATIONS) REGULATIONS 2000

(SI 2000/2794)

NOTES

Made: 10 October 2000.
Authority: Regulation of Investigatory Powers Act 2000, ss 45(4), (5).
Commencement: 6 November 2000.

1 Citation and commencement

These Regulations may be cited as the Regulation of Investigatory Powers (Cancellation of Authorisations) Regulations 2000, and shall come into force on 6th November 2000.

[1022]

2 Performance of duty to cancel

(1) Where any duty imposed by section 45 of the Regulation of Investigatory Powers Act 2000 would otherwise fall on a person who is no longer available to perform it, that duty is to be performed by—

(a) the person, if any, appointed for the purpose of these Regulations in accordance with paragraph (2);

(b) where no such person has been appointed, the person, if any, who holds the same office, rank or position in the same public authority as was held by the person who is no longer available and who has taken over that person's responsibilities or most of them.

(2) The person making an appointment for the purpose of these Regulations, and the person appointed, must each be a person holding the same office, rank or position (or a more senior one) in the same public authority as was held by the person who is no longer available.

[1023]

UTILITIES ACT 2000 (SUPPLY OF INFORMATION) REGULATIONS 2000

(SI 2000/2956)

NOTES

Made: 1 November 2000.
Authority: Utilities Act 2000, s 27(1), (6).
Commencement: 25 November 2000.

ARRANGEMENT OF REGULATIONS

1 Citation and Commencement

These Regulations may be cited as the Utilities Act 2000 (Supply of Information) Regulations 2000 and shall come into force on 25th November 2000.

[1024]

PART II DATA PROTECTION

2 Interpretation

In these Regulations—

"the Act" means the Utilities Act 2000;
"the Authority" means the Gas and Electricity Markets Authority;
"the Council" means the Gas and Electricity Consumer Council;
"electricity licence" means a licence under section 6 of the Electricity Act 1989;
"gas licence" means a licence under section 7 or 7A of the Gas Act 1986;
"licence holder" means the holder of a gas licence or an electricity licence.

[1025]

3 National security

(1) The Authority, a licence holder or the Council may refuse to supply under section 24 (provision of information to Council) or 26 (provision of information by Council to Authority) of the Act any information which it would be against the interests of national security to make public.

(2) The Secretary of State may certify for the purposes of paragraph (1) whether or not the making public of particular information would be against the interests of national security, and any such certificate shall, subject to any exercise of a court's jurisdiction to review it, be conclusive.

(3) A certificate under paragraph (2) may identify the information in question by means of a general description.

[1026]

4 Price sensitive information

(1) The Authority or a licence holder may refuse to supply under section 24 of the Act any information which—

(a) relates to particular securities or to a particular issuer of securities or to particular issuers of securities;
(b) is specific or precise;
(c) has not been made public; and
(d) if it were made public would be likely to have a significant effect on the price of the securities.

(2) For the purposes of this regulation—

(a) "price" includes value;
(b) information shall be treated as relating to a particular issuer of securities which is a company not only where it is about the company but also where it may affect the company's business prospects;
(c) "made public", in relation to information, shall be construed in accordance with subsection (1) of section 58 of the Criminal Justice Act 1993; and
(d) "securities" means any securities to which Part V of the Criminal Justice Act 1993 (insider dealing) applies.

[1027]

5 Information whose disclosure would be affected by the application of other legislation

(1) The Authority may refuse to supply under section 24 of the Act any information not falling within regulation 4(1) which—

(a) was disclosed to the Authority in circumstances in which that disclosure would have been prohibited by or under an enactment imposing general restrictions on the disclosure of information but for an exemption from those restrictions naming the Authority as a person to whom information may be disclosed whether generally or for specified purposes or in specified circumstances; or
(b) was obtained by the Authority in the exercise of functions which it may exercise concurrently with [the Office of Fair Trading] under [Part 4 of the Enterprise Act 2002] or under Part I of the Competition Act 1998.

(2) The Authority, a licence holder or the Council may refuse to supply under section 24 or 26 of the Act any information—

(a) whose disclosure would be prohibited by or under any enactment other than the Gas Act 1986 or the Electricity Act 1989; or
(b) whose disclosure is incompatible with any Community obligation.

(3) Subject to paragraph (4), the Authority, a licence holder or the Council may refuse to supply under section 24 or 26 of the Act any information which constitutes personal data within the meaning of section 1(1) of the Data Protection Act 1998 and where—

(a) in a case where the information falls within any of paragraphs (a) to (d) of the definition of "data" in that section, the disclosure of the information to a member of the public would contravene any of the data protection principles or section 10 of that Act (right to prevent processing likely to cause damage or distress); or

(b) in any other case, the disclosure of the information to a member of the public would contravene any of the data protection principles if the exemptions in section 33A(1) of the Data Protection Act 1998 (which relate to manual data held by public authorities) were disregarded.

(4) A licence holder may not, by virtue of paragraph (3), refuse to supply information which relates to a person who has made a complaint to which section 32 of the Gas Act 1986 or section 46 of the Electricity Act 1989 applies and which is being investigated by the Council.

[1028]

NOTES

Para (1): words in first pair of square brackets substituted by virtue of the Enterprise Act 2002, s 2 (for transitional and transitory provisions and savings see s 276 of, and Sch 24, para 6 to, that Act); words in second pair of square brackets substituted by the Enterprise Act 2002 (Consequential and Supplemental Provisions) Order 2003, SI 2003/1398, art 2, Schedule, para 40.

6 Information relevant to court proceedings or enforcement action

(1) The Authority, a licence holder or the Council may refuse to supply under section 24 or 26 of the Act any information whose disclosure would constitute or be punishable as a contempt of court.

(2) The Authority, a licence holder or the Council may refuse to supply under section 24 or 26 of the Act any information whose disclosure would, or would be likely to, prejudice any criminal proceedings.

(3) The Authority or a licence holder may refuse to supply under section 24 of the Act any information whose disclosure would, or would be likely to, prejudice—

(a) any action under sections 28 (orders for securing compliance) or 30A (penalties) of the Gas Act 1986; or

(b) any action under sections 25 (orders for securing compliance) or 27A (penalties) of the Electricity Act 1989.

(4) A licence holder may refuse to supply information under section 24 of the Act which the licence holder could not be compelled to give as evidence in civil proceedings or which is contained in documents or records which the licence holder could not be compelled to produce in evidence in any such proceedings.

[1029]

7 Information concerning internal discussions or deliberations

(1) Subject to paragraph (2), the Authority, a licence holder or the Council may refuse to supply under section 24 or 26 of the Act—

(a) any information concerning the discussions or deliberations of the Authority, a licence holder or the Council as to a decision or action to be taken or that may be taken by the Authority, a licence holder or the Council where the direction requiring the supply of that information is given before that decision or action has been taken;

(b) any information concerning the discussions or deliberations of the Authority, a licence holder or the Council as to a decision or action which has been taken and is to be announced or published by the Authority, a licence holder or the Council where the direction requiring the supply of that information is given before that decision or action has been announced or published;

(c) any information concerning the views of the Authority or a licence holder on its relationship with the Council or the performance by the Council of its functions;

(d) any information concerning the views of the Council on its relationship with the Authority or the performance by the Authority of its functions.

(2) A licence holder may not by virtue of sub-paragraphs (a) and (b) of paragraph (1) refuse to supply information which is relevant to the investigation of a complaint to which section 32 of the Gas Act 1986 or section 46 of the Electricity Act 1989 applies.

(3) The Authority may refuse to supply under section 24 of the Act any information which relates to the obtaining of information from confidential sources by the Authority for the purposes of its functions—

(a) under sections 28 or 30A of the Gas Act 1986;

(b) under sections 25 or 27A of the Electricity Act 1989; or

(c) in relation to any criminal proceedings which the Authority has power to conduct.

[1030]

8 Information the cost or other burden of whose provision is excessive

(1) A licence holder may refuse to supply under section 24 of the Act any information where the cost or effort that would be incurred or suffered by the licence holder in supplying that information would be excessive in relation to the likely benefit of the information to the Council.

(2) In determining the likely benefit of the information to the Council for the purposes of paragraph (1) the following shall be taken into account:

(a) the purposes for which the information is required by the Council; and

(b) the extent to which the provision of the information is necessary or expedient for those purposes.

[1031]

9 Information not held by the person to whom a direction is given

(1) A person may refuse to comply with a direction given to him under section 24 or section 26 of the Act if he does not hold the information specified or described in the direction.

(2) For the purposes of these Regulations, a person holds information if—

(a) he holds it, otherwise than on behalf of another person, or

(b) another person holds it on his behalf.

[1032]

10 Statistics on levels of performance or complaints

Nothing in these Regulations entitles a licence holder to refuse to supply information to the Council under section 24 of the Act, being information whose supply the Council has directed in accordance with the Council's duties under section 33DA of the Gas Act 1986 and section 42AA of the Electricity Act 1989.

[1033]

REGULATION OF INVESTIGATORY POWERS (BRITISH BROADCASTING CORPORATION) ORDER 2001

(SI 2001/1057)

NOTES

Made: 15 March 2001.
Authority: Regulation of Investigatory Powers Act 2000, s 47(1).
Commencement: 16 March 2001.

1 Citation, commencement and interpretation

(1) This Order may be cited as the Regulation of Investigatory Powers (British Broadcasting Corporation) Order 2001.

(2) This Order shall come into force on the day after the day on which it is made.

(3) In this Order "the 2000 Act" means the Regulation of Investigatory Powers Act 2000.

[1034]

2 Application of Part II of the 2000 Act to the detection of television receivers

(1) Part II of the 2000 Act (surveillance and covert human intelligence sources) shall apply to surveillance which—

(a) is carried out by means of apparatus designed or adapted for the purpose of detecting the installation or use in any residential or other premises of a television receiver (within the meaning of section 1 of the Wireless Telegraphy Act 1949), and

(b) is carried out from outside those premises exclusively for that purpose,

and such surveillance is referred to in this Order as "the detection of television receivers".

(2) In its application to the detection of television receivers, Part II of the 2000 Act shall have effect as if—

(a) the following provisions were omitted, namely, sections 28 to 42, in section 43, subsections (2), (6) to (8) and (10) and in subsection (4) the words "Subject to subsection (6)", section 44, section 45(2) to (7) and section 46, and

(b) the modifications set out in articles 3 to 5 were made.

[1035]

3 New section 27A

In its application to the detection of television receivers, Part II of the 2000 Act shall have effect as if the following section were inserted after section 27—

"27A Authorisation of detection of television receivers

(1) Subject to the following provisions of this Part, the persons designated for the purposes of this section shall each have power to grant authorisations for the detection of television receivers, that is to say, surveillance which—

(a) is carried out by means of apparatus designed or adapted for the purpose of detecting the installation or use in any residential or other premises of a television receiver (within the meaning of section 1 of the Wireless Telegraphy Act 1949), and

(b) is carried out from outside those premises exclusively for that purpose.

(2) The persons designated for the purposes of this section are—

(a) any person holding the position of head of sales or head of marketing within the Television Licence Management Unit of the British Broadcasting Corporation, and

(b) any person holding a position within that Unit which is more senior than the positions mentioned in paragraph (a).

(3) A person shall not grant an authorisation for the detection of television receivers unless he believes—

(a) that the authorisation is necessary—

(i) for the purpose of preventing or detecting crime constituting an offence under section 1 or 1A of the Wireless Telegraphy Act 1949; or

(ii) for the purpose of assessing or collecting sums payable to the British Broadcasting Corporation under regulations made under section 2 of the Wireless Telegraphy Act 1949; and

(b) that the authorised surveillance is proportionate to what is sought to be achieved by carrying it out.

(4) The conduct that is authorised by an authorisation for the detection of television receivers is any conduct that—

(a) consists in the carrying out of the detection of television receivers, and

(b) is carried out by the persons described in the authorisation in the circumstances described in the authorisation.".

[1036]

4 Modifications of section 43

In its application to the detection of television receivers, section 43 of the 2000 Act (general rules about grant, renewal and duration) shall have effect as if—

(a) in subsection (1), for paragraphs (a) and (b) there were substituted "must be in writing";

(b) for subsection (3) there were substituted—

PART II DATA PROTECTION

"(3) Subject to subsection (4), an authorisation under this Part shall cease to have effect—

(a) in the case of an authorisation which has not been renewed and in which is specified a period of less than eight weeks beginning with the day on which the grant of the authorisation takes effect, at the end of that period;

(b) in the case of an authorisation which has not been renewed and to which paragraph (a) does not apply, at the end of the period of eight weeks beginning with the day on which the grant of the authorisation takes effect;

(c) in the case of an authorisation which has been renewed, and in which is specified a period of less than eight weeks beginning with the day on which the grant of the authorisation takes effect, at the end of a period of the same length beginning with the day on which the latest renewal takes effect;

(d) in the case of an authorisation which has been renewed, and to which paragraph (c) does not apply, at the end of the period of eight weeks beginning with the day on which the latest renewal takes effect.";

(c) for subsection (5) there were substituted—

"(5) Section 27A shall have effect in relation to the renewal of an authorisation under this Part as if references to the grant of an authorisation included references to its renewal."; and

(d) in subsection (9) for paragraphs (a) to (c) there were substituted—

"(a) in the case of the grant of an authorisation, to the time at which or, as the case may be, day on which the authorisation is granted;

(b) in the case of the renewal of an authorisation, to the time at which or, as the case may be, day on which the authorisation would have ceased to have effect but for the renewal.".

[1037]

5 Modification of section 45(1)

In its application to the detection of television receivers, section 45 of the 2000 Act (cancellation of authorisations) shall have effect as if—

(a) in subsection (1) for the words from "if" to the end there were substituted "if he is satisfied that the authorisation is one in relation to which the requirements of section 27A(3)(a) and (b) are no longer satisfied"; and

(b) after subsection (1) there were inserted—

"(1A) Where any duty imposed by subsection (1) would otherwise fall on a person who is no longer available to perform it, that duty is to be performed by—

(a) the person, if any, appointed for the purpose of this subsection in accordance with subsection (1B);

(b) where no such person has been appointed, the person (if any) holding a position within the British Broadcasting Corporation who has taken over the responsibilities of the person who is no longer available, or most of them.

(1B) The person making an appointment for the purpose of subsection (1A), and the person appointed, must each be—

(a) a person designated for the purposes of section 27A, or

(b) a person holding a more senior position within the British Broadcasting Corporation than was held by the person who is no longer available.".

[1038]

REGULATION OF INVESTIGATORY POWERS (DESIGNATION OF PUBLIC AUTHORITIES FOR THE PURPOSES OF INTRUSIVE SURVEILLANCE) ORDER 2001

(SI 2001/1126)

NOTES

Made: 21 March 2001.
Authority: Regulation of Investigatory Powers Act 2000, s 41(3), (4).
Commencement: 22 March 2001.

1 Citation and commencement

This Order may be cited as the Regulation of Investigatory Powers (Designation of Public Authorities for the Purposes of Intrusive Surveillance) Order 2001 and shall come into force on the day after the day on which it is made.

[1039]

2 Designated public authority

The Home Office is hereby designated for the purposes of section 41 of the Regulation of Investigatory Powers Act 2000, as a public authority whose activities may require the carrying out of intrusive surveillance.

[1040]

3 Prescribed offices, ranks and positions

(1) In relation to the Home Office, an application for an authorisation for the carrying out of intrusive surveillance may be made by an individual holding an office, rank or position with the Home Office only where his office, rank or position is prescribed by paragraph (2).

(2) The offices, ranks and positions prescribed by this paragraph are all offices, ranks and positions in Her Majesty's Prison Service.

[1041]

REGULATION OF INVESTIGATORY POWERS (TECHNICAL ADVISORY BOARD) ORDER 2001

(SI 2001/3734)

NOTES

Made: 21 November 2001.
Authority: Regulation of Investigatory Powers Act 2000, s 13(1), (2).
Commencement: 22 November 2001.

1 Citation, commencement and interpretation

(1) This Order may be cited as the Regulation of Investigatory Powers (Technical Advisory Board) Order 2001 and shall come into force on the day after the day on which it is made.

(2) In this Order, "the 2000 Act" means the Regulation of Investigatory Powers Act 2000.

[1042]

2 Membership of the Board

(1) The Technical Advisory Board established by section 13(1) of the 2000 Act shall consist of 13 persons.

(2) Of that number one person, who does not fall within paragraph (3), shall be appointed chairman.

(3) Of the remaining number—

- (a) six shall be persons holding an office, rank or position with either—
  - (i) a person on whom obligations may be imposed under section 12 of the 2000 Act, or
  - (ii) a body representing the interests of such persons, and
- (b) six shall be persons holding an office, rank or position with either—
  - (i) a person by or on whose behalf applications for interception warrants may be made, or
  - (ii) a body representing the interests of such persons.

[1043]

REGULATION OF INVESTIGATORY POWERS (MAINTENANCE OF INTERCEPTION CAPABILITY) ORDER 2002

(SI 2002/1931)

NOTES

Made: 22 July 2002.
Authority: Regulation of Investigatory Powers Act 2000, ss 12(1), (2), (5), 78(5).
Commencement: 1 August 2002.

ARRANGEMENT OF ARTICLES

1 Citation, commencement and interpretation

(1) This Order may be cited as the Regulation of Investigatory Powers (Maintenance of Interception Capability) Order 2002 and shall come into force on 1st August 2002.

(2) In this Order "service provider" means a person providing a public postal service or a public telecommunications service, or proposing to do so.

[1044]

NOTES

Commencement: 1 August 2002.

2 Interception capability

(1) The Schedule to this Order sets out those obligations which appear to the Secretary of State reasonable to impose on service providers for the purpose of securing that it is and remains practicable for requirements to provide assistance in relation to interception warrants to be imposed and complied with.

(2) Subject to paragraph (3) the obligations in—

(a) Part I of the Schedule only apply to service providers who provide, or propose to provide, a public postal service; and
(b) Part II of the Schedule only apply to service providers who provide, or propose to provide, a public telecommunications service.

(3) The obligations in Part II of the Schedule shall not apply to service providers who—

(a) do not intend to provide a public telecommunications service to more than 10,000 persons in any one or more parts of the United Kingdom and do not do so; or
(b) only provide, or propose to provide, a public telecommunications service in relation to the provision of banking, insurance, investment or other financial services.

[1045]

NOTES

Commencement: 1 August 2002.

3 Interception capability notices

(1) The Secretary of State may give a service provider a notice requiring him to take all such steps falling within paragraph (2) as may be specified or described in the notice.

(2) Those steps are ones appearing to the Secretary of State to be necessary for securing that the service provider has the practical capability of meeting the obligations set out in the Schedule to this Order.

[1046]

NOTES

Commencement: 1 August 2002.

4 Referral of notices to the Technical Advisory Board

The period within which any person to whom a notice has been given under article 3 may refer the notice to the Technical Advisory Board is specified as being before the end of 28 days from the date of the notice.

[1047]

NOTES

Commencement: 1 August 2002.

SCHEDULE
OBLIGATIONS ON SERVICE PROVIDERS

Article 2

PART I
INTERCEPTION CAPABILITY FOR PUBLIC POSTAL SERVICES

1. To ensure the interception and temporary retention of postal items destined for addresses in the United Kingdom for provision to the person on whose application the interception warrant was issued.

2. To provide for the interception and retention of postal items sent by identified persons where the carrier keeps records of who sent which item in the course of their normal business.

3. To maintain a system of opening, copying and resealing of any postal item carried for less than £1.

4. To comply with the obligations set out in paragraphs 1 to 3 above in such a manner that the chance of the interception subject or other unauthorised persons becoming aware of any interception is minimised.

[1048]

NOTES

Commencement: 1 August 2002.

PART II
INTERCEPTION CAPABILITY FOR PUBLIC TELECOMMUNICATION SERVICES

5. To provide a mechanism for implementing interceptions within one working day of the service provider being informed that the interception has been appropriately authorised.

6. To ensure the interception, in their entirety, of all communications and related communications data authorised by the interception warrant and to ensure their simultaneous (ie in near real time) transmission to a hand-over point within the service provider's network as agreed with the person on whose application the interception warrant was issued.

7. To ensure that the intercepted communication and the related communications data will be transmitted so that they can be unambiguously correlated.

8. To ensure that the hand-over interface complies with any requirements communicated by the Secretary of State to the service provider, which, where practicable and appropriate, will be in line with agreed industry standards (such as those of the European Telecommunications Standards Institute).

9. To ensure filtering to provide only the traffic data associated with the warranted telecommunications identifier, where reasonable.

10. To ensure that the person on whose application the interception warrant was issued is able to remove any electronic protection applied by the service provider to the intercepted communication and the related communications data.

11. To enable the simultaneous interception of the communications of up to 1 in 10,000 of the persons to whom the service provider provides the public telecommunications service, provided that those persons number more than 10,000.

12. To ensure that the reliability of the interception capability is at least equal to the reliability of the public telecommunications service carrying the communication which is being intercepted.

13. To ensure that the intercept capability may be audited so that it is possible to confirm that the intercepted communications and related communications data are from, or intended for the interception subject, or originate from or are intended for transmission to, the premises named in the interception warrant.

14. To comply with the obligations set out in paragraphs 5 to 13 above in such a manner that the chance of the interception subject or other unauthorised persons becoming aware of any interception is minimised.

[1049]

NOTES

Commencement: 1 August 2002.

DATA PROTECTION (PROCESSING OF SENSITIVE PERSONAL DATA) (ELECTED REPRESENTATIVES) ORDER 2002

(SI 2002/2905)

NOTES

Made: 19 November 2002.
Authority: Data Protection Act 1998, s 67(2), Sch 3, para 10.
Commencement: 17 December 2002.

1 This Order may be cited as the Data Protection (Processing of Sensitive Personal Data) (Elected Representatives) Order 2002 and shall come into force on the twenty-eighth day after the day on which it is made.

[1050]

NOTES

Commencement: 17 December 2002.

2 For the purposes of paragraph 10 of Schedule 3 to the Data Protection Act 1998, the circumstances specified in any of paragraphs 3, 4, 5 or 6 in the Schedule to this Order are circumstances in which sensitive personal data may be processed.

[1051]

NOTES

Commencement: 17 December 2002.

SCHEDULE
CIRCUMSTANCES IN WHICH SENSITIVE PERSONAL DATA MAY BE PROCESSED

Article 2

Interpretation

1. In this Schedule, "elected representative" means—

(a) a Member of the House of Commons, a Member of the National Assembly for Wales, a Member of the Scottish Parliament or a Member of the Northern Ireland Assembly;
(b) a Member of the European Parliament elected in the United Kingdom;
(c) an elected member of a local authority within the meaning of section 270(1) of the Local Government Act 1972, namely—
  (i) in England, a county council, a district council, a London borough council or a parish council,
  (ii) in Wales, a county council, a county borough council or a community council;
(d) an elected mayor of a local authority within the meaning of Part II of the Local Government Act 2000;
(e) the Mayor of London or an elected member of the London Assembly;
(f) an elected member of—
  (i) the Common Council of the City of London, or
  (ii) the Council of the Isles of Scilly;
(g) an elected member of a council constituted under section 2 of the Local Government etc (Scotland) Act 1994; or
(h) an elected member of a district council within the meaning of the Local Government Act (Northern Ireland) 1972.

2. For the purposes of paragraph 1 above—
(a) a person who is—
  (i) a Member of the House of Commons immediately before Parliament is dissolved,
  (ii) a Member of the Scottish Parliament immediately before that Parliament is dissolved, or
  (iii) a Member of the Northern Ireland Assembly immediately before that Assembly is dissolved,

shall be treated as if he were such a member until the end of the fourth day after the day on which the subsequent general election in relation to that Parliament or Assembly is held;
(b) a person who is a Member of the National Assembly for Wales and whose term of office comes to an end, in accordance with section 2(5)(b) of the Government of Wales Act 1998, at the end of the day preceding an ordinary election (within the meaning of section 2(4) of that Act), shall be treated as if he were such a member until the end of the fourth day after the day on which that ordinary election is held; and
(c) a person who is an elected member of the Common Council of the City of London and whose term of office comes to an end at the end of the day preceding the annual Wardmotes shall be treated as if he were such a member until the end of the fourth day after the day on which those Wardmotes are held.

Processing by elected representatives

3. The processing—
(a) is carried out by an elected representative or a person acting with his authority;
(b) is in connection with the discharge of his functions as such a representative;
(c) is carried out pursuant to a request made by the data subject to the elected representative to take action on behalf of the data subject or any other individual; and
(d) is necessary for the purposes of, or in connection with, the action reasonably taken by the elected representative pursuant to that request.

4. The processing—
(a) is carried out by an elected representative or a person acting with his authority;
(b) is in connection with the discharge of his functions as such a representative;
(c) is carried out pursuant to a request made by an individual other than the data subject to the elected representative to take action on behalf of the data subject or any other individual;
(d) is necessary for the purposes of, or in connection with, the action reasonably taken by the elected representative pursuant to that request; and
(e) is carried out without the explicit consent of the data subject because the processing—
  (i) is necessary in a case where explicit consent cannot be given by the data subject,
  (ii) is necessary in a case where the elected representative cannot reasonably be expected to obtain the explicit consent of the data subject,

PART II DATA PROTECTION

(iii) must necessarily be carried out without the explicit consent of the data subject being sought so as not to prejudice the action taken by the elected representative, or

(iv) is necessary in the interests of another individual in a case where the explicit consent of the data subject has been unreasonably withheld.

Processing limited to disclosures to elected representatives

5. The disclosure—

(a) is made to an elected representative or a person acting with his authority;

(b) is made in response to a communication to the data controller from the elected representative, or a person acting with his authority, acting pursuant to a request made by the data subject;

(c) is of sensitive personal data which are relevant to the subject matter of that communication; and

(d) is necessary for the purpose of responding to that communication.

6. The disclosure—

(a) is made to an elected representative or a person acting with his authority;

(b) is made in response to a communication to the data controller from the elected representative, or a person acting with his authority, acting pursuant to a request made by an individual other than the data subject;

(c) is of sensitive personal data which are relevant to the subject matter of that communication;

(d) is necessary for the purpose of responding to that communication; and

(e) is carried out without the explicit consent of the data subject because the disclosure—

(i) is necessary in a case where explicit consent cannot be given by the data subject,

(ii) is necessary in a case where the data controller cannot reasonably be expected to obtain the explicit consent of the data subject,

(iii) must necessarily be carried out without the explicit consent of the data subject being sought so as not to prejudice the action taken by the elected representative, or

(iv) is necessary in the interests of another individual in a case where the explicit consent of the data subject has been unreasonably withheld.

[1052]

NOTES

Commencement: 17 December 2002.

PRIVACY AND ELECTRONIC COMMUNICATIONS (EC DIRECTIVE) REGULATIONS 2003

(SI 2003/2426)

NOTES

Made: 18 September 2003.
Authority: European Communities Act 1972, s 2(2).
Commencement: 11 December 2003.

ARRANGEMENT OF REGULATIONS

1 Citation and commencement

These Regulations may be cited as the Privacy and Electronic Communications (EC Directive) Regulations 2003 and shall come into force on 11th December 2003.

[1053]

NOTES

Commencement: 11 December 2003.

2 Interpretation

(1) In these Regulations—

"bill" includes an invoice, account, statement or other document of similar character and "billing" shall be construed accordingly;

"call" means a connection established by means of a telephone service available to the public allowing two-way communication in real time;

"communication" means any information exchanged or conveyed between a finite number of parties by means of a public electronic communications service, but does not include information conveyed as part of a programme service, except to the extent that such information can be related to the identifiable subscriber or user receiving the information;

"communications provider" has the meaning given by section 405 of the Communications Act 2003;

"corporate subscriber" means a subscriber who is—

(a) a company within the meaning of section 735(1) of the Companies Act 1985;

(b) a company incorporated in pursuance of a royal charter or letters patent;

(c) a partnership in Scotland;

(d) a corporation sole; or

(e) any other body corporate or entity which is a legal person distinct from its members;

"the Directive" means Directive 2002/58/EC of the European Parliament and of the Council of 12 July 2002 concerning the processing of personal data and the protection of privacy in the electronic communications sector (Directive on privacy and electronic communications);

"electronic communications network" has the meaning given by section 32 of the Communications Act 2003;

"electronic communications service" has the meaning given by section 32 of the Communications Act 2003;

"electronic mail" means any text, voice, sound or image message sent over a public electronic communications network which can be stored in the network or in the recipient's terminal equipment until it is collected by the recipient and includes messages sent using a short message service;

"enactment" includes an enactment comprised in, or in an instrument made under, an Act of the Scottish Parliament;

"individual" means a living individual and includes an unincorporated body of such individuals;

"the Information Commissioner" and "the Commissioner" both mean the Commissioner appointed under section 6 of the Data Protection Act 1998;

"information society service" has the meaning given in regulation 2(1) of the Electronic Commerce (EC Directive) Regulations 2002;

"location data" means any data processed in an electronic communications network indicating the geographical position of the terminal equipment of a user of a public electronic communications service, including data relating to—

(f) the latitude, longitude or altitude of the terminal equipment;

(g) the direction of travel of the user; or

(h) the time the location information was recorded;

"OFCOM" means the Office of Communications as established by section 1 of the Office of Communications Act 2002;

"programme service" has the meaning given in section 201 of the Broadcasting Act 1990;

"public communications provider" means a provider of a public electronic communications network or a public electronic communications service;

"public electronic communications network" has the meaning given in section 151 of the Communications Act 2003;

"public electronic communications service" has the meaning given in section 151 of the Communications Act 2003;

"subscriber" means a person who is a party to a contract with a provider of public electronic communications services for the supply of such services;

"traffic data" means any data processed for the purpose of the conveyance of a communication on an electronic communications network or for the billing in respect of that communication and includes data relating to the routing, duration or time of a communication;

"user" means any individual using a public electronic communications service; and

"value added service" means any service which requires the processing of traffic data or location data beyond that which is necessary for the transmission of a communication or the billing in respect of that communication.

(2) Expressions used in these Regulations that are not defined in paragraph (1) and are defined in the Data Protection Act 1998 shall have the same meaning as in that Act.

(3) Expressions used in these Regulations that are not defined in paragraph (1) or the Data Protection Act 1998 and are defined in the Directive shall have the same meaning as in the Directive.

(4) Any reference in these Regulations to a line shall, without prejudice to paragraph (3), be construed as including a reference to anything that performs the function of a line, and "connected", in relation to a line, is to be construed accordingly.

[1054]

NOTES

Commencement: 11 December 2003.

3 (*Revokes the Telecommunications* (*Data Protection and Privacy*) *Regulations 1999, SI 1999/2093 and the Telecommunications* (*Data Protection and Privacy*) (*Amendment*) *Regulations 2000, SI 2000/157.*)

4 Relationship between these Regulations and the Data Protection Act 1998

Nothing in these Regulations shall relieve a person of his obligations under the Data Protection Act 1998 in relation to the processing of personal data.

[1055]

NOTES

Commencement: 11 December 2003.

5 Security of public electronic communications services

(1) Subject to paragraph (2), a provider of a public electronic communications service ("the service provider") shall take appropriate technical and organisational measures to safeguard the security of that service.

(2) If necessary, the measures required by paragraph (1) may be taken by the service provider in conjunction with the provider of the electronic communications network by means of which the service is provided, and that network provider shall comply with any reasonable requests made by the service provider for these purposes.

(3) Where, notwithstanding the taking of measures as required by paragraph (1), there remains a significant risk to the security of the public electronic communications service, the service provider shall inform the subscribers concerned of—

(a) the nature of that risk;

(b) any appropriate measures that the subscriber may take to safeguard against that risk; and

(c) the likely costs to the subscriber involved in the taking of such measures.

(4) For the purposes of paragraph (1), a measure shall only be taken to be appropriate if, having regard to—

(a) the state of technological developments, and

(b) the cost of implementing it,

it is proportionate to the risks against which it would safeguard.

(5) Information provided for the purposes of paragraph (3) shall be provided to the subscriber free of any charge other than the cost to the subscriber of receiving or collecting the information.

[1056]

NOTES

Commencement: 11 December 2003.

6 Confidentiality of communications

(1) Subject to paragraph (4), a person shall not use an electronic communications network to store information, or to gain access to information stored, in the terminal equipment of a subscriber or user unless the requirements of paragraph (2) are met.

(2) The requirements are that the subscriber or user of that terminal equipment—

(a) is provided with clear and comprehensive information about the purposes of the storage of, or access to, that information; and

(b) is given the opportunity to refuse the storage of or access to that information.

(3) Where an electronic communications network is used by the same person to store or access information in the terminal equipment of a subscriber or user on more than one occasion, it is sufficient for the purposes of this regulation that the requirements of paragraph (2) are met in respect of the initial use.

(4) Paragraph (1) shall not apply to the technical storage of, or access to, information—

(a) for the sole purpose of carrying out or facilitating the transmission of a communication over an electronic communications network; or

(b) where such storage or access is strictly necessary for the provision of an information society service requested by the subscriber or user.

[1057]

NOTES

Commencement: 11 December 2003.

7 Restrictions on the processing of certain traffic data

(1) Subject to paragraphs (2) and (3), traffic data relating to subscribers or users which are processed and stored by a public communications provider shall, when no longer required for the purpose of the transmission of a communication, be—

(a) erased;

(b) in the case of an individual, modified so that they cease to constitute personal data of that subscriber or user; or

(c) in the case of a corporate subscriber, modified so that they cease to be data that would be personal data if that subscriber was an individual.

(2) Traffic data held by a public communications provider for purposes connected with the payment of charges by a subscriber or in respect of interconnection payments may be processed and stored by that provider until the time specified in paragraph (5).

(3) Traffic data relating to a subscriber or user may be processed and stored by a provider of a public electronic communications service if—

(a) such processing and storage are for the purpose of marketing electronic communications services, or for the provision of value added services to that subscriber or user; and

(b) the subscriber or user to whom the traffic data relate has given his consent to such processing or storage; and

(c) such processing and storage are undertaken only for the duration necessary for the purposes specified in subparagraph (a).

(4) Where a user or subscriber has given his consent in accordance with paragraph (3), he shall be able to withdraw it at any time.

(5) The time referred to in paragraph (2) is the end of the period during which legal proceedings may be brought in respect of payments due or alleged to be due or, where such proceedings are brought within that period, the time when those proceedings are finally determined.

(6) Legal proceedings shall not be taken to be finally determined—

(a) until the conclusion of the ordinary period during which an appeal may be brought by either party (excluding any possibility of an extension of that period, whether by order of a court or otherwise), if no appeal is brought within that period; or

(b) if an appeal is brought, until the conclusion of that appeal.

(7) References in paragraph (6) to an appeal include references to an application for permission to appeal.

[1058]

NOTES

Commencement: 11 December 2003.

8 Further provisions relating to the processing of traffic data under regulation 7

(1) Processing of traffic data in accordance with regulation 7(2) or (3) shall not be undertaken by a public communications provider unless the subscriber or user to whom the data relate has been provided with information regarding the types of traffic data which are to be processed and the duration of such processing and, in the case of processing in accordance with regulation 7(3), he has been provided with that information before his consent has been obtained.

(2) Processing of traffic data in accordance with regulation 7 shall be restricted to what is required for the purposes of one or more of the activities listed in paragraph (3) and shall be carried out only by the public communications provider or by a person acting under his authority.

(3) The activities referred to in paragraph (2) are activities relating to—

(a) the management of billing or traffic;

(b) customer enquiries;

(c) the prevention or detection of fraud;

(d) the marketing of electronic communications services; or

(e) the provision of a value added service.

(4) Nothing in these Regulations shall prevent the furnishing of traffic data to a person who is a competent authority for the purposes of any provision relating to the settling of disputes (by way of legal proceedings or otherwise) which is contained in, or made by virtue of, any enactment.

[1059]

NOTES

Commencement: 11 December 2003.

9 Itemised billing and privacy

(1) At the request of a subscriber, a provider of a public electronic communications service shall provide that subscriber with bills that are not itemised.

(2) OFCOM shall have a duty, when exercising their functions under Chapter 1 of Part 2 of the Communications Act 2003, to have regard to the need to reconcile the rights of subscribers receiving itemised bills with the rights to privacy of calling users and called subscribers, including the need for sufficient alternative privacy-enhancing methods of communications or payments to be available to such users and subscribers.

[1060]

NOTES

Commencement: 11 December 2003.

10 Prevention of calling line identification—outgoing calls

(1) This regulation applies, subject to regulations 15 and 16, to outgoing calls where a facility enabling the presentation of calling line identification is available.

(2) The provider of a public electronic communications service shall provide users originating a call by means of that service with a simple means to prevent presentation of the identity of the calling line on the connected line as respects that call.

(3) The provider of a public electronic communications service shall provide subscribers to the service, as respects their line and all calls originating from that line, with a simple means of preventing presentation of the identity of that subscriber's line on any connected line.

(4) The measures to be provided under paragraphs (2) and (3) shall be provided free of charge.

[1061]

NOTES

Commencement: 11 December 2003.

11 Prevention of calling or connected line identification—incoming calls

(1) This regulation applies to incoming calls.

(2) Where a facility enabling the presentation of calling line identification is available, the provider of a public electronic communications service shall provide the called subscriber with a simple means to prevent, free of charge for reasonable use of the facility, presentation of the identity of the calling line on the connected line.

(3) Where a facility enabling the presentation of calling line identification prior to the call being established is available, the provider of a public electronic communications service shall provide the called subscriber with a simple means of rejecting incoming calls where the presentation of the calling line identification has been prevented by the calling user or subscriber.

(4) Where a facility enabling the presentation of connected line identification is available, the provider of a public electronic communications service shall provide the called subscriber with a simple means to prevent, without charge, presentation of the identity of the connected line on any calling line.

(5) In this regulation "called subscriber" means the subscriber receiving a call by means of the service in question whose line is the called line (whether or not it is also the connected line).

[1062]

NOTES

Commencement: 11 December 2003.

12 Publication of information for the purposes of regulations 10 and 11

Where a provider of a public electronic communications service provides facilities for calling or connected line identification, he shall provide information to the public regarding the availability of such facilities, including information regarding the options to be made available for the purposes of regulations 10 and 11.

[1063]

NOTES

Commencement: 11 December 2003.

13 Co-operation of communications providers for the purposes of regulations 10 and 11

For the purposes of regulations 10 and 11, a communications provider shall comply with any reasonable requests made by the provider of the public electronic communications service by means of which facilities for calling or connected line identification are provided.

[1064]

NOTES

Commencement: 11 December 2003.

14 Restrictions on the processing of location data

(1) This regulation shall not apply to the processing of traffic data.

(2) Location data relating to a user or subscriber of a public electronic communications network or a public electronic communications service may only be processed—

(a) where that user or subscriber cannot be identified from such data; or

(b) where necessary for the provision of a value added service, with the consent of that user or subscriber.

(3) Prior to obtaining the consent of the user or subscriber under paragraph (2)(b), the public communications provider in question must provide the following information to the user or subscriber to whom the data relate—

(a) the types of location data that will be processed;

(b) the purposes and duration of the processing of those data; and

(c) whether the data will be transmitted to a third party for the purpose of providing the value added service.

(4) A user or subscriber who has given his consent to the processing of data under paragraph (2)(b) shall—

(a) be able to withdraw such consent at any time, and

(b) in respect of each connection to the public electronic communications network in question or each transmission of a communication, be given the opportunity to withdraw such consent, using a simple means and free of charge.

(5) Processing of location data in accordance with this regulation shall—

(a) only be carried out by—

(i) the public communications provider in question;

(ii) the third party providing the value added service in question; or

(iii) a person acting under the authority of a person falling within (i) or (ii); and

(b) where the processing is carried out for the purposes of the provision of a value added service, be restricted to what is necessary for those purposes.

[1065]

NOTES

Commencement: 11 December 2003.

15 Tracing of malicious or nuisance calls

(1) A communications provider may override anything done to prevent the presentation of the identity of a calling line where—

(a) a subscriber has requested the tracing of malicious or nuisance calls received on his line; and

(b) the provider is satisfied that such action is necessary and expedient for the purposes of tracing such calls.

(2) Any term of a contract for the provision of public electronic communications services which relates to such prevention shall have effect subject to the provisions of paragraph (1).

(3) Nothing in these Regulations shall prevent a communications provider, for the purposes of any action relating to the tracing of malicious or nuisance calls, from storing and making available to a person with a legitimate interest data containing the identity of a calling subscriber which were obtained while paragraph (1) applied.

[1066]

NOTES

Commencement: 11 December 2003.

16 Emergency calls

(1) For the purposes of this regulation, "emergency calls" means calls to either the national emergency call number 999 or the single European emergency call number 112.

(2) In order to facilitate responses to emergency calls—

(a) all such calls shall be excluded from the requirements of regulation 10;

(b) no person shall be entitled to prevent the presentation on the connected line of the identity of the calling line; and

(c) the restriction on the processing of location data under regulation 14(2) shall be disregarded.

[1067]

NOTES

Commencement: 11 December 2003.

17 Termination of automatic call forwarding

(1) Where—

(a) calls originally directed to another line are being automatically forwarded to a subscriber's line as a result of action taken by a third party, and

(b) the subscriber requests his provider of electronic communications services ("the subscriber's provider") to stop the forwarding of those calls,

the subscriber's provider shall ensure, free of charge, that the forwarding is stopped without any avoidable delay.

(2) For the purposes of paragraph (1), every other communications provider shall comply with any reasonable requests made by the subscriber's provider to assist in the prevention of that forwarding.

[1068]

NOTES

Commencement: 11 December 2003.

18 Directories of subscribers

(1) This regulation applies in relation to a directory of subscribers, whether in printed or electronic form, which is made available to members of the public or a section of the public, including by means of a directory enquiry service.

(2) The personal data of an individual subscriber shall not be included in a directory unless that subscriber has, free of charge, been—

(a) informed by the collector of the personal data of the purposes of the directory in which his personal data are to be included, and

(b) given the opportunity to determine whether such of his personal data as are considered relevant by the producer of the directory should be included in the directory.

(3) Where personal data of an individual subscriber are to be included in a directory with facilities which enable users of that directory to obtain access to that data solely on the basis of a telephone number—

(a) the information to be provided under paragraph (2)(a) shall include information about those facilities; and

(b) for the purposes of paragraph (2)(b), the express consent of the subscriber to the inclusion of his data in a directory with such facilities must be obtained.

(4) Data relating to a corporate subscriber shall not be included in a directory where that subscriber has advised the producer of the directory that it does not want its data to be included in that directory.

(5) Where the data of an individual subscriber have been included in a directory, that subscriber shall, without charge, be able to verify, correct or withdraw those data at any time.

(6) Where a request has been made under paragraph (5) for data to be withdrawn from or corrected in a directory, that request shall be treated as having no application in relation to an edition of a directory that was produced before the producer of the directory received the request.

(7) For the purposes of paragraph (6), an edition of a directory which is revised after it was first produced shall be treated as a new edition.

(8) In this regulation, "telephone number" has the same meaning as in section 56(5) of the Communications Act 2003 but does not include any number which is used as an internet domain name, an internet address or an address or identifier incorporating either an internet domain name or an internet address, including an electronic mail address.

[1069]

NOTES

Commencement: 11 December 2003.

19 Use of automated calling systems

(1) A person shall neither transmit, nor instigate the transmission of, communications comprising recorded matter for direct marketing purposes by means of an automated calling system except in the circumstances referred to in paragraph (2).

(2) Those circumstances are where the called line is that of a subscriber who has previously notified the caller that for the time being he consents to such communications being sent by, or at the instigation of, the caller on that line.

(3) A subscriber shall not permit his line to be used in contravention of paragraph (1).

(4) For the purposes of this regulation, an automated calling system is a system which is capable of—

(a) automatically initiating a sequence of calls to more than one destination in accordance with instructions stored in that system; and

(b) transmitting sounds which are not live speech for reception by persons at some or all of the destinations so called.

[1070]

NOTES

Commencement: 11 December 2003.

20 Use of facsimile machines for direct marketing purposes

(1) A person shall neither transmit, nor instigate the transmission of, unsolicited communications for direct marketing purposes by means of a facsimile machine where the called line is that of—

(a) an individual subscriber, except in the circumstances referred to in paragraph (2);

(b) a corporate subscriber who has previously notified the caller that such communications should not be sent on that line; or

(c) a subscriber and the number allocated to that line is listed in the register kept under regulation 25.

(2) The circumstances referred to in paragraph (1)(a) are that the individual subscriber has previously notified the caller that he consents for the time being to such communications being sent by, or at the instigation of, the caller.

(3) A subscriber shall not permit his line to be used in contravention of paragraph (1).

(4) A person shall not be held to have contravened paragraph (1)(c) where the number allocated to the called line has been listed on the register for less than 28 days preceding that on which the communication is made.

(5) Where a subscriber who has caused a number allocated to a line of his to be listed in the register kept under regulation 25 has notified a caller that he does not, for the time being, object to such communications being sent on that line by that caller, such communications may be sent by that caller on that line, notwithstanding that the number allocated to that line is listed in the said register.

(6) Where a subscriber has given a caller notification pursuant to paragraph (5) in relation to a line of his—

(a) the subscriber shall be free to withdraw that notification at any time, and

(b) where such notification is withdrawn, the caller shall not send such communications on that line.

(7) The provisions of this regulation are without prejudice to the provisions of regulation 19.

[1071]

NOTES

Commencement: 11 December 2003.

21 Unsolicited calls for direct marketing purposes

(1) A person shall neither use, nor instigate the use of, a public electronic communications service for the purposes of making unsolicited calls for direct marketing purposes where—

(a) the called line is that of a subscriber who has previously notified the caller that such calls should not for the time being be made on that line; or

(b) the number allocated to a subscriber in respect of the called line is one listed in the register kept under regulation 26.

(2) A subscriber shall not permit his line to be used in contravention of paragraph (1).

(3) A person shall not be held to have contravened paragraph (1)(b) where the number allocated to the called line has been listed on the register for less than 28 days preceding that on which the call is made.

(4) Where a subscriber who has caused a number allocated to a line of his to be listed in the register kept under regulation 26 has notified a caller that he does not, for the time being, object to such calls being made on that line by that caller, such calls may be made by that caller on that line, notwithstanding that the number allocated to that line is listed in the said register.

(5) Where a subscriber has given a caller notification pursuant to paragraph (4) in relation to a line of his—

(a) the subscriber shall be free to withdraw that notification at any time, and

(b) where such notification is withdrawn, the caller shall not make such calls on that line.

[1072]

NOTES

Commencement: 11 December 2003.

22 Use of electronic mail for direct marketing purposes

(1) This regulation applies to the transmission of unsolicited communications by means of electronic mail to individual subscribers.

(2) Except in the circumstances referred to in paragraph (3), a person shall neither transmit, nor instigate the transmission of, unsolicited communications for the purposes of direct marketing by means of electronic mail unless the recipient of the electronic mail has previously notified the sender that he consents for the time being to such communications being sent by, or at the instigation of, the sender.

(3) A person may send or instigate the sending of electronic mail for the purposes of direct marketing where—

(a) that person has obtained the contact details of the recipient of that electronic mail in the course of the sale or negotiations for the sale of a product or service to that recipient;

(b) the direct marketing is in respect of that person's similar products and services only; and

(c) the recipient has been given a simple means of refusing (free of charge except for the costs of the transmission of the refusal) the use of his contact details for the purposes of such direct marketing, at the time that the details were initially collected, and, where he did not initially refuse the use of the details, at the time of each subsequent communication.

(4) A subscriber shall not permit his line to be used in contravention of paragraph (2).

[1073]

NOTES

Commencement: 11 December 2003.

23 Use of electronic mail for direct marketing purposes where the identity or address of the sender is concealed

A person shall neither transmit, nor instigate the transmission of, a communication for the purposes of direct marketing by means of electronic mail—

(a) where the identity of the person on whose behalf the communication has been sent has been disguised or concealed; or

(b) where a valid address to which the recipient of the communication may send a request that such communications cease has not been provided.

[1074]

NOTES

Commencement: 11 December 2003.

24 Information to be provided for the purposes of regulations 19, 20 and 21

(1) Where a public electronic communications service is used for the transmission of a communication for direct marketing purposes the person using, or instigating the use of, the service shall ensure that the following information is provided with that communication—

(a) in relation to a communication to which regulations 19 (automated calling systems) and 20 (facsimile machines) apply, the particulars mentioned in paragraph (2)(a) and (b);

(b) in relation to a communication to which regulation 21 (telephone calls) applies, the particulars mentioned in paragraph (2)(a) and, if the recipient of the call so requests, those mentioned in paragraph (2)(b).

(2) The particulars referred to in paragraph (1) are—

(a) the name of the person;

(b) either the address of the person or a telephone number on which he can be reached free of charge.

[1075]

NOTES

Commencement: 11 December 2003.

25 Register to be kept for the purposes of regulation 20

(1) For the purposes of regulation 20 OFCOM shall maintain and keep up-to-date, in printed or electronic form, a register of the numbers allocated to subscribers, in respect of particular lines, who have notified them (notwithstanding, in the case of individual subscribers, that they enjoy the benefit of regulation 20(1)(a) and (2)) that they do not for the time being wish to receive unsolicited communications for direct marketing purposes by means of facsimile machine on the lines in question.

(2) OFCOM shall remove a number from the register maintained under paragraph (1) where they have reason to believe that it has ceased to be allocated to the subscriber by whom they were notified pursuant to paragraph (1).

(3) On the request of—

(a) a person wishing to send, or instigate the sending of, such communications as are mentioned in paragraph (1), or

(b) a subscriber wishing to permit the use of his line for the sending of such communications,

for information derived from the register kept under paragraph (1), OFCOM shall, unless it is not reasonably practicable so to do, on the payment to them of such fee as is, subject to paragraph (4), required by them, make the information requested available to that person or that subscriber.

(4) For the purposes of paragraph (3) OFCOM may require different fees—

(a) for making available information derived from the register in different forms or manners, or

(b) for making available information derived from the whole or from different parts of the register,

but the fees required by them shall be ones in relation to which the Secretary of State has notified OFCOM that he is satisfied that they are designed to secure, as nearly as may be and taking one year with another, that the aggregate fees received, or reasonably expected to be received, equal the costs incurred, or reasonably expected to be incurred, by OFCOM in discharging their duties under paragraphs (1), (2) and (3).

(5) The functions of OFCOM under paragraphs (1), (2) and (3), other than the function of determining the fees to be required for the purposes of paragraph (3), may be discharged on their behalf by some other person in pursuance of arrangements made by OFCOM with that other person.

[1076]

NOTES

Commencement: 11 December 2003.

26 Register to be kept for the purposes of regulation 21

(1) For the purposes of regulation 21 OFCOM shall maintain and keep up-to-date, in printed or electronic form, a register of the numbers allocated to … subscribers, in respect of particular lines, who have notified them that they do not for the time being wish to receive unsolicited calls for direct marketing purposes on the lines in question.

[(1A) Notifications to OFCOM made for the purposes of paragraph (1) by corporate subscribers shall be in writing.]

(2) OFCOM shall remove a number from the register maintained under paragraph (1) where they have reason to believe that it has ceased to be allocated to the subscriber by whom they were notified pursuant to paragraph (1).

[(2A) Where a number allocated to a corporate subscriber is listed in the register maintained under paragraph (1), OFCOM shall, within the period of 28 days following each anniversary of the date of that number being first listed in the register, send to the subscriber a written reminder that the number is listed in the register.]

(3) On the request of—

(a) a person wishing to make, or instigate the making of, such calls as are mentioned in paragraph (1), or

(b) a subscriber wishing to permit the use of his line for the making of such calls, for information derived from the register kept under paragraph (1), OFCOM shall, unless it is not reasonably practicable so to do, on the payment to them of such fee as is, subject to paragraph (4), required by them, make the information requested available to that person or that subscriber.

(4) For the purposes of paragraph (3) OFCOM may require different fees—

(a) for making available information derived from the register in different forms or manners, or

(b) for making available information derived from the whole or from different parts of the register,

but the fees required by them shall be ones in relation to which the Secretary of State has notified OFCOM that he is satisfied that they are designed to secure, as nearly as may be and taking one year with another, that the aggregate fees received, or reasonably expected to be received, equal the costs incurred, or reasonably expected to be incurred, by OFCOM in discharging their duties under paragraphs (1), (2) and (3).

(5) The functions of OFCOM under paragraphs (1), (2)[, (2A)] and (3), other than the function of determining the fees to be required for the purposes of paragraph (3), may be discharged on their behalf by some other person in pursuance of arrangements made by OFCOM with that other person.

[1077]

NOTES

Commencement: 11 December 2003.

Sub-s (1): word omitted revoked by the Privacy and Electronic Communications (EC Directive) (Amendment) Regulations 2004, SI 2004/1039, reg 2(1), (2).

Sub-ss (1A), (2A): inserted by SI 2004/1039, reg 2(1), (3), (4).

Sub-s (5): words in square brackets inserted by SI 2004/1039, reg 2(1), (5).

27 Modification of contracts

To the extent that any term in a contract between a subscriber to and the provider of a public electronic communications service or such a provider and the provider of an electronic communications network would be inconsistent with a requirement of these Regulations, that term shall be void.

[1078]

NOTES

Commencement: 11 December 2003.

28 National security

(1) Nothing in these Regulations shall require a communications provider to do, or refrain from doing, anything (including the processing of data) if exemption from the requirement in question is required for the purpose of safeguarding national security.

(2) Subject to paragraph (4), a certificate signed by a Minister of the Crown certifying that exemption from any requirement of these Regulations is or at any time was required for the purpose of safeguarding national security shall be conclusive evidence of that fact.

(3) A certificate under paragraph (2) may identify the circumstances in which it applies by means of a general description and may be expressed to have prospective effect.

(4) Any person directly affected by the issuing of a certificate under paragraph (2) may appeal to the Tribunal against the issuing of the certificate.

(5) If, on an appeal under paragraph (4), the Tribunal finds that, applying the principles applied by a court on an application for judicial review, the Minister did not have reasonable grounds for issuing the certificate, the Tribunal may allow the appeal and quash the certificate.

(6) Where, in any proceedings under or by virtue of these Regulations, it is claimed by a communications provider that a certificate under paragraph (2) which identifies the circumstances in which it applies by means of a general description applies in the circumstances in question, any other party to the proceedings may appeal to the Tribunal on the ground that the certificate does not apply in those circumstances and, subject to any determination under paragraph (7), the certificate shall be conclusively presumed so to apply.

(7) On any appeal under paragraph (6), the Tribunal may determine that the certificate does not so apply.

(8) In this regulation—

(a) "the Tribunal" means the Information Tribunal referred to in section 6 of the Data Protection Act 1998;

(b) subsections (8), (9), (10) and (12) of section 28 of and Schedule 6 to that Act apply for the purposes of this regulation as they apply for the purposes of section 28;

(c) section 58 of that Act shall apply for the purposes of this regulation as if the reference in that section to the functions of the Tribunal under that Act included a reference to the functions of the Tribunal under paragraphs (4) to (7) of this regulation; and

(d) subsections (1), (2) and (5)(f) of section 67 of that Act shall apply in respect of the making of rules relating to the functions of the Tribunal under this regulation.

[1079]

NOTES

Commencement: 11 December 2003.

29 Legal requirements, law enforcement etc

(1) Nothing in these Regulations shall require a communications provider to do, or refrain from doing, anything (including the processing of data)—

(a) if compliance with the requirement in question—

(i) would be inconsistent with any requirement imposed by or under an enactment or by a court order; or

(ii) would be likely to prejudice the prevention or detection of crime or the apprehension or prosecution of offenders; or

(b) if exemption from the requirement in question—

(i) is required for the purposes of, or in connection with, any legal proceedings (including prospective legal proceedings);

(ii) is necessary for the purposes of obtaining legal advice; or

(iii) is otherwise necessary for the purposes of establishing, exercising or defending legal rights.

[1080]

NOTES

Commencement: 11 December 2003.

30 Proceedings for compensation for failure to comply with requirements of the Regulations

(1) A person who suffers damage by reason of any contravention of any of the requirements of these Regulations by any other person shall be entitled to bring proceedings for compensation from that other person for that damage.

(2) In proceedings brought against a person by virtue of this regulation it shall be a defence to prove that he had taken such care as in all the circumstances was reasonably required to comply with the relevant requirement.

(3) The provisions of this regulation are without prejudice to those of regulation 31.

[1081]

NOTES

Commencement: 11 December 2003.

31 Enforcement—extension of Part V of the Data Protection Act 1998

(1) The provisions of Part V of the Data Protection Act 1998 and of Schedules 6 and 9 to that Act are extended for the purposes of these Regulations and, for those purposes, shall have effect subject to the modifications set out in Schedule 1.

(2) In regulations 32 and 33, "enforcement functions" means the functions of the Information Commissioner under the provisions referred to in paragraph (1) as extended by that paragraph.

(3) The provisions of this regulation are without prejudice to those of regulation 30.

[1082]

NOTES

Commencement: 11 December 2003.

32 Request that the Commissioner exercise his enforcement functions

Where it is alleged that there has been a contravention of any of the requirements of these Regulations either OFCOM or a person aggrieved by the alleged contravention may request the Commissioner to exercise his enforcement functions in respect of that contravention, but those functions shall be exercisable by the Commissioner whether or not he has been so requested.

[1083]

NOTES

Commencement: 11 December 2003.

33 Technical advice to the Commissioner

OFCOM shall comply with any reasonable request made by the Commissioner, in connection with his enforcement functions, for advice on technical and similar matters relating to electronic communications.

[1084]

NOTES

Commencement: 11 December 2003.

34 (*Amends the Telecommunications (Lawful Business Practice) (Interception of Communications) Regulations 2000, SI 2000/2699, reg 3.*)

35 Amendment to the Electronic Communications (Universal Service) Order 2003

(1) …

(2) Paragraph (1) shall have effect notwithstanding the provisions of section 65 of the Communications Act 2003 (which provides for the modification of the Universal Service Order made under that section).

[1085]

NOTES

Commencement: 11 December 2003.

Sub-s (1): amends the Electronic Communications (Universal Service) Order 2003, SI 2003/1904, Schedule at **[3565]**.

36 Transitional provisions

The provisions in Schedule 2 shall have effect.

[1086]

NOTES

Commencement: 11 December 2003.

SCHEDULE 1
MODIFICATIONS FOR THE PURPOSES OF THESE REGULATIONS TO PART V OF THE DATA PROTECTION ACT 1998 AND SCHEDULES 6 AND 9 TO THAT ACT AS EXTENDED BY REGULATION 31

Regulation 31

1. In section 40—
   (a) in subsection (1), for the words "data controller" there shall be substituted the word "person", for the words "data protection principles" there shall be substituted the words "requirements of the Privacy and Electronic Communications (EC Directive) Regulations 2003 (in this Part referred to as "the

relevant requirements")" and for the words "principle or principles" there shall be substituted the words "requirement or requirements";
(b) in subsection (2), the words "or distress" shall be omitted;
(c) subsections (3), (4), (5), (9) and (10) shall be omitted; and
(d) in subsection (6)(a), for the words "data protection principle or principles" there shall be substituted the words "relevant requirement or requirements."

2. In section 41(1) and (2), for the words "data protection principle or principles", in both places where they occur, there shall be substituted the words "relevant requirement or requirements".

3. Section 42 shall be omitted.

4. In section 43—
(a) for subsections (1) and (2) there shall be substituted the following provisions—

"(1) If the Commissioner reasonably requires any information for the purpose of determining whether a person has complied or is complying with the relevant requirements, he may serve that person with a notice (in this Act referred to as "an information notice") requiring him, within such time as is specified in the notice, to furnish the Commissioner, in such form as may be so specified, with such information relating to compliance with the relevant requirements as is so specified.

(2) An information notice must contain a statement that the Commissioner regards the specified information as relevant for the purpose of determining whether the person has complied or is complying with the relevant requirements and his reason for regarding it as relevant for that purpose."
(b) in subsection (6)(a), after the word "under" there shall be inserted the words "the Privacy and Electronic Communications (EC Directive) Regulations 2003 or";
(c) in subsection (6)(b), after the words "arising out of" there shall be inserted the words "the said Regulations or"; and
(d) subsection (10) shall be omitted.

5. Sections 44, 45 and 46 shall be omitted.

6. In section 47—
(a) in subsection (1), for the words "an information notice or special information notice" there shall be substituted the words "or an information notice"; and
(b) in subsection (2) the words "or a special information notice" shall be omitted.

7. In section 48—
(a) in subsections (1) and (3), for the words "an information notice or a special information notice", in both places where they occur, there shall be substituted the words "or an information notice";
(b) in subsection (3) for the words "43(5) or 44(6)" there shall be substituted the words "or 43(5)"; and
(c) subsection (4) shall be omitted.

8. In section 49 subsection (5) shall be omitted.

9. In paragraph 4(1) of Schedule (6), for the words "(2) or (4)" there shall be substituted the words "or (2)".

10. In paragraph 1 of Schedule 9—
(a) for subparagraph (1)(a) there shall be substituted the following provision—
"(a) that a person has contravened or is contravening any of the requirements of the Privacy and Electronic Communications (EC Directive) Regulations 2003 (in this Schedule referred to as "the 2003 Regulations") or";

and
(b) subparagraph (2) shall be omitted.

11. In paragraph 9 of Schedule 9—
(a) in subparagraph (1)(a) after the words "rights under" there shall be inserted the words "the 2003 Regulations or"; and
(b) in subparagraph (1)(b) after the words "arising out of" there shall be inserted the words "the 2003 Regulations or".

[1087]

NOTES
Commencement: 11 December 2003.

PART II DATA PROTECTION

SCHEDULE 2
TRANSITIONAL PROVISIONS

Regulation 36

Interpretation

1. In this Schedule "the 1999 Regulations" means the Telecommunications (Data Protection and Privacy) Regulations 1999 and "caller" has the same meaning as in regulation 21 of the 1999 Regulations.

Directories

2.—(1) Regulation 18 of these Regulations shall not apply in relation to editions of directories first published before 11th December 2003.

(2) Where the personal data of a subscriber have been included in a directory in accordance with Part IV of the 1999 Regulations, the personal data of that subscriber may remain included in that directory provided that the subscriber—

(a) has been provided with information in accordance with regulation 18 of these Regulations; and

(b) has not requested that his data be withdrawn from that directory.

(3) Where a request has been made under subparagraph (2) for data to be withdrawn from a directory, that request shall be treated as having no application in relation to an edition of a directory that was produced before the producer of the directory received the request.

(4) For the purposes of subparagraph (3), an edition of a directory, which is revised after it was first produced, shall be treated as a new edition.

Notifications

3.—(1) A notification of consent given to a caller by a subscriber for the purposes of regulation 22(2) of the 1999 Regulations is to have effect on and after 11th December 2003 as a notification given by that subscriber for the purposes of regulation 19(2) of these Regulations.

(2) A notification given to a caller by a corporate subscriber for the purposes of regulation 23(2)(a) of the 1999 Regulations is to have effect on and after 11th December 2003 as a notification given by that subscriber for the purposes of regulation 20(1)(b) of these Regulations.

(3) A notification of consent given to a caller by an individual subscriber for the purposes of regulation 24(2) of the 1999 Regulations is to have effect on and after 11th December 2003 as a notification given by that subscriber for the purposes of regulation 20(2) of these Regulations.

(4) A notification given to a caller by an individual subscriber for the purposes of regulation 25(2)(a) of the 1999 Regulations is to have effect on and after the 11th December 2003 as a notification given by that subscriber for the purposes of regulation 21(1) of these Regulations.

Registers Kept Under Regulations 25 and 26

4.—(1) A notification given by a subscriber pursuant to regulation 23(4)(a) of the 1999 Regulations to the Director General of Telecommunications (or to such other person as is discharging his functions under regulation 23(4) of the 1999 Regulations on his behalf by virtue of an arrangement made under regulation 23(6) of those Regulations) is to have effect on or after 11th December 2003 as a notification given pursuant to regulation 25(1) of these Regulations.

(2) A notification given by a subscriber who is an individual pursuant to regulation 25(4)(a) of the 1999 Regulations to the Director General of Telecommunications (or to such other person as is discharging his functions under regulation 25(4) of the 1999 Regulations on his behalf by virtue of an arrangement made under regulation 25(6) of those Regulations) is to have effect on or after 11th December 2003 as a notification given pursuant to regulation 26(1) of these Regulations.

References in these Regulations to OFCOM

5. In relation to times before an order made under section 411 of the Communications Act 2003 brings any of the provisions of Part 2 of Chapter 1 of that Act into force for the purpose of conferring on OFCOM the functions contained in those provisions, references to OFCOM in these Regulations are to be treated as references to the Director General of Telecommunications.

[1088]

NOTES

Commencement: 11 December 2003.

REGULATION OF INVESTIGATORY POWERS (DIRECTED SURVEILLANCE AND COVERT HUMAN INTELLIGENCE SOURCES) ORDER 2003

(SI 2003/3171)

NOTES

Made: 5 December 2003.
Authority: Regulation of Investigatory Powers Act 2000, ss 30(1), (3), (5), (6), 78(5).
Commencement: 5 January 2004.

ARRANGEMENT OF ARTICLES

1 Citation, commencement and interpretation

(1) This Order may be cited as the Regulation of Investigatory Powers (Directed Surveillance and Covert Human Intelligence Sources) Order 2003 and shall come into force one month after the day on which it is made.

(2) In this Order "the 2000 Act" means the Regulation of Investigatory Powers Act 2000.

[1089]

NOTES

Commencement: 5 January 2004.

2, 3 (*Amend the Regulation of Investigatory Powers Act 2000, Sch 1, Pts I, II at* **[715]**, **[716]**.)

4 Prescribed offices, ranks and positions

(1) The offices, ranks and positions listed in column 2 of Part I of the Schedule to this Order (being offices, ranks or positions with the relevant public authorities listed in column 1 of Part I of that Schedule which are relevant public authorities for the purposes of sections 28 and 29 of the 2000 Act) are hereby prescribed for the purpose of section 30(1) of the 2000 Act, subject to the restrictions in articles 7, 8 and 9.

(2) The offices, ranks and positions listed in column 2 of Part II of the Schedule to this Order (being offices, ranks or positions with the relevant public authorities listed in column 1 of Part II of that Schedule which are relevant public authorities for the purposes only of section 28 of the 2000 Act) are hereby prescribed for the purpose of section 30(1) of the 2000 Act, subject to the restrictions in articles 7, 8 and 9.

[1090]

NOTES

Commencement: 5 January 2004.

5 More senior offices, ranks and positions

(1) Where an office, rank or position with a relevant public authority is prescribed by virtue of article 4, all more senior offices, ranks or positions with that authority are also prescribed for the purpose of section 30(1) of the 2000 Act, subject to article 10.

(2) Where an office, rank or position with a relevant public authority is described in column 2 of the Schedule to this Order by reference to an agency, unit, branch, division or other part of that authority, the reference in paragraph (1) to all more senior offices, ranks or positions with that authority is a reference to all more senior offices, ranks or positions with that agency, unit, branch, division or part.

[1091]

NOTES

Commencement: 5 January 2004.

6 Additional offices, ranks and positions prescribed for urgent cases

(1) The additional offices, ranks and positions listed in column 3 of the Schedule to this Order (being offices, ranks or positions with the relevant public authorities listed in column 1) are hereby prescribed for the purposes of section 30(1) of the 2000 Act, subject to the restrictions in articles 7, 8 and 9 in the circumstances described in paragraph (2).

(2) An individual holding an office, rank or position which is listed in column 3 of the Schedule to this Order may only grant an authorisation where it is not reasonably practicable, having regard to the urgency of the case, for the application to be considered by an individual with the same authority holding an office, rank or position listed in column 2 of the Schedule to this Order.

(3) Where an office, rank or position with a relevant public authority is described in column 3 of the Schedule to this Order by reference to an agency, unit, branch, division or other part of that authority, the reference in paragraph (2) to an individual with the same authority is a reference to an individual with that agency, unit, branch, division or part.

[1092]

NOTES

Commencement: 5 January 2004.

7 Restrictions on the granting of authorisations

The restriction in this article is that an individual holding an office, rank or position which is listed in column 2 or 3 of the Schedule to this Order may not grant an authorisation unless he believes it is necessary on the grounds set out in one or more of the paragraphs of sections 28(3) and 29(3) of the 2000 Act listed in the corresponding entry in column 4 of that Schedule.

[1093]

NOTES

Commencement: 5 January 2004.

8 The restriction in this article is that where any entry in column 2 or 3 of Part I of the Schedule to this Order is headed by a reference to an authorisation under section 28 or section 29 of the 2000 Act, an individual holding an office, rank or position which is listed in that entry may only grant an authorisation under the section of the 2000 Act with which that entry is headed.

[1094]

NOTES

Commencement: 5 January 2004.

9 The restriction in this article is that an individual holding an office, rank or position with the Food Standards Agency or the Rural Payments Agency may not grant an authorisation for conduct in Northern Ireland.

[1095]

NOTES

Commencement: 5 January 2004.

10 The restrictions on the granting of authorisations under section 28 and 29 of the 2000 Act that apply to an individual holding an office, rank or position with a relevant public authority listed in column 2 of the Schedule to this Order shall also apply to individuals holding all more senior offices, ranks or positions with that authority that are prescribed by article 5.

[1096]

NOTES

Commencement: 5 January 2004.

11 (*Revokes the Regulation of Investigatory Powers (Prescription of Offices, Ranks and Positions) Order 2000, SI 2000/2417.*)

SCHEDULE

Article 4

PART I
(PRESCRIPTIONS FOR PUBLIC AUTHORITIES IN PART I OF SCHEDULE 1 TO THE 2000 ACT THAT ARE RELEVANT PUBLIC AUTHORITIES FOR THE PURPOSES OF SECTIONS 28 AND 29 OF THE 2000 ACT)

(1) Relevant public authorities in Part I of Schedule 1 to the 2000 Act	*(2) Prescribed offices etc*	*(3) Urgent cases*	*(4) Grounds set out in the paragraphs of sections 28(3) and 29(3) of the 2000 Act for which an authorisation can be given*
A police force maintained under section 2 of the Police Act 1996 (police forces in England and Wales outside London)	Superintendent	Inspector	(a)(b)(c)(d)(e)

PART II
DATA PROTECTION

(1) Relevant public authorities in Part I of Schedule 1 to the 2000 Act	(2) *Prescribed offices etc*	(3) *Urgent cases*	(4) *Grounds set out in the paragraphs of sections 28(3) and 29(3) of the 2000 Act for which an authorisation can be given*
A police force maintained under or by virtue of section 1 of the Police (Scotland) Act 1967	Superintendent	Inspector	(a)(b)(c)(d)(e)
The metropolitan police force	Superintendent	Inspector	(a)(b)(c)(d)(e)
The City of London police force	Superintendent	Inspector	(a)(b)(c)(d)(e)
The Police Service of Northern Ireland	Superintendent	Inspector	(a)(b)(c)(d)(e)
The Ministry of Defence Police	Superintendent	Inspector	(a)(b)(c)
The Royal Navy Regulating Branch	Provost Marshal		(a)(b)(c)
The Royal Military Police	Lieutenant Colonel	Major	(a)(b)(c)
The Royal Air Force Police	Wing Commander	Squadron Leader	(a)(b)(c)
The British Transport Police	Superintendent	Inspector	(a)(b)(c)(d)(e)
[The force comprising the special constables appointed under section 79 of the Harbours, Docks and Piers Clauses Act 1847 on the nomination of the Dover Harbour Board	Superintendent	Inspector	(a)(b)(d)(e)
The force comprising the constables appointed under article 3 of the Mersey Docks and Harbour (Police) Order 1975 on the nomination of the Mersey Docks and Harbour Company	Superintendent	Inspector	(a)(b)(d)(e)]
[The Civil Nuclear Constabulary	Superintendent	Inspector	(a)(b)]
…	…	…	…

(1) Relevant public authorities in Part I of Schedule 1 to the 2000 Act	*(2) Prescribed offices etc*	*(3) Urgent cases*	*(4) Grounds set out in the paragraphs of sections 28(3) and 29(3) of the 2000 Act for which an authorisation can be given*
…	…	…	…
[The Serious Organised Crime Agency	Senior Manager (Grade 2)	Principal Officer (Grade 3)	(b)]
The Serious Fraud Office	Assistant Director		(b)
Government Communications Headquarters	GC8		(a)(b)(c)
The Security Service	General Duties 3 or any other Officer at Level 3		(a)(b)(c)
The Secret Intelligence Service	Grade 6 or equivalent		(a)(b)(c)
The Royal Navy	Commander	Lieutenant Commander	(a)(b)(c)(d)(e)
The Army	Lieutenant Colonel	Major	(a)(b)(c)(d)(e)
The Royal Air Force	Wing Commander	Squadron Leader	(a)(b)(c)(d)(e)
The Commissioners of Customs and Excise	Band 9	Band 7 or 8	(a)(b)(c)(d)(e)(f)
The Commissioners of Inland Revenue	Band C1	Band C2	(b)(c)(f)
Ministry of Defence	Band C1	Band C2	(b)
Department for Environment, Food and Rural Affairs	Senior Investigation Officer in DEFRA Investigation [Services]		(b)
	…		…
	Senior Investigation Officer in Centre for Environment, Fisheries and Aquaculture Science		(b)
	[Section 28 authorisation District Inspector in Marine Fisheries Agency		(b)

PART II DATA PROTECTION

(1) Relevant public authorities in Part I of Schedule 1 to the 2000 Act	*(2) Prescribed offices etc*	*(3) Urgent cases*	*(4) Grounds set out in the paragraphs of sections 28(3) and 29(3) of the 2000 Act for which an authorisation can be given*
	Section 29 authorisation Deputy Chief Inspector in Marine Fisheries Agency		(b)]
	…		…
	…		…
	…		…
	…		…
The Department of Health	Integrated Payband 3 (Standard 2) in Medicines and Healthcare Products Regulatory Agency		(b)(d)(e)
The Home Office	[Operational manager responsible for security and operations in a directly managed prison	Duty Governor in a directly managed prison	(b)(d)]
	Immigration Inspector in the Immigration Service	Chief Immigration Officer in the Immigration Service	(b)(c)
	Section 28 authorisation The Head of the Unit responsible for Security and Anti Corruption within the Immigration and Nationality Directorate	**Section 28 authorisation** Senior Executive Officer within the Unit responsible for Security and Anti Corruption within the Immigration and Nationality Directorate	(b)
The Northern Ireland Office	Deputy Principal or Governor 3 in the Northern Ireland Prison Service	Staff Officer or Governor 4 in the Northern Ireland Prison Service	(b)(d)
The Department of Trade and Industry	Deputy Inspector of Companies in Companies Investigation Branch		(b)

(1) Relevant public authorities in Part I of Schedule 1 to the 2000 Act	*(2) Prescribed offices etc*	*(3) Urgent cases*	*(4) Grounds set out in the paragraphs of sections 28(3) and 29(3) of the 2000 Act for which an authorisation can be given*
	Chief Investigation Officer in the Investigation Officers Section of Legal Services Directorate D or a member of the Senior Civil Service in Legal Services Directorate D		(b)
	…	…	(b)
	…		(b)
	Section 28 authorisation Member of Senior Civil Service in British Trade International		(b)
	Section 28 authorisation Range 10 Officer in Coal Health Claims Unit	**Section 28 authorisation** Range 9 Officer in Coal Health Claims Unit	(b)
The Department for Transport	…		…
	…		…
	…		…
	…		…
	…		…
	…		…
	…		…
	…		…
	Section 28 authorisation Area Manager or National Intelligence Co-ordinator in the Vehicle and Operator Services Agency	**Section 28 authorisation** Senior Vehicle Examiner or Senior Traffic Examiner or Intelligence Officer in the Vehicle and Operator Services Agency	(b)(d)
	Section 29 authorisation Enforcement Manager in the Vehicle and Operator Services Agency	**Section 29 authorisation** Area Manager in the Vehicle and Operator Services Agency	(b)(d)(b)(d)

PART II DATA PROTECTION

(1) *Relevant public authorities in Part I of Schedule 1 to the 2000 Act*	(2) *Prescribed offices etc*	(3) *Urgent cases*	(4) *Grounds set out in the paragraphs of sections 28(3) and 29(3) of the 2000 Act for which an authorisation can be given*
	Principal Enforcement Officer in the Maritime and Coastguard Agency	Enforcement Officer in the Maritime and Coastguard Agency	(b)(d)
	[Chief Executive of the Driving Standards Agency		(d)]
The Department for Work and Pensions	Senior Executive Officer or equivalent grades in Jobcentre Plus	Higher Executive Officer or equivalent grades in Jobcentre Plus	(b)
	Senior Executive Officer or equivalent grades in DWP Internal Assurance Services		(b)
	Senior Executive Officer or equivalent grades in Child Support Agency	Higher Executive Officer or equivalent grades in Child Support Agency	(b)
National Assembly for Wales	Head of NHS Directorate	Member of NHS Directorate at a level equivalent to Grade 7	(b)(d)(e)
	Head of NHS Finance Division	Member of NHS Finance Division at a level equivalent to Grade 7	(b)(d)(e)
	Head of Common Agricultural Policy Management Division	Member of Common Agricultural Policy Management Division at a level equivalent to Grade 7	(b)(e)
	Regional Director in the Care Standards Inspectorate for Wales	Senior Inspector in the Care Standards Inspectorate for Wales	(b)(d)(e)

(1) Relevant public authorities in Part I of Schedule 1 to the 2000 Act	*(2) Prescribed offices etc*	*(3) Urgent cases*	*(4) Grounds set out in the paragraphs of sections 28(3) and 29(3) of the 2000 Act for which an authorisation can be given*
Any county council or district council in England, a London Borough Council, the Common Council of the City of London in its capacity as a local authority, the Council of the Isles of Scilly, and any county council or county borough council in Wales	Assistant Chief Officer, Assistant Head of Service, Service Manager or equivalent		(b)
Any fire authority within the meaning of the Fire Services Act 1947 (read with paragraph 2 of Schedule 11 to the Local Government Act 1985)	Divisional Officer 2	Divisional Officer 3	(b)(d)
The Charity Commission	Senior Investigations Manager	Investigations Manager	(b)
The Environment Agency	**Section 28 authorisation** Area Management Team Member	**Section 28 authorisation** Area Team Leader	(b)(d)(e)
	Section 29 authorisation Area Manager	**Section 29 authorisation** Area Management Team Member	(b)(d)(e)
The Financial Services Authority	Head of Department in Enforcement Division	Manager in Enforcement Division	(b)
The Food Standards Agency	**Section 28 authorisation** Head of Division or equivalent grade		(b)(d)(e)
	Section 29 authorisation Deputy Director of Legal Services or any Director		(b)(d)(e)

(1) Relevant public authorities in Part I of Schedule 1 to the 2000 Act	(2) *Prescribed offices etc*	*(3) Urgent cases*	(4) *Grounds set out in the paragraphs of sections 28(3) and 29(3) of the 2000 Act for which an authorisation can be given*
[The Gambling Commission	Director of Intelligence or Director of Monitoring and Enforcement		(b)]
The Office of Fair Trading	Director of Cartel Investigations	Principal Investigation Officer in the Cartel Investigation Branch	(b)(c)
The Office of the Police Ombudsman for Northern Ireland	Senior Investigating Officer	Deputy Senior Investigating Officer	(b)
The Postal Services Commission	**Section 28 authorisation** Legal Adviser	**Section 28 authorisation** Deputy Director	(b)
	Section 29 authorisation Chief Legal Adviser		(b)
A Universal Service Provider within the meaning of the Postal Services Act 2000	Senior Investigation Manager in Royal Mail Group plc		(b)
[The Gangmasters Licensing Authority	Head of Enforcement		(b)
The Commission for Healthcare Audit and Inspection	Head of Operations in a region	Area Manager	(b)(e)]
[The Office of Communications	Section 28 authorisation Manager of Spectrum Operations or Head of Enforcement and Interference Policy	Section 28 authorisation Area Manager or Senior Enforcement Policy Manager	(b)
	Section 29 authorisation Head of Field Operations		(b)]

[1097]

NOTES

Commencement: 5 January 2004.

Entries relating to "the Dover Harbour Board" and "the Mersey Docks and Harbour Company" inserted by the Regulation of Investigatory Powers (Directed Surveillance and Covert Human Intelligence Sources) (Amendment) Order 2005, SI 2005/1084, art 3(1), (2).

Entry relating to "The Civil Nuclear Constabulary" substituted, for original entry "The United Kingdom Atomic Energy Authority Constabulary" by SI 2005/1084, art 3(1), (3).

Entries relating to "The National Criminal Intelligence Service" and "The National Crime Squad" (omitted) revoked and entry relating to "The Serious Organised Crime Agency" inserted by the Serious Organised Crime and Police Act 2005 (Consequential and Supplementary Amendments to Secondary Legislation) Order 2006, SI 2006/594, art 2, Schedule, para 40(1)–(3), subject to transitional provisions in para 40(4) thereto.

In the entry relating to the "Department of Environment, Food and Rural Affairs", word in first pair of square brackets substituted, words omitted revoked and words in second pair of square brackets inserted by the Regulation of Investigatory Powers (Directed Surveillance and Covert Human Intelligence Sources) (Amendment) Order 2006, SI 2006/1874, art 4, Schedule, Pt 1, paras 1, 2.

In the entry relating to "The Home Office", words in square brackets substituted by SI 2006/1874, art 4, Schedule, Pt 1, paras 1, 3.

In the entry relating to "The Department of Trade and Industry", words omitted revoked by SI 2005/1084, art 3(1), (4).

In the entry relating to "The Department for Transport", words omitted revoked by SI 2005/1084, art 3(1), (5); words in square brackets inserted by SI 2006/1874, art 4, Schedule, Pt 1, paras 1, 4.

Entry relating to "The Gambling Commission" substituted for original entry "The Gaming Board for Great Britain" by SI 2006/1874, art 4, Schedule, Pt 1, paras 1, 5.

Entries relating to "The Gangmasters Licensing Authority" and "The Commission for Healthcare Audit and Inspection" inserted by 2006/1874, art 4, Schedule, Pt 1, paras 1, 6.

Entry relating to "The Office of Communications" inserted by SI 2005/1084, art 3(1), (6).

PART II
(PRESCRIPTIONS FOR PUBLIC AUTHORITIES IN PART II OF SCHEDULE 1 TO THE 2000 ACT THAT ARE RELEVANT PUBLIC AUTHORITIES FOR THE PURPOSES ONLY OF SECTION 28 OF THE 2000 ACT)

(1) Relevant public authorities in Part II of Schedule 1 to the 2000 Act	*(2) Prescribed offices etc*	*(3) Urgent cases*	*(4) Grounds set out in the paragraphs of section 28(3) of the 2000 Act for which an authorisation can be given*
The Health and Safety Executive	Band 2 Inspector		(b)(d)(e)
A Special Health Authority established under section 11 of the National Health Service Act 1977	…		…
	[Senior Manager (not below the grade of Agenda for Change pay band 8b) in the Counter Fraud and Security Management Services division of the NHS Business Services Authority]		(b)
…	…		…
…	…		…

PART II
DATA PROTECTION

(*1*) *Relevant public authorities in Part II of Schedule 1 to the 2000 Act*	(*2*) *Prescribed offices etc*	(*3*) *Urgent cases*	(*4*) *Grounds set out in the paragraphs of section 28(3) of the 2000 Act for which an authorisation can be given*
Her Majesty's Chief Inspector of Schools in England	[Compliance, Investigations and Enforcement Team Assistant Divisional Manager] in the Office of Her Majesty's Chief Inspector of Schools in England (OFSTED)	…	(b)
The Information Commissioner	Head of Investigations	Senior Investigating Officer	(b)
The Royal Parks Constabulary	Chief Officer	Inspector	(b)
The Royal Pharmaceutical Society of Great Britain	Director of Fitness to Practice and Legal Affairs or Director of Practice and Quality Improvement		(b)(d)(e)

[1098]

NOTES

Commencement: 5 January 2004.

In the entry relating to "A Special Health Authority", words omitted revoked by the Regulation of Investigatory Powers (Directed Surveillance and Covert Human Intelligence Sources) (Amendment) Order 2006, SI 2006/1874, art 4, Schedule, Pt 2, paras 7, 8; words in square brackets substituted by the Special Health Authorities Abolition Order 2006, SI 2006/635, art 3, Sch 2, para 13.

Entries relating to "A National Health Service trust" and "Local Health Boards" (omitted) revoked by SI 2006/1874, art 4, Schedule, Pt 2, paras 7, 9.

In the entry relating to "Her Majesty's Chief Inspector of Schools in England" words in square brackets substituted and words omitted revoked by SI 2006/1874, art 4, Schedule, Pt 2, paras 7, 10.

REGULATION OF INVESTIGATORY POWERS (COMMUNICATIONS DATA) ORDER 2003

(SI 2003/3172)

NOTES

Made: 5 December 2003.

Authority: Regulation of Investigatory Powers Act 2000, ss 25(2), (3), 78(5).

Commencement: 5 January 2004.

ARRANGEMENT OF ARTICLES

1 Citation, commencement and interpretation

(1) This Order may be cited as the Regulation of Investigatory Powers (Communications Data) Order 2003 and shall come into force one month after the day on which it is made.

(2) In this Order—

"the 2000 Act" means the Regulation of Investigatory Powers Act 2000;

["the 2006 Order" means the Regulation of Investigatory Powers (Communications Data) (Additional Purposes and Amendment) Order 2006;]

"authorisation" means an authorisation under section 22(3) of the 2000 Act; and

"notice" means a notice under section 22(4) of the 2000 Act.

[1099]

NOTES

Commencement: 5 January 2004.

Para (2): definition "the 2006 Order" inserted by the Regulation of Investigatory Powers (Communications Data) (Additional Functions and Amendment) Order 2006, SI 2006/1878, art 3.

2 Prescribed offices, ranks and positions

The offices, ranks and positions listed in columns 2 and 3 of Schedule 1 (being offices, ranks and positions with the relevant public authorities in column 1 of that Schedule) are hereby prescribed for the purposes of section 25(2) of the 2000 Act, subject to the restrictions in articles 6, 7 and 10.

[1100]

NOTES

Commencement: 5 January 2004.

3 Additional public authorities

The public authorities set out in column 1 of Parts I, III and IV of Schedule 2 are hereby specified as relevant public authorities for the purposes of section 25(1) of the 2000 Act.

[1101]

NOTES

Commencement: 5 January 2004.

4 Prescribed offices, ranks and positions in the additional public authorities

The offices, ranks and positions listed in columns 2 and 3 of Parts I, II, III and IV of Schedule 2 (being offices, ranks and positions with the relevant public authorities in column 1 of that Schedule) are hereby prescribed for the purposes of section 25(2) of the 2000 Act, subject to the restrictions in articles 6, 7, 8 and 9.

[1102]

NOTES
Commencement: 5 January 2004.

5 More senior offices, ranks and positions

(1) Where an office, rank or position with a relevant public authority listed in column 2 of Schedule 1 or column 2 of Schedule 2 is prescribed by virtue of article 2 or 4, all more senior offices, ranks or positions with that authority are also prescribed for the purposes of section 25(2) of the 2000 Act, subject to article 11.

(2) Where an office, rank or position with a relevant public authority is described in column 2 of Schedule 1 or column 2 of Schedule 2 by reference to an agency, unit, branch, division or other part of that authority, the reference in paragraph (1) to all more senior offices, ranks or positions with that authority is a reference to all more senior offices, ranks or positions with that agency, unit, branch, division or part.

[1103]

NOTES
Commencement: 5 January 2004.

[6 Restrictions on the granting of authorisations or the giving of notices

(1) The restriction in this article is that an individual holding an office, rank or position which is listed in column (2) or (3) of Schedule 1 or 2 may not grant an authorisation or give a notice unless he believes it is necessary for any purpose within section 22(2) of the 2000 Act which is listed in the corresponding entry in column (4) of those Schedules.

(2) In column (4) of those Schedules a letter refers to the paragraph in section 22(2) of the 2000 Act which is identified by that letter, except where there is a reference to article 2 of the 2006 Order.]

[1104]

NOTES
Commencement: 26 July 2006.
Substituted by the Regulation of Investigatory Powers (Communications Data) (Additional Functions and Amendment) Order 2006, SI 2006/1878, art 4.

7.—(1) The restriction in this paragraph is that an individual holding an office, rank or position which is listed in column 2 of Schedule 1 or column 2 of Schedule 2 may only grant an authorisation or give a notice that he believes is necessary on grounds other than those set out in paragraphs (a), (b), (c) and (g) of section 22(2) of the 2000 Act where that authorisation or notice satisfies the condition in paragraph (3).

(2) The restriction in this paragraph is that an individual holding an office, rank or position which is listed in column 3 of Schedule 1 or column 3 of Schedule 2 may only grant an authorisation or give a notice which satisfies the condition set out in paragraph (3).

(3) The condition referred to in paragraphs (1) and (2) is that the only communications data authorised to be obtained by the authorisation, or required to be obtained or disclosed by the notice, is communications data falling within section 21(4)(c) of the 2000 Act.

[1105]

NOTES
Commencement: 5 January 2004.

8.—(1) The restriction in this article is that an individual holding an office, rank or position which is listed in column 2 of Part II or Part III of Schedule 2 may only grant an authorisation or give a notice which satisfies the condition set out in paragraph (2).

(2) The condition referred to in paragraph (1) is that the only communications data authorised to be obtained by the authorisation, or required to be obtained or disclosed by the notice, is communications data falling within section 21(4)(b) or (c) of the 2000 Act.

[1106]

NOTES

Commencement: 5 January 2004.

9.—(1) The restriction in this article is that an individual holding an office, rank or position which is listed in column 2 of Part IV of Schedule 2 may only grant an authorisation or give a notice which satisfies the condition set out in paragraph (2).

(2) The condition referred to in paragraph (1) is that the only communications data authorised to be obtained by the authorisation, or required to be obtained or disclosed by the notice, is communications data relating to a postal service.

[1107]

NOTES

Commencement: 5 January 2004.

[10.—(1) The restriction in this article is that an individual holding an office, rank or position with the Commissioners for Her Majesty's Revenue and Customs (being a relevant public authority listed in Schedule 1 to the 2000 Act may only grant an authorisation or give a notice which satisfies the condition set out in paragraph (2).

(2) That condition is that, in connection with a function relating to a matter to which section 7 of the Commissioners for Revenue and Customs Act 2005 applies, the only communications data falling within section 21(4)(a) of the 2000 Act authorised to be obtained by the authorisation or required to be obtained or disclosed by the notice is communications data relating to a postal service.]

[1108]

NOTES

Commencement: 26 July 2006.

Substituted by the Regulation of Investigatory Powers (Communications Data) (Additional Functions and Amendment) Order 2006, SI 2006/1878, art 5.

11 The restrictions on the granting of authorisations and the giving of notices that apply to an individual holding an office, rank or position with a relevant public authority listed in column 2 of Schedule 1 or column 2 of Schedule 2 shall also apply to all individuals holding all more senior offices, ranks or positions with that authority that are prescribed by article 5.

[1109]

NOTES

Commencement: 5 January 2004.

SCHEDULE 1
INDIVIDUALS IN PUBLIC AUTHORITIES WITHIN SECTION 25(1) OF THE 2000 ACT

Article 2

(1) *Relevant public authorities*	(2) *Prescribed offices etc (All authorisations/ notices)*	*(3)* *Additional prescribed offices etc (Authorisations/ notices relating solely to communications data falling within section 21(4)(c))*	(4) *Purposes within section 22(2) for which an authorisation may be granted or a notice given*
Police Forces			
A police force maintained under section 2 of the Police Act 1996 (police forces in England and Wales outside London)	Superintendent	Inspector	(a)(b)(c)(d)(e)(g) [and article 2(b) of the 2006 Order]
A police force maintained under or by virtue of section 1 of the Police (Scotland) Act 1967	Superintendent	Inspector	(a)(b)(c)(d)(e)(g) [and article 2(b) of the 2006 Order]
The metropolitan police force	Superintendent	Inspector	(a)(b)(c)(d)(e)(g) [and article 2(b) of the 2006 Order]
The City of London police force	Superintendent	Inspector	(a)(b)(c)(d)(e)(g) [and article 2(b) of the 2006 Order]
The Police Service of Northern Ireland	Superintendent	Inspector	(a)(b)(c)(d)(e)(g) [and article 2(b) of the 2006 Order]
The Ministry of Defence Police	Superintendent	Inspector	(a)(b)(c)(g)
The Royal Navy Regulating Branch	Provost Marshal	—	(a)(b)(c)(g)
The Royal Military Police	Lieutenant Colonel	Major	(a)(b)(c)(g)
The Royal Air Force Police	Wing Commander	Squadron Leader	(a)(b)(c)(g)
The British Transport Police	Superintendent	Inspector	(a)(b)(c)(d)(e)(g) [and article 2(b) of the 2006 Order]
…	…	…	…
…	…	…	…

(1) *Relevant public authorities*	(2) *Prescribed offices etc (All authorisations/ notices)*	(3) *Additional prescribed offices etc (Authorisations/ notices relating solely to communications data falling within section 21(4)(c))*	(4) *Purposes within section 22(2) for which an authorisation may be granted or a notice given*
[The Commissioners for Her Majesty's Revenue and Customs	Senior Officer	Higher Officer	(b)(f)]
The Intelligence Services			
Government Communications Headquarters	GC8	—	(a)(b)(c)
The Security Service	General Duties 3 or any other Officer at Level 3	General Duties 4	(a)(b)(c)
The Secret Intelligence Service	Grade 6 or equivalent	—	(a)(b)(c)
[*Other bodies*]			
[The Serious Organised Crime Agency	Senior Manager (Grade 2)	Principal Officer (Grade 3)	(b) [and article 2(b) of the 2006 Order]]

[1110]

NOTES

Commencement: 5 January 2004.

Police Forces: words in first to sixth pairs of square brackets inserted by the Regulation of Investigatory Powers (Communications Data) (Additional Functions and Amendment) Order 2006, SI 2006/1878, art 6(1), (2); entries relating to "The National Criminal Intelligence Service" and "The National Crime Squad" (omitted) revoked by the Serious Organised Crime and Police Act 2005 (Consequential and Supplementary Amendments to Secondary Legislation) Order 2006, SI 2006/594, art 2, Schedule, para 41(1), (2), subject to transitional provisions in para 41(4) thereto; entry relating to "The Commissioners for Her Majesty's Revenue and Customs" substituted for original entries "The Commissioners of Customs and Excise" and "The Commissioners of Inland Revenue" by SI 2006/1878, art 6(1), (3).

Other bodies: heading "Other bodies" and the entry relating to "The Serious Organised Crime Agency" inserted by SI 2006/594, art 2, Schedule, para 41(1), (3), subject to transitional provisions in para 41(4) thereto; words in square brackets inserted by SI 2006/1878, art 6(1), (4).

SCHEDULE 2
INDIVIDUALS IN ADDITIONAL PUBLIC AUTHORITIES SPECIFIED BY THIS ORDER

Article 3

PART I
(INDIVIDUALS IN ADDITIONAL PUBLIC AUTHORITIES THAT MAY ACQUIRE ALL TYPES OF COMMUNICATIONS DATA WITHIN SECTION 21(4) OF THE 2000 ACT)

(1) *Additional public authorities specified for the purposes of section 25(1) of the 2000 Act*	*(2)* *Prescribed offices etc (All authorisations/ notices)*	*(3)* *Additional prescribed offices etc (Authorisations/ notices relating solely to communications data falling within section 21(4)(c))*	*(4)* *Purposes within section 22(2) for which an authorisation may be granted or a notice given*
The Financial Services Authority	Head of Department in Enforcement Division	—	(b)
[The Gangmasters Licensing Authority	Head of Enforcement	—	(b)
The Home Office	Immigration inspector in the Immigration Service	—	(b)
	Senior operational manager in a directly managed prison	—	(b)(d)
The Department for Transport	Inspector in the Air Accident Investigation Branch, the Marine Accident Investigation Branch or the Rail Accident Investigation Branch	—	(d)
The Gambling Commission	Director of Intelligence or Director of Monitoring and Enforcement	—	(b)
The Information Commissioner	Head of Regulatory Action Division	—	(b)
The Serious Fraud Office	Assistant Director for the Operations Division	—	(b)
The Criminal Cases Review Commission	An investigations Adviser	—	Article 2(a) of the 2006 Order
The Scottish Criminal Cases Review Commission	A Legal Officer	—	Article 2(a) of the 2006 Order

(1) *Additional public authorities specified for the purposes of section 25(1) of the 2000 Act*	(2) *Prescribed offices etc (All authorisations/ notices)*	*(3)* *Additional prescribed offices etc (Authorisations/ notices relating solely to communications data falling within section 21(4)(c))*	(4) *Purposes within section 22(2) for which an authorisation may be granted or a notice given*
The Royal Mail Group plc, by virtue of being a Universal Service Provider within the meaning of the Postal Services Act 2000	Senior Investigation Manager	—	(b)]
[The Scottish Drug Enforcement Agency, meaning the organisation known by that name and established under section 36(1)(a)(ii) of the Police (Scotland) Act 1967	Superintendent, Grade PO7 or any individual on secondment to the Scottish Drug Enforcement Agency who holds the rank of Superintendent or Grade PO7 with the police force from which that person is seconded	Inspector or any individual on secondment to the Scottish Drug Enforcement Agency who holds the rank of Inspector with the police force from which that person is seconded	(b)(d)(g)]
[The Civil Nuclear Constabulary	Superintendent	Inspector	(a)(b)]
…	…	…	…
The Office of the Police Ombudsman for Northern Ireland	Senior Investigating Officer	—	(b)
[The Independent Police Complaints Commission	Commissioner, Regional Director, Director of Investigations or Deputy Director of Investigations	—	(b)
The Office of Communications	Senior Enforcement Policy Manager	—	(b)
The force comprising the special constables appointed under section 79 of the Harbours, Docks and Piers Clauses Act 1847 on the nomination of the Dover Harbour Board	Superintendent	Inspector	(a)(b)(d)(e) [and article 2(b) of the 2006 Order]

PART II DATA PROTECTION

(1) *Additional public authorities specified for the purposes of section 25(1) of the 2000 Act*	(2) *Prescribed offices etc (All authorisations/ notices)*	(3) *Additional prescribed offices etc (Authorisations/ notices relating solely to communications data falling within section 21(4)(c))*	(4) *Purposes within section 22(2) for which an authorisation may be granted or a notice given*
The force comprising the constables appointed under article 3 of the Mersey Docks and Harbour (Police) Order 1975 on the nomination of the Mersey Docks and Harbour Company	Superintendent	Inspector	(a)(b)(d)(e) [and article 2(b) of the 2006 Order]]
Emergency Services			
A National Health Service trust established under section 5 of the National Health Service and Community Care Act 1990 whose functions, as specified in its Establishment Order, include the provision of emergency ambulance services	Duty Officer responsible for the Control Function	—	(g)
The Welsh Ambulance Services NHS Trust	Regional Control Manager	—	(g)
The Scottish Ambulance Service Board	Emergency Medical Dispatch Centre Officer in charge	—	(g)
The Northern Ireland Ambulance Service Health and Social Services Trust	Control Supervisor in Ambulance Control Room	—	(g)
The Department for Transport	Area Operations Manager in the Maritime and Coastguard Agency	—	(g)

(*1*) *Additional public authorities specified for the purposes of section 25*(*1*) *of the 2000 Act*	(*2*) *Prescribed offices etc* (*All authorisations/ notices*)	(*3*) *Additional prescribed offices etc* (*Authorisations/ notices relating solely to communications data falling within section 21*(*4*)(*c*))	(*4*) *Purposes within section 22*(*2*) *for which an authorisation may be granted or a notice given*
Any fire authority within the meaning of the Fire Services Act 1947 (read with paragraph 2 of Schedule 11 to the Local Government Act 1985) [or any fire and rescue authority under the Fire and Rescue Services Act 2004]	Fire Control Officer	—	(g)
A council constituted under section 2 of the Local Government etc (Scotland) Act 1994	Fire Control Officer	—	(g)
[A joint fire and rescue board constituted by an amalgamation scheme under section 2 of the Fire (Scotland) Act 2005 (asp 5) or a joint fire and rescue board within the meaning of section 5 of that Act]	Fire Control Officer	—	(g)
The Fire Authority for Northern Ireland	Fire Control Officer	—	(g)

[1111]

NOTES

Commencement: 5 January 2004.

Entries relating to "The Gangmasters Licensing Authority", "The Home Office", "The Department for Transport", "The Gambling Commission", "The Information Commissioner", "The Serious Fraud Office", "The Criminal Cases Review Commission", "The Scottish Criminal Cases Review Commission" and "The Royal Mail Group" inserted by the Regulation of Investigatory Powers (Communications Data) (Additional Functions and Amendment) Order 2006, SI 2006/1878, art 7(1), (2).

Entries relating to "The Scottish Drug Enforcement Agency" and "The Civil Nuclear Constabulary" substituted for original entries "The Scottish Crime Squad" and "The United Kingdom Atomic Energy Authority Constabulary" respectively, entry relating to "The Department of Trade and Industry" (omitted) revoked, and entries relating to "The Independent Police Complaints Commission" and "The Office of Communications" inserted by the Regulation of Investigatory Powers (Communications Data) (Amendment) Order 2005, SI 2005/1083, art 2.

Entries relating to the "Dover Harbour Board" and the "Mersey Docks and Harbour Company" inserted by SI 2005/1083, art 2(1), (5); words in square brackets therein inserted by SI 2006/1878, art 7(1), (3).

In the entry relating to "Any fire authority", words in square brackets inserted in relation to England by the Fire and Rescue Services Act 2004 (Consequential Amendments) (England) Order 2004,

SI 2004/3168, art 71(1), (2), and in relation to Wales by the Fire and Rescue Services Act 2004 (Consequential Amendments) (Wales) Order 2005, SI 2005/2929, art 77(1), (2).

In the entry relating to "A joint fire and rescue board", words in square brackets substituted by the Fire (Scotland) Act 2005 (Consequential Provisions and Modifications) Order 2005, SI 2005/2060, art 3, Schedule, Pt 2, para 17(1), (2).

PART II
(INDIVIDUALS IN THE PUBLIC AUTHORITIES SPECIFIED IN PART I THAT MAY ONLY ACQUIRE COMMUNICATIONS DATA FALLING WITHIN SECTIONS 21(4)(B) AND (C) OF THE 2000 ACT)

(*1*) *Additional public authorities specified for the purposes of section 25(1) of the 2000 Act*	(2) *Prescribed offices etc (All authorisations/ notices relating to communications data falling within sections 21(4)(b) and (c))*	(*3*) *Additional prescribed offices etc (Authorisations/ notices relating solely to communications data falling within section 21(4)(c))*	(*4*) *Purposes within section 22(2) for which an authorisation may be granted or a notice given*
The Department of Trade and Industry	Deputy Inspector of Companies in Companies Investigation Branch	—	(b)
	Deputy Chief Investigation Officer in the Investigation Officers Section of Legal Services Directorate D	—	(b)
Emergency Services			
A National Health Service Trust established under section 5 of the National Health Service and Community Care Act 1990 whose functions, as specified in its Establishment Order, include the provision of emergency ambulance services	Director of Operations or Director of Control and Communications	—	(b)
The Welsh Ambulance Services NHS Trust	Director of Operations	—	(b)
The Scottish Ambulance Service Board	Director of Operations	—	(b)

(1) *Additional public authorities specified for the purposes of section 25(1) of the 2000 Act*	*(2)* *Prescribed offices etc (All authorisations/ notices relating to communications data falling within sections 21(4)(b) and (c))*	*(3)* *Additional prescribed offices etc (Authorisations/ notices relating solely to communications data falling within section 21(4)(c))*	*(4)* *Purposes within section 22(2) for which an authorisation may be granted or a notice given*
The Northern Ireland Ambulance Service Health and Social Services Trust	Director of Operations	—	(b)
The Department for Transport	Principal Enforcement Officer in the Maritime and Coastguard Agency	—	(b)(d)
Any fire authority within the meaning of the Fire Services Act 1947 (read with paragraph 2 of Schedule 11 to the Local Government Act 1985) [or any fire and rescue authority under the Fire and Rescue Services Act 2004]	Principal Fire Control Officer or Divisional Officer 2	—	(b)(d)
A council constituted under section 2 of the Local Government etc (Scotland) Act 1994	Assistant Chief Officer, Assistant Head of Service, Service Manager or equivalent	—	(b)
	Principal Fire Control Officer or Divisional Officer 2	—	(b)(d)
[A joint fire and rescue board constituted by an amalgamation scheme under section 2 of the Fire (Scotland) Act 2005 (asp 5) or a joint fire and rescue board within the meaning of section 5 of that Act]	Principal Fire Control Officer or Divisional Officer 2	—	(b)(d)
The Fire Authority for Northern Ireland	Principal Fire Control Officer or Divisional Officer 2	—	(b)(d)

[1112]

PART II
DATA PROTECTION

NOTES

Commencement: 5 January 2004.

In the entry relating to "Any fire authority", words in square brackets inserted in relation to England by the Fire and Rescue Services Act 2004 (Consequential Amendments) (England) Order 2004, SI 2004/3168, art 71(1), (3), and in relation to Wales by the Fire and Rescue Services Act 2004 (Consequential Amendments) (Wales) Order 2005, SI 2005/2929, art 77(1), (3).

In the entry relating to "A joint fire and rescue board", words in square brackets substituted by the Fire (Scotland) Act 2005 (Consequential Provisions and Modifications) Order 2005, SI 2005/2060, art 3, Schedule, Pt 2, para 17(1), (3).

PART III

(INDIVIDUALS IN FURTHER ADDITIONAL PUBLIC AUTHORITIES THAT MAY ONLY ACQUIRE COMMUNICATIONS DATA FALLING WITHIN SECTIONS 21(4)(B) AND (C) OF THE 2000 ACT)

(1) *Additional public authorities specified for the purposes of section 25(1) of the 2000 Act*	*(2)* *Prescribed offices etc (All authorisations/ notices relating to communications data falling within sections 21(4)(b) and (c))*	*(3)* *Additional prescribed offices etc (Authorisations/ notices relating solely to communications data falling within section 21(4)(c))*	*(4)* *Purposes within section 22(2) for which an authorisation may be granted or a notice given*
Government Departments			
The Department for Environment, Food and Rural Affairs	Senior Investigation Officer in DEFRA Investigation [Services]	—	(b)
	Senior Investigation Officer in the Centre for Environment, Fisheries and Aquaculture Science	—	(b)
	[Deputy Chief Inspector in Marine Fisheries Agency]	—	(b)
The Food Standards Agency	Deputy Director of Legal Services or any Director	—	(b)(d)(e)
The Department of Health	Integrated Payband 3 (Standard 2) in the Medicines and Healthcare Products Regulatory Agency	—	(b)(d)(e)

(1) *Additional public authorities specified for the purposes of section 25(1) of the 2000 Act*	(2) *Prescribed offices etc (All authorisations/ notices relating to communications data falling within sections 21(4)(b) and (c))*	*(3)* *Additional prescribed offices etc (Authorisations/ notices relating solely to communications data falling within section 21(4)(c))*	*(4)* *Purposes within section 22(2) for which an authorisation may be granted or a notice given*
The Home Office	[Head of Investigations in the National Asylum Support Service]	—	(b)
The Department of Enterprise, Trade and Investment for Northern Ireland	Deputy Chief Inspector in Trading Standards Service	—	(b)
[The Department of Agriculture and Rural Development for Northern Ireland	Head of Financial Policy and Investigation Services	—	(b)]
Local Authorities			
Any county council or district council in England, a London borough council, the Common Council of the City of London in its capacity as a local authority, the Council of the Isles of Scilly, and any county council or county borough council in Wales	Assistant Chief Officer, Assistant Head of Service, Service Manager or equivalent	—	(b)
A district council within the meaning of the Local Government Act (Northern Ireland) 1972	Assistant Chief Officer	—	(b)
NHS Bodies			
[NHS Business Services Authority]	[Senior Manager (not below the grade of Agenda for Change pay band 8b) in the Counter Fraud and Security Management Services division of the NHS Business Services Authority]	—	(b)

PART II DATA PROTECTION

(1) *Additional public authorities specified for the purposes of section 25(1) of the 2000 Act*	*(2)* *Prescribed offices etc (All authorisations/ notices relating to communications data falling within sections 21(4)(b) and (c))*	*(3)* *Additional prescribed offices etc (Authorisations/ notices relating solely to communications data falling within section 21(4)(c))*	*(4)* *Purposes within section 22(2) for which an authorisation may be granted or a notice given*
The Common Services Agency for the Scottish Health Service	Head of NHS Scotland Counter Fraud Services	—	(b)
The Northern Ireland Health and Social Services Central Services Agency	Head of the Counter Fraud Unit	—	(b)
Other Bodies			
The Charity Commission	Senior Investigations Manager	—	(b)
The Environment Agency	Area Management Team Member	—	(b)(d)(e)
…	…	…	…
The Health and Safety Executive	Band 2 Inspector	—	(b)(d)(e)(g)
…	…	…	…
The Office of Fair Trading	Director of Cartel Investigations	—	(b)
[The Pensions Regulator	Regulatory manager	—	(b)]
…	…	…	…
The Scottish Environment Protection Agency	Director of Operations, any other Director	—	(b)(d)(e)
…	…	…	…

[1113]

NOTES

Commencement: 5 January 2004.

Words in square brackets in entries relating to "The Department for Environment, Food and Rural Affairs" and "The Home Office" substituted, entries relating to "The Department of Agriculture and Rural Development for Northern Ireland" and "The Pensions Regulator" inserted, and entries relating to "The Gaming Board for Great Britain", "The Information Commissioner", "The Serious Fraud Office" and "A Universal Service Provider" (omitted) revoked by the Regulation of Investigatory Powers (Communications Data) (Additional Functions and Amendment) Order 2006, SI 2006/1878, art 8; words in square brackets in the entry relating to "NHS Business Services Authority" substituted by the Special Health Authorities Abolition Order 2006, SI 2006/635, art 3, Sch 2, para 14.

PART IV
(INDIVIDUALS IN ADDITIONAL PUBLIC AUTHORITIES THAT MAY ONLY ACQUIRE COMMUNICATIONS DATA WITHIN SECTION 21(4) OF THE 2000 ACT RELATING TO A POSTAL SERVICE)

(1) *Additional public authorities specified for the purposes of section 25(1) of the 2000 Act*	*(2)* *Prescribed offices etc (All authorisations/ notices relating to communications data relating to postal services*	*(3)* *Additional prescribed offices etc (Authorisations/ notices relating solely to communications data falling within section 21(4)(c))*	*(4)* *Purposes within section 22(2) for which an authorisation may be granted or a notice given*
Postal Services Commission	Legal Adviser	—	(b)

[1114]

NOTES
Commencement: 5 January 2004.

REGULATION OF INVESTIGATORY POWERS (INTRUSIVE SURVEILLANCE) ORDER 2003

(SI 2003/3174)

NOTES
Made: 5 December 2003.
Authority: Regulation of Investigatory Powers Act 2000, s 41(3), (4).
Commencement: 5 January 2004.

1 Citation and commencement

This Order may be cited as the Regulation of Investigatory Powers (Intrusive Surveillance) Order 2003 and shall come into force one month after the day on which it is made.

[1115]

NOTES
Commencement: 5 January 2004.

2 Designated public authority

The Northern Ireland Office is hereby designated for the purposes of section 41 of the Regulation of Investigatory Powers Act 2000 as a public authority whose activities may require the carrying out of intrusive surveillance.

[1116]

NOTES
Commencement: 5 January 2004.

3 Prescribed offices, ranks and positions

An application for an authorisation for the carrying out of intrusive surveillance may be made only by an individual holding an office, rank or position in the Northern Ireland Prison Service.

[1117]

NOTES
Commencement: 5 January 2004.

REGULATION OF INVESTIGATORY POWERS (CONDITIONS FOR THE LAWFUL INTERCEPTION OF PERSONS OUTSIDE THE UNITED KINGDOM) REGULATIONS 2004

(SI 2004/157)

NOTES
Made: 27 January 2004.
Authority: Regulation of Investigatory Powers Act 2000, s 4(1)(d).
Commencement: to be appointed; see reg 2(1).

1 Citation

These Regulations may be cited as the Regulation of Investigatory Powers (Conditions for the Lawful Interception of Persons outside the United Kingdom) Regulations 2004.

[1118]

NOTES
Commencement: to be appointed; see reg 2(1) at **[1119]**.

2 Commencement

(1) These Regulations shall come into force—
   (a) if the United Kingdom is one of the first eight Member States of the European Union to ratify the Convention on Mutual Assistance in Criminal Matters established by Council Act of 29th May 2000 (2000/C197/01) ("the Convention"), 90 days after the day on which the eighth Member State ratifies; or
   (b) otherwise, 90 days after the day on which the United Kingdom ratifies the Convention.

(2) For the purposes of paragraph (1)—
   (a) a Member State ratifies the Convention when it notifies the Secretary-General of the Council of the European Union of the completion of its constitutional procedures for the adoption of the Convention, in accordance with Article 27(2) of the Convention;
   (b) the reference to a "Member State" is only to a state that was a Member State on 29th May 2000.

[1119]

NOTES
Commencement: to be appointed; see para (1) above.

3 Conditions for the lawful interception of persons outside the United Kingdom

For the purposes of section 4(1)(d) of the Regulation of Investigatory Powers Act 2000, the following conditions are prescribed—
   (a) the interception is carried out for the purposes of a criminal investigation;
   (b) the criminal investigation is being carried out in a country or territory that is party to an international agreement designated for the purposes of section 1(4) of that Act.

[1120]

NOTES
Commencement: to be appointed; see reg 2(1) at **[1119]**.

REGULATION OF INVESTIGATORY POWERS (DESIGNATION OF AN INTERNATIONAL AGREEMENT) ORDER 2004

(SI 2004/158)

NOTES

Made: 27 January 2004.
Authority: Regulation of Investigatory Powers Act 2000, s 1(4)(c).
Commencement: 1 April 2004.

1 Citation and commencement

This Order may be cited as the Regulation of Investigatory Powers (Designation of an International Agreement) Order 2004 and shall come into force on 1st April 2004.

[1121]

NOTES

Commencement: 1 April 2004.

2 Designation of an international agreement

The Convention on Mutual Assistance in Criminal Matters between the Member States of the European Union established by Council Act of 29th May 2000 (2000/C197/01) is hereby designated for the purposes of section 1(4) of the Regulation of Investigatory Powers Act 2000.

[1122]

NOTES

Commencement: 1 April 2004.

INFORMATION TRIBUNAL (NATIONAL SECURITY APPEALS) RULES 2005

(SI 2005/13)

NOTES

Made: 7 January 2005.
Authority: Data Protection Act 1998, s 67(2), Sch 6, para 7.
Commencement: 1 February 2005.

ARRANGEMENT OF RULES

PART II
DATA PROTECTION

1 Citation and commencement

These Rules may be cited as the Information Tribunal (National Security Appeals) Rules 2005 and shall come into force on 1st February 2005.

[1123]

NOTES

Commencement: 1 February 2005.

2 (*Revokes the Data Protection Tribunal (National Security Appeals) Rules 2000, SI 2000/206.*)

3 Application and interpretation

(1) These Rules apply to appeals under section 28 of the 1998 Act, section 60 of the 2000 Act and regulation 18(7) of the 2004 Regulations.

(2) In these Rules—

"the 1998 Act" means the Data Protection Act 1998;

"the 2000 Act" means the Freedom of Information Act 2000;

"the 2004 Regulations" means the Environmental Information Regulations 2004;

"appeal" means an appeal under—

(a) section 28 of the 1998 Act,

(b) section 60 of the 2000 Act, or

(c) section 60 as applied by regulation 18(1), as modified by regulation 18(7) of the 2004 Regulations, as the case may be;

"appellant" means—

(a) a person who brings or intends to bring an appeal under section 28 of the 1998 Act, or

(b) the Commissioner or an applicant who brings or intends to bring an appeal under section 60 of the 2000 Act or section 60 as applied by regulation 18(1), as modified by regulation 18(7) of the 2004 Regulations, as the case may be;

"costs"—

(a) except in Scotland, includes fees, charges, disbursements, expenses and remuneration;

(b) in Scotland means expenses, and includes fees, charges, disbursements and remuneration;

"disputed certification" means—

(a) in relation to an appeal under section 28(4) of the 1998 Act, section 60(1) of the 2000 Act or section 60(1) of the 2000 Act as applied by regulation 18(1), as modified by regulation 18(7) of the 2004 Regulations, the certificate against which the appeal is brought or intended to be brought;

(b) in relation to an appeal under section 28(6) of the 1998 Act, the claim by a data controller, against which the appeal is brought or intended to be brought, that a certificate applies to any personal data;

(c) in relation to an appeal under section 60(4) of the 2000 Act or section 60(4) as applied by regulation 18(1), as modified by regulation 18(7) of the 2004 Regulations, the claim by a public authority against which the appeal is brought or intended to be brought, that a certificate applies to any information, as the case may be;

"hearing" means a sitting of the Tribunal for the purposes of enabling the Tribunal to take a decision on an appeal, or on any matter raised in relation to an appeal, at which the parties are entitled to attend and be heard;

"party" has the meaning given in paragraph (3) below;

"president" means the person designated by the Lord Chancellor under paragraph 3 of Schedule 6 to the 1998 Act to preside when the Tribunal is constituted under that paragraph;

"proper officer" in relation to a rule means an officer or member of staff provided to the Tribunal under paragraph 14 of Schedule 5 to the 1998 Act and appointed by the chairman to perform the duties of a proper officer under that rule;

"relevant Minister" means the Minister of the Crown who is responsible for the signing of the certificate under section 28(2) of the 1998 Act, section 23(2) or 24(3) of the 2000 Act, or regulation 15(1) of the 2004 Regulations to which the appeal relates as the case may be, and except where the context otherwise requires, references in these Rules to the relevant Minister include a person appointed under rule 22 below to represent his interests or a person designated under regulation 15(2) of the 2004 Regulations; and

"respondent data controller" means, in relation to an appeal under section 28(6) of the 1998 Act, the data controller making the claim which constitutes the disputed certification.

(3) In these Rules, except where the context otherwise requires, "party" means the appellant or—

(a) in relation to an appeal under either section 28(4) of the 1998 Act, section 60 of the 2000 Act or section 60 of the 2000 Act as applied by regulation 18(1), as modified by regulation 18(7) of the 2004 Regulations, the relevant Minister,

(b) in relation to an appeal under section 28(6) of the 1998 Act, the respondent data controller,

and, except where the context otherwise requires, references in these Rules to a party or to any such party include a person appointed under rule 22 below to represent his interests.

(4) In relation to proceedings before the Tribunal in Scotland, for the words "on the trial of an action in rules 16(7) and 27(2) below, there is substituted "in a proof".

(5) Appeals brought before 1st January 2005 shall be determined in accordance with the Data Protection Tribunal (National Security Appeals) Rules 2000.

[1124]

NOTES

Commencement: 1 February 2005.

4 Constitution and general duty of the Tribunal

(1) When exercising its function under these Rules, the Tribunal shall secure that information is not disclosed contrary to the interests of national security.

(2) Subject to paragraph (3) below, the Tribunal's jurisdiction may be exercised ex parte by one or more of the persons designated under paragraph 2(1) of Schedule 6 to the 1998 Act.

(3) The Tribunal's jurisdiction may only be exercised ex parte in accordance with rule 12, in respect of appeals under either section 28 of the 1998 Act, section 60 of the 2000 Act or section 60 as applied by regulation 18(1), as modified by regulation 18(7) of the 2004 Regulations.

(4) For the purposes of paragraph (1) above, but without prejudice to the application of that paragraph, the disclosure of information is to be regarded as contrary to the interests of national security if it would indicate the existence or otherwise of any material, where that indication would itself be contrary to the interests of national security.

[1125]

NOTES

Commencement: 1 February 2005.

5 Method of appealing—notice of appeal

(1) An appeal must be brought by written notice of appeal served on the Tribunal.

(2) The notice of appeal shall—

(a) identify the disputed certification; and
(b) state—
   (i) the name and address of the appellant;
   (ii) the grounds of the appeal;
   (iii) the name and address of the public authority from which the disputed certification was received;
   (iv) the name and address of the appellant's representative, if he has appointed one; and
   (v) an address for the service of notices and other documents on the appellant, and
(c) be signed by or on behalf of the appellant.

(3) In the case of an appeal under section 28(6) of the 1998 Act, the notice of appeal shall also state—
(a) the date on which the respondent data controller made the claim constituting the disputed certification;
(b) an address for service of notices and other documents on the respondent data controller; and
(c) where applicable, the special circumstances which the appellant considers justify the Tribunal's accepting jurisdiction under rule 6(3) below.

(4) In the case of an appeal under section 60(4) of the 2000 Act or section 60(4) of the 2000 Act as applied by regulation 18(1), as modified by regulation 18(7) of the 2004 Regulations, the notice of appeal shall also state—
(a) the date on which the public authority made the claim constituting the disputed certification;
(b) an address for service of notices and other documents on the public authority; and
(c) where applicable, the special circumstances which the appellant considers justify the Tribunal's accepting jurisdiction under rule 6(3) below.

(5) A notice of appeal may include a request for an early determination of the appeal and the reasons for that request.

[1126]

NOTES

Commencement: 1 February 2005.

6 Time limit for appealing

(1) In the case of an appeal under section 28(4) of the 1998 Act, section 60(1) of the 2000 Act or section 60(1) of the 2000 Act as applied by regulation 18(1), as modified by regulation 18(7) of the 2004 Regulations, a notice of appeal may be served on the Tribunal at any time during the currency of the disputed certification to which it relates.

(2) In the case of an appeal under section 28(6) of the 1998 Act, section 60(4) of the 2000 Act or section 60(4) of the 2000 Act as applied by regulation 18(1), as modified by regulation 18(7) of the 2004 Regulations, subject to paragraph (3) below, a notice of appeal must be served on the Tribunal within 28 days of the date on which the claim constituting the disputed certification was made.

(3) The Tribunal may accept a notice of appeal served after the expiry of the period permitted by paragraph (2) above if it is of the opinion that, by reason of special circumstances, it is just and right to do so.

(4) A notice of appeal shall, if sent by post in accordance with rule 31(2) below, be treated as having been served on the date on which it is received for dispatch by the Post Office.

[1127]

NOTES

Commencement: 1 February 2005.

7 Acknowledgement of notice of appeal and notification by the Tribunal

(1) Upon receipt of a notice of appeal, the proper officer shall send—
(a) an acknowledgement of the service of a notice of appeal to the appellant, and

(b) a copy of the notice of appeal to—
(i) the relevant Minister,
(ii) the Commissioner, where he is not the appellant, and
(iii) in the case of appeal under section 28(6) of the 1998 Act, the respondent data controller.

(2) An acknowledgement of service under paragraph (1)(a) above shall be accompanied by a statement of the Tribunal's powers to award costs against the appellant under rule 29 below.

[1128]

NOTES

Commencement: 1 February 2005.

8 Relevant Minister's notice in reply

(1) No later than 42 days after receipt of a copy of a notice of appeal under rule 7(1)(b) above, the relevant Minister shall send to the Tribunal—
(a) a copy of the certificate to which the appeal relates, and
(b) a written notice in accordance with paragraph (2) below;

(2) The notice shall state—
(a) with regard to an appeal under section 28(4) of the 1998 Act, section 60(1) of the 2000 Act or section 60(1) of the 2000 Act as applied by regulation 18(1), as modified by regulation 18(7) of the 2004 Regulations, whether or not he intends to oppose the appeal and, if so—
(i) a summary of the circumstances relating to the issue of the certificate, and the reason for the issue of the certificate;
(ii) the grounds upon which he relies in opposing the appeal; and
(iii) a statement of the evidence upon which he relies in support of those grounds; and
(b) with regard to an appeal under section 28(6) of the 1998 Act, section 60(4) of the 2000 Act or section 60(4) as applied by regulation 18(1), as modified by regulation 18(7) of the 2004 Regulations, whether or not he wishes to make representations in relation to the appeal and, if so—
(i) the extent to which he intends to support or oppose the appeal;
(ii) the grounds upon which he relies in supporting or opposing the appeal; and
(iii) a statement of the evidence upon which he relies in support of those grounds.

(3) Except where the Tribunal proposes to determine the appeal in accordance with rule 12 below, and subject to rule 13 below, the proper office shall send a copy of the notice to—
(a) the appellant;
(b) the Commissioner; and
(c) in the case of an appeal under section 28(6) of the 1998 Act, the respondent data controller.

(4) A notice under this rule may include a request for an early determination of the appeal and the reasons for that request

[1129]

NOTES

Commencement: 1 February 2005.

9 Reply by respondent data controller

(1) A respondent data controller shall, within 42 days of the date on which he receives a copy of a notice of appeal under rule 7(1)(b) above, send to the Tribunal a written reply acknowledging service upon him of the notice of appeal, and stating—
(a) whether or not he intends to oppose the appeal and, if so,
(b) the grounds upon which he relies in opposing the appeal.

(2) Before the expiry of the period referred to in paragraph (1) above, the respondent data controller may apply to the Tribunal for an extension of that period, showing cause why, by

reason of special circumstances, it would be just and right to do so, and the Tribunal may grant such extension as it considers appropriate.

(3) Except where the Tribunal proposes to determine the appeal in accordance with rule 12 below, the proper officer shall send a copy of the reply to—

(a) the relevant Minister; and

(b) subject to paragraph (4) and rule 13 below, the appellant, the Commissioner and any other party to the proceedings.

(4) No copy may be sent under paragraph (3)(b) above before the period of 42 days referred to in rule 13(2)(b) below has expired unless the relevant Minister has indicated that he does not object.

(5) A reply under this rule may include a request for an early determination of the appeal and the reasons for that request.

[1130]

NOTES

Commencement: 1 February 2005.

10 Amendment and supplementary grounds

(1) With leave of the Tribunal, the appellant may amend his notice of appeal or deliver supplementary grounds of appeal.

(2) Rule 7(1) above and rule 12 below apply to an amended notice of appeal and to supplementary grounds of appeal provided under paragraph (1) above as they apply to a notice of appeal.

(3) Upon receipt of a copy of an amended notice of appeal or supplementary grounds of appeal under rule 7(1) above;

(a) the relevant Minister may amend his notice in reply, and

(b) in the case of an appeal under section 28(6) of the 1998 Act, the respondent data controller may amend his reply to the notice of appeal.

(4) An amended notice or reply under paragraph (3) above must be served on the Tribunal within 28 days of the date on which the copy referred to in that paragraph is received by

(a) the relevant Minister, or

(b) the respondent data controller,

as the case may be.

(5) Without prejudice to paragraph (3) above, and with the leave of the Tribunal—

(a) the relevant Minister may amend a notice in reply, and

(b) the respondent data controller,

may amend a reply to the notice of appeal.

(6) Rule 8(3) above and rules 12(1)(b) and 13(1)(a) below apply to an amended notice in reply by the relevant Minister provided under paragraph (3) or (5) above as they do to a reply.

(7) Rule 9(3) and (4) above and rules 12(1)(c) and 13(1)(b) below apply to an amended reply by the respondent data controller provided under paragraph (3) or (5) above as they do to a reply.

[1131]

NOTES

Commencement: 1 February 2005.

11 Application for striking out

(1) Where the relevant Minister or, in the case of an appeal under section 28(6) of the Act, the respondent data controller is of the opinion that an appeal does not lie to, or cannot be entertained by, the Tribunal, or that the notice of appeal discloses no reasonable grounds of appeal, he may include in his notice under rule 8 or, as the case may be, his reply under rule 9 above a notice to that effect stating the grounds for such contention and applying for the appeal to be struck out.

(2) An application under this rule may be heard as a preliminary issue or at the beginning of the hearing of the substantive appeal.

[1132]

NOTES

Commencement: 1 February 2005.

12 Summary disposal of appeals

(1) Where, having considered—

(a) the notice of appeal,

(b) the relevant Minister's notice in reply, and

(c) in the case of an appeal under section 28(6) of the 1998 Act, the respondent data controller's reply,

the Tribunal is of the opinion that the appeal is of such a nature that it can properly be determined by dismissing it forthwith, it may, subject to the provisions of this rule, so determine the appeal.

(2) Where the Tribunal proposes to determine an appeal under paragraph (1) above, it must first notify the appellant and the relevant Minister of the proposal.

(3) A notification to the appellant under paragraph (2) above must contain particulars of the appellant's entitlements set out in paragraph (4) below.

(4) An appellant notified in accordance with paragraph (2) above is entitled, within such time as the Tribunal may reasonably allow—

(a) to make written representations, and

(b) to request the Tribunal to hear oral representations

against the proposal to determine the appeal under paragraph (1) above.

(5) Where an appellant requests a hearing under paragraph (4)(b) above, the Tribunal shall, as soon as practicable and with due regard to the convenience of the appellant, appoint a time and place for a hearing accordingly.

(6) The proper officer shall send to the appellant a notice informing him of—

(a) the time and place of any hearing under paragraph (5) above which, unless the appellant otherwise agrees, shall not be earlier than 14 days after the date on which the notice is sent, and

(b) the effect of rule 23 below.

(7) The Tribunal must, as soon as practicable, notify the appellant and the relevant Minister if, having given a notification under paragraph (2) above, it ceases to propose to determine the appeal under paragraph (1) above.

[1133]

NOTES

Commencement: 1 February 2005.

13 Relevant Minister's objection to disclosure

(1) Where a Minister objects, on grounds of the need to secure that information is not disclosed contrary to the interests of national security, to the disclosure of—

(a) his notice in reply to the appellant, to the Commissioner or, in the case of an appeal under section 28(6) of the 1998 Act, to the respondent data controller; or

(b) the reply of a respondent data controller, to the appellant or the Commissioner,

he may send a notice of objection to the Tribunal.

(2) A notice of objection under paragraph (1) above must be sent—

(a) where paragraph (1)(a) above applies, with the notice in reply; and

(b) where paragraph (1)(b) above applies, within 42 days of the date on which he receives the copy mentioned in rule 9(3) above.

(3) A notice of objection under paragraph (1) above shall be in writing and shall—

(a) state the reasons for the objection; and

(b) where paragraph (1)(a) above applies, if and to the extent that it is possible to do so without disclosing information contrary to the interests of national security, be

PART II DATA PROTECTION

accompanied by a version of the relevant Minister's notice in a form which can be shown to the appellant, the Commissioner or, as the case may be, the respondent data controller.

(4) Where the relevant Minister sends a notice of objection under paragraph (1) above, the Tribunal must not disclose the material in question otherwise than in accordance with rule 18 below.

[1134]

NOTES

Commencement: 1 February 2005.

14 Withdrawal of appeal

(1) The appellant may at any time before a determination is made withdraw his appeal by sending to the Tribunal a notice of withdrawal in writing and signed by him or on his behalf.

(2) Upon receipt of a notice under paragraph (1) above, the proper officer shall send a copy of that notice to—

(a) the relevant Minister,
(b) the Commissioner, and
(c) in the case of an appeal under section 28(6) of the 1998 Act, the respondent data controller.

(3) A notice of withdrawal shall, if sent by post in accordance with rule 31(2) below, have effect on the date on which it is received for dispatch by the Post Office.

(4) Where an appeal is withdrawn under this rule, a fresh appeal may not be brought by the same appellant in relation to the same disputed certification except with the leave of the Tribunal.

[1135]

NOTES

Commencement: 1 February 2005.

15 Consolidation of appeals

(1) Subject to paragraph (2) below, where in the case of two or more appeals to which these Rules apply it appears to the Tribunal—

(a) that some common questions of law or fact arise in both or all of them, or
(b) that for some other reason it is desirable to proceed with the appeals under this rule,

the Tribunal may order that the appeals be consolidated or heard together.

(2) The Tribunal shall not make an order under this rule without giving the parties and the relevant Minister an opportunity to show cause why such an order should not be made.

[1136]

NOTES

Commencement: 1 February 2005.

16 Directions

(1) This rule is subject to rule 17 below.

(2) In this rule, references to a "party" include the relevant Minister notwithstanding that he may not be a party to an appeal under section 28(6) of the 1998 Act.

(3) Subject to paragraphs (7) and (8) below, the Tribunal may at any time of its own motion or on the application of any party give such direction as it thinks proper to enable the parties to prepare for the hearing of the appeal or to assist the Tribunal to determine the issues.

(4) Such directions may in particular—

(a) provide for a particular matter to be dealt with as a preliminary issue and for a pre-hearing review to be held;
(b) provide for—

(i) the exchange between the parties of lists of documents held by them which are relevant to the appeal,
(ii) the inspection by the parties of the documents so listed,
(iii) the exchange between the parties of statements of evidence, and
(iv) the provision by the parties to the Tribunal of statements or lists of agreed matters;

(c) require any party to send to the Tribunal and to the other parties—
(i) statements of facts and statements of the evidence which will be adduced, including such statements provided in modified or edited form;
(ii) a skeleton argument which summarises the submissions which will be made and cites the authorities which will be relied upon, identifying any particular passages to be relied upon;
(iii) a chronology of events;
(iv) any other particulars or supplementary statements which may reasonably be required for the determination of the appeal;
(v) any document or other material which the Tribunal may require and which it is in the power of that party to deliver;
(vi) an estimate of the time which will be needed for any hearing;
(vii) by a specified date, any written submissions on which the party intends to rely at a hearing that he does not intend to attend or at which he does not intend to be represented; and
(viii) a list of the witnesses he intends to call to give evidence at any hearing;

(d) limit the length of oral submissions and the time allowed for the examination and cross-examination of witnesses; and

(e) limit the number of expert witnesses to be heard on either side.

(5) If, following the determination of any matter at a pre-hearing review directed in accordance with paragraph (4)(a) above, the Tribunal is of the opinion that its decision as to that matter substantially disposes of the whole appeal, the Tribunal may treat the pre-hearing review as the hearing of the appeal and may give such direction as it thinks fit to dispose of the appeal.

(6) The Tribunal may, subject to any specific provision in these Rules, specify time limits for steps to be taken in the proceedings and may extend any time limit.

(7) Nothing in this rule may require the production of any document or other material which the party could not be compelled to produce on the trial of an action in a court of law in that part of the United Kingdom where the appeal is to be determined.

(8) It shall be a condition of the supply of any information or material provided under this rule that any recipient of that information or material may use it only for the purposes of the appeal.

(9) The power to give directions may be exercised in the absence of the parties.

(10) Notice of any directions given under this rule shall be served on all the parties, and the Tribunal may, on the application of any party, set aside or vary such direction.

(11) If a party does not comply with any direction given under these Rules, the Tribunal may—

(a) dismiss the whole or part of the appeal or application; or

(b) strike out the whole or part of a Minister's or a respondent data controller's reply or notice in reply and, where appropriate, direct that a Minister or a respondent data controller shall not contest the appeal.

(12) But the Tribunal must not dismiss, strike out or give a direction unless it has sent a notice to the party who has not complied giving that party the opportunity to comply within such period as the Tribunal may specify in the notice or to show cause why the Tribunal should not dismiss, strike out or give such a direction.

[1137]

NOTES

Commencement: 1 February 2005.

17 Applications by relevant Minister

(1) This rule applies in any case where the Tribunal proposes to—

(a) give or vary any direction under rule 16 above or rule 19(2) below,

PART II DATA PROTECTION

(b) issue a summons under rule 21 below, or
(c) certify or publish a determination under rule 28 below.

(2) Before the Tribunal proceeds as proposed in any case to which this rule applies, it must first notify the relevant Minister of the proposal.

(3) If the relevant Minister considers that proceeding as proposed by the Tribunal would cause information that is or would be exempt by virtue of a provision in Part II of the 2000 Act to be disclosed, he may make an application to the Tribunal requesting it to reconsider the proposal or reconsider it to any extent.

(4) An application by the relevant Minister under paragraph (3) above must be made within 14 days of receipt of notification under paragraph (2) above, and the Tribunal must not proceed as proposed in any case to which this rule applies before that period has expired, otherwise than in accordance with rule 18 below, unless the Minister has indicated that he does not object.

(5) Where the relevant Minister makes an application under this rule, the Tribunal must not proceed as proposed otherwise than in accordance with rule 18 below.

[1138]

NOTES

Commencement: 1 February 2005.

18 Determination on relevant Minister's objections and applications

(1) Except where rule 12 above applies, the Tribunal shall determine whether to uphold any objection of the relevant Minister under rule 13 above, and any application under rule 17 above, in accordance with this rule.

(2) Subject to paragraph (3) below, proceedings under this rule shall take place in the absence of the parties.

(3) The relevant Minister may attend any proceedings under this rule, whether or not he is a party to the appeal in question.

(4) An objection under rule 13 above must be considered under this rule as a preliminary issue, and an application under rule 17 above may be considered as a preliminary issue or at the hearing of the substantive appeal.

(5) Where, in the case of an objection under rule 13 above, the Tribunal is minded to overrule the relevant Minister's objection, or to require him to provide a version of his notice in a form other than that which he provided it under rule 13(3)(b) above, the Tribunal must invite the relevant Minister to make oral representations.

(6) Where the Tribunal under paragraph (5) above overrules an objection by the relevant Minister under rule 13 above, or requires him to provide a version of his notice in a form other than that in which he provided it under rule 13(3)(b) above, the Tribunal shall not disclose, and the relevant Minister shall not be required to disclose, any material which was the subject of the unsuccessful objection if the relevant Minister chooses not to rely upon it in opposing the appeal.

(7) Where, in the case of an objection under rule 13 above, the Tribunal upholds the relevant Minister's objection and either—

(a) approves the version of his notice provided under rule 13(3)(b), or
(b) requires him to provide a version of his notice in a form other than that in which he provided it under rule 13(3)(b),

rule 8(3) above applies to that version of the notice.

[1139]

NOTES

Commencement: 1 February 2005.

19 Power to determine without a hearing

(1) Without prejudice to rule 12 above, where either—

(a) the parties so agree in writing, or
(b) it appears to the Tribunal that the issues raised on the appeal have been determined

on a previous appeal brought by the appellant on the basis of facts which did not materially differ from those to which the appeal relates and the Tribunal has given the parties an opportunity of making representations to the effect that the appeal ought not to be determined without a hearing,

the Tribunal may determine an appeal, or any particular issue, without a hearing.

(2) Before determining any matter under this rule the Tribunal may, subject to rule 17 above, if it thinks fit direct any party to provide in writing further information about any matter relevant to the appeal within such time as the Tribunal may allow.

[1140]

NOTES

Commencement: 1 February 2005.

20 Time and place of hearings

(1) Subject to rules 12 and 19 above, where the Tribunal has directed that a hearing shall take place the Tribunal shall appoint a time and place for a hearing of the appeal as soon as practicable, with due regard to the convenience of the parties and to any request for an early hearing under any of rules 5(5), 8(4) or 9(5) above.

(2) Except in relation to a hearing under rule 12(5) above, the proper officer shall send to each party, the Commissioner and the relevant Minister a notice informing him of the time and place of any hearing, which, unless the parties otherwise agree, shall not be earlier than 14 days after the date on which the notice is sent.

(3) A notice to a party under this rule shall inform him of the effect of rule 23 below.

(4) The Tribunal may—

(a) postpone the time appointed for any hearing;

(b) adjourn a hearing to such time as the Tribunal may determine; or

(c) alter the place appointed for any hearing;

and, if it exercises any of the powers above, it shall notify each person previously notified of that hearing under this rule or rule 12(6) above, and any person summoned under rule 21 below to attend as a witness at that hearing, of the revised arrangements.

[1141]

NOTES

Commencement: 1 February 2005.
Order: the Disability Discrimination Act 2005 (Commencement No 2) Order 2005, SI 2005/2774.

21 Summoning of witnesses

(1) This rule is subject to rule 17 above.

(2) Subject to paragraph (3) below, the Tribunal may by summons require any person in the United Kingdom to attend as a witness at a hearing of an appeal at such time and place as may be specified in the summons and, subject to rule 27(2) and (3) below, at the hearing to answer any questions or produce any documents in his custody or under his control which relate to any matter in question in the appeal.

(3) No person shall be required to attend in obedience to a summons under paragraph (2) above unless he has been given at least 7 days' notice of the hearing or, if less than 7 days, he has informed the Tribunal that he accepts such notice as he has been given.

(4) The Tribunal may, upon the application of a person summoned under this rule, set the summons aside.

(5) A person who has attended a hearing as a witness in obedience to a summons shall be entitled to such sum as the Tribunal may consider reasonable in respect of his attendance at, and his travelling to and from, the hearing; and where the summons was issued at the request of a party, such sum shall be paid or tendered to him by that party.

(6) In relation to proceedings before the Tribunal in Scotland, in this rule "summons" means citation and the provisions of this rule are to be construed accordingly.

[1142]

NOTES
Commencement: 1 February 2005.

22 Representation at a hearing

(1) At any hearing by the Tribunal, other than a hearing under rule 12 above—
- (a) a party may, subject to rules 18(2) above and 24(3) below, conduct his case himself or may appear and be represented by any person whom he may appoint for the purpose, and
- (b) the relevant Minister may appear and be represented by any person whom he may appoint for the purpose.

(2) At any hearing by the Tribunal under rule 12(5) above, the appellant may conduct his case himself or may appear and be represented by any person whom he may appoint for the purpose.

(3) If the appellant or the relevant Minister does not intend to attend or be represented at a hearing, he must inform the Tribunal of his intention, and in such a case may send to the Tribunal additional written representations in support of his appeal.

[1143]

NOTES
Commencement: 1 February 2005.

23 Default of appearance at hearing

If, without furnishing the Tribunal with sufficient reason for his absence, a party fails to appear at a hearing, having been duly notified of the hearing, the Tribunal may, if that party is the appellant, dismiss the appeal or, in any case, hear and determine the appeal, or any particular issue, in the party's absence and may make such order as to costs as it thinks fit.

[1144]

NOTES
Commencement: 1 February 2005.

24 Hearings to be in private

(1) All hearings by the Tribunal (including preliminary hearings) shall be in private unless the Tribunal, with the consent of the parties and the relevant Minister, directs that the hearing or any part of the hearing shall take place in public.

(2) Where the Tribunal sits in private it may, with the consent of the parties and the relevant Minister, admit to a hearing such persons on such terms and conditions as it considers appropriate.

(3) Where the Tribunal considers it necessary for any party who is not the relevant Minister to be excluded from the proceedings or any part of them to secure that information is not disclosed contrary to the interests of national security, it must—
- (a) direct accordingly,
- (b) inform the person excluded of its reasons, to the extent that it is possible to do so without disclosing information contrary to the interests of national security, and record those reasons in writing, and
- (c) inform the relevant Minister.

(4) The relevant Minister, or a person authorised to act on his behalf, may attend any hearing, other than a hearing under rule 12 above, notwithstanding that it is in private.

[1145]

NOTES
Commencement: 1 February 2005.

25 Conduct of proceedings at hearing

(1) Subject to rules 23 and 24(3) above, the Tribunal shall at the hearing of an appeal give to each party and the relevant Minister an opportunity—

(a) to address the Tribunal and to amplify orally written statements previously furnished under these Rules, to give evidence and to call witnesses, and to put questions to any person giving evidence before the Tribunal, and
(b) to make representations on the evidence (if any) and on the subject matter of the appeal generally but, where evidence is taken, such opportunity shall not be given before the completion of the taking of evidence.

(2) Except as provided by these Rules, the Tribunal shall conduct the proceedings in such a manner as it considers appropriate in the circumstances for discharging its functions and shall so far as appears to it to be appropriate seek to avoid formality in its proceedings.

[1146]

NOTES

Commencement: 1 February 2005.

26 Preliminary and incidental matters

As regards matters preliminary or incidental to an appeal, the president may act for the Tribunal under rules 6(3), 9(2), 10, 14 to 16, 20(1) and (4)(a) and (c), 21 and 25.

[1147]

NOTES

Commencement: 1 February 2005.

27 Evidence

(1) The Tribunal may receive in evidence any document or information notwithstanding that such document or information would be inadmissible in a court of law.

(2) No person shall be compelled to give any evidence or produce any document which he could not be compelled to give or produce on the trial of an action in a court of law in that part of the United Kingdom where the appeal is to be determined.

(3) The Tribunal may require oral evidence of a witness (including a party) to be given on oath or affirmation and for that purpose the president or the proper officer shall have the power to administer oaths or take affirmations.

[1148]

NOTES

Commencement: 1 February 2005.

28 Determination of appeal

(1) As soon as practicable after the Tribunal has determined an appeal, the president shall certify in writing that determination and sign and date the certificate.

(2) If and to the extent that it is possible to do so without disclosing information which is or would be exempt by virtue of a provision in Part II of the 2000 Act, and subject to rule 17 above, the certificate shall include—
(a) any material finding of fact, and
(b) the reasons for the decision.

(3) The proper officer shall send a copy of the certificate to—
(a) the parties,
(b) the relevant Minister, and
(c) the Commissioner.

(4) Subject to rule 17 above, the Tribunal shall make arrangements for the publication of its determination but in doing so shall have regard to—
(a) the desirability of safeguarding—
(i) the privacy of data subjects,
(ii) commercially sensitive material,
(iii) any information which is or would be exempt by virtue of any provision in Part II of the 2000 Act, and
(b) the need to secure that information is not disclosed contrary to the interests of national security.

and for those purposes may make any necessary amendments to the text of the certificate.

(5) For the purposes of this rule (but without prejudice to its generality), the disclosure of information is to be regarded as contrary to the interests of national security if it would indicate the existence or otherwise of any material, where that indication would itself be contrary to the interests of national security.

[1149]

NOTES

Commencement: 1 February 2005.

29 Costs

(1) In any appeal before the Tribunal, including one withdrawn under rule 14 above, the Tribunal may make an order awarding costs—

(a) in the case of an appeal under section 28(4) of the 1998 Act, section 60(1) of the 2000 Act or section 60(1) of the 2000 Act as applied by regulation 18(1), as modified by regulation 18(7) of the 2004 Regulations—

(i) against the appellant and in favour of the relevant Minister where it considers that the appeal was manifestly unreasonable;

(ii) against the relevant Minister and in favour of the appellant where it allows the appeal and quashes the disputed certificate, or does so to any extent;

(iii) against the relevant Minister and in favour of the appellant where, before the Tribunal has made a determination, the relevant Minister withdraws the certificate to which the appeal relates

(b) in the case of an appeal under section 28(6) of the 1998 Act, section 60(4) of the 2000 Act or section 60(4) of the 2000 Act as applied by regulation 18(1), as modified by regulation 18(7) of the 2004 Regulations—

(i) against the appellant and in favour of any other party where it dismisses the appeal, or dismisses it to any extent;

(ii) in favour of the appellant and against any other party where it allows the appeal, or allows it to any extent; and

(c) where it considers that a party has been responsible for frivolous, vexatious, improper or unreasonable action, or for any failure to comply with a direction or any delay which with diligence could have been avoided, against that party and in favour of the other or others.

(2) The Tribunal shall not make an order under paragraph (1) above awarding costs against a party without first giving that party an opportunity of making representations against the making of the order.

(3) An order under paragraph (1) above may be to the party or parties in question to pay to the other party or parties either a specified sum in respect of the costs incurred by that other party or parties in connection with the proceedings or the whole or part of such costs as taxed (if not otherwise agreed).

(4) Any costs required by an order under this rule to be taxed must be taxed in the county court according to such of the scales prescribed by the county court rules for proceedings in the county court as shall be directed by the order.

(5) In relation to proceedings before the Tribunal in Scotland, for the purposes of the application of paragraph (4) above, for the reference to the county court and the county court rules there shall be substituted reference to the sheriff court and the sheriff court rules and for the reference to proceedings there shall be substituted a reference to civil proceedings.

[1150]

NOTES

Commencement: 1 February 2005.

30 Irregularities

(1) Any irregularity resulting from failure to comply with any provision of these Rules or of any direction of the Tribunal before the Tribunal has reached its decision shall not of itself render the proceedings void, but the Tribunal may, and shall if it considers that any person may have been prejudiced by that irregularity, give such directions or take such steps as it thinks fit before reaching its decision to cure or waive the irregularity, whether by amendment of any document, the giving of notice or otherwise.

(2) Clerical mistakes in any document recording or certifying a direction, decision or determination of the Tribunal or president, or errors arising in such document from an accidental slip or omission, may at any time be corrected by the president by certificate signed by him.

[1151]

NOTES

Commencement: 1 February 2005.

31 Notices, etc

(1) Any notice or document required or authorised by these Rules to be served on or sent to any person or authority may be—

- (a) sent by post in a registered letter or by the recorded delivery service, or delivered by hand in accordance with paragraph (2) below,
- (b) sent by means of electronic communication in accordance with paragraph (3) below.

(2) A notice or other document required or authorised by these Rules to be served on or sent to any person or authority that is sent by post in a registered letter or by the recorded delivery service, or delivered by hand, must be sent or delivered—

- (a) in the case of the Tribunal, to the proper officer of the Tribunal;
- (b) in the case of the Commissioner or the relevant Minister, to him at his office;
- (c) in the case of any other party, to him or his representative at the address for service under these Rules.

(3) Any notice or other document required or authorised by these Rules to be served on or sent to any person or authority that is to be sent by means of electronic communication, must be sent—

- (a) in the case of the Tribunal, by such means and to such address as the proper officer may specify;
- (b) in the case of the Commissioner or the relevant Minister, by such means and to such address as he may specify;
- (c) in the case of any other party, by such means and to such address as he or his appointed representative may specify.

(4) Without prejudice to paragraph (3) above, no person shall be required to accept service of documents sent by electronic means unless they have indicated that they are prepared to accept such service.

(5) An appellant or respondent data controller may at any time by notice to the Tribunal change his address for service, or the manner in which he wishes to have service effected on him, under these Rules.

[1152]

NOTES

Commencement: 1 February 2005.

PART II DATA PROTECTION

INFORMATION TRIBUNAL (ENFORCEMENT APPEALS) RULES 2005

(SI 2005/14)

NOTES

Made: 7 January 2005.
Authority: Data Protection Act 1998, s 67(2), Sch 6, para 7.
Commencement: 1 February 2005.

ARRANGEMENT OF RULES

1 Citation and commencement

These Rules may be cited as the Information Tribunal (Enforcement Appeals) Rules 2005 and shall come into force on 1st February 2005.

[1153]

NOTES

Commencement: 1 February 2005.

2 (*Revokes the Data Protection Tribunal (Enforcement Appeals) Rules 2000, SI 2000/189 and the Information Tribunal (Enforcement Appeals) (Amendment) Rules 2002, SI 2002/2722.*)

3 Application and interpretation

(1) These Rules apply to appeals under section 48 of the 1998 Act, section 57 of the 2000 Act, and section 57 of the 2000 Act as applied, as modified, by regulation 18 of the 2004 Regulations and the provisions of these Rules are to be construed accordingly.

(2) In these Rules—

"the 1998 Act" means the Data Protection Act 1998;

"the 2000 Act" means the Freedom of Information Act 2000;

"the 2004 Regulations" means the Environmental Information Regulations 2004;

"appeal" means an appeal under—

(a) section 48 of the 1998 Act,

(b) section 57 of the 2000 Act, or

(c) section 57 of the 2000 Act as applied, as modified, by regulation 18 of the 2004 Regulations,

as the case may be;

"appellant" means—

(a) a person who brings or intends to bring an appeal under section 48 of the 1998 Act, or

(b) a complainant who, or a public authority which brings, or intends to bring, an appeal under section 57(1) of the 2000 Act or section 57(1) of the 2000 Act as applied, as modified, by regulation 18 of the 2004 Regulations, or

(c) a public authority which brings or intends to bring an appeal under section 57(2) of the 2000 Act or section 57(2) of the 2000 Act as applied, as modified, by regulation 18 of the 2004 Regulations,

as the case may be;

"chairman" means the chairman of the Tribunal, and includes a deputy chairman of the Tribunal presiding or sitting alone;

"costs"—

(a) except in Scotland, includes fees, charges, disbursements, expenses and remuneration;

(b) in Scotland means expenses, and includes fees, charges, disbursements and remuneration;

"disputed decision" means—

(a) in relation to an appeal under section 48 of the 1998 Act other than an appeal under section 48(3)(b) of that Act, the decision of the Commissioner,

(b) in relation to an appeal under section 48(3)(b) of the 1998 Act, the effect of a decision of the Commissioner, and

(c) in relation to an appeal under section 57 of the 2000 Act or section 57 as applied, as modified, by regulation 18 of the 2004 Regulations, the decision of the Commissioner,

against which the appellant appeals or intends to appeal to the Tribunal, as the case may be;

"hearing" means a sitting of the Tribunal for the purposes of enabling the Tribunal to take a decision on an appeal, or on any matter raised in relation to an appeal, at which the parties are entitled to attend and be heard;

"party" has the meaning given in paragraph (3) below; and

"proper officer" in relation to a rule means an officer or member of staff provided to the Tribunal under paragraph 14 of Schedule 5 to the 1998 Act and appointed by the chairman to perform the duties of a proper officer under that rule.

(3) In these Rules, "party" means the appellant, or the Commissioner, or a person joined to an appeal in accordance with rule 7 below and, except where the context otherwise requires, references in these Rules to a party (including a reference in rule 15 below) include a person appointed under rule 19(1) to represent his interests.

(4) In relation to proceedings before the Tribunal in Scotland, for the words "on the trial of an action" in rules 14(5), 15(8) and 27(2) below there is substituted "in a proof".

(5) Appeals brought before 1st January 2005 shall be determined in accordance with the Data Protection Tribunal (Enforcement Appeals) Rules 2000 and the Information Tribunal (Enforcement Appeals) (Amendment) Rules 2002.

[1154]

NOTES

Commencement: 1 February 2005.

4 Method of appealing—notice of appeal

(1) An appeal must be brought by a written notice of appeal served on the Tribunal.

(2) The notice of appeal shall—

(a) identify the disputed decision and the date on which the notice relating to the disputed decision was served on or given to the appellant; and

(b) state—

(i) the name and address of the appellant;

(ii) the grounds of the appeal;

(iii) whether or not the appellant considers that he is likely to wish a hearing to be held;

[(iv) where the appeal is brought under a provision of the 2000 Act, or the 2000 Act as applied, as modified, by regulation 18 of the 2004 Regulations, the name and address of the public authority to which the disputed decision relates;]

(v) where applicable, the special circumstances which the appellant considers justify the Tribunal's accepting jurisdiction under rule 5(2) below; and

(vi) an address for service of notices and other documents on the appellant.

(c) be signed by or on behalf of the appellant.

PART II DATA PROTECTION

(3) Where an appeal is brought under section 48(1) of the 1998 Act, section 57(2) of the 2000 Act or section 57(2) as applied, as modified, by regulation 18 of the 2004 Regulations in relation to an information notice, the notice of appeal shall also contain a statement of any representations the appellant wishes to make as to why it might be necessary in the interests of justice for the appeal to be heard and determined otherwise than by the chairman sitting alone as provided by rule 21(2) below.

(4) A notice of appeal may include a request for an early determination of the appeal and the reasons for that request.

[1155]

NOTES

Commencement: 1 February 2005.

Para (2): sub-para (b)(iv) substituted by the Information Tribunal (Enforcement Appeals) (Amendment) Rules 2005, SI 2005/450, rr 2, 3.

5 Time limit for appealing

(1) Subject to paragraph (2) below, a notice of appeal must be served on the Tribunal within 28 days of the date on which the notice relating to the disputed decision was served on or given to the appellant.

(2) The Tribunal may accept a notice of appeal served after the expiry of the period permitted by paragraph (1) above if it is of the opinion that, by reason of special circumstances, it is just and right to do so.

(3) A notice of appeal shall, if sent by post in accordance with rule 31(2) below, be treated as having been served on the date on which it is received for dispatch by the Post Office.

[1156]

NOTES

Commencement: 1 February 2005.

6 Acknowledgement of notice of appeal and notification to the Commissioner

(1) Upon receipt of a notice of appeal, the proper officer shall send—

(a) an acknowledgement of the service of a notice of appeal to the appellant, or to his representative if one has been appointed; and

(b) subject to paragraph (3) below, a copy of the notice of appeal to the Commissioner and to any other party to the proceedings.

(2) An acknowledgement of service under paragraph (1)(a) above shall be accompanied by a statement of the Tribunal's powers to award costs against an appellant under rule 29 below.

(3) Paragraph (1)(b) above does not apply to a notice of appeal under section 48(3) of the 1998 Act, but in such a case—

(a) the proper officer shall send a copy of the notice of appeal to the Commissioner if the Tribunal is of the opinion that the interests of justice require the Commissioner to assist it by giving evidence or being heard on any matter relating to the appeal, and

(b) where a copy is sent to the Commissioner under subparagraph (a) above, the jurisdiction referred to in paragraph 6(2) of Schedule 6 to the 1998 Act shall not be exercised ex parte.

[1157]

NOTES

Commencement: 1 February 2005.

7 Joinder of other persons to appeals

(1) This rule applies to an appeal under section 57 of the 2000 Act and section 57 of the 2000 Act as applied, as modified, by regulation 18(1) of the 2004 Regulations.

(2) If the Tribunal considers, whether on the application of a party or otherwise, that it is desirable that any person be made a party to an appeal, the Tribunal may order that person to be joined as a party.

(3) Any person who receives a copy of a notice of appeal or reply naming him as a person having an interest in the proceedings, or who otherwise claims an interest in the proceedings, may give notice ("a joinder notice") to the Tribunal that he wishes to be joined to the appeal.

(4) Where the Tribunal decides to make a person a party to an appeal, it shall—
- (a) issue that person with an order to that effect ("an order of joinder"), and
- (b) send a copy of that order, together with a copy of the joinder notice given in accordance with paragraphs (3) and (6) of this rule, to all other parties to the appeal.

(5) The Tribunal may give directions with regard to the joining of persons to appeals.

(6) A joinder notice must be in writing and must include—
- (a) the full name and address of the person seeking to be joined to the appeal;
- (b) a statement of the person's interest and whether or not he opposes the appeal, together with any reasons on which he relies in support of his interest; and
- (c) the name and address of any representative the person appoints, and whether the Tribunal should send correspondence and notices concerning the appeal to the representative instead.

(7) A person who wishes to be joined as a party to an appeal must also deliver to the Tribunal at least 3 copies of the joinder notice and any accompanying documents to enable the Tribunal to send a copy to each of the other parties.

(8) A joinder notice given under this rule shall, if the person giving it is made a party to the appeal, be treated as that person's reply to the notice of appeal.

[1158]

NOTES

Commencement: 1 February 2005.

8 Reply by Commissioner

(1) The Commissioner shall take the steps specified in paragraph (2) below—
- (a) where he receives a copy of a notice of appeal under rule 6(1)(b) above, within 21 days of the date of that receipt, and
- (b) where he receives a copy of a notice of appeal under rule 6(3)(a) above, within such time, not exceeding 21 days from the date of that receipt, as the Tribunal may allow.

(2) The steps are that the Commissioner must—
- (a) send to the Tribunal a copy of the notice relating to the disputed decision, and
- (b) send to the Tribunal and the appellant a written reply acknowledging service upon him of the notice of appeal, and stating—
  - (i) whether or not he intends to oppose the appeal and, if so,
  - (ii) the grounds upon which he relies in opposing the appeal.

(3) Before the expiry of the period referred to in paragraph (1) above which applies to the case, the Commissioner may apply to the Tribunal for an extension of that period, showing cause why, by reason of special circumstances, it would be just and right to do so, and the Tribunal may grant such extension as it considers appropriate.

(4) Where the appellant's notice of appeal has stated that he is not likely to wish a hearing to be held, the Commissioner shall in his reply inform the Tribunal and the appellant whether he considers that a hearing is likely to be desirable.

(5) Where an appeal is brought under section 48(1) of the 1998 Act, section 57(2) of the 2000 Act or section 57(2) of the 2000 Act as applied, as modified, by regulation 18 of the 2004 Regulations in relation to an information notice, the Commissioner may include in his reply a statement of representations as to why it might be necessary in the interests of justice for the appeal to be heard and determined otherwise than by the chairman sitting alone as provided by rule 21(2) below.

(6) A reply under this rule may include a request for an early determination of the appeal and the reasons for that request.

[1159]

NOTES

Commencement: 1 February 2005.

9 Application for striking out

(1) Subject to paragraph (3) below, where the Commissioner is of the opinion that an appeal does not lie to, or cannot be entertained by, the Tribunal, or that the notice of appeal discloses no reasonable grounds of appeal, he may include in his reply under rule 8(2) above a notice to that effect stating the grounds for such contention and applying for the appeal to be struck out.

(2) An application under this rule may be heard as a preliminary issue or at the beginning of the substantive appeal.

(3) This rule does not apply in the case of an appeal under section 48(3) of the 1998 Act. **[1160]**

NOTES

Commencement: 1 February 2005.

10 Summary disposal of appeals

(1) Where, having considered—
- (a) the notice of appeal, and
- (b) any reply to the notice of appeal,

the Tribunal is of the opinion that the appeal is of such a nature that it can properly be determined by dismissing it forthwith it may, subject to the provisions of this rule, so determine the appeal.

(2) Where the Tribunal proposes to determine an appeal under paragraph (1) above, it must first notify the appellant of the proposal.

(3) A notification to the appellant under paragraph (2) above must contain particulars of the appellant's entitlements set out in paragraph (4) below.

(4) An appellant notified in accordance with paragraph (2) above is entitled, within such time as the Tribunal may reasonably allow—
- (a) to make written representations, and
- (b) to request the Tribunal to hear oral representations

against the proposal to determine the appeal under paragraph (1) above.

(5) Where an appellant requests a hearing under paragraph (4)(b) above the Tribunal shall, as soon as practicable and with due regard to the convenience of the appellant, appoint a time and place for a hearing.

(6) The proper officer shall send to the appellant a notice informing him of—
- (a) the time and place of any hearing under paragraph (5) above which, unless the appellant otherwise agrees, shall not be earlier than 14 days after the date on which the notice is sent, and
- (b) the effect of rule 20 below.

(7) The Tribunal must, as soon as practicable, notify the appellant and any other party if, having given a notice under paragraph (2) above, it ceases to propose to determine the appeal under paragraph (1) above. **[1161]**

NOTES

Commencement: 1 February 2005.

11 Amendment and supplementary grounds

(1) With the leave of the Tribunal, the appellant may amend his notice of appeal or deliver supplementary grounds of appeal.

(2) Paragraphs (1) and (3) of rule 6 above apply to an amended notice of appeal and supplementary grounds of appeal provided under paragraph (1) above as they do to a notice of appeal.

(3) Upon receipt of a copy of an amended notice of appeal or of supplementary grounds of appeal under rule 6(1)(b) or (3)(a) above, the Commissioner may amend his reply to the notice of appeal, and must send the amended reply to the Tribunal, the appellant and any other person that has been joined as a party to the appeal—

(a) Where he receives a copy of an amended notice of appeal under rule 6(1)(b) above, within 21 days of the date of that receipt, and

(b) Where he receives a copy of an amended notice of appeal under rule 6(3)(a) above, within such time, not exceeding 21 days from the date of that receipt, as the Tribunal may allow.

(4) Rule 8(3) above applies to the periods referred to in paragraph (3) above.

(5) Upon receipt of a copy of an amended notice of appeal or of supplementary grounds of appeal under rule 6(1)(b) above, a person who has been joined as a party to the appeal in accordance with rule 7 above may amend his reply to the notice of appeal, and must send the amended reply to the Tribunal, the appellant and any other party to the appeal within 21 days of the date of that receipt.

(6) Without prejudice to paragraph (3) above, the Commissioner may, with the leave of the Tribunal, amend his reply to the notice of appeal and must send the amended reply to the Tribunal, the appellant and any other party to the appeal.

[1162]

NOTES

Commencement: 1 February 2005.

12 Withdrawal of appeal

(1) The appellant may at any time before the determination of the appeal withdraw his appeal by sending to the Tribunal a notice of withdrawal, and the proper officer shall send a copy of that notice to the Commissioner.

(2) A notice of withdrawal given under this rule shall be in writing and shall be signed by the appellant or on his behalf.

(3) A notice of withdrawal shall, if sent by post in accordance with rule 31(2) below, have effect on the date on which it is received for dispatch by the Post Office.

(4) Where an appeal is withdrawn under this rule, a fresh appeal may not be brought by the appellant in relation to the same disputed decision except with the leave of the Tribunal.

[1163]

NOTES

Commencement: 1 February 2005.

13 Consolidation of appeals

(1) Subject to paragraph (2) below, where in the case of two or more appeals to which these Rules apply it appears to the Tribunal—

(a) that some common question of law or fact arises in both or all of them, or

(b) that for some other reason it is desirable to proceed with the appeals under this rule,

the Tribunal may order that the appeals be consolidated or heard together.

(2) The Tribunal shall not make an order under this rule without giving the parties an opportunity to show cause why such an order should not be made.

[1164]

NOTES

Commencement: 1 February 2005.

14 Directions

(1) Subject to paragraphs (5) and (6) below, the Tribunal may at any time of its own motion or on the application of any party give such directions as it thinks proper to enable the parties to prepare for the hearing or to assist the Tribunal to determine the issues.

(2) Such directions may in particular—

(a) provide for a particular matter to be dealt with as a preliminary issue and for a pre-hearing review to be held;

(b) provide for—

(i) the exchange between the parties of lists of documents held by them which are relevant to the appeal;

(ii) the inspection by the parties of the documents so listed;

(iii) the exchange between the parties of statements of evidence; and

(iv) the provision by the parties to the Tribunal of statements or lists of agreed matters;

(c) make provision as to applications for the joinder of other persons to appeals, including giving directions as to the delivery of notices and other documents in such cases;

(d) require any party to send to the Tribunal and to any other party—

(i) statements of facts and statements of the evidence which will be adduced, including such statements provided in modified or edited form;

(ii) a skeleton argument which summarises the submissions which will be made and cites the authorities which will be relied upon, identifying any particular passages to be relied upon;

(iii) a chronology of events;

(iv) any other particulars or supplementary statements which may reasonably be required for the determination of the appeal;

(v) any document or other material which the Tribunal may require and which it is in the power of that party to deliver;

(vi) an estimate of the time which will be needed for any hearing; and

(vii) a list of the witnesses the party intends to call to give evidence at any hearing;

(e) limit the length of oral submissions and the time allowed for examination and cross-examination of witnesses; and

(f) limit the number of expert witnesses to be heard on either side.

(3) If, following the determination of any matter at a pre-hearing review, the Tribunal is of the opinion that its decision as to that matter substantially disposes of the whole appeal, the Tribunal may treat the pre-hearing review as the hearing of the appeal and may give such direction as it thinks fit to dispose of the appeal.

(4) The Tribunal may, subject to any specific provision in these Rules, specify time limits for steps to be taken in the proceedings and may extend any time limit.

(5) Nothing in this rule may require the production of any document or other material which the party could not be compelled to produce on the trial of an action in a court of law in that part of the United Kingdom where the appeal is to be determined.

(6) It shall be a condition of the supply of any information or material provided under this rule that any recipient of that information or material may use it only for the purposes of the appeal.

(7) The power to give directions may be exercised in the absence of the parties.

(8) Notice of any directions given under this rule shall be served on the parties, and the Tribunal may, on the application of any party, set aside or vary such directions.

[(9) If a party does not comply with any direction given under these Rules, the Tribunal may—

(a) dismiss the whole or part of the appeal or application; or

(b) strike out the whole or part of a public authority's, the Commissioner's or another party's notice in reply and where it does so, it may direct that any of them shall not contest the appeal.]

(10) But the Tribunal must not dismiss an appeal, strike out a reply or notice in reply or give a direction unless it has sent a notice to the party who has not complied giving that party the opportunity to comply within such period as the Tribunal may specify in the notice or to show cause why the Tribunal should not dismiss, strike out or so direct.

[1165]

NOTES

Commencement: 1 February 2005.

Para (9): substituted by the Information Tribunal (Enforcement Appeals) (Amendment) Rules 2005, SI 2005/450, rr 2, 4.

15 Power to require entry of premises for testing of equipment or material

(1) Subject to paragraph (8) below, the Tribunal may, for the purpose of determining an appeal, make an order requiring the occupier of any premises ("the occupier") to permit the Tribunal to enter those premises at a specified time and inspect, examine, operate or test any equipment on those premises used or intended to be used in connection with the processing of personal data or the storage or recording of other information, and to inspect, examine or test any documents or other material on those premises connected with the processing of personal data or the storage or recording of other information.

(2) An order under paragraph (1) above shall also require the occupier to permit the Tribunal to be accompanied by—

(a) the parties, and

(b) such number of the officers or members of staff provided to the Tribunal under paragraph 14 of Schedule 5 to the 1998 Act as it considers necessary.

(3) The Tribunal shall serve a copy of the order on the occupier and the parties.

(4) The time specified in the order shall not be earlier than 7 days after the date of service of the copy.

(5) The Tribunal may upon the application of the occupier set the order aside.

(6) Subject to paragraph (4) above, the Tribunal may upon the application of any person mentioned in paragraph (3) above alter the time specified in the order without being obliged to serve further copies under that paragraph, but shall notify the other persons so mentioned of the revised time.

(7) This rule also applies where the occupier is a party to the appeal.

(8) Documents or other material which the appellant could not be compelled to produce on the trial of an action in that part of the United Kingdom where the appeal is to be determined shall be immune from inspection, examination or testing under this rule.

[1166]

NOTES

Commencement: 1 February 2005.

16 Determination of appeal without a hearing

(1) Subject to these Rules, the Tribunal may determine an appeal without a hearing.

(2) Where a party makes a request for a hearing, the Tribunal shall grant the request unless it is satisfied that the appeal can properly be determined without a hearing.

(3) Where the Tribunal decides to refuse a request for a hearing, it shall send written notice to the party making the request either before or at the same time as it makes its decision.

(4) A notice sent under paragraph (3) above shall specify the Tribunal's reasons for refusing the request.

(5) The Tribunal may of its own motion and at any stage of an appeal, direct a hearing.

[1167]

NOTES

Commencement: 1 February 2005.

17 Time and place of hearings

(1) Subject to rules 14(3) and 16 above, where the Tribunal has directed that a hearing shall take place, the Tribunal shall appoint a time and place for the hearing as soon as practicable and with due regard to the convenience of the parties and any request made under rule 4(4) or 8(6) above.

(2) The proper officer shall send to each party a notice informing him of the time and place of any hearing.

(3) The reference to a "party" in paragraph (2) above does not include the Commissioner in the case of an appeal under section 48(3) of the 1998 Act other than a case to which rule 6(3)(a) above applies.

(4) The time notified under paragraph (1) above shall not be earlier than 14 days after the date on which the notice is sent unless—

(a) the parties agree otherwise, or

(b) the appellant agrees otherwise, and the hearing relates to an appeal under section 48(3) of the 1998 Act.

(5) A notice to a party under this rule shall inform him of the effect of rule 20 below.

(6) The Tribunal may—

(a) postpone the time appointed for any hearing;

(b) adjourn a hearing to such time as the Tribunal may determine; or

(c) alter the time and place appointed for any hearing;

and, if it exercises any of the above powers, it shall notify each party previously notified of that hearing under this rule, and any person summoned under rule 18 below to attend as a witness at that hearing, of the revised arrangements.

[1168]

NOTES

Commencement: 1 February 2005.

18 Summoning of witnesses

(1) Subject to paragraph (2) below, the Tribunal may by summons require any person in the United Kingdom to attend as a witness at a hearing of an appeal at such time and place as may be specified in the summons and, subject to rule 27(2) and (3) below, at the hearing to answer any questions or produce any documents in his custody or under his control which relate to any matter in question in the appeal.

(2) No person shall be required to attend in obedience to a summons under paragraph (1) above unless he has been given at least 7 days' notice of the hearing or, if less than 7 days, he has informed the Tribunal that he accepts such notice as he has been given.

(3) The Tribunal may, upon the application of a person summoned under this rule, set the summons aside.

(4) A person who has attended a hearing as a witness in obedience to a summons shall be entitled to such sum as the Tribunal considers reasonable in respect of his attendance at, and his travelling to and from, the hearing; and where the summons was issued at the request of a party such sum shall be paid or tendered to him by that party.

(5) In relation to proceedings before the Tribunal in Scotland, in this rule "summons" means citation and the provisions of this rule are to be construed accordingly.

[1169]

NOTES

Commencement: 1 February 2005.

19 Representation at a hearing

(1) At any hearing by the Tribunal a party may conduct his case himself or may appear and be represented by any person whom he may appoint for the purpose.

(2) In this rule, references to a "party" do not include the Commissioner in the case of an appeal under section 48(3) of the 1998 Act other than a case to which rule 6(3)(a) above applies.

(3) If the appellant does not intend to attend or be represented at a hearing, he must inform the Tribunal of his intention, and in such a case may send to the Tribunal additional written representations in support of his appeal.

[1170]

NOTES

Commencement: 1 February 2005.

20 Default of appearance at hearing

If, without furnishing the Tribunal with sufficient reason for his absence, a party fails to appear at a hearing, having been duly notified of the hearing, the Tribunal may, if that party is the appellant, dismiss the appeal or, in any case, hear and determine the appeal, or any particular issue, in the party's absence and may make such order as to costs as it thinks fit.

[1171]

NOTES

Commencement: 1 February 2005.

21 Hearings and determinations in the case of appeals against an information notice

(1) This rule applies to any appeal under section 48(1) of the 1998 Act, section 57(2) of the 2000 Act or section 57(2) as applied, as modified, by regulation 18 of the 2004 Regulations in respect of an information notice.

(2) Subject to paragraph (3) below, any hearing of or relating to an appeal to which this rule applies shall be by the chairman sitting alone, and any appeal or issue relating to an appeal to which this rule applies shall be determined by the chairman sitting alone.

(3) Paragraph (2) above does not apply where it appears to the chairman that a hearing or determination by the Tribunal constituted in accordance with paragraph 4 of Schedule 6 to the 1998 Act is necessary in the interests of justice, taking into account any representations made under rule 4(3) or 8(5) above.

[1172]

NOTES

Commencement: 1 February 2005.

22 Hearings in public or in private

(1) All hearings by the Tribunal (including preliminary hearings) shall be in public unless, having heard representations on the matter from the parties and having regard to the desirability of safeguarding—

(a) the privacy of data subjects; or

(b) commercially sensitive information; or

(c) any matter in respect of which an exemption contained in Part II of the 2000 Act is claimed,

the Tribunal directs that the hearing or any part of the hearing shall take place in private.

(2) Without prejudice to paragraph (3) and rule 23 below, the following persons, in addition to the parties, may attend a hearing notwithstanding that it is in private—

(a) the chairman or any deputy chairman or member of the Tribunal in his capacity as such, notwithstanding that they do not constitute the Tribunal for the purpose of the hearing; and

(b) any other person with the leave of the Tribunal and the consent of the parties present.

(3) Whether or not a hearing is held in public, a member of the Council on Tribunals or the Scottish Committee of the Council on Tribunals in his capacity as such may attend the hearing, and may remain present during the deliberations of the Tribunal but must not take part in the deliberations.

[1173]

NOTES

Commencement: 1 February 2005.

23 Power to exclude parties from hearings

(1) Where an application is made to the Tribunal by a Minister of the Crown for a party or parties to the appeal to be excluded from the proceedings or any part of them, the Tribunal shall grant such application and exclude that party or parties, if and only if it is satisfied that it is necessary for reasons of substantial public interest to do so.

(2) An application under paragraph (1) above shall be made to the Tribunal ex parte.

(3) Where the Tribunal considers it necessary, for reasons of substantial public interest, for any party to be excluded from the proceedings, it must—

(a) direct accordingly,

(b) inform the party or parties excluded of it reasons, to the extent that it is possible to do so without disclosing information contrary to the public interest, and

(c) inform the relevant Minister.

[1174]

NOTES

Commencement: 1 February 2005.

24 Conduct of proceedings at hearing

(1) Subject to rules 20 and 23 above, the Tribunal shall at the hearing of an appeal give to each party an opportunity—

(a) to address the Tribunal and to amplify orally written statements previously furnished under these Rules, to give evidence and to call witnesses, and to put questions to any person giving evidence before the Tribunal, and

(b) to make representations on the evidence (if any) and on the subject matter of the appeal generally but, where evidence is taken, such opportunity shall not be given before the completion of the taking of evidence.

(2) Subject to paragraph (3) below, in this rule, references to a "party" do not include the Commissioner in the case of an appeal under section 48(3) of the 1998 Act.

(3) In a case to which rule 6(3)(a) above applies, the Tribunal shall give the Commissioner the opportunity referred to in paragraph (1) above to the extent that it is of the opinion that the interests of justice require the Commissioner to assist it by giving evidence or being heard on any matter relating to the appeal.

(4) Except as provided by these Rules, the Tribunal shall conduct the proceedings in such manner as it considers appropriate in the circumstances for discharging its functions and shall so far as appears to it appropriate seek to avoid formality in its proceedings.

[1175]

NOTES

Commencement: 1 February 2005.

25 Preliminary and incidental matters

As regards matters preliminary or incidental to an appeal the chairman may act for the Tribunal under rules 5(2), 8(1) and (3), [10 to 16], 17(1) and (6)(a) and (c), 18 and 24(1) and (3).

[1176]

NOTES

Commencement: 1 February 2005.

Words in square brackets substituted by the Information Tribunal (Enforcement Appeals) (Amendment) Rules 2005, SI 2005/450, rr 2, 5.

26 Burden of proof

In any proceedings before the Tribunal relating to an appeal to which these Rules apply, other than an appeal under section 48(3) of the 1998 Act [or section 57(1) of the 2000 Act], it shall be for the Commissioner to satisfy the Tribunal that the disputed decision should be upheld.

[1177]

NOTES

Commencement: 1 February 2005.

Words in square brackets inserted by the Information Tribunal (Enforcement Appeals) (Amendment) Rules 2005, SI 2005/450, rr 2, 6.

27 Evidence

(1) The Tribunal may receive in evidence any document or information notwithstanding that such document or information would be inadmissible in a court of law.

(2) No person shall be compelled to given any evidence or produce any document which he could not be compelled to produce on the trial of an action in a court of law in that part of the United Kingdom where the appeal is to be determined.

(3) The Tribunal may require oral evidence of a witness (including a party) to be given on oath or affirmation and for that purpose the chairman or the proper officer shall have power to administer oaths or take affirmations.

[1178]

NOTES

Commencement: 1 February 2005.

28 Determination of appeal

(1) As soon as practicable after the Tribunal has determined an appeal, the chairman shall certify in writing that determination and sign and date the certificate.

(2) If and to the extent that it is possible to do so without disclosing information which is or would be exempt by virtue of any provision in Part II of the 2000 Act, the certificate shall include—

- (a) any material finding of fact, and
- (b) the reasons for the decision.

(3) The proper officer shall send a copy of the certificate to the parties.

(4) The Tribunal shall make arrangements for the publication of its determination but in doing so shall have regard to the desirability of safeguarding —

- (a) the privacy of data subjects,
- (b) commercially sensitive information, and
- (c) any information which is or would be exempt by virtue of any provision in Part II of the 2000 Act,

and for that purpose may make any necessary amendments to the text of the certificate.

[1179]

NOTES

Commencement: 1 February 2005.

29 Costs

(1) In any appeal before the Tribunal, including one withdrawn under rule 12 above, the Tribunal may make an order awarding costs—

- (a) against the appellant and in favour of the Commissioner where it considers that the appeal was manifestly unreasonable;
- (b) against the Commissioner and in favour of the appellant where it considers that the disputed decision was manifestly unreasonable;
- (c) where it considers that a party has been responsible for frivolous, vexatious, improper or unreasonable action, or for any failure to comply with a direction or any delay which with diligence could have been avoided, against that party and in favour of any other.

(2) The Tribunal shall not make an order under paragraph (1) above awarding costs against a party without first giving that party an opportunity of making representations against the making of the order.

(3) An order under paragraph (1) above may be to the party or parties in question to pay to the other party or parties either a specified sum in respect of the costs incurred by that other party or parties in connection with the proceedings or the whole or part of such costs as taxed (if not otherwise agreed).

(4) Any costs required by an order under this rule to be taxed may be taxed in the county court according to such of the scales prescribed by the county court rules for proceedings in the county court as shall be directed by the order.

(5) In relation to proceedings before the Tribunal in Scotland, for the purposes of the application of paragraph (4) above, for the reference to the county court and the county court rules there shall be substituted reference to the sheriff court and the sheriff court rules and for the reference to proceedings there shall be substituted a reference to civil proceedings.

[1180]

NOTES

Commencement: 1 February 2005.

30 Irregularities

(1) Any irregularity resulting from failure to comply with any provision of these Rules or of any direction of the Tribunal before the Tribunal has reached a decision shall not of itself render the proceedings void, but the Tribunal may, and shall if it considers that any person may have been prejudiced by that irregularity, give such directions or take such steps as it thinks fit before reaching its decision to cure or waive the irregularity, whether by amendment of any document, the giving of notice or otherwise.

(2) Clerical mistakes in any document recording or certifying a direction, decision or determination of the Tribunal or chairman, or errors arising in such a document from an accidental slip or omission may, at any time, be corrected by the chairman, by certificate signed by him.

[1181]

NOTES

Commencement: 1 February 2005.

31 Notices, etc

(1) Any document or other notice required or authorised by these Rules to be served on or sent to any person or authority may be—

(a) sent by post in a registered letter or by the recorded delivery service, or delivered by hand in accordance with paragraph (2) below, or

(b) by means of electronic communication in accordance with paragraph (3) below.

(2) A document or other notice required or authorised by these Rules to be served on or sent to any person or authority that is sent by post in a registered letter or by the recorded delivery service, or is delivered by hand, must be sent or delivered—

(a) in the case of the Tribunal, to the proper officer of the Tribunal;

(b) in the case of the Commissioner, to him at his office;

(c) in the case of an appellant or any other party, to him or his representative at the address for service under these Rules; and

(d) in the case of an occupier within the provisions of rule 14 above, to him at the premises in question.

(3) A document or other notice required or authorised by these Rules to be served on or sent to any person or authority that is sent by means of an electronic communication, must be sent—

(a) in the case of the Tribunal, by such means and to such address as the proper officer of the Tribunal may specify;

(b) in the case of the Commissioner, by such means and to such address as may be specified by the Commissioner for such purposes;

(c) in the case of an appellant, a respondent data controller or any other party, by such means and to such address as he may specify for such purposes.

(4) Without prejudice to paragraph (3) above, no person shall be required to accept service of documents sent by electronic means unless they have indicated that they are prepared to accept such service.

(5) A party may at any time by notice to the Tribunal change his address for service under these Rules.

[1182]

NOTES

Commencement: 1 February 2005.

DATA PROTECTION (PROCESSING OF SENSITIVE PERSONAL DATA) ORDER 2006

(SI 2006/2068)

NOTES

Made: 25 July 2006.
Authority: Data Protection Act 1998, s 67(2), Sch 3, para 10.
Commencement: 26 July 2006.

1 Citation, commencement and interpretation

(1) This Order may be cited as the Data Protection (Processing of Sensitive Personal Data) Order 2006 and shall come into force on the day after the day on which it is made.

(2) In this Order—

"the Act" means the Data Protection Act 1998;

"caution" means a caution given to any person in England and Wales or Northern Ireland in respect of an offence which, at the time when the caution is given, is admitted and includes a reprimand or warning to which section 65 of the Crime and Disorder Act 1998 applies;

"conviction" has the same meaning as in section 56 of the Act;

"payment card" includes a credit card, a charge card and a debit card;

"pseudo-photograph" includes an image, whether made by computer-graphics or otherwise howsoever, which appears to be a photograph.

[1183]

NOTES

Commencement: 26 July 2006.

2 Condition relevant for purposes of the First Principle: processing of sensitive personal data

(1) For the purposes of paragraph 10 of Schedule 3 to the Act, the circumstances specified in paragraph (2) are circumstances in which sensitive personal data may be processed.

(2) The processing of information about a criminal conviction or caution for an offence listed in paragraph (3) relating to an indecent photograph or pseudo-photograph of a child is necessary for the purpose of administering an account relating to the payment card used in the commission of the offence or for cancelling that payment card.

(3) The offences listed are those under—

(a) section 1 of the Protection of Children Act 1978,
(b) section 160 of the Criminal Justice Act 1988,
(c) article 15 of the Criminal Justice (Evidence etc) (Northern Ireland) Order 1988,
(d) article 3 of the Protection of Children (Northern Ireland) Order 1978,
(e) section 52 of the Civic Government (Scotland) Act 1982, or
(f) incitement to commit any of the offences in sub-paragraphs (a)–(e).

[1184]–[1500]

NOTES

Commencement: 26 July 2006.

INTERCEPTION OF COMMUNICATIONS: CODE OF PRACTICE (2002)

NOTES

Authority: Regulation of Investigatory Powers Act 2000, s 71(5). This Code of Practice came into force on 1 July 2002 (see SI 2002/1693).

PART II DATA PROTECTION

1 GENERAL

1.1 This code of practice relates to the powers and duties conferred or imposed under Chapter I of Part I of the Regulation of Investigatory Powers Act 2000 ("the Act"). It provides guidance on the procedures that must be followed before interception of communications can take place under those provisions. It is primarily intended for use by those public authorities listed in section 6(2) of the Act. It will also prove useful to postal and telecommunication operators and other interested bodies to acquaint themselves with the procedures to be followed by those public authorities.

1.2 The Act provides that all codes of practice relating to the Act are admissible as evidence in criminal and civil proceedings. If any provision of this code appears relevant before any court or tribunal considering any such proceedings, or to the Tribunal established under the Act, or to one of the Commissioners responsible for overseeing the powers conferred by the Act, it must be taken into account.

[1501]

2 GENERAL RULES ON INTERCEPTION WITH A WARRANT

2.1 There are a limited number of persons by whom, or on behalf of whom, applications for interception warrants may be made. These persons are—

- The Director-General of the Security Service.
- The Chief of the Secret Intelligence Service.
- The Director of GCHQ.
- The Director-General of the National Criminal Intelligence Service (NCIS handle interception on behalf of police forces in England and Wales).
- The Commissioner of the Police of the Metropolis (the Metropolitan Police Special Branch handle interception on behalf of Special Branches in England and Wales).
- The Chief Constable of the Police Service of Northern Ireland.
- The Chief Constable of any police force maintained under or by virtue of section 1 of the Police (Scotland) Act 1967.
- The Commissioners of Customs and Excise.
- The Chief of Defence Intelligence.
- A person who, for the purposes of any international mutual assistance agreement, is the competent authority of a country or territory outside the United Kingdom.

Any application made on behalf of one of the above must be made by a person holding office under the Crown.

2.2 All interception warrants are issued by the Secretary of State.[1] Even where the urgency procedure is followed, the Secretary of State personally authorises the warrant, although it is signed by a senior official.

2.3 Before issuing an interception warrant, the Secretary of State must believe that what the action seeks to achieve is necessary for one of the following section 5(3) purposes—

- in the interests of national security;
- for the purpose of preventing or detecting serious crime; or
- for the purpose of safeguarding the economic well-being of the UK;

and that the conduct authorised by the warrant is proportionate to what is sought to be achieved by that conduct.

Necessity and Proportionality

2.4 Obtaining a warrant under the Act will only ensure that the interception authorised is a justifiable interference with an individual's rights under Article 8 of the European Convention of Human Rights (the right to privacy) if it is necessary and proportionate for the interception to take place. The Act recognises this by first requiring that the Secretary of State believes that the authorisation is necessary on one or more of the statutory grounds set out in section 5(3) of the Act. This requires him to believe that it is necessary to undertake the interception which is to be authorised for a particular purpose falling within the relevant statutory ground.

2.5 Then, if the interception is necessary, the Secretary of State must also believe that it is proportionate to what is sought to be achieved by carrying it out. This involves balancing the intrusiveness of the interference, against the need for it in operational terms. Interception of communications will not be proportionate if it is excessive in the circumstances of the case or if the information which is sought could reasonably be obtained by other means. Further, all interception should be carefully managed to meet the objective in question and must not be arbitrary or unfair.

Implementation of Warrants

2.6 After a warrant has been issued it will be forwarded to the person to whom it is addressed, in practice the intercepting agency which submitted the application. The Act (section 11) then permits the intercepting agency to carry out the interception, or to require the assistance of other persons in giving effect to the warrant. Warrants cannot be served on those outside the jurisdiction of the UK.

Provision of Reasonable Assistance

2.7 Any postal or telecommunications operator (referred to as communications service providers) in the United Kingdom may be required to provide assistance in giving effect to an interception. The Act places a requirement on postal and telecommunications operators to take all such steps for giving effect to the warrant as are notified to them (section 11(4) of the Act). But the steps which may be required are limited to those which it is reasonably practicable to take (section 11(5)). What is reasonably practicable should be agreed after consultation between the postal or telecommunications operator and the Government. If no agreement can be reached it will be for the Secretary of State to decide whether to press forward with civil proceedings. Criminal proceedings may also be instituted by or with the consent of the Director of Public Prosecutions.

2.8 Where the intercepting agency requires the assistance of a communications service provider in order to implement a warrant, they should provide the following to the communications service provider—

- A copy of the warrant instrument signed and dated by the Secretary of State (or in an urgent case, by a senior official);
- The relevant schedule for that service provider setting out the numbers, addresses or other factors identifying the communications to be intercepted;
- A covering document from the intercepting agency requiring the assistance of the communications service provider and specifying any other details regarding the means of interception and delivery as may be necessary. Contact details with respect to the intercepting agency will either be provided in this covering document or will be available in the handbook provided to all postal and telecommunications operators who maintain an intercept capability.

Provision of Intercept Capability

2.9 Whilst all persons who provide a postal or telecommunications service are obliged to provide assistance in giving effect to an interception, persons who provide a public postal or telecommunications service, or plan to do so, may also be required to provide a reasonable intercept capability. The obligations the Secretary of State considers reasonable to impose on such persons to ensure they have such a capability will be set out in an order made by the Secretary of State and approved by Parliament. The Secretary of State may then serve a notice upon a communications service provider setting out the steps they must take to ensure they can meet these obligations. A notice will not be served without consultation over the content of the notice between the Government and the service provider having previously taken place. When served with such a notice, a communications service provider, if he feels it unreasonable, will be able to refer that notice to the Technical Advisory Board (TAB) on the reasonableness of the technical requirements and capabilities that are being sought. Details of how to submit a notice to the TAB will be provided either before or at the time the notice is served.

2.10 Any communications service provider obliged to maintain a reasonable intercept capability will be provided with a handbook which will contain the basic information they require to respond to requests for reasonable assistance for the interception of communications.

Duration of Interception Warrants

2.11 All interception warrants are valid for an initial period of three months. Upon renewal, warrants issued on serious crime grounds are valid for a further period of three months. Warrants renewed on national security/economic well-being grounds are valid for a further period of six months. Urgent authorisations are valid for five working days following the date of issue unless renewed by the Secretary of State.

2.12 Where modifications take place, the warrant expiry date remains unchanged. However, where the modification takes place under the urgency provisions, the modification instrument expires after five working days following the date of issue unless renewed following the routine procedure.

2.13 Where a change in circumstance prior to the set expiry date leads the intercepting agency to consider it no longer necessary or practicable for the warrant to be in force, it should be cancelled with immediate effect.

Stored Communications

2.14 Section 2(7) of the Act defines a communication in the course of its transmission as also encompassing any time when the communication is being stored on the communication system in such a way as to enable the intended recipient to have access to it. This means that a warrant can be used to obtain both communications that are in the process of transmission and those that are being stored on the transmission system.

2.15 Stored communications may also be accessed by means other than a warrant. If a communication has been stored on a communication system it may be obtained with lawful authority by means of an existing statutory power such as a production order (under the Police and Criminal Evidence Act 1984) or a search warrant.

[1502]

NOTES

[1] Interception warrants may be issued on "serious crime" grounds by Scottish Ministers, by virtue of arrangements made under the Scotland Act 1998. In this Code references to the Secretary of State should be read as including Scottish Ministers where appropriate. The functions of the Scottish Ministers also cover renewal and cancellation arrangements.

3 SPECIAL RULES ON INTERCEPTION WITH A WARRANT

Collateral Intrusion

3.1 Consideration should be given to any infringement of the privacy of individuals who are not the subject of the intended interception, especially where communications relating to religious, medical, journalistic or legally privileged material may be involved. An application for an interception warrant should draw attention to any circumstances which give rise to an unusual degree of collateral infringement of privacy, and this will be taken into account by the Secretary of State when considering a warrant application. Should an interception operation reach the point where individuals other than the subject of the authorisation are identified as directly relevant to the operation, consideration should be given to applying for separate warrants covering those individuals.

Confidential Information

3.2 Particular consideration should also be given in cases where the subject of the interception might reasonably assume a high degree of privacy, or where confidential information is involved. Confidential information consists of matters subject to legal privilege, confidential personal information or confidential journalistic material (see paragraphs 3.9–3.11). For example, extra consideration should be given where interception might involve communications between a minister of religion and an individual relating to the latter's spiritual welfare, or where matters of medical or journalistic confidentiality or legal privilege may be involved.

Communications Subject to Legal Privilege

3.3 Section 98 of the Police Act 1997 describes those matters that are subject to legal privilege in England and Wales. In relation to Scotland, those matters subject to legal privilege contained in section 33 of the Criminal Law (Consolidation) (Scotland) Act 1995 should be adopted. With regard to Northern Ireland, Article 12 of the Police and Criminal Evidence (Northern Ireland) Order 1989 should be referred to.

3.4 Legal privilege does not apply to communications made with the intention of furthering a criminal purpose (whether the lawyer is acting unwittingly or culpably). Legally privileged communications will lose their protection if there are grounds to believe, for example, that the professional legal advisor is intending to hold or use the information for a criminal purpose. But privilege is not lost if a professional legal advisor is properly advising a person who is suspected of having committed a criminal offence. The concept of legal privilege applies to the provision of professional legal advice by any individual, agency or organisation qualified to do so.

3.5 The Act does not provide any special protection for legally privileged communications. Nevertheless, intercepting such communications is particularly sensitive and is therefore subject to additional safeguards under this Code. The guidance set out below may in part depend on whether matters subject to legal privilege have been obtained intentionally or incidentally to some other material which has been sought.

3.6 In general, any application for a warrant which is likely to result in the interception of legally privileged communications should include, in addition to the reasons why it is considered necessary for the interception to take place, an assessment of how likely it is that communications which are subject to legal privilege will be intercepted. In addition, it should state whether the purpose (or one of the purposes) of the interception is to obtain privileged communications. This assessment will be taken into account by the Secretary of State in deciding whether an interception is necessary under section 5(3) of the Act and whether it is proportionate. In such circumstances, the Secretary of State will be able to impose additional conditions such as regular reporting arrangements so as to be able to exercise his discretion on whether a warrant should continue to be authorised. In those cases where communications which include legally privileged communications have been intercepted and retained, the matter should be reported to the Interception of Communications Commissioner during his inspections and the material be made available to him if requested.

3.7 Where a lawyer is the subject of an interception, it is possible that a substantial proportion of the communications which will be intercepted will be between the lawyer and his client(s) and will be subject to legal privilege. Any case where a lawyer is the subject of an investigation should be notified to the Interception of Communications Commissioner during his inspections and any material which has been retained should be made available to him if requested.

3.8 In addition to safeguards governing the handling and retention of intercept material as provided for in section 15 of the Act, caseworkers who examine intercepted communications should be alert to any intercept material which may be subject to legal privilege. Where there is doubt as to whether the communications are subject to legal privilege, advice should be sought from a legal adviser within the intercepting agency. Similar advice should also be sought where there is doubt over whether communications are not subject to legal privilege due to the "in furtherance of a criminal purpose" exception.

PART II DATA PROTECTION

Communications involving Confidential Personal Information and Confidential Journalistic Material

3.9 Similar consideration to that given to legally privileged communications must also be given to the interception of communications that involve confidential personal information and confidential journalistic material. Confidential personal information is information held in confidence concerning an individual (whether living or dead) who can be identified from it, and the material in question relates to his physical or mental health or to spiritual counselling. Such information can include both oral and written communications. Such information as described above is held in confidence if it is held subject to an express or implied undertaking to hold it in confidence or it is subject to a restriction on disclosure or an obligation of confidentiality contained in existing legislation. For example, confidential personal information might include consultations between a health professional and a patient, or information from a patient's medical records.

3.10 Spiritual counselling is defined as conversations between an individual and a Minister of Religion acting in his official capacity, and where the individual being counselled is seeking or the Minister is imparting forgiveness, absolution or the resolution of conscience with the authority of the Divine Being(s) of their faith.

3.11 Confidential journalistic material includes material acquired or created for the purposes of journalism and held subject to an undertaking to hold it in confidence, as well as communications resulting in information being acquired for the purposes of journalism and held subject to such an undertaking.

[1503]

4 INTERCEPTION WARRANTS (SECTION 8(1))

4.1 This section applies to the interception of communications by means of a warrant complying with section 8(1) of the Act. This type of warrant may be issued in respect of the interception of communications carried on any postal service or telecommunications system as defined in section 2(1) of the Act (including a private telecommunications system). Responsibility for the issuing of interception warrants rests with the Secretary of State.

Application for a Section 8(1) Warrant

4.2 An application for a warrant is made to the Secretary of State. Interception warrants, when issued, are addressed to the person who submitted the application. This person may then serve a copy upon any person who may be able to provide assistance in giving effect to that warrant. Each application, a copy of which must be retained by the applicant, should contain the following information—

- Background to the operation in question.
- Person or premises to which the application relates (and how the person or premises feature in the operation).
- Description of the communications to be intercepted, details of the communications service provider(s) and an assessment of the feasibility of the interception operation where this is relevant.[1]
- Description of the conduct to be authorised as considered necessary in order to carry out the interception,[2] where appropriate.
- An explanation of why the interception is considered to be necessary under the provisions of section 5(3).
- A consideration of why the conduct to be authorised by the warrant is proportionate to what is sought to be achieved by that conduct.
- A consideration of any unusual degree of collateral intrusion and why that intrusion is justified in the circumstances. In particular, where the communications in question might affect religious, medical or journalistic confidentiality or legal privilege, this must be specified in the application.
- Where an application is urgent, supporting justification should be provided.
- An assurance that all material intercepted will be handled in accordance with the safeguards required by section 15 of the Act.

Authorisation of a Section 8(1) Warrant

4.3 Before issuing a warrant under section 8(1), the Secretary of State must believe the warrant is necessary[3]—

- in the interests of national security;
- for the purpose of preventing or detecting serious crime; or
- for the purpose of safeguarding the economic well-being of the United Kingdom.

4.4 In exercising his power to issue an interception warrant for the purpose of safeguarding the economic well-being of the United Kingdom (as provided for by section 5(3)(c) of the Act), the Secretary of State will consider whether the economic well-being of the United Kingdom which is to be safeguarded is, on the facts of each case, directly related to state security. The term "state security", which is used in Directive 97/66/EC (concerning the processing of personal data and the protection of privacy in the telecommunications sector), should be interpreted in the same way as the term "national security" which is used elsewhere in the Act and this Code. The Secretary of State will not issue a warrant on section 5(3)(c) grounds if this direct link between the economic well-being of the United Kingdom and state security is not established. Any application for a warrant on section 5(3)(c) grounds should therefore explain how, in the applicant's view, the economic well-being of the United Kingdom which is to be safeguarded is directly related to state security on the facts of the case.

4.5 The Secretary of State must also consider that the conduct authorised by the warrant is proportionate to what it seeks to achieve (section 5(2)(b)). In considering necessity and proportionality, the Secretary of State must take into account whether the information sought could reasonably be obtained by other means (section 5(4)).

Urgent Authorisation of a Section 8(1) Warrant

4.6 The Act makes provision (section 7(1)(b)) for cases in which an interception warrant is required urgently, yet the Secretary of State is not available to sign the warrant. In these cases the Secretary of State will still personally authorise the interception but the warrant is signed by a senior official, following discussion of the case between officials and the Secretary of State. The Act restricts issue of warrants in this way to urgent cases where the Secretary of State has himself expressly authorised the issue of the warrant (section 7(2)(a)), and requires the warrant to contain a statement to that effect (section 7(4)(a)). A warrant issued under the urgency procedure lasts for five working days following the day of issue unless renewed by the Secretary of State, in which case it expires after 3 months in the case of serious crime or 6 months in the case of national security or economic well-being in the same way as other non-urgent section 8(1) warrants. An urgent case is one in which interception authorisation is required within a twenty four hour period.

Format of a Section 8(1) Warrant

4.7 Each warrant comprises two sections, a warrant instrument signed by the Secretary of State listing the subject of the interception or set of premises, a copy of which each communications service provider will receive, and a schedule or set of schedules listing the communications to be intercepted. Only the schedule relevant to the communications that can be intercepted by the specified communications service provider will be provided to that service provider.

4.8 The warrant instrument should include—

- The name or description of the interception subject or of a set of premises in relation to which the interception is to take place.
- A warrant reference number.
- The persons who may subsequently modify the scheduled part of the warrant in an urgent case (if authorised in accordance with section 10(8) of the Act).

4.9 The scheduled part of the warrant will comprise one or more schedules. Each schedule should contain—

- The name of the communication service provider, or the other person who is to take action.
- A warrant reference number.
- A means of identifying the communications to be intercepted.[4]

Modification of Section 8(1) warrant

4.10 Interception warrants may be modified under the provisions of section 10 of the Act. The unscheduled part of a warrant may only be modified by the Secretary of State or, in an urgent case, by a senior official with the express authorisation of the Secretary of State. In these cases, a statement of that fact must be endorsed on the modifying instrument, and the modification ceases to have effect after five working days following the day of issue unless it is renewed by the Secretary of State. The modification will then expire upon the expiry date of the warrant.

4.11 Scheduled parts of a warrant may be modified by the Secretary of State, or by a senior official[5] acting upon his behalf. A modification to the scheduled part of the warrant may include the addition of a new schedule relating to a communication service provider on whom a copy of the warrant has not been previously served. Modifications made in this way expire at the same time as the warrant expires. There also exists a duty to modify a warrant by deleting a communication identifier if it is no longer relevant. When a modification is sought to delete a number or other communication identifier, the relevant communications service provider must be advised and interception suspended before the modification instrument is signed.

4.12 In an urgent case, and where the warrant specifically authorises it, scheduled parts of a warrant may be modified by the person to whom the warrant is addressed (the person who submitted the application) or a subordinate (where the subordinate is identified in the warrant). Modifications of this kind are valid for five working days following the day of issue unless the modification instrument is endorsed by a senior official acting on behalf of the Secretary of State. Where the modification is endorsed in this way, the modification expires upon the expiry date of the warrant.

Renewal of a Section 8(1) Warrant

4.13 The Secretary of State may renew a warrant at any point before its expiry date. Applications for renewals must be made to the Secretary of State and should contain an update of the matters outlined in paragraph 4.2 above. In particular, the applicant should give an assessment of the value of interception to the operation to date and explain why he considers that interception continues to be necessary for one or more of the purposes in section 5(3).

4.14 Where the Secretary of State is satisfied that the interception continues to meet the requirements of the Act he may renew the warrant. Where the warrant is issued on serious crime grounds, the renewed warrant is valid for a further three months. Where it is issued on national security/economic well-being grounds, the renewed warrant is valid for six months. These dates run from the date of signature on the renewal instrument.

4.15 A copy of the warrant renewal instrument will be forwarded by the intercepting agency to all relevant communications service providers on whom a copy of the original warrant instrument and a schedule have been served, providing they are still actively assisting. A warrant renewal instrument will include the reference number of the warrant and description of the person or premises described in the warrant.

Warrant Cancellation

4.16 The Secretary of State is under a duty to cancel an interception warrant if, at any time before its expiry date, he is satisfied that the warrant is no longer necessary on grounds falling

PART II DATA PROTECTION

within section 5(3) of the Act. Intercepting agencies will therefore need to keep their warrants under continuous review. In practice, cancellation instruments will be signed by a senior official on his behalf.

4.17 The cancellation instrument should be addressed to the person to whom the warrant was issued (the intercepting agency) and should include the reference number of the warrant and the description of the person or premises specified in the warrant. A copy of the cancellation instrument should be sent to those communications service providers who have held a copy of the warrant instrument and accompanying schedule during the preceding twelve months.

Records

4.18 The oversight regime allows the Interception of Communications Commissioner to inspect the warrant application upon which the Secretary of State based his decision, and the applicant may be required to justify the content. Each intercepting agency should keep the following to be made available for scrutiny by the Commissioner as he may require—

- all applications made for warrants complying with section 8(1) and applications made for the renewal of such warrants;
- all warrants, and renewals and copies of schedule modifications (if any);
- where any application is refused, the grounds for refusal as given by the Secretary of State;
- the dates on which interception is started and stopped.

4.19 Records shall also be kept of the arrangements by which the requirements of section 15(2) (minimisation of copying and destruction of intercepted material) and section 15(3) (destruction of intercepted material) are to be met. For further details see section on "Safeguards".

4.20 The term "intercepted material" is used throughout to embrace copies, extracts or summaries made from the intercepted material as well as the intercept material itself.

[1504]

NOTES

1 This assessment is normally based upon information provided by the relevant communication service provider.

2 This conduct may include the interception of other communications (section 5(6)(a)).

3 A single warrant can be justified on more than one of the grounds listed.

4 This may include addresses, numbers, apparatus or other factors, or combination of factors, that are to be used for identifying communications (section 8(2) of the Act).

5 Neither the senior official to whom the warrant is addressed, nor any of his subordinates may modify the scheduled parts of the warrant, except in an urgent case where the warrant contains an expressly authorised provision to this effect.

5 INTERCEPTION WARRANTS (SECTION 8(4))

5.1 This section applies to the interception of external communications by means of a warrant complying with section 8(4) of the Act. External communications are defined by the Act to be those which are sent or received outside the British Islands. They include those which are both sent and received outside the British Islands, whether or not they pass through the British Islands in course of their transit. They do not include communications both sent and received in the British Islands, even if they pass outside the British Islands en route. Responsibility for the issuing of such interception warrants rests with the Secretary of State.

Application for a Section 8(4) Warrant

5.2 An application for a warrant is made to the Secretary of State. Interception warrants, when issued, are addressed to the person who submitted the application. This person may then serve a copy upon any person who may be able to provide assistance in giving effect to that warrant. Each application, a copy of which must be retained by the applicant, should contain the following information—

- Background to the operation in question.
- Description of the communications to be intercepted, details of the communications service provider(s) and an assessment of the feasibility of the operation where this is relevant.[1]
- Description of the conduct to be authorised, which must be restricted to the interception of external communications, or to conduct necessary[2] in order to intercept those external communications, where appropriate.
- The certificate that will regulate examination of intercepted material.

- An explanation of why the interception is considered to be necessary for one or more of the section 5(3) purposes.
- A consideration of why the conduct to be authorised by the warrant is proportionate to what is sought to be achieved by that conduct.
- A consideration of any unusual degree of collateral intrusion, and why that intrusion is justified in the circumstances. In particular, where the communications in question might affect religious, medical or journalistic confidentiality or legal privilege, this must be specified in the application.
- Where an application is urgent, supporting justification should be provided.
- An assurance that intercepted material will be read, looked at or listened to only so far as it is certified, and it meets the conditions of sections 16(2)–16(6) of the Act.
- An assurance that all material intercepted will be handled in accordance with the safeguards required by sections 15 and 16 of the Act.

Authorisation of a Section 8(4) warrant

5.3 Before issuing a warrant under section 8(4), the Secretary of State must believe that the warrant is necessary[3]—

- in the interests of national security;
- for the purpose of preventing or detecting serious crime; or
- for the purpose of safeguarding the economic well-being of the United Kingdom.

5.4 In exercising his power to issue an interception warrant for the purpose of safeguarding the economic well-being of the United Kingdom (as provided for by section 5(3)(c) of the Act), the Secretary of State will consider whether the economic well-being of the United Kingdom which is to be safeguarded is, on the facts of each case, directly related to state security. The term "state security", which is used in Directive 97/66/EC (concerning the processing of personal data and the protection of privacy in the telecommunications sector), should be interpreted in the same way as the term "national security" which is used elsewhere in the Act and this Code. The Secretary of State will not issue a warrant on section 5(3)(c) grounds if this direct link between the economic well-being of the United Kingdom and state security is not established. Any application for a warrant on section 5(3)(c) grounds should therefore explain how, in the applicant's view, the economic well-being of the United Kingdom which is to be safeguarded is directly related to state security on the facts of the case.

5.5 The Secretary of State must also consider that the conduct authorised by the warrant is proportionate to what it seeks to achieve (section 5(2)(b)). In considering necessity and proportionality, the Secretary of State must take into account whether the information sought could reasonably be obtained by other means (section 5(4)).

5.6 When the Secretary of State issues a warrant of this kind, it must be accompanied by a certificate in which the Secretary of State certifies that he considers examination of the intercepted material to be necessary for one or more of the section 5(3) purposes. The Secretary of State has a duty to ensure that arrangements are in force for securing that only that material which has been certified as necessary for examination for a section 5(3) purpose, and which meets the conditions set out in section 16(2) to section 16(6) is, in fact, read, looked at or listened to. The Interception of Communications Commissioner is under a duty to review the adequacy of those arrangements.

Urgent Authorisation of a Section 8(4) Warrant

5.7 The Act makes provision (section 7(1)(b)) for cases in which an interception warrant is required urgently, yet the Secretary of State is not available to sign the warrant. In these cases the Secretary of State will still personally authorise the interception but the warrant is signed by a senior official, following discussion of the case between officials and the Secretary of State. The Act restricts issue of warrants in this way to urgent cases where the Secretary of State has himself expressly authorised the issue of the warrant (section 7(2)(a)), and requires the warrant to contain a statement to that effect (section 7(4)(a)).

5.8 A warrant issued under the urgency procedure lasts for five working days following the day of issue unless renewed by the Secretary of State, in which case it expires after 3 months in the case of serious crime or 6 months in the case of national security or economic well-being in the same way as other section 8(4) warrants.

Format of a Section 8(4) Warrant

5.9 Each warrant is addressed to the person who submitted the application. This person may then serve a copy upon such providers of communications services as he believes will be able to assist in implementing the interception. Communications service providers will not receive a copy of the certificate.

The warrant should include the following—

- A description of the communications to be intercepted.
- The warrant reference number.
- The persons who may subsequently modify the scheduled part of the warrant in an urgent case (if authorised in accordance with section 10(8) of the Act).

Modification of a Section 8(4) Warrant

5.10 Interception warrants may be modified under the provisions of section 10 of the Act. The warrant may only be modified by the Secretary of State or, in an urgent case, by a senior official with the express authorisation of the Secretary of State. In these cases a statement of that fact must be endorsed on the modifying instrument, and the modification ceases to have effect after five working days following the day of issue unless it is endorsed by the Secretary of State.

5.11 The certificate must be modified by the Secretary of State, save in an urgent case where a certificate may be modified under the hand of a senior official provided that the official holds a position in respect of which he is expressly authorised by provisions contained in the certificate to modify the certificate on the Secretary of State's behalf, or the Secretary of State has himself expressly authorised the modification and a statement of that fact is endorsed on the modifying instrument. Again the modification shall cease to have effect after five working days following the day of issue unless it is endorsed by the Secretary of State.

Renewal of a Section 8(4) Warrant

5.12 The Secretary of State may renew a warrant at any point before its expiry date. Applications for renewals are made to the Secretary of State and contain an update of the matters outlined in paragraph 5.2 above. In particular, the applicant must give an assessment of the value of interception to the operation to date and explain why he considers that interception continues to be necessary for one or more of purposes in section 5(3).

5.13 Where the Secretary of State is satisfied that the interception continues to meet the requirements of the Act he may renew the warrant. Where the warrant is issued on serious crime grounds, the renewed warrant is valid for a further three months. Where it is issued on national security/economic well-being grounds the renewed warrant is valid for six months. These dates run from the date of signature on the renewal instrument.

5.14 In those circumstances where the assistance of communications service providers has been sought, a copy of the warrant renewal instrument will be forwarded by the intercepting agency to all those on whom a copy of the original warrant instrument has been served, providing they are still actively assisting. A warrant renewal instrument will include the reference number of the warrant and description of the communications to be intercepted.

Warrant Cancellation

5.15 The Secretary of State shall cancel an interception warrant if, at any time before its expiry date, he is satisfied that the warrant is no longer necessary on grounds falling within Section 5(3) of the Act. In practice, cancellation instruments will be signed by a senior official on his behalf.

5.16 The cancellation instrument will be addressed to the person to whom the warrant was issued (the intercepting agency). A copy of the cancellation instrument should be sent to those communications service providers, if any, who have given effect to the warrant during the preceding twelve months.

Records

5.17 The oversight regime allows the Interception of Communications Commissioner to inspect the warrant application upon which the Secretary of State based his decision, and the applicant may be required to justify the content. Each intercepting agency should keep, so to be made available for scrutiny by the Interception of Communications Commissioner, the following—

- all applications made for warrants complying with section 8(4), and applications made for the renewal of such warrants;
- all warrants and certificates, and copies of renewal and modification instruments (if any);
- where any application is refused, the grounds for refusal as given by the Secretary of State;
- the dates on which interception is started and stopped.

Records shall also be kept of the arrangements in force for securing that only material which has been certified for examination for a purpose under section 5(3) and which meets the conditions set out in section 16(2)–16(6) of the Act in accordance with section 15 of the Act. Records shall be kept of the arrangements by which the requirements of section 15(2) (minimisation of copying and distribution of intercepted material) and section 15(3) (destruction of intercepted material) are to be met. For further details see section on "Safeguards".

[1505]

NOTES

1 This assessment is normally based upon information provided by the relevant communications service provider.

2 This conduct may include the interception of other communications (section 5(6)(a)).

3 A single warrant can be justified on more than one of the grounds listed.

6 SAFEGUARDS

6.1 All material (including related communications data) intercepted under the authority of a warrant complying with section 8(1) or section 8(4) of the Act must be handled in accordance with safeguards which the Secretary of State has approved in conformity with the duty imposed upon him by the Act. These safeguards are made available to the Interception of Communications Commissioner, and they must meet the requirements of section 15 of the Act which are set out below. In addition, the safeguards in section 16 of the Act apply to warrants complying with section 8(4). Any breach of these safeguards must be reported to the Interception of Communications Commissioner.

6.2 Section 15 of the Act requires that disclosure, copying and retention of intercept material be limited to the minimum necessary for the authorised purposes. The authorised purposes defined in section 15(4) of the Act include—

- if the material continues to be, or is likely to become, necessary for any of the purposes set out in section 5(3) – namely, in the interests of national security, for the purpose of preventing or detecting serious crime, for the purpose of safeguarding the economic well-being of the United Kingdom;
- if the material is necessary for facilitating the carrying out of the functions of the Secretary of State under Chapter I of Part I of the Act;
- if the material is necessary for facilitating the carrying out of any functions of the Interception of Communications Commissioner or the Tribunal;
- if the material is necessary to ensure that a person conducting a criminal prosecution has the information he needs to determine what is required of him by his duty to secure the fairness of the prosecution;
- if the material is necessary for the performance of any duty imposed by the Public Record Acts.

6.3 Section 16 provides for additional safeguards in relation to material gathered under section 8(4) warrants, requiring that the safeguards—

- ensure that intercepted material is read, looked at or listened to by any person only to the extent that the material is certified;
- regulate the use of selection factors that refer to individuals known to be for the time being in the British Islands.

The Secretary of State must ensure that the safeguards are in force before any interception under warrants complying with section 8(4) can begin. The Interception of Communications Commissioner is under a duty to review the adequacy of the safeguards.

Dissemination of Intercepted Material

6.4 The number of persons to whom any of the material is disclosed, and the extent of disclosure, must be limited to the minimum that is necessary for the authorised purposes set out in section 15(4) of the Act. This obligation applies equally to disclosure to additional persons within an agency, and to disclosure outside the agency. It is enforced by prohibiting disclosure to persons who do not hold the required security clearance, and also by the need-to-know principle: intercepted material must not be disclosed to any person unless that person's duties, which must relate to one of the authorised purposes, are such that he needs to know about the material to carry out those duties. In the same way only so much of the material may be disclosed as the recipient needs; for example if a summary of the material will suffice, no more than that should be disclosed.

6.5 The obligations apply not just to the original interceptor, but also to anyone to whom the material is subsequently disclosed. In some cases this will be achieved by requiring the latter to obtain the originator's permission before disclosing the material further. In others, explicit safeguards are applied to secondary recipients.

Copying

6.6 Intercepted material may only be copied to the extent necessary for the authorised purposes set out in section 15(4) of the Act. Copies include not only direct copies of the whole of the material, but also extracts and summaries which identify themselves as the product of an interception, and any record referring to an interception which is a record of the identities of the persons to or by whom the intercepted material was sent. The restrictions are implemented by requiring special treatment of such copies, extracts and summaries that are made by recording their making, distribution and destruction.

Storage

6.7 Intercepted material, and all copies, extracts and summaries of it, must be handled and stored securely, so as to minimise the risk of loss or theft. It must be held so as to be inaccessible to persons without the required level of security clearance. This requirement to store intercept product securely applies to all those who are responsible for the handling of this material, including communications service providers. The details of what such a requirement will mean in practice for communications service providers will be set out in the discussions they will be having with the Government before a Section 12 Notice is served (see paragraph 2.9).

Destruction

6.8 Intercepted material, and all copies, extracts and summaries which can be identified as the product of an interception, must be securely destroyed as soon as it is no longer needed for any of the authorised purposes. If such material is retained, it should be reviewed at appropriate intervals to confirm that the justification for its retention is still valid under section 15(3) of the Act.

Personnel security

6.9 Each intercepting agency maintains a distribution list of persons who may have access to intercepted material or need to see any reporting in relation to it. All such persons must be appropriately vetted. Any person no longer needing access to perform his duties should be removed from any such list. Where it is necessary for an officer of one agency to disclose material to another, it is the former's responsibility to ensure that the recipient has the necessary clearance.

[1506]

7 DISCLOSURE TO ENSURE FAIRNESS IN CRIMINAL PROCEEDINGS

7.1 Section 15(3) of the Act states the general rule that intercepted material must be destroyed as soon as its retention is no longer necessary for a purpose authorised under the Act. Section 15(4) specifies the authorised purposes for which retention is necessary.

7.2 This part of the Code applies to the handling of intercepted material in the context of criminal proceedings where the material has been retained for one of the purposes authorised in section 15(4) of the Act. For those who would ordinarily have had responsibility under the Criminal Procedure and Investigations Act 1996 to provide disclosure in criminal proceedings, this includes those rare situations where destruction of intercepted material has not taken place in accordance with section 15(3) and where that material is still in existence after the commencement of a criminal prosecution, retention having been considered necessary to ensure that a person conducting a criminal prosecution has the information he needs to discharge his duty of ensuring its fairness (section 15(4)(d)).

Exclusion of Matters from Legal Proceedings

7.3 The general rule is that neither the possibility of interception nor intercepted material itself plays any part in legal proceedings. This rule is set out in section 17 of the Act, which excludes evidence, questioning, assertion or disclosure in legal proceedings likely to reveal the existence (or the absence) of a warrant issued under this Act (or the Interception of Communications Act 1985). This rule means that the intercepted material cannot be used either by the prosecution or the defence. This preserves "equality of arms" which is a requirement under Article 6 of the European Convention on Human Rights.

7.4 Section 18 contains a number of tightly-drawn exceptions to this rule. This part of the Code deals only with the exception in subsections (7) to (11).

Disclosure to a Prosecutor

7.5 Section 18(7)(a) provides that intercepted material obtained by means of a warrant and which continues to be available, may, for a strictly limited purpose, be disclosed to a person conducting a criminal prosecution.

7.6 This may only be done for the purpose of enabling the prosecutor to determine what is required of him by his duty to secure the fairness of the prosecution. The prosecutor may not use intercepted material to which he is given access under section 18(7)(a) to mount a cross-examination, or to do anything other than ensure the fairness of the proceedings.

7.7 The exception does not mean that intercepted material should be retained against a remote possibility that it might be relevant to future proceedings. The normal expectation is, still, for the intercepted material to be destroyed in accordance with the general safeguards provided by section 15. The exceptions only come into play if such material has, in fact, been retained for an authorised purpose. Because the authorised purpose given in section 5(3)(b) (*"for the purpose of preventing or detecting serious crime"*) does not extend to gathering evidence for the purpose of a prosecution, material intercepted for this purpose may not have survived to the prosecution stage, as it will have been destroyed in accordance with the section 15(3) safeguards. There is, in these circumstances, no need to consider disclosure to a prosecutor if, in fact, no intercepted material remains in existence.

7.8 Be that as it may, section 18(7)(a) recognises the duty on prosecutors, acknowledged by common law, to review all available material to make sure that the prosecution is not proceeding unfairly. "Available material" will only ever include intercepted material at this stage if the conscious decision has been made to retain it for an authorised purpose.

7.9 If intercepted material does continue to be available at the prosecution stage, once this information has come to the attention of the holder of this material the prosecutor should be informed that a warrant has been issued under section 5 and that material of possible relevance to the case has been intercepted.

7.10 Having had access to the material, the prosecutor may conclude that the material affects the fairness of the proceedings. In these circumstances, he will decide how the prosecution, if it proceeds, should be presented.

Disclosure to a Judge

7.11 Section 18(7)(b) recognises that there may be cases where the prosecutor, having seen intercepted material under subsection (7)(a), will need to consult the trial Judge. Accordingly, it provides for the Judge to be given access to intercepted material, where there are exceptional circumstances making that disclosure essential in the interests of justice.

7.12 This access will be achieved by the prosecutor inviting the judge to make an order for disclosure to him alone, under this subsection. This is an exceptional procedure; normally, the prosecutor's functions under subsection (7)(a) will not fall to be reviewed by the judge. To comply with section 17(1), any consideration given to, or exercise of, this power must be carried out without notice to the defence. The purpose of this power is to ensure that the trial is conducted fairly.

7.13 The judge may, having considered the intercepted material disclosed to him, direct the prosecution to make an admission of fact. The admission will be abstracted from the interception; but, in accordance with the requirements of section 17(1), it must not reveal the fact of interception. This is likely to be a very unusual step. The Act only allows it where the judge considers it essential in the interests of justice.

7.14 Nothing in these provisions allows intercepted material, or the fact of interception, to be disclosed to the defence.

[1507]

8 OVERSIGHT

8.1 The Act provides for an Interception of Communications Commissioner whose remit is to provide independent oversight of the use of the powers contained within the warranted interception regime under Chapter I of Part I of the Act.

8.2 This Code does not cover the exercise of the Commissioner's functions. However, it will be the duty of any person who uses the above powers to comply with any request made by the Commissioner to provide any information as he requires for the purpose of enabling him to discharge his functions.

[1508]

9 COMPLAINTS

9.1 The Act establishes an independent Tribunal. This Tribunal will be made up of senior members of the judiciary and the legal profession and is independent of the Government. The Tribunal has full powers to investigate and decide any case within its jurisdiction.

9.2 This code does not cover the exercise of the Tribunal's functions. Details of the relevant complaints procedure can be obtained from the following address—

The Investigatory Powers Tribunal

PO Box 33220

London

SW1H 9ZQ

0207 273 4514

[1509]

10 INTERCEPTION WITHOUT A WARRANT

10.1 Section 1(5) of the Act permits interception without a warrant in the following circumstances—

- where it is authorised by or under sections 3 or 4 of the Act (see below);
- where it is in exercise, in relation to any stored communication, of some other statutory power exercised for the purpose of obtaining information or of taking possession of any document or other property, for example, the obtaining of a production order under Schedule 1 to the Police and Criminal Evidence Act 1984 for stored data to be produced.

Interception in accordance with a warrant under section 5 of the Act is dealt with under parts 2, 3, 4 and 5 of this Code.

10.2 For lawful interception which takes place without a warrant, pursuant to sections 3 or 4 of the Act or pursuant to some other statutory power, there is no prohibition in the Act on the evidential use of any material that is obtained as a result. The matter may still, however, be regulated by the exclusionary rules of evidence to be found in the common law, section 78 of the Police and Criminal Evidence Act 1984, and/or pursuant to the Human Rights Act 1998.

Interception with the Consent of both Parties

10.3 Section 3(1) of the Act authorises the interception of a communication if both the person sending the communication and the intended recipient(s) have consented to its interception, or where the person conducting the interception has reasonable grounds for believing that all parties have consented to the interception.

Interception with the Consent of one Party

10.4 Section 3(2) of the Act authorises the interception of a communication if either the sender or intended recipient of the communication has consented to its interception, and directed surveillance by means of that interception has been authorised under Part II of the Act. Further details can be found in chapter 4 of the Covert Surveillance Code of Practice and in chapter 2 of the Covert Human Intelligence Sources Code of Practice.

Interception for the Purposes of a Communication Service Provider

10.5 Section 3(3) of the Act permits a communication service provider or a person acting upon their behalf to carry out interception for purposes connected with the operation of that service or for purposes connected with the enforcement of any enactment relating to the use of the communication service.

Lawful Business Practice

10.6 Section 4(2) of the Act enables the Secretary of State to make regulations setting out those circumstances where it is lawful to intercept communications for the purpose of carrying on a business. These regulations apply equally to public authorities.

These Lawful Business Practice Regulations can be found on the following Department of Trade and Industry website: www.dti.gov.uk/cii/regulation.html

[1510]

COVERT HUMAN INTELLIGENCE SOURCES: CODE OF PRACTICE (2002)

NOTES

Authority: Regulation of Investigatory Powers Act 2000, s 71(5). This Code of Practice came into force on 1 August 2002 (see SI 2002/1932). This code applies to every authorisation of the use or conduct by public authorities of covert human intelligence sources carried out under Part II of the Regulation of Investigatory Powers Act 2000 which begins on or after the day on which this code comes into effect.

1 BACKGROUND

1.1 In this code the—

"1989 Act" means the Security Service Act 1989;
"1994 Act" means the Intelligence Services Act 1994;
"1997 Act" means the Police Act 1997;
"2000 Act" means the Regulation of Investigatory Powers Act 2000;
"RIP(S)A" means the Regulation of Investigatory Powers (Scotland) Act 2000.

1.2 This code of practice provides guidance on the authorisation of the use or conduct of covert human intelligence sources ("a source") by public authorities under Part II of the 2000 Act.

1.3 The provisions of the 2000 Act are not intended to apply in circumstances where members of the public volunteer information to the police or other authorities, as part of their normal civic duties, or to contact numbers set up to receive information (such as Crimestoppers, Customs Confidential, the Anti Terrorist Hotline, or the Security Service Public Telephone Number). Members of the public acting in this way would not generally be regarded as sources.

1.4 Neither Part II of the 2000 Act or this code of practice is intended to affect the practices and procedures surrounding criminal participation of sources.

1.5 The 2000 Act provides that all codes of practice relating to the 2000 Act are admissible as evidence in criminal and civil proceedings. If any provision of the code appears relevant to any court or tribunal considering any such proceedings, or to the Investigatory Powers Tribunal established under the 2000 Act, or to one of the Commissioners responsible for overseeing the powers conferred by the 2000 Act, it must be taken into account.

General extent of powers

1.6 Authorisations can be given for the use or conduct of a source both inside and outside the United Kingdom. Authorisations for actions outside the United Kingdom can only validate them for the purposes of proceedings in the United Kingdom. An authorisation under Part II of the 2000 Act does not take into account the requirements of the country outside the United Kingdom in which the investigation or operation is taking place.

1.7 Members of foreign law enforcement or other agencies or sources of those agencies may be authorised under the 2000 Act in the UK in support of domestic and international investigations.

1.8 Where the conduct authorised is likely to take place in Scotland, authorisations should be granted under RIP(S)A, unless the authorisation is being obtained by those public authorities listed in section 46(3) of the 2000 Act and the Regulation of Investigatory Powers (Authorisations Extending to Scotland) Order 2000). Additionally, any authorisation granted or renewed for the purposes of national security or the economic well-being of the UK must be made under the 2000 Act. This code of practice is extended to Scotland in relation to authorisations made under Part II of the 2000 Act which apply to Scotland. A separate code of practice applies in relation to authorisations made under RIP(S)A.

Use of material in evidence

1.9 Material obtained from a source may be used as evidence in criminal proceedings. The proper authorisation of a source should ensure the suitability of such evidence under the common law, section 78 of the Police and Criminal Evidence Act 1984 and the Human Rights Act 1998. Furthermore, the product obtained by a source described in this code is subject to the ordinary rules for retention and disclosure of material under the Criminal Procedure and

Investigations Act 1996, where those rules apply to the law enforcement body in question. There are also well-established legal procedures that will protect the identity of a source from disclosure in such circumstances.

[1511]

2 GENERAL RULES ON AUTHORISATIONS

2.1 An authorisation under Part II of the 2000 Act will provide lawful authority for the use of a source. Responsibility for giving the authorisation will depend on which public authority is responsible for the source.

2.2 Part II of the 2000 Act does not impose a requirement on public authorities to seek or obtain an authorisation where, under the 2000 Act, one is available (see section 80 of the 2000 Act). Nevertheless, where there is an interference by a public authority with the right to respect for private and family life guaranteed under Article 8 of the European Convention on Human Rights, and where there is no other lawful authority, the consequences of not obtaining an authorisation under the 2000 Act may be that the action is unlawful by virtue of section 6 of the Human Rights Act 1998.

2.3 Public authorities are therefore strongly recommended to seek an authorisation where the use or conduct of a source is likely to interfere with a person's Article 8 rights to privacy by obtaining information from or about a person, whether or not that person is the subject of the investigation or operation. Obtaining an authorisation will ensure that the action is carried out in accordance with law and subject to stringent safeguards against abuse.

Necessity and Proportionality

2.4 Obtaining an authorisation under the 2000 Act will only ensure that the authorised use or conduct of a source is a justifiable interference with an individual's Article 8 rights if it is necessary and proportionate for the source to be used. The 2000 Act first requires that the person granting an authorisation believe that the authorisation is necessary in the circumstances of the particular case for one or more of the statutory grounds in section 29(3) of the 2000 Act.

2.5 Then, if the use of the source is necessary, the person granting the authorisation must believe that the use of a source is proportionate to what is sought to be achieved by the conduct and use of that source. This involves balancing the intrusiveness of the use of the source on the target and others who might be affected by it against the need for the source to be used in operational terms. The use of a source will not be proportionate if it is excessive in the circumstances of the case or if the information which is sought could reasonably be obtained by other less intrusive means. The use of a source should be carefully managed to meet the objective in question and sources must not be used in an arbitrary or unfair way.

Collateral Intrusion

2.6 Before authorising the use or conduct of a source, the authorising officer should also take into account the risk of intrusion into the privacy of persons other than those who are directly the subjects of the operation or investigation (collateral intrusion). Measures should be taken, wherever practicable, to avoid unnecessary intrusion into the lives of those not directly connected with the operation.

2.7 An application for an authorisation should include an assessment of the risk of any collateral intrusion. The authorising officer should take this into account, when considering the proportionality of the use and conduct of a source.

2.8 Those tasking a source should inform the authorising officer if the investigation or operation unexpectedly interferes with the privacy of individuals who are not covered by the authorisation. When the original authorisation may not be sufficient, consideration should be given to whether the authorisation needs to be amended and reauthorised or a new authorisation is required.

2.9 Any person granting or applying for an authorisation will also need to be aware of any particular sensitivities in the local community where the source is being used and of similar activities being undertaken by other public authorities which could impact on the deployment of the source. Consideration should also be given to any adverse impact on community confidence or safety that may result from the use or conduct of a source or of information obtained from that source. In this regard, it is recommended that where the authorising officers in the National Criminal Intelligence Service (NCIS), the National Crime Squad (NCS) and HM Customs and Excise (HMCE) consider that conflicts might arise they should consult a senior officer within the police force area in which the source is deployed.

Additionally, the authorising officer should make an assessment of any risk to a source in carrying out the conduct in the proposed authorisation.

2.10 In a very limited range of circumstances an authorisation under Part II may, by virtue of sections 26(7) and 27 of the 2000 Act, render lawful conduct which would otherwise be criminal, if it is incidental to any conduct falling within section 26(8) of the 2000 Act which the source is authorised to undertake. This would depend on the circumstances of each individual case, and consideration should always be given to seeking advice from the legal adviser within the relevant public authority when such activity is contemplated. A source that acts beyond the limits recognised by the law will be at risk from prosecution. The need to protect the source cannot alter this principle.

Combined authorisations

2.11 A single authorisation may combine two or more different authorisations under Part II of the 2000 Act. For example, a single authorisation may combine authorisations for intrusive surveillance and the conduct of a source. In such cases the provisions applicable to each of the authorisations must be considered separately. Thus, a police superintendent can authorise the conduct of a source but an authorisation for intrusive surveillance by the police needs the separate authority of a chief constable, and in certain cases the approval of a Surveillance Commissioner will also be necessary. Where an authorisation for the use or conduct of a covert human intelligence source is combined with a Secretary of State authorisation for intrusive surveillance, the combined authorisation must be issued by the Secretary of State. However, this does not preclude public authorities from obtaining separate authorisations.

Directed surveillance against a potential source

2.12 It may be necessary to deploy directed surveillance against a potential source as part of the process of assessing their suitability for recruitment, or in planning how best to make the approach to them. An authorisation under this code authorising an officer to establish a covert relationship with a potential source could be combined with a directed surveillance authorisation so that both the officer and potential source could be followed. Directed surveillance is defined in section 26(2) of the 2000 Act. See the code of practice on Covert Surveillance.

Central Record of all authorisations

2.13 A centrally retrievable record of all authorisations should be held by each public authority and regularly updated whenever an authorisation is granted, renewed or cancelled. The record should be made available to the relevant Commissioner or an Inspector from the Office of Surveillance Commissioners, upon request. These records should be retained for a period of at least three years from the ending of the authorisation.

2.14 Proper records must be kept of the authorisation and use of a source. Section 29(5) of the 2000 Act provides that an authorising officer must not grant an authorisation for the use or conduct of a source unless he believes that there are arrangements in place for ensuring that there is at all times a person with the responsibility for maintaining a record of the use made of the source. The Regulation of Investigatory Powers (Source Records) Regulations 2000; SI No: 2725 details the particulars that must be included in the records relating to each source.

2.15 In addition, records or copies of the following, as appropriate, should be kept by the relevant authority—

- a copy of the authorisation together with any supplementary documentation and notification of the approval given by the authorising officer;
- a copy of any renewal of an authorisation, together with the supporting documentation submitted when the renewal was requested;
- the reason why the person renewing an authorisation considered it necessary to do so;
- any authorisation which was granted or renewed orally (in an urgent case) and the reason why the case was considered urgent;
- any risk assessment made in relation to the source;
- the circumstances in which tasks were given to the source;
- the value of the source to the investigating authority;
- a record of the results of any reviews of the authorisation;
- the reasons, if any, for not renewing an authorisation;
- the reasons for cancelling an authorisation;
- the date and time when any instruction was given by the authorising officer to cease using a source.

2.16 The records kept by public authorities should be maintained in such a way as to preserve the confidentiality of the source and the information provided by that source. There should, at

PART II DATA PROTECTION

all times, be a designated person within the relevant public authority who will have responsibility for maintaining a record of the use made of the source.

Retention and destruction of the product

2.17 Where the product obtained from a source could be relevant to pending or future criminal or civil proceedings, it should be retained in accordance with established disclosure requirements for a suitable further period, commensurate to any subsequent review.

2.18 In the cases of the law enforcement agencies (not including the Royal Navy Regulating Branch, the Royal Military Police and the Royal Air Force Police), particular attention is drawn to the requirements of the code of practice issued under the Criminal Procedure and Investigations Act 1996. This requires that material which is obtained in the course of a criminal investigation and which may be relevant to the investigation must be recorded and retained.

2.19 There is nothing in the 2000 Act which prevents material obtained from properly authorised use of a source being used in other investigations. Each public authority must ensure that arrangements are in place for the handling, storage and destruction of material obtained through the use of a source. Authorising officers must ensure compliance with the appropriate data protection requirements and any relevant codes of practice produced by individual authorities in the handling and storage of material.

The Intelligence services, MOD and HM Forces

2.20 The heads of these agencies are responsible for ensuring that arrangements exist to ensure that no information is stored by the authorities, except as necessary for the proper discharge of their functions. They are also responsible for arrangements to control onward disclosure. For the intelligence services, this is a statutory duty under the 1989 Act and the 1994 Act.

[1512]

3 SPECIAL RULES ON AUTHORISATIONS

Confidential Information

3.1 The 2000 Act does not provide any special protection for 'confidential information'. Nevertheless, particular care should be taken in cases where the subject of the investigation or operation might reasonably expect a high degree of privacy, or where confidential information is involved. Confidential information consists of matters subject to legal privilege, confidential personal information or confidential journalistic material.

3.2 In cases where through the use or conduct of a source it is likely that knowledge of confidential information will be acquired, the deployment of the source is subject to a higher level of authorisation. Annex A lists the authorising officer for each public authority permitted to authorise such use or conduct of a source.

Communications Subject to Legal Privilege

3.3 Section 98 of the 1997 Act describes those matters that are subject to legal privilege in England and Wales. In Scotland, the relevant description is contained in section 33 of the Criminal Law (Consolidation) (Scotland) Act 1995. With regard to Northern Ireland, Article 12 of the Police and criminal Evidence (Northern Ireland) Order 1989 should be referred to.

3.4 Legal privilege does not apply to communications made with the intention of furthering a criminal purpose (whether the lawyer is acting unwittingly or culpably). Legally privileged communications will lose their protection if there are grounds to believe, for example, that the professional legal adviser is intending to hold or use them for a criminal purpose. But privilege is not lost if a professional legal adviser is properly advising a person who is suspected of having committed a criminal offence. The concept of legal privilege applies to the provision of professional legal advice by any individual, agency or organisation qualified to do so.

3.5 The 2000 Act does not provide any special protection for legally privileged information. Nevertheless, such information is particularly sensitive and any source which acquires such material may engage Article 6 of the ECHR (right to a fair trial) as well as Article 8. Legally privileged information obtained by a source is extremely unlikely ever to be admissible as evidence in criminal proceedings. Moreover, the mere fact that use has been made of a source to obtain such information may lead to any related criminal proceedings being stayed as an abuse of process. Accordingly, action which may lead to such information being obtained is subject to additional safeguards under this code.

3.6 In general, an application for the use or conduct of a source which is likely to result in the acquisition of legally privileged information should only be made in exceptional and compelling circumstance. Full regard should be had to the particular proportionality issues such a use or conduct of a source raises. The application should include, in addition to the reasons why it is considered necessary for the use or conduct of a source to be used, an assessment of how likely it is that information subject to legal privilege will be acquired. The application should clearly state whether the purpose (or one of the purposes) of the use or conduct of the source is to obtain legally privileged information.

3.7 This assessment will be taken into account by the authorising officer in deciding whether the proposed use or conduct of a source is necessary and proportionate for a purpose under section 29 of the 2000 Act. The authorising officer may require regular reporting so as to be able to decide whether the authorisation should continue. In those cases where legally privileged information has been acquired and retained, the matter should be reported to the relevant Commissioner or Inspector during his next inspection and the material should be made available to him if requested.

3.8 A substantial proportion of the communications between a lawyer and his client(s) may be subject to legal privilege. Therefore, any case where a lawyer is the subject of an investigation or operation should be notified to the relevant Commissioner or Inspector during his next inspection and any material which has been retained should be made available to him if requested.

3.9 Where there is any doubt as to the handling and dissemination of information which may be subject to legal privilege, advice should be sought from a legal adviser within the relevant public authority before any further dissemination of the material takes place. Similar advice should also be sought where there is doubt over whether information is not subject to legal privilege due to the "in furtherance of a criminal purpose" exception. The retention of legally privileged information, or its dissemination to an outside body, should be accompanied by a clear warning that it is subject to legal privilege. It should be safeguarded by taking reasonable steps to ensure there is no possibility of it becoming available, or its contents becoming known to any person whose possession of it might prejudice any criminal or civil proceedings related to the information. Any dissemination of legally privileged material to an outside body should be notified to the relevant Commissioner or Inspector during his next inspection.

Communications involving Confidential Personal Information and Confidential Journalistic Material

3.10 Similar consideration must also be given to authorisations that involve confidential personal information and confidential journalistic material. In those cases where confidential personal information and confidential journalistic material has been acquired and retained, the matter should be reported to the relevant Commissioner or Inspector during his next inspection and the material be made available to him if requested. Confidential personal information is information held in confidence relating to the physical or mental health or spiritual counselling concerning an individual (whether living or dead) who can be identified from it. Such information, which can include both oral and written communications is held in confidence if it is held subject to an express or implied undertaking to hold it in confidence or it is subject to a restriction on disclosure or an obligation of confidentiality contained in existing legislation. Examples might include consultations between a health professional and a patient, or information from a patient's medical records.

3.11 Spiritual counselling means conversations between an individual and a Minister of Religion acting in his official capacity, where the individual being counselled is seeking or the Minister is imparting forgiveness, absolution or the resolution of conscience with the authority of the Divine Being(s) of their faith.

3.12 Confidential journalistic material includes material acquired or created for the purposes of journalism and held subject to an undertaking to hold it in confidence, as well as communications resulting in information being acquired for the purposes of journalism and held subject to such an undertaking.

Vulnerable individuals

3.13 A 'vulnerable individual' is a person who is or may be in need of community care services by reason of mental or other disability, age or illness and who is or may be unable to take care of himself, or unable to protect himself against significant harm or exploitation. Any individual of this description should only be authorised to act as a source in the most exceptional circumstances. In these cases, the attached table in Annex A lists the authorising officer for each public authority permitted to authorise the use of a vulnerable individual as a source.

Juvenile sources

3.14 Special safeguards also apply to the use or conduct of juvenile sources; that is sources under the age of 18 years. **On no occasion should the use or conduct of a source under 16 years of age be authorised to give information against his parents or any person who has parental responsibility for him.** In other cases, authorisations should not be granted unless the special provisions contained within The Regulation of Investigatory Powers (Juveniles) Order 2000; SI No: 2793 are satisfied. Authorisations for juvenile sources should be granted by those listed in the attached table at Annex A. The duration of such an authorisation is **one month** instead of twelve months.

[1513]

4 AUTHORISATION PROCEDURES FOR COVERT HUMAN INTELLIGENCE SOURCES

4.1 Under section 26(8) of the 2000 Act a person is a source if—

(a) he establishes or maintains a personal or other relationship with a person for the covert purpose of facilitating the doing of anything falling within paragraph (b) or (c);

(b) he covertly uses such a relationship to obtain information or to provide access to any information to another person; or

(c) he covertly discloses information obtained by the use of such a relationship or as a consequence of the existence of such a relationship.

4.2 A source may include those referred to as agents, informants and officers working undercover.

4.3 By virtue of section 26(9)(b) of the 2000 Act a purpose is covert, in relation to the establishment or maintenance of a personal or other relationship, if and only if, the relationship is conducted in a manner that is calculated to ensure that one of the parties to the relationship is unaware of the purpose.

4.4 By virtue of section 26(9)(c) of the 2000 Act a relationship is used covertly, and information obtained as mentioned in paragraph 4.1(c) above is disclosed covertly, if and only if it is used or, as the case may be, disclosed in a manner that is calculated to ensure that one of the parties to the relationship is unaware of the use or disclosure in question.

4.5 The use of a source involves inducing, asking or assisting a person to engage in the conduct of a source or to obtain information by means of the conduct of such a source.

4.6 The conduct of a source is any conduct falling within section 29(4) of the 2000 Act, or which is incidental to anything falling within section 29(4) of the 2000 Act.

Authorisation procedures

4.7 Under section 29(3) of the 2000 Act an authorisation for the use or conduct of a source may be granted by the authorising officer where he believes that the authorisation is necessary—

- in the interests of national security;[1, 2]
- for the purpose of preventing and detecting[3] crime or of preventing disorder;
- in the interests of the economic well-being of the UK;
- In the interests of public safety;
- for the purpose of protecting public health;[4]
- for the purpose of assessing or collecting any tax, duty, levy or other imposition, contribution or charge payable to a government department; or
- for any other purpose prescribed in an order made by the Secretary of State.[5]

4.8 The authorising officer must also believe that the authorised use or conduct of a source is proportionate to what is sought to be achieved by that use or conduct.

4.9 The public authorities entitled to authorise the use or conduct of a source are those listed in Schedule 1 to the 2000 Act. Responsibility for authorising the use or conduct of a source rests with the authorising officer and all authorisations require the personal authority of the authorising officer. An authorising officer is the person designated under section 29 of the 2000 Act to grant an authorisation for the use or conduct of a source. The Regulation of Investigatory Powers (Prescriptions of Offices, Ranks and Positions) Order 2000; SI No: 2417 designates the authorising officer for each different public authority and the officers entitled to act only in urgent cases. In certain circumstances the Secretary of State will be the authorising officer (see section 30(2) of the 2000 Act).

4.10 The authorising officer must give authorisations in writing, except that in urgent cases, they may be given orally by the authorising officer or the officer entitled to act in urgent cases. In such cases, a statement that the authorising officer has expressly authorised the action should be recorded in writing by the applicant as soon as is reasonably practicable.

4.11 A case is not normally to be regarded as urgent unless the time that would elapse before the authorising officer was available to grant the authorisation would, in the judgement of the person giving the authorisation, be likely to endanger life or jeopardise the operation or investigation for which the authorisation was being given. An authorisation is not to be regarded as urgent where the need for an authorisation has been neglected or the urgency is of the authorising officer's own making.

4.12 Authorising officers should not be responsible for authorising their own activities, e g those in which they, themselves, are to act as the source or in tasking the source. However, it is recognised that this is not always possible, especially in the cases of small organisations. Where an authorising officer authorises his own activity the authorisation record (see paragraphs 2.13–2.15) should highlight this and the attention of a Commissioner or Inspector should be invited to it during his next inspection.

4.13 The authorising officers within the police, NCIS and NCS may only grant authorisations on application by a member of their own force, Service or Squad. Authorising officers in HMCE may only grant authorisations on application by a customs officer.[6]

Information to be provided in applications for authorisation

4.14 In application for authorisation for the use or conduct of a source should be in writing and record—

- the reasons why the authorisation is necessary in the particular case and on the grounds (e g for the purpose of preventing or detecting crime) listed in section 29(3) of the 2000 Act;
- the reasons why the authorisation is considered proportionate to what it seeks to achieve;
- the purpose for which the source will be tasked or deployed (e g In relation to an organised serious crime, espionage, a series of racially motivated crimes etc);
- where a specific investigation or operation is involved, nature of that investigation or operation;
- the nature of what the source will be tasked to do;
- the level of authority required (or recommended, where that is different);
- the details of any potential collateral intrusion and why the intrusion is justified;
- the details of any confidential information that is likely to be obtained as a consequence of the authorisation; and
- a subsequent record of whether authority was given or refused, by whom and the time and date.

4.15 Additionally, in urgent cases, the authorisation should record (as the case may be)—

- the reasons why the authorising officer or the officer entitled to act in urgent cases considered the case so urgent that an oral instead of a written authorisation was given; and/or
- the reasons why it was not reasonably practicable for the application to be considered by the authorising officer.

4.16 Where the authorisation is oral, the detail referred to above should be recorded in writing by the applicant as soon as reasonably practicable.

Duration of authorisations

4.17 A written authorisation will, unless renewed, cease to have effect at the end of a period of **twelve months** beginning with the day on which it took effect.

4.18 Urgent oral authorisations or authorisations granted or renewed by a person who is entitled to act only in urgent cases will, unless renewed, cease to have effect after **seventy-two hours**, beginning with the time when the authorisation was granted or renewed.

Reviews

4.19 Regular reviews of authorisations should be undertaken to assess the need for the use of a source to continue. The review should include the use made of the source during the period authorised, the tasks given to the source and the information obtained from the source. The results of a review should be recorded on the authorisation record (see paragraphs 2.13–2.15). Particular attention is drawn to the need to review authorisations frequently where the use of a source provides access to confidential information or involves collateral intrusion.

4.20 In each case the authorising officer within each public authority should determine how often a review should take place. This should be as frequently as is considered necessary and practicable.

Renewals

4.21 Before an authorising officer renews an authorisation, he must be satisfied that a review has been carried out of the use of a source as outlined in paragraph 4.19.

4.22 If at any time before an authorisation would cease to have effect, the authorising officer considers it necessary for the authorisation to continue for the purpose for which it was given, he may renew it in writing for a further period of **twelve months**. Renewals may also be granted orally in urgent cases and last for a period of **seventy-two hours**.

4.23 A renewal takes effect at the time at which, or day on which the authorisation would have ceased to have effect but for the renewal. An application for renewal should not be made until shortly before the authorisation period is drawing to an end. Any person who would be entitled to grant a new authorisation can renew an authorisation. Authorisations may be renewed more than once, if necessary, provided they continue to meet the criteria for authorisation. The renewal should be kept/recorded as part of the authorisation record (see paragraphs 2.13–2.15).

4.24 All applications for the renewal of an authorisation should record—

- whether this is the first renewal or every occasion on which the authorisation has been renewed previously;
- any significant changes to the information in paragraph 4.14;
- the reasons why it is necessary to continue to use the source;
- the use made of the source in the period since the grant or, as the case may be, latest renewal of the authorisation;
- the tasks given to the source during that period and the information obtained from the conduct or use of the source;
- the results of regular reviews of the use of the source.

Cancellations

4.25 The authorising officer who granted or renewed the authorisation must cancel it if he is satisfied that the use or conduct of the source no longer satisfies the criteria for authorisation or that satisfactory arrangements for the source's case no longer exist. Where the authorising officer is no longer available, this duty will fall on the person who has taken over the role of authorising officer or the person who is acting as authorising officer (see the Regulation of Investigatory Powers (Cancellation of Authorisations) Order 2000; SI No: 2794). Where necessary, the safety and welfare of the source should continue to be taken into account after the authorisation has been cancelled.

MANAGEMENT OF SOURCES

Tasking

4.26 Tasking is the assignment given to the source by the persons defined at sections 29(5)(a) and (b) of the 2000 Act, asking him to obtain information, to provide access to information or to otherwise act, incidentally, for the benefit of the relevant public authority. Authorisation for the use or conduct of a source is required prior to any tasking where such tasking requires the source to establish or maintain a personal or other relationship for a covert purpose.

4.27 The person referred to in section 29(5)(a) of the 2000 Act will have day to day responsibility for—

- dealing with the source on behalf of the authority concerned;
- directing the day to day activities of the source;
- recording the information supplied by the source; and
- monitoring the source's security and welfare.

4.28 The person referred to in section 29(5)(b) of the 2000 Act will be responsible for the general oversight of the use of the source.

4.29 In some instances, the tasking given to a person will not require the source to establish a personal or other relationship for a covert purpose. For example a source may be tasked with finding out purely factual information about the layout of commercial premises. Alternatively, a trading standards officer may be involved in the test purchase of items which have been labelled misleadingly or are unfit for consumption. In such cases, it is for the relevant public authority to determine where, and in what circumstances, such activity may require authorisation.

4.30 It is not the intention that authorisations be drawn so narrowly that a separate authorisation is required each time the source is tasked. Rather, an authorisation might cover, in broad terms, the nature of the source's task. If this changes, then a new authorisation may need to be sought.

4.31 It is difficult to predict exactly what might occur each time a meeting with a source takes place, or the source meets the subject of an investigation. There may be occasions when unforeseen action or undertakings occur. When this happens, the occurrence must be recorded as soon as practicable after the event and, if the existing authorisation is insufficient it should either be updated and reauthorised (for minor amendments only) or it should cancelled and a new authorisation should be obtained before any further such action is carried out.

4.32 Similarly where it is intended to task a source in a new way or significantly greater way than previously identified, the persons defined at section 29(5)(a) or (b) of the 2000 Act must refer the proposed tasking to the authorising officer, who should consider whether a separate authorisation is required. This should be done in advance of any tasking and the details of such referrals must be recorded.

Management responsibility

4.33 Public authorities should ensure that arrangements are in place for the proper oversight and management of sources, including appointing individual officers as defined in section 29(5)(a) and (b) of the 2000 Act for each source.

4.34 The person responsible for the day-to-day contact between the public authority and the source will usually be of a rank or position below that of the authorising officer.

4.35 In cases where the authorisation is for the use or conduct of a source whose activities benefit more than a single public authority, responsibilities for the management and oversight of that source may be taken up by one authority or can be split between the authorities.

PART II
DATA PROTECTION

Security and welfare

4.36 Any public authority deploying a source should take into account the safety and welfare of that source, when carrying out actions in relation to an authorisation or tasking, and to foreseeable consequences to others of that tasking. Before authorising the use or conduct of a source, the authorising officer should ensure that a risk assessment is carried out to determine the risk to the source of any tasking and the likely consequences should the role of the source become known. The ongoing security and welfare of the source, after the cancellation of the authorisation, should also be considered at the outset.

4.37 The person defined at section 29(5)(a) of the 2000 Act is responsible for bringing to the attention of the person defined at section 29(5)(b) of the 2000 Act any concerns about the personal circumstances of the source, insofar as they might affect—

- the validity of the risk assessment;
- the conduct of the source, and
- the safety and welfare of the source.

4.38 Where deemed appropriate, concerns about such matters must be considered by the authorising officer, and a decision taken on whether or not to allow the authorisation to continue.

ADDITIONAL RULES

Recording of telephone conversations

4.39 Subject to paragraph 4.40 below, the interception of communications sent by post or by means of public telecommunications systems or private telecommunications systems attached to the public network may be authorised only by the Secretary of State, in accordance with the terms of Part I of the 2000 Act. Nothing in this code should be taken as granting dispensation from the requirements of that Part of the 2000 Act.

4.40 Part I of the 2000 Act provides certain exceptions to the rule that interception of telephone conversations must be warranted under that Part. This includes, where one party to the communication consents to the interception, it may be authorised in accordance with section 48(4) of the 2000 Act provided that there is no interception warrant authorising the interception. In such cases, the interception is treated as directed surveillance (see chapter 4 of the Covert Surveillance code of practice).

Use of covert human intelligence source with technical equipment

4.41 A source, whether or not wearing or carrying a surveillance device and invited into residential premises or a private vehicle, does not require additional authorisation to record any activity taking place inside those premises or vehicle which take place in his presence. This also applies to the recording of telephone conversations other than by interception which takes place in the source's presence. Authorisation for the use or conduct of that source may be obtained in the usual way.

4.42 However, if a surveillance device is to be used, other than in the presence of the source, an intrusive surveillance authorisation and if applicable an authorisation for interference with property should be obtained.

[1514]

NOTES

1 One of the functions of the Security Service is the protection of national security and in particular the protection against threats from terrorism. These functions extend throughout the United Kingdom, save that, in Northern Ireland, where the lead responsibility for investigating the threat from terrorism related to the affairs of Northern Ireland lies with the Police Service of Northern Ireland. An authorising officer in another public authority should not issue an authorisation under Part II of the 2000 Act where the operation or investigation falls within the responsibilities of the Security Service, as set out above, except where it is to be carried out by a Special Branch or where the Security Service has agreed that another public authority can authorise the use or conduct of a source which would normally fall within the responsibilities of the Security Service.

2 HM Forces may also undertake operations in connection with a military threat to national security and other operations in connection with national security in support of the Security Service, the Police Service of Northern Ireland or other Civil Powers.

3 Detecting crime is defined in section 81(5) of the 2000 Act.

4 This could include investigations into infectious diseases, contaminated products or the illicit sale of pharmaceuticals.

5 This could only be for a purpose which satisfies the criteria set out in Article 8(2) of the ECHR.

6 As defined in section 81(1) of the 2000 Act.

5 OVERSIGHT BY COMMISSIONERS

5.1 The 2000 Act requires the Chief Surveillance Commissioner to keep under review (with the assistance of the Surveillance Commissioners and Assistant Surveillance Commissioners) the performance of functions under Part III of the 1997 Act and Part II of the 2000 Act by the police (including the Royal Navy Regulating Branch, the Royal Military Police and the Royal Air Force Police and the Ministry of Defence Police and the British Transport Police), NCIS, NCS, HMCE and of the 2000 Act the other public authorities listed in Schedule 1 and in Northern Ireland officials of the Ministry of Defence and HM Forces.

5.2 The Intelligence Services Commissioner's remit is to provide independent oversight of the use of the powers contained within Part II of the 2000 Act by the Security Service, Secret Intelligence Service (SIS), the Governments Communication Headquarters (GCHQ) and the Ministry of Defence and HM Forces (excluding the Royal Navy Regulating Branch, the Royal Military Police and the Royal Air Force Police, and in Northern Ireland officials of the Ministry of Defence HM Forces).

5.3 This code does not cover the exercise of any of the Commissioners' functions. It is the duty of any person who uses these powers to comply with any request made by a Commissioner to disclose or provide any information he requires for the purpose of enabling him to carry out his functions.

5.4 References in this code to the performance of review functions by the Chief Surveillance Commissioner and other Commissioners apply also to Inspectors and other members of staff to whom such functions have been delegated.

[1515]

6 COMPLAINTS

6.1 The 2000 Act establishes an independent Tribunal. This Tribunal will be made up of senior members of the judiciary and the legal profession and is independent of the Government. The Tribunal has full powers to investigate and decide any case within its jurisdiction.

6.2 This code does not cover the exercise of the Tribunal's functions. Details of the relevant complaints procedure can be obtained from the following address—

Investigatory Powers Tribunal

PO Box 33220

London

SW1H 9ZQ

020 7273 4514

[1516]

ANNEX A
AUTHORISATION LEVELS WHEN KNOWLEDGE OF CONFIDENTIAL INFORMATION IS LIKELY TO BE ACQUIRED OR WHEN A VULNERABLE INDIVIDUAL OR JUVENILE IS TO BE USED AS A SOURCE

Government Department/Public Authority	Authorisation level for when knowledge of Confidential Information is likely to be acquired	Authorisation level for when a vulnerable individual or a Juvenile is to be used as a source
Police Forces – Any police force maintained under section 2 of the Police Act 1996 (police forces in England and Wales outside London).	Chief Constable	Assistant Chief Constable
Police Forces – Any police force maintained under or by virtue of section 1 of the Police (Scotland) Act 1967	Chief Constable	Assistant Chief Constable
The Metropolitan police force	Assistant Commissioner	Commander
The City of London police force	Commissioner	Commander
The Police Service of Northern Ireland	Deputy Chief Constable	Assistant Chief Constable
The Royal Navy Regulating Branch	Provost Marshal	Provost Marshal
Royal Military Police	Provost Marshal	Provost Marshal
Royal Air Force Police	Provost Marshal	Provost Marshal
National Criminal Intelligence Service (**NCIS**)	Director General	Assistant Chief Constable or Assistant Chief Investigation Officer
National Crime Squad (NCS)	Director General or Deputy Director General	Assistant Chief Constable
Serious Fraud Office	Director or Assistant Director	Director or Assistant Director
The Intelligence Services:		
Government Communications Headquarters	A Director of GCHQ	A Director of GCHQ
Security Service	Deputy Director General	Deputy Director General

PART II DATA PROTECTION

Government Department/Public Authority	Authorisation level for when knowledge of Confidential Information is likely to be acquired	Authorisation level for when a vulnerable individual or a Juvenile is to be used as a source
Secret Intelligence Service	A Director of the Secret Intelligence Service	A member of the Secret Intelligence Service not below the equivalent rank to that of a Grade 5 in the Home Civil Service)
HM Forces:		
Royal Navy	Rear Admiral	Rear Admiral
Army	Major General	Major General
Royal Air Force	Air-Vice Marshall	Air-Vice Marshall
HM Customs and Excise	Director Investigation or Regional Heads of Investigation	Band 11 (Intelligence)
Inland Revenue	Deputy Chairman of Inland Revenue	Head of Special Compliance Office
Department for the Environment, Food and Rural Affairs:		
DEFRA Investigation Branch	Immediate Senior Officer of Head of DEFRA Prosecution Division	Head of DEFRA Prosecution Division
Horticultural Marketing Inspectorate	Immediate Senior Officer of Head of DEFRA Prosecution Division	No
Plant Health and Seed Inspectorate	Immediate Senior Officer of Head of DEFRA Prosecution Division	No
Egg Marketing Inspectorate	Immediate Senior Officer of Head of DEFRA Prosecution Division	No
Sea Fisheries Inspectorate (SFI)	Immediate Senior Officer of Head of DEFRA Prosecution Division	No
Centre for Environment, Fisheries & Aquaculture Science (CEFAS)	Immediate Senior Officer of Head of DEFRA Prosecution Division	Head of DEFRA Prosecution Division
Ministry of Defence	Director General or equivalent	Director General or equivalent
Department for Transport, Local Government and the Regions:		
Vehicle Inspectorate	No	No
Transport Security (Transec)	Director of Transport Security	Deputy Director of Transport Security
Department of Health:		
Medical Devices Agency	Chief Executive	No
Medicine Control Agency	Chief Executive	Head of Division for Inspection and Enforcement

Government Department/Public Authority	**Authorisation level for when knowledge of Confidential Information is likely to be acquired**	**Authorisation level for when a vulnerable individual or a Juvenile is to be used as a source**
Welfare Foods Policy Unit	Deputy Chief Medical Officer	No
Directorate of Counter Fraud Services (DFCS)	Director of Counter Fraud Services	Director of Counter Fraud Services
Home Office:		
HM Prison Service	Deputy Director General	Area Managers
Immigration Service	Chief Inspector	Director
Department of Work and Pensions:		
Benefits Agency	Chief Executive	Head of Fraud Investigation
Department of Trade and Industry:		
Radiocommunications Agency	No	No
British Trade International	No	No
Coal Health Claims Unit	Director of Coal Health Claims unit	No
Companies Investigation Branch	The Inspector of Companies	The Inspector of Companies
Legal Services Directorate D	The Director of Legal Service D	The Director of Legal Service D
National Assembly for Wales	Health – Director, NHS Wales	Health – Director, NHS Wales
	Agriculture – Head, National Assembly for Wales Agriculture Department	Agriculture – Head, National Assembly for Wales Agriculture Department
Local Authorities	The Head of Paid Service or (in his absence) a Chief Officer	The Head of Paid Service or (in his absence) a Chief Officer
Environment Agency	Chief Executive	Executive Managers
Financial Services Authority	Chairman	Chairman
Food Standards Agency	Head of Group, Deputy Chief Executive and Chief Executive	Head of Group, Deputy Chief Executive and Chief Executive
The Intervention Board for Agricultural Produce	Chief Executive	Legal Director
Personal Investment Authority	Chairman	Chairman
Post Office	Director of Security	Head of Corporate Security/ Head of Security for the Royal Mail/Head of Security for Counter Business

[1517]

PART II DATA PROTECTION

COVERT SURVEILLANCE CODE OF PRACTICE (2002)

NOTES

Authority: Regulation of Investigatory Powers Act 2000, s 71(5). This Code of Practice came into force on 1 August 2002 (see SI 2002/1933). This code applies to every authorisation or with wireless telegraphy carried out under section 5 of the Intelligence Services Act 1994, Part III of the Police Act 1997 or Part II of the Regulation of Investigatory Powers Act 2000 by public authorities which begins on or after the day on which this code comes into effect.

1 BACKGROUND

1.1 In this code the—

- **"1989 Act"** means the Security Service Act 1989;
- **"1994 Act"** means the Intelligence Services Act 1994;
- **"1997 Act"** means the Police Act 1997;
- **"2000 Act"** means the Regulation of Investigatory Powers Act 2000;
- **"RIP(S)A"** means the Regulation of Investigatory Powers (Scotland) Act 2000.

1.2 This code of practice provides guidance on the use of covert surveillance by public authorities under Part II of the 2000 Act and on entry on, or interference with, property (or with wireless telegraphy) under section 5 of the 1994 Act or Part III of the 1997 Act. This code replaces the code of practice issued in 1999 pursuant to section 101(3) of the 1997 Act.

1.3 General observation forms part of the duties of many law enforcement officers and other public authorities and is not usually regulated by the 2000 Act. For example, police officers will be on patrol to prevent and detect crime, maintain public safety and prevent disorder or trading standards or HM Customs and Excise officers might covertly observe and then visit a shop as part of their enforcement function to verify the supply or level of supply of goods or services that may be liable to a restriction or tax. Such observation may involve the use of equipment to merely reinforce normal sensory perception, such as binoculars, or the use of cameras, where this does not involve systematic surveillance of an individual.

1.4 Although, the provisions of the 2000 Act or of this code of practice do not normally cover the use of overt CCTV surveillance systems, since members of the public are aware that such systems are in use, there may be occasions when public authorities use overt CCTV systems for the purposes of a specific investigation or operation. In such cases, authorisation for intrusive or directed surveillance may be necessary.

1.5 The 2000 Act provides that all codes of practice relating to the 2000 Act are admissible as evidence in criminal and civil proceedings. If any provision of the code appears relevant to any court or tribunal considering any such proceedings, or to the Investigatory Powers Tribunal established under the 2000 Act, or to one of the Commissioners responsible for overseeing the powers conferred by the 2000 Act, it must be taken into account.

General extent of powers

1.6 Authorisations under the 2000 Act can be given for surveillance both inside and outside the United Kingdom. Authorisations for actions outside the United Kingdom can only validate them for the purposes of proceedings in the United Kingdom. An authorisation under Part II of the 2000 Act does not take into account the requirements of the country outside the United Kingdom in which the investigation or operation is taking place.

1.7 Where the conduct authorised is likely to take place in Scotland, authorisations should be granted under RIP(S)A, unless the authorisation is being obtained by those public authorities listed in section 46(3) of the 2000 Act and the Regulation of Investigatory Powers (Authorisations Extending to Scotland) Order 2000; SI No 2418). Additionally any authorisation granted or renewed for the purposes of national security or the economic well-being of the United Kingdom must be made under the 2000 Act. This code of practice is extended to Scotland in relation to authorisations made under Part II of the 2000 Act which apply to Scotland. A separate code of practice applies in relation to authorisations made under RIP(S)A.

Use of material in evidence

1.8 Material obtained through covert surveillance may be used as evidence in criminal proceedings. The proper authorisation of surveillance should ensure the admissibility of such evidence under the common law, section 78 of the Police and Criminal Evidence Act 1984 and the Human Rights Act 1998. Furthermore, the product of the surveillance described in this code is subject to the ordinary rules for retention and disclosure of material under the Criminal Procedure and Investigations Act 1996, where those rules apply to the law enforcement body in question.

Directed surveillance, intrusive surveillance and entry on or interference with property or with wireless telegraphy

1.9 Directed surveillance is defined in section 26(2) of the 2000 Act as surveillance which is covert, but not intrusive, and undertaken—

(a) for the purposes of a specific investigation or specific operation;
(b) in such a manner as is likely to result in the obtaining of private information about a person (whether or not one specifically identified for the purposes of the investigation or operation); and
(c) otherwise than by way of an immediate response to events or circumstances the nature of which is such that it would not be reasonably practicable for an authorisation under Part II of the 2000 Act to be sought for the carrying out of the surveillance.

1.10 Directed surveillance investigations or operations can only be carried out by those public authorities who are listed in or added to Part I and Part II of Schedule 1 of the 2000 Act.

1.11 Intrusive surveillance is defined in section 26(3) of the 2000 Act as covert surveillance that—

(a) is carried out in relation to anything taking place on any residential premises or in any private vehicle; and
(b) involves the presence of an individual on the premises or in the vehicle or is carried out by means of a surveillance device.

1.12 Applications to carry out intrusive surveillance can only be made by the senior authorising officer of those public authorities listed in or added to section 32(6) of the 2000 Act or by a member or official of those public authorities listed in or added to section 41(1).

1.13 Applications to enter on or interfere with property or with wireless telegraphy can only be made by the authorising officers of those public authorities listed in or added to section 93(5) of the 1997 Act. Under section 5 of the 1994 Act only members of the intelligence services are able to make applications to enter on or interfere with property or with wireless telegraphy.

[1518]

2 GENERAL RULES ON AUTHORISATIONS

2.1 An authorisation under Part II of the 2000 Act will provide lawful authority for a public authority to carry out surveillance. Responsibility for authorising surveillance investigations or operations will vary, depending on whether the authorisation is for intrusive surveillance or directed surveillance, and which public authority is involved. For the purposes of Chapter 2 and 3 of this code the authorising officer, senior authorising officer or the person who makes an application to the Secretary of State will be referred to as an 'authorising officer'.

2.2 Part II of the 2000 Act does not impose a requirement on public authorities to seek or obtain an authorisation where, under the 2000 Act, one is available (see section 80 of the 2000 Act). Nevertheless, where there is an interference by a public authority with the right to respect for private and family life guaranteed under Article 8 of the European Convention on Human Rights, and where there is no other source of lawful authority, the consequence of not obtaining an authorisation under the 2000 Act may be that the action is unlawful by virtue of section 6 of the Human Rights Act 1998.

2.3 Public authorities are therefore strongly recommended to seek an authorisation where the surveillance is likely to interfere with a person's Article 8 rights to privacy by obtaining private information about that person, whether or not that person is the subject of the investigation or operation. Obtaining an authorisation will ensure that the action is carried out in accordance with law and subject to stringent safeguards against abuse.

Necessity and Proportionality

2.4 Obtaining an authorisation under the 2000 Act, the 1997 Act and 1994 Act will only ensure that there is a justifiable interference with an individual's Article 8 rights if it is necessary and proportionate for these activities to take place. The 2000 Act first requires that the person granting an authorisation believe that the authorisation is necessary in the circumstances of the particular case for one or more of the statutory grounds in section 28(3) of the 2000 Act for directed surveillance and in section 32(3) of the 2000 Act for intrusive surveillance.

2.5 Then, if the activities are necessary, the person granting the authorisation must believe that they are proportionate to what is sought to be achieved by carrying them out. This involves balancing the intrusiveness of the activity on the target and others who might be affected by it against the need for the activity in operational terms. The activity will not be proportionate if it is excessive in the circumstances of the case or if the information which is sought could reasonably be obtained by other less intrusive means. All such activity should be carefully managed to meet the objective in question and must not be arbitrary or unfair.

Collateral Intrusion

2.6 Before authorising surveillance the authorising officer should also take into account the risk of intrusion into the privacy of persons other than those who are directly the subjects of the investigation or operation (collateral intrusion). Measures should be taken, wherever practicable, to avoid or minimise unnecessary intrusion into the lives of those not directly connected with the investigation or operation.

2.7 An application for an authorisation should include an assessment of the risk of any collateral intrusion. The authorising officer should take this into account, when considering the proportionality of the surveillance.

2.8 Those carrying out the surveillance should inform the authorising officer if the investigation or operation unexpectedly interferes with the privacy of individuals who are not covered by the authorisation. When the original authorisation may not be sufficient, consideration should be given to whether the authorisation needs to be amended and reauthorised or a new authorisation is required.

2.9 Any person granting or applying for an authorisation or warrant will also need to be aware of particular sensitivities in the local community where the surveillance is taking place and of similar activities being undertaken by other public authorities which could impact on the deployment of surveillance. In this regard, it is recommended that where the authorising officers in the National Criminal Intelligence Service (NCIS), the National Crime Squad (NCS) and HM Customs and Excise (HMCE) consider that conflicts might arise they should consult a senior officer within the police force area in which the investigation or operation takes place.

2.10 The matters in paragraphs 2.1–2.9 above must also be taken into account when applying for authorisations or warrants for entry on or interference with property or with wireless telegraphy. In particular they must be necessary in the circumstances of the particular case for one of the statutory ground listed in section 93(2)(a) of the 1997 Act and section 5(2)(c) of the 1994 Act, proportionate and when exercised steps should be taken to minimise collateral intrusion.

Combined authorisations

2.11 A single authorisation may combine—

- two or more different authorisations under Part II of the 2000 Act;
- an authorisation under Part II of the 2000 Act and an authorisation under Part III of the 1997 Act;
- a warrant for intrusive surveillance under Part II of the 2000 Act and a warrant under section 5 of the 1994 Act.

2.12 For example, a single authorisation may combine authorisations for directed and intrusive surveillance. The provisions applicable in the case of each of the authorisations must be considered separately. Thus, a police superintendent can authorise the directed surveillance but the intrusive surveillance needs the separate authorisation of a chief constable, and in certain cases the approval of a Surveillance Commissioner will also be necessary. Where an authorisation for directed surveillance or the use or conduct of a covert human intelligence source is combined with a Secretary of State authorisation for intrusive surveillance, the combined authorisation must be issued by the Secretary of State. However, this does not preclude public authorities from obtaining separate authorisations.

2.13 In cases where one agency is acting on behalf of another, it is usually for the tasking agency to obtain or provide the authorisation. For example, where surveillance is carried out by the Armed Forces on behalf of the police, authorisations would be sought by the police and granted by the appropriate authorising officer. In cases where the Security Service is acting in support of the police or other law enforcement agencies in the field of serious crime, the Security Service would normally seek authorisations.

Central Record of all authorisations

2.14 A centrally retrievable record of all authorisations should be held by each public authority and regularly updated whenever an authorisation is granted, renewed or cancelled.

The record should be made available to the relevant Commissioner or an Inspector from the Office of Surveillance Commissioners, upon request. These records should be retained for a period of at least three years from the ending of the authorisation and should contain the following information—

- the type of authorisation;
- the date the authorisation was given;
- name and rank/grade of the authorising officer;
- the unique reference number (URN) of the investigation or operation;
- the title of the investigation or operation, including a brief description and names of subjects, if known;
- whether the urgency provisions were used, and if so why;
- if the authorisation is renewed, when it was renewed and who authorised the renewal, including the name and rank/grade of the authorising officer;
- whether the investigation or operation is likely to result in obtaining confidential information as defined in this code of practice;
- the date the authorisation was cancelled.

2.15 In all cases, the relevant authority should maintain the following documentation which need not form part of the centrally retrievable record—

- a copy of the application and a copy of the authorisation together with any supplementary documentation and notification of the approval given by the authorising officer;
- a record of the period over which the surveillance has taken place;
- the frequency of reviews prescribed by the authorising officer;
- a record of the result of each review of the authorisation;
- a copy of any renewal of an authorisation, together with the supporting documentation submitted when the renewal was requested;
- the date and time when any instruction was given by the authorising officer.

Retention and destruction of the product

2.16 Where the product of surveillance could be relevant to pending or future criminal or civil proceedings, it should be retained in accordance with established disclosure requirements for a suitable further period, commensurate to any subsequent review.

2.17 In the cases of the law enforcement agencies (not including the Royal Navy Regulating Branch, the Royal Military Police and the Royal Air Force Police), particular attention is drawn to the requirements of the code of practice issued under the Criminal Procedure and Investigations Act 1996. This requires that material which is obtained in the course of a criminal investigation and which may be relevant to the investigation must be recorded and retained.

2.18 There is nothing in the 2000 Act which prevents material obtained from properly authorised surveillance from being used in other investigations. Each public authority must ensure that arrangements are in place for the handling, storage and destruction of material obtained through the use of covert surveillance. Authorising officers must ensure compliance with the appropriate data protection requirements and any relevant codes of practice produced by individual authorities relating to the handling and storage of material.

The Intelligence Services, MOD and HM Forces

2.19 The heads of these agencies are responsible for ensuring that arrangements exist for securing that no information is stored by the authorities, except as necessary for the proper discharge of their functions. They are also responsible for arrangements to control onward disclosure. For the intelligence services, this is a statutory duty under the 1989 Act and the 1994 Act.

[1519]

3 SPECIAL RULES ON AUTHORISATIONS

3.1 The 2000 Act does not provide any special protection for 'confidential information'. Nevertheless, particular care should be taken in cases where the subject of the investigation or operation might reasonably expect a high degree of privacy, or where confidential information is involved. Confidential information consists of matters subject to legal privilege, confidential personal information or confidential journalistic material. So, for example, extra care should be given where, through the use of surveillance, it would be possible to acquire knowledge of discussions between a minister of religion and an individual relating to the latter's spiritual welfare, or where matters of medical or journalistic confidentiality or legal privilege may be involved.

3.2 In cases where through the use of surveillance it is likely that knowledge of confidential information will be acquired, the use of surveillance is subject to a higher level of authorisation. Annex A lists the authorising officer for each public authority permitted to authorise such surveillance.

Communications Subject to Legal Privilege

3.3 Section 98 of the 1997 Act describes those matters that are subject to legal privilege in England and Wales. In Scotland, the relevant description is contained in section 33 of the Criminal Law (Consolidation) (Scotland) Act 1995. With regard to Northern Ireland, Article 12 of the Police and Criminal Evidence (Northern Ireland) Order 1989 should be referred to.

3.4 Legal privilege does not apply to communications made with the intention of furthering a criminal purpose (whether the lawyer is acting unwittingly or culpably). Legally privileged communications will lose their protection if there are grounds to believe, for example, that the professional legal adviser is intending to hold or use them for a criminal purpose. But privilege is not lost if a professional legal adviser is properly advising a person who is suspected of having committed a criminal offence. The concept of legal privilege applies to the provision of professional legal advice by any individual, agency or organisation qualified to do so.

3.5 The 2000 Act does not provide any special protection for legally privileged information. Nevertheless, such information is particularly sensitive and surveillance which acquires such material may engage Article 6 of the ECHR (right to a fair trial) as well as Article 8. Legally privileged information obtained by surveillance is extremely unlikely ever to be admissible as evidence in criminal proceedings. Moreover, the mere fact that such surveillance has taken place may lead to any related criminal proceedings being stayed as an abuse of process. Accordingly, action which may lead to such information being acquired is subject to additional safeguards under this code.

3.6 In general, an application for surveillance which is likely to result in the acquisition of legally privileged information should only be made in exceptional and compelling circumstances. Full regard should be had to the particular proportionality issues such surveillance raises. The application should include, in addition to the reasons why it is considered necessary for the surveillance to take place, an assessment of how likely it is that information subject to legal privilege will be acquired. In addition, the application should clearly state whether the purpose (or one of the purposes) of the surveillance is to obtain legally privileged information.

3.7 This assessment will be taken into account by the authorising officer in deciding whether the proposed surveillance is necessary and proportionate under section 28 of the 2000 Act for directed surveillance and under section 32 for intrusive surveillance. The authorising officer may require regular reporting so as to be able to decide whether the authorisation should continue. In those cases where legally privileged information has been acquired and retained, the matter should be reported to the relevant Commissioner or Inspector during his next inspection and the material be made available to him if requested.

3.8 A substantial proportion of the communications between a lawyer and his client(s) may be subject to legal privilege. Therefore, any case where a lawyer is the subject of an investigation or operation should be notified to the relevant Commissioner during his next inspection and any material which has been retained should be made available to him if requested.

3.9 Where there is any doubt as to the handling and dissemination of information which may be subject to legal privilege, advice should be sought from a legal adviser within the relevant public authority before any further dissemination of the material takes place. Similar advice should also be sought where there is doubt over whether information is not subject to legal privilege due to the "in furtherance of a criminal purpose" exception. The retention of legally privileged information, or its dissemination to an outside body, should be accompanied by a clear warning that it is subject to legal privilege. It should be safeguarded by taking reasonable steps to ensure there is no possibility of it becoming available, or its contents becoming known, to any person whose possession of it might prejudice any criminal or civil proceedings related to the information. Any dissemination of legally privileged material to an outside body should be notified to the relevant Commissioner or Inspector during his next inspection.

Communications involving Confidential Personal Information and Confidential Journalistic Material

3.10 Similar consideration must also be given to authorisations that involve confidential personal information and confidential journalistic material. In those cases where confidential personal information and confidential journalistic material has been acquired and retained, the matter should be reported to the relevant Commissioner or Inspector during his next inspection and the material be made available to him if requested. Confidential personal information is information held in confidence relating to the physical or mental health or spiritual counselling concerning an individual (whether living or dead) who can be identified from it. Such information, which can include both oral and written communications, is held in confidence if it is held subject to an express or implied undertaking to hold it in confidence or it is subject to a restriction on disclosure or an obligation of confidentiality contained in existing legislation. Examples might include consultations between a health professional and a patient, or information from a patient's medical records.

3.11 Spiritual counselling means conversations between an individual and a Minister of Religion acting in his official capacity, where the individual being counselled is seeking or the Minister is imparting forgiveness, absolution or the resolution of conscience with the authority of the Divine Being(s) of their faith.

3.12 Confidential journalistic material includes material acquired or created for the purposes of journalism and held subject to an undertaking to hold it in confidence, as well as communications resulting in information being acquired for the purposes of journalism and held subject to such an undertaking.

[1520]

4 AUTHORISATION PROCEDURES FOR DIRECTED SURVEILLANCE

4.1 Directed surveillance is defined in section 26(2) of the 2000 Act as surveillance which is covert, but not intrusive, and undertaken—

(a) for the purposes of a specific investigation or specific operation;

(b) in such a manner as is likely to result in the obtaining of private information about a person (whether or not one specifically identified for the purposes of the investigation or operation); and

(c) otherwise than by way of an immediate response to events or circumstances the nature of which is such that it would not be reasonably practicable for an authorisation under Part II of the 2000 Act to be sought for the carrying out of the surveillance.

4.2 Covert surveillance is defined in section 26(9)(a) of the 2000 Act as any surveillance which is carried out in a manner calculated to ensure that the persons subject to the surveillance are unaware that it is or may be taking place.

4.3 Private information is defined in section 26(10) of the 2000 Act as including any information relating to a person's private or family life. The concept of private information should be broadly interpreted to include an individual's private or personal relationship with others. Family life should be treated as extending beyond the formal relationships created by marriage.

4.4 Directed surveillance does not include covert surveillance carried out by way of an immediate response to events or circumstances which, by their very nature, could not have been foreseen. For example, a police officer would not require an authorisation to conceal himself and observe a suspicious person that he came across in the course of a patrol.

4.5 By virtue of section 48(4) of the 2000 Act, surveillance includes the interception of postal and telephone communications where the sender or recipient consents to the reading of or listening to or recording of the communication (as the case may be). For further details see paragraphs 4.30–4.32 of this code.

4.6 Surveillance in residential premises or in private vehicles is defined as intrusive surveillance in section 26(3) of the 2000 Act and is dealt with in chapter 5 of this code. However, where surveillance is carried out by a device designed or adapted principally for the purpose of providing information about the location of a vehicle, the activity is directed surveillance and should be authorised accordingly.

4.7 Directed surveillance does not include entry on or interference with property or with wireless telegraphy. These activities are subject to a separate regime of authorisation or warrantry, as set out in chapter 6 of this code.

4.8 Directed surveillance includes covert surveillance within office premises, (as defined in paragraph 6.31 of this code). Authorising officers are reminded that confidential information should be afforded an enhanced level of protection. Chapter 3 of this code provides that in cases where the likely consequence of surveillance is to acquire confidential information, the authorisation should be given at a higher level.

Authorisation Procedures

4.9 Under section 28(3) of the 2000 Act an authorisation for directed surveillance may be granted by an authorising officer where he believes that the authorisation is necessary in the circumstances of the particular case—

- in the interests of national security;[1, 2]
- for the purpose of preventing and detecting[3] crime or of preventing disorder;
- in the interests of the economic well-being of the UK;
- in the interests of public safety;
- for the purpose of protecting public health;[4]
- for the purpose of assessing or collecting any tax, duty, levy or other imposition, contribution or charge payable to a government department; or
- for any other purpose prescribed by an order made by the Secretary of State.[5]

4.10 The authorising officer must also believe that the surveillance is proportionate to what it seeks to achieve.

4.11 The public authorities entitled to authorise directed surveillance are listed in Schedule 1 to the 2000 Act. Responsibility for authorising the carrying out of directed surveillance rests with the authorising officer and requires the personal authority of the authorising officer. The Regulation of Investigatory Powers (Prescriptions of Offices, Ranks and Positions) Order 2000; SI No: 2417 designates the authorising officer for each different public authority and the officers entitled to act only in urgent cases. Where an authorisation for directed surveillance is combined with a Secretary of State authorisation for intrusive surveillance, the combined authorisation must be issued by the Secretary of State.

4.12 The authorising officer must give authorisations in writing, except that in urgent cases, they may be given orally by the authorising officer or the officer entitled to act in urgent cases. In such cases, a statement that the authorising officer has expressly authorised the action should be recorded in writing by the applicant as soon as is reasonably practicable.

4.13 A case is not normally to be regarded as urgent unless the time that would elapse before the authorising officer was available to grant the authorisation would, in the judgement of the person giving the authorisation, be likely to endanger life or jeopardise the investigation or operation for which the authorisation was being given. An authorisation is not to be regarded as urgent where the need for an authorisation has been neglected or the urgency is of the authorising officer's own making.

4.14 Authorising officers should not be responsible for authorising investigations or operations in which they are directly involved, although it is recognised that this may sometimes be unavoidable, especially in the case of small organisations, or where it is necessary to act urgently. Where an authorising officer authorises such an investigation or operation the central record of authorisations (see paragraphs 2.14–2.15) should highlight this and the attention of a Commissioner or Inspector should be invited to it during his next inspection.

4.15 Authorising officers within the Police, NCIS and NCS may only grant authorisations on application by a member of their own force, Service or Squad. Authorising officers in HMCE may only grant an authorisation on application by a customs officer.[6]

Information to be provided in applications for authorisation

4.16 A written application for authorisation for directed surveillance should describe any conduct to be authorised and the purpose of the investigation or operation. The application should also include—

- the reasons why the authorisation is necessary in the particular case and on the grounds (eg for the purpose of preventing or detecting crime) listed in Section 28(3) of the 2000 Act;
- the reasons why the surveillance is considered proportionate to what it seeks to achieve;
- the nature of the surveillance;
- the identities, where known, of those to be the subject of the surveillance;
- an explanation of the information which it is desired to obtain as a result of the surveillance;
- the details of any potential collateral intrusion and why the intrusion is justified;
- the details of any confidential information that is likely to be obtained as a consequence of the surveillance;
- the level of authority required (or recommended where that is different) for the surveillance; and

- a subsequent record of whether authority was given or refused, by whom and the time and date.

4.17 Additionally, in urgent cases, the authorisation should record (as the case may be)—

- the reasons why the authorising officer or the officer entitled to act in urgent cases considered the case so urgent that an oral instead of a written authorisation was given; and/or
- the reasons why it was not reasonably practicable for the application to be considered by the authorising officer.

4.18 Where the authorisation is oral, the detail referred to above should be recorded in writing by the applicant as soon as reasonably practicable.

Duration of authorisations

4.19 A written authorisation granted by an authorising officer will cease to have effect (unless renewed) at the end of a period of **three months** beginning with the day on which it took effect.

4.20 Urgent oral authorisations or written authorisations granted by a person who is entitled to act only in urgent cases will, unless renewed, cease to have effect after **seventy-two hours**, beginning with the time when the authorisation was granted or renewed.

Reviews

4.21 Regular reviews of authorisations should be undertaken to assess the need for the surveillance to continue. The results of a review should be recorded on the central record of authorisations (see paragraphs 2.14–2.15). Particular attention is drawn to the need to review authorisations frequently where the surveillance provides access to confidential information or involves collateral intrusion.

4.22 In each case the authorising officer within each public authority should determine how often a review should take place. This should be as frequently as is considered necessary and practicable.

Renewals

4.23 If at any time before an authorisation would cease to have effect, the authorising officer considers it necessary for the authorisation to continue for the purpose for which it was given, he may renew it in writing for a further period of **three months** unless it is a case to which paragraph 4.25 applies. Renewals may also be granted orally in urgent cases and last for a period of **seventy-two hours**.

4.24 A renewal takes effect at the time at which, or day on which the authorisation would have ceased to have effect but for the renewal. An application for renewal should not be made until shortly before the authorisation period is drawing to an end. Any person who would be entitled to grant a new authorisation can renew an authorisation. Authorisations may be renewed more than once, provided they continue to meet the criteria for authorisation.

4.25 If at any time before an authorisation for directed surveillance, granted on the grounds of it being in the interests of national security or in the interests of the economic well-being of the UK, would cease to have effect, an authorising officer who is a member of the intelligence services considers it necessary for it to continue, he may renew it for a further period of **six months**, beginning with the day on which it would have ceased to have effect but for the renewal.

4.26 All applications for the renewal of an authorisation for directed surveillance should record—

- whether this is the first renewal or every occasion on which the authorisation has been renewed previously;
- any significant changes to the information in paragraph 4.16;
- the reasons why it is necessary to continue with the directed surveillance;
- the content and value to the investigation or operation of the information so far obtained by the surveillance;
- the results of regular reviews of the investigation or operation.

4.27 Authorisations may be renewed more than once, if necessary, and the renewal should be kept/recorded as part of the central record of authorisations (see paragraphs 2.14–2.15).

Cancellations

4.28 The authorising officer who granted or last renewed the authorisation must cancel it if he is satisfied that the directed surveillance no longer meets the criteria upon which it was

PART II
DATA PROTECTION

authorised. Where the authorising officer is no longer available, this duty will fall on the person who has taken over the role of authorising officer or the person who is acting as authorising officer (see the Regulation of Investigatory Powers (Cancellation of Authorisations) Order 2000; SI No: 2794).

Ceasing of surveillance activity

4.29 As soon as the decision is taken that directed surveillance should be discontinued, the instruction must be given to those involved to stop all surveillance of the subject(s). The date and time when such an instruction was given should be recorded in the central record of authorisations (see paragraphs 2.14–2.15) and the notification of cancellation where relevant.

ADDITIONAL RULES

Recording of telephone conversations

4.30 Subject to paragraph 4.31 below, the interception of communications sent by post or by means of public telecommunications systems or private telecommunications systems attached to the public network may be authorised only by the Secretary of State, in accordance with the terms of Part I of the 2000 Act. Nothing in this code should be taken as granting dispensation from the requirements of that Part of the 2000 Act.

4.31 Part I of the 2000 Act provides certain exceptions to the rule that interception of telephone conversations must be warranted under that Part. This includes, where one party to the communication consents to the interception, it may be authorised in accordance with section 48(4) of the 2000 Act provided that there is no interception warrant authorising the interception. In such cases, the interception is treated as directed surveillance.

4.32 The use of a surveillance device should not be ruled out simply because it may incidentally pick up one or both ends of a telephone conversation, and any such product can be treated as having been lawfully obtained. However, its use would not be appropriate where the sole purpose is to overhear speech which, at the time of monitoring, is being transmitted by a telecommunications system. In such cases an application should be made for an interception of communication warrant under section 5 of the 2000 Act.

[1521]

NOTES

1 One of the functions of the Security Service is the protection of national security and in particular the protection against threats from terrorism. These functions extend throughout the United Kingdom, save that, in Northern Ireland, where the lead responsibility for investigating the threat from terrorism related to the affairs of Northern Ireland lies with the Police Service of Northern Ireland. An authorising officer in another public authority should not issue an authorisation under Part II of the 2000 Act or under Part III of the 1997 Act where the operation or investigation falls within the responsibilities of the Security Service, as set out above, except where it is a directed surveillance investigation or operation that is to be carried out by a Special Branch or where the Security Service has agreed that another public authority can carry out a directed surveillance operation or investigation which would fall within the responsibilities of the Security Service.

2 HM Forces may also undertake operations in connection with a military threat to national security and other operations in connection with national security in support of the Security Service, the Police Service of Northern Ireland or other Civil Powers.

3 Detecting crime is defined in section 81(5) of the 2000 Act and is applied to the 1997 Act by section 134 of that Act (as amended).

4 This could include investigations into infectious diseases, contaminated products or the illicit sale of pharmaceuticals.

5 This could only be for a purpose which satisfies the criteria set out in Article 8(2) of the ECHR. As defined in section 81(1) of the 2000 Act.

6 As defined in section 81(1) of the 2000 Act.

5 AUTHORISATION PROCEDURES FOR INTRUSIVE SURVEILLANCE

5.1 Intrusive surveillance is defined in section 26(3) of the 2000 Act as covert surveillance that—

(a) is carried out in relation to anything taking place on any residential premises or in any private vehicle; and

(b) involves the presence of an individual on the premises or in the vehicle or is carried out by means of a surveillance device.

5.2 Covert surveillance is defined in section 26(9)(a) of the 2000 Act as any surveillance which is carried out in a manner calculated to ensure that the persons subject to the surveillance are unaware that it is or may be taking place.

5.3 Where surveillance is carried out in relation to anything taking place on any residential premises or in any private vehicle by means of a device, without that device being present on the premises, or in the vehicle, it is not intrusive unless the device consistently provides information of the same quality and detail as might be expected to be obtained from a device actually present on the premises or in the vehicle. Thus, an observation post outside premises, which provides a limited view and no sound of what is happening inside the premises would not be considered as intrusive surveillance.

5.4 Residential premises are defined in section 48(1) of the 2000 Act. The definition includes hotel rooms, bedrooms in barracks, and police and prison cells but not any common area to which a person is allowed access in connection with his occupation of such accommodation e g a hotel lounge.

5.5 A private vehicle is defined in section 48(1) of the 2000 Act as any vehicle which is used primarily for the private purposes of the person who owns it or of a person otherwise having the right to use it. A person does not have a right to use a motor vehicle if his right to use it derives only from his having paid, or undertaken to pay, for the use of the vehicle and its driver for a particular journey.

5.6 In many cases, a surveillance investigation or operation may involve both intrusive surveillance and entry on or interference with property or with wireless telegraphy. In such cases, both activities need authorisation. This can be done as a combined authorisation (see paragraph 2.11).

5.7 An authorisation for intrusive surveillance may be issued by the Secretary of State (for the intelligence services, the Ministry of Defence, HM Forces and any other public authority designated under section 41(1)) or by a senior authorising officer (for police, NCIS, NCS and HMCE).

5.8 All authorisations require the personal authority of the Secretary of State or the senior authorising officer. Any members or officials of the intelligence services, the Ministry of Defence and HM Forces can apply to the Secretary of State for an intrusive surveillance warrant. Under section 32(2) of the 2000 Act neither the Secretary of State or the senior authorising officer may authorise intrusive surveillance unless he believes—

(a) that the authorisation is necessary in the circumstances of the particular case on the grounds that it is—
- in the interests of national security;[1]
- for the purpose of preventing or detecting serious crime; or
- in the interests of the economic well-being of the UK;

and

(b) the authorising officer must also believe that the surveillance is proportionate to what it seeks to achieve.

5.9 A factor which must be taken into account in deciding whether an authorisation is necessary and proportionate is whether the information which it is thought necessary to obtain by means of the intrusive surveillance could reasonably be obtained by other less intrusive means.

Authorisations Procedures for Police, National Criminal Intelligence Service, the National Crime Squad and HM Customs and Excise

5.10 The senior authorising officer should generally give authorisations in writing. However, in urgent cases, they may be given orally. In an urgent oral case, a statement that the senior authorising officer has expressly authorised the conduct should be recorded in writing by the applicant as soon as is reasonably practicable.

5.11 If the senior authorising officer is absent then as provided for in section 12(4) of the Police Act 1996, section 5(4) of the Police (Scotland) Act 1967, section 25 of the City of London Police Act 1839, or sections 8 or 54 of the 1997 Act, an authorisation can be given in writing or, in urgent cases, orally by the designated deputy.

5.12 In an urgent case, where it is not reasonably practicable having regard to the urgency of the case for the designated deputy to consider the application, a written authorisation may be granted by a person entitled to act under section 34(4) of the 2000 Act.

5.13 A case is not normally to be regarded as urgent unless the time that would elapse before the authorising officer was available to grant the authorisation would, in the judgement of the person giving the authorisation, be likely to endanger life or jeopardise the investigation or operation for which the authorisation was being given. An authorisation is not to be regarded as urgent where the need for an authorisation has been neglected or the urgency is of the authorising officer's own making.

5.14 The consideration of an authorisation by the senior authorising officer is only to be regarded as not reasonably practicable (within the meaning of section 34(2) of the 2000 Act) if he is on annual leave, is absent from his office and his home, or is for some reason not able within a reasonable time to obtain access to a secure telephone or fax machine. Pressure of work is not normally to be regarded as rendering it impracticable for a senior authorising officer to consider an application. Where a designated deputy gives an authorisation this should be made clear and the reason for the absence of the senior authorising officer given.

5.15 A police, NCIS or NCS authorisation cannot be granted unless the application is made by a member of the same force, service or squad. For HMCE an authorisation cannot be granted unless the application is made by a customs officer. Where the surveillance is carried out in relation to any residential premises, the authorisation cannot be granted unless the residential premises are in the area of operation of the force, service, squad or organisation.

Information to be provided in applications for authorisation

5.16 Applications should be in writing and describe the conduct to be authorised and the purpose of the investigation or operation. The application should specify—

- the reasons why the authorisation is necessary in the particular case and on the grounds (eg for the purpose of preventing or detecting serious crime) listed in section 32(3) of the 2000 Act;
- the reasons why the surveillance is considered proportionate to what it seeks to achieve;
- the nature of the surveillance;
- the residential premises or private vehicle in relation to which the surveillance will take place;
- the identities, where known, of those to be the subject of the surveillance;
- an explanation of the information which it is desired to obtain as a result of the surveillance;
- details of any potential collateral intrusion and why the intrusion is justified;
- details of any confidential information that is likely to be obtained as a consequence of the surveillance;
- a subsequent record should be made of whether authority was given or refused, by whom and the time and date.

5.17 Additionally, in urgent cases, the authorisation should record (as the case may be)—

- the reasons why the authorising officer or designated deputy considered the case so urgent that an oral instead of a written authorisation was given; and/or
- the reasons why it was not reasonably practicable for the application to be considered by the senior authorising officer or the designated deputy.

5.18 Where the application is oral, the detail referred to above should be recorded in writing as soon as reasonably practicable.

Approval of Surveillance Commissioners

5.19 Except in urgent cases a police, NCIS, NCS or HMCE authorisation granted for intrusive surveillance will not take effect until it has been approved by a Surveillance Commissioner and written notice of the Commissioner's decision has been given to the person who granted the authorisation. This means that the approval will not take effect until the notice has been received in the office of the person who granted the authorisation within the relevant force, service, squad or HMCE.

5.20 When the authorisation is urgent it will take effect from the time it is granted provided notice is given to the Surveillance Commissioner in accordance with section 35(3)(b) (see section 36(3) of the 2000 Act).

5.21 There may be cases that become urgent after approval has been sought but before a response has been received from a Surveillance Commissioner. In such a case, the authorising officer should notify the Surveillance Commissioner that the case is now urgent (pointing out that it has become urgent since the notification). In these cases, the authorisation will take effect immediately.

Notifications to Surveillance Commissioners

5.22 Where a person grants, renews or cancels an authorisation, he must, as soon as is reasonably practicable, give notice in writing to a Surveillance Commissioner, in accordance with whatever arrangements have been made by the Chief Surveillance Commissioner.

5.23 In urgent cases, the notification must specify the grounds on which the case is believed to be one of urgency. The urgency provisions should not be used routinely. If the Surveillance

Commissioner is satisfied that there were no grounds for believing the case to be one of urgency, he has the power to quash the authorisation.

5.24 The information to be included in the notification to the Surveillance Commissioner is set out in the Regulation of Investigatory Powers (Notification of Authorisations etc) Order 2000; SI No: 2563.

Authorisation Procedures for Secretary of State Authorisations

Authorisations

5.25 An intrusive surveillance authorisation for any of the intelligence services, the Ministry of Defence, HM Forces or any other public authority designated for this purpose requires a Secretary of State authorisation/warrant, unless they are acting on behalf of another public authority that has obtained an authorisation. In this context, Secretary of State can mean any Secretary of State, although an authorisation or warrant should be obtained from the Secretary of State of the relevant department.

5.26 Intelligence services authorisations must be made by issue of a warrant. Such warrants will generally be given in writing by the Secretary of State. In urgent cases, a warrant may be signed (but not renewed) by a senior official, provided the Secretary of State has expressly authorised this.

5.27 Applications to the Secretary of State for authorisations should specify those matters listed in paragraph 5.16.

All intrusive surveillance authorisations

5.28 Paragraphs 5.29 to 5.42 deal with the duration, renewal and cancellation of authorisations. Unless otherwise specified the guidance below applies to all authorisations.

Duration of Authorisations

All authorisations except Secretary of State Intelligence Services authorisations

5.29 A written authorisation granted by a Secretary of State, a senior authorising officer or a designated deputy will cease to have effect (unless renewed) at the end of a period of **three months**, beginning with the day on which it took effect.

5.30 Oral authorisations given in urgent cases by a Secretary of State, a senior authorising officers or their designated deputies, and written authorisations given by those only entitled to act in urgent cases (see paragraph 5.11), will cease to have effect (unless renewed) at the end of the period of **seventy-two hours** beginning with the time when they took effect.

Secretary of State intelligence services authorisations

5.31 A warrant issued by the Secretary of State will cease to have effect at the end of a period of **six months** beginning with the day on which it was issued.

5.32 Warrants expressly authorised by a Secretary of State, and signed on his behalf by a senior civil servant, will cease to have effect at the end of the **second working day** following the day of issue of the warrant unless renewed by the Secretary of State.

Renewals

All authorisations except Secretary of State Intelligence Services authorisations

5.33 If at any time before an authorisation expires the senior authorising officer or, in his absence, the designated deputy considers the authorisation should continue to have effect for the purpose for which it was issued, he may renew it in writing for a further period of **three months**.

5.34 As with the initial authorisation, the senior authorising officer must (unless it is a case to which the urgency procedure applies) seek the approval of a Surveillance Commissioner. This means that the renewal will not take effect until the notice of it has been received in the office of the person who granted the authorisation within the relevant force, service, squad or HMCE (but not before the day on which the authorisation would have otherwise ceased to have effect). In urgent cases, a renewal can take effect immediately (provided this is not before the day on which the authorisation would have otherwise ceased to have effect). See section 35 and 36 of the 2000 Act and the Regulation of Investigatory Powers (Notification of Authorisations etc) Order 2000; SI No: 2563.

5.35 Subject to paragraph 5.36, if at any time before the day on which a Secretary of State authorisation expires, the Secretary of State considers it necessary for the warrant to be renewed for the purpose for which it was issued, he may renew it in writing for a further period of **three months**, beginning with the day on which it would have ceased to have effect, but for the renewal.

Secretary of State intelligence services authorisations

5.36 If at any time before an intelligence service warrant expires, the Secretary of State considers it necessary for the warrant to be renewed for the purpose for which it was issued, he may renew it in writing for a further period of **six months**, beginning with the day on which it would have ceased to have effect, but for the renewal.

5.37 All applications for a renewal of an authorisation or warrant should record—

- whether this is the first renewal or every occasion on which the warrant/authorisation has been renewed previously;
- any significant changes to the information listed in paragraph 5.16;
- the reasons why it is necessary to continue with the intrusive surveillance;
- the content and value to the investigation or operation of the product so far obtained by the surveillance;
- the results of regular reviews of the investigation or operation.

5.38 Authorisations may be renewed more than once, if necessary, and the renewal should be kept/recorded as part of the central record of authorisations (see paragraphs 2.14–2.15).

Reviews

5.39 Regular reviews of authorisations should be undertaken to assess the need for the surveillance to continue. The results of a review should be recorded on the central record of authorisations (see paragraphs 2.14–2.15). Particular attention is drawn to the need to review authorisations frequently where the intrusive surveillance provides access to confidential information or involves collateral intrusion.

5.40 The senior authorising officer or, for those subject to Secretary of State authorisation, the member or official who made the application within each public authority should determine how often a review should take place. This should be as frequently as is considered necessary and practicable.

Cancellations

5.41 The senior authorising officer who granted or last renewed the authorisation must cancel it, or the person who made the application to the Secretary of State must apply for its cancellation, if he is satisfied that the surveillance no longer meets the criteria upon which it was authorised. Where the senior authorising officer or person who made the application to the Secretary of State is no longer available, this duty will fall on the person who has taken over the role of senior authorising officer or taken over from the person who made the application to the Secretary of State or the person who is acting as the senior authorising officer (see the Regulation of Investigatory Powers (Cancellation of Authorisations) Order 2000; SI No: 2794).

5.42 The Surveillance Commissioners must be notified where police, NCIS, NCS or HMCE authorisations are cancelled (see the Regulation of Investigatory Powers (Notification of Authorisations etc) Order 2000; SI No: 2563).

Ceasing of surveillance activity

5.43 As soon as the decision is taken that the intrusive surveillance should be discontinued, instructions must be given to those involved to stop all surveillance of the subject(s). The date and time when such an instruction was given should be recorded in the central record of authorisations (see paragraphs 2.14–2.15) and the notification of cancellation where relevant.

Police, National Criminal Intelligence Service, the National Crime Squad and HM Customs and Excise authorisations

5.44 In cases where an authorisation is quashed or cancelled by a Surveillance Commissioner, the senior authorising officer must immediately instruct those carrying out the surveillance to stop monitoring, observing, listening or recording the activities of the subject of the authorisation. The date and time when such an instruction was given should be recorded on the central record of authorisations (see paragraphs 2.14–2.15).

[1522]

NOTES

1 A senior authorising officer of a law enforcement agency should not issue an authorisation for intrusive surveillance or entry on or interference with property or with wireless telegraphy where the operation is within the responsibilities of one of the intelligence services and properly falls to be authorised by warrant issued by the Secretary of State under Part II of the 2000 Act or the 1994 Act. Also see footnotes 1 and 2 to para 4.9.

6 AUTHORISATION PROCEDURES FOR ENTRY ON OR INTERFERENCE WITH PROPERTY OR WITH WIRELESS TELEGRAPHY

6.1 The 1994 Act and 1997 Act provide lawful authority for entry on or interference with property or with wireless telegraphy by the intelligence services and the police, NCIS, NCS and HMCE.

6.2 In many cases a covert surveillance operation may involve both intrusive surveillance and entry on or interference with property or with wireless telegraphy. This can be done as a combined authorisation, although the criteria for authorisation of each activity must be considered separately (see paragraph 2.11).

Authorisations for entry on or interference with property or with wireless telegraphy by the police, National Criminal Intelligence Service, the National Crime Squad and HM Customs and Excise

6.3 Responsibility for such authorisations rests with the authorising officer as defined in section 93(5) of the 1997 Act, that is the chief constable or equivalent. Authorisations require the personal authority of the authorising officer (or his designated deputy) except in urgent situations, where it is not reasonably practicable for the application to be considered by such person. The person entitled to act in such cases is set out in section 94 of the 1997 Act.

6.4 Authorisations under the 1997 Act may not be necessary where the public authority is acting with the consent of a person able to give permission in respect of relevant property, although consideration should still be given to the need to obtain an authorisation under Part II of the 2000 Act.

6.5 Authorisations for the police, NCIS and NCS may only be given by an authorising officer on application by a member of his own force, Service or Squad for entry on or interference with property or with wireless telegraphy within the authorising officer's own area of operation. For HMCE an authorisation may only be given by an authorising officer on application by a customs officer. An authorising officer may authorise the taking of action outside the relevant area solely for the purpose of maintaining or retrieving any device, apparatus or equipment.

6.6 Any person giving an authorisation for entry on or interference with property or with wireless telegraphy under section 93(2) of the 1997 Act must believe that—

- it is necessary for the action specified to be taken for the purpose of preventing or detecting serious crime (or in the case of the Police Service of Northern Ireland, in the interests of national security);[1] and
- that the taking of the action is proportionate to what the action seeks to achieve.

6.7 The authorising officer must take into account whether what it is thought necessary to achieve by the authorised conduct could reasonably be achieved by other means.

6.8 Any person granting or applying for an authorisation or warrant to enter on or interfere with property or with wireless telegraphy will also need to be aware of particular sensitivities in the local community where the entry or interference is taking place and of similar activities being undertaken by other public authorities which could impact on the deployment. In this regard, it is recommended that the authorising officers in NCIS, NCS and HMCE should consult a senior officer within the police force in which the investigation or operation takes place where the authorising officer considers that conflicts might arise. The Chief Constable of the Police Service of Northern Ireland should be informed of any surveillance operation undertaken by another law enforcement agency which involve its officers in maintaining or retrieving equipment in Northern Ireland.

Authorisation procedures for entry on or interference with property or with wireless telegraphy by the police, National Criminal Intelligence Service, the National Crime Squad and HM Customs and Excise

6.9 Authorisations will generally be given in writing by the authorising officer. However, in urgent cases, they may be given orally by the authorising officer. In such cases, a statement

PART II DATA PROTECTION

that the authorising officer has expressly authorised the action should be recorded in writing by the applicant as soon as is reasonably practicable. This should be done by the person with whom the authorising officer spoke.

6.10 If the authorising officer is absent then as provided for in section 12(4) of the Police Act 1996, section 5(4) of the Police (Scotland) Act 1967, section 25 of the City of London Police Act 1839, or sections 8 or 54 of the 1997 Act, an authorisation can be given in writing or, in urgent cases, orally by the designated deputy.

6.11 Where, however, in an urgent case, it is not reasonably practicable for the designated deputy to consider an application, then written authorisation may be given by the following—

- in the case of the police, by an assistant chief constable (other than a designated deputy);
- in the case of the Metropolitan Police and City of London Police, by a commander;
- in the case of NCIS and NCS, by a person designated by the relevant Director General;[2]
- in the case of HMCE, by a person designated by the Commissioners of Customs and Excise.[3]

6.12 Applications to the authorising officer for authorisation must be made in writing by a police or customs officer or a member of NCIS or NCS (within the terms of section 93(3) of the 1997 Act) and should specify—

- the identity or identities of those to be targeted (where known);
- the property which the entry or interference with will affect;
- the identity of individuals and/or categories of people, where known, who are likely to be affected by collateral intrusion;
- details of the offence planned or committed;
- details of the intrusive surveillance involved;
- how the authorisation criteria (as set out in paragraphs 6.6 and 6.7) have been met;
- any action which may be necessary to retrieve any equipment used in the surveillance;
- in case of a renewal, the results obtained so far, or a full explanation of the failure to obtain any results; and
- whether an authorisation was given or refused, by whom and the time and date.

6.13 Additionally, in urgent cases, the authorisation should record (as the case may be)—

- the reasons why the authorising officer or designated deputy considered the case so urgent that an oral instead of a written authorisation was given; and
- the reasons why (if relevant) the person granting the authorisation did not consider it reasonably practicable for the application to be considered by the senior authorising officer or the designated deputy.

6.14 Where the application is oral, the information referred to above should be recorded in writing by the applicant as soon as reasonably practicable.

Notifications to Surveillance Commissioners

6.15 Where a person gives, renews or cancels an authorisation, he must, as soon as is reasonably practicable, give notice of it in writing to a Surveillance Commissioner, in accordance with arrangements made by the Chief Surveillance Commissioner. In urgent cases which would otherwise have required the approval of a Surveillance Commissioner, the notification must specify the grounds on which the case is believed to be one of urgency.

6.16 There may be cases which become urgent after approval has been sought but before a response has been received from a Surveillance Commissioner. In such a case, the authorising officer should notify the Surveillance Commissioner that the case is urgent (pointing out that it has become urgent since the previous notification). In these cases, the authorisation will take effect immediately.

6.17 Notifications to Surveillance Commissioners in relation to the authorisation, renewal and cancellation of authorisations in respect of entry on or interference with property should be in accordance with the requirements of the Police Act 1997 (Notifications of Authorisations etc) Order 1998; SI No: 3241.

Duration of authorisations

6.18 Written authorisations given by authorising officers will cease to have effect at the end of a period of **three months** beginning with the day on which they took effect. In cases requiring prior approval by a Surveillance Commissioner this means from the time the Surveillance Commissioner has approved the authorisation and the person who gave the authorisation has been notified. This means that the approval will not take effect until the notice has been received in the office of the person who granted the authorisation within the relevant force, service, squad or HMCE. In cases not requiring prior approval, this means from the time the authorisation was given.

6.19 Oral authorisations given in urgent cases by—

- authorising officers;
- or designated deputies;

and written authorisations given by—

- assistant chief constables (other than a designated deputy);
- commanders in the Metropolitan Police and City of London Police;
- the person designated to act by the Director General of NCIS or of NCS;
- the person designated for the purpose by the Commissioners of Customs and Excise;

will cease at the end of the period of **seventy-two hours** beginning with the time when they took effect.

Renewals

6.20 If at any time before the day on which an authorisation expires the authorising officer or, in his absence, the designated deputy considers the authorisation should continue to have effect for the purpose for which it was issued, he may renew it in writing for a period of **three months** beginning with the day on which the authorisation would otherwise have ceased to have effect. Authorisations may be renewed more than once, if necessary, and the renewal should be recorded on the authorisation record (see paragraph 6.27).

6.21 Commissioners must be notified of renewals of authorisations. The information to be included in the notification is set out in the Police Act 1997 (Notifications of Authorisations etc) Order 1998; SI No: 3241.

6.22 If, at the time of renewal, the criteria in paragraph 6.30 exist, then the approval of a Surveillance Commissioner must be sought before the renewal can take effect. The fact that the initial authorisation required the approval of a Commissioner before taking effect does not mean that its renewal will automatically require such approval. It will only do so if, at the time of the renewal, it falls into one of the categories requiring approval (and is not urgent).

Reviews

6.23 Authorising officers should regularly review authorisations to assess the need for the entry on or interference with property or with wireless telegraphy to continue. This should be recorded on the authorisation record (see paragraph 6.27). The authorising officer should determine how often a review should take place when giving an authorisation. This should be as frequently as is considered necessary and practicable and at no greater interval than one month. Particular attention is drawn to the need to review authorisations and renewals regularly and frequently where the entry on or interference with property or with wireless telegraphy provides access to confidential information or involves collateral intrusion.

Cancellations

6.24 The senior authorising officer who granted or last renewed the authorisation must cancel it, or the person who made the application to the Secretary of State must apply for its cancellation, if he is satisfied that the authorisation no longer meets the criteria upon which it was authorised. Where the senior authorising officer or person who made the application to the Secretary of State is no longer available, this duty will fall on the person who has taken over the role of senior authorising officer or taken over from the person who made the application to the Secretary of State or the person who is acting as the senior authorising officer (see the Regulation of Investigatory Powers (Cancellation of Authorisations) Order 2000; SI No: 2794).

6.25 The Surveillance Commissioners must be notified of cancellations of authorisations. The information to be included in the notification is set out in the Police Act 1997 (Notifications of Authorisations etc) Order 1998; SI No: 3421.

6.26 The Surveillance Commissioners have the power to cancel an authorisation if they are satisfied that, at any time after an authorisation was given or renewed, there were no reasonable grounds for believing the matters set out in paragraphs 6.6 and 6.7 above. In such circumstances, a Surveillance Commissioner may order the destruction of records, in whole or in part, other than any that are required for pending criminal or civil proceedings.

Authorisation record

6.27 An authorisation record should be created which records—

- the time and date when an authorisation is given;
- whether an authorisation is in written or oral form;
- the time and date when it was notified to a Surveillance Commissioner;
- and the time and date when the Surveillance Commissioner notified his approval (where appropriate).

The authorisation record should also record—

- every occasion when entry on or interference with property or with wireless telegraphy has occurred;
- the result of periodic reviews of the authorisation;
- the date of every renewal; and
- it should record the time and date when any instruction was given by the authorising officer to cease the interference with property or with wireless telegraphy.

Ceasing of entry on or interference with property or with wireless telegraphy

6.28 Once an authorisation or renewal expires or is cancelled or quashed, the authorising officer must immediately instruct those carrying out the surveillance to cease all the actions authorised for the entry on or interference with property or with wireless telegraphy. The time and date when such an instruction was given should be recorded on the authorisation record (see paragraph 6.27).

Retrieval of equipment

6.29 Where a Surveillance Commissioner quashes or cancels an authorisation or renewal, he will, if there are reasonable grounds for doing so, order that the authorisation remain effective for a specified period, to enable officers to retrieve anything left on the property by virtue of the authorisation. He can only do so if the authorisation or renewal makes provision for this. A decision by the Surveillance Commissioner not to give such an order can be the subject of an appeal to the Chief Surveillance Commissioner.

Special Rules

Cases requiring prior approval of a Surveillance Commissioner

6.30 In certain cases, an authorisation for entry on or interference with property will not take effect until a Surveillance Commissioner has approved it and the notice has been received in the office of the person who granted the authorisation within the relevant force, service, squad or HMCE (unless the urgency procedures are used). These are cases where the person giving the authorisation believes that—

- any of the property specified in the authorisation—
  - is used wholly or mainly as a dwelling or as a bedroom in a hotel; or
  - constitutes office premises; or
- the action authorised is likely to result in any person acquiring knowledge of—
  - matters subject to legal privilege;
  - confidential personal information; or
  - confidential journalistic material.

6.31 Office premises are defined as any building or part of a building whose sole or principal use is as an office or for office purposes (which means purposes of administration, clerical work, handling money and telephone or telegraph operation).

Authorisations for entry on or interference with property or with wireless telegraphy by the intelligence services

6.32 Before granting a warrant, the Secretary of State must—

- think it necessary for the action to be taken for the purpose of assisting the relevant agency in carrying out its functions;
- be satisfied that the taking of the action is proportionate to what the action seeks to achieve;
- take into account in deciding whether an authorisation is necessary and proportionate is whether the information which it is thought necessary to obtain by the conduct authorised by the warrant could reasonably be obtained by other means; and
- be satisfied that there are satisfactory arrangements in force under the 1994 Act or the 1989 Act in respect of disclosure of any material obtained by means of the warrant, and that material obtained will be subject to those arrangements.

6.33 An application for a warrant must be made by a member of the intelligence services for the taking of action in relation to that agency. In addition, the Security Service may make an application for a warrant to act on behalf of the Secret Intelligence Service (SIS) and the Governments Communication Headquarters (GCHQ). SIS and GCHQ may not be granted a warrant for action in support of the prevention or detection of serious crime which relates to property in the British Islands.

6.34 A warrant shall, unless renewed, cease to have effect if the warrant was under the hand of the Secretary of State, at the end of the period of **six months** beginning with the day on which it was issued. In any other case, at the end of the period ending with the **second working day** following that day.

6.35 If at any time before the day on which a warrant would cease to have effect the Secretary of State considers it necessary for the warrant to continue to have effect for the purpose for which it was issued, he may by an instrument under his hand renew it for a period of **six months** beginning with that day. The Secretary of State shall cancel a warrant if he is satisfied that the action authorised by it is no longer necessary.

6.36 The intelligence services should provide the same information as the police, as and where appropriate, when making applications, requests for renewal and requests for cancellation of property warrants.

Retrieval of equipment

6.37 Because of the time it can take to remove equipment from a person's property it may also be necessary to renew a property warrant in order to complete the retrieval. Applications to the Secretary of State for renewal should state why it is being or has been closed down, why it has not been possible to remove the equipment and any timescales for removal, where known.

[1523]

NOTES

1. See footnotes 1 and 2 to para 4.9.
2. For police members of NCIS or NCS, this will be an officer who holds the rank of assistant chief constable in that Service or Squad. Additionally, in the case of NCIS, this may be an assistant chief investigation officer of HMCE.
3. This will be an officer of the rank of assistant chief investigation officer.

7 OVERSIGHT BY COMMISSIONERS

7.1 The 1997 and 2000 Acts require the Chief Surveillance Commissioner to keep under review (with the assistance of the Surveillance Commissioners and Assistant Surveillance Commissioners) the performance of functions under Part III of the 1997 Act and Part II of the 2000 Act by the police (including the Royal Navy Regulating Branch, the Royal Military Police and the Royal Air Force Police and the Ministry of Defence Police and the British Transport Police), NCIS, the NCS, HMCE and of the 2000 Act the other public authorities listed in Schedule 1 and in Northern Ireland officials of the Ministry of Defence and HM Forces.

7.2 The Intelligence Services Commissioner's remit is to provide independent oversight of the use of the powers contained within Part II of the 2000 Act and the 1994 Act by the Security Service, Secret Intelligence Service, GCHQ and the Ministry of Defence and HM Forces (excluding the Royal Navy Regulating Branch, the Royal Military Police and the Royal Air Force Police, and in Northern Ireland officials of the Ministry of Defence and HM Forces).

7.3 This code does not cover the exercise of any of the Commissioners' functions. It is the duty of any person who uses these powers to comply with any request made by a Commissioner to disclose or provide any information he requires for the purpose of enabling him to carry out his functions.

7.4 References in this code to the performance of review functions by the Chief Surveillance Commissioner and other Commissioners apply also to Inspectors and other members of staff to whom such functions have been delegated.

[1524]

8 COMPLAINTS

8.1 The 2000 Act establishes an independent Tribunal. This Tribunal will be made up of senior members of the judiciary and the legal profession and is independent of the Government. The Tribunal has full powers to investigate and decide any case within its jurisdiction.

This code does not cover the exercise of the Tribunal's functions. Details of the relevant complaints procedure can be obtained from the following address—

Investigatory Powers Tribunal

PO Box 33220

London

SW1H 9ZQ

020 7273 4514

[1525]

ANNEX A
AUTHORISATION LEVELS WHEN KNOWLEDGE OF CONFIDENTIAL INFORMATION IS LIKELY TO BE ACQUIRED

Relevant Public Authorities	*Authorisation level*
Police Forces – Any police force maintained under section 2 of the Police Act 1996 (police forces in England and Wales outside London).	Chief Constable
Police Forces – Any police force maintained under or by virtue of section 1 of the Police (Scotland) Act 1967.	Chief Constable
The Metropolitan police force	Assistant Commissioner
The City of London police force	Commissioner
The Police Service of Northern Ireland	Deputy Chief Constable
The Royal Navy Regulating Branch	The Royal Military Police
The Royal Air Force Police	Provost Marshal
Provost Marshal	Provost Marshal
National Criminal Intelligence Service (NCIS)	Director General
National Crime Squad (NCS)	Director General or Deputy Director General
Serious Fraud Office	Director or Assistant Director
The Intelligence Services:	
Government Communications Headquarters	A Director of GCHQ
Security Service	Deputy Director General
Secret Intelligence Service	A Director of the Secret Intelligence Service
HM Forces:	
Royal Navy	Rear Admiral
Army	Major General
Royal Air Force	Air-Vice Marshall
HM Customs and Excise	Director Investigation or Regional Heads of Investigation
Inland Revenue	Deputy Chairman of Inland Revenue
Department for Environment, Food and Rural Affairs:	
DEFRA Investigation Branch	Immediate Senior Officer of Head of DEFRA Prosecution Division

Relevant Public Authorities	*Authorisation level*
Horticultural Marketing Inspectorate	Immediate Senior Officer of Head of DEFRA Prosecution Division
Plant Health and Seed Inspectorate	Immediate Senior Officer of Head of DEFRA Prosecution Division
Egg Marketing Inspectorate	Immediate Senior Officer of Head of DEFRA Prosecution Division
Sea Fisheries Inspectorate (SFI)	Immediate Senior Officer of Head of DEFRA Prosecution Division
Centre for Environment, Fisheries & Aquaculture Science (CEFAS)	Immediate Senior Officer of Head of DEFRA Prosecution Division
Ministry of Defence	Director General or equivalent
Department for Transport, Local Government and Regions:	
Vehicle Inspectorate	No
Transport Security (Transec)	Director of Transport Security
Department of Health:	
Medical Devices Agency	Chief Executive
Medicine Control Agency	Chief Executive
Welfare Foods Policy Unit	Deputy Chief Medical Officer
Directorate of Counter Fraud Services (DFCS)	Director of Counter Fraud Services
Home Office:	
HM Prison Service	Deputy Director General of the Prison Service
Immigration Service	Chief Inspector of the Immigration Service
Department of Work and Pensions:	
Benefits Agency	Chief Executive of the Benefits Agency
Department of Trade and Industry:	
Radiocommunications Agency	No
British Trade International	No
Coal Health Claims Unit	Director of Coal Health Claims unit
Companies Investigation Branch	The Inspector of Companies
Legal Services Directorate D	The Director of Legal Service D
National Assembly for Wales	Head of NHS Directorate in the National Assembly for Wales
	Head of NHS Finance Division in the National Assembly for Wales
	Head of Common Agricultural Policy Management Division in the National Assembly for Wales
Local Authorities	The Head of Paid Service or (in his absence) a Chief Officer
Environment Agency	Chief Executive of the Environment Agency
Financial Services Authority	Chairman of the Financial Services Authority
Food Standards Agency	Head of Group, Deputy Chief Executive and Chief Executive of the Foods Standards Agency

Relevant Public Authorities	*Authorisation level*
The Intervention Board for Agricultural Produce	Chief Executive of the Intervention Board for Agricultural Produce
Personal Investment Authority	Chairman of the Personal Investment Authority
Post Office	Director of Security
Health & Safety Executive	Director of Field Operations, Director of Hazardous Installations Directorate, Her Majesty' s Chief Inspector of Nuclear Installations.
NHS bodies in England and Wales:	
A health authority established under section 8 of the National Health Service Act 1977	Chief Executive
A Special Health Authority established under section 11 of the National Health Service 1977	Chief Executive
A National Health Service Trust established under section 5 of the National Health Service and Community Care Act 1990	Chief Executive
Royal Pharmaceutical Society of Great Britain	Director of Professional Standards

[1526]

DIRECTIVE OF THE EUROPEAN PARLIAMENT AND OF THE COUNCIL

of 24 October 1995

on the protection of individuals with regard to the processing of personal data and on the free movement of such data

(95/46/EC)

NOTES

Date of publication in OJ: OJ L281, 23.11.95, p 31.

THE EUROPEAN PARLIAMENT AND THE COUNCIL OF THE EUROPEAN UNION,

Having regard to the Treaty establishing the European Community, and in particular Article 100a thereof,

Having regard to the proposal from the Commission,[1]

Having regard to the opinion of the Economic and Social Committee,[2]

Acting in accordance with the procedure referred to in Article 189b of the Treaty,

(1) Whereas the objectives of the Community, as laid down in the Treaty, as amended by the Treaty on European Union, include creating an ever closer union among the peoples of Europe, fostering closer relations between the States belonging to the Community, ensuring economic and social progress by common action to eliminate the barriers which divide Europe, encouraging the constant improvement of the living conditions of its peoples, preserving and strengthening peace and liberty and promoting democracy on the basis of the fundamental rights recognised in the constitution and laws of the Member States and in the European Convention for the Protection of Human Rights and Fundamental Freedoms;

(2) Whereas data-processing systems are designed to serve man; whereas they must, whatever the nationality or residence of natural persons, respect their fundamental rights and freedoms, notably the right to privacy, and contribute to economic and social progress, trade expansion and the well-being of individuals;

(3) Whereas the establishment and functioning of an internal market in which, in accordance with Article 7a of the Treaty, the free movement of goods, persons, services and capital is ensured require not only that personal data should be able to flow freely from one Member State to another, but also that the fundamental rights of individuals should be safeguarded;

(4) Whereas increasingly frequent recourse is being had in the Community to the processing of personal data in the various spheres of economic and social activity; whereas the progress made in information technology is making the processing and exchange of such data considerably easier;

(5) Whereas the economic and social integration resulting from the establishment and functioning of the internal market within the meaning of Article 7a of the Treaty will necessarily lead to a substantial increase in cross-border flows of personal data between all those involved in a private or public capacity in economic and social activity in the Member States; whereas the exchange of personal data between undertakings in different Member States is set to increase; whereas the national authorities in the various Member States are being called upon by virtue of Community law to collaborate and exchange personal data so as to be able to perform their duties or carry out tasks on behalf of an authority in another Member State within the context of the area without internal frontiers as constituted by the internal market;

(6) Whereas, furthermore, the increase in scientific and technical cooperation and the coordinated introduction of new telecommunications networks in the Community necessitate and facilitate cross-border flows of personal data;

(7) Whereas the difference in levels of protection of the rights and freedoms of individuals, notably the right to privacy, with regard to the processing of personal data afforded in the Member States may prevent the transmission of such data from the territory of one Member State to that of another Member State; whereas this difference may therefore constitute an obstacle to the pursuit of a number of economic activities at Community level, distort competition and impede authorities in the discharge of their responsibilities under Community law; whereas this difference in levels of protection is due to the existence of a wide variety of national laws, regulations and administrative provisions;

(8) Whereas, in order to remove the obstacles to flows of personal data, the level of protection of the rights and freedoms of individuals with regard to the processing of such data must be equivalent in all Member States; whereas this objective is vital to the internal market but cannot be achieved by the Member States alone, especially in view of the scale of the divergences which currently exist between the relevant laws in the Member States and the need to coordinate the laws of the Member States so as to ensure that the cross-border flow of personal data is regulated in a consistent manner that is in keeping with the objective of the internal market as provided for in Article 7a of the Treaty; whereas Community action to approximate those laws is therefore needed;

(9) Whereas, given the equivalent protection resulting from the approximation of national laws, the Member States will no longer be able to inhibit the free movement between them of personal data on grounds relating to protection of the rights and freedoms of individuals, and in particular the right to privacy; whereas Member States will be left a margin for manoeuvre, which may, in the context of implementation of the Directive, also be exercised by the business and social partners; whereas Member States will therefore be able to specify in their national law the general conditions governing the lawfulness of data processing; whereas in doing so the Member States shall strive to improve the protection currently provided by their legislation; whereas, within the limits of this margin for manoeuvre and in accordance with Community law, disparities could arise in the implementation of the Directive, and this could have an effect on the movement of data within a Member State as well as within the Community;

(10) Whereas the object of the national laws on the processing of personal data is to protect fundamental rights and freedoms, notably the right to privacy, which is recognised both in Article 8 of the European Convention for the Protection of Human Rights and Fundamental Freedoms and in the general principles of Community law; whereas, for that reason, the approximation of those laws must not result in any lessening of the protection they afford but must, on the contrary, seek to ensure a high level of protection in the Community;

(11) Whereas the principles of the protection of the rights and freedoms of individuals, notably the right to privacy, which are contained in this Directive, give substance to and amplify those contained in the Council of Europe Convention of 28 January 1981 for the Protection of Individuals with regard to Automatic Processing of Personal Data;

(12) Whereas the protection principles must apply to all processing of personal data by any person whose activities are governed by Community law; whereas there should be excluded the processing of data carried out by a natural person in the exercise of activities which are exclusively personal or domestic, such as correspondence and the holding of records of addresses;

(13) Whereas the activities referred to in Titles V and VI of the Treaty on European Union regarding public safety, defence, State security or the activities of the State in the area of criminal laws fall outside the scope of Community law, without prejudice to the obligations incumbent upon Member States under Article 56(2), Article 57 or Article 100a of the Treaty establishing the European Community; whereas the processing of personal data that is necessary to safeguard the economic well-being of the State does not fall within the scope of this Directive where such processing relates to State security matters;

(14) Whereas, given the importance of the developments under way, in the framework of the information society, of the techniques used to capture, transmit, manipulate, record, store or communicate sound and image data relating to natural persons, this Directive should be applicable to processing involving such data;

(15) Whereas the processing of such data is covered by this Directive only if it is automated or if the data processed are contained or are intended to be contained in a filing system structured according to specific criteria relating to individuals, so as to permit easy access to the personal data in question;

(16) Whereas the processing of sound and image data, such as in cases of video surveillance, does not come within the scope of this Directive if it is carried out for the purposes of public security, defence, national security or in the course of State activities relating to the area of criminal law or of other activities which do not come within the scope of Community law;

(17) Whereas, as far as the processing of sound and image data carried out for purposes of journalism or the purposes of literary or artistic expression is concerned, in particular in the audiovisual field, the principles of the Directive are to apply in a restricted manner according to the provisions laid down in Article 9;

(18) Whereas, in order to ensure that individuals are not deprived of the protection to which they are entitled under this Directive, any processing of personal data in the Community must be carried out in accordance with the law of one of the Member States; whereas, in this connection, processing carried out under the responsibility of a controller who is established in a Member State should be governed by the law of that State;

(19) Whereas establishment on the territory of a Member State implies the effective and real exercise of activity through stable arrangements; whereas the legal form of such an establishment, whether simply branch or a subsidiary with a legal personality, is not the determining factor in this respect; whereas, when a single controller is established on the territory of several Member States, particularly by means of subsidiaries, he must ensure, in order to avoid any circumvention of national rules, that each of the establishments fulfils the obligations imposed by the national law applicable to its activities;

(20) Whereas the fact that the processing of data is carried out by a person established in a third country must not stand in the way of the protection of individuals provided for in this Directive; whereas in these cases, the processing should be governed by the law of the Member State in which the means used are located, and there should be guarantees to ensure that the rights and obligations provided for in this Directive are respected in practice;

(21) Whereas this Directive is without prejudice to the rules of territoriality applicable in criminal matters;

(22) Whereas Member States shall more precisely define in the laws they enact or when bringing into force the measures taken under this Directive the general circumstances in which processing is lawful; whereas in particular Article 5, in conjunction with Articles 7 and 8, allows Member States, independently of general rules, to provide for special processing conditions for specific sectors and for the various categories of data covered by Article 8;

(23) Whereas Member States are empowered to ensure the implementation of the protection of individuals both by means of a general law on the protection of individuals as regards the processing of personal data and by sectorial laws such as those relating, for example, to statistical institutes;

(24) Whereas the legislation concerning the protection of legal persons with regard to the processing data which concerns them is not affected by this Directive;

(25) Whereas the principles of protection must be reflected, on the one hand, in the obligations imposed on persons, public authorities, enterprises, agencies or other bodies responsible for processing, in particular regarding data quality, technical security, notification to the supervisory authority, and the circumstances under which processing can be carried out, and, on the other hand, in the right conferred on individuals, the data on whom are the subject

of processing, to be informed that processing is taking place, to consult the data, to request corrections and even to object to processing in certain circumstances;

(26) Whereas the principles of protection must apply to any information concerning an identified or identifiable person; whereas, to determine whether a person is identifiable, account should be taken of all the means likely reasonably to be used either by the controller or by any other person to identify the said person; whereas the principles of protection shall not apply to data rendered anonymous in such a way that the data subject is no longer identifiable; whereas codes of conduct within the meaning of Article 27 may be a useful instrument for providing guidance as to the ways in which data may be rendered anonymous and retained in a form in which identification of the data subject is no longer possible;

(27) Whereas the protection of individuals must apply as much to automatic processing of data as to manual processing; whereas the scope of this protection must not in effect depend on the techniques used, otherwise this would create a serious risk of circumvention; whereas, nonetheless, as regards manual processing, this Directive covers only filing systems, not unstructured files; whereas, in particular, the content of a filing system must be structured according to specific criteria relating to individuals allowing easy access to the personal data; whereas, in line with the definition in Article 2(c), the different criteria for determining the constituents of a structured set of personal data, and the different criteria governing access to such a set, may be laid down by each Member State; whereas files or sets of files as well as their cover pages, which are not structured according to specific criteria, shall under no circumstances fall within the scope of this Directive;

(28) Whereas any processing of personal data must be lawful and fair to the individuals concerned; whereas, in particular, the data must be adequate, relevant and not excessive in relation to the purposes for which they are processed; whereas such purposes must be explicit and legitimate and must be determined at the time of collection of the data; whereas the purposes of processing further to collection shall not be incompatible with the purposes as they were originally specified;

(29) Whereas the further processing of personal data for historical, statistical or scientific purposes is not generally to be considered incompatible with the purposes for which the data have previously been collected provided that Member States furnish suitable safeguards; whereas these safeguards must in particular rule out the use of the data in support of measures or decisions regarding any particular individual;

(30) Whereas, in order to be lawful, the processing of personal data must in addition be carried out with the consent of the data subject or be necessary for the conclusion or performance of a contract binding on the data subject, or as a legal requirement, or for the performance of a task carried out in the public interest or in the exercise of official authority, or in the legitimate interests of a natural or legal person, provided that the interests or the rights and freedoms of the data subject are not overriding; whereas, in particular, in order to maintain a balance between the interests involved while guaranteeing effective competition, Member States may determine the circumstances in which personal data may be used or disclosed to a third party in the context of the legitimate ordinary business activities of companies and other bodies; whereas Member States may similarly specify the conditions under which personal data may be disclosed to a third party for the purposes of marketing whether carried out commercially or by a charitable organisation or by any other association or foundation, of a political nature for example, subject to the provisions allowing a data subject to object to the processing of data regarding him, at no cost and without having to state his reasons;

(31) Whereas the processing of personal data must equally be regarded as lawful where it is carried out in order to protect an interest which is essential for the data subject's life;

(32) Whereas it is for national legislation to determine whether the controller performing a task carried out in the public interest or in the exercise of official authority should be a public administration or another natural or legal person governed by public law, or by private law such as a professional association;

(33) Whereas data which are capable by their nature of infringing fundamental freedoms or privacy should not be processed unless the data subject gives his explicit consent; whereas, however, derogations from this prohibition must be explicitly provided for in respect of specific needs, in particular where the processing of these data is carried out for certain health-related purposes by persons subject to a legal obligation of professional secrecy or in the course of legitimate activities by certain associations or foundations the purpose of which is to permit the exercise of fundamental freedoms;

(34) Whereas Member States must also be authorised, when justified by grounds of important public interest, to derogate from the prohibition on processing sensitive categories of data where important reasons of public interest so justify in areas such as public health and social protection—especially in order to ensure the quality and cost-effectiveness of the procedures used for settling claims for benefits and services in the health insurance

system—scientific research and government statistics; whereas it is incumbent on them, however, to provide specific and suitable safeguards so as to protect the fundamental rights and the privacy of individuals;

(35) Whereas, moreover, the processing of personal data by official authorities for achieving aims, laid down in constitutional law or international public law, of officially recognised religious associations is carried out on important grounds of public interest;

(36) Whereas where, in the course of electoral activities, the operation of the democratic system requires in certain Member States that political parties compile data on people's political opinion, the processing of such data may be permitted for reasons of important public interest, provided that appropriate safeguards are established;

(37) Whereas the processing of personal data for purposes of journalism or for purposes of literary of artistic expression, in particular in the audiovisual field, should qualify for exemption from the requirements of certain provisions of this Directive in so far as this is necessary to reconcile the fundamental rights of individuals with freedom of information and notably the right to receive and impart information, as guaranteed in particular in Article 10 of the European Convention for the Protection of Human Rights and Fundamental Freedoms; whereas Member States should therefore lay down exemptions and derogations necessary for the purpose of balance between fundamental rights as regards general measures on the legitimacy of data processing, measures on the transfer of data to third countries and the power of the supervisory authority; whereas this should not, however, lead Member States to lay down exemptions from the measures to ensure security of processing; whereas at least the supervisory authority responsible for this sector should also be provided with certain ex-post powers, e g to publish a regular report or to refer matters to the judicial authorities;

(38) Whereas, if the processing of data is to be fair, the data subject must be in a position to learn of the existence of a processing operation and, where data are collected from him, must be given accurate and full information, bearing in mind the circumstances of the collection;

(39) Whereas certain processing operations involve data which the controller has not collected directly from the data subject; whereas, furthermore, data can be legitimately disclosed to a third party, even if the disclosure was not anticipated at the time the data were collected from the data subject; whereas, in all these cases, the data subject should be informed when the data are recorded or at the latest when the data are first disclosed to a third party;

(40) Whereas, however, it is not necessary to impose this obligation of the data subject already has the information; whereas, moreover, there will be no such obligation if the recording or disclosure are expressly provided for by law or if the provision of information to the data subject proves impossible or would involve disproportionate efforts, which could be the case where processing is for historical, statistical or scientific purposes; whereas, in this regard, the number of data subjects, the age of the data, and any compensatory measures adopted may be taken into consideration;

(41) Whereas any person must be able to exercise the right of access to data relating to him which are being processed, in order to verify in particular the accuracy of the data and the lawfulness of the processing; whereas, for the same reasons, every data subject must also have the right to know the logic involved in the automatic processing of data concerning him, at least in the case of the automated decisions referred to in Article 15(1); whereas this right must not adversely affect trade secrets or intellectual property and in particular the copyright protecting the software; whereas these considerations must not, however, result in the data subject being refused all information;

(42) Whereas Member States may, in the interest of the data subject or so as to protect the rights and freedoms of others, restrict rights of access and information; whereas they may, for example, specify that access to medical data may be obtained only through a health professional;

(43) Whereas restrictions on the rights of access and information and on certain obligations of the controller may similarly be imposed by Member States in so far as they are necessary to safeguard, for example, national security, defence, public safety, or important economic or financial interests of a Member State or the Union, as well as criminal investigations and prosecutions and action in respect of breaches of ethics in the regulated professions; whereas the list of exceptions and limitations should include the tasks of monitoring, inspection or regulation necessary in the three last-mentioned areas concerning public security, economic or financial interests and crime prevention; whereas the listing of tasks in these three areas does not affect the legitimacy of exceptions or restrictions for reasons of State security or defence;

(44) Whereas Member States may also be led, by virtue of the provisions of Community law, to derogate from the provisions of this Directive concerning the right of access, the obligation to inform individuals, and the quality of data, in order to secure certain of the purposes referred to above;

(45) Whereas, in cases where data might lawfully be processed on grounds of public interest, official authority or the legitimate interests of a natural or legal person, any data subject should nevertheless be entitled, on legitimate and compelling grounds relating to his particular situation, to object to the processing of any data relating to himself; whereas Member States may nevertheless lay down national provisions to the contrary;

(46) Whereas the protection of the rights and freedoms of data subjects with regard to the processing of personal data requires that appropriate technical and organisational measures be taken, both at the time of the design of the processing system and at the time of the processing itself, particularly in order to maintain security and thereby to prevent any unauthorised processing; whereas it is incumbent on the Member States to ensure that controllers comply with these measures; whereas these measures must ensure an appropriate level of security, taking into account the state of the art and the costs of their implementation in relation to the risks inherent in the processing and the nature of the data to be protected;

(47) Whereas where a message containing personal data is transmitted by means of a telecommunications or electronic mail service, the sole purpose of which is the transmission of such messages, the controller in respect of the personal data contained in the message will normally be considered to be the person from whom the message originates, rather than the person offering the transmission services; whereas, nevertheless, those offering such services will normally be considered controllers in respect of the processing of the additional personal data necessary for the operation of the service;

(48) Whereas the procedures for notifying the supervisory authority are designed to ensure disclosure of the purposes and main features of any processing operation for the purpose of verification that the operation is in accordance with the national measures taken under this Directive;

(49) Whereas, in order to avoid unsuitable administrative formalities, exemptions from the obligation to notify and simplification of the notification required may be provided for by Member States in cases where processing is unlikely adversely to affect the rights and freedoms of data subjects, provided that it is in accordance with a measure taken by a Member State specifying its limits; whereas exemption or simplification may similarly be provided for by Member States where a person appointed by the controller ensures that the processing carried out is not likely adversely to affect the rights and freedoms of data subjects; whereas such a data protection official, whether or not an employee of the controller, must be in a position to exercise his functions in complete independence;

(50) Whereas exemption or simplification could be provided for in cases of processing operations whose sole purpose is the keeping of a register intended, according to national law, to provide information to the public and open to consultation by the public or by any person demonstrating a legitimate interest;

(51) Whereas, nevertheless, simplification or exemption from the obligation to notify shall not release the controller from any of the other obligations resulting from this Directive;

(52) Whereas, in this context, *ex post facto* verification by the competent authorities must in general be considered a sufficient measure;

(53) Whereas, however, certain processing operation are likely to pose specific risks to the rights and freedoms of data subjects by virtue of their nature, their scope or their purposes, such as that of excluding individuals from a right, benefit or a contract, or by virtue of the specific use of new technologies; whereas it is for Member States, if they so wish, to specify such risks in their legislation;

(54) Whereas with regard to all the processing undertaken in society, the amount posing such specific risks should be very limited; whereas Member States must provide that the supervisory authority, or the data protection official in cooperation with the authority, check such processing prior to it being carried out; whereas following this prior check, the supervisory authority may, according to its national law, give an opinion or an authorisation regarding the processing; whereas such checking may equally take place in the course of the preparation either of a measure of the national parliament or of a measure based on such a legislative measure, which defines the nature of the processing and lays down appropriate safeguards;

(55) Whereas, if the controller fails to respect the rights of data subjects, national legislation must provide for a judicial remedy; whereas any damage which a person may suffer as a result of unlawful processing must be compensated for by the controller, who may be exempted from liability if he proves that he is not responsible for the damage, in particular in cases where he establishes fault on the part of the data subject or in case of *force majeure*;

whereas sanctions must be imposed on any person, whether governed by private of public law, who fails to comply with the national measures taken under this Directive;

(56) Whereas cross-border flows of personal data are necessary to the expansion of international trade; whereas the protection of individuals guaranteed in the Community by this Directive does not stand in the way of transfers of personal data to third countries which ensure an adequate level of protection; whereas the adequacy of the level of protection afforded by a third country must be assessed in the light of all the circumstances surrounding the transfer operation or set of transfer operations;

(57) Whereas, on the other hand, the transfer of personal data to a third country which does not ensure an adequate level of protection must be prohibited;

(58) Whereas provisions should be made for exemptions from this prohibition in certain circumstances where the data subject has given his consent, where the transfer is necessary in relation to a contract or a legal claim, where protection of an important public interest so requires, for example in cases of international transfers of data between tax or customs administrations or between services competent for social security matters, or where the transfer is made from a register established by law and intended for consultation by the public or persons having a legitimate interest; whereas in this case such a transfer should not involve the entirety of the data or entire categories of the data contained in the register and, when the register is intended for consultation by persons having a legitimate interest, the transfer should be made only at the request of those persons or if they are to be the recipients;

(59) Whereas particular measures may be taken to compensate for the lack of protection in a third country in cases where the controller offers appropriate safeguards; whereas, moreover, provision must be made for procedures for negotiations between the Community and such third countries;

(60) Whereas, in any event, transfers to third countries may be effected only in full compliance with the provisions adopted by the Member States pursuant to this Directive, and in particular Article 8 thereof;

(61) Whereas Member States and the Commission, in their respective spheres of competence, must encourage the trade associations and other representative organisations concerned to draw up codes of conduct so as to facilitate the application of this Directive, taking account of the specific characteristics of the processing carried out in certain sectors, and respecting the national provisions adopted for its implementation;

(62) Whereas the establishment in Member States of supervisory authorities, exercising their functions with complete independence, is an essential component of the protection of individuals with regard to the processing of personal data;

(63) Whereas such authorities must have the necessary means to perform their duties, including powers of investigation and intervention, particularly in cases of complaints from individuals, and powers to engage in legal proceedings; whereas such authorities must help to ensure transparency of processing in the Member States within whose jurisdiction they fall;

(64) Whereas the authorities in the different Member States will need to assist one another in performing their duties so as to ensure that the rules of protection are properly respected throughout the European Union;

(65) Whereas, at Community level, a Working Party on the Protection of Individuals with regard to the Processing of Personal Data must be set up and be completely independent in the performance of its functions; whereas, having regard to its specific nature, it must advise the Commission and, in particular, contribute to the uniform application of the national rules adopted pursuant to this Directive;

(66) Whereas, with regard to the transfer of data to third countries, the application of this Directive calls for the conferment of powers of implementation on the Commission and the establishment of a procedure as laid down in Council Decision 87/373/EEC;[3]

(67) Whereas an agreement on a *modus vivendi* between the European Parliament, the Council and the Commission concerning the implementing measures for acts adopted in accordance with the procedure laid down in Article 189b of the EC Treaty was reached on 20 December 1994;

(68) Whereas the principles set out in this Directive regarding the protection of the rights and freedoms of individuals, notably their right to privacy, with regard to the processing of personal data may be supplemented or clarified, in particular as far as certain sectors are concerned, by specific rules based on those principles;

(69) Whereas Member States should be allowed a period of not more than three years from the entry into force of the national measures transposing this Directive in which to apply such new national rules progressively to all processing operations already under way; whereas, in order to facilitate their cost-effective implementation, a further period expiring 12 years after the date on which this Directive is adopted will be allowed to Member States to ensure the conformity of existing manual filing systems with certain of the Directive's provisions; whereas, where data contained in such filing systems are manually processed

during this extended transition period, those systems must be brought into conformity with these provisions at the time of such processing;

(70) Whereas it is not necessary for the data subject to give his consent again so as to allow the controller to continue to process, after the national provisions taken pursuant to this Directive enter into force, any sensitive data necessary for the performance of a contract concluded on the basis of free and informed consent before the entry into force of these provisions;

(71) Whereas this Directive does not stand in the way of a Member State's regulating marketing activities aimed at consumers residing in territory in so far as such regulation does not concern the protection of individuals with regard to the processing of personal data;

(72) Whereas this Directive allows the principle of public access to official documents to be taken into account when implementing the principles set out in this Directive,

NOTES

1 OJ C277, 5.11.90, p 3 and OJ C311, 27.11.92, p 30.
2 OJ C159, 17.6.91, p 38.
3 OJ L197, 18.7.87, p 33.

HAVE ADOPTED THIS DIRECTIVE—

PART II DATA PROTECTION

CHAPTER I
GENERAL PROVISIONS

Article 1

Object of the Directive

1. In accordance with this Directive, Member States shall protect the fundamental rights and freedoms of natural persons, and in particular their right to privacy with respect to the processing of personal data.

2. Member States shall neither restrict nor prohibit the free flow of personal data between Member States for reasons connected with the protection afforded under paragraph 1.

[1527]

Article 2

Definitions

For the purposes of this Directive—

(a) "personal data" shall mean any information relating to an identified or identifiable natural person ("data subject"); an identifiable person is one who can be identified, directly or indirectly, in particular by reference to an identification number or to one or more factors specific to his physical, physiological, mental, economic, cultural or social identity;

(b) "processing of personal data" ("processing") shall mean any operation or set of operations which is performed upon personal data, whether or not by automatic means, such as collection, recording, organisation, storage, adaptation or alteration, retrieval, consultation, use, disclosure by transmission, dissemination or otherwise making available, alignment or combination, blocking, erasure or destruction;

(c) "personal data filing system" ("filing system") shall mean any structured set of personal data which are accessible according to specific criteria, whether centralised, decentralised or dispersed on a functional or geographical basis;

(d) "controller" shall mean the natural or legal person, public authority, agency or any other body which alone or jointly with others determines the purposes and means of the processing of personal data; where the purposes and means of processing are determined by national or Community laws or regulations, the controller or the specific criteria for his nomination may be designated by national or Community law;

(e) "processor" shall mean a natural or legal person, public authority, agency or any other body which processes personal data on behalf of the controller;

(f) "third party" shall mean any natural or legal person, public authority, agency or any other body other than the data subject, the controller, the processor and the persons who, under the direct authority of the controller or the processor, are authorised to process the data;

(g) "recipient" shall mean a natural or legal person, public authority, agency or any other body to whom data are disclosed, whether a third party or not; however, authorities which may receive data in the framework of a particular inquiry shall not be regarded as recipients;

(h) "the data subject's consent" shall mean any freely given specific and informed indication of his wishes by which the data subject signifies his agreement to personal data relating to him being processed.

[1528]

Article 3

Scope

1. This Directive shall apply to the processing of personal data wholly or partly by automatic means, and to the processing otherwise than by automatic means of personal data which form part of a filing system or are intended to form part of a filing system.

2. This Directive shall not apply to the processing of personal data—

— in the course of an activity which falls outside the scope of Community law, such as those provided for by Titles V and VI of the Treaty on European Union and in any case to processing operations concerning public security, defence, State security (including the economic well-being of the State when the processing operation relates to State security matters) and the activities of the State in areas of criminal law,

— by a natural person in the course of a purely personal or household activity.

[1529]

Article 4

National law applicable

1. Each Member State shall apply the national provisions it adopts pursuant to this Directive to the processing of personal data where—

(a) the processing is carried out in the context of the activities of an establishment of the controller on the territory of the Member State; when the same controller is established on the territory of several Member States, he must take the necessary measures to ensure that each of these establishments complies with the obligations laid down by the national law applicable;

(b) the controller is not established on the Member State's territory, but in a place where its national law applies by virtue of international public law;

(c) the controller is not established on Community territory and, for purposes of processing personal data makes use of equipment, automated or otherwise, situated on the territory of the said Member State, unless such equipment is used only for purposes of transit through the territory of the Community.

2. In the circumstances referred to in paragraph 1(c), the controller must designate a representative established in the territory of that Member State, without prejudice to legal actions which could be initiated against the controller himself.

[1530]

CHAPTER II

GENERAL RULES ON THE LAWFULNESS OF THE PROCESSING OF PERSONAL DATA

Article 5

Member States shall, within the limits of the provisions of this Chapter, determine more precisely the conditions under which the processing of personal data is lawful.

[1531]

SECTION I

PRINCIPLES RELATING TO DATA QUALITY

Article 6

1. Member States shall provide that personal data must be—

(a) processed fairly and lawfully;
(b) collected for specified, explicit and legitimate purposes and not further processed in a way incompatible with those purposes. Further processing of data for historical, statistical or scientific purposes shall not be considered as incompatible provided that Member States provide appropriate safeguards;
(c) adequate, relevant and not excessive in relation to the purposes for which they are collected and/or further processed;
(d) accurate and, where necessary, kept up to date; every reasonable step must be taken to ensure that data which are inaccurate or incomplete, having regard to the purposes for which they were collected or for which they are further processed, are erased or rectified;
(e) kept in a form which permits identification of data subjects for no longer than is necessary for the purposes for which the data were collected or for which they are further processed. Member States shall lay down appropriate safeguards for personal data stored for longer periods for historical, statistical or scientific use.

2. It shall be for the controller to ensure that paragraph 1 is complied with.

[1532]

SECTION II
CRITERIA FOR MAKING DATA PROCESSING LEGITIMATE

Article 7

Member States shall provide that personal data may be processed only if—
(a) the data subject has unambiguously given his consent; or
(b) processing is necessary for the performance of a contract to which the data subject is party or in order to take steps at the request of the data subject prior to entering into a contract; or
(c) processing is necessary for compliance with a legal obligation to which the controller is subject; or
(d) processing is necessary in order to protect the vital interests of the data subject; or
(e) processing is necessary for the performance of a task carried out in the public interest or in the exercise of official authority vested in the controller or in a third party to whom the data are disclosed; or
(f) processing is necessary for the purposes of the legitimate interests pursued by the controller or by the third party or parties to whom the data are disclosed, except where such interests are overridden by the interests for fundamental rights and freedoms of the data subject which require protection under Article 1(1).

[1533]

SECTION III
SPECIAL CATEGORIES OF PROCESSING

Article 8

The processing of special categories of data

1. Member States shall prohibit the processing of personal data revealing racial or ethnic origin, political opinions, religious or philosophical beliefs, trade-union membership, and the processing of data concerning health or sex life.

2. Paragraph 1 shall not apply where—
(a) the data subject has given his explicit consent to the processing of those data, except where the laws of the Member State provide that the prohibition referred to in paragraph 1 may not be lifted by the data subject's giving his consent; or
(b) processing is necessary for the purposes of carrying out the obligations and specific rights of the controller in the field of employment law in so far as it is authorised by national law providing for adequate safeguards; or
(c) processing is necessary to protect the vital interests of the data subject or of another person where the data subject is physically or legally incapable of giving his consent; or
(d) processing is carried out in the course of its legitimate activities with appropriate guarantees by a foundation, association or any other non-profit-seeking body with a political, philosophical, religious or trade-union aim and on condition that the processing relates solely to the members of the body or to persons who have

regular contact with it in connection with its purposes and that the data are not disclosed to a third party without the consent of the data subjects; or

(e) the processing relates to data which are manifestly made public by the data subject or is necessary for the establishment, exercise or defence of legal claims.

3. Paragraph 1 shall not apply where processing of the data is required for the purposes of preventive medicine, medical diagnosis, the provision of care or treatment or the management of health-care services, and where those data are processed by a health professional subject under national law or rules established by national competent bodies to the obligation of professional secrecy or by another person also subject to an equivalent obligation of secrecy.

4. Subject to the provision of suitable safeguards, Member States may, for reasons of substantial public interest, lay down exemptions in addition to those laid down in paragraph 2 either by national law or by decision of the supervisory authority.

5. Processing of data relating to offences, criminal convictions or security measures may be carried out only under the control of official authority, or if suitable specific safeguards are provided under national law, subject to derogations which may be granted by the Member State under national provisions providing suitable specific safeguards. However, a complete register of criminal convictions may be kept only under the control of official authority.

Member States may provide that data relating to administrative sanctions or judgements in civil cases shall also be processed under the control of official authority.

6. Derogations from paragraph 1 provided for in paragraphs 4 and 5 shall be notified to the Commission.

7. Member States shall determine the conditions under which a national identification number or any other identifier of general application may be processed.

[1534]

Article 9

Processing of personal data and freedom of expression

Member States shall provide for exemptions or derogations from the provisions of this Chapter, Chapter IV and Chapter VI for the processing of personal data carried out solely for journalistic purposes or the purpose of artistic or literary expression only if they are necessary to reconcile the right to privacy with the rules governing freedom of expression.

[1535]

SECTION IV
INFORMATION TO BE GIVEN TO THE DATA SUBJECT

Article 10

Information in cases of collection of data from the data subject

Member States shall provide that the controller or his representative must provide a data subject from whom data relating to himself are collected with at least the following information, except where he already has it—

(a) the identity of the controller and of his representative, if any;

(b) the purposes of the processing for which the data are intended;

(c) any further information such as

— the recipients or categories of recipients of the data,

— whether replies to the questions are obligatory or voluntary, as well as the possible consequences of failure to reply,

— the existence of the right of access to and the right to rectify the data concerning him

in so far as such further information is necessary, having regard to the specific circumstances in which the data are collected, to guarantee fair processing in respect of the data subject.

[1536]

Article 11

Information where the data have not been obtained from the data subject

1. Where the data have not been obtained from the data subject, Member States shall provide that the controller or his representative must at the time of undertaking the recording

of personal data or if a disclosure to a third party is envisaged, no later than the time when the data are first disclosed provide the data subject with at least the following information, except where he already has it—

(a) the identity of the controller and of his representative, if any;
(b) the purposes of the processing;
(c) any further information such as
— the categories of data concerned,
— the recipients or categories of recipients,
— the existence of the right of access to and the right to rectify the data concerning him

in so far as such further information is necessary, having regard to the specific circumstances in which the data are processed, to guarantee fair processing in respect of the data subject.

2. Paragraph 1 shall not apply where, in particular for processing for statistical purposes or for the purposes of historical or scientific research, the provision of such information proves impossible or would involve a disproportionate effort or if recording or disclosure is expressly laid down by law. In these cases Member States shall provide appropriate safeguards.

[1537]

SECTION V
THE DATA SUBJECT'S RIGHT OF ACCESS TO DATA

Article 12

Right of access

Member States shall guarantee every data subject the right to obtain from the controller—

(a) without constraint at reasonable intervals and without excessive delay or expense—
— confirmation as to whether or not data relating to him are being processed and information at least as to the purposes of the processing, the categories of data concerned, and the recipients or categories of recipients to whom the data are disclosed,
— communication to him in an intelligible form of the data undergoing processing and of any available information as to their source,
— knowledge of the logic involved in any automatic processing of data concerning him at least in the case of the automated decisions referred to in Article 15(1);
(b) as appropriate the rectification, erasure or blocking of data the processing of which does not comply with the provisions of this Directive, in particular because of the incomplete or inaccurate nature of the data;
(c) notification to third parties to whom the data have been disclosed of any rectification, erasure or blocking carried out in compliance with (b), unless this proves impossible or involves a disproportionate effort.

[1538]

SECTION VI
EXEMPTIONS AND RESTRICTIONS

Article 13

Exemptions and restrictions

1. Member States may adopt legislative measures to restrict the scope of the obligations and rights provided for in Articles 6(1), 10, 11(1), 12 and 21 when such a restriction constitutes a necessary measures to safeguard—

(a) national security;
(b) defence;
(c) public security;
(d) the prevention, investigation, detection and prosecution of criminal offences, or of breaches of ethics for regulated professions;
(e) an important economic or financial interest of a Member State or of the European Union, including monetary, budgetary and taxation matters;
(f) a monitoring, inspection or regulatory function connected, even occasionally, with the exercise of official authority in cases referred to in (c), (d) and (e);

(g) the protection of the data subject or of the rights and freedoms of others.

2. Subject to adequate legal safeguards, in particular that the data are not used for taking measures or decisions regarding any particular individual, Member States may, where there is clearly no risk of breaching the privacy of the data subject, restrict by a legislative measure the rights provided for in Article 12 when data are processed solely for purposes of scientific research or are kept in personal form for a period which does not exceed the period necessary for the sole purpose of creating statistics.

[1539]

SECTION VII
THE DATA SUBJECT'S RIGHT TO OBJECT

Article 14

The data subject's right to object

Member States shall grant the data subject the right—

(a) at least in the cases referred to in Article 7(e) and (f), to object at any time on compelling legitimate grounds relating to his particular situation to the processing of data relating to him, save where otherwise provided by national legislation. Where there is a justified objection, the processing instigated by the controller may no longer involve those data;

(b) to object, on request and free of charge, to the processing of personal data relating to him which the controller anticipates being processed for the purposes of direct marketing, or to be informed before personal data are disclosed for the first time to third parties or used on their behalf for the purposes of direct marketing, and to be expressly offered the right to object free of charge to such disclosures or uses.

Member States shall take the necessary measures to ensure that data subjects are aware of the existence of the right referred to in the first subparagraph of (b).

[1540]

Article 15

Automated individual decisions

1. Member States shall grant the right to every person not to be subject to a decision which produces legal effects concerning him or significantly affects him and which is based solely on automated processing of data intended to evaluate certain personal aspects relating to him, such as his performance at work, creditworthiness, reliability, conduct, etc.

2. Subject to the other Articles of this Directive, Member States shall provide that a person may be subjected to a decision of the kind referred to in paragraph 1 if that decision—

(a) is taken in the course of the entering into or performance of a contract, provided the request for the entering into or the performance of the contract, lodged by the data subject, has been satisfied or that there are suitable measures to safeguard his legitimate interests, such as arrangements allowing him to put his point of view; or

(b) is authorised by a law which also lays down measures to safeguard the data subject's legitimate interests.

[1541]

SECTION VIII
CONFIDENTIALITY AND SECURITY OF PROCESSING

Article 16

Confidentiality of processing

Any person acting under the authority of the controller or of the processor, including the processor himself, who has access to personal data must not process them except on instructions from the controller, unless he is required to do so by law.

[1542]

Article 17

Security of processing

1. Member States shall provide that the controller must implement appropriate technical and organisational measures to protect personal data against accidental or unlawful

destruction or accidental loss, alteration, unauthorised disclosure or access, in particular where the processing involves the transmission of data over a network, and against all other unlawful forms of processing.

Having regard to the state of the art and the cost of their implementation, such measures shall ensure a level of security appropriate to the risks represented by the processing and the nature of the data to be protected.

2. The Member States shall provide that the controller must, where processing is carried out on his behalf, choose a processor providing sufficient guarantees in respect of the technical security measures and organisational measures governing the processing to be carried out, and must ensure compliance with those measures.

3. The carrying out of processing by way of a processor must be governed by a contract or legal act binding the processor to the controller and stipulating in particular that—

- — the processor shall act only on instructions from the controller,
- — the obligations set out in paragraph 1, as defined by the law of the Member State in which the processor is established, shall also be incumbent on the processor.

4. For the purposes of keeping proof, the parts of the contract or the legal act relating to data protection and the requirements relating to the measures referred to in paragraph 1 shall be in writing or in another equivalent form.

[1543]

SECTION IX
NOTIFICATION

Article 18

Obligation to notify the supervisory authority

1. Member States shall provide that the controller or his representative, if any, must notify the supervisory authority referred to in Article 28 before carrying out any wholly or partly automatic processing operation or set of such operations intended to serve a single purpose or several related purposes.

2. Member States may provide for the simplification of or exemption from notification only in the following cases and under the following conditions—

- — where, for categories of processing operations which are unlikely, taking account of the data to be processed, to affect adversely the rights and freedoms of data subjects, they specify the purposes of the processing, the data or categories of data undergoing processing, the category or categories of data subject, the recipients or categories of recipient to whom the data are to be disclosed and the length of time the data are to be stored, and/or
- — where the controller, in compliance with the national law which governs him, appoints a personal data protection official, responsible in particular—
  - — for ensuring in an independent manner the internal application of the national provisions taken pursuant to this Directive
  - — for keeping the register of processing operations carried out by the controller, containing the items of information referred to in Article 21(2), thereby ensuring that the rights and freedoms of the data subjects are unlikely to be adversely affected by the processing operations.

3. Member States may provide that paragraph 1 does not apply to processing whose sole purpose is the keeping of a register which according to laws or regulations is intended to provide information to the public and which is open to consultation either by the public in general or by any person demonstrating a legitimate interest.

4. Member States may provide for an exemption from the obligation to notify or a simplification of the notification in the case of processing operations referred to in Article 8(2)(d).

5. Member States may stipulate that certain or all non-automatic processing operations involving personal data shall be notified, or provide for these processing operations to be subject to simplified notification.

[1544]

Article 19

Contents of notification

1. Member States shall specify the information to be given in the notification. It shall include at least—

(a) the name and address of the controller and of his representative, if any;
(b) the purpose or purposes of the processing;
(c) a description of the category or categories of data subject and of the data or categories of data relating to them;
(d) the recipients or categories of recipient to whom the data might be disclosed;
(e) proposed transfers of data to third countries;
(f) a general description allowing a preliminary assessment to be made of the appropriateness of the measures taken pursuant to Article 17 to ensure security of processing.

2. Member States shall specify the procedures under which any change affecting the information referred to in paragraph 1 must be notified to the supervisory authority.

[1545]

Article 20

Prior checking

1. Member States shall determine the processing operations likely to present specific risks to the rights and freedoms of data subjects and shall check that these processing operations are examined prior to the start thereof.

2. Such prior checks shall be carried out by the supervisory authority following receipt of a notification from the controller or by the data protection official, who, in cases of doubt, must consult the supervisory authority.

3. Member States may also carry out such checks in the context of preparation either of a measure of the national parliament or of a measure based on such a legislative measure, which define the nature of the processing and lay down appropriate safeguards.

[1546]

Article 21

Publicising of processing operations

1. Member States shall take measures to ensure that processing operations are publicised.

2. Member States shall provide that a register of processing operations notified in accordance with Article 18 shall be kept by the supervisory authority.

The register shall contain at least the information listed in Article 19(1)(a) to (e).

The register may be inspected by any person.

3. Member States shall provide, in relation to processing operations not subject to notification, that controllers or another body appointed by the Member States make available at least the information referred to in Article 19(1)(a) to (e) in an appropriate form to any person on request.

Member States may provide that this provision does not apply to processing whose sole purpose is the keeping of a register which according to laws or regulations is intended to provide information to the public and which is open to consultation either by the public in general or by any person who can provide proof of a legitimate interest.

[1547]

CHAPTER III
JUDICIAL REMEDIES, LIABILITY AND SANCTIONS

Article 22

Remedies

Without prejudice to any administrative remedy for which provision may be made, *inter alia* before the supervisory authority referred to in Article 28, prior to referral to the judicial authority, Member States shall provide for the right of every person to a judicial remedy for any breach of the rights guaranteed him by the national law applicable to the processing in question.

[1548]

Article 23

Liability

1. Member States shall provide that any person who has suffered damage as a result of an unlawful processing operation or of any act incompatible with the national provisions adopted pursuant to this Directive is entitled to receive compensation from the controller for the damage suffered.

2. The controller may be exempted from this liability, in whole or in part, if he proves that he is not responsible for the event giving rise to the damage.

[1549]

Article 24

Sanctions

The Member States shall adopt suitable measures to ensure the full implementation of the provisions of this Directive and shall in particular lay down the sanctions to be imposed in case of infringement of the provisions adopted pursuant to this Directive.

[1550]

CHAPTER IV
TRANSFER OF PERSONAL DATA TO THIRD COUNTRIES

Article 25

Principles

1. The Member States shall provide that the transfer to a third country of personal data which are undergoing processing or are intended for processing after transfer may take place only if, without prejudice to compliance with the national provisions adopted pursuant to the other provisions of this Directive, the third country in question ensures an adequate level of protection.

2. The adequacy of the level of protection afforded by a third country shall be assessed in the light of all the circumstances surrounding a data transfer operation or set of data transfer operations; particular consideration shall be given to the nature of the data, the purpose and duration of the proposed processing operation or operations, the country of origin and country of final destination, the rules of law, both general and sectoral, in force in the third country in question and the professional rules and security measures which are complied with in that country.

3. The Member States and the Commission shall inform each other of cases where they consider that a third country does not ensure an adequate level of protection within the meaning of paragraph 2.

4. Where the Commission finds, under the procedure provided for in Article 31(2), that a third country does not ensure an adequate level of protection within the meaning of paragraph 2 of this Article, Member States shall take the measures necessary to prevent any transfer of data of the same type to the third country in question.

5. At the appropriate time, the Commission shall enter into negotiations with a view to remedying the situation resulting from the finding made pursuant to paragraph 4.

6. The Commission may find, in accordance with the procedure referred to in Article 31(2), that a third country ensures an adequate level of protection within the meaning of paragraph 2 of this Article, by reason of its domestic law or of the international commitments it has entered into, particularly upon conclusion of the negotiations referred to in paragraph 5, for the protection of the private lives and basic freedoms and rights of individuals.

Member States shall take the measures necessary to comply with the Commission's decision.

[1551]

Article 26

Derogations

1. By way of derogation from Article 25 and save where otherwise provided by domestic law governing particular cases, Member States shall provide that a transfer or a set of transfers

of personal data to a third country which does not ensure an adequate level of protection within the meaning of Article 25(2) may take place on condition that—

(a) the data subject has given his consent unambiguously to the proposed transfer; or

(b) the transfer is necessary for the performance of a contract between the data subject and the controller or the implementation of precontractual measures taken in response to the data subject's request; or

(c) the transfer is necessary for the conclusion or performance of a contract concluded in the interest of the data subject between the controller and a third party; or

(d) the transfer is necessary or legally required on important public interest grounds, or for the establishment, exercise or defence of legal claims; or

(e) the transfer is necessary in order to protect the vital interests of the data subject; or

(f) the transfer is made from a register which according to laws or regulations is intended to provide information to the public and which is open to consultation either by the public in general or by any person who can demonstrate legitimate interest, to the extent that the conditions laid down in law for consultation are fulfilled in the particular case.

2. Without prejudice to paragraph 1, a Member State may authorise a transfer or a set of transfers of personal data to a third country which does not ensure an adequate level of protection within the meaning of Article 25(2), where the controller adduces adequate safeguards with respect to the protection of the privacy and fundamental rights and freedoms of individuals and as regards the exercise of the corresponding rights; such safeguards may in particular result from appropriate contractual clauses.

3. The Member State shall inform the Commission and the other Member States of the authorisations it grants pursuant to paragraph 2.

If a Member State or the Commission objects on justified grounds involving the protection of the privacy and fundamental rights and freedoms of individuals, the Commission shall take appropriate measures in accordance with the procedure laid down in Article 31(2).

Member States shall take the necessary measures to comply with the Commission's decision.

4. Where the Commission decides, in accordance with the procedure referred to in Article 31(2), that certain standard contractual clauses offer sufficient safeguards as required by paragraph 2, Member States shall take the necessary measures to comply with the Commission's decision.

[1552]

CHAPTER V
CODES OF CONDUCT

Article 27

1. The Member States and the Commission shall encourage the drawing up of codes of conduct intended to contribute to the proper implementation of the national provisions adopted by the Member States pursuant to this Directive, taking account of the specific features of the various sectors.

2. Member States shall make provision for trade associations and other bodies representing other categories of controllers which have drawn up draft national codes or which have the intention of amending or extending existing national codes to be able to submit them to the opinion of the national authority.

Member States shall make provision for this authority to ascertain, among other things, whether the drafts submitted to it are in accordance with the national provisions adopted pursuant to this Directive. If it sees fit, the authority shall seek the views of data subjects or their representatives.

3. Draft Community codes, and amendments or extensions to existing Community codes, may be submitted to the Working Party referred to in Article 29. This Working Party shall determine, among other things, whether the drafts submitted to it are in accordance with the national provisions adopted pursuant to this Directive. If it sees fit, the authority shall seek the views of data subjects or their representatives. The Commission may ensure appropriate publicity for the codes which have been approved by the Working Party.

[1553]

CHAPTER VI
SUPERVISORY AUTHORITY AND WORKING PARTY ON THE PROTECTION OF INDIVIDUALS WITH REGARD TO THE PROCESSING OF PERSONAL DATA

Article 28

Supervisory authority

1. Each Member State shall provide that one or more public authorities are responsible for monitoring the application within its territory of the provisions adopted by the Member States pursuant to this Directive.

These authorities shall act with complete independence in exercising the functions entrusted to them.

2. Each Member State shall provide that the supervisory authorities are consulted when drawing up administrative measures or regulations relating to the protection of individuals' rights and freedoms with regard to the processing of personal data.

3. Each authority shall in particular be endowed with—
- — investigative powers, such as powers of access to data forming the subject-matter of processing operations and powers to collect all the information necessary for the performance of its supervisory duties,
- — effective powers of intervention, such as, for example, that of delivering opinions before processing operations are carried out, in accordance with Article 20, and ensuring appropriate publication of such opinions, of ordering the blocking, erasure or destruction of data, of imposing a temporary or definitive ban on processing, of warning or admonishing the controller, or that of referring the matter to national parliaments or other political institutions,
- — the power to engage in legal proceedings where the national provisions adopted pursuant to this Directive have been violated or to bring these violations to the attention of the judicial authorities.

Decisions by the supervisory authority which give rise to complaints may be appealed against through the courts.

4. Each supervisory authority shall hear claims lodged by any person, or by an association representing that person, concerning the protection of his rights and freedoms in regard to the processing of personal data. The person concerned shall be informed of the outcome of the claim.

Each supervisory authority shall, in particular, hear claims for checks on the lawfulness of data processing lodged by any person when the national provisions adopted pursuant to Article 13 of this Directive apply. The person shall at any rate be informed that a check has taken place.

5. Each supervisory authority shall draw up a report on its activities at regular intervals. The report shall be made public.

6. Each supervisory authority is competent, whatever the national law applicable to the processing in question, to exercise, on the territory of its own Member State, the powers conferred on it in accordance with paragraph 3. Each authority may be requested to exercise its powers by an authority of another Member State.

The supervisory authorities shall cooperate with one another to the extent necessary for the performance of their duties, in particular by exchanging all useful information.

7. Member States shall provide that the members and staff of the supervisory authority, even after their employment has ended, are to be subject to a duty of professional secrecy with regard to confidential information to which they have access.

[1554]

Article 29

Working Party on the Protection of Individuals with regard to the Processing of Personal Data

1. A Working Party on the Protection of Individuals with regard to the Processing of Personal Data, hereinafter referred to as "the Working Party", is hereby set up.

It shall have advisory status and act independently.

2. The Working Party shall be composed of a representative of the supervisory authority or authorities designated by each Member State and of a representative of the authority or authorities established for the Community institutions and bodies, and of a representative of the Commission.

Each member of the Working Party shall be designated by the institution, authority or authorities which he represents. Where a Member State has designated more than one supervisory authority, they shall nominate a joint representative. The same shall apply to the authorities established for Community institutions and bodies.

3. The Working Party shall take decisions by a simple majority of the representatives of the supervisory authorities.

4. The Working Party shall elect its chairman. The chairman's term of office shall be two years. His appointment shall be renewable.

5. The Working Party's secretariat shall be provided by the Commission.

6. The Working Party shall adopt its own rules of procedure.

7. The Working Party shall consider items placed on its agenda by its chairman, either on his own initiative or at the request of a representative of the supervisory authorities or at the Commission's request.

[1555]

Article 30

1. The Working Party shall—
   (a) examine any question covering the application of the national measures adopted under this Directive in order to contribute to the uniform application of such measures;
   (b) give the Commission an opinion on the level of protection in the Community and in third countries;
   (c) advise the Commission on any proposed amendment of this Directive, on any additional or specific measures to safeguard the rights and freedoms of natural persons with regard to the processing of personal data and on any other proposed Community measures affecting such rights and freedoms;
   (d) give an opinion on codes of conduct drawn up at Community level.

2. If the Working Party finds that divergences likely to affect the equivalence of protection for persons with regard to the processing of personal data in the Community are arising between the laws or practices of Member States, it shall inform the Commission accordingly.

3. The Working Party may, on its own initiative, make recommendations on all matters relating to the protection of persons with regard to the processing of personal data in the Community.

4. The Working Party's opinions and recommendations shall be forwarded to the Commission and to the committee referred to in Article 31.

5. The Commission shall inform the Working Party of the action it has taken in response to its opinions and recommendations. It shall do so in a report which shall also be forwarded to the European Parliament and the Council. The report shall be made public.

6. The Working Party shall draw up an annual report on the situation regarding the protection of natural persons with regard to the processing of personal data in the Community and in third countries, which it shall transmit to the Commission, the European Parliament and the Council. The report shall be made public.

[1556]

CHAPTER VII
COMMUNITY IMPLEMENTING MEASURES

[Article 31

1. The Commission shall be assisted by a committee.

2. Where reference is made to this Article, Articles 4 and 7 of Decision 1999/468/EC[1] shall apply, having regard to the provisions of Article 8 thereof.

The period laid down in Article 4(3) of Decision 1999/468/EC shall be set at three months.

3. The committee shall adopt its rules of procedure.]

[1557]

NOTES

[1] OJ L184, 17.7.1999, p 23.

Substituted by European Parliament and Council Regulation 1882/2003/EC, Annex II(18).

FINAL PROVISIONS

Article 32

1. Member States shall bring into force the laws, regulations and administrative provisions necessary to comply with this Directive at the latest at the end of a period of three years from the date of its adoption.

When Member States adopt these measures, they shall contain a reference to this Directive or be accompanied by such reference on the occasion of their official publication. The methods of making such reference shall be laid down by the Member States.

2. Member States shall ensure that processing already under way on the date the national provisions adopted pursuant to this Directive enter into force, is brought into conformity with these provisions within three years of this date.

By way of derogation from the preceding subparagraph, Member States may provide that the processing of data already held in manual filing systems on the date of entry into force of the national provisions adopted in implementation of this Directive shall be brought into conformity with Articles 6, 7 and 8 of this Directive within 12 years of the date on which it is adopted. Member States shall, however, grant the data subject the right to obtain, at his request and in particular at the time of exercising his right of access, the rectification, erasure or blocking of data which are incomplete, inaccurate or stored in a way incompatible with the legitimate purposes pursued by the controller.

3. By way of derogation from paragraph 2, Member States may provide, subject to suitable safeguards, that data kept for the sole purpose of historical research need not be brought into conformity with Articles 6, 7 and 8 of this Directive.

4. Member States shall communicate to the Commission the text of the provisions of domestic law which they adopt in the field covered by this Directive.

[1558]

Article 33

The Commission shall report to the Council and the European Parliament at regular intervals, starting not later than three years after the date referred to in Article 32(1), on the implementation of this Directive, attaching to its report, if necessary, suitable proposals for amendments. The report shall be made public.

The Commission shall examine, in particular, the application of this Directive to the data processing of sound and image data relating to natural persons and shall submit any appropriate proposals which prove to be necessary, taking account of developments in information technology and in the light of the state of progress in the information society.

[1559]

Article 34

This Directive is addressed to the Member States.

[1560]

Done at Luxembourg, 24 October 1995.

DIRECTIVE OF THE EUROPEAN PARLIAMENT AND OF THE COUNCIL

of 12 July 2002

concerning the processing of personal data and the protection of privacy in the electronic communications sector (Directive on privacy and electronic communications)

(2002/58/EC)

NOTES

Date of publication in OJ: OJ L201, 31.7.2002, p 37.

THE EUROPEAN PARLIAMENT AND THE COUNCIL OF THE EUROPEAN UNION,

Having regard to the Treaty establishing the European Community, and in particular Article 95 thereof,

Having regard to the proposal from the Commission,[1]

Having regard to the opinion of the Economic and Social Committee,[2]

Having consulted the Committee of the Regions,

Acting in accordance with the procedure laid down in Article 251 of the Treaty,[3]

Whereas—

(1) Directive 95/46/EC of the European Parliament and of the Council of 24 October 1995 on the protection of individuals with regard to the processing of personal data and on the free movement of such data[4] requires Member States to ensure the rights and freedoms of natural persons with regard to the processing of personal data, and in particular their right to privacy, in order to ensure the free flow of personal data in the Community.

(2) This Directive seeks to respect the fundamental rights and observes the principles recognised in particular by the Charter of fundamental rights of the European Union. In particular, this Directive seeks to ensure full respect for the rights set out in Articles 7 and 8 of that Charter.

(3) Confidentiality of communications is guaranteed in accordance with the international instruments relating to human rights, in particular the European Convention for the Protection of Human Rights and Fundamental Freedoms, and the constitutions of the Member States.

(4) Directive 97/66/EC of the European Parliament and of the Council of 15 December 1997 concerning the processing of personal data and the protection of privacy in the telecommunications sector[5] translated the principles set out in Directive 95/46/EC into specific rules for the telecommunications sector. Directive 97/66/EC has to be adapted to developments in the markets and technologies for electronic communications services in order to provide an equal level of protection of personal data and privacy for users of publicly available electronic communications services, regardless of the technologies used. That Directive should therefore be repealed and replaced by this Directive.

(5) New advanced digital technologies are currently being introduced in public communications networks in the Community, which give rise to specific requirements concerning the protection of personal data and privacy of the user. The development of the information society is characterised by the introduction of new electronic communications services. Access to digital mobile networks has become available and affordable for a large public. These digital networks have large capacities and possibilities for processing personal data. The successful cross-border development of these services is partly dependent on the confidence of users that their privacy will not be at risk.

(6) The Internet is overturning traditional market structures by providing a common, global infrastructure for the delivery of a wide range of electronic communications services. Publicly available electronic communications services over the Internet open new possibilities for users but also new risks for their personal data and privacy.

(7) In the case of public communications networks, specific legal, regulatory and technical provisions should be made in order to protect fundamental rights and freedoms of natural persons and legitimate interests of legal persons, in particular with regard to the increasing capacity for automated storage and processing of data relating to subscribers and users.

(8) Legal, regulatory and technical provisions adopted by the Member States concerning the protection of personal data, privacy and the legitimate interest of legal persons, in the electronic communication sector, should be harmonised in order to avoid obstacles to the

internal market for electronic communication in accordance with Article 14 of the Treaty. Harmonisation should be limited to requirements necessary to guarantee that the promotion and development of new electronic communications services and networks between Member States are not hindered.

(9) The Member States, providers and users concerned, together with the competent Community bodies, should cooperate in introducing and developing the relevant technologies where this is necessary to apply the guarantees provided for by this Directive and taking particular account of the objectives of minimising the processing of personal data and of using anonymous or pseudonymous data where possible.

(10) In the electronic communications sector, Directive 95/46/EC applies in particular to all matters concerning protection of fundamental rights and freedoms, which are not specifically covered by the provisions of this Directive, including the obligations on the controller and the rights of individuals. Directive 95/46/EC applies to non-public communications services.

(11) Like Directive 95/46/EC, this Directive does not address issues of protection of fundamental rights and freedoms related to activities which are not governed by Community law. Therefore it does not alter the existing balance between the individual's right to privacy and the possibility for Member States to take the measures referred to in Article 15(1) of this Directive, necessary for the protection of public security, defence, State security (including the economic well-being of the State when the activities relate to State security matters) and the enforcement of criminal law. Consequently, this Directive does not affect the ability of Member States to carry out lawful interception of electronic communications, or take other measures, if necessary for any of these purposes and in accordance with the European Convention for the Protection of Human Rights and Fundamental Freedoms, as interpreted by the rulings of the European Court of Human Rights. Such measures must be appropriate, strictly proportionate to the intended purpose and necessary within a democratic society and should be subject to adequate safeguards in accordance with the European Convention for the Protection of Human Rights and Fundamental Freedoms.

(12) Subscribers to a publicly available electronic communications service may be natural or legal persons. By supplementing Directive 95/46/EC, this Directive is aimed at protecting the fundamental rights of natural persons and particularly their right to privacy, as well as the legitimate interests of legal persons. This Directive does not entail an obligation for Member States to extend the application of Directive 95/46/EC to the protection of the legitimate interests of legal persons, which is ensured within the framework of the applicable Community and national legislation.

(13) The contractual relation between a subscriber and a service provider may entail a periodic or a one-off payment for the service provided or to be provided. Prepaid cards are also considered as a contract.

(14) Location data may refer to the latitude, longitude and altitude of the user's terminal equipment, to the direction of travel, to the level of accuracy of the location information, to the identification of the network cell in which the terminal equipment is located at a certain point in time and to the time the location information was recorded.

(15) A communication may include any naming, numbering or addressing information provided by the sender of a communication or the user of a connection to carry out the communication. Traffic data may include any translation of this information by the network over which the communication is transmitted for the purpose of carrying out the transmission. Traffic data may, *inter alia*, consist of data referring to the routing, duration, time or volume of a communication, to the protocol used, to the location of the terminal equipment of the sender or recipient, to the network on which the communication originates or terminates, to the beginning, end or duration of a connection. They may also consist of the format in which the communication is conveyed by the network.

(16) Information that is part of a broadcasting service provided over a public communications network is intended for a potentially unlimited audience and does not constitute a communication in the sense of this Directive. However, in cases where the individual subscriber or user receiving such information can be identified, for example with video-on-demand services, the information conveyed is covered within the meaning of a communication for the purposes of this Directive.

(17) For the purposes of this Directive, consent of a user or subscriber, regardless of whether the latter is a natural or a legal person, should have the same meaning as the data subject's consent as defined and further specified in Directive 95/46/EC. Consent may be given by any appropriate method enabling a freely given specific and informed indication of the user's wishes, including by ticking a box when visiting an Internet website.

(18) Value added services may, for example, consist of advice on least expensive tariff packages, route guidance, traffic information, weather forecasts and tourist information.

(19) The application of certain requirements relating to presentation and restriction of calling and connected line identification and to automatic call forwarding to subscriber lines connected to analogue exchanges should not be made mandatory in specific cases where such application would prove to be technically impossible or would require a disproportionate economic effort. It is important for interested parties to be informed of such cases and the Member States should therefore notify them to the Commission.

(20) Service providers should take appropriate measures to safeguard the security of their services, if necessary in conjunction with the provider of the network, and inform subscribers of any special risks of a breach of the security of the network. Such risks may especially occur for electronic communications services over an open network such as the Internet or analogue mobile telephony. It is particularly important for subscribers and users of such services to be fully informed by their service provider of the existing security risks which lie outside the scope of possible remedies by the service provider. Service providers who offer publicly available electronic communications services over the Internet should inform users and subscribers of measures they can take to protect the security of their communications for instance by using specific types of software or encryption technologies. The requirement to inform subscribers of particular security risks does not discharge a service provider from the obligation to take, at its own costs, appropriate and immediate measures to remedy any new, unforeseen security risks and restore the normal security level of the service. The provision of information about security risks to the subscriber should be free of charge except for any nominal costs which the subscriber may incur while receiving or collecting the information, for instance by downloading an electronic mail message. Security is appraised in the light of Article 17 of Directive 95/46/EC.

(21) Measures should be taken to prevent unauthorised access to communications in order to protect the confidentiality of communications, including both the contents and any data related to such communications, by means of public communications networks and publicly available electronic communications services. National legislation in some Member States only prohibits intentional unauthorised access to communications.

(22) The prohibition of storage of communications and the related traffic data by persons other than the users or without their consent is not intended to prohibit any automatic, intermediate and transient storage of this information in so far as this takes place for the sole purpose of carrying out the transmission in the electronic communications network and provided that the information is not stored for any period longer than is necessary for the transmission and for traffic management purposes, and that during the period of storage the confidentiality remains guaranteed. Where this is necessary for making more efficient the onward transmission of any publicly accessible information to other recipients of the service upon their request, this Directive should not prevent such information from being further stored, provided that this information would in any case be accessible to the public without restriction and that any data referring to the individual subscribers or users requesting such information are erased.

(23) Confidentiality of communications should also be ensured in the course of lawful business practice. Where necessary and legally authorised, communications can be recorded for the purpose of providing evidence of a commercial transaction. Directive 95/46/EC applies to such processing. Parties to the communications should be informed prior to the recording about the recording, its purpose and the duration of its storage. The recorded communication should be erased as soon as possible and in any case at the latest by the end of the period during which the transaction can be lawfully challenged.

(24) Terminal equipment of users of electronic communications networks and any information stored on such equipment are part of the private sphere of the users requiring protection under the European Convention for the Protection of Human Rights and Fundamental Freedoms. So-called spyware, web bugs, hidden identifiers and other similar devices can enter the user's terminal without their knowledge in order to gain access to information, to store hidden information or to trace the activities of the user and may seriously intrude upon the privacy of these users. The use of such devices should be allowed only for legitimate purposes, with the knowledge of the users concerned.

(25) However, such devices, for instance so-called "cookies", can be a legitimate and useful tool, for example, in analysing the effectiveness of website design and advertising, and in verifying the identity of users engaged in on-line transactions. Where such devices, for instance cookies, are intended for a legitimate purpose, such as to facilitate the provision of information society services, their use should be allowed on condition that users are provided with clear and precise information in accordance with Directive 95/46/EC about the purposes of cookies or similar devices so as to ensure that users are made aware of information being placed on the terminal equipment they are using. Users should have the opportunity to refuse to have a cookie or similar device stored on their terminal equipment. This is particularly important where users other than the original user have access to the terminal equipment and

thereby to any data containing privacy-sensitive information stored on such equipment. Information and the right to refuse may be offered once for the use of various devices to be installed on the user's terminal equipment during the same connection and also covering any further use that may be made of those devices during subsequent connections. The methods for giving information, offering a right to refuse or requesting consent should be made as user-friendly as possible. Access to specific website content may still be made conditional on the well-informed acceptance of a cookie or similar device, if it is used for a legitimate purpose.

(26) The data relating to subscribers processed within electronic communications networks to establish connections and to transmit information contain information on the private life of natural persons and concern the right to respect for their correspondence or concern the legitimate interests of legal persons. Such data may only be stored to the extent that is necessary for the provision of the service for the purpose of billing and for interconnection payments, and for a limited time. Any further processing of such data which the provider of the publicly available electronic communications services may want to perform, for the marketing of electronic communications services or for the provision of value added services, may only be allowed if the subscriber has agreed to this on the basis of accurate and full information given by the provider of the publicly available electronic communications services about the types of further processing it intends to perform and about the subscriber's right not to give or to withdraw his/her consent to such processing. Traffic data used for marketing communications services or for the provision of value added services should also be erased or made anonymous after the provision of the service. Service providers should always keep subscribers informed of the types of data they are processing and the purposes and duration for which this is done.

(27) The exact moment of the completion of the transmission of a communication, after which traffic data should be erased except for billing purposes, may depend on the type of electronic communications service that is provided. For instance for a voice telephony call the transmission will be completed as soon as either of the users terminates the connection. For electronic mail the transmission is completed as soon as the addressee collects the message, typically from the server of his service provider.

(28) The obligation to erase traffic data or to make such data anonymous when it is no longer needed for the purpose of the transmission of a communication does not conflict with such procedures on the Internet as the caching in the domain name system of IP addresses or the caching of IP addresses to physical address bindings or the use of log-in information to control the right of access to networks or services.

(29) The service provider may process traffic data relating to subscribers and users where necessary in individual cases in order to detect technical failure or errors in the transmission of communications. Traffic data necessary for billing purposes may also be processed by the provider in order to detect and stop fraud consisting of unpaid use of the electronic communications service.

(30) Systems for the provision of electronic communications networks and services should be designed to limit the amount of personal data necessary to a strict minimum. Any activities related to the provision of the electronic communications service that go beyond the transmission of a communication and the billing thereof should be based on aggregated, traffic data that cannot be related to subscribers or users. Where such activities cannot be based on aggregated data, they should be considered as value added services for which the consent of the subscriber is required.

(31) Whether the consent to be obtained for the processing of personal data with a view to providing a particular value added service should be that of the user or of the subscriber, will depend on the data to be processed and on the type of service to be provided and on whether it is technically, procedurally and contractually possible to distinguish the individual using an electronic communications service from the legal or natural person having subscribed to it.

(32) Where the provider of an electronic communications service or of a value added service subcontracts the processing of personal data necessary for the provision of these services to another entity, such subcontracting and subsequent data processing should be in full compliance with the requirements regarding controllers and processors of personal data as set out in Directive 95/46/EC. Where the provision of a value added service requires that traffic or location data are forwarded from an electronic communications service provider to a provider of value added services, the subscribers or users to whom the data are related should also be fully informed of this forwarding before giving their consent for the processing of the data.

(33) The introduction of itemised bills has improved the possibilities for the subscriber to check the accuracy of the fees charged by the service provider but, at the same time, it may jeopardise the privacy of the users of publicly available electronic communications services.

PART II
DATA PROTECTION

Therefore, in order to preserve the privacy of the user, Member States should encourage the development of electronic communication service options such as alternative payment facilities which allow anonymous or strictly private access to publicly available electronic communications services, for example calling cards and facilities for payment by credit card. To the same end, Member States may ask the operators to offer their subscribers a different type of detailed bill in which a certain number of digits of the called number have been deleted.

(34) It is necessary, as regards calling line identification, to protect the right of the calling party to withhold the presentation of the identification of the line from which the call is being made and the right of the called party to reject calls from unidentified lines. There is justification for overriding the elimination of calling line identification presentation in specific cases. Certain subscribers, in particular help lines and similar organisations, have an interest in guaranteeing the anonymity of their callers. It is necessary, as regards connected line identification, to protect the right and the legitimate interest of the called party to withhold the presentation of the identification of the line to which the calling party is actually connected, in particular in the case of forwarded calls. The providers of publicly available electronic communications services should inform their subscribers of the existence of calling and connected line identification in the network and of all services which are offered on the basis of calling and connected line identification as well as the privacy options which are available. This will allow the subscribers to make an informed choice about the privacy facilities they may want to use. The privacy options which are offered on a per-line basis do not necessarily have to be available as an automatic network service but may be obtainable through a simple request to the provider of the publicly available electronic communications service.

(35) In digital mobile networks, location data giving the geographic position of the terminal equipment of the mobile user are processed to enable the transmission of communications. Such data are traffic data covered by Article 6 of this Directive. However, in addition, digital mobile networks may have the capacity to process location data which are more precise than is necessary for the transmission of communications and which are used for the provision of value added services such as services providing individualised traffic information and guidance to drivers. The processing of such data for value added services should only be allowed where subscribers have given their consent. Even in cases where subscribers have given their consent, they should have a simple means to temporarily deny the processing of location data, free of charge.

(36) Member States may restrict the users' and subscribers' rights to privacy with regard to calling line identification where this is necessary to trace nuisance calls and with regard to calling line identification and location data where this is necessary to allow emergency services to carry out their tasks as effectively as possible. For these purposes, Member States may adopt specific provisions to entitle providers of electronic communications services to provide access to calling line identification and location data without the prior consent of the users or subscribers concerned.

(37) Safeguards should be provided for subscribers against the nuisance which may be caused by automatic call forwarding by others. Moreover, in such cases, it must be possible for subscribers to stop the forwarded calls being passed on to their terminals by simple request to the provider of the publicly available electronic communications service.

(38) Directories of subscribers to electronic communications services are widely distributed and public. The right to privacy of natural persons and the legitimate interest of legal persons require that subscribers are able to determine whether their personal data are published in a directory and if so, which. Providers of public directories should inform the subscribers to be included in such directories of the purposes of the directory and of any particular usage which may be made of electronic versions of public directories especially through search functions embedded in the software, such as reverse search functions enabling users of the directory to discover the name and address of the subscriber on the basis of a telephone number only.

(39) The obligation to inform subscribers of the purpose(s) of public directories in which their personal data are to be included should be imposed on the party collecting the data for such inclusion. Where the data may be transmitted to one or more third parties, the subscriber should be informed of this possibility and of the recipient or the categories of possible recipients. Any transmission should be subject to the condition that the data may not be used for other purposes than those for which they were collected. If the party collecting the data from the subscriber or any third party to whom the data have been transmitted wishes to use the data for an additional purpose, the renewed consent of the subscriber is to be obtained either by the initial party collecting the data or by the third party to whom the data have been transmitted.

(40) Safeguards should be provided for subscribers against intrusion of their privacy by unsolicited communications for direct marketing purposes in particular by means of

automated calling machines, telefaxes, and e-mails, including SMS messages. These forms of unsolicited commercial communications may on the one hand be relatively easy and cheap to send and on the other may impose a burden and/or cost on the recipient. Moreover, in some cases their volume may also cause difficulties for electronic communications networks and terminal equipment. For such forms of unsolicited communications for direct marketing, it is justified to require that prior explicit consent of the recipients is obtained before such communications are addressed to them. The single market requires a harmonised approach to ensure simple, Community-wide rules for businesses and users.

(41) Within the context of an existing customer relationship, it is reasonable to allow the use of electronic contact details for the offering of similar products or services, but only by the same company that has obtained the electronic contact details in accordance with Directive 95/46/EC. When electronic contact details are obtained, the customer should be informed about their further use for direct marketing in a clear and distinct manner, and be given the opportunity to refuse such usage. This opportunity should continue to be offered with each subsequent direct marketing message, free of charge, except for any costs for the transmission of this refusal.

(42) Other forms of direct marketing that are more costly for the sender and impose no financial costs on subscribers and users, such as person-to-person voice telephony calls, may justify the maintenance of a system giving subscribers or users the possibility to indicate that they do not want to receive such calls. Nevertheless, in order not to decrease existing levels of privacy protection, Member States should be entitled to uphold national systems, only allowing such calls to subscribers and users who have given their prior consent.

(43) To facilitate effective enforcement of Community rules on unsolicited messages for direct marketing, it is necessary to prohibit the use of false identities or false return addresses or numbers while sending unsolicited messages for direct marketing purposes.

(44) Certain electronic mail systems allow subscribers to view the sender and subject line of an electronic mail, and also to delete the message, without having to download the rest of the electronic mail's content or any attachments, thereby reducing costs which could arise from downloading unsolicited electronic mails or attachments. These arrangements may continue to be useful in certain cases as an additional tool to the general obligations established in this Directive.

(45) This Directive is without prejudice to the arrangements which Member States make to protect the legitimate interests of legal persons with regard to unsolicited communications for direct marketing purposes. Where Member States establish an opt-out register for such communications to legal persons, mostly business users, the provisions of Article 7 of Directive 2000/31/EC of the European Parliament and of the Council of 8 June 2000 on certain legal aspects of information society services, in particular electronic commerce, in the internal market (Directive on electronic commerce)[6] are fully applicable.

(46) The functionalities for the provision of electronic communications services may be integrated in the network or in any part of the terminal equipment of the user, including the software. The protection of the personal data and the privacy of the user of publicly available electronic communications services should be independent of the configuration of the various components necessary to provide the service and of the distribution of the necessary functionalities between these components. Directive 95/46/EC covers any form of processing of personal data regardless of the technology used. The existence of specific rules for electronic communications services alongside general rules for other components necessary for the provision of such services may not facilitate the protection of personal data and privacy in a technologically neutral way. It may therefore be necessary to adopt measures requiring manufacturers of certain types of equipment used for electronic communications services to construct their product in such a way as to incorporate safeguards to ensure that the personal data and privacy of the user and subscriber are protected. The adoption of such measures in accordance with Directive 1999/5/EC of the European Parliament and of the Council of 9 March 1999 on radio equipment and telecommunications terminal equipment and the mutual recognition of their conformity[7] will ensure that the introduction of technical features of electronic communication equipment including software for data protection purposes is harmonised in order to be compatible with the implementation of the internal market.

(47) Where the rights of the users and subscribers are not respected, national legislation should provide for judicial remedies. Penalties should be imposed on any person, whether governed by private or public law, who fails to comply with the national measures taken under this Directive.

(48) It is useful, in the field of application of this Directive, to draw on the experience of the Working Party on the Protection of Individuals with regard to the Processing of Personal Data composed of representatives of the supervisory authorities of the Member States, set up by Article 29 of Directive 95/46/EC.

(49) To facilitate compliance with the provisions of this Directive, certain specific arrangements are needed for processing of data already under way on the date that national implementing legislation pursuant to this Directive enters into force,

NOTES

1 OJ C365 E, 19.12.2000, p 223.
2 OJ C123, 25.4.2001, p 53.
3 Opinion of the European Parliament of 13 November 2001 (not yet published in the Official Journal), Council Common Position of 28 January 2002 (OJ C113 E, 14.5.2002, p 39) and Decision of the European Parliament of 30 May 2002 (not yet published in the Official Journal). Council Decision of 25 June 2002.
4 OJ L281, 23.11.1995, p 31.
5 OJ L24, 30.1.1998, p 1.
6 OJ L178, 17.7.2000, p 1.
7 OJ L91, 7.4.1999, p 10.

HAVE ADOPTED THIS DIRECTIVE—

Article 1

Scope and aim

1. This Directive harmonises the provisions of the Member States required to ensure an equivalent level of protection of fundamental rights and freedoms, and in particular the right to privacy, with respect to the processing of personal data in the electronic communication sector and to ensure the free movement of such data and of electronic communication equipment and services in the Community.

2. The provisions of this Directive particularise and complement Directive 95/46/EC for the purposes mentioned in paragraph 1. Moreover, they provide for protection of the legitimate interests of subscribers who are legal persons.

3. This Directive shall not apply to activities which fall outside the scope of the Treaty establishing the European Community, such as those covered by Titles V and VI of the Treaty on European Union, and in any case to activities concerning public security, defence, State security (including the economic well-being of the State when the activities relate to State security matters) and the activities of the State in areas of criminal law.

[1561]

Article 2

Definitions

Save as otherwise provided, the definitions in Directive 95/46/EC and in Directive 2002/21/EC of the European Parliament and of the Council of 7 March 2002 on a common regulatory framework for electronic communications networks and services (Framework Directive)[1] shall apply.

The following definitions shall also apply—

(a) "user" means any natural person using a publicly available electronic communications service, for private or business purposes, without necessarily having subscribed to this service;

(b) "traffic data" means any data processed for the purpose of the conveyance of a communication on an electronic communications network or for the billing thereof;

(c) "location data" means any data processed in an electronic communications network, indicating the geographic position of the terminal equipment of a user of a publicly available electronic communications service;

(d) "communication" means any information exchanged or conveyed between a finite number of parties by means of a publicly available electronic communications service. This does not include any information conveyed as part of a broadcasting service to the public over an electronic communications network except to the extent that the information can be related to the identifiable subscriber or user receiving the information;

(e) "call" means a connection established by means of a publicly available telephone service allowing two-way communication in real time;

(f) "consent" by a user or subscriber corresponds to the data subject's consent in Directive 95/46/EC;

(g) "value added service" means any service which requires the processing of traffic data or location data other than traffic data beyond what is necessary for the transmission of a communication or the billing thereof;

(h) "electronic mail" means any text, voice, sound or image message sent over a public communications network which can be stored in the network or in the recipient's terminal equipment until it is collected by the recipient.

[1562]

NOTES

[1] OJ L108, 24.4.2002, p 33.

Article 3

Services concerned

1. This Directive shall apply to the processing of personal data in connection with the provision of publicly available electronic communications services in public communications networks in the Community.

2. Articles 8, 10 and 11 shall apply to subscriber lines connected to digital exchanges and, where technically possible and if it does not require a disproportionate economic effort, to subscriber lines connected to analogue exchanges.

3. Cases where it would be technically impossible or require a disproportionate economic effort to fulfil the requirements of Articles 8, 10 and 11 shall be notified to the Commission by the Member States.

[1563]

Article 4

Security

1. The provider of a publicly available electronic communications service must take appropriate technical and organisational measures to safeguard security of its services, if necessary in conjunction with the provider of the public communications network with respect to network security. Having regard to the state of the art and the cost of their implementation, these measures shall ensure a level of security appropriate to the risk presented.

2. In case of a particular risk of a breach of the security of the network, the provider of a publicly available electronic communications service must inform the subscribers concerning such risk and, where the risk lies outside the scope of the measures to be taken by the service provider, of any possible remedies, including an indication of the likely costs involved.

[1564]

Article 5

Confidentiality of the communications

1. Member States shall ensure the confidentiality of communications and the related traffic data by means of a public communications network and publicly available electronic communications services, through national legislation. In particular, they shall prohibit listening, tapping, storage or other kinds of interception or surveillance of communications and the related traffic data by persons other than users, without the consent of the users concerned, except when legally authorised to do so in accordance with Article 15(1). This paragraph shall not prevent technical storage which is necessary for the conveyance of a communication without prejudice to the principle of confidentiality.

2. Paragraph 1 shall not affect any legally authorised recording of communications and the related traffic data when carried out in the course of lawful business practice for the purpose of providing evidence of a commercial transaction or of any other business communication.

3. Member States shall ensure that the use of electronic communications networks to store information or to gain access to information stored in the terminal equipment of a subscriber or user is only allowed on condition that the subscriber or user concerned is

provided with clear and comprehensive information in accordance with Directive 95/46/EC, *inter alia* about the purposes of the processing, and is offered the right to refuse such processing by the data controller. This shall not prevent any technical storage or access for the sole purpose of carrying out or facilitating the transmission of a communication over an electronic communications network, or as strictly necessary in order to provide an information society service explicitly requested by the subscriber or user.

[1565]

Article 6

Traffic data

1. Traffic data relating to subscribers and users processed and stored by the provider of a public communications network or publicly available electronic communications service must be erased or made anonymous when it is no longer needed for the purpose of the transmission of a communication without prejudice to paragraphs 2, 3 and 5 of this Article and Article 15(1).

2. Traffic data necessary for the purposes of subscriber billing and interconnection payments may be processed. Such processing is permissible only up to the end of the period during which the bill may lawfully be challenged or payment pursued.

3. For the purpose of marketing electronic communications services or for the provision of value added services, the provider of a publicly available electronic communications service may process the data referred to in paragraph 1 to the extent and for the duration necessary for such services or marketing, if the subscriber or user to whom the data relate has given his/her consent. Users or subscribers shall be given the possibility to withdraw their consent for the processing of traffic data at any time.

4. The service provider must inform the subscriber or user of the types of traffic data which are processed and of the duration of such processing for the purposes mentioned in paragraph 2 and, prior to obtaining consent, for the purposes mentioned in paragraph 3.

5. Processing of traffic data, in accordance with paragraphs 1, 2, 3 and 4, must be restricted to persons acting under the authority of providers of the public communications networks and publicly available electronic communications services handling billing or traffic management, customer enquiries, fraud detection, marketing electronic communications services or providing a value added service, and must be restricted to what is necessary for the purposes of such activities.

6. Paragraphs 1, 2, 3 and 5 shall apply without prejudice to the possibility for competent bodies to be informed of traffic data in conformity with applicable legislation with a view to settling disputes, in particular interconnection or billing disputes.

[1566]

Article 7

Itemised billing

1. Subscribers shall have the right to receive non-itemised bills.

2. Member States shall apply national provisions in order to reconcile the rights of subscribers receiving itemised bills with the right to privacy of calling users and called subscribers, for example by ensuring that sufficient alternative privacy enhancing methods of communications or payments are available to such users and subscribers.

[1567]

Article 8

Presentation and restriction of calling and connected line identification

1. Where presentation of calling line identification is offered, the service provider must offer the calling user the possibility, using a simple means and free of charge, of preventing the presentation of the calling line identification on a per-call basis. The calling subscriber must have this possibility on a per-line basis.

2. Where presentation of calling line identification is offered, the service provider must offer the called subscriber the possibility, using a simple means and free of charge for reasonable use of this function, of preventing the presentation of the calling line identification of incoming calls.

3. Where presentation of calling line identification is offered and where the calling line identification is presented prior to the call being established, the service provider must offer the called subscriber the possibility, using a simple means, of rejecting incoming calls where the presentation of the calling line identification has been prevented by the calling user or subscriber.

4. Where presentation of connected line identification is offered, the service provider must offer the called subscriber the possibility, using a simple means and free of charge, of preventing the presentation of the connected line identification to the calling user.

5. Paragraph 1 shall also apply with regard to calls to third countries originating in the Community. Paragraphs 2, 3 and 4 shall also apply to incoming calls originating in third countries.

6. Member States shall ensure that where presentation of calling and/or connected line identification is offered, the providers of publicly available electronic communications services inform the public thereof and of the possibilities set out in paragraphs 1, 2, 3 and 4.

[1568]

Article 9

Location data other than traffic data

1. Where location data other than traffic data, relating to users or subscribers of public communications networks or publicly available electronic communications services, can be processed, such data may only be processed when they are made anonymous, or with the consent of the users or subscribers to the extent and for the duration necessary for the provision of a value added service. The service provider must inform the users or subscribers, prior to obtaining their consent, of the type of location data other than traffic data which will be processed, of the purposes and duration of the processing and whether the data will be transmitted to a third party for the purpose of providing the value added service. Users or subscribers shall be given the possibility to withdraw their consent for the processing of location data other than traffic data at any time.

2. Where consent of the users or subscribers has been obtained for the processing of location data other than traffic data, the user or subscriber must continue to have the possibility, using a simple means and free of charge, of temporarily refusing the processing of such data for each connection to the network or for each transmission of a communication.

3. Processing of location data other than traffic data in accordance with paragraphs 1 and 2 must be restricted to persons acting under the authority of the provider of the public communications network or publicly available communications service or of the third party providing the value added service, and must be restricted to what is necessary for the purposes of providing the value added service.

[1569]

Article 10

Exceptions

Member States shall ensure that there are transparent procedures governing the way in which a provider of a public communications network and/or a publicly available electronic communications service may override—

(a) the elimination of the presentation of calling line identification, on a temporary basis, upon application of a subscriber requesting the tracing of malicious or nuisance calls. In this case, in accordance with national law, the data containing the identification of the calling subscriber will be stored and be made available by the provider of a public communications network and/or publicly available electronic communications service;

(b) the elimination of the presentation of calling line identification and the temporary denial or absence of consent of a subscriber or user for the processing of location data, on a per-line basis for organisations dealing with emergency calls and recognised as such by a Member State, including law enforcement agencies, ambulance services and fire brigades, for the purpose of responding to such calls.

[1570]

Article 11

Automatic call forwarding

Member States shall ensure that any subscriber has the possibility, using a simple means and free of charge, of stopping automatic call forwarding by a third party to the subscriber's terminal.

[1571]

Article 12

Directories of subscribers

1. Member States shall ensure that subscribers are informed, free of charge and before they are included in the directory, about the purpose(s) of a printed or electronic directory of subscribers available to the public or obtainable through directory enquiry services, in which their personal data can be included and of any further usage possibilities based on search functions embedded in electronic versions of the directory.

2. Member States shall ensure that subscribers are given the opportunity to determine whether their personal data are included in a public directory, and if so, which, to the extent that such data are relevant for the purpose of the directory as determined by the provider of the directory, and to verify, correct or withdraw such data. Not being included in a public subscriber directory, verifying, correcting or withdrawing personal data from it shall be free of charge.

3. Member States may require that for any purpose of a public directory other than the search of contact details of persons on the basis of their name and, where necessary, a minimum of other identifiers, additional consent be asked of the subscribers.

4. Paragraphs 1 and 2 shall apply to subscribers who are natural persons. Member States shall also ensure, in the framework of Community law and applicable national legislation, that the legitimate interests of subscribers other than natural persons with regard to their entry in public directories are sufficiently protected.

[1572]

Article 13

Unsolicited communications

1. The use of automated calling systems without human intervention (automatic calling machines), facsimile machines (fax) or electronic mail for the purposes of direct marketing may only be allowed in respect of subscribers who have given their prior consent.

2. Notwithstanding paragraph 1, where a natural or legal person obtains from its customers their electronic contact details for electronic mail, in the context of the sale of a product or a service, in accordance with Directive 95/46/EC, the same natural or legal person may use these electronic contact details for direct marketing of its own similar products or services provided that customers clearly and distinctly are given the opportunity to object, free of charge and in an easy manner, to such use of electronic contact details when they are collected and on the occasion of each message in case the customer has not initially refused such use.

3. Member States shall take appropriate measures to ensure that, free of charge, unsolicited communications for purposes of direct marketing, in cases other than those referred to in paragraphs 1 and 2, are not allowed either without the consent of the subscribers concerned or in respect of subscribers who do not wish to receive these communications, the choice between these options to be determined by national legislation.

4. In any event, the practice of sending electronic mail for purposes of direct marketing disguising or concealing the identity of the sender on whose behalf the communication is made, or without a valid address to which the recipient may send a request that such communications cease, shall be prohibited.

5. Paragraphs 1 and 3 shall apply to subscribers who are natural persons. Member States shall also ensure, in the framework of Community law and applicable national legislation, that the legitimate interests of subscribers other than natural persons with regard to unsolicited communications are sufficiently protected.

[1573]

Article 14

Technical features and standardisation

1. In implementing the provisions of this Directive, Member States shall ensure, subject to paragraphs 2 and 3, that no mandatory requirements for specific technical features are imposed on terminal or other electronic communication equipment which could impede the placing of equipment on the market and the free circulation of such equipment in and between Member States.

2. Where provisions of this Directive can be implemented only by requiring specific technical features in electronic communications networks, Member States shall inform the Commission in accordance with the procedure provided for by Directive 98/34/EC of the European Parliament and of the Council of 22 June 1998 laying down a procedure for the provision of information in the field of technical standards and regulations and of rules on information society services.[1]

3. Where required, measures may be adopted to ensure that terminal equipment is constructed in a way that is compatible with the right of users to protect and control the use of their personal data, in accordance with Directive 1999/5/EC and Council Decision 87/95/EEC of 22 December 1986 on standardisation in the field of information technology and communications.[2]

[1574]

NOTES

[1] OJ L204, 21.7.1998, p 37. Directive as amended by Directive 98/48/EC (OJ L217, 5.8.1998, p 18).

[2] OJ L36, 7.2.1987, p 31. Decision as last amended by the 1994 Act of Accession.

Article 15

Application of certain provisions of Directive 95/46/EC

1. Member States may adopt legislative measures to restrict the scope of the rights and obligations provided for in Article 5, Article 6, Article 8(1), (2), (3) and (4), and Article 9 of this Directive when such restriction constitutes a necessary, appropriate and proportionate measure within a democratic society to safeguard national security (ie State security), defence, public security, and the prevention, investigation, detection and prosecution of criminal offences or of unauthorised use of the electronic communication system, as referred to in Article 13(1) of Directive 95/46/EC. To this end, Member States may, *inter alia*, adopt legislative measures providing for the retention of data for a limited period justified on the grounds laid down in this paragraph. All the measures referred to in this paragraph shall be in accordance with the general principles of Community law, including those referred to in Article 6(1) and (2) of the Treaty on European Union.

[1a. Paragraph 1 shall not apply to data specifically required by Directive 2006/24/EC of the European Parliament and of the Council of 15 March 2006 on the retention of data generated or processed in connection with the provision of publicly available electronic communications services or of public communications networks[1] to be retained for the purposes referred to in Article 1(1) of that Directive.]

2. The provisions of Chapter III on judicial remedies, liability and sanctions of Directive 95/46/EC shall apply with regard to national provisions adopted pursuant to this Directive and with regard to the individual rights derived from this Directive.

3. The Working Party on the Protection of Individuals with regard to the Processing of Personal Data instituted by Article 29 of Directive 95/46/EC shall also carry out the tasks laid down in Article 30 of that Directive with regard to matters covered by this Directive, namely the protection of fundamental rights and freedoms and of legitimate interests in the electronic communications sector.

[1575]

NOTES

Para 1a: inserted by European Parliament and Council Directive 2006/24/EC, Art 11.

[1] OJ L105, 13.4.2006, p 54.

Article 16

Transitional arrangements

1. Article 12 shall not apply to editions of directories already produced or placed on the market in printed or off-line electronic form before the national provisions adopted pursuant to this Directive enter into force.

2. Where the personal data of subscribers to fixed or mobile public voice telephony services have been included in a public subscriber directory in conformity with the provisions of Directive 95/46/EC and of Article 11 of Directive 97/66/EC before the national provisions adopted in pursuance of this Directive enter into force, the personal data of such subscribers may remain included in this public directory in its printed or electronic versions, including versions with reverse search functions, unless subscribers indicate otherwise, after having received complete information about purposes and options in accordance with Article 12 of this Directive.

[1576]

Article 17

Transposition

1. Before 31 October 2003 Member States shall bring into force the provisions necessary to comply with this Directive. They shall forthwith inform the Commission thereof.

When Member States adopt those provisions, they shall contain a reference to this Directive or be accompanied by such a reference on the occasion of their official publication. The methods of making such reference shall be laid down by the Member States.

2. Member States shall communicate to the Commission the text of the provisions of national law which they adopt in the field governed by this Directive and of any subsequent amendments to those provisions.

[1577]

Article 18

Review

The Commission shall submit to the European Parliament and the Council, not later than three years after the date referred to in Article 17(1), a report on the application of this Directive and its impact on economic operators and consumers, in particular as regards the provisions on unsolicited communications, taking into account the international environment. For this purpose, the Commission may request information from the Member States, which shall be supplied without undue delay. Where appropriate, the Commission shall submit proposals to amend this Directive, taking account of the results of that report, any changes in the sector and any other proposal it may deem necessary in order to improve the effectiveness of this Directive.

[1578]

Article 19

Repeal

Directive 97/66/EC is hereby repealed with effect from the date referred to in Article 17(1).

References made to the repealed Directive shall be construed as being made to this Directive.

[1579]

Article 20

Entry into force

This Directive shall enter into force on the day of its publication in the *Official Journal of the European Communities*.

[1580]

Article 21

Addressees

This Directive is addressed to the Member States.

[1581]

Done at Brussels, 12 July 2002.

DIRECTIVE OF THE EUROPEAN PARLIAMENT AND OF THE COUNCIL

of 15 March 2006

on the retention of data generated or processed in connection with the provision of publicly available electronic communications services or of public communications networks and amending Directive 2002/58/EC

(2006/24/EC)

NOTES

Date of publication in OJ: OJ L105, 13.4.2006, p 54.

THE EUROPEAN PARLIAMENT AND THE COUNCIL OF THE EUROPEAN UNION,

Having regard to the Treaty establishing the European Community, and in particular Article 95 thereof,

Having regard to the proposal from the Commission,

Having regard to the Opinion of the European Economic and Social Committee[1],

Acting in accordance with the procedure laid down in Article 251 of the Treaty[2],

Whereas:

(1) Directive 95/46/EC of the European Parliament and of the Council of 24 October 1995 on the protection of individuals with regard to the processing of personal data and on the free movement of such data[3] requires Member States to protect the rights and freedoms of natural persons with regard to the processing of personal data, and in particular their right to privacy, in order to ensure the free flow of personal data in the Community.

(2) Directive 2002/58/EC of the European Parliament and of the Council of 12 July 2002 concerning the processing of personal data and the protection of privacy in the electronic communications sector (Directive on privacy and electronic communications)[4] translates the principles set out in Directive 95/46/EC into specific rules for the electronic communications sector.

(3) Articles 5, 6 and 9 of Directive 2002/58/EC lay down the rules applicable to the processing by network and service providers of traffic and location data generated by using electronic communications services. Such data must be erased or made anonymous when no longer needed for the purpose of the transmission of a communication, except for the data necessary for billing or interconnection payments. Subject to consent, certain data may also be processed for marketing purposes and the provision of value-added services.

(4) Article 15(1) of Directive 2002/58/EC sets out the conditions under which Member States may restrict the scope of the rights and obligations provided for in Article 5, Article 6, Article 8(1), (2), (3) and (4), and Article 9 of that Directive. Any such restrictions must be necessary, appropriate and proportionate within a democratic society for specific public order purposes, i.e. to safeguard national security (i.e. State security), defence, public security or the prevention, investigation, detection and prosecution of criminal offences or of unauthorised use of the electronic communications systems.

(5) Several Member States have adopted legislation providing for the retention of data by service providers for the prevention, investigation, detection, and prosecution of criminal offences. Those national provisions vary considerably.

(6) The legal and technical differences between national provisions concerning the retention of data for the purpose of prevention, investigation, detection and prosecution of criminal offences present obstacles to the internal market for electronic communications, since service providers are faced with different requirements regarding the types of traffic and location data to be retained and the conditions and periods of retention.

(7) The Conclusions of the Justice and Home Affairs Council of 19 December 2002 underline that, because of the significant growth in the possibilities afforded by electronic communications, data relating to the use of electronic communications are particularly important and therefore a valuable tool in the prevention, investigation, detection and prosecution of criminal offences, in particular organised crime.

(8) The Declaration on Combating Terrorism adopted by the European Council on 25 March 2004 instructed the Council to examine measures for establishing rules on the retention of communications traffic data by service providers.

PART II
DATA PROTECTION

(9) Under Article 8 of the European Convention for the Protection of Human Rights and Fundamental Freedoms (ECHR), everyone has the right to respect for his private life and his correspondence. Public authorities may interfere with the exercise of that right only in accordance with the law and where necessary in a democratic society, inter alia, in the interests of national security or public safety, for the prevention of disorder or crime, or for the protection of the rights and freedoms of others. Because retention of data has proved to be such a necessary and effective investigative tool for law enforcement in several Member States, and in particular concerning serious matters such as organised crime and terrorism, it is necessary to ensure that retained data are made available to law enforcement authorities for a certain period, subject to the conditions provided for in this Directive. The adoption of an instrument on data retention that complies with the requirements of Article 8 of the ECHR is therefore a necessary measure.

(10) On 13 July 2005, the Council reaffirmed in its declaration condemning the terrorist attacks on London the need to adopt common measures on the retention of telecommunications data as soon as possible.

(11) Given the importance of traffic and location data for the investigation, detection, and prosecution of criminal offences, as demonstrated by research and the practical experience of several Member States, there is a need to ensure at European level that data that are generated or processed, in the course of the supply of communications services, by providers of publicly available electronic communications services or of a public communications network are retained for a certain period, subject to the conditions provided for in this Directive.

(12) Article 15(1) of Directive 2002/58/EC continues to apply to data, including data relating to unsuccessful call attempts, the retention of which is not specifically required under this Directive and which therefore fall outside the scope thereof, and to retention for purposes, including judicial purposes, other than those covered by this Directive.

(13) This Directive relates only to data generated or processed as a consequence of a communication or a communication service and does not relate to data that are the content of the information communicated. Data should be retained in such a way as to avoid their being retained more than once. Data generated or processed when supplying the communications services concerned refers to data which are accessible. In particular, as regards the retention of data relating to Internet e-mail and Internet telephony, the obligation to retain data may apply only in respect of data from the providers' or the network providers' own services.

(14) Technologies relating to electronic communications are changing rapidly and the legitimate requirements of the competent authorities may evolve. In order to obtain advice and encourage the sharing of experience of best practice in these matters, the Commission intends to establish a group composed of Member States' law enforcement authorities, associations of the electronic communications industry, representatives of the European Parliament and data protection authorities, including the European Data Protection Supervisor.

(15) Directive 95/46/EC and Directive 2002/58/EC are fully applicable to the data retained in accordance with this Directive. Article 30(1)(c) of Directive 95/46/EC requires the consultation of the Working Party on the Protection of Individuals with regard to the Processing of Personal Data established under Article 29 of that Directive.

(16) The obligations incumbent on service providers concerning measures to ensure data quality, which derive from Article 6 of Directive 95/46/EC, and their obligations concerning measures to ensure confidentiality and security of processing of data, which derive from Articles 16 and 17 of that Directive, apply in full to data being retained within the meaning of this Directive.

(17) It is essential that Member States adopt legislative measures to ensure that data retained under this Directive are provided to the competent national authorities only in accordance with national legislation in full respect of the fundamental rights of the persons concerned.

(18) In this context, Article 24 of Directive 95/46/EC imposes an obligation on Member States to lay down sanctions for infringements of the provisions adopted pursuant to that Directive. Article 15(2) of Directive 2002/58/EC imposes the same requirement in relation to national provisions adopted pursuant to Directive 2002/58/EC. Council Framework Decision 2005/222/JHA of 24 February 2005 on attacks against information systems[5] provides that the intentional illegal access to information systems, including to data retained therein, is to be made punishable as a criminal offence.

(19) The right of any person who has suffered damage as a result of an unlawful processing operation or of any act incompatible with national provisions adopted pursuant to Directive 95/46/EC to receive compensation, which derives from Article 23 of that Directive, applies also in relation to the unlawful processing of any personal data pursuant to this Directive.

(20) The 2001 Council of Europe Convention on Cybercrime and the 1981 Council of Europe Convention for the Protection of Individuals with Regard to Automatic Processing of Personal Data also cover data being retained within the meaning of this Directive.

(21) Since the objectives of this Directive, namely to harmonise the obligations on providers to retain certain data and to ensure that those data are available for the purpose of the investigation, detection and prosecution of serious crime, as defined by each Member State in its national law, cannot be sufficiently achieved by the Member States and can therefore, by reason of the scale and effects of this Directive, be better achieved at Community level, the Community may adopt measures, in accordance with the principle of subsidiarity as set out in Article 5 of the Treaty. In accordance with the principle of proportionality, as set out in that Article, this Directive does not go beyond what is necessary in order to achieve those objectives.

(22) This Directive respects the fundamental rights and observes the principles recognised, in particular, by the Charter of Fundamental Rights of the European Union. In particular, this Directive, together with Directive 2002/58/EC, seeks to ensure full compliance with citizens' fundamental rights to respect for private life and communications and to the protection of their personal data, as enshrined in Articles 7 and 8 of the Charter.

(23) Given that the obligations on providers of electronic communications services should be proportionate, this Directive requires that they retain only such data as are generated or processed in the process of supplying their communications services. To the extent that such data are not generated or processed by those providers, there is no obligation to retain them. This Directive is not intended to harmonise the technology for retaining data, the choice of which is a matter to be resolved at national level.

(24) In accordance with paragraph 34 of the Interinstitutional agreement on better law-making[6], Member States are encouraged to draw up, for themselves and in the interests of the Community, their own tables illustrating, as far as possible, the correlation between this Directive and the transposition measures, and to make them public.

(25) This Directive is without prejudice to the power of Member States to adopt legislative measures concerning the right of access to, and use of, data by national authorities, as designated by them. Issues of access to data retained pursuant to this Directive by national authorities for such activities as are referred to in the first indent of Article 3(2) of Directive 95/46/EC fall outside the scope of Community law. However, they may be subject to national law or action pursuant to Title VI of the Treaty on European Union. Such laws or action must fully respect fundamental rights as they result from the common constitutional traditions of the Member States and as guaranteed by the ECHR. Under Article 8 of the ECHR, as interpreted by the European Court of Human Rights, interference by public authorities with privacy rights must meet the requirements of necessity and proportionality and must therefore serve specified, explicit and legitimate purposes and be exercised in a manner that is adequate, relevant and not excessive in relation to the purpose of the interference,

NOTES

1 Opinion delivered on 19 January 2006 (not yet published in the Official Journal).

2 Opinion of the European Parliament of 14 December 2005 (not yet published in the Official Journal) and Council Decision of 21 February 2006.

3 OJ L 281, 23.11.1995, p 31. Directive as amended by Regulation (EC) No 1882/2003 (OJ L 284, 31.10.2003, p 1).

4 OJ L 201, 31.7.2002, p 37.

5 OJ L 69, 16.3.2005, p 67.

6 OJ C 321, 31.12.2003, p 1.

HAS ADOPTED THIS DIRECTIVE—

Article 1

Subject matter and scope

1. This Directive aims to harmonise Member States' provisions concerning the obligations of the providers of publicly available electronic communications services or of public communications networks with respect to the retention of certain data which are generated or processed by them, in order to ensure that the data are available for the purpose of the investigation, detection and prosecution of serious crime, as defined by each Member State in its national law.

2. This Directive shall apply to traffic and location data on both legal entities and natural persons and to the related data necessary to identify the subscriber or registered user. It shall not apply to the content of electronic communications, including information consulted using an electronic communications network.

[1582]

Article 2

Definitions

1. For the purpose of this Directive, the definitions in Directive 95/46/EC, in Directive 2002/21/EC of the European Parliament and of the Council of 7 March 2002 on a common regulatory framework for electronic communications networks and services (Framework Directive) [1], and in Directive 2002/58/EC shall apply.

2. For the purpose of this Directive:

(a) "data" means traffic data and location data and the related data necessary to identify the subscriber or user;

(b) "user" means any legal entity or natural person using a publicly available electronic communications service, for private or business purposes, without necessarily having subscribed to that service;

(c) "telephone service" means calls (including voice, voicemail and conference and data calls), supplementary services (including call forwarding and call transfer) and messaging and multi-media services (including short message services, enhanced media services and multi-media services);

(d) "user ID" means a unique identifier allocated to persons when they subscribe to or register with an Internet access service or Internet communications service;

(e) "cell ID" means the identity of the cell from which a mobile telephony call originated or in which it terminated;

(f) "unsuccessful call attempt" means a communication where a telephone call has been successfully connected but not answered or there has been a network management intervention.

[1583]

NOTES

[1] OJ L 108, 24.4.2002, p 33.

Article 3

Obligation to retain data

1. By way of derogation from Articles 5, 6 and 9 of Directive 2002/58/EC, Member States shall adopt measures to ensure that the data specified in Article 5 of this Directive are retained in accordance with the provisions thereof, to the extent that those data are generated or processed by providers of publicly available electronic communications services or of a public communications network within their jurisdiction in the process of supplying the communications services concerned.

2. The obligation to retain data provided for in paragraph 1 shall include the retention of the data specified in Article 5 relating to unsuccessful call attempts where those data are generated or processed, and stored (as regards telephony data) or logged (as regards Internet data), by providers of publicly available electronic communications services or of a public communications network within the jurisdiction of the Member State concerned in the process of supplying the communication services concerned. This Directive shall not require data relating to unconnected calls to be retained.

[1584]

Article 4

Access to data

Member States shall adopt measures to ensure that data retained in accordance with this Directive are provided only to the competent national authorities in specific cases and in accordance with national law. The procedures to be followed and the conditions to be fulfilled in order to gain access to retained data in accordance with necessity and proportionality requirements shall be defined by each Member State in its national law, subject to the relevant provisions of European Union law or public international law, and in particular the ECHR as interpreted by the European Court of Human Rights.

[1585]

Article 5

Categories of data to be retained

1. Member States shall ensure that the following categories of data are retained under this Directive:
   - (a) data necessary to trace and identify the source of a communication:
     - (1) concerning fixed network telephony and mobile telephony:
       - (i) the calling telephone number;
       - (ii) the name and address of the subscriber or registered user;
     - (2) concerning Internet access, Internet e-mail and Internet telephony:
       - (i) the user ID(s) allocated;
       - (ii) the user ID and telephone number allocated to any communication entering the public telephone network;
       - (iii) the name and address of the subscriber or registered user to whom an Internet Protocol (IP) address, user ID or telephone number was allocated at the time of the communication;
   - (b) data necessary to identify the destination of a communication:
     - (1) concerning fixed network telephony and mobile telephony:
       - (i) the number(s) dialled (the telephone number(s) called), and, in cases involving supplementary services such as call forwarding or call transfer, the number or numbers to which the call is routed;
       - (ii) the name(s) and address(es) of the subscriber(s) or registered user(s);
     - (2) concerning Internet e-mail and Internet telephony:
       - (i) the user ID or telephone number of the intended recipient(s) of an Internet telephony call;
       - (ii) the name(s) and address(es) of the subscriber(s) or registered user(s) and user ID of the intended recipient of the communication;
   - (c) data necessary to identify the date, time and duration of a communication:
     - (1) concerning fixed network telephony and mobile telephony, the date and time of the start and end of the communication;
     - (2) concerning Internet access, Internet e-mail and Internet telephony:
       - (i) the date and time of the log-in and log-off of the Internet access service, based on a certain time zone, together with the IP address, whether dynamic or static, allocated by the Internet access service provider to a communication, and the user ID of the subscriber or registered user;
       - (ii) the date and time of the log-in and log-off of the Internet e-mail service or Internet telephony service, based on a certain time zone;
   - (d) data necessary to identify the type of communication:
     - (1) concerning fixed network telephony and mobile telephony: the telephone service used;
     - (2) concerning Internet e-mail and Internet telephony: the Internet service used;
   - (e) data necessary to identify users' communication equipment or what purports to be their equipment:
     - (1) concerning fixed network telephony, the calling and called telephone numbers;
     - (2) concerning mobile telephony:
       - (i) the calling and called telephone numbers;
       - (ii) the International Mobile Subscriber Identity (IMSI) of the calling party;
       - (iii) the International Mobile Equipment Identity (IMEI) of the calling party;
       - (iv) the IMSI of the called party;
       - (v) the IMEI of the called party;
       - (vi) in the case of pre-paid anonymous services, the date and time of the initial activation of the service and the location label (Cell ID) from which the service was activated;
     - (3) concerning Internet access, Internet e-mail and Internet telephony:
       - (i) the calling telephone number for dial-up access;

PART II DATA PROTECTION

(ii) the digital subscriber line (DSL) or other end point of the originator of the communication;

(f) data necessary to identify the location of mobile communication equipment:
(1) the location label (Cell ID) at the start of the communication;
(2) data identifying the geographic location of cells by reference to their location labels (Cell ID) during the period for which communications data are retained.

2. No data revealing the content of the communication may be retained pursuant to this Directive.

[1586]

Article 6

Periods of retention

Member States shall ensure that the categories of data specified in Article 5 are retained for periods of not less than six months and not more than two years from the date of the communication.

[1587]

Article 7

Data protection and data security

Without prejudice to the provisions adopted pursuant to Directive 95/46/EC and Directive 2002/58/EC, each Member State shall ensure that providers of publicly available electronic communications services or of a public communications network respect, as a minimum, the following data security principles with respect to data retained in accordance with this Directive:

(a) the retained data shall be of the same quality and subject to the same security and protection as those data on the network;

(b) the data shall be subject to appropriate technical and organisational measures to protect the data against accidental or unlawful destruction, accidental loss or alteration, or unauthorised or unlawful storage, processing, access or disclosure;

(c) the data shall be subject to appropriate technical and organisational measures to ensure that they can be accessed by specially authorised personnel only;

and

(d) the data, except those that have been accessed and preserved, shall be destroyed at the end of the period of retention.

[1588]

Article 8

Storage requirements for retained data

Member States shall ensure that the data specified in Article 5 are retained in accordance with this Directive in such a way that the data retained and any other necessary information relating to such data can be transmitted upon request to the competent authorities without undue delay.

[1589]

Article 9

Supervisory authority

1. Each Member State shall designate one or more public authorities to be responsible for monitoring the application within its territory of the provisions adopted by the Member States pursuant to Article 7 regarding the security of the stored data. Those authorities may be the same authorities as those referred to in Article 28 of Directive 95/46/EC.

2. The authorities referred to in paragraph 1 shall act with complete independence in carrying out the monitoring referred to in that paragraph.

[1590]

Article 10

Statistics

1. Member States shall ensure that the Commission is provided on a yearly basis with statistics on the retention of data generated or processed in connection with the provision of publicly available electronic communications services or a public communications network. Such statistics shall include:

— the cases in which information was provided to the competent authorities in accordance with applicable national law,

— the time elapsed between the date on which the data were retained and the date on which the competent authority requested the transmission of the data,

— the cases where requests for data could not be met.

2. Such statistics shall not contain personal data.

[1591]

Article 11

(*Amends Directive 2002/58/EC, Art 15 at* **[1575]**.)

Article 12

Future measures

1. A Member State facing particular circumstances that warrant an extension for a limited period of the maximum retention period referred to in Article 6 may take the necessary measures. That Member State shall immediately notify the Commission and inform the other Member States of the measures taken under this Article and shall state the grounds for introducing them.

2. The Commission shall, within a period of six months after the notification referred to in paragraph 1, approve or reject the national measures concerned, after having examined whether they are a means of arbitrary discrimination or a disguised restriction of trade between Member States and whether they constitute an obstacle to the functioning of the internal market. In the absence of a decision by the Commission within that period the national measures shall be deemed to have been approved.

3. Where, pursuant to paragraph 2, the national measures of a Member State derogating from the provisions of this Directive are approved, the Commission may consider whether to propose an amendment to this Directive.

[1592]

Article 13

Remedies, liability and penalties

1. Each Member State shall take the necessary measures to ensure that the national measures implementing Chapter III of Directive 95/46/EC providing for judicial remedies, liability and sanctions are fully implemented with respect to the processing of data under this Directive.

2. Each Member State shall, in particular, take the necessary measures to ensure that any intentional access to, or transfer of, data retained in accordance with this Directive that is not permitted under national law adopted pursuant to this Directive is punishable by penalties, including administrative or criminal penalties, that are effective, proportionate and dissuasive.

[1593]

Article 14

Evaluation

1. No later than 15 September 2010, the Commission shall submit to the European Parliament and the Council an evaluation of the application of this Directive and its impact on economic operators and consumers, taking into account further developments in electronic communications technology and the statistics provided to the Commission pursuant to Article 10 with a view to determining whether it is necessary to amend the provisions of this Directive, in particular with regard to the list of data in Article 5 and the periods of retention provided for in Article 6. The results of the evaluation shall be made public.

2. To that end, the Commission shall examine all observations communicated to it by the Member States or by the Working Party established under Article 29 of Directive 95/46/EC. **[1594]**

Article 15

Transposition

1. Member States shall bring into force the laws, regulations and administrative provisions necessary to comply with this Directive by no later than 15 September 2007. They shall forthwith inform the Commission thereof. When Member States adopt those measures, they shall contain a reference to this Directive or shall be accompanied by such reference on the occasion of their official publication. The methods of making such reference shall be laid down by Member States.

2. Member States shall communicate to the Commission the text of the main provisions of national law which they adopt in the field covered by this Directive.

3. Until 15 March 2009, each Member State may postpone application of this Directive to the retention of communications data relating to Internet Access, Internet telephony and Internet e-mail. Any Member State that intends to make use of this paragraph shall, upon adoption of this Directive, notify the Council and the Commission to that effect by way of a declaration. The declaration shall be published in the Official Journal of the European Union. **[1595]**

Article 16

Entry into force

This Directive shall enter into force on the twentieth day following that of its publication in the Official Journal of the European Union.

[1596]

Article 17

Addressees

This Directive is addressed to the Member States.

[1597]

Done at Strasbourg, 15 March 2006.

DECLARATION BY THE NETHERLANDS
PURSUANT TO ARTICLE 15(3) OF DIRECTIVE 2006/24/EC

Regarding the Directive of the European Parliament and of the Council on the retention of data processed in connection with the provision of publicly available electronic communications services and amending Directive 2002/58/EC, the Netherlands will be making use of the option of postponing application of the Directive to the retention of communications data relating to Internet access, Internet telephony and Internet e-mail, for a period not exceeding 18 months following the date of entry into force of the Directive.

DECLARATION BY AUSTRIA
PURSUANT TO ARTICLE 15(3) OF DIRECTIVE 2006/24/EC

Austria declares that it will be postponing application of this Directive to the retention of communications data relating to Internet access, Internet telephony and Internet e-mail, for a period of 18 months following the date specified in Article 15(1).

DECLARATION BY ESTONIA
PURSUANT TO ARTICLE 15(3) OF DIRECTIVE 2006/24/EC

In accordance with Article 15(3) of the Directive of the European Parliament and of the Council on the retention of data generated or processed in connection with the provision of publicly available electronic communications services or of public communications networks and amending Directive 2002/58/EC, Estonia hereby states its intention to make use of use that paragraph and to postpone application of the Directive to retention of communications data relating to Internet access, Internet telephony and Internet e-mail until 36 months after the date of adoption of the Directive.

DECLARATION BY THE UNITED KINGDOM PURSUANT TO ARTICLE 15(3) OF DIRECTIVE 2006/24/EC

The United Kingdom declares in accordance with Article 15(3) of the Directive on the retention of data generated or processed in connection with the provision of publicly available electronic communications services or of public communications networks and amending Directive 2002/58/EC that it will postpone application of that Directive to the retention of communications data relating to Internet access, Internet telephony and Internet e-mail.

DECLARATION BY THE REPUBLIC OF CYPRUS PURSUANT TO ARTICLE 15(3) OF DIRECTIVE 2006/24/EC

The Republic of Cyprus declares that it is postponing application of the Directive in respect of the retention of communications data relating to Internet access, Internet telephony and Internet e-mail until the date fixed in Article 15(3).

DECLARATION BY THE HELLENIC REPUBLIC PURSUANT TO ARTICLE 15(3) OF DIRECTIVE 2006/24/EC

Greece declares that, pursuant to Article 15(3), it will postpone application of this Directive in respect of the retention of communications data relating to Internet access, Internet telephony and Internet e-mail until 18 months after expiry of the period provided for in Article 15(1).

DECLARATION BY THE GRAND DUCHY OF LUXEMBOURG PURSUANT TO ARTICLE 15(3) OF DIRECTIVE 2006/24/EC

Pursuant to Article 15(3) of the Directive of the European Parliament and of the Council on the retention of data generated or processed in connection with the provision of publicly available electronic communications services or of public communications networks and amending Directive 2002/58/EC, the Government of the Grand Duchy of Luxembourg declares that it intends to make use of Article 15(3) of the Directive in order to have the option of postponing application of the Directive to the retention of communications data relating to Internet access, Internet telephony and Internet e-mail.

DECLARATION BY SLOVENIA PURSUANT TO ARTICLE 15(3) OF DIRECTIVE 2006/24/EC

Slovenia is joining the group of Member States which have made a declaration under Article 15(3) of the Directive of the European Parliament and the Council on the retention of data generated or processed in connection with the provision of publicly available electronic communications services or of public communications networks, for the 18 months postponement of the application of the Directive to the retention of communication data relating to Internet, Internet telephony and Internet e-mail.

DECLARATION BY SWEDEN PURSUANT TO ARTICLE 15(3) OF DIRECTIVE 2006/24/EC

Pursuant to Article 15(3), Sweden wishes to have the option of postponing application of this Directive to the retention of communications data relating to Internet access, Internet telephony and Internet e-mail.

DECLARATION BY THE REPUBLIC OF LITHUANIA PURSUANT TO ARTICLE 15(3) OF DIRECTIVE 2006/24/EC

Pursuant to Article 15(3) of the draft Directive of the European Parliament and of the Council on the retention of data generated or processed in connection with the provision of publicly available electronic communications services or public communications networks and amending Directive 2002/58/EC (hereafter the "Directive"), the Republic of Lithuania declares that once the Directive has been adopted it will postpone the application thereof to the retention of communications data relating to Internet access, Internet telephony and Internet e-mail for the period provided for in Article 15(3).

DECLARATION BY THE REPUBLIC OF LATVIA PURSUANT TO ARTICLE 15(3) OF DIRECTIVE 2006/24/EC

Latvia states in accordance with Article 15(3) of Directive 2006/24/EC of 15 March 2006 on the retention of data generated or processed in connection with the provision of publicly available electronic communications services or of public communications networks and amending Directive 2002/58/EC that it is postponing application of the Directive to the retention of communications data relating to Internet access, Internet telephony and Internet e-mail until 15 March 2009.

DECLARATION BY THE CZECH REPUBLIC
PURSUANT TO ARTICLE 15(3) OF DIRECTIVE 2006/24/EC

Pursuant to Article 15(3), the Czech Republic hereby declares that it is postponing application of this Directive to the retention of communications data relating to Internet access, Internet telephony and Internet e-mail until 36 months after the date of adoption thereof.

DECLARATION BY BELGIUM
PURSUANT TO ARTICLE 15(3) OF DIRECTIVE 2006/24/EC

Belgium declares that, taking up the option available under Article 15(3), it will postpone application of this Directive, for a period of 36 months after its adoption, to the retention of communications data relating to Internet access, Internet telephony and Internet e-mail.

DECLARATION BY THE REPUBLIC OF POLAND
PURSUANT TO ARTICLE 15(3) OF DIRECTIVE 2006/24/EC

Poland hereby declares that it intends to make use of the option provided for under Article 15(3) of the Directive of the European Parliament and of the Council on the retention of data processed in connection with the provision of publicly available electronic communications services and amending Directive 2002/58/EC and postpone application of the Directive to the retention of communications data relating to Internet access, Internet telephony and Internet e-mail for a period of 18 months following the date specified in Article 15(1).

DECLARATION BY FINLAND
PURSUANT TO ARTICLE 15(3) OF DIRECTIVE 2006/24/EC

Finland declares in accordance with Article 15(3) of the Directive on the retention of data generated or processed in connection with the provision of publicly available electronic communications services or of public communications networks and amending Directive 2002/58/EC that it will postpone application of that Directive to the retention of communications data relating to Internet access, Internet telephony and Internet e-mail.

DECLARATION BY GERMANY
PURSUANT TO ARTICLE 15(3) OF DIRECTIVE 2006/24/EC

Germany reserves the right to postpone application of this Directive to the retention of communications data relating to Internet access, Internet telephony and Internet e-mail for a period of 18 months following the date specified in the first sentence of Article 15(1).

[1598]–[2000]

PART III
INTERNET AND DOMAIN NAMES

PART III
INTERNET AND DOMAIN NAMES

TELEVISION LICENCES (DISCLOSURE OF INFORMATION) ACT 2000 (PRESCRIPTION OF INFORMATION) ORDER 2000

(SI 2000/1955)

NOTES

Made: 21 July 2000.
Authority: Television Licences (Disclosure of Information) Act 2000, s 1(3), (4).
Commencement: 1 August 2000.

1 Citation and commencement

This Order may be cited as the Television Licences (Disclosure of Information) Act 2000 (Prescription of Information) Order 2000 and shall come into force on 1st August 2000.

[2001]

2 Prescription of "social security information"

(1) Information of the description mentioned in paragraph (2) is hereby prescribed, in relation to the Secretary of State and the Department for Social Development ("the Northern Ireland department"), as "social security information" for the purposes of section 1 of the Television Licences (Disclosure of Information) Act 2000 (supply of information to the BBC etc by the Secretary of State and the Northern Ireland department).

(2) The description of information referred to in paragraph (1) is information consisting of—

(a) the name, date of birth, address and national insurance number of an individual aged 74 years or over, and

(b) in a case where such an individual has died, that fact and the date on which he died.

[2002]

EUROPEAN PARLIAMENT AND COUNCIL REGULATION

of 22 April 2002

on the implementation of the .eu Top Level Domain

(733/2002/EC)

(Text with EEA relevance)

NOTES

Date of publication in OJ: OJ L113, 30.4.2002, p 1.

THE EUROPEAN PARLIAMENT AND THE COUNCIL OF THE EUROPEAN UNION,

Having regard to the Treaty establishing the European Community, and in particular Article 156 thereof,

Having regard to the proposal from the Commission,[1]

Having regard to the opinion of the Economic and Social Committee,[2]

Following consultation of the Committee of the Regions,

Acting in accordance with the procedure laid down in Article 251 of the Treaty,[3]

Whereas—

(1) The creation of the .eu Top Level Domain (TLD) is included as one of the targets to accelerate electronic commerce in the e-Europe initiative as endorsed by the European Council at its meeting in Lisbon on 23 and 24 March 2000.

(2) The communication from the Commission to the Council and the European Parliament on the organisation and management of the Internet refers to the creation of the .eu TLD and the Council resolution of 3 October 2000 on the organisation and management of the Internet[4] charges the Commission to encourage the coordination of policies in relation to the management of the Internet.

(3) TLDs are an integral part of the Internet infrastructure. They are an essential element of the global interoperability of the World Wide Web ("WWW" or "the Web"). The connection and presence permitted by the allocation of domain names and the related addresses allow users to locate computers and websites on the Web. TLDs are also an integral part of every Internet e-mail address.

(4) The .eu TLD should promote the use of, and access to, the Internet networks and the virtual market place based on the Internet, in accordance with Article 154(2) of the Treaty, by providing a complementary registration domain to existing country code Top Level Domains (ccTLDs) or global registration in the generic Top Level Domains, and should in consequence increase choice and competition.

(5) The .eu TLD should improve the interoperability of trans-European networks, in accordance with Articles 154 and 155 of the Treaty, by ensuring the availability of .eu name servers in the Community. This will affect the topology and technical infrastructure of the Internet in Europe which will benefit from an additional set of name servers in the Community.

(6) Through the .eu TLD, the Internal market should acquire higher visibility in the virtual market place based on the Internet. The .eu TLD should provide a clearly identified link with the Community, the associated legal framework, and the European market place. It should enable undertakings, organisations and natural persons within the Community to register in a specific domain which will make this link obvious. As such, the .eu TLD will not only be a key building block for electronic commerce in Europe but will also support the objectives of Article 14 of the Treaty.

(7) The .eu TLD can accelerate the benefits of the information society in Europe as a whole, play a role in the integration of future Member States into the European Union, and help combat the risk of digital divide with neighbouring countries. It is therefore to be expected that this Regulation will be extended to the European Economic Area and that amendments may be sought to the existing arrangements between the European Union and European third countries, with a view to accommodating the requirements of the .eu TLD so that entities in those countries may participate in it.

(8) This Regulation is without prejudice to Community law in the field of personal data protection. This Regulation should be implemented in compliance with the principles relating to privacy and the protection of personal data.

(9) Internet management has generally been based on the principles of non-interference, self-management and self-regulation. To the extent possible and without prejudice to Community law, these principles should also apply to the .eu ccTLD. The implementation of the .eu TLD may take into consideration best practices in this regard and could be supported by voluntary guidelines or codes of conduct where appropriate.

(10) The establishment of the .eu TLD should contribute to the promotion of the European Union image on the global information networks and bring an added value to the Internet naming system in addition to the national ccTLDs.

(11) The objective of this Regulation is to establish the conditions of implementation of the .eu TLD, to provide for the designation of a Registry and establish the general policy framework within which the Registry will function. National ccTLDs are not covered by this Regulation.

(12) The Registry is the entity charged with the organisation, administration and management of the .eu TLD, including maintenance of the corresponding databases and the associated public query services, the accreditation of Registrars, the registration of domain names applied for by accredited Registrars, the operation of the TLD name servers and the dissemination of TLD zone files. Public query services associated with the TLD are referred to as "Who is" queries. "Who is"-type databases should be in conformity with Community law on data protection and privacy. Access to these databases provides information on a domain name holder and is an essential tool in boosting user confidence.

(13) After publishing a call for expressions of interest in the *Official Journal of the European Communities*, the Commission should, on the basis of an open, transparent and nondiscriminatory selection procedure, designate a Registry. The Commission should enter into a contract with the selected Registry which should specify the conditions applying to the Registry for the organisation, administration and management of the .eu TLD and which should be limited in time and renewable.

(14) The Commission, acting on behalf of the Community, has requested the delegation of the EU code for the purpose of creating an Internet ccTLD. On 25 September 2000, the Internet Corporation for Assigned Names and Numbers (ICANN) issued a resolution providing that "alpha-2 codes are delegable as ccTLDs only in cases where the ISO 3166 Maintenance Agency, on its exceptional reservation list, has issued a reservation of the code

that covers any application of ISO 3166–1 that needs a coded representation in the name of the country, territory or area involved". Such conditions are met by the EU code which is therefore "delegable" to the Community.

(15) ICANN is at present responsible for coordinating the delegation of codes representing ccTLD to Registries. The Council resolution of 3 October 2000 encourages the implementation of the principles applied to ccTLD Registries adopted by the Governmental Advisory Committee (GAC). The Registry should enter into a contract with ICANN respecting the GAC principles.

(16) The adoption of a public policy addressing speculative and abusive registration of domain names should provide that holders of prior rights recognised or established by national and/or Community law and public bodies will benefit from a specific period of time (a "sunrise period") during which the registration of their domain names is exclusively reserved to such holders of prior rights recognised or established by national and/or Community law and public bodies.

(17) Domain names should not be revoked arbitrarily. A revocation may, however, be obtained in particular should a domain name be manifestly contrary to public order. The revocation policy should nevertheless provide for a timely and efficient mechanism.

(18) Rules should be adopted on the question of *bona vacantia* to address the status of domain names the registration of which is not renewed or which, for example because of succession law, are left without holder.

(19) The new .eu TLD registry should not be empowered to create second-level domains using alpha-2 codes representing countries.

(20) Within the framework established by this Regulation, the public policy rules concerning the implementation and functions of the .eu TLD and the public policy principles on registration, various options including the "first come, first served" method should be considered when registration policy is formulated.

(21) When reference is made to interested parties, provision should be made for consultation encompassing, in particular, public authorities, undertakings, organisations and natural persons. The Registry could establish an advisory body to organise such consultation.

(22) The measures necessary for the implementation of this Regulation, including criteria for the selection procedure of the Registry, the designation of the Registry, as well as the adoption of public policy rules, should be adopted in accordance with Council Decision 1999/468/EC of 28 June 1999 laying down the procedures for the exercise of implementing powers conferred on the Commission.[5]

(23) Since the objective of the proposed action, namely to implement the .eu TLD, cannot be sufficiently achieved by the Member States and can therefore, by reason of the scale and effects of the action, be better achieved at Community level, the Community may adopt measures, in accordance with the principle of subsidiarity as set out in Article 5 of the Treaty. In accordance with the principle of proportionality as set out in that Article, this Regulation does not go beyond what is necessary in order to achieve that objective,

NOTES

1 OJ C96 E, 27.3.2001, p 333.

2 OJ C155, 29.5.2001, p 10.

3 Opinion of the European Parliament of 4 July 2001 (OJ C65 E, 14.3.2002, p 147), Council Common Position of 6 November 2001 (OJ C45 E, 19.2.2002, p 53) and Decision of the European Parliament of 28 February 2002 (not yet published in the Official Journal). Council Decision of 25 March 2002.

4 OJ C293, 14.10.2000, p 3.

5 OJ L184, 17.7.1999, p 23.

HAVE ADOPTED THIS REGULATION—

Article 1

Objective and Scope

1. The objective of this Regulation is to implement the .eu country code Top Level Domain (ccTLD) within the Community. The Regulation sets out the conditions for such implementation, including the designation of a Registry, and establishes the general policy framework within which the Registry will function.

2. This Regulation shall apply without prejudice to arrangements in Member States regarding national ccTLDs.

[2003]

Article 2

Definitions

For the purposes of this Regulation—

(a) "Registry" means the entity entrusted with the organisation, administration and management of the .eu TLD including maintenance of the corresponding databases and the associated public query services, registration of domain names, operation of the Registry of domain names, operation of the Registry TLD name servers and dissemination of TLD zone files;

(b) "Registrar" means a person or entity that, via contract with the Registry, provides domain name registration services to registrants.

[2004]

Article 3

Characteristics of the Registry

1. The Commission shall—

(a) establish, in accordance with the procedure referred to in Article 6(3), the criteria and the procedure for the designation of the Registry;

(b) designate, in accordance with the procedure referred to in Article 6(2), the Registry after publishing a call for expressions of interest in the *Official Journal of the European Communities* and after the procedure for such call has been completed;

(c) enter into, in accordance with the procedure referred to in Article 6(2), a contract which shall specify the conditions according to which the Commission supervises the organisation, administration and management of the .eu TLD by the Registry. The contract between the Commission and the Registry shall be limited in time and renewable.

The Registry may not accept registrations until the registration policy is in place.

2. The Registry shall be a non-profit organisation, formed in accordance with the law of a Member State and having its registered office, central administration and principal place of business within the Community.

3. Having obtained the prior consent of the Commission, the Registry shall enter into the appropriate contract providing for the delegation of the .eu ccTLD code. To this effect the relevant principles adopted by the Governmental Advisory Committee shall be taken into account.

4. The .eu TLD Registry shall not act itself as Registrar.

[2005]

Article 4

Obligations of the Registry

1. The Registry shall observe the rules, policies and procedures laid down in this Regulation and the contracts referred to in Article 3. The Registry shall observe transparent and non-discriminatory procedures.

2. The Registry shall—

(a) organise, administer and manage the .eu TLD in the general interest and on the basis of principles of quality, efficiency, reliability and accessibility;

(b) register domain names in the .eu TLD through any accredited .eu Registrar requested by any—

  (i) undertaking having its registered office, central administration or principal place of business within the Community, or

  (ii) organisation established within the Community without prejudice to the application of national law, or

  (iii) natural person resident within the Community;

(c) impose fees directly related to costs incurred;

(d) implement the extra-judicial settlement of conflicts policy based on recovery of costs and a procedure to resolve promptly disputes between domain name holders regarding rights relating to names including intellectual property rights as well as disputes in relation to individual decisions by the Registry. This policy shall be adopted in accordance with Article 5(1) and take into consideration the recommendations of the World Intellectual Property Organisation. The policy shall provide adequate procedural guarantees for the parties concerned, and shall apply without prejudice to any court proceeding;

(e) adopt procedures for, and carry out, accreditation of .eu Registrars and ensure effective and fair conditions of competition among .eu Registrars;

(f) ensure the integrity of the databases of domain names.

[2006]

Article 5

Policy framework

1. After consulting the Registry and following the procedure referred to in Article 6(3), the Commission shall adopt public policy rules concerning the implementation and functions of the .eu TLD and the public policy principles on registration. Public policy shall include—

(a) an extra-judicial settlement of conflicts policy;

(b) public policy on speculative and abusive registration of domain names including the possibility of registrations of domain names in a phased manner to ensure appropriate temporary opportunities for the holders of prior rights recognised or established by national and/or Community law and for public bodies to register their names;

(c) policy on possible revocation of domain names, including the question of *bona vacantia*;

(d) issues of language and geographical concepts;

(e) treatment of intellectual property and other rights.

2. Within three months of the entry into force of this Regulation, Member States may notify to the Commission and to the other Member States a limited list of broadly-recognised names with regard to geographical and/or geopolitical concepts which affect their political or territorial organisation that may either—

(a) not be registered, or

(b) be registered only under a second level domain according to the public policy rules.

The Commission shall notify to the Registry without delay the list of notified names to which such criteria apply. The Commission shall publish the list at the same time as it notifies the Registry.

Where a Member State or the Commission within 30 days of publication raises an objection to an item included in a notified list, the Commission shall take measures, in accordance with the procedure referred to in Article 6(3), to remedy the situation.

3. Before starting registration operations, the Registry shall adopt the initial registration policy for the .eu TLD in consultation with the Commission and other interested parties. The Registry shall implement in the registration policy the public policy rules adopted pursuant to paragraph 1 taking into account the exception lists referred to in paragraph 2.

4. The Commission shall periodically inform the Committee referred to in Article 6 on the activities referred to in paragraph 3 of this Article.

[2007]

Article 6

Committee

1. The Commission shall be assisted by the Communications Committee established by Article 22(1) of Directive 2002/21/EC of the European Parliament and of the Council of 7 March 2002 on a common regulatory framework for electronic communications networks and services (Framework Directive).[1] Until the Communications Committee is established pursuant to Decision 1999/468/EC, the Commission shall be assisted by the Committee established by Article 9 of Council Directive 90/387/EEC of 28 June 1990 on the establishment of the internal market for telecommunication services through the implementation of open network provision.[2]

2. Where reference is made to this paragraph, Articles 3 and 7 of Decision 1999/468/EC shall apply, having regard to the provisions of Article 8 thereof.

3. Where reference is made to this paragraph, Articles 5 and 7 of Decision 1999/468/EC shall apply, having regard to the provisions of Article 8 thereof.

The period laid down in Article 5(6) of Decision 1999/468/EC shall be set at three months.

4. The Committee shall adopt its rules of procedure.

[2008]

NOTES

[1] OJ L108, 24.4.2002, p 33.

[2] OJ L192, 24.7.1990, p 1. Directive as last amended by Directive 97/51/EC of the European Parliament and of the Council (OJ L295, 29.10.1997, p 23).

Article 7

Reservation of rights

The Community shall retain all rights relating to the .eu TLD including, in particular, intellectual property rights and other rights to the Registry databases required to ensure the implementation of this Regulation and the right to re-designate the Registry.

[2009]

Article 8

Implementation report

The Commission shall submit a report to the European Parliament and the Council on the implementation, effectiveness and functioning of the .eu TLD one year after the adoption of this Regulation and thereafter every two years.

[2010]

Article 9

Entry into force

This Regulation shall enter into force on the day of its publication in the *Official Journal of the European Communities*.

This Regulation shall be binding in its entirety and directly applicable in all Member States.

[2011]

Done at Luxembourg, 22 April 2002.

COMMISSION REGULATION

of 28 April 2004

laying down public policy rules concerning the implementation and functions of the .eu Top Level Domain and the principles governing registration

(2004/874/EC)

(Text with EEA relevance)

NOTES

Date of publication in OJ: OJ L162, 30/04/2004, p 40–50.

THE COMMISSION OF THE EUROPEAN COMMUNITIES,

Having regard to the Treaty establishing the European Community,

Having regard to Regulation (EC) No 733/2002 of the European Parliament and of the Council of 22 April 2002 on the implementation of the .eu Top Level Domain,[1] and in particular Article 5(1) thereof,

Having consulted the Registry in accordance with Article 5(1) of Regulation (EC) No 733/2002,

Whereas:

(1) The initial implementation stages of the .eu Top Level Domain (TLD), to be created pursuant to Regulation (EC) No 733/2002, have been completed by designating a legal entity, established within the Community to administer and manage the .eu TLD Registry function. The Registry, designated by Commission Decision 2003/375/EC,[2] is required to be a non-profit organisation that should operate and provide services on a cost covering basis and at an affordable price.

(2) Requesting a domain name should be possible through electronic means in a simple, speedy and efficient procedure, in all official languages of the Community, through accredited registrars.

(3) Accreditation of registrars should be carried out by the Registry following a procedure that ensures fair and open competition between Registrars. The accreditation process should be objective, transparent and non-discriminatory. Only parties who meet certain basic technical requirements to be determined by the Registry should be eligible for accreditation.

(4) Registrars should only accept applications for the registration of domain names filed after their accreditation and should forward them in the chronological order in which they were received.

(5) To ensure better protection of consumers' rights, and without prejudice to any Community rules concerning jurisdiction and applicable law, the applicable law in disputes between registrars and registrants on matters concerning Community titles should be the law of one of the Member States.

(6) Registrars should require accurate contact information from their clients, such as full name, address of domicile, telephone number and electronic mail, as well as information concerning a natural or legal person responsible for the technical operation of the domain name.

(7) The Registry policy should promote the use of all the official languages of the Community.

(8) Pursuant to Regulation (EC) No 733/2002, Member States may request that their official name and the name under which they are commonly known should not be registered directly under .eu TLD otherwise than by their national government. Countries that are expected to join the European Union later than May 2004 should be enabled to block their official names and the names under which they are commonly known, so that they can be registered at a later date.

(9) A Member State should be authorised to designate an operator that will register as a domain name its official name and the name under which it is commonly known. Similarly, the Commission should be authorised to select domain names for use by the institutions of the Community, and to designate the operator of those domain names. The Registry should be empowered to reserve a number of specified domain names for its operational functions.

(10) In accordance with Article 5(2) of Regulation (EC) No 733/2002, a number of Member States have notified to the Commission and to other Member States a limited list of broadly-recognised names with regard to geographical and/or geopolitical concepts which affect their political or territorial organisation. Such lists include names that could either not be registered or which could be registered only under the second level domain in accordance with the public policy rules. The names included in these lists are not subject to the first-come first-served principle.

(11) The principle of first-come-first-served should be the basic principle for resolving a dispute between holders of prior rights during the phased registration. After the termination of the phased registration the principle of first come first served should apply in the allocation of domain names.

(12) In order to safeguard prior rights recognised by Community or national law, a procedure for phased registration should be put in place. Phased registration should take place in two phases, with the aim of ensuring that holders of prior rights have appropriate opportunities to register the names on which they hold prior rights. The Registry should ensure that validation of the rights is performed by appointed validation agents. On the basis of evidence provided by the applicants, validation agents should assess the right which is claimed for a particular name. Allocation of that name should then take place on a first-come, first-served basis if there are two or more applicants for a domain name, each having a prior right.

(13) The Registry should enter into an appropriate escrow agreement to ensure continuity of service, and in particular to ensure that in the event of re-delegation or other unforeseen circumstances it is possible to continue to provide services to the local Internet community with minimum disruption. The Registry should also comply with the relevant data protection rules, principles, guidelines and best practices, notably concerning the amount and type of data displayed in the WHOIS database. Domain names considered by a Member State court to

be defamatory, racist or contrary to public policy should be blocked and eventually revoked once the court decision becomes final. Such domain names should be blocked from future registrations.

(14) In the event of the death or insolvency of a domain name holder, if no transfer has been initiated at the expiry of the registration period, the domain name should be suspended for 40 calendar days. If the heirs or administrators concerned have not registered the name during that period it should become available for general registration.

(15) Domain names should be open to revocation by the Registry on a limited number of specified grounds, after giving the domain name holder concerned an opportunity to take appropriate measures. Domain names should also be capable of revocation through an alternative dispute resolution (ADR) procedure.

(16) The Registry should provide for an ADR procedure which takes into account the international best practices in this area and in particular the relevant World Intellectual Property Organization (WIPO) recommendations, to ensure that speculative and abusive registrations are avoided as far as possible.

(17) The Registry should select service providers that have appropriate expertise on the basis of objective, transparent and non-discriminatory criteria. ADR should respect a minimum of uniform procedural rules, similar to the ones set out in the Uniform Dispute Resolution Policy adopted by the Internet Corporation of Assigned Names and Numbers (ICANN).

(18) In view of the impending enlargement of the Union it is imperative that the system of public policy rules set up by this Regulation enter into force without delay.

(19) The measures provided for in this Regulation are in accordance with the opinion of the Communications Committee established by Article 22(1) of Directive 2002/21/EC of the European Parliament and of the Council,[3]

NOTES

[1] OJ L113, 30.4.2002, p 1.
[2] OJ L128, 24.5.2003, p 29.
[3] OJ L108, 24.4.2002, p 13.

HAS ADOPTED THIS REGULATION:

CHAPTER I
SUBJECT MATTER

Article 1

Subject matter

This Regulation sets out the public policy rules concerning the implementation and functions of the .eu Top Level Domain (TLD) and the public policy principles on registration referred to in Article 5(1) of Regulation (EC) No 733/2002.

[2012]

CHAPTER II
PRINCIPLES ON REGISTRATION

Article 2

Eligibility and general principles for registration

An eligible party, as listed in Article 4(2)(b) of Regulation (EC) No 733/2002, may register one or more domain names under .eu TLD.

Without prejudice to Chapter IV, a specific domain name shall be allocated for use to the eligible party whose request has been received first by the Registry in the technically correct manner and in accordance with this Regulation. For the purposes of this Regulation, this criterion of first receipt shall be referred to as the 'first-come-first-served' principle.

Once a domain name is registered it shall become unavailable for further registration until the registration expires without renewal, or until the domain name is revoked.

Unless otherwise specified in this Regulation, domain names shall be registered directly under the .eu TLD.

Domain name registration shall be valid only after the appropriate fee has been paid by the requesting party.

Domain names registered under the .eu TLD shall only be transferable to parties that are eligible for registration of .eu domain names.

[2013]

Article 3

Requests for domain name registration

The request for domain name registration shall include all of the following:

(a) the name and address of the requesting party;

(b) a confirmation by electronic means from the requesting party that it satisfies the general eligibility criteria set out in Article 4(2)(b) of Regulation (EC) No 733/2002;

(c) an affirmation by electronic means from the requesting party that to its knowledge the request for domain name registration is made in good faith and does not infringe any rights of a third party;

(d) an undertaking by electronic means from the requesting party that it shall abide by all the terms and conditions for registration, including the policy on the extra-judicial settlement of conflicts set out in Chapter VI.

Any material inaccuracy in the elements set out in points (a) to (d) shall constitute a breach of the terms of registration.

Any verification by the Registry of the validity of registration applications shall take place subsequently to the registration at the initiative of the Registry or pursuant to a dispute for the registration of the domain name in question, except for applications filed in the course of the phased registration procedure under Articles 10, 12, and 14.

[2014]

Article 4

Accreditation of registrars

Only registrars accredited by the Registry shall be permitted to offer registration services for names under the .eu TLD.

The procedure for the accreditation of registrars shall be determined by the Registry and shall be reasonable, transparent and non-discriminatory, and shall ensure effective and fair conditions of competition.

Registrars are required to access and use the Registry's automated registration systems. The Registry may set further basic technical requirements for the accreditation of registrars.

The Registry may ask registrars for advance payment of registration fees, to be set annually by the Registry based on a reasonable market estimate.

The procedure, terms of accreditation of registrars and the list of accredited registrars shall be made publicly available by the Registry in readily accessible form.

Each registrar shall be bound by contract with the Registry to observe the terms of accreditation and in particular to comply with the public policy principles set out in this Regulation.

[2015]

Article 5

Provisions for registrars

Without prejudice to any rule governing jurisdiction and applicable law, agreements between the Registrar and the registrant of a domain name cannot designate, as applicable law, a law other than the law of one of the Member States, nor can they designate a dispute-resolution body, unless selected by the Registry pursuant to Article 23, nor an arbitration court or a court located outside the Community.

A registrar who receives more than one registration request for the same name shall forward those requests to the Registry in the chronological order in which they were received.

Only applications received after the date of accreditation shall be forwarded to the Registry.

Registrars shall require all applicants to submit accurate and reliable contact details of at least one natural or legal person responsible for the technical operation of the domain name that is requested.

Registrars may develop label, authentication and trustmark schemes in order to promote consumer confidence in the reliability of information that is available under a domain name that is registered by them, in accordance with applicable national and Community law.

[2016]

CHAPTER III
LANGUAGES AND GEOGRAPHICAL CONCEPTS

Article 6

Languages

Registrations of .eu domain names shall start only after the Registry has informed the Commission that the filing of applications for the registration of .eu domain names and communications of decisions concerning registration is possible in all official languages of the Community, hereinafter referred to as 'official languages'.

For any communication by the Registry that affects the rights of a party in conjunction with a registration, such as the grant, transfer, cancellation or revocation of a domain, the Registry shall ensure that these communications are possible in all official languages.

The Registry shall perform the registration of domain names in all the alphabetic characters of the official languages when adequate international standards become available.

The Registry shall not be required to perform functions using languages other than the official languages.

[2017]

Article 7

Procedure for reserved geographical and geopolitical names

For the procedure of raising objections to the lists of broadly recognised names in accordance with the third subparagraph of Article 5(2) of Regulation (EC) No 733/2002, objections shall be notified to the members of the Communications Committee established by Article 22(1) of Directive 2002/21/EC and to the Director-General of the Commission's Directorate-General Information Society. The members of the Communications Committee and the Director-General may designate other contact points for these notifications.

Objections and designations of contact points shall be notified in the form of electronic mail, delivery by courier or in person, or by postal delivery effected by way of registered letter and acknowledgement of receipt.

Upon the resolution of any objections, the Registry shall publish on its web site two lists of names. The one list shall contain the list of names that the Commission shall have notified as 'not registrable'. The other list shall contain the list of names that the Commission shall have notified to the Registry as 'registrable only under a second level domain'.

[2018]

[Article 8

Reservation of names by countries and alpha-2 codes representing countries

1. The list of names set out in the Annex to this Regulation shall only be reserved or registered as second level domain names directly under the .eu TLD by the countries indicated in the list.

2. Alpha-2 codes representing countries shall not be registered as second level domain names directly under the .eu TLD.]

[2019]

NOTES

Substituted by Commission Regulation 1654/2005/EC, Art 1(1).

Article 9

Second level domain name for geographical and geopolitical names

Registration of geographical and geopolitical concepts as domain names in accordance with Article 5(2)(b) of Regulation (EC) No 733/2002 may be provided for by a Member State that has notified the names. This may be done under any domain name that has been registered by that Member State.

The Commission may ask the Registry to introduce domain names directly under the .eu TLD for use by the Community institutions and bodies. After the entry into force of this Regulation and not later than a week before the beginning of the phased registration period provided for in Chapter IV, the Commission shall notify the Registry of the names that are to be reserved and the bodies that represent the Community institutions and bodies in registering the names.

[2020]

CHAPTER IV
PHASED REGISTRATION

Article 10

Eligible parties and the names they can register

1. Holders of prior rights recognised or established by national and/or Community law and public bodies shall be eligible to apply to register domain names during a period of phased registration before general registration of .eu domain starts.

'Prior rights' shall be understood to include, *inter alia*, registered national and community trademarks, geographical indications or designations of origin, and, in as far as they are protected under national law in the Member-State where they are held: unregistered trademarks, trade names, business identifiers, company names, family names, and distinctive titles of protected literary and artistic works.

'Public bodies' shall include: institutions and bodies of the Community, national and local governments, governmental bodies, authorities, organisations and bodies governed by public law, and international and intergovernmental organisations.

2. The registration on the basis of a prior right shall consist of the registration of the complete name for which the prior right exists, as written in the documentation which proves that such a right exists.

3. The registration by a public body may consist of the complete name of the public body or the acronym that is generally used. Public bodies that are responsible for governing a particular geographic territory may also register the complete name of the territory for which they are responsible, and the name under which the territory is commonly known.

[2021]

Article 11

Special characters

As far as the registration of complete names is concerned, where such names comprise a space between the textual or word elements, identicality shall be deemed to exist between such complete names and the same names written with a hyphen between the word elements or combined in one word in the domain name applied for.

Where the name for which prior rights are claimed contains special characters, spaces, or punctuations, these shall be eliminated entirely from the corresponding domain name, replaced with hyphens, or, if possible, rewritten.

Special character and punctuations as referred to in the second paragraph shall include the following:

~ @ # $ % ^ & * ( ) + = < > { } [...] | \ / : ; ' , . ?

Without prejudice to the third paragraph of Article 6, if the prior right name contains letters which have additional elements that cannot be reproduced in ASCII code, such as ä, é or ñ, the letters concerned shall be reproduced without these elements (such as a, e, n), or shall be replaced by conventionally accepted spellings (such as ae). In all other respects, the domain name shall be identical to the textual or word elements of the prior right name.

[2022]

Article 12

Principles for phased registration

1. [Phased registration shall not start before the requirement of the first paragraph of Article 6 is fulfilled.]

The Registry shall publish the date on which phased registration shall start at least two months in advance and shall inform all accredited Registrars accordingly.

The Registry shall publish on its website two months before the beginning of the phased registration a detailed description of all the technical and administrative measures that it shall use to ensure a proper, fair and technically sound administration of the phased registration period.

2. The duration of the phased registration period shall be four months. General registration of domain names shall not start prior to the completion of the phased registration period.

Phased registration shall be comprised of two parts of two months each.

During the first part of phased registration, only registered national and Community trademarks, geographical indications, and the names and acronyms referred to in Article 10(3), may be applied for as domain names by holders or licensees of prior rights and by the public bodies mentioned in Article 10(1).

During the second part of phased registration, the names that can be registered in the first part as well as names based on all other prior rights can be applied for as domain names by holders of prior rights on those names.

3. The request to register a domain name based on a prior right under Article 10(1) and (2) shall include a reference to the legal basis in national or Community law for the right to the name, as well as other relevant information, such as trademark registration number, information concerning publication in an official journal or government gazette, registration information at professional or business associations and chambers of commerce.

4. The Registry may make the requests for domain name registration subject to payment of additional fees, provided that these serve merely to cover the costs generated by the application of this Chapter. The Registry may charge differential fees depending upon the complexity of the process required to validate prior rights.

5. At the end of the phased registration an independent audit shall be performed at the expense of the Registry and shall report its findings to the Commission. The auditor shall be appointed by the Registry after consulting the Commission. The purpose of the audit shall be to confirm the fair, appropriate and sound operational and technical administration of the phased registration period by the Registry.

6. To resolve a dispute over a domain name the rules provided in Chapter VI shall apply.

[2023]

NOTES

Para 1: words in square brackets substituted by Commission Regulation 1654/2005/EC, Art 1(2).

Article 13

Selection of validation agents

Validation agents shall be legal persons established within the territory of the Community. Validation agents shall be reputable bodies with appropriate expertise. The Registry shall select the validation agents in an objective, transparent and non-discriminatory manner, ensuring the widest possible geographical diversity. The Registry shall require the validation agent to execute the validation in an objective, transparent and non-discriminatory manner.

Member States shall provide for validation concerning the names mentioned in Article 10(3). To that end, the Member States shall send to the Commission within two months following entry into force of this Regulation, a clear indication of the addresses to which documentary evidence is to be sent for verification. The Commission shall notify the Registry of these addresses.

The Registry shall publish information about the validation agents at its website.

[2024]

Article 14

Validation and registration of applications received during phased registration

All claims for prior rights under Article 10(1) and (2) must be verifiable by documentary evidence which demonstrates the right under the law by virtue of which it exists.

The Registry, upon receipt of the application, shall block the domain name in question until validation has taken place or until the deadline passes for receipt of documentation. If the Registry receives more than one claim for the same domain during the phased registration period, applications shall be dealt with in strict chronological order.

The Registry shall make available a database containing information about the domain names applied for under the procedure for phased registration, the applicants, the Registrar that submitted the application, the deadline for submission of validation documents, and subsequent claims on the names.

Every applicant shall submit documentary evidence that shows that he or she is the holder of the prior right claimed on the name in question. The documentary evidence shall be submitted to a validation agent indicated by the Registry. The applicant shall submit the evidence in such a way that it shall be received by the validation agent within forty days from the submission of the application for the domain name. If the documentary evidence has not been received by this deadline, the application for the domain name shall be rejected.

Validation agents shall time-stamp documentary evidence upon receipt.

Validation agents shall examine applications for any particular domain name in the order in which the application was received at the Registry.

The relevant validation agent shall examine whether the applicant that is first in line to be assessed for a domain name and that has submitted the documentary evidence before the deadline has prior rights on the name. If the documentary evidence has not been received in time or if the validation agent finds that the documentary evidence does not substantiate a prior right, he shall notify the Registry of this.

If the validation agent finds that prior rights exist regarding the application for a particular domain name that is first in line, he shall notify the Registry accordingly.

This examination of each claim in chronological order of receipt shall be followed until a claim is found for which prior rights on the name in question are confirmed by a validation agent.

The Registry shall register the domain name, on the first come first served basis, if it finds that the applicant has demonstrated a prior right in accordance with the procedure set out in the second, third and fourth paragraphs.

[2025]

CHAPTER V
RESERVATIONS, WHOIS DATA AND IMPROPER REGISTRATIONS

Article 15

Escrow agreement

1. The Registry shall, at its own expense, enter into an agreement with a reputable trustee or other escrow agent established within the territory of the Community designating the Commission as the beneficiary of the escrow agreement. The Commission shall give its consent to that agreement before it is concluded. The Registry shall submit to the escrow agent on a daily basis an electronic copy of the current content of the .eu database.

2. The agreement shall provide that the data shall be held by the escrow agent on the following terms and conditions:

(a) the data shall be received and held in escrow, undergoing no procedure other than verification that it is complete, consistent, and in proper format, until it is released to the Commission;

(b) the data shall be released from escrow upon expiration without renewal or upon termination of the contract between the Registry and the Commission for any of the reasons described therein and irrespectively of any disputes or litigation between the Commission and the Registry;

PART III INTERNET AND DOMAIN NAMES

(c) in the event that the escrow is released, the Commission shall have the exclusive, irrevocable, royalty-free right to exercise or to have exercised all rights necessary to re-designate the Registry;

(d) if the contract with the Registry is terminated the Commission, with the cooperation of the Registry, shall take all necessary steps to transfer the administrative and operational responsibility for the .eu TLD and any reserve funds to such party as the Commission may designate: in that event, the Registry shall make all efforts to avoid disruption of the service and shall in particular continue to update the information that is subject to the escrow until the time of completion of the transfer.

[2026]

Article 16

WHOIS database

The purpose of the WHOIS database shall be to provide reasonably accurate and up to date information about the technical and administrative points of contact administering the domain names under the .eu TLD.

The WHOIS database shall contain information about the holder of a domain name that is relevant and not excessive in relation to the purpose of the database. In as far as the information is not strictly necessary in relation to the purpose of the database, and if the domain name holder is a natural person, the information that is to be made publicly available shall be subject to the unambiguous consent of the domain name holder. The deliberate submission of inaccurate information shall constitute grounds for considering the domain name registration to have been in breach of the terms of registration.

[2027]

Article 17

Names reserved by the Registry

The following names shall be reserved for the operational functions of the Registry:

eurid.eu, registry.eu, nic.eu, dns.eu, internic.eu, whois.eu, das.eu, coc.eu, eurethix.eu, eurethics.eu, euthics.eu

[2028]

Article 18

Improper registrations

Where a domain name is considered by a Court of a Member State to be defamatory, racist or contrary to public policy, it shall be blocked by the Registry upon notification of a Court decision and shall be revoked upon notification of a final court decision. The Registry shall block from future registration those names which have been subject to such a court order for as long as such order remains valid.

[2029]

Article 19

Death and winding up

1. If the domain name holder dies during the registration period of the domain name, the executors of his or her estate, or his or her legal heirs, may request transfer of the name to the heirs along with submission of the appropriate documentation. If, on expiry of the registration period, no transfer has been initiated, the domain name shall be suspended for a period of 40 calendar days and shall be published on the Registry's website. During this period the executors or the legal heirs may apply to register the name along with submission of the appropriate documentation. If the heirs have not registered the name during that 40-day period, the domain name shall thereafter become available for general registration.

2. If the domain name holder is an undertaking, a legal or natural person, or an organisation that becomes subject to insolvency proceedings, winding up, cessation of trading, winding up by court order or any similar proceeding provided for by national law, during the registration period of the domain name, then the legally appointed administrator of the domain name holder may request transfer to the purchaser of the domain name holders

assets along with submission of the appropriate documentation. If, on expiry of the registration period, no transfer has been initiated, the domain name shall be suspended for a period of forty calendar days and shall be published on the registry's website. During this period the administrator may apply to register the name along with submission of appropriate documentation. If the administrator has not registered the name during that 40-day period, the domain name shall thereafter become available for general registration.

[2030]

CHAPTER VI
REVOCATION AND SETTLEMENT OF CONFLICTS

Article 20

Revocation of domain names

The Registry may revoke a domain name at its own initiative and without submitting the dispute to any extrajudicial settlement of conflicts, exclusively on the following grounds:

(a) outstanding unpaid debts owed to the Registry;
(b) holder's non-fulfilment of the general eligibility criteria pursuant to Article 4(2)(b) of Regulation (EC) 733/2002;
(c) holder's breach of the terms of registration under Article 3.

The Registry shall lay down a procedure in accordance with which it may revoke domain names on these grounds. This procedure shall include a notice to the domain name holder and shall afford him an opportunity to take appropriate measures.

Revocation of a domain name, and where necessary its subsequent transfer, may also be effected in accordance with a decision issued by an extrajudicial settlement body.

[2031]

Article 21

Speculative and abusive registrations

1. A registered domain name shall be subject to revocation, using an appropriate extra-judicial or judicial procedure, where that name is identical or confusingly similar to a name in respect of which a right is recognised or established by national and/or Community law, such as the rights mentioned in Article 10(1), and where it:

(a) has been registered by its holder without rights or legitimate interest in the name; or
(b) has been registered or is being used in bad faith.

2. A legitimate interest within the meaning of point (a) of paragraph 1 may be demonstrated where:

(a) prior to any notice of an alternative dispute resolution (ADR) procedure, the holder of a domain name has used the domain name or a name corresponding to the domain name in connection with the offering of goods or services or has made demonstrable preparation to do so;
(b) the holder of a domain name, being an undertaking, organisation or natural person, has been commonly known by the domain name, even in the absence of a right recognised or established by national and/or Community law;
(c) the holder of a domain name is making a legitimate and non-commercial or fair use of the domain name, without intent to mislead consumers or harm the reputation of a name on which a right is recognised or established by national and/or Community law.

3. Bad faith, within the meaning of point (b) of paragraph 1 may be demonstrated, where:

(a) circumstances indicate that the domain name was registered or acquired primarily for the purpose of selling, renting, or otherwise transferring the domain name to the holder of a name in respect of which a right is recognised or established by national and/or Community law or to a public body; or
(b) the domain name has been registered in order to prevent the holder of such a name in respect of which a right is recognised or established by national and/or Community law, or a public body, from reflecting this name in a corresponding domain name, provided that:

PART III INTERNET AND DOMAIN NAMES

(i) a pattern of such conduct by the registrant can be demonstrated; or
(ii) the domain name has not been used in a relevant way for at least two years from the date of registration; or
(iii) in circumstances where, at the time the ADR procedure was initiated, the holder of a domain name in respect of which a right is recognised or established by national and/or Community law or the holder of a domain name of a public body has declared his/its intention to use the domain name in a relevant way but fails to do so within six months of the day on which the ADR procedure was initiated;

(c) the domain name was registered primarily for the purpose of disrupting the professional activities of a competitor; or
(d) the domain name was intentionally used to attract Internet users, for commercial gain, to the holder of a domain name website or other on-line location, by creating a likelihood of confusion with a name on which a right is recognised or established by national and/or Community law or a name of a public body, such likelihood arising as to the source, sponsorship, affiliation or endorsement of the website or location or of a product or service on the website or location of the holder of a domain name; or
(e) the domain name registered is a personal name for which no demonstrable link exists between the domain name holder and the domain name registered.

4. The provisions in paragraphs 1, 2 and 3 may not be invoked so as to obstruct claims under national law.

[2032]

Article 22

Alternative dispute resolution (ADR) procedure

1. An ADR procedure may be initiated by any party where:
(a) the registration is speculative or abusive within the meaning of Article 21; or
(b) a decision taken by the Registry conflicts with this Regulation or with Regulation (EC) No 733/2002.

2. Participation in the ADR procedure shall be compulsory for the holder of a domain name and the Registry.

3. A fee for the ADR shall be paid by the complainant.

4. Unless otherwise agreed by the parties, or specified otherwise in the registration agreement between registrar and domain name holder, the language of the administrative proceeding shall be the language of that agreement. This rule shall be subject to the authority of the panel to determine otherwise, having regard to the circumstances of the case.

5. The complaints and the responses to those complaints must be submitted to an ADR provider chosen by the complainant from the list referred to in the first paragraph of Article 23. That submission shall be made in accordance with this Regulation and the published supplementary procedures of the ADR provider.

6. As soon as a request for ADR is properly filed with the ADR provider and the appropriate fee is paid, the ADR provider shall inform the Registry of the identity of the complainant and the domain name involved. The Registry shall suspend the domain name involved from cancellation or transfer until the dispute resolution proceedings or subsequent legal proceedings are complete and the decision has been notified to the Registry.

7. The ADR provider shall examine the complaint for compliance with its rules of procedure, with the provisions of this Regulation and with Regulation (EC) No 733/2002, and, unless non-compliance is established, shall forward the complaint to the respondent within five working days following receipt of the fees to be paid by the complainant.

8. Within 30 working days of the date of receipt of the complaint the respondent shall submit a response to the provider.

9. Any written communication to a complainant or respondent shall be made by the preferred means stated by the complainant or respondent, respectively, or in the absence of such specification electronically via the Internet, provided that a record of transmission is available.

All communications concerning the ADR procedure to the holder of a domain name that is subject to an ADR procedure shall be sent to the address information that is available to the Registrar that maintains the registration of the domain name in accordance with the terms and conditions of registration.

10. Failure of any of the parties involved in an ADR procedure to respond within the given deadlines or appear to a panel hearing may be considered as grounds to accept the claims of the counterparty.

11. In the case of a procedure against a domain name holder, the ADR panel shall decide that the domain name shall be revoked, if it finds that the registration is speculative or abusive as defined in Article 21. The domain name shall be transferred to the complainant if the complainant applies for this domain name and satisfies the general eligibility criteria set out in Article 4(2)(b) of Regulation (EC) No 733/2002.

In the case of a procedure against the Registry, the ADR panel shall decide whether a decision taken by the Registry conflicts with this Regulation or with Regulation (EC) No 733/2002. The ADR panel shall decide that the decision shall be annulled and may decide in appropriate cases that the domain name in question shall be transferred, revoked or attributed, provided that, where necessary, the general eligibility criteria set out in Article 4(2)(b) of Regulation (EC) No 733/2002 are fulfilled.

The decision of the ADR panel shall state the date for implementation of the decision.

Decisions of the panel are taken by simple majority. The alternative dispute panel shall issue its decision within one month from the date of receipt of the response by the ADR provider. The decision shall be duly motivated. The decisions of the panel shall be published.

12. Within three working days after receiving the decision from the panel, the provider shall notify the full text of the decision to each party, the concerned registrar(s) and the Registry. The decision shall be notified to the Registry and the complainant by registered post or other equivalent electronic means.

13. The results of ADR shall be binding on the parties and the Registry unless court proceedings are initiated within 30 calendar days of the notification of the result of the ADR procedure to the parties.

[2033]

Article 23

Selection of providers and panellists for alternative dispute resolution

1. The Registry may select ADR providers, who shall be reputable bodies with appropriate expertise in an objective, transparent and non-discriminatory manner. A list of the ADR providers shall be published on the Registry's website.

2. A dispute which is submitted to the ADR procedure shall be examined by arbitrators appointed to a panel of one or three members.

The panellists shall be selected in accordance to the internal procedures of the selected ADR providers. They shall have appropriate expertise and shall be selected in an objective, transparent and non-discriminatory manner. Each provider shall maintain a publicly available list of panellists and their qualifications.

A panellist shall be impartial and independent and shall have, before accepting appointment, disclosed to the provider any circumstances giving rise to justifiable doubt as to their impartiality or independence. If, at any stage during the administrative proceedings, new circumstances arise that could give rise to justifiable doubt as to the impartiality or independence of the panellist, that panellist shall promptly disclose such circumstances to the provider.

In such event, the provider shall appoint a substitute panellist.

[2034]

CHAPTER VII
FINAL PROVISIONS

Article 24

Entry into force

This Regulation shall enter into force on the day of its publication in the Official Journal of the European Union.

This Regulation shall be binding in its entirety and directly applicable in all Member States.

[2035]

Done at Brussels, 28 April 2004.

[ANNEX

1. List of names per country and the countries that can register them

AUSTRIA

1. österreich	2. oesterreich	3. republik-österreich
4. republik-oesterreich	5. afstria	6. dimokratia-afstria
7. østrig	8. republikken-østrig	9. oestrig
10. austria	11. republic-austria	12. república-austria
13. autriche	14. république-autriche	15. oostenrijk
16. republiek-oostenrijk	17. república-austria	18. itävalta
19. itävallan-tasavalta	20. itaevalta	21. österrike
22. oesterrike	23. republik-österrike	24. rakousko
25. republika-rakousko	26. repubblica-austria	27. austrija
28. republika-austrija	29. respublika-austrija	30. ausztria
31. Osztrák-Köztársaság	32. Republika-Austriacka	33. rakúsko
34. republika-rakúsko	35. avstrija	36. republika-avstrija
37. awstrija	38. republika-awstrija	39. republiköstereich
40. republikoesterreich	41. dimokratiaafstria	42. republikkenøstrig
43. republicaustria	44. repúblicaaustria	45. républiqueautriche
46. repubblicaaustria	47. republiekoostenrijk	48. repúblicaaustria
49. tasavaltaitävalta	50. republikösterrike	51. republikarakousko
52. republikaaustrija	53. respublikaaustrija	54. OsztrákKöztársaság
55. RepublikaAustriacka	56. republikarakúsko	57. republikaavstrija
58. republikaawstrija	59. aostria	60. vabariik-aostria
61. vabariikaostria		

BELGIUM

1. belgie	2. belgië	3. belgique
4. belgien	5. belgium	6. bélgica
7. belgica	8. belgio	9. belgia
10. belgija	11. vlaanderen	12. wallonie
13. wallonië	14. brussel	15. vlaamse-gemeenschap
16. franse-gemeenschap	17. duitstalige-gemeenschap	18. vlaams-gewest
19. waals-gewest	20. brussels-hoofdstedelijk-gewest	21. flandre
22. bruxelles	23. communauté-flamande	24. communaute-flamande
25. communauté-française	26. communaute-francaise	27. communaute-germanophone
28. communauté-germanophone	29. région-flamande	30. region-flamande
31. région-wallonne	32. region-wallonne	33. région-de-bruxelles-capitale
34. region-de-bruxelles-capitale	35. flandern	36. wallonien
37. bruessel	38. brüssel	39. flaemische-gemeinschaft
40. flämische-gemeinschaft	41. franzoesische-gemeinschaft	42. französische-gemeinschaft

43. deutschsprachige-gemeinschaft	44. flaemische-region	45. flämische-region
46. wallonische-region	47. region-bruessel-hauptstadt	48. region-brüssel-hauptstadt
49. flanders	50. wallonia	51. brussels
52. flemish-community	53. french-community	54. german-speaking-community
55. flemish-region	56. walloon-region	57. brussels-capital-region
58. flandes	59. valonia	60. bruselas
61. comunidad-flamenca	62. comunidad-francesa	63. comunidad-germanófona
64. comunidad-germanofona	65. region-flamenca	66. región-flamenca
67. region-valona	68. región-valona	69. region-de-bruselas-capital
70. región-de-bruselas-capital	71. fiandre	72. vallonia
73. communita-fiamminga	74. communità-fiamminga	75. communita-francese
76. communità-francese	77. communita-di-lingua-tedesca	78. communità-di-lingua-tedesca
79. regione-fiamminga	80. regione-vallona	81. regione-di-bruxelles-capitale
82. flandres	83. bruxelas	84. comunidade-flamenga
85. comunidade-francofona	86. comunidade-germanofona	87. regiao-flamenga
88. região-flamenga	89. regiao-vala	90. região-vala
91. regiao-de-bruxelas-capital	92. região-de-bruxelas-capital	93. vallonien
94. bryssel	95. flamlaendskt-spraakomraade	96. fransktalande-spraakomraade
97. tysktalande-spraakomraade	98. flamlaendska-regionen	99. vallonska-regionen
100. bryssel-huvustad	101. det-flamske-sprogsamfund	102. det-franske-sprogsamfund
103. det-tysktalende-sprogsamfund	104. den-flamske-region	105. den-vallonske-region
106. regionen-bruxelles-hovedstadsomraadet	107. flanderi	108. flaaminkielinen-yhteiso
109. ranskankielinen-yhteiso	110. saksankielinen-yhteiso	111. flanderin-alue
112. vallonian-alue	113. brysselin-alue	114. flandry
115. valonsko	116. brusel	117. vlamske-spolecenstvi
118. francouzske-spolecenstvi	119. germanofonni-spolecenstvi	120. vlamsky-region
121. valonsky-region	122. region-brusel	123. flandrija
124. valonija	125. bruselj	126. flamska-skupnost
127. frankofonska-skupnost	128. germanofonska-skupnost	129. flamska-regija
130. valonska-regija	131. regija-bruselj	

PART III INTERNET AND DOMAIN NAMES

CYPRUS

1. cypern	2. cyprus	3. cyprus
4. kypros	5. chypre	6. zypern
7. κυπρος	8. cipro	9. chipre
10. chipre	11. cypern	12. anchipír
13. kypr	14. küpros	15. ciprus
16. kipras	17. kipra	18. ćipru
19. cypr	20. ciper	21. cyprus
22. kibris	23. republikkencypern	24. republiekcyprus
25. republicofcyprus	26. kyproksentasavalta	27. republiquedechypre

28. republikzypern
29. κυπριακηδημοκρατια
30. repubblicadicipro
31. republicadechipre
32. republicadechipre
33. cypernsrepublik
34. poblachtnacipíre
35. kyperskarepublika
36. küprosevabariik
37. ciprusiköztàrsasàg
38. kiprorespublika
39. kiprasrepublika
40. republikata'ćipru
41. republikacypryjska
42. republikaciper
43. cyperskarepublika
44. kibriscumhuriyeti

CZECH REPUBLIC

1. ceska-republika
2. den-tjekkiske-republik
3. tschechische-republik
4. tsehhi-vabariik
5. τσεχικη-δημοκρατια
6. czech-republic
7. repulica-checa
8. republique-tcheque
9. repubblica-ceca
10. cehijas-republika
11. cekijos-respublika
12. cseh-koztarsasag
13. repubblica-ceka
14. tsjechische-republiek
15. republika-czeska
16. republica-checa
17. ceska-republika
18. ceska-republika
19. tsekin-tasavalta
20. tjeckiska-republiken
21. ceskarepublika
22. dentjekkiskerepublik
23. tschechischerepublik
24. tsehhivabariik
25. τσεχικηδημοκρατια
26. czechrepublic
27. repulicacheca
28. republiquetcheque
29. repubblicaceca
30. cehijasrepublika
31. cekijosrespublika
32. csehkoztarsasag
33. repubblicaceka
34. tsjechischerepubliek
35. republikaczeska
36. republicacheca
37. ceskarepublika
38. ceskarepublika
39. tsekintasavalta
40. tjeckiskarepubliken
41. czech
42. cesko
43. tjekkiet
44. tschechien
45. tsehhi
46. τσεχια
47. czechia
48. chequia
49. tchequie
50. cechia
51. cehija
52. cekija
53. csehorszag
54. tsjechie
55. czechy
56. chequia
57. ceska
58. tsekinmaa
59. tjeckien
60. cechy
61. česka-republika
62. tsehhi-vabariik
63. republica-checa
64. republique-tcheque
65. čehijas-republika
66. cseh-köztarsasag
67. republica-checa
68. česka-republika
69. českarepublika
70. tsehhivabariik
71. republicacheca
72. republiquetcheque
73. čehijasrepublika
74. csehköztarsasag
75. republicacheca
76. českarepublika
77. česko
78. tsjechië
79. tsehhi
80. chequia
81. tchequie
82. čehija
83. csehorszag
84. česka
85. čechy

DENMARK

1. danemark
2. denemarken
3. danmark
4. denmark
5. tanska
6. δανία
7. danimarca
8. dinamarca
9. dänemark
10. dánsko
11. taani
12. danija

13. dānija
14. id-danimarka
15. dania
16. danska
17. dánia

ESTONIA

1. eesti
2. estija
3. estland
4. estonia
5. estónia
6. estonie
7. estonija
8. estonja
9. εσθονία
10. igaunija
11. viro

FINLAND

1. suomi
2. finland
3. finska
4. finskó
5. finlândia
6. finlandia
7. finlandja
8. finnország
9. suomija
10. somija
11. finlande
12. φινλανδία
13. soomi
14. finnland
15. finsko

FRANCE

1. francia
2. francie
3. frankrig
4. frankreich
5. prantsusmaa
6. γαλλια
7. gallia
8. france
9. france
10. francia
11. francija
12. prancūzija
13. prancuzija
14. franciaország
15. franciaorszag
16. franza
17. frankrijk
18. francja
19. França
20. francúzsko
21. francuzsko
22. francija
23. ranska
24. frankrike
25. französischerepublik
26. französische-republik
27. französische_republik
28. franzosischerepublik
29. franzosische-republik
30. franzosische_republik
31. franzoesischerepublik
32. franzoesische-republik
33. franzoesische_republik
34. frenchrepublic
35. french-republic
36. french_republic
37. republiquefrançaise
38. republique-française
39. republique_française
40. républiquefrançaise
41. république-française
42. république_française
43. republiquefrancaise
44. republique-francaise
45. republique_francaise
46. républiquefrancaise
47. république-francaise
48. république_francaise
49. alsace
50. auvergne
51. aquitaine
52. basse-normandie
53. bassenormandie
54. bourgogne
55. bretagne
56. centre
57. champagne-ardenne

58. champagneardenne	59. corse	60. franche-comte
61. franche-comté	62. franchecomte	63. franchecomté
64. haute-normandie	65. hautenormandie	66. ile-de-France
67. île-de-France	68. iledeFrance	69. îledeFrance
70. languedoc-roussillon	71. languedocroussillon	72. limousin
73. lorraine	74. midi-pyrenees	75. midi-pyrénées
76. midipyrenees	77. midipyrénées	78. nord-pas-de-calais
79. nordpasdecalais	80. paysdelaloire	81. pays-de-la-loire
82. picardie	83. poitou-charentes	84. poitoucharentes
85. provence-alpes-cote-d-azur	86. provence-alpes-côte-d-azur	87. provencealpescotedazur
88. provencealpescôtedazur	89. rhone-alpes	90. rhône-alpes
91. rhonealpes	92. rhônealpes	93. guadeloupe
94. guyane	95. martinique	96. reunion
97. réunion	98. mayotte	99. saint-pierre-et-miquelon
100. saintpierreetmiquelon	101. polynesie-française	102. polynésie-française
103. polynesie-francaise	104. polynésie-francaise	105. polynesiefrançaise
106. polynésiefrançaise	107. polynesiefrancaise	108. polynésiefrancaise
109. nouvelle-caledonie	110. nouvelle-calédonie	111. nouvellecaledonie
112. nouvellecalédonie	113. wallis-et-futuna	114. wallisetfutuna
115. terres-australes-et-antarctiques-françaises	116. terres-australes-et-antarctiques-françaises	117. terresaustralesetantarctiques françaises
118. terresaustralesetantarctique-françaises	119. saint-barthélémy	120. saintbarthélémy
121. saint-barthelemy	122. saintbarthelemy	123. saint-martin
124. saintmartin		

GERMANY

1. deutschland	2. federalrepublicofgermany	3. bundesrepublik-deutschland
4. bundesrepublikdeutschland	5. allemagne	6. republiquefederaled'allemagne
7. alemanna	8. repúblicafederaldealemania	9. germania
10. repubblicafederaledigermania	11. germany	12. federalrepublicofgermany
13. tyskland	14. forbundsrepublikkentyskland	15. duitsland
16. bondsrepubliekduitsland	17. nemecko	18. spolkovárepublikanemecko
19. alemanha	20. republicafederaldaalemanha	21. niemczech
22. republikafederalnaniemiec	23. németország	24. németországiszövetségiköztársaság
25. vokietijos	26. vokietijosfederacine respublika	27. vacija
28. vacijasfederativarepublika	29. däitschland	30. bundesrepublikdäitschland
31. germanja	32. repubblikafederalita germanja	33. gearmaine

34. poblachtchnaidhmena gearmaine	35. saksamaa	36. saksamaaliitvabariik
37. nemcija	38. zweznarepublikanemcija	39. γερμανία
40. saksa	41. saksanliittotasavalta	42. Baden-Württemberg
43. Bavaria	44. Bayern	45. Berlin
46. Brandenburg	47. Bremen	48. Hamburg
49. Hessen	50. Lower-Saxony	51. Mecklenburg-Western-Pomerania
52. Mecklenburg-Vorpommern	53. niedersachsen	54. nordrhein-Westfalen
55. northrhine-Westphalia	56. Rheinland-Pfalz	57. Rhineland-Palatinate
58. Saarland	59. Sachsen	60. Sachsen-Anhalt
61. Saxony	62. Saxony-Anhalt	63. Schleswig-Holstein
64. Thüringen	65. Thuringia	66. Baden-Wuerttemberg
67. bade-wurtemberg	68. le-bade-wurtemberg	69. Baden-Wurttemberg
70. BadenWürttemberg	71. BadenWuerttemberg	72. badewurtemberg
73. lebadewurtemberg	74. BadenWurttemberg	75. Baviera
76. Bavière	77. Freistaat-Bayern	78. FreistaatBayern
79. Free-State-of-Bavaria	80. Stato-Libero-di-Baviera	81. Etat-Libre-Bavière
82. Brandebourg	83. Brandeburgo	84. Brandenburgii
85. freieundhansestadthamburg	86. freie-und-hansestadt-hamburg	87. freiehansestadthamburg
88. freie-hansestadt-hamburg	89. hansestadt-hamburg	90. hansestadthamburg
91. stadthamburg	92. stadt-hamburg	93. hamburg-stadt
94. hamburg	95. landhamburg	96. land-hamburg
97. hamburku	98. hampuriin	99. hamborg
100. hamburgo	101. hambourg	102. amburgo
103. hamburgu	104. hanbao	105. hamburuku
106. hamburk	107. hesse	108. hassia
109. nordrheinwestfalen	110. northrhinewestphalia	111. northrhine-westfalia
112. northrhinewestfalia	113. rhenanie-du-nord-westphalie	114. rhenaniedunordwestphalie
115. lasaxe	116. sachsen	117. sajonia
118. sajónia	119. saksen	120. saksimaa
121. saksio	122. saksonia	123. saksonijos
124. saška	125. saska	126. sasko
127. sassonia	128. saxe	129. saxonia
130. saxónia	131. szászország	132. szaszorszag
133. Σαξωνία	134. саксония	135. freistaat-sachsen
136. sorben	137. serbja	138. Sorben-Wenden
139. Wenden	140. lausitzer-sorben	141. domowina

GREECE

1. Grecia	2. Graekenland	3. Griechenland
4. Hellas	5. Greece	6. Grece
7. Grecia	8. Griekenland	9. Grecia
10. Kreikka	11. Grekland	12. Recko

PART III INTERNET AND DOMAIN NAMES

13. Kreeka	14. Graecia	15. Graikija
16. Gorogorszag	17. Grecja	18. Grecja
19. Grecko	20. Grcija	

HUNGARY

1. magyarkoztarsasag	2. republicofhungary	3. republiquedehongrie
4. republikungarn	5. republicadehungria	6. repubblicadiungheria
7. republicadahungria	8. ungerskarepubliken	9. unkarintasavalta
10. denungarskerepublik	11. derepublikhongarije	12. republikawegierska
13. ungarivabariik	14. ungarijasrepublika	15. vengrijosrespublika
16. magyarorszag	17. hungary	18. hongrie
19. ungarn	20. hungria	21. ungheria
22. ungern	23. unkari	24. hongarije
25. wegry	26. madarsko	27. ungari
28. ungarija	29. vengrija	30. magyarköztársaság
31. magyarország	32. madarskarepublika	33. republikamadzarska
34. madzarsko	35. ουγγαρια	36. ουγριкιδεμοκρατια
37. nyugatdunántúl	38. középdunántúl	39. déldunántúl
40. középmagyarország	41. északmagyarország	42. északalföld
43. délalföld	44. nyugatdunantul	45. kozepdunantul
46. deldunantul	47. kozepmagyarorszag	48. eszakmagyarorszag
49. eszakalfold	50. delalfold	

IRELAND

1. irlanda	2. irsko	3. irland
4. iirimaa	5. ireland	6. irlande
7. irlanda	8. Īrija	9. Airija
10. Írország	11. L-Irlanda	12. ιρλανδία
13. ierland	14. irlandia	15. Írsko
16. irska	17. irlanti	18. irland
19. .irlande	20. Ιρλανδία	21. irlande
22. republicofireland	23. eire	

ITALY

1. Repubblica-Italiana	2. RepubblicaItaliana	3. Italia
4. Italy	5. Italian	6. Italien
7. Italija	8. Itália	9. Italië
10. Italien	11. Itálie	12. Italie
13. Olaszország	14. Itālija	15. Włochy
16. Ιταλία	17. Italja	18. Taliansko
19. Itaalia	20. Abruzzo	21. Basilicata

22. Calabria
23. Campania
24. Emilia-Romagna
25. Friuli-VeneziaGiulia
26. Lazio
27. Liguria
28. Lombardia
29. Marche
30. Molise
31. Piemonte
32. Puglia
33. Sardegna
34. Sicilia
35. Toscana
36. Trentino-AltoAdige
37. Umbria
38. Valled'Aosta
39. Veneto

LATVIA

1. Λετονία
2. Lettorszag
3. Latvja
4. Letland
5. Lotwa
6. Letonia
7. Lotyssko
8. Latvija
9. Lettland
10. Latvia
11. Lotyssko
12. Letland
13. Lettland
14. Lati
15. Letonia
16. Lettonie
17. Lettonia
18. Republicoflatvia
19. Latvijskajarespublika

LITHUANIA

1. lietuva
2. leedu
3. liettua
4. litauen
5. lithouania
6. lithuania
7. litouwen
8. lituania
9. lituanie
10. litva
11. litván
12. litvania
13. litvanya
14. litwa
15. litwanja
16. liettuan
17. litevská
18. lietuvas
19. litwy
20. litovska
21. aukstaitija
22. zemaitija
23. dzukija
24. suvalkija
25. suduva
26. lietuvos-respublika
27. lietuvos_respublika
28. lietuvosrespublika
29. republic-of-lithuania
30. republic_of_lithuania
31. republiclithuania
32. republicoflithuania
33. republique-de-lituanie
34. republique_de_lituanie
35. republiquelituanie
36. republiquedelituanie
37. republica-de-lituania
38. republica_de_lituania
39. republicalituania
40. republicadelituania
41. litovskajarespublika
42. litovskaja-respublika
43. litovskaja_respublika
44. litauensrepublik
45. litauens-republik
46. litauens_republic
47. republiklitauen
48. republik-litauen
49. republic_litauen
50. δημοκρατιατησλιθουανιας
51. δημοκρατια-της-λιθουανιας
52. δημοκρατια_της_λιθουανιας
53. δημοκρατίατηςΛιθουανίας
54. δημοκρατία-της-Λιθουανίας
55. δημοκρατία_της_Λιθουανίας
56. repubblicadilituania
57. repubblica-di-lituania
58. repubblica_di_lituania
59. republieklitouwen
60. republiek-litouwen
61. republiek_litouwen
62. republicadalituania
63. republica-da-lituania
64. republica_da_lituania
65. liettuantasavalta
66. liettuan-tasavalta
67. liettuan_tasavalta
68. republikenLitauen
69. republiken-litauen
70. republiken_litauen
71. litevskárepublika
72. litevská-republika

73. litevská_republika
74. leeduvabariik
75. leedu-vabariik
76. leedu_vabariik
77. lietuvasrepublika
78. lietuvas-republika
79. lietuvas_republika
80. litvánköztársaság
81. litván-köztársaság
82. litván_köztársaság
83. repubblikatallitwanja
84. repubblika-tal-litwanja
85. repubblika_tal_litwanja
86. republikalitwy
87. republika-litwy
88. republika_litwy
89. litovskarepublika
90. litovska-republika
91. litovska_republika
92. republikalitva
93. republika-litva
94. republika_litva

LUXEMBOURG

1. luxembourg
2. luxemburg
3. letzebuerg

MALTA

1. malta
2. malte
3. melita
4. republicofmalta
5. republic-of-malta
6. therepublicofmalta
7. the-republic-of-malta
8. repubblikatamalta
9. repubblika-ta-malta
10. maltarepublic
11. maltarepubblika
12. gozo
13. ghawdex

NETHERLANDS

1. nederland
2. holland
3. thenetherlands
4. netherlands
5. lespaysbas
6. hollande
7. dieniederlande
8. lospaisesbajos
9. holanda

POLAND

1. rzeczpospolitapolska
2. rzeczpospolita_polska
3. rzeczpospolita-polska
4. polska
5. polonia
6. lenkija
7. poland
8. polen
9. pologne
10. polsko
11. poola
12. puola

PORTUGAL

1. republicaportuguesa
2. portugal
3. portugália
4. portugalia
5. portugali
6. portugalska
7. portugalsko
8. portogallo
9. portugalija
10. portekiz
11. πορτογαλία
12. portugāle
13. aveiro
14. beja
15. braga

16. bragança
17. castelobranco
18. coimbra
19. evora
20. faro
21. guarda
22. leiria
23. lisboa
24. portalegre
25. porto
26. santarem
27. setubal
28. vianadocastelo
29. viseu
30. vilareal
31. madeira
32. açores
33. alentejo
34. algarve
35. altoalentejo
36. baixoalentejo
37. beiraalta
38. beirabaixa
39. beirainterior
40. beiralitoral
41. beiratransmontana
42. douro
43. dourolitoral
44. entredouroeminho
45. estremadura
46. minho
47. ribatejo
48. tras-os-montes-e-alto-douro
49. acores

SLOVAKIA

1. slowakische-republik
2. republique-slovaque
3. slovakiki-dimokratia
4. slovenska-republika
5. slovakiske-republik
6. slovaki-vabariik
7. slovakian-tasavalta
8. slovakikidimokratia
9. slovakiki-dimokratia
10. szlovak-koztarsasag
11. slovak-republic
12. repubblica-slovacca
13. slovakijas-republika
14. slovakijos-respublika
15. repubblika-slovakka
16. slowaakse-republiek
17. republika-slowacka
18. republica-eslovaca
19. slovaska-republika
20. republica-eslovaca
21. slovakiska-republiken
22. σλοβακικη-δημοκρατια
23. slowakischerepublik
24. republiqueslovaque
25. slovenskarepublika
26. slovakiskerepublik
27. slovakivabariik
28. slovakiantasavalta
29. szlovakkoztarsasag
30. slovakrepublic
31. repubblicaslovacca
32. slovakijasrepublika
33. slovakijosrespublika
34. repubblikaslovakka
35. slowaakserepubliek
36. republikaslowacka
37. republicaeslovaca
38. slovaskarepublika
39. republicaeslovaca
40. slovakiskarepubliken
41. σλοβακικηδημοκρατια
42. slowakei
43. slovaquie
44. slovakia
45. slovensko
46. slovakiet
47. slovakkia
48. szlovakia
49. slovacchia
50. slovakija
51. slowakije
52. slowacija
53. eslovaquia
54. slovaska
55. σλοβακικη
56. slovakien
57. république-slovaque
58. slovenská-republika
59. szlovák-köztársaság
60. slovākijos-respublika
61. republika-słowacka
62. república-eslovaca
63. slovaška-republika
64. slovačka-republika
65. lýdveldid-slovakia
66. républiqueslovaque
67. slovenskárepublika
68. szlovákköztársaság
69. slovākijosrespublika
70. republikasłowacka
71. repúblicaeslovaca
72. slovaškarepublika
73. slovačkarepublika
74. lýdveldidslovakia
75. szlovákia
76. slovākija
77. słowacija
78. slovaška
79. slovačka

SLOVENIA

1. slovenija
2. slovenia
3. slowenien
4. slovenie
5. la-slovenie
6. laslovenie
7. eslovenia
8. republikaslovenija
9. republika-slovenija
10. republicofslovenia
11. republic-of-slovenia
12. szlovenia
13. szlovenkoztarsasag
14. szloven-koztarsasag
15. repubblicadislovenia
16. repubblica-di-slovenia

SPAIN

1. españa
2. reinodeespana
3. reino-de-espana
4. espagne
5. espana
6. espanha
7. espanja
8. espanya
9. hispaania
10. hiszpania
11. ispanija
12. spagna
13. spain
14. spanielsko
15. spanien
16. spanija
17. spanje
18. reinodeespaña
19. reino-de-españa
20. španielsko
21. spānija
22. španija
23. španiělsko
24. espainia
25. ispania
26. ισπανια
27. andalucia
28. andalucía
29. andalousie
30. andalusia
31. andalusien
32. juntadeandalucia
33. juntadeandalucía
34. aragon
35. aragón
36. gobiernodearagon
37. gobiernoaragón
38. principadodeasturias
39. principaudasturies
40. asturias
41. asturies
42. illesbalears
43. islasbaleares
44. canarias
45. gobiernodecanarias
46. canaryisland
47. kanarischeinseln
48. cantabria
49. gobiernodecantabria
50. castillalamancha
51. castilla-lamancha
52. castillayleon
53. castillayleón
54. juntadecastillayleon
55. juntadecastillayleón
56. generalitatdecatalunya
57. generalitatdecataluña
58. catalunya
59. cataluña
60. katalonien
61. catalonia
62. catalogna
63. catalogne
64. cataloniě
65. katalonias
66. catalunha
67. kataloniens
68. katalonian
69. catalonië
70. extremadura
71. comunidadautonomade extremadura
72. comunidadautónomade extremadura
73. xuntadegalicia
74. comunidadautonomadegalicia
75. comunidaautónomade galicia
76. comunidadeautonomade galicia
77. comunidadeautónomade galicia
78. larioja
79. gobiernodelarioja
80. comunidadmadrid
81. madridregion
82. regionmadrid
83. madrid
84. murciaregion
85. murciaregión
86. murciaregione
87. murciaregiao
88. regiondemurcia
89. regióndemurcia
90. regionofmurcia
91. regionvonmurcia
92. regionedimurcia
93. regiaodomurcia
94. navarra
95. nafarroa
96. navarre
97. navarracomunidadforal
98. nafarroaforukomunitatea
99. nafarroaforuerkidegoa

100. communauteforaledenavarre
101. communautéforaledenavarre
102. foralcommunityofnavarra
103. paisvasco
104. paísvasco
105. euskadi
106. euskalherria
107. paisbasc
108. basquecountry
109. paysbasque
110. paesebasco
111. baskenland
112. paisbasco
113. χώρατωνβάσκων
114. gobiernovasco
115. euskojaurlaritza
116. governbasc
117. basquegovernment
118. gouvernementbasque
119. governobasco
120. baskischeregierung
121. baskitschebestuur
122. κυβέρνησητωνβάσκων
123. comunidad-valenciana
124. comunidadvalenciana
125. comunitat-valenciana
126. comunitatvalenciana
127. ceuta
128. gobiernoceuta
129. melilla
130. gobiernomelilla

SWEDEN

1. suecia
2. reinodesuecia
3. sverige
4. kongerietsverige
5. schweden
6. königreichschweden
7. konigreichschweden
8. σουηδία
9. Βασίλειοτης Σουηδίας
10. sweden
11. kingdomofsweden
12. suède
13. suede
14. royaumedesuède
15. royaumedesuede
16. svezia
17. regnodisvezia
18. zweden
19. koninkrijkzweden
20. suécia
21. reinodasuécia
22. reinodasuecia
23. ruotsi
24. ruotsinkuningaskunta
25. konungariketsverige
26. švédsko
27. rootsi
28. svedija
29. svédorszag
30. svedorszag
31. l-isvezja
32. szweja
33. švedska
34. svedska

UNITED KINGDOM

1. unitedkingdom
2. united-kingdom
3. united_kingdom
4. greatbritain
5. great-britain
6. great_britain
7. britain
8. cymru
9. england
10. northernireland
11. northern-ireland
12. northern_ireland
13. scotland
14. wales

2. List of names per country and the countries that can reserve them

BULGARIA

1. българия
2. bulgaria
3. bulharsko
4. bulgarien
5. bulgaaria
6. βουλγαρία
7. bulgarie
8. bulgarija
9. bulgarije
10. bolgarija
11. republicofbulgaria
12. the-republic-of-bulgaria
13. the_republic_of_bulgaria
14. republic-of-bulgaria
15. republic_of_bulgaria

16. republicbulgaria
17. republic-bulgaria
18. republic_bulgaria
19. repubblicadibulgaria
20. repubblica-di-bulgaria
21. repubblica_di_bulgaria
22. repubblicabulgaria
23. repubblica-bulgaria
24. repubblica_bulgaria
25. republikbulgarien
26. republik-bulgarien
27. republik_bulgarien
28. bulgaariavabariik
29. bulgaaria-vabariik
30. bulgaaria_vabariik
31. δημοκρατιατησβουλγαριας
32. δημοκρατια-της-βουλγαριας
33. δημοκρατια_της_βουλγαριας
34. republiekbulgarije
35. republiek-bulgarije
36. republiek_bulgarije
37. republikabolgarija
38. republika-bolgarija
39. republika_bolgarija
40. republikabulgaria
41. republika-bulgaria
42. republika_bulgaria
43. bulharskarepublica
44. bulharska-republica
45. bulharska_republica
46. republiquebulgarie
47. republique-bulgarie
48. republique_bulgarie
49. republicabulgarija
50. republica-bulgārija
51. republica_bulgārija
52. repúblikabulgária
53. repúblika-bulgária
54. repúblika_bulgária
55. repúblicabulgaria
56. república-bulgaria
57. república_bulgaria
58. bulgarja
59. bãlgarija
60. bulgariantasavalta
61. bulgarian-tasavalta
62. bulgarian_tasavalta
63. republikenbulgarien
64. republiken-bulgarien
65. republiken_bulgarien
66. repulicabulgaria
67. repulica-bulgaria
68. repulica_bulgaria
69. köztársaságbulgária
70. köztársaság-bulgária
71. köztársaság_bulgária

CROATIA

1. croatia
2. kroatia
3. kroatien
4. kroatien
5. croazia
6. kroatien
7. croacia
8. croatie
9. horvátország
10. horvatorszag
11. kroatië
12. kroatie
13. chorwacja
14. κροατία
15. chorvatsko
16. charvátsko
17. horvaatia
18. kroaatia
19. croácia
20. croacia
21. horvātija
22. horvatija
23. kroatija
24. kroazja
25. chorvátsko
26. chrovatsko
27. hrvaška
28. hrvaska

ICELAND

1. arepublicadeislândia
2. deijslandrepubliek
3. deijslandrepubliek
4. derepubliekvanijsland
5. derepubliekvanijsland
6. iceland
7. icelandrepublic
8. iepublikaislande
9. ijsland
10. island
11. islanda
12. islande
13. islandia
14. islândia
15. islandica
16. islandrepublik
17. islandskylisejnik
18. islannintasavalta
19. islanti
20. izland
21. ísland
22. íslenskalýđveldiđ
23. köztársaságizland
24. larepubblicadiislanda
25. larepúblicadeislandia
26. larépubliquedislande
27. lislande

28. lýđveldiđísland	29. puklerkaislandska	30. rahvavabariikisland
31. repubblicadiislanda	32. repubblikataisland	33. republicoficeland
34. republikaisland	35. republikaislandia	36. republikavisland
37. republikkenisland	38. republikvonisland	39. repúblicadeislandia
40. repúblicadeislândia	41. républiquedislande	42. Δημοκρατίατης Ισλανδίας
43. Ισλανδία		

LIECHTENSTEIN

1. fyrstendømmetliechtenstein	2. fürstentumliechtenstein	3. principalityofliechtenstein
4. liechtensteinivürstiriiki	5. liechtensteininruhtinaskunta	6. principautédeliechtenstein
7. πριγκιπάτοτουλιχτενστάιν	8. furstadæmisinsliechtensteins	9. principatodelliechtenstein
10. lichtenšteinokunigaikštystė	11. lihtenšteinasfirstiste	12. prinċipalitàtal-liechtenstein
13. vorstendomliechtenstein	14. fyrstedømmetliechtenstein	15. księstwoliechtenstein
16. principadodoliechtenstein	17. furstendömetliechtenstein	18. lichtenštajnskékniežatstvo
19. kneževinolihtenštajn	20. principadodeliechtenstein	21. lichtenštejnskéknížectví
22. lichtensteinihercegség		

NORWAY

1. norge	2. noreg	3. norway
4. norwegen	5. norvege	6. norvège
7. noruega	8. norvegia	9. norvégia
10. norsko	11. nórsko	12. norra
13. norja	14. norvegija	15. norvēģija
16. noorwegen	17. Νορβηγία	18. norvegja
19. norveġja	20. norveska	21. norveška
22. norwegia	23. norga	

ROMANIA

1. românia	2. romania	3. roumanie
4. rumänien	5. rumanien	6. rumanía
7. rumænien	8. roménia	9. romênia
10. romenia	11. rumunia	12. rumunsko
13. romunija	14. rumānija	15. rumunija
16. rumeenia	17. ρουμανία	18. románia
19. rumanija	20. roemenië	

TURKEY

1. turkiye	2. türkiye	3. turkiyecumhuriyeti
4. türkiyecumhuriyeti]		

[2036]

PART III INTERNET AND DOMAIN NAMES

NOTES

Added by Commission Regulation 1654/2005/EC, Art 1(3).

.EU ALTERNATIVE DISPUTE RESOLUTION RULES (THE "ADR RULES")

NOTES

The ADR Rules can be found at www.adr.eu.

Alternative dispute resolution proceedings for the resolution of disputes under Paragraph 22(1)(a) and (b) of Commission Regulation (EC) No 874/2004 of 28 April 2004 laying down public policy rules concerning the implementation and functions of the .eu Top Level Domain and principles governing registration shall be governed by these *ADR Rules* and the *Supplemental ADR Rules* of the *Provider* administering the *ADR Proceedings*, as far as available and posted on its web site. The interpretation and application of these ADR Rules will be done in the light of the EU legal framework which will prevail in case of conflict.

A GENERAL

1 Definitions

In these ADR Rules:

ADR means an alternative dispute resolution.

ADR Proceeding is a proceeding initiated in accordance with the Procedural Rules.

Complaint means the document including all annexes prepared by the *Complainant* to initiate a cause of action under the *ADR Proceeding*.

Complainant means the *Party* initiating a *Complaint* concerning a .eu domain name registration or requesting to change the language of the *ADR Proceeding*.

Date of Commencement of an ADR Proceeding means a date on which all the following conditions are fulfilled:

(a) an administratively compliant *Complaint* has been properly filed with the *Provider*; and

(b) the appropriate fee for the *ADR Proceeding* is paid.

Domain Name Holder means a legal or natural person who holds an activated registration of a .eu domain name.

European Union Regulations refer to Regulation (EC) No 733/2002 of the European Parliament and of the Council of 22 April 2002 on the implementation of the .eu Top Level Domain[1] and Commission Regulation (EC) No 874/2004 of 28 April 2004 laying down public policy rules concerning the implementation and functions of the .eu Top Level Domain and principles governing registration[2] and any further regulation that would replace, amend or complete such rules and principles.

Registry means the entity entrusted by the European Commission with the organization, administration and management of the .eu designated in accordance with the procedure established in Article 3 of Regulation (EC) No 733/2002.

Mutual Jurisdiction means a court jurisdiction at the location of either

(a) the principal office of the *Registrar* (provided the *Respondent* has submitted in its *Registration Agreement* to that jurisdiction for court adjudication of disputes concerning or arising from the use of the domain name, and provided that the court thus designated is located within the European Union) or

(b) the *Respondent's* address as shown for the registration of the domain name in the *Registry*'s Whois database at the time the *Complaint* is submitted to the *Provider* or as received from *the Registry* by the *Complainant* if such information is not available in *the Registry*'s Whois database or

(c) the principal office of *the Registry* in case of *ADR Proceeding*s against *the Registry*.[3]

Panel means an *ADR* panel appointed by a *Provider* to decide a *Complaint* concerning a .eu domain name registration.

Panelist means an individual appointed by a *Provider* to be a member of a *Panel*.

Party means a *Complainant* or a *Respondent*; **Parties** means both of them.

Procedural Rules means these *ADR Rules, Provider's Supplemental ADR Rules* and *European Union Regulations*. In case of conflict between any of these rules, the European Union Regulations take precedence.

Provider means a dispute resolution service provider selected by *the Registry*.

Registrar means an entity with which the *Respondent* has registered a domain name that is the subject of a *Complaint*.

Registration Agreement means the agreement between a *Registrar* and a domain name holder.

Registration Policy means the .eu Domain Name Registration Policy issued by *the Registry*.

Respondent means the holder of a .eu domain name registration (or the holder's legal heirs or *the Registry* in case of an *ADR Proceeding* against *the Registry*) in respect of which a *Complaint* and/or a request to change the language of the *ADR Proceeding* is initiated.

Response means the document including all annexes filed by the *Respondent* responding to the allegations set forth in the *Complaint* in accordance with these *ADR Rules* and the *Supplemental ADR Rules*.

Sunrise Appeal Period means a 40 day period during which a *Complaint* against *the Registry*'s decision to register a domain name within the Sunrise period can be filed as specified in the *Sunrise Rules*.

Sunrise Rules means the .eu *Registration Policy* and the Terms and Conditions for Domain Name Applications made during the Phased Registration Period issued by *the Registry*.

Supplemental ADR Rules means the rules adopted by the *Provider* administering *ADR Proceedings* to supplement these *ADR Rules*.

Terms and Conditions mean the .eu Domain Name Registration Terms and Conditions issued by *the Registry*.

Time of Filing means a point in time when the following conditions are fulfilled:

(a) a *Complaint* or a request to change the language of the *ADR Proceeding* has been properly filed with the *Provider*; and

(b) the appropriate fee for the *ADR Proceeding* is received by the *Provider*.

Working days mean all days falling between Monday and Friday other than those which are public holidays in the country or the state where the Provider or either of the *Parties*, as the case may be, is subject to an obligation to adhere to a period of time as specified under these *ADR Rules*.

2 Communications and Periods of Time

(a) When forwarding a *Complaint* to the *Respondent*, it shall be the *Provider's* responsibility to employ reasonably available means calculated to achieve actual notice to the *Respondent*.

(b) The *Provider* shall discharge its obligation to achieve actual notice by (i) sending the *Complaint* or a notice with information how to access the *Complaint* (*e g* for the purposes of an on-line platform operated by the *Provider*) to the *Respondent* employing the means stipulated in (c) below to the address which *the Registry* has communicated to the *Provider* for the registered domain name holder or to *the Registry*'s seat in case of a *Complaint* against *the Registry*'s decision; and (ii) in case the Respondent does not confirm receiving the electronic communication made pursuant to (i) above within five (5) days from sending the communication, by forwarding the *Complaint* by registered postal or courier service, postage pre-paid and return receipt requested, to the address(es) specified in (i) above.

(c) Unless specified otherwise in these *ADR Rules*, any written communication to the *Complainant*, the *Respondent* or the *Provider* provided for under these *ADR Rules*, shall be made by the preferred means stated by the *Complainant* or *Respondent*, respectively, or in the absence of such specification:

(1) electronically via the Internet, provided a record of its transmission is available; or

(2) by telecopy or facsimile transmission, with a confirmation of transmission; or
(3) by registered postal or courier service, postage pre-paid and return receipt requested.

(d) Either *Party* may update its contact details by notifying the *Provider* and *the Registry*.

(e) Except as otherwise provided in these *ADR Rules*, all communications provided for under these *ADR Rules* shall be deemed to have been received, in accordance with this provision:

(1) if via the Internet, on the date that the communication was transmitted, provided that the date of transmission is verifiable; or
(2) if delivered by facsimile transmission, on the date shown on the confirmation of transmission; or
(3) if by registered postal or courier service, on the date marked on the receipt, or, if it is not possible to deliver the communication in this way, on the expiry of twelve (12) *days* from the handing over of the communication to a postal or courier service provider.

(f) It shall be the responsibility of the sender to retain records of the fact and circumstances of delivery, which shall be available for inspection by the *Provider* and for reporting purposes.

(g) A system log of data messages of the *Provider* shall be considered as valid records in the absence of any evidence of malfunction of the *Provider's* system.

(h) Except as otherwise provided in these *ADR Rules*, all time periods calculated under these ADR Rules begin on the earliest date that the communication is deemed to have been made in accordance with Paragraph A2(e).

(i) At the request of a *Party* filed before the expiration of the relevant period(s) of time, the *Provider* and, after its appointment, the *Panel*, may – in its sole discretion—extend the periods of time laid down in these *ADR Rules* which are applicable to the *Parties* in exceptional circumstances or upon agreement by both *Parties*. The *Provider* and, after its appointment, the *Panel*, shall decide on any such limited period of extension.

(j) No *Party* or anyone acting on its behalf may engage in any unilateral communication with the *Panel*. All communications between a *Party*, on the one hand, and the *Panel* or the *Provider* on the other shall be made to a case administrator appointed by the *Provider* by the means and in the manner prescribed in the *Provider's Supplemental ADR Rules*.

(k) Any communication in an *ADR Proceeding* initiated by

(1) a *Panel* to a *Party* shall be made through the *Provider*;
(2) a *Party* shall be made through the *Provider*;
(3) the *Provider* to any *Party* or by a *Party* on after the *Date of Commencement of an ADR Proceeding* shall be copied by the Provider to the other *Party* and the *Panel*.

(l) In the event a *Party* sending a communication receives notification of non-delivery of the communication, the *Party* shall promptly notify the *Provider* of the circumstances of the notification.

3 Language of Proceedings

(a) The language of the *ADR Proceedings* must be one of the official EU languages. Unless otherwise agreed by the *Parties*, or specified otherwise in the *Registration Agreement*, the language of the *ADR Proceeding* shall be the language of the *Registration Agreement* for the disputed domain name. In the absence of an agreement between the parties, the *Panel* may in its sole discretion, having regard to the exceptional circumstances of the *ADR Proceeding*, decide on the written request of a Complainant, filed before initiating a *Complaint*, that the language of the *ADR Proceeding* will be different than the language of the *Registration Agreement* for the disputed domain name.

(b) The procedure related to the request of a change of the language of the *ADR Proceeding* shall be as follows:

(1) The request shall be submitted to the *Provider* in hard copy and in electronic form and shall:
   (i) specify the information under Paragraphs B1 (b)(2), (b)(3), (b)(5), (b)(6), and (b)(7) of the *ADR Rules*;
   (ii) specify the requested change of the language of *ADR Proceeding*;
   (iii) specify the exceptional circumstances that would justify such a change of the language of an *ADR Proceeding*;

(iv) conclude with the statement under B1(b)(15) of the *ADR Rules*.

(2) The *Provider* will acknowledge receiving the request from the *Complainant*, subject to the receipt of the fees due hereunder, and, if applicable, shall notify *the Registry* of the *Time of Filing* in accordance withB1(e) of the *ADR Rules*, having the same consequences as under B1(e) of the *ADR Rules*.

(3) The *Provider* shall notify the *Respondent* of the request to change the language of the *ADR Proceeding* within five (5) *days* following receipt of the fees payable hereunder.

(4) The *Respondent* shall have a right to submit a response to the *Provider* within twelve (12) *days* of the date of notification of the request to change the language of the *ADR Proceeding*. The response shall be submitted in hard copy and in electronic form.

(5) The *Provider* will acknowledge receiving the response from the *Respondent* and will appoint a single *Panel* to decide the request. Paragraph B5 applies accordingly.

(6) The *Panel* shall issue a decision whether or not to allow the requested change of the language of the *ADR Proceeding* within twelve (12) *days* from the date of its appointment. The *Panel's* decision shall be final and not subject to appeal. The decision shall be communicated to the *Parties* without delay.

(7) In case the *Complainant* files the *Complaint* within thirty (30) *Working days* from receiving the decision under (b)(6) above, the *Time of Filing* of the request to change the language of the *ADR Proceeding* shall apply with respect to the *Complaint*, provided the appropriate fee is paid.

(c) All documents including communications made as part of the *ADR Proceeding* shall be made in the language of the *ADR Proceeding*. The *Panel* may disregard documents submitted in other languages than the language of the *ADR Proceeding* without requesting their translation. Any communication by the *Provider* which, from its content, cannot be regarded as amounting to procedural documents (such as cover letters with which the *Provider* sends procedural documents or automatic system notifications generated by the *Provider*'s application) shall be made in the language of the *ADR Proceeding* or in English.

(d) The *Provider* and, after its constitution, the *Panel* by itself or upon the request of a *Party*, may order that any documents submitted in languages other than the language of the *ADR Proceeding* be accompanied by a translation in whole or in part into the language of the *ADR Proceeding*.

4 Settlement or Other Grounds for Termination

(a) The *ADR Proceeding* will be understood to be concluded once the *Panel* has received confirmation from both *Parties* that an agreement has been entered into by the *Parties* concerning the object of the dispute.

(b) If the *Parties* wish to negotiate a settlement, the *Complainant* may request that the *Provider* or, after its constitution, the *Panel* suspend the *ADR Proceeding* for a limited period. The suspension period may be extended by the *Panel* upon the *Complainant*'s request. Any such suspension shall be without prejudice to the obligation of the *Panel* to forward its decision on the *Complaint* to the *Provider* within the time period specified in Paragraph B12(b) below. Resumption of the ADR Proceeding shall take place automatically upon receipt of a request thereto from either the *Respondent* or the *Complainant* or upon the expiration of such limited and specified time period.

(c) The *Panel* shall terminate the *ADR Proceeding* if it becomes aware that the dispute that is the subject of the *Complaint* has been finally decided by a court of competent jurisdiction or an alternative dispute resolution body.

(d) The *Panel* shall suspend *ADR Proceeding*(s) pursuant to Paragraphs B1(f) , B2(e) and B3(d) below.

5 Court Proceedings

The conduct of the *ADR Proceeding* shall not be prejudiced by any court proceeding, subject to Paragraph (c)A4(c) above.

6 Fees

(a) The *Complainant* shall pay to the *Provider* an initial fixed fee, in accordance with the *Supplemental ADR Rules*. Until the *Provider* has received this initial fee, it is not obliged to take any action on the *Complaint*. If the *Provider* has not received the fee within ten (10) days of the date of notification of unpaid fees, the *Complaint* shall be deemed withdrawn and the *ADR Proceeding* canceled.

(b) A *Complainant* initiating a request to change the language of the *ADR Proceeding* under Section above or initiating a challenge to the withdrawal of Complaint due to its administrative deficiency under Paragraph B2(c) below shall pay to the *Provider* separate fees in accordance with the *Supplemental ADR Rules*. If the *Provider* has not received the fee within five (5) days of the date of notification of unpaid fees, the request shall be deemed as withdrawn.

(c) A *Respondent* electing under Paragraph B3(b)(4) to have the dispute decided by a three-member *Panel*, rather than single-member *Panel* elected by the *Complainant*, shall pay the *Provider* an additional fee specified in the *Supplemental ADR Rules*. In all other cases, the *Complainant* shall bear all of the *Provider's* fees.

(d) In exceptional circumstances, for example in the event an in-person hearing is held, the *Provider* shall request the *Party* or the *Parties* requesting such event respectively to pay additional fees, which, after its constitution, shall be established in consultation with the *Panel* before scheduling any such hearing.

(e) Subject to Paragraph B1(f) below, the fees paid are not reimbursable. **[2037]**

NOTES

[1] OJ L113 of 30.04.2002, p 1.
[2] OJ. L162 of 30.04.2004, p 40.
[3] OJ. L12 of 16.01.2001, p 1.

B CONDUCT OF THE PROCEEDINGS

1 The Complaint

(a) Any person or entity may initiate an *ADR Proceeding* by submitting a *Complaint* in accordance with the *Procedural Rules* to any *Provider*. A *Complaint* may be filed:

(1) against a *Domain Name Holder* in respect of which domain name the *Complaint* is initiated; or

(2) against *the Registry*.

For the avoidance of doubt, until the domain name in respect of which the *Complaint* is initiated has been registered and activated, a party can initiate an *ADR Proceeding* only against *the Registry*.

(b) The *Complaint* shall be submitted in hard copy and in electronic form and shall:

(1) Request that the *Complaint* be submitted for a decision in an *ADR Proceeding* in accordance with the *Procedural Rules*;

(2) Provide the name, postal and e-mail addresses, and the telephone and fax numbers of the *Complainant* and of any representative authorized to act for the *Complainant* in the *ADR Proceeding*;

(3) Specify a preferred method for communication directed to the *Complainant* in the *ADR Proceeding* (including the person to be contacted, means of communication, and address information);

(4) Designate whether the *Complainant* elects to have the dispute decided by a single-member or a three-member *Panel* and, in the event the *Complainant* elects a three-member *Panel*, provide the names of three candidates to serve as one of the *Panelists* (these candidates may be drawn from the list of panelists of the *Provider* dealing with the proceedings); to the maximum extent practicable, such candidates should not have been involved in the past three (3) years in any prior *ADR Proceeding* where the *Complainant* was a *Party*;

(5) Provide the name of the *Respondent* and, in case of an ADR Proceeding against a *Domain Name Holder* provide all information (including any postal and e-mail addresses and telephone and fax numbers) known to the *Complainant* on how to contact the *Respondent* or any representative of the *Respondent*, including contact information based on pre-*Complaint* dealings, in sufficient detail to allow the *Provider* to send the *Complaint* to the *Respondent* as described in Paragraph A2(a);

(6) Specify the domain name(s) that is/are the subject of the *Complaint*;

(7) Identify the *Registrar(s)* with whom the domain name(s) is/are registered at the time the *Complaint* is filed (not applicable for *Complaints* filed against the decision(s) of *the Registry* before the registration of the disputed domain name);

(8) In case the *Complaint* is filed against the decision(s) of *the Registry*, identify the disputed *the Registry* decision(s) and whether or not the disputed decision deals with the registration of a domain name within the Sunrise Period.

(9) Specify the names in respect of which a right is recognized or established by the national law of a Member State and/or Community law. For each such name, describe exactly the type of right(s) claimed, specify the law or law(s) as well as the conditions under which the right is recognized and/or established.

(10) Describe, in accordance with these *ADR Rules*, the grounds on which the *Complaint* is made including, in particular,

(i) In case of an *ADR Proceeding* against the *Domain Name Holder* in respect of which domain name the *Complaint* is initiated:

A. why the domain name is identical or confusingly similar to the name or names in respect of which a right or rights are recognized or established by national and/or Community law (as specified and described in accordance with Paragraph B 1 (b) (9)); and, either

B. why the domain name has been registered by its holder without rights or legitimate interests in respect of the domain name that is the subject of the *Complaint*; or

C. why the domain name should be considered as having been registered or being used in bad faith.

(ii) In case of an *ADR Proceeding* against *the Registry*, the reasons why a decision taken by *the Registry* conflicts with *European Union Regulations*.

(11) Specify, in accordance with these *ADR Rules*, the remedies sought (see Paragraph B11 (b) and (c) below);

(12) If the *Complainant* requests transfer of the domain name, provide evidence that the *Complainant* satisfies the general eligibility criteria for registration set out in Paragraph 4(2)(b) of Regulation (EC) No 733/2002;

(13) Identify any other legal proceedings that have been commenced or terminated in connection with or relating to any of the domain name(s) that is/are the subject of the *Complaint*;

(14) State that the *Complainant* will submit, with respect to any challenges to a decision in the *ADR Proceeding* revoking or transferring the domain name, to the jurisdiction of the courts in at least one specified *Mutual Jurisdiction* in accordance with Paragraph A1;

(15) Conclude with the following statement followed by the signature of the *Complainant* or its authorized representative:

"*Complainant* warrants that all information provided hereunder is complete and accurate.

Complainant agrees with the processing of his personal data by the *Provider* to the extent necessary for the due performance of the *Provider's* responsibilities hereunder.

Complainant also agrees with the publication of the full decision (including personal details contained in the decision) issued in the *ADR Proceeding* initiated by this *Complaint* in the language of the *ADR Proceeding* and in an unofficial English translation secured by the *Provider*.

Complainant further agrees that its claims and remedies concerning the registration of the domain name, the dispute, or the dispute's resolution shall be solely against the domain name holder and hereby waives any and all claims and remedies against

(i) the *Provider*, as well as its directors, officers, employees, advisors and agents, except in the case of deliberate wrongdoing;

(ii) *Panelists*, except in the case of deliberate wrongdoing;

(iii) the *Registrar*, except in the case of deliberate wrongdoing; and

(iv) *the Registry*, as well as its directors, officers, employees, advisors, and agents, except in the case of deliberate wrongdoing."

(16) Annex any documentary or other evidence, including any evidence concerning the rights upon which the *Complaint* relies, together with a schedule indexing such evidence.

(17) Include any forms prescribed in the *Supplemental ADR Rules* and comply with any formal requirements contained in the *Supplemental ADR Rules*, including any word limit.

(c) The *Complaint* may relate to more than one domain name, provided that the *Parties* and the language of the *ADR Proceedings* are the same.

(d) The *Provider* will acknowledge receiving the *Complaint* from the *Complainant*, subject to the receipt of the fees due above.

(e) As soon as practicable after the *Time of Filing*, but in any event not later than five (5) *days* from the date of *Time of Filing* and before notifying the *Respondent* pursuant to Article B2 below, the *Provider* shall inform *the Registry* of the identity of the *Complainant* and the domain name(s) involved. Upon receiving information from the *Provider*, *the Registry* shall block the disputed domain name pursuant to eu Domain Name Registration *Terms and Conditions*.

(f) Any *ADR Proceeding*(s) against a *Domain Name Holder* with a later *Time of Filing* with respect to the same domain name(s) shall be suspended pending the outcome of the ADR Proceeding initiated by the *Complaint* with the earliest *Time of Filing*. If in such *ADR Proceeding* the *Panel* decides to grant the *Complainant* the remedies requested, all suspended *ADR Proceedings* will be terminated and any fees paid shall be reimbursed. If in the *ADR Proceeding* the *Panel* rejects the *Complaint*, the *Provider* shall activate the *Complaint* next in time to the *Time of Filing*. The *Provider* shall notify the respective *Complainant(s)* of the termination, activation, or continued suspension of their *Complaint(s)* in writing within five (5) days from the date the *Panel* decision related to the prior *Complaint* is issued.

(g) In case an *ADR Proceeding* is initiated against *the Registry* with a later *Time of Filing* than another *ADR Proceeding* against the *Registry* with respect to the same decision taken by the *Registry*, the *ADR Proceeding* against the *Registry* with a later *Time of Filing* shall be terminated and any fees paid shall be reimbursed.

(h) Nothing mentioned in Paragraph 15, (i) to (iii) above, prevents the *Complainant* from initiating an *ADR Proceeding* against *the Registry* where a decision taken by *the Registry* conflicts with *European Union Regulations*.

(i) In case of an *ADR Proceeding* against the *Registry*, any request of a *Complainant* for documents or other information related to the *Registry* decision challenged in the *ADR Proceeding* must be made directly to the *Registry* in accordance with the *Registration Policy*.

2 Notification of Complaint

(a) The *Provider* shall review the *Complaint* for administrative compliance with the *Procedural Rules* and, if in compliance, shall forward the *Complaint* (together with the explanatory cover sheet prescribed by the *Provider's Supplemental ADR Rules*) to the *Respondent*, in the manner prescribed by Paragraphs A2(a) and A2(b), within five (5) *Working days* following receipt of the fees to be paid by the *Complainant* in accordance with Paragraph A6.

(b) If the *Provider* finds the *Complaint* not to be in administrative compliance with the *Procedural Rules*, it shall promptly notify the *Complainant* of the nature of the deficiencies identified. If the deficiencies are capable of being corrected, the *Complainant* shall have seven (7) *days* within which to correct any such deficiencies and submit an amended *Complaint*, after which, if not corrected, the *Provider* shall inform the *Complainant* that the *ADR Proceeding* is deemed to be withdrawn due to administrative deficiency and without prejudice to submission of a different *Complaint* by the *Complainant*.

(c) A *Complainant* can challenge the withdrawal of its *Complaint* due to administrative deficiency pursuant to Paragraph B2(b) above. The procedure related to such a challenge shall be as follows:

(1) The request shall be submitted to the *Provider* within 5 days from receiving the information about the withdrawal and shall:
   - (i) specify the information under Paragraphs B1 (b)(2), B1 (b)(6) and B1 (b)(8) (if applicable) of the *ADR Rules*;
   - (ii) specify the requested cancellation of the withdrawal of the *Complaint* due to administrative deficiency;
   - (iii) specify the reasons of the requested cancellation;
   - (iv) conclude with the statement under B1(b)(15) of the *ADR Rules*.

(2) The *Provider* will acknowledge receiving the request from the *Complainant*, subject to the receipt of the fees due pursuant to Paragraph A6(a) above and will appoint a single *Panel* to decide the request. Paragraph B5 applies accordingly.

(3) The *Panel* shall issue a decision whether or not to allow the requested challenge

within twelve (12) *days* from the date of its appointment. The *Panel's* decision shall be final and not subject to appeal. The decision shall be communicated to the *Complainant* without delay.

(d) The Provider shall immediately notify the Complainant, the Respondent, and the Registry of the Date of Commencement of an ADR Proceeding.

(e) The Provider shall suspend the ADR Proceeding until the procedures specified in Paragraphs B2(b) and B2(c) above are completed.

3 The Response

(a) Within thirty (30) *Working days* of the date of delivery of the *Complaint* in accordance with Paragraph A2(b), the *Respondent* shall submit a *Response* to the *Provider*.

(b) The *Response* shall be submitted in hard copy and in electronic form and shall:

(1) Provide the name, postal and e-mail addresses, and the telephone and fax numbers of the *Respondent* and of any representative authorized to act for the *Respondent* in the *ADR Proceeding*;

(2) Specify a preferred method for communication directed to the *Respondent* in the *ADR Proceeding* (including person to be contacted, medium, and address information);

(3) If the *Complainant* has elected a single-member *Panel* in the *Complaint* (see Paragraph B1(b)(3)), state whether the *Respondent* elects instead to have the dispute decided by a three-member *Panel*;

(4) If either *Complainant* or *Respondent* elects a three-member *Panel*, provide the names and contact details of three candidates to serve as one of the *Panelists* (these candidates may be drawn from any *Provider's* list of panelists; to the maximum extent practicable, such candidates should not have been involved in the past three (3) years in any prior *ADR Proceeding* where the *Respondent* was a *Party*;

(5) Identify any other legal proceedings that have been commenced or terminated in connection with or relating to any of the domain name(s) that is/are the subject of the *Complaint*;

(6) Describe, in accordance with these *ADR Rules*, the grounds on which the *Response* is made.

(7) Conclude with the following statement followed by the signature of the *Respondent* or its authorized representative:

"*Respondent* warrants that all information provided hereunder is complete and accurate.

Respondent agrees with the processing of his personal data by the *Provider* to the extent necessary for the due performance of the *Provider's* responsibilities hereunder.

Respondent also agrees with the publication of the full decision (including personal data contained in the decision) issued in this *ADR Proceeding* in the language of the *ADR Proceeding* and in an unofficial English translation secured by the *Provider.*

Respondent hereby waives any and all claims and remedies related to the current *ADR Proceeding* against

(i) the *Provider* as well as its directors, officers, employees, advisors and agents, except in the case of deliberate wrongdoing;

(ii) *Panelists*, except in the case of deliberate wrongdoing,

(iii) the *Registrar*, except in the case of deliberate wrongdoing and

(iv) *the Registry*, as well as its directors, officers, employees, and agents, except in the case of deliberate wrongdoing."

(8) Attach any documentary or other evidence, including any evidence concerning the rights upon which the *Respondent* relies, together with a schedule indexing such evidence.

(9) Include any forms prescribed in the *Supplemental ADR Rules* and comply with any formal requirements contained in the *Supplemental ADR Rules*, including any word limit.

(c) If the *Complainant* has elected to have the dispute decided by a single-member *Panel* and the *Respondent* elects a three-member *Panel*, the *Respondent* shall be required to pay a fee in accordance with Paragraph A6(b). This payment shall be made together with the submission of the *Response* to the *Provider*. In the event that the required payment is not made, the dispute shall be decided by a single-member *Panel*.

(d) The *Provider* shall confirm receipt of the *Response* to the *Respondent*. If the *Provider* finds the *Response* not to be in administrative compliance with the *Procedural Rules*, it shall promptly notify the *Respondent* of the nature of the deficiencies identified. If the deficiencies are capable of being remedied, the *Respondent* shall have seven (7) *days* within which to correct any such deficiencies and submit an amended *Response*, after which the *Response* shall be deemed not submitted by the *Respondent*. The *Provider* shall suspend the *ADR Proceeding* until either of the two actions happens first: (i) it receives the amended *Response* or (ii) the time period mentioned in this Paragraph expires.

(e) The *Provider* shall forward the administratively compliant *Response* to the *Complainant* without delay.

(f) If a *Respondent* does not submit a *Response* or submits solely an administratively deficient *Response*, the *Provider* shall notify the *Parties* of *Respondent*'s default. The *Provider* shall send to the *Panel* for its information and to the *Complainant* the administratively deficient *Response* submitted by the *Respondent*. The *Provider's* notification of the *Respondent*'s default shall be without prejudice to the *Respondent*'s right to have the dispute decided by a three member Panel pursuant to Paragraph B3(b)(4) above, provided the fees under Paragraph A.6(c) above have been paid.

(g) The *Respondent* can challenge the *Provider's* notification of the *Respondent*'s default in a written submission to the *Provider* filed within five (5) days from receiving the notification of *Respondent*'s default. The *Provider* shall acknowledge receiving the *Respondent*'s challenge and shall forward the *Respondent*'s challenge to the *Panel* within three (3) days from its receipt. The *Respondent*'s challenge shall be considered by the *Panel* in its sole discretion as part of its decision making. If the *Panel* confirms that the *Response* is administratively deficient, the *Panel* may decide the dispute based upon the *Complaint* only.

(h) Nothing mentioned in Paragraph 7, (i) to (iii) above, prevents the *Respondent* from initiating an *ADR Proceeding* against a decision taken by *the Registry* which conflicts with *European Union Regulations*.

4 Appointment of the Panel and Timing of Decision

(a) The *Panelists* shall be selected in accordance to the internal procedures of the *Providers*. They shall have appropriate expertise and shall be selected in an objective, transparent and non-discriminatory manner. Each *Provider* shall maintain and publish a publicly available list of panelists and their qualifications.

(b) If neither the *Complainant* nor the *Respondent* has elected a three-member *Panel* (Paragraphs B1(b)(3) and B3(b)(4)), the *Provider* shall appoint a single *Panelist* from its list of panelists.

(c) Unless it has already elected a three-member *Panel*, the *Complainant* shall submit to the *Provider*, within four (4) days of communication of a *Response* in which the *Respondent* elects a three-member *Panel*, the names and contact details of three candidates to serve as one of the *Panelists*. These candidates may be drawn from the *Provider's* list of panelists; to the maximum extent practicable, such candidates should not have been involved in the last three (3) years in any prior *ADR Proceeding* where the *Complainant* was a *Party*.

(d) In the event that either the *Complainant* or the *Respondent* elects a three-member *Panel*, the *Provider* shall appoint one *Panelist* from the list of candidates submitted by the *Complainant*, one *Panelist* from the list of candidates submitted by the *Respondent*, and one *Panelist* from its list of panelists. If either *Party* does not duly submit its list of candidates, the *Provider* shall appoint an additional *Panelist* from its list of Panelists.

(e) Once the entire *Panel* is appointed, the *Provider* shall notify the *Parties* of the identity of the *Panelists* appointed and the date by which, absent exceptional circumstances, the *Panel* shall forward its decision on the *Complaint* to the *Provider*.

5 Impartiality and Independence

(a) The *Panelists* shall have no personal or economic interests in the results of the dispute, and they undertake to resolve the dispute under the principles of good faith, fairness and due diligence. The *Panelists* shall maintain the confidential character of the information disclosed to them during the *ADR Proceedings* as far as such information is not included in the decision to be published.

(b) A *Panelist* shall be impartial and independent and shall have, before accepting appointment, disclosed to the *Provider* any circumstances giving rise to justifiable doubt as to the *Panelist's* impartiality or independence. If, at any stage during the *ADR Proceeding*, new circumstances arise that could give rise to justifiable doubt as to the impartiality or independence of a *Panelist*, that *Panelist* shall promptly disclose such circumstances to the *Provider*. In such event, the *Provider* shall have the sole discretion to appoint a substitute *Panelist*.

(c) Apart from the above, the *Parties* can also challenge the appointment of a *Panelist*. The *Party* that challenges a *Panelist* should explain to the *Provider* his reasons for the challenge. The challenge shall be filed within two (2) *days* from receiving the notice of the subject *Panelist's* appointment, or after having become aware of the circumstances giving rise to justifiable doubt in regard to the impartiality or independence of the *Panelist*.

(d) When a *Panelist* has been challenged by one *Party*, the other *Party* and/or the challenged *Panelist* will be entitled to submit a response. This right will be exercised within two (2) *days* after receiving the communication to which the previous Paragraph refers.

(e) The *Provider* will decide on the challenge, and its decision will be final and not subject to appeal.

6 Transmission of the File to the Panel

The *Provider* shall forward the file to the *Panel* as soon as the *Panelist* is appointed in the case of a *Panel* consisting of a single member, or as soon as the last *Panelist* is appointed in the case of a three-member *Panel*.

7 General Powers of the Panel

(a) The *Panel* shall conduct the *ADR Proceeding* in such manner as it considers appropriate in accordance with the *Procedural Rules*. The Panel is not obliged, but is permitted in its sole discretion, to conduct its own investigations on the circumstances of the case.

(b) In all cases, the *Panel* shall ensure that the *Parties* are treated fairly and with equality.

(c) The *Panel* shall ensure that the *ADR Proceeding* takes place with due expedition.

(d) The *Panel* shall determine in its sole discretion the admissibility, relevance, materiality and weight of the evidence.

8 Further Statements

In addition to the *Complaint* and the *Response*, the *Panel* may request or admit, in its sole discretion, further statements or documents from either of the *Parties*.

9 In-Person Hearings

There shall be no in-person hearings (including hearings by teleconference, videoconference, and web conference). The decision will be handled based on documents or other types of written evidence unless the *Panel* determines, in its sole discretion and as a matter of exceptional circumstances, that such a hearing is necessary for rendering a decision on the *Complaint*.

10 Default

(a) In the event that a *Party* does not comply with any of the time periods established by these *ADR Rules* or the *Panel*, the *Panel* shall proceed to a decision on the *Complaint* and may consider this failure to comply as grounds to accept the claims of the other *Party*.

(b) Unless provided differently in these *ADR Rules,* if a *Party* does not comply with any provision of, or requirement under, these *ADR Rules*, the *Supplemental ADR Rules* or any request from the *Panel*, the *Panel* shall draw such inferences therefrom as it considers appropriate.

11 Basis for Decision

(a) A *Panel* shall decide a *Complaint* on the basis of the statements and documents submitted and in accordance with the *Procedural Rules*.

(b) The remedies available pursuant to an *ADR Proceeding* where the *Respondent* is the *Domain Name Holder* in respect of which domain name the *Complaint* was initiated shall be limited to the revocation of the disputed domain name(s) /or, if the *Complainant* satisfies the general eligibility criteria for registration set out in Paragraph 4(2)(b) of Regulation (EC) No 733/2002, the transfer of the disputed domain name(s) to the *Complainant*.

(c) The main remedy available pursuant to an ADR Proceeding where the *Respondent* is the *Registry* shall be the annulment of the disputed decision taken by the *Registry*. The *Panel* may decide in appropriate cases pursuant to the *Procedural Rules*, *Registration Policy*, *Sunrise Rules* and/or the *Terms and Conditions* that the domain name in question shall be transferred, revoked or attributed. However, with regard to any *Registry* decision relating to a prior right invoked during the phased registration period such measures of transfer and attribution will only be granted by the *Panel* if the *Complainant* is the next applicant in the queue for the domain name concerned and subject to the decision by the *Registry* that the *Complainant* satisfies all registration criteria set out in *the European Union Regulations* and to the subsequent activation by the *Registry* of the domain name in the name of the *Complainant* who is the next applicant in the queue.

(d) The *Panel* shall issue a decision granting the remedies requested under the *Procedural Rules* in the event that the *Complainant* proves

(1) in *ADR Proceeding*s where the *Respondent* is the holder of a .eu domain name registration in respect of which the *Complaint* was initiated that

(i) The domain name is identical or confusingly similar to a name in respect of which a right is recognized or established by the national law of a Member State and/or Community law and; either

(ii) The domain name has been registered by the *Respondent* without rights or legitimate interest in the name; or

(iii) The domain name has been registered or is being used in bad faith.

(2) in ADR Proceedings where the Respondent is the Registry that the decision taken by the Registry conflicts with the European Union Regulations.

(e) Any of the following circumstances, in particular but without limitation, if found by the *Panel* to be proved based on its evaluation of all evidence presented, may demonstrate the *Respondent's* rights or legitimate interests to the domain name for purposes of Paragraph B11(d)(1)(ii):

(1) prior to any notice of the dispute, the *Respondent* has used the domain name or a name corresponding to the domain name in connection with the offering of goods or services or has made demonstrable preparation to do so;

(2) the *Respondent*, being an undertaking, organization or natural person, has been commonly known by the domain name, even in the absence of a right recognized or established by national and/or Community law;

(3) the *Respondent* is making a legitimate and non-commercial or fair use of the domain name, without intent to mislead consumers or harm the reputation of a name in which a right is recognized or established by national law and/or Community law.

(f) For purposes of Paragraph B11(d)(1)(iii), the following circumstances, in particular but without limitation, if found by the *Panel* to be present, shall be evidence of the registration or use of a domain name in bad faith:

(1) circumstances indicating that the domain name was registered or acquired primarily for the purpose of selling, renting, or otherwise transferring the domain name to the holder of a name, in respect of which a right is recognized or established by national and/or Community law, or to a public body; or

(2) the domain name has been registered in order to prevent the holder of such a name in respect of which a right is recognized or established by national and/or Community law, or a public body, from reflecting this name in a corresponding domain name, provided that:

(i) the *Respondent* has engaged in a pattern of such conduct; or

(ii) the domain name has not been used in a relevant way for at least two years from the date of registration; or

(iii) there are circumstances where, at the time the *ADR Proceeding* was initiated, the *Respondent* has declared its intention to use the domain name, in respect of which a right is recognized or established by national and/or Community law or which corresponds to the name of a public body, in a relevant way but failed to do so within six months of the day on which the *ADR Proceeding* was initiated;

(3) the domain name was registered primarily for the purpose of disrupting the professional activities of a competitor; or

(4) the domain name was intentionally used to attract Internet users, for commercial gain to the *Respondent's* website or other on-line location, by creating a likelihood

of confusion with a name on which a right is recognized or established, by national and/or Community law, or it is a name of a public body, such likelihood arising as to the source, sponsorship, affiliation or endorsement of the website or location or of a product or service on the website or location of the Respondent; or

(5) the domain name is a personal name for which no demonstrable link exists between the *Respondent* and the domain name registered.

12 Decision-Making and Form of Decisions

(a) The decisions of the *Panelists* will be final, not subject to appeal, and compulsory for the *Parties*, without detriment to the right of the *Parties* to initiate a court proceeding in a *Mutual Jurisdiction* which will have consequences to the implementation of the decision as described in the *Terms and Conditions*.

(b) The *Panel* shall forward its decision on the *Complaint* to the *Provider* within one month of the *Provider's* receipt of administratively compliant *Response* or the lapse of the time period for its submission.

(c) In the case of a three-member *Panel*, the *Panel's* decision shall be made by simple majority.

(d) The *Panel's* decision shall be in writing, provide the reasons on which it is based, indicate the date on which it was rendered and identify the name(s) of the *Panelist(s)*. If the *Panel* decides that the disputed domain name be revoked or transferred to the *Complainant*, it shall state that the decision shall be implemented by *the Registry* within thirty (30) days after the notification of the decision to the *Parties*, unless the *Respondent* initiates court proceedings in a *Mutual Jurisdiction* (see Paragraphs B12(a) and B14).

(e) *Panel* decisions shall comply with formal requirements set forth in the *Provider's Supplemental ADR Rules*.

(f) If the *Panel* concludes that the dispute is not within the scope of the Regulation (EC) No 874/2004, it shall so state.

(g) If the *Complainant* has

(1) proved that the domain name is identical or confusingly similar to a name in respect of which *Complainant* owns a right that is recognized or established by a Member State's national law and/or Community law; and

(2) failed to prove the *Respondent's* lack of rights and legitimate interests, as specified in Paragraph B11(d)(1)(ii) of these *ADR Rules*; and

(3) relied on Paragraph B11(f)(2)(iii) of these *ADR Rules* to prove bad faith; and

(4) failed to prove bad faith on any other grounds;

the *Panel* shall issue an interim decision setting out its findings on issues (1) to (4) above and shall suspend the proceedings until a date six months after the *Time of Filing*. In such an event (and should the *Respondent* not submit evidence of relevant use by the postponed date and the *Complainant* prove the remaining elements required by Paragraph B11(f)(2)(iii)), the *Panel* shall decide whether or not to grant to the *Complainant* the requested remedy. Under all other circumstances, the *Panel* shall proceed to a decision without reference to Paragraph B11(f)(2)(iii).

All evidence submitted by the *Respondent* must be accompanied by a declaration of completeness and accuracy and be given to the *Complainant*. The *Complainant* shall have a right to submit a response to the *Respondent*'s evidence within fifteen (15) days from receiving the evidence.

(h) If after considering the submissions the *Panel* finds that the *Complaint* was initiated in bad faith, the *Panel* shall declare in its decision that the *Complaint* was brought in bad faith and constitutes an abuse of administrative proceeding.

Each *Panel* decision shall contain a brief summary in English in accordance with guidelines prepared by the *Provider*.

13 Communication of Decision to Parties

(a) Within three (3) *Working days* after receiving the final decision from the *Panel*, the *Provider* shall communicate the full text of the decision to each *Party*, the concerned *Registrar(s)* and to *the Registry*.

(b) The *Provider* shall publish the full decision on a publicly accessible web site.

14 Implementation of Decision

The implementation of the decision shall follow the *Terms and Conditions*. [2038]

C CONCLUDING PROVISIONS

1 Exclusion of Liability

Except in the case of deliberate wrongdoing, neither the *Provider* nor a *Panelist* shall be liable to a *Party* for any act or omission in connection with any *ADR Proceeding* under these *ADR Rules*.

2 Amendments

The version of these *ADR Rules* in effect at the time of the submission of the *Complaint* to the *Provider* shall apply to the *ADR Proceeding* commenced thereby. The *Registry* may amend these *ADR Rules* at any time after having consulted all the *Providers*.

3 Effective Date

These *ADR Rules* apply to all *Complaints* filed on or after 7 December 2005. [2039]

SUPPLEMENTAL ADR RULES OF THE ARBITRATION COURT ATTACHED TO THE ECONOMIC CHAMBER OF THE CZECH REPUBLIC AND AGRICULTURAL CHAMBER OF THE CZECH REPUBLIC

NOTES

The ADR Supplemental Rules can be found at www.adr.eu. © Arbitration Court attached to the Economic Chamber of the Czech Republic and Agricultural Chamber of the Czech Republic (Czech Arbitration Court), 2006.

A GENERAL

1 Scope

(a) **Relationship to ADR Rules and EU legislation**. These *Supplemental ADR Rules* are to be read and used in connection with the *.eu Dispute Resolution Rules*, adopted by the European Registry of Internet Domain names (*EURid*) (the "*ADR Rules*") and with the Regulations (EC) No 733/2002 and No 874/2004 and with any other applicable EU legislation. These supplemental rules may not derogate from either the *ADR Rules* or the *European Union Regulations*.

(b) **Version of Supplemental Rules**. The version of these *Supplemental ADR Rules* in effect on the date of the submission of the *Complaint* shall apply to the administrative proceeding commenced thereby.

2 Definitions

Provider means the Arbitration Court attached to the Economic Chamber of the Czech Republic and Agricultural Chamber of the Czech Republic.

Any other term defined in the *ADR Rules* shall have the same meaning when used in these *Supplemental ADR Rules*.

3 Fees and Payment Instructions

The fees applicable for administrative procedures and obligatory payment instructions are specified in Annex A hereto and posted on the *Provider's* website.

4 Communication Instructions

The *Parties* shall be required to adhere to communication instructions contained in Annex C hereto.

B CONDUCT OF THE PROCEEDINGS

1 Submission of Complaint

(a) The *Complaint* must include all elements listed in Paragraph B1(b) of the *ADR Rules*.

(b) **Complaint Form**. In accordance with Paragraph B1(b)(17) of the *ADR Rules*, the *Complainant* shall be required to prepare its *Complaint* using the *Complaint Form* included in the list of Forms contained in Annex B hereto and posted on the *Provider's* web site.

(c) **Number of Copies**. When a hard-copy submission is to be made to the *Provider* by a *Party*, it shall be submitted in three (3) copies together with one (1) original of such submission.

(d) **Language of the ADR Proceeding.** In accordance with Paragraph A3(d) of the *ADR Rules*, all relevant parts of the documents submitted as part of the *Complaint* including any annexes and schedules submitted in languages other than the language of the *ADR Proceeding* must be accompanied by a translation into the language of the *ADR Proceeding*. Documents or their parts not submitted in the language of the *ADR Proceeding* shall not be taken into account by the *Panel*.

2 Appointment of Case Administrator

(a) **Notification**. The *Provider* shall advise the *Parties* of the name and contact details of a member of its staff who shall be the *Case Administrator* and who shall be responsible for all administrative matters relating to the dispute and communications to the *ADR Panel*.

(b) **Responsibilities**. *The Case Administrator* may provide administrative assistance to the *Panel* or *Panelist(s)*, but shall have no authority to decide matters of a substantive nature concerning the dispute.

3 Submission of Response

(a) The *Response* must include all elements listed in Paragraph B3(b) of the *ADR Rules*.

(b) *Response Form*. In accordance with Paragraph B3(b)(9) of the *ADR Rules*, the *Respondent* shall be required to prepare its *Response* using the *Response Form* included in the list of Forms contained in Annex B hereto and posted on the *Provider's* web site.

4 Panelist Appointment Procedures

(a) **Party Candidates**. Where a Party is required to submit the names of three (3) candidates for consideration for appointment by the *Provider* as a *Panelist* (ie, in accordance with paragraphs B1(b)(4), B3(b)(4) and B4(c) of the *ADR Rules*), that *Party* shall provide the names and contact details of its three candidates in the order of its preference. In appointing a *Panelist*, the *Provider* shall, subject to availability, respect the order of preference indicated by a *Party*.

(b) **Presiding Panelist**. The *Panelist* appointed in accordance with Paragraph B4(d) of the *ADR Rules* from the *Provider's* list of Panelists shall be the *Presiding Panelist*, coordinating the *Panel*.

(c) **Respondent Default.** Where the *Respondent* does not submit a *Response* or does not submit the payment provided for in Paragraph B3(c) of the *ADR Rules* by the deadline specified by the *Provider*, the *Provider* shall proceed to appoint the *Panel*.

5 Declaration

In accordance with Paragraph B5 of the *ADR Rules*, prior to appointment as a *Panelist*, a candidate shall be required to submit to the *Provider* a *Declaration of Independence and Impartiality* using the form included in the list of Forms contained in Annex B hereto and posted on the *Provider's* web site.

6 Forms

In addition to the Form Complaint in relation to the Complaint (Section B above) and Form Response in relation to the *Response* (Section 3 above) the *Parties* shall be required to use for their other communication during the *ADR Proceeding* form documents set out in Annex B hereto and posted on the *Provider's* web site.

7 In-Person Hearings

In case the *Panel* determines, in its sole discretion, that an in-person hearing is necessary, the hearing will be carried out by teleconference, videoconference, or web conference at the CHAT address of the *Provider* if both Parties agree with the use of such technology; otherwise, the hearing will be carried out in-person at the location specified by the *Panel*. The *Panel* will give the *Parties* seven (7) days notice that the aforementioned hearing will be held, including the date, time and electronic place or physical location where it will take place.

8 Panel Decision

The Panel decision will meet the requirements set forth in Article B13 of the *ADR Rules* and will comply with all formal requirements contained in these *Supplemental ADR Rules*, with the exception of the limit of number of pages pursuant to Paragraph 11 below where the *Panel* will exercise its discretion. A model decision is included in the list of Forms contained in Annex B hereto and posted in the *Provider's* website.

9 Correction of Clerical Mistakes

Within seven (7) days of receiving the decision, a *Party* may, by written notice to the *Panel* and the other *Party*, request the *Panel* to correct in the decision any errors in computation, any clerical or typographical errors, or any errors of a similar nature. Any such corrections shall be given in writing to the *Parties* and shall become a part of the decision.

The *Panel* may correct any errors on its own initiative of the type referred to in the preceding Paragraph within seven (7) days of the date of the decision being rendered.

10 Publication of the Decision

The *Provider* shall submit the decision of the *Panel* to the *Parties*, the *Registrar(s)* and *EURid* as required by the *ADR Rules* and the *Registration Policy*. The *Provider* shall publish the full decision on the *Provider's* Website, listing:

(a) the Domain Name that is in dispute and is the subject of a *Complaint*;
(b) the case number;
(c) the *Date of Commencement of ADR Proceeding*.

The decision shall be published in the language of the ADR Proceeding and in an unofficial translation into English language secured by the *Provider*.

11 Word Limits

Panelists shall exercise reasonable efforts to adhere the following guidelines as to length of the decisions:

(a) The word limit under Paragraph B1(b)(10) of the *ADR Rules* shall be 5,000 words.
(b) The word limit under Paragraph B3(b)(6) of the *ADR Rules* shall be 5,000 words.
(c) The word limit under Paragraph B13(e) of the *ADR Rules* shall be 5,000 words.

C CONCLUDING PROVISIONS

1 Amendments

(a) Subject to the *ADR Rules*, the *Provider* may amend these *Supplemental ADR Rules* in its sole discretion.

(b) The version of these *Supplemental ADR Rules* in effect at the time of the submission of the *Complaint* to the *Provider* shall apply to the *ADR Proceedings* commenced thereby. *EURid* may amend these *ADR Supplemental Rules* at any time after consultation with the *Provider*.

2 Effective date

These *Supplemental ADR Rules* apply to all cases filed on or after 7 December 2005.

3 List of Annexes

Annex A: Fee Schedule;

Annex B: List of Forms;

Annex C: Communication Instructions.

[2040]

UNIFORM DOMAIN NAME DISPUTE RESOLUTION POLICY

(As Approved by ICANN on October 24, 1999)

NOTES

The original source for this document is ICANN (Internet Corporation for Assigned Names and Numbers).

1. Purpose

This Uniform Domain Name Dispute Resolution Policy (the "Policy") has been adopted by the Internet Corporation for Assigned Names and Numbers ("ICANN"), is incorporated by reference into your Registration Agreement, and sets forth the terms and conditions in connection with a dispute between you and any party other than us (the registrar) over the registration and use of an Internet domain name registered by you. Proceedings under Paragraph 4 of this Policy will be conducted according to the Rules for Uniform Domain Name Dispute Resolution Policy (the "Rules of Procedure"), which are available at www.icann.org/udrp/udrp-rules-24oct99.htm, and the selected administrative-dispute-resolution service provider's supplemental rules.

2. Your Representations

By applying to register a domain name, or by asking us to maintain or renew a domain name registration, you hereby represent and warrant to us that—

(a) the statements that you made in your Registration Agreement are complete and accurate;

(b) to your knowledge, the registration of the domain name will not infringe upon or otherwise violate the rights of any third party;

(c) you are not registering the domain name for an unlawful purpose; and

(d) you will not knowingly use the domain name in violation of any applicable laws or regulations. It is your responsibility to determine whether your domain name registration infringes or violates someone else's rights.

3. Cancellations, Transfers, and Changes

We will cancel, transfer or otherwise make changes to domain name registrations under the following circumstances—

(a) subject to the provisions of Paragraph 8, our receipt of written or appropriate electronic instructions from you or your authorised agent to take such action;

(b) our receipt of an order from a court or arbitral tribunal, in each case of competent jurisdiction, requiring such action; and/or

(c) our receipt of a decision of an Administrative Panel requiring such action in any administrative proceeding to which you were a party and which was conducted under this Policy or a later version of this Policy adopted by ICANN. (See Paragraph 4(i) and (k) below.)

We may also cancel, transfer or otherwise make changes to a domain name registration in accordance with the terms of your Registration Agreement or other legal requirements.

4. Mandatory Administrative Proceeding

This Paragraph sets forth the type of disputes for which you are required to submit to a mandatory administrative proceeding. These proceedings will be conducted before one of the administrative-dispute-resolution service providers listed at www.icann.org/udrp/approved-providers.htm (each, a "Provider").

a. Applicable Disputes

You are required to submit to a mandatory administrative proceeding in the event that a third party (a "complainant") asserts to the applicable Provider, in compliance with the Rules of Procedure, that

(i) your domain name is identical or confusingly similar to a trademark or service mark in which the complainant has rights; and
(ii) you have no rights or legitimate interests in respect of the domain name; and
(iii) your domain name has been registered and is being used in bad faith.

In the administrative proceeding, the complainant must prove that each of these three elements are present.

b. *Evidence of Registration and Use in Bad Faith*
For the purposes of Paragraph 4(a)(iii), the following circumstances, in particular but without limitation, if found by the Panel to be present, shall be evidence of the registration and use of a domain name in bad faith—

(i) circumstances indicating that you have registered or you have acquired the domain name primarily for the purpose of selling, renting, or otherwise transferring the domain name registration to the complainant who is the owner of the trademark or service mark or to a competitor of that complainant, for valuable consideration in excess of your documented out-of-pocket costs directly related to the domain name; or
(ii) you have registered the domain name in order to prevent the owner of the trademark or service mark from reflecting the mark in a corresponding domain name, provided that you have engaged in a pattern of such conduct; or
(iii) you have registered the domain name primarily for the purpose of disrupting the business of a competitor; or
(iv) by using the domain name, you have intentionally attempted to attract, for commercial gain, Internet users to your web site or other on-line location, by creating a likelihood of confusion with the complainant's mark as to the source, sponsorship, affiliation, or endorsement of your web site or location or of a product or service on your web site or location.

c. *How to Demonstrate Your Rights to and Legitimate Interests in the Domain Name in Responding to a Complaint*
When you receive a complaint, you should refer to Paragraph 5 of the Rules of Procedure in determining how your response should be prepared. Any of the following circumstances, in particular but without limitation, if found by the Panel to be proved based on its evaluation of all evidence presented, shall demonstrate your rights or legitimate interests to the domain name for purposes of Paragraph 4(a)(ii)—

(i) before any notice to you of the dispute, your use of, or demonstrable preparations to use, the domain name or a name corresponding to the domain name in connection with a bona fide offering of goods or services; or
(ii) you (as an individual, business, or other organisation) have been commonly known by the domain name, even if you have acquired no trademark or service mark rights; or
(iii) you are making a legitimate noncommercial or fair use of the domain name, without intent for commercial gain to misleadingly divert consumers or to tarnish the trademark or service mark at issue.

d. *Selection of Provider*
The complainant shall select the Provider from among those approved by ICANN by submitting the complaint to that Provider. The selected Provider will administer the proceeding, except in cases of consolidation as described in Paragraph 4(f).

e. *Initiation of Proceeding and Process and Appointment of Administrative Panel*
The Rules of Procedure state the process for initiating and conducting a proceeding and for appointing the panel that will decide the dispute (the "Administrative Panel").

f. *Consolidation*
In the event of multiple disputes between you and a complainant, either you or the complainant may petition to consolidate the disputes before a single Administrative Panel. This petition shall be made to the first Administrative Panel appointed to hear a pending dispute between the parties. This Administrative

Panel may consolidate before it any or all such disputes in its sole discretion, provided that the disputes being consolidated are governed by this Policy or a later version of this Policy adopted by ICANN.

g. *Fees*

All fees charged by a Provider in connection with any dispute before an Administrative Panel pursuant to this Policy shall be paid by the complainant, except in cases where you elect to expand the Administrative Panel from one to three panellists as provided in Paragraph 5(b)(iv) of the Rules of Procedure, in which case all fees will be split evenly by you and the complainant.

h. *Our Involvement in Administrative Proceedings*

We do not, and will not, participate in the administration or conduct of any proceeding before an Administrative Panel. In addition, we will not be liable as a result of any decisions rendered by the Administrative Panel.

i. *Remedies*

The remedies available to a complainant pursuant to any proceeding before an Administrative Panel shall be limited to requiring the cancellation of your domain name or the transfer of your domain name registration to the complainant.

j. *Notification and Publication*

The Provider shall notify us of any decision made by an Administrative Panel with respect to a domain name you have registered with us. All decisions under this Policy will be published in full over the Internet, except when an Administrative Panel determines in an exceptional case to redact portions of its decision.

k. *Availability of Court Proceedings*

The mandatory administrative proceeding requirements set forth in Paragraph 4 shall not prevent either you or the complainant from submitting the dispute to a court of competent jurisdiction for independent resolution before such mandatory administrative proceeding is commenced or after such proceeding is concluded. If an Administrative Panel decides that your domain name registration should be cancelled or transferred, we will wait ten (10) business days (as observed in the location of our principal office) after we are informed by the applicable Provider of the Administrative Panel's decision before implementing that decision. We will then implement the decision unless we have received from you during that ten (10) business day period official documentation (such as a copy of a complaint, file-stamped by the clerk of the court) that you have commenced a lawsuit against the complainant in a jurisdiction to which the complainant has submitted under Paragraph 3(b)(xiii) of the Rules of Procedure. (In general, that jurisdiction is either the location of our principal office or of your address as shown in our Who is database. See Paragraphs 1 and 3(b)(xiii) of the Rules of Procedure for details.) If we receive such documentation within the ten (10) business day period, we will not implement the Administrative Panel's decision, and we will take no further action, until we receive (i) evidence satisfactory to us of a resolution between the parties; (ii) evidence satisfactory to us that your lawsuit has been dismissed or withdrawn; or (iii) a copy of an order from such court dismissing your lawsuit or ordering that you do not have the right to continue to use your domain name.

5. All Other Disputes and Litigation

All other disputes between you and any party other than us regarding your domain name registration that are not brought pursuant to the mandatory administrative proceeding provisions of Paragraph 4 shall be resolved between you and such other party through any court, arbitration or other proceeding that may be available.

6. Our Involvement in Disputes

We will not participate in any way in any dispute between you and any party other than us regarding the registration and use of your domain name. You shall not name us as a party or otherwise include us in any such proceeding. In the event that we are named as a party in any such proceeding, we reserve the right to raise any and all defenses deemed appropriate, and to take any other action necessary to defend ourselves.

7. Maintaining the Status Quo

We will not cancel, transfer, activate, deactivate, or otherwise change the status of any domain name registration under this Policy except as provided in Paragraph 3 above.

8. Transfers During a Dispute

a. *Transfers of a Domain Name to a New Holder*

You may not transfer your domain name registration to another holder

(i) during a pending administrative proceeding brought pursuant to Paragraph 4 or for a period of fifteen (15) business days (as observed in the location of our principal place of business) after such proceeding is concluded; or

(ii) during a pending court proceeding or arbitration commenced regarding your domain name unless the party to whom the domain name registration is being transferred agrees, in writing, to be bound by the decision of the court or arbitrator. We reserve the right to cancel any transfer of a domain name registration to another holder that is made in violation of this subparagraph.

b. *Changing Registrars*

You may not transfer your domain name registration to another registrar during a pending administrative proceeding brought pursuant to Paragraph 4 or for a period of fifteen (15) business days (as observed in the location of our principal place of business) after such proceeding is concluded. You may transfer administration of your domain name registration to another registrar during a pending court action or arbitration, provided that the domain name you have registered with us shall continue to be subject to the proceedings commenced against you in accordance with the terms of this Policy. In the event that you transfer a domain name registration to us during the pendency of a court action or arbitration, such dispute shall remain subject to the domain name dispute policy of the registrar from which the domain name registration was transferred.

9. Policy Modifications

We reserve the right to modify this Policy at any time with the permission of ICANN. We will post our revised Policy at <URL> at least thirty (30) calendar days before it becomes effective. Unless this Policy has already been invoked by the submission of a complaint to a Provider, in which event the version of the Policy in effect at the time it was invoked will apply to you until the dispute is over, all such changes will be binding upon you with respect to any domain name registration dispute, whether the dispute arose before, on or after the effective date of our change. In the event that you object to a change in this Policy, your sole remedy is to cancel your domain name registration with us, provided that you will not be entitled to a refund of any fees you paid to us. The revised Policy will apply to you until you cancel your domain name registration.

[2041]

RULES FOR UNIFORM DOMAIN NAME DISPUTE RESOLUTION POLICY (THE "RULES")

(As Approved by ICANN on October 24, 1999)

NOTES

The original source for this document is ICANN (Internet Corporation for Assigned Names and Numbers).

Administrative proceedings for the resolution of disputes under the Uniform Dispute Resolution Policy adopted by ICANN shall be governed by these Rules and also the Supplemental Rules of the Provider administering the proceedings, as posted on its web site.

1. Definitions

In these Rules—

"Complainant" means the party initiating a complaint concerning a domain-name registration.

"ICANN" refers to the Internet Corporation for Assigned Names and Numbers.

"Mutual Jurisdiction" means a court jurisdiction at the location of either

(a) the principal office of the Registrar (provided the domain-name holder has submitted in its Registration Agreement to that jurisdiction for court adjudication of disputes concerning or arising from the use of the domain name) or

(b) the domain-name holder's address as shown for the registration of the domain name in Registrar's Whois database at the time the complaint is submitted to the Provider.

"Panel" means an administrative panel appointed by a Provider to decide a complaint concerning a domain-name registration.

"panellist" means an individual appointed by a Provider to be a member of a Panel.

"Party" means a Complainant or a Respondent.

"Policy" means the Uniform Domain Name Dispute Resolution Policy that is incorporated by reference and made a part of the Registration Agreement.

"Provider" means a dispute-resolution service provider approved by ICANN. A list of such Providers appears at www.icann.org/udrp/approved-providers.htm.

"Registrar" means the entity with which the Respondent has registered a domain name that is the subject of a complaint.

"Registration Agreement" means the agreement between a Registrar and a domain-name holder.

"Respondent" means the holder of a domain-name registration against which a complaint is initiated.

"Reverse Domain Name Hijacking" means using the Policy in bad faith to attempt to deprive a registered domain-name holder of a domain name.

"Supplemental Rules" means the rules adopted by the Provider administering a proceeding to supplement these Rules. Supplemental Rules shall not be inconsistent with the Policy or these Rules and shall cover such topics as fees, word and page limits and guidelines, the means for communicating with the Provider and the Panel, and the form of cover sheets.

2. Communications

(a) When forwarding a complaint to the Respondent, it shall be the Provider's responsibility to employ reasonably available means calculated to achieve actual notice to Respondent. Achieving actual notice, or employing the following measures to do so, shall discharge this responsibility—

(i) sending the complaint to all postal-mail and facsimile addresses (A) shown in the domain name's registration data in Registrar's Whois database for the registered domain-name holder, the technical contact, and the administrative contact and (B) supplied by Registrar to the Provider for the registration's billing contact; and

(ii) sending the complaint in electronic form (including annexes to the extent available in that form) by e-mail to—

(A) the e-mail addresses for those technical, administrative, and billing contacts;

(B) postmaster@<the contested domain name>; and

(C) if the domain name (or "www." followed by the domain name) resolves to an active web page (other than a generic page the Provider concludes is maintained by a registrar or ISP for parking domain-names registered by multiple domain-name holders), any e-mail address shown or e-mail links on that web page; and

(iii) sending the complaint to any address the Respondent has notified the Provider it prefers and, to the extent practicable, to all other addresses provided to the Provider by Complainant under Paragraph 3(b)(v).

(b) Except as provided in Paragraph 2(a), any written communication to Complainant or Respondent provided for under these Rules shall be made by the preferred means stated by the Complainant or Respondent, respectively (see Paragraphs 3(b)(iii) and 5(b)(iii)), or in the absence of such specification

(i) by telecopy or facsimile transmission, with a confirmation of transmission; or

(ii) by postal or courier service, postage pre-paid and return receipt requested; or

(iii) electronically via the Internet, provided a record of its transmission is available.

(c) Any communication to the Provider or the Panel shall be made by the means and in the manner (including number of copies) stated in the Provider's Supplemental Rules.

(d) Communications shall be made in the language prescribed in Paragraph 11. E-mail communications should, if practicable, be sent in plaintext.

(e) Either Party may update its contact details by notifying the Provider and the Registrar.

(f) Except as otherwise provided in these Rules, or decided by a Panel, all communications provided for under these Rules shall be deemed to have been made—

(i) if delivered by telecopy or facsimile transmission, on the date shown on the confirmation of transmission; or
(ii) if by postal or courier service, on the date marked on the receipt; or
(iii) if via the Internet, on the date that the communication was transmitted, provided that the date of transmission is verifiable.

(g) Except as otherwise provided in these Rules, all time periods calculated under these Rules to begin when a communication is made shall begin to run on the earliest date that the communication is deemed to have been made in accordance with Paragraph 2(f).

(h) Any communication by
(i) a Panel to any Party shall be copied to the Provider and to the other Party;
(ii) the Provider to any Party shall be copied to the other Party; and
(iii) a Party shall be copied to the other Party, the Panel and the Provider, as the case may be.

(i) It shall be the responsibility of the sender to retain records of the fact and circumstances of sending, which shall be available for inspection by affected parties and for reporting purposes.

(j) In the event a Party sending a communication receives notification of non-delivery of the communication, the Party shall promptly notify the Panel (or, if no Panel is yet appointed, the Provider) of the circumstances of the notification. Further proceedings concerning the communication and any response shall be as directed by the Panel (or the Provider).

3. The Complaint

(a) Any person or entity may initiate an administrative proceeding by submitting a complaint in accordance with the Policy and these Rules to any Provider approved by ICANN. (Due to capacity constraints or for other reasons, a Provider's ability to accept complaints may be suspended at times. In that event, the Provider shall refuse the submission. The person or entity may submit the complaint to another Provider.)

(b) The complaint shall be submitted in hard copy and (except to the extent not available for annexes) in electronic form and shall—
(i) Request that the complaint be submitted for decision in accordance with the Policy and these Rules;
(ii) Provide the name, postal and e-mail addresses, and the telephone and telefax numbers of the Complainant and of any representative authorised to act for the Complainant in the administrative proceeding;
(iii) Specify a preferred method for communications directed to the Complainant in the administrative proceeding (including person to be contacted, medium, and address information) for each of (A) electronic-only material and (B) material including hard copy;
(iv) Designate whether Complainant elects to have the dispute decided by a single-member or a three-member Panel and, in the event Complainant elects a three-member Panel, provide the names and contact details of three candidates to serve as one of the panellists (these candidates may be drawn from any ICANN-approved Provider's list of panellists);
(v) Provide the name of the Respondent (domain-name holder) and all information (including any postal and e-mail addresses and telephone and telefax numbers) known to Complainant regarding how to contact Respondent or any representative of Respondent, including contact information based on pre-complaint dealings, in sufficient detail to allow the Provider to send the complaint as described in Paragraph 2(a);
(vi) Specify the domain name(s) that is/are the subject of the complaint;
(vii) Identify the Registrar(s) with whom the domain name(s) is/are registered at the time the complaint is filed;
(viii) Specify the trademark(s) or service mark(s) on which the complaint is based and, for each mark, describe the goods or services, if any, with which the mark is used (Complainant may also separately describe other goods and services with which it intends, at the time the complaint is submitted, to use the mark in the future.);
(ix) Describe, in accordance with the Policy, the grounds on which the complaint is made including, in particular,
(1) the manner in which the domain name(s) is/are identical or confusingly similar to a trademark or service mark in which the Complainant has rights; and

(2) why the Respondent (domain-name holder) should be considered as having no rights or legitimate interests in respect of the domain name(s) that is/are the subject of the complaint; and

(3) why the domain name(s) should be considered as having been registered and being used in bad faith

(The description should, for elements (2) and (3), discuss any aspects of Paragraphs 4(b) and 4(c) of the Policy that are applicable. The description shall comply with any word or page limit set forth in the Provider's Supplemental Rules.);

(x) Specify, in accordance with the Policy, the remedies sought;

(xi) Identify any other legal proceedings that have been commenced or terminated in connection with or relating to any of the domain name(s) that are the subject of the complaint;

(xii) State that a copy of the complaint, together with the cover sheet as prescribed by the Provider's Supplemental Rules, has been sent or transmitted to the Respondent (domain-name holder), in accordance with Paragraph 2(b);

(xiii) State that Complainant will submit, with respect to any challenges to a decision in the administrative proceeding canceling or transferring the domain name, to the jurisdiction of the courts in at least one specified Mutual Jurisdiction;

(xiv) Conclude with the following statement followed by the signature of the Complainant or its authorised representative—

"Complainant agrees that its claims and remedies concerning the registration of the domain name, the dispute, or the dispute's resolution shall be solely against the domain-name holder and waives all such claims and remedies against (a) the dispute-resolution provider and panellists, except in the case of deliberate wrongdoing, (b) the registrar, (c) the registry administrator, and (d) the Internet Corporation for Assigned Names and Numbers, as well as their directors, officers, employees, and agents."

"Complainant certifies that the information contained in this Complaint is to the best of Complainant's knowledge complete and accurate, that this Complaint is not being presented for any improper purpose, such as to harass, and that the assertions in this Complaint are warranted under these Rules and under applicable law, as it now exists or as it may be extended by a good-faith and reasonable argument."; and

(xv) Annex any documentary or other evidence, including a copy of the Policy applicable to the domain name(s) in dispute and any trademark or service mark registration upon which the complaint relies, together with a schedule indexing such evidence.

(c) The complaint may relate to more than one domain name, provided that the domain names are registered by the same domain-name holder.

4. Notification of Complaint

(a) The Provider shall review the complaint for administrative compliance with the Policy and these Rules and, if in compliance, shall forward the complaint (together with the explanatory cover sheet prescribed by the Provider's Supplemental Rules) to the Respondent, in the manner prescribed by Paragraph 2(a), within three (3) calendar days following receipt of the fees to be paid by the Complainant in accordance with Paragraph 19.

(b) If the Provider finds the complaint to be administratively deficient, it shall promptly notify the Complainant and the Respondent of the nature of the deficiencies identified. The Complainant shall have five (5) calendar days within which to correct any such deficiencies, after which the administrative proceeding will be deemed withdrawn without prejudice to submission of a different complaint by Complainant.

(c) The date of commencement of the administrative proceeding shall be the date on which the Provider completes its responsibilities under Paragraph 2(a) in connection with forwarding the Complaint to the Respondent.

(d) The Provider shall immediately notify the Complainant, the Respondent, the concerned Registrar(s), and ICANN of the date of commencement of the administrative proceeding.

5. The Response

(a) Within twenty (20) days of the date of commencement of the administrative proceeding the Respondent shall submit a response to the Provider.

(b) The response shall be submitted in hard copy and (except to the extent not available for annexes) in electronic form and shall—

(i) Respond specifically to the statements and allegations contained in the complaint and include any and all bases for the Respondent (domain-name holder) to retain registration and use of the disputed domain name (This portion of the response shall comply with any word or page limit set forth in the Provider's Supplemental Rules.);

(ii) Provide the name, postal and e-mail addresses, and the telephone and telefax numbers of the Respondent (domain-name holder) and of any representative authorised to act for the Respondent in the administrative proceeding;

(iii) Specify a preferred method for communications directed to the Respondent in the administrative proceeding (including person to be contacted, medium, and address information) for each of (A) electronic-only material and (B) material including hard copy;

(iv) If Complainant has elected a single-member panel in the Complaint (see Paragraph 3(b)(iv)), state whether Respondent elects instead to have the dispute decided by a three-member panel;

(v) If either Complainant or Respondent elects a three-member Panel, provide the names and contact details of three candidates to serve as one of the panellists (these candidates may be drawn from any ICANN-approved Provider's list of panellists);

(vi) Identify any other legal proceedings that have been commenced or terminated in connection with or relating to any of the domain name(s) that are the subject of the complaint;

(vii) State that a copy of the response has been sent or transmitted to the Complainant, in accordance with Paragraph 2(b); and

(viii) Conclude with the following statement followed by the signature of the Respondent or its authorised representative—

"Respondent certifies that the information contained in this Response is to the best of Respondent's knowledge complete and accurate, that this Response is not being presented for any improper purpose, such as to harass, and that the assertions in this Response are warranted under these Rules and under applicable law, as it now exists or as it may be extended by a good-faith and reasonable argument."; and

(ix) Annex any documentary or other evidence upon which the Respondent relies, together with a schedule indexing such documents.

(c) If Complainant has elected to have the dispute decided by a single-member Panel and Respondent elects a three-member Panel, Respondent shall be required to pay one-half of the applicable fee for a three-member Panel as set forth in the Provider's Supplemental Rules. This payment shall be made together with the submission of the response to the Provider. In the event that the required payment is not made, the dispute shall be decided by a single-member Panel.

(d) At the request of the Respondent, the Provider may, in exceptional cases, extend the period of time for the filing of the response. The period may also be extended by written stipulation between the Parties, provided the stipulation is approved by the Provider.

(e) If a Respondent does not submit a response, in the absence of exceptional circumstances, the Panel shall decide the dispute based upon the complaint.

6. Appointment of the Panel and Timing of Decision

(a) Each Provider shall maintain and publish a publicly available list of panellists and their qualifications.

(b) If neither the Complainant nor the Respondent has elected a three-member Panel (Paragraphs 3(b)(iv) and 5(b)(iv)), the Provider shall appoint, within five (5) calendar days following receipt of the response by the Provider, or the lapse of the time period for the submission thereof, a single panellist from its list of panellists. The fees for a single-member Panel shall be paid entirely by the Complainant.

(c) If either the Complainant or the Respondent elects to have the dispute decided by a three-member Panel, the Provider shall appoint three panellists in accordance with the procedures identified in Paragraph 6(e). The fees for a three-member Panel shall be paid in their entirety by the Complainant, except where the election for a three-member Panel was made by the Respondent, in which case the applicable fees shall be shared equally between the Parties.

(d) Unless it has already elected a three-member Panel, the Complainant shall submit to the Provider, within five (5) calendar days of communication of a response in which the

Respondent elects a three-member Panel, the names and contact details of three candidates to serve as one of the panellists. These candidates may be drawn from any ICANN-approved Provider's list of panellists.

(e) In the event that either the Complainant or the Respondent elects a three-member Panel, the Provider shall endeavor to appoint one panellist from the list of candidates provided by each of the Complainant and the Respondent. In the event the Provider is unable within five (5) calendar days to secure the appointment of a panellist on its customary terms from either Party's list of candidates, the Provider shall make that appointment from its list of panellists. The third panellist shall be appointed by the Provider from a list of five candidates submitted by the Provider to the Parties, the Provider's selection from among the five being made in a manner that reasonably balances the preferences of both Parties, as they may specify to the Provider within five (5) calendar days of the Provider's submission of the five-candidate list to the Parties.

(f) Once the entire Panel is appointed, the Provider shall notify the Parties of the panellists appointed and the date by which, absent exceptional circumstances, the Panel shall forward its decision on the complaint to the Provider.

7. Impartiality and Independence

A panellist shall be impartial and independent and shall have, before accepting appointment, disclosed to the Provider any circumstances giving rise to justifiable doubt as to the panellist's impartiality or independence. If, at any stage during the administrative proceeding, new circumstances arise that could give rise to justifiable doubt as to the impartiality or independence of the panellist, that panellist shall promptly disclose such circumstances to the Provider. In such event, the Provider shall have the discretion to appoint a substitute panellist.

8. Communication Between Parties and the Panel

No Party or anyone acting on its behalf may have any unilateral communication with the Panel. All communications between a Party and the Panel or the Provider shall be made to a case administrator appointed by the Provider in the manner prescribed in the Provider's Supplemental Rules.

9. Transmission of the File to the Panel

The Provider shall forward the file to the Panel as soon as the panellist is appointed in the case of a Panel consisting of a single member, or as soon as the last panellist is appointed in the case of a three-member Panel.

10. General Powers of the Panel

(a) The Panel shall conduct the administrative proceeding in such manner as it considers appropriate in accordance with the Policy and these Rules.

(b) In all cases, the Panel shall ensure that the Parties are treated with equality and that each Party is given a fair opportunity to present its case.

(c) The Panel shall ensure that the administrative proceeding takes place with due expedition. It may, at the request of a Party or on its own motion, extend, in exceptional cases, a period of time fixed by these Rules or by the Panel.

(d) The Panel shall determine the admissibility, relevance, materiality and weight of the evidence.

(e) A Panel shall decide a request by a Party to consolidate multiple domain name disputes in accordance with the Policy and these Rules.

11. Language of Proceedings

(a) Unless otherwise agreed by the Parties, or specified otherwise in the Registration Agreement, the language of the administrative proceeding shall be the language of the Registration Agreement, subject to the authority of the Panel to determine otherwise, having regard to the circumstances of the administrative proceeding.

(b) The Panel may order that any documents submitted in languages other than the language of the administrative proceeding be accompanied by a translation in whole or in part into the language of the administrative proceeding.

12. Further Statements

In addition to the complaint and the response, the Panel may request, in its sole discretion, further statements or documents from either of the Parties.

13. In-Person Hearings

There shall be no in-person hearings (including hearings by teleconference, videoconference, and web conference), unless the Panel determines, in its sole discretion and as an exceptional matter, that such a hearing is necessary for deciding the complaint.

14. Default

(a) In the event that a Party, in the absence of exceptional circumstances, does not comply with any of the time periods established by these Rules or the Panel, the Panel shall proceed to a decision on the complaint.

(b) If a Party, in the absence of exceptional circumstances, does not comply with any provision of, or requirement under, these Rules or any request from the Panel, the Panel shall draw such inferences therefrom as it considers appropriate.

15. Panel Decisions

(a) A Panel shall decide a complaint on the basis of the statements and documents submitted and in accordance with the Policy, these Rules and any rules and principles of law that it deems applicable.

(b) In the absence of exceptional circumstances, the Panel shall forward its decision on the complaint to the Provider within fourteen (14) days of its appointment pursuant to Paragraph 6.

(c) In the case of a three-member Panel, the Panel's decision shall be made by a majority.

(d) The Panel's decision shall be in writing, provide the reasons on which it is based, indicate the date on which it was rendered and identify the name(s) of the panellist(s).

(e) Panel decisions and dissenting opinions shall normally comply with the guidelines as to length set forth in the Provider's Supplemental Rules. Any dissenting opinion shall accompany the majority decision. If the Panel concludes that the dispute is not within the scope of Paragraph 4(a) of the Policy, it shall so state. If after considering the submissions the Panel finds that the complaint was brought in bad faith, for example in an attempt at Reverse Domain Name Hijacking or was brought primarily to harass the domain-name holder, the Panel shall declare in its decision that the complaint was brought in bad faith and constitutes an abuse of the administrative proceeding.

16. Communication of Decision to Parties

(a) Within three (3) calendar days after receiving the decision from the Panel, the Provider shall communicate the full text of the decision to each Party, the concerned Registrar(s), and ICANN. The concerned Registrar(s) shall immediately communicate to each Party, the Provider, and ICANN the date for the implementation of the decision in accordance with the Policy.

(b) Except if the Panel determines otherwise (see Paragraph 4(j) of the Policy), the Provider shall publish the full decision and the date of its implementation on a publicly accessible web site. In any event, the portion of any decision determining a complaint to have been brought in bad faith (see Paragraph 15(e) of these Rules) shall be published.

17. Settlement or Other Grounds for Termination

(a) If, before the Panel's decision, the Parties agree on a settlement, the Panel shall terminate the administrative proceeding.

(b) If, before the Panel's decision is made, it becomes unnecessary or impossible to continue the administrative proceeding for any reason, the Panel shall terminate the administrative proceeding, unless a Party raises justifiable grounds for objection within a period of time to be determined by the Panel.

18. Effect of Court Proceedings

(a) In the event of any legal proceedings initiated prior to or during an administrative proceeding in respect of a domain-name dispute that is the subject of the complaint, the Panel shall have the discretion to decide whether to suspend or terminate the administrative proceeding, or to proceed to a decision.

(b) In the event that a Party initiates any legal proceedings during the pendency of an administrative proceeding in respect of a domain-name dispute that is the subject of the complaint, it shall promptly notify the Panel and the Provider. See Paragraph 8 above.

19. Fees

(a) The Complainant shall pay to the Provider an initial fixed fee, in accordance with the Provider's Supplemental Rules, within the time and in the amount required. A Respondent electing under Paragraph 5(b)(iv) to have the dispute decided by a three-member Panel, rather than the single-member Panel elected by the Complainant, shall pay the Provider one-half the fixed fee for a three-member Panel. See Paragraph 5(c). In all other cases, the Complainant shall bear all of the Provider's fees, except as prescribed under Paragraph 19(d). Upon appointment of the Panel, the Provider shall refund the appropriate portion, if any, of the initial fee to the Complainant, as specified in the Provider's Supplemental Rules.

(b) No action shall be taken by the Provider on a complaint until it has received from Complainant the initial fee in accordance with Paragraph 19(a).

(c) If the Provider has not received the fee within ten (10) calendar days of receiving the complaint, the complaint shall be deemed withdrawn and the administrative proceeding terminated.

(d) In exceptional circumstances, for example in the event an in-person hearing is held, the Provider shall request the Parties for the payment of additional fees, which shall be established in agreement with the Parties and the Panel.

20. Exclusion of Liability

Except in the case of deliberate wrongdoing, neither the Provider nor a panellist shall be liable to a Party for any act or omission in connection with any administrative proceeding under these Rules.

21. Amendments

The version of these Rules in effect at the time of the submission of the complaint to the Provider shall apply to the administrative proceeding commenced thereby. These Rules may not be amended without the express written approval of ICANN.

[2042]

NOMINET UK
DISPUTE RESOLUTION SERVICE POLICY AND DISPUTE RESOLUTION SERVICE PROCEDURE

NOTES

The Dispute Resolution Service (DRS) Policy and Procedure are published by Nominet UK and are reproduced with its kind permission. Copyright of the Policy and Procedure remains with Nominet UK.

DISPUTE RESOLUTION SERVICE POLICY

NOTES

Version 2: issued September 2004 (applies to all disputes filed on or after 25 October 2004).

At the time of going to press, there is a consultation about future changes to the DRS. To ensure that you are referring to the most up to date version of the DRS Policy, see www.nominet.org.uk.

1. Definitions

Abusive Registration means a Domain Name which either:

i. was registered or otherwise acquired in a manner which, at the time when the registration or acquisition took place, took unfair advantage of or was unfairly detrimental to the Complainant's Rights; OR

ii. has been used in a manner which took unfair advantage of or was unfairly detrimental to the Complainant's Rights;

Complainant means a third party who asserts to us the elements set out in paragraph 2 of this Policy and according to the Procedure, or, if there are multiple complainants, the 'lead complainant' (see Procedure paragraph 3(b));

Contract means the contract between us and the Respondent, made up of our Terms and Conditions, the Rules for .uk domain and sub-domains, this Policy and the Procedure;

Days means unless otherwise stated any day other than Saturday, Sunday or any Bank or public holiday in England and Wales;

Decision means the decision reached by an Expert and where applicable includes decisions of an appeal panel;

Dispute Resolution Service means the service provided by us according to this Policy and the Procedure;

Domain Name means a domain name registered in any sub-domain of the .uk domain;

Expert means the expert(s) we appoint under paragraphs 8 or 18 of the Procedure;

Informal Mediation means impartial mediation which we conduct to facilitate an acceptable resolution to the dispute;

ISP means the internet service provider through which the Domain Name in dispute has been registered or is hosted;

Party means a Complainant or Respondent and 'Parties' has a corresponding meaning;

Procedure means the Procedure for the conduct of proceedings under the Dispute Resolution Service;

Respondent means the person (including a legal person) in whose name or on whose behalf a Domain Name is registered and against whom the Complainant makes a complaint;

Rights includes, but is not limited to, rights enforceable under English law. However, a Complainant will be unable to rely on rights in a name or term which is wholly descriptive of the Complainant's business;

We means Nominet UK (company no 3203859) whose registered office is at Sandford Gate, Sandy Lane West, Littlemore, Oxford, OX4 6LB and 'us' and 'our' have corresponding meanings.

2. Dispute Resolution Service

a. A Respondent must submit to proceedings under the Dispute Resolution Service if a Complainant asserts to us, according to the Procedure, that:

- i. The Complainant has Rights in respect of a name or mark which is identical or similar to the Domain Name; and
- ii. The Domain Name, in the hands of the Respondent, is an Abusive Registration.

b. The Complainant is required to prove to the Expert that both elements are present on the balance of probabilities.

c. We recommend that both Parties use our guidance and help information, which can be found on our website.

3. Evidence of Abusive Registration

a. A non-exhaustive list of factors which may be evidence that the Domain Name is an Abusive Registration is as follows:

- i. Circumstances indicating that the Respondent has registered or otherwise acquired the Domain Name primarily:
  - A. for the purposes of selling, renting or otherwise transferring the Domain Name to the Complainant or to a competitor of the Complainant, for valuable consideration in excess of the Respondent's documented out-of-pocket costs directly associated with acquiring or using the Domain Name;
  - B. as a blocking registration against a name or mark in which the Complainant has Rights; or
  - C. for the purpose of unfairly disrupting the business of the Complainant;
- ii. Circumstances indicating that the Respondent is using the Domain Name in a way which has confused people or businesses into believing that the Domain Name is registered to, operated or authorised by, or otherwise connected with the Complainant;

iii. The Complainant can demonstrate that the Respondent is engaged in a pattern of registrations where the Respondent is the registrant of domain names (under .uk or otherwise) which correspond to well known names or trade marks in which the Respondent has no apparent rights, and the Domain Name is part of that pattern;

iv. It is independently verified that the Respondent has given false contact details to us; or

v. The domain name was registered as a result of a relationship between the Complainant and the Respondent, and the Complainant:

A. has been using the domain name registration exclusively; and

B. paid for the registration and/or renewal of the domain name registration.

b. Failure on the Respondent's part to use the Domain Name for the purposes of e-mail or a web-site is not in itself evidence that the Domain Name is an Abusive Registration.

c. There shall be a presumption of Abusive Registration if the Complainant proves that Respondent has been found to have made an Abusive Registration in three (3) or more Dispute Resolution Service cases in the two (2) years before the Complaint was filed. This presumption can be rebutted (see paragraph 4(c)).

4. How the Respondent may demonstrate in its response that the Domain Name is not an Abusive Registration

a. A non-exhaustive list of factors which may be evidence that the Domain Name is not an Abusive Registration is as follows:

i. Before being aware of the Complainant's cause for complaint (not necessarily the 'complaint' under the DRS), the Respondent has

A. used or made demonstrable preparations to use the Domain Name or a Domain Name which is similar to the Domain Name in connection with a genuine offering of goods or services;

B. been commonly known by the name or legitimately connected with a mark which is identical or similar to the Domain Name;

C. made legitimate non-commercial or fair use of the Domain Name; or

ii. The Domain Name is generic or descriptive and the Respondent is making fair use of it;

iii. In relation to paragraph 3(a)(v); that the Registrant's holding of the Domain Name is consistent with an express term of a written agreement entered into by the Parties; or

iv. In relation to paragraphs 3(a)(iii) and/or 3(c); that the Domain Name is not part of a wider pattern or series of registrations because the Domain Name is of a significantly different type or character to the other domain names registered by the Respondent.

b. Fair use may include sites operated solely in tribute to or in criticism of a person or business.

c. If paragraph 3(c) applies, to succeed the Respondent must rebut the presumption by proving in the Response that the registration of the Domain Name is not an Abusive Registration.

5. Informal Mediation

a. After we have received the Parties' submissions under the Procedure, we will initiate and conduct a period of Informal Mediation under paragraph 7 of the Procedure.

6. Without Prejudice

a. Documents and information which are 'without prejudice' (or are marked as being 'without prejudice') may be used in submissions and may be considered by the Expert except that the Expert will not consider such materials if:

i. they are generated within Informal Mediation; or

ii. the Expert believes that it is in the interests of justice that the document or information be excluded from consideration.

7. Appointment of Expert

a. If an acceptable resolution cannot be found by Informal Mediation we will notify the Parties that we will appoint an Expert when the Complainant has paid the applicable fees set out in paragraph 21(a) of the Procedure and within the time specified in paragraph 21(c) of the Procedure. The Expert will come to a written Decision.

8. Notification and Publication

a. We will communicate a Decision to the Parties according to paragraph 17 of the Procedure and will publish all Decisions in full on our web site.

b. Fees are payable by the Complainant or otherwise according to paragraph 22 of the Procedure only if an acceptable resolution has not been reached by Informal Mediation and once we have notified the Parties that an Expert is to be appointed.

c. Decisions may contain the contact details of the Parties and the Parties consent to contact details being displayed in this way.

9. Exclusion of Liability

a. Neither we nor our directors, officers, employees or servants nor any Expert shall be liable to a party for anything done or omitted in connection with any proceedings under the Dispute Resolution Service unless the act or omission is shown to have been in bad faith.

10. Appeal, Repeat Complaints and Availability of Court Proceedings

a. Either Party will have the right to appeal a Decision under paragraph 18 of the Procedure. The appeal panel will consider appeals on the basis of a full review of the matter and may review procedural matters.

b. We may refer questions of interpretation of the Policy and Procedure to the appeal panel. Any decision rendered as a result of our referral will not affect any Decision previously made under the Dispute Resolution Service.

c. We will publish decisions of the appeal panel. Appeal decisions will not have precedent value, but will be of persuasive value to Experts in future decisions.

d. The operation of the Dispute Resolution Service will not prevent either the Complainant or the Respondent from submitting the dispute to a court of competent jurisdiction.

e. If a complaint has reached the Decision stage on a previous occasion it will not be reconsidered (but it may be appealed, see paragraph 10(a) and Procedure paragraph 18) by an Expert. If the Expert finds that the complaint is a resubmission of an earlier complaint he or she shall reject the complaint without a consideration of its merits.

f. In determining whether a complaint is a resubmission of an earlier complaint, or contains a material difference that justifies a re-hearing the Expert shall consider the following questions:

- i. Are the Complainant, the Respondent and the domain name in issue the same as in the earlier case?
- ii. Does the substance of the complaint relate to acts that occurred prior to or subsequent to the close of submissions in the earlier case?
- iii. If the substance of the complaint relates to acts that occurred prior to the close of submissions in the earlier case, are there any exceptional grounds for the rehearing or reconsideration, bearing in mind the need to protect the integrity and smooth operation of the Policy and Procedure?
- iv. If the substance of the complaint relates to acts that occurred subsequent to the close of submissions in the earlier decision, acts on which the re-filed complaint is based should not be, in substance, the same as the acts on which the previous complaint was based.

g. A non-exhaustive list of examples which may be exceptional enough to justify a re-hearing under paragraph 10(f)(iii) include:

- i. serious misconduct on the part of the Expert, a party, witness or lawyer;
- ii. false evidence having been offered to the Expert;
- iii. the discovery of credible and material evidence which could not have been reasonably foreseen or known for the Complainant to have included it in the evidence in support of the earlier complaint;
- iv. a breach of natural justice; and
- v. the avoidance of an unconscionable result.

11. Implementation of Expert Decisions

a. If the Expert makes a Decision that a Domain Name registration should be cancelled, suspended, transferred or otherwise amended, we will implement that Decision by making any necessary changes to the Register according to the process set out in paragraph 17 of the Procedure. We will use the details set out in the Complaint form unless you specify other details to us in good time.

12. Other action by us

a. We will not cancel, transfer, activate, deactivate or otherwise change any Domain Name registration except as set out in paragraph 11 above and as provided under paragraphs 6.3 or 16 to 19 of the Terms and Conditions.

13. Transfers During a Dispute

a. A Respondent may not transfer a Domain Name registration:

i. if the electronic form of a complaint has been received by our Dispute Resolution Service staff and the matter is pending the receipt of a valid paper copy to confirm the complaint (to a maximum of five (5) Days); or

ii. whilst proceedings under the Dispute Resolution Service are ongoing in relation to the Domain Name or for a period of ten (10) Days after their conclusion, unless to the Complainant as a result of a settlement reached between the Parties and approved by us whether or not pursuant to Informal Mediation; or

iii. whilst a court proceeding or arbitration in respect of the Domain Name registration is ongoing in a court of competent jurisdiction.

We reserve the right to reverse any transfer of a Domain Name registration which does not comply with this paragraph.

b. A Respondent may not without the Complainant's consent (which the Complainant will not unreasonably withhold) transfer the hosting of a Domain Name to another ISP whilst proceedings under the Dispute Resolution Service are ongoing in relation to the Domain Name or for a period of ten (10) Days after the conclusion of the Dispute Resolution Service.

14. Modifications to the Policy and Procedure of the Dispute Resolution Service

a. The internet is an emerging and evolving medium and the regulatory and administrative framework under which we operate is constantly developing. For these reasons we reserve the right to make reasonable modifications to the Policy and Procedure at any time. We will only do so when we have good reason. Except where we are acting in pursuance of a statutory requirement or a court order, changes will be implemented following a process of open public consultation. Each such change will be published in advance (where practicable, 30 calendar days in advance) on our web site: http://www.nominet.org.uk/ and will become binding and effective upon the date specified therein.

b. The Respondent will be bound by the Policy and Procedure which are current at the time the Dispute Resolution Service is commenced until the dispute is concluded.

[2043]

PROCEDURE FOR THE CONDUCT OF PROCEEDINGS UNDER THE DISPUTE RESOLUTION SERVICE

NOTES

Version 2: issued September 2004 (applies to all disputes filed on or after 25 October 2004).

At the time of going to press, there is a consultation about future changes to the DRS. To ensure that you are referring to the most up to date version of the DRS Procedure, see www.nominet.org.uk.

1. Definitions

Abusive Registration means a Domain Name which either:

i. was registered or otherwise acquired in a manner which, at the time when the registration or acquisition took place, took unfair advantage of or was unfairly detrimental to the Complainant's Rights; OR

ii. has been used in a manner which took unfair advantage of or was unfairly detrimental to the Complainant's Rights;

Complainant means a third party who asserts to us the elements set out in paragraph 2 of the Policy and according to this Procedure, or, if there are multiple Complainants, the 'lead complainant' (see paragraph 3(b));

Contract means the contract between us and the Respondent, made up of our Terms and Conditions, the Rules for .uk domain and sub-domains, the Policy and this Procedure;

Days means unless otherwise stated any day other than Saturday, Sunday or any Bank or public holiday in England and Wales;

Decision means the decision reached by an Expert and where applicable includes decisions of an appeal panel;

Dispute Resolution Service means the service provided by us according to the Policy and this Procedure;

Domain Name means a domain name registered in any sub-domain of the .uk domain;

Expert means the expert(s) we appoint under paragraphs 8 or 18 of this Procedure;

Informal Mediation means impartial mediation which we conduct to facilitate an acceptable resolution to the dispute;

ISP means the internet service provider through which the Domain Name in dispute has been registered or is hosted;

Party means a Complainant or Respondent and 'Parties' has a corresponding meaning;

Policy means Nominet's Dispute Resolution Service Policy;

Respondent means the person (including a legal person) in whose name or on whose behalf a Domain Name is registered and against whom the Complainant makes a complaint;

Reverse Domain Name Hijacking means using the Policy in bad faith in an attempt to deprive a registered domain-name holder of a domain name;

Rights includes, but is not limited to, rights enforceable under English law. However, a Complainant will be unable to rely on rights in a name or term which is wholly descriptive of the Complainant's business;

We means Nominet UK (company no 3203859) whose registered office is at Sandford Gate, Sandy Lane West, Littlemore, Oxford, OX4 6LB and 'us' and 'our' have corresponding meanings.

2. Communication

a. We will send a complaint (see paragraph 3) to the Respondent by using, in our discretion, any of the following means:

- i. sending the complaint by first class post, fax or e-mail to the Respondent at the contact details shown as the registrant or other contacts in our Domain Name register database entry for the Domain Name in dispute;
- ii. sending the complaint in electronic form (including attachments to the extent available in that form) by e-mail to;
  - A. postmaster@<the Domain Name in dispute>; or
  - B. if the Domain Name resolves to an active web page (other than a generic page which we conclude is maintained by an ISP for parking Domain Names), to any e-mail address shown or e-mail links on that web page so far as this is practicable; or
- iii. sending the complaint to any addresses provided to us by the Complainant under paragraph 3(b)(iii) so far as this is practicable.

b. Except as set out in paragraph 2(a) above, all written communication to a Party or a Party's representative under the Policy or this Procedure shall be made by fax, first class post or e-mail.

c. Communication shall be made in English. E-mail communications should be sent in plain text so far as this is practicable.

d. During the course of proceedings under the Dispute Resolution Service, if either Party wishes to change its contact details it must notify us of all changes.

e. Except as otherwise provided in this Procedure or as otherwise decided by us or if appointed, the Expert, all communications provided for under this Procedure shall be deemed to have been received:

- i. if sent by facsimile, on the date transmitted; or
- ii. if sent by first class post, on the second Day after posting; or
- iii. if sent via the Internet, on the date that the communication was transmitted;

iv. and, unless otherwise provided in this Procedure, the time periods provided for under the Policy and this Procedure shall be calculated accordingly.

f. Any communication (except for communications relating to Informal Mediation) between:

i. us and any Party shall be copied by us to the other Party and if appointed, the Expert, subject to paragraph (13), below; and

ii. a Party to another Party shall be copied by the sender to us and we will copy such correspondence to the Expert, if appointed.

3. The Complaint

a. Any person or entity may submit a complaint to us in accordance with the Policy and this Procedure. In exceptional circumstances, we may have to suspend our ability to accept complaints. If so, we will post a message to that effect on our web-site which will indicate when the suspension is likely to be lifted.

b. More than one person or entity may jointly make a complaint. Where this occurs the joint Complainants must:

i. all sign the hard copy of the complaint (or have it signed on their behalf);

ii. specify one of the Complainants, or a single representative, who will be the 'lead Complainant' who will receive correspondence on behalf of all the Complainants and is entitled to act on behalf of them all (eg in Informal Mediation); and

iii. specify which Complainant the Complainants wish to become the sole registrant of each Domain Name(s) which are the subject of the complaint if the Complainants are successful (this does not bind the Expert).

c. The Complainant must send the complaint to us in hard copy and (except to the extent not available for attachments) in electronic form. The complaint shall:—

i. not exceed 2000 words (not including the text set out in paragraph 3(c)(ix) below and annexes);

ii. specify whether the Complainant wishes to be contacted direct or through an authorised representative, and set out the e-mail address, telephone number, fax number and postal address which should be used;

iii. set out any of the Respondent's contact details which are known to the Complainant;

iv. specify the Domain Name which is the subject of the dispute and the name or mark which is identical or similar to the Domain Name and in which the Complainant asserts it has Rights;

v. describe in accordance with the Policy the grounds on which the complaint is made including in particular: what Rights the Complainant asserts in the name or mark; why the Domain Name should be considered to be an Abusive Registration in the hands of the Respondent; and discuss any applicable aspects of paragraph 3 of the Policy, as well as any other grounds which support the Complainant's assertion;

vi. specify whether the Complainant is seeking to have the Domain Name transferred, suspended, cancelled or otherwise amended;

vii. tell us whether any legal proceedings have been commenced or terminated in connection with the Domain Name which is the subject of the complaint;

viii. state that the Complainant will submit to the exclusive jurisdiction of the English courts with respect to any legal proceedings seeking to reverse the effect of a Decision requiring the suspension, cancellation, transfer or other amendment to a Domain Name registration, and that the Complainant agrees that any such legal proceedings will be governed by English law;

ix. conclude with the following statement followed by the signature of the Complainant or its authorised representative:—

"The Complainant agrees that its claims and remedies concerning the registration of the Domain Name, the dispute, or the dispute's resolution shall be solely against the Respondent and that neither Nominet UK nor its directors, officers, employees or servants nor any Expert shall be liable for anything done or omitted in connection with any proceedings under the Dispute Resolution Service unless the act or omission is shown to have been in bad faith.";

"The information contained in this complaint is to the best of the Complainant's knowledge true and complete. This complaint is not being presented in bad faith and the matters stated in this complaint comply with the Procedure and applicable law."; and

"If the Expert orders a transfer of the domain name(s) then I agree to be bound by Nominet's Terms and Conditions for the Registration of Domain Names, and in particular the provisions relating to Nominet's processing of personal data."

x. attach three copies of any documentary or other evidence on which the Complainant relies including correspondence and any trade mark registration and/or evidence of use of or reputation in a name or mark, together with an index of the material attached.

d. The complaint may relate to more than one Domain Name, provided that those Domain Names are registered in the name of the Respondent.

4. Notification of Complaint

a. We will check that the complaint complies with the Policy and this Procedure and, if so, we will forward it to the Respondent together with our explanatory coversheet within three (3) Days of our receipt of the complaint.

b. If we find that the complaint does not comply with the Policy and this Procedure, we will promptly notify the Complainant of the deficiencies we have identified. The Complainant shall have three (3) Days from receipt of notification within which to correct the deficiencies and return the complaint to us, failing which we will deem the complaint to be withdrawn. This will not prevent the Complainant submitting a different complaint to us.

c. Proceedings under the Dispute Resolution Service will commence on the earliest date upon which the complaint is deemed to have been received by the Respondent in accordance with paragraph 2(e) of this Procedure. We will promptly notify the Parties of the date of commencement of such proceedings.

5. The Response

a. Within fifteen (15) Days of the date of commencement of proceedings under the Dispute Resolution Service, the Respondent shall submit a response to us.

b. Within three (3) Days following our receipt of the response, we will forward the response to the Complainant.

c. The Respondent must send the response to us in hard copy and (except to the extent not available for attachments) in electronic form to us at the addresses set out in our explanatory coversheet. The response shall:

i. not exceed 2000 words (not including the text set out in paragraph 5(c)(v) and annexes);
ii. include any grounds the Respondent wishes to rely upon to rebut the Complainant's assertions under 3(c)(v) above including any relevant factors set out in paragraph 4 of the Policy;
iii. specify whether the Respondent wishes to be contacted direct or through an authorised representative, and set out the e-mail address, telephone number, fax number and postal address which should be used;
iv. tell us whether any legal proceedings have been commenced or terminated in connection with the Domain Name which is the subject of the complaint;
v. conclude with the following statement followed by the signature of the Respondent or its authorised representative:—
"The information contained in this response is to the best of the Respondent's knowledge true and complete and the matters stated in this response comply with the Procedure and applicable law."; and
vi. attach three copies of any documentary or other evidence on which the Respondent relies including correspondence and any trade mark registration and/or evidence of use of or reputation in a name or mark together with an index of the material attached.

d. If the Respondent does not submit a response, we will notify the Parties that we will appoint the Expert on our receipt from the Complainant of the applicable fees according to paragraph 21 and in the absence of exceptional circumstances.

6. Reply by the Complainant

a. Within five (5) Days of receiving the response from us, the Complainant may submit to us a reply to the Respondent's response, which shall not exceed 2000 words (not including annexes). If a reply is submitted it must be submitted in hard copy (including three copies of all annexes) and as far as possible in electronic form to us. If the Complainant does not submit a reply to us within five (5) Days we will proceed to Informal Mediation.

7. Informal Mediation

a. Within three (3) Days of our receipt of the Complainant's reply (or the expiry of the deadline to do so), we will begin to conduct Informal Mediation. Informal Mediation will be conducted in a manner which we, in our sole discretion, consider appropriate. No Informal Mediation will occur if the Respondent does not file a Response.

b. Negotiations conducted between the Parties during Informal Mediation (including any information obtained from or in connection to negotiations) shall be confidential, that is they will not be shown to the Expert. Neither we nor any Party may reveal details of such negotiations to any third parties unless a court of competent jurisdiction orders disclosure, or we or either Party are required to do so by applicable laws or regulations. Neither Party shall use any information gained during mediation for any ulterior or collateral purpose or include it in any submission likely to be seen by any Expert, judge or arbitrator in this dispute or any later dispute or litigation.

c. If the Parties reach a settlement during Informal Mediation then the existence, nature and terms of the settlement shall be confidential, unless the Parties specifically agree otherwise or a court of competent jurisdiction orders otherwise.

d. No binding verbal agreements can be reached as part of the Informal Mediation: any settlement reached by the Parties must be in writing or similar electronic form to be enforceable.

e. If the Parties do not achieve an acceptable resolution through Informal Mediation within ten (10) Days, we will send notice to the Parties that we will appoint an Expert when the Complainant has paid the applicable fees set out under paragraph 21(a) within the time limit specified in paragraph 21(c). We will tell the Expert whether or not Informal Mediation occurred, but we will not tell the Expert what happened during Informal Mediation or why it failed to resolve the dispute.

f. No Party may ask us (including our directors, officers, employees, contractors, agents and any Expert) to reveal information or materials gained as a result of any Informal Mediation under the Dispute Resolution Service unless such disclosure has been ordered by a court of competent jurisdiction. Neither Party shall call the Expert or us (including our directors, officers, employees, contractors, or agents) as a witness (either in person or to produce documents or other materials) in any proceedings which arise from, or are in connection with, the matters discussed in the mediation.

8. Appointment of the Expert and Timing of Decision

a. If we do not receive the Complainant's request to refer the matter to an Expert together with the applicable fees within ten (10) Days of the Complainant's receipt of the notice referred to in paragraph 7(e) above, we will deem the complaint to be withdrawn. This will not prevent the Complainant submitting a different complaint to us.

b. Within five (5) Days of our receipt of the applicable fees from the Complainant, we will appoint an Expert on a rotational basis from our list of Experts.

c. We will maintain and publish a list of Experts and their qualifications.

d. Once we have appointed the Expert, we will notify the Parties of the name of the Expert appointed and the date by which, except in exceptional circumstances, the Expert will forward his or her Decision to us.

9. Impartiality and Independence

a. The Expert shall be impartial and independent and both before accepting the appointment and during the proceedings will disclose to us any circumstances giving rise to justifiable doubt as to his or her impartiality or independence. We will have the discretion to appoint a substitute Expert if necessary in which case we will adjust the timetable accordingly.

10. Communication Between Parties and the Expert

a. A Party and the Expert must not communicate directly. All communication between a Party and the Expert must be made through us.

11. Transmission of the File to the Expert

a. We will forward the file except for documents relating to Informal Mediation to the Expert as soon as the Expert is appointed.

12. General Powers of Nominet and the Expert

a. We, or the Expert if appointed, may in exceptional cases extend any period of time in proceedings under the Dispute Resolution Service.

b. The Expert shall determine the admissibility, relevance, materiality and weight of the evidence.

c. We shall decide a request by a Party to consolidate multiple Domain Name disputes in accordance with the Policy and this Procedure.

13. Further Statement

a. In addition to the complaint, the response and if applicable the reply and any appeal, the Expert may request further statements or documents from the Parties. The Expert will not be obliged to consider any statements or documents from the Parties which he or she has not received according to the Policy or this Procedure or which he or she has not requested.

b. Any communication with us intended to be passed to the Expert which is not part of the standard process (e g other than a complaint, response, reply, submissions requested by the Expert, appeal notice or appeal notice response) is a 'non-standard submission'. Any non-standard submission must contain as a separate, first paragraph, a brief explanation of why there is an exceptional need for the non-standard submission. We will pass this explanation to the Expert, and the remainder will only be passed to the Expert at his or her sole discretion. If there is no explanation, we may not pass on the document or information.

14. In Person Hearings

a. No in person hearings (including hearings by conference call, video conference and web conference) will be held unless the Expert determines in his or her sole discretion and in exceptional cases, that such a hearing is necessary to enable him or her to come to a Decision.

15. Default

a. If we find that a submission by a Party exceeds the word limit, we will return the submission to that Party who will within three (3) Days return a submission to us which complies with the word limits. If we do not receive the submission back from:

i. the Complainant, we will deem the complaint to be withdrawn, which will not stop the Complainant from submitting a different complaint; or

ii. the Respondent, we will notify the Parties that we will appoint the Expert when the Complainant has paid the applicable fees set out in paragraph 21 and in the absence of exceptional circumstances. Once appointed the Expert will decide the dispute based upon the complaint and evidence attached to it.

b. If, in the absence of exceptional circumstances, a Party does not comply with any time period laid down in the Policy or this Procedure, the Expert will proceed to a Decision on the complaint. If the Expert has not been appointed Nominet shall take any action which it deems appropriate in its sole discretion, unless prescribed by this Procedure.

c. If, in the absence of exceptional circumstances, a Party does not comply with any provision in the Policy or this Procedure or any request by us or the Expert, the Expert will draw such inferences from the Party's non compliance as he or she considers appropriate.

16. Expert Decision

a. The Expert will decide a complaint on the basis of the Parties' submissions, the Policy and the Procedure.

b. Unless exceptional circumstances apply, an Expert shall forward his or her Decision to us within ten (10) Days of his or her appointment pursuant to paragraph 8.

c. The Decision shall be in writing and signed, provide the reasons on which it is based, indicate the date on which it was made and identify the name of the Expert.

d. If the Expert concludes that the dispute is not within the scope of paragraph 2 of the Policy, he or she shall state that this is the case. If, after considering the submissions, the Expert finds that the complaint was brought in bad faith, for example in an attempt at Reverse Domain Name Hijacking, the Expert shall state this finding in the Decision. If the Complainant is found on three separate occasions within a 2-year period to have brought a complaint in bad faith, Nominet will not accept any further complaints from that Complainant for a period of 2 years.

17. Communication of Decision to Parties and Implementation of Decision

a. Within three (3) Days of our receipt of a Decision from the Expert, we will communicate the full text of the Decision to each Party and the date for the implementation of the Decision in accordance with the Policy.

b. We will publish the full Decision and the date that any action which the Decision requires will be taken, on our website.

c. If the Expert makes a Decision that a Domain Name registration should be cancelled, suspended, transferred or otherwise amended, we will implement that Decision by making any necessary changes to the Domain Name register database after ten (10) Days of the date that the parties were notified, unless, during the ten (10) Days following the date that the parties were notified we receive from either Party:

i. an appeal or statement of intention to appeal complying with paragraph 18 of the Procedure, in which case we will take no further action in respect of the Domain Name until the appeal is concluded; or

ii. official documentation showing that the Party has issued and served (or in the case of service outside England and Wales, commenced the process of serving) legal proceedings against the other Party in respect of the domain name. In this case, we will take no further action in respect of the Domain Name unless we receive:

A. evidence which satisfies us that the Parties have reached a settlement; or

B. evidence which satisfies us that such proceedings have been dismissed, withdrawn or are otherwise unsuccessful.

18. Appeal

a. Either Party shall have the right to appeal a Decision by submitting either:

i. a statement of the intention to appeal (see paragraph 18(b)), plus the non-refundable deposit (see paragraph 21(e)), which must be followed within fifteen (15) Days by an appeal notice (see paragraph 18(c)) and the balance of the fee (see paragraph 21(e)); or

ii. an appeal notice (see paragraph 18(c)) and the whole fee (see paragraph 21(e)).

b. A statement of intention to appeal should only contain sufficient information to make it clear that an appeal is requested. The statement of intention to appeal should not contain the actual grounds or reasons for appeal.

c. An appeal notice should not exceed 1000 words, should set out detailed grounds and reasons for the appeal, but shall contain no new evidence or annexes.

d. Within three (3) Days of our receipt of the:

i. statement of the intention to appeal and deposit; or

ii. appeal notice and the full fee

we will forward the statement of intention to appeal or appeal notice (as the case may be) to the other Party.

e. Within ten (10) Days of receiving the appeal notice from us, the other Party may submit to us an appeal notice response (paragraph 18(f)).

f. An appeal notice response must not exceed 1000 words, should set out detailed grounds and reasons why the appeal should be rejected but should contain no new evidence or annexes.

g. Following the filing of an appeal notice response (or the expiry of the deadline to do so) we will appoint an appeal panel of three Experts. The test of impartiality shall apply to each appeal Expert subject to this the appeal panel shall consist of:

i. the chairman of the group of Experts, or at his or her discretion, an Expert of his or her choice; and

ii. the next available two Independent Experts appointed by rotation from our list.

h. The appeal panel should not normally take into consideration any new evidence presented in an appeal notice or appeal notice response, unless they believe that it is in the interests of justice to do so.

i. So far as is appropriate in the circumstances paragraphs 16 and 17 apply equally to appeal Decisions, except that:

i. appeal Decisions should be returned by the appeal panel to us within thirty (30) days of the appointment of the last panellist, but this deadline may be extended by up to ten (10) Days by agreement with us; and

ii. appeal Decisions cannot be subject to any appeal within the Dispute Resolution Service.

19. Settlement or Other Grounds for Termination

a. If, before a Decision is made the Parties agree and notify us of a settlement which we approve, whether or not pursuant to Informal Mediation, we will terminate proceedings under the Dispute Resolution Service.

b. If, before a Decision is made, it becomes unnecessary or impossible to continue proceedings under the Dispute Resolution Service for any reason, we will terminate proceedings under the Dispute Resolution Service unless a Party raises justifiable grounds for objection within a period of time which we will determine.

20. Effect of Court Proceedings

a. If legal proceedings relating to a Domain Name which is the subject of a complaint are issued in a court of competent jurisdiction before or during the course of proceedings under the Dispute Resolution Service and are brought to our attention, we will suspend the proceedings, pending the outcome of the legal proceedings.

b. A Party must promptly notify us if it initiates legal proceedings in a court of competent jurisdiction in relating to a Domain Name which is the subject of a complaint during the course of proceedings under the Dispute Resolution Service.

21. Fees

a. The applicable fees in respect of the referral of proceedings under the Dispute Resolution Service to an Expert are £750 + VAT for disputes involving 1–5 Domain Names and only one Complainant. For disputes involving 6 or more Domain Names, and/or more than one Complainant, we will set a fee in consultation with the Complainant. Fees are calculated on a cost-recovery basis, and are passed on in their entirety to the Expert(s). Nominet does not charge for its mediation or administration services in respect of the Dispute Resolution Service.

b. Fees are payable by the Complainant only if an acceptable resolution has not been reached and we notify the Parties that an Expert is to be appointed.

c. If we have not received the fees from the Complainant as set out in paragraph 21(a) above within ten (10) Days of receipt by the Complainant of notice from us that an Expert is to be appointed under paragraphs 5(d), 7(e) or 15(a)(ii) we will deem the complaint to be withdrawn.

d. In exceptional circumstances, for example if an in person hearing is held, we will request that the Parties pay additional fees to be agreed between us, the Parties and the Expert.

e. The applicable fees for the submission of an appeal are £3,000 + VAT. If the option is used to pay a deposit and the balance, the deposit is £300 + VAT and non-refundable, and the balance is £2,700 + VAT. If the deposit is paid, and the balance of the fee and/or appeal notice are not filed in time, that appeal is deemed withdrawn and the case will be closed.

22. Exclusion of Liability

a. Neither we nor our directors, officers, employees or servants nor any Expert shall be liable to a party for anything done or omitted in connection with any proceedings under the Dispute Resolution Service unless the act or omission is shown to have been in bad faith.

23. Modifications to the Policy and Procedure of the Dispute Resolution Service

a. The internet is an emerging and evolving medium and the regulatory and administrative framework under which we operate is constantly developing. For these reasons we reserve the right to make reasonable modifications to the Policy and Procedure at any time. We will only do so when we have good reason. Except where we are acting in pursuance of a statutory requirement or a court order, changes will be implemented following a process of open public consultation. Each such change will be published in advance (where practicable, thirty (30) calendar days in advance) on our web site: http://www.nominet.org.uk/ and will become binding and effective upon the date specified therein.

b. The Respondent will be bound by the Policy and Procedure which are current at the time the Dispute Resolution Service is commenced until the dispute is concluded.

[2044]–[2500]

PART IV
INTELLECTUAL PROPERTY

COPYRIGHT, DESIGNS AND PATENTS ACT 1988

(1988 c 48)

An Act to restate the law of copyright, with amendments; to make fresh provision as to the rights of performers and others in performances; to confer a design right in original designs; to amend the Registered Designs Act 1949; to make provision with respect to patent agents and trade mark agents; to confer patents and designs jurisdiction on certain county courts; to amend the law of patents; to make provision with respect to devices designed to circumvent copy-protection of works in electronic form; to make fresh provision penalising the fraudulent reception of transmissions; to make the fraudulent application or use of a trade mark an offence; to make provision for the benefit of the Hospital for Sick Children, Great Ormond Street, London; to enable financial assistance to be given to certain international bodies; and for connected purposes

[15 November 1988]

ARRANGEMENT OF SECTIONS

PART I
COPYRIGHT

CHAPTER I
SUBSISTENCE, OWNERSHIP AND DURATION OF COPYRIGHT

Introductory

Descriptions of work and related provisions

Authorship and ownership of copyright

Duration of copyright

CHAPTER III
ACTS PERMITTED IN RELATION TO COPYRIGHT WORKS

Computer programs: lawful users

Databases: permitted acts

Works in electronic form

Miscellaneous: broadcasts

PART VII
MISCELLANEOUS AND GENERAL

Devices designed to circumvent copy-protection

Rights management information

Computer programs

Databases

Fraudulent reception of transmissions

PART I
COPYRIGHT

CHAPTER I
SUBSISTENCE, OWNERSHIP AND DURATION OF COPYRIGHT

Introductory

1 Copyright and copyright works

(1) Copyright is a property right which subsists in accordance with this Part in the following descriptions of work—

(a) original literary, dramatic, musical or artistic works,
(b) sound recordings, films [or broadcasts], and
(c) the typographical arrangement of published editions.

(2) In this Part "copyright work" means a work of any of those descriptions in which copyright subsists.

(3) Copyright does not subsist in a work unless the requirements of this Part with respect to qualification for copyright protection are met (see section 153 and the provisions referred to there).

[2501]

NOTES

Sub-s (1): words in square brackets in para (b) substituted for original words ", broadcasts or cable programmes" by the Copyright and Related Rights Regulations 2003, SI 2003/2498, regs 3, 5(2), subject to transitional provisions as noted below.

Transitional provisions: the Copyright and Related Rights Regulations 2003, SI 2003/2498 came into force on 31 October 2003 and, except as expressly provided, apply to: (i) works made, (ii) performances given, (iii) databases in which database right vests which are made, and (iv) works in which publication right vests which are first published, before or after that date (see reg 31 of the 2003 Regulations at **[2582C]**). Savings and transitional provisions are provided for in regs 32–40 of those Regulations at **[2582D]–[2582L]**.

2 Rights subsisting in copyright works

(1) The owner of the copyright in a work of any description has the exclusive right to do the acts specified in Chapter II as the acts restricted by the copyright in a work of that description.

(2) In relation to certain descriptions of copyright work the following rights conferred by Chapter IV (moral rights) subsist in favour of the author, director or commissioner of the work, whether or not he is the owner of the copyright—

(a) section 77 (right to be identified as author or director),
(b) section 80 (right to object to derogatory treatment of work), and
(c) section 85 (right to privacy of certain photographs and films).

[2502]

Descriptions of work and related provisions

3 Literary, dramatic and musical works

(1) In this Part—

"literary work" means any work, other than a dramatic or musical work, which is written, spoken or sung, and accordingly includes—
(a) a table or compilation [other than a database], …
(b) a computer program[, …
(c) preparatory design material for a computer program]; [and
(d) a database;]

"dramatic work" includes a work of dance or mime; and
"musical work" means a work consisting of music, exclusive of any words or action intended to be sung, spoken or performed with the music.

(2) Copyright does not subsist in a literary, dramatic or musical work unless and until it is recorded, in writing or otherwise; and references in this Part to the time at which such a work is made are to the time at which it is so recorded.

(3) It is immaterial for the purposes of subsection (2) whether the work is recorded by or with the permission of the author; and where it is not recorded by the author, nothing in that subsection affects the question whether copyright subsists in the record as distinct from the work recorded.

[2503]

NOTES

Sub-s (1): words in square brackets in para (a) inserted, word omitted from para (b) repealed, and para (d) and word immediately preceding it inserted by the Copyright and Rights in Databases Regulations 1997, SI 1997/3032, reg 5, subject to savings and transitional provisions in Pt IV of those Regulations at **[2576]–[2580]**; word omitted from para (a) repealed and para (c) and word immediately preceding it (now repealed) inserted by the Copyright (Computer Programs) Regulations 1992, SI 1992/3233, regs 2, 3, subject to reg 12(2) thereof (agreements entered into before 1 January 1993 to remain unaffected).

[3A Databases

(1) In this Part "database" means a collection of independent works, data or other materials which—
(a) are arranged in a systematic or methodical way, and
(b) are individually accessible by electronic or other means.

(2) For the purposes of this Part a literary work consisting of a database is original if, and only if, by reason of the selection or arrangement of the contents of the database the database constitutes the author's own intellectual creation.]

[2504]

NOTES

Inserted by the Copyright and Rights in Databases Regulations 1997, SI 1997/3032, reg 6, subject to savings and transitional provisions in Pt IV of those Regulations at **[2576]–[2580]**.

4 Artistic works

(1) In this Part "artistic work" means—
(a) a graphic work, photograph, sculpture or collage, irrespective of artistic quality,
(b) a work of architecture being a building or a model for a building, or
(c) a work of artistic craftsmanship.

(2) In this Part—
"building" includes any fixed structure, and a part of a building or fixed structure;
"graphic work" includes—
(a) any painting, drawing, diagram, map, chart or plan, and
(b) any engraving, etching, lithograph, woodcut or similar work;

"photograph" means a recording of light or other radiation on any medium on which an image is produced or from which an image may by any means be produced, and which is not part of a film;
"sculpture" includes a cast or model made for purposes of sculpture.

[2505]

[5A Sound recordings

(1) In this Part "sound recording" means—
(a) a recording of sounds, from which the sounds may be reproduced, or

(b) a recording of the whole or any part of a literary, dramatic or musical work, from which sounds reproducing the work or part may be produced,

regardless of the medium on which the recording is made or the method by which the sounds are reproduced or produced.

(2) Copyright does not subsist in a sound recording which is, or to the extent that it is, a copy taken from a previous sound recording.]

[2506]

NOTES

Substituted, together with s 5B, for original s 5, by the Duration of Copyright and Rights in Performances Regulations 1995, SI 1995/3297, regs 4, 9(1), subject to transitional provisions and savings in regs 12–35 thereof.

[5B Films

(1) In this Part "film" means a recording on any medium from which a moving image may by any means be produced.

(2) The sound track accompanying a film shall be treated as part of the film for the purposes of this Part.

(3) Without prejudice to the generality of subsection (2), where that subsection applies—

(a) references in this Part to showing a film include playing the film sound track to accompany the film, …

[(b) references in this Part to playing a sound recording, or to communicating a sound recording to the public, do not include playing or communicating the film sound track to accompany the film,

(c) references in this Part to copying a work, so far as they apply to a sound recording, do not include copying the film sound track to accompany the film, and

(d) references in this Part to the issuing, rental or lending of copies of a work, so far as they apply to a sound recording, do not include the issuing, rental or lending of copies of the sound track to accompany the film.]

(4) Copyright does not subsist in a film which is, or to the extent that it is, a copy taken from a previous film.

(5) Nothing in this section affects any copyright subsisting in a film sound track as a sound recording.]

[2507]

NOTES

Substituted as noted to s 5A at **[2506]**.

Sub-s (3): word omitted from para (a) repealed and paras (b)–(d) substituted for original para (b) by the Performances (Moral Rights, etc) Regulations 2006, SI 2006/18, reg 2, Schedule, paras 1, 2.

6 Broadcasts

[(1) In this Part a "broadcast" means an electronic transmission of visual images, sounds or other information which—

(a) is transmitted for simultaneous reception by members of the public and is capable of being lawfully received by them, or

(b) is transmitted at a time determined solely by the person making the transmission for presentation to members of the public,

and which is not excepted by subsection (1A); and references to broadcasting shall be construed accordingly.

(1A) Excepted from the definition of "broadcast" is any internet transmission unless it is—

(a) a transmission taking place simultaneously on the internet and by other means,

(b) a concurrent transmission of a live event, or

(c) a transmission of recorded moving images or sounds forming part of a programme service offered by the person responsible for making the transmission, being a service in which programmes are transmitted at scheduled times determined by that person.]

(2) An encrypted transmission shall be regarded as capable of being lawfully received by members of the public only if decoding equipment has been made available to members of the public by or with the authority of the person making the transmission or the person providing the contents of the transmission.

(3) References in this Part to the person making a broadcast [or a transmission which is a broadcast] are—

(a) to the person transmitting the programme, if he has responsibility to any extent for its contents, and

(b) to any person providing the programme who makes with the person transmitting it the arrangements necessary for its transmission;

and references in this Part to a programme, in the context of broadcasting, are to any item included in a broadcast.

[(4) For the purposes of this Part, the place from which a [wireless] broadcast is made is the place where, under the control and responsibility of the person making the broadcast, the programme-carrying signals are introduced into an uninterrupted chain of communication (including, in the case of a satellite transmission, the chain leading to the satellite and down towards the earth).]

[(4A) Subsections (3) and (4) have effect subject to section 6A (safeguards in case of certain satellite broadcasts).]

(5) References in this Part to the reception of a broadcast include reception of a broadcast relayed by means of a telecommunications system.

[(5A) The relaying of a broadcast by reception and immediate re-transmission shall be regarded for the purposes of this Part as a separate act of broadcasting from the making of the broadcast which is so re-transmitted.]

(6) Copyright does not subsist in a broadcast which infringes, or to the extent that it infringes, the copyright in another broadcast …

[2508]

NOTES

Sub-ss (1), (1A): substituted, for original sub-s (1), by the Copyright and Related Rights Regulations 2003, SI 2003/2498, regs 3, 4(a), subject to transitional provisions as noted to s 1 at **[2501]**.

Sub-s (3): words in square brackets substituted by SI 2003/2498, regs 3, 4(b), subject to transitional provisions as noted to s 1 at **[2501]**.

Sub-s (4): substituted by the Copyright and Related Rights Regulations 1996, SI 1996/2967, regs 4, 5, subject to transitional provisions and savings in regs 25–36 thereof; word in square brackets inserted by SI 2003/2498, regs 3, 4(c), subject to transitional provisions as noted to s 1 at **[2501]**.

Sub-s (4A): inserted by SI 1996/2967, regs 4, 6(1), subject to transitional provisions and savings in regs 25–36 thereof.

Sub-s (5A): inserted by SI 2003/2498, regs 3, 4(d), subject to transitional provisions as noted to s 1 at **[2501]**.

Sub-s (6): words omitted repealed by SI 2003/2498, reg 2(2), Sch 2, subject to transitional provisions as noted to s 1 at **[2501]**.

This section, as it applied before the amendments made by the 2003 Regulations (and as amended by SI 1996/2967), is set out below for reference purposes—

"6 Broadcasts

(1) In this Part a "broadcast" means a transmission by wireless telegraphy of visual images, sounds or other information which—

(a) is capable of being lawfully received by members of the public, or

(b) is transmitted for presentation to members of the public;

and references to broadcasting shall be construed accordingly.

(2) An encrypted transmission shall be regarded as capable of being lawfully received by members of the public only if decoding equipment has been made available to members of the public by or with the authority of the person making the transmission or the person providing the contents of the transmission.

(3) References in this Part to the person making a broadcast, broadcasting a work, or including a work in a broadcast are—

(a) to the person transmitting the programme, if he has responsibility to any extent for its contents, and

(b) to any person providing the programme who makes with the person transmitting it the arrangements necessary for its transmission; and references in this Part to a programme, in the context of broadcasting, are to any item included in a broadcast.

[(4) For the purposes of this Part, the place from which a broadcast is made is the place where, under the control and responsibility of the person making the broadcast, the programme-carrying signals are introduced into an uninterrupted chain of communication (including, in the case of a satellite transmission, the chain leading to the satellite and down towards the earth).]

[(4A) Subsections (3) and (4) have effect subject to section 6A (safeguards in case of certain satellite broadcasts).]

(5) References in this Part to the reception of a broadcast include reception of a broadcast relayed by means of a telecommunications system.

(6) Copyright does not subsist in a broadcast which infringes, or to the extent that it infringes, the copyright in another broadcast or in a cable programme.".

[6A Safeguards in relation to certain satellite broadcasts

(1) This section applies where the place from which a broadcast by way of satellite transmission is made is located in a country other than an EEA State and the law of that country fails to provide at least the following level of protection—

(a) exclusive rights in relation to [wireless] broadcasting equivalent to those conferred by section 20 ([infringement by communication to the public]) on the authors of literary, dramatic, musical and artistic works, films and broadcasts;

(b) a right in relation to live [wireless] broadcasting equivalent to that conferred on a performer by section 182(1)(b) (consent required for live broadcast of performance); and

(c) a right for authors of sound recordings and performers to share in a single equitable remuneration in respect of the [wireless] broadcasting of sound recordings.

(2) Where the place from which the programme-carrying signals are transmitted to the satellite ("the uplink station") is located in an EEA State—

(a) that place shall be treated as the place from which the broadcast is made, and

(b) the person operating the uplink station shall be treated as the person making the broadcast.

(3) Where the uplink station is not located in an EEA State but a person who is established in an EEA State has commissioned the making of the broadcast—

(a) that person shall be treated as the person making the broadcast, and

(b) the place in which he has his principal establishment in the European Economic Area shall be treated as the place from which the broadcast is made.]

[2509]

NOTES

Inserted by the Copyright and Related Rights Regulations 1996, SI 1996/2967, regs 4, 6(2), subject to transitional provisions and savings in regs 25–36 thereof.

Sub-s (1): words in second pair of square brackets in para (a) substituted, and other words in square brackets inserted, by the Copyright and Related Rights Regulations 2003, SI 2003/2498, regs 3, 5(3), subject to transitional provisions as noted to s 1 at **[2501]**. Sub-s (1), as it applied before the amendments made by the 2003 Regulations, is set out below for reference purposes—

"(1) This section applies where the place from which a broadcast by way of satellite transmission is made is located in a country other than an EEA State and the law of that country fails to provide at least the following level of protection—

(a) exclusive rights in relation to broadcasting equivalent to those conferred by section 20 (infringement by broadcasting) on the authors of literary, dramatic, musical and artistic works, films and broadcasts;

(b) a right in relation to live broadcasting equivalent to that conferred on a performer by section 182(1)(b) (consent required for live broadcast of performance); and

(c) a right for authors of sound recordings and performers to share in a single equitable remuneration in respect of the broadcasting of sound recordings.".

7 Cable programmes

(1) In this Part—

"cable programme" means any item included in a cable programme service; and

"cable programme service" means a service which consists wholly or mainly in sending visual images, sounds or other information by means of a telecommunications system, otherwise than by wireless telegraphy, for reception—

(a) at two or more places (whether for simultaneous reception or at different times in response to requests by different users), or

(b) for presentation to members of the public,

and which is not, or so far as it is not, excepted by or under the following provisions of this section.

(2) *The following are excepted from the definition of "cable programme service"—*

(*a*) *a service or part of a service of which it is an essential feature that while visual images, sounds or other information are being conveyed by the person providing the service there will or may be sent from each place of reception, by means of the same system or (as the case may be) the same part of it, information (other than signals sent for the operation or control of the service) for reception by the person providing the service or other persons receiving it;*

(*b*) *a service run for the purposes of a business where—*

(*i*) *no person except the person carrying on the business is concerned in the control of the apparatus comprised in the system,*

(*ii*) *the visual images, sounds or other information are conveyed by the system solely for purposes internal to the running of the business and not by way of rendering a service or providing amenities for others, and*

(*iii*) *the system is not connected to any other telecommunications system;*

(*c*) *a service run by a single individual where—*

(*i*) *all the apparatus comprised in the system is under his control,*

(*ii*) *the visual images, sounds or other information conveyed by the system are conveyed solely for domestic purposes of his, and*

(*iii*) *the system is not connected to any other telecommunications system;*

(*d*) *services where—*

(*i*) *all the apparatus comprised in the system is situated in, or connects, premises which are in single occupation, and*

(*ii*) *the system is not connected to any other telecommunications system,*

other than services operated as part of the amenities provided for residents or inmates of premises run as a business;

(*e*) *services which are, or to the extent that they are, run for persons providing broadcasting or cable programme services or providing programmes for such services.*

(3) *The Secretary of State may by order amend subsection (2) so as to add or remove exceptions, subject to such transitional provision as appears to him to be appropriate.*

(4) *An order shall be made by statutory instrument; and no order shall be made unless a draft of it has been laid before and approved by resolution of each House of Parliament.*

(5) *References in this Part to the inclusion of a cable programme or work in a cable programme service are to its transmission as part of the service; and references to the person including it are to the person providing the service.*

(6) *Copyright does not subsist in a cable programme—*

(*a*) *if it is included in a cable programme service by reception and immediate re-transmission of a broadcast, or*

(*b*) *if it infringes, or to the extent that it infringes, the copyright in another cable programme or in a broadcast.*

[2510]

NOTES

Repealed by the Copyright and Related Rights Regulations 2003, SI 2003/2498, regs 3, 5(1), subject to transitional provisions as noted to s 1 at **[2501]**.

8 Published editions

(1) In this Part "published edition", in the context of copyright in the typographical arrangement of a published edition, means a published edition of the whole or any part of one or more literary, dramatic or musical works.

(2) Copyright does not subsist in the typographical arrangement of a published edition if, or to the extent that, it reproduces the typographical arrangement of a previous edition.

[2511]

Authorship and ownership of copyright

9 Authorship of work

(1) In this Part "author", in relation to a work, means the person who creates it.

(2) That person shall be taken to be—

[(aa) in the case of a sound recording, the producer;

(ab) in the case of a film, the producer and the principal director;]

(b) in the case of a broadcast, the person making the broadcast (see section 6(3)) or, in the case of a broadcast which relays another broadcast by reception and immediate re-transmission, the person making that other broadcast;

(c) …

(d) in the case of the typographical arrangement of a published edition, the publisher.

(3) In the case of a literary, dramatic, musical or artistic work which is computer-generated, the author shall be taken to be the person by whom the arrangements necessary for the creation of the work are undertaken.

(4) For the purposes of this Part a work is of "unknown authorship" if the identity of the author is unknown or, in the case of a work of joint authorship, if the identity of none of the authors is known.

(5) For the purposes of this Part the identity of an author shall be regarded as unknown if it is not possible for a person to ascertain his identity by reasonable inquiry; but if his identity is once known it shall not subsequently be regarded as unknown.

[2512]

NOTES

Sub-s (2): paras (aa), (ab) substituted for original para (a), by the Copyright and Related Rights Regulations 1996, SI 1996/2967, regs 4, 18(1), subject to transitional provisions and savings in regs 25–36 thereof; para (c) repealed by the Copyright and Related Rights Regulations 2003, SI 2003/2498, regs 2(2), 3, 5(4), Sch 2, subject to transitional provisions as noted to s 1 at **[2501]**, and previously read as follows—

"(c) in the case of a cable programme, the person providing the cable programme service in which the programme is included;".

10 Works of joint authorship

(1) In this Part a "work of joint authorship" means a work produced by the collaboration of two or more authors in which the contribution of each author is not distinct from that of the other author or authors.

[(1A) A film shall be treated as a work of joint authorship unless the producer and the principal director are the same person.]

(2) A broadcast shall be treated as a work of joint authorship in any case where more than one person is to be taken as making the broadcast (see section 6(3)).

(3) References in this Part to the author of a work shall, except as otherwise provided, be construed in relation to a work of joint authorship as references to all the authors of the work.

[2513]

NOTES

Sub-s (1A): inserted by the Copyright and Related Rights Regulations 1996, SI 1996/2967, regs 4, 18(2), subject to transitional provisions and savings in regs 25–36 thereof.

11 First ownership of copyright

(1) The author of a work is the first owner of any copyright in it, subject to the following provisions.

(2) Where a literary, dramatic, musical or artistic work[, or a film,] is made by an employee in the course of his employment, his employer is the first owner of any copyright in the work subject to any agreement to the contrary.

(3) This section does not apply to Crown copyright or Parliamentary copyright (see sections 163 and 165) or to copyright which subsists by virtue of section 168 (copyright of certain international organisations).

[2514]

NOTES

Sub-s (2): words in square brackets inserted by the Copyright and Related Rights Regulations 1996, SI 1996/2967, regs 4, 18(3), subject to transitional provisions and savings in regs 25–36 thereof.

Duration of copyright

[12 Duration of copyright in literary, dramatic, musical or artistic works

(1) The following provisions have effect with respect to the duration of copyright in a literary, dramatic, musical or artistic work.

(2) Copyright expires at the end of the period of 70 years from the end of the calendar year in which the author dies, subject as follows.

(3) If the work is of unknown authorship, copyright expires—

(a) at the end of the period of 70 years from the end of the calendar year in which the work was made, or

(b) if during that period the work is made available to the public, at the end of the period of 70 years from the end of the calendar year in which it is first so made available,

subject as follows.

(4) Subsection (2) applies if the identity of the author becomes known before the end of the period specified in paragraph (a) or (b) of subsection (3).

(5) For the purposes of subsection (3) making available to the public includes—

(a) in the case of a literary, dramatic or musical work—
(i) performance in public, or
[(ii) communication to the public;]

(b) in the case of an artistic work—
(i) exhibition in public,
(ii) a film including the work being shown in public, or
[(iii) communication to the public;]

but in determining generally for the purposes of that subsection whether a work has been made available to the public no account shall be taken of any unauthorised act.

(6) Where the country of origin of the work is not an EEA state and the author of the work is not a national of an EEA state, the duration of copyright is that to which the work is entitled in the country of origin, provided that does not exceed the period which would apply under subsections (2) to (5).

(7) If the work is computer-generated the above provisions do not apply and copyright expires at the end of the period of 50 years from the end of the calendar year in which the work was made.

(8) The provisions of this section are adapted as follows in relation to a work of joint authorship—

(a) the reference in subsection (2) to the death of the author shall be construed—
(i) if the identity of all the authors is known, as a reference to the death of the last of them to die, and
(ii) if the identity of one or more of the authors is known and the identity of one or more others is not, as a reference to the death of the last whose identity is known;

(b) the reference in subsection (4) to the identity of the author becoming known shall be construed as a reference to the identity of any of the authors becoming known;

(c) the reference in subsection (6) to the author not being a national of an EEA state shall be construed as a reference to none of the authors being a national of an EEA state.

(9) This section does not apply to Crown copyright or Parliamentary copyright (see sections 163 to [*166B*]) or to copyright which subsists by virtue of section 168 (copyright of certain international organisations).]

[2515]

NOTES

Substituted by the Duration of Copyright and Rights in Performances Regulations 1995, SI 1995/3297, regs 4, 5(1), subject to transitional provisions and savings in regs 12–35 thereof.

Sub-s (5): sub-paras (a)(ii), (b)(iii) substituted by the Copyright and Related Rights Regulations 2003, SI 2003/2498, reg 2(1), Sch 1, Pt 1, paras 1, 4(1), subject to transitional provisions as noted to s 1 at **[2501]**. Sub-s (5), as it applied before the amendments made by the 2003 Regulations, is set out below for reference purposes—

"(5) For the purposes of subsection (3) making available to the public includes—

(a) in the case of a literary, dramatic or musical work—

(i) performance in public, or

(ii) being broadcast or included in a cable programme service;

(b) in the case of an artistic work—

(i) exhibition in public,

(ii) a film including the work being shown in public, or

(iii) being included in a broadcast or cable programme service;

but in determining generally for the purposes of that subsection whether a work has been made available to the public no account shall be taken of any unauthorised act.".

Sub-s (9): figure (in italics) in square brackets substituted by the Northern Ireland Act 1998, s 99, Sch 13, para 8(1), (2) and further substituted by the figure "166D" by the Government of Wales Act 2006, s 160(1), Sch 10, paras 22, 23, with effect immediately after the ordinary election (under the Government of Wales Act 1998, s 3) to be held in 2007 (see s 161(1) of the 2006 Act).

[13A Duration of copyright in sound recordings

(1) The following provisions have effect with respect to the duration of copyright in a sound recording.

[(2) Subject to subsections (4) and (5), copyright expires—

(a) at the end of the period of 50 years from the end of the calendar year in which the recording is made, or

(b) if during that period the recording is published, 50 years from the end of the calendar year in which it is first published, or

(c) if during that period the recording is not published but is made available to the public by being played in public or communicated to the public, 50 years from the end of the calendar year in which it is first so made available,

but in determining whether a sound recording has been published, played in public or communicated to the public, no account shall be taken of any unauthorised act.]

(3) …

(4) Where the author of a sound recording is not a national of an EEA state, the duration of copyright is that to which the sound recording is entitled in the country of which the author is a national, provided that does not exceed the period which would apply under [subsection (2)].

(5) If or to the extent that the application of subsection (4) would be at variance with an international obligation to which the United Kingdom became subject prior to 29th October 1993, the duration of copyright shall be as specified in [subsection (2)].]

[2516]

NOTES

Substituted, together with s 13B, for original s 13, by the Duration of Copyright and Rights in Performances Regulations 1995, SI 1995/3297, regs 4, 6(1), subject to transitional provisions and savings in regs 12–35 thereof.

Sub-s (2): substituted by the Copyright and Related Rights Regulations 2003, SI 2003/2498, regs 3, 29(a), subject to transitional provisions as noted to s 1 at **[2501]**.

Sub-s (3): repealed by SI 2003/2498, regs 2(2), 3, 29(b), Sch 2, subject to transitional provisions as noted to s 1 at **[2501]**.

Sub-ss (4), (5): words in square brackets substituted by SI 2003/2498, regs 3, 29(c), subject to transitional provisions as noted to s 1 at **[2501]**.

This section, as it applied before the amendments made by the 2003 Regulations (and as substituted by SI 1995/3297), is set out below for reference purposes—

"[13A Duration of copyright in sound recordings

(1) The following provisions have effect with respect to the duration of copyright in a sound recording.

(2) Copyright expires—

(a) at the end of the period of 50 years from the end of the calendar year in which it is made, or
(b) if during that period it is released, 50 years from the end of the calendar year in which it is released;

subject as follows.

(3) For the purposes of subsection (2) a sound recording is "released" when it is first published, played in public, broadcast or included in a cable programme service; but in determining whether a sound recording has been released no account shall be taken of any unauthorised act.

(4) Where the author of a sound recording is not a national of an EEA state, the duration of copyright is that to which the sound recording is entitled in the country of which the author is a national, provided that does not exceed the period which would apply under subsections (2) and (3).

(5) If or to the extent that the application of subsection (4) would be at variance with an international obligation to which the United Kingdom became subject prior to 29th October 1993, the duration of copyright shall be as specified in subsections (2) and (3).]".

[13B Duration of copyright in films

(1) The following provisions have effect with respect to the duration of copyright in a film.

(2) Copyright expires at the end of the period of 70 years from the end of the calendar year in which the death occurs of the last to die of the following persons—

(a) the principal director,
(b) the author of the screenplay,
(c) the author of the dialogue, or
(d) the composer of music specially created for and used in the film;

subject as follows.

(3) If the identity of one or more of the persons referred to in subsection (2)(a) to (d) is known and the identity of one or more others is not, the reference in that subsection to the death of the last of them to die shall be construed as a reference to the death of the last whose identity is known.

(4) If the identity of the persons referred to in subsection (2)(a) to (d) is unknown, copyright expires at—

(a) the end of the period of 70 years from the end of the calendar year in which the film was made, or
(b) if during that period the film is made available to the public, at the end of the period of 70 years from the end of the calendar year in which it is first so made available.

(5) Subsections (2) and (3) apply if the identity of any of those persons becomes known before the end of the period specified in paragraph (a) or (b) of subsection (4).

(6) For the purposes of subsection (4) making available to the public includes—

(a) showing in public, or
[(b) communicating to the public;]

but in determining generally for the purposes of that subsection whether a film has been made available to the public no account shall be taken of any unauthorised act.

(7) Where the country of origin is not an EEA state and the author of the film is not a national of an EEA state, the duration of copyright is that to which the work is entitled in the country of origin, provided that does not exceed the period which would apply under subsections (2) to (6).

(8) In relation to a film of which there are joint authors, the reference in subsection (7) to the author not being a national of an EEA state shall be construed as a reference to none of the authors being a national of an EEA state.

(9) If in any case there is no person falling within paragraphs (a) to (d) of subsection (2), the above provisions do not apply and copyright expires at the end of the period of 50 years from the end of the calendar year in which the film was made.

(10) For the purposes of this section the identity of any of the persons referred to in subsection (2)(a) to (d) shall be regarded as unknown if it is not possible for a person to ascertain his identity by reasonable inquiry; but if the identity of any such person is once known it shall not subsequently be regarded as unknown.]

[2517]

NOTES

Substituted as noted to s 13A at **[2516]**.

Sub-s (6): para (b) substituted by the Copyright and Related Rights Regulations 2003, SI 2003/2498, reg 2(1), Sch 1, Pt 1, paras 1, 4(3), subject to transitional provisions as noted to s 1 at **[2501]**, and previously read as follows—

"(b) being broadcast or included in a cable programme service;".

[14 Duration of copyright in broadcasts …

(1) The following provisions have effect with respect to the duration of copyright in a broadcast …

(2) Copyright in a broadcast … expires at the end of the period of 50 years from the end of the calendar year in which the broadcast was made … , subject as follows.

(3) Where the author of the broadcast … is not a national of an EEA state, the duration of copyright in the broadcast … is that to which it is entitled in the country of which the author is a national, provided that does not exceed the period which would apply under subsection (2).

(4) If or to the extent that the application of subsection (3) would be at variance with an international obligation to which the United Kingdom became subject prior to 29th October 1993, the duration of copyright shall be as specified in subsection (2).

(5) Copyright in a repeat broadcast … expires at the same time as the copyright in the original broadcast … ; and accordingly no copyright arises in respect of a repeat broadcast … which is broadcast … after the expiry of the copyright in the original broadcast …

(6) A repeat broadcast … means one which is a repeat … of a broadcast previously made …]

[2518]

NOTES

Substituted by the Duration of Copyright and Rights in Performances Regulations 1995, SI 1995/3297, regs 4, 7(1), subject to transitional provisions and savings in regs 12–35 thereof.

Words omitted repealed by the Copyright and Related Rights Regulations 2003, SI 2003/2498, reg 2(2), Sch 2, subject to transitional provisions as noted to s 1 at **[2501]**.

This section, as it applied before the amendments made by the 2003 Regulations (and as substituted by SI 1995/3297), is set out below for reference purposes—

"14 Duration of copyright in broadcasts and cable programmes

(1) The following provisions have effect with respect to the duration of copyright in a broadcast or cable programme.

(2) Copyright in a broadcast or cable programme expires at the end of the period of 50 years from the end of the calendar year in which the broadcast was made or the programme was included in a cable programme service, subject as follows.

(3) Where the author of the broadcast or cable programme is not a national of an EEA state, the duration of copyright in the broadcast or cable programme is that to which it is entitled in the country of which the author is a national, provided that does not exceed the period which would apply under subsection (2).

(4) If or to the extent that the application of subsection (3) would be at variance with an international obligation to which the United Kingdom became subject prior to 29th October 1993, the duration of copyright shall be as specified in subsection (2).

(5) Copyright in a repeat broadcast or cable programme expires at the same time as the copyright in the original broadcast or cable programme; and accordingly no copyright arises in respect of a repeat broadcast or cable programme which is broadcast or included in a cable programme service after the expiry of the copyright in the original broadcast or cable programme.

(6) A repeat broadcast or cable programme means one which is a repeat either of a broadcast previously made or of a cable programme previously included in a cable programme service.".

15 Duration of copyright in typographical arrangement of published editions

Copyright in the typographical arrangement of a published edition expires at the end of the period of 25 years from the end of the calendar year in which the edition was first published.

[2519]

[15A Meaning of country of origin

(1) For the purposes of the provisions of this Part relating to the duration of copyright the country of origin of a work shall be determined as follows.

(2) If the work is first published in a Berne Convention country and is not simultaneously published elsewhere, the country of origin is that country.

(3) If the work is first published simultaneously in two or more countries only one of which is a Berne Convention country, the country of origin is that country.

(4) If the work is first published simultaneously in two or more countries of which two or more are Berne Convention countries, then—

- (a) if any of those countries is an EEA state, the country of origin is that country; and
- (b) if none of those countries is an EEA state, the country of origin is the Berne Convention country which grants the shorter or shortest period of copyright protection.

(5) If the work is unpublished or is first published in a country which is not a Berne Convention country (and is not simultaneously published in a Berne Convention country), the country of origin is—

- (a) if the work is a film and the maker of the film has his headquarters in, or is domiciled or resident in a Berne Convention country, that country;
- (b) if the work is—
  - (i) a work of architecture constructed in a Berne Convention country, or
  - (ii) an artistic work incorporated in a building or other structure situated in a Berne Convention country,

  that country;
- (c) in any other case, the country of which the author of the work is a national.

(6) In this section—

- (a) a "Berne Convention country" means a country which is a party to any Act of the International Convention for the Protection of Literary and Artistic Works signed at Berne on 9th September 1886; and
- (b) references to simultaneous publication are to publication within 30 days of first publication.]

[2520]

NOTES

Inserted by the Duration of Copyright and Rights in Performances Regulations 1995, SI 1995/3297, regs 4, 8(1), subject to transitional provisions and savings in regs 12–35 thereof.

16–27 (*Outside the scope of this work.*)

CHAPTER III
ACTS PERMITTED IN RELATION TO COPYRIGHT WORKS

28–50 (*Outside the scope of this work.*)

[Computer programs: lawful users

50A Back up copies

(1) It is not an infringement of copyright for a lawful user of a copy of a computer program to make any back up copy of it which it is necessary for him to have for the purposes of his lawful use.

(2) For the purposes of this section and sections 50B[, 50BA] and 50C a person is a lawful user of a computer program if (whether under a licence to do any acts restricted by the copyright in the program or otherwise), he has a right to use the program.

(3) Where an act is permitted under this section, it is irrelevant whether or not there exists any term or condition in an agreement which purports to prohibit or restrict the act (such terms being, by virtue of section 296A, void).]

[2521]

NOTES

Inserted, together with preceding heading and ss 50B, 50C, by the Copyright (Computer Programs) Regulations 1992, SI 1992/3233, regs 2, 8, subject to reg 12(2) thereof (agreements entered into before 1 January 1993 to remain unaffected).

Sub-s (2): figure in square brackets inserted by the Copyright and Related Rights Regulations 2003, SI 2003/2498, regs 3, 15(2), subject to transitional provisions as noted to s 1 at **[2501]**.

[50B Decompilation

(1) It is not an infringement of copyright for a lawful user of a copy of a computer program expressed in a low level language—

(a) to convert it into a version expressed in a higher level language, or

(b) incidentally in the course of so converting the program, to copy it,

(that is, to "decompile" it), provided that the conditions in subsection (2) are met.

(2) The conditions are that—

(a) it is necessary to decompile the program to obtain the information necessary to create an independent program which can be operated with the program decompiled or with another program ("the permitted objective"); and

(b) the information so obtained is not used for any purpose other than the permitted objective.

(3) In particular, the conditions in subsection (2) are not met if the lawful user—

(a) has readily available to him the information necessary to achieve the permitted objective;

(b) does not confine the decompiling to such acts as are necessary to achieve the permitted objective;

(c) supplies the information obtained by the decompiling to any person to whom it is not necessary to supply it in order to achieve the permitted objective; or

(d) uses the information to create a program which is substantially similar in its expression to the program decompiled or to do any act restricted by copyright.

(4) Where an act is permitted under this section, it is irrelevant whether or not there exists any term or condition in an agreement which purports to prohibit or restrict the act (such terms being, by virtue of section 296A, void).]

[2522]

NOTES

Inserted as noted to s 50A at **[2521]**.

[50BA Observing, studying and testing of computer programs

(1) It is not an infringement of copyright for a lawful user of a copy of a computer program to observe, study or test the functioning of the program in order to determine the ideas and principles which underlie any element of the program if he does so while performing any of the acts of loading, displaying, running, transmitting or storing the program which he is entitled to do.

(2) Where an act is permitted under this section, it is irrelevant whether or not there exists any term or condition in an agreement which purports to prohibit or restrict the act (such terms being, by virtue of section 296A, void).]

[2522A]

NOTES

Commencement: 31 October 2003.

Inserted by the Copyright and Related Rights Regulations 2003, SI 2003/2498, regs 3, 15(1), subject to transitional provisions as noted to s 1 at **[2501]**.

[50C Other acts permitted to lawful users

(1) It is not an infringement of copyright for a lawful user of a copy of a computer program to copy or adapt it, provided that the copying or adapting—

(a) is necessary for his lawful use; and

(b) is not prohibited under any term or condition of an agreement regulating the circumstances in which his use is lawful.

(2) It may, in particular, be necessary for the lawful use of a computer program to copy it or adapt it for the purpose of correcting errors in it.

(3) This section does not apply to any copying or adapting permitted under [section 50A, 50B or 50BA].]

[2523]

NOTES

Inserted as noted to s 50A at **[2521]**.

Sub-s (3): words in square brackets substituted for original words "section 50A or 50B" by the Copyright and Related Rights Regulations 2003, SI 2003/2498, regs 3, 15(3), subject to transitional provisions as noted to s 1 at **[2501]**.

[Databases: permitted acts

50D Acts permitted in relation to databases

(1) It is not an infringement of copyright in a database for a person who has a right to use the database or any part of the database, (whether under a licence to do any of the acts restricted by the copyright in the database or otherwise) to do, in the exercise of that right, anything which is necessary for the purposes of access to and use of the contents of the database or of that part of the database.

(2) Where an act which would otherwise infringe copyright in a database is permitted under this section, it is irrelevant whether or not there exists any term or condition in any agreement which purports to prohibit or restrict the act (such terms being, by virtue of section 296B, void).]

[2524]

NOTES

Inserted, together with preceding heading, by the Copyright and Rights in Databases Regulations 1997, SI 1997/3032, reg 9, subject to savings and transitional provisions in Pt IV of those Regulations at **[2576]–[2580]**.

51–55 (*Outside the scope of this work.*)

Works in electronic form

56 Transfers of copies of works in electronic form

(1) This section applies where a copy of a work in electronic form has been purchased on terms which, expressly or impliedly or by virtue of any rule of law, allow the purchaser to copy the work, or to adapt it or make copies of an adaptation, in connection with his use of it.

(2) If there are no express terms—

(a) prohibiting the transfer of the copy by the purchaser, imposing obligations which continue after a transfer, prohibiting the assignment of any licence or terminating any licence on a transfer, or

(b) providing for the terms on which a transferee may do the things which the purchaser was permitted to do,

anything which the purchaser was allowed to do may also be done without infringement of copyright by a transferee; but any copy, adaptation or copy of an adaptation made by the purchaser which is not also transferred shall be treated as an infringing copy for all purposes after the transfer.

(3) The same applies where the original purchased copy is no longer usable and what is transferred is a further copy used in its place.

(4) The above provisions also apply on a subsequent transfer, with the substitution for references in subsection (2) to the purchaser of references to the subsequent transferor.

[2525]

57–67 (*Outside the scope of this work.*)

Miscellaneous: broadcasts …

68 Incidental recording for purposes of broadcast …

(1) This section applies where by virtue of a licence or assignment of copyright a person is authorised to broadcast … —

(a) a literary, dramatic or musical work, or an adaptation of such a work,
(b) an artistic work, or
(c) a sound recording or film.

(2) He shall by virtue of this section be treated as licensed by the owner of the copyright in the work to do or authorise any of the following for the purposes of the broadcast … —

(a) in the case of a literary, dramatic or musical work, or an adaptation of such a work, to make a sound recording or film of the work or adaptation;
(b) in the case of an artistic work, to take a photograph or make a film of the work;
(c) in the case of a sound recording or film, to make a copy of it.

(3) That licence is subject to the condition that the recording, film, photograph or copy in question—

(a) shall not be used for any other purpose, and
(b) shall be destroyed within 28 days of being first used for broadcasting the work …

(4) A recording, film, photograph or copy made in accordance with this section shall be treated as an infringing copy—

(a) for the purposes of any use in breach of the condition mentioned in subsection (3)(a), and
(b) for all purposes after that condition or the condition mentioned in subsection (3)(b) is broken.

[2526]

NOTES

Words omitted (including from the heading preceding this section) repealed by the Copyright and Related Rights Regulations 2003, SI 2003/2498, reg 2(2), Sch 2, subject to transitional provisions as noted to s 1 at **[2501]**.

This section (and preceding heading), as it applied before the amendments made by the 2003 Regulations, is set out below for reference purposes—

"Miscellaneous: broadcasts and cable programmes

68 Incidental recording for purposes of broadcast or cable programme

(1) This section applies where by virtue of a licence or assignment of copyright a person is authorised to broadcast or include in a cable programme service—

(a) a literary, dramatic or musical work, or an adaptation of such a work,
(b) an artistic work, or
(c) a sound recording or film.

(2) He shall by virtue of this section be treated as licensed by the owner of the copyright in the work to do or authorise any of the following for the purposes of the broadcast or cable programme—

(a) in the case of a literary, dramatic or musical work, or an adaptation of such a work, to make a sound recording or film of the work or adaptation;
(b) in the case of an artistic work, to take a photograph or make a film of the work;
(c) in the case of a sound recording or film, to make a copy of it.

(3) That licence is subject to the condition that the recording, film, photograph or copy in question—

(a) shall not be used for any other purpose, and
(b) shall be destroyed within 28 days of being first used for broadcasting the work or, as the case may be, including it in a cable programme service.

(4) A recording, film, photograph or copy made in accordance with this section shall be treated as an infringing copy—

(a) for the purposes of any use in breach of the condition mentioned in subsection (3)(a), and
(b) for all purposes after that condition or the condition mentioned in subsection (3)(b) is broken.".

69 Recording for purposes of supervision and control of broadcasts and [other services]

(1) Copyright is not infringed by the making or use by the British Broadcasting Corporation, for the purpose of maintaining supervision and control over programmes broadcast by them, of recordings of those programmes.

[(2) Copyright is not infringed by anything done in pursuance of—
[(a) section 167(1) of the Broadcasting Act 1990, section 115(4) or (6) or 117 of the Broadcasting Act 1996 or paragraph 20 of Schedule 12 to the Communications Act 2003;]
(b) a condition which, [by virtue of section 334(1) of the Communications Act 2003], is included in a licence granted under Part I or III of that Act or Part I or II of the Broadcasting Act 1996; …
(c) a direction given under section 109(2) of the Broadcasting Act 1990 (power of [OFCOM] to require production of recordings etc);
[(d) section 334(3) of the Communications Act 2003].]

[(3) Copyright is not infringed by the use by OFCOM in connection with the performance of any of their functions under the Broadcasting Act 1990, the Broadcasting Act 1996 or the Communications Act 2003 of—
(a) any recording, script or transcript which is provided to them under or by virtue of any provision of those Acts; or
(b) any existing material which is transferred to them by a scheme made under section 30 of the Communications Act 2003.

(4) In subsection (3), "existing material" means—
(a) any recording, script or transcript which was provided to the Independent Television Commission or the Radio Authority under or by virtue of any provision of the Broadcasting Act 1990 or the Broadcasting Act 1996; and
(b) any recording or transcript which was provided to the Broadcasting Standards Commission under section 115(4) or (6) or 116(5) of the Broadcasting Act 1996.]

[2527]

NOTES

Section heading: words in square brackets substituted for original words "cable programmes" by the Copyright and Related Rights Regulations 2003, SI 2003/2498, reg 2(1), Sch 1, Pt 1, paras 1, 2(1), subject to transitional provisions as noted to s 1 at **[2501]**.

Sub-s (2): substituted by the Broadcasting Act 1996, s 148(1), Sch 10, para 31; para (a) and words in square brackets in paras (b), (c) substituted, word omitted from para (b) repealed, and para (d) inserted, by the Communications Act 2003, s 406(1), (7), Sch 17, para 91(1), (2), Sch 19(1).

Sub-ss (3), (4): substituted, for original sub-s (3), by the Communications Act 2003, s 406(1), Sch 17, para 91(1), (3).

70 Recording for purposes of time-shifting

[(1)] The making [in domestic premises] for private and domestic use of a recording of a broadcast … solely for the purpose of enabling it to be viewed or listened to at a more convenient time does not infringe any copyright in the broadcast … or in any work included in it.

[(2) Where a copy which would otherwise be an infringing copy is made in accordance with this section but is subsequently dealt with—
(a) it shall be treated as an infringing copy for the purposes of that dealing; and
(b) if that dealing infringes copyright, it shall be treated as an infringing copy for all subsequent purposes.

(3) In subsection (2), "dealt with" means sold or let for hire, offered or exposed for sale or hire or communicated to the public.]

[2528]

NOTES

Sub-s (1): numbered as such, words in square brackets inserted, and words omitted repealed, by the Copyright and Related Rights Regulations 2003, SI 2003/2498, regs 2(2), 3, 19(1), (2), Sch 2, subject to transitional provisions as noted to s 1 at **[2501]**.

Sub-ss (2), (3): added by SI 2003/2498, regs 3, 19(1), (2), subject to transitional provisions as noted to s 1 at **[2501]**.

This section, as it applied before the amendments made by the 2003 Regulations, is set out below for reference purposes—

"70 Recording for purposes of time-shifting

The making for private and domestic use of a recording of a broadcast or cable programme solely for the purpose of enabling it to be viewed or listened to at a more convenient time does not infringe any copyright in the broadcast or cable programme or in any work included in it.".

[71 Photographs of broadcasts

(1) The making in domestic premises for private and domestic use of a photograph of the whole or any part of an image forming part of a broadcast, or a copy of such a photograph, does not infringe any copyright in the broadcast or in any film included in it.

(2) Where a copy which would otherwise be an infringing copy is made in accordance with this section but is subsequently dealt with—

(a) it shall be treated as an infringing copy for the purposes of that dealing; and

(b) if that dealing infringes copyright, it shall be treated as an infringing copy for all subsequent purposes.

(3) In subsection (2), "dealt with" means sold or let for hire, offered or exposed for sale or hire or communicated to the public.]

[2529]

NOTES

Commencement: 31 October 2003.

Substituted by the Copyright and Related Rights Regulations 2003, SI 2003/2498, regs 3, 20(1), subject to transitional provisions as noted to s 1 at **[2501]**, and this section, as it applied before the substitution made by the 2003 Regulations, is set out below for reference purposes—

"71 Photographs of television broadcasts or cable programmes

The making for private and domestic use of a photograph of the whole or any part of an image forming part of a television broadcast or cable programme, or a copy of such a photograph, does not infringe any copyright in the broadcast or cable programme or in any film included in it.".

72 Free public showing or playing of broadcast ...

(1) The showing or playing in public of a broadcast ... to an audience who have not paid for admission to the place where the broadcast ... is to be seen or heard does not infringe any copyright in—

[(a) the broadcast;

(b) any sound recording (except so far as it is an excepted sound recording) included in it; or

(c) any film included in it.]

[(1A) For the purposes of this Part an "excepted sound recording" is a sound recording—

(a) whose author is not the author of the broadcast in which it is included; and

(b) which is a recording of music with or without words spoken or sung.

(1B) Where by virtue of subsection (1) the copyright in a broadcast shown or played in public is not infringed, copyright in any excepted sound recording included in it is not infringed if the playing or showing of that broadcast in public—

(a) forms part of the activities of an organisation that is not established or conducted for profit; or

(b) is necessary for the purposes of—

(i) repairing equipment for the reception of broadcasts;

(ii) demonstrating that a repair to such equipment has been carried out; or

(iii) demonstrating such equipment which is being sold or let for hire or offered or exposed for sale or hire.]

(2) The audience shall be treated as having paid for admission to a place—

(a) if they have paid for admission to a place of which that place forms part; or

(b) if goods or services are supplied at that place (or a place of which it forms part)—

(i) at prices which are substantially attributable to the facilities afforded for seeing or hearing the broadcast ... , or

(ii) at prices exceeding those usually charged there and which are partly attributable to those facilities.

(3) The following shall not be regarded as having paid for admission to a place—

(a) persons admitted as residents or inmates of the place;

(b) persons admitted as members of a club or society where the payment is only for membership of the club or society and the provision of facilities for seeing or hearing broadcasts ... is only incidental to the main purposes of the club or society.

PART IV INTELLECTUAL PROPERTY

(4) Where the making of the broadcast … was an infringement of the copyright in a sound recording or film, the fact that it was heard or seen in public by the reception of the broadcast … shall be taken into account in assessing the damages for that infringement.

[2530]

NOTES

Section heading: words omitted repealed by the Copyright and Related Rights Regulations 2003, SI 2003/2498, reg 2(2), Sch 2, subject to transitional provisions as noted to s 1 at **[2501]**.

Sub-s (1): words omitted repealed, and paras (a)–(c) substituted, for original paras (a), (b), by SI 2003/2498, regs 3, 21(1)(a), subject to transitional provisions as noted to s 1 at **[2501]**.

Sub-ss (1A), (1B): inserted by SI 2003/2498, regs 3, 21(1)(b), subject to transitional provisions as noted to s 1 at **[2501]**.

Sub-ss (2)–(4): words omitted repealed by SI 2003/2498, reg 2(2), Sch 2, subject to transitional provisions as noted to s 1 at **[2501]**.

This section, as it applied before the amendments made by the 2003 Regulations, is set out below for reference purposes—

"72 Free public showing or playing of broadcast or cable programme

(1) The showing or playing in public of a broadcast or cable programme to an audience who have not paid for admission to the place where the broadcast or programme is to be seen or heard does not infringe any copyright in—

(a) the broadcast or cable programme, or
(b) any sound recording or film included in it.

(2) The audience shall be treated as having paid for admission to a place—

(a) if they have paid for admission to a place of which that place forms part; or
(b) if goods or services are supplied at that place (or a place of which it forms part)—
  (i) at prices which are substantially attributable to the facilities afforded for seeing or hearing the broadcast or programme, or
  (ii) at prices exceeding those usually charged there and which are partly attributable to those facilities.

(3) The following shall not be regarded as having paid for admission to a place—

(a) persons admitted as residents or inmates of the place;
(b) persons admitted as members of a club or society where the payment is only for membership of the club or society and the provision of facilities for seeing or hearing broadcasts or programmes is only incidental to the main purposes of the club or society.

(4) Where the making of the broadcast or inclusion of the programme in a cable programme service was an infringement of the copyright in a sound recording or film, the fact that it was heard or seen in public by the reception of the broadcast or programme shall be taken into account in assessing the damages for that infringement.".

[73 Reception and re-transmission of [wireless broadcast by cable]

(1) This section applies where a [wireless] broadcast made from a place in the United Kingdom is [received and immediately re-transmitted by cable].

(2) The copyright in the broadcast is not infringed—

(a) if the [re-transmission by cable] is in pursuance of a relevant requirement, or
(b) if and to the extent that the broadcast is made for reception in the area in which [it is re-transmitted by cable] and forms part of a qualifying service.

(3) The copyright in any work included in the broadcast is not infringed if and to the extent that the broadcast is made for reception in the area in which [it is retransmitted by cable]; but where the making of the broadcast was an infringement of the copyright in the work, the fact that the broadcast was re-transmitted [by cable] shall be taken into account in assessing the damages for that infringement.

(4) Where—

(a) the [re-transmission by cable] is in pursuance of a relevant requirement, but
(b) to any extent, the area in which the [re-transmission by cable takes place] ("the cable area") falls outside the area for reception in which the broadcast is made ("the broadcast area"),

the [re-transmission by cable] (to the extent that it is provided for so much of the cable area as falls outside the broadcast area) of any work included in the broadcast shall, subject to subsection (5), be treated as licensed by the owner of the copyright in the work, subject only to the payment to him by the person making the broadcast of such reasonable royalty or other payment in respect of the [re-transmission by cable of the broadcast] as may be agreed or determined in default of agreement by the Copyright Tribunal.

(5) Subsection (4) does not apply if, or to the extent that, the [re-transmission of the work by cable] is (apart from that subsection) licensed by the owner of the copyright in the work.

(6) In this section "qualifying service" means, subject to subsection (8), any of the following services—

(a) a regional or national Channel 3 service,
(b) Channel 4, Channel 5 and S4C,
[(c) the public teletext service,
(d) S4C Digital, and]
(e) the television broadcasting services and teletext service of the British Broadcasting Corporation;

[and expressions used in this subsection have the same meanings as in Part 3 of the Communications Act 2003.]

[(7) In this section "relevant requirement" means a requirement imposed by a general condition (within the meaning of Chapter 1 of Part 2 of the Communications Act 2003) the setting of which is authorised under section 64 of that Act (must-carry obligations).]

(8) The Secretary of State may by order amend subsection (6) so as to add any service to, or remove any service from, the definition of "qualifying service".

(9) The Secretary of State may also by order—

(a) provide that in specified cases subsection (3) is to apply in relation to broadcasts of a specified description which are not made as mentioned in that subsection, or
(b) exclude the application of that subsection in relation to broadcasts of a specified description made as mentioned in that subsection.

(10) Where the Secretary of State exercises the power conferred by subsection (9)(b) in relation to broadcasts of any description, the order may also provide for subsection (4) to apply, subject to such modifications as may be specified in the order, in relation to broadcasts of that description.

(11) An order under this section may contain such transitional provision as appears to the Secretary of State to be appropriate.

(12) An order under this section shall be made by statutory instrument which shall be subject to annulment in pursuance of a resolution of either House of Parliament.

[(13) In this section references to re-transmission by cable include the transmission of microwave energy between terrestrial fixed points.]]

[2531]

NOTES

Substituted, together with s 73A, for original s 73, by the Broadcasting Act 1996, s 138, Sch 9, para 1.

Section heading: words in square brackets substituted for original words "broadcast in cable programme service" by the Copyright and Related Rights Regulations 2003, SI 2003/2498, regs 3, 22(1)(a), subject to transitional provisions as noted to s 1 at **[2501]**.

Sub-ss (1)–(5): words in square brackets inserted and substituted by SI 2003/2498, regs 3, 22(1)(b)–(g), subject to transitional provisions as noted to s 1 at **[2501]**. Sub-ss (1)–(5) as they applied before the amendments made by the 2003 Regulations, are set out below for reference purposes—

"(1) This section applies where a broadcast made from a place in the United Kingdom is, by reception and immediate re-transmission, included in a cable programme service.

(2) The copyright in the broadcast is not infringed—

(a) if the inclusion is in pursuance of a relevant requirement, or
(b) if and to the extent that the broadcast is made for reception in the area in which the cable programme service is provided and forms part of a qualifying service.

(3) The copyright in any work included in the broadcast is not infringed if and to the extent that the broadcast is made for reception in the area in which the cable programme service is provided; but where the making of the broadcast was an infringement of the copyright in the work, the fact that the broadcast was re-transmitted as a programme in a cable programme service shall be taken into account in assessing the damages for that infringement.

(4) Where—

(a) the inclusion is in pursuance of a relevant requirement, but
(b) to any extent, the area in which the cable programme service is provided ("the cable area") falls outside the area for reception in which the broadcast is made ("the broadcast area"),

the inclusion in the cable programme service (to the extent that it is provided for so much of the cable area as falls outside the broadcast area) of any work included in the broadcast shall, subject to subsection (5), be treated as licensed by the owner of the copyright in the work, subject only to the payment to him by the person making the broadcast of such reasonable royalty or other payment in respect of the inclusion of the broadcast in the cable programme service as may be agreed or determined in default of agreement by the Copyright Tribunal.

(5) Subsection (4) does not apply if, or to the extent that, the inclusion of the work in the cable programme service is (apart from that subsection) licensed by the owner of the copyright in the work.".

Sub-s (6): paras (c), (d) and words in square brackets following para (e) substituted by the Communications Act 2003, s 406(1), Sch 17, para 92(1), (2).

Sub-s (7): substituted by the Communications Act 2003, s 406(1), Sch 17, para 92(1), (3).

Sub-s (13): added by SI 2003/2498, regs 3, 22(1)(h), subject to transitional provisions as noted to s 1 at **[2501]**.

[73A Royalty or other sum payable in pursuance of section 73(4)

(1) An application to settle the royalty or other sum payable in pursuance of subsection (4) of section 73 (reception and re-transmission of [wireless broadcast by cable]) may be made to the Copyright Tribunal by the copyright owner or the person making the broadcast.

(2) The Tribunal shall consider the matter and make such order as it may determine to be reasonable in the circumstances.

(3) Either party may subsequently apply to the Tribunal to vary the order, and the Tribunal shall consider the matter and make such order confirming or varying the original order as it may determine to be reasonable in the circumstances.

(4) An application under subsection (3) shall not, except with the special leave of the Tribunal, be made within twelve months from the date of the original order or of the order on a previous application under that subsection.

(5) An order under subsection (3) has effect from the date on which it is made or such later date as may be specified by the Tribunal.]

[2532]

NOTES

Substituted as noted to s 73 at **[2531]**.

Sub-s (1): words in square brackets substituted for original words "broadcast in cable programme service" by the Copyright and Related Rights Regulations 2003, SI 2003/2498, regs 3, 22(2), subject to transitional provisions as noted to s 1 at **[2501]**.

74 Provision of sub-titled copies of broadcast ...

(1) A designated body may, for the purpose of providing people who are deaf or hard of hearing, or physically or mentally handicapped in other ways, with copies which are sub-titled or otherwise modified for their special needs, make copies of ... broadcasts ... and issue [or lend] copies to the public, without infringing any copyright in the broadcasts ... or works included in them.

(2) A "designated body" means a body designated for the purposes of this section by order of the Secretary of State, who shall not designate a body unless he is satisfied that it is not established or conducted for profit.

(3) An order under this section shall be made by statutory instrument which shall be subject to annulment in pursuance of a resolution of either House of Parliament.

(4) This section does not apply if, or to the extent that, there is a licensing scheme certified for the purposes of this section under section 143 providing for the grant of licences.

[2533]

NOTES

Section heading: words "or cable programme" (omitted) repealed by the Copyright and Related Rights Regulations 2003, SI 2003/2498, reg 2(2), Sch 2, subject to transitional provisions as noted to s 1 at **[2501]**.

Sub-s (1): words omitted repealed, and words in square brackets inserted, by SI 2003/2498, regs 2(2), 3, 23(1), Sch 2, subject to transitional provisions as noted to s 1 at **[2501]**, and sub-s (1), as it applied before the amendments made by the 2003 Regulations, is set out below for reference purposes—

"(1) A designated body may, for the purpose of providing people who are deaf or hard of hearing, or physically or mentally handicapped in other ways, with copies which are sub-titled or otherwise modified for their special needs, make copies of television broadcasts or cable programmes and issue copies to the public, without infringing any copyright in the broadcasts or cable programmes or works included in them.".

Orders: the Copyright (Sub-titling of Broadcasts and Cable Programmes) (Designated Body) Order 1989, SI 1989/1013.

75 Recording for archival purposes

(1) A recording of a broadcast … of a designated class, or a copy of such a recording, may be made for the purpose of being placed in an archive maintained by a designated body without thereby infringing any copyright in the broadcast … or in any work included in it.

(2) In subsection (1) "designated" means designated for the purposes of this section by order of the Secretary of State, who shall not designate a body unless he is satisfied that it is not established or conducted for profit.

(3) An order under this section shall be made by statutory instrument which shall be subject to annulment in pursuance of a resolution of either House of Parliament.

[2534]

NOTES

Sub-s (1): words "or cable programme" (omitted in both places) repealed by the Copyright and Related Rights Regulations 2003, SI 2003/2498, reg 2(2), Sch 2, subject to transitional provisions as noted to s 1 at **[2501]**.

Orders: the Copyright (Recording for Archives of Designated Class of Broadcasts and Cable Programmes) (Designated Bodies) Order 1993, SI 1993/74.

76–295 (*Outside the scope of this work.*)

PART VII
MISCELLANEOUS AND GENERAL

[Circumvention of protection measures

296 Circumvention of technical devices applied to computer programs

(1) This section applies where—

(a) a technical device has been applied to a computer program; and

(b) a person (A) knowing or having reason to believe that it will be used to make infringing copies—

(i) manufactures for sale or hire, imports, distributes, sells or lets for hire, offers or exposes for sale or hire, advertises for sale or hire or has in his possession for commercial purposes any means the sole intended purpose of which is to facilitate the unauthorised removal or circumvention of the technical device; or

(ii) publishes information intended to enable or assist persons to remove or circumvent the technical device.

(2) The following persons have the same rights against A as a copyright owner has in respect of an infringement of copyright—

(a) a person—

(i) issuing to the public copies of, or

(ii) communicating to the public,

the computer program to which the technical device has been applied;

(b) the copyright owner or his exclusive licensee, if he is not the person specified in paragraph (a);

(c) the owner or exclusive licensee of any intellectual property right in the technical device applied to the computer program.

(3) The rights conferred by subsection (2) are concurrent, and sections 101(3) and 102(1) to (4) apply, in proceedings under this section, in relation to persons with concurrent rights as they apply, in proceedings mentioned in those provisions, in relation to a copyright owner and exclusive licensee with concurrent rights.

(4) Further, the persons in subsection (2) have the same rights under section 99 or 100 (delivery up or seizure of certain articles) in relation to any such means as is referred to in

subsection (1) which a person has in his possession, custody or control with the intention that it should be used to facilitate the unauthorised removal or circumvention of any technical device which has been applied to a computer program, as a copyright owner has in relation to an infringing copy.

(5) The rights conferred by subsection (4) are concurrent, and section 102(5) shall apply, as respects anything done under section 99 or 100 by virtue of subsection (4), in relation to persons with concurrent rights as it applies, as respects anything done under section 99 or 100, in relation to a copyright owner and exclusive licensee with concurrent rights.

(6) In this section references to a technical device in relation to a computer program are to any device intended to prevent or restrict acts that are not authorised by the copyright owner of that computer program and are restricted by copyright.

(7) The following provisions apply in relation to proceedings under this section as in relation to proceedings under Part 1 (copyright)—

(a) sections 104 to 106 of this Act (presumptions as to certain matters relating to copyright); and

(b) section 72 of the *Supreme Court Act 1981*, section 15 of the Law Reform (Miscellaneous Provisions) (Scotland) Act 1985 and section 94A of the Judicature (Northern Ireland) Act 1978 (withdrawal of privilege against self-incrimination in certain proceedings relating to intellectual property);

and section 114 of this Act applies, with the necessary modifications, in relation to the disposal of anything delivered up or seized by virtue of subsection (4).

(8) Expressions used in this section which are defined for the purposes of Part 1 of this Act (copyright) have the same meaning as in that Part.]

[2535]

NOTES

Commencement: 31 October 2003.

Substituted, together with preceding heading and ss 296ZA–296ZF, for original s 296 (and preceding heading) by the Copyright and Related Rights Regulations 2003, SI 2003/2498, regs 3, 24(1), subject to transitional provisions as noted to s 1 at **[2501]**, and this section, as it applied before the substitution made by the 2003 Regulations (and as amended by SI 1992/3233), is set out below for reference purposes—

"Devices designed to circumvent copy-protection

296 Devices designed to circumvent copy-protection

(1) This section applies where copies of a copyright work are issued to the public, by or with the licence of the copyright owner, in an electronic form which is copy-protected.

(2) The person issuing the copies to the public has the same rights against a person who, knowing or having reason to believe that it will be used to make infringing copies—

(a) makes, imports, sells or lets for hire, offers or exposes for sale or hire, or advertises for sale or hire, any device or means specifically designed or adapted to circumvent the form of copy-protection employed, or

(b) publishes information intended to enable or assist persons to circumvent that form of copy-protection,

as a copyright owner has in respect of an infringement of copyright.

[(2A) Where the copies being issued to the public as mentioned in subsection (1) are copies of a computer program, subsection (2) applies as if for the words "or advertises for sale or hire" there were substituted "advertises for sale or hire or possesses in the course of a business.]

(3) Further, he has the same rights under section 99 or 100 (delivery up or seizure of certain articles) in relation to any such device or means which a person has in his possession, custody or control with the intention that it should be used to make infringing copies of copyright works, as a copyright owner has in relation to an infringing copy.

(4) References in this section to copy-protection include any device or means intended to prevent or restrict copying of a work or to impair the quality of copies made.

(5) Expressions used in this section which are defined for the purposes of Part I of this Act (copyright) have the same meaning as in that Part.

(6) The following provisions apply in relation to proceedings under this section as in relation to proceedings under Part I (copyright)—

(a) sections 104 to 106 of this Act (presumptions as to certain matters relating to copyright), and

(b) section 72 of the Supreme Court Act 1981, section 15 of the Law Reform (Miscellaneous

Provisions) (Scotland) Act 1985 and section 94A of the Judicature (Northern Ireland) Act 1978 (withdrawal of privilege against self-incrimination in certain proceedings relating to intellectual property);

and section 114 of this Act applies, with the necessary modifications, in relation to the disposal of anything delivered up or seized by virtue of subsection (3) above.".

Sub-s (7): for the words in italics in para (b) there are substituted the words "Senior Courts Act 1981" by the Constitutional Reform Act 2005, s 59(5), Sch 11, Pt 1, para 1(2), as from a day to be appointed.

[296ZA Circumvention of technological measures

(1) This section applies where—

(a) effective technological measures have been applied to a copyright work other than a computer program; and

(b) a person (B) does anything which circumvents those measures knowing, or with reasonable grounds to know, that he is pursuing that objective.

(2) This section does not apply where a person, for the purposes of research into cryptography, does anything which circumvents effective technological measures unless in so doing, or in issuing information derived from that research, he affects prejudicially the rights of the copyright owner.

(3) The following persons have the same rights against B as a copyright owner has in respect of an infringement of copyright—

(a) a person—

(i) issuing to the public copies of, or

(ii) communicating to the public,

the work to which effective technological measures have been applied; and

(b) the copyright owner or his exclusive licensee, if he is not the person specified in paragraph (a).

(4) The rights conferred by subsection (3) are concurrent, and sections 101(3) and 102(1) to (4) apply, in proceedings under this section, in relation to persons with concurrent rights as they apply, in proceedings mentioned in those provisions, in relation to a copyright owner and exclusive licensee with concurrent rights.

(5) The following provisions apply in relation to proceedings under this section as in relation to proceedings under Part 1 (copyright)—

(a) sections 104 to 106 of this Act (presumptions as to certain matters relating to copyright); and

(b) section 72 of the *Supreme Court Act 1981*, section 15 of the Law Reform (Miscellaneous Provisions) (Scotland) Act 1985 and section 94A of the Judicature (Northern Ireland) Act 1978 (withdrawal of privilege against self-incrimination in certain proceedings relating to intellectual property).

(6) Subsections (1) to (4) and (5)(b) and any other provision of this Act as it has effect for the purposes of those subsections apply, with any necessary adaptations, to rights in performances, publication right and database right.

(7) The provisions of regulation 22 (presumptions relevant to database right) of the Copyright and Rights in Databases Regulations 1997 (SI 1997/3032) apply in proceedings brought by virtue of this section in relation to database right.]

[2535A]

NOTES

Commencement: 31 October 2003.

Substituted as noted to s 296 at **[2535]**.

Sub-s (5): for the words in italics in para (b) there are substituted the words "Senior Courts Act 1981" by the Constitutional Reform Act 2005, s 59(5), Sch 11, Pt 1, para 1(2), as from a day to be appointed.

[296ZB Devices and services designed to circumvent technological measures

(1) A person commits an offence if he—

(a) manufactures for sale or hire, or

(b) imports otherwise than for his private and domestic use, or

(c) in the course of a business—

(i) sells or lets for hire, or

(ii) offers or exposes for sale or hire, or

(iii) advertises for sale or hire, or
(iv) possesses, or
(v) distributes, or
(d) distributes otherwise than in the course of a business to such an extent as to affect prejudicially the copyright owner,

any device, product or component which is primarily designed, produced, or adapted for the purpose of enabling or facilitating the circumvention of effective technological measures.

(2) A person commits an offence if he provides, promotes, advertises or markets—
(a) in the course of a business, or
(b) otherwise than in the course of a business to such an extent as to affect prejudicially the copyright owner,

a service the purpose of which is to enable or facilitate the circumvention of effective technological measures.

(3) Subsections (1) and (2) do not make unlawful anything done by, or on behalf of, law enforcement agencies or any of the intelligence services—
(a) in the interests of national security; or
(b) for the purpose of the prevention or detection of crime, the investigation of an offence, or the conduct of a prosecution,

and in this subsection "intelligence services" has the meaning given in section 81 of the Regulation of Investigatory Powers Act 2000.

(4) A person guilty of an offence under subsection (1) or (2) is liable—
(a) on summary conviction, to imprisonment for a term not exceeding three months, or to a fine not exceeding the statutory maximum, or both;
(b) on conviction on indictment to a fine or imprisonment for a term not exceeding two years, or both.

(5) It is a defence to any prosecution for an offence under this section for the defendant to prove that he did not know, and had no reasonable ground for believing, that—
(a) the device, product or component; or
(b) the service,

enabled or facilitated the circumvention of effective technological measures.]

[2535B]

NOTES

Commencement: 31 October 2003.
Substituted as noted to s 296 at **[2535]**.

[296ZC Devices and services designed to circumvent technological measures: search warrants and forfeiture

(1) The provisions of sections 297B (search warrants), 297C (forfeiture of unauthorised decoders: England and Wales or Northern Ireland) and 297D (forfeiture of unauthorised decoders: Scotland) apply to offences under section 296ZB with the following modifications.

(2) In section 297B the reference to an offence under section 297A(1) shall be construed as a reference to an offence under section 296ZB(1) or (2).

(3) In sections 297C(2)(a) and 297D(15) the references to an offence under section 297A(1) shall be construed as a reference to an offence under section 296ZB(1).

(4) In sections 297C and 297D references to unauthorised decoders shall be construed as references to devices, products or components for the purpose of circumventing effective technological measures.]

[2535C]

NOTES

Commencement: 31 October 2003.
Substituted as noted to s 296 at **[2535]**.

[296ZD Rights and remedies in respect of devices and services designed to circumvent technological measures

(1) This section applies where—

(a) effective technological measures have been applied to a copyright work other than a computer program; and

(b) a person (C) manufactures, imports, distributes, sells or lets for hire, offers or exposes for sale or hire, advertises for sale or hire, or has in his possession for commercial purposes any device, product or component, or provides services which—

(i) are promoted, advertised or marketed for the purpose of the circumvention of, or

(ii) have only a limited commercially significant purpose or use other than to circumvent, or

(iii) are primarily designed, produced, adapted or performed for the purpose of enabling or facilitating the circumvention of,

those measures.

(2) The following persons have the same rights against C as a copyright owner has in respect of an infringement of copyright—

(a) a person—

(i) issuing to the public copies of, or

(ii) communicating to the public,

the work to which effective technological measures have been applied;

(b) the copyright owner or his exclusive licensee, if he is not the person specified in paragraph (a); and

(c) the owner or exclusive licensee of any intellectual property right in the effective technological measures applied to the work.

(3) The rights conferred by subsection (2) are concurrent, and sections 101(3) and 102(1) to (4) apply, in proceedings under this section, in relation to persons with concurrent rights as they apply, in proceedings mentioned in those provisions, in relation to a copyright owner and exclusive licensee with concurrent rights.

(4) Further, the persons in subsection (2) have the same rights under section 99 or 100 (delivery up or seizure of certain articles) in relation to any such device, product or component which a person has in his possession, custody or control with the intention that it should be used to circumvent effective technological measures, as a copyright owner has in relation to any infringing copy.

(5) The rights conferred by subsection (4) are concurrent, and section 102(5) shall apply, as respects anything done under section 99 or 100 by virtue of subsection (4), in relation to persons with concurrent rights as it applies, as respects anything done under section 99 or 100, in relation to a copyright owner and exclusive licensee with concurrent rights.

(6) The following provisions apply in relation to proceedings under this section as in relation to proceedings under Part 1 (copyright)—

(a) sections 104 to 106 of this Act (presumptions as to certain matters relating to copyright); and

(b) section 72 of the *Supreme Court Act 1981*, section 15 of the Law Reform (Miscellaneous Provisions) (Scotland) Act 1985 and section 94A of the Judicature (Northern Ireland) Act 1978 (withdrawal of privilege against self-incrimination in certain proceedings relating to intellectual property);

and section 114 of this Act applies, with the necessary modifications, in relation to the disposal of anything delivered up or seized by virtue of subsection (4).

(7) In section 97(1) (innocent infringement of copyright) as it applies to proceedings for infringement of the rights conferred by this section, the reference to the defendant not knowing or having reason to believe that copyright subsisted in the work shall be construed as a reference to his not knowing or having reason to believe that his acts enabled or facilitated an infringement of copyright.

(8) Subsections (1) to (5), (6)(b) and (7) and any other provision of this Act as it has effect for the purposes of those subsections apply, with any necessary adaptations, to rights in performances, publication right and database right.

(9) The provisions of regulation 22 (presumptions relevant to database right) of the Copyright and Rights in Databases Regulations 1997 (SI 1997/3032) apply in proceedings brought by virtue of this section in relation to database right.]

[2535D]

NOTES

Commencement: 31 October 2003.

Substituted as noted to s 296 at **[2535]**.

Sub-s (6): for the words in italics in para (b) there are substituted the words "Senior Courts Act 1981" by the Constitutional Reform Act 2005, s 59(5), Sch 11, Pt 1, para 1(2), as from a day to be appointed.

[296ZE Remedy where effective technological measures prevent permitted acts

(1) In this section—

"permitted act" means an act which may be done in relation to copyright works, notwithstanding the subsistence of copyright, by virtue of a provision of this Act listed in Part 1 of Schedule 5A;

"voluntary measure or agreement" means—

(a) any measure taken voluntarily by a copyright owner, his exclusive licensee or a person issuing copies of, or communicating to the public, a work other than a computer program, or

(b) any agreement between a copyright owner, his exclusive licensee or a person issuing copies of, or communicating to the public, a work other than a computer program and another party,

the effect of which is to enable a person to carry out a permitted act.

(2) Where the application of any effective technological measure to a copyright work other than a computer program prevents a person from carrying out a permitted act in relation to that work then that person or a person being a representative of a class of persons prevented from carrying out a permitted act may issue a notice of complaint to the Secretary of State.

(3) Following receipt of a notice of complaint, the Secretary of State may give to the owner of that copyright work or an exclusive licensee such directions as appear to the Secretary of State to be requisite or expedient for the purpose of—

(a) establishing whether any voluntary measure or agreement relevant to the copyright work the subject of the complaint subsists; or

(b) (where it is established there is no subsisting voluntary measure or agreement) ensuring that the owner or exclusive licensee of that copyright work makes available to the complainant the means of carrying out the permitted act the subject of the complaint to the extent necessary to so benefit from that permitted act.

(4) The Secretary of State may also give directions—

(a) as to the form and manner in which a notice of complaint in subsection (2) may be delivered to him;

(b) as to the form and manner in which evidence of any voluntary measure or agreement may be delivered to him; and

(c) generally as to the procedure to be followed in relation to a complaint made under this section;

and shall publish directions given under this subsection in such manner as in his opinion will secure adequate publicity for them.

(5) It shall be the duty of any person to whom a direction is given under subsection (3)(a) or (b) to give effect to that direction.

(6) The obligation to comply with a direction given under subsection (3)(b) is a duty owed to the complainant or, where the complaint is made by a representative of a class of persons, to that representative and to each person in the class represented; and a breach of the duty is actionable accordingly (subject to the defences and other incidents applying to actions for breach of statutory duty).

(7) Any direction under this section may be varied or revoked by a subsequent direction under this section.

(8) Any direction given under this section shall be in writing.

(9) This section does not apply to copyright works made available to the public on agreed contractual terms in such a way that members of the public may access them from a place and at a time individually chosen by them.

(10) This section applies only where a complainant has lawful access to the protected copyright work, or where the complainant is a representative of a class of persons, where the class of persons have lawful access to the work.

(11) Subsections (1) to (10) apply with any necessary adaptations to—
- (a) rights in performances, and in this context the expression "permitted act" refers to an act that may be done by virtue of a provision of this Act listed in Part 2 of Schedule 5A;
- (b) database right, and in this context the expression "permitted act" refers to an act that may be done by virtue of a provision of this Act listed in Part 3 of Schedule 5A; and
- (c) publication right.]

[2535E]

NOTES

Commencement: 31 October 2003.
Substituted as noted to s 296 at **[2535]**.

[296ZF Interpretation of sections 296ZA to 296ZE

(1) In sections 296ZA to 296ZE, "technological measures" are any technology, device or component which is designed, in the normal course of its operation, to protect a copyright work other than a computer program.

(2) Such measures are "effective" if the use of the work is controlled by the copyright owner through—
- (a) an access control or protection process such as encryption, scrambling or other transformation of the work, or
- (b) a copy control mechanism,

which achieves the intended protection.

(3) In this section, the reference to—
- (a) protection of a work is to the prevention or restriction of acts that are not authorised by the copyright owner of that work and are restricted by copyright; and
- (b) use of a work does not extend to any use of the work that is outside the scope of the acts restricted by copyright.

(4) Expressions used in sections 296ZA to 296ZE which are defined for the purposes of Part 1 of this Act (copyright) have the same meaning as in that Part.]

[2535F]

NOTES

Commencement: 31 October 2003.
Substituted as noted to s 296 at **[2535]**.

[Rights management information

296ZG Electronic rights management information

(1) This section applies where a person (D), knowingly and without authority, removes or alters electronic rights management information which—
- (a) is associated with a copy of a copyright work, or
- (b) appears in connection with the communication to the public of a copyright work, and

where D knows, or has reason to believe, that by so doing he is inducing, enabling, facilitating or concealing an infringement of copyright.

(2) This section also applies where a person (E), knowingly and without authority, distributes, imports for distribution or communicates to the public copies of a copyright work from which electronic rights management information—
- (a) associated with the copies, or
- (b) appearing in connection with the communication to the public of the work,

has been removed or altered without authority and where E knows, or has reason to believe, that by so doing he is inducing, enabling, facilitating or concealing an infringement of copyright.

(3) A person issuing to the public copies of, or communicating, the work to the public, has the same rights against D and E as a copyright owner has in respect of an infringement of copyright.

(4) The copyright owner or his exclusive licensee, if he is not the person issuing to the public copies of, or communicating, the work to the public, also has the same rights against D and E as he has in respect of an infringement of copyright.

(5) The rights conferred by subsections (3) and (4) are concurrent, and sections 101(3) and 102(1) to (4) apply, in proceedings under this section, in relation to persons with concurrent rights as they apply, in proceedings mentioned in those provisions, in relation to a copyright owner and exclusive licensee with concurrent rights.

(6) The following provisions apply in relation to proceedings under this section as in relation to proceedings under Part 1 (copyright)—

(a) sections 104 to 106 of this Act (presumptions as to certain matters relating to copyright); and

(b) section 72 of the *Supreme Court Act 1981*, section 15 of the Law Reform (Miscellaneous Provisions) (Scotland) Act 1985 and section 94A of the Judicature (Northern Ireland) Act 1978 (withdrawal of privilege against self-incrimination in certain proceedings relating to intellectual property).

(7) In this section—

(a) expressions which are defined for the purposes of Part 1 of this Act (copyright) have the same meaning as in that Part; and

(b) "rights management information" means any information provided by the copyright owner or the holder of any right under copyright which identifies the work, the author, the copyright owner or the holder of any intellectual property rights, or information about the terms and conditions of use of the work, and any numbers or codes that represent such information.

(8) Subsections (1) to (5) and (6)(b), and any other provision of this Act as it has effect for the purposes of those subsections, apply, with any necessary adaptations, to rights in performances, publication right and database right.

(9) The provisions of regulation 22 (presumptions relevant to database right) of the Copyright and Rights in Databases Regulations 1997 (SI 1997/3032) apply in proceedings brought by virtue of this section in relation to database right.]

[2535G]

NOTES

Commencement: 31 October 2003.

Inserted by the Copyright and Related Rights Regulations 2003, SI 2003/2498, regs 3, 25, subject to transitional provisions as noted to s 1 at **[2501]**.

Sub-s (6): for the words in italics in para (b) there are substituted the words "Senior Courts Act 1981" by the Constitutional Reform Act 2005, s 59(5), Sch 11, Pt 1, para 1(2), as from a day to be appointed.

[Computer programs

296A Avoidance of certain terms

(1) Where a person has the use of a computer program under an agreement, any term or condition in the agreement shall be void in so far as it purports to prohibit or restrict—

(a) the making of any back up copy of the program which it is necessary for him to have for the purposes of the agreed use;

(b) where the conditions in section 50B(2) are met, the decompiling of the program; or

[(c) the observing, studying or testing of the functioning of the program in accordance with section 50BA].

(2) In this section, decompile, in relation to a computer program, has the same meaning as in section 50B.]

[2536]

NOTES

Inserted, together with preceding cross-heading, by the Copyright (Computer Programs) Regulations 1992, SI 1992/3233, regs 2, 11, 12(2), although not so as to affect agreements entered into before 1 January 1993.

Sub-s (1): para (c) substituted by the Copyright and Related Rights Regulations 2003, SI 2003/2498, regs 3, 15(4), subject to transitional provisions as noted to s 1 at **[2501]**, and para (c), as it applied before the amendment made by the 2003 Regulations, is set out below for reference purposes—

"(c) the use of any device or means to observe, study or test the functioning of the program in order to understand the ideas and principles which underlie any element of the program.".

[Databases

296B Avoidance of certain terms relating to databases

Where under an agreement a person has a right to use a database or part of a database, any term or condition in the agreement shall be void in so far as it purports to prohibit or restrict the performance of any act which would but for section 50D infringe the copyright in the database.]

[2537]

NOTES

Inserted, together with preceding cross-heading, by the Copyright and Rights in Databases Regulations 1997, SI 1997/3032, reg 10, subject to savings and transitional provisions in Pt IV of those Regulations at **[2576]–[2580]**.

Fraudulent reception of transmissions

297 Offence of fraudulently receiving programmes

(1) A person who dishonestly receives a programme included in a broadcasting … service provided from a place in the United Kingdom with intent to avoid payment of any charge applicable to the reception of the programme commits an offence and is liable on summary conviction to a fine not exceeding level 5 on the standard scale.

(2) Where an offence under this section committed by a body corporate is proved to have been committed with the consent or connivance of a director, manager, secretary or other similar officer of the body, or a person purporting to act in any such capacity, he as well as the body corporate is guilty of the offence and liable to be proceeded against and punished accordingly.

In relation to a body corporate whose affairs are managed by its members "director" means a member of the body corporate.

[2538]

NOTES

Sub-s (1): words "or cable programme" (omitted) repealed by the Copyright and Related Rights Regulations 2003, SI 2003/ 2498, reg 2(2), Sch 2, subject to transitional provisions as noted to s 1 at **[2501]**.

[297A Unauthorised decoders

(1) A person commits an offence if he—

(a) makes, imports, distributes, sells or lets for hire or offers or exposes for sale or hire any unauthorised decoder;

(b) has in his possession for commercial purposes any unauthorised decoder;

(c) instals, maintains or replaces for commercial purposes any unauthorised decoder; or

(d) advertises any unauthorised decoder for sale or hire or otherwise promotes any unauthorised decoder by means of commercial communications.

(2) A person guilty of an offence under subsection (1) is liable—

[(a) on summary conviction, to imprisonment for a term not exceeding six months, or to a fine not exceeding the statutory maximum, or to both;]

(b) on conviction on indictment, to imprisonment for a term not exceeding [ten] years, or to a fine, or to both.

(3) It is a defence to any prosecution for an offence under this section for the defendant to prove that he did not know, and had no reasonable ground for believing, that the decoder was an unauthorised decoder.

(4) In this section—

"apparatus" includes any device, component or electronic data (including software);

"conditional access technology" means any technical measure or arrangement whereby access to encrypted transmissions in an intelligible form is made conditional on prior individual authorisation;

"decoder" means any apparatus which is designed or adapted to enable (whether on its own or with any other apparatus) an encrypted transmission to be decoded;

"encrypted" includes subjected to scrambling or the operation of cryptographic envelopes, electronic locks, passwords or any other analogous application;

"transmission" means—

(a) any programme included in a broadcasting ... service which is provided from a place in the United Kingdom or any other member State; or

(b) an information society service (within the meaning of Directive 98/34/EC of the European Parliament and of the Council of 22nd June 1998, as amended by Directive 98/48/EC of the European Parliament and of the Council of 20th July 1998) which is provided from a place in the United Kingdom or any other member State; and

"unauthorised", in relation to a decoder, means that the decoder is designed or adapted to enable an encrypted transmission, or any service of which it forms part, to be accessed in an intelligible form without payment of the fee (however imposed) which the person making the transmission, or on whose behalf it is made, charges for accessing the transmission or service (whether by the circumvention of any conditional access technology related to the transmission or service or by any other means).]

[2539]

NOTES

Inserted by the Broadcasting Act 1990, s 179(1); substituted by the Conditional Access (Unauthorised Decoders) Regulations 2000, SI 2000/1175, reg 2(1), (2).

Sub-s (2): para (a) substituted, and word in square brackets in para (b) substituted (for the original word "two"), by the Copyright, etc and Trade Marks (Offences and Enforcement) Act 2002, s 1(1), (4), except in relation to offences committed before 20 November 2002. The original para (a) read as follows—

"(a) on summary conviction, to a fine not exceeding the statutory maximum;".

Sub-s (4): words "or cable programme" (omitted from definition "transmission") repealed by the Copyright and Related Rights Regulations 2003, SI 2003/2498, reg 2(2), Sch 2, subject to transitional provisions as noted to s 1 at **[2501]**.

[297B Search warrants

(1) Where a justice of the peace (in Scotland, a sheriff or justice of the peace) is satisfied by information on oath given by a constable (in Scotland, by evidence on oath) that there are reasonable grounds for believing—

(a) that an offence under section 297A(1) has been or is about to be committed in any premises, and

(b) that evidence that such an offence has been or is about to be committed is in those premises,

he may issue a warrant authorising a constable to enter and search the premises, using such reasonable force as is necessary.

(2) The power conferred by subsection (1) does not, in England and Wales, extend to authorising a search for material of the kinds mentioned in section 9(2) of the Police and Criminal Evidence Act 1984 (c 60) (certain classes of personal or confidential material).

(3) A warrant under subsection (1)—

(a) may authorise persons to accompany any constable executing the warrant, and

(b) remains in force for [three months] from the date of its issue.

(4) In executing a warrant issued under subsection (1) a constable may seize an article if he reasonably believes that it is evidence that any offence under section 297A(1) has been or is about to be committed.

(5) In this section "premises" includes land, buildings, fixed or moveable structures, vehicles, vessels, aircraft and hovercraft.]

[2540]

NOTES

Commencement: 20 November 2002.

Inserted by the Copyright, etc and Trade Marks (Offences and Enforcement) Act 2002, s 2(1), (4).

Sub-s (3): words in square brackets substituted for original words "28 days" in relation to England and Wales by the Serious Organised Crime and Police Act 2005, s 174(1), Sch 16, para 6(1), (4).

[297C Forfeiture of unauthorised decoders: England and Wales or Northern Ireland

(1) In England and Wales or Northern Ireland where unauthorised decoders have come into the possession of any person in connection with the investigation or prosecution of a relevant offence, that person may apply under this section for an order for the forfeiture of the unauthorised decoders.

(2) For the purposes of this section "relevant offence" means—

(a) an offence under section 297A(1) (criminal liability for making, importing, etc unauthorised decoders),

(b) an offence under the Trade Descriptions Act 1968, or

(c) an offence involving dishonesty or deception.

(3) An application under this section may be made—

(a) where proceedings have been brought in any court for a relevant offence relating to some or all of the unauthorised decoders, to that court, or

(b) where no application for the forfeiture of the unauthorised decoders has been made under paragraph (a), by way of complaint to a magistrates' court.

(4) On an application under this section, the court shall make an order for the forfeiture of any unauthorised decoders only if it is satisfied that a relevant offence has been committed in relation to the unauthorised decoders.

(5) A court may infer for the purposes of this section that such an offence has been committed in relation to any unauthorised decoders if it is satisfied that such an offence has been committed in relation to unauthorised decoders which are representative of the unauthorised decoders in question (whether by reason of being of the same design or part of the same consignment or batch or otherwise).

(6) Any person aggrieved by an order made under this section by a magistrates' court, or by a decision of such a court not to make such an order, may appeal against that order or decision—

(a) in England and Wales, to the Crown Court, or

(b) in Northern Ireland, to the county court.

(7) An order under this section may contain such provision as appears to the court to be appropriate for delaying the coming into force of the order pending the making and determination of any appeal (including any application under section 111 of the Magistrates' Courts Act 1980 (c 43) or Article 146 of the Magistrates' Courts (Northern Ireland) Order 1981 (SI 1981/1675 (NI 26)) (statement of case)).

(8) Subject to subsection (9), where any unauthorised decoders are forfeited under this section they shall be destroyed in accordance with such directions as the court may give.

(9) On making an order under this section the court may direct that the unauthorised decoders to which the order relates shall (instead of being destroyed) be forfeited to a person who has rights or remedies under section 298 in relation to the unauthorised decoders in question, or dealt with in such other way as the court considers appropriate.]

[2541]

NOTES

Commencement: 20 November 2002.

Inserted, together with s 297D, by the Copyright, etc and Trade Marks (Offences and Enforcement) Act 2002, s 5.

[297D Forfeiture of unauthorised decoders: Scotland

(1) In Scotland the court may make an order under this section for the forfeiture of unauthorised decoders.

(2) An order under this section may be made—

(a) on an application by the procurator-fiscal made in the manner specified in section 134 of the Criminal Procedure (Scotland) Act 1995 (c 46), or

(b) where a person is convicted of a relevant offence, in addition to any other penalty which the court may impose.

(3) On an application under subsection (2)(a), the court shall make an order for the forfeiture of any unauthorised decoders only if it is satisfied that a relevant offence has been committed in relation to the unauthorised decoders.

(4) The court may infer for the purposes of this section that such an offence has been committed in relation to any unauthorised decoders if it is satisfied that such an offence has been committed in relation to unauthorised decoders which are representative of the unauthorised decoders in question (whether by reason of being of the same design or part of the same consignment or batch or otherwise).

(5) The procurator-fiscal making the application under subsection (2)(a) shall serve on any person appearing to him to be the owner of, or otherwise to have an interest in, the unauthorised decoders to which the application relates a copy of the application, together with a notice giving him the opportunity to appear at the hearing of the application to show cause why the unauthorised decoders should not be forfeited.

(6) Service under subsection (5) shall be carried out, and such service may be proved, in the manner specified for citation of an accused in summary proceedings under the Criminal Procedure (Scotland) Act 1995 (c 46).

(7) Any person upon whom notice is served under subsection (5) and any other person claiming to be the owner of, or otherwise to have an interest in, unauthorised decoders to which an application under this section relates shall be entitled to appear at the hearing of the application to show cause why the unauthorised decoders should not be forfeited.

(8) The court shall not make an order following an application under subsection (2)(a)—

(a) if any person on whom notice is served under subsection (5) does not appear, unless service of the notice on that person is proved, or

(b) if no notice under subsection (5) has been served, unless the court is satisfied that in the circumstances it was reasonable not to serve such notice.

(9) Where an order for the forfeiture of any unauthorised decoders is made following an application under subsection (2)(a), any person who appeared, or was entitled to appear, to show cause why the unauthorised decoders should not be forfeited may, within 21 days of the making of the order, appeal to the High Court by Bill of Suspension.

(10) Section 182(5)(a) to (e) of the Criminal Procedure (Scotland) Act 1995 shall apply to an appeal under subsection (9) as it applies to a stated case under Part 2 of that Act.

(11) An order following an application under subsection (2)(a) shall not take effect—

(a) until the end of the period of 21 days beginning with the day after the day on which the order is made, or

(b) if an appeal is made under subsection (9) above within that period, until the appeal is determined or abandoned.

(12) An order under subsection (2)(b) shall not take effect—

(a) until the end of the period within which an appeal against the order could be brought under the Criminal Procedure (Scotland) Act 1995 (c 46), or

(b) if an appeal is made within that period, until the appeal is determined or abandoned.

(13) Subject to subsection (14), where any unauthorised decoders are forfeited under this section they shall be destroyed in accordance with such directions as the court may give.

(14) On making an order under this section the court may direct that the unauthorised decoders to which the order relates shall (instead of being destroyed) be forfeited to a person who has rights or remedies under section 298 in relation to the unauthorised decoders in question, or dealt with in such other way as the court considers appropriate.

(15) For the purposes of this section—

"relevant offence" means an offence under section 297A(1) (criminal liability for making, importing, etc unauthorised decoders), or under the Trade Descriptions Act 1968 (c 29) or any offence involving dishonesty or deception;

"the court" means—

(a) in relation to an order made on an application under subsection (2)(a), the sheriff, and

(b) in relation to an order made under subsection (2)(b), the court which imposed the penalty.]

[2542]

NOTES

Commencement: 20 November 2002.
Inserted as noted to s 297C at **[2541]**.

[298 Rights and remedies in respect of apparatus, &c for unauthorised reception of transmissions

(1) A person who—

(a) makes charges for the reception of programmes included in a broadcasting ... service provided from a place in the United Kingdom or any other member State,

(b) sends encrypted transmissions of any other description from a place in the United Kingdom or any other member State, or

(c) provides conditional access services from a place in the United Kingdom or any other member State,

is entitled to the following rights and remedies.

(2) He has the same rights and remedies against a person—

(a) who—

(i) makes, imports, distributes, sells or lets for hire, offers or exposes for sale or hire, or advertises for sale or hire,

(ii) has in his possession for commercial purposes, or

(iii) instals, maintains or replaces for commercial purposes,

any apparatus designed or adapted to enable or assist persons to access the programmes or other transmissions or circumvent conditional access technology related to the programmes or other transmissions when they are not entitled to do so, or

(b) who publishes or otherwise promotes by means of commercial communications any information which is calculated to enable or assist persons to access the programmes or other transmissions or circumvent conditional access technology related to the programmes or other transmissions when they are not entitled to do so,

as a copyright owner has in respect of an infringement of copyright.

(3) Further, he has the same rights under section 99 or 100 (delivery up or seizure of certain articles) in relation to any such apparatus as a copyright owner has in relation to an infringing copy.

(4) Section 72 of the *Supreme Court Act 1981*, section 15 of the Law Reform (Miscellaneous Provisions) (Scotland) Act 1985 and section 94A of the Judicature (Northern Ireland) Act 1978 (withdrawal of privilege against self-incrimination in certain proceedings relating to intellectual property) apply to proceedings under this section as to proceedings under Part I of this Act (copyright).

(5) In section 97(1) (innocent infringement of copyright) as it applies to proceedings for infringement of the rights conferred by this section, the reference to the defendant not knowing or having reason to believe that copyright subsisted in the work shall be construed as a reference to his not knowing or having reason to believe that his acts infringed the rights conferred by this section.

(6) Section 114 applies, with the necessary modifications, in relation to the disposal of anything delivered up or seized by virtue of subsection (3) above.

(7) In this section "apparatus", "conditional access technology" and "encrypted" have the same meanings as in section 297A, "transmission" includes transmissions as defined in that section and "conditional access services" means services comprising the provision of conditional access technology.]

[2543]

NOTES

Substituted by the Conditional Access (Unauthorised Decoders) Regulations 2000, SI 2000/1175, reg 2(1), (3).

Sub-s (1): words "or cable programme" omitted from para (a), repealed by the Copyright and Related Rights Regulations 2003, SI 2003/2498, reg 2(2), Sch 2, subject to transitional provisions as noted to s 1 at **[2501]**.

Sub-s (4): for the words in italics there are substituted the words "Senior Courts Act 1981" by the Constitutional Reform Act 2005, s 59(5), Sch 11, Pt 1, para 1(2), as from a day to be appointed.

299 Supplementary provisions as to fraudulent reception

(1) Her Majesty may by Order in Council—

(a) provide that section 297 applies in relation to programmes included in services provided from a country or territory outside the United Kingdom, and

(b) provide that section 298 applies in relation to such programmes and to encrypted transmissions sent from such a country or territory.

(2) …

(3) A statutory instrument containing an Order in Council under subsection (1) shall be subject to annulment in pursuance of a resolution of either House of Parliament.

(4) Where sections 297 and 298 apply in relation to a broadcasting service … , they also apply to any service run for the person providing that service, or a person providing programmes for that service, which consists wholly or mainly in the sending by means of a telecommunications system of sounds or visual images, or both.

(5) In sections 297[, 297A] and 298, and this section, "programme" [and "broadcasting"], and related expressions, have the same meaning as in Part I (copyright).
[2544]

NOTES

Sub-s (2): repealed by the Broadcasting Act 1990, ss 179(2), 203(3), Sch 21.

Sub-s (4): words "or cable programme service" (omitted) repealed by the Copyright and Related Rights Regulations 2003, SI 2003/2498, reg 2(2), Sch 2, subject to transitional provisions as noted to s 1 at **[2501]**.

Sub-s (5): figure in first pair of square brackets inserted by the Broadcasting Act 1990, s 179(2); words in second pair of square brackets substituted for original words ", "broadcasting" and "cable programme service"" by SI 2003/2498, reg 2(1), Sch 1, Pt 1, paras 1, 3(3), subject to transitional provisions as noted to s 1 at **[2501]**.

Orders in Council: the Fraudulent Reception of Transmissions (Guernsey) Order 1989, SI 1989/2003.

300–305 *(S 300 repealed by the Trade Marks Act 1994, s 106(2), Sch 5; ss 301–305 outside the scope of this work.)*

306 Short title

This Act may be cited as the Copyright, Designs and Patents Act 1988.
[2545]

(Schs 1–5 outside the scope of this work.)

[SCHEDULE 5A
PERMITTED ACTS TO WHICH SECTION 296ZE APPLIES

Section 296ZE

PART 1
COPYRIGHT EXCEPTIONS

section 29 (research and private study)

[section 31A (making a single accessible copy for personal use)

section 31B (multiple copies for visually impaired persons)

section 31C (intermediate copies and records)]

section 32(1), (2) and (3) (things done for purposes of instruction or examination)

section 35 (recording by educational establishments of broadcasts)

section 36 (reprographic copying by educational establishments of passages from published works)

section 38 (copying by librarians: articles in periodicals)

section 39 (copying by librarians: parts of published works)

section 41 (copying by librarians: supply of copies to other libraries) section 42 (copying by librarians or archivists: replacement copies of works)

section 43 (copying by librarians or archivists: certain unpublished works)

section 44 (copy of work required to be made as condition of export)

section 45 (Parliamentary and judicial proceedings)

section 46 (Royal Commissions and statutory inquiries)

section 47 (material open to public inspection or on official register)

section 48 (material communicated to the Crown in the course of public business)

section 49 (public records)

section 50 (acts done under statutory authority)

section 61 (recordings of folksongs)

section 68 (incidental recording for purposes of broadcast)

section 69 (recording for purposes of supervision and control of broadcasts)

section 70 (recording for purposes of time-shifting)

section 71 (photographs of broadcasts)

section 74 (provision of sub-titled copies of broadcast)

section 75 (recording for archival purposes)]

[2545A]

NOTES

Commencement: 31 October 2003.

Inserted by the Copyright and Related Rights Regulations 2003, SI 2003/2498, regs 3, 24(2), Sch 3, subject to transitional provisions as noted to s 1 at **[2501]**; entries in square brackets inserted by the Copyright (Visually Impaired Persons) Act 2002, s 7(3) (as inserted by SI 2003/2498, reg 2(1), Sch 1, Pt 2, para 22(c)).

[PART 2
RIGHTS IN PERFORMANCES EXCEPTIONS

paragraph 4 of Schedule 2 (things done for purposes of instruction or examination)

paragraph 6 of Schedule 2 (recording of broadcasts by educational establishments)

paragraph 7 of Schedule 2 (copy of work required to be made as condition of export)

paragraph 8 of Schedule 2 (Parliamentary and judicial proceedings)

paragraph 9 of Schedule 2 (Royal Commissions and statutory inquiries)

paragraph 10 of Schedule 2 (public records)

paragraph 11 of Schedule 2 (acts done under statutory authority)

paragraph 14 of Schedule 2 (recordings of folksongs)

paragraph 16 of Schedule 2 (incidental recording for purposes of broadcast)

paragraph 17 of Schedule 2 (recordings for purposes of supervision and control of broadcasts)

paragraph 17A of Schedule 2 (recording for the purposes of time-shifting)

paragraph 17B of Schedule 2 (photographs of broadcasts)

paragraph 20 of Schedule 2 (provision of sub-titled copies of broadcast)

paragraph 21 of Schedule 2 (recording of broadcast for archival purposes)]

[2545B]

NOTES

Commencement: 31 October 2003.

Inserted as noted to Pt I at **[2545A]**.

[PART 3
DATABASE RIGHT EXCEPTIONS

regulation 20 of and Schedule 1 to the Copyright and Rights in Databases Regulations 1997 (SI 1997/3032)]

[2545C]

NOTES

Commencement: 31 October 2003.
Inserted as noted to Pt 1 at **[2545A]**.

(*Schs 6–8 outside the scope of this work.*)

DESIGN RIGHT (SEMICONDUCTOR TOPOGRAPHIES) REGULATIONS 1989

(SI 1989/1100)

NOTES

Made: 29 June 1989.
Authority: European Communities Act 1972, s 2(2).
Commencement: 1 August 1989.

ARRANGEMENT OF REGULATIONS

1 Citation and commencement

These Regulations may be cited as the Design Right (Semiconductor Topographies) Regulations 1989 and shall come into force on 1st August 1989.

[2546]

2 Interpretation

(1) In these Regulations—

"the Act" means the Copyright, Designs and Patents Act 1988;

"semiconductor product" means an article the purpose, or one of the purposes, of which is the performance of an electronic function and which consists of two or more layers, at least one of which is composed of semiconducting material and in or upon one or more of which is fixed a pattern appertaining to that or another function; and

"semiconductor topography" means a design within the meaning of section 213(2) of the Act which is a design of either of the following—

(a) the pattern fixed, or intended to be fixed, in or upon—

(i) a layer of a semiconductor product, or

(ii) a layer of material in the course of and for the purpose of the manufacture of a semiconductor product, or

(b) the arrangement of the patterns fixed, or intended to be fixed, in or upon the layers of a semiconductor product in relation to one another.

(2) Except where the context otherwise requires, these Regulations shall be construed as one with Part III of the Act (design right).

[2547]

3 Application of Copyright, Designs and Patents Act 1988, Part III

In its application to a design which is a semiconductor topography, Part III of the Act shall have effect subject to regulations 4 to 9 below.

[2548]

4 Qualification

(1) Section 213(5) of the Act has effect subject to paragraphs (2) to (4) below.

[(2) Part III of the Act has effect as if for section 217(3) there was substituted the following—

"(3) In this section "qualifying country" means—
(a) the United Kingdom,
(b) another member State,
(c) the Isle of Man, Gibraltar, the Channel Islands or any colony,
(d) a country listed in the Schedule to the Design Right (Semiconductor Topographies) Regulations 1989.".]

(3) Where a semiconductor topography is created in pursuance of a commission or in the course of employment and the designer of the topography is, by virtue of section 215 of the Act (as substituted by regulation 5 below), the first owner of design right in that topography, section 219 of the Act does not apply and section 218(2) to (4) of the Act shall apply to the topography as if it had not been created in pursuance of a commission or in the course of employment.

(4) Section 220 of the Act has effect subject to regulation 7 below and as if for subsection (1) there was substituted the following—

"220—(1) A design which does not qualify for design right protection under section 218 or 219 (as modified by regulation 4(3) of the Design Right (Semiconductor Topographies) Regulations 1989) or under the said regulation 4(3) qualifies for design right protection if the first marketing of articles made to the design—
(a) is by a qualifying person who is exclusively authorised to put such articles on the market in every member State of the European Economic Community, and
(b) takes place within the territory of any member State.";

and subsection (4) of section 220 accordingly has effect as if the words "in the United Kingdom" were omitted.

[2549]

NOTES

Para (2): substituted by the Design Right (Semiconductor Topographies) (Amendment) Regulations 2006, SI 2006/1833, regs 2, 3.

5 Ownership of design right

Part III of the Act has effect as if for section 215 of the Act there was substituted the following—

"215—(1) The designer is the first owner of any design right in a design which is not created in pursuance of a commission or in the course of employment.

(2) Where a design is created in pursuance of a commission, the person commissioning the design is the first owner of any design right in it subject to any agreement in writing to the contrary.

(3) Where, in a case not falling within subsection (2) a design is created by an employee in the course of his employment, his employer is the first owner of any design right in the design subject to any agreement in writing to the contrary.

(4) If a design qualifies for design right protection by virtue of section 220 (as modified by regulation 4(4) of the Design Right (Semiconductor Topographies) Regulations 1989), the above rules do not apply and, subject to regulation 7 of the said Regulations, the person by whom the articles in question are marketed is the first owner of the design right.".

[2550]

6 Duration of design right

(1) Part III of the Act has effect as if for section 216 of the Act there was substituted the following—

"216 The design right in a semiconductor topography expires—

(a) ten years from the end of the calendar year in which the topography or articles made to the topography were first made available for sale or hire anywhere in the world by or with the licence of the design right owner, or

(b) if neither the topography nor articles made to the topography are so made available within a period of fifteen years commencing with the earlier of the time when the topography was first recorded in a design document or the time when an article was first made to the topography, at the end of that period.".

(2) Subsection (2) of section 263 of the Act has effect as if the words "or a semiconductor topography" were inserted after the words "in relation to an article".

(3) The substitute provision set out in paragraph (1) above has effect subject to regulation 7 below.

[2551]

7 Confidential information

In determining, for the purposes of section 215(4), 216 or 220 of the Act (as modified by these Regulations), whether there has been any marketing, or anything has been made available for sale or hire, no account shall be taken of any sale or hire, or any offer or exposure for sale or hire, which is subject to an obligation of confidence in respect of information about the semiconductor topography in question unless either—

(a) the article or semiconductor topography sold or hired or offered or exposed for sale or hire has been sold or hired on a previous occasion (whether or not subject to an obligation of confidence), or

(b) the obligation is imposed at the behest of the Crown, or of the government of any country outside the United Kingdom, for the protection of security in connection with the production of arms, munitions or war material.

[2552]

8 Infringement

(1) Section 226 of the Act has effect as if for subsection (1) there was substituted the following—

"226—(1) Subject to subsection (1A), the owner of design right in a design has the exclusive right to reproduce the design—

(a) by making articles to that design, or

(b) by making a design document recording the design for the purpose of enabling such articles to be made.

(1A) Subsection (1) does not apply to—

(a) the reproduction of a design privately for non-commercial aims; or

(b) the reproduction of a design for the purpose of analysing or evaluating the design or analysing, evaluating or teaching the concepts, processes, systems or techniques embodied in it.".

(2) Section 227 of the Act does not apply if the article in question has previously been sold or hired within—

(a) the United Kingdom by or with the licence of the owner of design right in the semiconductor topography in question, or

(b) the territory of any other member State of the European Economic Community or the territory of Gibraltar by or with the consent of the person for the time being entitled to import it into or sell or hire it within that territory.

(3) Section 228(6) of the Act does not apply.

(4) It is not an infringement of design right in a semiconductor topography to—

(a) create another original semiconductor topography as a result of an analysis or evaluation of the first topography or of the concepts, processes, systems or techniques embodied in it, or

(b) reproduce that other topography.

(5) Anything which would be an infringement of the design right in a semiconductor topography if done in relation to the topography as a whole is an infringement of the design right in the topography if done in relation to a substantial part of the topography.

[2553]

9 Licences of right

Section 237 of the Act does not apply.

[2554]

10 Revocation and transitional provisions

(1) …

(2) Sub-paragraph (1) of paragraph 19 of Schedule 1 to the Act shall not apply in respect of a semiconductor topography created between 7th November 1987 and 31st July 1989.

(3) In its application to copyright in a semiconductor topography created before 7th November 1987, sub-paragraph (2) of the said paragraph 19 shall have effect as if the reference to sections 237 to 239 were a reference to sections 238 and 239; and sub-paragraph (3) of that paragraph accordingly shall not apply to such copyright.

[2555]

NOTES

Para (1): revokes the Semiconductor Products (Protection of Topography) Regulations 1987, SI 1987/1497.

[SCHEDULE
QUALIFYING COUNTRIES

Albania

Angola

Antigua and Barbuda

Argentina

Armenia

Australia

Bahrain, Kingdom of

Bangladesh

Barbados

Belize

Benin

Bolivia

Botswana

Brazil

Brunei Darussalam

Bulgaria

Burkina Faso

Burundi

Cambodia

Cameroon

Canada

Central African Republic

Chad

Chile

China

Colombia

Congo

Costa Rica

Côte d'Ivoire

Croatia

Cuba

Democratic Republic of the Congo

Djibouti

Dominica

Dominican Republic

Ecuador

Egypt

El Salvador

Fiji

Former Yugoslav Republic of Macedonia

French overseas territories

Gabon

The Gambia

Georgia

Ghana

Grenada

Guatemala

Guinea

Guinea Bissau

Guyana

Haiti

Honduras

Hong Kong

Iceland

India

Indonesia

Israel

Jamaica

Japan

Jordan

Kenya

Korea, Republic of

Kuwait

Kyrgyz Republic

Lesotho

Liechtenstein

Macao, China

Madagascar

Malawi

Malaysia

Maldives

Mali

Mauritania

Mauritius

Mexico

Moldova

Mongolia

Morocco

Mozambique

Myanmar

Namibia

Nepal

Netherlands Antilles

New Zealand

Nicaragua

Niger

Nigeria

Norway

Oman

Pakistan

Panama

Papua New Guinea

Paraguay

Peru

Philippines

Qatar

Romania

Rwanda

Saint Kitts and Nevis

Saint Lucia

Saint Vincent & the Grenadines

Saudi Arabia

Senegal

Sierra Leone

Singapore

Solomon Islands

South Africa

Sri Lanka

Suriname

Swaziland

Switzerland

Chinese Taipei

Tanzania

Thailand

Togo

Trinidad and Tobago

Tunisia

Turkey

Uganda

United Arab Emirates

United States of America

Uruguay

Venezuela

Zambia

Zimbabwe]

[2556]–[2557]

NOTES

Commencement: 1 August 2006.

Substituted by the Design Right (Semiconductor Topographies) (Amendment) Regulations 2006, SI 2006/1833, regs 2, 4, Sch 1.

COPYRIGHT AND RIGHTS IN DATABASES REGULATIONS 1997

(SI 1997/3032)

NOTES

Made: 18 December 1997.

Authority: European Communities Act 1972, s 2(2).

Commencement: 1 January 1998.

ARRANGEMENT OF REGULATIONS

PART I
INTRODUCTORY PROVISIONS

PART III
DATABASE RIGHT

PART IV
SAVINGS AND TRANSITIONAL PROVISIONS

PART I
INTRODUCTORY PROVISIONS

1 Citation, commencement and extent

(1) These Regulations may be cited as the Copyright and Rights in Databases Regulations 1997.

(2) These Regulations come into force on 1st January 1998.

(3) These Regulations extend to the whole of the United Kingdom.

[2558]

2 Implementation of Directive

(1) These Regulations make provision for the purpose of implementing—

(a) Council Directive No 96/9/EC of 11 March 1996 on the legal protection of databases, …

(b) certain obligations of the United Kingdom created by or arising under the EEA Agreement so far as relating to the implementation of that Directive[, and]

[(c) an Agreement in the form of an exchange of letters between the United Kingdom of Great Britain and Northern Ireland on behalf of the Isle of Man and the European Community extending to the Isle of Man the legal protection of databases as provided for in Chapter III of that Directive.]

(2) In this Regulation "the EEA Agreement" means the Agreement on the European Economic Area signed at Oporto on 2nd May 1992, as adjusted by the Protocol signed at Brussels on 17th March 1993.

[2559]

NOTES

Para (1): word omitted from sub-para (a) revoked, word in square brackets in sub-para (b) substituted, sub-para (c) inserted, by the Copyright and Rights in Databases (Amendment) Regulations 2003, SI 2003/2501, regs 2, 3.

Council Directive 96/9/EC: OJ L77, 27.3.96, p 20.

3 Interpretation

In these Regulations "the 1988 Act" means the Copyright, Designs and Patents Act 1988.

[2560]

4 Scheme of the Regulations

(1) The 1988 Act is amended in accordance with the provisions of Part II of these Regulations, subject to the savings and transitional provisions in Part IV of these Regulations.

(2) Part III of these Regulations has effect subject to those savings and transitional provisions.

[2561]

5–11 *((Pt II) amends the Copyright, Designs and Patents Act 1988 as follows: reg 5 amends s 3 at* **[2503]***; reg 6 inserts s 3A at* **[2504]***; regs 7, 8 amend ss 21, 29 (outside the scope of this work); reg 9 inserts s 50D and the preceding heading at* **[2524]***; reg 10 inserts s 296B and the preceding heading at* **[2537]***; reg 11 amends s 179 (outside the scope of this work).)*

PART III
DATABASE RIGHT

12 Interpretation

(1) In this Part—

"database" has the meaning given by section 3A(1) of the 1988 Act (as inserted by Regulation 6);

"extraction", in relation to any contents of a database, means the permanent or temporary transfer of those contents to another medium by any means or in any form;

"insubstantial", in relation to part of the contents of a database, shall be construed subject to Regulation 16(2);

"investment" includes any investment, whether of financial, human or technical resources;

"jointly", in relation to the making of a database, shall be construed in accordance with Regulation 14(6);

"lawful user", in relation to a database, means any person who (whether under a licence to do any of the acts restricted by any database right in the database or otherwise) has a right to use the database;

"maker", in relation to a database, shall be construed in accordance with Regulation 14;

"re-utilisation", in relation to any contents of a database, means making those contents available to the public by any means;

"substantial", in relation to any investment, extraction or re-utilisation, means substantial in terms of quantity or quality or a combination of both.

(2) The making of a copy of a database available for use, on terms that it will or may be returned, otherwise than for direct or indirect economic or commercial advantage, through an establishment which is accessible to the public shall not be taken for the purposes of this Part to constitute extraction or re-utilisation of the contents of the database.

(3) Where the making of a copy of a database available through an establishment which is accessible to the public gives rise to a payment the amount of which does not go beyond what is necessary to cover the costs of the establishment, there is no direct or indirect economic or commercial advantage for the purposes of paragraph (2).

(4) Paragraph (2) does not apply to the making of a copy of a database available for on-the-spot reference use.

(5) Where a copy of a database has been sold within the EEA [or the Isle of Man] by, or with the consent of, the owner of the database right in the database, the further sale within the EEA [or the Isle of Man] of that copy shall not be taken for the purposes of this Part to constitute extraction or re-utilisation of the contents of the database.

[2562]

NOTES

Para (5): words in square brackets inserted by the Copyright and Rights in Databases (Amendment) Regulations 2003, SI 2003/2501, regs 2, 4.

13 Database right

(1) A property right ("database right") subsists, in accordance with this Part, in a database if there has been a substantial investment in obtaining, verifying or presenting the contents of the database.

(2) For the purposes of paragraph (1) it is immaterial whether or not the database or any of its contents is a copyright work, within the meaning of Part I of the 1988 Act.

(3) This Regulation has effect subject to Regulation 18.

[2563]

14 The maker of a database

(1) Subject to paragraphs (2) to (4), the person who takes the initiative in obtaining, verifying or presenting the contents of a database and assumes the risk of investing in that obtaining, verification or presentation shall be regarded as the maker of, and as having made, the database.

(2) Where a database is made by an employee in the course of his employment, his employer shall be regarded as the maker of the database, subject to any agreement to the contrary.

(3) Subject to paragraph (4), where a database is made by Her Majesty or by an officer or servant of the Crown in the course of his duties, Her Majesty shall be regarded as the maker of the database.

(4) Where a database is made by or under the direction or control of the House of Commons or the House of Lords—

(a) the House by whom, or under whose direction or control, the database is made shall be regarded as the maker of the database, and

(b) if the database is made by or under the direction or control of both Houses, the two Houses shall be regarded as the joint makers of the database.

[(4A) Where a database is made by or under the direction or control of the Scottish Parliament, the Scottish Parliamentary Corporate Body shall be regarded as the maker of the database.]

(5) For the purposes of this Part a database is made jointly if two or more persons acting together in collaboration take the initiative in obtaining, verifying or presenting the contents of the database and assume the risk of investing in that obtaining, verification or presentation.

(6) References in this Part to the maker of a database shall, except as otherwise provided, be construed, in relation to a database which is made jointly, as references to all the makers of the database.

[2564]

NOTES

Para (4A): inserted by the Scotland Act 1998 (Consequential Modifications) (No 1) Order 1999, SI 1999/1042, art 3, Sch 1, Pt II, para 26.

15 First ownership of database right

The maker of a database is the first owner of database right in it.

[2565]

16 Acts infringing database right

(1) Subject to the provisions of this Part, a person infringes database right in a database if, without the consent of the owner of the right, he extracts or re-utilises all or a substantial part of the contents of the database.

(2) For the purposes of this Part, the repeated and systematic extraction or re-utilisation of insubstantial parts of the contents of a database may amount to the extraction or re-utilisation of a substantial part of those contents.

[2566]

17 Term of protection

(1) Database right in a database expires at the end of the period of fifteen years from the end of the calendar year in which the making of the database was completed.

(2) Where a database is made available to the public before the end of the period referred to in paragraph (1), database right in the database shall expire fifteen years from the end of the calendar year in which the database was first made available to the public.

(3) Any substantial change to the contents of a database, including a substantial change resulting from the accumulation of successive additions, deletions or alterations, which would result in the database being considered to be a substantial new investment shall qualify the database resulting from that investment for its own term of protection.

(4) This Regulation has effect subject to Regulation 30.

[2567]

18 Qualification for database right

(1) Database right does not subsist in a database unless, at the material time, its maker, or if it was made jointly, one or more of its makers, was—

(a) an individual who was a national of an EEA state or habitually resident within the EEA,

(b) a body which was incorporated under the law of an EEA state and which, at that time, satisfied one of the conditions in paragraph (2), …

(c) a partnership or other unincorporated body which was formed under the law of an EEA state and which, at that time, satisfied the condition in paragraph (2)(a)[,]

[(d) an individual who was habitually resident within the Isle of Man,

(e) a body which was incorporated under the law of the Isle of Man and which, at that time, satisfied one of the conditions in paragraph (2A), or

(f) a partnership or other unincorporated body which was formed under the law of the Isle of Man and which, at that time, satisfied the condition in paragraph (2A)(a).]

(2) The conditions mentioned in paragraphs (1)(b) and (c) are—

(a) that the body has its central administration or principal place of business within the EEA, or

(b) that the body has its registered office within the EEA and the body's operations are linked on an ongoing basis with the economy of an EEA state.

[(2A) The conditions mentioned in paragraphs (1)(e) and (f) are—

(a) that the body has its central administration or principal place of business within the Isle of Man, or

(b) that the body has its registered office within the Isle of Man and the body's operations are linked on an ongoing basis with the economy of the Isle of Man.]

(3) Paragraph (1) does not apply in any case falling within Regulation 14(4).

(4) In this Regulation—

(a) "EEA" and "EEA state" have the meaning given by section 172A of the 1988 Act;

(b) "the material time" means the time when the database was made, or if the making extended over a period, a substantial part of that period.

[2568]

NOTES

Para (1): word omitted from sub-para (b) revoked, comma in square brackets in sub-para (c) substituted, and sub-paras (d)–(f) inserted, by the Copyright and Rights in Databases (Amendment) Regulations 2003, SI 2003/2501, regs 2, 5(a)–(c).

Para (2A): inserted by SI 2003/2501, regs 2, 5(d).

19 Avoidance of certain terms affecting lawful users

(1) A lawful user of a database which has been made available to the public in any manner shall be entitled to extract or re-utilise insubstantial parts of the contents of the database for any purpose.

(2) Where under an agreement a person has a right to use a database, or part of a database, which has been made available to the public in any manner, any term or condition in the agreement shall be void in so far as it purports to prevent that person from extracting or re-utilising insubstantial parts of the contents of the database, or of that part of the database, for any purpose.

[2569]

20 Exceptions to database right

(1) Database right in a database which has been made available to the public in any manner is not infringed by fair dealing with a substantial part of its contents if—

(a) that part is extracted from the database by a person who is apart from this paragraph a lawful user of the database,

(b) it is extracted for the purpose of illustration for teaching or research and not for any commercial purpose, and

(c) the source is indicated.

(2) The provisions of Schedule 1 specify other acts which may be done in relation to a database notwithstanding the existence of database right.

[2570]

[20A Exceptions to database right: deposit libraries

(1) Database right in a database is not infringed by the copying of a work from the internet by a deposit library or person acting on its behalf if—

(a) the work is of a description prescribed by regulations under section 10(5) of the 2003 Act,

(b) its publication on the internet, or a person publishing it there, is connected with the United Kingdom in a manner so prescribed, and

(c) the copying is done in accordance with any conditions so prescribed.

(2) Database right in a database is not infringed by the doing of anything in relation to relevant material permitted to be done under regulations under section 7 of the 2003 Act.

(3) Regulations under section 44A(3) of the 1988 Act exclude the application of paragraph (2) in relation to prescribed activities in relation to relevant material as (and to the extent that) they exclude the application of section 44A(2) of that Act in relation to those activities.

(4) In this Regulation—

(a) "the 2003 Act" means the Legal Deposit Libraries Act 2003;

(b) "deposit library" and "relevant material" have the same meaning as in section 7 of the 2003 Act.]

[2570A]

NOTES

Commencement: 30 October 2003 (so far as confers power to make regulations); 1 February 2004 (otherwise).

Inserted by the Legal Deposit Libraries Act 2003, s 8(2).

21 Acts permitted on assumption as to expiry of database right

(1) Database right in a database is not infringed by the extraction or re-utilisation of a substantial part of the contents of the database at a time when, or in pursuance of arrangements made at a time when—

(a) it is not possible by reasonable inquiry to ascertain the identity of the maker, and

(b) it is reasonable to assume that database right has expired.

(2) In the case of a database alleged to have been made jointly, paragraph (1) applies in relation to each person alleged to be one of the makers.

[2571]

22 Presumptions relevant to database right

(1) The following presumptions apply in proceedings brought by virtue of this Part of these Regulations with respect to a database.

(2) Where a name purporting to be that of the maker appeared on copies of the database as published, or on the database when it was made, the person whose name appeared shall be presumed, until the contrary is proved—

(a) to be the maker of the database, and

(b) to have made it in circumstances not falling within Regulation 14(2) to (4).

(3) Where copies of the database as published bear a label or a mark stating—

(a) that a named person was the maker of the database, or

(b) that the database was first published in a specified year, the label or mark shall be admissible as evidence of the facts stated and shall be presumed to be correct until the contrary is proved.

(4) In the case of a database alleged to have been made jointly, paragraphs (2) and (3), so far as is applicable, apply in relation to each person alleged to be one of the makers.

[2572]

[23 Application of copyright provisions to database right

The following provisions of the 1988 Act apply in relation to database right and databases in which that right subsists as they apply in relation to copyright and copyright works—

sections 90 to 93 (dealing with rights in copyright works)
sections 96 to 102 (rights and remedies of copyright owner and exclusive licensee)
sections 113 and 114 (supplementary provisions relating to delivery up)
section 115 (jurisdiction of county court and sheriff court).]

[2573]

NOTES

Commencement: 29 April 2006.

Substituted by the Intellectual Property (Enforcement, etc) Regulations 2006, SI 2006/1028, reg 2(3), Sch 3, para 6.

24 Licensing of database right

The provisions of Schedule 2 have effect with respect to the licensing of database right.

[2574]

25 Database right: jurisdiction of Copyright Tribunal

(1) The Copyright Tribunal has jurisdiction under this Part to hear and determine proceedings under the following provisions of Schedule 2—

(a) paragraph 3, 4 or 5 (reference of licensing scheme);
(b) paragraph 6 or 7 (application with respect to licence under licensing scheme);
(c) paragraph 10, 11 or 12 (reference or application with respect to licence by licensing body).

(2) The provisions of Chapter VIII of Part I of the 1988 Act (general provisions relating to the Copyright Tribunal) apply in relation to the Tribunal when exercising any jurisdiction under this Part.

(3) Provision shall be made by rules under section 150 of the 1988 Act prohibiting the Tribunal from entertaining a reference under paragraph 3, 4 or 5 of Schedule 2 (reference of licensing scheme) by a representative organisation unless the Tribunal is satisfied that the organisation is reasonably representative of the class of persons which it claims to represent.

[2575]

PART IV
SAVINGS AND TRANSITIONAL PROVISIONS

[26 Introductory

Expressions used in this Part which are defined for the purposes of Part I of the 1988 Act have the same meaning as in that Part.]

[2576]

NOTES

Commencement: 1 November 2003.

Substituted by the Copyright and Rights in Databases (Amendment) Regulations 2003, SI 2003/2501, regs 2, 6.

27 General rule

Subject to Regulations 28 and 29, these Regulations apply to databases made before or after [1st January 1998].

[2577]

NOTES

Words in square brackets substituted by the Copyright and Rights in Databases (Amendment) Regulations 2003, SI 2003/2501, regs 2, 7.

[28 General savings

(1) Nothing in these Regulations affects any agreement made before 1st January 1998.

(2) Nothing in these Regulations affects any agreement made after 31st December 1997 and before 1st November 2003 in so far as the effect would only arise as a result of the amendment of these Regulations by the Copyright and Rights in Databases (Amendment) Regulations 2003.

(3) No act done in respect of any database, in which database right subsists by virtue of the maker of the database (or one or more of its makers) falling within one of the provisions contained in Regulations 14(4) and 18(1)(a), (b) and (c),—

(a) before 1st January 1998, or

(b) after 31st December 1997, in pursuance of an agreement made before 1st January 1998,

shall be regarded as an infringement of database right in the database.

(4) No act done in respect of any database, in which database right subsists by virtue of its maker (or one or more of its makers) falling within one of the provisions contained in Regulation 18(1)(d), (e) and (f),—

(a) before 1st November 2003, or

(b) after 31st October 2003, in pursuance of an agreement made before 1st November 2003,

shall be regarded as an infringement of database right in the database.]

[2578]

NOTES

Commencement: 1 November 2003.

Substituted by the Copyright and Rights in Databases (Amendment) Regulations 2003, SI 2003/2501, regs 2, 8.

29 Saving for copyright in certain existing databases

(1) Where a database—

(a) was created on or before 27th March 1996, and

(b) is a copyright work immediately before [1st January 1998],

copyright shall continue to subsist in the database for the remainder of its copyright term.

(2) In this Regulation "copyright term" means the period of the duration of copyright under section 12 of the 1988 Act (duration of copyright in literary, dramatic, musical or artistic works).

[2579]

NOTES

Para (1): words in square brackets in sub-para (b) substituted by the Copyright and Rights in Databases (Amendment) Regulations 2003, SI 2003/2501, regs 2, 9.

[30 Database right: term applicable to certain existing databases

Where—

(a) the making of any database is completed on or after 1st January 1983, and before 1st January 1998, and

(b) either—

(i) the database is a database in which database right subsists by virtue of the maker of the database (or one or more of its makers) falling within one of the provisions contained in Regulations 14(4) and 18(1)(a), (b) and (c) and database right begins to subsist in the database on 1st January 1998, or

(ii) the database is a database in which database right subsists by virtue of its maker (or one or more of its makers) falling within one of the provisions contained in Regulation 18(1)(d), (e) and (f) and database right begins to subsist in the database on 1st November 2003,

then database right shall subsist in the database for a period of fifteen years beginning with 1st January 1998.]

[2580]

NOTES

Commencement: 1 November 2003.

Substituted by the Copyright and Rights in Databases (Amendment) Regulations 2003, SI 2003/2501, regs 2, 10.

SCHEDULE 1
EXCEPTIONS TO DATABASE RIGHT FOR PUBLIC ADMINISTRATION

Regulation 20(2)

Parliamentary and judicial proceedings

1. Database right in a database is not infringed by anything done for the purposes of parliamentary or judicial proceedings or for the purposes of reporting such proceedings.

Royal Commissions and statutory inquiries

2.—(1) Database right in a database is not infringed by anything done for—

(a) the purposes of the proceedings of a Royal Commission or statutory inquiry, or

(b) the purpose of reporting any such proceedings held in public.

(2) Database right in a database is not infringed by the issue to the public of copies of the report of a Royal Commission or statutory inquiry containing the contents of the database.

(3) In this paragraph "Royal Commission" and "statutory inquiry" have the same meaning as in section 46 of the 1988 Act.

Material open to public inspection or on official register

3.—(1) Where the contents of a database are open to public inspection pursuant to a statutory requirement, or are on a statutory register, database right in the database is not infringed by the extraction of all or a substantial part of the contents containing factual information of any description, by or with the authority of the appropriate person, for a purpose which does not involve re-utilisation of all or a substantial part of the contents.

(2) Where the contents of a database are open to public inspection pursuant to a statutory requirement, database right in the database is not infringed by the extraction or re-utilisation of all or a substantial part of the contents, by or with the authority of the appropriate person, for the purpose of enabling the contents to be inspected at a more convenient time or place or otherwise facilitating the exercise of any right for the purpose of which the requirement is imposed.

(3) Where the contents of a database which is open to public inspection pursuant to a statutory requirement, or which is on a statutory register, contain information about matters of general scientific, technical, commercial or economic interest, database right in the database is not infringed by the extraction or re-utilisation of all or a substantial part of the contents, by or with the authority of the appropriate person, for the purpose of disseminating that information.

(4) In this paragraph—

"appropriate person" means the person required to make the contents of the database open to public inspection or, as the case may be, the person maintaining the register;

"statutory register" means a register maintained in pursuance of a statutory requirement; and

"statutory requirement" means a requirement imposed by provision made by or under an enactment.

Material communicated to the Crown in the course of public business

4.—(1) This paragraph applies where the contents of a database have in the course of public business been communicated to the Crown for any purpose, by or with the licence of the owner of the database right and a document or other material thing recording or embodying the contents of the database is owned by or in the custody or control of the Crown.

(2) The Crown may, for the purpose for which the contents of the database were communicated to it, or any related purpose which could reasonably have been anticipated by the owner of the database right in the database, extract or re-utilise all or a substantial part of the contents without infringing database right in the database.

(3) The Crown may not re-utilise the contents of a database by virtue of this paragraph if the contents have previously been published otherwise than by virtue of this paragraph.

(4) In sub-paragraph (1) "public business" includes any activity carried on by the Crown.

(5) This paragraph has effect subject to any agreement to the contrary between the Crown and the owner of the database right in the database.

Public records

5. The contents of a database which are comprised in public records within the meaning of the Public Records Act 1958, the Public Records (Scotland) Act 1937 or the Public Records Act (Northern Ireland) 1923 which are open to public inspection in pursuance of that Act, may be re-utilised by or with the authority of any officer appointed under that Act, without infringement of database right in the database.

Acts done under statutory authority

6.—(1) Where the doing of a particular act is specifically authorised by an Act of Parliament, whenever passed, then, unless the Act provides otherwise, the doing of that act does not infringe database right in a database.

(2) Sub-paragraph (1) applies in relation to an enactment contained in Northern Ireland legislation as it applies in relation to an Act of Parliament.

(3) Nothing in this paragraph shall be construed as excluding any defence of statutory authority otherwise available under or by virtue of any enactment.

[2581]

SCHEDULE 2
LICENSING OF DATABASE RIGHT

Regulation 24

Licensing scheme and licensing bodies

1.—(1) In this Schedule a "licensing scheme" means a scheme setting out—

(a) the classes of case in which the operator of the scheme, or the person on whose behalf he acts, is willing to grant database right licences, and

(b) the terms on which licences would be granted in those classes of case;

and for this purpose a "scheme" includes anything in the nature of a scheme, whether described as a scheme or as a tariff or by any other name.

(2) In this Schedule a "licensing body" means a society or other organisation which has as its main object, or one of its main objects, the negotiating or granting, whether as owner or prospective owner of a database right or as agent for him, of database right licences, and whose objects include the granting of licences covering the databases of more than one maker.

(3) In this paragraph "database right licences" means licences to do, or authorise the doing of, any of the things for which consent is required under Regulation 16.

2. Paragraphs 3 to 8 apply to licensing schemes which are operated by licensing bodies and cover databases of more than one maker so far as they relate to licences for extracting or

re-utilising all or a substantial part of the contents of a database; and references in those paragraphs to a licensing scheme shall be construed accordingly.

Reference of proposed licensing scheme to tribunal

3.—(1) The terms of a licensing scheme proposed to be operated by a licensing body may be referred to the Copyright Tribunal by an organisation claiming to be representative of persons claiming that they require licences in cases of a description to which the scheme would apply, either generally or in relation to any description of case.

(2) The Tribunal shall first decide whether to entertain the reference, and may decline to do so on the ground that the reference is premature.

(3) If the Tribunal decides to entertain the reference it shall consider the matter referred and make such order, either confirming or varying the proposed scheme, either generally or so far as it relates to cases of the description to which the reference relates, as the Tribunal may determine to be reasonable in the circumstances.

(4) The order may be made so as to be in force indefinitely or for such period as the Tribunal may determine.

Reference of licensing scheme to tribunal

4.—(1) If while a licensing scheme is in operation a dispute arises between the operator of the scheme and—

(a) a person claiming that he requires a licence in a case of a description to which the scheme applies, or

(b) an organisation claiming to be representative of such persons,

that person or organisation may refer the scheme to the Copyright Tribunal in so far as it relates to cases of that description.

(2) A scheme which has been referred to the Tribunal under this paragraph shall remain in operation until proceedings on the reference are concluded.

(3) The Tribunal shall consider the matter in dispute and make such order, either confirming or varying the scheme so far as it relates to cases of the description to which the reference relates, as the Tribunal may determine to be reasonable in the circumstances.

(4) The order may be made so as to be in force indefinitely or for such period as the Tribunal may determine.

Further reference of scheme to tribunal

5.—(1) Where the Copyright Tribunal has on a previous reference of a licensing scheme under paragraph 3 or 4, or under this paragraph, made an order with respect to the scheme, then, while the order remains in force—

(a) the operator of the scheme,

(b) a person claiming that he requires a licence in a case of the description to which the order applies, or

(c) an organisation claiming to be representative of such persons,

may refer the scheme again to the Tribunal so far as it relates to cases of that description.

(2) A licensing scheme shall not, except with the special leave of the Tribunal, be referred again to the Tribunal in respect of the same description of cases—

(a) within twelve months from the date of the order on the previous reference, or

(b) if the order was made so as to be in force for 15 months or less, until the last three months before the expiry of the order.

(3) A scheme which has been referred to the Tribunal under this section shall remain in operation until proceedings on the reference are concluded.

(4) The Tribunal shall consider the matter in dispute and make such order, either confirming, varying or further varying the scheme so far as it relates to cases of the description to which the reference relates, as the Tribunal may determine to be reasonable in the circumstances.

(5) The order may be made so as to be in force indefinitely or for such period as the Tribunal may determine.

Application for grant of licence in connection with licensing scheme

6.—(1) A person who claims, in a case covered by a licensing scheme, that the operator of the scheme has refused to grant him or procure the grant to him of a licence in accordance with the scheme, or has failed to do so within a reasonable time after being asked, may apply to the Copyright Tribunal.

(2) A person who claims, in a case excluded from a licensing scheme, that the operator of the scheme either—

(a) has refused to grant him a licence or procure the grant to him of a licence, or has failed to do so within a reasonable time of being asked, and that in the circumstances it is unreasonable that a licence should not be granted, or

(b) proposes terms for a licence which are unreasonable,

may apply to the Copyright Tribunal.

(3) A case shall be regarded as excluded from a licensing scheme for the purposes of sub-paragraph (2) if—

(a) the scheme provides for the grant of licences subject to terms excepting matters from the licence and the case falls within such an exception, or

(b) the case is so similar to those in which licences are granted under the scheme that it is unreasonable that it should not be dealt with in the same way.

(4) If the Tribunal is satisfied that the claim is well-founded, it shall make an order declaring that, in respect of the matters specified in the order, the applicant is entitled to a licence on such terms as the Tribunal may determine to be applicable in accordance with the scheme or, as the case may be, to be reasonable in the circumstances.

(5) The order may be made so as to be in force indefinitely or for such period as the Tribunal may determine.

Application for review of order as to entitlement to licence

7.—(1) Where the Copyright Tribunal has made an order under paragraph 6 that a person is entitled to a licence under a licensing scheme, the operator of the scheme or the original applicant may apply to the Tribunal to review its order.

(2) An application shall not be made, except with the special leave of the Tribunal—

(a) within twelve months from the date of the order, or of the decision on a previous application under this section, or

(b) if the order was made so as to be in force for 15 months or less, or as a result of the decision on a previous application under this section is due to expire within 15 months of that decision, until the last three months before the expiry date.

(3) The Tribunal shall on an application for review confirm or vary its order as the Tribunal may determine to be reasonable having regard to the terms applicable in accordance with the licensing scheme or, as the case may be, the circumstances of the case.

Effect of order of tribunal as to licensing scheme

8.—(1) A licensing scheme which has been confirmed or varied by the Copyright Tribunal—

(a) under paragraph 3 (reference of terms of proposed scheme), or

(b) under paragraph 4 or 5 (reference of existing scheme to Tribunal),

shall be in force or, as the case may be, remain in operation, so far as it relates to the description of case in respect of which the order was made, so long as the order remains in force.

(2) While the order is in force a person who in a case of a class to which the order applies—

(a) pays to the operator of the scheme any charges payable under the scheme in respect of a licence covering the case in question or, if the amount cannot be ascertained, gives an undertaking to the operator to pay them when ascertained, and

(b) complies with the other terms applicable to such a licence under the scheme,

shall be in the same position as regards infringement of database right as if he had at all material times been the holder of a licence granted by the owner of the database right in question in accordance with the scheme.

(3) The Tribunal may direct that the order, so far as it varies the amount of charges payable, has effect from a date before that on which it is made, but not earlier than the date on which the reference was made or, if later, on which the scheme came into operation.

If such a direction is made—

(a) any necessary repayments, or further payments, shall be made in respect of charges already paid, and

(b) the reference in sub-paragraph (2)(a) to the charges payable under the scheme shall be construed as a reference to the charges so payable by virtue of the order.

No such direction may be made where sub-paragraph (4) below applies.

(4) Where the Tribunal has made an order under paragraph 6 (order as to entitlement to licence under licensing scheme) and the order remains in force, the person in whose favour the order is made shall if he—

(a) pays to the operator of the scheme any charges payable in accordance with the order or, if the amount cannot be ascertained, gives an undertaking to pay the charges when ascertained, and

(b) complies with the other terms specified in the order,

be in the same position as regards infringement of database right as if he had at all material times been the holder of a licence granted by the owner of the database right in question on the terms specified in the order.

References and applications with respect to licences by licensing bodies

9. Paragraphs 10 to 13 (references and applications with respect to licensing by licensing bodies) apply to licences relating to database right which cover databases of more than one maker granted by a licensing body otherwise than in pursuance of a licensing scheme, so far as the licences authorise extracting or re-utilising all or a substantial part of the contents of a database; and references in those paragraphs to a licence shall be construed accordingly.

Reference to tribunal of proposed licence

10.—(1) The terms on which a licensing body proposes to grant a licence may be referred to the Copyright Tribunal by the prospective licensee.

(2) The Tribunal shall first decide whether to entertain the reference, and may decline to do so on the ground that the reference is premature.

(3) If the Tribunal decides to entertain the reference it shall consider the terms of the proposed licence and make such order, either confirming or varying the terms, as it may determine to be reasonable in the circumstances.

(4) The order may be made so as to be in force indefinitely or for such period as the Tribunal may determine.

Reference to tribunal of expiring licence

11.—(1) A licensee under a licence which is due to expire, by effluxion of time or as a result of notice given by the licensing body, may apply to the Copyright Tribunal on the ground that it is unreasonable in the circumstances that the licence should cease to be in force.

(2) Such an application may not be made until the last three months before the licence is due to expire.

(3) A licence in respect of which a reference has been made to the Tribunal shall remain in operation until proceedings on the reference are concluded.

(4) If the Tribunal finds the application well-founded, it shall make an order declaring that the licensee shall continue to be entitled to the benefit of the licence on such terms as the Tribunal may determine to be reasonable in the circumstances.

(5) An order of the Tribunal under this section may be made so as to be in force indefinitely or for such period as the Tribunal may determine.

Application for review of order as to licence

12.—(1) Where the Copyright Tribunal has made an order under paragraph 10 or 11, the licensing body or the person entitled to the benefit of the order may apply to the Tribunal to review its order.

(2) An application shall not be made, except with the special leave of the Tribunal—

(a) within twelve months from the date of the order or of the decision on a previous application under this paragraph, or

(b) if the order was made so as to be in force for 15 months or less, or as a result of the decision on a previous application under this section is due to expire within 15 months of that decision, until the last three months before the expiry date.

(3) The Tribunal shall on an application for review confirm or vary its order as the Tribunal may determine to be reasonable in the circumstances.

Effect of order of tribunal as to licence

13.—(1) Where the Copyright Tribunal has made an order under paragraph 10 or 11 and the order remains in force, the person entitled to the benefit of the order shall if he—

(a) pays to the licensing body any charges payable in accordance with the order or, if the amount cannot be ascertained, gives an undertaking to pay the charges when ascertained, and

(b) complies with the other terms specified in the order,

be in the same position as regards infringement of database right as if he had at all material times been the holder of a licence granted by the owner of the database right in question on the terms specified in the order.

(2) The benefit of the order may be assigned—

(a) in the case of an order under paragraph 10, if assignment is not prohibited under the terms of the Tribunal's order; and

(b) in the case of an order under paragraph 11, if assignment was not prohibited under the terms of the original licence.

(3) The Tribunal may direct that an order under paragraph 10 or 11, or an order under paragraph 12 varying such an order, so far as it varies the amount of charges payable, has effect from a date before that on which it is made, but not earlier than the date on which the reference or application was made or, if later, on which the licence was granted or, as the case may be, was due to expire.

If such a direction is made—

(a) any necessary repayments, or further payments, shall be made in respect of charges already paid, and

(b) the reference in sub-paragraph (1)(a) to the charges payable in accordance with the order shall be construed, where the order is varied by a later order, as a reference to the charges so payable by virtue of the later order.

General considerations: unreasonable discrimination

14. In determining what is reasonable on a reference or application under this Schedule relating to a licensing scheme or licence, the Copyright Tribunal shall have regard to—

(a) the availability of other schemes, or the granting of other licences, to other persons in similar circumstances, and

(b) the terms of those schemes or licences,

and shall exercise its powers so as to secure that there is no unreasonable discrimination between licensees, or prospective licensees, under the scheme or licence to which the reference or application relates and licensees under other schemes operated by, or other licences granted by, the same person.

Powers exercisable in consequence of competition report

15.—[(1) Sub-paragraph (1A) applies where whatever needs to be remedied, mitigated or prevented by the Secretary of State, the Office of Fair Trading or (as the case may be) the Competition Commission under section 12(5) of the Competition Act 1980 or section 41(2), 55(2), 66(6), 75(2), 83(2), 138(2), 147(2) or 160(2) of, or paragraph 5(2) or 10(2) of Schedule 7 to, the Enterprise Act 2002 (powers to take remedial action following references to the Commission in connection with public bodies and certain other persons, mergers or market investigations) or article 12(7) of, or paragraph 5(2) or 10(2) of Schedule 2 to, the Enterprise Act 2002 (Protection of Legitimate Interests) Order 2003 (power to take remedial action following references to the Commission in connection with European mergers) consists of or includes—

(a) conditions in licences granted by the owner of database right in a database restricting the use of the database by the licensee or the right of the owner of the database right to grant other licences; or

(b) a refusal of an owner of database right to grant licences on reasonable terms.

(1A) The powers conferred by Schedule 8 to the Enterprise Act 2002 include power to cancel or modify those conditions and, instead or in addition, to provide that licences in respect of the database right shall be available as of right.

(2) The references to anything permitted by Schedule 8 to the Enterprise Act 2002 in section 12(5A) of the Competition Act 1980 and in sections 75(4)(a), 83(4)(a), 84(2)(a), 89(1), 160(4)(a), 161(3)(a) and 164(1) of, and paragraphs 5, 10 and 11 of Schedule 7 to, the Act of 2002 and paragraphs 5, 10 and 11 of Schedule 2 to the Enterprise Act 2002 (Protection of Legitimate Interests) Order 2003 shall be construed accordingly.]

(3) The terms of a licence available by virtue of this paragraph shall, in default of agreement, be settled by the Copyright Tribunal on an application by the person requiring the licence; and terms so settled shall authorise the licensee to do everything in respect of which a licence is so available.

(4) Where the terms of a licence are settled by the Tribunal, the licence has effect from the date on which the application to the Tribunal was made.

[2582]

NOTES

Para 15: sub-paras (1), (1A), (2) substituted, for original sub-paras (1), (2), by the Enterprise Act 2002 (Consequential and Supplemental Provisions) Order 2003, SI 2003/1398, art 2, Schedule, para 31, except in relation to the making by the Secretary of State of references under the Water Industry Act 1991, s 32.

COPYRIGHT AND RELATED RIGHTS REGULATIONS 2003

(SI 2003/2498)

NOTES

Made: 27 September 2003.
Authority: European Communities Act 1972, s 2(2).
Commencement: 31 October 2003.

ARRANGEMENT OF REGULATIONS

PART 1
INTRODUCTORY PROVISIONS

PART 3
SAVINGS AND TRANSITIONAL PROVISIONS

PART 1
INTRODUCTORY PROVISIONS

1 Citation and commencement

These Regulations may be cited as the Copyright and Related Rights Regulations 2003 and shall come into force on 31st October 2003.

[2582A]

NOTES
Commencement: 31 October 2003.

2–29 (*Reg 2 introduces Schs 1, 2 to these Regulations; regs 3–29* (*Pt 2*) *amend the Copyright, Designs and Patents Act 1988 at* **[2501]–[2545C]**.)

PART 3
SAVINGS AND TRANSITIONAL PROVISIONS

General provisions

30 Introductory

(1) In this Part—

"commencement" means the date upon which these regulations come into force;

"extended copyright" means any copyright in sound recordings which subsists by virtue of section 13A of the 1988 Act (as amended by regulation 29) after the date on which it would have expired under the 1988 provisions;

"prospective owner" includes a person who is prospectively entitled to extended copyright in a sound recording by virtue of such an agreement as is mentioned in regulation 37(1);

"the 1988 Act" means the Copyright, Designs and Patents Act 1988; and

"the 1988 provisions" means the provisions of the 1988 Act as they stood immediately before commencement (including the provisions of Schedule 1 to that Act continuing the effect of earlier enactments).

(2) Expressions used in this Part which are defined for the purposes of Part 1 or 2 of the 1988 Act have the same meaning as in that Part.

[2582B]

NOTES
Commencement: 31 October 2003.

31 General rules

(1) Subject to regulation 32, these Regulations apply to—

(a) copyright works made,

(b) performances given,

(c) databases, in which database right vests, made, and

(d) works, in which publication right vests, first published,

before or after commencement.

(2) No act done before commencement shall be regarded as an infringement of any new or extended right arising by virtue of these Regulations.

[2582C]

NOTES

Commencement: 31 October 2003.

32 Savings for certain existing agreements

(1) Nothing in these Regulations affects any agreement made before 22nd December 2002.

(2) No act done after commencement, in pursuance of an agreement made before 22nd December 2002, shall be regarded as an infringement of any new or extended right arising by virtue of these Regulations.

[2582D]

NOTES

Commencement: 31 October 2003.

Special provisions

33 Permitted acts

The provisions of Chapter 3 of Part 1 (acts permitted in relation to copyright works) and Schedule 2 (rights in performances: permitted acts) in the 1988 provisions shall continue to apply to anything done after commencement in completion of an act begun before commencement which was permitted by those provisions.

[2582E]

NOTES

Commencement: 31 October 2003.

34 Performers' rights: making available to the public

(1) Those parts of section 182D in the 1988 provisions which confer a right to equitable remuneration in relation to the making available to the public in the way mentioned in section 182CA(1) (regulation 7) of a commercially published sound recording shall cease to apply on commencement.

(2) Any assignment made before commencement under the provisions of section 182D(2) shall, on commencement, cease to apply insofar as it relates to the new making available to the public right conferred by section 182CA (regulation 7).

[2582F]

NOTES

Commencement: 31 October 2003.

35 Exercise of rights in relation to performances

(1) The new right conferred by section 182CA (consent required for making available to the public) (in regulation 7) is exercisable as from commencement by the performer or (if he has died) by the person who immediately before commencement was entitled by virtue of section 192A(2) to exercise the rights conferred on the performer by Part 2 in relation to that performance.

(2) Any damages received by a person's personal representatives by virtue of the right conferred by paragraph (1) shall devolve as part of that person's estate as if the right had subsisted and been vested in him immediately before his death.

[2582G]

NOTES

Commencement: 31 October 2003.

36 Ownership of extended copyright in sound recordings

The person who is the owner of the copyright in a sound recording immediately before commencement is as from commencement the owner of any extended copyright in that sound recording.

[2582H]

NOTES

Commencement: 31 October 2003.

37 Prospective ownership of extended copyright in sound recordings

(1) Where by an agreement made before commencement in relation to extended copyright in a sound recording, and signed by or on behalf of the prospective owner of the copyright, the prospective owner purports to assign the extended copyright (wholly or partially) to another person, then, if on commencement the assignee or another person claiming under him would be entitled as against all other persons to require the copyright to be vested in him, the copyright shall vest in the assignee or his successor in title by virtue of this paragraph.

(2) A licence granted by a prospective owner of extended copyright in a sound recording is binding on every successor in title to his interest (or prospective interest) in the right, except a purchaser in good faith for valuable consideration and without notice (actual or constructive) of the licence or a person deriving title from such a purchaser; and references in Part 1 of the 1988 Act to doing anything with, or without, the licence of the copyright owner shall be construed accordingly.

[2582I]

NOTES

Commencement: 31 October 2003.

38 Extended copyright in sound recordings: existing licences, agreements, etc

(1) Any copyright licence or any term or condition of an agreement relating to the exploitation of a sound recording which—

(a) subsists immediately before commencement in relation to an existing sound recording, and

(b) is not to expire before the end of the copyright period under the 1988 provisions,

shall continue to have effect during the period of any extended copyright in that sound recording, subject to any agreement to the contrary.

(2) Any copyright licence, or term or condition relating to the exploitation of a sound recording, imposed by order of the Copyright Tribunal which—

(a) subsists immediately before commencement in relation to an existing sound recording, and

(b) is not to expire before the end of the copyright period under the 1988 provisions,

shall continue to have effect during the period of any extended copyright, subject to any further order of the Tribunal.

[2582J]

NOTES

Commencement: 31 October 2003.

39 Duration of copyright in sound recordings: general saving

Copyright in an existing sound recording shall continue to subsist until the date it would have expired under Regulation 15 of the Duration of Copyright and Rights in Performances Regulations 1995 (SI 1995/3297) if that date is later than the date on which copyright would expire under the provisions of section 13A of the 1988 Act as amended by regulation 29.

[2582K]

NOTES

Commencement: 31 October 2003.

40 Sanctions and remedies

(1) Section 296 in the 1988 provisions (devices designed to circumvent copy-protection) shall continue to apply to acts done in relation to computer programs or other works prior to commencement.

(2) Section 296 as substituted by regulation 24(1) (circumvention of technical devices applied to computer programs), and sections 296ZA (circumvention of technological measures) and 296ZD (rights and remedies in respect of devices designed to circumvent technological measures), introduced by regulation 24(1), shall apply to acts done in relation to computer programs or other works on or after commencement.

(3) Sections 107(2A), 198(1A) and 296ZB(1) and (2) (offences) do not have effect in relation to any act committed before commencement.

[2582L]

NOTES

Commencement: 31 October 2003.

(Schs 1, 2 contain consequential amendments and repeals and in so far as relevant to this work they have been incorporated at the appropriate place; Sch 3 inserts Sch 5A to the Copyright, Designs and Patents Act 1988 at **[2545A]–[2545C]**.)

COUNCIL DIRECTIVE

of 16 December 1986

on the legal protection of topographies of semiconductor products

(87/54/EEC)

NOTES

Date of publication in OJ: OJ L24, 27.1.87, p 36.

THE COUNCIL OF THE EUROPEAN COMMUNITIES,

Having regard to the Treaty establishing the European Economic Community and in particular Article 100 thereof,

Having regard to the proposal from the Commission,[1]

Having regard to the opinion of the European Parliament,[2]

Having regard to the opinion of the Economic and Social Committee,[3]

Whereas semiconductor products are playing an increasingly important role in a broad range of industries and semiconductor technology can accordingly be considered as being of fundamental importance for the Community's industrial development;

Whereas the functions of semiconductor products depend in large part on the topographies of such products and whereas the development of such topographies requires the investment of considerable resources, human, technical and financial, while topographies of such products can be copied at a fraction of the cost needed to develop them independently;

Whereas topographies of semiconductor products are at present not clearly protected in all Member States by existing legislation and such protection, where it exists, has different attributes;

Whereas certain existing differences in the legal protection of semiconductor products offered by the laws of the Member States have direct and negative effects on the functioning of the common market as regards semiconductor products and such differences could well become greater as Member States introduce new legislation on this subject;

Whereas existing differences having such effects need to be removed and new ones having a negative effect on the common market prevented from arising;

Whereas, in relation to extension of protection to persons outside the Community, Member States should be free to act on their own behalf in so far as Community decisions have not been taken within a limited period of time;

Whereas the Community's legal framework on the protection of topographies of semiconductor products can, in the first instance, be limited to certain basic principles by provisions specifying whom and what should be protected, the exclusive rights on which protected persons should be able to rely to authorise or prohibit certain acts, exceptions to these rights and for how long the protection should last;

Whereas other matters can for the time being be decided in accordance with national law, in particular, whether registration or deposit is required as a condition for protection and, subject to an exclusion of licences granted for the sole reason that a certain period of time has elapsed, whether and on what conditions non-voluntary licences may be granted in respect of protected topographies;

Whereas protection of topographies of semiconductor products in accordance with this Directive should be without prejudice to the application of some other forms of protection;

Whereas further measures concerning the legal protection of topographies of semiconductor products in the Community can be considered at a later stage, if necessary, while the application of common basic principles by all Member States in accordance with the provisions of this Directive is an urgent necessity,

NOTES

[1] OJ C360, 31.12.85, p 14.
[2] OJ C255, 13.10.86, p 249.
[3] OJ C189, 28.7.86, p 5.

HAS ADOPTED THIS DIRECTIVE—

CHAPTER 1 DEFINITIONS

Article 1

1. For the purposes of this Directive—

(a) a "semiconductor product" shall mean the final or an intermediate form of any product—

(i) consisting of a body of material which includes a layer of semiconducting material; and

(ii) having one or more other layers composed of conducting, insulating or semiconducting material, the layers being arranged in accordance with a predetermined three-dimensional pattern; and

(iii) intended to perform, exclusively or together with other functions, an electronic function;

(b) the "topography" of a semiconductor product shall mean a series of related images, however fixed or encoded;

(i) representing the three-dimensional pattern of the layers of which a semiconductor product is composed; and

(ii) in which series, each image has the pattern or part of the pattern of a surface of the semiconductor product at any stage of its manufacture;

(c) "commercial exploitation" means the sale, rental, leasing or any other method of commercial distribution, or an offer for these purposes. However, for the purposes of Articles 3(4), 4(1), 7(1), (3) and (4) "commercial exploitation" shall not include exploitation under conditions of confidentiality to the extent that no further distribution to third parties occurs, except where exploitation of a topography takes place under conditions of confidentiality required by a measure taken in conformity with Article 223(1)(b) of the Treaty.

2. The Council acting by qualified majority on a proposal from the Commission, may amend paragraph 1(a)(i) and (ii) in order to adapt these provisions in the light of technical progress.

[2583]

CHAPTER 2 PROTECTION OF TOPOGRAPHIES OF SEMICONDUCTOR PRODUCTS

Article 2

1. Member States shall protect the topographies of semiconductor products by adopting legislative provisions conferring exclusive rights in accordance with the provisions of the Directive.

2. The topography of a semiconductor product shall be protected in so far as it satisfies the conditions that it is the result of its creator's own intellectual effort and is not commonplace in the semiconductor industry. Where the topography of a semiconductor product consists of elements that are commonplace in the semiconductor industry, it shall be protected only to the extent that the combination of such elements, taken as a whole, fulfils the abovementioned conditions.

[2584]

Article 3

1. Subject to paragraphs 2 to 5, the right to protection shall apply in favour of persons who are the creators of the topographies of semiconductor products.

2. Member States may provide that,

(a) where a topography is created in the course of the creator's employment, the right to protection shall apply in favour of the creator's employer unless the terms of employment provide to the contrary;

(b) where a topography is created under a contract other than a contract of employment, the right to protection shall apply in favour of a party to the contract by whom the topography has been commissioned, unless the contract provides to the contrary.

3.

(a) As regards the persons referred to in paragraph 1, the right to protection shall apply in favour of natural persons who are nationals of a Member State or who have their habitual residence on the territory of a Member State.

(b) Where Member States make provision in accordance with paragraph 2, the right to protection shall apply in favour of—

(i) natural persons who are nationals of a Member State or who have their habitual residence on the territory of a Member State;

(ii) companies or other legal persons which have a real and effective industrial or commercial establishment on the territory of a Member State.

4. Where no right to protection exists in accordance with other provisions of this Article, the right to protection shall also apply in favour of the persons referred to in paragraph 3(b)(i) and (ii) who—

(a) first commercially exploit within a Member State a topography which has not yet been exploited commercially anywhere in the world; and

(b) have been exclusively authorised to exploit commercially the topography throughout the Community by the person entitled to dispose of it.

5. The right to protection shall also apply in favour of the successors in title of the persons mentioned in paragraphs 1 to 4.

6. Subject to paragraph 7, Member States may negotiate and conclude agreements or understandings with third States and multilateral Conventions concerning the legal protection of topographies of semiconductor products whilst respecting Community law and in particular the rules laid down in this Directive.

7. Member States may enter into negotiations which third States with a view to extending the right to protection to persons who do not benefit from the right to protection according to the provisions of this Directive. Member States who enter into such negotiations shall inform the Commission thereof.

When a Member State wishes to extend protection to persons who otherwise do not benefit from the right to protection according to the provisions of this Directive or to conclude an agreement or understanding on the extension of protection with a non-Member State it shall notify the Commission. The Commission shall inform the other Member States thereof.

The Member State shall hold the extension of protection or the conclusion of the agreement or understanding in abeyance for one month from the date on which it notifies the Commission. However, if within that period the Commission notifies the Member State concerned of its intention to submit a proposal to the Council for all Member States to extend protection in respect of the persons or non-Member State concerned, the Member State shall hold the extension of protection or the conclusion of the agreement or understanding in abeyance for a period of two months from the date of the notification by the Member State.

Where, before the end of this two-month period, the Commission submits such a proposal to the Council, the Member State shall hold the extension of protection or the conclusion of the agreement or understanding in abeyance for a further period of four months from the date on which the proposal was submitted.

In the absence of a Commission notification or proposal or a Council decision within the time limits prescribed above, the Member State may extend protection or conclude the agreement or understanding.

A proposal by the Commission to extend protection, whether or not it is made following a notification by a Member State in accordance with the preceding paragraphs shall be adopted by the Council acting by qualified majority.

A Decision of the Council on the basis of a Commission proposal shall not prevent a Member State from extending protection to persons, in addition to those to benefit from protection in all Member States, who were included in the envisaged extension, agreement or understanding as notified, unless the Council acting by qualified majority has decided otherwise.

8. Commission proposals and Council decisions pursuant to paragraph 7 shall be published for information in the *Official Journal of the European Communities.*

[2585]

Article 4

1. Member States may provide that the exclusive rights conferred in conformity with Article 2 shall not come into existence or shall no longer apply to the topography of a semiconductor product unless an application for registration in due form has been filed with a public authority within two years of its first commercial exploitation. Member States may require in addition to such registration that material identifying or exemplifying the topography or any combination thereof has been deposited with a public authority, as well as a statement as to the date of first commercial exploitation of the topography where it precedes the date of the application for registration.

2. Member States shall ensure that material deposited in conformity with paragraph 1 is not made available to the public where it is a trade secret. This provision shall be without prejudice to the disclosure of such material pursuant to an order of a court or other competent authority to persons involved in litigation concerning the validity or infringement of the exclusive rights referred to in Article 2.

3. Member States may require that transfers of rights in protected topographies be registered.

4. Member States may subject registration and deposit in accordance with paragraphs 1 and 3 to the payment of fees not exceeding their administrative costs.

5. Conditions prescribing the fulfilment of additional formalities for obtaining or maintaining protection shall not be admitted.

6. Member States which require registration shall provide for legal remedies in favour of a person having the right to protection in accordance with the provisions of this Directive who can prove that another person has applied for or obtained the registration of a topography without his authorisation.

[2586]

Article 5

1. The exclusive rights referred to in Article 2 shall include the rights to authorise or prohibit any of the following acts—

(a) reproduction of a topography in so far as it is protected under Article 2(2);

(b) commercial exploitation or the importation for that purpose of a topography or of a semiconductor product manufactured by using the topography.

2. Notwithstanding paragraph 1, a Member State may permit the reproduction of a topography privately for non commercial aims.

3. The exclusive rights referred to in paragraph 1(a) shall not apply to reproduction for the purpose of analysing, evaluating or teaching the concepts, processes, systems or techniques embodied in the topography or the topography itself.

4. The exclusive rights referred to in paragraph 1 shall not extend to any such act in relation to a topography meeting the requirements of Article 2(2) and created on the basis of an analysis and evaluation of another topography, carried out in conformity with paragraph 3.

5. The exclusive rights to authorise or prohibit the acts specified in paragraph 1(b) shall not apply to any such act committed after the topography or the semiconductor product has been put on the market in a Member State by the person entitled to authorise its marketing or with his consent.

6. A person who, when he acquires a semiconductor product, does not know, or has no reasonable grounds to believe, that the product is protected by an exclusive right conferred by a Member State in conformity with this Directive shall not be prevented from commercially exploiting that product.

However, for acts committed after that person knows, or has reasonable grounds to believe, that the semiconductor product is so protected, Member States shall ensure that on the demand of the rightholder a tribunal may require, in accordance with the provisions of the national law applicable, the payment of adequate remuneration.

7. The provisions of paragraph 6 shall apply to the successors in title of the person referred to in the first sentence of that paragraph.

[2587]

Article 6

Member States shall not subject the exclusive rights referred to in Article 2 to licences granted, for the sole reason that a certain period of time has elapsed, automatically, and by operation of law.

[2588]

Article 7

1. Member States shall provide that the exclusive rights referred to in Article 2 shall come into existence—
   (a) where registration is the condition for the coming into existence of the exclusive rights in accordance with Article 4, on the earlier of the following dates—
      (i) the date when the topography is first commercially exploited anywhere in the world;
      (ii) the date when an application or registration has been filed in due form; or
   (b) when the topography is first commercially exploited anywhere in the world; or
   (c) when the topography is first fixed or encoded.

2. Where the exclusive rights come into existence in accordance with paragraph 1(a) or (b), the Member States shall provide, for the period prior to those rights coming into existence, legal remedies in favour of a person having the right to protection in accordance with the provisions of this Directive who can prove that another person has fraudulently reproduced or commercially exploited or imported for that purpose a topography. This paragraph shall be without prejudice to legal remedies made available to enforce the exclusive rights conferred in conformity with Article 2.

3. The exclusive rights shall come to an end 10 years from the end of the calendar year in which the topography is first commercially exploited anywhere in the world or, where registration is a condition for the coming into existence or continuing application of the exclusive rights, 10 years from the earlier of the following dates—
   (a) the end of the calendar year in which the topography is first commercially exploited anywhere in the world;
   (b) the end of the calendar year in which the application for registration has been filed in due form.

4. Where a topography has not been commercially exploited anywhere in the world within a period of 15 years from its first fixation or encoding, any exclusive rights in existence pursuant to paragraph 1 shall come to an end and no new exclusive rights shall come into existence unless an application for registration in due form has been filed within that period in those Member States where registration is a condition for the coming into existence or continuing application of the exclusive rights.

[2589]

Article 8

The protection granted to the topographies of semiconductor products in accordance with Article 2 shall not extend to any concept, process, system, technique or encoded information embodied in the topography other than the topography itself.

[2590]

Article 9

Where the legislation of Member States provides that semiconductor products manufactured using protected topographies may carry an indication, the indication to be used shall be a capital T as follows: T, 'T', [T], [T], T* or Ⓣ

.

[2591]

CHAPTER 3
CONTINUED APPLICATION OF OTHER LEGAL PROVISIONS

Article 10

1. The provisions of this Directive shall be without prejudice to legal provisions concerning patent and utility model rights.

2. The provisions of this Directive shall be without prejudice—
   (a) to rights conferred by the Member States in fulfilment of their obligations under international agreements, including provisions extending such rights to nationals of, or residents in, the territory of the Member State concerned;
   (b) to the law of copyright in Member States, restricting the reproduction of drawing or other artistic representations of topographies by copying them in two dimensions.

3. Protection granted by national law to topographies of semiconductor products fixed or encoded before the entry into force of the national provisions enacting the Directive, but no later than the date set out in Article 11(1), shall not be affected by the provisions of this Directive.

[2592]

CHAPTER 4
FINAL PROVISIONS

Article 11

1. Member States shall bring into force the laws, regulations or administrative provisions necessary to comply with this Directive by 7 November 1987.

2. Member States shall ensure that they communicate to the Commission the texts of the main provisions of national law which they adopt in the field covered by this Directive.

[2593]

Article 12

This Directive is addressed to the Member States.

[2594]

Done at Brussels, 16 December 1986.

COUNCIL DIRECTIVE

of 14 May 1991

on the legal protection of computer programs

(91/250/EEC)

NOTES

Date of publication in OJ: OJ L122, 17.5.91, p 42.

THE COUNCIL OF THE EUROPEAN COMMUNITIES,

Having regard to the Treaty establishing the European Economic Community and in particular Article 100a thereof,

Having regard to the proposal from the Commission,[1]

In co-operation with the European Parliament,[2]

Having regard to the opinion of the Economic and Social Committee,[3]

Whereas computer programs are at present not clearly protected in all Member States by existing legislation and such protection, where it exists, has different attributes;

Whereas the development of computer programs requires the investment of considerable human, technical and financial resources while computer programs can be copied at a fraction of the cost needed to develop them independently;

Whereas computer programs are playing an increasingly important role in a broad range of industries and computer program technology can accordingly be considered as being of fundamental importance for the Community's industrial development;

Whereas certain differences in the legal protection of computer programs offered by the laws of the Member States have direct and negative effects on the functioning of the common market as regards computer programs and such differences could well become greater as Member States introduce new legislation on this subject;

Whereas existing differences having such effects need to be removed and new ones prevented from arising, while differences not adversely affecting the functioning of the common market to a substantial degree need not be removed or prevented from arising;

Whereas the Community's legal framework on the protection of computer programs can accordingly in the first instance be limited to establishing that Member States should accord protection to computer programs under copyright law as literary works and, further, to establishing who and what should be protected, the exclusive rights on which protected persons should be able to rely in order to authorise or prohibit certain acts and for how long the protection should apply;

Whereas, for the purpose of this Directive, the term "computer program" shall include programs in any form, including those which are incorporated into hardware; whereas this term also includes preparatory design work leading to the development of a computer program provided that the nature of the preparatory work is such that a computer program can result from it at a later stage;

Whereas, in respect of the criteria to be applied in determining whether or not a computer program is an original work, no tests as to the qualitative or aesthetic merits of the program should be applied;

Whereas the Community is fully committed to the promotion of international standardisation;

Whereas the function of a computer program is to communicate and work together with other components of a computer system and with users and, for this purpose, a logical and, where appropriate, physical interconnection and interaction is required to permit all elements of software and hardware to work with other software and hardware and with users in all the ways in which they are intended to function;

Whereas the parts of the program which provide for such interconnection and interaction between elements of software and hardware are generally known as "interfaces";

Whereas this functional interconnection and interaction is generally known as "interoperability"; whereas such interoperability can be defined as the ability to exchange information and mutually to use the information which has been exchanged;

Whereas, for the avoidance of doubt, it has to be made clear that only the expression of a computer program is protected and that ideas and principles which underlie any element of a program, including those which underlie its interfaces, are not protected by copyright under this Directive;

Whereas, in accordance with this principle of copyright, to the extent that logic, algorithms and programming languages comprise ideas and principles, those ideas and principles are not protected under this Directive;

Whereas, in accordance with the legislation and jurisprudence of the Member States and the international copyright conventions, the expression of those ideas and principles is to be protected by copyright;

Whereas, for the purposes of this Directive, the term "rental" means the making available for use, for a limited period of time and for profit-making purposes, of a computer program or a copy thereof; whereas this term does not include public lending, which, accordingly, remains outside the scope of this Directive;

Whereas the exclusive rights of the author to prevent the unauthorised reproduction of his work have to be subject to a limited exception in the case of a computer program to allow the reproduction technically necessary for the use of that program by the lawful acquirer;

Whereas this means that the acts of loading and running necessary for the use of a copy of a program which has been lawfully acquired, and the act of correction of its errors, may not be prohibited by contract; whereas, in the absence of specific contractual provisions, including when a copy of the program has been sold, any other act necessary for the use of the copy of a program may be performed in accordance with its intended purpose by a lawful acquirer of that copy;

Whereas a person having a right to use a computer program should not be prevented from performing acts necessary to observe, study or test the functioning of the program, provided that these acts do not infringe the copyright in the program;

Whereas the unauthorised reproduction, translation, adaptation or transformation of the form of the code in which a copy of a computer program has been made available constitutes an infringement of the exclusive rights of the author;

Whereas, nevertheless, circumstances may exist when such a reproduction of the code and translation of its form within the meaning of Article 4(a) and (b) are indispensable to obtain the necessary information to achieve the interoperability of an independently created program with other programs;

Whereas it has therefore to be considered that in these limited circumstances only, performance of the acts of reproduction and translation by or on behalf of a person having a right to use a copy of the program is legitimate and compatible with fair practice and must therefore be deemed not to require the authorisation of the rightholder;

Whereas an objective of this exception is to make it possible to connect all components of a computer system, including those of different manufacturers, so that they can work together;

Whereas such an exception to the author's exclusive rights may not be used in a way which prejudices the legitimate interests of the rightholder or which conflicts with a normal exploitation of the program;

Whereas, in order to remain in accordance with the provisions of the Berne Convention for the Protection of Literary and Artistic Works, the term of protection should be the life of the author and fifty years from the first of January of the year following the year of his death or, in the case of an anonymous or pseudonymous work, 50 years from the first of January of the year following the year in which the work is first published;

Whereas protection of computer programs under copyright laws should be without prejudice to the application, in appropriate cases, of other forms of protection; whereas, however, any contractual provisions contrary to Article 6 or to the exceptions provided for in Article 5(2) and (3) should be null and void;

Whereas the provisions of this Directive are without prejudice to the application of the competition rules under Articles 85 and 86 of the Treaty if a dominant supplier refuses to make information available which is necessary for interoperability as defined in this Directive;

Whereas the provisions of this Directive should be without prejudice to specific requirements of Community law already enacted in respect of the publication of interfaces in the telecommunications sector or Council Decisions relating to standardisation in the field of information technology and telecommunication;

Whereas this Directive does not affect derogations provided for under national legislation in accordance with the Berne Convention on points not covered by this Directive,

NOTES

1 OJ C91, 12.4.89, p 4; and OJ C320, 20.12.90, p 22.

2 OJ C231, 17.9.90, p 78; and OJ C129, 20.5.91, p 93.

3 OJ C329, 30.12.89, p 4.

HAS ADOPTED THIS DIRECTIVE—

Article 1

1. In accordance with the provisions of this Directive, Member States shall protect computer programs, by copyright, as literary works within the meaning of the Berne Convention for the Protection of Literary and Artistic Works. For the purposes of this Directive, the term "computer programs" shall include their preparatory design material.

2. Protection in accordance with this Directive shall apply to the expression in any form of a computer program. Ideas and principles which underlie any element of a computer program, including those which underlie its interfaces, are not protected by copyright under this Directive.

3. A computer program shall be protected if it is original in the sense that it is the author's own intellectual creation. No other criteria shall be applied to determine its eligibility for protection.

[2595]

Article 2

Authorship of computer programs

1. The author of a computer program shall be the natural person or group of natural persons who has created the program or, where the legislation of the Member State permits, the legal person designated as the rightholder by that legislation. Where collective works are recognised by the legislation of a Member State, the person considered by the legislation of the Member State to have created the work shall be deemed to be its author.

2. In respect of a computer program created by a group of natural persons jointly, the exclusive rights shall be owned jointly.

3. Where a computer program is created by an employee in the execution of his duties or following the instructions given by his employer, the employer exclusively shall be entitled to exercise all economic rights in the program so created, unless otherwise provided by contract.

[2596]

Article 3

Beneficiaries of protection

Protection shall be granted to all natural or legal persons eligible under national copyright legislation as applied to literary works.

[2597]

Article 4

Restricted Acts

Subject to the provisions of Articles 5 and 6, the exclusive rights of the rightholder within the meaning of Article 2, shall include the right to do or to authorise—

(a) the permanent or temporary reproduction of a computer program by any means and in any form, in part or in whole. Insofar as loading, displaying, running, transmission or storage of the computer program necessitate such reproduction, such acts shall be subject to authorisation by the rightholder;

(b) the translation, adaptation, arrangement and any other alteration of a computer program and the reproduction of the results thereof, without prejudice to the rights of the person who alters the program;

(c) any form of distribution to the public, including the rental, of the original computer program or of copies thereof. The first sale in the Community of a copy of a program by the rightholder or with his consent shall exhaust the distribution right within the Community of that copy, with the exception of the right to control further rental of the program or a copy thereof.

[2598]

Article 5

Exceptions to the restricted acts

1. In the absence of specific contractual provisions, the acts referred to in Article 4(a) and (b) shall not require authorisation by the rightholder where they are necessary for the use of the computer program by the lawful acquirer in accordance with its intended purpose, including for error correction.

2. The making of a back-up copy by a person having a right to use the computer program may not be prevented by contract insofar as it is necessary for that use.

3. The person having a right to use a copy of a computer program shall be entitled, without the authorisation of the rightholder, to observe, study or test the functioning of the program in order to determine the ideas and principles which underlie any element of the program if he does so while performing any of the acts of loading, displaying, running, transmitting or storing the program which he is entitled to do.

[2599]

Article 6

Decompilation

1. The authorisation of the rightholder shall not be required where reproduction of the code and translation of its form within the meaning of Article 4(a) and (b) are indispensable to

obtain the information necessary to achieve the interoperability of an independently created computer program with other programs, provided that the following conditions are met—

(a) these acts are performed by the licensee or by another person having a right to use a copy of a program, or on their behalf by a person authorised to do so;

(b) the information necessary to achieve interoperability has not previously been readily available to the persons referred to in subparagraph (a); and

(c) these acts are confined to the parts of the original program which are necessary to achieve interoperability.

2. The provisions of paragraph 1 shall not permit the information obtained through its application—

(a) to be used for goals other than to achieve the interoperability of the independently created computer program;

(b) to be given to others, except when necessary for the interoperability of the independently created computer program; or

(c) to be used for the development, production or marketing of a computer program substantially similar in its expression, or for any other act which infringes copyright.

3. In accordance with the provisions of the Berne Convention for the protection of Literary and Artistic Works, the provisions of this Article may not be interpreted in such a way as to allow its application to be used in a manner which unreasonably prejudices the right holder's legitimate interests or conflicts with a normal exploitation of the computer program.

[2600]

Article 7

Special measures of protection

1. Without prejudice to the provisions of Articles 4, 5 and 6, Member States shall provide, in accordance with their national legislation, appropriate remedies against a person committing any of the acts listed in subparagraphs (a), (b) and (c) below—

(a) any act of putting into circulation a copy of a computer program knowing, or having reason to believe, that it is an infringing copy;

(b) the possession, for commercial purposes, of a copy of a computer program knowing, or having reason to believe, that it is an infringing copy;

(c) any act of putting into circulation, or the possession for commercial purposes of, any means the sole intended purpose of which is to facilitate the unauthorised removal or circumvention of any technical device which may have been applied to protect a computer program.

2. Any infringing copy of a computer program shall be liable to seizure in accordance with the legislation of the Member State concerned.

3. Member States may provide for the seizure of any means referred to in paragraph 1(c).

[2601]

Article 8

(*Repealed by Council Directive 93/38/EEC, Art 11*(*1*).)

Article 9

Continued application of other legal provisions

1. The provisions of this Directive shall be without prejudice to any other legal provisions such as those concerning patent rights, trade-marks, unfair competition, trade secrets, protection of semi-conductor products or the law of contract. Any contractual provisions contrary to Article 6 or to the exceptions provided for in Article 5(2) and (3) shall be null and void.

2. The provisions of this Directive shall apply also to programs created before 1 January 1993 without prejudice to any acts concluded and rights acquired before that date.

[2602]

Article 10

Final provisions

1. Member States shall bring into force the laws, regulations and administrative provisions necessary to comply with this Directive before 1 January 1993.

When Member States adopt these measures, the latter shall contain a reference to this Directive or shall be accompanied by such reference on the occasion of their official publication. The methods of making such a reference shall be laid down by the Member States.

2. Member States shall communicate to the Commission the provisions of national law which they adopt in the field governed by this Directive.

[2603]

Article 11

This Directive is addressed to the Member States.

[2604]

Done at Brussels, 14 May 1991.

DIRECTIVE OF THE EUROPEAN PARLIAMENT AND OF THE COUNCIL

of 11 March 1996

on the legal protection of databases

(96/9/EC)

NOTES

Date of publication in OJ: OJ L77, 27.3.96, p 20.

THE EUROPEAN PARLIAMENT AND THE COUNCIL OF THE EUROPEAN UNION,

Having regard to the Treaty establishing the European Community, and in particular Article 57(2), 66 and 100a thereof,

Having regard to the proposal from the Commission,[1]

Having regard to the opinion of the Economic and Social Committee,[2]

Acting in accordance with the procedure laid down in Article 189b of the Treaty,[3]

(1) Whereas databases are at present not sufficiently protected in all Member States by existing legislation; whereas such protection, where it exists, has different attributes;

(2) Whereas such differences in the legal protection of databases offered by the legislation of the Member States have direct negative effects on the functioning of the internal market as regards databases and in particular on the freedom of natural and legal persons to provide on-line database goods and services on the basis of harmonised legal arrangements throughout the Community; whereas such differences could well become more pronounced as Member States introduce new legislation in this field, which is now taking on an increasingly international dimension;

(3) Whereas existing differences distorting the functioning of the internal market need to be removed and new ones prevented from arising, while differences not adversely affecting the functioning of the internal market or the development of an information market within the Community need not be removed or prevented from arising;

(4) Whereas copyright protection for databases exists in varying forms in the Member States according to legislation or case-law, and whereas, if differences in legislation in the scope and conditions of protection remain between the Member States, such unharmonised intellectual property rights can have the effect of preventing the free movement of goods or services within the Community;

(5) Whereas copyright remains an appropriate form of exclusive right for authors who have created databases;

(6) Whereas, nevertheless, in the absence of a harmonised system of unfair-competition legislation or of case-law, other measures are required in addition to prevent the unauthorised extraction and/or re-utilisation of the contents of a database;

(7) Whereas the making of databases requires the investment of considerable human, technical and financial resources while such databases can be copied or accessed at a fraction of the cost needed to design them independently;

(8) Whereas the unauthorised extraction and/or re-utilisation of the contents of a database constitute acts which can have serious economic and technical consequences;

(9) Whereas databases are a vital tool in the development of an information market within the Community; whereas this tool will also be of use in many other fields;

(10) Whereas the exponential growth, in the Community and worldwide, in the amount of information generated and processed annually in all sectors of commerce and industry calls for investment in all the Member States in advanced information processing systems;

(11) Whereas there is at present a very great imbalance in the level of investment in the database sector both as between the Member States and between the Community and the world's largest database-producing third countries;

(12) Whereas such an investment in modern information storage and processing systems will not take place within the Community unless a stable and uniform legal protection regime is introduced for the protection of the rights of makers of databases;

(13) Whereas this Directive protects collections, sometimes called "compilations", of works, data or other materials which are arranged, stored and accessed by means which include electronic, electromagnetic or electro-optical processes or analogous processes;

(14) Whereas protection under this Directive should be extended to cover non-electronic databases;

(15) Whereas the criteria used to determine whether a database should be protected by copyright should be defined to the fact that the selection or the arrangement of the contents of the database is the author's own intellectual creation; whereas such protection should cover the structure of the database;

(16) Whereas no criterion other than originality in the sense of the author's intellectual creation should be applied to determine the eligibility of the database for copyright protection, and in particular no aesthetic or qualitative criteria should be applied;

(17) Whereas the term "database" should be understood to include literary, artistic, musical or other collections of works or collections of other material such as texts, sound, images, numbers, facts, and data; whereas it should cover collections of independent works, data or other materials which are systematically or methodically arranged and can be individually accessed; whereas this means that a recording or an audiovisual, cinematographic, literary or musical work as such does not fall within the scope of this Directive;

(18) Whereas this Directive is without prejudice to the freedom of authors to decide whether, or in what manner, they will allow their works to be included in a database, in particular whether or not the authorisation given is exclusive; whereas the protection of databases by the *sui generis* right is without prejudice to existing rights over their contents, and whereas in particular where an author or the holder of a related right permits some of his works or subject matter to be included in a database pursuant to a non-exclusive agreement a third party may make use of those works or subject matter subject to the required consent of the author or of the holder of the related right without the *sui generis* right of the maker of the database being invoked to prevent him doing so, on condition that those works or subject matter are neither extracted from the database nor re-utilised on the basis thereof;

(19) Whereas, as a rule, the compilation of several recordings of musical performances on a CD does not come within the scope of this Directive, both because, as a compilation, it does not meet the conditions for copyright protection and because it does not represent a substantial enough investment to be eligible under the *sui generis* right;

(20) Whereas protection under this Directive may also apply to the materials necessary for the operation or consultation of certain databases such as thesaurus and indexation systems;

(21) Whereas the protection provided for in this Directive relates to databases in which works, data or other materials have been arranged systematically or methodically; whereas it is not necessary for those materials to have been physically stored in an organised manner;

(22) Whereas electronic databases within the meaning of this Directive may also include devices such as CD-ROM and CD-i;

(23) Whereas the term "database" should not be taken to extend to computer programs used in the making or operation of a database, which are protected by Council Directive 91/250/EEC of 14 May 1991 on the legal protection of computer programs;[4]

(24) Whereas the rental and lending of databases in the field of copyright and related rights are governed exclusively by Council Directive 92/100/EEC of 19 November 1992 on rental right and lending right and on certain rights related to copyright in the field of intellectual property;[5]

(25) Whereas the term of copyright is already governed by Council Directive 93/98/EEC of 29 October 1993 harmonising the term of protection of copyright and certain related rights;[6]

(26) Whereas works protected by copyright and subject matter protected by related rights, which are incorporated into a database, remain nevertheless protected by the respective

exclusive rights and may not be incorporated into, or extracted from, the database without the permission of the rightholder or his successors in title;

(27) Whereas copyright in such works and related rights in subject matter thus incorporated into a database are in no way affected by the existence of a separate right in the selection or arrangement of these works and subject matter in a database;

(28) Whereas the moral rights of the natural person who created the database belong to the author and should be exercised according to the legislation of the Member States and the provisions of the Berne Convention for the Protection of Literary and Artistic Works; whereas such moral rights remain outside the scope of this Directive;

(29) Whereas the arrangements applicable to databases created by employees are left to the discretion of the Member States; whereas, therefore nothing in this Directive prevents Member States from stipulating in their legislation that where a database is created by an employee in the execution of his duties or following the instructions given by his employer, the employer exclusively shall be entitled to exercise all economic rights in the database so created, unless otherwise provided by contract;

(30) Whereas the author's exclusive rights should include the right to determine the way in which his work is exploited and by whom, and in particular to control the distribution of his work to unauthorised persons;

(31) Whereas the copyright protection of databases includes making databases available by means other than the distribution of copies;

(32) Whereas Member States are required to ensure that their national provisions are at least materially equivalent in the case of such acts subject to restrictions as are provided for by this Directive;

(33) Whereas the question of exhaustion of the right of distribution does not arise in the case of on-line databases, which come within the field of provision of services; whereas this also applies with regard to a material copy of such a database made by the user of such a service with the consent of the rightholder; whereas, unlike CD-ROM or CD-i, where the intellectual property is incorporated in a material medium, namely an item of goods, every on-line service is in fact an act which will have to be subject to authorisation where the copyright so provides;

(34) Whereas, nevertheless, once the rightholder has chosen to make available a copy of the database to a user, whether by an on-line service or by other means of distribution, that lawful user must be able to access and use the database for the purposes and in the way set out in the agreement with the rightholder, even if such access and use necessitate performance of otherwise restricted acts;

(35) Whereas a list should be drawn up of exceptions to restricted acts, taking into account the fact that copyright as covered by this Directive applies only to the selection or arrangements of the contents of a database; whereas Member States should be given the option of providing for such exceptions in certain cases; whereas, however, this option should be exercised in accordance with the Berne Convention and to the extent that the exceptions relate to the structure of the database; whereas a distinction should be drawn between exceptions for private use and exceptions for reproduction for private purposes, which concerns provisions under national legislation of some Member States on levies on blank media or recording equipment;

(36) Whereas the term "scientific research" within the meaning of this Directive covers both the natural sciences and the human sciences;

(37) Whereas Article 10(1) of the Berne Convention is not affected by this Directive;

(38) Whereas the increasing use of digital recording technology exposes the database maker to the risk that the contents of his database may be copied and rearranged electronically, without his authorisation, to produce a database of identical content which, however, does not infringe any copyright in the arrangement of his database;

(39) Whereas, in addition to aiming to protect the copyright in the original selection or arrangement of the contents of a database, this Directive seeks to safeguard the position of makers of databases against misappropriation of the results of the financial and professional investment made in obtaining and collection the contents by protecting the whole or substantial parts of a database against certain acts by a user or competitor;

(40) Whereas the object of this *sui generis* right is to ensure protection of any investment in obtaining, verifying or presenting the contents of a database for the limited duration of the right; whereas such investment may consist in the deployment of financial resources and/or the expending of time, effort and energy;

(41) Whereas the objective of the *sui generis* right is to give the maker of a database the option of preventing the unauthorised extraction and/or re-utilisation of all or a substantial part of the contents of that database; whereas the maker of a database is the person who takes the initiative and the risk of investing; whereas this excludes subcontractors in particular from the definition of maker;

(42) Whereas the special right to prevent unauthorised extraction and/or re-utilisation relates to acts by the user which go beyond his legitimate rights and thereby harm the investment; whereas the right to prohibit extraction and/or re-utilisation of all or a substantial part of the contents relates not only to the manufacture of a parasitical competing product but also to any user who, through his acts, causes significant detriment, evaluated qualitatively or quantitatively, to the investment;

(43) Whereas, in the case of on-line transmission, the right to prohibit re-utilisation is not exhausted either as regards the database or as regards a material copy of the database or of part thereof made by the addressee of the transmission with the consent of the rightholder;

(44) Whereas, when on-screen display of the contents of a database necessitates the permanent or temporary transfer of all or a substantial part of such contents to another medium, that act should be subject to authorisation by the rightholder;

(45) Whereas the right to prevent unauthorised extraction and/or re-utilisation does not in any way constitute an extension of copyright protection to mere facts or data;

(46) Whereas the existence of a right to prevent the unauthorised extraction and/or re-utilisation of the whole or a substantial part of works, data or materials from a database should not give rise to the creation of a new right in the works, data or materials themselves;

(47) Whereas, in the interests of competition between suppliers of information products and services, protection by the *sui generis* right must not be afforded in such a way as to facilitate abuses of a dominant position, in particular as regards the creation and distribution of new products and services which have an intellectual, documentary, technical, economic or commercial added value; whereas, therefore, the provisions of this Directive are without prejudice to the application of Community or national competition rules;

(48) Whereas the objective of this Directive, which is to afford an appropriate and uniform level of protection of databases as a means to secure the remuneration of the maker of the database, is different from the aim of Directive 95/46/EC of the European Parliament and of the Council of 24 October 1995 on the protection of individuals with regard to the processing of personal data and on the free movement of such data,[7] which is to guarantee free circulation of personal data on the basis of harmonised rules designed to protect fundamental rights, notably the right to privacy which is recognised in Article 8 of the European Convention for the Protection of Human Rights and Fundamental Freedoms; whereas the provisions of this Directive are without prejudice to data protection legislation;

(49) Whereas, notwithstanding the right to prevent extraction and/or re-utilisation of all or a substantial part of a database, it should be laid down that the maker of a database or rightholder may not prevent a lawful user of the database from extracting and re-utilising insubstantial parts; whereas, however, that user may not unreasonably prejudice either the legitimate interests of the holder of the *sui generis* right or the holder of copyright or a related right in respect of the works or subject matter contained in the database;

(50) Whereas the Member States should be given the option of providing for exceptions to the right to prevent the unauthorised extraction and/or re-utilisation of a substantial part of the contents of a database in the case of extraction for private purposes, for the purposes of illustration for teaching or scientific research, or where extraction and/or re-utilisation are/is carried out in the interests of public security or for the purposes of an administrative or judicial procedure; whereas such operations must not prejudice the exclusive rights of the maker to exploit the database and their purpose must not be commercial;

(51) Whereas the Member States, where they avail themselves of the option to permit a lawful user of a database to extract a substantial part of the contents for the purposes of illustration for teaching or scientific research, may limit that permission to certain categories of teaching or scientific research institution;

(52) Whereas those Member States which have specific rules providing for a right comparable to the *sui generis* right provided for in this Directive should be permitted to retain, as far as the new right is concerned, the exceptions traditionally specified by such rules;

(53) Whereas the burden of proof regarding the date of completion of the making of a database lies with the maker of the database;

(54) Whereas the burden of proof that the criteria exist for concluding that a substantial modification of the contents of a database is to be regarded as a substantial new investment lies with the maker of the database resulting from such investment;

(55) Whereas a substantial new investment involving a new term of protection may include a substantial verification of the contents of the database;

(56) Whereas the right to prevent unauthorised extraction and/or re-utilisation in respect of a database should apply to databases whose makers are nationals or habitual residents of third countries or to those produced by legal persons not established in a Member State,

within the meaning of the Treaty, only if such third countries offer comparable protection to databases produced by nationals of a Member State or persons who have their habitual residence in the territory of the Community;

(57) Whereas, in addition to remedies provided under the legislation of the Member States for infringements of copyright or other rights, Member States should provide for appropriate remedies against unauthorised extraction and/or re-utilisation of the contents of a database;

(58) Whereas, in addition to the protection given under this Directive to the structure of the database by copyright, and to its contents against unauthorised extraction and/or re-utilisation under the *sui generis* right, other legal provisions in the Member States relevant to the supply of database goods and services continue to apply;

(59) Whereas this Directive is without prejudice to the application to databases composed of audiovisual works of any rules recognised by a Member State's legislation concerning the broadcasting of audiovisual programmes;

(60) Whereas some Member States currently protect under copyright arrangements databases which do not meet the criteria for eligibility for copyright protection laid down in this Directive; whereas, even if the databases concerned are eligible for protection under the right laid down in this Directive to prevent unauthorised extraction and/or re-utilisation of their contents, the term of protection under that right is considerably shorter than that which they enjoy under the national arrangements currently in force; whereas harmonisation of the criteria for determining whether a database is to be protected by copyright may not have the effect of reducing the term of protection currently enjoyed by the rightholders concerned; whereas a derogation should be laid down to that effect; whereas the effects of such derogation must be confined to the territories of the Member States concerned,

NOTES

1 OJ C156, 23.6.92, p 4 and OJ C308, 15.11.93, p 1.
2 OJ C19, 25.1.93, p 3.
3 Opinion of the European Parliament of 23 June 1993, OJ C194, 19.7.93, p 144, Common Position of the Council of 10 July 1995, OJ C288, 30.10.95, p 14, Decision of the European Parliament of 14 December 1995, OJ C17, 22.1.96, and Council Decision of 26 February 1996.
4 OJ L122, 17.5.91, p 42, as amended by OJ L290, 24.11.93, p 9.
5 OJ L346, 27.11.92, p 61.
6 OJ L290, 24.11.93, p 9.
7 OJ L281, 23.11.95, p 31.

HAVE ADOPTED THIS DIRECTIVE—

CHAPTER I
SCOPE

Article 1

Scope

1. This Directive concerns the legal protection of databases in any form.

2. For the purposes of this Directive, "database" shall mean a collection of independent works, data or other materials arranged in a systematic or methodical way and individually accessible by electronic or other means.

3. Protection under this Directive shall not apply to computer programs used in the making or operation of databases accessible by electronic means.

[2605]

Article 2

Limitations on the scope

This Directive shall apply without prejudice to Community provisions relating to—

(a) the legal protection of computer programs;
(b) rental right, lending right and certain rights related to copyright in the field of intellectual property;
(c) the term of protection of copyright and certain related rights.

[2606]

CHAPTER II
COPYRIGHT

Article 3

Object of protection

1. In accordance with this Directive, databases which, by reason of the selection or arrangement of their contents, constitute the author's own intellectual creation shall be protected as such by copyright. No other criteria shall be applied to determine their eligibility for that protection.

2. The copyright protection of databases provided for by this Directive shall not extend to their contents and shall be without prejudice to any rights subsisting in those contents themselves.

[2607]

Article 4

Database authorship

1. The author of a database shall be the natural person or group of natural persons who created the base or, where the legislation of the Member States so permits, the legal person designated as the rightholder by that legislation.

2. Where collective works are recognised by the legislation of a Member State, the economic rights shall be owned by the person holding the copyright.

3. In respect of a database created by a group of natural persons jointly, the exclusive rights shall be owned jointly.

[2608]

Article 5

Restricted acts

In respect of the expression of the database which is protectable by copyright, the author of a database shall have the exclusive right to carry out or to authorise—

(a) temporary or permanent reproduction by any means and in any form, in whole or in part;
(b) translation, adaptation, arrangement and any other alteration;
(c) any form of distribution to the public of the database or of copies thereof. The first sale in the Community of a copy of the database by the rightholder or with his consent shall exhaust the right to control resale of that copy within the Community;
(d) any communication, display or performance to the public;
(e) any reproduction, distribution, communication, display or performance to the public of the results of the acts referred to in (b).

[2609]

Article 6

Exceptions to restricted acts

1. The performance by the lawful user of a database or of a copy thereof of any of the acts listed in Article 5 which is necessary for the purposes of access to the contents of the databases and normal use of the contents by the lawful user shall not require the authorisation of the author of the database. Where the lawful user is authorised to use only part of the database, this provision shall apply only to that part.

2. Member States shall have the option of providing for limitations on the rights set out in Article 5 in the following cases—

(a) in the case of reproduction for private purposes of a non-electronic database;
(b) where there is use for the sole purpose of illustration for teaching or scientific research, as long as the source is indicated and to the extent justified by the non-commercial purpose to be achieved;
(c) where there is use for the purposes of public security of for the purposes of an administrative or judicial procedure;

(d) where other exceptions to copyright which are traditionally authorised under national law are involved, without prejudice to points (a), (b) and (c).

3. In accordance with the Berne Convention for the protection of Literary and Artistic Works, this Article may not be interpreted in such a way as to allow its application to be used in a manner which unreasonably prejudices the rightholder's legitimate interests or conflicts with normal exploitation of the database.

[2610]

CHAPTER III
SUI GENERIS RIGHT

Article 7

Object of protection

1. Member States shall provide for a right for the maker of a database which shows that there has been qualitatively and/or quantitatively a substantial investment in either the obtaining, verification or presentation of the contents to prevent extraction and/or re-utilisation of the whole or of a substantial part, evaluated qualitatively and/or quantitatively, of the contents of that database.

2. For the purposes of this Chapter—

(a) "extraction" shall mean the permanent or temporary transfer of all or a substantial part of the contents of a database to another medium by any means or in any form;

(b) "re-utilisation" shall mean any form of making available to the public all or a substantial part of the contents of a database by the distribution of copies, by renting, by on-line or other forms of transmission. The first sale of a copy of a database within the Community by the rightholder or with his consent shall exhaust the right to control resale of that copy within the Community;

Public lending is not an act of extraction or re-utilisation.

3. The right referred to in paragraph 1 may be transferred, assigned or granted under contractual licence.

4. The right provided for in paragraph 1 shall apply irrespective of the eligibility of that database for protection by copyright or by other rights. Moreover, it shall apply irrespective of eligibility of the contents of that database for protection by copyright or by other rights. Protection of databases under the right provided for in paragraph 1 shall be without prejudice to rights existing in respect of their contents.

5. The repeated and systematic extraction and/or re-utilisation of insubstantial parts of the contents of the database implying acts which conflict with a normal exploitation of that database or which unreasonably prejudice the legitimate interests of the maker of the database shall not be permitted.

[2611]

Article 8

Rights and obligations of lawful users

1. The maker of a database which is made available to the public in whatever manner may not prevent a lawful user of the database from extracting and/or re-utilising insubstantial parts of its contents, evaluated qualitatively and/or quantitatively, for any purposes whatsoever. Where the lawful user is authorised to extract and/or re-utilise only part of the database, this paragraph shall apply only to that part.

2. A lawful user of a database which is made available to the public in whatever manner may not perform acts which conflict with normal exploitation of the database or unreasonably prejudice the legitimate interests of the maker of the database.

3. A lawful user of a database which is made available to the public in any manner may not cause prejudice to the holder of a copyright or related right in respect of the works or subject matter contained in the database.

[2612]

Article 9

Exceptions to the *sui generis* right

Member States may stipulate that lawful users of a database which is made available to the public in whatever manner may, without the authorisation of its maker, extract or re-utilise a substantial part of its contents—

(a) in the case of extraction for private purposes of the contents of a non-electronic database;

(b) in the case of extraction for the purposes of illustration for teaching or scientific research, as long as the source is indicated and to the extent justified by the non-commercial purpose to be achieved;

(c) in the case of extraction and/or re-utilisation for the purposes of public security or an administrative or judicial procedure.

[2613]

Article 10

Term of protection

1. The right provided for in Article 7 shall run from the date of completion of the making of the database. It shall expire fifteen years from the first of January of the year following the date of completion.

2. In the case of a database which is made available to the public in whatever manner before expiry of the period provided for in paragraph 1, the term of protection by that right shall expire fifteen years from the first of January of the year following the date when the database was first made available to the public.

3. Any substantial change, evaluated qualitatively or quantitatively, to the contents of a database, including any substantial change resulting from the accumulation of successive additions, deletions or alterations, which would result in the database being considered to be a substantial new investment, evaluated qualitatively or quantitatively, shall qualify the database resulting from that investment for its own term of protection.

[2614]

Article 11

Beneficiaries of protection under the *sui generis* right

1. The right provided for in Article 7 shall apply to database whose makers or rightholders are nationals of a Member State or who have their habitual residence in the territory of the Community.

2. Paragraph 1 shall also apply to companies and firms formed in accordance with the law of a Member State and having their registered office, central administration or principal place of business within the Community; however, where such a company or firm has only its registered office in the territory of the Community, its operations must be genuinely linked on an ongoing basis with the economy of a Member State.

3. Agreements extending the right provided for in Article 7 to databases made in third countries and falling outside the provisions of paragraphs 1 and 2 shall be concluded by the Council acting on a proposal from the Commission. The term of any protection extended to databases by virtue of that procedure shall not exceed that available pursuant to Article 10.

[2615]

CHAPTER IV
COMMON PROVISIONS

Article 12

Remedies

Member States shall provide appropriate remedies in respect of infringements of the rights provided for in this Directive.

[2616]

Article 13

Continued application of other legal provisions

This Directive shall be without prejudice to provisions concerning in particular copyright, rights related to copyright or any other rights or obligations subsisting in the data, works or other materials incorporated into a database, patent rights, trade marks, design rights, the protection of national treasures, laws on restrictive practices and unfair competition, trade secrets, security, confidentiality, data protection and privacy, access to public documents, and the law of contract.

[2617]

Article 14

Application over time

1. Protection pursuant to this Directive as regards copyright shall also be available in respect of databases created prior to the date referred to Article 16(1) which on that date fulfil the requirements laid down in this Directive as regards copyright protection of databases.

2. Notwithstanding paragraph 1, where a database protected under copyright arrangements in a Member State on the date of publication of this Directive does not fulfil the eligibility criteria for copyright protection laid down in Article 3(1), this Directive shall not result in any curtailing in that Member State of the remaining term of protection afforded under those arrangements.

3. Protection pursuant to the provisions of this Directive as regards the right provided for in Article 7 shall also be available in respect of databases the making of which was completed not more than fifteen years prior to the date referred to in Article 16(1) and which on that date fulfil the requirements laid down in Article 7.

4. The protection provided for in paragraphs 1 and 3 shall be without prejudice to any acts concluded and rights acquired before the date referred to in those paragraphs.

5. In the case of a database the making of which was completed not more than fifteen years prior to the date referred to in Article 16(1), the term of protection by the right provided for in Article 7 shall expire fifteen years from the first of January following that date.

[2618]

Article 15

Binding nature of certain provisions

Any contractual provision contrary to Articles 6(1) and 8 shall be null and void.

[2619]

Article 16

Final provisions

1. Member States shall bring into force the laws, regulations and administrative provisions necessary to comply with this Directive before 1 January 1998.

When Member States adopt these provisions, they shall contain a reference to this Directive or shall be accompanied by such reference on the occasion of their official publication. The methods of making such reference shall be laid down by Member States.

2. Member States shall communicate to the Commission the text of the provisions of domestic law which they adopt in the field governed by this Directive.

3. Not later than at the end of the third year after the date referred to in paragraph 1, and every three years thereafter, the Commission shall submit to the European Parliament, the Council and the Economic and Social Committee a report on the application of this Directive, in which, inter alia, on the basis of specific information supplied by the Member States, it shall examine in particular the application of the *sui generis* right, including Articles 8 and 9, and shall verify especially whether the application of this right has led to abuse of a dominant position or other interference with free competition which would justify appropriate measures being taken, including the establishment of non-voluntary licensing arrangements. Where necessary, it shall submit proposals for adjustment of this Directive in line with developments in the area of databases.

[2620]

Article 17

This Directive is addressed to the Member States.

[2621]

Done at Strasbourg, 11 March 1996.

DIRECTIVE OF THE EUROPEAN PARLIAMENT AND OF THE COUNCIL

of 22 May 2001

on the harmonisation of certain aspects of copyright and related rights in the information society

(2001/29/EC)

NOTES

Date of publication in OJ: OJ L167, 22.6.01, p 10 (as amended by Corrigendum (see OJ L 6, 10.01.02)).

THE EUROPEAN PARLIAMENT AND THE COUNCIL OF THE EUROPEAN UNION,

Having regard to the Treaty establishing the European Community, and in particular Articles 47(2), 55 and 95 thereof,

Having regard to the proposal from the Commission,[1]

Having regard to the opinion of the Economic and Social Committee,[2]

Acting in accordance with the procedure laid down in Article 251 of the Treaty,[3]

Whereas—

(1) The Treaty provides for the establishment of an internal market and the institution of a system ensuring that competition in the internal market is not distorted. Harmonisation of the laws of the Member States on copyright and related rights contributes to the achievement of these objectives.

(2) The European Council, meeting at Corfu on 24 and 25 June 1994, stressed the need to create a general and flexible legal framework at Community level in order to foster the development of the information society in Europe. This requires, *inter alia*, the existence of an internal market for new products and services. Important Community legislation to ensure such a regulatory framework is already in place or its adoption is well under way. Copyright and related rights play an important role in this context as they protect and stimulate the development and marketing of new products and services and the creation and exploitation of their creative content.

(3) The proposed harmonisation will help to implement the four freedoms of the internal market and relates to compliance with the fundamental principles of law and especially of property, including intellectual property, and freedom of expression and the public interest.

(4) A harmonised legal framework on copyright and related rights, through increased legal certainty and while providing for a high level of protection of intellectual property, will foster substantial investment in creativity and innovation, including network infrastructure, and lead in turn to growth and increased competitiveness of European industry, both in the area of content provision and information technology and more generally across a wide range of industrial and cultural sectors. This will safeguard employment and encourage new job creation.

(5) Technological development has multiplied and diversified the vectors for creation, production and exploitation. While no new concepts for the protection of intellectual property are needed, the current law on copyright and related rights should be adapted and supplemented to respond adequately to economic realities such as new forms of exploitation.

(6) Without harmonisation at Community level, legislative activities at national level which have already been initiated in a number of Member States in order to respond to the technological challenges might result in significant differences in protection and thereby in restrictions on the free movement of services and products incorporating, or based on, intellectual property, leading to a refragmentation of the internal market and legislative inconsistency. The impact of such legislative differences and uncertainties will become more significant with the further development of the information society, which has already greatly increased transborder exploitation of intellectual property. This development will and should further increase. Significant legal differences and uncertainties in protection may hinder economies of scale for new products and services containing copyright and related rights.

(7) The Community legal framework for the protection of copyright and related rights must, therefore, also be adapted and supplemented as far as is necessary for the smooth

functioning of the internal market. To that end, those national provisions on copyright and related rights which vary considerably from one Member State to another or which cause legal uncertainties hindering the smooth functioning of the internal market and the proper development of the information society in Europe should be adjusted, and inconsistent national responses to the technological developments should be avoided, whilst differences not adversely affecting the functioning of the internal market need not be removed or prevented.

(8) The various social, societal and cultural implications of the information society require that account be taken of the specific features of the content of products and services.

(9) Any harmonisation of copyright and related rights must take as a basis a high level of protection, since such rights are crucial to intellectual creation. Their protection helps to ensure the maintenance and development of creativity in the interests of authors, performers, producers, consumers, culture, industry and the public at large. Intellectual property has therefore been recognised as an integral part of property.

(10) If authors or performers are to continue their creative and artistic work, they have to receive an appropriate reward for the use of their work, as must producers in order to be able to finance this work. The investment required to produce products such as phonograms, films or multimedia products, and services such as "on-demand" services, is considerable. Adequate legal protection of intellectual property rights is necessary in order to guarantee the availability of such a reward and provide the opportunity for satisfactory returns on this investment.

(11) A rigorous, effective system for the protection of copyright and related rights is one of the main ways of ensuring that European cultural creativity and production receive the necessary resources and of safeguarding the independence and dignity of artistic creators and performers.

(12) Adequate protection of copyright works and subject-matter of related rights is also of great importance from a cultural standpoint. Article 151 of the Treaty requires the Community to take cultural aspects into account in its action.

(13) A common search for, and consistent application at European level of, technical measures to protect works and other subject-matter and to provide the necessary information on rights are essential insofar as the ultimate aim of these measures is to give effect to the principles and guarantees laid down in law.

(14) This Directive should seek to promote learning and culture by protecting works and other subject-matter while permitting exceptions or limitations in the public interest for the purpose of education and teaching.

(15) The Diplomatic Conference held under the auspices of the World Intellectual Property Organisation (WIPO) in December 1996 led to the adoption of two new Treaties, the 'WIPO Copyright Treaty' and the 'WIPO Performances and Phonograms Treaty', dealing respectively with the protection of authors and the protection of performers and phonogram producers. Those Treaties update the international protection for copyright and related rights significantly, not least with regard to the so-called 'digital agenda', and improve the means to fight piracy world-wide. The Community and a majority of Member States have already signed the Treaties and the process of making arrangements for the ratification of the Treaties by the Community and the Member States is under way. This Directive also serves to implement a number of the new international obligations.

(16) Liability for activities in the network environment concerns not only copyright and related rights but also other areas, such as defamation, misleading advertising, or infringement of trademarks, and is addressed horizontally in Directive 2000/31/EC of the European Parliament and of the Council of 8 June 2000 on certain legal aspects of information society services, in particular electronic commerce, in the internal market ('Directive on electronic commerce'),[4] which clarifies and harmonises various legal issues relating to information society services including electronic commerce. This Directive should be implemented within a timescale similar to that for the implementation of the Directive on electronic commerce, since that Directive provides a harmonised framework of principles and provisions relevant *inter alia* to important parts of this Directive. This Directive is without prejudice to provisions relating to liability in that Directive.

(17) It is necessary, especially in the light of the requirements arising out of the digital environment, to ensure that collecting societies achieve a higher level of rationalisation and transparency with regard to compliance with competition rules.

(18) This Directive is without prejudice to the arrangements in the Member States concerning the management of rights such as extended collective licences.

(19) The moral rights of rightholders should be exercised according to the legislation of the Member States and the provisions of the Berne Convention for the Protection of Literary and Artistic Works, of the WIPO Copyright Treaty and of the WIPO Performances and Phonograms Treaty. Such moral rights remain outside the scope of this Directive.

(20) This Directive is based on principles and rules already laid down in the Directives currently in force in this area, in particular Directives 91/250/EEC,[5] 92/100/EEC,[6] 93/83/EEC,[7] 93/98/EEC[8] and 96/9/EC,[9] and it develops those principles and rules and places them in the context of the information society. The provisions of this Directive should be without prejudice to the provisions of those Directives, unless otherwise provided in this Directive.

(21) This Directive should define the scope of the acts covered by the reproduction right with regard to the different beneficiaries. This should be done in conformity with the acquis communautaire. A broad definition of these acts is needed to ensure legal certainty within the internal market.

(22) The objective of proper support for the dissemination of culture must not be achieved by sacrificing strict protection of rights or by tolerating illegal forms of distribution of counterfeited or pirated works.

(23) This Directive should harmonise further the author's right of communication to the public. This right should be understood in a broad sense covering all communication to the public not present at the place where the communication originates. This right should cover any such transmission or retransmission of a work to the public by wire or wireless means, including broadcasting. This right should not cover any other acts.

(24) The right to make available to the public subject-matter referred to in Article 3(2) should be understood as covering all acts of making available such subject-matter to members of the public not present at the place where the act of making available originates, and as not covering any other acts.

(25) The legal uncertainty regarding the nature and the level of protection of acts of on-demand transmission of copyright works and subject-matter protected by related rights over networks should be overcome by providing for harmonised protection at Community level. It should be made clear that all rightholders recognised by this Directive should have an exclusive right to make available to the public copyright works or any other subject-matter by way of interactive on-demand transmissions. Such interactive on-demand transmissions are characterised by the fact that members of the public may access them from a place and at a time individually chosen by them.

(26) With regard to the making available in on-demand services by broadcasters of their radio or television productions incorporating music from commercial phonograms as an integral part thereof, collective licensing arrangements are to be encouraged in order to facilitate the clearance of the rights concerned.

(27) The mere provision of physical facilities for enabling or making a communication does not in itself amount to communication within the meaning of this Directive.

(28) Copyright protection under this Directive includes the exclusive right to control distribution of the work incorporated in a tangible article. The first sale in the Community of the original of a work or copies thereof by the rightholder or with his consent exhausts the right to control resale of that object in the Community. This right should not be exhausted in respect of the original or of copies thereof sold by the rightholder or with his consent outside the Community. Rental and lending rights for authors have been established in Directive 92/100/EEC. The distribution right provided for in this Directive is without prejudice to the provisions relating to the rental and lending rights contained in Chapter I of that Directive.

(29) The question of exhaustion does not arise in the case of services and on-line services in particular. This also applies with regard to a material copy of a work or other subject-matter made by a user of such a service with the consent of the rightholder. Therefore, the same applies to rental and lending of the original and copies of works or other subject-matter which are services by nature. Unlike CD-ROM or CD-I, where the intellectual property is incorporated in a material medium, namely an item of goods, every on-line service is in fact an act which should be subject to authorisation where the copyright or related right so provides.

(30) The rights referred to in this Directive may be transferred, assigned or subject to the granting of contractual licences, without prejudice to the relevant national legislation on copyright and related rights.

(31) A fair balance of rights and interests between the different categories of rightholders, as well as between the different categories of rightholders and users of protected subject-matter must be safeguarded. The existing exceptions and limitations to the rights as set out by the Member States have to be reassessed in the light of the new electronic environment. Existing differences in the exceptions and limitations to certain restricted acts have direct negative effects on the functioning of the internal market of copyright and related rights. Such differences could well become more pronounced in view of the further development of transborder exploitation of works and cross-border activities. In order to ensure the proper functioning of the internal market, such exceptions and limitations should

be defined more harmoniously. The degree of their harmonisation should be based on their impact on the smooth functioning of the internal market.

(32) This Directive provides for an exhaustive enumeration of exceptions and limitations to the reproduction right and the right of communication to the public. Some exceptions or limitations only apply to the reproduction right, where appropriate. This list takes due account of the different legal traditions in Member States, while, at the same time, aiming to ensure a functioning internal market. Member States should arrive at a coherent application of these exceptions and limitations, which will be assessed when reviewing implementing legislation in the future.

(33) The exclusive right of reproduction should be subject to an exception to allow certain acts of temporary reproduction, which are transient or incidental reproductions, forming an integral and essential part of a technological process and carried out for the sole purpose of enabling either efficient transmission in a network between third parties by an intermediary, or a lawful use of a work or other subject-matter to be made. The acts of reproduction concerned should have no separate economic value on their own. To the extent that they meet these conditions, this exception should include acts which enable browsing as well as acts of caching to take place, including those which enable transmission systems to function efficiently, provided that the intermediary does not modify the information and does not interfere with the lawful use of technology, widely recognised and used by industry, to obtain data on the use of the information. A use should be considered lawful where it is authorised by the rightholder or not restricted by law.

(34) Member States should be given the option of providing for certain exceptions or limitations for cases such as educational and scientific purposes, for the benefit of public institutions such as libraries and archives, for purposes of news reporting, for quotations, for use by people with disabilities, for public security uses and for uses in administrative and judicial proceedings.

(35) In certain cases of exceptions or limitations, rightholders should receive fair compensation to compensate them adequately for the use made of their protected works or other subject-matter. When determining the form, detailed arrangements and possible level of such fair compensation, account should be taken of the particular circumstances of each case. When evaluating these circumstances, a valuable criterion would be the possible harm to the rightholders resulting from the act in question. In cases where rightholders have already received payment in some other form, for instance as part of a licence fee, no specific or separate payment may be due. The level of fair compensation should take full account of the degree of use of technological protection measures referred to in this Directive. In certain situations where the prejudice to the rightholder would be minimal, no obligation for payment may arise.

(36) The Member States may provide for fair compensation for rightholders also when applying the optional provisions on exceptions or limitations which do not require such compensation.

(37) Existing national schemes on reprography, where they exist, do not create major barriers to the internal market. Member States should be allowed to provide for an exception or limitation in respect of reprography.

(38) Member States should be allowed to provide for an exception or limitation to the reproduction right for certain types of reproduction of audio, visual and audiovisual material for private use, accompanied by fair compensation. This may include the introduction or continuation of remuneration schemes to compensate for the prejudice to rightholders. Although differences between those remuneration schemes affect the functioning of the internal market, those differences, with respect to analogue private reproduction, should not have a significant impact on the development of the information society. Digital private copying is likely to be more widespread and have a greater economic impact. Due account should therefore be taken of the differences between digital and analogue private copying and a distinction should be made in certain respects between them.

(39) When applying the exception or limitation on private copying, Member States should take due account of technological and economic developments, in particular with respect to digital private copying and remuneration schemes, when effective technological protection measures are available. Such exceptions or limitations should not inhibit the use of technological measures or their enforcement against circumvention.

(40) Member States may provide for an exception or limitation for the benefit of certain non-profit making establishments, such as publicly accessible libraries and equivalent institutions, as well as archives. However, this should be limited to certain special cases covered by the reproduction right. Such an exception or limitation should not cover uses made in the context of on-line delivery of protected works or other subject-matter. This Directive should be without prejudice to the Member States' option to derogate from the exclusive public lending right in accordance with Article 5 of Directive 92/100/EEC. Therefore, specific

contracts or licences should be promoted which, without creating imbalances, favour such establishments and the disseminative purposes they serve.

(41) When applying the exception or limitation in respect of ephemeral recordings made by broadcasting organisations it is understood that a broadcaster's own facilities include those of a person acting on behalf of and under the responsibility of the broadcasting organisation.

(42) When applying the exception or limitation for non-commercial educational and scientific research purposes, including distance learning, the non-commercial nature of the activity in question should be determined by that activity as such. The organisational structure and the means of funding of the establishment concerned are not the decisive factors in this respect.

(43) It is in any case important for the Member States to adopt all necessary measures to facilitate access to works by persons suffering from a disability which constitutes an obstacle to the use of the works themselves, and to pay particular attention to accessible formats.

(44) When applying the exceptions and limitations provided for in this Directive, they should be exercised in accordance with international obligations. Such exceptions and limitations may not be applied in a way which prejudices the legitimate interests of the rightholder or which conflicts with the normal exploitation of his work or other subject-matter. The provision of such exceptions or limitations by Member States should, in particular, duly reflect the increased economic impact that such exceptions or limitations may have in the context of the new electronic environment. Therefore, the scope of certain exceptions or limitations may have to be even more limited when it comes to certain new uses of copyright works and other subject-matter.

(45) The exceptions and limitations referred to in Article 5(2), (3) and (4) should not, however, prevent the definition of contractual relations designed to ensure fair compensation for the rightholders insofar as permitted by national law.

(46) Recourse to mediation could help users and rightholders to settle disputes. The Commission, in cooperation with the Member States within the Contact Committee, should undertake a study to consider new legal ways of settling disputes concerning copyright and related rights.

(47) Technological development will allow rightholders to make use of technological measures designed to prevent or restrict acts not authorised by the rightholders of any copyright, rights related to copyright or the *sui generis* right in databases. The danger, however, exists that illegal activities might be carried out in order to enable or facilitate the circumvention of the technical protection provided by these measures. In order to avoid fragmented legal approaches that could potentially hinder the functioning of the internal market, there is a need to provide for harmonised legal protection against circumvention of effective technological measures and against provision of devices and products or services to this effect.

(48) Such legal protection should be provided in respect of technological measures that effectively restrict acts not authorised by the rightholders of any copyright, rights related to copyright or the *sui generis* right in databases without, however, preventing the normal operation of electronic equipment and its technological development. Such legal protection implies no obligation to design devices, products, components or services to correspond to technological measures, so long as such device, product, component or service does not otherwise fall under the prohibition of Article 6. Such legal protection should respect proportionality and should not prohibit those devices or activities which have a commercially significant purpose or use other than to circumvent the technical protection. In particular, this protection should not hinder research into cryptography.

(49) The legal protection of technological measures is without prejudice to the application of any national provisions which may prohibit the private possession of devices, products or components for the circumvention of technological measures.

(50) Such a harmonised legal protection does not affect the specific provisions on protection provided for by Directive 91/250/EEC. In particular, it should not apply to the protection of technological measures used in connection with computer programs, which is exclusively addressed in that Directive. It should neither inhibit nor prevent the development or use of any means of circumventing a technological measure that is necessary to enable acts to be undertaken in accordance with the terms of Article 5(3) or Article 6 of Directive 91/250/EEC. Articles 5 and 6 of that Directive exclusively determine exceptions to the exclusive rights applicable to computer programs.

(51) The legal protection of technological measures applies without prejudice to public policy, as reflected in Article 5, or public security. Member States should promote voluntary measures taken by rightholders, including the conclusion and implementation of agreements between rightholders and other parties concerned, to accommodate achieving the objectives of certain exceptions or limitations provided for in national law in accordance with this Directive. In the absence of such voluntary measures or agreements within a reasonable

period of time, Member States should take appropriate measures to ensure that rightholders provide beneficiaries of such exceptions or limitations with appropriate means of benefiting from them, by modifying an implemented technological measure or by other means. However, in order to prevent abuse of such measures taken by right-holders, including within the framework of agreements, or taken by a Member State, any technological measures applied in implementation of such measures should enjoy legal protection.

(52) When implementing an exception or limitation for private copying in accordance with Article 5(2)(b), Member States should likewise promote the use of voluntary measures to accommodate achieving the objectives of such exception or limitation. If, within a reasonable period of time, no such voluntary measures to make reproduction for private use possible have been taken, Member States may take measures to enable beneficiaries of the exception or limitation concerned to benefit from it. Voluntary measures taken by right-holders, including agreements between rightholders and other parties concerned, as well as measures taken by Member States, do not prevent rightholders from using technological measures which are consistent with the exceptions or limitations on private copying in national law in accordance with Article 5(2)(b), taking account of the condition of fair compensation under that provision and the possible differentiation between various conditions of use in accordance with Article 5(5), such as controlling the number of reproductions. In order to prevent abuse of such measures, any technological measures applied in their implementation should enjoy legal protection.

(53) The protection of technological measures should ensure a secure environment for the provision of interactive on-demand services, in such a way that members of the public may access works or other subject-matter from a place and at a time individually chosen by them. Where such services are governed by contractual arrangements, the first and second subparagraphs of Article 6(4) should not apply. Non-interactive forms of online use should remain subject to those provisions.

(54) Important progress has been made in the international standardisation of technical systems of identification of works and protected subject-matter in digital format. In an increasingly networked environment, differences between technological measures could lead to an incompatibility of systems within the Community. Compatibility and interoperability of the different systems should be encouraged. It would be highly desirable to encourage the development of global systems.

(55) Technological development will facilitate the distribution of works, notably on networks, and this will entail the need for rightholders to identify better the work or other subject-matter, the author or any other rightholder, and to provide information about the terms and conditions of use of the work or other subject-matter in order to render easier the management of rights attached to them. Rightholders should be encouraged to use markings indicating, in addition to the information referred to above, *inter alia* their authorisation when putting works or other subject-matter on networks.

(56) There is, however, the danger that illegal activities might be carried out in order to remove or alter the electronic copyright-management information attached to it, or otherwise to distribute, import for distribution, broadcast, communicate to the public or make available to the public works or other protected subject-matter from which such information has been removed without authority. In order to avoid fragmented legal approaches that could potentially hinder the functioning of the internal market, there is a need to provide for harmonised legal protection against any of these activities.

(57) Any such rights-management information systems referred to above may, depending on their design, at the same time process personal data about the consumption patterns of protected subject-matter by individuals and allow for tracing of on-line behaviour. These technical means, in their technical functions, should incorporate privacy safeguards in accordance with Directive 95/46/EC of the European Parliament and of the Council of 24 October 1995 on the protection of individuals with regard to the processing of personal data and the free movement of such data.[10]

(58) Member States should provide for effective sanctions and remedies for infringements of rights and obligations as set out in this Directive. They should take all the measures necessary to ensure that those sanctions and remedies are applied. The sanctions thus provided for should be effective, proportionate and dissuasive and should include the possibility of seeking damages and/or injunctive relief and, where appropriate, of applying for seizure of infringing material.

(59) In the digital environment, in particular, the services of intermediaries may increasingly be used by third parties for infringing activities. In many cases such intermediaries are best placed to bring such infringing activities to an end. Therefore, without prejudice to any other sanctions and remedies available, rightholders should have the possibility of applying for an injunction against an intermediary who carries a third party's infringement of a protected work or other subject-matter in a network. This possibility should

be available even where the acts carried out by the intermediary are exempted under Article 5. The conditions and modalities relating to such injunctions should be left to the national law of the Member States.

(60) The protection provided under this Directive should be without prejudice to national or Community legal provisions in other areas, such as industrial property, data protection, conditional access, access to public documents, and the rule of media exploitation chronology, which may affect the protection of copyright or related rights.

(61) In order to comply with the WIPO Performances and Phonograms Treaty, Directives 92/100/EEC and 93/ 98/EEC should be amended,

NOTES

1 OJ C108, 7.4.98, p 6 and OJ C180, 25.6.99, p 6.
2 OJ C407, 28.12.98, p 30.
3 Opinion of the European Parliament of 10 February 1999 (OJ C150, 28.5.99, p 171), Council Common Position of 28 September 2000 (OJ C344, 1.12.2000, p 1) and Decision of the European Parliament of 14 February 2001 (not yet published in the Official Journal). Council Decision of 9 April 2001.
4 OJ L178, 17.7.2000, p 1.
5 Council Directive 91/250/EEC of 14 May 1991 on the legal protection of computer programs (OJ L122, 17.5.1991, p 42). Directive as amended by Directive 93/98/EEC.
6 Council Directive 92/100/EEC of 19 November 1992 on rental right and lending right and on certain rights related to copyright in the field of intellectual property (OJ L346, 27.11.92, p 61). Directive as amended by Directive 93/98/EEC.
7 Council Directive 93/83/EEC of 27 September 1993 on the coordination of certain rules concerning copyright and rights related to copyright applicable to satellite broadcasting and cable retransmission (OJ L248, 6.10.93, p 15).
8 Council Directive 93/98/EEC of 29 October 1993 harmonising the term of protection of copyright and certain related rights (OJ L290, 24.11.93, p 9).
9 Directive 96/9/EC of the European Parliament and of the Council of 11 March 1996 on the legal protection of databases (OJ L77, 27.3.1996, p 20).
10 OJ L281, 23.11.95, p 31.

HAVE ADOPTED THIS DIRECTIVE—

CHAPTER I
OBJECTIVE AND SCOPE

Article 1
Scope

1. This Directive concerns the legal protection of copyright and related rights in the framework of the internal market, with particular emphasis on the information society.

2. Except in the cases referred to in Article 11, this Directive shall leave intact and shall in no way affect existing Community provisions relating to—
   (a) the legal protection of computer programs;
   (b) rental right, lending right and certain rights related to copyright in the field of intellectual property;
   (c) copyright and related rights applicable to broadcasting of programmes by satellite and cable retransmission;
   (d) the term of protection of copyright and certain related rights;
   (e) the legal protection of databases.

[2622]

CHAPTER II
RIGHTS AND EXCEPTIONS

Article 2

Reproduction right

Member States shall provide for the exclusive right to authorise or prohibit direct or indirect, temporary or permanent reproduction by any means and in any form, in whole or in part—
   (a) for authors, of their works;
   (b) for performers, of fixations of their performances;

(c) for phonogram producers, of their phonograms;
(d) for the producers of the first fixations of films, in respect of the original and copies of their films;
(e) for broadcasting organisations, of fixations of their broadcasts, whether those broadcasts are transmitted by wire or over the air, including by cable or satellite.

[2623]

Article 3

Right of communication to the public of works and right of making available to the public other subject-matter

1. Member States shall provide authors with the exclusive right to authorise or prohibit any communication to the public of their works, by wire or wireless means, including the making available to the public of their works in such a way that members of the public may access them from a place and at a time individually chosen by them.

2. Member States shall provide for the exclusive right to authorise or prohibit the making available to the public, by wire or wireless means, in such a way that members of the public may access them from a place and at a time individually chosen by them—

(a) for performers, of fixations of their performances;
(b) for phonogram producers, of their phonograms;
(c) for the producers of the first fixations of films, of the original and copies of their films;
(d) for broadcasting organisations, of fixations of their broadcasts, whether these broadcasts are transmitted by wire or over the air, including by cable or satellite.

3. The rights referred to in paragraphs 1 and 2 shall not be exhausted by any act of communication to the public or making available to the public as set out in this Article.

[2624]

Article 4

Distribution right

1. Member States shall provide for authors, in respect of the original of their works or of copies thereof, the exclusive right to authorise or prohibit any form of distribution to the public by sale or otherwise.

2. The distribution right shall not be exhausted within the Community in respect of the original or copies of the work, except where the first sale or other transfer of ownership in the Community of that object is made by the rightholder or with his consent.

[2625]

Article 5

Exceptions and limitations

1. Temporary acts of reproduction referred to in Article 2, which are transient or incidental, which are an integral and essential part of a technological process and the sole purpose of which is to enable—

(a) a transmission in a network between third parties by an intermediary, or
(b) a lawful use

of a work or other subject-matter to be made, and which have no independent economic significance, shall be exempted from the reproduction right provided for in Article 2.

2. Member States may provide for exceptions or limitations to the reproduction right provided for in Article 2 in the following cases—

(a) in respect of reproductions on paper or any similar medium, effected by the use of any kind of photographic technique or by some other process having similar effects, with the exception of sheet music, provided that the right-holders receive fair compensation;
(b) in respect of reproductions on any medium made by a natural person for private use and for ends that are neither directly nor indirectly commercial, on condition that the rightholders receive fair compensation which takes account of the application or non-application of technological measures referred to in Article 6 to the work or subject-matter concerned;
(c) in respect of specific acts of reproduction made by publicly accessible libraries,

educational establishments or museums, or by archives, which are not for direct or indirect economic or commercial advantage;

(d) in respect of ephemeral recordings of works made by broadcasting organisations by means of their own facilities and for their own broadcasts; the preservation of these recordings in official archives may, on the grounds of their exceptional documentary character, be permitted;

(e) in respect of reproductions of broadcasts made by social institutions pursuing non-commercial purposes, such as hospitals or prisons, on condition that the rightholders receive fair compensation.

3. Member States may provide for exceptions or limitations to the rights provided for in Articles 2 and 3 in the following cases—

(a) use for the sole purpose of illustration for teaching or scientific research, as long as the source, including the author's name, is indicated, unless this turns out to be impossible and to the extent justified by the non-commercial purpose to be achieved;

(b) uses, for the benefit of people with a disability, which are directly related to the disability and of a non-commercial nature, to the extent required by the specific disability;

(c) reproduction by the press, communication to the public or making available of published articles on current economic, political or religious topics or of broadcast works or other subject-matter of the same character, in cases where such use is not expressly reserved, and as long as the source, including the author's name, is indicated, or use of works or other subject-matter in connection with the reporting of current events, to the extent justified by the informatory purpose and as long as the source, including the author's name, is indicated, unless this turns out to be impossible;

(d) quotations for purposes such as criticism or review, provided that they relate to a work or other subject-matter which has already been lawfully made available to the public, that, unless this turns out to be impossible, the source, including the author's name, is indicated, and that their use is in accordance with fair practice, and to the extent required by the specific purpose;

(e) use for the purposes of public security or to ensure the proper performance or reporting of administrative, parliamentary or judicial proceedings;

(f) use of political speeches as well as extracts of public lectures or similar works or subject-matter to the extent justified by the informatory purpose and provided that the source, including the author's name, is indicated, except where this turns out to be impossible;

(g) use during religious celebrations or official celebrations organised by a public authority;

(h) use of works, such as works of architecture or sculpture, made to be located permanently in public places;

(i) incidental inclusion of a work or other subject-matter in other material;

(j) use for the purpose of advertising the public exhibition or sale of artistic works, to the extent necessary to promote the event, excluding any other commercial use;

(k) use for the purpose of caricature, parody or pastiche;

(l) use in connection with the demonstration or repair of equipment;

(m) use of an artistic work in the form of a building or a drawing or plan of a building for the purposes of reconstructing the building;

(n) use by communication or making available, for the purpose of research or private study, to individual members of the public by dedicated terminals on the premises of establishments referred to in paragraph 2(c) of works and other subject-matter not subject to purchase or licensing terms which are contained in their collections;

(o) use in certain other cases of minor importance where exceptions or limitations already exist under national law, provided that they only concern analogue uses and do not affect the free circulation of goods and services within the Community, without prejudice to the other exceptions and limitations contained in this Article.

4. Where the Member States may provide for an exception or limitation to the right of reproduction pursuant to paragraphs 2 and 3, they may provide similarly for an exception or limitation to the right of distribution as referred to in Article 4 to the extent justified by the purpose of the authorised act of reproduction.

5. The exceptions and limitations provided for in paragraphs 1, 2, 3 and 4 shall only be applied in certain special cases which do not conflict with a normal exploitation of the work or other subject-matter and do not unreasonably prejudice the legitimate interests of the rightholder.

[2626]

CHAPTER III
PROTECTION OF TECHNOLOGICAL MEASURES AND RIGHTS-MANAGEMENT INFORMATION

Article 6

Obligations as to technological measures

1. Member States shall provide adequate legal protection against the circumvention of any effective technological measures, which the person concerned carries out in the knowledge, or with reasonable grounds to know, that he or she is pursuing that objective.

2. Member States shall provide adequate legal protection against the manufacture, import, distribution, sale, rental, advertisement for sale or rental, or possession for commercial purposes of devices, products or components or the provision of services which—

(a) are promoted, advertised or marketed for the purpose of circumvention of, or

(b) have only a limited commercially significant purpose or use other than to circumvent, or

(c) are primarily designed, produced, adapted or performed for the purpose of enabling or facilitating the circumvention of,

any effective technological measures.

3. For the purposes of this Directive, the expression "technological measures" means any technology, device or component that, in the normal course of its operation, is designed to prevent or restrict acts, in respect of works or other subject-matter, which are not authorised by the rightholder of any copyright or any right related to copyright as provided for by law or the *sui generis* right provided for in Chapter III of Directive 96/9/EC. Technological measures shall be deemed "effective" where the use of a protected work or other subject-matter is controlled by the rightholders through application of an access control or protection process, such as encryption, scrambling or other transformation of the work or other subject-matter or a copy control mechanism, which achieves the protection objective.

4. Notwithstanding the legal protection provided for in paragraph 1, in the absence of voluntary measures taken by rightholders, including agreements between rightholders and other parties concerned, Member States shall take appropriate measures to ensure that rightholders make available to the beneficiary of an exception or limitation provided for in national law in accordance with Article 5(2)(a), (2)(c), (2)(d), (2)(e), (3)(a), (3)(b) or (3)(e) the means of benefiting from that exception or limitation, to the extent necessary to benefit from that exception or limitation and where that beneficiary has legal access to the protected work or subject-matter concerned.

A Member State may also take such measures in respect of a beneficiary of an exception or limitation provided for in accordance with Article 5(2)(b), unless reproduction for private use has already been made possible by rightholders to the extent necessary to benefit from the exception or limitation concerned and in accordance with the provisions of Article 5(2)(b) and (5), without preventing rightholders from adopting adequate measures regarding the number of reproductions in accordance with these provisions.

The technological measures applied voluntarily by rightholders, including those applied in implementation of voluntary agreements, and technological measures applied in implementation of the measures taken by Member States, shall enjoy the legal protection provided for in paragraph 1.

The provisions of the first and second subparagraphs shall not apply to works or other subject-matter made available to the public on agreed contractual terms in such a way that members of the public may access them from a place and at a time individually chosen by them.

When this Article is applied in the context of Directives 92/100/EEC and 96/9/EC, this paragraph shall apply *mutatis mutandis*

[2627]

Article 7

Obligations concerning rights-management information

1. Member States shall provide for adequate legal protection against any person knowingly performing without authority any of the following acts—

(a) the removal or alteration of any electronic rights-management information;

(b) the distribution, importation for distribution, broadcasting, communication or making available to the public of works or other subject-matter protected under this Directive or under Chapter III of Directive 96/9/EC from which electronic rights-management information has been removed or altered without authority,

if such person knows, or has reasonable grounds to know, that by so doing he is inducing, enabling, facilitating or concealing an infringement of any copyright or any rights related to copyright as provided by law, or of the *sui generis* right provided for in Chapter III of Directive 96/9/EC.

2. For the purposes of this Directive, the expression "rights-management information" means any information provided by rightholders which identifies the work or other subject-matter referred to in this Directive or covered by the *sui generis* right provided for in Chapter III of Directive 96/9/EC, the author or any other rightholder, or information about the terms and conditions of use of the work or other subject-matter, and any numbers or codes that represent such information.

The first subparagraph shall apply when any of these items of information is associated with a copy of, or appears in connection with the communication to the public of, a work or other subject-matter referred to in this Directive or covered by the *sui generis* right provided for in Chapter III of Directive 96/9/EC.

[2628]

CHAPTER IV
COMMON PROVISIONS

Article 8

Sanctions and remedies

1. Member States shall provide appropriate sanctions and remedies in respect of infringements of the rights and obligations set out in this Directive and shall take all the measures necessary to ensure that those sanctions and remedies are applied. The sanctions thus provided for shall be effective, proportionate and dissuasive.

2. Each Member State shall take the measures necessary to ensure that rightholders whose interests are affected by an infringing activity carried out on its territory can bring an action for damages and/or apply for an injunction and, where appropriate, for the seizure of infringing material as well as of devices, products or components referred to in Article 6(2).

3. Member States shall ensure that rightholders are in a position to apply for an injunction against intermediaries whose services are used by a third party to infringe a copyright or related right.

[2629]

Article 9

Continued application of other legal provisions

This Directive shall be without prejudice to provisions concerning in particular patent rights, trade marks, design rights, utility models, topographies of semi-conductor products, type faces, conditional access, access to cable of broadcasting services, protection of national treasures, legal deposit requirements, laws on restrictive practices and unfair competition, trade secrets, security, confidentiality, data protection and privacy, access to public documents, the law of contract.

[2630]

Article 10

Application over time

1. The provisions of this Directive shall apply in respect of all works and other subject-matter referred to in this Directive which are, on 22 December 2002, protected by the

Member States' legislation in the field of copyright and related rights, or which meet the criteria for protection under the provisions of this Directive or the provisions referred to in Article 1(2).

2. This Directive shall apply without prejudice to any acts concluded and rights acquired before 22 December 2002.

[2631]

Article 11

(*Repeals Directive 92/100/EEC, Art 7, and amends Art 10 and Directive 93/98/EEC, Art 3.*)

Article 12

Final provisions

1. Not later than 22 December 2004 and every three years thereafter, the Commission shall submit to the European Parliament, the Council and the Economic and Social Committee a report on the application of this Directive, in which, *inter alia*, on the basis of specific information supplied by the Member States, it shall examine in particular the application of Articles 5, 6 and 8 in the light of the development of the digital market. In the case of Article 6, it shall examine in particular whether that Article confers a sufficient level of protection and whether acts which are permitted by law are being adversely affected by the use of effective technological measures. Where necessary, in particular to ensure the functioning of the internal market pursuant to Article 14 of the Treaty, it shall submit proposals for amendments to this Directive.

2. Protection of rights related to copyright under this Directive shall leave intact and shall in no way affect the protection of copyright.

3. A contact committee is hereby established. It shall be composed of representatives of the competent authorities of the Member States. It shall be chaired by a representative of the Commission and shall meet either on the initiative of the chairman or at the request of the delegation of a Member State.

4. The tasks of the committee shall be as follows—

(a) to examine the impact of this Directive on the functioning of the internal market, and to highlight any difficulties;

(b) to organise consultations on all questions deriving from the application of this Directive;

(c) to facilitate the exchange of information on relevant developments in legislation and case-law, as well as relevant economic, social, cultural and technological developments;

(d) to act as a forum for the assessment of the digital market in works and other items, including private copying and the use of technological measures.

[2632]

Article 13

Implementation

1. Member States shall bring into force the laws, regulations and administrative provisions necessary to comply with this Directive before 22 December 2002. They shall forthwith inform the Commission thereof.

When Member States adopt these measures, they shall contain a reference to this Directive or shall be accompanied by such reference on the occasion of their official publication. The methods of making such reference shall be laid down by Member States.

2. Member States shall communicate to the Commission the text of the provisions of domestic law which they adopt in the field governed by this Directive.

[2633]

Article 14

Entry into force

This Directive shall enter into force on the day of its publication in the *Official Journal of the European Communities*.

[2634]

Article 15

Addressees

This Directive is addressed to the Member States.

[2635]

Done at Brussels, 22 May 2001.

TREATY ON INTELLECTUAL PROPERTY IN RESPECT OF INTEGRATED CIRCUITS

Adopted at Washington on May 26, 1989

NOTES

The original source for this Treaty is the World Intellectual Property Organisation (WIPO).

Article 1

Establishment of a Union

The Contracting Parties constitute themselves into a Union for the purposes of this Treaty.

[2636]

Article 2

Definitions

For the purposes of this Treaty—

(i) "integrated circuit" means a product, in its final form or an intermediate form, in which the elements, at least one of which is an active element, and some or all of the interconnections are integrally formed in and/or on a piece of material and which is intended to perform an electronic function,

(ii) "layout-design (topography)" means the three-dimensional disposition, however expressed, of the elements, at least one of which is an active element, and of some or all of the interconnections of an integrated circuit, or such a three-dimensional disposition prepared for an integrated circuit intended for manufacture,

(iii) "holder of the right" means the natural person who, or the legal entity which, according to the applicable law, is to be regarded as the beneficiary of the protection referred to in Article 6,

(iv) "protected layout-design (topography)" means a layout-design (topography) in respect of which the conditions of protection referred to in this Treaty are fulfilled,

(v) "Contracting Party" means a State, or an Intergovernmental Organisation meeting the requirements of item (x), party to this Treaty,

(vi) "territory of a Contracting Party" means, where the Contracting Party is a State, the territory of that State and, where the Contracting Party is an Intergovernmental Organisation, the territory in which the constituting treaty of that Intergovernmental Organisation applies,

(vii) "Union" means the Union referred to in Article 1,

(viii) "Assembly" means the Assembly referred to in Article 9,

(ix) "Director General" means the Director General of the World Intellectual Property Organisation,

(x) "Intergovernmental Organisation" means an organisation constituted by, and composed of, States of any region of the world, which has competence in respect of matters governed by this Treaty, has its own legislation providing for intellectual property protection in respect of layout-designs (topographies) and binding on all its member States, and has been duly authorised, in accordance with its internal procedures, to sign, ratify, accept, approve or accede to this Treaty.

[2637]

PART IV INTELLECTUAL PROPERTY

Article 3

The Subject Matter of the Treaty

(1) [*Obligation to Protect Layout-Designs* (*Topographies*)] (a) Each Contracting Party shall have the obligation to secure, throughout its territory, intellectual property protection in respect of layout-designs (topographies) in accordance with this Treaty. It shall, in particular, secure adequate measures to ensure the prevention of acts considered unlawful under Article 6 and appropriate legal remedies where such acts have been committed.

(b) The right of the holder of the right in respect of an integrated circuit applies whether or not the integrated circuit is incorporated in an article.

(c) Notwithstanding Article 2(i), any Contracting Party whose law limits the protection of layout-designs (topographies) to layout-designs (topographies) of semiconductor integrated circuits shall be free to apply that limitation as long as its law contains such limitation.

(2) [*Requirement of Originality*] (a) The obligation referred to in paragraph (1)(a) shall apply to layout-designs (topographies) that are original in the sense that they are the result of their creators' own intellectual effort and are not commonplace among creators of layout-designs (topographies) and manufacturers of integrated circuits at the time of their creation.

(b) A layout-design (topography) that consists of a combination of elements and interconnections that are commonplace shall be protected only if the combination, taken as a whole, fulfils the conditions referred to in subparagraph (a).

[2638]

Article 4

The Legal Form of the Protection

Each Contracting Party shall be free to implement its obligations under this Treaty through a special law on layout-designs (topographies) or its law on copyright, patents, utility models, industrial designs, unfair competition or any other law or a combination of any of those laws.

[2639]

Article 5

National Treatment

(1) [*National Treatment*] Subject to compliance with its obligation referred to in Article 3(1)(a), each Contracting Party shall, in respect of the intellectual property protection of layout-designs (topographies), accord, within its territory,

(i) to natural persons who are nationals of, or are domiciled in the territory of, any of the other Contracting Parties, and

(ii) to legal entities which or natural persons who, in the territory of any of the other Contracting Parties, have a real and effective establishment for the creation of layout-designs (topographies) or the production of integrated circuits,

the same treatment that it accords to its own nationals.

(2) [*Agents, Addresses for Service, Court Proceedings*] Notwithstanding paragraph (1), any Contracting Party is free not to apply national treatment as far as any obligations to appoint an agent or to designate an address for service are concerned or as far as the special rules applicable to foreigners in court proceedings are concerned.

(3) [*Application of Paragraphs (1) and (2) to Intergovernmental Organisations*] Where the Contracting Party is an Intergovernmental Organisation, "nationals" in paragraph (1) means nationals of any of the States members of that Organisation.

[2640]

Article 6

The Scope of the Protection

(1) [*Acts Requiring the Authorisation of the Holder of the Right*] (a) Any Contracting Party shall consider unlawful the following acts if performed without the authorisation of the holder of the right—

(i) the act of reproducing, whether by incorporation in an integrated circuit or otherwise, a protected layout-design (topography) in its entirety or any part thereof, except the act of reproducing any part that does not comply with the requirement of originality referred to in Article 3(2),

(ii) the act of importing, selling or otherwise distributing for commercial purposes a protected layout-design (topography) or an integrated circuit in which a protected layout-design (topography) is incorporated.

(b) Any Contracting Party shall be free to consider unlawful also acts other than those specified in subparagraph (a) if performed without the authorisation of the holder of the right.

(2) [*Acts Not Requiring the Authorisation of the Holder of the Right*] (a) Notwithstanding paragraph (1), no Contracting Party shall consider unlawful the performance, without the authorisation of the holder of the right, of the act of reproduction referred to in paragraph (1)(a)(i) where that act is performed by a third party for private purposes or for the sole purpose of evaluation, analysis, research or teaching.

(b) Where the third party referred to in subparagraph (a), on the basis of evaluation or analysis of the protected layout-design (topography) ("the first layout-design (topography)"), creates a layout-design (topography) complying with the requirement of originality referred to in Article 3(2) ("the second layout-design (topography)"), that third party may incorporate the second layout-design (topography) in an integrated circuit or perform any of the acts referred to in paragraph (1) in respect of the second layout-design (topography) without being regarded as infringing the rights of the holder of the right in the first layout-design (topography).

(c) The holder of the right may not exercise his right in respect of an identical original layout-design (topography) that was independently created by a third party.

(3) [*Measures Concerning Use Without the Consent of the Holder of the Right*] (a) Notwithstanding paragraph (1), any Contracting Party may, in its legislation, provide for the possibility of its executive or judicial authority granting a non-exclusive license, in circumstances that are not ordinary, for the performance of any of the acts referred to in paragraph (1) by a third party without the authorisation of the holder of the right ("non-voluntary license"), after unsuccessful efforts, made by the said third party in line with normal commercial practices, to obtain such authorisation, where the granting of the non-voluntary license is found, by the granting authority, to be necessary to safeguard a national purpose deemed to be vital by that authority; the non-voluntary license shall be available for exploitation only in the territory of that country and shall be subject to the payment of an equitable remuneration by the third party to the holder of the right.

(b) The provisions of this Treaty shall not affect the freedom of any Contracting Party to apply measures, including the granting, after a formal proceeding by its executive or judicial authority, of a non-voluntary license, in application of its laws in order to secure free competition and to prevent abuses by the holder of the right.

(c) The granting of any non-voluntary license referred to in subparagraph (a) or subparagraph (b) shall be subject to judicial review. Any non-voluntary license referred to in subparagraph (a) shall be revoked when the conditions referred to in that subparagraph cease to exist.

(4) [*Sale and Distribution of Infringing Integrated Circuits Acquired Innocently*] Notwithstanding paragraph (1)(a)(ii), no Contracting Party shall be obliged to consider unlawful the performance of any of the acts referred to in that paragraph in respect of an integrated circuit incorporating an unlawfully reproduced layout-design (topography) where the person performing or ordering such acts did not know and had no reasonable ground to know, when acquiring the said integrated circuit, that it incorporates an unlawfully reproduced layout-design (topography).

(5) [*Exhaustion of Rights*] Notwithstanding paragraph (1)(a)(ii), any Contracting Party may consider lawful the performance, without the authorisation of the holder of the right, of any of the acts referred to in that paragraph where the act is performed in respect of a protected layout-design (topography), or in respect of an integrated circuit in which such a layout-design (topography) is incorporated, that has been put on the market by, or with the consent of, the holder of the right.

[2641]

Article 7

Exploitation; Registration, Disclosure

(1) [*Faculty to Require Exploitation*] Any Contracting Party shall be free not to protect a layout-design (topography) until it has been ordinarily commercially exploited, separately or as incorporated in an integrated circuit, somewhere in the world.

(2) [*Faculty to Require Registration; Disclosure*] (a) Any Contracting Party shall be free not to protect a layout-design (topography) until the layout-design (topography) has been the subject of an application for registration, filed in due form with the competent public authority, or of a registration with that authority; it may be required that the application be accompanied by the filing of a copy or drawing of the layout-design (topography) and, where the integrated circuit has been commercially exploited, of a sample of that integrated circuit, along with information defining the electronic function which the integrated circuit is intended to perform; however, the applicant may exclude such parts of the copy or drawing that relate to the manner of manufacture of the integrated circuit, provided that the parts submitted are sufficient to allow the identification of the layout-design (topography).

(b) Where the filing of an application for registration according to subparagraph (a) is required, the Contracting Party may require that such filing be effected within a certain period of time from the date on which the holder of the right first exploits ordinarily commercially anywhere in the world the layout-design (topography) of an integrated circuit; such period shall not be less than two years counted from the said date.

(c) Registration under subparagraph (a) may be subject to the payment of a fee.

[2642]

Article 8

The Duration of the Protection

Protection shall last at least eight years.

[2643]

Article 9

Assembly

(1) [*Composition*] (a) The Union shall have an Assembly consisting of the Contracting Parties.

(b) Each Contracting Party shall be represented by one delegate who may be assisted by alternate delegates, advisors and experts.

(c) Subject to subparagraph (d), the expenses of each delegation shall be borne by the Contracting Party that has appointed the delegation.

(d) The Assembly may ask the World Intellectual Property Organisation to grant financial assistance to facilitate the participation of delegations of Contracting Parties that are regarded as developing countries in conformity with the established practice of the General Assembly of the United Nations.

(2) [*Functions*] (a) The Assembly shall deal with matters concerning the maintenance and development of the Union and the application and operation of this Treaty.

(b) The Assembly shall decide the convocation of any diplomatic conference for the revision of this Treaty and give the necessary instructions to the Director General for the preparation of such diplomatic conference.

(c) The Assembly shall perform the functions allocated to it under Article 14 and shall establish the details of the procedures provided for in that Article, including the financing of such procedures.

(3) [*Voting*] (a) Each Contracting Party that is a State shall have one vote and shall vote only in its own name.

(b) Any Contracting Party that is an Intergovernmental Organisation shall exercise its right to vote, in place of its member States, with a number of votes equal to the number of its member States which are party to this Treaty and which are present at the time the vote is taken. No such Intergovernmental Organisation shall exercise its right to vote if any of its member States participates in the vote.

(4) [*Ordinary Sessions*] The Assembly shall meet in ordinary session once every two years upon convocation by the Director General.

(5) [*Rules of Procedure*] The Assembly shall establish its own rules of procedure, including the convocation of extraordinary sessions, the requirements of a quorum and, subject to the provisions of this Treaty, the required majority for various kinds of decisions.

[2644]

Article 10

International Bureau

(1) [*International Bureau*] (a) The International Bureau of the World Intellectual Property Organisation shall—

(i) perform the administrative tasks concerning the Union, as well as any tasks specially assigned to it by the Assembly;

(ii) subject to the availability of funds, provide technical assistance, on request, to the Governments of Contracting Parties that are States and are regarded as developing countries in conformity with the established practice of the General Assembly of the United Nations.

(b) No Contracting Party shall have any financial obligations; in particular, no Contracting Party shall be required to pay any contributions to the International Bureau on account of its membership in the Union.

(2) [*Director General*] The Director General shall be the chief executive of the Union and shall represent the Union.

[2645]

Article 11

Amendment of Certain Provisions of the Treaty

(1) [*Amending of Certain Provisions by the Assembly*] The Assembly may amend the definitions contained in Article 2(i) and 2(ii), as well as Articles 3(1)(c), 9(1)(c) and (d), 9(4), 10(1)(a) and 14.

(2) [*Initiation and Notice of Proposals for Amendment*] (a) Proposals under this Article for amendment of the provisions of this Treaty referred to in paragraph (1) may be initiated by any Contracting Party or by the Director General.

(b) Such proposals shall be communicated by the Director General to the Contracting Parties at least six months in advance of their consideration by the Assembly.

(c) No such proposal shall be made before the expiration of five years from the date of entry into force of this Treaty under Article 16(1).

(3) [*Required Majority*] Adoption by the Assembly of any amendment under paragraph (1) shall require four-fifths of the votes cast.

(4) [*Entry Into Force*] (a) Any amendment to the provisions of this Treaty referred to in paragraph (1) shall enter into force three months after written notifications of acceptance, effected in accordance with their respective constitutional processes, have been received by the Director General from three-fourths of the Contracting Parties members of the Assembly at the time the Assembly adopted the amendment. Any amendment to the said provisions thus accepted shall bind all States and Intergovernmental Organisations that were Contracting Parties at the time the amendment was adopted by the Assembly or that become Contracting Parties thereafter, except Contracting Parties which have notified their denunciation of this Treaty in accordance with Article 17 before the entry into force of the amendment.

(b) In establishing the required three-fourths referred to in subparagraph (a), a notification made by an Intergovernmental Organisation shall only be taken into account if no notification has been made by any of its member States.

[2646]

Article 12

Safeguard of Paris and Berne Conventions

This Treaty shall not affect the obligations that any Contracting Party may have under the Paris Convention for the Protection of Industrial Property or the Berne Convention for the Protection of Literary and Artistic Works.

[2647]

Article 13

Reservations

No reservations to this Treaty shall be made.

[2648]

Article 14

Settlement of Disputes

(1) [*Consultations*] (a) Where any dispute arises concerning the interpretation or implementation of this Treaty, a Contracting Party may bring the matter to the attention of another Contracting Party and request the latter to enter into consultations with it.

(b) The Contracting Party so requested shall provide promptly an adequate opportunity for the requested consultations.

(c) The Contracting Parties engaged in consultations shall attempt to reach, within a reasonable period of time, a mutually satisfactory solution of the dispute.

(2) [*Other Means of Settlement*] If a mutually satisfactory solution is not reached within a reasonable period of time through the consultations referred to in paragraph (1), the parties to the dispute may agree to resort to other means designed to lead to an amicable settlement of their dispute, such as good offices, conciliation, mediation and arbitration.

(3) [*Panel*] (a) If the dispute is not satisfactorily settled through the consultations referred to in paragraph (1), or if the means referred to in paragraph (2) are not resorted to, or do not lead to an amicable settlement within a reasonable period of time, the Assembly, at the written request of either of the parties to the dispute, shall convene a panel of three members to examine the matter. The members of the panel shall not, unless the parties to the dispute agree otherwise, be from either party to the dispute. They shall be selected from a list of designated governmental experts established by the Assembly. The terms of reference for the panel shall be agreed upon by the parties to the dispute. If such agreement is not achieved within three months, the Assembly shall set the terms of reference for the panel after having consulted the parties to the dispute and the members of the panel. The panel shall give full opportunity to the parties to the dispute and any other interested Contracting Parties to present to it their views. If both parties to the dispute so request, the panel shall stop its proceedings.

(b) The Assembly shall adopt rules for the establishment of the said list of experts, and the manner of selecting the members of the panel, who shall be governmental experts of the Contracting Parties, and for the conduct of the panel proceedings, including provisions to safeguard the confidentiality of the proceedings and of any material designated as confidential by any participant in the proceedings.

(c) Unless the parties to the dispute reach an agreement between themselves prior to the panel's concluding its proceedings, the panel shall promptly prepare a written report and provide it to the parties to the dispute for their review. The parties to the dispute shall have a reasonable period of time, whose length will be fixed by the panel, to submit any comments on the report to the panel, unless they agree to a longer time in their attempts to reach a mutually satisfactory resolution to their dispute. The panel shall take into account the comments and shall promptly transmit its report to the Assembly. The report shall contain the facts and recommendations for the resolution of the dispute, and shall be accompanied by the written comments, if any, of the parties to the dispute.

(4) [*Recommendation by the Assembly*] The Assembly shall give the report of the panel prompt consideration. The Assembly shall, by consensus, make recommendations to the parties to the dispute, based upon its interpretation of this Treaty and the report of the panel. **[2649]**

Article 15

Becoming Party to the Treaty

(1) [*Eligibility*] (a) Any State member of the World Intellectual Property Organisation or of the United Nations may become party to this Treaty.

(b) Any Intergovernmental Organisation which meets the requirements of Article 2(x) may become party to this Treaty. The Organisation shall inform the Director General of its competence, and any subsequent changes in its competence, with respect to the matters governed by this Treaty. The Organisation and its member States may, without, however, any derogation from the obligations under this Treaty, decide on their respective responsibilities for the performance of their obligations under this Treaty.

(2) [*Adherence*] A State or Intergovernmental Organisation shall become party to this Treaty by—

(i) signature followed by the deposit of an instrument of ratification, acceptance or approval, or

(ii) the deposit of an instrument of accession.

(3) [*Deposit of Instruments*] The instruments referred to in paragraph (2) shall be deposited with the Director General.

[2650]

Article 16

Entry Into Force of the Treaty

(1) [*Initial Entry Into Force*] This Treaty shall enter into force, with respect to each of the first five States or Intergovernmental Organisations which have deposited their instruments of ratification, acceptance, approval or accession, three months after the date on which the fifth instrument of ratification, acceptance, approval or accession has been deposited.

(2) [*States and Intergovernmental Organisations Not Covered by the Initial Entry Into Force*] This Treaty shall enter into force with respect to any State or Intergovernmental Organisation not covered by paragraph (1) three months after the date on which that State or Intergovernmental Organisation has deposited its instrument of ratification, acceptance, approval or accession unless a later date has been indicated in the instrument; in the latter case, this Treaty shall enter into force with respect to the said State or Intergovernmental Organisation on the date thus indicated.

(3) [*Protection of Layout-Designs (Topographies) Existing at Time of Entry Into Force*] Any Contracting Party shall have the right not to apply this Treaty to any layout-design (topography) that exists at the time this Treaty enters into force in respect of that Contracting Party, provided that this provision does not affect any protection that such layout-design (topography) may, at that time, enjoy in the territory of that Contracting Party by virtue of international obligations other than those resulting from this Treaty or the legislation of the said Contracting Party.

[2651]

Article 17

Denunciation of the Treaty

(1) [*Notification*] Any Contracting Party may denounce this Treaty by notification addressed to the Director General.

(2) [*Effective Date*] Denunciation shall take effect one year after the day on which the Director General has received the notification of denunciation.

[2652]

Article 18

Texts of the Treaty

(1) [*Original Texts*] This Treaty is established in a single original in the English, Arabic, Chinese, French, Russian and Spanish languages, all texts being equally authentic.

(2) [*Official Texts*] Official texts shall be established by the Director General, after consultation with the interested Governments, in such other languages as the Assembly may designate.

[2653]

Article 19

Depositary

The Director General shall be the depositary of this Treaty.

[2654]

Article 20

Signature

This Treaty shall be open for signature between May 26, 1989, and August 25, 1989, with the Government of the United States of America, and between August 26, 1989, and May 25, 1990, at the headquarters of WIPO.

[2655]

IN WITNESS WHEREOF the undersigned, being duly authorised thereto, have signed this Treaty.

Done at Washington, May 26, 1989.

WIPO COPYRIGHT TREATY

Adopted by the Diplomatic Conference on December 20, 1996

NOTES

The original source for this Treaty is the World Intellectual Property Organisation (WIPO).

PREAMBLE

THE CONTRACTING PARTIES,

Desiring to develop and maintain the protection of the rights of authors in their literary and artistic works in a manner as effective and uniform as possible,

Recognising the need to introduce new international rules and clarify the interpretation of certain existing rules in order to provide adequate solutions to the questions raised by new economic, social, cultural and technological developments,

Recognising the profound impact of the development and convergence of information and communication technologies on the creation and use of literary and artistic works,

Emphasising the outstanding significance of copyright protection as an incentive for literary and artistic creation,

Recognising the need to maintain a balance between the rights of authors and the larger public interest, particularly education, research and access to information, as reflected in the Berne Convention,

HAVE AGREED AS FOLLOWS—

Article 1

Relation to the Berne Convention

(1) This Treaty is a special agreement within the meaning of Article 20 of the Berne Convention for the Protection of Literary and Artistic Works, as regards Contracting Parties that are countries of the Union established by that Convention. This Treaty shall not have any connection with treaties, other than the Berne Convention, nor shall it prejudice any rights and obligations under any other treaties.

(2) Nothing in this Treaty shall derogate from existing obligations that Contracting Parties have to each other under the Berne Convention for the Protection of Literary and Artistic Works.

(3) Hereinafter, "Berne Convention" shall refer to the Paris Act of July 24, 1971 of the Berne Convention for the Protection of Literary and Artistic Works.

(4) Contracting Parties shall comply with Articles 1 to 21 and the Appendix of the Berne Convention.

[2656]

Article 2

Scope of Copyright Protection

Copyright protection extends to expressions and not to ideas, procedures, methods of operation or mathematical concepts as such.

[2657]

Article 3

Application of Articles 2 to 6 of the Berne Convention

Contracting Parties shall apply *mutatis mutandis* the provisions of Articles 2 to 6 of the Berne Convention in respect of the protection provided for in this Treaty.

[2658]

Article 4

Computer Programs

Computer programs are protected as literary works within the meaning of Article 2 of the Berne Convention. Such protection applies to computer programs, whatever may be the mode or form of their expression.

[2659]

Article 5

Compilations of Data (Databases)

Compilations of data or other material, in any form, which by reason of the selection or arrangement of their contents constitute intellectual creations, arc protected as such. This protection does not extend to the data or the material itself and is without prejudice to any copyright subsisting in the data or material contained in the compilation

[2660]

Article 6

Right of Distribution

(1) Authors of literary and artistic works shall enjoy the exclusive right of authorising the making available to the public of the original and copies of their works through sale or other transfer of ownership.

(2) Nothing in this Treaty shall affect the freedom of Contracting Parties to determine the conditions, if any, under which the exhaustion of the right in paragraph (1) applies after the first sale or other transfer of ownership of the original or a copy of the work with the authorisation of the author.

[2661]

Article 7

Right of Rental

(1) Authors of—

(i) computer programs;

(ii) cinematographic works; and

(iii) works embodied in phonograms as determined in the national law of Contracting Parties,

shall enjoy the exclusive right of authorising commercial rental to the public of the originals or copies of their works.

(2) Paragraph (1) shall not apply—

(i) in the case of computer programs, where the program itself is not the essential object of the rental, and

(ii) in the case of cinematographic works, unless such commercial rental has led to widespread copying of such works materially impairing the exclusive right of reproduction.

(3) Notwithstanding the provisions of paragraph (1), a Contracting Party that, on April 15, 1994, had and continues to have in force a system of equitable remuneration of authors for the rental of copies of their works embodied in phonograms may maintain that system provided that the commercial rental of works embodied in phonograms is not giving rise to the material impairment of the exclusive right of reproduction of authors.

[2662]

Article 8

Right of Communication to the Public

Without prejudice to the provisions of Articles 11(1)(ii), 11*bis*(1)(i) and (ii), 11*ter*(1)(ii), 14(1)(ii) and 14*bis*(1) of the Berne Convention, authors of literary and artistic works shall enjoy the exclusive right of authorising any communication to the public of their works, by wire or wireless means, including the making available to the public of their works in such a way that members of the public may access these works from a place and at a time individually chosen by them.

[2663]

Article 9

Duration of the Protection of Photographic Works

In respect of photographic works, the Contracting Parties shall not apply the provisions of Article 7(4) of the Berne Convention.

[2664]

Article 10

Limitations and Exceptions

(1) Contracting Parties may, in their national legislation, provide for limitations of or exceptions to the rights granted to authors of literary and artistic works under this Treaty in certain special cases that do not conflict with a normal exploitation of the work and do not unreasonably prejudice the legitimate interests of the author.

(2) Contracting Parties shall, when applying the Berne Convention, confine any limitations of or exceptions to rights provided for therein to certain special cases that do not conflict with a normal exploitation of the work and do not unreasonably prejudice the legitimate interests of the author.

[2665]

Article 11

Obligations Concerning Technological Measures

Contracting Parties shall provide adequate legal protection and effective legal remedies against the circumvention of effective technological measures that are used by authors in connection with the exercise of their rights under this Treaty or the Berne Convention and that restrict acts, in respect of their works, which are not authorised by the authors concerned or permitted by law.

[2666]

Article 12

Obligations concerning Rights Management Information

(1) Contracting Parties shall provide adequate and effective legal remedies against any person knowingly performing any of the following acts knowing, or with respect to civil remedies having reasonable grounds to know that it will induce, enable, facilitate or conceal an infringement of any right covered by this Treaty or the Berne Convention—

(i) to remove or alter any electronic rights management information without authority;

(ii) to distribute, import for distribution, broadcast or communicate to the public, without authority, works or copies of works knowing that electronic rights management information has been removed or altered without authority.

(2) As used in this Article, "rights management information" means information which identifies the work, the author of the work, the owner of any right in the work, or information about the terms and conditions of use of the work, and any numbers or codes that represent such information, when any of these items of information is attached to a copy of a work or appears in connection with the communication of a work to the public.

[2667]

Article 13

Application in Time

Contracting Parties shall apply the provisions of Article 18 of the Berne Convention to all protection provided for in this Treaty.

[2668]

Article 14

Provisions on Enforcement of Rights

(1) Contracting Parties undertake to adopt, in accordance with their legal systems, the measures necessary to ensure the application of this Treaty.

(2) Contracting Parties shall ensure that enforcement procedures are available under their law so as to permit effective action against any act of infringement of rights covered by this Treaty, including expeditious remedies to prevent infringements and remedies which constitute a deterrent to further infringements.

[2669]

Article 15

Assembly

(1)

(a) The Contracting Parties shall have an Assembly.

(b) Each Contracting Party shall be represented by one delegate who may be assisted by alternate delegates, advisors and experts.

(c) The expenses of each delegation shall be borne by the Contracting Party that has appointed the delegation. The Assembly may ask the World Intellectual Property Organisation (hereinafter referred to as "WIPO") to grant financial assistance to facilitate the participation of delegations of Contracting Parties that are regarded as developing countries in conformity with the established practice of the General Assembly of the United Nations or that are countries in transition to a market economy.

(2)

(a) The Assembly shall deal with matters concerning the maintenance and development of this Treaty and the application and operation of this Treaty.

(b) The Assembly shall perform the function allocated to it under Article 17(2) in respect of the admission of certain intergovernmental organisations to become party to this Treaty.

(c) The Assembly shall decide the convocation of any diplomatic conference for the revision of this Treaty and give the necessary instructions to the Director General of WIPO for the preparation of such diplomatic conference.

(3)

(a) Each Contracting Party that is a State shall have one vote and shall vote only in its own name.

(b) Any Contracting Party that is an intergovernmental organisation may participate in the vote, in place of its Member States, with a number of votes equal to the number of its Member States which are party to this Treaty. No such intergovernmental organisation shall participate in the vote if any one of its Member States exercises its right to vote and vice versa.

(4) The Assembly shall meet in ordinary session once every two years upon convocation by the Director General of WIPO.

(5) The Assembly shall establish its own rules of procedure, including the convocation of extraordinary sessions, the requirements of a quorum and, subject to the provisions of this Treaty, the required majority for various kinds of decisions.

[2670]

Article 16

International Bureau

The International Bureau of WIPO shall perform the administrative tasks concerning the Treaty.

[2671]

Article 17

Eligibility for Becoming Party to the Treaty

(1) Any Member State of WIPO may become party to this Treaty.

(2) The Assembly may decide to admit any intergovernmental organisation to become party to this Treaty which declares that it is competent in respect of, and has its own legislation binding on all its Member States on, matters covered by this Treaty and that it has been duly authorised, in accordance with its internal procedures, to become party to this Treaty.

(3) The European Community, having made the declaration referred to in the preceding paragraph in the Diplomatic Conference that has adopted this Treaty may become party to this Treaty.

[2672]

Article 18

Rights and Obligations under the Treaty

Subject to any specific provisions to the contrary in this Treaty, each Contracting Party shall enjoy all of the rights and assume all of the obligations under this Treaty.

[2673]

Article 19

Signature of the Treaty

This Treaty shall be open for signature until December 31, 1997, by any Member Stare of WIPO and by the European Community.

[2674]

Article 20

Entry into Force of the Treaty

This Treaty shall enter into force three months after 30 instruments of ratification or accession by States have been deposited with the Director General of WIPO.

[2675]

Article 21

Effective Date of Becoming Party to the Treaty

This Treaty shall bind—

(i) the 30 States referred to in Article 20, from the date on which this Treaty has entered into force;

(ii) each other State from the expiration of three months from the date on which the State has deposited its instrument with the Director General of WIPO;

(iii) the European Community, from the expiration of three months after the deposit of its instrument of ratification or accession if such instrument has been deposited after the entry into force of this Treaty according to Article 20, or, three months after the entry into force of this Treaty if such instrument has been deposited before the entry into force of this Treaty;

(iv) any other intergovernmental organisation that is admitted to become party to this Treaty, from the expiration of three months after the deposit of its instrument of accession.

[2676]

Article 22

No Reservations to the Treaty

No reservation to this Treaty shall be admitted.

[2677]

Article 23

Denunciation of the Treaty

This Treaty may be denounced by any Contracting Party by notification addressed to the Director General of WIPO. Any denunciation shall take effect one year from the date on which the Director General of WIPO received the notification.

[2678]

Article 24

Languages of the Treaty

(1) This Treaty is signed in a single original in English, Arabic, Chinese, French, Russian and Spanish languages, the versions in all these languages being equally authentic.

(2) An official text in any language other than those referred to in paragraph (1) shall be established by the Director General of WIPO on the request of an interested party, after consultation with all the interested parties. For the purposes of this paragraph, "interested party" means any Member State of WIPO whose official language, or one of whose official languages, is involved and the European Community, and any other intergovernmental organisation that may become party to this Treaty, if one of its official languages is involved.

[2679]

Article 25

Depositary

The Director General of WIPO is the depositary of this Treaty.

[2680]

WIPO PERFORMANCES AND PHONOGRAMS TREATY

Adopted by the Diplomatic Conference on December 20, 1996

NOTES

The original source for this Treaty is the World Intellectual Property Organisation (WIPO).

PREAMBLE

THE CONTRACTING PARTIES,

Desiring to develop and maintain the protection of the rights of performers and producers of phonograms in a manner as effective and uniform as possible,

Recognising the need to introduce new international rules in order to provide adequate solutions to the questions raised by economic, social, cultural and technological developments,

Recognising the profound impact of the development and convergence of information and communication technologies on the production and use of performances and phonograms,

Recognising the need to maintain a balance between the rights of the performers and producers of phonograms and the larger public interest, particularly education, research and access to information,

HAVE AGREED AS FOLLOWS—

CHAPTER I
GENERAL PROVISIONS

Article 1

Relation to Other Conventions

(1) Nothing in this Treaty shall derogate from existing obligations that Contracting Parties have to each other under the International Convention for the Protection of Performers, Producers of Phonograms and Broadcasting Organisations done in Rome, October 26, 1961 (hereinafter the "Rome Convention").

(2) Protection granted under this Treaty shall leave intact and shall in no way affect the protection of copyright in literary and artistic works. Consequently, no provision of this Treaty may be interpreted as prejudicing such protection.

(3) This Treaty shall not have any connection with, nor shall it prejudice any rights and obligations under, any other treaties.

[2681]

Article 2

Definitions

For the purposes of this Treaty—

(a) "performers" are actors, singers, musicians, dancers, and other persons who act, sing, deliver, declaim, play in, interpret, or otherwise perform literary or artistic works or expressions of folklore;
(b) "phonogram" means the fixation of the sounds of a performance or of other sounds, or of a representation of sounds, other than in the form of a fixation incorporated in a cinematographic or other audiovisual work;
(c) "fixation" means the embodiment of sounds, or of the representations thereof, from which there can be perceived, reproduced or communicated through a device;
(d) "producer of a phonogram" means the person, or the legal entity, who or which takes the initiative and has the responsibility for the first fixation of the sounds of a performance or other sounds, or the representations of sounds;
(e) "publication" of a fixed performance or a phonogram means the offering of copies of the fixed performance or the phonogram to the public, with the consent of the rightholder, and provided that copies are offered to the public in reasonable quantity;
(f) "broadcasting" means the transmission by wireless means for public reception of sounds or of images and sounds or of the representations thereof; such transmission by satellite is also "broadcasting"; transmission of encrypted signals is "broadcasting" where the means for decrypting are provided to the public by the broadcasting organisation or with its consent;
(g) "communication to the public" of a performance or a phonogram means the transmission to the public by any medium, otherwise than by broadcasting, of sounds of a performance or the sounds or the representations of sounds fixed in a phonogram. For the purposes of Article 15, "communication to the public" includes making the sounds or representations of sounds fixed in a phonogram audible to the public.

[2682]

Article 3

Beneficiaries of Protection under this Treaty

(1) Contracting Parties shall accord the protection provided under this Treaty to the performers and producers of phonograms who are nationals of other Contracting Parties.

(2) The nationals of other Contracting Parties shall be understood to be those performers or producers of phonograms who would meet the criteria for eligibility for protection provided under the Rome Convention, were all the Contracting Parties to this Treaty Contracting States of that Convention. In respect of these criteria of eligibility Contracting Parties shall apply the relevant definitions in Article 2 of this Treaty.

(3) Any Contracting Party availing itself of the possibilities provided in Article 5(3) of the Rome Convention or, for the purposes of Article 5 of the same Convention, Article 17 thereof shall make a notification as foreseen in those provisions to the Director General of the World intellectual Property Organisation (WIPO).

[2683]

Article 4

National Treatment

(1) Each Contracting Party shall accord to nationals of other Contracting Parties, as defined in Article 3(2), the treatment it accords to its own nationals with regard to the exclusive rights specifically granted in this Treaty and to the right to equitable remuneration provided for in Article 15 of this Treaty.

(2) The obligation provided for in paragraph (1) does not apply to the extent that another Contracting Party makes use of the reservations permitted by Article 15(3) of this Treaty.

[2684]

CHAPTER II
RIGHT OF PERFORMERS

Article 5

Moral Rights of Performers

(1) Independently of a performer's economic rights, and even after the transfer of those rights, the performer shall, as regards his live aural performances or performances fixed in

phonograms have the right to claim to be identified as the performer of his performances, except where omission is dictated by the manner of the use of the performance, and to object to any distortion, mutilation or other modification of his performances that would be prejudicial to his reputation.

(2) The rights granted to a performer in accordance with paragraph (1) shall, after his death, be maintained, at least until the expiry of the economic rights, and shall be exercisable by the persons or institutions authorised by the legislation of the Contracting Party where protection is claimed. However, those Contracting Parties whose legislation, at the moment of their ratification of or accession to this Treaty, does not provide for protection after the death of the performer of all rights set out in the preceding paragraph may provide that some of these rights will, after his death, cease to be maintained.

(3) The means of redress for safeguarding the rights granted under this Article shall be governed by the legislation of the Contracting Party where protection is claimed.

[2685]

Article 6

Economic Rights of Performers in their Unfixed Performances

Performers shall enjoy the exclusive right of authorising, as regards their performances—

(i) the broadcasting and communication to the public of their unfixed performances except where the performance is already a broadcast performance; and

(ii) the fixation of their unfixed performance.

[2686]

Article 7

Right of Reproduction

Performers shall enjoy the exclusive right of authorising the direct or indirect reproduction of their performances fixed in phonograms, in any manner or form.

[2687]

Article 8

Right of Distribution

(1) Performers shall enjoy the exclusive right of authorising the making available to the public of the original and copies of their performances fixed in phonograms through sale or other transfer of ownership.

(2) Nothing in this Treaty shall affect the freedom of Contracting Parties to determine the conditions, if any, under which the exhaustion of the right in paragraph (1) applies after the first sale or other transfer of ownership of the original or a copy of the fixed performance with the authorisation of the performer.

[2688]

Article 9

Right of Rental

(1) Performers shall enjoy the exclusive right of authorising the commercial rental to the public of the original and copies of their performances fixed in phonograms as determined in the national law of Contracting Parties, even after distribution of them by, or pursuant to, authorisation by the performer.

(2) Notwithstanding the provisions of paragraph (1), a Contracting Party that, on April 15, 1994, had and continues to have in force a system of equitable remuneration of performers for the rental of copies of their performances fixed in phonograms, may maintain that system provided that the commercial rental of phonograms is not giving rise to the material impairment of the exclusive rights of reproduction of performers.

[2689]

Article 10

Right of Making Available of Fixed Performances

Performers shall enjoy the exclusive right of authorising the making available to the public of their performances fixed in phonograms, by wire or wireless means, in such a way that members of the public may access them from a place and at a time individually chosen by them.

[2690]

CHAPTER III
RIGHTS OF PRODUCERS OF PHONOGRAMS

Article 11

Right of Reproduction

Producers of phonograms shall enjoy the exclusive right of authorising the direct or indirect reproduction of their phonograms, in any manner or form.

[2691]

Article 12

Right of Distribution

(1) Producers of phonograms shall enjoy the exclusive right of authorising the making available to the public of the original and copies of their phonograms through sale or other transfer of ownership.

(2) Nothing in this Treaty shall affect the freedom of Contracting Parties to determine the conditions, if any, under which the exhaustion of the right in paragraph (1) applies after the first sale or transfer of ownership of the original or a copy of the phonogram with the authorisation of the producer of the phonograms.

[2692]

Article 13

Right of Rental

(1) Producers of phonograms shall enjoy the exclusive right of authorising the commercial rental to the public of the original and copies of their phonograms, even after distribution of them by or pursuant to authorisation by the producer.

(2) Notwithstanding the provisions of paragraph (1), a Contracting Party that, on April 15, 1994, had and continues to have in force a system of equitable remuneration of producers of phonograms for the rental of copies of their phonograms, may maintain that system provided that the commercial rental of phonograms is not giving rise to the material impairment of the exclusive rights of reproduction of producers of phonograms.

[2693]

Article 14

Right of Making Available of Phonograms

Producers of phonograms shall enjoy the exclusive right of authorising the making available to the public of their phonograms, by wire or wireless means, in such a way that members of the public may access them from a place and at a time individually chosen by them.

[2694]

CHAPTER IV
COMMON PROVISIONS

Article 15

Right to Remuneration for Broadcasting and Communication to the Public

(1) Performers and producers of phonogram shall enjoy the right to a single equitable remuneration for the direct or indirect use of phonograms published for commercial purposes for broadcasting or for any communication to the public.

(2) Contracting Parties may establish in their national legislation that the single equitable remuneration shall be claimed from the user by the performer or by the producer of a phonogram or by both. Contracting Parties may enact national legislation that in the absence of an agreement between the performer and the producer of a phonogram, sets the terms according to which performers and producers of phonograms shall share the single equitable remuneration.

(3) Any Contracting Party may in a notification deposited with the Director General of WIPO, declare that it will apply the provisions of paragraph (1) only in respect of certain uses, or that it will limit their application in some other way, or that it will not apply these provisions at all.

(4) For the purposes of this Article, phonograms made available to the to the public by wire or wireless means in such a way that members of the public may access them from a place and at a time individually chosen by them shall be considered as if they had been published for commercial purposes.

[2695]

Article 16

Limitations and Exceptions

(1) Contracting Parties may, in their national legislation, provide for the same kinds of limitations or exceptions with regard to the protection of performers and producers of phonograms as they provide for, in their national legislation, in connection with the protection of copyright in literary and artistic works.

(2) Contracting Parties shall confine any limitations of or exceptions to rights provided for in this Treaty to certain special cases which do not conflict with a normal exploitation of the performance or phonogram and do not unreasonably prejudice the legitimate interests of the performer or of the producer of the phonograms.

[2696]

Article 17

Term of Protection

(1) The term of protection to be granted to performers under this Treaty shall last, at least, until the end of a period of 50 years computed from the end of the year in which the performance was fixed in a phonogram.

(2) The term of protection to be granted to producers of phonograms under this Treaty shall last, at least, until the end of a period of 50 years computed from the end of the year in which the phonogram was published, or failing such publication within 50 years from fixation of the phonogram, 30 years from the end of the year in which the fixation was made.

[2697]

Article 18

Obligations concerning Technological Measures

Contracting Parties shall provide adequate legal protection and effective legal remedies against the circumvention of effective technological measures that are used by performers or producers of phonograms in connection with the exercise of their rights under this Treaty and that restrict acts, in respect of their performances or phonograms, which are not authorised by the performers or the producers of phonograms concerned or permitted by law.

[2698]

Article 19

Obligations concerning Rights Management Information

(1) Contracting Parties shall provide adequate and effective legal remedies against any person knowingly performing any of the following acts knowing, or with respect to civil remedies, having reasonable grounds to know, that it will induce, enable, facilitate or conceal an infringement of any right covered by this Treaty—

- (i) to remove or alter any electronic rights management information without authority;
- (ii) to distribute, import for distribution, broadcast, communicate or make available to the public, without authority, performances, copies of fixed performances or phonograms knowing that electronic rights management information has been removed or altered without authority.

(2) As used in this Article, "rights management information" means information which identifies the performer, the performance of the performer, the producer of the phonogram, the phonogram, the owner of any right in the performance or phonogram, or information about the terms and conditions of use of the performance or phonogram, and any numbers or codes that represent such information, when any of these items of information is attached to a copy of a fixed performance or a phonogram or appears in connection with the communication or making available of a fixed performance or a phonogram to the public.

[2699]

Article 20

Formalities

The enjoyment and exercise of the rights provided for in this Treaty shall not be subject to any formality.

[2700]

Article 21

Reservations

Subject to the provisions of Article 15(3), no reservations to this Treaty shall be permitted.

[2701]

Article 22

Application in Time

(1) Contracting Parties shall apply the provisions of Article 15(3) of the Berne Convention, *mutatis mutandis,* to the rights of performers and producers of phonograms provided for in this Treaty.

(2) Notwithstanding paragraph (1), a Contracting Party may limit the application of Article 5 of this Treaty to performances which occurred after the entry into force of this Treaty for that Party.

[2702]

Article 23

Provisions on Enforcement of Rights

(1) Contracting Parties undertake to adopt, in accordance with their legal systems, the measures necessary to ensure the application of this Treaty.

(2) Contracting Parties shall ensure that enforcement procedures are available under their law so as to permit effective action against any act of infringement of rights covered by this Treaty, including expeditious remedies to prevent infringements and remedies which constitute a deterrent to further infringements.

[2703]

CHAPTER V
ADMINISTRATIVE AND FINAL CLAUSES

Article 24

Assembly

(1)

(a) The Contracting Parties shall have an Assembly.
(b) Each Contracting Party shall be represented by one delegate who may be assisted by alternate delegates, advisors and experts.
(c) The expenses of each delegation shall be borne by the Contracting Party that has appointed the delegation. The Assembly may ask WIPO to grant financial assistance to facilitate the participation of delegations of Contracting Parties that are regarded as developing countries in conformity with the established practice of the General Assembly of the United Nations or that are countries in transition to a market economy.

(2)

(a) The Assembly shall deal with matters concerning the maintenance and development of this Treaty and the application and operation of this Treaty.
(b) The Assembly shall perform the function allocated to it under Article 26(2) in respect of the admission of certain intergovernmental organisations to become party to this Treaty.
(c) The Assembly shall decide the convocation of any diplomatic conference for the revision of this Treaty and give the necessary instructions to the Director General of WIPO for the preparation of such diplomatic conference.

(3)
(a) Each Contracting Party that is a State shall have one vote and shall vote only in its own name.
(b) Any Contracting Party that is an intergovernmental organisation may participate in the vote, in place of its Member States, with a number of votes equal to the number of its Member States which are party to this Treaty. No such intergovernmental organisation shall participate in the vote if any one of its Member States exercises its right to vote and vice versa.

(4) The Assembly shall meet in ordinary session once every two years upon convocation by the Director General of WIPO.

(5) The Assembly shall establish its own rules of procedure, including the convocation of extraordinary sessions, the requirements of a quorum and, subject to the provisions of this Treaty, the required majority for various kinds of decisions.

[2704]

Article 25

International Bureau

The International Bureau of WIPO shall perform the administrative tasks concerning the Treaty.

[2705]

Article 26

Eligibility for Becoming Party to the Treaty

(1) Any Member State of WIPO may become party to this Treaty.

(2) The Assembly may decide to admit any intergovernmental organisation to become party to this Treaty which declares that it is competent in respect of, and has its own legislation binding on all its Member States on, matters covered by this Treaty and that it has been duly authorised, in accordance with its internal procedures, to become party to this Treaty.

(3) The European Community, having made the declaration referred to in the preceding paragraph in the Diplomatic Conference that has adopted this Treaty may become party to this Treaty.

[2706]

Article 27

Rights and Obligations under the Treaty

Subject to any specific provisions to the contrary in this Treaty, each Contracting Party shall enjoy all of the rights and assume all of the obligations under this Treaty.

[2707]

Article 28

Signature of the Treaty

This Treaty shall be open for signature until December 31, 1997, by any Member State of WIPO and by the European Community.

[2708]

Article 29

Entry into Force of the Treaty

This Treaty shall enter into force three months after 30 instruments of ratification or accession by States have been deposited with the Director General of WIPO.

[2709]

Article 30

Effective Date of Becoming Party to the Treaty

This Treaty shall bind—

(i) the 30 States referred to in Article 29, from the date on which this Treaty has entered into force;

(ii) each other State from the expiration of three months from the date on which the State has deposited its instrument with the Director General of WIPO;

(iii) the European Community, from the expiration of three months after the deposit of its instrument of ratification or accession if such instrument has been deposited after the entry into force of this Treaty according to Article 29, on three months after the entry into force of this Treaty if such instrument has been deposited before the entry into force of this Treaty;

(iv) any other intergovernmental organisation that is admitted to become party to this Treaty, from the expiration of three months after the deposit of its instrument of accession.

[2710]

Article 31

Denunciation of the Treaty

This Treaty may be denounced by any Contracting Party by notification addressed to the Director General of WIPO. Any denunciation shall take effect one year from the date on which the Director General of WIPO received the notification.

[2711]

Article 32

Languages of the Treaty

(1) This Treaty is signed in a single original in English, Arabic, Chinese, French, Russian and Spanish languages, the versions in all these languages being equally authentic.

(2) An official text in any language other than those referred to in paragraph (1) shall be established by the Director General of WIPO on the request of an interested party, after consultation with all the interested parties. For the purposes of this paragraph, "interested party" means any Member State of WIPO whose official language, or one of whose official languages, is involved and the European Community, and any other intergovernmental organisation that may become party to this Treaty if one of its official languages is involved.

[2712]

Article 33

Depositary

The Director General of WIPO is the depositary of this Treaty.

[2713]–[3000]

PART V
BROADCASTING AND TRANSMISSION

MARINE, &C, BROADCASTING (OFFENCES) ACT 1967

(1967 c 41)

ARRANGEMENT OF SECTIONS

An Act to suppress broadcasting from ships, aircraft and certain marine structures

[14 July 1967]

1 Prohibition of broadcasting from ships and aircraft

(*1*) *It shall not be lawful for a broadcast to be made from a ship or aircraft while it is in or over the United Kingdom or external waters, nor shall it be lawful for a broadcast to be made from a ship registered in the United Kingdom, the Isle of Man or any of the Channel Islands or an aircraft so registered while the ship or aircraft is elsewhere than in or over the United Kingdom or external waters.*

(*2*) *If a broadcast is made from a ship in contravention of the foregoing subsection, the owner of the ship, the master of the ship and every person who operates, or participates in the operation of, the apparatus by means of which the broadcast is made shall be guilty of an offence; and if a broadcast is made from an aircraft in contravention of that subsection, the operator of the aircraft, the commander of the aircraft and every person who operates, or participates in the operation of, the apparatus by means of which the broadcast is made shall be guilty of an offence.*

(*3*) *A person who procures the making of a broadcast in contravention of subsection* (*1*) *above shall be guilty of an offence.*

(*4*) *In subsection* (*2*) *above—*
- (*a*) *"master", in relation to a ship, includes any other person* (*except a pilot*) *having command or charge of the ship;*
- (*b*) *"operator", in relation to an aircraft, means the person for the time being having the management of the aircraft.*

[3001]

NOTES

Whole Act repealed by the Wireless Telegraphy Act 2006, s 125(1), Sch 9, Pt 1, subject to transitional provisions and savings in s 124 of, Sch 8, Pt 1, paras 1–8, 24 to, that Act at **[4230]**, **[4239]**.

2 Prohibition of broadcasting from marine structures

(*1*) *It shall not be lawful for a broadcast to be made from—*
- (*a*) *a structure in [any waters to which this section applies], being a structure affixed to, or supported by, the bed of those waters and not being a ship; or*
- (*b*) *any other object in such waters, being neither a structure affixed or supported as aforesaid nor a ship or aircraft;*

and if a broadcast is made in contravention of the foregoing provision, every person who operates, or participates in the operation of, the apparatus by means of which the broadcast is made shall be guilty of an offence.

(2) A person who procures the making of a broadcast in contravention of the foregoing subsection shall be guilty of an offence.

[(3) This section applies to—
(a) tidal waters in the United Kingdom;
(b) external waters; and
(c) waters in a designated area within the meaning of the Continental Shelf Act 1964.]

[3002]

NOTES

Repealed as noted to s 1 at **[3001]**.
Sub-s (1): words in square brackets substituted by the Broadcasting Act 1990, s 171, Sch 16, para 1.
Sub-s (3): added by the Broadcasting Act 1990, s 171, Sch 16, para 1.

[2A Unlawful broadcasting from within prescribed areas of the high seas

(1) Subject to subsection (4) below, it shall not be lawful to make a broadcast which—
(a) is made from a ship (other than one registered in the United Kingdom, the Isle of Man or any of the Channel Islands) while the ship is within any area of the high seas prescribed for the purposes of this section by an order made by the Secretary of State; and
(b) is capable of being received in, or causes interference with any wireless telegraphy in, the United Kingdom.

(2) If a broadcast is made from a ship in contravention of subsection (1) above, the owner of the ship, the master of the ship and every person who operates, or participates in the operation of, the apparatus by means of which the broadcast is made shall be guilty of an offence.

(3) A person who procures the making of a broadcast in contravention of subsection (1) above shall be guilty of an offence.

(4) The making of a broadcast does not contravene subsection (1) above if it is shown to have been authorised under the law of any country or territory outside the United Kingdom.

(5) Any order under this section shall be made by statutory instrument subject to annulment in pursuance of a resolution of either House of Parliament.]

[3003]

NOTES

Repealed as noted to s 1 at **[3001]**.
Inserted by the Broadcasting Act 1990, s 171, Sch 16, para 2.
Orders: the Marine, etc, Broadcasting (Offences) (Prescribed Areas of the High Seas) Order 1990, SI 1990/2503 at **[3464]**.

3 Prohibition of acts connected with broadcasting from certain ships and aircraft, and from marine structures outside United Kingdom

(1) [Subject to subsection (1A) below,] if a broadcast is made—
(a) from a ship other than one registered in the United Kingdom, the Isle of Man or any of the Channel Islands while the ship is on the high seas; or
(b) from an aircraft other than one so registered while the aircraft is on or over the high seas; or
(c) from a structure on the high seas, being a structure affixed to, or supported by, the bed of those seas and not being a ship; or
(d) from any object on those seas, being neither a structure affixed or supported as aforesaid nor a ship or aircraft;

any of the persons mentioned in subsection (3) below who operates, or participates in the operation of, the apparatus by means of which the broadcast is made shall be guilty of an offence.

[(1A) Subsection (1)(a) above does not apply to any broadcast made in contravention of section 2A(1) of this Act, and subsections (1)(c) and (d) above do not apply to structures or other objects in waters falling within section 2(3)(c) of this Act.]

(2) A person who procures a broadcast to be made as mentioned in the foregoing subsection shall be guilty of an offence.

(3) The persons referred to in subsection (1) above are the following, namely—

[(a) a British citizen, a [British overseas territories citizen][, a British National (Overseas)] or a British Overseas citizen; or

(b) a person who under the British Nationality Act 1981 is a British subject; or

(c) a British protected person (within the meaning of that Act)].

[3004]

NOTES

Repealed as noted to s 1 at **[3001]**.

Sub-s (1): words in square brackets inserted by the Broadcasting Act 1990, s 171, Sch 16, para 3.

Sub-s (1A): inserted by the Broadcasting Act 1990, s 171, Sch 16, para 3.

Sub-s (3): paras (a)–(c) substituted for original paras (a)–(e) by the British Nationality Act 1981, s 52(6), Sch 7; words in first pair of square brackets in para (a) substituted by virtue of the British Overseas Territories Act 2002, s 2(3); words in second pair of square brackets in para (a) inserted by the Hong Kong (British Nationality) Order 1986, SI 1986/948, art 8, Schedule.

[3A Prohibition of management of stations broadcasting from ships, aircraft etc

(1) Any person who, from any place in the United Kingdom or external waters, participates in the management, financing, operation or day-to-day running of any broadcasting station by which broadcasts are made—

(a) in contravention of section 1, 2 or 2A(1) of this Act, or

(b) as mentioned in section 3(1)(a) of this Act,

shall be guilty of an offence.

(2) In this section "broadcasting station" means any business or other operation (whether or not in the nature of a commercial venture) which is engaged in the making of broadcasts.]

[3005]

NOTES

Repealed as noted to s 1 at **[3001]**.

Inserted by the Broadcasting Act 1990, s 171, Sch 16, para 4.

4 Prohibition of acts facilitating broadcasting from ships, aircraft, etc

(1) A person who does any of the acts mentioned in subsection (3) below, while satisfying the condition as to knowledge or belief mentioned in the case of that act, shall be guilty of an offence if—

(a) he does the act in the United Kingdom or external waters or in a ship registered in the United Kingdom, the Isle of Man or any of the Channel Islands or an aircraft so registered while the ship or aircraft is elsewhere than in or over the United Kingdom or external waters; or

[(aa) where paragraph (a) above does not apply but the broadcasts in question are made, or are to be made, from any structure or other object (not being a ship or aircraft) in waters falling within section 2(3)(c) of this Act, he does the act on that structure or other object within those waters; or

(ab) where paragraph (a) above does not apply but the broadcasts in question are made, or are to be made, from a ship in contravention of section 2A(1) of this Act, he does the act in that ship within any such area of the high seas as is mentioned in paragraph (a) of that provision; or]

(b) being a person mentioned in section 3(3) of this Act, he does the act on or over the high seas.

(2) A person who, in the United Kingdom, procures another person to do, outside the United Kingdom, anything which, if it had been done in the United Kingdom by the last-mentioned person, would have constituted an offence under the foregoing subsection, shall be guilty of an offence.

(3) The acts, and conditions as to knowledge or belief, referred to in subsection (1) above are the following, namely:—

(a) furnishing or agreeing to furnish to another a ship or aircraft knowing, or having reasonable cause to believe, that broadcasts are to be made from it in contravention of section 1(1) of this Act or while it is on or over the high seas;

(b) carrying or agreeing to carry in a ship or aircraft wireless telegraphy apparatus

knowing, or having reasonable cause to believe, that by means thereof broadcasts are to be made from the ship or aircraft as aforesaid;

(*c*) *supplying to, or installing in, a ship or aircraft wireless telegraphy apparatus knowing, or having reasonable cause to believe, that by means thereof broadcasts are to be made from the ship or aircraft as aforesaid;*

(*d*) *supplying any wireless telegraphy apparatus for installation on or in, or installing any such apparatus on or in, any structure or other object (not being, in either case, a ship or aircraft) knowing, or having reasonable cause to believe, that by means of that apparatus broadcasts are to be made from the object in contravention of section 2(1) of this Act or while the object is on the high seas;*

(*e*) *repairing or maintaining any wireless telegraphy apparatus knowing, or having reasonable cause to believe, that, by means thereof, broadcasts are made, or are to be made, in contravention of section 1(1)[, 2(1) or 2A(1)] of this Act or as mentioned in section 3(1) of this Act;*

(*f*) *knowing, or having reasonable cause to believe, in the case of a ship or aircraft, that broadcasts are made, or are to be made, from it in contravention of section 1(1) of this Act or while it is on or over the high seas—*

(*i*) *supplying any goods or materials for its operation or maintenance, for the operation or maintenance of wireless telegraphy apparatus installed therein or for the sustentation or comfort of the persons on board of it;*

(*ii*) *carrying by water or air goods or persons to or from it;*

(*iii*) *engaging a person as an officer or one of the crew of it;*

(*g*) *knowing, or having reasonable cause to believe, in the case of a structure or other object (not being, in either case, a ship or aircraft), that broadcasts are made, or are to be made, from it in contravention of section 2(1) of this Act or while it is on the high seas—*

(*i*) *supplying any goods or materials for its maintenance, for the operation or maintenance of wireless telegraphy apparatus installed therein or thereon or for the sustentation or comfort of the persons therein or thereon;*

(*ii*) *carrying by water or air goods or persons thereto or therefrom;*

(*iii*) *engaging a person to render services therein or thereon.*

[(3A) Section 46 of the Consumer Protection Act 1987 (meaning of supply) shall have effect for construing references in this section to the supply of any thing as it has effect for the purpose of construing references in that Act to the supply of goods.]

[3006]

NOTES

Repealed as noted to s 1 at **[3001]**.

Sub-s (1): paras (aa), (ab) inserted by the Broadcasting Act 1990, s 171, Sch 16, para 5(1), (2).

Sub-s (3): words in square brackets in para (e) substituted by the Broadcasting Act 1990, s 171, Sch 16, para 5(1), (3).

Sub-s (3A): added by the Communications Act 2003, s 406(1), Sch 17, para 32.

5 Prohibition of acts relating to matter broadcast from ships, aircraft, etc

(1) A person who does any of the acts mentioned in subsection (3) below, and, if any intent or circumstances is or are specified in relation to the act, does it with that intent or in those circumstances, shall be guilty of an offence if—

(*a*) *he does the act in the United Kingdom or external waters or in a ship registered in the United Kingdom, the Isle of Man or any of the Channel Islands or an aircraft so registered while the ship or aircraft is elsewhere than in or over the United Kingdom or external waters; or*

[(aa) where paragraph (a) above does not apply but the broadcasts in question are made, or are to be made, from any structure or other object (not being a ship or aircraft) in waters falling within section 2(3)(c) of this Act, he does the act on that structure or other object within those waters; or

(ab) where paragraph (a) above does not apply but the broadcasts in question are made, or are to be made, from a ship in contravention of section 2A(1) of this Act, he does the act in that ship within any such area of the high seas as is mentioned in paragraph (a) of that provision; or]

(*b*) *being a person mentioned in section 3(3) of this Act he does the act on or over the high seas.*

(2) *A person who, in the United Kingdom, procures another person to do, outside the United Kingdom, anything which, if it had been done in the United Kingdom by the last-mentioned person, would have constituted an offence under the foregoing subsection, shall be guilty of an offence.*

(3) *The acts, and, where relevant, the intent and circumstances, referred to in subsection (1) above are the following namely:—*

(*a*) *supplying a [film or sound recording [knowing, or having reasonable cause to believe, that a broadcast of the work is to]] be made in contravention of section 1(1)[, 2(1) or 2A(1)] of this Act or as mentioned in section 3(1) thereof;*

(*b*) *making a literary, dramatic or musical work [knowing, or having reasonable cause to believe, that a broadcast of the work is to] be made as aforesaid;*

(*c*) *making an artistic work [knowing, or having reasonable cause to believe, that a broadcast of the work is to] be included in a television broadcast made as aforesaid;*

(*d*) *participating in a broadcast made as aforesaid, being actually present as an announcer, as a performer or one of the performers concerned in an entertainment given, or as the deliverer of a speech;*

(*e*) *advertising by means of a broadcast made as aforesaid or inviting another to advertise by means of a broadcast to be so made;*

(*f*) *publishing the times or other details of any broadcasts which are to be so made, or (otherwise than by publishing such details) publishing an advertisement of matter calculated to promote, directly or indirectly, the interests of a business whose activities consist in or include the operation of a station from which broadcasts are or are to be so made.*

[(3A) Section 46 of the Consumer Protection Act 1987 (meaning of supply) shall have effect for construing references in this section to the supply of any thing as it has effect for the purpose of construing references in that Act to the supply of goods.]

[(4) The cases in which a person is to be taken for the purposes of this section as advertising by means of a broadcast include any case in which he causes or allows it to be stated, suggested or implied that entertainment included in the broadcast—

(*a*) *has been supplied by him; or*

(*b*) *is provided wholly or partly at his expense.]*

(5) *For the purposes of this section advertising by means of a broadcast shall be deemed to take place as well wherever the broadcast is received as where it is made.*

(6) *In this section "speech" includes lecture, address and sermon, [and "film", "sound recording", "literary, dramatic or musical work" and "artistic work" have the same meanings as in Part I of the Copyright, Designs and Patents Act 1988 (copyright)].*

[3007]

NOTES

Repealed as noted to s 1 at **[3001]**.

Sub-s (1): paras (aa), (ab) inserted by the Broadcasting Act 1990, s 171(1), (2), Sch 16, para 6(1), (2).

Sub-s (3): words in first (outer) pair of square brackets in para (a) substituted by the Copyright, Designs and Patents Act 1988, s 303(1), Sch 7, para 9; words in second (inner) pair of square brackets in para (a) and words in square brackets in paras (b), (c) substituted by the Communications Act 2003, s 406(1), Sch 17, para 33(1), (2); words in third pair of square brackets in para (a) substituted by the Broadcasting Act 1990, s 171, Sch 16, para 6(1), (3).

Sub-s (3A): inserted by the Communications Act 2003, s 406(1), Sch 17, para 32.

Sub-s (4): substituted by the Communications Act 2003, s 406(1), Sch 17, para 33(1), (3).

Sub-s (6): words in square brackets substituted by the Copyright, Designs and Patents Act 1988, s 303(1), Sch 7, para 9.

6 Penalties and legal proceedings

(1) *A person guilty of an offence under this Act shall be liable—*

(*a*) *on summary conviction, to imprisonment for a term not exceeding [six] months or to a fine not exceeding [the prescribed sum], or to both;*

(*b*) *on conviction on indictment, to imprisonment for a term not exceeding two years or to a fine, or to both.*

(2) …

(3) Proceedings for an offence under this Act may be taken, and the offence may for all incidental purposes be treated as having been committed, in any place in the United Kingdom.

(4) Notwithstanding anything in any enactment relating to courts of summary jurisdiction, summary proceedings for an offence under this Act may be instituted at any time within two years from the time when the offence was committed.

(5) Proceedings for an offence under this Act shall not, in England or Wales, be instituted otherwise than [by OFCOM or] by or [with the consent of the Secretary of State or] the Director of Public Prosecutions and shall not, in Northern Ireland, be instituted otherwise than [by OFCOM or] by or [with the consent of the Secretary of State or] the Attorney General for Northern Ireland; …

(6) A member of a police force shall, for the purpose of the enforcement of this Act, have in external waters all the powers, protection and privileges which he has in the area for which he acts as constable.

(7) …

(8) In the application of this section to Northern Ireland, the following subsection shall be substituted for subsection (6)—

> *"(6) A member of the [Police Service of Northern Ireland] shall, for the purpose of the enforcement of this Act, have in external waters all the powers, protection and privileges which he has in Northern Ireland".*

[3008]

NOTES

Repealed as noted to s 1 at **[3001]**.

Sub-s (1): number in first pair of square brackets substituted by the Broadcasting Act 1990, s 171, Sch 16, para 7(1), (2), and words in second pair of square brackets substituted by virtue of the Magistrates' Courts Act 1980, s 32(2).

Sub-ss (2), (7): repealed by the Communications Act 2003, s 406(7), Sch 19(1).

Sub-s (5): words in first and third pairs of square brackets inserted by the Communications Act 2003, s 406(1), Sch 17, para 34; words in second and fourth pairs of square brackets substituted by the Broadcasting Act 1990, s 171, Sch 16, para 7(1), (3); words omitted repealed by the Criminal Jurisdiction Act 1975, s 14(5), Sch 6, Pt I; for the words "Attorney General for Northern Ireland" there are substituted the words "Advocate General for Northern Ireland" by the Justice (Northern Ireland) Act 2002, s 28(1), Sch 7, para 25, as from a day to be appointed.

Sub-s (8): words in square brackets substituted by the Police (Northern Ireland) Act 2000, s 78(2)(f).

7 Special defence available in proceedings for carrying goods or persons in contravention of section 4

(1) In any proceedings against a person for an offence under section 4 of this Act consisting in the carriage of goods or persons to or from a ship or aircraft it shall be a defence for him to prove—

- *(a) that the ship or aircraft was, or was believed to be, wrecked, stranded or in distress, and that the goods or persons carried were carried for the purpose of preserving the ship or aircraft, or its cargo or apparel, or saving the lives of persons on board of it; or*
- *(b) that a person on board of the ship or aircraft was, or was believed to be, suffering from hurt, injury or illness, and that the goods or persons were carried for the purpose of securing that the necessary surgical or medical advice and attendance were rendered to him.*

(2) In any proceedings against a person for an offence under section 4 of this Act consisting in the carriage of goods or persons to or from an object other than a ship or aircraft it shall be a defence for him to prove—

- *(a) that the object was, or was believed to be, unsafe, and that the goods or persons carried were carried for the purpose of saving the lives of persons therein or thereon; or*
- *(b) that a person therein or thereon was, or was believed to be, suffering from hurt, injury or illness, and that the goods or persons were carried for the purpose of securing that the necessary surgical or medical advice and attendance were rendered to him.*

(3) In any proceedings against a person for an offence under section 4 of this Act consisting in the carriage of a person to or from a ship or aircraft or to or from an object

other than a ship or aircraft, it shall be a defence for him to prove that the person carried was visiting the ship, aircraft or object, as the case may be, for the purpose of exercising or performing any power or duty conferred or imposed on him by law.

(*4*) *The references in subsections (1)(a) and (2)(a) above to persons having been carried for the purpose of saving lives shall not be construed so as to exclude the persons whose lives it was the purpose to save and the references in subsections (1)(b) and (2)(b) above to persons having been carried as therein mentioned shall not be construed so as to exclude the person who was, or was believed to be, suffering as so mentioned.*

[3009]

NOTES

Repealed as noted to s 1 at **[3001]**.

[7A Powers of enforcement in relation to marine offences under this Act

(*1*) *The following persons are enforcement officers for the purposes of this section—*

(*a*) *persons authorised by the Secretary of State [or OFCOM] to exercise the powers conferred by subsection (5) below;*

(*b*) *police officers;*

(*c*) *commissioned officers of Her Majesty's armed forces;*

(*d*) *officers commissioned by the Commissioners of Customs and Excise under section 6(3) of the Customs and Excise Management Act 1979; and*

(*e*) *persons not falling within any of the preceding paragraphs who are British sea-fishery officers by virtue of section 7(1) of the Sea Fisheries Act 1968;*

and in this subsection "armed forces" means the Royal Navy, the Royal Marines, the regular army and the regular air force, and any reserve or auxiliary force of any of those services which has been called out on permanent service, ... , or embodied.

(2) *If an enforcement officer has reasonable grounds for suspecting—*

(*a*) *that an offence under this Act has been or is being committed by the making of a broadcast from any ship, structure or other object in external waters or in tidal waters in the United Kingdom or from a ship registered in the United Kingdom, the Isle of Man or any of the Channel Islands while on the high seas,*

(*b*) *that an offence under section 2 of this Act has been or is being committed by the making of a broadcast from a structure or other object in waters falling within subsection (3)(c) of that section, or*

(*c*) *that an offence under section 2A of this Act has been or is being committed by the making of a broadcast from a ship,*

and [a written authorisation has been issued by the Secretary of State or OFCOM] for the exercise of the powers conferred by subsection (5) below in relation to that ship, structure or other object, then (subject to subsections (6) and (7) below) the officer may, with or without persons assigned to assist him in his duties, so exercise those powers.

(*3*) *If—*

(*a*) *[an authorisation has been issued by the Secretary of State or OFCOM] under subsection (2) above for the exercise of the powers conferred by subsection (5) below in relation to any ship, structure or other object, and*

(*b*) *an enforcement officer has reasonable grounds for suspecting that an offence under section 4 or 5 of this Act has been or is being committed in connection with the making of a broadcast from that ship, structure or other object,*

then (subject to subsections (6) and (7) below) the officer may, with or without persons assigned to assist him in his duties, also exercise those powers in relation to any ship, structure or other object which he has reasonable grounds to suspect has been or is being used in connection with the commission of that offence.

(*4*) *Where—*

(*a*) *an enforcement officer has reasonable grounds for suspecting that an offence under section 4 or 5 of this Act has been or is being committed in connection with the making of a broadcast from a ship, structure or other object, but*

(*b*) *an authorisation has not been issued under subsection (2) above for the exercise of the powers conferred by subsection (5) below in relation to that ship, structure or other object,*

then (subject to subsections (6) and (7) below) the officer may, with or without persons assigned to assist him in his duties, nevertheless exercise those powers in relation to any ship, structure or other object which he has reasonable grounds to suspect has been or is being used in connection with the commission of that offence if [a written authorisation has been issued by the Secretary of State or OFCOM] for the exercise of those powers in relation to that ship, structure or other object.

(5) The powers conferred by this subsection on an enforcement officer in relation to any ship, structure or other object are—

- *(a) to board and search the ship, structure or other object;*
- *(b) to seize and detain the ship, structure or other object and any apparatus or other thing found in the course of the search which appears to him to have been used, or to have been intended to be used, in connection with, or to be evidence of, the commission of the suspected offence;*
- *(c) to arrest and search any person who he has reasonable grounds to suspect has committed or is committing an offence under this Act if—*
  - *(i) that person is on board the ship, structure or other object, or*
  - *(ii) the officer has reasonable grounds for suspecting that that person was so on board at, or shortly before, the time when the officer boarded the ship, structure or other object;*
- *(d) to arrest any person who assaults him, or a person assigned to assist him in his duties, while exercising any of the powers conferred by this subsection or who intentionally obstructs him or any such person in the exercise of any of those powers;*
- *(e) to require any person on board the ship, structure or other object to produce any documents or other items which are in his custody or possession and are or may be evidence of the commission of any offence under this Act;*
- *(f) to require any such person to do anything for the purpose of facilitating the exercise of any of the powers conferred by this subsection, including enabling any apparatus or other thing to be rendered safe and, in the case of a ship, enabling the ship to be taken to a port;*
- *(g) to use reasonable force, if necessary, in exercising any of those powers;*

and references in paragraphs (a) to (c) and (e) above to the ship, structure or other object include references to any ship's boat or other vessel used from the ship, structure or other object.

(6) Except as provided in subsection (7) below, the powers conferred by subsection (5) above shall only be exercised in tidal waters in the United Kingdom or in external waters.

(7) Those powers [except so far as exercisable by virtue of an authorisation issued by OFCOM] may in addition—

- *(a) in relation to a suspected offence under this Act committed in a ship registered in the United Kingdom, the Isle of Man or any of the Channel Islands while on the high seas, be exercised in relation to that ship on the high seas;*
- *(b) in relation to a suspected offence under section 2 of this Act committed on a structure or other object within waters falling within subsection (3)(c) of that section, be exercised in relation to that structure or other object within those waters; and*
- *(c) in relation to a suspected offence under section 2A of this Act committed in a ship within any such area of the high seas as is mentioned in subsection (1)(a) of that section, be exercised in relation to that ship within that area of the high seas.*

(8) Any person who—

- *(a) assaults an enforcement officer, or a person assigned to assist him in his duties, while exercising any of the powers conferred by subsection (5) above or intentionally obstructs him or any such person in the exercise of any of those powers, or*
- *(b) without reasonable excuse fails or refuses to comply with any such requirement as is mentioned in paragraph (e) or (f) of that subsection,*

shall be guilty of an offence under this Act.

(9) Neither an enforcement officer nor a person assigned to assist him in his duties shall be liable in any civil or criminal proceedings for anything done in purported exercise of any of the powers conferred by subsection (5) above if the court is satisfied that the act was done in good faith and that there were reasonable grounds for doing it.

(10) Nothing in this section shall have effect so as to prejudice the exercise of any powers exercisable apart from this section.

(11) Any reference in this section, in relation to a person assigned to assist an enforcement officer in his duties, to the exercise of any of the powers conferred by subsection (5) above is a reference to the exercise by that person of any of those powers on behalf of that officer.]

[3010]

NOTES

Repealed as noted to s 1 at **[3001]**.

Inserted by the Broadcasting Act 1990, s 171, Sch 16, para 8.

Sub-s (1): words in square brackets inserted by the Communications Act 2003, s 406(1), Sch 17, para 35(1), (2); words omitted repealed by the Reserve Forces Act 1996 (Consequential Provisions etc) Regulations 1998, SI 1998/3086, reg 10(2).

Sub-ss (2)–(4): words in square brackets substituted by the Communications Act 2003, s 406(1), Sch 17, para 35(1), (3), (4).

Sub-s (7): words in square brackets inserted by the Communications Act 2003, s 406(1), Sch 17, para 35(1), (5).

8 Saving for things done under wireless telegraphy licence

Nothing in this Act shall render it unlawful to do anything under and in accordance with a wireless telegraphy licence, or to procure anything to be so done.

[3011]

NOTES

Repealed as noted to s 1 at **[3001]**.

9 Interpretation

(1) In this Act—

"broadcast" means a broadcast by wireless telegraphy of sounds or visual images intended for general reception (whether the sounds or images are actually received by any person or not), but does not include a broadcast consisting in a message or signal sent in connection with navigation or for the purpose of securing safety;

"external waters" means the whole of the sea adjacent to the United Kingdom which is within the seaward limits of the territorial waters adjacent thereto;

"the high seas" means the seas outside the seaward limits of the territorial waters adjacent to the United Kingdom or to any country or territory outside the United Kingdom;

["OFCOM" means the Office of Communications;]

"ship" includes every description of vessel used in navigation;

"wireless telegraphy", "wireless telegraphy apparatus" and "wireless telegraphy licence" have the same meanings respectively as in the Wireless Telegraphy Act 1949.

(2) …

[3012]

NOTES

Repealed as noted to s 1 at **[3001]**.

Sub-s (1): definition "OFCOM" inserted by the Communications Act 2003, s 406(1), Sch 17, para 36.

Sub-s (2): repealed by the Territorial Sea Act 1987, s 3(4), Sch 2.

10 Power to extend Act to Isle of Man and Channel Islands

(1) Her Majesty may by Order in Council direct that this Act shall extend to the Isle of Man or any of the Channel Islands, with such exceptions, adaptations and modifications as may be specified in the Order.

(2) An Order in Council under this section may be varied or revoked by a subsequent Order of Her Majesty in Council.

[3013]

NOTES

Repealed as noted to s 1 at **[3001]**.

Orders in Council: the Marine, &c, Broadcasting (Offences) (Guernsey) Order 1967, SI 1967/1274; the Marine, &c, Broadcasting (Offences) (Jersey) Order 1967, SI 1967/1275; the Marine, &c, Broadcasting

(Offences) (Isle of Man) Order 1967, SI 1967/1276; the Wireless Telegraphy (Guernsey) Order 1994, SI 1994/1064; the Wireless Telegraphy (Isle of Man) Order 1995, SI 1995/268.

11 Short title and commencement

(*1*) *This Act may be cited as the Marine, &c, Broadcasting* (*Offences*) *Act 1967.*

(*2*) *This Act shall not come into operation before the expiry of one month beginning with the day on which it is passed, but subject thereto it shall come into operation on a day to be appointed by Her Majesty in Council.*

[3014]

NOTES

Repealed as noted to s 1 at **[3001]**.

BROADCASTING ACT 1990

(1990 c 42)

ARRANGEMENT OF SECTIONS

PART I
INDEPENDENT TELEVISION SERVICES

CHAPTER V
ADDITIONAL SERVICES PROVIDED ON
TELEVISION BROADCASTING FREQUENCIES

CHAPTER VII
SUPPLEMENTAL

PART III
INDEPENDENT RADIO SERVICES

CHAPTER I
REGULATION BY AUTHORITY OF
INDEPENDENT RADIO SERVICES GENERALLY

Function of OFCOM

General provisions about licences

Prohibition on providing unlicensed independent radio services

CHAPTER II
SOUND BROADCASTING SERVICES

National services

Local and other services

Miscellaneous provisions relating to national and local services

Enforcement of licences

CHAPTER IV
ADDITIONAL SERVICES PROVIDED ON
SOUND BROADCASTING FREQUENCIES

PART VI
THE BROADCASTING STANDARDS COUNCIL

PART X
MISCELLANEOUS AND GENERAL

Television licensing

General

An Act to make new provision with respect to the provision and regulation of independent television and sound programme services and of other services provided on television or radio frequencies; to make provision with respect to the provision and regulation of local delivery services; to amend in other respects the law relating to broadcasting and the provision of television and sound programme services and to make provision with respect to the supply and use of information about programmes; to make provision with respect to the transfer of the property, rights and liabilities of the Independent Broadcasting Authority and the Cable Authority and the dissolution of those bodies; to make new provision relating to the Broadcasting Complaints Commission; to provide for the establishment and functions of a Broadcasting Standards Council; to amend the Wireless Telegraphy Acts 1949 to 1967 and the Marine, &c, Broadcasting (Offences) Act 1967; to revoke a class licence granted under the Telecommunications Act 1984 to run broadcast relay systems; and for connected purposes

[1 November 1990]

PART I
INDEPENDENT TELEVISION SERVICES

1–47 ((*Chs I–IV*) *outside the scope of this work.*)

CHAPTER V
ADDITIONAL SERVICES PROVIDED ON TELEVISION BROADCASTING FREQUENCIES

48 Additional services

(1) In this Part "additional service" means any service which consists in the sending of [electronic] signals for transmission by wireless telegraphy by means of the use of the spare capacity within the signals carrying any television broadcasting service provided [on a relevant frequency].

(2) For the purposes of this Part the spare capacity within the signals carrying any such broadcasting service shall be taken to be [any part of the signals which—

(a) is not required for the purposes of the television broadcasting service for the purposes of which the frequency has been made available; and

(b) is determined by OFCOM to be available for the provision of additional services;]

and references in this Part to spare capacity shall be construed accordingly.

[(2A) For the purposes of this Part, if they consider it appropriate to do so, OFCOM may, while an additional services licence is in force, from time to time modify the determination made under subsection (2)(b) for the purposes of that licence in any manner that does not reduce the amount of spare capacity made available for the licensed services; and when so modified any such licence shall have effect accordingly.]

(3) [OFCOM] shall, when determining under subsection [(2)(b)] the extent and nature of the spare capacity available for the provision of additional services in the case of any frequency, have regard—

[(a) to the obligations contained in any code under section 303 of the Communications Act 2003 by virtue of subsection (5) of that section; and

(aa) to any need of the person providing the television broadcasting service in question to be able to use part of the signals carrying it for providing services (in addition to those provided for satisfying those obligations) which—

(i) are ancillary to programmes included in the service and directly related to their contents; or

(ii) relate to the promotion or listing of such programmes].

(4) A person holding a licence to provide a Channel 3 service or Channel 4 or 5 shall be taken for the purposes of this Part to be authorised by his licence—

[(a) to provide services for the satisfaction in his case of obligations mentioned in subsection (3)(a); and

(b) to provide in relation to his television broadcasting service any such services as are mentioned in subsection (3)(aa).]

(5) …

[(6) In this section—

"electronic signals" means signals within the meaning of section 32 of the Communications Act 2003;

"relevant frequency" means a frequency made available by OFCOM for the purposes of a television broadcasting service.]

[3015]

NOTES

Sub-ss (1), (2), (3), (4): words in square brackets substituted by the Communications Act 2003, s 360(3), Sch 15, Pt 1, para 20(1)–(3), (5), (6), subject to transitional provisions in s 406(6) of, and Sch 18, paras 5, 30, 64 to, that Act at **[3434]**, **[3460]** and subject to further transitional provisions as noted below.

Sub-s (2A): inserted by the Communications Act 2003, s 360(3), Sch 15, Pt 1, para 20(1), (4), subject to transitional provisions in s 406(6) of, and Sch 18, paras 30, 64 to, that Act at **[3434]**, **[3460]** and subject to further transitional provisions as noted below.

Sub-s (5): repealed by the Communications Act 2003, s 406(7), Sch 19(1), subject to transitional provisions in s 406(6) of, and Sch 18, paras 5, 30, 64 to, that Act at **[3434]**, **[3460]**.

Sub-s (6): substituted by the Communications Act 2003, s 360(3), Sch 15, Pt 1, para 20(1), (7), subject to transitional provisions in s 406(6) of, and Sch 18, paras 30, 64 to, that Act at **[3434]**, **[3460]** and subject to further transitional provisions as noted below

Transitional provisions: the Communications Act 2003, Sch 15, Pt 1, para 20(8) provides that the amendments made by Sch 15, Pt 1, para 20(1)–(7) to that Act do not affect the validity of a licence granted or last renewed before the television transfer date, or the services licensed by any such licence.

49 Licensing of additional services

(1) Subject to subsection (2), [OFCOM] shall do all that they can to secure that, in the case of each [relevant frequency], all of the spare capacity available for the provision of additional services on that frequency is used for the provision of such services under additional services licences granted by [OFCOM] in accordance with this section.

[(1A) An additional services licence is not required for an additional service that is comprised in the public teletext service (within the meaning of Part 3 of the Communications Act 2003).]

(4) An additional services licence may relate to the use of spare capacity within more than one frequency; and two or more additional services licences may relate to the use of spare capacity within the same frequency where it is to be used at different times, or in different areas, in the case of each of those licences.

(5) An additional services licence may include provisions enabling the licence holder, subject to and in accordance with such conditions as [OFCOM] may impose, to authorise any person to whom this subsection applies to provide any additional service on the spare capacity allocated by the licence.

(6) Subsection (5) applies to any person who is not a disqualified person in relation to an additional services licence by virtue of Part II of Schedule 2 to this Act.

(7) Any conditions included in an additional services licence shall apply in relation to the provision of additional services by a person authorised as mentioned in subsection (5) as they apply in relation to the provision of such services by the licence holder; and any failure by such a person to comply with any such conditions shall be treated for the purposes of this Part as a failure on the part of the licence holder to comply with those conditions.

(8) Every licence under this Part to provide a television broadcasting service shall include such conditions as appear to [OFCOM] to be appropriate for securing that the licence holder grants—

- (a) to any person who holds a licence to provide additional services on the frequency on which that broadcasting service is provided, and
- (b) to any person who is authorised by any such person as mentioned in subsection (5) to provide additional services on that frequency,

access to facilities reasonably required by that person for the purposes of, or in connection with, the provision of any such additional services.

(9) Any person who grants to any other person access to facilities in accordance with conditions imposed under subsection (8) may require that other person to pay a reasonable charge in respect thereof; and any dispute as to the amount of any such charge shall be determined by [OFCOM].

(10) In this Part "additional services licence" means a licence to provide additional services [and "relevant frequency" has the same meaning as in section 48].

[3016]

NOTES

Sub-ss (1), (5), (8), (9): words in square brackets substituted by the Communications Act 2003, s 360(3), Sch 15, Pt 1, para 21(1)–(3), subject to transitional provisions in s 406(6) of, and Sch 18, paras 30, 64 to, that Act at **[3434]**, **[3460]**.

Sub-s (1A): substituted, for original sub-ss (2), (3), by the Communications Act 2003, s 360(3), Sch 15, Pt 1, para 21(1), (4), subject to transitional provisions in s 406(6) of, and Sch 18, paras 5, 30, 64 to, that Act at **[3434]**, **[3460]** and subject to further transitional provisions in the Office of Communications Act 2002 (Commencement No 3) and Communications Act 2003 (Commencement No 2) Order 2003, SI 2003/3142, art 8(2) at **[3597]**.

Sub-s (10): words in square brackets added by the Communications Act 2003, s 360(3), Sch 15, Pt 1, para 21(1), (5), subject to transitional provisions in s 406(6) of, and Sch 18, paras 5, 30, 64 to, that Act at **[3434]**, **[3460]**.

50 Applications for additional services licences

(1) Where [OFCOM] propose to grant a licence to provide additional services they shall publish, in such manner as they consider appropriate, a notice—

- (a) stating that they propose to grant such a licence;
- (b) specifying—
  - (i) the television broadcasting service or services on whose frequency or frequencies the services are to be provided, and
  - (ii) … the extent and nature of the spare capacity which is to be allocated by the licence;
- (c) inviting applications for the licence and specifying the closing date for such applications; and
- (d) specifying—
  - (i) the fee payable on any application made in pursuance of the notice, and
  - (ii) the percentage of qualifying revenue for each accounting period that would be payable by an applicant in pursuance of section 52(1)(c) if he were granted the licence.

(2) [OFCOM] may, if they think fit, specify under subsection (1)(d)(ii)—

(a) different percentages in relation to different accounting periods falling within the period for which the licence would be in force;

(b) a nil percentage in relation to any accounting period so falling.

(3) Any application made in pursuance of a notice under this section must be in writing and accompanied by—

(a) the fee specified in the notice under subsection (1)(d)(i);

(b) a technical plan indicating—

(i) the nature of any additional services which the applicant proposes to provide, and

(ii) so far as known to the applicant, the nature of any additional services which any other person proposes to provide in accordance with section 49(5);

(c) the applicant's cash bid in respect of the licence; and

(d) such information as [OFCOM] may reasonably require as to the applicant's present financial position and his projected financial position during the period for which the licence would be in force.

(4) At any time after receiving such an application and before determining it [OFCOM] may require the applicant to furnish additional information under subsection (3)(b) or (d).

(5) Any information to be furnished to [OFCOM] under this section shall, if they so require, be in such form or verified in such manner as they may specify.

(6) [OFCOM] shall, as soon as reasonably practicable after the date specified in a notice under this section as the closing date for applications, publish in such manner as they consider appropriate—

(a) the name of every person who has made an application to them in pursuance of the notice;

(b) particulars of the technical plan submitted by him under subsection (3)(b); and

(c) such other information connected with his application as [OFCOM] consider appropriate.

(7) …

[3017]

NOTES

Sub-s (1): words in square brackets substituted, and words omitted repealed, by the Communications Act 2003, ss 360(3), 406(7), Sch 15, Pt 1, para 22(1)–(3), Sch 19(1), subject to transitional provisions in s 406(6) of, and Sch 18, paras 30, 64 to, that Act at **[3434]**, **[3460]**.

Sub-ss (2)–(6): words in square brackets substituted by the Communications Act 2003, s 360(3), Sch 15, Pt 1, para 22(1), (2), subject to transitional provisions in s 406(6) of, and Sch 18, paras 30, 64 to, that Act at **[3434]**, **[3460]**.

Sub-s (7): repealed by the Communications Act 2003, ss 360(3), 406(7), Sch 15, Pt 1, para 22(1), (4), Sch 19(1), subject to transitional provisions in s 406(6) of, and Sch 18, paras 30, 64 to, that Act at **[3434]**, **[3460]**.

51 Procedure to be followed by [OFCOM] in connection with consideration of applications for, and awarding of, licences

(1) Where a person has made an application for an additional services licence in accordance with section 50, [OFCOM] shall not proceed to consider whether to award him the licence on the basis of his cash bid in accordance with subsections (3) and (4) below unless it appears to them—

[(a) that the technical plan submitted under section 50(3)(b), in so far as it involves the use of an electronic communications network (within the meaning of the Communications Act 2003), contains proposals that are acceptable to them; and]

(b) that the services proposed to be provided under the licence would be capable of being maintained throughout the period for which the licence would be in force;

and any reference to an applicant in section 17 (as applied by subsection (3) below) is accordingly a reference to an applicant in whose case it appears to [OFCOM] that the requirements of paragraphs (a) and (b) above are satisfied.

(2) …

(3) Subject to subsection (4), [sections 17 and 17A] shall apply in relation to an additional services licence as [they apply] in relation to a Channel 3 licence.

(4) In the application of section 17 in relation to an additional services licence—

(a) the provisions of subsection (4) down to the end of paragraph (b) shall be omitted;
(b) in subsection (7)(a), the reference to section 19(1) shall be construed as a reference to section 52(1); and
(c) subsection (12) shall have effect with the substitution of the following paragraph for paragraph (b)—
"(b) the name of every other applicant in whose case it appeared to [OFCOM] that the requirement specified in section 51(1)(a) was satisfied;".

(5) If at any time after an additional services licence has been granted to any person but before the licence has come into force—
(a) that person indicates to [OFCOM] that none of the services in question will be provided once the licence has come into force, or
(b) [OFCOM] for any other reason have reasonable grounds for believing that none of those services will be so provided,
then, subject to subsection (6)—
(i) [OFCOM] shall serve on him a notice revoking the licence as from the time the notice is served on him, and
(ii) section 17 (as applied by subsection (3) above) shall, subject to section 17(14), have effect as if he had not made an application for the licence.

(6) Subsection (5) shall not apply in the case of any person by virtue of paragraph (b) of that subsection unless [OFCOM] have served on him a notice stating their grounds for believing that none of the services in question will be provided once his licence has come into force; and they shall not serve such a notice on him unless they have given him a reasonable opportunity of making representations to them about the matters complained of.

(7) …

[3018]

NOTES

Section heading: word in square brackets substituted by virtue of the Communications Act 2003, s 360(3), Sch 15, Pt 1, para 23(1), (2), subject to transitional provisions in s 406(6) of, and Sch 18, paras 30, 64 to, that Act at **[3434]**, **[3460]**.

Sub-ss (1), (4)–(6): words in square brackets substituted by the Communications Act 2003, s 360(3), Sch 15, Pt 1, para 23(1)–(3), subject to transitional provisions in s 406(6) of, and Sch 18, paras 30, 64 to, that Act at **[3434]**, **[3460]**.

Sub-ss (2), (7): repealed by the Communications Act 2003, ss 360(3), 406(7), Sch 15, Pt 1, para 23(1), (4), Sch 19(1), subject to transitional provisions in s 406(6) of, and Sch 18, paras 30, 64 to, that Act at **[3434]**, **[3460]**.

Sub-s (3): words in square brackets substituted by the Broadcasting Act 1996, s 86(2).

52 Additional payments to be made in respect of additional services licences

(1) An additional services licence shall include conditions requiring the licence holder to pay to [OFCOM] (in addition to any fees required to be so paid by virtue of section 4(1)(b))—
(a) in respect of the first complete calendar year falling within the period for which the licence is in force, the amount specified in his cash bid;
(b) in respect of each subsequent year falling wholly or partly within that period, the amount so specified as increased by the appropriate percentage; and
(c) in respect of each accounting period of his falling within the period referred to in paragraph (a), an amount representing such percentage of the qualifying revenue for that accounting period as was specified in relation to the licence under section 50(1)(d)(ii).

(2) For the purposes of subsection (1)(c) the qualifying revenue for any accounting period of the licence holder shall consist of all amounts which are received or to be received by him or by any connected person and are referable to the right under his licence to use, or to authorise any other person to use, in that period the spare capacity allocated by the licence.

(3) An additional services licence may include conditions—
(a) enabling [OFCOM] to estimate before the beginning of an accounting period the amount due for that period by virtue of subsection (1)(c); and
(b) requiring the licence holder to pay the estimated amount by monthly instalments throughout that period.

(4) Such a licence may in particular include conditions—

(a) authorising [OFCOM] to revise any estimate on one or more occasions, and to adjust the instalments payable by the licence holder to take account of the revised estimate;

(b) providing for the adjustment of any overpayment or underpayment.

(5) Where—

(a) the first complete accounting period of the licence holder falling within the period referred to in subsection (1)(a) ("the licence period") does not begin at the same time as that period, or

(b) the last complete accounting period of his falling within the licence period does not end at the same time as that period,

any reference in subsection (1)(c) to an accounting period of his shall include a reference to such part of the accounting period preceding that first complete accounting period, or (as the case may be) following that last complete accounting period, as falls within the licence period; and other references to accounting periods in this Part shall be construed accordingly. **[3019]**

NOTES

Sub-ss (1), (3), (4): words in square brackets substituted by the Communications Act 2003, s 360(3), Sch 15, Pt 1, para 24, subject to transitional provisions in s 406(6) of, and Sch 18, paras 30, 64 to, that Act at **[3434]**, **[3460]**.

53 Duration of licences, and renewal of licences for provision of services on assigned frequencies

[(1) A licence to provide additional services on a frequency which is a relevant frequency for the purposes of section 48 or (in the case of a licence granted before the television transfer date) was assigned under section 65—]

(a) shall, subject to the provisions of this Part, continue in force for a period of ten years, and

(b) may (subject to the following provisions of this section) be renewed on one or more occasions for a period of ten years beginning with the date of renewal.

(2) An application for the renewal of a licence under subsection (1) may be made by the licence holder not earlier than four years before the date on which it would otherwise cease to be in force and not later than [the day falling three months before] the relevant date.

(3) …

(4) Where an application is made for the renewal of a licence under subsection (1) … , [OFCOM] may postpone the consideration of it by them for as long as they think appropriate having regard to subsection (9).

(5) Where an application for the renewal of an additional services licence has been duly made to [OFCOM], they may only (subject to subsection (6)) refuse the application if—

(a) they are not satisfied that any additional service specified in the technical plan submitted under section 50(3)(b) would, if the licence were renewed, be provided as proposed in that plan, or

(b) they propose to grant a fresh additional services licence for the provision of any additional service which would differ in any material respect from any such service authorised to be provided under the applicant's licence, or

(c) they propose to determine that all or part of the spare capacity allocated by the licence is to cease to be available for the provision of additional services in order that it may be used by any relevant person for the purpose of enhancing the technical quality of his television broadcasting service;

and in paragraph (c) "relevant person" means the person providing a television broadcasting service on whose frequency the licensed service has been provided.

(6) Section 17(5) to (7) shall apply in relation to an applicant for the renewal of an additional services licence as those provisions apply in relation to such an applicant as is mentioned in section 17(5), but as if—

(a) any reference to the awarding of a Channel 3 licence to the applicant were a reference to the renewal of the applicant's licence under this section; and

(b) in section 17(7), the reference to section 19(1) were a reference to section 52(1).

(7) On the grant of any such application [OFCOM]—

(a) shall determine an amount which is to be payable to [OFCOM] by the licence holder in respect of the first complete calendar year falling within the period for which the licence is to be renewed; and

(b) may specify a different percentage from that specified under section 50(1)(d)(ii) as the percentage of qualifying revenue for each accounting period of his that will be payable by the applicant in pursuance of section 52(1)(c) during the period for which the licence is to be renewed;

and [OFCOM] may specify under paragraph (b) either of the things mentioned in section 50(2).

(8) The amount determined by [OFCOM] under subsection (7)(a) in connection with the renewal of a licence shall be such amount as would, in their opinion, be [the cash bid of the licence holder were the licence (instead of being renewed) to be granted for the period of the renewal on an application made in accordance with section 50(3)].

[(8A) For the purposes of subsection (7)(b)—

(a) different percentages may be specified for different accounting periods, and

(b) the percentages that may be specified for an accounting period include a nil percentage.]

(9) Where [OFCOM] have granted a person's application under this section they shall formally renew his licence not later than the relevant date or, if that is not reasonably practicable, as soon after that date as is reasonably practicable; and they shall not so renew his licence unless they have notified him of—

(a) the amount determined by them under subsection (7)(a), and

(b) any percentage specified by them under subsection (7)(b),

and he has, within such period as is specified in that notification, notified them that he consents to the licence being renewed on those terms.

(10) Where an additional services licence is renewed under this section—

(a) any conditions included in it in pursuance of section 52 shall have effect during the period for which the licence has been renewed—

(i) as if the amount determined by [OFCOM] under subsection (7)(a) above were an amount specified in a cash bid submitted by the licence holder, and

(ii) subject to any determination made under subsection (7)(b) above; and

(b) (subject to paragraph (a)) that section shall have effect in relation to the period for which the licence has been renewed as it has effect in relation to the period for which an additional services licence is originally in force.

(11) In this section "the relevant date", in relation to an additional services licence, means the date which [OFCOM] determine to be that by which they would need to publish a notice under section 50 if they were to grant, as from the date on which that licence would expire if not renewed, a fresh licence to provide the additional services formerly provided under that licence.

[(12) A determination for the purposes of subsection (11)—

(a) must be made at least one year before the date determined; and

(b) must be notified by OFCOM to the person who holds the licence in question.

(13) In this section "the television transfer date" has the same meaning as in the Communications Act 2003.]

[3020]

NOTES

Sub-ss (1), (5), (7), (8), (9)–(11): words in square brackets substituted by the Communications Act 2003, s 360(3), Sch 15, Pt 1, para 25(1), (2), (4), (5), subject to transitional provisions in s 406(6) of, and Sch 18, paras 5, 30, 64 to, that Act at **[3434]**, **[3460]**.

Sub-s (2): words in square brackets inserted by the Communications Act 2003, s 360(3), Sch 15, Pt 1, para 25(1), (3), subject to transitional provisions in s 406(6) of, and Sch 18, paras 30, 50, 64 to, that Act at **[3434]**, **[3460]**.

Sub-s (3): repealed by the Satellite Television Service Regulations 1997, SI 1997/1682, reg 2, Schedule, para 8.

Sub-s (4): words omitted repealed, and word in square brackets substituted, by the Communications Act 2003, ss 360(3), 406(7), Sch 15, Pt 1, para 25(1), (4), Sch 19(1), subject to transitional provisions in s 406(6) of, and Sch 18, paras 5, 30, 64 to, that Act at **[3434]**, **[3460]**.

Sub-s (8A): inserted by the Communications Act 2003, s 360(3), Sch 15, Pt 1, para 25(1), (6), subject to transitional provisions in s 406(6) of, and Sch 18, paras 30, 64 to, that Act at **[3434]**, **[3460]**.

Sub-ss (12), (13): added by the Communications Act 2003, s 360(3), Sch 15, Pt 1, para 25(1), (7), subject to transitional provisions in s 406(6) of, and Sch 18, paras 30, 50, 64 to, that Act at **[3434]**, **[3460]**.

54 Additional services not to interfere with other transmissions

(1) An additional services licence may include such conditions as [OFCOM] consider appropriate for securing that the provision of any additional service under the licence does not cause any interference with—

(a) the television broadcasting service or services on whose frequency or frequencies it is provided, or

(b) any other wireless telegraphy transmissions.

(2) …

[3021]

NOTES

Sub-s (1): word in square brackets substituted by the Communications Act 2003, s 360(3), Sch 15, Pt 1, para 26(1), (2), subject to transitional provisions in s 406(6) of, and Sch 18, paras 30, 64 to, that Act at **[3434]**, **[3460]**.

Sub-s (2): repealed by the Communications Act 2003, ss 360(3), 406(7), Sch 15, Pt 1, para 26(1), (3), Sch 19(1), subject to transitional provisions in s 406(6) of, and Sch 18, paras 30, 64 to, that Act at **[3434]**, **[3460]**.

55 Enforcement of additional services licences

(1) If [OFCOM] are satisfied that the holder of an additional services licence has failed to comply with any condition of the licence or with any direction given by [OFCOM] under or by virtue of any provision of this Part, they may (subject to subsection (3)) serve on him a notice requiring him to pay, within a specified period, a specified financial penalty to [OFCOM].

[(1A) The amount of a financial penalty imposed on a person in pursuance of subsection (1) shall not exceed 5 per cent of the qualifying revenue for the licence holder's last complete accounting period falling within the period for which his licence has been in force ("the relevant period").

(1B) In relation to a person whose first complete accounting period falling within the relevant period has not ended when the penalty is imposed, subsection (1A) is to be construed as referring to 5 per cent of the amount which OFCOM estimate to be the qualifying revenue for that accounting period.

(1C) Section 52(2) applies for determining or estimating qualifying revenue for the purposes of subsection (1A) or (1B) above.]

(3) [OFCOM] shall not serve on any person a notice under subsection (1) unless they have given him a reasonable opportunity of making representations to them about the matters complained of.

(4) Section 42 shall apply in relation to an additional services licence as it applies in relation to a licence to provide a Channel 3 service, but with the omission of subsection (7) [and, in the case of a licence renewed under section 53 as if the reference in section 42(4) to the end of the period for which the licence is to continue in force were a reference to the end of the period for which it has been renewed].

[3022]

NOTES

Sub-ss (1), (3): words in square brackets substituted by the Communications Act 2003, s 360(3), Sch 15, Pt 1, para 27(1), (2), subject to transitional provisions in s 406(6) of, and Sch 18, paras 30, 64 to, that Act at **[3434]**, **[3460]**.

Sub-ss (1A)–(1C): substituted, for original sub-s (2), by the Communications Act 2003, s 345, Sch 13, Pt I, paras 1, 5(1), subject to savings and transitional provisions in ss 345, 406(6) of, and Sch 13, Pt 1, para 5(2), Sch 18, paras 5, 30 to, that Act at **[3393]**, **[3434]**, **[3454]**, **[3460]**.

Sub-s (4): words in square brackets added by the Communications Act 2003, s 360(3), Sch 15, Pt 1, para 27(1), (3), subject to transitional provisions in s 406(6) of, and Sch 18, paras 30, 64 to, that Act at **[3434]**, **[3460]**.

56–64 ((*Ch VI*) *outside the scope of this work.*)

CHAPTER VII
SUPPLEMENTAL

65 (*Repealed by the Communications Act 2003, s 406(7), Sch 19(1), subject to transitional provisions in s 406(6) of, and Sch 18, paras 5, 30, 64 to, that Act at* **[3434]**, **[3460]**.)

66 Requirements relating to transmission and distribution of services

(1) During such period as the Secretary of State may by order specify, all Channel 3 services shall be broadcast [so as to be available for reception by members of the public] by a single person under arrangements made with him by the persons licensed to provide those services; and every Channel 3 licence shall include such conditions as appear to [OFCOM] to be appropriate—

(a) for securing that result and

(b) for securing that the costs incurred in respect of the broadcasting of those services (taken as a whole) during that period in accordance with those arrangements are shared by those persons in such manner as may be approved by the Secretary of State.

(2) Any Channel 3 licence shall include such conditions as appear to [OFCOM] to be appropriate for securing that the costs incurred in respect of the distribution of Channel 3 services (taken as a whole) during such period as the Secretary of State may by order specify are shared by the persons licensed to provide those services in such manner as may be approved by the Secretary of State.

In this subsection "distribution", in relation to Channel 3 services, means the conveyance of those services (by whatever means and whether directly or indirectly) to the broadcasting stations from which they are broadcast [so as to be available for reception by members of the public].

[(2A) In subsections (1) and (2) "available for reception by members of the public" shall be construed in accordance with section 361 of the Communications Act 2003.]

(3) The Secretary of State may, at any time during the period referred to in subsection (1) or (2), by order provide for that period to be extended by such further period as is specified in the order; and any conditions included in a Channel 3 licence in pursuance of that subsection shall accordingly, in any such case, have effect in relation to that period as so extended.

(4) Any Channel 3 licence or licence to provide Channel 4 or 5 shall include such conditions as appear to [OFCOM] to be appropriate for requiring the signals carrying the licensed service to attain high standards in terms of technical quality and reliability throughout so much of the relevant area as is for the time being reasonably practicable.

(5) Before imposing any conditions in pursuance of subsection (4) [OFCOM] shall consult the Secretary of State as to how much of the relevant area is to be specified in the conditions as the area throughout which the required standards are to be attained.

(6) In subsections (4) and (5) "the relevant area"—

(a) in relation to a Channel 3 or Channel 5 licence, means the area for which the licensed service is to be provided; and

(b) in relation to the licence to provide Channel 4, means England, Scotland and Northern Ireland.

(7) The Welsh Authority shall do all that they can to ensure that the signals carrying S4C attain high standards in terms of technical quality and reliability throughout so much of Wales as is for the time being reasonably practicable.

(8) Any order under this section shall be subject to annulment in pursuance of a resolution of either House of Parliament.

[3023]

NOTES

Sub-ss (1), (2), (4), (5): words in square brackets substituted by the Communications Act 2003, s 360(3), Sch 15, Pt 1, para 29(1)–(3), subject to transitional provisions in s 406(6) of, and Sch 18, paras 30, 64 to, that Act at **[3434]**, **[3460]**.

Sub-s (2A): inserted by the Communications Act 2003, s 360(3), Sch 15, Pt 1, para 29(1), (4), subject to transitional provisions in s 406(6) of, and Sch 18, paras 30, 64 to, that Act at **[3434]**, **[3460]**.

[66A Enforcement of licences held by BBC companies

(1) Where [OFCOM]—

(a) give a direction to a BBC company under section 40(1),

(b) serve a notice on a BBC company under any provision of section 41 or 42, or

(c) receive any written representations from a BBC company under section 40(2), 41(3) or 42(8),

[OFCOM] shall send a copy of the direction, notice or representations to the Secretary of State.

(2) References in subsection (1) to any of the provisions of sections 40 to 42 are references to that provision as applied—

(a) by section 42B(2), in relation to a licence to provide a restricted service,

(b)–(d) …

(e) by section 55(4), in relation to an additional services licence.]

[3024]

NOTES

Inserted by the Broadcasting Act 1996, s 136, Sch 8, para 3.

Sub-s (1): words in square brackets substituted by the Communications Act 2003, s 360(3), Sch 15, Pt 1, para 30, subject to transitional provisions in s 406(6) of, and Sch 18, paras 30, 64 to, that Act at **[3434]**, **[3460]**.

Sub-s (2): para (b) repealed by the Satellite Television Service Regulations 1997, SI 1997/1682, reg 2, Schedule, para 9; paras (c), (d) repealed by the Communications Act 2003, s 406(7), Sch 19(1), subject to transitional provisions in s 406(6) of, and Sch 18, paras 5, 30, 64 to, that Act at **[3434]**, **[3460]**.

67 Computation of qualifying revenue

Part I of Schedule 7 (which contains provisions relating to the computation of qualifying revenue for the purposes of this Part and Part II) shall have effect.

[3025]

68–70 (*Repealed by the Communications Act 2003, s 406(7), Sch 19(1), subject to transitional provisions in s 406(6) of, and Sch 18, paras 5, 30, 64 to, that Act at* **[3434]**, **[3460]**.)

71 Interpretation of Part I

(1) In this Part (unless the context otherwise requires)—

"the 1981 Act" means the Broadcasting Act 1981;

"additional service" and "additional services licence" have the meaning given by section 48(1) and section 49(10) respectively;

"the appropriate percentage", in relation to any year, has the meaning given by section 19(10);

"cash bid", in relation to a licence, has the meaning given by section 15(7);

"Channel 3" means the system of television broadcasting services established … under section 14, and "a Channel 3 licence" means a licence to provide one of the services comprised within that system;

"Channel 4" means the television broadcasting service referred to in section 24(1), and "on Channel 4" means in that service;

"Channel 5" means the television broadcasting service referred to in section 28(1), and "a Channel 5 licence" means a licence to provide that service;

…

"the Corporation" means the Channel Four Television Corporation established by section 23;

…

"licence" means a licence under this Part, and "licensed" shall be construed accordingly;

…

"national Channel 3 service" has the meaning given by section 14(6), and "a national Channel 3 licence" means a licence to provide a national Channel 3 service;

…

"regional Channel 3 service" has the meaning given by section 14(6), and "a regional Channel 3 licence" means a licence to provide a regional Channel 3 service;

["restricted service" has the meaning given by section 42A;]

["S4C" has the same meaning as in Part 3 of the Communications Act 2003;]

[…]

"spare capacity" shall be construed in accordance with section 48(2);

["television broadcasting service", "television licensable content service" and "television programme service" each has the same meaning as in Part 3 of the Communications Act 2003].

(2) Where the person who is for the time being the holder of any licence ("the present licence holder") is not the person to whom the licence was originally granted, any reference in this Part (however expressed) to the holder of the licence shall be construed, in relation to any time falling before the date when the present licence holder became the holder of it, as including a reference to a person who was previously the holder of the licence.

[3026]

NOTES

Sub-s (1): words omitted from definition "Channel 3" and definitions "the Commission", "licensable programme service" (omitted) repealed, and definitions "S4C", "television broadcasting service", "television licensable content service" and "television programme service" substituted, by the Communications Act 2003, ss 360(3), 406(7), Sch 15, Pt 1, para 31, Sch 19(1), subject to transitional provisions in s 406(6) of, and Sch 18, paras 5, 30, 64 to, that Act at **[3434]**, **[3460]**; definition "restricted service" inserted by the Broadcasting Act 1996, s 148(1), Sch 10, Pt II, para 17; definitions "domestic satellite service" and "non-domestic satellite service" (omitted) repealed by the Satellite Television Service Regulations 1997, SI 1997/1682, reg 2, Schedule, para 10; definition "satellite television service" (omitted) inserted by SI 1997/1682, reg 2, Schedule, para 10, and repealed by the Communications Act 2003, s 406(7), Sch 19(1), subject to transitional provisions in s 406(6) of, and Sch 18, paras 5, 30, 64 to, that Act at **[3434]**, **[3460]**.

72–82 ((*Pt II) repealed by the Communications Act 2003, s 406(7), Sch 19(1), subject to transitional provisions in s 406(6) of, and Sch 18, paras 5, 30, 64 to, that Act at* **[3434]**, **[3460]**.)

PART III
INDEPENDENT RADIO SERVICES

CHAPTER I
REGULATION BY AUTHORITY OF INDEPENDENT RADIO SERVICES GENERALLY

83 (*Repealed by the Communications Act 2003, s 406(7), Sch 19(1), subject to transitional provisions in s 406(6) of, and Sch 18, paras 30, 64 to, that Act at* **[3434]**, **[3460]**.)

Function of [OFCOM]

NOTES

Cross-heading: word in square brackets substituted by virtue of the Communications Act 2003, s 360(3), Sch 15, Pt 1, para 32(1), (2), subject to transitional provisions in s 406(6) of, and Sch 18, paras 30, 64 to, that Act at **[3434]**, **[3460]**.

84 (*Repealed by the Communications Act 2003, s 406(7), Sch 19(1), subject to transitional provisions in s 406(6) of, and Sch 18, paras 5, 30, 64 to, that Act at* **[3434]**, **[3460]**, *and subject to further transitional provisions in the Office of Communications Act 2002 (Commencement No 3) and Communications Act 2003 (Commencement No 2) Order 2003, SI 2003/3142, art 6(2) at* **[3595]**.)

85 Licensing functions of [OFCOM]

(1) Subject to subsection (2), [OFCOM] may, in accordance with the following provisions of this Part, grant [licences to provide relevant independent radio services].

(2) [OFCOM] shall do all that they can to secure the provision within the United Kingdom of—

(a) a diversity of national services each catering for tastes and interests different from those catered for by the others and of which—

(i) one is a service the greater part of which consists in the broadcasting of spoken material, and

(ii) another is a service which consists, wholly or mainly, in the broadcasting of music which, in the opinion of [OFCOM], is not pop music; and

(b) a range and diversity of local services.

(3), (4) …

(5) The Secretary of State may by order make such amendments of subsection (2)(a) as he considers appropriate—

(a) for including in that provision a requirement that one of the national services there referred to should be a service of a particular description, or

(b) for removing such a requirement from that provision;

and (without prejudice to the generality of section 200(2)(b)) any such order may make such consequential amendments of section 98(1)(b)(iii) as the Secretary of State considers appropriate.

(6) In subsection (2)(a)(ii) "pop music" includes rock music and other kinds of modern popular music which are characterised by a strong rhythmic element and a reliance on electronic amplification for their performance (whether or not, in the case of any particular piece of rock or other such music, the music in question enjoys a current popularity as measured by the number of recordings sold).

(7) An order shall not be made under subsection (5) unless a draft of it has been laid before and approved by a resolution of each House of Parliament.

[(8) In this section "relevant independent radio services" means the following services so far as they are services falling to be regulated under section 245 of the Communications Act 2003—

(a) sound broadcasting services,

(b) radio licensable content services,

(c) additional radio services.]

[3027]

NOTES

Section heading: word in square brackets substituted by virtue of the Communications Act 2003, s 360(3), Sch 15, Pt 1, para 32(1), (2), subject to transitional provisions in s 406(6) of, and Sch 18, paras 30, 64 to, that Act at **[3434]**, **[3460]**.

Sub-ss (1), (2): words in square brackets substituted by the Communications Act 2003, s 360(3), Sch 15, Pt 1, para 32(1)–(3), subject to transitional provisions in s 406(6) of, and Sch 18, paras 30, 64 to, that Act at **[3434]**, **[3460]**.

Sub-ss (3), (4): repealed by the Communications Act 2003, ss 360(3), 406(7), Sch 15, Pt 1, para 32(1), (4), Sch 19(1), subject to transitional provisions in s 406(6) of, and Sch 18, paras 30, 64 to, that Act at **[3434]**, **[3460]**.

Sub-s (8): added by the Communications Act 2003, s 360(3), Sch 15, Pt 1, para 32(1), (5), subject to transitional provisions in s 406(6) of, and Sch 18, paras 30, 64 to, that Act at **[3434]**, **[3460]**.

General provisions about licences

86 Licences under Part III

(1) A licence shall be in writing and (subject to the provisions of this Part) shall continue in force [(subject to a suspension of the licence under section 111B)—

(a) in the case of a licence to provide radio licensable content services, until such time as it is surrendered or is revoked in accordance with any of the following provisions of this Part; and

(b) in any other case, until whichever is the earlier of any such time or the end of the period specified in the licence].

(2) A licence may be granted by [OFCOM] for the provision of such a service as is specified in the licence or for the provision of a service of such a description as is so specified; and (without prejudice to the generality of the preceding provision) a licence may be so granted for the provision of a service which to any extent consists in the simultaneous broadcasting of different programmes on different frequencies.

[(3) A licence to provide a local or national service or to provide an additional service must specify a period of no more than twelve years as the period for which it is to be in force.]

(4) [OFCOM]—

(a) shall not grant a licence to any person unless they are satisfied that he is a fit and proper person to hold it; and

(b) shall do all that they can to secure that, if they cease to be so satisfied in the case of any person holding a licence, that person does not remain the holder of the licence;

and nothing in this Part shall be construed as affecting the operation of this subsection or of section 88(1) or (2)(b) or (c) or 89(1).

[(4A) Where [OFCOM] are not satisfied that a BBC company which has applied for a licence is a fit and proper person to hold it, they shall, before refusing the application, notify the Secretary of State that they are not so satisfied.]

(5) [OFCOM] may vary a licence by a notice served on the licence holder if—

(a) in the case of a variation of the period for which the licence is to continue in force, the licence holder consents; or

(b) in the case of any other variation, the licence holder has been given a reasonable opportunity of making representations to [OFCOM] about the variation.

(6) Paragraph (a) of subsection (5) does not affect the operation of section 110(1)(b); and that subsection shall not authorise the variation of any conditions included in a licence in pursuance of section 102(1) or section 118(1).

(7) A licence granted to any person under this Part shall not be transferable to any other person without the previous consent in writing of [OFCOM].

(8) Without prejudice to the generality of subsection (7), [OFCOM] shall not give their consent for the purposes of that subsection unless they are satisfied that any such other person would be in a position to comply with all of the conditions included in the licence which would have effect during the period for which it is to be in force.

[(9) The holding of a licence by a person shall not relieve him of—

(a) any liability in respect of a failure to hold [a licence under section 8 of the Wireless Telegraphy Act 2006]; or

(b) any obligation to comply with requirements imposed by or under Chapter 1 of Part 2 of the Communications Act 2003 (electronic communications networks and electronic communications services).]

[3028]

NOTES

Sub-ss (1), (2), (4), (5), (7), (8): words in square brackets substituted by the Communications Act 2003, ss 252(1), 360(3), Sch 15, Pt 1, para 33(1), (2), subject to transitional provisions in s 406(6) of, and Sch 18, paras 30, 64 to, that Act at **[3434]**, **[3460]**.

Sub-s (3): substituted by the Communications Act 2003, s 252(2).

Sub-s (4A): inserted by the Broadcasting Act 1996, s 136, Sch 8, para 5; word in square brackets substituted by the Communications Act 2003, s 360(3), Sch 15, Pt 1, para 33(1), (2), subject to transitional provisions in s 406(6) of, and Sch 18, paras 30, 64 to, that Act at **[3434]**, **[3460]**.

Sub-s (9): substituted by the Communications Act 2003, s 360(3), Sch 15, Pt 1, para 33(1), (3), subject to transitional provisions in s 406(6) of, and Sch 18, paras 5, 30, 64 to, that Act at **[3434]**, **[3460]**; words in square brackets substituted by the Wireless Telegraphy Act 2006, s 123, Sch 7, paras 9, 11.

Modification: sub-s (3) is modified in its application to community radio services by the Community Radio Order 2004, SI 2004/1944, art 4, Schedule, Pt 1, paras 1, 2 at **[3624]**.

87 General licence conditions

(1) A licence may include—

(a) such conditions as appear to [OFCOM] to be appropriate having regard to any duties which are or may be imposed on them, or on the licence holder, by or under this Act[, the Broadcasting Act 1996 or the Communications Act 2003];

(b) conditions enabling [OFCOM] to supervise and enforce technical standards in connection with the provision of the licensed service;

(c) conditions requiring the payment by the licence holder to [OFCOM] (whether on the grant of the licence or at such times thereafter as may be determined by or under the licence, or both) of a fee or fees of an amount or amounts so determined;

(d) conditions requiring the licence holder to furnish [OFCOM], in such manner and at such times as they may reasonably require, with such information as they may require for the purpose of exercising the functions assigned to them by or under this Act[, the Broadcasting Act 1996 or the Communications Act 2003];

(e) conditions requiring the licence holder, if found by [OFCOM] to be in breach of any condition of his licence, to reimburse to [OFCOM], in such circumstances as are specified in any conditions, any costs reasonably incurred by them in connection with the breach of that condition;

(f) conditions providing for such incidental and supplemental matters as appear to [OFCOM] to be appropriate.

(2) A licence may in particular include—

(a) conditions requiring the licence holder—

(i) to comply with any direction given by [OFCOM] as to such matters as are specified in the licence or are of a description so specified, or

(ii) (except to the extent that [OFCOM] consent to his doing or not doing them) not to do or to do such things as are specified in the licence or are of a description so specified; and

(b) conditions requiring the licence holder to permit—

(i) any employee of, or person authorised by, [OFCOM], …

(ii) …

to enter any premises which are used in connection with the broadcasting of the licensed service and to inspect, examine, operate or test any equipment on the premises which is used in that connection.

(3) The fees required to be paid to [OFCOM] by virtue of subsection (1)(c) shall be in accordance with such tariff as may from time to time be fixed by [OFCOM]; …

(4) A tariff fixed under subsection (3) may specify different fees in relation to different cases or circumstances; and [OFCOM] shall publish every such tariff in such manner as they consider appropriate.

(5) Where the holder of any licence—

(a) is required by virtue of any condition imposed under this Part to provide [OFCOM] with any information, and

(b) in purported compliance with that condition provides them with any information which is false in a material particular,

he shall be taken for the purposes of sections 110 and 111 to have failed to comply with that condition.

(6) Nothing in this Act which authorises or requires the inclusion in a licence of conditions relating to any particular matter or having effect for any particular purpose shall be taken as derogating from the generality of subsection (1).

[3029]

NOTES

Sub-s (1): word "OFCOM" in square brackets wherever it appears substituted, and other words in square brackets inserted, by the Communications Act 2003, s 360(3), Sch 15, Pt 1, para 34(1)–(3), subject to transitional provisions in s 406(6) of, and Sch 18, paras 30, 64 to, that Act at **[3434]**, **[3460]**.

Sub-ss (2), (3): words in square brackets substituted, and words omitted repealed, by the Communications Act 2003, ss 360(3), 406(7), Sch 15, Pt 1, para 34(1), (2), (4), (5), Sch 19(1), subject to transitional provisions in s 406(6) of, and Sch 18, paras 5, 30, 64 to, that Act at **[3434]**, **[3460]**.

Sub-ss (4), (5): words in square brackets substituted by the Communications Act 2003, s 360(3), Sch 15, Pt 1, para 34(1), (2), subject to transitional provisions in s 406(6) of, and Sch 18, paras 30, 64 to, that Act at **[3434]**, **[3460]**.

88 Restrictions on the holding of licences

(1) [OFCOM] shall do all that they can to secure—

(a) that a person does not become or remain the holder of a licence if he is a person who is a disqualified person in relation to that licence by virtue of Part II of Schedule 2 to this Act; and

[(b) that a person does not become the holder of a licence if requirements imposed by or under Schedule 14 to the Communications Act 2003 would be contravened were he to do so; and

(c) that those requirements are not contravened in the case of a person who already holds a licence].

(2) [OFCOM] may accordingly—

(a) require any applicant for a licence to provide them with such information as they may reasonably require for the purpose of determining—

(i) whether he is such a disqualified person as is mentioned in subsection (1)(a),

(ii) whether any such requirements as are mentioned in subsection (1)(b) would preclude them from granting a licence to him, and

(iii) if so, what steps would be required to be taken by or in relation to him in order for any such requirements to be complied with;

(b) revoke the award of a licence to a body where a relevant change takes place after the award, but before the grant, of the licence;

(c) make the grant of a licence to any person conditional on the taking of any specified steps that appear to them to be required to be taken as mentioned in paragraph (a)(iii);

(d) impose conditions in any licence enabling them to require the licence holder, if a body corporate, to give to them advance notice of proposals affecting—

(i) shareholdings in the body, or

(ii) the directors of the body,

where such proposals are known to the body;

[(da) impose conditions in a licence requiring the licence holder, if a body corporate, to give OFCOM notice, after they have occurred and irrespective of whether proposals for them have fallen to be notified, of changes, transactions or events affecting—

(i) shareholdings in the body; or

(ii) the directors of the body;

(db) impose conditions in a licence enabling OFCOM to require the licence holder to provide them with such information as they may reasonably require for determining—

(i) whether the licence holder is a disqualified person in relation to that licence by virtue of Part 2 of Schedule 2; or

(ii) whether any such requirements as are mentioned in subsection (1)(b) have been and are being complied with by or in relation to the licence holder;]

(e) impose conditions in any licence enabling them to give the licence holder directions requiring him to take, or arrange for the taking of, any specified steps appearing to them to be required to be taken in order for any such requirements as are mentioned in subsection (1)(b) to be complied with.

[(2A) Before revoking in pursuance of subsection (2)(b) the award of a licence to a BBC company, [OFCOM] shall give the Secretary of State notice of their intention to do so, specifying the relevant change.]

(3) Where [OFCOM]—

(a) revoke the award of any licence in pursuance of subsection (2)(b), or

(b) determine that any condition imposed by them in relation to any licence in pursuance of subsection (2)(c) has not been satisfied,

any provisions of this Part relating to the awarding of licences of the kind in question shall (subject to subsection (4)) have effect as if the person to whom the licence was awarded or granted had not made an application for it.

(4) Those provisions shall not so have effect if [OFCOM] decide that it would be desirable to publish a fresh notice under this Part in respect of the grant of a licence, or (as the case may be) a further licence, to provide the service in question.

(5) Every licence shall include such conditions as [OFCOM] consider necessary or expedient to ensure that where—

(a) the holder of the licence is a body, and

(b) a relevant change takes place after the grant of the licence,

[OFCOM] may revoke the licence by notice served on the holder of the licence and taking effect forthwith or on a date specified in the notice.

[(6) [OFCOM] shall not serve any such notice on the licence holder unless—

(a) [OFCOM] have notified him of the matters [constituting their grounds for revoking the licence] and given him a reasonable opportunity of making representations to them about those matters, and

(b) in a case where the relevant change is one falling within subsection (6A)—

(i) they have also given him an opportunity of complying with [the requirements imposed by or under Schedule 14 to the Communications Act 2003] within a period specified in the notification, and

(ii) the period specified in the notification has elapsed.

(6A) A relevant change falls within this subsection if it consists only in one or more of the following—

(a) …
(b) a change in the national market share (within the meaning of [Part 1 of Schedule 14 to the Communications Act 2003]) of one or more national newspapers (within the meaning of that Part of that Schedule);
(c) a change in the local market share (within the meaning of that Part of that Schedule) in a particular area of one or more local newspapers (within the meaning of that Part of that Schedule).

(6B) …]

[(6C) [OFCOM] shall not serve any such notice as is mentioned in subsection (5) on a BBC company unless they have given the Secretary of State notice of their intention to do so, specifying the relevant change.

(6D) Where [OFCOM] receive any written representations from a BBC company under subsection (6), they shall send a copy of the representations to the Secretary of State.]

(7) In this section "relevant change", in relation to a body to which a licence had been awarded or granted, means—
(a) any change affecting the nature or characteristics of the body, or
(b) any change in the persons having control over or interests in the body, [or
(c) any other change giving rise to [a disqualification under Part 2 of Schedule 2 to this Act or a contravention of a requirement imposed by or under Schedule 14 to the Communications Act 2003,]]

being [(in any case)] a change which is such that, if it fell to [OFCOM] to determine whether to award the licence to the body in the new circumstances of the case, they would be induced by the change to refrain from so awarding it.
[3030]

NOTES

Sub-s (1): reference to "OFCOM" in square brackets substituted, and paras (b), (c) substituted, for original para (b), by the Communications Act 2003, ss 350(2), 360(3), Sch 15, Pt 1, para 35(1), (2), subject to transitional provisions in s 406(6) of, and Sch 18, paras 5, 30, 54(5)–(7), 39, 64 to, that Act at **[3434]**, **[3460]**.

Sub-s (2): reference to "OFCOM" in square brackets substituted, and paras (da), (db) inserted, by the Communications Act 2003, s 360(3), Sch 15, Pt 1, para 35(1)–(3), subject to transitional provisions in s 406(6) of, and Sch 18, paras 30, 39, 64 to, that Act at **[3434]**, **[3460]**.

Sub-s (2A): inserted by the Broadcasting Act 1996, s 136, Sch 8, para 6; word in square brackets substituted by the Communications Act 2003, s 360(3), Sch 15, Pt 1, para 35(1), (2), subject to transitional provisions in s 406(6) of, and Sch 18, paras 30, 39, 64 to, that Act at **[3434]**, **[3460]**.

Sub-ss (3)–(5): words in square brackets substituted by the Communications Act 2003, s 360(3), Sch 15, Pt 1, para 35(1), (2), subject to transitional provisions in s 406(6) of, and Sch 18, paras 30, 39, 64 to, that Act at **[3434]**, **[3460]**.

Sub-s (6): substituted, together with sub-ss (6A), (6B), for original sub-s (6), by the Broadcasting Act 1996, s 73, Sch 2, para 13(2); words in square brackets substituted by the Communications Act 2003, s 360(3), Sch 15, Pt 1, para 35(1), (2), (4), subject to transitional provisions in s 406(6) of, and Sch 18, paras 5, 30, 39, 64 to, that Act at **[3434]**, **[3460]**.

Sub-s (6A): substituted, together with sub-ss (6), (6B), for original sub-s (6), by the Broadcasting Act 1996, s 73, Sch 2, para 13(2); para (a) repealed, and words in square brackets in para (b) substituted, by the Communications Act 2003, ss 360(3), 406(7), Sch 15, Pt 1, para 35(1), (5), Sch 19(1), subject to transitional provisions in s 406(6) of, and Sch 18, paras 5, 30, 39, 64 to, that Act at **[3434]**, **[3460]**.

Sub-s (6B): substituted, together with sub-ss (6), (6A), for original sub-s (6), by the Broadcasting Act 1996, s 73, Sch 2, para 13(2); repealed by the Communications Act 2003, ss 360(3), 406(7), Sch 15, Pt 1, para 35(1), (6), Sch 19(1), subject to transitional provisions in s 406(6) of, and Sch 18, paras 5, 30, 39, 64 to, that Act at **[3434]**, **[3460]**.

Sub-ss (6C), (6D): inserted by the Broadcasting Act 1996, s 136, Sch 8, para 6; words in square brackets substituted by the Communications Act 2003, s 360(3), Sch 15, Pt 1, para 35(1), (2), subject to transitional provisions in s 406(6) of, and Sch 18, paras 30, 39, 64 to, that Act at **[3434]**, **[3460]**.

Sub-s (7): words in first (outer) pair of square brackets inserted, and words in third pair of square brackets substituted, by the Broadcasting Act 1996, s 73, Sch 2, Pt V, para 13(1), (3); words in second (inner) and fourth pairs of square brackets substituted by the Communications Act 2003, s 360(3), Sch 15, Pt 1, para 35(1), (2), (7), subject to transitional provisions in s 406(6) of, and Sch 18, paras 5, 30, 39, 64 to, that Act at **[3434]**, **[3460]**.

89 Disqualification for holding licence on grounds of conviction for transmitting offence

(1) Subject to subsection (2), a person shall be disqualified for holding a licence under this Part if within the last five years he has been convicted of—
[(a) an offence under section 35 of the Wireless Telegraphy Act 2006 (unauthorised

use etc of wireless telegraphy station or apparatus) consisting in the establishment or use of a wireless telegraphy station, or the installation or use of wireless telegraphy apparatus, for the purpose of making a broadcast (within the meaning of Part 5 of that Act);

(aa) an offence under section 36 of that Act (keeping wireless telegraphy station or apparatus available for unauthorised use) where the relevant contravention of section 8 of that Act would constitute an offence falling within paragraph (a);

(ab) an offence under section 37 or 38 of that Act (unlawful broadcasting offences);

(b) an offence under Part 5 of that Act (prohibition of broadcasting from sea or air); or]

(c) an offence under section 97 below.

(2) …

(3) Every licence granted under this Part shall include conditions requiring the holder of the licence to do all that he can to ensure that no person who is disqualified for holding a licence by virtue of subsection (1) is [concerned in—

(a) the provision of the licensed service or the making of programmes included in it; or

(b) the operation of [a wireless telegraphy station] used for broadcasting the service]. **[3031]**

NOTES

Sub-s (1): paras (a), (aa), (ab), (b) substituted by the Wireless Telegraphy Act 2006, s 123, Sch 7, paras 9, 12(1), (2). Paras (a), (aa), (ab) were previously substituted, for original para (a), by the Communications Act 2003, s 360(3), Sch 15, Pt 1, para 36(1), (2), subject to transitional provisions in s 406(6) of, and Sch 18, paras 30, 64 to, that Act at **[3434]**, **[3460]**, and subject to further transitional provisions as noted below.

Sub-s (2): repealed by the Communications Act 2003, s 406(7), Sch 19(1), subject to transitional provisions in s 406(6) of, and Sch 18, paras 5, 30, 64 to, that Act at **[3434]**, **[3460]**.

Sub-s (3): words in first (outer) pair of square brackets substituted by the Communications Act 2003, s 360(3), Sch 15, Pt 1, para 36(1), (3), subject to transitional provisions in s 406(6) of, and Sch 18, paras 30, 64 to, that Act at **[3434]**, **[3460]**, and subject to further transitional provisions as noted below; words in square brackets in para (b) substituted by the Wireless Telegraphy Act 2006, s 123, Sch 7, paras 9, 12(1), (3).

Transitional provisions: the Communications Act 2003, Sch 15, Pt 1, para 36(4) provides that the amendments made by Sch 15, Pt 1, para 36(1)–(3) to that Act do not impose a disqualification in respect of any offence committed before 29 December 2003.

90–96 (*Repealed by the Communications Act 2003, s 406(7), Sch 19(1), subject to transitional provisions in s 406(6) of, and Sch 18, paras 5, 30, 42, 43, 64 to, that Act at* **[3434]**, **[3460]**.)

Prohibition on providing unlicensed independent radio services

97 Prohibition on providing independent radio services without a licence

(1) Subject to subsection (2), any person who provides any [relevant regulated radio service] without being authorised to do so by or under a licence under this Part [or Part II of the Broadcasting Act 1996] shall be guilty of an offence.

[(1A) In subsection (1) "relevant regulated radio service" means a service falling to be regulated by OFCOM under section 245 of the Communications Act 2003, other than a radio multiplex service.]

(2) The Secretary of State may, after consultation with [OFCOM], by order provide that subsection (1) shall not apply to such services or descriptions of services as are specified in the order.

(3) A person guilty of an offence under this section shall be liable—

(a) on summary conviction, to a fine not exceeding the statutory maximum;

(b) on conviction on indictment, to a fine.

(4) No proceedings in respect of an offence under this section shall be instituted—

(a) in England and Wales, except by or with the consent of the Director of Public Prosecutions;

(b) in Northern Ireland, except by or with the consent of the Director of Public Prosecutions for Northern Ireland.

(5) Without prejudice to subsection (3) above, compliance with this section shall be enforceable by civil proceedings by the Crown for an injunction or interdict or for any other appropriate relief.

(6) Any order under this section shall be subject to annulment in pursuance of a resolution of either House of Parliament.

[3032]

NOTES

Sub-s (1): words in first pair of square brackets substituted by the Communications Act 2003, s 360(3), Sch 15, Pt 1, para 37(1), (2), subject to transitional provisions in s 406(6) of, and Sch 18, paras 5, 30, 64 to, that Act at **[3434]**, **[3460]**; words in second pair of square brackets inserted by the Broadcasting Act 1996, s 148(1), Sch 10, Pt 1, para 7.

Sub-s (1A): inserted by the Communications Act 2003, s 360(3), Sch 15, Pt 1, para 37(1), (3), subject to transitional provisions in s 406(6) of, and Sch 18, paras 30, 64 to, that Act at **[3434]**, **[3460]**.

Sub-s (2): word in square brackets substituted by the Communications Act 2003, s 360(3), Sch 15, Pt 1, para 37(1), (4), subject to transitional provisions in s 406(6) of, and Sch 18, paras 30, 64 to, that Act at **[3434]**, **[3460]**.

Orders: the Broadcasting Act 1990 (Independent Radio Services: Exceptions) Order 1990, SI 1990/2536 at **[3468]**.

CHAPTER II
SOUND BROADCASTING SERVICES

National services

98 Applications for national licences

(1) Where [OFCOM] propose to grant a licence to provide a national service, they shall publish, in such manner as they consider appropriate, a notice—

(a) stating that they propose to grant such a licence;

(b) specifying—

(i) the period for which the licence is to be granted,

(ii) the minimum area of the United Kingdom for which the service is to be provided,

[(iia) the digital capacity that is likely, in their opinion, to be available from the holders of national radio multiplex licences for the broadcasting of a simulcast radio service corresponding to the service,]

(iii) if the service is to be one falling within section 85(2)(a)(i) or (ii), that the service is to be such a service, and

(iv) if there is any existing licensed national service, that the service is to be one which caters for tastes and interests different from those already catered for by any such service (as described in the notice);

(c) inviting applications for the licence and specifying the closing date for such applications; and

(d) specifying—

(i) the fee payable on any application made in pursuance of the notice, and

(ii) the percentage of qualifying revenue for each accounting period that would be payable by an applicant in pursuance of section 102(1)(c) if he were granted the licence.

(2) In determining the minimum area of the United Kingdom for which a national service is to be provided [OFCOM] shall have regard to the following considerations, namely—

(a) that the service in question should, so far as is reasonably practicable, make the most effective use of the frequency or frequencies on which it is to be provided; but

(b) that the area for which it is to be provided should not be so extensive that the costs of providing it would be likely to affect the ability of the person providing the service to maintain it.

(3) Any application made in pursuance of a notice under this section must be in writing and accompanied by—

(a) the applicant's proposals for providing a service that would … —

(i) comply with any requirement specified in the notice under subsection (1)(b)(iii) or (iv), …

(ii) …

[(aa) the applicant's proposals (if any) for providing a simulcast radio service corresponding to the service,]

(b) the fee specified in the notice under subsection (1)(d)(i);

(c) the applicant's proposals for training or retraining persons employed or to be employed by him in order to help fit them for employment in, or in connection with, the making of programmes to be included in his proposed service;

(d) the applicant's cash bid in respect of the licence;

(e) such information as [OFCOM] may reasonably require—

(i) as to the applicant's present financial position and his projected financial position during the period for which the licence would be in force, and

(ii) as to the arrangements which the applicant proposes to make for, and in connection with, the transmission of his proposed service; and

(f) such other information as [OFCOM] may reasonably require for the purpose of considering the application.

[(3A) For the purposes of subsection (1)(d)(ii)—

(a) different percentages may be specified for different accounting periods, and

(b) the percentages that may be specified for an accounting period include a nil percentage.]

(4) At any time after receiving such an application and before determining it [OFCOM] may require the applicant to furnish additional information under any of paragraphs (a), [(aa),] (c), (e) and (f) of subsection (3).

(5) Any information to be furnished to [OFCOM] under this section shall, if they so require, be in such form or verified in such manner as they may specify.

(6) [OFCOM] shall, as soon as reasonably practicable after the date specified in a notice under this section as the closing date for applications, publish in such manner as they consider appropriate—

(a) the name of every person who has made an application to them in pursuance of the notice;

(b) the proposals submitted by him under subsection (3)(a) [and (aa)]; and

(c) such other information connected with his application as [OFCOM] consider appropriate.

(7) In this section ["national radio multiplex licence" has the same meaning as in Part 2 of the Broadcasting Act 1996; and] "programme" does not include an advertisement.

(8) In this Part "cash bid", in relation to a licence, means an offer to pay to [OFCOM] a specified amount of money in respect of the first complete calendar year falling within the period for which the licence is in force (being an amount which, as increased by the appropriate percentage, is also to be payable in respect of subsequent years falling wholly or partly within that period).

[3033]

NOTES

Sub-s (1): word in square brackets substituted, and sub-para (b)(iia) inserted, by the Communications Act 2003, ss 257(1), (2), 360(3), Sch 15, Pt 1, para 38(1), (2), subject to transitional provisions in s 406(6) of, and Sch 18, paras 30, 44(2), (4), 64 to, that Act at **[3434]**, **[3460]**.

Sub-ss (2), (5), (8): words in square brackets substituted by the Communications Act 2003, s 360(3), Sch 15, Pt 1, para 38(1), (2), subject to transitional provisions in s 406(6) of, and Sch 18, paras 30, 44(2), (4), 64 to, that Act at **[3434]**, **[3460]**.

Sub-s (3): words omitted repealed, para (aa) inserted, and other words in square brackets substituted, by the Communications Act 2003, ss 257(1), (3), 360(3), 406(7), Sch 15, Pt 1, para 38(1)–(3), Sch 19(1), subject to transitional provisions in s 406(6) of, and Sch 18, paras 30, 44(2), (4), 64 to, that Act at **[3434]**, **[3460]**.

Sub-s (3A): inserted by the Communications Act 2003, s 360(3), Sch 15, Pt 1, para 38(1), (4), subject to transitional provisions in s 406(6) of, and Sch 18, paras 30, 44(2), (4), 64 to, that Act at **[3434]**, **[3460]**.

Sub-s (4): word in first pair of square brackets substituted, and number in second pair of square brackets inserted, by the Communications Act 2003, s 360(3), Sch 15, Pt 1, para 38(1), (2), (5), subject to transitional provisions in s 406(6) of, and Sch 18, paras 30, 44(2), (4), 64 to, that Act at **[3434]**, **[3460]**.

Sub-s (6): references to "OFCOM" in square brackets substituted, and words in square brackets in para (b) inserted, by the Communications Act 2003, s 360(3), Sch 15, Pt 1, para 38(1), (2), (6), subject to transitional provisions in s 406(6) of, and Sch 18, paras 30, 44(2), (4), 64 to, that Act at **[3434]**, **[3460]**.

Sub-s (7): words in square brackets inserted by the Communications Act 2003, s 257(1), (4), subject to transitional provisions in s 406(6) of, and Sch 18, para 44(2), (4) to, that Act at **[3434]**, **[3460]**.

99 Procedure to be followed by [OFCOM] in connection with consideration of applications for national licences

(1) Where a person has made an application for a national licence in accordance with section 98, [OFCOM] shall not proceed to consider whether to award him the licence on the basis of his cash bid in accordance with section 100 unless it appears to them—

(a) that his proposed service would … —

(i) comply with any requirement specified under subsection (1)(b)(iii) or (iv) of section 98, …

(ii) … ; and

(b) that he would be able to maintain that service [and any proposed simulcast radio service corresponding to that service] throughout the period for which the licence would be in force.

(2) Any reference to an applicant in section 100 (except in section 100(9)(b)) is accordingly a reference to an applicant in whose case it appears to [OFCOM] that the requirements of subsection (1)(a) and (b) above are satisfied.

[3034]

NOTES

Section heading: word in square brackets substituted by virtue of the Communications Act 2003, s 360(3), Sch 15, Pt 1, para 39(1), (2), subject to transitional provisions in s 406(6) of, and Sch 18, paras 30, 44(2), (4), 64 to, that Act at **[3434]**, **[3460]**.

Sub-s (1): word in first pair of square brackets substituted, words omitted repealed, and words in square brackets in para (b) inserted, by the Communications Act 2003, ss 360(3), 406(7), Sch 15, Pt 1, para 39(1)–(3), Sch 19(1), subject to transitional provisions in s 406(6) of, and Sch 18, paras 30, 44(2), (4), 64 to, that Act at **[3434]**, **[3460]**.

Sub-s (2): word in square brackets substituted by the Communications Act 2003, s 360(3), Sch 15, Pt 1, para 39(1), (2), subject to transitional provisions in s 406(6) of, and Sch 18, paras 30, 44(2), (4), 64 to, that Act at **[3434]**, **[3460]**.

100 Award of national licence to person submitting highest cash bid

(1) Subject to the following provisions of this section, [OFCOM] shall, after considering all the cash bids submitted by the applicants for a national licence, award the licence to the applicant who submitted the highest bid.

[(1A) If, in a case in which one or more of the applicants has made a proposal to provide a simulcast radio service corresponding to the service to be licensed (a "simulcast applicant"), the highest cash bid is made by an applicant who is not a simulcast applicant, OFCOM may—

(a) disregard the requirement imposed by subsection (1); and

(b) award the licence to the simulcast applicant whose cash bid is the highest of the bids submitted by simulcast applicants.

(2) Where—

(a) two or more applicants for a licence have submitted cash bids specifying an identical amount and that amount is higher than the amount of every other bid, or

(b) two or more simulcast applicants have submitted cash bids specifying an identical amount and that amount is higher than the amount of every other bid submitted by a simulcast applicant,

OFCOM must invite those applicants and (in a case falling within paragraph (b)) every applicant who has made a higher bid to submit further cash bids in respect of that licence.

(2A) OFCOM may decide not to invite an applicant to submit a further cash bid under subsection (2) if—

(a) the applicant is not a simulcast applicant and they propose to exercise their power under subsection (1A); or

(b) they propose to exercise their power under subsection (3).

(2B) Subsection (2A) is not to be construed as preventing OFCOM from making a decision to exercise their power under subsection (1A) or (3) after they have received further bids in response to invitations under subsection (2).

(2C) In this Part references to a person's cash bid, in relation to a person who has submitted a further cash bid in pursuance of subsection (2), have effect as references to his further bid.]

(3) [OFCOM] may disregard the requirement imposed by subsection (1) and award the licence to an applicant who has not submitted the highest bid if it appears to them that there

are exceptional circumstances which make it appropriate for them to award the licence to that applicant; and where it appears to [OFCOM], in the context of the licence, that any circumstances are to be regarded as exceptional circumstances for the purposes of this subsection, those circumstances may be so regarded by them despite the fact that similar circumstances have been so regarded by them in the context of any other licence or licences.

(4) If it appears to [OFCOM], in the case of the applicant to whom (apart from this subsection) they would award the licence in accordance with the preceding provisions of this section, that there are grounds for suspecting that any relevant source of funds is such that it would not be in the public interest for the licence to be awarded to him—

(a) they shall refer his application to the Secretary of State, together with—

(i) a copy of all documents submitted to them by the applicant, and

(ii) a summary of their deliberations on the application; and

(b) they shall not award the licence to him unless the Secretary of State has given his approval.

(5) On such a reference the Secretary of State may only refuse to give his approval to the licence being awarded to the applicant in question if he is satisfied that any relevant source of funds is such that it would not be in the public interest for the licence to be so awarded.

(6) In subsections (4) and (5) "relevant source of funds", in relation to an applicant, means any source of funds to which he might (directly or indirectly) have recourse for the purpose of—

(a) paying any amounts payable by him by virtue of section 102(1), or

(b) otherwise financing the provision of his proposed service.

(7) Where [OFCOM] are, by virtue of subsection (4), precluded from awarding the licence to an applicant, the preceding provisions of this section shall (subject to subsection (11)) have effect as if that person had not made an application for the licence.

(8) Where [OFCOM] have awarded a national licence to any person in accordance with this section, they shall, as soon as reasonably practicable after awarding the licence—

(a) publish the matters specified in subsection (9) in such manner as they consider appropriate; and

(b) grant the licence to that person.

(9) The matters referred to in subsection (8)(a) are—

(a) the name of the person to whom the licence has been awarded and the amount of his cash bid;

(b) the name of every other applicant in whose case it appeared to [OFCOM] that the requirement specified in section 99(1)(a) was satisfied;

(c) where the licence has, by virtue of subsection (3) above, been awarded to an applicant who has not submitted the highest cash bid, [OFCOM's] reasons for the licence having been so awarded; and

(d) such other information as [OFCOM] consider appropriate.

(10) In a case where the licence has been awarded to any person by virtue of the operation of this section, in accordance with any provision of this Part, on the revocation of an earlier grant of the licence, subsection (9) shall have effect as if—

(a) paragraph (b) were omitted; and

(b) the matters specified in that subsection included an indication of the circumstances in which the licence has been awarded to that person.

(11) Subsections (1) to (6) shall not have effect as mentioned in subsection (7) if [OFCOM] decide that it would be desirable to publish a fresh notice under section 98 in respect of the grant of the licence; and similarly, where any of the following provisions of this Part provides, in connection with the revocation of a licence, for this section to have effect as if the former holder of the licence had not made an application for it, this section shall not so have effect if [OFCOM] decide that it would be desirable to publish a fresh notice under this Part in respect of the grant of a further licence to provide the service in question.

[3035]

NOTES

Sub-ss (1), (3), (4), (7)–(9), (11): words in square brackets substituted by the Communications Act 2003, s 360(3), Sch 15, Pt 1, para 40, subject to transitional provisions in s 406(6) of, and Sch 18, paras 30, 44(2), (4), 64 to, that Act at **[3434]**, **[3460]**.

Sub-ss (1A)–(2C): substituted, for original sub-s (2), by the Communications Act 2003, s 257(1), (5), subject to transitional provisions in s 406(6) of, and Sch 18, para 44(2), (4) to, that Act at **[3434]**, **[3460]**.

[100A Licence conditions relating to simulcast radio services

Where OFCOM award a national licence to a person whose application for that licence included proposals to provide a simulcast radio service, that licence must include a condition requiring the licence holder—

(a) to provide, from a date specified in the licence, a simulcast radio service corresponding to the licensed service, and

(b) to do all that he can to secure the broadcasting of that service.]

[3036]

NOTES

Commencement: 29 December 2003.

Inserted by the Communications Act 2003, s 257(1), (6), subject to transitional provisions in s 406(6) of, and Sch 18, para 44(2), (4) to, that Act at **[3434]**, **[3460]**.

101 Failure to begin providing licensed service and financial penalties on revocation of licence

(1) If at any time after a national licence has been granted to any person but before the licence has come into force—

(a) that person indicates to [OFCOM] that he does not intend to provide [the licensed national service or that he does not intend to provide a corresponding simulcast radio service that he is required to provide by a condition imposed under section 100A], or

(b) [OFCOM] for any other reason have reasonable grounds for believing that that person will not provide [the licensed national service or any such simulcast radio service] once the licence has come into force,

then, subject to subsection (2)—

(i) [OFCOM] shall serve on him a notice revoking the licence as from the time the notice is served on him, and

(ii) section 100 shall (subject to section 100(11)) have effect as if he had not made an application for the licence.

(2) Subsection (1) shall not apply in the case of any person by virtue of paragraph (b) of that subsection unless [OFCOM] have served on him a notice stating their grounds for believing that he will not provide [the licensed national service or the simulcast radio service] once his licence has come into force; and they shall not serve such a notice on him unless they have given him a reasonable opportunity of making representations to them about the matters complained of.

(3) Where [OFCOM] revoke a national licence under this section or under any other provision of this Part, they shall serve on the licence holder a notice requiring him to pay to them, within a specified period, [a specified financial penalty].

[(3A) The maximum amount which a person may be required to pay by way of a penalty under subsection (3) is the maximum penalty given by subsections (3B) and (3C).

(3B) In a case where the licence is revoked under this section or the penalty is imposed before the end of the first complete accounting period of the licence holder to fall within the period for which the licence is in force, the maximum penalty is whichever is the greater of—

(a) £250,000; and

(b) 7 per cent of the amount which OFCOM estimate would have been the qualifying revenue for the first complete accounting period of the licence holder falling within the period for which the licence would have been in force.

(3C) In any other case, the maximum penalty is whichever is the greater of—

(a) £250,000; and

(b) 7 per cent of the qualifying revenue for the last complete accounting period of the licence holder falling within the period for which the licence is in force.

(3D) Section 102(2) to (6) applies for estimating or determining qualifying revenue for the purposes of subsection (3B) or (3C) above.]

(5) Any financial penalty payable by any body by virtue of subsection (3) shall, in addition to being recoverable from that body as provided by section 122(4), be recoverable by [OFCOM] as a debt due to them from any person who controls that body.

[3037]

NOTES

Sub-ss (1)–(3), (5): words in square brackets substituted by the Communications Act 2003, ss 345, 360(3), Sch 13, Pt 1, paras 1, 6(1), Sch 15, Pt 1, para 41, subject to savings and transitional provisions in ss 345, 406(6) of, and Sch 13, Pt 1, para 6(3), Sch 18, paras 5, 30, 44(2), (4), 64 to, that Act at **[3393]**, **[3434]**, **[3454]**, **[3460]**.

Sub-ss (3A)–(3D): substituted, for original sub-s (4), by the Communications Act 2003, s 345, Sch 13, Pt 1, paras 1, 6(2), subject to savings and transitional provisions in ss 345, 406(6) of, and Sch 13, Pt 1, para 6(3), Sch 18, paras 5, 30 to, that Act at **[3393]**, **[3434]**, **[3454]**, **[3460]**.

102 Additional payments to be made in respect of national licences

(1) A national licence shall include conditions requiring the licence holder to pay to [OFCOM] (in addition to any fees required to be so paid by virtue of section 87(1)(c))—

(a) in respect of the first complete calendar year falling within the period for which the licence is in force, the amount specified in his cash bid;

(b) in respect of each subsequent year falling wholly or partly within that period, the amount so specified as increased by the appropriate percentage; and

(c) in respect of each accounting period of his falling within the period referred to in paragraph (a), an amount representing such percentage of the qualifying revenue for that accounting period as was specified in relation to the licence under section 98(1)(d)(ii).

(2) For the purposes of subsection (1)(c) the qualifying revenue for any accounting period of the licence holder shall (subject to subsection (6)) consist of all payments received or to be received by him or by any connected person—

(a) in consideration of the inclusion in the licensed service in that period of advertisements or other programmes, or

(b) in respect of charges made in that period for the reception of programmes included in that service.

(3) If, in connection with the inclusion of any advertisements or other programmes whose inclusion is paid for by payments falling within subsection (2), any payments are made to the licence holder or any connected person to meet any payments payable by the licence holder by virtue of subsection (1)(c), those payments shall be regarded as made in consideration of the inclusion of the programmes in question.

(4) In the case of an advertisement included under arrangements made between—

(a) the licence holder or any connected person, and

(b) a person acting as an advertising agent,

the amount of any receipt by the licence holder or any connected person that represents a payment by the advertiser from which the advertising agent has deducted any amount by way of commission shall, except in a case falling within subsection (5), be the amount of the payment by the advertiser after the deduction of the commission.

(5) If the amount deducted by way of commission as mentioned in subsection (4) exceeds 15 per cent of the payment by the advertiser, the amount of the receipt in question shall be taken to be the amount of the payment less 15 per cent.

(6) If, in any accounting period of the licence holder, the licence holder or any connected person derives, in relation to any programme to be included in the licensed service, any financial benefit (whether direct or indirect) from payments made by any person, by way of sponsorship, for the purpose of defraying or contributing towards costs incurred or to be incurred in connection with that programme, the qualifying revenue for that accounting period shall be taken for the purposes of subsection (1)(c) to include the amount of the financial benefit so derived by the licence holder or the connected person, as the case may be.

(7) A national licence may include conditions—

(a) enabling [OFCOM] to estimate before the beginning of an accounting period the amount due for that period by virtue of subsection (1)(c); and

(b) requiring the licence holder to pay the estimated amount by monthly instalments throughout that period.

(8) Such a licence may in particular include conditions—

(a) authorising [OFCOM] to revise any estimate on one or more occasions, and to adjust the instalments payable by the licence holder to take account of the revised estimate;

(b) providing for the adjustment of any overpayment or underpayment.

(9) Where—

(a) the first complete accounting period of the licence holder falling within the period referred to in subsection (1)(a) ("the licence period") does not begin at the same time as that period, or

(b) the last complete accounting period of his falling within the licence period does not end at the same time as that period,

any reference in subsection (1)(c) to an accounting period of his shall include a reference to such part of the accounting period preceding that first complete accounting period, or (as the case may be) following that last complete accounting period, as falls within the licence period; and other references to accounting periods in this Part shall be construed accordingly.

(10) In this Part "the appropriate percentage", in relation to any year ("the relevant year"), means the percentage which corresponds to the percentage increase between—

(a) the retail prices index for the month of November in the year preceding the first complete calendar year falling within the period for which the licence in question is in force; and

(b) the retail prices index for the month of November in the year preceding the relevant year;

and for this purpose "the retail prices index" means the general index of prices (for all items) published by the [Office for National Statistics].

[3038]

NOTES

Sub-ss (1), (7), (8): words in square brackets substituted by the Communications Act 2003, s 360(3), Sch 15, Pt 1, para 42, subject to transitional provisions in s 406(6) of, and Sch 18, paras 30, 44(2), (4), 64 to, that Act at **[3434]**, **[3460]**.

Sub-s (10): words in square brackets substituted by the Transfer of Functions (Registration and Statistics) Order 1996, SI 1996/273, art 5(1), Sch 2, para 25.

103 Restriction on changes in control over holder of national licence

(1) Where—

(a) any change in the persons having control over—

(i) a body to which a national licence has been awarded or transferred in accordance with this Part of this Act, or

(ii) an associated programme provider,

takes place within the relevant period, and

(b) that change takes place without having been previously approved for the purposes of this section by [OFCOM],

then (subject to subsection (5)) [OFCOM] may, if the licence has not yet been granted, refuse to grant it to the body referred to in paragraph (a)(i) above or, if it has already been granted, serve on that body a notice revoking it.

(2) In subsection (1)—

"associated programme provider", in relation to such a body as is mentioned in paragraph (a)(i) of that subsection, means any body which is connected with that body and [is or is likely to be involved, to a substantial extent, in the provision of the programmes included] in the licensed service; and

"the relevant period", in relation to a national licence, means the period beginning with the date of the award of the licence and ending on the first anniversary of the date of its coming into force;

and paragraph 3 in Part I of Schedule 2 to this Act shall have effect for the purposes of this subsection [as it has effect for the purposes of that Schedule.]

(3) [OFCOM] shall refuse to approve for the purposes of this section such a change as is mentioned in subsection (1)(a) if it appears to them that the change would be prejudicial to the provision under the licence, by the body referred to in subsection (1)(a)(i), of a service which accords with the proposals submitted under section 98(3)(a) by that body (or, as the case may be, by the person to whom the licence was originally awarded).

(4) [OFCOM] may refuse so to approve any such change if, in any circumstances not falling within subsection (3), they consider it appropriate to do so.

(5) [OFCOM] shall not under subsection (1) refuse to grant a licence to, or serve a notice on, any body unless they have given it a reasonable opportunity of making representations to them about the matters complained of.

(6) Where under subsection (1) [OFCOM] refuse to grant a licence to any body, section 100 shall (subject to section 100(11)) have effect as if that body had not made an application for the licence; and, where under that subsection they serve on any body a notice revoking its licence, subsections (6) and (7) of section 111 shall apply in relation to that notice as they apply in relation to a notice served under subsection (3) of that section.

[3039]

NOTES

Sub-ss (1)–(6): words in square brackets substituted by the Communications Act 2003, s 360(3), Sch 15, Pt 1, para 43, subject to transitional provisions in s 406(6) of, and Sch 18, paras 30, 44(1), (4), 64 to, that Act at **[3434]**, **[3460]**.

[103A Renewal of national licences

(1) A national licence may (subject to the following provisions of this section) be renewed on one occasion for a period of [twelve] years beginning with the date of renewal.

(2) An application for the renewal of a national licence under subsection (1) may be made by the licence holder not earlier than three years before the date on which it would otherwise cease to be in force and not later than [the day falling three months before] the relevant date.

(3) Where any such application is made … —

(a) …

(b) … , [OFCOM] may postpone the consideration of the application for so long as they think appropriate having regard to subsection (8).

(4) Where an application for the renewal of a national licence has been duly made to [OFCOM], they shall (subject to subsection (5)) grant the application if, but only if—

(a) [OFCOM] are satisfied that the applicant would, if his licence were renewed, provide a national service which complied with the conditions included in the licence in pursuance of section 106 (whether as originally imposed or as varied under that section),

[(b) the applicant gave notice to OFCOM, within the period of one month beginning with the commencement of section 42 of the Broadcasting Act 1996, of his intention to provide a simulcast radio service, and]

(c) a simulcast radio service provided by the applicant is being broadcast in digital form or [OFCOM] are satisfied that by the relevant date the applicant has done all that it would in the circumstances be reasonable to expect him to do by that date to procure the broadcasting of such a service within such time as [OFCOM] consider reasonable.

(5) Section 100(4) to (6) shall apply in relation to an applicant for the renewal of a national licence as those provisions apply in relation to such an applicant as is mentioned in section 100(4), but as if any reference to the awarding of such a licence to the applicant were a reference to the renewal of the applicant's licence under this section.

(6) On the grant of any application under this section [OFCOM]—

(a) may, in a case where a simulcast radio service provided by the applicant is not yet being broadcast in digital form on the relevant date, determine a date by which the broadcasting of such a service in that form must begin;

(b) shall determine an amount which is to be payable to [OFCOM] by the applicant in respect of the first complete calendar year falling within the period for which the licence is to be renewed; and

(c) may specify a different percentage from that specified under section 98(1)(d)(ii) as the percentage of qualifying revenue for each accounting period of his that will be payable by the applicant in pursuance of section 102(1)(c) during the period for which the licence is to be renewed.

[(7) The amount determined under subsection (6)(b) must be equal to the amount which, in OFCOM's opinion, would have been the cash bid of the licence holder were the licence (instead of being renewed) to be granted for the period of the renewal on an application made in accordance with section 98.

(7A) For the purposes of subsection (6)(c)—

(a) different percentages may be specified for different accounting periods, and

(b) the percentages that may be specified for an accounting period include a nil percentage.]

(8) Where [OFCOM] have granted a person's application under this section they shall formally renew his licence not later than the relevant date or, if that is not reasonably practicable …, as soon after that date as is reasonably practicable; and they shall not so renew his licence unless they have notified him of—

(a) any date determined by them under subsection (6)(a),
(b) the amount determined by them under subsection (6)(b), and
(c) any percentage specified by them under subsection (6)(c),

and he has, within such period as is specified in that notification, notified them that he consents to the licence being renewed on those terms.

(9) Where a national licence has been renewed under this section—

(a) any conditions included in it in pursuance of section 102 shall have effect during the period for which the licence has been renewed—
  (i) as if the amount determined by [OFCOM] under subsection (6)(b) were an amount specified in a cash bid submitted by the licence holder, and
  (ii) subject to any determination made under subsection (6)(c);
(b) (subject to paragraph (a)) that section shall have effect in relation to the period for which the licence has been renewed as it has effect in relation to the period for which a national licence is originally in force;
(c) where [OFCOM] have determined a date under subsection (6)(a), they shall include in the licence as renewed a condition requiring a simulcast radio service to be broadcast in digital form throughout the period beginning with the date determined under subsection (6)(a) and ending with the date on which the licence (as renewed) is to expire; and
(d) the reference in section 111(4) to the end of the period for which a national licence is to continue in force shall, in relation to the licence, be construed as a reference to the end of the period for which it has been renewed.

(10) …

[(10A) In the case of a pre-transfer national licence (including one for a period extended under section 253 of the Communications Act 2003)—

(a) the licence is not to be capable of being renewed under this section if it has already been renewed under this section before the radio transfer date, and
(b) on the renewal of the licence, it shall be the duty of OFCOM to secure that the renewed licence contains only such provision as would be included in a national licence granted by OFCOM under this Part after the radio transfer date.]

(11) In this section—

…

"the relevant date", in relation to a national licence, means the date which [OFCOM] determine to be that by which they would need to publish a notice under section 98(1) if they were to grant, as from the date on which that licence would expire if not renewed, a fresh licence to provide the national service formerly provided under that licence.]

[(12) A determination for the purposes of subsection (11)—

(a) must be made at least one year before the date determined, and
(b) must be notified by OFCOM to the person who holds the licence in question.]

[3040]

NOTES

Inserted by the Broadcasting Act 1996, s 92.

Sub-ss (1), (4), (6), (9): words in square brackets substituted by the Communications Act 2003, s 360(3), Sch 15, Pt 1, para 44(1)–(3), (6), subject to transitional provisions in s 406(6) of, and Sch 18, paras 5, 30, 44(2), (4), 64 to, that Act at **[3434]**, **[3460]**.

Sub-s (2): words in square brackets inserted by the Communications Act 2003, s 360(3), Sch 15, Pt 1, para 44(1), (4), subject to transitional provisions in s 406(6) of, and Sch 18, paras 5, 30, 44(2), (4), 50, 64 to, that Act at **[3434]**, **[3460]**.

Sub-ss (3), (8), (11): words omitted repealed, and words in square brackets substituted, by the Communications Act 2003, ss 360(3), 406(7), Sch 15, Pt 1, para 44(1), (2), (5), Sch 19(1), subject to transitional provisions in s 406(6) of, and Sch 18, paras 5, 30, 44(2), (4), 64 to, that Act at **[3434]**, **[3460]**.

Sub-ss (7), (7A): substituted, for original sub-s (7), by the Communications Act 2003, s 360(3), Sch 15, Pt 1, para 44(1), (7), subject to transitional provisions in s 406(6) of, and Sch 18, paras 5, 30, 44(2), (4), 64 to, that Act at **[3434]**, **[3460]**.

Sub-s (10): repealed by the Communications Act 2003, s 406(7), Sch 19(1), subject to transitional provisions in s 406(6) of, and Sch 18, paras 5, 30, 44(2), (4), 64 to, that Act at **[3434]**, **[3460]**.

Sub-s (10A): inserted by the Communications Act 2003, s 360(3), Sch 15, Pt 1, para 44(1), (8), subject to transitional provisions in s 406(6) of, and Sch 18, paras 30, 44(2), (4), 64 to, that Act at **[3434]**, **[3460]**.

Sub-s (12): added by the Communications Act 2003, s 360(3), Sch 15, Pt 1, para 44(1), (9), subject to transitional provisions in s 406(6) of, and Sch 18, paras 30, 44(2), (4), 50, 64 to, that Act at **[3434]**, **[3460]**.

Local and other services

104 Applications for other licences

(1) Where [OFCOM] propose to grant a licence to provide a local service, they shall publish, in such manner as they consider appropriate, a notice—

(a) stating that they propose to grant such a licence;

(b) specifying the area or locality in the United Kingdom for which the service is to be provided;

(c) inviting applications for the licence and specifying the closing date for applications; and

(d) stating the fee payable on any application made in pursuance of the notice.

(2) Any application made in pursuance of a notice under subsection (1) must be in writing and accompanied by—

(a) the fee specified in the notice under paragraph (d) of that subsection;

(b) the applicant's proposals for providing a service that would—

(i) cater for the tastes and interests of persons living in the area or locality for which it would be provided or for any particular tastes and interests of such persons, and

(ii) broaden the range of programmes available by way of local services to persons living in that area or locality;

(c) such information as [OFCOM] may reasonably require—

(i) as to the applicant's present financial position and his projected financial position during the period for which the licence would be in force, and

(ii) as to the arrangements which the applicant proposes to make for, and in connection with, the transmission of his proposed service; and

(d) such other information as [OFCOM] may reasonably require for the purpose of considering the application.

(3) At any time after receiving such an application and before determining it [OFCOM] may require the applicant to furnish additional information under subsection (2)(b), (c) or (d).

(4) [OFCOM] shall, at the request of any person and on the payment by him of such sum (if any) as [OFCOM] may reasonably require, make available for inspection by that person any information furnished under subsection (2)(b) by the applicants for a local licence.

(5) …

(6) [An application for a licence to provide a restricted service shall be made] in such manner as [OFCOM] may determine, and shall be accompanied by such fee (if any) as [OFCOM] may determine.

(7) In this section and sections 105 and 106 "programme" does not include an advertisement.

[3041]

NOTES

Sub-ss (1)–(4), (6): words in square brackets substituted by the Communications Act 2003, s 360(3), Sch 15, Pt 1, para 45, subject to transitional provisions in s 406(6) of, and Sch 18, paras 30, 44(3), (4), 64 to, that Act at **[3434]**, **[3460]**.

Sub-s (5): repealed by the Broadcasting Act 1996, ss 94(2), 148(2), Sch 11, Pt I.

Modification: this section is modified in its application to community radio services by the Community Radio Order 2004, SI 2004/1944, art 4, Schedule, Pt 1, paras 1, 3 at **[3624]**.

[104A Renewal of local licences

(1) A local licence may (subject to the following provisions of this section) be renewed on one occasion for a period of [twelve] years beginning with the date of renewal.

(2) No application for the renewal of a local licence under subsection (1) may be made before [OFCOM] first publish a notice pursuant to section 50(2) of the Broadcasting Act 1996 inviting applications for a licence to provide a relevant local radio multiplex service.

(3) Subject to subsection (2), an application for the renewal of a local licence under subsection (1) may be made by the licence holder not earlier than three years before the date on which it would otherwise cease to be in force and not later than [the day falling three months before] the relevant date.

(4) The applicant must, in his application or at any time before the consideration of his application, nominate—

(a) a local digital sound programme service provided or to be provided by him, and
(b) a relevant local radio multiplex service,

but may not nominate together a local digital sound programme service and a local radio multiplex service if another local licence held by him includes a condition in pursuance of subsection (12) relating to the broadcasting of that local digital sound programme service by that local radio multiplex service.

(5) Where an application for the renewal of a local licence has been duly made to [OFCOM], they shall grant the application if—

(a) they are satisfied that the applicant would, if his licence were renewed, provide a local service which complied with the conditions included in the licence in pursuance of section 106 (whether as originally imposed or as varied under that section), …
(b) the nominated local digital sound programme service provided by the applicant is being broadcast by means of the nominated local radio multiplex service,
[(c) they are satisfied that the period for which the nominated local digital sound programme service will be available for reception and the times at which it will be available will not be significantly different, week by week, from those for which and at which the licensed local service will be broadcast].

(6) Where the condition specified in subsection (5)(a) is satisfied, [OFCOM] may grant the application even though the condition specified in subsection (5)(b) is not satisfied if—

(a) the applicant holds a licence to provide local digital sound programme services,
(b) a licence to provide the nominated local radio multiplex service has been awarded, and
(c) it appears to [OFCOM] that, under a contract between the applicant and the person to whom that licence has been awarded, the applicant is obliged to provide the nominated local digital sound programme service for broadcasting by means of the nominated local radio multiplex service.

(7) [OFCOM] may in any case postpone consideration of the application until the relevant date.

(8) If, at the relevant date, the condition specified in subsection (5)(b) is not satisfied, and any of the conditions specified in subsection (6) is not satisfied, [OFCOM] may postpone consideration of the application for such period not exceeding twelve months as they think appropriate.

(9) Where [OFCOM] postpone consideration of an application under this section for any period beyond the relevant date (the "postponement period"), they shall extend the period for which the licence is in force by a period equal to the postponement period; and section 86(3) shall not limit the powers of [OFCOM] under this subsection.

(10) On the grant of any application under this section [OFCOM] shall—

(a) where the nominated local digital sound programme service provided by the applicant is not being broadcast by means of the nominated local radio multiplex service, determine a date by which that service must have begun to be so broadcast; and
(b) specify a fee payable to [OFCOM] in respect of the renewal.

(11) Where [OFCOM] have granted a person's application under this section they shall formally renew his licence as soon afterwards as is reasonably practicable; and they shall not so renew his licence unless they have notified him of—

(a) any date determined by them under subsection (10)(a), and
(b) the renewal fee specified by them under subsection (10)(b),

and he has, within such period as is specified in that notification, notified them that he consents to the licence being renewed on those terms.

(12) Where [OFCOM] renew a licence under this section they shall include in the licence as renewed a condition requiring the licence holder to do all that he can to ensure that the

nominated local digital sound programme service is broadcast by means of the nominated local radio multiplex service throughout the period beginning with whichever is the later of—

(a) the date on which the licence would expire if not renewed, and

(b) any date determined by them under subsection (10)(a),

and ending with the date on which the licence (as renewed) is to expire.

[(12A) In the case of a pre-transfer local licence (including one for a period extended under section 253 of the Communications Act 2003)—

(a) the licence is not to be capable of being renewed under this section if it has already been renewed under this section before the radio transfer date; and

(b) on the renewal of the licence, it shall be the duty of OFCOM to secure that the renewed licence contains only such provision as would be included in a local licence granted by OFCOM under this Part after the radio transfer date.]

(13) In this section—

(a) "local digital sound programme service" has the same meaning as in Part II of the Broadcasting Act 1996;

(b) "nominated" means nominated by the applicant under subsection (4);

(c) "relevant date", in relation to a local licence, means the date which [OFCOM] determine to be that by which they would need to publish a notice under section 104(1) if they were to grant, as from the date on which that licence would expire if not renewed, a fresh licence to provide the local service formerly provided under that licence; and

(d) "relevant local radio multiplex service", in relation to a local licence, means a local radio multiplex service (within the meaning of Part II of the Broadcasting Act 1996) with a coverage area which to a significant extent includes the coverage area of the local service provided under the local licence; and for this purpose "coverage area", in relation to a service, has the meaning given by [paragraph 8(2) of Schedule 14 to the Communications Act 2003].]

[(14) A determination for the purposes of subsection (13)(c)—

(a) must be made at least one year before the date determined; and

(b) must be notified by OFCOM to the person who holds the licence in question.]

[3042]

NOTES

Inserted by the Broadcasting Act 1996, s 94(1).

Sub-ss (1), (2), (6)–(12), (13): words in square brackets substituted by the Communications Act 2003, s 360(3), Sch 15, Pt 1, para 46(1)–(3), (6), subject to transitional provisions in s 406(6) of, and Sch 18, paras 30, 44(3), (4), 50, 64 to, that Act at **[3434]**, **[3460]**.

Sub-s (3): words in square brackets inserted by the Communications Act 2003, s 360(3), Sch 15, Pt 1, para 46(1), (4), subject to transitional provisions in s 406(6) of, and Sch 18, paras 30, 44(3), (4), 50, 64 to, that Act at **[3434]**, **[3460]**.

Sub-s (5): word in first pair of square brackets substituted, word omitted repealed, and para (c) added, by the Communications Act 2003, ss 254, 360(3), 406(7), Sch 15, Pt 1, para 46(1), (2), Sch 19(1), subject to transitional provisions in s 406(6) of, and Sch 18, paras 5, 30, 44(3), (4), 50, 64 to, that Act at **[3434]**, **[3460]**.

Sub-s (12A): inserted by the Communications Act 2003, s 360(3), Sch 15, Pt 1, para 46(1), (5), subject to transitional provisions in s 406(6) of, and Sch 18, paras 30, 44(3), (4), 64 to, that Act at **[3434]**, **[3460]**.

Sub-s (14): added by the Communications Act 2003, s 360(3), Sch 15, Pt 1, para 46(1), (7), subject to transitional provisions in s 406(6) of, and Sch 18, paras 30, 44(3), (4), 50, 64 to, that Act at **[3434]**, **[3460]**.

Modification: this section is modified in its application to community radio services by the Community Radio Order 2004, SI 2004/1944, art 4, Schedule, Pt 1, paras 1, 4 at **[3624]**.

[104B Special application procedure for local licences

(1) Where—

(a) a local licence is due to expire (otherwise than by virtue of section 110), [and]

(b) …

(c) [OFCOM] propose to grant a further licence to provide the service in question,

[OFCOM] may if they think fit publish a notice under subsection (2) instead of a notice under section 104(1).

[(1A) In subsection (1)(c) the reference to the service in question, in relation to a case in which it is a pre-transfer local licence that is due to expire, is a reference to the equivalent local service for which a licence is capable of being granted at times on or after the radio transfer date.]

(2) A notice under this subsection is a notice—

(a) stating that [OFCOM] propose to grant a further licence to provide a specified local service,

(b) specifying the area or locality in the United Kingdom for which the service is to be provided,

(c) inviting declarations of intent to apply for a licence to provide the service,

(d) specifying the closing date for such declarations, and

(e) specifying—

(i) the application fee payable on any declaration made in pursuance of the notice, and

(ii) a deposit of such amount as [OFCOM] may think fit.

(3) A declaration of intent made in pursuance of a notice under subsection (2) must be in writing and accompanied by the application fee and deposit specified under subsection (2)(e)(i) and (ii).

(4) Where [OFCOM] receive a declaration of intent in accordance with the provisions of this section from a person other than the licence holder in relation to the service in question, they shall—

(a) publish a notice under section 104(1),

(b) specify—

(i) in relation to persons who have made a declaration of intent in accordance with the provisions of this section, no further application fee, and

(ii) in relation to all other applicants, an application fee of the same amount as the fee referred to in subsection (2)(e)(i), and

(c) repay the deposit referred to in subsection (2)(e)(ii) to every person—

(i) who has made a declaration of intent in accordance with the provisions of this section, and

(ii) who duly submits an application in pursuance of the notice referred to in paragraph (a).

(5) Where [OFCOM] receive a declaration of intent in accordance with the provisions of this section from the licence holder in relation to the service in question, and no such declaration from any other person, they shall—

(a) invite the licence holder to apply for the licence in such manner as they may determine (but without requiring any further application fee), and

(b) on receiving an application duly made by him, repay to him the deposit referred to in subsection (2)(e)(ii).

(6), (7) ...]

[3043]

NOTES

Inserted by the Broadcasting Act 1996, s 94(1).

Sub-s (1): word in first pair of square brackets inserted, para (b) repealed, and other words in square brackets substituted, by the Communications Act 2003, ss 255, 360(3), 406(7), Sch 15, Pt 1, para 47(1), (2), Sch 19(1), subject to transitional provisions in s 406(6) of, and Sch 18, paras 30, 44(3), (4), 64 to, that Act at **[3434]**, **[3460]**.

Sub-s (1A): inserted by the Communications Act 2003, s 360(3), Sch 15, Pt 1, para 47(1), (3), subject to transitional provisions in s 406(6) of, and Sch 18, para 44(3), (4) to, that Act at **[3434]**, **[3460]**.

Sub-ss (2), (4), (5): words in square brackets substituted by the Communications Act 2003, s 360(3), Sch 15, Pt 1, para 47(1), (2), subject to transitional provisions in s 406(6) of, and Sch 18, paras 30, 44(3), (4), 64 to, that Act at **[3434]**, **[3460]**.

Sub-ss (6), (7): repealed by the Communications Act 2003, s 406(7), Sch 19(1), subject to transitional provisions in s 406(6) of, and Sch 18, para 44(3), (4) to, that Act at **[3434]**, **[3460]**.

Modification: this section is modified in its application to community radio services by the Community Radio Order 2004, SI 2004/1944, art 4, Schedule, Pt 1, paras 1, 4 at **[3624]**.

105 Special requirements relating to grant of local licences

Where [OFCOM] have published a notice under section 104(1), they shall, in determining whether, or to whom, to grant the local licence in question, have regard to the following matters, namely—

(a) the ability of each of the applicants for the licence to maintain, throughout the period for which the licence would be in force, the service which he proposes to provide;

(b) the extent to which any such proposed service would cater for the tastes and interests of persons living in the area or locality for which the service would be provided, and, where it is proposed to cater for any particular tastes and interests of such persons, the extent to which the service would cater for those tastes and interests;

(c) the extent to which any such proposed service would broaden the range of programmes available by way of local services to persons living in the area or locality for which it would be provided, and, in particular, the extent to which the service would cater for tastes and interests different from those already catered for by local services provided for that area or locality; and

[(d) the extent to which there is evidence that, amongst persons living in that area or locality, there is a demand for, or support for, the provision of the proposed service.]

[3044]

NOTES

Words in square brackets substituted by the Communications Act 2003, s 360(3), Sch 15, Pt 1, para 48, subject to transitional provisions in s 406(6) of, and Sch 18, paras 30, 44(3), (4), 64 to, that Act at **[3434]**, **[3460]**.

Modification: this section is modified in its application to community radio services by the Community Radio Order 2004, SI 2004/1944, art 4, Schedule, Pt 1, paras 1, 5 at **[3624]**.

Miscellaneous provisions relating to national and local services

106 Requirements as to character and coverage of national and local services

(1) A national or local licence shall include such conditions as appear to [OFCOM] to be appropriate for securing that the character of the licensed service, as proposed by the licence holder when making his application, is maintained during the period for which the licence is in force …

[(1A) Conditions included in a licence for the purposes of subsection (1) may provide that OFCOM may consent to a departure from the character of the licensed service if, and only if, they are satisfied—

(a) that the departure would not substantially alter the character of the service,

(b) that the departure would not narrow the range of programmes available by way of relevant independent radio services to persons living in the area or locality for which the service is licensed to be provided,

(c) that, in the case of a local licence, the departure would be conducive to the maintenance or promotion of fair and effective competition in that area or locality, or

(d) that, in the case of a local licence, there is evidence that, amongst persons living in that area or locality, there is a significant demand for, or significant support for, the change that would result from the departure.

(1B) The matters to which OFCOM must have regard in determining for the purposes of this section the character of a service provided under a local licence include, in particular, the selection of spoken material and music in programmes included in the service.]

(2) A national or local licence shall include conditions requiring the licence holder to secure that the licensed service serves so much of the area or locality for which it is licensed to be provided as is for the time being reasonably practicable.

(3) A national licence shall include conditions enabling [OFCOM], where it appears to them to be reasonably practicable for the licensed service to be provided for any additional area falling outside the minimum area determined by them in accordance with section 98(2), to require the licence holder to provide the licensed service for any such additional area.

(4) Subject to subsection (5), [OFCOM] may, if they think fit, authorise the holder of a local licence, by means of a variation of his licence to that effect, to provide the licensed service for any additional area or locality adjoining the area or locality for which that service has previously been licensed to be provided.

[(5) OFCOM shall only exercise the power conferred on them by subsection (4) if it appears to them—

(a) that to do so would not result in a significant increase of the area or locality for which the service in question is licensed to be provided, or

(b) that the increase that would result is justifiable in the exceptional circumstances of the case.]

(6) As soon as practicable after [OFCOM] have exercised that power in relation to any service, they shall publish, in such manner as they consider appropriate, a notice—

(a) stating that they have exercised that power in relation to that service; and

(b) giving details of the additional area or locality for which that service is licensed to be provided.

[(7) In this section "relevant independent radio services" means the following services so far as they are services falling to be regulated under section 245 of the Communications Act 2003—

(a) sound broadcasting services;

(b) radio licensable content services;

(c) additional services;

but, in relation to a departure from the character of a service provided under a local licence, does not include a service that is provided otherwise than wholly or mainly for reception by persons living and working in the area or locality in question.]

[3045]

NOTES

Sub-s (1): words in square brackets substituted, and words omitted repealed, by the Communications Act 2003, ss 312(1), (2), 360(3), 406(7), Sch 15, Pt 1, para 49, Sch 19(1), subject to transitional provisions in s 406(6), Sch 18, paras 30, 64 to, that Act at **[3434]**, **[3460]**.

Sub-ss (1A), (1B): inserted by the Communications Act 2003, s 312(1), (3).

Sub-ss (3), (4), (6): words in square brackets substituted by the Communications Act 2003, s 360(3), Sch 15, Pt 1, para 49, subject to transitional provisions in s 406(6) of, and Sch 18, paras 30, 64 to, that Act at **[3434]**, **[3460]**.

Sub-s (5): substituted by the Communications Act 2003, s 312(1), (4).

Sub-s (7): added by the Communications Act 2003, s 312(1), (5).

Modification: this section is modified in its application to community radio services by the Community Radio Order 2004, SI 2004/1944, art 4, Schedule, Pt 1, paras 1, 6 at **[3624]**.

[106ZA Consultation about change of character of local services

(1) Before deciding for the purposes of a condition imposed under subsection (1A) of section 106 whether to consent to a departure from the character of a service provided under a local licence on any of the grounds mentioned in paragraphs (b) to (d) of that subsection, OFCOM must publish a notice specifying—

(a) the proposed departure; and

(b) the period in which representations may be made to OFCOM about the proposal.

(2) That period must end not less than 28 days after the date of publication of the notice.

(3) The notice must be published in such manner as appears to OFCOM to be appropriate for bringing it to the attention of the persons who, in OFCOM's opinion, are likely to be affected by the departure.

(4) OFCOM—

(a) are not required to publish a notice under this section, and

(b) may specify a period of less than 28 days in such a notice as the period for representations,

if they consider that the publication of the notice, or allowing a longer period for representations, would result in a delay that would be likely prejudicially to affect the interests of the licence holder.

(5) OFCOM are not required under this section—

(a) to publish any matter that is confidential in accordance with subsection (6) or (7); or

(b) to publish anything that it would not be reasonably practicable to publish without disclosing such a matter.

(6) A matter is confidential under this subsection if—

(a) it relates specifically to the affairs of a particular body; and

(b) its publication would or might, in OFCOM's opinion, seriously and prejudicially affect the interests of that body.

(7) A matter is confidential under this subsection if—

(a) it relates specifically to the private affairs of an individual; and

(b) its publication would or might, in OFCOM's opinion, seriously and prejudicially affect the interests of that individual.]

[3046]

NOTES

Commencement: 29 December 2003.
Inserted by the Communications Act 2003, s 313.

106A–108 *(S 106A inserted by the Broadcasting Act 1996, s 93, repealed, together with ss 107, 108, by the Communications Act 2003, s 406(7), Sch 19(1), subject to transitional provisions in s 406(6) of, and Sch 18, paras 5, 30, 64 to, that Act at* **[3434], [3460]**.)

Enforcement of licences

109 Power to require scripts etc or broadcasting of correction or [a statement of findings]

(1) If [OFCOM] are satisfied that the holder of a licence granted under this Chapter has failed to comply with any condition of the licence or with any direction given by [OFCOM] under or by virtue of any provision of this Part, they may serve on him a notice—

(a) stating that [OFCOM] are so satisfied as respects any specified condition or direction;

(b) stating the effect of subsection (2); and

(c) specifying for the purposes of that subsection a period not exceeding twelve months.

(2) If, at any time during the period specified in a notice under subsection (1), [OFCOM] are satisfied that the licence holder has again failed to comply with any such condition or direction as is mentioned in that subsection (whether or not the same as the one specified in the notice), [OFCOM] may direct him—

(a) to provide [OFCOM] in advance with such scripts and particulars of the programmes to be included in the licensed service as are specified in the direction; and

(b) in relation to such of those programmes as will consist of or include recorded matter, to produce to [OFCOM] in advance for examination or reproduction such recordings of that matter as are so specified;

and a direction under this subsection shall have effect for such period, not exceeding six months, as is specified in the direction.

(3) If [OFCOM] are satisfied—

(a) that the holder of a licence has failed to comply with any condition of the licence, and

(b) that that failure can be appropriately remedied by the inclusion in the licensed service of a correction or [a statement of findings] (or both) under this subsection,

they may (subject to subsection (4)) direct the licence holder to include in the licensed service a correction or [a statement of findings] (or both) in such form, and at such time or times, as they may determine.

(4) [OFCOM] shall not give any person a direction under subsection (3) unless they have given him a reasonable opportunity of making representations to [OFCOM] about the matters complained of.

(5) Where the holder of a licence includes a correction or [a statement of findings] in the licensed service in pursuance of a direction under subsection (3), he may announce that he is doing so in pursuance of such a direction.

[(6) For the purposes of this section a statement of findings, in relation to a case in which OFCOM are satisfied that the holder of a licence has contravened the conditions of his licence, is a statement of OFCOM's findings in relation to that contravention.]

[3047]

NOTES

Section heading: words in square brackets substituted by the Communications Act 2003, s 344(1), (2).
Sub-ss (1)–(5): words in square brackets substituted by the Communications Act 2003, ss 344(1), (2), 360(3), Sch 15, Pt 1, para 50, subject to transitional provisions in s 406(6) of, and Sch 18, paras 30, 64 to, that Act at **[3434]**, **[3460]**.
Sub-s (6): added by the Communications Act 2003, s 344(1), (3).

110 Power to impose financial penalty or suspend or shorten licence period

(1) If [OFCOM] are satisfied that the holder of a licence granted under this Chapter has failed to comply with any condition of the licence or with any direction given by them under or by virtue of any provision of this Part, they may (subject to the following provisions of this section) serve on him—

(a) a notice requiring him to pay, within a specified period, a specified financial penalty to [OFCOM];

(b) a notice reducing the period for which the licence is to be in force by a specified period not exceeding two years; or

(c) a notice suspending the licence for a specified period not exceeding six months.

[(1A) The maximum amount which the holder of a national licence may be required to pay by way of a financial penalty imposed in pursuance of subsection (1)(a) is the maximum penalty given by subsection (1B).

(1B) The maximum penalty is whichever is the greater of—

(a) £250,000; and

(b) 5 per cent of the qualifying revenue for his last complete accounting period falling within the period for which his licence has been in force ("the relevant period").

(1C) In relation to a person whose first complete accounting period falling within the relevant period has not ended when the penalty is imposed, subsection (1B)(b) is to be construed as referring to 5 per cent of the amount which OFCOM estimate to be the qualifying revenue for that accounting period.

(1D) Section 102(2) to (6) applies for determining or estimating qualifying revenue for the purposes of subsection (1B) or (1C) above.]

(3) The amount of any financial penalty imposed in pursuance of subsection (1)(a) on the holder of any other licence shall not exceed [£250,000].

(4) [OFCOM] shall not serve on any person such a notice as is mentioned in subsection (1)(a), (b) or (c) unless they have given him a reasonable opportunity of making representations to them about the matters complained of.

(5) Where a licence is due to expire on a particular date by virtue of a notice served on any person under subsection (1)(b), [OFCOM] may, on the application of that person, revoke that notice by a further notice served on him at any time before that date, if they are satisfied that, since the date of the earlier notice, his conduct in relation to the operation of the licensed service has been such as to justify the revocation of that notice.

(6) It is hereby declared that any exercise by [OFCOM] of their powers under subsection (1) of this section in respect of any failure to comply with any condition or direction shall not preclude any exercise by them of their powers under section 109 in respect of that failure.

(7) …

[3048]

NOTES

Sub-ss (1), (3)–(6): words in square brackets substituted by the Communications Act 2003, ss 345, 360(3), Sch 13, paras 1, 7(2), Sch 15, Pt 1, para 50 (for effect and transitional provisions see ss 345, 406(6) of, and Sch 13, Pt 1, para 7(3), Sch 18, paras 5, 30, 64 to, that Act at **[3393]**, **[3434]**, **[3454]**, **[3460]**).

Sub-ss (1A)–(1D): substituted, for original sub-s (2), by the Communications Act 2003, s 345, Sch 13, Pt 1, paras 1, 7(1) (for effect and transitional provisions see ss 345, 406(6) of, and Sch 13, Pt 1, para 7(3), Sch 18, para 5 to, that Act at **[3393]**, **[3434]**, **[3454]**, **[3460]**).

Sub-s (7): repealed by the Communications Act 2003, s 406(7), Sch 19(1).

111 Power to revoke licences

(1) If [OFCOM] are satisfied—

(a) that the holder of a licence granted under this Chapter is failing to comply with any condition of the licence or with any direction given by them under or by virtue of any provision of this Part, and

(b) that that failure is such that, if not remedied, it would justify the revocation of the licence,

they shall (subject to subsection (8)) serve on the holder of the licence a notice under subsection (2).

(2) A notice under this subsection is a notice—
(a) stating that [OFCOM] are satisfied as mentioned in subsection (1);
(b) specifying the respects in which, in their opinion, the licence holder is failing to comply with any such condition or direction as is there mentioned; and
(c) stating that, unless the licence holder takes, within such period as is specified in the notice, such steps to remedy the failure as are so specified, [OFCOM] will revoke his licence under subsection (3).

(3) If at the end of the period specified in a notice under subsection (2) [OFCOM] are satisfied—
(a) that the person on whom the notice was served has failed to take the steps specified in it, and
(b) that it is necessary in the public interest to revoke his licence,
they shall (subject to subsection (8)) serve on him a notice revoking his licence.

(4) If [OFCOM] are satisfied in the case of any national licence—
(a) that the holder of the licence has ceased to provide the licensed service before the end of the period for which the licence is to continue in force, and
(b) that it is appropriate for them to do so,
they shall (subject to subsection (8)) serve on him a notice revoking his licence.

(5) If [OFCOM] are satisfied—
(a) that the holder of a licence granted under this Chapter provided them, in connection with his application for the licence, with information which was false in a material particular, or
(b) that, in connection with his application for the licence, the holder of such a licence withheld any material information with the intention of causing them to be misled,
they may (subject to subsection (8)) serve on him a notice revoking his licence.

(6) Subject to subsection (7), any notice served under subsection (3), (4) or (5) shall take effect as from the time when it is served on the licence holder.

(7) If it appears to [OFCOM] to be appropriate to do so for the purpose of preserving continuity in the provision of the service in question, they may provide in any such notice for it to take effect as from a date specified in it.

(8) [OFCOM] shall not serve any notice on a person under this section unless they have given him a reasonable opportunity of making representations to them about the matters complained of.

[3049]

NOTES

Sub-ss (1)–(5), (7), (8): words in square brackets substituted by the Communications Act 2003, s 360(3), Sch 15, Pt 1, para 50, subject to transitional provisions in s 406(6) of, and Sch 18, paras 30, 64 to, that Act at **[3434]**, **[3460]**.

[111A Enforcement of licences held by BBC companies

Where [OFCOM]—
(a) serve a notice on a BBC company under any provision of section 109, 110 or 111, or
(b) receive any written representations from a BBC company under section 109(4), 110(4) or 111(8),
[OFCOM] shall send a copy of the direction, notice or representations to the Secretary of State.]

[3050]

NOTES

Inserted by the Broadcasting Act 1996, s 136, Sch 8, para 7.
Words in square brackets substituted by the Communications Act 2003, s 360(3), Sch 15, Pt 1, para 50, subject to transitional provisions in s 406(6) of, and Sch 18, paras 30, 64 to, that Act at **[3434]**, **[3460]**.

[111B Power to suspend licence to provide satellite service

(1) If [OFCOM] are satisfied—
(a) that the holder of a licence to provide a [radio licensable content service] has

included in the service one or more programmes containing material likely to encourage or incite to crime or to lead to disorder,

(b) that he has thereby failed to comply with the condition [which in compliance with section 263 of the Communications Act 2003 is included in the licence for the purpose of securing the objective mentioned in section 319(2)(b) of that Act, and]

(c) that the failure is such as to justify the revocation of the licence,

they shall serve on the holder of the licence a notice under subsection (2).

(2) A notice under this subsection is a notice—

(a) stating that [OFCOM] are satisfied as mentioned in subsection (1),

(b) specifying the respects in which, in their opinion, the licence holder has failed to comply with the condition mentioned in paragraph (b) of that subsection,

(c) stating that [OFCOM] may revoke his licence after the end of the period of twenty-one days beginning with the date on which the notice is served on the licence holder,

(d) informing the licence holder of his right to make representations to [OFCOM] within that period about the matters complained of, and

(e) suspending the licence as from the time when the notice is served on the licence holder until the revocation takes effect or [OFCOM] decide not to revoke the licence.

(3) If [OFCOM], having considered any representations about the matters complained of made to them within the period referred to in subsection (2)(c) by the licence holder, are satisfied that it is necessary in the public interest to revoke the licence in question, they shall serve on the licence holder a notice revoking the licence.

(4) A notice under subsection (3) shall not take effect until the end of the period of twenty-eight days beginning with the day on which that notice was served on the licence holder.

(5) Section 111 shall not have effect in relation to the revocation of a licence in pursuance of a notice under subsection (1).]

[3051]

NOTES

Inserted by the Broadcasting Act 1996, s 96.

Sub-ss (1)–(3): words in square brackets substituted by the Communications Act 2003, s 360(3), Sch 15, Pt 1, para 51, subject to transitional provisions in s 406(6) of, and Sch 18, paras 30, 45, 64 to, that Act at **[3434]**, **[3460]**.

112, 113 ((*Ch III*) *repealed by the Communications Act 2003, s 406(7), Sch 19(1), subject to transitional provisions in s 406(6) of, and Sch 18, paras 5, 30, 64 to, that Act at* **[3434]**, **[3460]**.)

CHAPTER IV
ADDITIONAL SERVICES PROVIDED ON SOUND BROADCASTING FREQUENCIES

114 Additional services

(1) In this Part "additional service" means any service which consists in the sending of [electronic] signals for transmission by wireless telegraphy by means of the use of the spare capacity within the signals carrying any sound broadcasting service provided [on a relevant frequency].

(2) For the purposes of this Part the spare capacity within the signals carrying any such broadcasting service shall be taken to be [any part of the signals which—

(a) is not required for the purposes of the sound broadcasting service for the purposes of which the frequency has been made available; and

(b) is determined by OFCOM to be available for the provision of additional services;]

and references in this Part to spare capacity shall be construed accordingly.

[(2A) At any time while an additional services licence is in force, OFCOM may, if they consider it appropriate to do so, modify or further modify the determination made for the purposes of that licence under subsection (2)(b); and where there has been such a modification or further modification, the licence shall have effect accordingly.

(2B) A modification or further modification under subsection (2A) must not reduce the amount of spare capacity made available for the licensed services.]

(3) [OFCOM shall, when determining under subsection (2)] the extent and nature of the spare capacity available for the provision of additional services in the case of any frequency on which a national service is provided, have regard to any need of the person providing that service to be able to use part of the signals carrying it for providing services which are ancillary to programmes included in the service.

(4) A person holding a national licence shall be taken for the purposes of this Part to be authorised by his licence to provide any such services as are mentioned in subsection (3).

(5) …

[(6) In this section "electronic signal" means a signal within the meaning of section 32 of the Communications Act 2003.

(7) In this section and section 115 "relevant frequency" means a frequency made available by OFCOM for the purposes of a sound broadcasting service.]

[3052]

NOTES

Sub-ss (1), (2), (3): words in square brackets substituted by the Communications Act 2003, s 360(3), Sch 15, Pt 1, para 52(1)–(3), (5), subject to transitional provisions in s 406(6) of, and Sch 18, paras 30, 64 to, that Act at **[3434]**, **[3460]** and subject to further transitional provisions as noted below.

Sub-ss (2A), (2B): inserted by the Communications Act 2003, s 360(3), Sch 15, Pt 1, para 52(1), (4), subject to transitional provisions in s 406(6) of, and Sch 18, paras 30, 64 to, that Act at **[3434]**, **[3460]** and subject to further transitional provisions as noted below.

Sub-s (5): repealed by the Communications Act 2003, s 406(7), Sch 19(1), subject to transitional provisions in s 406(6) of, and Sch 18, paras 30, 64 to, that Act at **[3434]**, **[3460]**.

Sub-ss (6), (7): substituted, for original sub-s (6), by the Communications Act 2003, s 360(3), Sch 15, Pt 1, para 52(1), (6), subject to transitional provisions in s 406(6) of, and Sch 18, paras 30, 64 to, that Act at **[3434]**, **[3460]** and subject to further transitional provisions as noted below.

Transitional provisions: the Communications Act 2003, Sch 15, Pt 1, para 52(7) provides that the amendments made by Sch 15, Pt 1, para 52(1)–(6) to that Act do not affect the validity of a licence granted or last renewed before the television transfer date, or the services licensed by any such licence.

115 Licensing of additional services

(1) [OFCOM] shall do all that they can to secure that, in the case of each [relevant frequency] all of the spare capacity available for the provision of additional services on that frequency is used for the provision of such services under additional services licences granted by [OFCOM] in accordance with this section.

(2) An additional services licence may relate to the use of spare capacity within more than one frequency; and two or more additional services licences may relate to the use of spare capacity within the same frequency where it is to be used at different times, or in different areas, in the case of each of those licences.

(3) An additional services licence may include provisions enabling the licence holder, subject to and in accordance with such conditions as [OFCOM] may impose, to authorise any person to whom this subsection applies to provide any additional service on the spare capacity allocated by the licence.

(4) Subsection (3) applies to any person who is not a disqualified person in relation to an additional services licence by virtue of Part II of Schedule 2 to this Act [and who would not be in contravention of the requirements imposed by or under Schedule 14 to the Communications Act 2003 if he held such a licence].

(5) Any conditions included in an additional services licence shall apply in relation to the provision of additional services by a person authorised as mentioned in subsection (3) as they apply in relation to the provision of such services by the licence holder; and any failure by such a person to comply with any such conditions shall be treated for the purposes of this Part as a failure on the part of the licence holder to comply with those conditions.

(6) Every licence to provide a national service shall include such conditions as appear to [OFCOM] to be appropriate for securing that the licence holder grants—

(a) to any person who holds a licence to provide additional services on the frequency on which that national service is provided, and

(b) to any person who is authorised by any such person as mentioned in subsection (3) to provide additional services on that frequency, access to facilities reasonably required by that person for the purposes of, or in connection with, the provision of any such additional services.

(7) Any person who grants to any other person access to facilities in accordance with conditions imposed under subsection (6) may require that other person to pay a reasonable charge in respect thereof; and any dispute as to the amount of any such charge shall be determined by [OFCOM].

(8) The holder of a licence to provide a [local or restricted service or to provide a radio licensable content service] shall be taken for the purposes of this Part to be authorised by his licence to provide, or to authorise another person to provide, additional services on the frequency on which the licensed service is provided.

(9) In this Part "additional services licence" means a licence to provide additional services.

[3053]

NOTES

Sub-ss (1), (3), (6)–(8): words in square brackets substituted by the Communications Act 2003, s 360(3), Sch 15, Pt 1, para 53(1)–(3), (5), subject to transitional provisions in s 406(6) of, and Sch 18, paras 30, 64 to, that Act at **[3434]**, **[3460]**.

Sub-s (4): words in square brackets inserted by the Communications Act 2003, s 360(3), Sch 15, Pt 1, para 53(1), (4), subject to transitional provisions in s 406(6) of, and Sch 18, paras 30, 64 to, that Act at **[3434]**, **[3460]**.

116 Applications for additional services licences

(1) Where [OFCOM] propose to grant a licence to provide additional services they shall publish, in such manner as they consider appropriate, a notice—

- (a) stating that they propose to grant such a licence;
- (b) specifying—
  - (i) the period for which the licence is to be granted,
  - (ii) the sound broadcasting service or services on whose frequency or frequencies the services are to be provided, and
  - (iii) … the extent and nature of the spare capacity which is to be allocated by the licence;
- (c) inviting applications for the licence and specifying the closing date for such applications; and
- (d) specifying—
  - (i) the fee payable on any application made in pursuance of the notice, and
  - (ii) the percentage of qualifying revenue for each accounting period that would be payable by an applicant in pursuance of section 118(1)(c) if he were granted the licence.

(2) [OFCOM] may, if they think fit, specify under subsection (1)(d)(ii)—

- (a) different percentages in relation to different accounting periods falling within the period for which the licence would be in force;
- (b) a nil percentage in relation to any accounting period so falling.

(3) Any application made in pursuance of a notice under this section must be in writing and accompanied by—

- (a) the fee specified in the notice under subsection (1)(d)(i);
- (b) a technical plan indicating—
  - (i) the nature of any additional services which the applicant proposes to provide, and
  - (ii) so far as known to the applicant, the nature of any additional services which any other person proposes to provide in accordance with section 115(3);
- (c) the applicant's cash bid in respect of the licence; and
- (d) such information as [OFCOM] may reasonably require as to the applicant's present financial position and his projected financial position during the period for which the licence would be in force.

(4) At any time after receiving such an application and before determining it [OFCOM] may require the applicant to furnish additional information under subsection (3)(b) or (d).

(5) Any information to be furnished to [OFCOM] under this section shall, if they so require, be in such form or verified in such manner as they may specify.

(6) [OFCOM] shall, as soon as reasonably practicable after the date specified in a notice under this section as the closing date for applications, publish in such manner as they consider appropriate—

(a) the name of every person who has made an application to them in pursuance of the notice;

(b) particulars of the technical plan submitted by him under subsection (3)(b); and

(c) such other information connected with his application as [OFCOM] consider appropriate.

[3054]

NOTES

Sub-s (1): words in square brackets substituted, and words omitted repealed, by the Communications Act 2003, ss 360(3), 406(7), Sch 15, Pt 1, para 54, Sch 19(1), subject to transitional provisions in s 406(6) of, and Sch 18, paras 30, 64 to, that Act at **[3434]**, **[3460]**.

Sub-ss (2)–(6): words in square brackets substituted by the Communications Act 2003, s 360(3), Sch 15, Pt 1, para 54(1), (2), subject to transitional provisions in s 406(6) of, and Sch 18, paras 30, 64 to, that Act at **[3434]**, **[3460]**.

117 Procedure to be followed by [OFCOM] in connection with consideration of applications for, and awarding of, licences

(1) Where a person has made an application for an additional services licence in accordance with section 116, [OFCOM] shall not proceed to consider whether to award him the licence on the basis of his cash bid in accordance with subsections (3) and (4) below unless it appears to them—

[(a) that the technical plan submitted under section 116(3)(b), in so far as it involves the use of an electronic communications network (within the meaning of the Communications Act 2003), contains proposals that are acceptable to them; and]

(b) that the services proposed to be provided under the licence would be capable of being maintained throughout the period for which the licence would be in force;

and any reference to an applicant in section 100 (as applied by subsection (3) below) is accordingly a reference to an applicant in whose case it appears to [OFCOM] that the requirements of paragraphs (a) and (b) above are satisfied.

(2) …

(3) Subject to subsection (4), section 100 shall apply in relation to an additional services licence as it applies in relation to a national licence.

(4) In the application of section 100 in relation to an additional services licence—

(a) subsection (6) shall have effect with the substitution in paragraph (a) of a reference to section 118(1) for the reference to section 102(1); and

(b) subsection (9) shall have effect with the substitution in paragraph (b) of a reference to the requirement specified in subsection (1)(a) above for the reference to the requirement specified in section 99(1)(a).

(5) If at any time after an additional services licence has been granted to any person but before the licence has come into force—

(a) that person indicates to [OFCOM] that none of the services in question will be provided once the licence has come into force, or

(b) [OFCOM] for any other reason have reasonable grounds for believing that none of those services will be so provided,

then, subject to subsection (6)—

(i) [OFCOM] shall serve on him a notice revoking the licence as from the time the notice is served on him, and

(ii) section 100 (as applied by subsection (3) above) shall, subject to section 100(11), have effect as if he had not made an application for the licence.

(6) Subsection (5) shall not apply in the case of any person by virtue of paragraph (b) of that subsection unless [OFCOM] have served on him a notice stating their grounds for believing that none of the services in question will be provided once his licence has come into force; and they shall not serve such a notice on him unless they have given him a reasonable opportunity of making representations to them about the matters complained of.

(7) …

[3055]

NOTES

Section heading: words in square brackets substituted by virtue of the Communications Act 2003, s 360(3), Sch 15, Pt 1, para 55(1), (2), subject to transitional provisions in s 406(6) of, and Sch 18, paras 30, 64 to, that Act at **[3434]**, **[3460]**.

Sub-ss (1), (5), (6): words in square brackets substituted by the Communications Act 2003, s 360(3), Sch 15, Pt 1, para 55(1)–(3), subject to transitional provisions in s 406(6) of, and Sch 18, paras 30, 64 to, that Act at **[3434]**, **[3460]**.

Sub-ss (2), (7): repealed by the Communications Act 2003, ss 360(3), 406(7), Sch 15, Pt 1, para 55(1), (4), Sch 19(1), subject to transitional provisions in s 406(6) of, and Sch 18, paras 30, 64 to, that Act at **[3434]**, **[3460]**.

118 Additional payments to be made in respect of additional services licences

(1) An additional services licence shall include conditions requiring the licence holder to pay to [OFCOM] (in addition to any fees required to be so paid by virtue of section 87(1)(c))—

(a) in respect of the first complete calendar year falling within the period for which the licence is in force, the amount specified in his cash bid;

(b) in respect of each subsequent year falling wholly or partly within that period, the amount so specified as increased by the appropriate percentage; and

(c) in respect of each accounting period of his falling within the period referred to in paragraph (a), an amount representing such percentage of the qualifying revenue for that accounting period as was specified in relation to the licence under section 116(1)(d)(ii).

(2) For the purposes of subsection (1)(c) the qualifying revenue for any accounting period of the licence holder shall consist of all amounts which are received or to be received by him or by any connected person and are referable to the right under his licence to use, or to authorise any other person to use, in that period the spare capacity allocated by the licence.

(3) An additional services licence may include conditions—

(a) enabling [OFCOM] to estimate before the beginning of an accounting period the amount due for that period by virtue of subsection (1)(c); and

(b) requiring the licence holder to pay the estimated amount by monthly instalments throughout that period.

(4) Such a licence may in particular include conditions—

(a) authorising [OFCOM] to revise any estimate on one or more occasions, and to adjust the instalments payable by the licence holder to take account of the revised estimate;

(b) providing for the adjustment of any overpayment or underpayment.

(5) Where—

(a) the first complete accounting period of the licence holder falling within the period referred to in subsection (1)(a) ("the licence period") does not begin at the same time as that period, or

(b) the last complete accounting period of his falling within the licence period does not end at the same time as that period,

any reference in subsection (1)(c) to an accounting period of his shall include a reference to such part of the accounting period preceding that first complete accounting period, or (as the case may be) following that last complete accounting period, as falls within the licence period; and other references to accounting periods in this Part shall be construed accordingly. **[3056]**

NOTES

Sub-ss (1), (3), (4): words in square brackets substituted by the Communications Act 2003, s 360(3), Sch 15, Pt 1, para 56, subject to transitional provisions in s 406(6) of, and Sch 18, paras 30, 64 to, that Act at **[3434]**, **[3460]**.

119 Additional services not to interfere with other transmissions

(1) An additional services licence may include such conditions as [OFCOM] consider appropriate for securing that the provision of any additional service under the licence does not cause any interference with—

(a) the sound broadcasting service or services on whose frequency or frequencies it is provided, or

(b) any other wireless telegraphy transmission.

(2) …

[3057]

NOTES

Sub-s (1): word in square brackets substituted by the Communications Act 2003, s 360(3), Sch 15, Pt 1, para 57(1), (2), subject to transitional provisions in s 406(6) of, and Sch 18, paras 30, 64 to, that Act at **[3434]**, **[3460]**.

Sub-s (2): repealed by the Communications Act 2003, ss 360(3), 406(7), Sch 15, Pt 1, para 57(1), (3), Sch 19(1), subject to transitional provisions in s 406(6) of, and Sch 18, paras 30, 64 to, that Act at **[3434]**, **[3460]**.

120 Enforcement of additional services licences

(1) If [OFCOM] are satisfied that the holder of an additional services licence has failed to comply with any condition of the licence or with any direction given by [OFCOM] under or by virtue of any provision of this Part, they may (subject to subsection (3)) serve on him a notice requiring him to pay, within a specified period, a specified financial penalty to [OFCOM].

[(1A) The amount of a financial penalty imposed on a person in pursuance of subsection (1) shall not exceed 5 per cent of the qualifying revenue for the licence holder's last complete accounting period falling within the period for which his licence has been in force ("the relevant period").

(1B) In relation to a person whose first complete accounting period falling within the relevant period has not ended when the penalty is imposed, subsection (1A) is to be construed as referring to 5 per cent of the amount which OFCOM estimate to be the qualifying revenue for that accounting period.

(1C) Section 118(2) applies for determining or estimating qualifying revenue for the purposes of subsection (1A) or (1B) above.]

(3) [OFCOM] shall not serve on any person a notice under subsection (1) unless they have given him a reasonable opportunity of making representations to them about the matters complained of.

(4) Section 111 shall apply in relation to an additional services licence as it applies in relation to a licence granted under Chapter II of this Part, but with the omission of subsection (7).

[3058]

NOTES

Sub-ss (1), (3): words in square brackets substituted by the Communications Act 2003, s 360(3), Sch 15, Pt 1, para 58, subject to transitional provisions in s 406(6) of, and Sch 18, paras 30, 64 to, that Act at **[3434]**, **[3460]**.

Sub-ss (1A)–(1C): substituted, for original sub-s (2), by the Communications Act 2003, s 345, Sch 13, Pt 1, paras 1, 8(1), subject to savings and transitional provisions in ss 345, 406(6) of, and Sch 13, Pt 1, para 8(2), Sch 18, paras 5, 30 to, that Act at **[3393]**, **[3434]**, **[3454]**, **[3460]**.

121–161 *(Pt III, Ch V (ss 121–126) and Pt IV (ss 127–141) outside the scope of this work; Pts V, VI (ss 142–161) repealed by the Broadcasting Act 1996, s 148(2), Sch 11, Pt I.)*

PART VII
PROHIBITION ON INCLUSION OF OBSCENE AND OTHER MATERIAL IN PROGRAMME SERVICES

Obscenity

162 Obscenity in programme services: England and Wales

(1) …

(2) Schedule 15 to this Act shall have effect for the purpose of supplementing subsection (1) above.

[3059]

NOTES

Sub-s (1): amends the Obscene Publications Act 1959, s 1.

163–165 (*S 163 amends the Civic Government* (*Scotland*) *Act 1982, s 51; s 164 amends the Public Order Act 1986, ss 18, 20–23, 29; s 165 amends the Public Order* (*Northern Ireland*) *Order 1987, SI 1987/463* (*outside the scope of this work*).)

Defamation

166 Defamatory material

(1) For the purposes of the law of libel and slander (including the law of criminal libel so far as it relates to the publication of defamatory matter) the publication of words in the course of any programme included in a programme service shall be treated as publication in permanent form.

(2) Subsection (1) above shall apply for the purposes of section 3 of each of the Defamation Acts (slander of title etc) as it applies for the purposes of the law of libel and slander.

(3) …

(4) In this section "the Defamation Acts" means the Defamation Act 1952 and the Defamation Act (Northern Ireland) 1955.

(5) Subsections (1) and (2) above do not extend to Scotland.

[3060]

NOTES

Sub-s (3): repealed by the Defamation Act 1996, s 16, Sch 2.

Supplementary

167 Power to make copies of recordings

(1) If a justice of the peace is satisfied by information on oath laid by a constable that there is reasonable ground for suspecting that a relevant offence has been committed by any person in respect of a programme included in a programme service, he may make an order authorising any constable to require that person—

(a) to produce to the constable a visual or sound recording of any matter included in that programme, if and so far as that person is able to do so; and
(b) on the production of such a recording, to afford the constable an opportunity of causing a copy of it to be made.

(2) An order made under this section shall describe the programme to which it relates in a manner sufficient to enable that programme to be identified.

(3) A person who without reasonable excuse fails to comply with any requirement of a constable made by virtue of subsection (1) shall be guilty of an offence and liable on summary conviction to a fine not exceeding the third level on the standard scale.

(4) No order shall be made under this section in respect of any recording in respect of which a warrant could be granted under any of the following provisions, namely—

(a) section 3 of the Obscene Publications Act 1959;
(b) section 24 of the Public Order Act 1986; and
(c) Article 14 of the Public Order (Northern Ireland) Order 1987.

(5) In the application of subsection (1) to England and Wales "relevant offence" means an offence under—

(a) section 2 of the Obscene Publications Act 1959; or
(b) section 22 of the Public Order Act 1986.

(6) In the application of subsection (1) to Scotland—

(a) "relevant offence" means an offence under—
    (i) section 51 of the Civic Government (Scotland) Act 1982, or

(ii) section 22 of the Public Order Act 1986;

(b) the reference to a justice of the peace shall include a reference to the sheriff; and

(c) for the reference to information on oath there shall be substituted a reference to evidence on oath.

(7) In the application of subsection (1) to Northern Ireland—

(a) "relevant offence" means an offence under Article 12 of the Public Order (Northern Ireland) Order 1987;

(b) for the reference to a justice of the peace there shall be substituted a reference to a resident magistrate; and

(c) for the reference to information on oath laid by a constable there shall be substituted a reference to a complaint on oath made by a constable.

[3061]

168–176 (*Ss 168–174 (Pt XIII) repealed by the Wireless Telegraphy Act 2006, s 125(1), Sch 9, Pt 1, subject to transitional provisions and savings in s 124 of, Sch 8, Pt 1, paras 1–8, 24 to, that Act at* **[4230]**, **[4239]**; *ss 175, 176 (Pt IX) outside the scope of this work.*)

PART X
MISCELLANEOUS AND GENERAL

Foreign satellite services

177–179 (*Ss 177, 178 outside the scope of this work; s 179 inserts the Copyright, Designs and Patents Act 1988, s 297A at* **[2539]**, *and amends s 299 of that Act at* **[2544]**.)

Television licensing

180 Transfer to BBC of functions connected with television licences

(1)–(3) …

(4) Part I of the Wireless Telegraphy Act 1967 (obtaining of information as to sale and hire of television sets) shall have effect subject to the amendments specified in Part II of Schedule 18 to this Act (by virtue of which all of the functions of the Secretary of State under that Part of that Act, apart from his power to make regulations under section 2(7) or 6(1), are transferred to the BBC).

[3062]

NOTES

Sub-s (1): repealed by the Wireless Telegraphy Act 2006, s 125(1), Sch 9, Pt 1, subject to transitional provisions and savings in s 124 of, Sch 8, Pt 1, paras 1–8, 24 to, that Act at **[4230]**, **[4239]**, and previously read as follows:

"(1) The Wireless Telegraphy Act 1949 ("the 1949 Act") shall have effect subject to the amendments specified in Part I of Schedule 18 to this Act (by virtue of which functions of the Secretary of State as respects the issue and renewal of television licences are transferred to the BBC).".

Sub-ss (2), (3): repealed by the Communications Act 2003, s 406(7), Sch 19(1), subject to transitional provisions in s 406(6) of, and Sch 18, paras 5, 55 to, that Act at **[3434]**, **[3460]**.

181–194A (*Ss 181, 186, 187, 189–191 repealed by the Communications Act 2003, s 406(7), Sch 19(1), subject to transitional provisions in s 406(6) of, and Sch 18, paras 3–5, 9, 11–14, 16–18, 64 to, that Act at* **[3434]**, **[3460]**; *s 182 repealed by the Broadcasting Act 1996, ss 105(2), 148(2), Sch 11, Pt I; ss 183–185, 188, 193, 194A outside the scope of this work; s 192 repealed by the Enterprise Act 2002, s 278(2), Sch 26; s 194 repealed by the Competition Act 1998 (Transitional, Consequential and Supplemental Provisions) Order 2000, SI 2000/311, art 26(1), (2).*)

General

195–200 (*Outside the scope of this work.*)

201 Programme services

(1) In this Act "programme service" means any of the following services (whether or not it is, or it requires to be, licensed …), namely—

[(aa) any service which is a programme service within the meaning of the Communications Act 2003;]

(c) any other service which consists in the sending, by means of [an electronic communications network (within the meaning of the Communications Act 2003)], of sounds or visual images or both either—

(i) for reception at two or more places in the United Kingdom (whether they are so sent for simultaneous reception or at different times in response to requests made by different users of the service); or

(ii) for reception at a place in the United Kingdom for the purpose of being presented there to members of the public or to any group of persons.

[(2A) Subsection (1)(c) does not apply to so much of a service consisting only of sound programmes as—

(a) is a two-way service (within the meaning of section 248(4) of the Communications Act 2003);

(b) satisfies the conditions in section 248(5) of that Act; or

(c) is provided for the purpose only of being received by persons who have qualified as users of the service by reason of being persons who fall within paragraph (a) or (b) of section 248(7) of that Act.

(2B) Subsection (1)(c) does not apply to so much of a service not consisting only of sound programmes as—

(a) is a two-way service (within the meaning of section 232 of the Communications Act 2003);

(b) satisfies the conditions in section 233(5) of that Act; or

(c) is provided for the purpose only of being received by persons who have qualified as users of the service by reason of being persons who fall within paragraph (a) or (b) of section 233(7) of that Act.]

[3063]

NOTES

Sub-s (1): words omitted repealed, para (aa) substituted, for original paras (a), (b), and para (bb) (as inserted by the Broadcasting Act 1996, s 148(1), Sch 10, para 11), and other words in square brackets substituted, by the Communications Act 2003, ss 360(1), 406(7), Sch 19(1).

Sub-ss (2A), (2B): substituted, for original sub-s (2), by the Communications Act 2003, s 360(2).

202 General interpretation

(1) In this Act (unless the context otherwise requires)—

"advertising agent" shall be construed in accordance with subsection (7);

"the BBC" means the British Broadcasting Corporation;

["a BBC company" means—

(a) any body corporate which is controlled by the BBC, or

(b) any body corporate in which the BBC or any body corporate falling within paragraph (a) above is (to any extent) a participant (as defined in paragraph 1(1) of Part I of Schedule 2);]

"body", without more, means a body of persons whether incorporated or not, and includes a partnership;

"broadcast" means broadcast by wireless telegraphy;

["a Channel 4 company" means—

(a) any body corporate which is controlled by the Channel Four Television Corporation, or

(b) any body corporate in which the Corporation or any body corporate falling within paragraph (a) above is (to any extent) a participant (as defined in paragraph 1(1) of Part I of Schedule 2);]

"connected", in relation to any [person], shall be construed in accordance with paragraph 3 in Part I of Schedule 2;

"control", in relation to a body, has the meaning given by paragraph 1(1) in that Part of that Schedule;

"dwelling-house" includes a hotel, inn, boarding-house or other similar establishment;

["EEA Agreement" means the Agreement on the European Economic Area signed at Oporto on 2nd May 1992 as adjusted by the Protocol signed at Brussels on 17th March 1993;

"EEA State" means a State which is a contracting party to the EEA Agreement;]

"financial year" shall be construed in accordance with subsection (2);

"frequency" includes frequency band;

"modifications" includes additions, alterations and omissions;

["OFCOM" means the Office of Communications;]

"pension scheme" means a scheme for the payment of pensions, allowances or gratuities;

"programme" includes an advertisement and, in relation to any service, includes any item included in that service;

["an S4C company" means—

(a) any body corporate which is controlled by the Welsh Authority, or

(b) any body corporate in which the Welsh Authority or any body corporate falling within paragraph (a) above is (to any extent) a participant (as defined in paragraph 1(1) of Part I of Schedule 2);]

.....

"the Welsh Authority" means the authority renamed Sianel Pedwar Cymru by section 56(1);

["wireless telegraphy" and "wireless telegraphy station" each has the same meaning as in the Wireless Telegraphy Act 2006.]

(2) In any provision of—

(a) …

(b) Schedule … , 2, 3, 6, … or 19,

"financial year" means a financial year of the body with which that provision is concerned; and in any other provision of this Act "financial year" means the twelve months ending with 31st March.

(3) In this Act—

(a) references to pensions, allowances or gratuities include references to like benefits to be given on death or retirement; and

(b) any reference to the payment of pensions, allowances or gratuities to or in respect of any persons includes a reference to the making of payments towards provision for the payment of pensions, allowances or gratuities to or in respect of those persons.

(4) Any reference in this Act (however expressed) to a licence under this Act being in force is a reference to its being in force so as to authorise the provision under the licence of the licensed service; and any such reference shall accordingly not be construed as prejudicing the operation of any provisions of such a licence which are intended to have effect otherwise than at a time when the licensed service is authorised to be so provided.

[(4A) Any reference in this Act to Council Directive 89/552/EEC is a reference to that Directive as amended by Directive 97/36/EC of the European Parliament and the Council.]

(5) It is hereby declared that, for the purpose of determining for the purposes of any provision of this Act whether a service is—

(a) … capable of being received, within the United Kingdom or elsewhere, or

(b) for reception at any place or places, or in any area, in the United Kingdom,

the fact that the service has been encrypted to any extent shall be disregarded.

[(5A) …]

(6) Any reference in this Act, in relation to a service consisting of programmes transmitted by satellite—

(a) to a person by whom the programmes are transmitted, or

(b) to a place from which the programmes are transmitted,

is a reference to a person by whom, or a place from which, the programmes are transmitted to the satellite by means of which the service is provided.

[(6A) Subsections (2) and (3) of section 362 of the Communications Act 2003 (persons by whom services provided) are to apply for the purposes of this Act as they apply for the purposes of Part 3 of that Act.]

(7) For the purposes of this Act—

(a) a person shall not be regarded as carrying on business as an advertising agent, or as acting as such an agent, unless he carries on a business involving the selection and purchase of advertising time or space for persons wishing to advertise;

(b) a person who carries on such a business shall be regarded as carrying on business as an advertising agent irrespective of whether in law he is the agent of those for whom he acts;

(c) a person who is the proprietor of a newspaper shall not be regarded as carrying on business as an advertising agent by reason only that he makes arrangements on behalf of advertisers whereby advertisements appearing in the newspaper are also to appear in one or more other newspapers;

(d) a company or other body corporate shall not be regarded as carrying on business as an advertising agent by reason only that its objects or powers include or authorise that activity.

[3064]

NOTES

Sub-s (1): definitions "a BBC company", "a Channel 4 company" and "an S4C company" inserted, and in definition "connected" word in square brackets substituted, by the Broadcasting Act 1996, ss 136, 148(1), Sch 8, para 8, Sch 10, para 21; definitions "EEA Agreement", "EEA State" inserted by the Satellite Television Service Regulations 1997, SI 1997/1682, reg 2, Schedule, para 14(2); definition "OFCOM" inserted, and definition "telecommunication system" (omitted) repealed, by the Communications Act 2003, ss 360(3), 406(7), Sch 15, Pt 1, para 68(1), (2), Sch 19(1), subject to transitional provisions in s 406(6) of, and Sch 18, paras 30, 64 to, that Act at **[3434]**, **[3460]**; definition beginning "wireless telegraphy" substituted by the Wireless Telegraphy Act 2006, s 123, Sch 7, paras 9, 13.

Sub-s (2): para (a) repealed by the Broadcasting Act 1996, s 148(2), Sch 11, Pt I; words omitted from para (b) repealed by the Communications Act 2003, s 406(7), Sch 19(1) and the Broadcasting Act 1996, s 148(2), Sch 11, Pt I.

Sub-s (4A): inserted by the Television Broadcasting Regulations 1998, SI 1998/3196, reg 2, Schedule, para 6(1), (2).

Sub-s (5): words omitted repealed by the Communications Act 2003, s 406(7), Sch 19(1).

Sub-s (5A): inserted by SI 1997/1682, reg 2, Schedule, para 14(3); repealed by SI 1998/3196, reg 2, Schedule, para 6(1), (3).

Sub-s (6A): inserted by the Communications Act 2003, s 360(3), Sch 15, Pt 1, para 68(1), (3), subject to transitional provisions in s 406(6) of, and Sch 18, paras 30, 64 to, that Act at **[3434]**, **[3460]**.

203 Consequential and transitional provisions

(1)–(3) …

(4) The transitional provisions and savings contained in Schedule 22 to this Act shall have effect.

[3065]

NOTES

Sub-ss (1)–(3): outside the scope of this work.

204 Short title, commencement and extent

(1) This Act may be cited as the Broadcasting Act 1990.

(2) This Act shall come into force on such day as the Secretary of State may by order appoint; and different days may be so appointed for different provisions or for different purposes.

(3) Subject to subsections (4) and (5), this Act extends to the whole of the United Kingdom.

(4) In Part VII—

(a) section 162 and Schedule 15 extend to England and Wales only;

(b) section 163 extends to Scotland only;

(c) section 164 extends to England and Wales and Scotland; and

(d) section 165 extends to Northern Ireland only.

(5) The amendments and repeals in Schedules 20 and 21 have the same extent as the enactments to which they refer.

(6) Her Majesty may by Order in Council direct that any of the provisions of this Act shall extend to the Isle of Man or any of the Channel Islands with such modifications, if any, as appear to Her Majesty to be appropriate.

[3066]

NOTES

Orders: the Broadcasting Act 1990 (Commencement No 1 and Transitional Provisions) Order 1990, SI 1990/2347.

Orders in Council: the Broadcasting Act 1990 (Guernsey) Order 1991, SI 1991/191; the Broadcasting Act 1990 (Isle of Man) Order 1991, SI 1991/192; the Broadcasting Act 1990 (Jersey) Order 1991, SI 1991/193; the Broadcasting Act (Isle of Man) (No 2) Order 1991, SI 1991/998; the Broadcasting Act 1990 (Guernsey) (No 2) Order 1991, SI 1991/1709; the Broadcasting Act 1990 (Jersey) (No 2) Order 1991, SI 1991/1710; the Wireless Telegraphy (Guernsey) Order 1994, SI 1994/1064; the Wireless Telegraphy (Isle of Man) Order 1995, SI 1995/268; the Broadcasting (Guernsey) Order 1999, SI 1999/1314; the Broadcasting (Jersey) Order 1999, SI 1999/1315; the Broadcasting (Guernsey) Order 2003, SI 2003/3192; the Broadcasting (Isle of Man) Order 2003, SI 2003/3193; the Wireless Telegraphy (Jersey) Order 2003, SI 2003/3196; the Broadcasting (Jersey) Order 2003, SI 2003/3203; the Broadcasting and Communications (Jersey) Order 2004, SI 2004/308.

SCHEDULES

(*Sch 1 repealed by the Communications Act 2003, s 406(7), Sch 19(1), subject to transitional provisions in s 406(6) of, and Sch 18, paras 30, 64 to, that Act at* **[3434]**, **[3460]**.)

SCHEDULE 2
RESTRICTIONS ON THE HOLDING OF LICENCES

Sections 5 and 88

PART I
GENERAL

1.—(1) In this Schedule—

["the 1996 Act" means the Broadcasting Act 1996;]

"advertising agency" means an individual or a body corporate who carries on business as an advertising agent (whether alone or in partnership) or has control over any body corporate which carries on business as an advertising agent, and any reference to an advertising agency includes a reference to an individual who—

(a) is a director or officer of any body corporate which carries on such a business, or

(b) is employed by any person who carries on such a business;

"associate"—

[(a) in relation to a body corporate, shall be construed in accordance with paragraph (1A), and]

(b) in relation to an individual, shall be construed in accordance with sub-paragraph (2);

["Broadcasting Act licence" means a licence under Part 1 or 3 of this Act or Part 1 or 2 of the Broadcasting Act 1996;]

"control"—

(a) in relation to a body corporate, shall be construed in accordance with sub-paragraph (3), and

(b) in relation to any body other than a body corporate, means the power of a person to secure, [by whatever means and whether directly or indirectly], that the affairs of the first-mentioned body are conducted in accordance with the wishes of that person;

[. . .]

"equity share capital" has the same meaning as in the Companies Act 1985;

"local authority"—

(a) in relation to England . . . , means any of the following, that is to say, the council of a county, district or London borough, the Common Council of the City of London and the Council of the Isles of Scilly;

[(aa) in relation to Wales, means a county council or county borough council;]

(b) in relation to Scotland, means a [council constituted under section 2 of the Local Government etc (Scotland) Act 1994]; and

(c) in relation to Northern Ireland, means a district council;

. . .

[. . .]

"participant", in relation to a body corporate, means a person who holds or is beneficially entitled to shares in that body or who possesses voting power in that body.

[…]

[(1A) For the purpose of determining the persons who are the associates of a body corporate for the purposes of this Schedule—

(a) an individual shall be regarded as an associate of a body corporate if he is a director of that body corporate, and

(b) a body corporate and another body corporate shall be regarded as associates of each other if one controls the other or if the same person controls both.]

(2) For the purpose of determining the persons who are an individual's associates for the purposes of this Schedule, the following persons shall be regarded as associates of each other, namely—

(a) any individual and that individual's husband or wife [or civil partner] and any relative, or husband or wife [or civil partner] of a relative, of that individual or of that individual's husband or wife [or civil partner];

(b) any individual and any body corporate of which that individual is a director;

(c) any person in his capacity as trustee of a settlement and the settlor or grantor and any person associated with the settlor or grantor;

(d) persons carrying on business in partnership and the husband or wife [or civil partner] and relatives of any of them;

(e) any two or more persons acting together to secure or exercise control of a body corporate or other association or to secure control of any enterprise or assets;

and in this sub-paragraph "relative" means a brother, sister, uncle, aunt, nephew, niece, lineal ancestor or descendant (the stepchild or illegitimate child of any person, or anyone adopted by a person, whether legally or otherwise, as his child, being regarded as a relative or taken into account to trace a relationship in the same way as that person's child); and references to a wife or husband shall include a former wife or husband and a reputed wife or husband [and references to a civil partner shall include a former civil partner] [and a reputed civil partner].

[(3) For the purposes of this Schedule a person controls a body corporate if—

(a) he holds, or is beneficially entitled to, more than 50 per cent of the equity share capital in the body, or possesses more than 50 per cent of the voting power in it; or

(b) although he does not have such an interest in the body, it is reasonable, having regard to all the circumstances, to expect that he [would (if he chose to) be able in most cases or in significant respects], by whatever means and whether directly or indirectly, to achieve the result that [affairs] of the body are conducted in accordance with his wishes; or

(c) he holds, or is beneficially entitled to, 50 per cent of the equity share capital in that body, or possesses 50 per cent of the voting power in it, and an arrangement exists between him and any other participant in the body as to the manner in which any voting power in the body possessed by either of them is to be exercised, or as to the omission by either of them to exercise such voting power.

(3A) For the purposes of sub-paragraph (3)(c)—

(a) "arrangement" includes any agreement or arrangement, whether or not it is, or is intended to be, legally enforceable, and

(b) a person shall be treated—

  (i) as holding, or being beneficially entitled to, any equity share capital which is held by a body corporate which he controls or to which such a body corporate is beneficially entitled, and

  (ii) as possessing any voting power possessed by such a body corporate.]

(4) …

(5) For the purposes of any provision of this Schedule which refers to a body controlled by two or more persons or bodies of any description taken together, the persons or bodies in question shall not be regarded as controlling the body by virtue of paragraph (b) of sub-paragraph (3) unless they are acting together in concert.

[(6) In this Schedule any reference to a participant with more than a [5 per cent] interest in a body corporate is a reference to a person who—

(a) holds or is beneficially entitled to more than [5 per cent] of the shares in that body, or

(b) possesses more than [5 per cent] of the voting power in that body.

(7) Sub-paragraph (6) shall have effect subject to the necessary modifications in relation to other references in this Schedule—

(a) to an interest of more than a specified percentage in a body corporate, or

(b) to an interest of a specified percentage or more in a body corporate.

(8) …]

2.—(1) [Subject to sub-paragraph (1A)] any reference in paragraph 1 above to a person—

(a) holding or being entitled to shares, or any amount of the shares or equity share capital, in a body corporate, or

(b) possessing voting power, or any amount of the voting power, in a body corporate,

is a reference to his doing so, or being so entitled, whether alone or jointly with one or more other persons and whether directly or through one or more nominees.

[(1A) For the purposes of this Schedule, a person's holding of shares, or possession of voting power, in a body corporate shall be disregarded if, or to the extent that—

(a) he holds the shares concerned—

(i) as a nominee,

(ii) as a custodian (whether under a trust or by a contract), or

(iii) under an arrangement pursuant to which he has issued, or is to issue, depositary receipts, as defined by section 220(1) of the Companies Act 1985, in respect of the shares concerned, and

(b) he is not entitled to exercise or control the exercise of voting rights in respect of the shares concerned.

(1B) For the purposes of sub-paragraph (1A)(b)—

(a) a person is not entitled to exercise or control the exercise of voting rights in respect of shares if he is bound (whether by contract or otherwise) not to exercise the voting rights, or not to exercise them otherwise than in accordance with the instructions of another, and

(b) voting rights which a person is entitled to exercise or of which he is entitled to control the exercise only in certain circumstances shall be taken into account only when those circumstances have arisen and for as long as they continue to obtain.]

(2), (3) …

[3. For the purposes of this Schedule the following persons shall be treated as connected with a particular person—

(a) a person who controls that person,

(b) an associate of that person or of a person falling within paragraph (a), and

(c) a body which is controlled by that person or by an associate of that person.]

[3A, 3B. …]

4. …

[3067]

NOTES

Para 1: in sub-para (1) definition "the 1996 Act" inserted, in definition "associate" para (a) substituted, and in definition "control" words in square brackets substituted, by the Broadcasting Act 1996, s 73, Sch 2, Pt I, para 1(1), (2); definition "Broadcasting Act licence" inserted, and definition omitted in the second place repealed, by the Communications Act 2003, ss 360(3), 406(7), Sch 15, Pt 1, para 69(1), (2), Sch 19(1), subject to transitional provisions in s 406(6) of, and Sch 18, para 5 to, that Act at **[3434]**, **[3460]**; definitions omitted from square brackets inserted by the Broadcasting Act 1996, s 73, Sch 2, Pt I, para 1(1), (2), repealed by the Communications Act 2003, s 406(7), Sch 19(1); in definition "local authority", words omitted from para (a) repealed, and para (aa) inserted, by the Local Government (Wales) Act 1994, s 66(6), (8), Sch 16, para 89, Sch 18, in para (b) words in square brackets substituted by the Local Government etc (Scotland) Act 1994, s 180(1), Sch 13, para 166; sub-para (1A) inserted, sub-paras (3), (3A) substituted, for original sub-para (3), sub-para (4) repealed, and sub-paras (6)–(8) substituted, for original sub-para (6), by the Broadcasting Act 1996, ss 73, 148(2), Sch 2, para 1(3)–(6), Sch 11, Pt I; in sub-para (2), words in square brackets in paras (a), (d), and words in fifth pair of square brackets inserted by the Civil Partnership Act 2004, s 261(1), Sch 27, para 139, words in sixth pair of square brackets inserted by the Civil Partnership Act 2004 (Overseas Relationships and Consequential, etc Amendments) Order 2005, SI 2005/3129, art 4(4), Sch 4, para 10; words in square brackets in sub-paras (3), (6) substituted, and sub-para (8) repealed, by the Communications Act 2003, ss 357(1), 360(6), 406(7), Sch 15, Pt 1, para 69(1), (3), Sch 19(1), subject to transitional provisions in s 406(6) of, and Sch 18, para 5 to, that Act at **[3434]**, **[3460]**.

Para 2: words in square brackets in sub-para (1), and sub-paras (1A), (1B) inserted, and sub-paras (2), (3) repealed, by the Broadcasting Act 1996, ss 73, 148(2), Sch 2, para 2, Sch 11, Pt I.

Para 3: substituted by the Broadcasting Act 1996, s 73, Sch 2, para 3.

Paras 3A, 3B: inserted by the Broadcasting Act 1996, s 73, Sch 2, para 4; repealed by the Communications Act 2003, s 406(7), Sch 19(1), subject to transitional provisions in s 406(6) of, and Sch 18, paras 5, 30, 64 to, that Act at **[3434]**, **[3460]**.

Para 4: repealed by the Communications Act 2003, s 406(7), Sch 19(1).

PART II
DISQUALIFICATION FOR HOLDING LICENCES

General disqualification of non-EEC nationals and bodies having political connections

1.—(1) Subject to [sub-paragraph (1A)], the following persons are disqualified persons in relation to [a Broadcasting Act licence]—

(a), (b)..

(c) a local authority;

(d) a body whose objects are wholly or mainly of a political nature;

(e) a body affiliated to a body falling within paragraph (d);

(f) an individual who is an officer of a body falling within paragraph (d) or (e);

(g) a body corporate which is an associate of a body corporate falling within paragraph (d) or (e);

(h) a body corporate in which a body falling within any of paragraphs (c) to (e) and (g) is a participant with more than a 5 per cent interest;

[(hh) a body corporate which is controlled by a body corporate falling within paragraph (h);]

(i) a body which is controlled by a person falling within any of paragraphs [(c)] to (g) or by two or more such persons taken together; and

(j) a body corporate in which a body falling within paragraph (i), other than one which is controlled—

(i) by a person falling within paragraph … (f), or

(ii) by two or more such persons taken together,

is a participant with more than a 5 per cent interest.

[(1A) Where a service is provided exclusively for the purposes of the carrying out of the functions of a local authority under section 142 of the Local Government Act 1972 (provision by local authorities of information relating to their activities), a person is disqualified by virtue of sub-paragraph (1) in relation to a licence to provide that service only if he would be so disqualified disregarding paragraph (c) of that sub-paragraph.]

(2), (3) …

Disqualification of religious bodies

2.—[(1) The following persons are disqualified persons in relation only to licences falling within sub-paragraph (1A)—]

(a) a body whose objects are wholly or mainly of a religious nature;

(b) a body which is controlled by a body falling within paragraph (a) or by two or more such bodies taken together;

(c) a body which controls a body falling within paragraph (a);

(d) a body corporate which is an associate of a body corporate falling within paragraph (a), (b) or (c);

(e) a body corporate in which a body falling within any of paragraphs (a) to (d) is a participant with more than a 5 per cent interest;

(f) an individual who is an officer of a body falling within paragraph (a); and

(g) a body which is controlled by an individual falling within paragraph (f) or by two or more such individuals taken together.

[(1A) A licence falls within this sub-paragraph if it is—

(a) a Channel 3 licence,

(b) a Channel 5 licence,

(c) a national sound broadcasting licence,

(d) a public teletext licence,

(e) an additional television service licence,

(f) a television multiplex licence, or

(g) a radio multiplex licence.

(1B) In this paragraph—

"additional television service licence" means a licence under Part 1 of this Act to provide an additional television service within the meaning of Part 3 of the Communications Act 2003,

"Channel 3 licence" and "Channel 5 licence" each has the same meaning as in Part 1 of this Act, "national sound broadcasting licence" means a licence to provide a sound broadcasting service (within the meaning of Part 3 of this Act) which is a national service (within the meaning of that Part),

"public teletext licence" means a licence to provide the public teletext service (within the meaning of Part 3 of the Communications Act 2003),

"radio multiplex licence" means a licence under Part 2 of the Broadcasting Act 1996 to provide a radio multiplex service within the meaning of that Part, and

"television multiplex licence" means a licence under Part 1 of the Broadcasting Act 1996 to provide a multiplex service within the meaning of that Part.]

Disqualification of publicly-funded bodies for radio service licences

3.—(1) The following persons are disqualified persons in relation to any licence granted [under Part 3 of this Act or Part 2 of the Broadcasting Act 1996] other than a licence to provide a restricted service—

(a) a body [(other than a local authority, the Welsh Authority or the BBC)] which has, in its last financial year, received more than half its income from public funds;

(b) a body which is controlled by a body falling within paragraph (a) or by two or more such bodies taken together; and

(c) a body corporate in which a body falling within paragraph (a) or (b) is a participant with more than a 5 per cent interest.

(2) For the purposes of sub-paragraph (1)(a) money is received from public funds if it is paid—

(a) by a Minister of the Crown out of money provided by Parliament or out of the National Loans Fund;

(b) by a Northern Ireland department out of the Consolidated Fund of Northern Ireland or out of money appropriated by Measure of the Northern Ireland Assembly; or

(c) by a body which itself falls within sub-paragraph (1)(a), including a body which falls within that provision by virtue of this paragraph;

but, in each case, there shall be disregarded any money paid as consideration for the acquisition of property or the supply of goods or services or as remuneration, expenses, pensions, allowances or similar benefits for or in respect of a person as the holder of an office.

General disqualification on grounds of undue influence

4.—(1) A person is a disqualified person in relation to [a Broadcasting Act licence] if in the opinion of [OFCOM]—

(a) any relevant body is, by the giving of financial assistance or otherwise, exerting influence over the activities of that person, and

(b) that influence has led, is leading or is likely to lead to results which are adverse to the public interest.

(2) In sub-paragraph (1) "relevant body"—

(a) in relation to a licence granted [under Part 1 of this Act or Part 1 of the Broadcasting Act 1996, means a person] falling within paragraph 1(1)(c) to (h) or (j) above or a body which is controlled—

(i) by a person falling within paragraph 1(1)(c) to (g) above, or

(ii) by two or more such persons taken together; and

(b) in relation to a licence granted [under Part 3 of this Act or Part 2 of the Broadcasting Act 1996, means a person] falling within paragraph 1(1)(c) or (h) or (j) or 3 above or a body which is controlled—

[(i) by a person falling within paragraph 1(1)(c) to (g) above,

(ii) by a person falling within paragraph 3 above, or

(iii) by two or more persons taken together each of whom falls within sub-paragraph (i) or (ii) (whether or not they all fall within the same sub-paragraph).]

General disqualification of broadcasting bodies

5. The following persons are disqualified persons in relation to [a Broadcasting Act licence]—

(a) the BBC;

(b) the Welsh Authority;

(c), (d) …

[Disqualification of certain companies for certain licences

5A.—(1) A BBC company, a Channel 4 company or an S4C company is a disqualified person in relation to—

(a) any licence … to provide regional or national Channel 3 services or Channel 5, …

(b) …

(2) A BBC company is also a disqualified person in relation to any licence … to provide a national, local or restricted service within the meaning of Part III of this Act.

(3) …]

General disqualification of advertising agencies

6. The following persons are disqualified persons in relation to [a Broadcasting Act licence]—

(a) an advertising agency;

(b) an associate of an advertising agency;

(c) any body which is controlled by a person falling within sub-paragraph (a) or (b) or by two or more such persons taken together;

(d) any body corporate in which a person falling within any of sub-paragraphs (a) to (c) is a participant with more than a 5 per cent interest.

[3068]

NOTES

Para 1: sub-para (1)(hh) inserted by the Broadcasting Act 1996, ss 73, 148(2), Sch 2, para 6, Sch 11, Pt I; in sub-para (1) other words in square brackets substituted, and words omitted from sub-para (1) and the whole of sub-paras (2), (3) repealed, and sub-para (1A) inserted, by the Communications Act 2003, ss 348(1), 349(1), 360(3), 406(7), Sch 15, Pt 1, para 69(1), (4), (5), Sch 19(1), subject to transitional provisions in s 406(6) of, and Sch 18, para 5 to, that Act at **[3434]**, **[3460]**.

Para 2: words in square brackets in sub-para (1) substituted, and sub-paras (1A), (1B) substituted, for original sub-paras (2), (3), by the Communications Act 2003, s 348(2), (3), subject to transitional provisions in s 406(6) of, and Sch 18, paras 5, 54(1)–(4), (7), 64 to, that Act at **[3434]**, **[3460]**.

Para 3: words in first pair of square brackets substituted by the Communications Act 2003, s 360(3), Sch 15, Pt 1, para 69(1), (6), subject to transitional provisions in s 406(6) of, and Sch 18, para 5 to, that Act at **[3434]**, **[3460]**; words in square brackets in sub-para (1)(a) substituted by the Broadcasting Act 1996, s 73, Sch 2, para 7.

Paras 4, 6: words in square brackets substituted by the Communications Act 2003, ss 348(4), 360(3), Sch 15, Pt 1, para 69(1), (4), (7), (8), subject to transitional provisions in s 406(6) of, and Sch 18, para 5 to, that Act at **[3434]**, **[3460]**.

Para 5: words in square brackets substituted by the Communications Act 2003, s 360(3), Sch 15, Pt 1, para 69(1), (4), subject to transitional provisions in s 406(6) of, and Sch 18, para 5 to, that Act at **[3434]**, **[3460]**; paras (c), (d) repealed by the Broadcasting Act 1996, ss 73, 148(2), Sch 2, para 8, Sch 11, Pt I.

Para 5A: inserted, together with preceding cross heading, by the Broadcasting Act 1996, s 73, Sch 2, para 9; words omitted repealed by the Communications Act 2003, ss 360(3), 406(7), Sch 15, Pt 1, para 69(1), (9), Sch 19(1), subject to transitional provisions in s 406(6) of, and Sch 18, paras 5, 30, 64 to, that Act at **[3434]**, **[3460]**.

Modification: this Part is modified in its application to community radio services by the Community Radio Order 2004, SI 2004/1944, art 4, Schedule, Pt 1, paras 1, 8 at **[3624]**.

(*Sch 2, Pts 3–5, Schs 4, 5 repealed by the Communications Act 2003, ss 350(1), 406(7), Sch 19(1), subject to transitional provisions in s 406(6) of, and Sch 18, paras 5, 30, 36(2), 54(5)–(7), 64 to, that Act at* **[3434]**, **[3460]**; *Schs 3, 6 outside the scope of this work.*)

SCHEDULE 7
QUALIFYING REVENUE: SUPPLEMENTARY PROVISIONS
Sections 67, 77 and 121

PART I
QUALIFYING REVENUE FOR PURPOSES OF PART I OR II OF THIS ACT

Computation of qualifying revenue

1.—(1) It shall be the duty of [OFCOM] to draw up, and from time to time review, a statement setting out the principles to be followed in ascertaining the qualifying revenue in relation to a person—
(a) for any accounting period of his, or
(b) for any year,
for the purposes of any provision of Part I or Part II of this Act.

(2) A statement under this paragraph may set out different principles for persons holding different kinds of licences.

(3) Before drawing up or revising a statement under this paragraph [OFCOM] shall consult the Secretary of State and the Treasury.

(4) [OFCOM] shall—
(a) publish the statement drawn up under this paragraph and every revision of that statement; and
(b) transmit a copy of that statement, and every revision of it, to the Secretary of State; and the Secretary of State shall lay copies of the statement and of every such revision before each House of Parliament.

Disputes

2.—(1) For the purposes of any provision of Part I or Part II of this Act—
(a) the amount of the qualifying revenue in relation to any person for any accounting period of his, or (as the case may be) for any year, or
(b) the amount of any payment to be made to [OFCOM] by any person in respect of any such revenue, or of an instalment of any such payment,
shall, in the event of a disagreement between [OFCOM] and that person, be the amount determined by [OFCOM].

(2) No determination of [OFCOM] under this paragraph shall be called in question in any court of law, or be the subject of any arbitration; but nothing in this sub-paragraph shall prevent the bringing of proceedings for judicial review.

[3069]

NOTES

Words in square brackets substituted by the Communications Act 2003, s 360(3), Sch 15, Pt 1, para 72(1), (2), subject to transitional provisions in s 406(6) of, and Sch 18, paras 30, 37, 64 to, that Act at **[3434]**, **[3460]**.

PART II
QUALIFYING REVENUE FOR PURPOSES OF PART III OF THIS ACT

Computation of qualifying revenue

1.—(1) It shall be the duty of [OFCOM] to draw up, and from time to time review, a statement setting out the principles to be followed in ascertaining the qualifying revenue for any accounting period of a licence holder for the purposes of any provision of Part III of this Act.

(2) A statement under this paragraph may set out different principles for persons holding different kinds of licences.

(3) Before drawing up or revising a statement under this paragraph [OFCOM] shall consult the Secretary of State and the Treasury.

(4) [OFCOM] shall—

(a) publish the statement drawn up under this paragraph and every revision of that statement; and

(b) transmit a copy of that statement, and every revision of it, to the Secretary of State;

and the Secretary of State shall lay copies of the statement and of every such revision before each House of Parliament.

Disputes

2.—(1) For the purposes of any provision of Part III of this Act—

(a) the amount of the qualifying revenue for any accounting period of a person, or

(b) the amount of any payment to be made to [OFCOM] by any person in respect of any such revenue, or of an instalment of any such payment,

shall, in the event of a disagreement between [OFCOM] and that person, be the amount determined by [OFCOM].

(2) No determination of [OFCOM] under this paragraph shall be called in question in any court of law, or be the subject of any arbitration; but nothing in this sub-paragraph shall prevent the bringing of proceedings for judicial review. **[3070]**

NOTES

Words in square brackets substituted by the Communications Act 2003, s 360(3), Sch 15, Pt 1, para 72(1), (3), subject to transitional provisions in s 406(6) of, and Sch 18, paras 30, 37, 64 to, that Act at **[3434]**, **[3460]**.

(*Sch 8 repealed by the Communications Act 2003, s 406(7), Sch 19(1), subject to transitional provisions in s 406(6) of, and Sch 18, paras 30, 64 to, that Act at* **[3434]**, **[3460]** *and subject to further transitional provisions in the Office of Communications Act 2002 (Commencement No 3) and Communications Act 2003 (Commencement No 2) Order 2003, SI 2003/3142, art 6(2) at* **[3595]**.)

SCHEDULE 9
SCHEME PROVIDING FOR DIVISION OF ASSETS OF IBA

Section 127

Preliminary

1. In this Schedule—

"relevant transferee" shall be construed in accordance with paragraph 2(1) below; and

"transfer scheme" means a scheme under this Schedule made either by the IBA under paragraph 2(1) below or by the Secretary of State under paragraph 2(4) below.

Making and modification of transfer scheme

2.—(1) The IBA shall make a scheme under this Schedule for the division of all their property, rights and liabilities between—

(a) the Commission,

(b) the Radio Authority, and

(c) the nominated company;

and references in this Schedule to the relevant transferees are references to the bodies specified in paragraphs (a) to (c) above.

(2) Where such a scheme is made by the IBA, it shall not be capable of coming into force in accordance with section 127(1) of this Act unless it is approved by the Secretary of State.

(3) Where such a scheme is submitted to the Secretary of State for his approval, he may modify the scheme before approving it.

(4) If—

(a) the IBA have not, before such time as the Secretary of State may notify to them as the latest time for the submission of such a scheme, submitted such a scheme for his approval, or

(b) the Secretary of State decides not to approve (either with or without modifications) a scheme that has been submitted to him by the IBA,

the Secretary of State may himself make a scheme for the division of the IBA's property, rights and liabilities between the relevant transferees.

(5) If, at any time after the Secretary of State has either—

(a) approved (either with or without modifications) a scheme under this Schedule made by the IBA, or

(b) himself made such a scheme,

but before the scheme has come into force in accordance with section 127(1) of this Act, the Secretary of State considers it appropriate to do so, he may determine that the scheme shall, on its so coming into force, come into force with such modifications as may be specified in his determination; and, in any such case, the scheme shall accordingly, on its coming into force, come into force with those modifications.

(6) If at any time after a transfer scheme has come into force—

(a) the Secretary of State considers it appropriate to make an order under this sub-paragraph, and

(b) every relevant transferee who would be affected by the order either—

(i) (in a case where any such transferee is the nominated company and that company has ceased to be wholly owned by the Crown) has consented to the making of the order, or

(ii) (in any other case) has been consulted by the Secretary of State,

the Secretary of State may by order provide that the scheme shall for all purposes be deemed to have come into force with such modifications as may be specified in the order.

(7) Any power to modify a transfer scheme which is conferred on the Secretary of State by this paragraph may be so exercised as to make any such provision as could have been made by the scheme, and an order under sub-paragraph (6) above may provide for any of its provisions to have effect as from the coming into force of the scheme to which it relates.

(8) In determining whether and in what manner to exercise any power conferred on him by this paragraph the Secretary of State shall have regard to the need to ensure that the division of property, rights and liabilities between the relevant transferees which is effected under this Schedule allocates property, rights and liabilities to those transferees in such a manner as appears to him to be appropriate—

(a) in the case of the Commission and the Radio Authority, in the light of the functions conferred on those bodies by this Act; and

(b) in the case of the nominated company, with a view to the carrying on by that company of a business consisting of—

(i) the provision of broadcasting transmission services and services related to such services, and

(ii) the carrying out of research and development work relating to broadcasting.

(9) It shall be the duty of the IBA and each of the relevant transferees to provide the Secretary of State with all such information and other assistance as he may reasonably require for the purposes of, or in connection with, the exercise of any power conferred on him by this paragraph.

(10) Nothing in this paragraph shall require a scheme under this Schedule to make provision—

(a) with respect to any equipment or other asset which the IBA have agreed to dispose of in pursuance of section 132(1) or 133(6) of this Act, or

(b) with respect to any liabilities of the IBA which—

(i) have not yet become enforceable against the IBA, and

(ii) are not specifically and exclusively referable to any particular part or parts of the undertaking of the IBA which is or are transferred in accordance with any such scheme to one or more of the relevant transferees, or

(c) with respect to any such rights or liabilities as are mentioned in sub-paragraph (11).

(11) Those rights and liabilities are rights and liabilities acquired by the IBA in connection with the sharing by the IBA and the BBC of the use of facilities (of whatever description) in connection with the transmission of television programmes or local sound broadcasts.

Content of transfer scheme

3.—(1) A transfer scheme may—

(a) define the property, rights and liabilities to be allocated to a particular relevant transferee—

(i) by specifying or describing the property, rights and liabilities in question,

(ii) by referring to all the property, rights and liabilities comprised in a specified part of the IBA's undertaking, or

(ii) partly in the one way and partly in the other;

(b) provide that any rights or liabilities specified or described in the scheme shall be enforceable either by or against either or any, or by or against both or all, of two or more relevant transferees;

(c) impose on any relevant transferee an obligation to enter into such written agreements with, or execute such instruments in favour of, such other relevant transferee as may be specified in the scheme;

(d) create for any of the relevant transferees an interest in or right over property transferred in accordance with the scheme to any other of those transferees;

(e) in connection with any provision made by virtue of paragraph (d), make incidental provision as to the interests, rights and liabilities of other persons with respect to the property in question.

(2) Without prejudice to the generality of sub-paragraph (1)(a), a transfer scheme may, in connection with any transfer to be made in accordance with the scheme, exclude from the transfer any rights and liabilities falling within paragraph 2(11) above and described in the scheme.

(3) A transfer scheme may also allocate to any of the relevant transferees such property, rights and liabilities to which the IBA may become entitled or subject after the making of the scheme and before the transfer date as may be described in the scheme.

(4) The property, rights and liabilities of the IBA that are capable of being transferred in accordance with a transfer scheme include—

(a) property, rights and liabilities that would not otherwise be capable of being transferred or assigned by the IBA;

(b) property situated anywhere in the United Kingdom or elsewhere; and

(c) rights and liabilities under the law of any part of the United Kingdom or of any country or territory outside the United Kingdom.

(5) It is hereby declared for the avoidance of doubt that the rights and liabilities capable of being so transferred include rights and liabilities of the IBA under any agreement or arrangement for the payment of pensions, allowances or gratuities.

(6) An obligation imposed by a provision included in a transfer scheme by virtue of sub-paragraph (1)(c) shall be enforceable by civil proceedings brought by the other relevant transferee in question for an injunction or interdict or for any other appropriate relief.

Effect of transfer scheme

4.—(1) Where a transfer scheme comes into force on the transfer date, this sub-paragraph shall have effect on that date so as to transfer to each of the relevant transferees, in accordance with the scheme's provisions and without further assurance, such of the property, rights and liabilities of the IBA as are allocated to that transferee by the scheme.

(2) A transaction of any description which is effected in pursuance of any provision included in a transfer scheme in accordance with this Schedule shall be binding on all persons, notwithstanding that it would, apart from this sub-paragraph, have required the consent or concurrence of any person other than the IBA or any relevant transferee.

(3) Where apart from this sub-paragraph any person would have power, in consequence of anything done or likely to be done by or under this Act, to terminate or modify an interest or right which is vested in the IBA at the passing of this Act, then—

(a) for the purposes of the transfer of the interest or right in accordance with a transfer scheme, that power shall not be exercisable in relation to the interest or right at any time before its transfer in accordance with the scheme; and

(b) without prejudice to any other provision of this Schedule, that power shall be exercisable in relation to the interest or right after its transfer only in so far as the scheme provides for it to be transferred subject to the power.

(4) Where, in consequence of any transfer made in accordance with a transfer scheme, all the property, rights and liabilities comprised in a particular part of the IBA's undertaking are transferred to a relevant transferee—

(a) the Transfer of Undertakings (Protection of Employment) Regulations 1981 shall apply to the transfer, whether or not they would otherwise so apply, and

(b) that undertaking shall accordingly (whether or not it would otherwise be so regarded) be regarded for the purposes of those Regulations as an undertaking in the nature of a commercial venture.

Third parties affected by transfer scheme

5.—(1) This paragraph applies where—

(a) in consequence of any transfer made in accordance with a transfer scheme, any right or liability of a person other than the IBA or any relevant transferee) which was enforceable against or by the IBA becomes enforceable against or by one or more relevant transferees; and

(b) apart from this Schedule that person's consent or concurrence would have been required for that right or liability to become so enforceable;

and in this paragraph references to a third party are references to any such person.

(2) Subject to sub-paragraph (3), the IBA shall take reasonable steps to identify any third party and to notify him of the effect of the transfer in question on any right or liability of his falling within sub-paragraph (1), and of the effect of sub-paragraph (4).

(3) A transfer scheme may provide that the duties imposed on the IBA by sub-paragraph (2) in relation to a transfer shall be imposed instead on such one of the relevant transferees as may be specified in the scheme.

(4) Where—

(a) any right or liability of a third party has become enforceable against or by more than one relevant transferee, and

(b) the value of any property or interest of the third party is diminished thereby,

such compensation as is just shall be paid to the third party by one or more of the relevant transferees.

(5) Any dispute as to whether, and if so how much, compensation is payable under sub-paragraph (4), or as to the person to or by whom it shall be paid, shall be referred to and determined by—

(a) an arbitrator appointed by the Lord Chancellor; or

(b) where the proceedings are to be held in Scotland, an arbiter appointed by the Lord President of the Court of Session.

Supplemental provisions of scheme

6.—(1) A transfer scheme may contain supplemental, consequential and transitional provisions for the purposes of, or in connection with, the division effected or any other provision made by the scheme.

(2) Without prejudice to the generality of sub-paragraph (1) above, a transfer scheme may provide—

(a) that for purposes connected with any transfer made in accordance with the scheme a relevant transferee to whom anything is transferred in accordance with the scheme is to be treated as the same person in law as the IBA;

(b) that, so far as may be necessary for the purposes of or in connection with any such transfer, agreements made, transactions effected and other things done by or in relation to the IBA are to be treated as made, effected or done by or in relation to the relevant transferee to whom the transfer is made;

(c) that, so far as may be necessary for the purposes of or in connection with any such transfer, references in any agreement (whether or not in writing) or in any deed, bond, instrument or other document to, or to any member or officer of, the IBA are to have effect with such modifications as are specified in the scheme;

(d) that proceedings commenced by or against the IBA are to be continued by or against such one of the relevant transferees as the scheme may provide in relation to any circumstances specified or described in it;

(e) that the effect of any transfer made in accordance with the scheme in relation to contracts of employment with the IBA is not to be to terminate any such contracts but is to be that periods of employment with the IBA are to count for all purposes as periods of employment with the relevant transferee to whom the transfer is made;

(f) that disputes as to the effect of the scheme between any of the relevant transferees are to be referred to such arbitration as may be specified in or determined under the scheme;

(g) that determinations on such arbitrations, and certificates given jointly by all or any two of the relevant transferees as to the effect of the scheme as between the transferees concerned, are to be conclusive for all purposes.

Vesting of IBA's property after coming into force of scheme

7.—(1) A transfer scheme may provide for the imposition of duties—

(a) on the IBA, and

(b) on all or any of the relevant transferees,

to take all such steps as may be requisite to secure that the vesting in any of those transferees, by virtue of the scheme, of any foreign property, right or liability is effective under the relevant foreign law.

(2) The provisions of a transfer scheme may require the IBA to comply with any directions of any of the relevant transferees in performing any duty imposed on the IBA by virtue of a provision included in the scheme by virtue of sub-paragraph (1).

(3) A transfer scheme may provide that, until the vesting of any foreign property, right or liability of the IBA in a relevant transferee is effective under the relevant foreign law, it shall be the duty of the IBA to hold that property or right for the benefit of, or to discharge that liability on behalf of, that transferee.

(4) Nothing in any provision included in a transfer scheme by virtue of this paragraph shall be taken as prejudicing the effect under the law of any part of the United Kingdom of the vesting in a relevant transferee, by virtue of the scheme, of any foreign property, right or liability.

(5) The IBA shall have all such powers as may be requisite for the performance of any duty imposed on them by any provision included in a transfer scheme by virtue of this paragraph; but such a scheme may require a relevant transferee to act on behalf of the IBA (so far as possible) for the purposes of, or in connection with, the performance of any such duty in relation to any property, right or liability vested in the transferee by virtue of the scheme.

(6) A transfer scheme may provide that any foreign property, rights or liabilities that are acquired or incurred by the IBA after the scheme comes into force are immediately to become property, rights or liabilities of such one of the relevant transferees as is specified in the scheme; and such a scheme may make the same provision in relation to any such property, rights or liabilities as can be made, by virtue of the preceding provisions of this paragraph, in relation to foreign property, rights and liabilities vested in the IBA when the scheme comes into force.

(7) References in this paragraph to any foreign property, right or liability are references to any property, right or liability as respects which any issue arising in any proceedings would have to be determined (in accordance with the rules of private international law) by reference to the law of a country or territory outside the United Kingdom.

(8) Any expenses incurred by the IBA in consequence of any provision included in a transfer scheme by virtue of this paragraph shall be met by the relevant transferees in such proportions as may be determined by or under the scheme.

Certificate of Secretary of State as to vesting of property etc

8.—(1) Subject to sub-paragraph (2), a certificate issued by the Secretary of State to the effect that any property, right or liability of the IBA vested at a particular time by virtue of this Schedule in one or more of the relevant transferees shall be conclusive evidence of the matters stated in the certificate.

(2) Nothing in any such certificate shall prejudice the operation of a certificate issued by virtue of a provision included in a transfer scheme by virtue of paragraph 6(2)(g) above.

Power of Secretary of State to control division of IBA's pension fund

9.—(1) If the Secretary of State so determines, the trustees of the Independent Broadcasting Authority Staff Pensions Plan shall refer to him, before such date as he may specify, the division and distribution of the relevant assets which is to be made by them for the purpose of making a transfer payment to a pension scheme established by the nominated company for its employees; and, if he does so, any such division and distribution of those assets and liabilities shall not be made by the trustees except—

(a) with his consent, or

(b) in accordance with an order made by him under sub-paragraph (2).

(2) Where any such division and distribution is referred to the Secretary of State under sub-paragraph (1), he may by order direct that the relevant assets shall be divided and distributed by the trustees in such manner, and at such time, as is specified in the order; and any provision of—

(a) the Plan referred to in sub-paragraph (1), or

(b) any enactment relating to occupational pension schemes, including any enactment relating to transfer values,

shall not have effect to the extent that it is inconsistent with the division and distribution of those assets in accordance with any such order.

(3) When making an order under sub-paragraph (2) the Secretary of State shall have regard to the interests of all classes of persons who are for the time being beneficiaries or potential beneficiaries under the Plan referred to in sub-paragraph (1).

(4) In this paragraph—

"the relevant assets" means the assets held by or on behalf of the trustees; and

"the trustees" means the trustees of the Plan referred to in sub-paragraph (1).

(5) An order under sub-paragraph (2) shall be subject to annulment in pursuance of a resolution of either House of Parliament.

Discharge by IBA of contingent etc liabilities

10.—(1) This paragraph applies to any liabilities to which the IBA are subject on or after the transfer date, being liabilities which—

(a) had not become enforceable against the IBA before that date, and

(b) are not specifically and exclusively referable to any particular part or parts of the undertaking of the IBA which has or have been transferred in accordance with a transfer scheme to one or more of the relevant transferees.

(2) Any sums required by the IBA for the purpose of discharging any liabilities to which this paragraph applies shall be paid to them by the Secretary of State out of money provided by Parliament.

(3) Any payments made to the IBA under sub-paragraph (2) may be so made subject to such conditions as the Secretary of State may determine with the approval of the Treasury.

Final accounts and annual report of IBA

11.—(1) The IBA shall, as soon as possible after the transfer date, prepare such a statement of accounts as is mentioned in subsection (1) of section 42 of the Broadcasting Act 1981 (accounts and audit) in respect of the period between—

(a) the end of the financial year for which the last statement of accounts was prepared by them under that section, and

(b) the transfer date,

whether that period is a financial year or not; and that section shall continue to apply on and after that date in relation to the auditing of accounts kept in accordance with that subsection in respect of that period.

(2) The IBA shall, as soon as possible after the transfer date, prepare and transmit to the Secretary of State, in accordance with section 43 of that Act (annual reports), such a report as is mentioned in subsection (1) of that section in respect of the period between—

(a) the end of the financial year for which the last such report was prepared by them under that section, and

(b) the transfer date,

whether that period is a financial year or not.

(3) Subsection (2) of that section shall apply to any such report as if the references to the statement of accounts for the year in question included references to the statement of accounts prepared in accordance with sub-paragraph (1) above.

(4) The Secretary of State shall lay copies of any such report before each House of Parliament.

(5) Any expenses incurred by the IBA under this paragraph shall be met by such one or more of the relevant transferees, and (if more than one) in such proportions, as may be determined by or under a transfer scheme.

[3071]

(Schs 10, 11 outside the scope of this work; Sch 12 repealed by the Communications Act 2003, s 406(7), Sch 19(1), subject to transitional provisions in s 406(6) of, and Sch 18, paras 5, 30, 64 to, that Act at **[3434]**, **[3460]***; Schs 13, 14 repealed by the Broadcasting Act 1996, s 148(2), Sch 11, Pt I.)*

SCHEDULE 15
APPLICATION OF 1959 ACT TO TELEVISION AND SOUND PROGRAMMES

Section 162

Interpretation

1. In this Schedule—

"the 1959 Act" means the Obscene Publications Act 1959;

"relevant programme" means a programme included in a programme service;

and other expressions used in this Schedule which are also used in the 1959 Act have the same meaning as in that Act.

Liability of person providing live programme material

2. Where—

(a) any matter is included by any person in a relevant programme in circumstances falling within section 1(5) of the 1959 Act, and

(b) that matter has been provided, for inclusion in that programme, by some other person,

the 1959 Act shall have effect as if that matter had been included in that programme by that other person (as well as by the person referred to in sub-paragraph (a)).

Obscene articles kept for inclusion in programmes

3. It is hereby declared that where a person has an obscene article in his ownership, possession or control with a view to the matter recorded on it being included in a relevant programme, the article shall be taken for the purposes of the 1959 Act to be an obscene article had or kept by that person for publication for gain.

Requirement for consent of Director of Public Prosecutions

4.—(1) Proceedings for an offence under section 2 of the 1959 Act for publishing an obscene article shall not be instituted except by or with the consent of the Director of Public Prosecutions in any case where—

(a) the relevant publication, or

(b) the only other publication which following from the relevant publication,

took place in the course of the inclusion of a programme in a programme service; and in this sub-paragraph "the relevant publication" means the publication in respect of which the defendant would be charged if the proceedings were brought.

(2) Proceedings for an offence under section 2 of the 1959 Act for having an obscene article for publication for gain shall not be instituted except by or with the consent of the Director of Public Prosecutions in any case where—

(a) the relevant publication, or

(b) the only other publication which could reasonably have been expected to follow from the relevant publication,

was to take place in the course of the inclusion of a programme in a programme service; and in this sub-paragraph "the relevant publication" means the publication which, if the proceedings were brought, the defendant would be alleged to have had in contemplation.

(3) Without prejudice to the duty of a court to make an order for the forfeiture of an article under section 1(4) of the Obscene Publications Act 1964 (orders on conviction), in a case where by virtue of sub-paragraph (2) above proceedings under section 2 of the 1959 Act for having an article for publication for gain could not be instituted except by or with the consent of the Director of Public Prosecutions, no order for the forfeiture of the article shall be made under section 3 of the 1959 Act (power of search and seizure) unless the warrant under which the article was seized was issued on an information laid by or on behalf of the Director of Public Prosecutions.

Defences

5.—(1) A person shall not be convicted of an offence under section 2 of the 1959 Act in respect of the inclusion of any matter in a relevant programme if he proves that he did not know and had no reason to suspect that the programme would include matter rendering him liable to be convicted of such an offence.

(2) Where the publication in issue in any proceedings under that Act consists of the inclusion of any matter in a relevant programme, section 4(1) of that Act (general defence of public good) shall not apply; but—

(a) a person shall not be convicted of an offence under section 2 of that Act, and
(b) an order for forfeiture shall not be made under section 3 of that Act,

if it is proved that the inclusion of the matter in question in a relevant programme is justified as being for the public good on the ground that it is in the interests of—

(i) drama, opera, ballet or any other art,
(ii) science, literature or learning, or
(iii) any other objects of general concern.

(3) Section 4(2) of that Act (admissibility of opinions of experts) shall apply for the purposes of sub-paragraph (2) above as it applies for the purposes of section 4(1) and (1A) of that Act.

Exclusion of proceedings under common law

6. Without prejudice to section 2(4) of the 1959 Act, a person shall not be proceeded against for an offence at common law—

(a) in respect of a relevant programme or anything said or done in the course of such a programme, where it is of the essence of the common law offence that the programme or (as the case may be) what was said or done was obscene, indecent, offensive, disgusting or injurious to morality; or
(b) in respect of an agreement to cause a programme to be included in a programme service or to cause anything to be said or done in the course of a programme which is to be so included, where the common law offence consists of conspiring to corrupt public morals or to do any act contrary to public morals or decency.

[3072]

(*Sch 16 repealed by the Wireless Telegraphy Act 2006, s 125(1), Sch 9, Pt 1, subject to transitional provisions and savings in s 124 of, Sch 8, Pt 1, paras 1–8, 24 to, that Act at* **[4230]**, **[4239]**; *Schs 17, 19 outside the scope of this work; Schs 18, 20, 21 contain amendments and repeals, which in so far as relevant to this work, have been incorporated at the appropriate place.*)

SCHEDULE 22
TRANSITIONAL PROVISIONS AND SAVINGS

Section 203(4)

Saving of amendments made by Cable and Broadcasting Act 1984

1–3. …

4. The amendments made by paragraphs 12, … , 32 … of Schedule 5 to the Cable and Broadcasting Act 1984 shall not be affected by the repeals made by this Act but shall continue to have effect, subject to any amendments made by Schedule 20 to this Act.

5–7. …

[3073]

NOTES

Paras 1–3, 5: repealed by the Communications Act 2003, s 406(7), Sch 19(1), subject to transitional provisions in s 406(6) of, and Sch 18, paras 5, 30, 64 to, that Act at **[3434]**, **[3460]**.

Para 4: number omitted in the first place repealed by the Children (Northern Ireland) Order 1995, SI 1995/755, art 185(2), Sch 10; number omitted in the second place repealed by the Communications Act 2003, s 406(7), Sch 19(1).

Para 6, 7: outside the scope of this work.

OFFICE OF COMMUNICATIONS ACT 2002

(2002 c 11)

An Act to establish a body corporate to be known as the Office of Communications; and to confer functions in relation to proposals about the regulation of communications on that body, on certain existing regulators and on the Secretary of State

[19 March 2002]

1 The Office of Communications

(1) There shall be a body corporate to be known as the Office of Communications (in this Act referred to as "OFCOM").

(2) OFCOM shall consist of such number of members as the Secretary of State may determine; but he shall not determine a membership for OFCOM of less than three or more than six.

(3) The membership of OFCOM shall comprise—
- (a) a chairman appointed by the Secretary of State;
- (b) such number of other members appointed by the Secretary of State as he may determine; and
- (c) the executive members.

(4) The executive members of OFCOM shall comprise—
- (a) the chief executive of OFCOM; and
- (b) such other persons (if any) as may be appointed to membership of OFCOM from amongst their employees.

(5) It shall be for the members of OFCOM mentioned in subsection (3)(a) and (b), after consulting the chief executive of OFCOM—
- (a) to determine whether there should be any executive members falling within subsection (4)(b) and (subject to subsections (2) and (6)(a)) how many; and
- (b) to make any appointments of executive members required for the purposes of any such determination.

(6) The Secretary of State—
- (a) may, by a direction to OFCOM, set a maximum and a minimum number for the executive members of OFCOM; and
- (b) shall exercise his powers under this section to secure that the number of executive members of OFCOM is, so far as practicable, at all times less than the number of other members.

(7) The Secretary of State may by order made by statutory instrument modify the numbers for the time being specified in subsection (2) as the maximum and minimum membership for OFCOM.

(8) A statutory instrument containing an order under subsection (7) shall be subject to annulment in pursuance of a resolution of either House of Parliament; and the power to make such an order shall include power to make such incidental, supplemental, consequential and transitional provision as the Secretary of State thinks fit.

(9) OFCOM shall not be treated for any purposes as a body exercising functions on behalf of the Crown; and, accordingly, no person shall be treated as a servant of the Crown by reason only of his membership of, or employment by, OFCOM.

(10) The Schedule (which makes provision in relation to OFCOM) shall have effect.

[3074]

NOTES

Commencement: 1 July 2002 (sub-ss (1)–(6), (9), (10)); 29 November 2002 (otherwise).

Orders: the Office of Communications (Membership) Order 2002, SI 2002/2956 at **[3505]**; the Office of Communications (Membership) Order 2005, SI 2005/2718 at **[3625A]**.

2 (*Repealed by the Communications Act 2003, s 406(1), (7), Sch 17, para 171, Sch 19(1)*).)

3 Management of OFCOM

OFCOM shall, in managing their affairs, have regard—

(a) to such general guidance concerning the management of the affairs of public bodies as OFCOM consider appropriate; and

(b) subject to any such guidance and only to the extent that they may reasonably be regarded as applicable in relation to a statutory corporation, to generally accepted principles of good corporate governance.

[3075]

NOTES

Commencement: 1 July 2002.

4–6 (*Repealed by the Communications Act 2003, s 406(1), (7), Sch 17, para 171, Sch 19(1)*).)

7 Short title, commencement and extent

(1) This Act may be cited as the Office of Communications Act 2002.

(2) Sections 1, 2 and 3 and the Schedule shall come into force on such day as the Secretary of State may by order made by statutory instrument appoint; and different days may be appointed under this subsection for different purposes.

(3) This Act extends to Northern Ireland.

(4) Her Majesty may by Order in Council extend the provisions of this Act, with such modifications as appear to Her Majesty in Council to be appropriate, to any of the Channel Islands or to the Isle of Man.

[3076]

NOTES

Commencement: 19 March 2002.

Orders: the Office of Communications Act 2002 (Commencement No 1) Order 2002, SI 2002/1483; the Office of Communications Act 2002 (Commencement No 2) Order 2002, SI 2002/2955; the Office of Communications Act 2002 (Commencement No 3) and Communications Act 2003 (Commencement No 2) Order 2003, 2003/3142 at **[3590]**.

Orders in Council: the Communications (Bailiwick of Guernsey) Order 2003, SI 2003/3195; the Communications (Jersey) Order 2003, SI 2003/3197; the Communications (Isle of Man) Order 2003, SI 2003/3198.

SCHEDULE
FURTHER PROVISION ABOUT OFCOM

Section 1

Qualification for membership of non-executive members

1.—(1) Before appointing a person to be the chairman or another non-executive member of OFCOM, the Secretary of State shall satisfy himself that that person will have no such financial or other interest as is likely to affect prejudicially the carrying out by him of his functions as a member of OFCOM.

(2) The Secretary of State shall also satisfy himself from time to time with respect to the chairman and every other non-executive member of OFCOM that that member has no such interest.

(3) Every person who—

(a) is a person whom the Secretary of State proposes to appoint to be the chairman or another non-executive member of OFCOM, or

(b) is the chairman or another non-executive member of OFCOM,

shall, whenever requested by the Secretary of State to do so, furnish him with such information as the Secretary of State considers necessary for the performance by him of his duties under sub-paragraphs (1) and (2).

(4) …

Tenure of office

2.—(1) Subject to the following provisions of this paragraph, the chairman and every other non-executive member of OFCOM shall each hold and vacate office in accordance with the terms of his appointment.

(2) A person's appointment to be the chairman or another non-executive member of OFCOM must state the period for which the appointment is made; but a person shall be eligible for re-appointment at the end of any such period.

(3) The chairman and every other non-executive member of OFCOM may at any time resign his office by notice in writing to the Secretary of State.

(4) If the Secretary of State is satisfied that the chairman or another non-executive member of OFCOM—

(a) is an undischarged bankrupt or has had his estate sequestrated without being discharged,

(b) has made an arrangement with his creditors, or has entered into a trust deed for creditors, or has made a composition contract with his creditors,

(c) has such a financial or other interest as is likely to affect prejudicially the carrying out by him of his functions as a member of OFCOM,

(d) has been guilty of misbehaviour, or

(e) is otherwise incapable of carrying out, or unfit to carry out, the functions of his office,

the Secretary of State may by notice in writing remove him from office.

Remuneration and pensions of non-executive members

3.—(1) OFCOM may pay to the chairman and other non-executive members of OFCOM such remuneration and allowances as the Secretary of State may determine.

(2) OFCOM may pay, or make provision for paying, to or in respect of the chairman and other non-executive members of OFCOM, such sums by way of pensions, allowances or gratuities as the Secretary of State may determine.

(3) Where—

(a) a person ceases, otherwise than on the expiry of his term of office, to be the chairman or to be a non-executive member other than the chairman, and

(b) it appears to the Secretary of State that there are special circumstances which make it right for him to receive compensation,

OFCOM may make a payment to him of such amount as the Secretary of State may determine.

(4) If any non-executive member of OFCOM—

(a) is a participant in any pension scheme applicable to his membership of OFCOM, and

(b) on ceasing to be a non-executive member of OFCOM, becomes an employee of OFCOM or both such an employee and an executive member,

he may, if the Secretary of State so determines, be treated for the purposes of the pension scheme as if his service (after ceasing to be a non-executive member of OFCOM) as an employee or executive member of OFCOM were service as a non-executive member of OFCOM.

Deputy chairman

4.—(1) The Secretary of State may appoint any member of OFCOM who is a non-executive member to be the deputy chairman of OFCOM.

(2) A person appointed to be the deputy chairman—
 (a) shall cease to be the deputy chairman if he ceases to be a member of OFCOM; but
 (b) shall otherwise hold and vacate that office in accordance with the terms of his appointment.

(3) The deputy chairman of OFCOM shall be entitled to carry out the functions of the chairman, in such cases and in such manner as may be determined by or in accordance with any directions given by the chairman or the Secretary of State.

Chief executive and other employees of OFCOM

5.—(1) There shall be a chief executive of OFCOM.

(2) The chief executive shall be appointed by the chairman and other non-executive members of OFCOM with the approval of the Secretary of State.

(3) OFCOM may appoint such other employees as they may determine and make such other arrangements for the staffing of OFCOM as they think fit.

(4) Sub-paragraph (1) shall not apply in relation to any time before such date as the Secretary of State may notify to OFCOM as the date from which they are required to have a chief executive; and the membership of OFCOM shall not be required at any time before that date to include any executive member.

Terms and conditions of executive members of OFCOM

6.—(1) The chief executive shall be appointed to hold his office, and the other executive members of OFCOM shall be appointed as executive members and employed by OFCOM, on such terms and conditions, including terms and conditions as to remuneration, as the chairman and other non-executive members may determine.

(2) If the chairman and other non-executive members of OFCOM so determine in the case of any of the employees of OFCOM who are executive members, OFCOM shall—
 (a) pay, to or in respect of those employees, such pensions, allowances or gratuities, or
 (b) provide and maintain for them such pension schemes (whether contributory or not),

as the chairman and the other non-executive members may determine.

(3) If any employee of OFCOM who is an executive member—
 (a) is a participant in any pension scheme applicable to his employment, and
 (b) becomes a non-executive member of OFCOM,

he may, if the Secretary of State so determines, be treated for the purposes of the pension scheme as if his service as a non-executive member were service as an employee of OFCOM.

(4) If any employee of OFCOM who is an executive member—
 (a) is a participant in any pension scheme applicable to his membership of OFCOM, and
 (b) ceases to be an executive member without ceasing to be an employee of OFCOM,

he may, if the Secretary of State so determines, be treated for the purposes of the pension scheme as if his service (after ceasing to be an executive member) as an employee of OFCOM were service as an executive member of OFCOM.

Other employees of OFCOM

7.—(1) The employees of OFCOM who are not executive members shall be appointed to and hold their employments on such terms and conditions, including terms and conditions as to remuneration, as OFCOM may determine.

(2) If OFCOM so determine in the case of any of the employees of OFCOM who are not executive members, OFCOM shall—

(a) pay to or in respect of those employees such pensions, allowances or gratuities, or
(b) provide and maintain for them such pension schemes (whether contributory or not),

as OFCOM may determine.

(3) If any employee of OFCOM—
(a) is a participant in any pension scheme applicable to his employment, and
(b) becomes an executive member or a non-executive member of OFCOM,

he may, if the Secretary of State so determines, be treated for the purposes of the pension scheme as if his service as a member of OFCOM were service as an employee of OFCOM.

Finances of OFCOM

8.—[(1) It shall be the duty of OFCOM so to conduct their affairs as to secure that their revenues so far as they—
(a) derive from the exercise of powers to impose charges or fees in respect of the carrying out of particular functions, and
(b) do not fall to be paid into the Consolidated Fund of the United Kingdom or of Northern Ireland,

are at least sufficient to enable OFCOM to meet the costs of carrying out the functions to which the revenues relate.]

(2) Any excess of OFCOM's revenues for any financial year over the sums required by them for that year for meeting their obligations and carrying out their functions shall be applied by OFCOM in such manner as the Secretary of State, after consultation with OFCOM, may direct.

(3) A direction under sub-paragraph (2) may require the whole or any part of any such excess to be paid to the Secretary of State.

(4) The Secretary of State shall pay any sums received by him under sub-paragraph (3) into the Consolidated Fund.

(5) …

Grants to OFCOM

9.—(1) The Secretary of State may, with the consent of the Treasury, make grants to OFCOM of such sums as he may think fit for the purpose of enabling OFCOM to incur or meet liabilities in respect of capital and revenue expenditure.

(2) Grants under this paragraph shall be paid out of money provided by Parliament.

Advances to OFCOM

10.—(1) The Secretary of State may make advances to OFCOM out of money provided by Parliament.

(2) Any sums advanced under this paragraph shall be repaid to the Secretary of State at such times and by such methods, and interest on those sums shall be paid to him at such times and at such rates, as he may from time to time direct.

Accounts and audit

11.—(1) OFCOM shall—
(a) keep proper accounts and proper records in relation to the accounts, and
(b) prepare in respect of each financial year a statement of accounts in such form as the Secretary of State may direct.

(2) OFCOM shall, within such period after the end of the financial year to which it relates as the Secretary of State may direct, send copies of every statement prepared under sub-paragraph (1)(b) to—
(a) the Secretary of State; and
(b) the Comptroller and Auditor General.

(3) The Comptroller and Auditor General shall—

(a) examine, certify and report on every statement sent to him under sub-paragraph (2); and

(b) lay a copy of the statement and of his report before each House of Parliament.

Annual report

12.—(1) As soon as possible after the end of each financial year, OFCOM shall prepare and send to the Secretary of State a report of the carrying out of their functions during that financial year.

(2) Every report under this paragraph shall incorporate—

(a) a report of OFCOM's proceedings during that year; and

(b) such information relating to the financial position of OFCOM, and to any other matters that he considers appropriate, as the Secretary of State may direct.

(3) The Secretary of State shall lay a copy of every report sent to him under this paragraph before each House of Parliament.

Authentication of OFCOM's seal

13.—(1) The application of OFCOM's seal shall be authenticated by the signature of—

(a) the chairman or another member of OFCOM; or

(b) any other person authorised by OFCOM (whether generally or specially) for the purpose.

(2) Subject to sub-paragraph (3), a document purporting to be duly executed under the seal of OFCOM or to be signed on behalf of OFCOM, shall be received in evidence and, except to the extent that the contrary is shown, taken to be duly so executed or signed.

(3) This paragraph shall not extend to Scotland.

Committees of OFCOM and advisory committees

14.—(1) OFCOM may make such arrangements as they think fit—

(a) for the carrying out of any of their functions by committees established by them; and

(b) for committees established by OFCOM to give advice to them about matters relating to the carrying out of OFCOM's functions.

(2) Subject to sub-paragraph (3), the committees established by OFCOM may include committees the membership of which comprises or includes persons (including persons constituting a majority of the committee) who are neither members nor employees of OFCOM.

(3) Except where—

(a) the committee is established for the sole purpose of advising OFCOM on matters relating to the carrying out of their functions, and

(b) is not authorised under paragraph 18 to carry out functions on behalf of OFCOM,

the membership of every committee established by OFCOM must contain at least one person who is either a member or an employee of OFCOM, or who is both.

[(3A) Sub-paragraph (3) has effect in the case of a committee of OFCOM which—

(a) is not the Content Board, but

(b) has functions that are confined to functions falling within section 13(2) of the Communications Act 2003 (functions within the Content Board's remit),

as if the reference in that sub-paragraph to a member of OFCOM included a reference to a member of the Content Board who is not a member of OFCOM.]

(4) Where a person who is neither a member nor an employee of OFCOM is a member of any committee established by OFCOM, OFCOM may pay to that person such remuneration and expenses as they may determine.

Proceedings of OFCOM and their committees etc

15.—(1) OFCOM may make such other arrangements for regulating their own procedure, and such arrangements for regulating the procedure of the committees established by them, as they think fit.

(2) The procedure for the carrying out of the separate functions which under this Schedule are conferred on the chairman and non-executive members of OFCOM shall be in accordance with such arrangements as may be determined by a majority of the non-executive members.

(3) Arrangements under this paragraph may include arrangements as to quorums and as to the making of decisions by a majority.

(4) OFCOM shall publish, in such manner as they consider appropriate, any arrangements which they make under this paragraph.

(5) This paragraph has effect subject to paragraph 17.

16. OFCOM shall make arrangements for the keeping of proper records—
- (a) of their proceedings;
- (b) of the proceedings of any committee established by them;
- (c) of the proceedings at any meeting of the chairman and other non-executive members of OFCOM; and
- (d) of anything done by an employee or member of OFCOM under paragraph 18(a).

Disqualification for acting in relation to certain matters

17.—(1) This paragraph applies if at any meeting of—
- (a) OFCOM,
- (b) the chairman and other non-executive members of OFCOM, or
- (c) any committee established by OFCOM,

any member of OFCOM or, as the case may be, of the committee has any form of direct or indirect interest in any matter falling to be considered at that meeting.

(2) The person with the interest shall declare it and the declaration shall be recorded in the minutes of the meeting.

(3) The person with the interest shall not take part in any discussion or decision relating to the matter in which he has an interest, unless—
- (a) in the case of a meeting of OFCOM or of the chairman and other non-executive members of OFCOM, the other members of OFCOM who are present when the discussion or decision falls to take place or is made have resolved unanimously that the interest is to be disregarded; or
- (b) in any other case, the other members of the committee who are present when the discussion or decision falls to take place or is made have so resolved in the manner authorised by OFCOM.

(4) It shall be the duty of OFCOM, in granting authorisations for the purposes of sub-paragraph (3)(b), to secure that a resolution for those purposes does not allow a person to take part in a discussion or decision at a meeting of a committee established by virtue of paragraph 14(1)(a) unless at least the following requirements are met—
- (a) the number of other members of the committee in favour of the resolution is not less than two thirds of those who are both present and entitled to vote on the resolution; and
- (b) the number of other members of the committee in favour of the resolution is not less than its quorum.

(5) For the purposes of this paragraph a general notification given at or sent to a meeting of OFCOM, of the chairman and other non-executive members of OFCOM or of a committee established by OFCOM that—
- (a) a person is a member of a company or firm, and
- (b) is to be regarded as interested in any matter involving that company or firm,

shall be regarded (subject to sub-paragraph (6)(b)), as compliance in relation to any such matter with sub-paragraph (2) for the purposes of that meeting and any subsequent meeting of OFCOM, of the chairman and other non-executive members of OFCOM or of the committee established by OFCOM which is held while the notification is in force.

(6) A notification for the purposes of sub-paragraph (5)—

(a) shall remain in force until it is withdrawn, and

(b) if given at or sent to a meeting of the chairman and other non-executive members of OFCOM or to a committee shall have effect in relation only to meetings of the chairman and other non-executive members or, as the case may be, to meetings of that committee.

(7) A person required to make a declaration for the purposes of this paragraph in relation to any meeting—

(a) shall not be required to attend the meeting; but

(b) shall be taken to have complied with the requirements of this paragraph if he takes reasonable steps to secure that notice of his interest is read out at, and taken into consideration at, the meeting in question.

(8), (9) …

Delegation of functions

18. Anything that is authorised or required by or under any enactment to be done by OFCOM may be done on their behalf by—

(a) any employee or member of OFCOM who has been authorised by OFCOM (whether generally or specially) for the purpose;

(b) any committee established by OFCOM which has been so authorised.

Validity of proceedings

19.—(1) The validity of any proceedings of OFCOM, of the chairman and other non-executive members of OFCOM or of any committee established by OFCOM shall not be affected by—

(a) any vacancy in the membership of OFCOM or of such a committee;

(b) any defect in the appointment of the chairman, deputy chairman or any other member of OFCOM;

(c) any failure of the Secretary of State to comply with the requirements of section 1(6)(b); or

(d) any failure to comply with any arrangements under paragraph 15 or with any of the requirements of paragraph 17.

(2) Nothing in sub-paragraph (1)(d) shall validate any proceedings of a meeting which (apart from any matter falling within sub-paragraph (1)(b) or (c)) is inquorate.

Membership of OFCOM not a disqualification for membership of an existing regulator etc

20–23. …

Interpretation

24.—(1) In this Schedule—

"employee", in relation to OFCOM, includes the chief executive;

"financial year" means—

(a) the period of not more than twelve months beginning with the date on which OFCOM are established under this Act and ending with 31st March; and

(b) every subsequent period of twelve months ending with 31st March;

and

"non-executive member", in relation to OFCOM, means a member of OFCOM who is not an executive member.

(2) In this Schedule—

(a) references to pensions, allowances or gratuities include references to any similar benefits provided on death or retirement; and

(b) references to the payment of pensions, allowances or gratuities to or in respect of any persons includes a reference to the making of payments towards the provision of the payment of pensions, allowances or gratuities to or in respect of those persons.

(3) In this Schedule references to functions of OFCOM include references to functions conferred by any enactment or subordinate legislation at any time after the passing of this Act. **[3077]**

NOTES

Commencement: 1 July 2002 (paras 1–11, 13–24); 29 December 2003 (para 12).

Para 1: sub-para (4) repealed by the Communications Act 2003, s 406(1), (7), Sch 17, para 172(1), (2)(a), Sch 19(1).

Para 8: sub-para (1) substituted, and sub-para (5) repealed, by the Communications Act 2003, s 406(1), (7), Sch 17, para 172(1), (2)(b), (3), Sch 19(1).

Para 14: sub-para (3A) inserted by the Communications Act 2003, s 406(1), Sch 17, para 172(1), (4).

Para 17: sub-paras (8), (9) repealed by the Communications Act 2003, s 406(1), (7), Sch 17, para 172(1), (2)(c), Sch 19(1).

Para 20: repealed by the Communications Act 2003, s 406(1), (7), Sch 17, para 172(1), (2)(d), Sch 19(1).

Para 21: amends the House of Commons Disqualification Act 1975, Sch 1, Pt 2 and the Northern Ireland Assembly Disqualification Act 1975, Sch 1, Pt 2.

Para 22: amends the Freedom of Information Act 2000, Sch 1, Pt 6.

Para 23: amends the Public Records Act 1958, Sch 1, para 3, Table, Pt 2.

COMMUNICATIONS ACT 2003

(2003 c 21)

ARRANGEMENT OF SECTIONS

PART 1
FUNCTIONS OF OFCOM

Transferred and assigned functions

General duties in carrying out functions

Accessible domestic communications apparatus

Media literacy

OFCOM's Content Board

Functions for the protection of consumers

Advisory committees

International matters

General information functions

Employment in broadcasting

Charging

Guarantees

Provisions supplemental to transfer of functions

PART 2
NETWORKS, SERVICES AND THE RADIO SPECTRUM

CHAPTER 1
ELECTRONIC COMMUNICATIONS NETWORKS AND SERVICES

Preliminary

Notification by providers

Administrative charges imposed on providers

Register of providers required to notify or to pay charges

Conditions of entitlement to provide network or service etc

General conditions: subject-matter

General conditions: customer interests

General conditions: telephone numbers

General conditions: must-carry obligations

Universal service conditions

Electronic communications code

Regulation of premium rate services

Offences relating to networks and services

Persistent misuse of network or service

Powers to deal with emergencies

Restrictions in leases and licences

Information provisions

Local authority powers in relation to networks and services

Grants for networks and services in Northern Ireland

Interpretation of Chapter 1

CHAPTER 2
SPECTRUM USE

General functions relating to spectrum use

Reservation of spectrum for multiplex use

Recognised spectrum access

Crown use of the radio spectrum

Limitations and exemptions applied to spectrum use

Award and transfer of licences

Variation and revocation of licences

Wireless telegraphy register

Criminal proceedings etc

Construction of 1949 Act

CHAPTER 3
DISPUTES AND APPEALS

Disputes

Appeals

Interpretation of Chapter 3

PART 3
TELEVISION AND RADIO SERVICES

CHAPTER 1
THE BBC, C4C THE WELSH AUTHORITY
AND THE GAELIC MEDIA SERVICE

The BBC

C4C

The Welsh Authority

The Gaelic Media Service

CHAPTER 2
REGULATORY STRUCTURE FOR INDEPENDENT TELEVISION SERVICES

Preliminary

Channels 3 and 5

The public teletext service

Meaning of initial expiry date

Reviews relating to licensing of Channels 3 & 5 and teletext

Replacement of Channel 4 licence

Television licensable content services

Television multiplex services

Local digital television services

CHAPTER 3
REGULATORY STRUCTURE FOR INDEPENDENT RADIO SERVICES

Preliminary

Radio licensable content services

Licence periods etc

Multiplexes broadcasting sound programmes

Community radio

CHAPTER 4
REGULATORY PROVISIONS

Application of regulatory regimes

The public service remit for television

Must-offer obligations etc affecting public service television

Programming quotas for public service television

News provision etc on public service television

Independent and regional productions and programmes for public service television

Networking arrangements for Channel 3

Special obligations for Channel 4

Special obligation for the public teletext provider

Sporting and other events of national interest

Television services for the deaf and visually impaired

Programming quotas for digital television programme services

Regulation of electronic programme guides

Character and coverage of radio services

Competition between licensed providers etc

Programme and fairness standards for television and radio

Power to proscribe unacceptable foreign television and radio services

Party political broadcasts on television and radio

CHAPTER 6
OTHER PROVISIONS ABOUT TELEVISION AND RADIO SERVICES

Annual report on television and radio

Community radio and local digital television

Supplemental provisions of Part 3

PART 4
LICENSING OF TV RECEPTION

PART 5
COMPETITION IN COMMUNICATIONS MARKETS

CHAPTER 1
FUNCTIONS OF OFCOM UNDER COMPETITION LEGISLATION

CHAPTER 2
MEDIA MERGERS

Supplemental provisions of Chapter 2

PART 6
MISCELLANEOUS AND SUPPLEMENTAL

Annual report

Review of media ownership

Guidelines as to penalties

Disclosure of information

Notifications etc and electronic working

Other miscellaneous provisions

Supplemental

An Act to confer functions on the Office of Communications; to make provision about the regulation of the provision of electronic communications networks and services and of the use of the electro-magnetic spectrum; to make provision about the regulation of broadcasting and of the provision of television and radio services; to make provision about mergers involving newspaper and other media enterprises and, in that connection, to amend the Enterprise Act 2002; and for connected purposes.

[17 July 2003]

PART 1
FUNCTIONS OF OFCOM

Transferred and assigned functions

1 Functions and general powers of OFCOM

(1) The Office of Communications ("OFCOM") shall have the following functions—

(a) the functions transferred to OFCOM under section 2; and

(b) such other functions as may be conferred on OFCOM by or under any enactment (including this Act).

(2) OFCOM shall also have any functions in relation to telephone numbers that are conferred on them by the law of the Isle of Man or of any of the Channel Islands.

(3) OFCOM may do anything which appears to them to be incidental or conducive to the carrying out of their functions, including borrow money.

(4) OFCOM are not to borrow money except with the consent of the Secretary of State, or in accordance with a general authorisation given by him.

(5) OFCOM's powers under subsection (3) include, in particular—

(a) power to undertake research and development work in connection with any matter in relation to which they have functions;

(b) power to promote the carrying out of such research and development by others, or otherwise to arrange for it to be carried out by others;

(c) power to institute and carry on criminal proceedings in England and Wales or Northern Ireland for an offence relating to a matter in relation to which they have functions; and

(d) power, in such cases and in such circumstances as they may think fit, to make payments (where no legal liability arises) to persons adversely affected by the carrying out by OFCOM of any of their functions.

(6) In exercise of their powers under subsection (3), OFCOM must establish and maintain separate offices in each of the following parts of the United Kingdom—

(a) England;

(b) Wales;

(c) Scotland; and

(d) Northern Ireland.

(7) Part 2 of the Deregulation and Contracting Out Act 1994 (c 40) (contracting out) is to have effect in relation to the functions conferred on OFCOM by or under any enactment as if—

(a) OFCOM were an office holder within the meaning of that Part; and

(b) a power of OFCOM to make subordinate legislation were excluded from section 69 of that Act to the extent only that it is exercisable by statutory instrument.

(8) In this section "telephone numbers" has the same meaning as in Chapter 1 of Part 2.

[3078]

NOTES

Commencement: 25 July 2003 (sub-ss (3) in part, (5)(c), and to the extent that these sub-ss are taken for the purposes of s 408(3) of this Act to be brought into force for the purpose of enabling network and service functions and spectrum functions to be carried out during the transitional period by the Director General of Telecommunications and the Secretary of State respectively) (see further s 408 and Sch 18 at **[3434]**, **[3460]**, and the Communications Act 2003 (Commencement No 1) Order 2003, SI 2003/1900 at **[3507]**); 29 December 2003 (otherwise).

2 Transfer of functions of pre-commencement regulators

(1) As from such date as the Secretary of State may appoint for the coming into force of this section, the functions that are set out in Schedule 1 (functions of the Secretary of State and of the pre-commencement regulators) shall become functions of OFCOM in accordance with that Schedule.

(2) References in any enactment to a person who is a person from whom functions are transferred by virtue of this section are to have effect, so far as necessary for the purposes of the transfers, as references to OFCOM.

(3) The functions of OFCOM are to include the carrying out of the transferred functions, at times after the time when they become functions of OFCOM, in relation to anything occurring before that time.

(4) The provisions of this section have effect subject to—

(a) the modifications made by this Act of the enactments relating to the transferred functions; and

(b) any express transitional or consequential provisions made by or under this Act in relation to those enactments.

[3079]

NOTES

Commencement: 29 December 2003 (except in relation to television licences); 1 April 2004 (otherwise).

General duties in carrying out functions

3 General duties of OFCOM

(1) It shall be the principal duty of OFCOM, in carrying out their functions—

(a) to further the interests of citizens in relation to communications matters; and

(b) to further the interests of consumers in relevant markets, where appropriate by promoting competition.

(2) The things which, by virtue of subsection (1), OFCOM are required to secure in the carrying out of their functions include, in particular, each of the following—

(a) the optimal use for wireless telegraphy of the electro-magnetic spectrum;

(b) the availability throughout the United Kingdom of a wide range of electronic communications services;

(c) the availability throughout the United Kingdom of a wide range of television and radio services which (taken as a whole) are both of high quality and calculated to appeal to a variety of tastes and interests;

(d) the maintenance of a sufficient plurality of providers of different television and radio services;

(e) the application, in the case of all television and radio services, of standards that provide adequate protection to members of the public from the inclusion of offensive and harmful material in such services;

(f) the application, in the case of all television and radio services, of standards that provide adequate protection to members of the public and all other persons from both—

(i) unfair treatment in programmes included in such services; and

(ii) unwarranted infringements of privacy resulting from activities carried on for the purposes of such services.

(3) In performing their duties under subsection (1), OFCOM must have regard, in all cases, to—

(a) the principles under which regulatory activities should be transparent, accountable, proportionate, consistent and targeted only at cases in which action is needed; and

(b) any other principles appearing to OFCOM to represent the best regulatory practice.

(4) OFCOM must also have regard, in performing those duties, to such of the following as appear to them to be relevant in the circumstances—

(a) the desirability of promoting the fulfilment of the purposes of public service television broadcasting in the United Kingdom;

(b) the desirability of promoting competition in relevant markets;

(c) the desirability of promoting and facilitating the development and use of effective forms of self-regulation;

(d) the desirability of encouraging investment and innovation in relevant markets;

(e) the desirability of encouraging the availability and use of high speed data transfer services throughout the United Kingdom;

(f) the different needs and interests, so far as the use of the electro-magnetic spectrum for wireless telegraphy is concerned, of all persons who may wish to make use of it;

(g) the need to secure that the application in the case of television and radio services of standards falling within subsection (2)(e) and (f) is in the manner that best guarantees an appropriate level of freedom of expression;

(h) the vulnerability of children and of others whose circumstances appear to OFCOM to put them in need of special protection;

(i) the needs of persons with disabilities, of the elderly and of those on low incomes;

(j) the desirability of preventing crime and disorder;

(k) the opinions of consumers in relevant markets and of members of the public generally;

(l) the different interests of persons in the different parts of the United Kingdom, of the different ethnic communities within the United Kingdom and of persons living in rural and in urban areas;

(m) the extent to which, in the circumstances of the case, the furthering or securing of the matters mentioned in subsections (1) and (2) is reasonably practicable.

(5) In performing their duty under this section of furthering the interests of consumers, OFCOM must have regard, in particular, to the interests of those consumers in respect of choice, price, quality of service and value for money.

(6) Where it appears to OFCOM, in relation to the carrying out of any of the functions mentioned in section 4(1), that any of their general duties conflict with one or more of their duties under sections 4, 24 and 25, priority must be given to their duties under those sections.

(7) Where it appears to OFCOM that any of their general duties conflict with each other in a particular case, they must secure that the conflict is resolved in the manner they think best in the circumstances.

(8) Where OFCOM resolve a conflict in an important case between their duties under paragraphs (a) and (b) of subsection (1), they must publish a statement setting out—

(a) the nature of the conflict;

(b) the manner in which they have decided to resolve it; and

(c) the reasons for their decision to resolve it in that manner.

(9) Where OFCOM are required to publish a statement under subsection (8), they must—

(a) publish it as soon as possible after making their decision but not while they would (apart from a statutory requirement to publish) be subject to an obligation not to publish a matter that needs to be included in the statement; and

(b) so publish it in such manner as they consider appropriate for bringing it to the attention of the persons who, in OFCOM's opinion, are likely to be affected by the matters to which the decision relates.

(10) Every report under paragraph 12 of the Schedule to the Office of Communications Act 2002 (c 11) (OFCOM's annual report) for a financial year must contain a summary of the manner in which, in that year, OFCOM resolved conflicts arising in important cases between their general duties.

(11) A case is an important case for the purposes of subsection (8) or (10) only if—

(a) it involved one or more of the matters mentioned in subsection (12); or

(b) it otherwise appears to OFCOM to have been of unusual importance.

(12) Those matters are—

(a) a major change in the activities carried on by OFCOM;

(b) matters likely to have a significant impact on persons carrying on businesses in any of the relevant markets; or

(c) matters likely to have a significant impact on the general public in the United Kingdom or in a part of the United Kingdom.

(13) This section is subject to sections 370(11) and 371(11) of this Act and to section 119A(4) of the Enterprise Act 2002 (c 40) (which applies to functions conferred on OFCOM by Chapter 2 of Part 5 of this Act).

(14) In this section—

"citizens" means all members of the public in the United Kingdom;

"communications matters" means the matters in relation to which OFCOM have functions;

"general duties", in relation to OFCOM, means—

(a) their duties under subsections (1) to (5); and

(b) the duty which, under section 107(5), is to rank equally for the purposes of subsections (6) and (7) with their duties under this section;

"relevant markets" means markets for any of the services, facilities, apparatus or directories in relation to which OFCOM have functions.

[3080]

NOTES

Commencement: 29 December 2003.

4 Duties for the purpose of fulfilling Community obligations

(1) This section applies to the following functions of OFCOM—

(a) their functions under Chapter 1 of Part 2;

(b) their functions under the enactments relating to the management of the radio spectrum;

(c) their functions under Chapter 3 of Part 2 in relation to disputes referred to them under section 185;

(d) their functions under sections 24 and 25 so far as they relate to information required for purposes connected with matters in relation to which functions specified in this subsection are conferred on OFCOM; and

(e) their functions under section 26 so far as they are carried out for the purpose of making information available to persons mentioned in subsection (2)(a) to (c) of that section.

(2) It shall be the duty of OFCOM, in carrying out any of those functions, to act in accordance with the six Community requirements (which give effect, amongst other things, to the requirements of Article 8 of the Framework Directive and are to be read accordingly).

(3) The first Community requirement is a requirement to promote competition—

(a) in relation to the provision of electronic communications networks and electronic communications services;

(b) in relation to the provision and making available of services and facilities that are provided or made available in association with the provision of electronic communications networks or electronic communications services; and

(c) in relation to the supply of directories capable of being used in connection with the use of electronic communications networks or electronic communications services.

(4) The second Community requirement is a requirement to secure that OFCOM's activities contribute to the development of the European internal market.

(5) The third Community requirement is a requirement to promote the interests of all persons who are citizens of the European Union (within the meaning of Article 17 of the Treaty establishing the European Community).

(6) The fourth Community requirement is a requirement to take account of the desirability of OFCOM's carrying out their functions in a manner which, so far as practicable, does not favour—

(a) one form of electronic communications network, electronic communications service or associated facility; or

(b) one means of providing or making available such a network, service or facility,

over another.

(7) The fifth Community requirement is a requirement to encourage, to such extent as OFCOM consider appropriate for the purpose mentioned in subsection (8), the provision of network access and service interoperability.

(8) That purpose is the purpose of securing—

(a) efficiency and sustainable competition in the markets for electronic communications networks, electronic communications services and associated facilities; and
(b) the maximum benefit for the persons who are customers of communications providers and of persons who make such facilities available.

(9) The sixth Community requirement is a requirement to encourage such compliance with the standards mentioned in subsection (10) as is necessary for—
(a) facilitating service interoperability; and
(b) securing freedom of choice for the customers of communications providers.

(10) Those standards are—
(a) standards or specifications from time to time drawn up and published in accordance with Article 17 of the Framework Directive;
(b) the standards and specifications from time to time adopted by—
(i) the European Committee for Standardisation;
(ii) the European Committee for Electrotechnical Standardisation; or
(iii) the European Telecommunications Standards Institute; and
(c) the international standards and recommendations from time to time adopted by—
(i) the International Telecommunication Union;
(ii) the International Organisation for Standardisation; or
(iii) the International Electrotechnical Committee.

(11) Where it appears to OFCOM that any of the Community requirements conflict with each other, they must secure that the conflict is resolved in the manner they think best in the circumstances.

(12) In this section—
"the Framework Directive" means Directive 2002/21/EC of the European Parliament and of the Council on a common regulatory framework for electronic communications networks and services;
"network access" and "service interoperability" each has the same meaning as in Chapter 1 of Part 2.

[3081]

NOTES

Commencement: 25 July 2003 (for the purpose of enabling network and service functions and spectrum functions to be carried out during the transitional period by the Director General of Telecommunications and the Secretary of State respectively) (see further s 408 and Sch 18 at **[3436]**, **[3460]**, and the Communications Act 2003 (Commencement No 1) Order 2003, SI 2003/1900 at **[3507]**); 29 December 2003 (for the purpose of enabling OFCOM to perform those functions) (see the Office of Communications Act 2002 (Commencement No 3) and Communications Act 2003 (Commencement No 2) Order 2003, SI 2003/3142 at **[3590]**).

5 Directions in respect of networks and spectrum functions

(1) This section applies to the following functions of OFCOM—
(a) their functions under Part 2; and
(b) their functions under the enactments relating to the management of the radio spectrum that are not contained in that Part.

(2) It shall be the duty of OFCOM to carry out those functions in accordance with such general or specific directions as may be given to them by the Secretary of State.

(3) The Secretary of State's power to give directions under this section shall be confined to a power to give directions for one or more of the following purposes—
(a) in the interests of national security;
(b) in the interests of relations with the government of a country or territory outside the United Kingdom;
(c) for the purpose of securing compliance with international obligations of the United Kingdom;
(d) in the interests of the safety of the public or of public health.

(4) The Secretary of State is not entitled by virtue of any provision of this section to direct OFCOM to suspend or restrict—
(a) a person's entitlement to provide an electronic communications network or electronic communications service; or
(b) a person's entitlement to make available associated facilities.

(5) The Secretary of State must publish a direction under this section in such manner as appears to him to be appropriate for bringing it to the attention of the persons who, in his opinion, are likely to be affected by it.

(6) The Secretary of State is not required by subsection (5) to publish a direction, and he may exclude matter from a direction he does publish, if he considers the publication of the direction or matter to be—

- (a) against the interests of national security; or
- (b) against the interests of relations with the government of a country or territory outside the United Kingdom.

(7) Subsection (4) does not affect the Secretary of State's powers under section 132. **[3082]**

NOTES

Commencement: 25 July 2003 (for the purpose of enabling network and service functions and spectrum functions to be carried out during the transitional period by the Director General of Telecommunications and the Secretary of State respectively) (see further s 408 and Sch 18 at **[3436]**, **[3460]**, and the Communications Act 2003 (Commencement No 1) Order 2003, SI 2003/1900 at **[3507]**); 18 September 2003 (otherwise) (see the Office of Communications Act 2002 (Commencement No 3) and Communications Act 2003 (Commencement No 2) Order 2003, SI 2003/3142 at **[3590]**).

6 Duties to review regulatory burdens

(1) OFCOM must keep the carrying out of their functions under review with a view to securing that regulation by OFCOM does not involve—

- (a) the imposition of burdens which are unnecessary; or
- (b) the maintenance of burdens which have become unnecessary.

(2) In reviewing their functions under this section it shall be the duty of OFCOM—

- (a) to have regard to the extent to which the matters which they are required under section 3 to further or to secure are already furthered or secured, or are likely to be furthered or secured, by effective self-regulation; and
- (b) in the light of that, to consider to what extent it would be appropriate to remove or reduce regulatory burdens imposed by OFCOM.

(3) In determining for the purposes of this section whether procedures for self-regulation are effective OFCOM must consider, in particular—

- (a) whether those procedures are administered by a person who is sufficiently independent of the persons who may be subjected to the procedures; and
- (b) whether adequate arrangements are in force for funding the activities of that person in relation to those procedures.

(4) OFCOM must, from time to time, publish a statement setting out how they propose, during the period for which the statement is made, to secure that regulation by OFCOM does not involve the imposition or maintenance of unnecessary burdens.

(5) The first statement to be published under this section—

- (a) must be published as soon as practicable after the commencement of this section; and
- (b) shall be a statement for the period of twelve months beginning with the day of its publication.

(6) A subsequent statement—

- (a) must be published during the period to which the previous statement related; and
- (b) must be a statement for the period of twelve months beginning with the end of the previous period.

(7) It shall be the duty of OFCOM, in carrying out their functions at times during a period for which a statement is in force under this section, to have regard to that statement.

(8) OFCOM may, if they think fit, revise a statement under this section at any time before or during the period for which it is made.

(9) Where OFCOM revise a statement, they must publish the revision as soon as practicable.

(10) The publication under this section of a statement, or of a revision of a statement, must be in such manner as OFCOM consider appropriate for bringing it to the attention of the persons who, in their opinion, are likely to be affected by the matters to which it relates.

[3083]

NOTES

Commencement: 29 December 2003.

7 Duty to carry out impact assessments

(1) This section applies where—

(a) OFCOM are proposing to do anything for the purposes of, or in connection with, the carrying out of their functions; and

(b) it appears to them that the proposal is important;

but this section does not apply if it appears to OFCOM that the urgency of the matter makes it impracticable or inappropriate for them to comply with the requirements of this section.

(2) A proposal is important for the purposes of this section only if its implementation would be likely to do one or more of the following—

(a) to involve a major change in the activities carried on by OFCOM;

(b) to have a significant impact on persons carrying on businesses in the markets for any of the services, facilities, apparatus or directories in relation to which OFCOM have functions; or

(c) to have a significant impact on the general public in the United Kingdom or in a part of the United Kingdom.

(3) Before implementing their proposal, OFCOM must either—

(a) carry out and publish an assessment of the likely impact of implementing the proposal; or

(b) publish a statement setting out their reasons for thinking that it is unnecessary for them to carry out an assessment.

(4) An assessment under subsection (3)(a) must set out how, in OFCOM's opinion, the performance of their general duties (within the meaning of section 3) is secured or furthered by or in relation to what they propose.

(5) An assessment carried out under this section—

(a) may take such form, and

(b) must relate to such matters,

as OFCOM consider appropriate.

(6) In determining the matters to which an assessment under this section should relate, OFCOM must have regard to such general guidance relating to the carrying out of impact assessments as they consider appropriate.

(7) Where OFCOM publish an assessment under this section—

(a) they must provide an opportunity of making representations to them about their proposal to members of the public and other persons who, in OFCOM's opinion, are likely to be affected to a significant extent by its implementation;

(b) the published assessment must be accompanied by a statement setting out how representations may be made; and

(c) OFCOM are not to implement their proposal unless the period for making representations about it has expired and they have considered all the representations that were made in that period.

(8) Where OFCOM are required (apart from this section)—

(a) to consult about a proposal to which this section applies, or

(b) to give a person an opportunity of making representations about it,

the requirements of this section are in addition to, but may be performed contemporaneously with, the other requirements.

(9) Every report under paragraph 12 of the Schedule to the Office of Communications Act 2002 (c 11) (OFCOM's annual report) must set out—

(a) a list of the assessments under this section carried out during the financial year to which the report relates; and

(b) a summary of the decisions taken during that year in relation to proposals to which assessments carried out in that year or previous financial years relate.

(10) The publication of anything under this section must be in such manner as OFCOM consider appropriate for bringing it to the attention of the persons who, in OFCOM's opinion, are likely to be affected if their proposal is implemented.

[3084]

NOTES
Commencement: 29 December 2003.

8 Duty to publish and meet promptness standards

(1) It shall be the duty of OFCOM to publish a statement setting out the standards they are proposing to meet with respect to promptness in—

(a) the carrying out of their different functions; and
(b) the transaction of business for purposes connected with the carrying out of those functions.

(2) This section does not require standards to be set out with respect to anything which (apart from this section) is required to be done by a time, or within a period, provided for by or under an enactment.

(3) OFCOM may, if they think fit, at any time revise the statement for the time being in force under this section.

(4) It shall be the duty of OFCOM—

(a) in carrying out their functions, and
(b) in transacting business for purposes connected with the carrying out of their functions,

to have regard to the statement for the time being in force under this section.

(5) Where OFCOM revise a statement under this section, they must publish the revision as soon as practicable.

(6) The publication under this section of a statement, or of a revision of a statement, must be in such manner as OFCOM consider appropriate for bringing it to the attention of the persons who, in their opinion, are likely to be affected by the matters to which it relates.

(7) OFCOM's report under paragraph 12 of the Schedule to the Office of Communications Act 2002 (c 11) (annual report) for each financial year must contain a statement by OFCOM summarising the extent to which they have complied during that year with the standards set out under this section.

[3085]

NOTES
Commencement: 29 December 2003.

9 Secretary of State's powers in relation to promptness standards

(1) Where the Secretary of State considers that the statement published by OFCOM under section 8 is not adequate for securing that they meet satisfactory promptness standards, he may give them a notification to that effect.

(2) If the period of three months after the date of the giving of a notification under subsection (1) expires without OFCOM taking steps which the Secretary of State is satisfied remedy the situation, he may give them a direction under this section.

(3) A direction under this section is one requiring OFCOM to issue a new or revised statement under section 8 in accordance with the direction.

(4) Before giving a direction under this section, the Secretary of State must—

(a) give OFCOM an opportunity of making representations to him about his proposed direction; and
(b) have regard to any representations made to him by them.

(5) Where the Secretary of State gives a direction to OFCOM under this section, he must publish a copy of it in such manner as he considers appropriate for bringing it to the attention of persons who, in his opinion, are likely to be affected by OFCOM's promptness standards.

(6) It shall be the duty of OFCOM to revise their statement under section 8 in accordance with any direction of the Secretary of State under this section.

(7) In this section "promptness standards" means standards of promptness in—
(a) the carrying out by OFCOM of their different functions; and
(b) the transaction by them of business for purposes connected with the carrying out of those functions.

(8) No notification is to be given under subsection (1) at any time in the period of twelve months beginning with the commencement of section 8.

[3086]

NOTES
Commencement: 29 December 2003.

Accessible domestic communications apparatus

10 Duty to encourage availability of easily usable apparatus

(1) It shall be the duty of OFCOM to take such steps, and to enter into such arrangements, as appear to them calculated to encourage others to secure—
(a) that domestic electronic communications apparatus is developed which is capable of being used with ease, and without modification, by the widest possible range of individuals (including those with disabilities); and
(b) that domestic electronic communications apparatus which is capable of being so used is as widely available as possible for acquisition by those wishing to use it.

(2) It shall be the duty of OFCOM from time to time to review whether they need to take further steps, or to enter into further arrangements, for the purpose of performing their duty under this section.

(3) OFCOM must not do anything under this section that would be inconsistent with the Community requirements set out in section 4.

(4) In this section "electronic communications apparatus" means apparatus that is designed or adapted for a use which consists of or includes the sending or receiving of communications or other signals that are transmitted by means of an electronic communications network.

(5) For the purposes of this section electronic communications apparatus is domestic electronic communications apparatus except to the extent that it is designed or adapted for use solely for the purposes of, or in connection with, a business.

(6) In this section "signal" includes—
(a) anything comprising speech, music, sounds, visual images or communications or data of any description; and
(b) signals serving for the impartation of anything between persons, between a person and a thing or between things, or for the actuation or control of apparatus.

[3087]

NOTES
Commencement: 29 December 2003.

Media literacy

11 Duty to promote media literacy

(1) It shall be the duty of OFCOM to take such steps, and to enter into such arrangements, as appear to them calculated—
(a) to bring about, or to encourage others to bring about, a better public understanding of the nature and characteristics of material published by means of the electronic media;
(b) to bring about, or to encourage others to bring about, a better public awareness and understanding of the processes by which such material is selected, or made available, for publication by such means;
(c) to bring about, or to encourage others to bring about, the development of a better public awareness of the available systems by which access to material published by means of the electronic media is or can be regulated;

(d) to bring about, or to encourage others to bring about, the development of a better public awareness of the available systems by which persons to whom such material is made available may control what is received and of the uses to which such systems may be put; and

(e) to encourage the development and use of technologies and systems for regulating access to such material, and for facilitating control over what material is received, that are both effective and easy to use.

(2) In this section, references to the publication of anything by means of the electronic media are references to its being—

(a) broadcast so as to be available for reception by members of the public or of a section of the public; or

(b) distributed by means of an electronic communications network to members of the public or of a section of the public.

[3088]

NOTES

Commencement: 29 December 2003.

OFCOM's Content Board

12 Duty to establish and maintain Content Board

(1) It shall be the duty of OFCOM, in accordance with the following provisions of this section, to exercise their powers under paragraph 14 of the Schedule to the Office of Communications Act 2002 (c 11) (committees of OFCOM) to establish and maintain a committee to be known as "the Content Board".

(2) The Content Board shall consist of—

(a) a chairman appointed by OFCOM; and

(b) such number of other members appointed by OFCOM as OFCOM think fit.

(3) The chairman of the Content Board must be a non-executive member of OFCOM but is not to be the chairman of OFCOM.

(4) At least one of the other members of the Content Board must also be a nonexecutive member of OFCOM other than the chairman of OFCOM.

(5) In appointing persons to be members of the Content Board, OFCOM must secure that, for each of the following parts of the United Kingdom—

(a) England,

(b) Scotland,

(c) Wales, and

(d) Northern Ireland,

there is a different member of the Board capable of representing the interests and opinions of persons living in that part of the United Kingdom.

(6) In appointing a person for the purposes of subsection (5)(a), OFCOM must have regard to the desirability of ensuring that the person appointed is able to represent the interests and opinions of persons living in all the different regions of England.

(7) The validity of any proceedings of the Content Board shall not be affected by any failure by OFCOM to comply with subsection (5) or (6).

(8) It shall be the duty of OFCOM when appointing members of the Content Board to secure, so far as practicable, that a majority of the members of the Board (counting the chairman) consists of persons who are neither members nor employees of OFCOM.

(9) The following shall be disqualified from being the chairman or another member of the Content Board—

(a) governors and employees of the BBC;

(b) members and employees of the Welsh Authority; and

(c) members and employees of C4C.

(10) Before appointing a person to be the chairman or another member of the Content Board, OFCOM must satisfy themselves that he will not have any financial or other interest which would be likely prejudicially to affect the carrying out by him of any of his functions as chairman or member of the Content Board.

(11) A person is not to be taken to have such an interest by reason only that he is or will be a member or employee of OFCOM.

(12) Every person whom OFCOM propose to appoint to be the chairman or another member of the Content Board, shall, whenever requested to do so by OFCOM, furnish OFCOM with any information they consider necessary for the performance of their duty under subsection (10).

(13) In addition to paying remuneration and expenses under paragraph 14(4) of the Schedule to the Office of Communications Act 2002 (c 11), OFCOM may—

(a) pay to, or in respect of, any member of the Content Board who is not a member or employee of OFCOM, such sums by way of pensions, allowances or gratuities as OFCOM may determine; and

(b) provide for the making of such payments to or in respect of any such member of the Content Board.

(14) In subsection (13)—

(a) the reference to pensions, allowances and gratuities includes a reference to similar benefits payable on death or retirement; and

(b) the reference to providing for the payment of a pension, allowance or gratuity to, or in respect of, a person includes a reference to the making of payments towards the provision or payment of a pension, allowance or gratuity, or of any such similar benefits, to or in respect of that person.

[3089]

NOTES

Commencement: 29 December 2003.

13 Functions of the Content Board

(1) The Content Board shall have such functions as OFCOM, in exercise of their powers under the Schedule to the Office of Communications Act 2002 (c 11), may confer on the Board.

(2) The functions conferred on the Board must include, to such extent and subject to such restrictions and approvals as OFCOM may determine, the carrying out on OFCOM's behalf of—

(a) functions in relation to matters that concern the contents of anything which is or may be broadcast or otherwise transmitted by means of electronic communications networks; and

(b) functions in relation to the promotion of public understanding or awareness of matters relating to the publication of matter by means of the electronic media.

(3) In determining what functions to confer on the Content Board, OFCOM must have particular regard to the desirability of securing that the Board have at least a significant influence on decisions which—

(a) relate to the matters mentioned in subsection (2); and

(b) involve the consideration of different interests and other factors as respects different parts of the United Kingdom.

(4) It shall be the duty of the Content Board to ensure, in relation to—

(a) the carrying out of OFCOM's functions under Part 3 of this Act, Parts 1 and 3 of the 1990 Act and Parts 1 and 2 of the 1996 Act,

(b) the matters with respect to which functions are conferred on the Board, and

(c) such other matters mentioned in subsection (2) as OFCOM may determine,

that OFCOM are aware of the different interests and other factors which, in the Board's opinion, need to be taken into account as respects the different parts of the United Kingdom in relation to the carrying out of OFCOM's functions.

(5) The power of OFCOM to determine the Content Board's functions includes power to authorise the Board to establish committees and panels to advise the Board on the carrying out of some or all of the Board's functions.

(6) The power of OFCOM to authorise the establishment of a committee or panel by the Content Board includes power to authorise the establishment of a committee or panel that includes persons who are not members of the Board.

(7) In this section references to the publication of anything by means of the electronic media are references to its being—

(a) broadcast so as to be available for reception by members of the public or of a section of the public; or
(b) distributed by means of an electronic communications network to members of the public or of a section of the public.

[3090]

NOTES

Commencement: 29 December 2003.

Functions for the protection of consumers

14 Consumer research

(1) OFCOM must make arrangements for ascertaining—
(a) the state of public opinion from time to time about the manner in which electronic communications networks and electronic communications services are provided;
(b) the state of public opinion from time to time about the manner in which associated facilities are made available;
(c) the experiences of consumers in the markets for electronic communications services and associated facilities, in relation to the manner in which electronic communications networks and electronic communications services are provided and associated facilities made available;
(d) the experiences of such consumers in relation to the handling, by communications providers and by persons making such facilities available, of complaints made to them by such consumers;
(e) the experiences of such consumers in relation to the resolution of disputes with communications providers or with persons making associated facilities available; and
(f) the interests and experiences of such consumers in relation to other matters that are incidental to, or are otherwise connected with, their experiences of the provision of electronic communications networks and electronic communications services or of the availability of associated facilities.

(2) The matters to which the arrangements must relate do not include the incidence or investigation of interference (within the meaning of [the Wireless Telegraphy Act 2006]) with wireless telegraphy.

(3) The matters to which the arrangements must relate do not (except so far as authorised or required by subsections (4) to (6)) include public opinion with respect to—
(a) the contents of anything broadcast or otherwise published by means of an electronic communications network; or
(b) the experiences or interests of consumers in any market for electronic communications services with respect to anything so broadcast or published.

(4) OFCOM must make arrangements for ascertaining—
(a) the state of public opinion from time to time concerning programmes included in television and radio services;
(b) any effects of such programmes, or of other material published by means of the electronic media, on the attitudes or behaviour of persons who watch, listen to or receive the programmes or material; and
(c) so far as necessary for the purpose mentioned in subsection (5), the types of programmes that members of the public would like to see included in television and radio services.

(5) That purpose is the carrying out by OFCOM of their functions under Chapter 4 of Part 3 of this Act.

(6) OFCOM must make arrangements for the carrying out of research into the following—
(a) the matters mentioned in section 11(1);
(b) matters relating to, or connected with, the setting of standards under section 319 of this Act;
(c) matters relating to, or connected with, the observance of those standards by persons providing television and radio services;
(d) matters relating to, or connected with, the prevention of unjust or unfair treatment in programmes included in such services; and

(e) matters relating to, or connected with, the prevention of unwarranted infringements of privacy resulting from activities carried on for the purposes of such services.

(7) Arrangements made by OFCOM for the purposes of this section may include arrangements for the carrying out of research in one or more of the following ways—

(a) by members or employees of OFCOM;
(b) by the Content Board;
(c) in accordance with arrangements made by that Board;
(d) by persons who are neither members nor employees of OFCOM.

(8) In this section references to the publication of anything by means of the electronic media are references to its being—

(a) broadcast so as to be available for reception by members of the public or of a section of the public; or
(b) distributed by means of an electronic communications network to members of the public or of a section of the public.

(9) This section does not restrict OFCOM's power to make any arrangements they consider to be incidental or conducive to the carrying out of any of their functions.

[3091]

NOTES

Commencement: 29 December 2003.

Sub-s (2): words in square brackets substituted by the Wireless Telegraphy Act 2006, s 123, Sch 7, paras 25, 26.

15 Duty to publish and take account of research

(1) It shall be the duty of OFCOM—

(a) to publish the results of any research carried out by them or on their behalf under section 14; and
(b) to consider and, to such extent as they think fit, to take account of the results of such research in the carrying out of their functions.

(2) OFCOM are not required under this section—

(a) to publish any matter that is confidential in accordance with subsection (3) or (4); or
(b) to publish anything that it would not be reasonably practicable to publish without disclosing such a matter.

(3) A matter is confidential under this subsection if—

(a) it relates specifically to the affairs of a particular body; and
(b) publication of that matter would or might, in OFCOM's opinion, seriously and prejudicially affect the interests of that body.

(4) A matter is confidential under this subsection if—

(a) it relates to the private affairs of an individual; and
(b) publication of that matter would or might, in OFCOM's opinion, seriously and prejudicially affect the interests of that individual.

(5) The publication of research under this section must be in such manner as OFCOM consider appropriate.

[3092]

NOTES

Commencement: 29 December 2003.

16 Consumer consultation

(1) It shall be the duty of OFCOM to establish and maintain effective arrangements for consultation about the carrying out of their functions with—

(a) consumers in the markets for the services and facilities in relation to which OFCOM have functions;
(b) consumers in the markets for apparatus used in connection with any such services or facilities;

(c) consumers in the markets for directories capable of being used in connection with the use of an electronic communications network or electronic communications service.

(2) The arrangements must include the establishment and maintenance of a panel of persons (in this Act referred to as "the Consumer Panel") with the function of advising both—

(a) OFCOM; and
(b) such other persons as the Panel think fit.

(3) The arrangements must secure that the matters about which the Consumer Panel are able to give advice include the interests of domestic and small business consumers in relation to the following matters—

(a) the provision of electronic communications networks;
(b) the provision and making available of the services and facilities mentioned in subsection (4);
(c) the supply of apparatus designed or adapted for use in connection with any such services or facilities;
(d) the supply of directories capable of being used in connection with the use of an electronic communications network or electronic communications service;
(e) the financial and other terms on which such services or facilities are provided or made available, or on which such apparatus or such a directory is supplied;
(f) standards of service, quality and safety for such services, facilities, apparatus and directories;
(g) the handling of complaints made by persons who are consumers in the markets for such services, facilities, apparatus or directories to the persons who provide the services or make the facilities available, or who are suppliers of the apparatus or directories;
(h) the resolution of disputes between such consumers and the persons who provide such services or make such facilities available, or who are suppliers of such apparatus or directories;
(i) the provision of remedies and redress in respect of matters that form the subject-matter of such complaints or disputes;
(j) the information about service standards and the rights of consumers that is made available by persons who provide or make available such services or facilities, or who are suppliers of such apparatus or directories;
(k) any other matter appearing to the Panel to be necessary for securing effective protection for persons who are consumers in the markets for any such services, facilities, apparatus or directories.

(4) Those services and facilities are—

(a) electronic communications services;
(b) associated facilities;
(c) directory enquiry facilities;
(d) a service consisting in the supply of information for use in responding to directory enquiries or of an electronic programme guide; and
(e) every service or facility not falling within any of the preceding paragraphs which is provided or made available to members of the public—
  (i) by means of an electronic communications network; and
  (ii) in pursuance of agreements entered into between the person by whom the service or facility is provided or made available and each of those members of the public.

(5) The matters about which the Consumer Panel are to be able to give advice do not include any matter that concerns the contents of anything which is or may be broadcast or otherwise transmitted by means of electronic communications networks.

(6) The arrangements made by OFCOM under this section must also secure that the Consumer Panel are able, in addition to giving advice on the matters mentioned in subsection (3), to do each of the following—

(a) at the request of OFCOM, to carry out research for OFCOM in relation to any of the matters in relation to which OFCOM have functions under section 14;
(b) to make arrangements for the carrying out of research into such other matters appearing to the Panel to be relevant to the carrying out of the Panel's functions as they think fit;
(c) to give advice to OFCOM in relation to any matter referred to the Panel by OFCOM for advice;

(d) to publish such information as the Panel think fit about the advice they give, about the carrying out of the Panel's other functions and about the results of research carried out by them or on their behalf.

(7) It shall be the duty of OFCOM, in the carrying out of their functions, to consider and, to such extent as they think appropriate, to have regard to—

(a) any advice given to OFCOM by the Consumer Panel; and

(b) any results notified to OFCOM of any research undertaken by that Panel.

(8) It shall also be the duty of OFCOM (subject to subsection (9))—

(a) to provide the Consumer Panel with all such information as, having regard, in particular, to the need to preserve commercial confidentiality, OFCOM consider appropriate to disclose to the Panel for the purpose of enabling the Panel to carry out their functions; and

(b) to provide the Panel with all such further information as the Panel may require.

(9) OFCOM are not required to provide information by virtue of subsection (8)(b) if, having regard to—

(a) the need to preserve commercial confidentiality; and

(b) any other matters that appear to OFCOM to be relevant;

it is reasonable for OFCOM to refuse to disclose it to the Panel.

(10) It shall be the duty of OFCOM, in the case of any advice or opinion received from and published by the Panel which OFCOM propose to disregard in whole or in part, or with which OFCOM disagree in whole or in part—

(a) to ensure that the Panel know OFCOM's reasons for disregarding or disagreeing with the advice or opinion; and

(b) to ensure that those reasons are or have been published in such manner as OFCOM consider appropriate for bringing them to the attention of persons who are aware of the Panel's advice or opinion.

(11) The Consumer Panel must—

(a) as soon as practicable after the end of the period of twelve months beginning with the commencement of this section; and

(b) as soon as practicable after the end of each subsequent period of twelve months;

prepare a report on the carrying out of their functions in that period.

(12) The Consumer Panel must publish each report—

(a) as soon as practicable after its preparation is complete, and

(b) in such manner as they consider appropriate.

(13) In this section—

"domestic and small business consumer" means a person who—

(a) is a consumer in the market for services or facilities mentioned in subsection (4) or for apparatus designed or adapted for use in connection with any such services or facilities; but

(b) is neither—

(i) a communications provider or a person who makes associated facilities available; nor

(ii) a person who is a consumer in the market in respect of an undertaking carried on by him for which more than ten individuals work (whether as employees or volunteers or otherwise);

"electronic programme guide" means a service which consists of—

(a) the listing or promotion, or both the listing and the promotion, of some or all of the programmes included in any one or more programme services the providers of which are or include persons other than the provider of the guide; and

(b) a facility for obtaining access, in whole or in part, to the programme service or services listed or promoted in the guide.

[3093]

NOTES

Commencement: 29 December 2003.

17 Membership etc of the Consumer Panel

(1) The members of the Consumer Panel shall be appointed by OFCOM and shall comprise a chairman and such other members as OFCOM may determine.

(2) The approval of the Secretary of State is required for the appointment of a person to be the chairman or to be another member of the Panel.

(3) In appointing persons to be members of the Consumer Panel, OFCOM must secure that, for each of the following parts of the United Kingdom—

(a) England,
(b) Scotland,
(c) Wales, and
(d) Northern Ireland,

there is a different member of the Panel capable of representing the interests and opinions of persons living in that part of the United Kingdom.

(4) In appointing persons to be members of the Consumer Panel, OFCOM must secure, so far as practicable, that the Panel are able to give informed advice about matters referable to each of the following—

(a) the interests of persons living in rural areas;
(b) the interests of persons living in urban areas;
(c) the interests of small businesses;
(d) the interests of disadvantaged persons, persons with low incomes and persons with disabilities; and
(e) the interests of the elderly.

(5) The validity of any proceedings of the Consumer Panel shall not be affected by any failure by OFCOM to comply with subsection (3) or (4).

(6) It shall be the duty of the Consumer Panel, in carrying out their functions, to have regard to the following interests—

(a) the interests of persons from the different parts of the United Kingdom; and
(b) the interests specified in subsection (4).

(7) A person shall be disqualified from being the chairman or a member of the Consumer Panel if he is a member or employee of OFCOM.

(8) The chairman and every member of the Consumer Panel—

(a) shall be appointed for a fixed period specified in the terms of his appointment but shall be eligible for re-appointment at the end of that period; and
(b) may at any time be removed from the Panel by a notice given by OFCOM with the approval of the Secretary of State.

(9) OFCOM may pay to the chairman and to any other member of the Consumer Panel such remuneration and allowances as OFCOM consider appropriate.

[3094]

NOTES

Commencement: 29 December 2003.

18 Committees and other procedure of the Consumer Panel

(1) The Consumer Panel may make such arrangements as they think fit for committees established by the Panel to give advice to them about matters relating to the carrying out of the Panel's functions.

(2) The Consumer Panel may make such other arrangements for regulating their own procedure, and for regulating the procedure of the committees established by them, as they think fit.

(3) Those arrangements may include arrangements as to quorums and as to the making of decisions by a majority.

(4) The committees established by the Panel may include committees the membership of which includes persons (including persons constituting a majority of the committee) who are not members of the Panel.

(5) The membership of every committee established by the Consumer Panel must contain at least one person who is a member of the Panel.

(6) Where a person who is not a member of the Consumer Panel is a member of a committee established by the Panel, OFCOM may pay to that person such remuneration and expenses as OFCOM may determine.

[3095]

NOTES

Commencement: 29 December 2003.

19 Power to amend remit of Consumer Panel

(1) The Secretary of State may by order modify subsection (3) of section 16 so as to add to the matters about which the Consumer Panel are required to be able to give advice.

(2) Before making an order under this section the Secretary of State must consult OFCOM and such other persons as he thinks fit.

(3) No order is to be made containing provision authorised by this section unless a draft of the order has been laid before Parliament and approved by a resolution of each House.

(4) The power to amend or revoke an order under this section does not include power to provide for a matter to cease to be a matter about which the Consumer Panel are required to be able to give advice.

[3096]

NOTES

Commencement: 29 December 2003.

Advisory committees

20 Advisory committees for different parts of the United Kingdom

(1) It shall be the duty of OFCOM, in accordance with the following provisions of this section, to exercise their powers under paragraph 14 of the Schedule to the Office of Communications Act 2002 (c 11) (committees of OFCOM) to establish and maintain a committee for each of the following parts of the United Kingdom—

- (a) England;
- (b) Wales;
- (c) Scotland; and
- (d) Northern Ireland.

(2) Each committee shall consist of—

- (a) a chairman appointed by OFCOM; and
- (b) such number of other members appointed by OFCOM as OFCOM think fit.

(3) In appointing a person in accordance with this section to be a member of a committee, OFCOM must have regard to the desirability of ensuring that the person appointed is able to represent the interests and opinions, in relation to communications matters, of persons living in the part of the United Kingdom for which the committee has been established.

(4) The function of each committee shall be to provide advice to OFCOM (including other committees established by OFCOM) about the interests and opinions, in relation to communications matters, of persons living in the part of the United Kingdom for which the committee has been established.

(5) A committee established under this section may also, at the request of the Consumer Panel, provide advice about those interests and opinions to the Consumer Panel.

(6) The consent of OFCOM is required for the giving of advice under subsection (5).

(7) In this section "communications matters" has the same meaning as in section 3.

[3097]

NOTES

Commencement: 29 December 2003.

21 Advisory committee on elderly and disabled persons

(1) It shall be the duty of OFCOM, in accordance with the following provisions of this section, to exercise their powers under paragraph 14 of the Schedule to the Office of Communications Act 2002 (c 11) (committees of OFCOM) to establish and maintain a committee to provide the advice specified in this section.

(2) The committee shall consist of—

(a) a chairman appointed by OFCOM; and

(b) such number of other members appointed by OFCOM as OFCOM think fit.

(3) In appointing persons to be members of the committee, OFCOM must have regard to the desirability of ensuring that the members of the committee include—

(a) persons who are familiar with the needs of the elderly; and

(b) persons who are familiar with the needs of persons with disabilities.

(4) The function of the committee shall be to provide advice to OFCOM (including other committees established by OFCOM) about the interests, in relation to communications matters, of—

(a) the elderly; and

(b) persons with disabilities.

(5) The committee may also, at the request of the Consumer Panel, provide advice about those interests to the Consumer Panel.

(6) The consent of OFCOM is required for the giving of advice under subsection (5).

(7) In this section "communications matters" has the same meaning as in section 3.

[3098]

NOTES

Commencement: 29 December 2003.

International matters

22 Representation on international and other bodies

(1) It shall be the duty of OFCOM to do, as respects the United Kingdom, such of the following things as they are required to do by the Secretary of State—

(a) provide representation on behalf of Her Majesty's Government in the United Kingdom on international and other bodies having communications functions;

(b) become or serve as a member of an international or other body having such functions;

(c) subscribe to such a body;

(d) provide representation on behalf of Her Majesty's Government in the United Kingdom at international meetings about communications.

(2) OFCOM shall also have the power, if requested to do so by the Secretary of State, to do one or more of those things as respects any of the Channel Islands, the Isle of Man or a British overseas territory.

(3) It shall be the duty of OFCOM to carry out their functions under this section in accordance with such general or specific directions as may be given to them by the Secretary of State.

(4) The Secretary of State—

(a) is not entitled to direct OFCOM to comply with a request made under subsection (2); but

(b) may give directions about how OFCOM are to carry out any representative role that they undertake in accordance with such a request.

(5) In this section—

"communications functions" means—

(a) functions relating to the use of the electro-magnetic spectrum for wireless telegraphy;

(b) functions relating to the regulation of television or radio broadcasting or the provision of television and radio services; and

(c) any other function which relates to, or is connected with, a matter in respect of which OFCOM have functions;

"international meetings about communications" means international meetings relating to, or to matters connected with, one or more of the following—

(a) the use of the electro-magnetic spectrum for wireless telegraphy;

(b) the regulation of television or radio broadcasting or of the provision of television and radio services;

(c) any other matter in respect of which OFCOM have functions.

(6) In relation to—

(a) a part of the British Islands outside the United Kingdom, or

(b) a British overseas territory,

the references in subsection (5) to matters in respect of which OFCOM have functions include references to matters corresponding, in the case of that part of those Islands or of that territory, to matters in respect of which OFCOM's functions are confined to the United Kingdom.

(7) In subsection (5) "television or radio broadcasting" includes the provision by means other than broadcasting of services similar to those provided by television or radio broadcasts.

[3099]

NOTES

Commencement: 29 December 2003.

23 Directions for international purposes in respect of broadcasting functions

(1) This section applies to—

(a) OFCOM's functions under the enactments relating to broadcasting; and

(b) the matters in relation to which those functions are conferred.

(2) It shall be the duty of OFCOM—

(a) to carry out those functions in accordance with any general or specific directions given to them by the Secretary of State for the purpose mentioned in subsection (3); and

(b) to carry out such other functions in relation to the matters to which this section applies as they are required to carry out by any general or specific directions so given.

(3) The Secretary of State is not to give a direction under this section except for the purpose of securing compliance, in relation to a matter to which this section applies, with an international obligation of the United Kingdom.

(4) A direction under this section must be contained in an order made by the Secretary of State.

(5) In this section "the enactments relating to broadcasting" means—

(a) the 1990 Act;

(b) the 1996 Act;

(c) Part 3 of this Act; and

(d) the other provisions of this Act so far as relating to the 1990 Act, the 1996 Act or that Part.

[3100]

NOTES

Commencement: 29 December 2003.

General information functions

24 Provision of information to the Secretary of State

(1) It shall be the duty of OFCOM to comply with a direction by the Secretary of State to provide him with information falling within subsection (2).

(2) The information that may be the subject of a direction under this section is any information reasonably required by the Secretary of State for the purpose of enabling him to secure compliance with an international obligation of the United Kingdom.

(3) Information that is required to be provided by a direction under this section must be provided in such manner and at such times as may be required by the direction.

[3101]

NOTES

Commencement: 25 July 2003 (for the purpose of enabling network and service functions and spectrum functions to be carried out during the transitional period by the Director General of Telecommunications and the Secretary of State respectively) (see further s 408 and Sch 18 at **[3436]**, **[3460]**, and the Communications Act 2003 (Commencement No 1) Order 2003, SI 2003/1900 at **[3507]**); 29 December 2003 (for the purpose of enabling OFCOM to perform those functions) (see the Office of Communications Act 2002 (Commencement No 3) and Communications Act 2003 (Commencement No 2) Order 2003, SI 2003/3142 at **[3590]**).

25 Community requirement to provide information

(1) This section applies if—

- (a) the European Commission requires OFCOM to provide it with information for the purpose of enabling it to perform any of its functions in relation to electronic communications networks, electronic communications services or associated facilities; and
- (b) the information is information obtained by OFCOM in the course of carrying out any of their functions under—
  - (i) Part 2; or
  - (ii) the enactments relating to the management of the radio spectrum that are not contained in that Part.

(2) It shall be the duty of OFCOM to comply with the requirement.

(3) If information provided to the European Commission under this section has been obtained by OFCOM from a person who is or, at the time the information was obtained from him, was—

- (a) a communications provider, or
- (b) a person making associated facilities available,

OFCOM must notify him that they have provided the information to the Commission.

(4) It shall be for OFCOM to determine the manner in which a notification is given under subsection (3).

[3102]

NOTES

Commencement: 25 July 2003 (for the purpose of enabling network and service functions and spectrum functions to be carried out during the transitional period by the Director General of Telecommunications and the Secretary of State respectively) (see further s 408 and Sch 18 at **[3436]**, **[3460]**, and the Communications Act 2003 (Commencement No 1) Order 2003, SI 2003/1900 at **[3507]**); 29 December 2003 (for the purpose of enabling OFCOM to perform those functions) (see the Office of Communications Act 2002 (Commencement No 3) and Communications Act 2003 (Commencement No 2) Order 2003, SI 2003/3142 at **[3590]**).

26 Publication of information and advice for consumers etc

(1) OFCOM may arrange for the publication of such information and advice about matters in relation to which they have functions as it appears to them to be appropriate to make available to the persons mentioned in subsection (2).

(2) Those persons are—

- (a) the customers of communications providers;
- (b) the customers of persons who make associated facilities available;
- (c) persons who use electronic communications networks, electronic communications services or associated facilities; and
- (d) persons to whom radio and television services are provided or who are otherwise able or likely to take advantage of any of those services.

(3) In arranging for the publication of information or advice under this section, OFCOM must have regard to the need to exclude from publication, so far as that is practicable, the matters which are confidential in accordance with subsections (4) and (5).

(4) A matter is confidential under this subsection if—

- (a) it relates specifically to the affairs of a particular body; and

(b) publication of that matter would or might, in OFCOM's opinion, seriously and prejudicially affect the interests of that body.

(5) A matter is confidential under this subsection if—

(a) it relates to the private affairs of an individual; and

(b) publication of that matter would or might, in OFCOM's opinion, seriously and prejudicially affect the interests of that individual.

(6) The publication of information or advice under this section must be in such manner as OFCOM consider appropriate.

[3103]

NOTES

Commencement: 25 July 2003 (sub-ss (1), (2)(a)–(c), (3)–(6), for the purpose of enabling network and service functions and spectrum functions to be carried out during the transitional period by the Director General of Telecommunications and the Secretary of State respectively) (see further s 408 and Sch 18 at **[3436]**, **[3460]**, and the Communications Act 2003 (Commencement No 1) Order 2003, SI 2003/1900 at **[3507]**); 29 December 2003 (otherwise).

Employment in broadcasting

27 Training and equality of opportunity

(1) It shall be the duty of OFCOM to take all such steps as they consider appropriate for promoting the development of opportunities for the training and retraining of persons—

(a) for employment by persons providing television and radio services; and

(b) for work in connection with the provision of such services otherwise than as an employee.

(2) It shall be the duty of OFCOM to take all such steps as they consider appropriate for promoting equality of opportunity in relation to both—

(a) employment by those providing television and radio services; and

(b) the training and retraining of persons for such employment.

(3) It shall also be the duty of OFCOM, in relation to such employment, training and retraining, to take all such steps as they consider appropriate for promoting the equalisation of opportunities for disabled persons.

(4) The reference in subsection (2) to equality of opportunity is a reference to equality of opportunity—

(a) between men and women; and

(b) between persons of different racial groups.

(5) In this section—

"disabled" has the same meaning as in the Disability Discrimination Act 1995 (c 50);

"racial group" has the same meaning as in the Race Relations Act 1976 (c 74) or, in Northern Ireland, the Race Relations (Northern Ireland) Order 1997 (SI 1997/869 (NI 6)).

(6) The Secretary of State may by order amend subsection (4) by adding any other form of equality of opportunity that he considers appropriate.

(7) No order is to be made containing provision authorised by subsection (6) unless a draft of the order has been laid before Parliament and approved by a resolution of each House.

[3104]

NOTES

Commencement: 29 December 2003.

Charging

28 General power to charge for services

(1) OFCOM may provide a service to which this section applies to any person on such terms as to the making of payments to OFCOM—

(a) as they may determine in advance; or

(b) as may be agreed between that person and OFCOM.

(2) This section applies to a service which is provided by OFCOM to a person in the course of carrying out their functions and is neither—

(a) a service which OFCOM are under a duty to provide to that person; nor
(b) one in respect of which express provision is made by or under an enactment for authorising or forbidding the payment of fees or charges.

(3) In this section references to providing a service to a person include references to a service consisting in—

(a) the giving of advice to that person;
(b) the entry of his particulars in a register or other record kept by OFCOM otherwise than in pursuance of an express statutory duty to keep the register or record; or
(c) the taking of steps for the purposes of determining whether to grant an application for an entry in a register or record so kept.

[3105]

NOTES

Commencement: 18 September 2003.

Guarantees

29 Secretary of State guarantees for OFCOM borrowing

(1) The Secretary of State may guarantee—

(a) the repayment of the principal of any borrowing by OFCOM;
(b) the payment of interest on any such borrowing; and
(c) the discharge of other financial obligations incurred by OFCOM in connection with any such borrowing.

(2) The power of the Secretary of State to give a guarantee under this section is a power (subject to subsection (3)) to give it in such manner and on such conditions as he thinks fit.

(3) The Secretary of State must not give a guarantee under this section if the aggregate of—

(a) the amounts that he may be required to pay for fulfilling that guarantee, and
(b) the amounts that he may be required to pay for fulfilling other guarantees previously given under this section and still in force,

exceeds £5 million.

(4) The Secretary of State may by order substitute another amount for the amount for the time being specified in subsection (3).

(5) No order is to be made containing provision authorised by subsection (4) unless a draft of the order has been laid before Parliament and approved by a resolution of the House of Commons.

(6) Immediately after a guarantee is given under this section, the Secretary of State must lay a statement of the guarantee before each House of Parliament.

(7) Where any sum is paid by the Secretary of State under a guarantee given under this section, he must lay a statement relating to that sum before each House of Parliament as soon as practicable after the end of each of the financial years—

(a) beginning with the one in which the sum is paid; and
(b) ending with the one in which OFCOM's liabilities under subsection (8) in respect of that sum are finally discharged.

(8) If sums are paid by the Secretary of State in fulfilment of a guarantee given under this section OFCOM must pay him—

(a) such amounts in or towards the repayment to him of those sums as he may direct; and
(b) interest, at such rates as he may determine, on amounts outstanding under this subsection.

(9) Payments to the Secretary of State under subsection (8) must be made at such times and in such manner as he may determine.

[3106]

NOTES

Commencement: 18 September 2003.

Provisions supplemental to transfer of functions

30 Transfers of property etc from pre-commencement regulators

(1) The Secretary of State may, by a direction to any of the pre-commencement regulators, require that regulator to make one or more schemes for the transfer from that regulator to OFCOM of such of the regulator's property, rights and liabilities as may be specified or described in the direction.

(2) Where a pre-commencement regulator is required to make a scheme, the scheme must be made by such date as may be specified in the direction.

(3) Before making a scheme in pursuance of a direction under subsection (1), a pre-commencement regulator must consult OFCOM.

(4) A pre-commencement regulator who makes a scheme in pursuance of a direction under subsection (1) shall submit that scheme to the Secretary of State for approval.

(5) A scheme that is required to be so submitted shall have effect only if, and to the extent that, it is approved by the Secretary of State.

(6) The Secretary of State, in approving a scheme, may do so subject to such modifications as he thinks fit.

(7) Where the Secretary of State approves a scheme subject to modifications specified by him, it shall have effect with those modifications.

(8) A scheme approved by the Secretary of State under this section shall come into force either—

- (a) if no time is appointed under paragraph (b), at the time when the approval is given; or
- (b) if the Secretary of State appoints a later time for the coming into force of the scheme (whether when approving the scheme or by subsequently varying a time appointed under this paragraph), at that later time.

(9) Where a scheme is submitted to the Secretary of State under this section, he must—

- (a) consult OFCOM about any proposal of his to approve the scheme; and
- (b) consult both OFCOM and the pre-commencement regulator in question about any modifications subject to which he proposes to give his approval, or about any proposal of his to refuse approval.

(10) The Secretary of State may, after consulting OFCOM, himself make a scheme for the transfer of property, rights and liabilities—

- (a) from a pre-commencement regulator to OFCOM; or
- (b) from himself to OFCOM;

and such a scheme shall come into force on such day as the Secretary of State may appoint (whether in the scheme or subsequently).

(11) The Secretary of State is not to make a scheme for the transfer of property, rights and liabilities from a pre-commencement regulator to OFCOM unless—

- (a) that regulator has failed to comply with a direction under subsection (1); or
- (b) that regulator has complied with such a direction by submitting a scheme to the Secretary of State that he has decided not to approve (with or without modifications).

(12) Schedule 2 (which makes further provision about schemes under this section) shall have effect.

[3107]

NOTES

Commencement: 18 September 2003.

31 Transitional functions and abolition of pre-commencement regulators

(1) It shall be the duty of the pre-commencement regulators to take all such steps as are necessary or expedient for ensuring that OFCOM are able effectively to carry out OFCOM's functions from the time when they are vested in OFCOM.

(2) The pre-commencement regulators, in taking those steps, must comply with every direction given to them by the Secretary of State.

(3) The pre-commencement regulators and OFCOM shall each have a duty to provide the Secretary of State with all such information and assistance as he may require for the purposes of, or in connection with—

(a) his power to give directions under subsection (1) of section 30; and

(b) his powers and duties in relation to the approval and making of schemes under that section.

(4) On such day as the Secretary of State may by order appoint—

(a) the office of the Director General of Telecommunications shall be abolished; and

(b) the Broadcasting Standards Commission, the Independent Television Commission and the Radio Authority shall cease to exist.

(5) Section 54 of the Telecommunications Act 1984 (c 12) (which provides for the establishment of advisory bodies) shall cease to have effect; and each of the bodies established under that section shall cease to exist on such day as the Secretary of State may by order appoint.

(6) Different days may be appointed under this section for the Director General of Telecommunications and for each of the different bodies mentioned in subsections (4)(b) and (5).

[3108]

NOTES

Commencement: 17 July 2003 (sub-ss (1)–(4), (6)); 29 December 2003 (otherwise).

PART 2
NETWORKS, SERVICES AND THE RADIO SPECTRUM

CHAPTER 1
ELECTRONIC COMMUNICATIONS NETWORKS AND SERVICES

Preliminary

32 Meaning of electronic communications networks and services

(1) In this Act "electronic communications network" means—

(a) a transmission system for the conveyance, by the use of electrical, magnetic or electro-magnetic energy, of signals of any description; and

(b) such of the following as are used, by the person providing the system and in association with it, for the conveyance of the signals—

(i) apparatus comprised in the system;

(ii) apparatus used for the switching or routing of the signals; and

(iii) software and stored data.

(2) In this Act "electronic communications service" means a service consisting in, or having as its principal feature, the conveyance by means of an electronic communications network of signals, except in so far as it is a content service.

(3) In this Act "associated facility" means a facility which—

(a) is available for use in association with the use of an electronic communications network or electronic communications service (whether or not one provided by the person making the facility available); and

(b) is so available for the purpose of—

(i) making the provision of that network or service possible;

(ii) making possible the provision of other services provided by means of that network or service; or

(iii) supporting the provision of such other services.

(4) In this Act—

(a) references to the provision of an electronic communications network include references to its establishment, maintenance or operation;

(b) references, where one or more persons are employed or engaged to provide the network or service under the direction or control of another person, to the person by whom an electronic communications network or electronic communications service is provided are confined to references to that other person; and

(c) references, where one or more persons are employed or engaged to make facilities available under the direction or control of another person, to the person by whom any associated facilities are made available are confined to references to that other person.

(5) Paragraphs (a) and (b) of subsection (4) apply in relation to references in subsection (1) to the provision of a transmission system as they apply in relation to references in this Act to the provision of an electronic communications network.

(6) The reference in subsection (1) to a transmission system includes a reference to a transmission system consisting of no more than a transmitter used for the conveyance of signals.

(7) In subsection (2) "a content service" means so much of any service as consists in one or both of the following—

(a) the provision of material with a view to its being comprised in signals conveyed by means of an electronic communications network;

(b) the exercise of editorial control over the contents of signals conveyed by means of a such a network.

(8) In this section references to the conveyance of signals include references to the transmission or routing of signals or of parts of signals and to the broadcasting of signals for general reception.

(9) For the purposes of this section the cases in which software and stored data are to be taken as being used for a particular purpose include cases in which they—

(a) have been installed or stored in order to be used for that purpose; and

(b) are available to be so used.

(10) In this section "signal" includes—

(a) anything comprising speech, music, sounds, visual images or communications or data of any description; and

(b) signals serving for the impartation of anything between persons, between a person and a thing or between things, or for the actuation or control of apparatus.

[3109]

NOTES

Commencement: 25 July 2003 (for the purpose of enabling network and service functions and spectrum functions to be carried out during the transitional period by the Director General of Telecommunications and the Secretary of State respectively) (see further s 408 and Sch 18 at **[3436]**, **[3460]**, and the Communications Act 2003 (Commencement No 1) Order 2003, SI 2003/1900 at **[3507]**); 29 December 2003 (for the purpose of enabling OFCOM to perform those functions) (see the Office of Communications Act 2002 (Commencement No 3) and Communications Act 2003 (Commencement No 2) Order 2003, SI 2003/3142 at **[3590]**).

Notification by providers

33 Advance notification to OFCOM

(1) A person shall not—

(a) provide a designated electronic communications network,

(b) provide a designated electronic communications service, or

(c) make available a designated associated facility,

unless, before beginning to provide it or to make it available, he has given a notification to OFCOM of his intention to provide that network or service, or to make that facility available.

(2) An electronic communications network, electronic communications service or associated facility is designated for the purposes of this section if it is of a description of

networks, services or facilities that is for the time being designated by OFCOM as a description of networks, services or facilities for which notification under this section is required.

(3) A person who has given a notification for the purposes of subsection (1) must, before—

(a) providing or making available the notified network, service or facility with any significant differences, or

(b) ceasing to provide it or to make it available,

give a notification to OFCOM of the differences or (as the case may be) of his intention to cease to provide the network or service or to make the facility available.

(4) A notification for the purposes of this section must—

(a) be sent to OFCOM in such manner as OFCOM may require; and

(b) contain all such information as OFCOM may require.

(5) The only information OFCOM may require a notification to contain is—

(a) a declaration of the relevant proposal of the person giving the notification;

(b) the time when it is intended that effect should be given to the relevant proposal;

(c) particulars identifying the person giving the notification;

(d) particulars identifying one or more persons with addresses in the United Kingdom who, for the purposes of matters relating to the notified network, service or facility, are authorised to accept service at an address in the United Kingdom on behalf of the person giving the notification;

(e) particulars identifying one or more persons who may be contacted if there is an emergency that is caused by or affects the provision of the notified network, service or facility;

(f) addresses and other particulars necessary for effecting service on or contacting each of the persons mentioned in paragraphs (c) to (e).

(6) The declaration of the relevant proposal that may be required under subsection (5) is whichever of the following is appropriate in the case of the person giving the notification—

(a) a declaration of his proposal to provide the network or service described in the notification or to make available the facility so described;

(b) a declaration of his proposal to make the modifications that are so described of the network, service or facility specified in the notification; or

(c) a declaration of his proposal to cease to provide the network or service so specified or to cease to make available the facility so specified.

(7) Requirements imposed under subsection (4) are not to require a notification by a person to contain particulars falling within subsection (5)(d) in a case in which—

(a) that person is resident in a member State or has a place of business in a member State;

(b) the notification contains a statement under subsection (8);

(c) the notification sets out an address in a member State at which service will be accepted by the person who, in accordance with that statement, is authorised to accept it; and

(d) OFCOM are satisfied that adequate arrangements exist for effecting service on that person at that address.

(8) That statement is one which—

(a) declares that the person authorised, for the purposes of matters relating to the notified network, service or facilities, to accept service on behalf of the person giving the notification is that person himself; or

(b) identifies another person who is resident in a member State, or has a place of business in such State, as the person so authorised.

(9) The reference in subsection (3) to providing or making available a notified network, service or facility with significant differences is a reference to continuing to provide it, or to make it available, after a change in whatever falling within subsection (5)(a) to (f) was last notified to OFCOM under this section.

(10) References in this section to accepting service at an address are references—

(a) to accepting service of documents or process at that address; or

(b) otherwise to receiving notifications at that address;

and the reference in subsection (7) to effecting service at an address is to be construed accordingly.

(11) Where a description of electronic communications network, electronic communications service or associated facility is designated for the purposes of this section at a time when a network, service or facility of that description is already being provided or made available by a person—

(a) that person's obligation under this section to give a notification before beginning to provide or make available that network, service or facility shall have effect as an obligation to give a notification within such period after the coming into force of the designation as may be specified in the notice in which the designation is contained; and

(b) that notification is to be one stating that that person is already providing the network or service, or making the facility available (rather than that it is his intention to do so).

(12) Subsection (11) has effect subject to any transitional provision—

(a) which is contained in the notification setting out the designation; and

(b) treats a person as having given the notification required by that subsection.

[3110]

NOTES

Commencement: 25 July 2003 (for the purpose of enabling network and service functions and spectrum functions to be carried out during the transitional period by the Director General of Telecommunications and the Secretary of State respectively) (see further s 408 and Sch 18 at **[3436]**, **[3460]**, and the Communications Act 2003 (Commencement No 1) Order 2003, SI 2003/1900 at **[3507]**); 29 December 2003 (for the purpose of enabling OFCOM to perform those functions) (see the Office of Communications Act 2002 (Commencement No 3) and Communications Act 2003 (Commencement No 2) Order 2003, SI 2003/3142 at **[3590]**).

34 Designations and requirements for the purposes of s 33

(1) Before—

(a) making or withdrawing a designation for the purposes of section 33, or

(b) imposing or modifying a requirement under subsection (4) of that section,

OFCOM must consult such of the persons who, in their opinion, are likely to be affected by it as they think fit.

(2) Before making or withdrawing a designation for the purposes of section 33 OFCOM must also consult the Secretary of State.

(3) The way in which a designation for the purposes of section 33 or a requirement under subsection (4) of that section—

(a) is to be made or imposed, or

(b) may be withdrawn or modified,

is by a notice published in such manner as OFCOM consider appropriate for bringing the designation, requirement, withdrawal or modification to the attention of the persons who, in their opinion, are likely to be affected by it.

(4) A designation for the purposes of section 33 may be framed by reference to any such description of networks, services or facilities, or such other factors, as OFCOM think fit.

(5) Requirements imposed under section 33(4) may make different provision for different cases.

[3111]

NOTES

Commencement: 25 July 2003 (for the purpose of enabling network and service functions and spectrum functions to be carried out during the transitional period by the Director General of Telecommunications and the Secretary of State respectively) (see further s 408 and Sch 18 at **[3436]**, **[3460]**, and the Communications Act 2003 (Commencement No 1) Order 2003, SI 2003/1900 at **[3507]**); 29 December 2003 (for the purpose of enabling OFCOM to perform those functions) (see the Office of Communications Act 2002 (Commencement No 3) and Communications Act 2003 (Commencement No 2) Order 2003, SI 2003/3142 at **[3590]**).

35 Notification of contraventions of s 33

(1) Where OFCOM determine that there are reasonable grounds for believing that a person has contravened section 33, they may give him a notification under this section.

(2) A notification under this section is one which—

(a) sets out the determination made by OFCOM; and
(b) specifies the period during which the person notified has an opportunity of doing the things specified in subsection (3).

(3) Those things are—
(a) making representations about the determination; and
(b) providing OFCOM with the information which the notified person should have provided for the purposes of section 33 but has not.

(4) Subject to subsections (5) to (7), the period for doing those things must be the period of one month beginning with the day after the one on which the notification was given.

(5) OFCOM may, if they think fit, allow a longer period for doing those things either—
(a) by specifying a longer period in the notification; or
(b) by subsequently, on one or more occasions, extending the specified period.

(6) The person notified shall have a shorter period for doing those things if a shorter period is agreed between OFCOM and the person notified.

(7) The person notified shall also have a shorter period if—
(a) OFCOM have reasonable grounds for believing that the contravention is a repeated contravention;
(b) they have determined that, in those circumstances, a shorter period would be appropriate; and
(c) the shorter period has been specified in the notification.

(8) A notification under this section—
(a) may be given in respect of more than one contravention of section 33; and
(b) if it is given in respect of a continuing contravention, may be given in respect of any period during which the contravention has continued.

(9) Where a notification under this section has been given to a person in respect of a contravention of section 33, OFCOM may give a further notification in respect of the same contravention if, and only if—
(a) the subsequent notification is in respect of so much of a period during which the contravention in question was continuing as falls after a period to which the earlier notification relates; or
(b) the earlier notification has been withdrawn without a penalty having been imposed by reference to the notified contravention.

(10) For the purposes of this section a contravention is a repeated contravention, in relation to a notification with respect to that contravention, if—
(a) a previous notification under this section has been given in respect of the same contravention or in respect of another contravention of section 33; and
(b) the subsequent notification is given no more than twelve months after the day of the making by OFCOM of a determination for the purposes of section 36(2) or 37(2) that the contravention to which the previous notification related did occur.

[3112]

NOTES

Commencement: 25 July 2003 (for the purpose of enabling network and service functions and spectrum functions to be carried out during the transitional period by the Director General of Telecommunications and the Secretary of State respectively) (see further s 408 and Sch 18 at **[3436]**, **[3460]**, and the Communications Act 2003 (Commencement No 1) Order 2003, SI 2003/1900 at **[3507]**); 29 December 2003 (for the purpose of enabling OFCOM to perform those functions) (see the Office of Communications Act 2002 (Commencement No 3) and Communications Act 2003 (Commencement No 2) Order 2003, SI 2003/3142 at **[3590]**).

36 Enforcement notification for contravention of s 33

(1) This section applies where—
(a) a person ("the notified provider") has been given a notification under section 35;
(b) OFCOM have allowed the notified provider an opportunity of making representations about the notified determination; and
(c) the period allowed for the making of the representations has expired.

(2) OFCOM may give the notified provider an enforcement notification if they are satisfied—

(a) that he has, in one or more of the respects notified, been in contravention of section 33; and
(b) that he has not, during the period allowed under section 35, provided OFCOM with all the information which he should have provided to them to remedy the contravention.

(3) An enforcement notification is a notification which imposes a requirement on the notified provider to take all such steps for providing OFCOM with that information as may be specified in the notification.

(4) A decision of OFCOM to give an enforcement notification to a person—
(a) must be notified to that person, together with the reasons for the decision, no later than a week after the day on which it is taken; and
(b) must fix a reasonable period for the taking of the steps required by the notification.

(5) It shall be the duty of a person to whom an enforcement notification has been given to comply with it.

(6) That duty shall be enforceable in civil proceedings by OFCOM—
(a) for an injunction;
(b) for specific performance of a statutory duty under section 45 of the Court of Session Act 1988 (c 36); or
(c) for any other appropriate remedy or relief.

[3113]

NOTES

Commencement: 25 July 2003 (for the purpose of enabling network and service functions and spectrum functions to be carried out during the transitional period by the Director General of Telecommunications and the Secretary of State respectively) (see further s 408 and Sch 18 at **[3436]**, **[3460]**, and the Communications Act 2003 (Commencement No 1) Order 2003, SI 2003/1900 at **[3507]**); 29 December 2003 (for the purpose of enabling OFCOM to perform those functions) (see the Office of Communications Act 2002 (Commencement No 3) and Communications Act 2003 (Commencement No 2) Order 2003, SI 2003/3142 at **[3590]**).

37 Penalties for contravention of s 33

(1) This section applies (in addition to section 36) where—
(a) a person ("the notified provider") has been given a notification under section 35;
(b) OFCOM have allowed the notified provider an opportunity of making representations about the matters notified; and
(c) the period allowed for the making of the representations has expired.

(2) OFCOM may impose a penalty on the notified provider if he—
(a) has, in one or more of the respects notified, been in contravention of section 33; and
(b) has not, during the period allowed under section 35, provided OFCOM with all the information which he should have provided to remedy the contravention.

(3) Where a notification under section 35 relates to more than one contravention, a separate penalty may be imposed in respect of each contravention.

(4) Where such a notification relates to a continuing contravention, no more than one penalty may be imposed in respect of the period of contravention specified in the notification.

(5) OFCOM may also impose a penalty on the notified provider if he has contravened, or is contravening, a requirement of an enforcement notification given under section 36 in respect of the notified contravention.

(6) The amount of a penalty imposed under this section is to be such amount not exceeding £10,000 as OFCOM determine to be—
(a) appropriate; and
(b) proportionate to the contravention in respect of which it is imposed.

(7) In making that determination OFCOM must have regard to—
(a) any representations made to them by the notified provider; and
(b) any steps taken by him towards complying with his obligations under section 33.

(8) Where OFCOM impose a penalty on a person under this section, they shall—

(a) within one week of making their decision to impose the penalty, notify that person of that decision and of their reasons for that decision; and
(b) in that notification, fix a reasonable period after it is given as the period within which the penalty is to be paid.

(9) A penalty imposed under this section—
(a) must be paid to OFCOM; and
(b) if not paid within the period fixed by them, is to be recoverable by them accordingly.

(10) The Secretary of State may by order amend this section so as to substitute a different maximum penalty for the maximum penalty for the time being specified in subsection (6).

(11) No order is to be made containing provision authorised by subsection (10) unless a draft of the order has been laid before Parliament and approved by a resolution of each House. **[3114]**

NOTES

Commencement: 25 July 2003 (for the purpose of enabling network and service functions and spectrum functions to be carried out during the transitional period by the Director General of Telecommunications and the Secretary of State respectively) (see further s 408 and Sch 18 at **[3436]**, **[3460]**, and the Communications Act 2003 (Commencement No 1) Order 2003, SI 2003/1900 at **[3507]**); 29 December 2003 (for the purpose of enabling OFCOM to perform those functions) (see the Office of Communications Act 2002 (Commencement No 3) and Communications Act 2003 (Commencement No 2) Order 2003, SI 2003/3142 at **[3590]**).

Administrative charges imposed on providers

38 Fixing of charges

(1) A person who, at any time in a charging year, is a person to whom this section applies shall—
(a) in respect of the network, service or facility provided or made available by him,
(b) in respect of the application to him of a universal service condition relating to matters mentioned in section 66(3),
(c) in respect of the application to him of an SMP apparatus condition, or
(d) in respect of the application of the electronic communications code in his case,
pay to OFCOM the administrative charge (if any) that is fixed by them for the case that is applicable to him.

(2) This section applies to a person at a time if, at that time, he is—
(a) providing an electronic communications network of a description which is, at that time, designated for the purposes of this section;
(b) providing an electronic communications service of a description which is, at that time, so designated;
(c) making available an associated facility of a description which is, at that time, so designated;
(d) a person who without being a communications provider is designated in accordance with regulations under section 66;
(e) a supplier of apparatus to whom an SMP apparatus condition applies; or
(f) a person in whose case the electronic communications code applies by virtue of a direction given under section 106 otherwise than for the purposes of the provision by him of an electronic communications network of a designated description.

(3) OFCOM are not to fix the administrative charge for a charging year unless—
(a) at the time the charge is fixed there is in force a statement by OFCOM of the principles that OFCOM are proposing to apply in fixing charges under this section for that year; and
(b) the charge is fixed in accordance with those charging principles.

(4) Those principles must be such as appear to OFCOM to be likely to secure, on the basis of such estimates of the likely costs as it is practicable for them to make—
(a) that, on a year by year basis, the aggregate amount of the charges payable to OFCOM is sufficient to meet, but does not exceed, the annual cost to OFCOM of carrying out the functions mentioned in subsection (5);

(b) that the cost of carrying out those functions is met by the imposition of charges that are objectively justifiable and proportionate to the matters in respect of which they are imposed;

(c) that the relationship between meeting the cost of carrying out those functions and the amounts of the charges is transparent;

(d) that the charges fixed for persons who are liable to charges by reason only of being persons to whom SMP apparatus conditions apply are referable only to things done in, or in connection with, the setting, modification or enforcement of SMP apparatus conditions or the carrying out of the functions mentioned in subsection (6)(l); and

(e) that the charges fixed for persons who are liable to charges by reason only of being persons falling within subsection (2)(f), are referable only to costs incurred in, or in connection with, the carrying out of the functions mentioned in subsection (6)(g) and (l).

(5) Those functions are—

(a) the relevant Chapter 1 functions;

(b) the carrying out for a Chapter 1 purpose of any research by OFCOM or the Consumer Panel into any of the matters mentioned in section 14(1)(c) to (f);

(c) the publication under section 26 of any information or advice that it appears to OFCOM to be appropriate to make available to the persons mentioned in subsection (2)(a) to (c) of that section; and

(d) the function of taking any steps that OFCOM consider it necessary to take—

(i) in preparation for the carrying out of any of the functions mentioned in paragraphs (a) to (c) of this subsection; or

(ii) for the purpose of facilitating the carrying out of those functions or otherwise in connection with carrying them out.

(6) The relevant Chapter 1 functions are—

(a) OFCOM's functions under sections 33 to 37 and 44;

(b) the setting, modification and enforcement of conditions under section 45;

(c) the supervision, as respects the requirements of sections 33 to 37 and of any such conditions, of communications providers and of persons who make associated facilities available;

(d) the monitoring of compliance with those requirements and with any such conditions;

(e) the functions conferred on OFCOM by or under section 55;

(f) their functions under section 105;

(g) their functions under sections 106 to 119;

(h) their functions under sections 185 to 191;

(i) securing international co-operation in relation to the regulation of electronic communications networks, electronic communications services and associated facilities;

(j) securing the harmonisation and standardisation of the regulation of electronic communications networks, electronic communications services and associated facilities;

(k) market analysis and any monitoring of the controls operating in the markets for electronic communications networks, electronic communications services and associated facilities;

(l) OFCOM's functions under this section and sections 39 to 43.

(7) A purpose is a Chapter 1 purpose for the purposes of subsection (5)(b) if it is the purpose of ascertaining the effectiveness of one or more of the following—

(a) the regulation of the provision of electronic communications networks or electronic communications services;

(b) the regulation of the making available of associated facilities;

(c) the mechanisms in place for the handling, by communications providers and by persons making such facilities available, of complaints made to them by consumers in markets for such services or facilities;

(d) the mechanisms in place for resolving disputes between such consumers and communications providers or persons who make such facilities available.

(8) OFCOM's power to fix charges for a particular case includes—

(a) power to provide that the charges in that case are to be equal to the amounts produced by a computation made in the manner, and by reference to the factors, specified by them;

(b) power to provide for different charges to be imposed in that case on different descriptions of persons; and

(c) power to provide for particular descriptions of persons falling within subsection (2)(d) to (f) to be excluded from the liability to pay charges in that case.

(9) As soon as reasonably practicable after the end of each charging year, OFCOM must publish a statement setting out, in respect of that year—

(a) the aggregate amounts of the administrative charges for that year that have been received by OFCOM;

(b) the aggregate amount of the administrative charges for that year that remain outstanding and are likely to be paid or recovered; and

(c) the cost to OFCOM of carrying out the functions mentioned in subsection (5).

(10) Any deficit or surplus shown (after applying this subsection for all previous years) by a statement under subsection (9) shall be carried forward and taken into account in determining what is required to satisfy the requirement imposed by virtue of subsection (4)(a) in relation to the following year.

(11) Section 34 applies in relation to the making and withdrawal of a designation for the purposes of this section as it applies to the making and withdrawal of a designation for the purposes of section 33.

(12) In this section "charging year" means—

(a) the period beginning with the commencement of this section and ending with the next 31st March; or

(b) any subsequent period of twelve months beginning with 1st April.

[3115]

NOTES

Commencement: 25 July 2003 (for the purpose of enabling network and service functions and spectrum functions to be carried out during the transitional period by the Director General of Telecommunications and the Secretary of State respectively) (see further s 408 and Sch 18 at **[3436]**, **[3460]**, and the Communications Act 2003 (Commencement No 1) Order 2003, SI 2003/1900 at **[3507]**); 29 December 2003 (for the purpose of enabling OFCOM to perform those functions) (see the Office of Communications Act 2002 (Commencement No 3) and Communications Act 2003 (Commencement No 2) Order 2003, SI 2003/3142 at **[3590]**).

---

39 Supplemental provision about fixing charges

(1) OFCOM's power to fix a charge under section 38—

(a) is to be exercisable only by the publication or giving of such notification as they consider appropriate for bringing the charge to the attention of the persons who, in their opinion, are likely to be affected by it; and

(b) includes power, by setting it out in that notification, to fix the time at which the charge is to become due to OFCOM.

(2) A charge fixed under section 38 for a charging year may be fixed in terms providing for a deduction from the charge on a proportionate basis to be made for a part of the year during which—

(a) the network, service or facility in respect of which it is fixed is not provided or made available by the person otherwise liable to the charge;

(b) the universal service condition in respect of which it is fixed does not apply in that person's case;

(c) the SMP apparatus condition in respect of which it is fixed does not apply in that person's case; or

(d) the electronic communications code does not apply in that person's case.

(3) Such a charge may also be fixed (subject to subsection (4)) so that it is referable, in whole or in part—

(a) to the provision or making available of a network, service or facility during a part of the year falling before the fixing of the charge;

(b) to the application of a universal service condition to a person for a part of the year so falling;

(c) to a person's being a person to whom an SMP apparatus condition applies for a part of the year so falling; or

(d) to the application of the electronic communications code in a person's case during a part of the year so falling.

(4) A charge may be fixed so as to be referable to a time before it is fixed to the extent only that both—

(a) the imposition of the charge, and

(b) the amount of the charge,

are required by, and consistent with, the statement of charging principles in force at the beginning of the charging year.

(5) Before making or revising a statement of charging principles, OFCOM must consult such of the persons who, in OFCOM's opinion, are likely to be affected by those principles as they think fit.

(6) The way in which a statement of charging principles must be made or may be revised is by the publication of the statement or revised statement in such manner as OFCOM consider appropriate for bringing it to the attention of the persons who, in their opinion, are likely to be affected by it.

(7) References in this section to a statement of charging principles are references to a statement by OFCOM of the principles that they are proposing to apply in fixing charges under section 38 for a charging year.

(8) In this section "charging year" has the same meaning as in section 38. **[3116]**

NOTES

Commencement: 25 July 2003 (for the purpose of enabling network and service functions and spectrum functions to be carried out during the transitional period by the Director General of Telecommunications and the Secretary of State respectively) (see further s 408 and Sch 18 at **[3436]**, **[3460]**, and the Communications Act 2003 (Commencement No 1) Order 2003, SI 2003/1900 at **[3507]**); 29 December 2003 (for the purpose of enabling OFCOM to perform those functions) (see the Office of Communications Act 2002 (Commencement No 3) and Communications Act 2003 (Commencement No 2) Order 2003, SI 2003/3142 at **[3590]**).

40 Notification of non-payment of charges

(1) OFCOM are not entitled to bring proceedings for the recovery from a person of an administrative charge fixed for any year under section 38 unless they have given that person a notification under this section with respect to the amount they are seeking to recover.

(2) Where OFCOM determine that there are reasonable grounds for believing that a person is in contravention (whether in respect of the whole or a part of a charge) of a requirement to pay such an administrative charge, they may give him a notification under this section.

(3) A notification under this section is one which—

(a) sets out the determination made by OFCOM; and

(b) specifies the period during which the person notified has an opportunity of doing the things specified in subsection (4).

(4) Those things are—

(a) making representations about the notified determination; and

(b) paying the unpaid charge or (as the case may be) the amount outstanding.

(5) Subject to subsections (6) to (8), the period for doing those things must be the period of one month beginning with the day after the one on which the notification was given.

(6) OFCOM may, if they think fit, allow a longer period for doing those things either—

(a) by specifying a longer period in the notification; or

(b) by subsequently, on one or more occasions, extending the specified period.

(7) The person notified shall have a shorter period for doing those things if a shorter period is agreed between OFCOM and the person notified.

(8) The person notified shall also have a shorter period if—

(a) OFCOM have reasonable grounds for believing that the contravention is a repeated contravention;

(b) they have determined that, in those circumstances, a shorter period would be appropriate; and

(c) the shorter period has been specified in the notification.

(9) A notification under this section—

(a) may be given in respect of contraventions of more than one requirement to pay an administrative charge; and
(b) if it is given in respect of a continuing contravention, may be given in respect of any period during which the contravention has continued.

(10) Where a notification under this section has been given to a person in respect of an amount outstanding, OFCOM may give a further notification in respect of the whole or a part of that amount if, and only if—
(a) the subsequent notification is in respect of so much of a period during which that amount was outstanding as falls after a period to which the earlier notification relates; or
(b) the earlier notification has been withdrawn without a penalty having been imposed in respect of the matters notified.

(11) For the purposes of this section a contravention is a repeated contravention, in relation to a notification with respect to that contravention, if—
(a) a previous notification under this section has been given in respect of the same contravention or in respect of another contravention of a requirement to pay an administrative charge; and
(b) the subsequent notification is given no more than twelve months after the day of the making by OFCOM of a determination for the purposes of section 41(2) that the contravention to which the previous notification related did occur.

[3117]

NOTES

Commencement: 25 July 2003 (for the purpose of enabling network and service functions and spectrum functions to be carried out during the transitional period by the Director General of Telecommunications and the Secretary of State respectively) (see further s 408 and Sch 18 at **[3436]**, **[3460]**, and the Communications Act 2003 (Commencement No 1) Order 2003, SI 2003/1900 at **[3507]**); 29 December 2003 (for the purpose of enabling OFCOM to perform those functions) (see the Office of Communications Act 2002 (Commencement No 3) and Communications Act 2003 (Commencement No 2) Order 2003, SI 2003/3142 at **[3590]**).

41 Penalties for non-payment of charges

(1) This section applies where—
(a) a person ("the notified charge payer") has been given a notification under section 40;
(b) OFCOM have allowed the notified charge payer an opportunity of making representations about the notified determination; and
(c) the period allowed for the making of the representations has expired.

(2) OFCOM may impose a penalty on the notified charge payer if he—
(a) has, in one or more of the respects notified, been in contravention of a requirement to pay an administrative charge fixed under section 38; and
(b) has not, during the period allowed under section 40, paid the whole of the notified amount outstanding.

(3) Where a notification under section 40 relates to more than one contravention, a separate penalty may be imposed in respect of each contravention.

(4) Where such a notification relates to a continuing contravention, no more than one penalty may be imposed in respect of the period of contravention specified in the notification.

(5) The amount of a penalty imposed under this section is to be such amount, not exceeding twice the amount of the charge fixed for the relevant year, as OFCOM determine to be—
(a) appropriate; and
(b) proportionate to the contravention in respect of which it is imposed.

(6) In making that determination OFCOM must have regard to—
(a) any representations made to them by the notified charge payer; and
(b) any steps taken by him towards paying the amounts that he was notified under section 40 were outstanding.

(7) Where OFCOM impose a penalty on a person under this section, they shall—
(a) within one week of making their decision to impose the penalty, notify that person of that decision and of their reasons for that decision; and

(b) in that notification, fix a reasonable period after it is given as the period within which the penalty is to be paid.

(8) A penalty imposed under this section—

(a) must be paid to OFCOM; and

(b) if not paid within the period fixed by them, is to be recoverable by them accordingly.

(9) In this section "the relevant year", in relation to a contravention of a requirement to pay the whole or a part of the administrative charge fixed for any year, means that year.

(10) The provisions of this section do not affect OFCOM's power, apart from those provisions, to bring proceedings (whether before or after the imposition of a penalty under this section) for the recovery of the whole or part of an amount due to them under section 38(1).

[3118]

NOTES

Commencement: 25 July 2003 (for the purpose of enabling network and service functions and spectrum functions to be carried out during the transitional period by the Director General of Telecommunications and the Secretary of State respectively) (see further s 408 and Sch 18 at **[3436]**, **[3460]**, and the Communications Act 2003 (Commencement No 1) Order 2003, SI 2003/1900 at **[3507]**); 29 December 2003 (for the purpose of enabling OFCOM to perform those functions) (see the Office of Communications Act 2002 (Commencement No 3) and Communications Act 2003 (Commencement No 2) Order 2003, SI 2003/3142 at **[3590]**).

42 Suspending service provision for non-payment

(1) OFCOM may give a direction under this section to a person who is a communications provider or who makes associated facilities available ("the contravening provider") if they are satisfied—

(a) that he is or has been in serious and repeated contravention of requirements to pay administrative charges fixed under section 38 (whether in respect of the whole or a part of the charges);

(b) that the contraventions are not contraventions relating only to charges in respect of the application to the contravening provider of SMP apparatus conditions;

(c) that the bringing of proceedings for the recovery of the amounts outstanding has failed to secure complete compliance by the contravening provider with the requirements to pay the charges fixed in his case, or has no reasonable prospect of securing such compliance;

(d) that an attempt, by the imposition of penalties under section 41, to secure such compliance has failed; and

(e) that the giving of the direction is appropriate and proportionate to the seriousness (when repeated as they have been) of the contraventions.

(2) A direction under this section is—

(a) a direction that the entitlement of the contravening provider to provide electronic communications networks or electronic communications services, or to make associated facilities available, is suspended (either generally or in relation to particular networks, services or facilities); or

(b) a direction that that entitlement is restricted in the respects set out in the direction.

(3) A direction under this section—

(a) must specify the networks, services and facilities to which it relates; and

(b) except so far as it otherwise provides, takes effect for an indefinite period beginning with the time at which it is notified to the person to whom it is given.

(4) A direction under this section—

(a) in providing for the effect of a suspension or restriction to be postponed may provide for it to take effect only at a time determined by or in accordance with the terms of the direction; and

(b) in connection with the suspension or restriction contained in the direction or with the postponement of its effect, may impose such conditions on the contravening provider as appear to OFCOM to be appropriate for the purpose of protecting that provider's customers.

(5) Those conditions may include a condition requiring the making of payments—

(a) by way of compensation for loss or damage suffered by the contravening provider's customers as a result of the direction; or
(b) in respect of annoyance, inconvenience or anxiety to which they have been put in consequence of the direction.

(6) OFCOM are not to give a direction under this section unless they have—
(a) notified the contravening provider of the proposed direction and of the conditions (if any) which they are proposing to impose by that direction;
(b) provided him with an opportunity of making representations about the proposals and of proposing steps for remedying the situation; and
(c) considered every representation and proposal made to them during the period allowed by them for the contravening provider to take advantage of that opportunity.

(7) That period must be one ending not less than one month after the day of the giving of the notification.

(8) If OFCOM consider it appropriate to do so (whether or not in consequence of any representations or proposals made to them), they may revoke a direction under this section, or modify its conditions—
(a) with effect from such time as they may direct;
(b) subject to compliance with such requirements as they may specify; and
(c) to such extent and in relation to such networks, services or facilities, or parts of a network, service or facility, as they may determine.

(9) For the purposes of this section there are repeated contraventions by a person of requirements to pay administrative charges to the extent that—
(a) in the case of a previous notification given to that person under section 40, OFCOM have determined for the purposes of section 41(2) that such a contravention did occur; and
(b) in the period of twelve months following the day of the making of that determination, one or more further notifications have been given to that person in respect of the same or different failures to pay administrative charges.

[3119]

NOTES

Commencement: 25 July 2003 (for the purpose of enabling network and service functions and spectrum functions to be carried out during the transitional period by the Director General of Telecommunications and the Secretary of State respectively) (see further s 408 and Sch 18 at **[3436]**, **[3460]**, and the Communications Act 2003 (Commencement No 1) Order 2003, SI 2003/1900 at **[3507]**); 29 December 2003 (for the purpose of enabling OFCOM to perform those functions) (see the Office of Communications Act 2002 (Commencement No 3) and Communications Act 2003 (Commencement No 2) Order 2003, SI 2003/3142 at **[3590]**).

43 Enforcement of directions under s 42

(1) A person is guilty of an offence if he provides an electronic communications network or electronic communications service, or makes available any associated facility—
(a) while his entitlement to do so is suspended by a direction under section 42; or
(b) in contravention of a restriction contained in such a direction.

(2) A person guilty of an offence under subsection (1) shall be liable—
(a) on summary conviction, to a fine not exceeding the statutory maximum;
(b) on conviction on indictment, to a fine.

(3) The duty of a person to comply with a condition of a direction under section 42 shall be a duty owed to every person who may be affected by a contravention of the condition.

(4) Where a duty is owed by virtue of subsection (3) to a person—
(a) a breach of the duty that causes that person to sustain loss or damage, and
(b) an act which—
(i) by inducing a breach of the duty or interfering with its performance, causes that person to sustain loss or damage, and
(ii) is done wholly or partly for achieving that result,
shall be actionable at the suit or instance of that person.

(5) In proceedings brought against a person by virtue of subsection (4)(a) it shall be a defence for that person to show that he took all reasonable steps and exercised all due diligence to avoid contravening the condition in question.

(6) Sections 94 to 99 apply in relation to a contravention of conditions imposed by a direction under section 42 as they apply in relation to a contravention of conditions set under section 45.

[3120]

NOTES

Commencement: 25 July 2003 (for the purpose of enabling network and service functions and spectrum functions to be carried out during the transitional period by the Director General of Telecommunications and the Secretary of State respectively) (see further s 408 and Sch 18 at **[3436]**, **[3460]**, and the Communications Act 2003 (Commencement No 1) Order 2003, SI 2003/1900 at **[3507]**); 29 December 2003 (for the purpose of enabling OFCOM to perform those functions) (see the Office of Communications Act 2002 (Commencement No 3) and Communications Act 2003 (Commencement No 2) Order 2003, SI 2003/3142 at **[3590]**).

Register of providers required to notify or to pay charges

44 Duty of OFCOM to keep publicly accessible register

(1) It shall be the duty of OFCOM to establish and maintain a register for the purposes of section 33.

(2) OFCOM must record in the register—

(a) every designation by them for the purposes of section 33 or 38;
(b) every withdrawal by them of such a designation;
(c) every notification given to them under section 33; and
(d) every notification treated as given to them under that section by a transitional provision made under subsection (12) of that section.

(3) Information recorded in the register must be so recorded in such manner as OFCOM consider appropriate.

(4) It shall be the duty of OFCOM to publish a notification setting out—

(a) the times at which the register is for the time being available for public inspection; and
(b) the fees that must be paid for, or in connection with, an inspection of the register.

(5) The publication of a notification under subsection (4) must be in such manner as OFCOM consider appropriate for bringing it to the attention of the persons who, in their opinion, are likely to be affected by it.

(6) OFCOM must make the register available for public inspection—

(a) during such hours, and
(b) on payment of such fees,

as are set out in the notification for the time being in force under subsection (4).

[3121]

NOTES

Commencement: 25 July 2003 (for the purpose of enabling network and service functions and spectrum functions to be carried out during the transitional period by the Director General of Telecommunications and the Secretary of State respectively) (see further s 408 and Sch 18 at **[3436]**, **[3460]**, and the Communications Act 2003 (Commencement No 1) Order 2003, SI 2003/1900 at **[3507]**); 29 December 2003 (for the purpose of enabling OFCOM to perform those functions) (see the Office of Communications Act 2002 (Commencement No 3) and Communications Act 2003 (Commencement No 2) Order 2003, SI 2003/3142 at **[3590]**).

Conditions of entitlement to provide network or service etc

45 Power of OFCOM to set conditions

(1) OFCOM shall have the power to set conditions under this section binding the persons to whom they are applied in accordance with section 46.

(2) A condition set by OFCOM under this section must be either—

(a) a general condition; or
(b) a condition of one of the following descriptions—
    (i) a universal service condition;

(ii) an access-related condition;
(iii) a privileged supplier condition;
(iv) a significant market power condition (an "SMP condition").

(3) A general condition is a condition which contains only provisions authorised or required by one or more of sections 51, 52, 57, 58 or 64.

(4) A universal service condition is a condition which contains only provisions authorised or required by section 67.

(5) An access-related condition is a condition which contains only provisions authorised by section 73.

(6) A privileged supplier condition is a condition which contains only the provision required by section 77.

(7) An SMP condition is either—
(a) an SMP services condition; or
(b) an SMP apparatus condition.

(8) An SMP services condition is a condition which contains only provisions which—
(a) are authorised or required by one or more of sections 87 to 92; or
(b) in the case of a condition applying to a person falling within section 46(8)(b), correspond to provision authorised or required by one or more of sections 87 to 89.

(9) An SMP apparatus condition is a condition containing only provisions authorised by section 93.

(10) OFCOM's power to set a condition under this section making provision authorised or required by this Chapter includes each of the following—
(a) power to impose a requirement on the person or persons to whom the condition is applied to comply with such directions with respect to the matters to which the condition relates as may be given from time to time by OFCOM or by another person specified in the condition;
(b) power to impose an obligation with respect to those matters that is framed by reference to, or is conditional upon, the giving of a consent or of an approval, or on the making of a recommendation, by OFCOM or by another person so specified;
(c) power, for the purposes of provision made by virtue of either of the preceding paragraphs, to confer a discretion exercisable from time to time by OFCOM or by another person specified in the condition or determined in accordance with provision contained in it;
(d) power (subject to section 51(3)) to set different conditions for different cases (including different conditions in relation to different parts of the United Kingdom); and
(e) power to revoke or modify the conditions for the time being in force.

(11) The directions that may be authorised by virtue of subsection (10) do not include directions withdrawing, suspending or restricting a person's entitlement—
(a) to provide, in whole or in part, any electronic communications network or electronic communications service; or
(b) to make available, in whole or in part, any associated facilities.

[3122]

NOTES

Commencement: 25 July 2003 (for the purpose of enabling network and service functions and spectrum functions to be carried out during the transitional period by the Director General of Telecommunications and the Secretary of State respectively) (see further s 408 and Sch 18 at **[3436]**, **[3460]**, and the Communications Act 2003 (Commencement No 1) Order 2003, SI 2003/1900 at **[3507]**); 29 December 2003 (for the purpose of enabling OFCOM to perform those functions) (see the Office of Communications Act 2002 (Commencement No 3) and Communications Act 2003 (Commencement No 2) Order 2003, SI 2003/3142 at **[3590]**).

46 Persons to whom conditions may apply

(1) A condition set under section 45 is not to be applied to a person except in accordance with the following provisions of this section.

(2) A general condition may be applied generally—

(a) to every person providing an electronic communications network or electronic communications service; or
(b) to every person providing such a network or service of a particular description specified in the condition.

(3) A universal service condition, access-related condition, privileged supplier condition or SMP condition may be applied to a particular person specified in the condition.

(4) A privileged supplier condition may also be applied generally—
(a) to every person to whom such a condition is required to apply under section 77; or
(b) to every such person who is of a particular description specified in the condition.

(5) The particular person to whom a universal service condition is applied—
(a) except in the case of a condition relating to matters mentioned in subsection (3) of section 66, must be a communications provider designated in accordance with regulations under that section; and
(b) in that excepted case, must be a communications provider so designated or a person who is not such a provider but who is so designated for the purposes only of conditions relating to those matters.

(6) The particular person to whom an access-related condition is applied—
(a) in the case of a condition falling within section 74(1), may be any person whatever; and
(b) in any other case, must be a person who provides an electronic communications network or makes associated facilities available.

(7) The particular person to whom an SMP services condition is applied must—
(a) be a communications provider or a person who makes associated facilities available; and
(b) fall within subsection (8).

(8) A person falls within this subsection if—
(a) he is a person whom OFCOM have determined to be a person having significant market power in a specific market for electronic communications networks, electronic communications services or associated facilities (a "services market"); or
(b) it appears to OFCOM that he is a person on whom it is necessary, for the purpose of securing compliance with an international obligation of the United Kingdom, to impose a condition containing provision that corresponds to provision which, in the case of a person falling within paragraph (a), must be made (or may be made) under any of sections 87 to 89.

(9) The particular person to whom an SMP apparatus condition is applied must be—
(a) a person who supplies electronic communications apparatus; and
(b) a person whom OFCOM have determined to be a person having significant market power in a specific market for electronic communications apparatus (an "apparatus market").

[3123]

NOTES

Commencement: 25 July 2003 (for the purpose of enabling network and service functions and spectrum functions to be carried out during the transitional period by the Director General of Telecommunications and the Secretary of State respectively) (see further s 408 and Sch 18 at **[3436]**, **[3460]**, and the Communications Act 2003 (Commencement No 1) Order 2003, SI 2003/1900 at **[3507]**); 29 December 2003 (for the purpose of enabling OFCOM to perform those functions) (see the Office of Communications Act 2002 (Commencement No 3) and Communications Act 2003 (Commencement No 2) Order 2003, SI 2003/3142 at **[3590]**).

47 Test for setting or modifying conditions

(1) OFCOM must not, in exercise or performance of any power or duty under this Chapter—
(a) set a condition under section 45, or
(b) modify such a condition,

unless they are satisfied that the condition or (as the case may be) the modification satisfies the test in subsection (2).

(2) That test is that the condition or modification is—

(a) objectively justifiable in relation to the networks, services, facilities, apparatus or directories to which it relates;
(b) not such as to discriminate unduly against particular persons or against a particular description of persons;
(c) proportionate to what the condition or modification is intended to achieve; and
(d) in relation to what it is intended to achieve, transparent.

[3124]

NOTES

Commencement: 25 July 2003 (for the purpose of enabling network and service functions and spectrum functions to be carried out during the transitional period by the Director General of Telecommunications and the Secretary of State respectively) (see further s 408 and Sch 18 at **[3436]**, **[3460]**, and the Communications Act 2003 (Commencement No 1) Order 2003, SI 2003/1900 at **[3507]**); 29 December 2003 (for the purpose of enabling OFCOM to perform those functions) (see the Office of Communications Act 2002 (Commencement No 3) and Communications Act 2003 (Commencement No 2) Order 2003, SI 2003/3142 at **[3590]**).

48 Procedure for setting, modifying and revoking conditions

(1) Subject to the following provisions of this Chapter—
(a) the way in which conditions are to be set or modified under section 45 is by the publication of a notification setting out the conditions or modifications; and
(b) the way in which such a condition is to be revoked is by the publication of a notification stating that the condition is revoked.

(2) Before setting conditions under section 45, or modifying or revoking a condition so set, OFCOM must publish a notification—
(a) stating that they are proposing to set, modify or revoke the conditions that are specified in the notification;
(b) setting out the effect of those conditions, modifications or revocations;
(c) giving their reasons for making the proposal; and
(d) specifying the period within which representations may be made to OFCOM about their proposal.

(3) That period must end no less than one month after the day of the publication of the notification.

(4) In the case of a notification under subsection (2) with respect to an SMP condition, the applicable requirements of sections 79 to 86 must also be complied with.

(5) OFCOM may give effect, with or without modifications, to a proposal with respect to which they have published a notification under subsection (2) only if—
(a) they have considered every representation about the proposal that is made to them within the period specified in the notification; and
(b) they have had regard to every international obligation of the United Kingdom (if any) which has been notified to them for the purposes of this paragraph by the Secretary of State.

(6) The publication of a notification under this section must be in such manner as appears to OFCOM to be appropriate for bringing the contents of the notification—
(a) in the case of a notification setting general conditions, to the attention of such persons as OFCOM consider appropriate; and
(b) in any other case, to the attention of the persons who, in OFCOM's opinion, are likely to be affected by the contents of the notification.

(7) Nothing in the following provisions of this Chapter imposing a duty on OFCOM to set or modify a condition shall be taken as dispensing with any of the requirements of this section.

[3125]

NOTES

Commencement: 25 July 2003 (for the purpose of enabling network and service functions and spectrum functions to be carried out during the transitional period by the Director General of Telecommunications and the Secretary of State respectively) (see further s 408 and Sch 18 at **[3436]**, **[3460]**, and the Communications Act 2003 (Commencement No 1) Order 2003, SI 2003/1900 at **[3507]**); 29 December 2003 (for the purpose of enabling OFCOM to perform those functions) (see the Office of Communications Act 2002 (Commencement No 3) and Communications Act 2003 (Commencement No 2) Order 2003, SI 2003/3142 at **[3590]**).

49 Directions and approvals for the purposes of a s 45 condition

(1) This section applies where—

(a) a condition set under section 45 has effect by reference to directions, approvals or consents given by a person (whether OFCOM themselves or another); and

(b) that person is proposing to give a direction, approval or consent that affects the operation of that condition or to modify or withdraw a direction, approval or consent so as to affect the condition's operation.

(2) A person must not give, modify or withdraw the direction, approval or consent unless he is satisfied that to do so is—

(a) objectively justifiable in relation to the networks, services, facilities, apparatus or directories to which it relates;

(b) not such as to discriminate unduly against particular persons or against a particular description of persons;

(c) proportionate to what it is intended to achieve; and

(d) in relation to what it is intended to achieve, transparent.

(3) In giving, modifying or withdrawing the direction, approval or consent, a person other than OFCOM shall be under the same duty as OFCOM to act in accordance with the six Community requirements set out in section 4.

(4) Before the direction, approval or consent is given, modified or withdrawn, a notification must be published—

(a) stating that there is a proposal to give, modify or withdraw it;

(b) identifying the person whose proposal it is;

(c) setting out the direction, approval or consent to which the proposal relates;

(d) setting out the effect of the direction, approval or consent or of its proposed modification or withdrawal;

(e) giving reasons for the making of the proposal; and

(f) specifying the period within which representations may be made about the proposal to the person whose proposal it is.

(5) That period must be one ending not less than one month after the day of the publication of the notification.

(6) But, where—

(a) the person giving the notification is satisfied that there are exceptional circumstances justifying the use of a shorter period, and

(b) the notification is not one that is required to be sent to the European Commission under section 50(4) or (5),

the period specified as the period for making representations may be whatever shorter period that person considers reasonable in those circumstances.

(7) In a case in which—

(a) a person other than OFCOM is proposing to give, modify or withdraw a direction, approval or consent, and

(b) the condition for the purposes of which the direction, approval or consent has effect, or will have effect, provides for notifications of proposals for the purposes of that condition to be given by that person,

the obligation of publishing the notification for the purposes of subsection (4) of that proposal falls on that person.

(8) In any other case, the obligation of publishing a notification for the purposes of subsection (4) falls on OFCOM.

(9) The person who is authorised to give the direction, approval or consent may give effect, with or without modifications, to a proposal with respect to which a notification has been given under subsection (4) only if—

(a) he has considered every representation about the proposal that is made to him within the period specified in the notification; and

(b) he has had regard to every international obligation of the United Kingdom (if any) which has been notified to OFCOM for the purposes of this paragraph by the Secretary of State.

(10) The publication of a notification under this section must be in such manner as appears to the person publishing it to be appropriate for bringing the contents of the notification to the attention of such persons as he considers appropriate.

[3126]

NOTES

Commencement: 25 July 2003 (for the purpose of enabling network and service functions and spectrum functions to be carried out during the transitional period by the Director General of Telecommunications and the Secretary of State respectively) (see further s 408 and Sch 18 at **[3436]**, **[3460]**, and the Communications Act 2003 (Commencement No 1) Order 2003, SI 2003/1900 at **[3507]**); 29 December 2003 (for the purpose of enabling OFCOM to perform those functions) (see the Office of Communications Act 2002 (Commencement No 3) and Communications Act 2003 (Commencement No 2) Order 2003, SI 2003/3142 at **[3590]**).

50 Delivery of copies of notifications etc

(1) The relevant person must send to the Secretary of State—

(a) a copy of every notification published under section 48(1) or (2);

(b) a copy of every notification published under section 49(4);

(c) a copy of every direction, approval or consent given for the purpose of giving effect to a proposal required to be published under section 49(4); and

(d) a copy of every instrument modifying or withdrawing a direction, approval or consent for the purpose of giving effect to such a proposal.

(2) The relevant person must send to the European Commission—

(a) a copy of every notification published under section 48(1) with respect to an SMP services condition;

(b) a copy of every direction, approval or consent given for the purposes of such a condition; and

(c) a copy of every instrument modifying or withdrawing such a direction, approval or consent.

(3) OFCOM must send to the European Commission and to the regulatory authorities of every other member State a copy of every notification published by them under section 48(2) with respect to a proposal which—

(a) relates to the setting, modification or revocation of an access-related condition falling within section 73(2) or (4) or of an SMP services condition; and

(b) is a proposal which, in OFCOM's opinion, would affect trade between member States.

(4) OFCOM must send to the European Commission and to the regulatory authorities of every other member State a copy of every notification published by them under section 49(4) with respect to a proposal which—

(a) relates to the giving of a direction, approval or consent for the purposes of—

(i) an access-related condition falling within section 73(2) or (4), or

(ii) an SMP services condition,

or to the modification or withdrawal of such a direction, approval or consent; and

(b) is a proposal which, in OFCOM's opinion, would affect trade between member States.

(5) Where it is a person other than OFCOM who is the relevant person who is required to publish a notification under section 49(4) relating to the giving, modification or withdrawal of a direction, approval or consent given for purposes mentioned in subsection (4)(a) of this section—

(a) that person must refer to OFCOM the question whether, in their opinion, the proposal would affect trade between member States;

(b) OFCOM must immediately determine that question on that reference; and

(c) the relevant person must send a copy of the notification to the European Commission and to the regulatory authorities of every other member State if OFCOM determine that the proposal is one which, in their opinion, would affect trade between member States.

(6) The relevant person must, in every other case in which it appears to him appropriate to do so, send a copy of—

(a) every notification published under section 48(1) or (2) or 49(4),

(b) every direction, approval or consent given for the purposes of a condition set under section 45, and

(c) every instrument modifying or withdrawing such a direction, approval or consent,

to the European Commission and to such of the regulatory authorities of the other member States as the relevant person thinks fit.

(7) Subsection (6) does not apply where—

(a) the notification or the notified proposal relates to an SMP apparatus condition, or to a direction, approval or consent for the purposes of such a condition; or

(b) the direction, approval or consent given, modified or withdrawn is for the purposes of such a condition.

(8) In this section "the relevant person", in relation to a notification, direction, approval or consent—

(a) except in a case falling within paragraph (b), means the person by whom it is published or (as the case may be) the person by whom it has been or is to be given, modified or withdrawn; and

(b) in the case of a direction, approval or consent given, modified or withdrawn by a person other than OFCOM for the purpose of giving effect to a proposal published by OFCOM under section 49(4), means OFCOM.

[3127]

NOTES

Commencement: 25 July 2003 (for the purpose of enabling network and service functions and spectrum functions to be carried out during the transitional period by the Director General of Telecommunications and the Secretary of State respectively) (see further s 408 and Sch 18 at **[3436]**, **[3460]**, and the Communications Act 2003 (Commencement No 1) Order 2003, SI 2003/1900 at **[3507]**); 29 December 2003 (for the purpose of enabling OFCOM to perform those functions) (see the Office of Communications Act 2002 (Commencement No 3) and Communications Act 2003 (Commencement No 2) Order 2003, SI 2003/3142 at **[3590]**).

General conditions: subject-matter

51 Matters to which general conditions may relate

(1) Subject to sections 52 to 64, the only conditions that may be set under section 45 as general conditions are conditions falling within one or more of the following paragraphs—

(a) conditions making such provision as OFCOM consider appropriate for protecting the interests of the end-users of public electronic communications services;

(b) conditions making such provision as OFCOM consider appropriate for securing service interoperability and for securing, or otherwise relating to, network access;

(c) conditions making such provision as OFCOM consider appropriate for securing the proper and effective functioning of public electronic communications networks;

(d) conditions for giving effect to determinations or regulations made under section 71;

(e) conditions requiring or regulating the provision, availability and use, in the event of a disaster, of electronic communications networks, electronic communications services and associated facilities;

(f) conditions making such provision as OFCOM consider appropriate for securing the protection of public health by the prevention or avoidance of the exposure of individuals to electro-magnetic fields created in connection with the operation of electronic communications networks;

(g) conditions requiring compliance with relevant international standards.

(2) The power under subsection (1)(a) to set conditions for protecting the interests of the end-users of public electronic communications services includes power to set conditions for that purpose which—

(a) relate to the supply, provision or making available of goods, services or facilities in association with the provision of public electronic communications services; and

(b) give effect to Community obligations to provide protection for such end-users in relation to the supply, provision or making available of those goods, services or facilities.

(3) The power to set general conditions in relation to a description of electronic communications network or electronic communications service does not include power—

(a) to set conditions that are made applicable according to the identity of the provider of a network or service; or

(b) to set conditions that differ according to the identity of the provider of the networks or services to which they relate.

(4) The power to set general conditions falling within subsection (1)(b) does not include power to set conditions containing provision which under—

(a) section 73, or

(b) any of sections 87 to 92,

must be or may be included, in a case in which it appears to OFCOM to be appropriate to do so, in an access-related condition or SMP condition.

(5) The conditions falling within subsection (1)(c) include conditions making such provision as OFCOM consider appropriate for the purpose, in accordance with Community obligations, of preventing or restricting electro-magnetic interference—

(a) with the provision of an electronic communications network or electronic communications service; or

(b) with, or with the receipt of, anything conveyed or provided by means of such a network or service.

(6) In this section "electro-magnetic interference" means interference by means of the emission or reflection of electro-magnetic energy in the course of, or in connection with, the provision any electronic communications network or electronic communications service.

(7) In this section "disaster" includes any major incident having a significant effect on the general public; and for this purpose a major incident includes any incident of contamination involving radioactive substances or other toxic materials.

[3128]

NOTES

Commencement: 25 July 2003 (for the purpose of enabling network and service functions and spectrum functions to be carried out during the transitional period by the Director General of Telecommunications and the Secretary of State respectively) (see further s 408 and Sch 18 at **[3436]**, **[3460]**, and the Communications Act 2003 (Commencement No 1) Order 2003, SI 2003/1900 at **[3507]**); 29 December 2003 (for the purpose of enabling OFCOM to perform those functions) (see the Office of Communications Act 2002 (Commencement No 3) and Communications Act 2003 (Commencement No 2) Order 2003, SI 2003/3142 at **[3590]**).

General conditions: customer interests

52 Conditions relating to customer interests

(1) It shall be the duty of OFCOM to set such general conditions (if any) as they consider appropriate for securing that—

(a) public communications providers, or

(b) such descriptions of them as OFCOM consider appropriate,

establish and maintain procedures, standards and policies with respect to the matters mentioned in subsection (2).

(2) Those matters are—

(a) the handling of complaints made to public communications providers by any of their domestic and small business customers;

(b) the resolution of disputes between such providers and any of their domestic and small business customers;

(c) the provision of remedies and redress in respect of matters that form the subject-matter of such complaints or disputes;

(d) the information about service standards and about the rights of domestic and small business customers that is to be made available to those customers by public communications providers;

(e) any other matter appearing to OFCOM to be necessary for securing effective protection for the domestic and small business customers of such providers.

(3) It shall be the duty of OFCOM, in setting conditions in accordance with subsection (1), to secure so far as they consider appropriate—

(a) that the procedures established and maintained for the handling of complaints and the resolution of disputes are easy to use, transparent and effective;

(b) that domestic and small business customers have the right to use those procedures free of charge; and

(c) that where public communications providers are in contravention of conditions set in accordance with the preceding provisions of this section, the providers follow such procedures as may be required by the general conditions.

(4) Subject to section 55, OFCOM's duties under subsections (1) and (3) so far as relating to procedures for the handling of complaints are to be performed, to such extent as they consider appropriate, by the setting of general conditions requiring public communications providers to establish and maintain procedures that conform with a code of practice which is—

(a) applicable to the providers to whom the conditions apply; and
(b) for the time being approved by OFCOM for the purposes of this subsection.

(5) Subject to section 55, OFCOM's duties under subsections (1) and (3) so far as relating to procedures for resolving disputes are to be performed, to such extent as they consider appropriate, by the setting of general conditions requiring public communications providers—

(a) to establish and maintain procedures for resolving disputes; and
(b) to secure that those procedures are, and continue to be, approved by OFCOM.

(6) In this section "domestic and small business customer", in relation to a public communications provider, means a customer of that provider who is neither—

(a) himself a communications provider; nor
(b) a person who is such a customer in respect of an undertaking carried on by him for which more than ten individuals work (whether as employees or volunteers or otherwise).

[3129]

NOTES

Commencement: 25 July 2003 (for the purpose of enabling network and service functions and spectrum functions to be carried out during the transitional period by the Director General of Telecommunications and the Secretary of State respectively) (see further s 408 and Sch 18 at **[3436]**, **[3460]**, and the Communications Act 2003 (Commencement No 1) Order 2003, SI 2003/1900 at **[3507]**); 29 December 2003 (for the purpose of enabling OFCOM to perform those functions) (see the Office of Communications Act 2002 (Commencement No 3) and Communications Act 2003 (Commencement No 2) Order 2003, SI 2003/3142 at **[3590]**).

53 Approval of codes of practice for the purposes of s 52

(1) Where a code of practice is submitted to OFCOM for approval, they shall approve that code if and only if, in their opinion, it makes all such provision as they consider necessary in relation to the matters dealt with in the code for the protection of the domestic and small business customers of the public communications providers to whom the code applies.

(2) It shall be the duty of OFCOM to keep under review the codes of practice for the time being approved by them.

(3) OFCOM may at any time, by a notification given or published in such manner as they consider appropriate—

(a) approve modifications that have been made to an approved code;
(b) withdraw their approval from a code; or
(c) give notice that the withdrawal of their approval will take effect from such time as may be specified in the notification unless such modifications of the code as are specified in the notification are made before that time.

(4) In considering—

(a) whether to approve a code of practice, or
(b) whether or in what manner to exercise their powers under subsections (2) and (3) of this section,

OFCOM must have regard to the matters mentioned in subsection (5).

(5) Those matters are—

(a) the need to secure that customers are able readily to comprehend the procedures that are provided for by an approved code of practice;
(b) the need to secure that there is consistency between the different codes for the time being approved by OFCOM; and
(c) the need to secure that the number of different codes so approved is kept to a minimum.

(6) In this section—

"approval" means approval for the purposes of section 52(4) and "approve" and "approved" are to be construed accordingly; and

PART V BROADCASTING AND TRANSMISSION

"domestic and small business customer" has the same meaning as in section 52.

[3130]

NOTES

Commencement: 25 July 2003 (for the purpose of enabling network and service functions and spectrum functions to be carried out during the transitional period by the Director General of Telecommunications and the Secretary of State respectively) (see further s 408 and Sch 18 at **[3436]**, **[3460]**, and the Communications Act 2003 (Commencement No 1) Order 2003, SI 2003/1900 at **[3507]**); 29 December 2003 (for the purpose of enabling OFCOM to perform those functions) (see the Office of Communications Act 2002 (Commencement No 3) and Communications Act 2003 (Commencement No 2) Order 2003, SI 2003/3142 at **[3590]**).

54 Approval of dispute procedures for the purposes of s 52

(1) Before giving their approval to any dispute procedures, OFCOM must consult the Secretary of State.

(2) OFCOM are not to approve dispute procedures unless they are satisfied that the arrangements under which the procedures have effect—

(a) are administered by person who is for practical purposes independent (so far as decisions in relation to disputes are concerned) of both OFCOM and the communications providers to whom the arrangements apply;
(b) give effect to procedures that are easy to use, transparent and effective;
(c) give, in the case of every communications provider to whom the arrangements apply, a right to each of his domestic and small business customers to use the procedures free of charge;
(d) ensure that all information necessary for giving effect to the procedures is obtained;
(e) ensure that disputes are effectively investigated;
(f) include provision conferring power to make awards of appropriate compensation; and
(g) are such as to enable awards of compensation to be properly enforced.

(3) OFCOM may approve dispute procedures subject to such conditions (including conditions as to the provision of information to OFCOM) as they may think fit.

(4) It shall be the duty of OFCOM to keep under review the dispute procedures for the time being approved by them.

(5) OFCOM may at any time, by a notification given or published in such manner as they consider appropriate—

(a) modify the conditions of their approval of any dispute procedures or withdraw such an approval; or
(b) give notice that the modification of those conditions, or the withdrawal of such an approval, will take effect from such time as may be specified in the notification unless the procedures (or the arrangements under which they have effect) are modified before that time in the manner required by the notification.

(6) In considering—

(a) whether to approve dispute procedures, or
(b) whether or in what manner to exercise their powers under subsections (3) to (5),

OFCOM must have regard to the matters mentioned in subsection (7).

(7) Those matters are—

(a) the need to secure that customers are able readily to comprehend dispute procedures;
(b) the need to secure that there is consistency between the different procedures for the time being approved by OFCOM; and
(c) the need to secure that the number of different sets of procedures so approved is kept to a minimum.

(8) In this section—

"approval" means approval for the purposes of subsection (5) of section 52 and "approve" and "approved" are to be construed accordingly;

"dispute procedures" means any such procedures as may fall to be approved for the purposes of that subsection; and "domestic and small business customer" has the same meaning as in section 52.

[3131]

NOTES

Commencement: 25 July 2003 (for the purpose of enabling network and service functions and spectrum functions to be carried out during the transitional period by the Director General of Telecommunications and the Secretary of State respectively) (see further s 408 and Sch 18 at **[3436]**, **[3460]**, and the Communications Act 2003 (Commencement No 1) Order 2003, SI 2003/1900 at **[3507]**); 29 December 2003 (for the purpose of enabling OFCOM to perform those functions) (see the Office of Communications Act 2002 (Commencement No 3) and Communications Act 2003 (Commencement No 2) Order 2003, SI 2003/3142 at **[3590]**).

55 Orders by OFCOM in the absence of conditions under s 52

(1) OFCOM may make an order under this section if, at any time, they consider in relation to any one or more public communications providers—

(a) that it is not practicable, or at least not appropriate, for OFCOM's duties under subsections (1) and (3) of section 52 to be performed in a particular respect by the setting of general conditions; and

(b) that it is necessary to make the order for the purpose—

(i) of securing the necessary protection for the customers of that provider or of those providers; or

(ii) of securing compliance with a Community obligation.

(2) An order under this section may make such of the following provisions as OFCOM think fit—

(a) provision imposing requirements with respect to the complaints and disputes mentioned in section 52(2);

(b) provision for the enforcement of those requirements;

(c) provision making other arrangements for the purposes of those requirements.

(3) The power to make provision by an order under this section includes, in particular—

(a) power to establish a body corporate with the capacity to make its own rules and to establish its own procedures;

(b) power to determine the jurisdiction of a body established by such an order or, for the purposes of the order, of any other person;

(c) power to confer jurisdiction with respect to any matter on OFCOM themselves;

(d) power to provide for a person on whom jurisdiction is conferred by the arrangements to make awards of compensation, to direct the reimbursement of costs or expenses, or to do both;

(e) power to provide for such a person to enforce, or to participate in the enforcement of, any awards or directions made under such an order; and

(f) power to make such other provision as OFCOM think fit for the enforcement of such awards and directions.

(4) An order under this section may require such public communications providers as may be determined by or under the order to make payments to OFCOM in respect of expenditure incurred by OFCOM in connection with—

(a) the establishment and maintenance, in accordance with such an order, of a body corporate or of a procedure; or

(b) the making of any other arrangements for the purposes of the requirements of such an order.

(5) The consent of the Secretary of State is required for the making by OFCOM of an order under this section.

(6) Section 403 applies to the power of OFCOM to make an order under this section.

(7) A statutory instrument containing an order made by OFCOM under this section shall be subject to annulment in pursuance of a resolution of either House of Parliament.

[3132]

NOTES

Commencement: 25 July 2003 (for the purpose of enabling network and service functions and spectrum functions to be carried out during the transitional period by the Director General of Telecommunications and the Secretary of State respectively) (see further s 408 and Sch 18 at **[3436]**, **[3460]**, and the Communications Act 2003 (Commencement No 1) Order 2003, SI 2003/1900 at **[3507]**);

PART V BROADCASTING AND TRANSMISSION

29 December 2003 (for the purpose of enabling OFCOM to perform those functions) (see the Office of Communications Act 2002 (Commencement No 3) and Communications Act 2003 (Commencement No 2) Order 2003, SI 2003/3142 at **[3590]**).

General conditions: telephone numbers

56 The National Telephone Numbering Plan

(1) It shall be the duty of OFCOM to publish a document (to be known as "the National Telephone Numbering Plan") setting out—

(a) the numbers that they have determined to be available for allocation by them as telephone numbers;

(b) such restrictions as they consider appropriate on the adoption of numbers available for allocation in accordance with the plan; and

(c) such restrictions as they consider appropriate on the other uses to which numbers available for allocation in accordance with the plan may be put.

(2) It shall be OFCOM's duty—

(a) from time to time to review the National Telephone Numbering Plan; and

(b) to make any revision of that plan that they think fit in consequence of such a review;

but this duty must be performed in compliance with the requirements, so far as applicable, of section 60.

(3) OFCOM must also keep such day to day records as they consider appropriate of the telephone numbers allocated by them in accordance with the National Telephone Numbering Plan.

(4) The publication of the National Telephone Numbering Plan, or of a revision of it, must be in such manner as appears to OFCOM to be appropriate for bringing the contents of the Plan, or of the revised Plan, to the attention of such persons as OFCOM consider appropriate.

(5) In this Chapter references to a telephone number are (subject to subsection (7)) references to any number that is used (whether or not in connection with telephony) for any one or more of the following purposes—

(a) identifying the destination for, or recipient of, an electronic communication;

(b) identifying the origin, or sender, of an electronic communication;

(c) identifying the route for an electronic communication;

(d) identifying the source from which an electronic communication or electronic communications service may be obtained or accessed;

(e) selecting the service that is to be obtained or accessed, or required elements or characteristics of that service; or

(f) identifying the communications provider by means of whose network or service an electronic communication is to be transmitted, or treated as transmitted.

(6) In this Chapter references to the adoption of a telephone number by a communications provider are references to his doing any of the following in relation to a number allocated (whether or not to that provider) by OFCOM—

(a) allocating or transferring that number to a particular customer or piece of apparatus;

(b) using that number for identifying a service or route used by that provider or by any of his customers;

(c) using that number for identifying a communication as one to be transmitted by that provider;

(d) designating that number for use in selecting a service or the required elements or characteristics of a service;

(e) authorising the use of that number by others for any of the purposes mentioned in subsection (5).

(7) The Secretary of State may by order exclude such numbers as may be described in the order from the numbers that are to be treated as telephone numbers for the purposes of this Chapter.

(8) No order is to be made containing provision authorised by subsection (7) unless a draft of the order has been laid before Parliament and approved by a resolution of each House.

(9) References in this section to the allocation of a number are references to its allocation for the purposes of general conditions under section 58 or in accordance with conditions under section 59.

(10) In this section—

"electronic communication" means a communication for transmission by means of an electronic communications network; and

"number" includes data of any description.

[3133]

NOTES

Commencement: 25 July 2003 (except in respect of any number which is used as an internet domain name, an internet address or an address or identifier incorporating either an internet domain name or an internet address, including an email address and only for the purpose of enabling network and service functions and spectrum functions to be carried out during the transitional period by the Director General of Telecommunications and the Secretary of State respectively) (see further s 408 and Sch 18 at **[3436]**, **[3460]**, and the Communications Act 2003 (Commencement No 1) Order 2003, SI 2003/1900 at **[3507]**); 29 December 2003 (otherwise).

Orders: the Telephone Number Exclusion (Domain Names and Internet Addresses) Order 2003, SI 2003/3281 at **[3603]**.

57 Conditions to secure access to telephone numbers

(1) General conditions may impose such requirements as OFCOM consider appropriate for securing that every end-user of a public electronic communications service is able, by means of that service—

(a) to make calls or otherwise transmit electronic communications to every normal telephone number; and

(b) to receive every call or other electronic communication that is made or transmitted to him using such a service from apparatus identified by a normal telephone number.

(2) A normal telephone number is one which—

(a) has been made available, in accordance with the National Telephone Numbering Plan, as a number to be used for the purpose of identifying the destination for, or the recipient of, electronic communications; and

(b) is for the time being—

(i) a number adopted by a communications provider to be used for such a purpose; or

(ii) a number in use for such a purpose by a person other than a communications provider to whom it has been allocated in accordance with conditions under section 59.

(3) In this section "electronic communication" has the same meaning as in section 56.

[3134]

NOTES

Commencement: 25 July 2003 (except in respect of any number which is used as an internet domain name, an internet address or an address or identifier incorporating either an internet domain name or an internet address, including an email address and only for the purpose of enabling network and service functions and spectrum functions to be carried out during the transitional period by the Director General of Telecommunications and the Secretary of State respectively) (see further s 408 and Sch 18 at **[3436]**, **[3460]**, and the Communications Act 2003 (Commencement No 1) Order 2003, SI 2003/1900 at **[3507]**); 29 December 2003 (otherwise).

58 Conditions about allocation and adoption of numbers

(1) General conditions may include conditions which—

(a) prohibit the adoption of telephone numbers by a communications provider except in cases where the numbers have been allocated by OFCOM to a person;

(b) regulate the use by a communications provider, for the purpose of providing an electronic communications network or electronic communications service, of telephone numbers not allocated to that provider;

(c) impose restrictions on the adoption of telephone numbers by a communications provider, and on other practices by communications providers in relation to telephone numbers allocated to them;

(d) impose requirements on a communications provider in connection with the adoption by him of telephone numbers;
(e) require an allocation of particular telephone numbers to be transferred from one communications provider to another in the circumstances provided for in the conditions;
(f) impose such requirements and restrictions on a communications provider from whom an allocation is required to be transferred as may be provided for, in relation to the transfer, in the conditions;
(g) require payments of such amounts as may be determined by OFCOM to be made to them by a person in respect of the allocation to him of telephone numbers;
(h) require payments of such amounts as may be determined by OFCOM to be made to them by a person in respect of transfers of allocations from one person to another; and
(i) require communications providers to secure compliance with such rules relating to the use of telephone numbers by their customers as OFCOM may set out in general conditions or determine in accordance with provision made by the general conditions.

(2) General conditions may also—
(a) provide for the procedure to be followed on the making of applications to OFCOM for the allocation of telephone numbers;
(b) provide for the information that must accompany such applications and for the handling of such applications;
(c) provide a procedure for telephone numbers to be reserved pending the making and disposal of an application for their allocation;
(d) provide for the procedure to be followed on the making of applications for telephone numbers to be reserved, and for the handling of such applications;
(e) regulate the procedures to be followed, the system to be applied and the charges to be imposed for the purposes of, or in connection with, the adoption by a communications provider of telephone numbers allocated to that provider;
(f) regulate the procedures to be followed, the system to be applied and the charges to be imposed for the purposes of, or in connection with, the transfer of an allocation from one person to another.

(3) The conditions that may be set under subsection (1)(d) include conditions imposing requirements with respect to the provision of information for purposes connected with—
(a) the compilation of directories; and
(b) the provision of directory enquiry facilities.

(4) The procedure to be followed on the making of an application for the allocation of numbers that are available for allocation in accordance with the National Telephone Numbering Plan must require OFCOM's determination of the application to be made—
(a) in the case of an application made in response to an invitation in accordance with subsection (5), before the end of six weeks after the day on which the application is received; and
(b) in any other case, before the end of three weeks after that day.

(5) Where OFCOM are proposing to allocate any telephone numbers, they may—
(a) invite persons to indicate the payments each would be willing to make to OFCOM if allocated the numbers; and
(b) make the allocation according to the amounts indicated.

(6) General conditions providing for payments to be made to OFCOM in respect of anything mentioned in subsection (1)(g) or (h)—
(a) must set out the principles according to which the amounts of the payments are to be determined;
(b) may provide for the payments to consist of a lump sum in respect of a particular allocation or transfer or of sums payable periodically while an allocation remains in force, or of both;
(c) may provide for the amounts to be determined by reference to—
(i) any indication according to which the allocation has been made as mentioned in subsection (5); or
(ii) any other factors (including the costs incurred by OFCOM in connection with the carrying out of their functions by virtue of section 56 and this section) as OFCOM think fit.

(7) General conditions may—

(a) make modifications from time to time of, or of the method of determining, the amounts of periodic payments falling to be made by virtue of conditions containing provision authorised by this section; and
(b) make different provision in relation to different descriptions of communications provider and different descriptions of telephone number.

(8) Nothing in subsection (7) authorises the modification, after it has been fixed, of the amount of a periodic payment fixed in accordance with arrangements made in relation to numbers allocated as mentioned in subsection (5)(b).

(9) Payments that are required to be made to OFCOM in respect of anything mentioned in subsection (1)(g) or (h)—
(a) must be paid to them as soon as they become due in accordance with the conditions imposing the obligation to pay; and
(b) if not so paid, are to be recoverable by them accordingly.

[3135]

NOTES

Commencement: 25 July 2003 (except in respect of any number which is used as an internet domain name, an internet address or an address or identifier incorporating either an internet domain name or an internet address, including an email address and only for the purpose of enabling network and service functions and spectrum functions to be carried out during the transitional period by the Director General of Telecommunications and the Secretary of State respectively) (see further s 408 and Sch 18 at **[3436]**, **[3460]**, and the Communications Act 2003 (Commencement No 1) Order 2003, SI 2003/1900 at **[3507]**); 29 December 2003 (otherwise).

59 Telephone numbering conditions binding non-providers

(1) OFCOM may set conditions under this section that apply to persons other than communications providers and relate to—
(a) the allocation of telephone numbers to such persons;
(b) the transfer of allocations to and from such persons; and
(c) the use of telephone numbers by such persons.

(2) The conditions that may be set under this section include conditions imposing obligations corresponding to any of the obligations that may be imposed on communications providers by general conditions making provision for, or in connection with—
(a) the allocation of telephone numbers;
(b) the transfer of allocations; or
(c) the use of telephone numbers.

(3) Subsection (10) of section 45 applies to OFCOM's power to set a condition under this section as it applies to their power to set a condition under that section.

(4) Sections 47 to 49 apply in relation to—
(a) the setting of conditions under this section and the modification and revocation of such conditions; and
(b) the giving, modification or withdrawal of any direction, approval or consent for the purposes of a condition under this section,

as they apply in the case of general conditions and in the case of directions, approvals and consents given for the purposes of general conditions.

(5) It shall be the duty of a person who—
(a) is not a communications provider, but
(b) applies for the allocation of a telephone number, or is allocated such a number,

to comply with any conditions set under this section.

(6) That duty shall be enforceable in civil proceedings by OFCOM—
(a) for an injunction;
(b) for specific performance of a statutory duty under section 45 of the Court of Session Act 1988 (c 36); or
(c) for any other appropriate remedy or relief.

(7) Subsection (6) does not apply in the case of a person against whom the obligations contained in the condition in question are enforceable (by virtue of his having become a communications provider) as obligations imposed by general conditions.

[3136]

NOTES

Commencement: 25 July 2003 (except in respect of any number which is used as an internet domain name, an internet address or an address or identifier incorporating either an internet domain name or an internet address, including an email address and only for the purpose of enabling network and service functions and spectrum functions to be carried out during the transitional period by the Director General of Telecommunications and the Secretary of State respectively) (see further s 408 and Sch 18 at **[3436]**, **[3460]**, and the Communications Act 2003 (Commencement No 1) Order 2003, SI 2003/1900 at **[3507]**); 29 December 2003 (otherwise).

60 Modification of documents referred to in numbering conditions

(1) This section applies where numbering conditions for the time being have effect by reference to provisions, as they have effect from time to time, of—

(a) the National Telephone Numbering Plan; or

(b) another document published by OFCOM.

(2) OFCOM must not revise or otherwise modify the relevant provisions unless they are satisfied that the revision or modification is—

(a) objectively justifiable in relation to the matters to which it relates;

(b) not such as to discriminate unduly against particular persons or against a particular description of persons;

(c) proportionate to what the modification is intended to achieve; and

(d) in relation to what it is intended to achieve, transparent.

(3) Before revising or otherwise modifying the relevant provisions, OFCOM must publish a notification—

(a) stating that they are proposing to do so;

(b) specifying the Plan or other document that they are proposing to revise or modify;

(c) setting out the effect of their proposed revisions or modifications;

(d) giving their reasons for making the proposal; and

(e) specifying the period within which representations may be made to OFCOM about their proposal.

(4) That period must be one ending not less than one month after the day of the publication of the notification.

(5) OFCOM may give effect, with or without modifications, to a proposal with respect to which they have published a notification under subsection (3) only if—

(a) they have considered every representation about the proposal that is made to them within the period specified in the notification; and

(b) they have had regard to every international obligation of the United Kingdom (if any) which has been notified to them for the purposes of this paragraph by the Secretary of State.

(6) The publication of a notification under this section must be in such manner as appears to OFCOM to be appropriate for bringing the contents of the notification to the attention of such persons as OFCOM consider appropriate.

(7) In this section—

"numbering conditions" means—

(a) general conditions the making of which is authorised by section 57 or 58;

(b) conditions set under section 59;

"the relevant provisions", in relation to the Plan or document, means the provisions of the Plan or document by reference to which (as they have effect from time to time) the numbering conditions in question have effect.

[3137]

NOTES

Commencement: 25 July 2003 (except in respect of any number which is used as an internet domain name, an internet address or an address or identifier incorporating either an internet domain name or an internet address, including an email address and only for the purpose of enabling network and service functions and spectrum functions to be carried out during the transitional period by the Director General of Telecommunications and the Secretary of State respectively) (see further s 408 and Sch 18 at **[3436]**, **[3460]**, and the Communications Act 2003 (Commencement No 1) Order 2003, SI 2003/1900 at **[3507]**); 29 December 2003 (otherwise).

61 Withdrawal of telephone number allocations

(1) Where OFCOM have allocated telephone numbers for the purposes of any numbering conditions, they may withdraw that allocation if, and only if, the case is one in which the withdrawal of an allocation is authorised by this section.

(2) The withdrawal of an allocation is authorised (subject to section 62) if—

(a) consent to the withdrawal is given by the person to whom the numbers are for the time being allocated;
(b) the withdrawal is made for the purposes of a transfer of the allocation required by numbering conditions;
(c) the withdrawal is made for the purposes of a numbering reorganisation applicable to a particular series of telephone numbers;
(d) the withdrawal is made in circumstances specified in the numbering conditions and for the purpose of securing that what appears to OFCOM to be the best and most efficient use is made of the numbers and other data that are appropriate for use as telephone numbers;
(e) the allocated numbers are numbers that have not been adopted during such period after their allocation as may be specified in the numbering conditions; or
(f) the allocated numbers are comprised in a series of numbers which have not to a significant extent been adopted or used during such period as may be so specified.

(3) The withdrawal of an allocation is also authorised where—

(a) there have been serious and repeated contraventions, by the person to whom the allocation is for the time being allocated, of the numbering conditions; and
(b) it appears to OFCOM that the taking of other steps in respect of the contraventions is likely to prove ineffective for securing future compliance.

(4) The withdrawal of an allocation is also authorised where—

(a) the person to whom the allocation is for the time being allocated is not a communications provider; and
(b) it appears to OFCOM that contraventions by that person of numbering conditions makes the withdrawal of the allocation appropriate.

(5) OFCOM's power to set conditions specifying circumstances for the purposes of subsection (2)(d), and their power to withdraw an allocation in the specified circumstances, are each exercisable only in a manner that does not discriminate unduly—

(a) against particular communications providers;
(b) against particular users of the allocated numbers; or
(c) against a particular description of such providers or users;

and the purposes for which those powers may be exercised do not include the carrying out of a numbering reorganisation of the sort mentioned in subsection (2)(c).

(6) Where OFCOM are proposing to withdraw an allocation in exercise of the power conferred by virtue of subsection (2)(e) or (f), they must—

(a) give a notification of their proposal;
(b) consider any representations made to them about the proposal within the period of one month following the day on which the notification is given; and
(c) ensure that the withdrawal (if OFCOM decide to proceed with it after considering those representations) does not take effect until the end of the three months beginning with the end of the period mentioned in paragraph (b).

(7) A notification for the purposes of subsection (6) must be given in such manner as OFCOM consider appropriate for bringing it to the attention of—

(a) the person to whom the numbers to which the proposed withdrawal relates are for the time being allocated;
(b) every person appearing to OFCOM to be a person to whom communications are or may be transmitted using one of those numbers for identifying the destination or route;
(c) every person who uses one or more of those numbers for obtaining access to services or for communication; and
(d) every other person who, in OFCOM's opinion, is likely to be affected by the proposal.

(8) For the purposes of this section there are repeated contraventions by a person of numbering conditions to the extent that—

(a) in the case of a previous notification given to that person under section 94,

OFCOM have determined for the purposes of section 95(2) or 96(2) that a contravention of a numbering condition did occur; and

(b) in the period of twelve months following the day of the making of that determination, one or more further notifications have been given to that person in respect of contraventions of numbering conditions;

and for the purposes of this subsection it shall be immaterial whether the notifications related to the same contravention or to different contraventions of the same or different conditions.

(9) In this section "numbering conditions" means—

(a) general conditions the making of which is authorised by section 58; or

(b) conditions set under section 59.

[3138]

NOTES

Commencement: 25 July 2003 (except in respect of any number which is used as an internet domain name, an internet address or an address or identifier incorporating either an internet domain name or an internet address, including an email address and only for the purpose of enabling network and service functions and spectrum functions to be carried out during the transitional period by the Director General of Telecommunications and the Secretary of State respectively) (see further s 408 and Sch 18 at **[3436]**, **[3460]**, and the Communications Act 2003 (Commencement No 1) Order 2003, SI 2003/1900 at **[3507]**); 29 December 2003 (otherwise).

62 Numbering reorganisations

(1) This section applies to the withdrawal of an allocation for the purposes of a numbering reorganisation that is applicable to a particular series of telephone numbers.

(2) The allocation is to be withdrawn only if the reorganisation, so far as it relates to numbers of any description, is not such as to discriminate unduly—

(a) against particular communications providers;

(b) against particular users of the allocated numbers; or

(c) against a particular description of such providers or users.

(3) The allocation must not be withdrawn if the reorganisation fails to provide for withdrawn allocations to be replaced by allocations of telephone numbers so nearly resembling the numbers to which the withdrawal relates as the purpose of the reorganisation allows.

(4) Where a replacement allocation is made for the purposes of the re-organisation—

(a) no payment is to be made to OFCOM in respect of the making of the replacement allocation; but

(b) subsection (5) is to apply.

(5) Where this subsection applies—

(a) a provision for the making of periodic payments in respect of the withdrawn allocation is to be treated, to the extent that OFCOM determine that it should, as a provision requiring the making of periodic payments in respect of the replacement allocation; and

(b) OFCOM may, if they think fit, make such repayments or adjustments of a provision for payment as appear to them to be appropriate in consequence of differences between—

(i) the numbers to which the withdrawn allocation relates; and

(ii) the numbers to which the replacement allocation relates.

[3139]

NOTES

Commencement: 25 July 2003 (except in respect of any number which is used as an internet domain name, an internet address or an address or identifier incorporating either an internet domain name or an internet address, including an email address and only for the purpose of enabling network and service functions and spectrum functions to be carried out during the transitional period by the Director General of Telecommunications and the Secretary of State respectively) (see further s 408 and Sch 18 at **[3436]**, **[3460]**, and the Communications Act 2003 (Commencement No 1) Order 2003, SI 2003/1900 at **[3507]**); 29 December 2003 (otherwise).

63 General duty as to telephone numbering functions

(1) It shall be the duty of OFCOM, in the carrying out of their functions under sections 56 to 62—

(a) to secure that what appears to them to be the best use is made of the numbers that are appropriate for use as telephone numbers; and
(b) to encourage efficiency and innovation for that purpose.

(2) It shall also be the duty of OFCOM, in carrying out those functions, to secure that there is no undue discrimination by communications providers against other communications providers in relation to the adoption of telephone numbers for purposes connected with the use by one communications provider, or his customers, of an electronic communications network or electronic communications service provided by another.

(3) In this section "number" has the same meaning as in section 56.

[3140]

NOTES

Commencement: 25 July 2003 (except in respect of any number which is used as an internet domain name, an internet address or an address or identifier incorporating either an internet domain name or an internet address, including an email address and only for the purpose of enabling network and service functions and spectrum functions to be carried out during the transitional period by the Director General of Telecommunications and the Secretary of State respectively) (see further s 408 and Sch 18 at **[3436]**, **[3460]**, and the Communications Act 2003 (Commencement No 1) Order 2003, SI 2003/1900 at **[3507]**); 29 December 2003 (otherwise).

General conditions: must-carry obligations

64 Must-carry obligations

(1) General conditions may include conditions making any provision that OFCOM consider appropriate for securing that particular services are broadcast or otherwise transmitted by means of the electronic communications networks described in the conditions.

(2) A general condition containing provision authorised by this section is not (subject to subsection (4)) to require a service to be broadcast or otherwise transmitted by means of an electronic communications network unless—
(a) the service is included in the list of must-carry services; and
(b) the effect of the requirement is confined to networks by means of which public electronic communications services are provided that are used by a significant number of end-users as their principal means of receiving television programmes.

(3) That list is as follows—
(a) any service of television programmes provided by the BBC so far as it is provided in digital form and is a service in relation to which OFCOM have functions;
(b) the Channel 3 services so far as provided in digital form;
(c) Channel 4 so far as provided in digital form;
(d) Channel 5 so far as provided in digital form;
(e) S4C Digital;
(f) the digital public teletext service.

(4) General conditions making provision authorised by this section in relation to a listed service must, to such extent as OFCOM consider appropriate (and subject to subsection (5))—
(a) apply the requirement to broadcast or otherwise transmit that service to every service which is an ancillary service by reference to the listed service; and
(b) provide for the listed service to be treated for the purposes of the conditions as constituting such other services comprised in or provided with that service as may be determined by OFCOM.

(5) General conditions making provision authorised by this section must also comply with all such restrictions (if any) as may be imposed by order made by the Secretary of State as to the maximum and minimum amounts, or proportions, of available capacity that are to be required by such conditions to be used in the case of a network for the broadcasting or other transmission of particular services, or descriptions of service.

(6) In making an order under subsection (5) the Secretary of State must have regard to—
(a) the objective of securing that services included in the list of must-carry services, and the other services to which conditions set in accordance with this section are likely to be applied by virtue of subsection (4), are available for reception by as many members of the public in the United Kingdom as practicable; and

(b) the need to secure that the amount of capacity available in the case of every network for making other services available is reasonable and, accordingly, that the burden of complying with conditions set in accordance with this section is proportionate to the public benefit to be secured by that objective.

(7) It shall be the duty of the Secretary of State from time to time to review—

(a) the list of must-carry services; and

(b) any requirements for the time being in force under this section with respect to the terms on which services must be broadcast or otherwise transmitted.

(8) Where the Secretary of State carries out such a review, he must consult the following about the matters under review—

(a) OFCOM; and

(b) such persons who, in his opinion, are likely to be affected by a modification of the list of must-carry services, or who represent any of those persons, as he thinks fit.

(9) If, on such a review, he considers it appropriate to do so, the Secretary of State may by order modify the list of must-carry services.

(10) In determining whether it is appropriate for the purposes of subsection (9) to add a service to the list of must-carry services or to remove it, the Secretary of State must have regard, in particular, to—

(a) the public benefit to be secured by the addition of the service to the list, or by its retention in the list;

(b) the extent to which the service (if it were not included in the list) would nevertheless be made available to an acceptable technical standard by means of the networks to which conditions set in accordance with this section apply;

(c) the capacity left available, after the requirements of those conditions have been complied with, for the broadcasting or other transmission of material by means of each of those networks; and

(d) the need to secure that the burden of complying with conditions so set is proportionate to the objective of securing that the services in the list of must-carry services, and the other services to which conditions set in accordance with this section are likely to applied by virtue of subsection (4), are available for reception by as many members of the public in the United Kingdom as practicable.

(11) The Secretary of State may also, if (whether on such a review or in any other circumstances) he considers it appropriate to do so, by order make provision imposing requirements as to what, as between—

(a) the person providing a must-carry service, and

(b) the person providing a network by means of which it is to be provided,

are to be the terms on which the service is to be broadcast or otherwise transmitted, in pursuance of general conditions set in accordance with this section, by means of that network.

(12) An order under subsection (11) may provide for the terms to be determined by OFCOM in accordance with the provisions of the order.

(13) Before making an order under subsection (5), and before making an order under subsection (11) in a case in which there has been no review under subsection (7), the Secretary of State must consult—

(a) OFCOM; and

(b) such persons who, in his opinion, are likely to be affected by the order, or who represent any of those persons, as he thinks fit.

(14) Section 362 applies for construing this section as it applies for the purposes of Part 3.

[3141]

NOTES

Commencement: 25 July 2003 (for the purpose of enabling network and service functions and spectrum functions to be carried out during the transitional period by the Director General of Telecommunications and the Secretary of State respectively) (see further s 408 and Sch 18 at **[3436]**, **[3460]**, and the Communications Act 2003 (Commencement No 1) Order 2003, SI 2003/1900 at **[3507]**); 29 December 2003 (for the purpose of enabling OFCOM to perform those functions) (see the Office of Communications Act 2002 (Commencement No 3) and Communications Act 2003 (Commencement No 2) Order 2003, SI 2003/3142 at **[3590]**).

Universal service conditions

65 Obligations to be secured by universal service conditions

(1) The Secretary of State must by order ("the universal service order") set out the extent to which the things falling within subsection (2) must, for the purpose of securing compliance with Community obligations for the time being in force, be provided, made available or supplied throughout the United Kingdom.

(2) Those things are—

(a) electronic communications networks and electronic communications services;
(b) facilities capable of being made available as part of or in connection with an electronic communications service;
(c) particular methods of billing for electronic communications services or of accepting payment for them;
(d) directories capable of being used in connection with the use of an electronic communications network or electronic communications service; and
(e) directory enquiry facilities capable of being used for purposes connected with the use of such a network or service.

(3) The universal service order may contain guidance about matters relating to the pricing of things that the order says must be provided, made available or supplied.

(4) Before making or varying the universal service order, the Secretary of State must consult OFCOM and such other persons as he considers appropriate.

[3142]

NOTES

Commencement: 25 July 2003 (for the purpose of enabling network and service functions and spectrum functions to be carried out during the transitional period by the Director General of Telecommunications and the Secretary of State respectively) (see further s 408 and Sch 18 at **[3436]**, **[3460]**, and the Communications Act 2003 (Commencement No 1) Order 2003, SI 2003/1900 at **[3507]**); 29 December 2003 (for the purpose of enabling OFCOM to perform those functions) (see the Office of Communications Act 2002 (Commencement No 3) and Communications Act 2003 (Commencement No 2) Order 2003, SI 2003/3142 at **[3590]**).

66 Designation of universal service providers

(1) OFCOM may by regulations make provision for the designation of the persons to whom universal service conditions are to be applicable.

(2) Subject to subsection (3), those regulations are not to authorise the designation of a person other than a communications provider.

(3) The regulations may provide for a person other than a communications provider to be designated for the purposes only of conditions relating to—

(a) the supply of directories capable of being used in connection with the use of an electronic communications network or electronic communications service; and
(b) the making available of directory enquiry facilities capable of being used for purposes connected with the use of such a network or service.

(4) OFCOM may from time to time—

(a) review the designations for the time being in force in accordance with regulations under this section; and
(b) on such a review, consider what (if any) universal service conditions should continue to apply to each of the designated persons.

(5) The procedure to be followed in the case of every such review must be the procedure provided for in regulations made by OFCOM.

(6) Regulations made by OFCOM under this section must provide for a person's designation as a person to whom universal service conditions are to be applicable to cease to have effect where, in any such case as may be described in the regulations, the universal service conditions applied to him are all revoked.

(7) Regulations made by OFCOM under this section providing a procedure for the designation of persons, or for the conduct of a review under subsection (4), must not provide for any procedure other than one appearing to OFCOM—

(a) to be efficient, objective and transparent; and

(b) not to involve, or to tend to give rise to, any undue discrimination against any person or description of persons.

(8) Where—

(a) OFCOM designate a person in accordance with regulations under this section, or

(b) a designation of a person in accordance with any such regulations ceases to have effect,

they must give a notification of that designation, or of that fact, to the European Commission.

(9) A notification under this section must identify the person who has been designated, or the person whose designation has ceased to have effect.

(10) Section 403 applies to the power of OFCOM to make regulations under this section. **[3143]**

NOTES

Commencement: 25 July 2003 (for the purpose of enabling network and service functions and spectrum functions to be carried out during the transitional period by the Director General of Telecommunications and the Secretary of State respectively) (see further s 408 and Sch 18 at **[3436]**, **[3460]**, and the Communications Act 2003 (Commencement No 1) Order 2003, SI 2003/1900 at **[3507]**); 29 December 2003 (for the purpose of enabling OFCOM to perform those functions) (see the Office of Communications Act 2002 (Commencement No 3) and Communications Act 2003 (Commencement No 2) Order 2003, SI 2003/3142 at **[3590]**).

67 Subject-matter of universal service conditions

(1) OFCOM may set any such universal service conditions as they consider appropriate for securing compliance with the obligations set out in the universal service order.

(2) Universal service conditions applied to a person must include a condition requiring him to publish information about his performance in complying with the universal service conditions that apply to him.

(3) A condition set in accordance with subsection (2) must contain provision which—

(a) requires information published in accordance with it to be updated from time to time and published again;

(b) requires information so published to satisfy the requirements that OFCOM consider appropriate for securing that it is adequate; and

(c) requires information so published to be framed by reference to the quality of service parameters, definitions and measurement methods for the time being set out in Annex III to the Universal Service Directive.

(4) A condition set in accordance with that subsection may impose requirements as to—

(a) the times at which information published in accordance with it is to be published; and

(b) the manner in which that information is to be published.

(5) Universal service conditions may impose an obligation on a person to whom they apply to do one or both of the following, if required to do so by OFCOM—

(a) to make facilities available for enabling information published in pursuance of a condition applied to that person under subsection (2) to be independently audited;

(b) to meet the costs of any independent auditing of that information that is required by OFCOM.

(6) The reference in subsection (5) to the independent auditing of information is a reference to its being audited by a qualified auditor—

(a) for accuracy; and

(b) for its usefulness in the making of comparisons with information published by other designated universal service providers.

(7) Universal service conditions may impose performance targets on designated universal service providers with respect to any of the matters in relation to which obligations may be imposed by such conditions.

(8) In setting a universal service condition, OFCOM must have regard to any guidance about matters relating to pricing that is contained in the universal service order.

(9) In this section "qualified auditor" means a person eligible, in accordance with Part 2 of the Companies Act 1989 (c 40), for appointment as a company auditor.

[3144]

NOTES

Commencement: 25 July 2003 (for the purpose of enabling network and service functions and spectrum functions to be carried out during the transitional period by the Director General of Telecommunications and the Secretary of State respectively) (see further s 408 and Sch 18 at **[3436]**, **[3460]**, and the Communications Act 2003 (Commencement No 1) Order 2003, SI 2003/1900 at **[3507]**); 29 December 2003 (for the purpose of enabling OFCOM to perform those functions) (see the Office of Communications Act 2002 (Commencement No 3) and Communications Act 2003 (Commencement No 2) Order 2003, SI 2003/3142 at **[3590]**).

68 Tariffs etc for universal services

(1) It shall be the duty of OFCOM—

(a) to keep under review universal service tariffs; and

(b) to monitor changes to those tariffs.

(2) Universal service conditions may require one or more of the following—

(a) the use of a common tariff, or of common tariffs, in relation to anything mentioned in section 65(2);

(b) the use, in such cases as may be specified or described in the conditions, of such special tariffs in relation to anything so mentioned as may be so specified or described;

(c) the fixing of tariffs used in accordance with the conditions by the use of such methods, and by reference to such methods of computing costs, as may be so specified or described.

(3) Universal service conditions must secure that the terms on which a person is provided with anything required by the universal service order do not require him—

(a) to pay for an unnecessary additional service; or

(b) to pay, in respect of anything required by the order, any amount that is attributable to the provision to him of such a service.

(4) The references in subsection (3), in relation to a person, to an unnecessary additional service are references to anything the provision of which—

(a) he has to accept by reason of his being provided, at his request, with something required by the order ("the requested service"); and

(b) is not necessary for the purpose of providing him with the requested service.

(5) It shall be the duty of OFCOM, in setting a universal service condition about universal service tariffs, to have regard to anything ascertained by them in the performance of their duty under subsection (1).

(6) References in this section to a universal service tariff are references to any of the tariffs used by designated universal service providers in relation to the things for the time being required by the universal service order.

(7) References in this section to providing a person with anything include references to making it available or supplying it to him.

(8) In this section "tariff" includes a pricing structure.

[3145]

NOTES

Commencement: 25 July 2003 (for the purpose of enabling network and service functions and spectrum functions to be carried out during the transitional period by the Director General of Telecommunications and the Secretary of State respectively) (see further s 408 and Sch 18 at **[3436]**, **[3460]**, and the Communications Act 2003 (Commencement No 1) Order 2003, SI 2003/1900 at **[3507]**); 29 December 2003 (for the purpose of enabling OFCOM to perform those functions) (see the Office of Communications Act 2002 (Commencement No 3) and Communications Act 2003 (Commencement No 2) Order 2003, SI 2003/3142 at **[3590]**).

69 Directories and directory enquiry facilities

(1) This section applies where universal service conditions require a designated universal service provider—

(a) to supply a directory capable of being used in connection with the use of an electronic communications network or electronic communications service; or

(b) to make available directory enquiry facilities capable of being used for purposes connected with use of such a network or service.

(2) The universal service conditions applied to the provider must include the conditions that OFCOM consider appropriate for securing that the provider does not unduly discriminate against a source of relevant information—

(a) in the compiling of the directory or the answering of directory enquiries; or

(b) in the treatment in the directory, or for the purposes of the facilities, of any relevant information from that source.

(3) In this section—

(a) references to relevant information are references to information provided for inclusion in the directory or for use in the answering of directory enquiries; and

(b) references to a source of relevant information are references to a communications provider or designated universal service provider who provides relevant information.

[3146]

NOTES

Commencement: 25 July 2003 (for the purpose of enabling network and service functions and spectrum functions to be carried out during the transitional period by the Director General of Telecommunications and the Secretary of State respectively) (see further s 408 and Sch 18 at **[3436]**, **[3460]**, and the Communications Act 2003 (Commencement No 1) Order 2003, SI 2003/1900 at **[3507]**); 29 December 2003 (for the purpose of enabling OFCOM to perform those functions) (see the Office of Communications Act 2002 (Commencement No 3) and Communications Act 2003 (Commencement No 2) Order 2003, SI 2003/3142 at **[3590]**).

70 Review of compliance costs

(1) OFCOM may from time to time review the extent (if any) of the financial burden for a particular designated universal service provider of complying in relation to any matter with any one or more of the universal service conditions applied to him.

(2) Where—

(a) regulations under section 66 require the financial burden of so complying to be taken into account in determining whom to designate, and

(b) the regulations provide for a particular method of calculating that burden to be used for the purposes of that determination,

that must be the method of calculation applied on a review under this section.

(3) Where subsection (2) does not apply, the financial burden of so complying is to be taken to be the amount calculated by OFCOM to be the net cost of compliance after allowing for market benefits accruing to the designated universal service provider from—

(a) his designation; and

(b) the application to him of universal service conditions.

(4) After carrying out a review under this section OFCOM must either—

(a) cause the calculations made by them on the review to be audited by a person who appears to them to be independent of designated universal service providers; or

(b) themselves carry out an audit of those calculations.

(5) OFCOM must ensure, in the case of every audit carried out under subsection (4), that a report on the audit—

(a) is prepared; and

(b) if not prepared by OFCOM, is provided to them.

(6) It shall be the duty of OFCOM, in the case of every review under this section, to publish—

(a) their conclusions on the review; and

(b) a summary of the report of the audit which was carried out as respects the calculations made for the purposes of that review.

(7) The publication of anything under subsection (6) must be a publication in such manner as OFCOM consider appropriate for bringing it to the attention of the persons who, in their opinion, are likely to be affected by it.

[3147]

NOTES

Commencement: 25 July 2003 (for the purpose of enabling network and service functions and spectrum functions to be carried out during the transitional period by the Director General of Telecommunications and the Secretary of State respectively) (see further s 408 and Sch 18 at **[3436]**,

[3460], and the Communications Act 2003 (Commencement No 1) Order 2003, SI 2003/1900 at **[3507]**); 29 December 2003 (for the purpose of enabling OFCOM to perform those functions) (see the Office of Communications Act 2002 (Commencement No 3) and Communications Act 2003 (Commencement No 2) Order 2003, SI 2003/3142 at **[3590]**).

71 Sharing of burden of universal service obligations

(1) This section applies where OFCOM—

(a) have concluded, on a review under section 70, that complying in relation to any matter with universal service conditions imposes a financial burden on a particular designated universal service provider; and

(b) have published that conclusion in accordance with that section.

(2) OFCOM must determine, in the case of the designated universal service provider, whether they consider it would be unfair for that provider to bear, or to continue to bear, the whole or any part of so much of the burden.

(3) If—

(a) OFCOM determine that it would be unfair for the designated universal service provider to bear, or to continue to bear, the whole or a part of the burden, and

(b) an application for a determination under this subsection is made to OFCOM by that provider,

OFCOM may determine that contributions are to be made by communications providers to whom general conditions are applicable for meeting that burden.

(4) The making of any of the following must be in accordance with regulations made by OFCOM—

(a) a determination by OFCOM of the extent of the financial burden that exists for the designated universal service provider of complying in relation to any matter with universal service conditions;

(b) an application for the purposes of subsection (3)(b);

(c) a determination by OFCOM of whether it is or would be unfair for the designated universal service provider to bear, or to continue to bear, the burden of complying in relation to any matter with universal service conditions;

(d) a determination of the extent (if any) to which that is or would be unfair.

(5) The assessment, collection and distribution of contributions under subsection (3) is not to be carried out except in accordance with a mechanism provided for in a scheme contained in regulations made by OFCOM.

(6) It shall be the duty of OFCOM to exercise their power to make regulations under this section in the manner which they consider will secure that the assessment, collection and distribution of contributions under subsection (3) is carried out—

(a) in an objective and transparent manner;

(b) in a manner that does not involve, or tend to give rise to, any undue discrimination against particular communications providers or particular designated universal service providers, or against a particular description of them; and

(c) in a manner that avoids, or (if that is impracticable) at least minimises, any distortion of competition or of customer demand.

(7) Regulations made by OFCOM under this section may provide for a scheme containing the provision mentioned in subsection (5), and for any fund set up for the purposes of such a scheme, to be administered either—

(a) by OFCOM; or

(b) by such other person as may be specified in the regulations.

(8) A person other than OFCOM is not to be specified in regulations under this section as the administrator of such a scheme or fund unless he is a person who OFCOM are satisfied is independent of both—

(a) the persons who are designated universal service providers; and

(b) communications providers to whom general conditions are applicable.

(9) Section 403 applies to the powers of OFCOM to make regulations under this section. **[3148]**

NOTES

Commencement: 25 July 2003 (for the purpose of enabling network and service functions and spectrum functions to be carried out during the transitional period by the Director General of

Telecommunications and the Secretary of State respectively) (see further s 408 and Sch 18 at **[3436]**, **[3460]**, and the Communications Act 2003 (Commencement No 1) Order 2003, SI 2003/1900 at **[3507]**); 29 December 2003 (for the purpose of enabling OFCOM to perform those functions) (see the Office of Communications Act 2002 (Commencement No 3) and Communications Act 2003 (Commencement No 2) Order 2003, SI 2003/3142 at **[3590]**).

72 Report on sharing mechanism

(1) This section applies where regulations under section 71 provide for a scheme for the assessment, collection and distribution of contributions under subsection (3) of that section.

(2) OFCOM must prepare and publish a report setting out, in relation to the period to which it applies—

- (a) every determination by OFCOM that has had effect in relation to a time in that period as a determination of the costs of providing anything contained in the universal service order;
- (b) the market benefits for each designated universal service provider that have accrued to him during that period from his designation and from the application to him of universal service conditions; and
- (c) the contribution made under section 71(3) by every person who has made a contribution during that period.

(3) The first report under this section must be prepared in relation to the period of twelve months beginning with the coming into force of the first regulations to be made under section 71.

(4) Every subsequent report must be prepared in relation to the period of twelve months beginning with the end of the period to which the previous report applied.

(5) Every report under this section—

- (a) must be prepared as soon as practicable after the end of the period to which it is to apply; and
- (b) must be published as soon as practicable after its preparation is complete.

(6) OFCOM are not required under this section—

- (a) to publish any matter that is confidential in accordance with subsection (7) or (8); or
- (b) to publish anything that it would not be reasonably practicable to publish without disclosing such a matter.

(7) A matter is confidential under this subsection if—

- (a) it relates specifically to the affairs of a particular body; and
- (b) publication of that matter would or might, in OFCOM's opinion, seriously and prejudicially affect the interests of that body.

(8) A matter is confidential under this subsection if—

- (a) it relates to the private affairs of an individual; and
- (b) publication of that matter would or might, in OFCOM's opinion, seriously and prejudicially affect the interests of that individual.

(9) The publication of a report under this section must be a publication in such manner as OFCOM consider appropriate for bringing it to the attention of the persons who, in their opinion, are affected by the matters to which it relates.

[3149]

NOTES

Commencement: 25 July 2003 (for the purpose of enabling network and service functions and spectrum functions to be carried out during the transitional period by the Director General of Telecommunications and the Secretary of State respectively) (see further s 408 and Sch 18 at **[3436]**, **[3460]**, and the Communications Act 2003 (Commencement No 1) Order 2003, SI 2003/1900 at **[3507]**); 29 December 2003 (for the purpose of enabling OFCOM to perform those functions) (see the Office of Communications Act 2002 (Commencement No 3) and Communications Act 2003 (Commencement No 2) Order 2003, SI 2003/3142 at **[3590]**).

Access-related conditions

73 Permitted subject-matter of access-related conditions

(1) The only conditions that may be set under section 45 as access-related conditions are those authorised by this section.

(2) Access-related conditions may include conditions relating to the provision of such network access and service interoperability as appears to OFCOM appropriate for the purpose of securing—

(a) efficiency on the part of communications providers and persons making associated facilities available;
(b) sustainable competition between them; and
(c) the greatest possible benefit for the end-users of public electronic communications services.

(3) Access-related conditions may include conditions appearing to OFCOM to be appropriate for securing that persons to whom the electronic communications code applies participate, in cases where there are no viable alternative arrangements that may be made, in arrangements for—

(a) sharing the use of electronic communications apparatus; and
(b) apportioning and making contributions towards costs incurred in relation to shared electronic communications apparatus.

(4) Access-related conditions may include one which—

(a) is of a technical or operational nature;
(b) appears to OFCOM to be appropriate for securing the proper operation of an electronic communications network in compliance with any SMP services condition falling within section 87(3); and
(c) is applied to—
   (i) a person who is required by such an SMP services condition to confer any entitlements to network access; or
   (ii) a person on whom such an entitlement is or may be conferred in pursuance of a requirement imposed by such an SMP services condition.

(5) Access-related conditions may include conditions containing any provision required by section 75(2).

[3150]

NOTES

Commencement: 25 July 2003 (for the purpose of enabling network and service functions and spectrum functions to be carried out during the transitional period by the Director General of Telecommunications and the Secretary of State respectively) (see further s 408 and Sch 18 at **[3436]**, **[3460]**, and the Communications Act 2003 (Commencement No 1) Order 2003, SI 2003/1900 at **[3507]**); 29 December 2003 (for the purpose of enabling OFCOM to perform those functions) (see the Office of Communications Act 2002 (Commencement No 3) and Communications Act 2003 (Commencement No 2) Order 2003, SI 2003/3142 at **[3590]**).

74 Specific types of access-related conditions

(1) The conditions that may be set by virtue of section 73(2) include conditions which, for the purpose of securing end-to-end connectivity for the end-users of public electronic communications services provided by means of a series of electronic communications networks—

(a) impose obligations on a person controlling network access to any of those networks; and
(b) require the interconnection of the networks.

(2) The conditions that may be set by virtue of section 73(2) also include such conditions imposing obligations on a person providing facilities for the use of application programme interfaces or electronic programme guides as OFCOM consider to be necessary for securing—

(a) that persons are able to have access to such programme services provided in digital form as OFCOM may determine; and
(b) that the facility for using those interfaces or guides is provided on terms which—
   (i) are fair and reasonable; and
   (ii) do not involve, or tend to give rise to, any undue discrimination against any person or description of persons.

(3) In this section—

"application programme interface" means a facility for allowing software to make use, in connection with any of the matters mentioned in subsection (4), of facilities contained in other software;

"electronic programme guide" means a facility by means of which a person has access to any service which consists of—

(a) the listing or promotion, or both the listing and the promotion, of some or all of the programmes included in any one or more programme services; and

(b) a facility for obtaining access, in whole or in part, to the programme service or services listed or promoted in the guide;

"end-to-end connectivity" means the facility—

(a) for different end-users of the same public electronic communications service to be able to communicate with each other; and

(b) for the end-users of different such services to be able, each using the service of which he is the end-user, to communicate with each other.

(4) The matters mentioned in subsection (3), in the definition of "application programme interface", are—

(a) allowing a person to have access to programme services;

(b) allowing a person, other than a communications provider or a person who makes associated facilities available, to make use of an electronic communications network by means of which a programme service is broadcast or otherwise transmitted;

(c) allowing a person to become the end-user of a description of public electronic communications service.

(5) This section is not to be construed as restricting the provision that may be made under section 73(2).

[3151]

NOTES

Commencement: 25 July 2003 (for the purpose of enabling network and service functions and spectrum functions to be carried out during the transitional period by the Director General of Telecommunications and the Secretary of State respectively) (see further s 408 and Sch 18 at **[3436]**, **[3460]**, and the Communications Act 2003 (Commencement No 1) Order 2003, SI 2003/1900 at **[3507]**); 29 December 2003 (for the purpose of enabling OFCOM to perform those functions) (see the Office of Communications Act 2002 (Commencement No 3) and Communications Act 2003 (Commencement No 2) Order 2003, SI 2003/3142 at **[3590]**).

75 Conditional access systems and access to digital services

(1) It shall be the duty of OFCOM, when setting a condition falling within section 73(4), to ensure that it contains all such provision as they consider appropriate for the purpose of taking account of the relevant international standards.

(2) It shall be the duty of OFCOM to ensure—

(a) that access-related conditions are applied to every person who provides a conditional access system in relation to a protected programme service; and

(b) that those conditions make all such provision as is required by the provision contained from time to time in Part I of Annex I to the Access Directive (conditions relating to access to digital programme services).

(3) In this section—

"conditional access system" means any system, facility, arrangements or technical measure under or by means of which access to programme services requires—

(a) a subscription to the service or to a service that includes that service; or

(b) an authorisation to view it, or to listen to it, on a particular occasion;

"protected programme service" means a programme service the programmes included in which cannot be viewed or listened to in an intelligible form except by the use of a conditional access system.

[3152]

NOTES

Commencement: 25 July 2003 (for the purpose of enabling network and service functions and spectrum functions to be carried out during the transitional period by the Director General of Telecommunications and the Secretary of State respectively) (see further s 408 and Sch 18 at **[3436]**,

[3460], and the Communications Act 2003 (Commencement No 1) Order 2003, SI 2003/1900 at **[3507]**); 29 December 2003 (for the purpose of enabling OFCOM to perform those functions) (see the Office of Communications Act 2002 (Commencement No 3) and Communications Act 2003 (Commencement No 2) Order 2003, SI 2003/3142 at **[3590]**).

76 Modification and revocation of conditions imposed under s 75

(1) This section applies in the case of conditions falling within section 75(2) which have been set by OFCOM in relation to a particular person ("the system provider").

(2) OFCOM must not give effect to a proposal to modify or revoke any of the conditions unless—

- (a) they have carried out an analysis for the purpose of determining in accordance with this Chapter whether that person is or remains a person on whom SMP services conditions are capable of being imposed;
- (b) they have determined in consequence of that analysis that he is not; and
- (c) they are satisfied that the modification or revocation will not have an adverse effect on any or all of the matters mentioned in subsection (3).

(3) Those matters are—

- (a) the accessibility to any persons of services that are for the time being included in the list of must-carry services in section 64;
- (b) the prospects for effective competition in the market for programme services provided by being broadcast or otherwise transmitted in digital form; and
- (c) the prospects for effective competition in the markets for conditional access systems and other associated facilities.

(4) In this section "conditional access system" has the same meaning as in section 75.

[3153]

NOTES

Commencement: 25 July 2003 (for the purpose of enabling network and service functions and spectrum functions to be carried out during the transitional period by the Director General of Telecommunications and the Secretary of State respectively) (see further s 408 and Sch 18 at **[3436]**, **[3460]**, and the Communications Act 2003 (Commencement No 1) Order 2003, SI 2003/1900 at **[3507]**); 29 December 2003 (for the purpose of enabling OFCOM to perform those functions) (see the Office of Communications Act 2002 (Commencement No 3) and Communications Act 2003 (Commencement No 2) Order 2003, SI 2003/3142 at **[3590]**).

Privileged supplier conditions

77 Imposition of privileged supplier conditions

(1) It shall be the duty of OFCOM to secure that privileged supplier conditions containing all such provision falling within subsection (3) as they consider appropriate are applied to every public communications provider to whom this section applies.

(2) This section applies to every public communications provider who—

- (a) enjoys special or exclusive rights in relation to the provision of any non-communications services; and
- (b) is not such a provider in respect only of associated facilities.

(3) The provision that may be contained in a condition set under section 45 as a privileged supplier condition is any provision that OFCOM consider appropriate for any one or more of the following purposes—

- (a) requiring the provider to whom it applies to keep separate accounts in relation to his public electronic communications network or public electronic communications service and other matters;
- (b) requiring that provider to submit the accounts of the different parts of his undertaking, and any financial report relating to a part of that undertaking, to a qualified auditor for auditing;
- (c) requiring the accounts of the different parts of his undertaking to be published;
- (d) securing, by means other than the keeping of separate accounts, the structural separation of the different parts of his undertaking.

(4) OFCOM are not required under this section to apply a condition to a person where they are satisfied that that person has an annual turnover in relation to all his communications activities that is less than £50 million.

(5) Where in a case falling within subsection (4) OFCOM are not required to apply a privileged supplier condition to a person, they may apply such a condition to him if they think fit.

(6) The reference in subsection (4) to a person's communications activities is a reference to any activities of his that consist in, or are connected with, either or both of the following—

(a) the provision of any one or more electronic communications networks;
(b) the provision of any one or more electronic communications services.

(7) The making, for the purposes of subsection (4), of—

(a) a determination of the period in respect of which a person's annual turnover in relation to any activities is computed, and
(b) a determination of the amount in Euros of that turnover for any period,

must be in accordance with such rules as OFCOM consider to be reasonable.

(8) OFCOM must publish any rules made by them for the purposes of subsection (7) in such manner as they consider appropriate for bringing them to the attention of the persons who, in their opinion, are likely to be affected by them.

(9) In this section—

"non-communications services", in relation to a person, means services other than those consisting in, or connected with, the provision by him of—

(a) an electronic communications network; or
(b) an electronic communications service;

"qualified auditor" means a person eligible, in accordance with Part 2 of the Companies Act 1989 (c 40), for appointment as a company auditor;

"special or exclusive rights" has the same meaning as in Article 86 of the Treaty establishing the European Community.

[3154]

NOTES

Commencement: 25 July 2003 (for the purpose of enabling network and service functions and spectrum functions to be carried out during the transitional period by the Director General of Telecommunications and the Secretary of State respectively) (see further s 408 and Sch 18 at **[3436]**, **[3460]**, and the Communications Act 2003 (Commencement No 1) Order 2003, SI 2003/1900 at **[3507]**); 29 December 2003 (for the purpose of enabling OFCOM to perform those functions) (see the Office of Communications Act 2002 (Commencement No 3) and Communications Act 2003 (Commencement No 2) Order 2003, SI 2003/3142 at **[3590]**).

SMP conditions: procedure

78 Circumstances required for the setting of SMP conditions

(1) For the purposes of this Chapter a person shall be taken to have significant market power in relation to a market if he enjoys a position which amounts to or is equivalent to dominance of the market.

(2) References in this section to dominance of a market must be construed in accordance with any applicable provisions of Article 14 of the Framework Directive.

(3) A person is to be taken to enjoy a position of dominance of a market if he is one of a number of persons who enjoy such a position in combination with each other.

(4) A person or combination of persons may also be taken to enjoy a position of dominance of a market by reason wholly or partly of his or their position in a closely related market if the links between the two markets allow the market power held in the closely related market to be used in a way that influences the other market so as to strengthen the position in the other market of that person or combination of persons.

(5) The matters that must be taken into account in determining whether a combination of persons enjoys a position of dominance of a services market include, in particular, the matters set out in Annex II to the Framework Directive.

[3155]

NOTES

Commencement: 25 July 2003 (for the purpose of enabling network and service functions and spectrum functions to be carried out during the transitional period by the Director General of Telecommunications and the Secretary of State respectively) (see further s 408 and Sch 18 at **[3436]**, **[3460]**, and the Communications Act 2003 (Commencement No 1) Order 2003, SI 2003/1900 at **[3507]**); 29 December 2003 (for the purpose of enabling OFCOM to perform those functions) (see the Office of Communications Act 2002 (Commencement No 3) and Communications Act 2003 (Commencement No 2) Order 2003, SI 2003/3142 at **[3590]**).

79 Market power determinations

(1) Before making a market power determination, OFCOM must—

(a) identify (by reference, in particular, to area and locality) the markets which in their opinion are the ones which in the circumstances of the United Kingdom are the markets in relation to which it is appropriate to consider whether to make the determination; and

(b) carry out an analysis of the identified markets.

(2) In identifying or analysing any services market for the purposes of this Chapter, OFCOM must take due account of all applicable guidelines and recommendations which—

(a) have been issued or made by the European Commission in pursuance of the provisions of a Community instrument; and

(b) relate to market identification and analysis.

(3) In considering whether to make or revise a market power determination in relation to a services market, OFCOM must take due account of all applicable guidelines and recommendations which—

(a) have been issued or made by the European Commission in pursuance of the provisions of a Community instrument; and

(b) relate to market analysis or the determination of what constitutes significant market power.

(4) The way in which—

(a) a market is to be identified for the purposes of this section, or

(b) a market power determination is to be made,

is by the publication of a notification containing the identification or determination.

(5) Notifications for the purposes of subsection (4)—

(a) may be given separately;

(b) may be contained in a single notification relating to both the identification of a market and the making of a market determination in relation to that market; or

(c) may be contained in a single notification under section 48(1) with respect to the setting or modification of an SMP condition and either—

(i) the making of the market power determination by reference to which OFCOM set or modify that condition; or

(ii) the making of that market power determination and the identification of the market in relation to which they make that determination.

(6) The publication of a notification under this section must be in such manner as appears to OFCOM to be appropriate for bringing the contents of the notification to the attention of the persons who, in OFCOM's opinion, are likely to be affected by the matters notified.

(7) References in this section to guidelines and recommendations issued by the European Commission and to a Community instrument include references, respectively, to guidelines and recommendations issued after the commencement of this section and to a Community instrument made after the commencement of this section.

[3156]

NOTES

Commencement: 25 July 2003 (for the purpose of enabling network and service functions and spectrum functions to be carried out during the transitional period by the Director General of Telecommunications and the Secretary of State respectively) (see further s 408 and Sch 18 at **[3436]**, **[3460]**, and the Communications Act 2003 (Commencement No 1) Order 2003, SI 2003/1900 at **[3507]**); 29 December 2003 (for the purpose of enabling OFCOM to perform those functions) (see the Office of Communications Act 2002 (Commencement No 3) and Communications Act 2003 (Commencement No 2) Order 2003, SI 2003/3142 at **[3590]**).

80 Proposals for identifying markets and for market power determinations

(1) Before OFCOM—

(a) identify a market for the purposes of making a market power determination, or

(b) make a market power determination,

they must publish a notification of what they are proposing to do.

(2) Notifications for the purposes of subsection (1)—

(a) may be given separately;

(b) may be contained in a single notification relating to both the identification of a market and the making of a market determination in relation to that market; or

(c) may be contained in a single notification under section 48(2) with respect to the setting or modification of an SMP condition and either—

(i) the making of the market power determination by reference to which OFCOM are proposing to set or modify that condition; or

(ii) the making of that market power determination and the identification of the market in relation to which they are proposing to make that determination.

(3) A notification under this section relating to a proposal to identify a market or to make a market power determination must—

(a) state that OFCOM are proposing to identify that market or to make that market power determination;

(b) set out the effect of the proposal;

(c) give their reasons for making the proposal; and

(d) specify the period within which representations may be made to OFCOM about their proposal.

(4) That period must be a period of not less than one month after the day of the publication of the notification.

(5) The publication of a notification under this section must be in such manner as appears to OFCOM to be appropriate for bringing the contents of the notification to the attention of the persons who, in OFCOM's opinion, are likely to be affected by the matters notified.

(6) OFCOM may give effect, with or without modifications, to a proposal with respect to which they have given a notification under this section only if—

(a) they have considered every representation about the proposal that is made to them within the period specified in the notification; and

(b) they have had regard to every international obligation of the United Kingdom (if any) which has been notified to them for the purposes of this paragraph by the Secretary of State.

(7) The power of OFCOM to give effect to such a proposal is subject to sections 82 and 83.

[3157]

NOTES

Commencement: 25 July 2003 (for the purpose of enabling network and service functions and spectrum functions to be carried out during the transitional period by the Director General of Telecommunications and the Secretary of State respectively) (see further s 408 and Sch 18 at **[3436]**, **[3460]**, and the Communications Act 2003 (Commencement No 1) Order 2003, SI 2003/1900 at **[3507]**); 29 December 2003 (for the purpose of enabling OFCOM to perform those functions) (see the Office of Communications Act 2002 (Commencement No 3) and Communications Act 2003 (Commencement No 2) Order 2003, SI 2003/3142 at **[3590]**).

81 Delivery of copies of notifications under ss 79 and 80

(1) OFCOM must send a copy of every notification published under section 79(4) or 80 to the Secretary of State.

(2) OFCOM must send to the European Commission a copy of every notification published under section 79(4) with respect to a market power determination in relation to a services market.

(3) OFCOM must send a copy of every notification published under section 80 which—

(a) relates to a proposal to identify a services market or to make a market power determination in relation to such a market; and

(b) in OFCOM's opinion would affect trade between member States, to the European Commission and to the regulatory authorities of every other member State.

(4) OFCOM must, in every other case in which it appears to them appropriate to do so, send—

(a) to the European Commission, and
(b) to such of the regulatory authorities of the other member States as OFCOM think fit,

a copy of a notification published under section 80 which relates to a proposal to identify a services market or to make a market power determination in relation to such a market.

[3158]

NOTES

Commencement: 25 July 2003 (for the purpose of enabling network and service functions and spectrum functions to be carried out during the transitional period by the Director General of Telecommunications and the Secretary of State respectively) (see further s 408 and Sch 18 at **[3436]**, **[3460]**, and the Communications Act 2003 (Commencement No 1) Order 2003, SI 2003/1900 at **[3507]**); 29 December 2003 (for the purpose of enabling OFCOM to perform those functions) (see the Office of Communications Act 2002 (Commencement No 3) and Communications Act 2003 (Commencement No 2) Order 2003, SI 2003/3142 at **[3590]**).

82 European Commission's powers in respect of proposals

(1) This section applies, in the case of a notification under section 80 with respect to a proposal—

(a) to identify a particular market; or
(b) to make a market power determination.

(2) If, within the representations period, OFCOM are notified by the European Commission for the purposes of Article 7(4) of the Framework Directive (market identifications that do not conform to Commission recommendations and determinations that affect trade between member States)—

(a) that the Commission considers that giving effect to the proposal would create a barrier in relation to the single European market, or
(b) that the Commission has serious doubts as to whether giving effect to the proposal would be compatible with the requirements of any Community obligations,

OFCOM are not to give effect to the proposal before the end of a further two months beginning with the end of the representations period.

(3) Where, before the end of that two month period, the European Commission makes a decision in accordance with Article 7(4) of the Framework Directive that the proposal should be withdrawn, OFCOM—

(a) must withdraw it; and
(b) shall not be entitled to give effect to it.

(4) In this section "the representations period", in relation to a notification under section 80, means the period specified in that notification for the making of representations about the proposals contained in it.

[3159]

NOTES

Commencement: 25 July 2003 (for the purpose of enabling network and service functions and spectrum functions to be carried out during the transitional period by the Director General of Telecommunications and the Secretary of State respectively) (see further s 408 and Sch 18 at **[3436]**, **[3460]**, and the Communications Act 2003 (Commencement No 1) Order 2003, SI 2003/1900 at **[3507]**); 29 December 2003 (for the purpose of enabling OFCOM to perform those functions) (see the Office of Communications Act 2002 (Commencement No 3) and Communications Act 2003 (Commencement No 2) Order 2003, SI 2003/3142 at **[3590]**).

83 Special rules for transnational markets

(1) This section applies where a services market is for the time being identified by a decision of the European Commission under Article 15(4) of the Framework Directive as a transnational market.

(2) Where the market area includes the whole or a part of the United Kingdom, OFCOM must enter into and maintain arrangements with the other relevant regulatory authorities about—

(a) the extent to which the agreement of all the relevant regulatory authorities is required for the doing of any of the things mentioned in subsection (3); and
(b) the procedures to be followed for securing that agreement where it is required.

(3) Those things are—
(a) the identification of the whole or a part of the market as a market in relation to which it is appropriate to determine whether a person has significant market power;
(b) the making of such a determination in relation to the whole or a part of the market;
(c) the setting of a condition the setting of which requires such a determination to have been made;
(d) the modification or revocation of such a condition.

(4) OFCOM must not do any of the things mentioned in subsection (3) except in accordance with arrangements maintained under that subsection.

(5) Those arrangements may include arrangements requiring OFCOM, when doing any of those things, to comply with—
(a) a decision made, by one or more other regulatory authorities; or
(b) a decision made by a person appointed under the arrangements to act on behalf of some or all of the relevant regulatory authorities.

(6) In this section—
"market area", in relation to a services market identified by the European Commission as a transnational market, means the area identified by that Commission as the area for which the market operates; and
"relevant regulatory authorities", in relation to such a market, means the regulatory authorities for each member State the whole or a part of which is comprised in the market area.

[3160]

NOTES

Commencement: 25 July 2003 (for the purpose of enabling network and service functions and spectrum functions to be carried out during the transitional period by the Director General of Telecommunications and the Secretary of State respectively) (see further s 408 and Sch 18 at **[3436]**, **[3460]**, and the Communications Act 2003 (Commencement No 1) Order 2003, SI 2003/1900 at **[3507]**); 29 December 2003 (for the purpose of enabling OFCOM to perform those functions) (see the Office of Communications Act 2002 (Commencement No 3) and Communications Act 2003 (Commencement No 2) Order 2003, SI 2003/3142 at **[3590]**).

84 Review of services market identifications and determinations

(1) This section applies where OFCOM have identified and analysed a services market for the purposes of making a market power determination.

(2) OFCOM must, at such intervals as they consider appropriate, carry out further analyses of the identified market for one or both of the following purposes—
(a) reviewing market power determinations made on the basis of an earlier analysis;
(b) deciding whether to make proposals for the modification of SMP conditions set by reference to a market power determination made on such a basis.

(3) It shall be the duty of OFCOM to carry out such a further analysis of a services market as soon as reasonably practicable after recommendations are made by the European Commission that affect the matters that were taken into account, or could have been taken into account, in the case of the last analysis by OFCOM of that market.

(4) Where on, or in consequence of, a further analysis under this section, OFCOM determine that a person to whom any SMP conditions apply is no longer a person with significant market power in that market, they must revoke every SMP services condition applied to that person by reference to the market power determination made on the basis of the earlier analysis.

(5) Before carrying out a further analysis under subsection (2), OFCOM may review any decision of theirs identifying the markets which it was appropriate to consider for the purpose of carrying out an earlier analysis.

(6) Where, on such a review, OFCOM conclude that the appropriate markets have changed—
(a) they must identify the markets they now consider to be the appropriate ones; and

(b) those markets shall be the identified markets for the purposes of the further analysis.

(7) Sections 79 to 83 apply—

(a) in relation to the identification of a services market for the purposes of reviewing a market power determination under this section, as they apply in relation to the identification of such a market for the purpose of making a market determination; and

(b) in relation to the review of such a determination, as they apply in relation to the making of such a determination.

[3161]

NOTES

Commencement: 25 July 2003 (for the purpose of enabling network and service functions and spectrum functions to be carried out during the transitional period by the Director General of Telecommunications and the Secretary of State respectively) (see further s 408 and Sch 18 at **[3436]**, **[3460]**, and the Communications Act 2003 (Commencement No 1) Order 2003, SI 2003/1900 at **[3507]**); 29 December 2003 (for the purpose of enabling OFCOM to perform those functions) (see the Office of Communications Act 2002 (Commencement No 3) and Communications Act 2003 (Commencement No 2) Order 2003, SI 2003/3142 at **[3590]**).

85 Review of apparatus market identifications and determinations

(1) This section applies where OFCOM have identified and analysed an apparatus market for the purposes of making a market power determination.

(2) OFCOM must, at such intervals as they consider appropriate, carry out further analyses of the identified market for one or both of the following purposes—

(a) reviewing market power determinations made on the basis of an earlier analysis;

(b) deciding whether to make proposals for the modification of SMP conditions set by reference to any such market power determination.

(3) Where on, or in consequence of, a further analysis under this section, OFCOM determine that a person to whom any SMP conditions apply is no longer a person with significant market power in that market, they shall revoke every SMP apparatus condition applied to that person by reference to the market power determination made on the basis of the earlier analysis.

(4) Before carrying out any further analysis under subsection (2), OFCOM may review any decision of theirs identifying the markets which it was appropriate to consider for the purpose of carrying out any earlier analysis.

(5) Where on such a review OFCOM conclude that the appropriate markets have changed—

(a) they shall identify the markets they now consider to be the appropriate ones; and

(b) those markets shall be the identified markets for the purposes of the further analysis.

(6) Where on such a review OFCOM conclude that there is no person at all with significant market power in relation to the identified market—

(a) they must so inform the Secretary of State; and

(b) the Secretary of State may by order remove or restrict OFCOM's power under this Chapter to set SMP apparatus conditions by reference to that market.

(7) Sections 79, 80 and 81(1) apply—

(a) in relation to the identification of a apparatus market for the purposes of reviewing a market power determination under this section, as they apply in relation to the identification of such a market for the purpose of making a market determination; and

(b) in relation to the review of such a determination, as they apply in relation to the making of such a determination.

[3162]

NOTES

Commencement: 25 July 2003 (for the purpose of enabling network and service functions and spectrum functions to be carried out during the transitional period by the Director General of Telecommunications and the Secretary of State respectively) (see further s 408 and Sch 18 at **[3436]**, **[3460]**, and the Communications Act 2003 (Commencement No 1) Order 2003, SI 2003/1900 at **[3507]**);

29 December 2003 (for the purpose of enabling OFCOM to perform those functions) (see the Office of Communications Act 2002 (Commencement No 3) and Communications Act 2003 (Commencement No 2) Order 2003, SI 2003/3142 at **[3590]**).

86 Cases where review required

(1) OFCOM must not set an SMP services condition by a notification which does not also make the market power determination by reference to which the condition is set unless—

(a) the condition is set by reference to a market power determination which has been reviewed under section 84 and, in consequence of that review, is confirmed in the notification setting the condition; or

(b) the condition is set by reference to a market power determination made in relation to a market in which OFCOM are satisfied there has been no material change since the determination was made.

(2) OFCOM must not modify or revoke SMP services conditions applying to a person except in a case falling within subsection (3) or (4).

(3) The first case is where, for the purpose of determining whether to make the modification or revocation, OFCOM have—

(a) carried out a further analysis under section 84 of the market in question; and

(b) reviewed the market power determination for the time being in force in that person's case.

(4) The second case is where OFCOM are satisfied that there has not—

(a) in the case of an unmodified condition, since the condition was set, or

(b) in any other case, since the condition was last modified,

been a material change in the market identified or otherwise used for the purposes of the market power determination by reference to which the condition was set or last modified.

(5) OFCOM must not modify SMP apparatus conditions applying to a person except where, for the purpose of determining whether to make the modification or revocation, they have—

(a) carried out a further analysis under section 85 of the market in question; and

(b) reviewed the market power determination for the time being in force in that person's case.

(6) A change is a material change for the purposes of subsection (1) or (4) if it is one that is material to—

(a) the setting of the condition in question; or

(b) the modification or revocation in question.

[3163]

NOTES

Commencement: 25 July 2003 (for the purpose of enabling network and service functions and spectrum functions to be carried out during the transitional period by the Director General of Telecommunications and the Secretary of State respectively) (see further s 408 and Sch 18 at **[3436]**, **[3460]**, and the Communications Act 2003 (Commencement No 1) Order 2003, SI 2003/1900 at **[3507]**); 29 December 2003 (for the purpose of enabling OFCOM to perform those functions) (see the Office of Communications Act 2002 (Commencement No 3) and Communications Act 2003 (Commencement No 2) Order 2003, SI 2003/3142 at **[3590]**).

SMP services conditions: subject-matter

87 Conditions about network access etc

(1) Where OFCOM have made a determination that a person to whom this section applies ("the dominant provider") has significant market power in an identified services market, they shall—

(a) set such SMP conditions authorised by this section as they consider it appropriate to apply to that person in respect of the relevant network or relevant facilities; and

(b) apply those conditions to that person.

(2) This section applies to—

(a) a person who provides a public electronic communications network; and

(b) a person who makes available facilities that are associated facilities by reference to such a network.

(3) This section authorises SMP conditions requiring the dominant provider to give such entitlements as OFCOM may from time to time direct as respects—
- (a) the provision of network access to the relevant network;
- (b) the use of the relevant network; and
- (c) the availability of the relevant facilities.

(4) In determining what conditions authorised by subsection (3) to set in a particular case, OFCOM must take into account, in particular, the following factors—
- (a) the technical and economic viability, having regard to the state of market development, of installing and using facilities that would make the proposed network access unnecessary;
- (b) the feasibility of the provision of the proposed network access;
- (c) the investment made by the person initially providing or making available the network or other facility in respect of which an entitlement to network access is proposed;
- (d) the need to secure effective competition in the long term;
- (e) any rights to intellectual property that are relevant to the proposal; and
- (f) the desirability of securing that electronic communications services are provided that are available throughout the member States.

(5) The conditions authorised by subsection (3) may include provision—
- (a) for securing fairness and reasonableness in the way in which requests for network access are made and responded to; and
- (b) for securing that the obligations contained in the conditions are complied with within the periods and at the times required by or under the conditions.

(6) The SMP conditions authorised by this section also include one or more of the following—
- (a) a condition requiring the dominant provider not to discriminate unduly against particular persons, or against a particular description of persons, in relation to matters connected with network access to the relevant network or with the availability of the relevant facilities;
- (b) a condition requiring the dominant provider to publish, in such manner as OFCOM may from time to time direct, all such information as they may direct for the purpose of securing transparency in relation to such matters;
- (c) a condition requiring the dominant provider to publish, in such manner as OFCOM may from time to time direct, the terms and conditions on which he is willing to enter into an access contract;
- (d) a condition requiring the terms and conditions on which the dominant provider is willing to enter into an access contract to include such terms and conditions as may be specified or described in the condition;
- (e) a condition requiring the dominant provider to make such modifications as OFCOM may direct of any offer by that provider which sets out the terms and conditions on which he is willing to enter into an access contract.

(7) The SMP conditions authorised by this section also include conditions requiring the dominant provider to maintain a separation for accounting purposes between such different matters relating—
- (a) to network access to the relevant network, or
- (b) to the availability of the relevant facilities,

as OFCOM may from time to time direct.

(8) The SMP conditions authorised by subsection (7) include conditions imposing requirements about the accounting methods to be used in maintaining the separation.

(9) The SMP conditions authorised by this section also include (subject to section 88) conditions imposing on the dominant provider—
- (a) such price controls as OFCOM may direct in relation to matters connected with the provision of network access to the relevant network, or with the availability of the relevant facilities;
- (b) such rules as they may make in relation to those matters about the recovery of costs and cost orientation;
- (c) such rules as they may make for those purposes about the use of cost accounting systems; and
- (d) obligations to adjust prices in accordance with such directions given by OFCOM as they may consider appropriate.

(10) The SMP conditions authorised by subsection (9) include conditions requiring the application of presumptions in the fixing and determination of costs and charges for the purposes of the price controls, rules and obligations imposed by virtue of that subsection.

(11) Where OFCOM set a condition authorised by this section which imposes rules on the dominant provider about the use of cost accounting systems, it shall be their duty also to set, and to apply to him, an SMP condition which imposes on him an obligation—

(a) to make arrangements for a description to be made available to the public of the cost accounting system used in pursuance of that condition; and

(b) to include in that description details of—

(i) the main categories under which costs are brought into account for the purposes of that system; and

(ii) the rules applied for the purposes of that system with respect to the allocation of costs.

(12) In this section—

"access contract" means—

(a) a contract for the provision by a person to whom this section applies to another person of network access to the relevant network; or

(b) a contract under which the relevant facilities are made available by a person to whom this section applies to another person;

"the relevant facilities", in relation to a person to whom this section applies, means the associated facilities made available by that person in relation to a public electronic communications network; and

"the relevant network", in relation to such a person, means the public electronic communications network provided by him.

[3164]

NOTES

Commencement: 25 July 2003 (for the purpose of enabling network and service functions and spectrum functions to be carried out during the transitional period by the Director General of Telecommunications and the Secretary of State respectively) (see further s 408 and Sch 18 at **[3436]**, **[3460]**, and the Communications Act 2003 (Commencement No 1) Order 2003, SI 2003/1900 at **[3507]**); 29 December 2003 (for the purpose of enabling OFCOM to perform those functions) (see the Office of Communications Act 2002 (Commencement No 3) and Communications Act 2003 (Commencement No 2) Order 2003, SI 2003/3142 at **[3590]**).

88 Conditions about network access pricing etc

(1) OFCOM are not to set an SMP condition falling within section 87(9) except where—

(a) it appears to them from the market analysis carried out for the purpose of setting that condition that there is a relevant risk of adverse effects arising from price distortion; and

(b) it also appears to them that the setting of the condition is appropriate for the purposes of—

(i) promoting efficiency;

(ii) promoting sustainable competition; and

(iii) conferring the greatest possible benefits on the end-users of public electronic communications services.

(2) In setting an SMP condition falling within section 87(9) OFCOM must take account of the extent of the investment in the matters to which the condition relates of the person to whom it is to apply.

(3) For the purposes of this section there is a relevant risk of adverse affects arising from price distortion if the dominant provider might—

(a) so fix and maintain some or all of his prices at an excessively high level, or

(b) so impose a price squeeze,

as to have adverse consequences for end-users of public electronic communications services.

(4) In considering the matters mentioned in subsection (1)(b) OFCOM may—

(a) have regard to the prices at which services are available in comparable competitive markets;

(b) determine what they consider to represent efficiency by using such cost accounting methods as they think fit.

(5) In this section "the dominant provider" has the same meaning as in section 87.

[3165]

NOTES

Commencement: 25 July 2003 (for the purpose of enabling network and service functions and spectrum functions to be carried out during the transitional period by the Director General of Telecommunications and the Secretary of State respectively) (see further s 408 and Sch 18 at **[3436]**, **[3460]**, and the Communications Act 2003 (Commencement No 1) Order 2003, SI 2003/1900 at **[3507]**); 29 December 2003 (for the purpose of enabling OFCOM to perform those functions) (see the Office of Communications Act 2002 (Commencement No 3) and Communications Act 2003 (Commencement No 2) Order 2003, SI 2003/3142 at **[3590]**).

89 Conditions about network access in exceptional cases

(1) This section applies where—

(a) OFCOM have made a determination that a person ("the dominant provider") has significant market power in an identified services market;

(b) that person is the provider of an electronic communications network or a person who makes associated facilities available; and

(c) OFCOM consider that there are exceptional circumstances making it appropriate for conditions with respect to the provision of network access to be applied to the dominant provider in addition to those that are required to be or may be applied to him apart from this section.

(2) OFCOM may set the additional SMP conditions and apply them to the dominant provider if—

(a) they have submitted the additional conditions to the European Commission for approval; and

(b) the Commission has approved the imposition on the dominant provider of the obligations contained in those conditions.

[3166]

NOTES

Commencement: 25 July 2003 (for the purpose of enabling network and service functions and spectrum functions to be carried out during the transitional period by the Director General of Telecommunications and the Secretary of State respectively) (see further s 408 and Sch 18 at **[3436]**, **[3460]**, and the Communications Act 2003 (Commencement No 1) Order 2003, SI 2003/1900 at **[3507]**); 29 December 2003 (for the purpose of enabling OFCOM to perform those functions) (see the Office of Communications Act 2002 (Commencement No 3) and Communications Act 2003 (Commencement No 2) Order 2003, SI 2003/3142 at **[3590]**).

90 Conditions about carrier selection and pre-selection

(1) This section applies where—

(a) OFCOM have made a determination that a person ("the dominant provider") has significant market power in an identified services market; and

(b) it appears to OFCOM that the market is a market relating to services for the provision of public electronic communications networks for use by means of connections at fixed locations.

(2) It shall be the duty of OFCOM to set, and to apply to the dominant provider, such SMP conditions authorised by this section as they think fit.

(3) The SMP conditions authorised by this section are conditions requiring the dominant provider to do one or both of the following—

(a) to make a relevant connection facility available to every person to whom he provides a public electronic communications service;

(b) for the purpose of making such a connection facility available to such persons, to make facilities for interconnection available to a person providing an electronic communications service.

(4) Where OFCOM set a condition requiring the dominant provider to make a relevant connection facility available, they shall also set such SMP conditions as they consider appropriate—

(a) with respect to the relationship to costs of any prices fixed for the use of the facility; and

(b) for the purpose of securing that prices and other charges imposed on the persons to whom public electronic communications services are provided by the dominant provider do not constitute a disincentive to the use of the facility.

(5) Where OFCOM set conditions authorised by this section, those conditions may include provision imposing obligations as to the manner in which one or both of the following are to be made available in accordance with the conditions—

(a) the relevant connection facility in question;

(b) the facilities for interconnection that are to be made available to a person providing an electronic communications service.

(6) In this section "relevant connection facility" is a facility which—

(a) allows a person to whom a public electronic communications service is provided by means of an electronic communications network to select which public electronic communications service provided wholly or partly by means of that network is the service that he wishes to use; and

(b) enables that selection to be made either—

(i) by the use of a telephone number on each separate occasion on which a selection is made; or

(ii) by designating in advance the selection that is to apply on every occasion when no such selection as is mentioned in sub-paragraph (i) is made.

[3167]

NOTES

Commencement: 25 July 2003 (for the purpose of enabling network and service functions and spectrum functions to be carried out during the transitional period by the Director General of Telecommunications and the Secretary of State respectively) (see further s 408 and Sch 18 at **[3436]**, **[3460]**, and the Communications Act 2003 (Commencement No 1) Order 2003, SI 2003/1900 at **[3507]**); 29 December 2003 (for the purpose of enabling OFCOM to perform those functions) (see the Office of Communications Act 2002 (Commencement No 3) and Communications Act 2003 (Commencement No 2) Order 2003, SI 2003/3142 at **[3590]**).

91 Conditions about regulation of services etc for end-users

(1) Where—

(a) OFCOM have made a determination that a person ("the dominant provider") has significant market power in an identified services market ("the relevant market"),

(b) the relevant market is one for the end-users of public electronic communications services that are available in that market, and

(c) it appears to OFCOM that the test in subsection (2) is satisfied in the case of that provider,

they shall set, and apply to that provider, such SMP conditions authorised by this section as they consider appropriate.

(2) That test is that OFCOM are unable, by the setting of conditions of the sorts specified in subsection (3), to perform, or fully to perform, their duties under section 4 in relation to the market situation in the relevant market.

(3) The sorts of conditions referred to in subsection (2) are—

(a) access-related conditions; and

(b) SMP conditions authorised or required by sections 87 to 90.

(4) The reference in subsection (2) to the market situation in the relevant market is a reference to the situation revealed by such market analyses of that market as may have been carried out for the purposes of this Chapter.

(5) The SMP conditions authorised by this section are conditions imposing on the dominant provider such regulatory controls as OFCOM may from time to time direct in relation to the provision by that provider of any public electronic communications service to the end-users of that service.

(6) Where OFCOM set a condition which is authorised by this section and imposes regulatory control on tariffs or other matters to which costs are relevant, they shall also set, and apply to the dominant provider, an SMP condition which requires him, to the extent that they consider it appropriate—

(a) to use such cost accounting systems as may be determined by them;

(b) to have the use of those systems audited annually by a qualified auditor; and

(c) to publish an annual statement about compliance by the dominant provider with the obligations imposed by virtue of paragraph (a).

(7) It shall be the duty of OFCOM to provide the European Commission with all such information as the Commission requires them to provide about—

(a) conditions authorised by this section that are set by OFCOM; and
(b) the cost accounting systems used, by the persons to whom those conditions apply, in relation to the services regulated in accordance with the conditions.

(8) In this section "qualified auditor" means a person eligible, in accordance with Part 2 of the Companies Act 1989 (c 40), for appointment as a company auditor.

[3168]

NOTES

Commencement: 25 July 2003 (for the purpose of enabling network and service functions and spectrum functions to be carried out during the transitional period by the Director General of Telecommunications and the Secretary of State respectively) (see further s 408 and Sch 18 at **[3436]**, **[3460]**, and the Communications Act 2003 (Commencement No 1) Order 2003, SI 2003/1900 at **[3507]**); 29 December 2003 (for the purpose of enabling OFCOM to perform those functions) (see the Office of Communications Act 2002 (Commencement No 3) and Communications Act 2003 (Commencement No 2) Order 2003, SI 2003/3142 at **[3590]**).

92 Conditions about leased lines

(1) This section applies where—
(a) OFCOM have made a determination that a person ("the dominant provider") has significant market power in an identified services market; and
(b) it appears to OFCOM that the market in relation to which that market power determination has been made is a market relating to the provision of any such leased lines as are for the time being identified by the European Commission in the List of Standards published in the Official Journal of the European Communities.

(2) It shall be the duty of OFCOM to set, and to apply to the dominant provider, such SMP conditions authorised by this section as they consider appropriate.

(3) The SMP conditions authorised by this section are conditions for applying, so far as required by the provisions for the time being contained in Annex VII to the Universal Service Directive, the principles of non-discrimination, cost orientation and transparency in relation to the leased lines identified as mentioned in subsection (1).

(4) In this section "leased line" means an electronic communications service the provision of which consists in the reservation of a fixed amount of transmission capacity between fixed points on the same or different electronic communications networks.

[3169]

NOTES

Commencement: 25 July 2003 (for the purpose of enabling network and service functions and spectrum functions to be carried out during the transitional period by the Director General of Telecommunications and the Secretary of State respectively) (see further s 408 and Sch 18 at **[3436]**, **[3460]**, and the Communications Act 2003 (Commencement No 1) Order 2003, SI 2003/1900 at **[3507]**); 29 December 2003 (for the purpose of enabling OFCOM to perform those functions) (see the Office of Communications Act 2002 (Commencement No 3) and Communications Act 2003 (Commencement No 2) Order 2003, SI 2003/3142 at **[3590]**).

SMP apparatus conditions: subject-matter

93 Conditions about apparatus supply

(1) Where OFCOM have made a determination that a person ("the dominant supplier") has significant market power in an identified apparatus market, they may—
(a) set such SMP conditions authorised by this section as they consider it appropriate to apply to that person in respect of the supply of electronic communications apparatus; and
(b) apply those conditions to that person.

(2) This section authorises the setting of SMP conditions of each of the following descriptions—
(a) conditions requiring the dominant supplier to maintain such a separation for accounting purposes between matters relating to the supply of electronic communications apparatus and other matters as may be described in the conditions;

(b) conditions imposing requirements about the accounting methods to be used in maintaining the separation; and

(c) conditions imposing such rules as OFCOM may make, for the purpose of securing the maintenance of the separation, about the use of cost accounting systems.

(3) This section also authorises the setting of SMP conditions imposing price controls in relation to the hiring of telephones which are hardwired to an electronic communications network.

(4) Conditions set under this section must not make provision in relation to the supply of electronic communications apparatus unless the apparatus is of a description of apparatus as respects the supply of which the dominant supplier has been found to have significant market power.

(5) For the purposes of this section a telephone is hardwired to an electronic communications network where, in order for it to be used with that network—

(a) it has to be physically attached to apparatus comprised in the network; and

(b) the attachment has to be effected by a process that requires the use of a tool.

[3170]

NOTES

Commencement: 25 July 2003 (for the purpose of enabling network and service functions and spectrum functions to be carried out during the transitional period by the Director General of Telecommunications and the Secretary of State respectively) (see further s 408 and Sch 18 at **[3436]**, **[3460]**, and the Communications Act 2003 (Commencement No 1) Order 2003, SI 2003/1900 at **[3507]**); 29 December 2003 (for the purpose of enabling OFCOM to perform those functions) (see the Office of Communications Act 2002 (Commencement No 3) and Communications Act 2003 (Commencement No 2) Order 2003, SI 2003/3142 at **[3590]**).

Enforcement of conditions

94 Notification of contravention of conditions

(1) Where OFCOM determine that there are reasonable grounds for believing that a person is contravening, or has contravened, a condition set under section 45, they may give that person a notification under this section.

(2) A notification under this section is one which—

(a) sets out the determination made by OFCOM;

(b) specifies the condition and contravention in respect of which that determination has been made; and

(c) specifies the period during which the person notified has an opportunity of doing the things specified in subsection (3).

(3) Those things are—

(a) making representations about the matters notified;

(b) complying with notified conditions of which he remains in contravention; and

(c) remedying the consequences of notified contraventions.

(4) Subject to subsections (5) to (7) and section 98(3), the period for doing those things must be the period of one month beginning with the day after the one on which the notification was given.

(5) OFCOM may, if they think fit, allow a longer period for doing those things either—

(a) by specifying a longer period in the notification; or

(b) by subsequently, on one or more occasions, extending the specified period.

(6) The person notified shall have a shorter period for doing those things if a shorter period is agreed between OFCOM and the person notified.

(7) The person notified shall also have a shorter period if—

(a) OFCOM have reasonable grounds for believing that the contravention is a repeated contravention;

(b) they have determined that, in those circumstances, a shorter period would be appropriate; and

(c) the shorter period has been specified in the notification.

(8) A notification under this section—

(a) may be given in respect of more than one contravention; and

(b) if it is given in respect of a continuing contravention, may be given in respect of any period during which the contravention has continued.

(9) Where a notification under this section has been given to a person in respect of a contravention of a condition, OFCOM may give a further notification in respect of the same contravention of that condition if, and only if—

(a) the contravention is one occurring after the time of the giving of the earlier notification;

(b) the contravention is a continuing contravention and the subsequent notification is in respect of so much of a period as falls after a period to which the earlier notification relates; or

(c) the earlier notification has been withdrawn without a penalty having been imposed in respect of the notified contravention.

(10) OFCOM must not give a notification under this section in a case in which—

(a) they decide that a more appropriate way of proceeding in relation to the contravention in question would be under the Competition Act 1998 (c 41); and

(b) they publish a statement to that effect in such manner as they consider appropriate for bringing their decision to the attention of the persons who, in their opinion, are likely to be affected by it.

(11) For the purposes of this section a contravention is a repeated contravention, in relation to a notification with respect to that contravention, if—

(a) a previous notification under this section has been given in respect of same contravention or in respect of another contravention of the same condition; and

(b) the subsequent notification is given no more than twelve months after day of the making by OFCOM of a determination for the purposes section 95(2) or 96(2) that the contravention to which the previous notification related did occur.

[3171]

NOTES

Commencement: 25 July 2003 (for the purpose of enabling network and service functions spectrum functions to be carried out during the transitional period by the Director General Telecommunications and the Secretary of State respectively) (see further s 408 and Sch 18 at **[3436]**, **[3460]**, and the Communications Act 2003 (Commencement No 1) Order 2003, SI 2003/1900 at **[3507]**); 29 December 2003 (for the purpose of enabling OFCOM to perform those functions) (see the Office Communications Act 2002 (Commencement No 3) and Communications Act 2003 (Commencement No 2) Order 2003, SI 2003/3142 at **[3590]**).

Application: this section, and ss 95–98, apply for the purposes of enforcement of the Radio Equipment and Telecommunications Terminal Equipment Regulations 2000, SI 2000/730, regs 7, 13, as if the requirements in those regulations were conditions set under s 45 of this Act: see the Radio Equipment and Telecommunications Terminal Equipment Regulations 2000, SI 2000/730, reg 18(5) at **[4354]**.

95 Enforcement notification for contravention of conditions

(1) This section applies where—

(a) a person ("the notified provider") has been given a notification under section 94;

(b) OFCOM have allowed the notified provider an opportunity of making representations about the matters notified; and

(c) the period allowed for the making of the representations has expired.

(2) OFCOM may give the notified provider an enforcement notification if they are satisfied—

(a) that he has, in one or more of the respects notified, been in contravention a condition specified in the notification under section 94; and

(b) that he has not, during the period allowed under that section, taken all such steps as they consider appropriate—

(i) for complying with that condition; and

(ii) for remedying the consequences of the notified contravention of condition.

(3) An enforcement notification is a notification which imposes one or both the following requirements on the notified provider—

(a) a requirement to take such steps for complying with the notified condition as may be specified in the notification;

(b) a requirement to take such steps for remedying the consequences of notified contravention as may be so specified.

(4) A decision of OFCOM to give an enforcement notification to a person—

(a) must be notified by them to that person, together with the reasons for decision, no later than one week after the day on which it is taken; and

(b) must fix a reasonable period for the taking of the steps required by notification.

(5) It shall be the duty of a person to whom an enforcement notification been given to comply with it.

(6) That duty shall be enforceable in civil proceedings by OFCOM—

(a) for an injunction;

(b) for specific performance of a statutory duty under section 45 of the Court of Session Act 1988 (c 36); or

(c) for any other appropriate remedy or relief.

[3172]

NOTES

Commencement: 25 July 2003 (for the purpose of enabling network and service functions and spectrum functions to be carried out during the transitional period by the Director General of Telecommunications and the Secretary of State respectively) (see further s 408 and Sch 18 at **[3436]**, **[3460]**, and the Communications Act 2003 (Commencement No 1) Order 2003, SI 2003/1900 at **[3507]**); 29 December 2003 (for the purpose of enabling OFCOM to perform those functions) (see the Office of Communications Act 2002 (Commencement No 3) and Communications Act 2003 (Commencement No 2) Order 2003, SI 2003/3142 at **[3590]**).

Application: see the note to s 94 at **[3171]**.

96 Penalties for contravention of conditions

(1) This section applies (in addition to section 95) where—

(a) a person ("the notified provider") has been given a notification under section 94;

(b) OFCOM have allowed the notified provider an opportunity of making representations about the matters notified; and

(c) the period allowed for the making of the representations has expired.

(2) OFCOM may impose a penalty on the notified provider if he—

(a) has, in one or more of the respects notified, been in contravention of a condition specified in the notification under section 94; and

(b) has not, during the period allowed under that section, taken the steps OFCOM consider appropriate—

(i) for complying with the notified condition; and

(ii) for remedying the consequences of the notified contravention of that condition.

(3) Where a notification under section 94 relates to more than one contravention, a separate penalty may be imposed in respect of each contravention.

(4) Where such a notification relates to a continuing contravention, no more than one penalty may be imposed in respect of the period of contravention specified in the notification.

(5) OFCOM may also impose a penalty on the notified provider if he has contravened, or is contravening, a requirement of an enforcement notification given under section 95 in respect of the notified contravention.

(6) Where OFCOM impose a penalty on a person under this section, they shall—

(a) within one week of making their decision to impose the penalty, notify that person of that decision and of their reasons for that decision; and

(b) in that notification, fix a reasonable period after it is given as the period within which the penalty is to be paid.

(7) A penalty imposed under this section—

(a) must be paid to OFCOM; and

(b) if not paid within the period fixed by them, is to be recoverable by them accordingly.

[3173]

NOTES

Commencement: 25 July 2003 (for the purpose of enabling network and service functions and spectrum functions to be carried out during the transitional period by the Director General of Telecommunications and the Secretary of State respectively) (see further s 408 and Sch 18 at **[3436]**, **[3460]**, and the Communications Act 2003 (Commencement No 1) Order 2003, SI 2003/1900 at **[3507]**);

29 December 2003 (for the purpose of enabling OFCOM to perform those functions) (see the Office of Communications Act 2002 (Commencement No 3) and Communications Act 2003 (Commencement No 2) Order 2003, SI 2003/3142 at **[3590]**).

Application: see the note to s 94 at **[3171]**.

97 Amount of penalty under s 96

(1) The amount of a penalty imposed under section 96 is to be such amount not exceeding ten per cent of the turnover of the notified provider's relevant business for the relevant period as OFCOM determine to be—

(a) appropriate; and

(b) proportionate to the contravention in respect of which it is imposed.

(2) In making that determination OFCOM must have regard to—

(a) any representations made to them by the notified provider;

(b) any steps taken by him towards complying with the conditions contraventions of which have been notified to him under section 94; and

(c) any steps taken by him for remedying the consequences of those contraventions.

(3) For the purposes of this section—

(a) the turnover of a person's relevant business for a period shall be calculated in accordance with such rules as may be set out by order made by the Secretary of State; and

(b) provision may also be made by such an order for determining what is to be treated as the network, service, facility or business by reference to which the calculation of that turnover falls to be made.

(4) No order is to be made containing provision authorised by subsection (3) unless a draft of the order has been laid before Parliament and approved by a resolution of each House.

(5) In this section—

"relevant business" means (subject to the provisions of an order under subsection (3) and to subsections (6) and (7)) so much of any business carried on by the notified provider as consists in any one or more of the following—

(a) the provision of an electronic communications network;

(b) the provision of an electronic communications service;

(c) the making available of associated facilities;

(d) the supply of directories for use in connection with the use of such a network or service;

(e) the making available of directory enquiry facilities for use for purposes connected with the use of such a network or service;

(f) any business not falling within any of the preceding paragraphs which is carried on in association with any business in respect of which any access-related condition is applied to the person carrying it on;

"relevant period", in relation to a contravention by a person of a condition set under section 45, means—

(a) except in a case falling within paragraph (b) or (c), the period of one year ending with the 31st March next before the time when notification of the contravention was given under section 94;

(b) in the case of a person who at that time has been carrying on that business for a period of less than a year, the period, ending with that time, during which he has been carrying it on; and

(c) in the case of a person who at that time has ceased to carry on that business, the period of one year ending with the time when he ceased to carry it on.

(6) In the case of a contravention of an SMP apparatus condition the relevant business is so much of any business carried on by the person in respect of whose contravention the penalty is imposed as consists in the supply of electronic communications apparatus.

(7) So much of any business of a person on whom the penalty is imposed as falls within paragraph (f) of the definition of a relevant business shall be disregarded for the purposes of this section except in relation to—

(a) a contravention of an access-related condition imposed in respect of that business; or

(b) a contravention of an enforcement notification given under section 95 relating to such a condition.

(8) In this section "the notified provider" has the same meaning as in section 96. **[3174]**

NOTES

Commencement: 25 July 2003 (for the purpose of enabling network and service functions and spectrum functions to be carried out during the transitional period by the Director General of Telecommunications and the Secretary of State respectively) (see further s 408 and Sch 18 at **[3436]**, **[3460]**, and the Communications Act 2003 (Commencement No 1) Order 2003, SI 2003/1900 at **[3507]**); 29 December 2003 (for the purpose of enabling OFCOM to perform those functions) (see the Office of Communications Act 2002 (Commencement No 3) and Communications Act 2003 (Commencement No 2) Order 2003, SI 2003/3142 at **[3590]**).

Application: see the note to s 94 at **[3171]**.

Orders: the Electronic Communications (Networks and Services) (Penalties) (Rules for Calculation of Turnover) Order 2003, SI 2003/2712 at **[3586]**.

98 Power to deal with urgent cases

(1) This section applies where OFCOM determine—

(a) that they are entitled to give a notification under section 94 with respect to a contravention by a person ("the contravening provider") of a condition set under section 45, other than an SMP apparatus condition;

(b) that there are reasonable grounds for suspecting that the case is an urgent case; and

(c) that the urgency of the case makes it appropriate for OFCOM to take action under this section.

(2) A case is an urgent case for the purposes of this section if the contravention has resulted in, or creates an immediate risk of—

(a) a serious threat to the safety of the public, to public health or to national security;

(b) serious economic or operational problems for persons (other than the contravening provider) who are communications providers or persons who make associated facilities available; or

(c) serious economic or operational problems for persons who make use of electronic communications networks, electronic communications services or associated facilities.

(3) OFCOM may, in a notification under section 94 with respect to the contravention, specify a period of less than one month for doing the things mentioned in subsection (3) of that section.

(4) OFCOM shall also have power to give to the contravening provider—

(a) a direction that his entitlement to provide electronic communications networks or electronic communications services, or to make associated facilities available, is suspended (either generally or in relation to particular networks, services or facilities); or

(b) a direction that that entitlement is restricted in the respects set out in the direction.

(5) A direction under subsection (4)—

(a) must specify the networks, services and facilities to which it relates; and

(b) except so far as it otherwise provides, takes effect for an indefinite period beginning with the time at which it is notified to the person to whom it is given.

(6) A direction under subsection (4)—

(a) in providing for the effect of a suspension or restriction to be postponed, may provide for it to take effect only at a time determined by or in accordance with the terms of the direction; and

(b) in connection with the suspension or restriction contained in the direction or with the postponement of its effect, may impose such conditions on the contravening provider as appear to OFCOM to be appropriate for the purpose of protecting his customers.

(7) Those conditions may include a condition requiring the making of payments—

(a) by way of compensation for loss or damage suffered by the contravening provider's customers as a result of the direction; or

(b) in respect of annoyance, inconvenience or anxiety to which they have been put in consequence of the direction.

(8) OFCOM have power to revoke a direction given under subsection (4)—

(a) with effect from such time as they may direct;
(b) subject to compliance with such requirements as they may specify; and
(c) to such extent and in relation to such networks, services or facilities, or parts of a network, service or facility, as they may determine.

[3175]

NOTES

Commencement: 25 July 2003 (for the purpose of enabling network and service functions and spectrum functions to be carried out during the transitional period by the Director General of Telecommunications and the Secretary of State respectively) (see further s 408 and Sch 18 at **[3436]**, **[3460]**, and the Communications Act 2003 (Commencement No 1) Order 2003, SI 2003/1900 at **[3507]**); 29 December 2003 (for the purpose of enabling OFCOM to perform those functions) (see the Office of Communications Act 2002 (Commencement No 3) and Communications Act 2003 (Commencement No 2) Order 2003, SI 2003/3142 at **[3590]**).

Application: see the note to s 94 at **[3171]**.

99 Confirmation of directions under s 98

(1) As soon as reasonably practicable after giving a direction under section 98(4), OFCOM must give the person to whom it is given—
(a) an opportunity of making representations to them about the grounds on which it was given and its effect; and
(b) an opportunity of proposing steps to remedy the situation.

(2) As soon as practicable after the period allowed by OFCOM for making those representations has ended, they must determine—
(a) whether the contravention providing the grounds for the giving of the direction did occur; and
(b) whether the circumstances made it an urgent case justifying the giving of the direction.

(3) If OFCOM decide that the contravention did occur and that the direction was justified, they may confirm the direction.

(4) If not, they must exercise their power to revoke it.

(5) As soon as reasonably practicable after determining whether to confirm the direction, OFCOM must notify the person to whom it was given of their decision.

(6) Conditions included in a direction by virtue of section 98(7) have effect only if the direction is confirmed.

[3176]

NOTES

Commencement: 25 July 2003 (for the purpose of enabling network and service functions and spectrum functions to be carried out during the transitional period by the Director General of Telecommunications and the Secretary of State respectively) (see further s 408 and Sch 18 at **[3436]**, **[3460]**, and the Communications Act 2003 (Commencement No 1) Order 2003, SI 2003/1900 at **[3507]**); 29 December 2003 (for the purpose of enabling OFCOM to perform those functions) (see the Office of Communications Act 2002 (Commencement No 3) and Communications Act 2003 (Commencement No 2) Order 2003, SI 2003/3142 at **[3590]**).

100 Suspending service provision for contraventions of conditions

(1) OFCOM may give a direction under this section to a person who is a communications provider or makes associated facilities available ("the contravening provider") if they are satisfied—
(a) that he is or has been in serious and repeated contravention of conditions set under section 45, other than an SMP apparatus condition;
(b) that an attempt, by the imposition of penalties or the giving of enforcement notifications under section 95 or both, to secure compliance with the contravened conditions has failed; and
(c) that the giving of the direction is appropriate and proportionate to the seriousness (when repeated as they have been) of the contraventions.

(2) A direction under this section is—
(a) a direction that the entitlement of the contravening provider to provide electronic communications networks or electronic communications services, or to make

associated facilities available, is suspended (either generally or in relation to particular networks, services or facilities); or

(b) a direction that that entitlement is restricted in the respects set out in the direction.

(3) A direction under this section—

(a) must specify the networks, services and facilities to which it relates; and

(b) except so far as it otherwise provides, takes effect for an indefinite period beginning with the time at which it is notified to the person to whom it is given.

(4) A direction under this section—

(a) in providing for the effect of a suspension or restriction to be postponed, may provide for it to take effect only at a time determined by or in accordance with the terms of the direction; and

(b) in connection with the suspension or restriction contained in the direction or with the postponement of its effect, may impose such conditions on the contravening provider as appear to OFCOM to be appropriate for the purpose of protecting that provider's customers.

(5) Those conditions may include a condition requiring the making of payments—

(a) by way of compensation for loss or damage suffered by the contravening provider's customers as a result of the direction; or

(b) in respect of annoyance, inconvenience or anxiety to which they have been put in consequence of the direction.

(6) If OFCOM consider it appropriate to do so (whether or not in consequence of representations or proposals made to them), they may revoke a direction under this section or modify its conditions—

(a) with effect from such time as they may direct;

(b) subject to compliance with such requirements as they may specify; and

(c) to such extent and in relation to such networks, services or facilities, or parts of a network, service or facility, as they may determine.

(7) For the purposes of this section there are repeated contraventions by a person of conditions set under section 45 to the extent that—

(a) in the case of a previous notification given to that person under section 94, OFCOM have determined for the purposes of section 95(2) or 96(2) that such a contravention did occur;

(b) in the period of twelve months following the day of the making of that determination, one or more further notifications have been given to that person in respect of contraventions of a condition set under section 45; and

(c) the previous notification and the subsequent ones all relate to contraventions of the same condition (whether the same contravention or different contraventions).

[3177]

NOTES

Commencement: 25 July 2003 (for the purpose of enabling network and service functions and spectrum functions to be carried out during the transitional period by the Director General of Telecommunications and the Secretary of State respectively) (see further s 408 and Sch 18 at **[3436]**, **[3460]**, and the Communications Act 2003 (Commencement No 1) Order 2003, SI 2003/1900 at **[3507]**); 29 December 2003 (for the purpose of enabling OFCOM to perform those functions) (see the Office of Communications Act 2002 (Commencement No 3) and Communications Act 2003 (Commencement No 2) Order 2003, SI 2003/3142 at **[3590]**).

101 Suspending apparatus supply for contraventions of conditions

(1) OFCOM may give a direction under this section to a person who supplies electronic communications apparatus ("the contravening supplier") if they are satisfied—

(a) that he is or has been in serious and repeated contravention of any SMP apparatus conditions;

(b) that an attempt, by the imposition of penalties or the giving of enforcement notifications under section 95 or both, to secure compliance with the contravened conditions has failed; and

(c) that the giving of the direction is appropriate and proportionate to the seriousness (when repeated as they have been) of the contraventions.

(2) A direction under this section is—

(a) a direction to the contravening supplier to cease to act as a supplier of electronic communications apparatus (either generally or in relation to apparatus of a particular description); or

(b) a direction imposing such restrictions as may be set out in the direction on the supply by that supplier of electronic communications apparatus (either generally or in relation to apparatus of a particular description).

(3) A direction under this section takes effect, except so far as it otherwise provides, for an indefinite period beginning with the time at which it is notified to the person to whom it is given.

(4) A direction under this section—

(a) may provide for a prohibition or restriction to take effect only at a time determined by or in accordance with the terms of the direction; and

(b) in connection with a prohibition or restriction contained in the direction or with the postponement of its effect, may impose such conditions on the contravening supplier as appear to OFCOM to be appropriate for the purpose of protecting that supplier's customers.

(5) Those conditions may include a condition requiring the making of payments—

(a) by way of compensation for loss or damage suffered by the contravening supplier's customers as a result of the direction; or

(b) in respect of annoyance, inconvenience or anxiety to which they have been put in consequence of the direction.

(6) If OFCOM consider it appropriate to do so (whether or not in consequence of representations or proposals made to them), they may at any time revoke a direction under this section or modify its conditions—

(a) with effect from such time as they may direct;

(b) subject to compliance with such requirements as they may specify; and

(c) to such extent and in relation to such apparatus or descriptions of apparatus as they may determine.

(7) For the purposes of this section there are repeated contraventions by a person of SMP apparatus conditions to the extent that—

(a) in the case of a previous notification given to that person under section 94, OFCOM have determined for the purposes of section 95(2) or 96(2) that such a contravention did occur;

(b) in the period of twelve months following the day of the making of that determination, one or more further notifications have been given to that person in respect of contraventions of an SMP apparatus condition; and

(c) the previous notification and the subsequent ones all relate to contraventions of the same condition (whether the same contravention or different contraventions).

[3178]

NOTES

Commencement: 25 July 2003 (for the purpose of enabling network and service functions and spectrum functions to be carried out during the transitional period by the Director General of Telecommunications and the Secretary of State respectively) (see further s 408 and Sch 18 at **[3436]**, **[3460]**, and the Communications Act 2003 (Commencement No 1) Order 2003, SI 2003/1900 at **[3507]**); 29 December 2003 (for the purpose of enabling OFCOM to perform those functions) (see the Office of Communications Act 2002 (Commencement No 3) and Communications Act 2003 (Commencement No 2) Order 2003, SI 2003/3142 at **[3590]**).

102 Procedure for directions under ss 100 and 101

(1) Except in an urgent case, OFCOM are not to give a direction under section 100 or 101 unless they have—

(a) notified the contravening provider or contravening supplier of the proposed direction and of the conditions (if any) which they are proposing to impose by that direction;

(b) provided him with an opportunity of making representations about the proposals and of proposing steps for remedying the situation; and

(c) considered every representation and proposal made to them during the period allowed by them for the contravening provider or the contravening supplier to take advantage of that opportunity.

(2) That period must be one ending not less than one month after the day of the giving of the notification.

(3) As soon as practicable after giving a direction under section 100 or 101 in an urgent case, OFCOM must, provide the contravening provider or contravening supplier with an opportunity of—

(a) making representations about the effect of the direction and of any of its conditions; and
(b) proposing steps for remedying the situation.

(4) A case is an urgent case for the purposes of this section if OFCOM—

(a) consider that it would be inappropriate, because the contraventions in question fall within subsection (5), to allow time, before giving a direction under section 100 or 101, for the making and consideration of representations; and
(b) decide for that reason to act in accordance with subsection (3), instead of subsection (1).

(5) The contraventions fall within this subsection if they have resulted in, or create an immediate risk of—

(a) a serious threat to the safety of the public, to public health or to national security;
(b) serious economic or operational problems for persons (apart from the contravening provider or contravening supplier) who are communications providers or persons who make associated facilities available; or
(c) serious economic or operational problems for persons who make use of electronic communications networks, electronic communications services or associated facilities.

(6) In this section—

"contravening provider" has the same meaning as in section 100; and
"contravening supplier" has the same meaning as in section 101.

[3179]

NOTES

Commencement: 25 July 2003 (for the purpose of enabling network and service functions and spectrum functions to be carried out during the transitional period by the Director General of Telecommunications and the Secretary of State respectively) (see further s 408 and Sch 18 at **[3436]**, **[3460]**, and the Communications Act 2003 (Commencement No 1) Order 2003, SI 2003/1900 at **[3507]**); 29 December 2003 (for the purpose of enabling OFCOM to perform those functions) (see the Office of Communications Act 2002 (Commencement No 3) and Communications Act 2003 (Commencement No 2) Order 2003, SI 2003/3142 at **[3590]**).

103 Enforcement of directions under ss 98, 100 and 101

(1) A person is guilty of an offence if he provides an electronic communications network or electronic communications service, or makes available any associated facility—

(a) while his entitlement to do so is suspended by a direction under section 98(4) or 100; or
(b) in contravention of a restriction contained in such a direction.

(2) A person is guilty of an offence if he supplies electronic communications apparatus—

(a) while prohibited from doing so by a direction under section 101; or
(b) in contravention of a restriction contained in such a direction.

(3) A person guilty of an offence under this section shall be liable—

(a) on summary conviction, to a fine not exceeding the statutory maximum;
(b) on conviction on indictment, to a fine.

(4) Sections 94 to 99 apply in relation to a contravention of conditions imposed by a direction under section 98, 100 or 101 as they apply in relation to a contravention of conditions set under section 45.

[3180]

NOTES

Commencement: 25 July 2003 (for the purpose of enabling network and service functions and spectrum functions to be carried out during the transitional period by the Director General of Telecommunications and the Secretary of State respectively) (see further s 408 and Sch 18 at **[3436]**, **[3460]**, and the Communications Act 2003 (Commencement No 1) Order 2003, SI 2003/1900 at **[3507]**);

29 December 2003 (for the purpose of enabling OFCOM to perform those functions) (see the Office of Communications Act 2002 (Commencement No 3) and Communications Act 2003 (Commencement No 2) Order 2003, SI 2003/3142 at **[3590]**).

104 Civil liability for breach of conditions or enforcement notification

(1) The obligation of a person to comply with—

(a) the conditions set under section 45 which apply to him,

(b) requirements imposed on him by an enforcement notification under section 95, and

(c) the conditions imposed by a direction under section 98 or 100,

shall be a duty owed to every person who may be affected by a contravention of the condition or requirement.

(2) Where a duty is owed by virtue of this section to a person—

(a) a breach of the duty that causes that person to sustain loss or damage, and

(b) an act which—

(i) by inducing a breach of the duty or interfering with its performance, causes that person to sustain loss or damage, and

(ii) is done wholly or partly for achieving that result,

shall be actionable at the suit or instance of that person.

(3) In proceedings brought against a person by virtue of subsection (2)(a) it shall be a defence for that person to show that he took all reasonable steps and exercised all due diligence to avoid contravening the condition or requirement in question.

(4) The consent of OFCOM is required for the bringing of proceedings by virtue of subsection (1)(a).

(5) Where OFCOM give a consent for the purposes of subsection (4) subject to conditions relating to the conduct of the proceedings, the proceedings are not to be carried on by that person except in compliance with those conditions.

[3181]

NOTES

Commencement: 25 July 2003 (for the purpose of enabling network and service functions and spectrum functions to be carried out during the transitional period by the Director General of Telecommunications and the Secretary of State respectively) (see further s 408 and Sch 18 at **[3436]**, **[3460]**, and the Communications Act 2003 (Commencement No 1) Order 2003, SI 2003/1900 at **[3507]**); 29 December 2003 (for the purpose of enabling OFCOM to perform those functions) (see the Office of Communications Act 2002 (Commencement No 3) and Communications Act 2003 (Commencement No 2) Order 2003, SI 2003/3142 at **[3590]**).

OFCOM's duty to intervene on network access issues

105 Consideration and determination of network access questions

(1) This section applies where—

(a) it appears to OFCOM that a network access question has arisen and needs to be determined; and

(b) they consider that, for the purpose of determining that question, it would be appropriate for them to exercise their powers under this Chapter to set, modify or revoke conditions falling within subsection (2).

(2) Conditions falling within this subsection are—

(a) access-related conditions authorised by section 73(2) or (4); and

(b) SMP services conditions authorised by section 87.

(3) Before considering whether, for the purpose of determining the question that has arisen, to set, modify or revoke conditions falling within subsection (2), OFCOM must publish a notification of their proposal to consider that matter.

(4) If, after considering that matter, OFCOM decide not to exercise their powers to set, modify or revoke conditions falling within subsection (2), they must publish a notification of their decision.

(5) A notification under this section must be published in the manner that OFCOM consider appropriate for bringing it to the attention of the persons who, in OFCOM's opinion, would be likely to be affected by action taken for determining the network access question that appears to them to have arisen.

(6) In this section "network access question" means a question relating to network access or the terms or conditions on which it is or may be provided in a particular case.

[3182]

NOTES

Commencement: 25 July 2003 (for the purpose of enabling network and service functions and spectrum functions to be carried out during the transitional period by the Director General of Telecommunications and the Secretary of State respectively) (see further s 408 and Sch 18 at **[3436]**, **[3460]**, and the Communications Act 2003 (Commencement No 1) Order 2003, SI 2003/1900 at **[3507]**); 29 December 2003 (for the purpose of enabling OFCOM to perform those functions) (see the Office of Communications Act 2002 (Commencement No 3) and Communications Act 2003 (Commencement No 2) Order 2003, SI 2003/3142 at **[3590]**).

Electronic communications code

106 Application of the electronic communications code

(1) In this Chapter "the electronic communications code" means the code set out in Schedule 2 to the Telecommunications Act 1984 (c 12).

(2) Schedule 3 (which amends Schedule 2 to the Telecommunications Act 1984 (c 12) for the purpose of translating the telecommunications code into a code applicable in the context of the new regulatory regime established by this Act) shall have effect.

(3) The electronic communications code shall have effect—

(a) in the case of a person to whom it is applied by a direction given by OFCOM; and

(b) in the case of the Secretary of State or any Northern Ireland department where the Secretary of State or that department is providing or proposing to provide an electronic communications network.

(4) The only purposes for which the electronic communications code may be applied in a person's case by a direction under this section are—

(a) the purposes of the provision by him of an electronic communications network; or

(b) the purposes of the provision by him of a system of conduits which he is making available, or proposing to make available, for use by providers of electronic communications networks for the purposes of the provision by them of their networks.

(5) A direction applying the electronic communications code in any person's case may provide for that code to have effect in his case—

(a) in relation only to such places or localities as may be specified or described in the direction;

(b) for the purposes only of the provision of such electronic communications network, or part of an electronic communications network, as may be so specified or described; or

(c) for the purposes only of the provision of such conduit system, or part of a conduit system, as may be so specified or described.

(6) The Secretary of State may by order provide for the electronic communications code to have effect for all purposes with a different amount substituted for the amount for the time being specified in paragraph 16(3) of the code (minimum compensation).

(7) In this section "conduit" includes a tunnel, subway, tube or pipe.

[3183]

NOTES

Commencement: 25 July 2003 (for the purpose of enabling network and service functions and spectrum functions to be carried out during the transitional period by the Director General of Telecommunications and the Secretary of State respectively) (see further s 408 and Sch 18 at **[3436]**, **[3460]**, and the Communications Act 2003 (Commencement No 1) Order 2003, SI 2003/1900 at **[3507]**); 29 December 2003 (for the purpose of enabling OFCOM to perform those functions) (see the Office of Communications Act 2002 (Commencement No 3) and Communications Act 2003 (Commencement No 2) Order 2003, SI 2003/3142 at **[3590]**).

107 Procedure for directions applying code

(1) OFCOM are not to give a direction applying the electronic communications code in any person's case except on an application made for the purpose by that person.

(2) If OFCOM publish a notification setting out their requirements with respect to—

(a) the content of an application for a direction applying the electronic communications code, and

(b) the manner in which such an application is to be made,

such an application must be made in accordance with the requirements for the time being in force.

(3) OFCOM may—

(a) from time to time review the requirements for the time being in force for the purposes of subsection (2); and

(b) on any such review, modify them in such manner as they think fit by giving a notification of the revised requirements.

(4) In considering whether to apply the electronic communications code in any person's case, OFCOM must have regard, in particular, to each of the following matters—

(a) the benefit to the public of the electronic communications network or conduit system by reference to which the code is to be applied to that person;

(b) the practicability of the provision of that network or system without the application of the code;

(c) the need to encourage the sharing of the use of electronic communications apparatus;

(d) whether the person in whose case it is proposed to apply the code will be able to meet liabilities arising as a consequence of—

(i) the application of the code in his case; and

(ii) any conduct of his in relation to the matters with which the code deals.

(5) For the purposes of subsections (6) and (7) of section 3 OFCOM's duty under subsection (4) ranks equally with their duties under that section.

(6) Before giving a direction under section 106, OFCOM must—

(a) publish a notification of their proposal to give the direction; and

(b) consider any representations about that proposal that are made to them within the period specified in the notification.

(7) A notification for the purposes of subsection (6)(a) must contain the following—

(a) a statement of OFCOM's proposal;

(b) a statement of their reasons for that proposal;

(c) a statement of the period within which representations may be made to them about the proposal.

(8) The statement of OFCOM's proposal must—

(a) contain a statement that they propose to apply the code in the case of the person in question;

(b) set out any proposals of theirs to impose terms under section 106(5);

but this subsection is subject to sections 113(7) and 115(5).

(9) The period specified as the period within which representations may be made must end no less than one month after the day of the publication of the notification.

(10) The publication by OFCOM of a notification for any of the purposes of this section must be a publication in such manner as OFCOM consider appropriate for bringing the notification to the attention of the persons who, in their opinion, are likely to be affected by it. **[3184]**

NOTES

Commencement: 25 July 2003 (for the purpose of enabling network and service functions and spectrum functions to be carried out during the transitional period by the Director General of Telecommunications and the Secretary of State respectively) (see further s 408 and Sch 18 at **[3436]**, **[3460]**, and the Communications Act 2003 (Commencement No 1) Order 2003, SI 2003/1900 at **[3507]**); 29 December 2003 (for the purpose of enabling OFCOM to perform those functions) (see the Office of Communications Act 2002 (Commencement No 3) and Communications Act 2003 (Commencement No 2) Order 2003, SI 2003/3142 at **[3590]**).

108 Register of persons in whose case code applies

(1) It shall be the duty of OFCOM to establish and maintain a register of persons in whose case the electronic communications code applies by virtue of a direction under section 106.

(2) OFCOM must record in the register every direction given under that section.

(3) Information recorded in the register must be recorded in such manner as OFCOM consider appropriate.

(4) It shall be the duty of OFCOM to publish a notification setting out—

(a) the times at which the register is for the time being available for public inspection; and

(b) the fees that must be paid for, or in connection with, an inspection of the register.

(5) The publication of a notification under subsection (4) must be a publication in such manner as OFCOM consider appropriate for bringing it to the attention of the persons who, in their opinion, are likely to be affected by it.

(6) OFCOM must make the register available for public inspection—

(a) during such hours, and

(b) on payment of such fees,

as are set out in the notification for the time being in force under subsection (4).

[3185]

NOTES

Commencement: 25 July 2003 (for the purpose of enabling network and service functions and spectrum functions to be carried out during the transitional period by the Director General of Telecommunications and the Secretary of State respectively) (see further s 408 and Sch 18 at **[3436]**, **[3460]**, and the Communications Act 2003 (Commencement No 1) Order 2003, SI 2003/1900 at **[3507]**); 29 December 2003 (for the purpose of enabling OFCOM to perform those functions) (see the Office of Communications Act 2002 (Commencement No 3) and Communications Act 2003 (Commencement No 2) Order 2003, SI 2003/3142 at **[3590]**).

109 Restrictions and conditions subject to which code applies

(1) Where the electronic communications code is applied in any person's case by a direction given by OFCOM, that code is to have effect in that person's case subject to such restrictions and conditions as may be contained in regulations made by the Secretary of State.

(2) In exercising his power to make regulations under this section it shall be the duty of the Secretary of State to have regard to each of the following—

(a) the duties imposed on OFCOM by sections 3 and 4;

(b) the need to protect the environment and, in particular, to conserve the natural beauty and amenity of the countryside;

(c) the need to ensure that highways are not damaged or obstructed, and traffic not interfered with, to any greater extent than is reasonably necessary;

(d) the need to encourage the sharing of the use of electronic communications apparatus;

(e) the need to secure that a person in whose case the code is applied will be able to meet liabilities arising as a consequence of—

(i) the application of the code in his case; and

(ii) any conduct of his in relation to the matters with which the code deals.

(3) The power of the Secretary of State to provide by regulations for the restrictions and conditions subject to which the electronic communications code has effect includes power to provide for restrictions and conditions which are framed by reference to any one or more of the following—

(a) the making of a determination in accordance with the regulations by a person specified in the regulations;

(b) the giving of an approval or consent by a person so specified; or

(c) the opinion of any person.

(4) Before making any regulations under this section, the Secretary of State must consult—

(a) OFCOM; and

(b) such other persons as he considers appropriate.

[3186]

NOTES

Commencement: 25 July 2003 (for the purpose of enabling network and service functions and spectrum functions to be carried out during the transitional period by the Director General of Telecommunications and the Secretary of State respectively) (see further s 408 and Sch 18 at **[3436]**, **[3460]**, and the Communications Act 2003 (Commencement No 1) Order 2003, SI 2003/1900 at **[3507]**); 29 December 2003 (for the purpose of enabling OFCOM to perform those functions) (see the Office of Communications Act 2002 (Commencement No 3) and Communications Act 2003 (Commencement No 2) Order 2003, SI 2003/3142 at **[3590]**).

Regulations: the Electronic Communications Code (Conditions and Restrictions) Regulations 2003, SI 2003/2553 at **[3566]**.

110 Enforcement of restrictions and conditions

(1) Where OFCOM determine that there are reasonable grounds for believing that a person in whose case the electronic communications code applies is contravening, or has contravened, a requirement imposed by virtue of any restrictions or conditions under section 109, they may give him a notification under this section.

(2) A notification under this section is one which—
- (a) sets out the determination made by OFCOM;
- (b) specifies the requirement and the contravention in respect of which that determination has been made; and
- (c) specifies the period during which the person notified has an opportunity of doing the things specified in subsection (3).

(3) Those things are—
- (a) making representations about the matters notified;
- (b) complying with any notified requirement of which he remains in contravention; and
- (c) remedying the consequences of notified contraventions.

(4) Subject to subsections (5) to (7), the period for doing those things must be the period of one month beginning with the day after the one on which the notification was given.

(5) OFCOM may, if they think fit, allow a longer period for doing those things either—
- (a) by specifying a longer period in the notification; or
- (b) by subsequently, on one or more occasions, extending the specified period.

(6) The person notified shall have a shorter period for doing those things if a shorter period is agreed between OFCOM and the person notified.

(7) The person notified shall also have a shorter period if—
- (a) OFCOM have reasonable grounds for believing that the contravention is a repeated contravention;
- (b) they have determined that, in those circumstances, a shorter period would be appropriate; and
- (c) the shorter period has been specified in the notification.

(8) A notification under this section—
- (a) may be given in respect of more than one contravention; and
- (b) if it is given in respect of a continuing contravention, may be given in respect of any period during which the contravention has continued.

(9) Where a notification under this section has been given to a person in respect of a contravention of a requirement, OFCOM may give a further notification in respect of the same contravention of that requirement if, and only if—
- (a) the contravention is one occurring after the time of the giving of the earlier notification;
- (b) the contravention is a continuing contravention and the subsequent notification is in respect of so much of a period as falls after a period to which the earlier notification relates; or
- (c) the earlier notification has been withdrawn without a penalty having been imposed in respect of the notified contravention.

(10) For the purposes of this section a contravention is a repeated contravention, in relation to a notification with respect to that contravention, if—
- (a) a previous notification under this section has been given in respect of the same contravention or in respect of another contravention of the same requirement; and

(b) the subsequent notification is given no more than twelve months after the day of the making by OFCOM of a determination for the purposes of section 111(2) or 112(2) that the contravention to which the previous notification related did occur.

[3187]

NOTES

Commencement: 25 July 2003 (for the purpose of enabling network and service functions and spectrum functions to be carried out during the transitional period by the Director General of Telecommunications and the Secretary of State respectively) (see further s 408 and Sch 18 at **[3436]**, **[3460]**, and the Communications Act 2003 (Commencement No 1) Order 2003, SI 2003/1900 at **[3507]**); 29 December 2003 (for the purpose of enabling OFCOM to perform those functions) (see the Office of Communications Act 2002 (Commencement No 3) and Communications Act 2003 (Commencement No 2) Order 2003, SI 2003/3142 at **[3590]**).

111 Enforcement notification for contravention of code restrictions

(1) This section applies where—

(a) a person ("the notified provider") has been given a notification under section 110;

(b) OFCOM have allowed the notified provider an opportunity of making representations about the matters notified; and

(c) the period allowed for the making of the representations has expired.

(2) OFCOM may give the notified provider an enforcement notification if they are satisfied—

(a) that he has been in contravention, in one or more of the respects notified, of a requirement specified in the notification under section 110; and

(b) that he has not, during the period allowed under section 110, taken all such steps as they consider appropriate—

(i) for complying with that requirement; and

(ii) for remedying the consequences of the notified contravention of that requirement.

(3) An enforcement notification is a notification which imposes one or both of the following requirements on the notified provider—

(a) a requirement to take such steps for complying with the notified requirement as may be specified in the notification;

(b) a requirement to take such steps for remedying the consequences of the notified contravention as may be so specified.

(4) A decision of OFCOM to give an enforcement notification to a person—

(a) must be notified by them to that person, together with the reasons for the decision, no later than one week after the day on which it is taken; and

(b) must fix a reasonable period for the taking of the steps required by the notification.

(5) It shall be the duty of a person to whom an enforcement notification has been given to comply with it.

(6) That duty shall be enforceable in civil proceedings by OFCOM—

(a) for an injunction;

(b) for specific performance of a statutory duty under section 45 of the Court of Session Act 1988 (c 36); or

(c) for any other appropriate remedy or relief.

[3188]

NOTES

Commencement: 25 July 2003 (for the purpose of enabling network and service functions and spectrum functions to be carried out during the transitional period by the Director General of Telecommunications and the Secretary of State respectively) (see further s 408 and Sch 18 at **[3436]**, **[3460]**, and the Communications Act 2003 (Commencement No 1) Order 2003, SI 2003/1900 at **[3507]**); 29 December 2003 (for the purpose of enabling OFCOM to perform those functions) (see the Office of Communications Act 2002 (Commencement No 3) and Communications Act 2003 (Commencement No 2) Order 2003, SI 2003/3142 at **[3590]**).

112 Penalties for contravention of code restrictions

(1) This section applies (in addition to section 111) where—

(a) a person ("the notified provider") has been given a notification under section 110;
(b) OFCOM have allowed the notified provider an opportunity of making representations about the matters notified; and
(c) the period allowed for the making of the representations has expired.

(2) OFCOM may impose a penalty on the notified provider if he—
(a) has been in contravention, in any of the respects notified, of a requirement specified in the notification under section 110; and
(b) has not, during the period allowed under that section, taken all such steps as they consider appropriate—
(i) for complying with the notified requirement; and
(ii) for remedying the consequences of the notified contravention of that requirement.

(3) Where a notification under section 110 relates to more than one contravention, a separate penalty may be imposed in respect of each contravention.

(4) Where such a notification relates to a continuing contravention, no more than one penalty may be imposed under this section in respect of the period of contravention specified in the notification.

(5) OFCOM may also impose a penalty on the notified provider if he has contravened, or is contravening, a requirement of an enforcement notification.

(6) The amount of a penalty imposed under this section is to be such amount not exceeding £10,000 as OFCOM determine to be—
(a) appropriate; and
(b) proportionate to the contravention in respect of which it is imposed.

(7) In making that determination OFCOM must have regard to—
(a) any representations made to them by the notified provider;
(b) any steps taken by him towards complying with the requirements contraventions of which have been notified to him under section 110; and
(c) any steps taken by him for remedying the consequences of those contraventions.

(8) Where OFCOM impose a penalty on a person under this section, they shall—
(a) within one week of making their decision to impose the penalty, notify that person of that decision and of their reasons for that decision; and
(b) in that notification, fix a reasonable period after it is given as the period within which the penalty is to be paid.

(9) A penalty imposed under this section—
(a) must be paid to OFCOM; and
(b) if not paid within the period fixed by them, is to be recoverable by them accordingly.

(10) The Secretary of State may by order amend this section so as to substitute a different maximum penalty for the maximum penalty for the time being specified in subsection (6).

(11) No order is to be made containing provision authorised by subsection (10) unless a draft of the order has been laid before Parliament and approved by a resolution of each House.
[3189]

NOTES

Commencement: 25 July 2003 (for the purpose of enabling network and service functions and spectrum functions to be carried out during the transitional period by the Director General of Telecommunications and the Secretary of State respectively) (see further s 408 and Sch 18 at **[3436]**, **[3460]**, and the Communications Act 2003 (Commencement No 1) Order 2003, SI 2003/1900 at **[3507]**); 29 December 2003 (for the purpose of enabling OFCOM to perform those functions) (see the Office of Communications Act 2002 (Commencement No 3) and Communications Act 2003 (Commencement No 2) Order 2003, SI 2003/3142 at **[3590]**).

113 Suspension of application of code

(1) OFCOM may suspend the application of the electronic communications code in any person's case if they are satisfied—
(a) that he is or has been in serious and repeated contravention of requirements to pay administrative charges fixed under section 38 (whether in respect of the whole or a part of the charges);

(b) that the bringing of proceedings for the recovery of the amounts outstanding has failed to secure complete compliance by the contravening provider with the requirements to pay the charges fixed in his case, or has no reasonable prospect of securing such compliance;

(c) that an attempt, by the imposition of penalties under section 41, to secure such compliance has failed; and

(d) that the suspension of the application of the code is appropriate and proportionate to the seriousness (when repeated as they have been) of the contraventions.

(2) OFCOM may, to the extent specified in subsection (3), suspend the application in that person's case of the electronic communications code if—

(a) the electronic communications code has been applied by a direction under section 106 in any person's case; and

(b) OFCOM give a direction under section 42, 100, 132 or 140 for the suspension or restriction of that person's entitlement to provide an electronic communications network, or a part of such a network.

(3) The extent, in any person's case, of a suspension under subsection (2) must not go beyond the application of the code for the purposes of so much of an electronic communications network as that person is prohibited from providing by virtue of the suspension or restriction of his entitlement to provide such a network, or part of a network.

(4) OFCOM may, to the extent specified in subsection (5), suspend the application in that person's case of the electronic communications code if—

(a) the electronic communications code has been applied by a direction under section 106 in any person's case; and

(b) that person is a person in whose case there have been repeated and serious contraventions of requirements imposed by virtue of any restrictions or conditions under section 109.

(5) The extent, in any person's case, of a suspension under subsection (4) must not go beyond the following applications of the code in his case—

(a) its application for the purposes of electronic communications networks, or parts of such a network, which are not yet in existence at the time of the suspension;

(b) its application for the purposes of conduit systems, or parts of such systems, which are not yet in existence or not yet used for the purposes of electronic communications networks; and

(c) its application for other purposes in circumstances in which the provision of an electronic communications network, or part of such a network, would not have to cease if its application for those purposes were suspended.

(6) A suspension under this section of the application of the code in any person's case must be by a further direction given to that person by OFCOM under section 106.

(7) The statement required by section 107(8) to be included, in the case of a direction for the purposes of this section, in the statement of OFCOM's proposal is a statement of their proposal to suspend the application of the code.

(8) A suspension of the application of the electronic communications code in any person's case—

(a) shall cease to have effect if the suspension is under subsection (2) and the network suspension or restriction ceases to have effect; but

(b) subject to that shall continue in force until such time (if any) as it is withdrawn by OFCOM.

(9) In subsection (8) the reference to the network suspension or restriction, in relation to a suspension of the application of the electronic communications code, is a reference to the suspension or restriction of an entitlement to provide an electronic communications network, or part of such a network, which is the suspension or restriction by reference to which the application of the code was suspended under subsection (2).

(10) Subject to subsection (11), where the application of the electronic communications code is suspended in a person's case, he shall not, while it is so suspended, be entitled to exercise any right conferred on him by or by virtue of the code.

(11) The suspension, in a person's case, of the application of the electronic communications code does not, except so far as otherwise provided by a scheme contained in an order under section 117—

(a) affect (as between the original parties to it) any agreement entered into for the purposes of the code or any agreement having effect in accordance with it;
(b) affect anything done under the code before the suspension of its application; or
(c) require the removal of, or prohibit the use of, any apparatus lawfully installed on, in or over any premises before that suspension.

(12) Subsection (9) of section 42 applies for the purposes of subsection (1) as it applies for the purposes of that section.

[3190]

NOTES

Commencement: 25 July 2003 (for the purpose of enabling network and service functions and spectrum functions to be carried out during the transitional period by the Director General of Telecommunications and the Secretary of State respectively) (see further s 408 and Sch 18 at **[3436]**, **[3460]**, and the Communications Act 2003 (Commencement No 1) Order 2003, SI 2003/1900 at **[3507]**); 29 December 2003 (for the purpose of enabling OFCOM to perform those functions) (see the Office of Communications Act 2002 (Commencement No 3) and Communications Act 2003 (Commencement No 2) Order 2003, SI 2003/3142 at **[3590]**).

114 Procedure for directions under s 113

(1) Except in an urgent case, OFCOM are not to give a direction under section 113(4) suspending the application of the electronic communications code in the case of any person ("the operator") unless they have—

(a) notified the operator of the proposed suspension and of the steps (if any) that they are proposing to take under section 117;
(b) provided him with an opportunity of making representations about the proposals and of proposing steps for remedying the situation that has given rise to the proposed suspension; and
(c) considered every representation and proposal made to them during the period allowed by them for the operator to take advantage of that opportunity.

(2) That period must be one ending not less than one month after the day of the giving of the notification.

(3) As soon as practicable after giving a direction under section 113 in an urgent case, OFCOM must provide the operator with an opportunity of—

(a) making representations about the effect of the direction and of any steps taken under section 117 in connection with the suspension; and
(b) proposing steps for remedying the situation that has given rise to the situation.

(4) A case is an urgent case for the purposes of this section if OFCOM—

(a) consider that it would be inappropriate, because the circumstances appearing to OFCOM to require the suspension fall within subsection (5), to allow time, before giving a direction under section 113, for the making and consideration of representations; and
(b) decide for that reason to act in accordance with subsection (3), instead of subsection (1).

(5) Circumstances fall within this subsection if they have resulted in, or create an immediate risk of—

(a) a serious threat to the safety of the public, to public health or to national security;
(b) serious economic or operational problems for persons (apart from the operator) who are communications providers or persons who make associated facilities available; or
(c) serious economic or operational problems for persons who make use of electronic communications networks, electronic communications services or associated facilities.

[3191]

NOTES

Commencement: 25 July 2003 (for the purpose of enabling network and service functions and spectrum functions to be carried out during the transitional period by the Director General of Telecommunications and the Secretary of State respectively) (see further s 408 and Sch 18 at **[3436]**, **[3460]**, and the Communications Act 2003 (Commencement No 1) Order 2003, SI 2003/1900 at **[3507]**); 29 December 2003 (for the purpose of enabling OFCOM to perform those functions) (see the Office of Communications Act 2002 (Commencement No 3) and Communications Act 2003 (Commencement No 2) Order 2003, SI 2003/3142 at **[3590]**).

115 Modification and revocation of application of code

(1) OFCOM may at any time modify the terms on which, by virtue of section 106(5), the code is applied in a person's case.

(2) OFCOM may revoke a direction applying the electronic communications code in a person's case if an application for the revocation has been made by that person.

(3) If at any time it appears to OFCOM that a person in whose case the electronic communications code has been applied is not the provider of an electronic communications network or conduit system for the purposes of which the code applies, OFCOM may revoke the direction applying the code in his case.

(4) A modification or revocation under this section shall be by a further direction under section 106 to the person in whose case the electronic communications code has been applied by the direction being modified or revoked.

(5) The matters required by section 107(8) to be included, in the case of a direction for the purposes of this section, in the statement of OFCOM's proposal are whichever of the following is applicable—

(a) a statement of their proposal to modify terms imposed under section 106(5);

(b) a statement of their proposal to revoke the direction applying the code.

[3192]

NOTES

Commencement: 25 July 2003 (for the purpose of enabling network and service functions and spectrum functions to be carried out during the transitional period by the Director General of Telecommunications and the Secretary of State respectively) (see further s 408 and Sch 18 at **[3436]**, **[3460]**, and the Communications Act 2003 (Commencement No 1) Order 2003, SI 2003/1900 at **[3507]**); 29 December 2003 (for the purpose of enabling OFCOM to perform those functions) (see the Office of Communications Act 2002 (Commencement No 3) and Communications Act 2003 (Commencement No 2) Order 2003, SI 2003/3142 at **[3590]**).

116 Notification of cessation by person to whom code applies

(1) This section applies where, by virtue of a direction under section 106, the electronic communications code applies in any person's case for the purposes of the provision by him of—

(a) an electronic communications network which is not of a description designated for the purposes of section 33; or

(b) such a system of conduits as is mentioned in section 106(4)(b).

(2) If that person ceases to provide that network or conduit system, he must notify OFCOM of that fact.

(3) A notification under this section must be given within such period and in such manner as may be required by OFCOM.

(4) OFCOM may impose a penalty on a person who fails to comply with a requirement imposed by or under this section.

(5) The amount of a penalty imposed on a person under this section is to be such amount not exceeding £1,000 as OFCOM may determine to be both—

(a) appropriate; and

(b) proportionate to the matter in respect of which it is imposed.

(6) Where OFCOM impose a penalty on a person under this section, they shall—

(a) within one week of making their decision to impose the penalty, notify that person of that decision and of their reasons for that decision; and

(b) in that notification, fix a reasonable period after it is given as the period within which the penalty is to be paid.

(7) A penalty imposed under this section—

(a) must be paid to OFCOM; and

(b) if not paid within the period fixed by them, is to be recoverable by them accordingly.

(8) The Secretary of State may by order amend this section so as to substitute a different maximum penalty for the maximum penalty for the time being specified in subsection (5).

(9) No order is to be made containing provision authorised by subsection (8) unless a draft of the order has been laid before Parliament and approved by a resolution of each House.
[3193]

NOTES

Commencement: 25 July 2003 (for the purpose of enabling network and service functions and spectrum functions to be carried out during the transitional period by the Director General of Telecommunications and the Secretary of State respectively) (see further s 408 and Sch 18 at **[3436]**, **[3460]**, and the Communications Act 2003 (Commencement No 1) Order 2003, SI 2003/1900 at **[3507]**); 29 December 2003 (for the purpose of enabling OFCOM to perform those functions) (see the Office of Communications Act 2002 (Commencement No 3) and Communications Act 2003 (Commencement No 2) Order 2003, SI 2003/3142 at **[3590]**).

117 Transitional schemes on cessation of application of code

(1) Where it appears to OFCOM—

- (a) that the electronic communications code has ceased or is to cease to apply, to any extent, in the case of any person ("the former operator"),
- (b) that it has ceased or will cease so to apply for either of the reasons specified in subsection (2), and
- (c) that it is appropriate for transitional provision to be made in connection with it ceasing to apply in the case of the former operator,

they may by order make a scheme containing any such transitional provision as they think fit in that case.

(2) Those reasons are—

- (a) the suspension under section 113 of the application of the code in the former operator's case;
- (b) the revocation or modification under section 115 of the direction applying the code in his case.

(3) A scheme contained in an order under this section may, in particular—

- (a) impose any one or more obligations falling within subsection (4) on the former operator;
- (b) provide for those obligations to be enforceable in such manner (otherwise than by criminal penalties) and by such persons as may be specified in the scheme;
- (c) authorise the retention of apparatus on any land pending its subsequent use for the purposes of an electronic communications network, electronic communications service or conduit system to be provided by any person;
- (d) provide for the transfer to such persons as may be specified in, or determined in accordance with, the scheme of any rights or liabilities arising out of any agreement or other obligation entered into or incurred in pursuance of the code by the former operator;
- (e) provide, for the purposes of any provision contained in the scheme by virtue of any of the preceding paragraphs, for such questions arising under the scheme as are specified in the scheme, or are of a description so specified, to be referred to, and determined by, OFCOM.

(4) The obligations referred to in subsection (3)(a) are—

- (a) an obligation to remove anything installed in pursuance of any right conferred by or in accordance with the code;
- (b) an obligation to restore land to its condition before anything was done in pursuance of any such right; or
- (c) an obligation to pay the expenses of any such removal or restoration.

(5) Sections 110 to 112 apply in relation to the requirements imposed by virtue of a scheme contained in an order under this section as they apply in relation to a requirement imposed by virtue of restrictions or conditions under section 109.

(6) Section 403 applies to the power of OFCOM to make an order under this section.
[3194]

NOTES

Commencement: 25 July 2003 (for the purpose of enabling network and service functions and spectrum functions to be carried out during the transitional period by the Director General of Telecommunications and the Secretary of State respectively) (see further s 408 and Sch 18 at **[3436]**, **[3460]**, and the Communications Act 2003 (Commencement No 1) Order 2003, SI 2003/1900 at **[3507]**);

29 December 2003 (for the purpose of enabling OFCOM to perform those functions) (see the Office of Communications Act 2002 (Commencement No 3) and Communications Act 2003 (Commencement No 2) Order 2003, SI 2003/3142 at **[3590]**).

118 Compulsory acquisition of land etc

Schedule 4 (which provides for compulsory acquisition of land by the provider of an electronic communications network in whose case the electronic communications code applies and for entry on land by persons nominated by such a provider) shall have effect.

[3195]

NOTES

Commencement: 25 July 2003 (for the purpose of enabling network and service functions and spectrum functions to be carried out during the transitional period by the Director General of Telecommunications and the Secretary of State respectively) (see further s 408 and Sch 18 at **[3436]**, **[3460]**, and the Communications Act 2003 (Commencement No 1) Order 2003, SI 2003/1900 at **[3507]**); 29 December 2003 (for the purpose of enabling OFCOM to perform those functions) (see the Office of Communications Act 2002 (Commencement No 3) and Communications Act 2003 (Commencement No 2) Order 2003, SI 2003/3142 at **[3590]**).

119 Power to give assistance in relation to certain proceedings

(1) This section applies where any actual or prospective party to any proceedings falling within subsection (2) (other than the operator, within the meaning of the electronic communications code) applies to OFCOM for assistance under this section in relation to those proceedings.

(2) The proceedings falling within this subsection are any actual or prospective proceedings in which there falls to be determined any question arising under, or in connection with—

- (a) the electronic communications code as applied in any person's case by a direction under section 106; or
- (b) any restriction or condition subject to which that code applies.

(3) OFCOM may grant the application if, on any one or more of the following grounds, they think fit to do so—

- (a) on the ground that the case raises a question of principle;
- (b) on the ground that it is unreasonable, having regard to the complexity of the case or to any other matter, to expect the applicant to deal with the case without assistance under this section;
- (c) by reason of any other special consideration.

(4) Assistance by OFCOM under this section may include—

- (a) giving advice or arranging for the giving of advice by a solicitor or counsel;
- (b) procuring or attempting to procure the settlement of the matter in dispute;
- (c) arranging for the giving of any assistance usually given by a solicitor or counsel—
  - (i) in the steps preliminary or incidental to proceedings; or
  - (ii) in arriving at, or giving effect to, a compromise to avoid proceedings or to bring them to an end;
- (d) arranging for representation by a solicitor or counsel;
- (e) arranging for the giving of any other assistance by a solicitor or counsel;
- (f) any other form of assistance which OFCOM consider appropriate.

(5) Nothing in subsection (4)(d) shall be taken to affect the law and practice regulating the descriptions of persons who may appear in, conduct or defend any proceedings, or who may address the court in any proceedings.

(6) In so far as expenses are incurred by OFCOM in providing the applicant with assistance under this section, the recovery of those expenses (as taxed or assessed in such manner as may be prescribed by rules of court) shall constitute a first charge for the benefit of OFCOM—

- (a) on any costs or expenses which (whether by virtue of a judgement or order of a court, or an agreement or otherwise) are payable to the applicant by any other person in respect of the matter in connection with which the assistance is given; and

(b) so far as relates to costs or expenses, on the applicant's rights under a compromise or settlement arrived at in connection with that matter to avoid proceedings, or to bring them to an end.

(7) A charge conferred by subsection (6) is subject to—

(a) any charge imposed by section 10(7) of the Access to Justice Act 1999 (c 22) and any provision made by or under Part 1 of that Act for the payment of any sum to the Legal Services Commission;

(b) any charge or obligation for payment in priority to other debts under the Legal Aid (Scotland) Act 1986 (c 47); or

(c) any charge under the Legal Aid, Advice and Assistance (Northern Ireland) Order 1981 (SI 1981/228 (NI 8)).

[3196]

NOTES

Commencement: 25 July 2003 (for the purpose of enabling network and service functions and spectrum functions to be carried out during the transitional period by the Director General of Telecommunications and the Secretary of State respectively) (see further s 408 and Sch 18 at **[3436]**, **[3460]**, and the Communications Act 2003 (Commencement No 1) Order 2003, SI 2003/1900 at **[3507]**); 29 December 2003 (for the purpose of enabling OFCOM to perform those functions) (see the Office of Communications Act 2002 (Commencement No 3) and Communications Act 2003 (Commencement No 2) Order 2003, SI 2003/3142 at **[3590]**).

Regulation of premium rate services

120 Conditions regulating premium rate services

(1) OFCOM shall have the power, for the purpose of regulating the provision, content, promotion and marketing of premium rate services, to set conditions under this section that bind the persons to whom they are applied.

(2) Conditions under this section may be applied either—

(a) generally to every person who provides a premium rate service; or

(b) to every person who is of a specified description of such persons, or who provides a specified description of such services.

(3) The only provision that may be made by conditions under this section is provision requiring the person to whom the condition applies to comply, to the extent required by the condition, with—

(a) directions given in accordance with an approved code by the enforcement authority and for the purpose of enforcing its provisions; and

(b) if there is no such code, the provisions of the order for the time being in force under section 122.

(4) The power to set a condition under this section includes power to modify or revoke the conditions for the time being in force under this section.

(5) Sections 47 and 48 apply to the setting, modification and revocation of a condition under this section as they apply to the setting, modification and revocation of a condition under section 45.

(6) OFCOM must send a copy of every notification published under section 48(1) with respect to a condition under this section to the Secretary of State.

(7) A service is a premium rate service for the purposes of this Chapter if—

(a) it is a service falling within subsection (8);

(b) there is a charge for the provision of the service;

(c) the charge is required to be paid to a person providing an electronic communications service by means of which the service in question is provided; and

(d) that charge is imposed in the form of a charge made by that person for the use of the electronic communications service.

(8) A service falls within this subsection if its provision consists in—

(a) the provision of the contents of communications transmitted by means of an electronic communications network; or

(b) allowing the user of an electronic communications service to make use, by the making of a transmission by means of that service, of a facility made available to the users of the electronic communications service.

(9) For the purposes of this Chapter a person provides a premium rate service ("the relevant service") if—

(a) he provides the contents of the relevant service;

(b) he exercises editorial control over the contents of the relevant service;

(c) he is a person who packages together the contents of the relevant service for the purpose of facilitating its provision;

(d) he makes available a facility comprised in the relevant service; or

(e) he falls within subsection (10), (11) or (12).

(10) A person falls within this subsection if—

(a) he is the provider of an electronic communications service used for the provision of the relevant service; and

(b) under arrangements made with a person who is a provider of the relevant service falling within subsection (9)(a) to (d), he is entitled to retain some or all of the charges received by him in respect of the provision of the relevant service or of the use of his electronic communications service for the purposes of the relevant service.

(11) A person falls within this subsection if—

(a) he is the provider of an electronic communications network used for the provision of the relevant service; and

(b) an agreement relating to the use of the network for the provision of that service subsists between the provider of the network and a person who is a provider of the relevant service falling within subsection (9)(a) to (d).

(12) A person falls within this subsection if—

(a) he is the provider of an electronic communications network used for the provision of the relevant service; and

(b) the use of that network for the provision of premium rate services, or of services that include or may include premium rate services, is authorised by an agreement subsisting between that person and either an intermediary service provider or a person who is a provider of the relevant service by virtue of subsection (10) or (11).

(13) Where one or more persons are employed or engaged under the direction of another to do any of the things mentioned in subsection (9)(a) to (d), only that other person shall be a provider of the relevant service for the purposes of this Chapter.

(14) References in this section to a facility include, in particular, references to—

(a) a facility for making a payment for goods or services;

(b) a facility for entering a competition or claiming a prize; and

(c) a facility for registering a vote or recording a preference.

(15) In this section—

"approved code" means a code for the time being approved under section 121;

"enforcement authority", in relation to such a code, means the person who under the code has the function of enforcing it; and

"intermediary service provider" means a person who—

(a) provides an electronic communications service used for the provision of the relevant service or an electronic communications network so used; and

(b) is a party to an agreement with—

(i) a provider of the relevant service falling within subsection (9)(a) to (d), or

(ii) another intermediary service provider,

which relates to the use of that electronic communications service or network for the provision of premium rate services, or of services that include or may include premium rate services.

[3197]

NOTES

Commencement: 29 December 2003.

121 Approval of code for premium rate services

(1) If it appears to OFCOM—

(a) that a code has been made by any person for regulating the provision and contents of premium rate services, and the facilities made available in the provision of such services;

(b) that the code contains provision for regulating, to such extent (if any) as they think fit, the arrangements made by the providers of premium rate services for promoting and marketing those services; and

(c) that it would be appropriate for them to approve that code for the purposes of section 120,

they may approve that code for those purposes.

(2) OFCOM are not to approve a code for those purposes unless they are satisfied—

(a) that there is a person who, under the code, has the function of administering and enforcing it; and

(b) that that person is sufficiently independent of the providers of premium rate services;

(c) that adequate arrangements are in force for funding the activities of that person in relation to the code;

(d) that the provisions of the code are objectively justifiable in relation to the services to which it relates;

(e) that those provisions are not such as to discriminate unduly against particular persons or against a particular description of persons;

(f) that those provisions are proportionate to what they are intended to achieve; and

(g) that, in relation to what those provisions are intended to achieve, they are transparent.

(3) OFCOM are not for those purposes to approve so much of a code as imposes an obligation as respects a premium rate service on a person who is a provider of the service by virtue only of section 120(12) ("the relevant provider") unless they are satisfied that the obligation—

(a) arises only if there is no one who is a provider of the service otherwise than by virtue of section 120(12) against whom it is practicable to take action;

(b) arises only after a notice identifying the service and setting out respects in which requirements of the code have been contravened in relation to it has been given to the relevant provider by the person responsible for enforcing the code; and

(c) is confined to an obligation to secure that electronic communications networks provided by the relevant provider are not used for making the service available to persons who are in the United Kingdom.

(4) The provision that may be contained in a code and approved under this section includes, in particular, provision about the pricing of premium rate services and provision for the enforcement of the code.

(5) The provision for the enforcement of a code that may be approved under this section includes—

(a) provision for the payment, to a person specified in the code, of a penalty not exceeding the maximum penalty for the time being specified in section 123(2);

(b) provision requiring a provider of a premium rate service to secure that the provision of the service is suspended or otherwise ceases or is restricted in any respect;

(c) provision for the imposition on a person, in respect of a contravention of the code, of a temporary or permanent prohibition or restriction on his working in connection with the provision of premium rate services or, in the case of a body corporate, on its providing such services or on its carrying on other activities in connection with their provision.

(6) OFCOM may, at any time, for the purposes of section 120—

(a) approve modifications that have been made to an approved code; or

(b) withdraw their approval from an approved code.

(7) Where OFCOM give or withdraw an approval for the purposes of section 120, they must give notification of their approval or of its withdrawal.

(8) The notification must be published in such manner as OFCOM consider appropriate for bringing it to the attention of the persons who, in OFCOM's opinion, are likely to be affected by the approval or withdrawal.

[3198]

NOTES

Commencement: 29 December 2003.

122 Orders by OFCOM in the absence of a code under s 121

(1) OFCOM may make an order under this section if, at any time, they consider that there is no code in force to which they think it would be appropriate to give, or to continue to give, their approval under section 121.

(2) An order under this section may make such of the following provisions as OFCOM think fit—

(a) provision imposing requirements with respect to the provision and contents of premium rate services, and with respect to the facilities made available in the provision of such services (including provision about pricing);
(b) provision imposing requirements with respect to the arrangements made by the providers of premium rate services for the promotion and marketing of those services;
(c) provision for the enforcement of requirements imposed by virtue of paragraph (a) or (b);
(d) provision making other arrangements for the purposes of those requirements.

(3) The power to make provision by an order under this section includes, in particular—

(a) power to establish a body corporate with the capacity to make its own rules and to establish its own procedures;
(b) power to determine the jurisdiction of a body established by such an order or, for the purposes of the order, of any other person;
(c) power to confer jurisdiction with respect to any matter on OFCOM themselves;
(d) power to provide for a person on whom jurisdiction is conferred by the arrangements to make awards of compensation, to direct the reimbursement of costs or expenses, or to do both;
(e) power to provide for such a person to enforce, or to participate in the enforcement of, any awards or directions made under such an order;
(f) power to make provision falling within section 121(5)(c) for the enforcement of the provisions of the order; and
(g) power to make such other provision as OFCOM think fit for the enforcement of such awards and directions.

(4) An order under this section may require such providers of premium rate services as may be determined by or under the order to make payments to OFCOM in respect of expenditure incurred by OFCOM in connection with—

(a) the establishment and maintenance, in accordance with such an order, of any body corporate or procedure; or
(b) the making of other arrangements for the purposes of the requirements of such an order.

(5) An order under this section is not to impose an obligation as respects a premium rate service on a person who is a provider of the service by virtue only of section 120(12) ("the relevant provider") unless the obligation—

(a) arises only if there is no one who is a provider of the service otherwise than by virtue of section 120(12) against whom it is practicable to take action;
(b) arises only after a notice identifying the service and setting out respects in which requirements of the order have been contravened in relation to it has been given to the relevant provider by OFCOM; and
(c) is confined to an obligation to secure that electronic communications networks provided by the relevant provider are not used for making the service available to persons who are in the United Kingdom.

(6) The consent of the Secretary of State is required for the making by OFCOM of an order under this section.

(7) Section 403 applies to the power of OFCOM to make an order under this section.

(8) A statutory instrument containing an order made by OFCOM under this section shall be subject to annulment in pursuance of a resolution of either House of Parliament.
[3199]

NOTES

Commencement: 29 December 2003.

123 Enforcement of s 120 conditions

(1) Sections 94 to 96 apply in relation to a contravention of conditions set under section 120 as they apply in relation to a contravention of a condition set under section 45.

(2) The amount of the penalty imposed under section 96 as applied by this section is to be such amount not exceeding [£250,000] as OFCOM determine to be—

(a) appropriate; and
(b) proportionate to the contravention in respect of which it is imposed.

(3) In making that determination OFCOM must have regard to—

(a) any representations made to them by the notified provider;
(b) any steps taken by him towards complying with the conditions contraventions of which have been notified to him under section 94 (as applied); and
(c) any steps taken by him for remedying the consequences of those contraventions.

(4) The Secretary of State may by order amend this section so as to substitute a different maximum penalty for the maximum penalty for the time being specified in subsection (2).

(5) No order is to be made containing provision authorised by subsection (4) unless a draft of the order has been laid before Parliament and approved by a resolution of each House.
[3200]

NOTES

Commencement: 29 December 2003.

Sub-s (2): sum in square brackets substituted for original sum "£100,000" by the Communications Act 2003 (Maximum Penalty and Disclosure of Information) Order 2005, SI 2005/3469, art 2, except in relation to contraventions of conditions set under s 120 which occurred before 30 December 2005.

Orders: the Communications Act 2003 (Maximum Penalty and Disclosure of Information) Order 2005, SI 2005/3469.

124 Suspending service provision for contraventions of s 120 conditions

(1) OFCOM may give a direction under this section to a person who is a communications provider ("the contravening provider") if they are satisfied—

(a) that he is or has been in serious and repeated contravention of conditions set under section 120;
(b) that an attempt, by the imposition of penalties or the giving of enforcement notifications under section 95 (as applied by section 123) or both, to secure compliance with the contravened conditions has failed;
(c) that the giving of the direction is appropriate and proportionate to the seriousness (when repeated as they have been) of the contraventions; and
(d) that the giving of the direction is required for reasons of public policy.

(2) OFCOM may also give a direction under this section to a person who is a communications provider ("the contravening provider") if they are satisfied—

(a) that he is, or has been, in contravention of conditions set under section 120 in respect of a premium rate service;
(b) that the circumstances of the contravention make it appropriate for OFCOM to suspend or restrict the provision of premium rate services provided by the contravening provider without the conditions set out in subsection (1) being satisfied; and
(c) that in those circumstances the giving of the direction is urgently required for reasons of public policy.

(3) A direction under this section is—

(a) a direction to the contravening provider to secure the suspension of the provision of premium rate services provided by him; or
(b) a direction requiring him to secure compliance with restrictions, set out in the direction, on the provision of such services.

(4) A direction under this section—

(a) must specify the services to which it relates; and

(b) except so far as it otherwise provides, takes effect for an indefinite period beginning with the time at which it is notified to the person to whom it is given.

(5) A direction under this section—

(a) in providing for the effect of a suspension or restriction to be postponed, may provide for it to take effect only at a time determined by or in accordance with the terms of the direction; and

(b) in connection with the suspension or restriction contained in the direction or with the postponement of its effect, may impose such conditions on the contravening provider as appear to OFCOM to be appropriate for the purpose of protecting that provider's customers.

(6) Those conditions may include a condition requiring the making of payments—

(a) by way of compensation for loss or damage suffered by the contravening provider's customers as a result of the direction; or

(b) in respect of annoyance, inconvenience or anxiety to which they have been put in consequence of the direction.

(7) If OFCOM consider it appropriate to do so (whether or not in consequence of representations or proposals made to them), they may revoke a direction under this section or modify its conditions—

(a) with effect from such time as they may direct;

(b) subject to compliance with such requirements as they may specify; and

(c) to such extent and in relation to such services as they may determine.

(8) Sections 102 and 103 apply in the case of a direction under this section as they apply in the case of a direction under section 100, but as if references in section 103(1) to an electronic communications network or electronic communications service were references to a premium rate service.

(9) For the purposes of this section there are repeated contraventions by a person of conditions set under section 120 to the extent that—

(a) in the case of a previous notification given to that person under section 94 (as applied by section 123), OFCOM have determined for the purposes of section 95(2) or 96(2) (as so applied) that such a contravention did occur; and

(b) in the period of twelve months following the day of the making of that determination, one or more further notifications have been given to that person in respect of contraventions of a condition set under section 120.

(10) For the purposes of this section the seriousness of repeated contraventions of conditions set under section 120 has to be determined by reference to the seriousness of the contraventions of the approved code or order by reference to which the conditions have effect. **[3201]**

NOTES

Commencement: 29 December 2003.

Offences relating to networks and services

125 Dishonestly obtaining electronic communications services

(1) A person who—

(a) dishonestly obtains an electronic communications service, and

(b) does so with intent to avoid payment of a charge applicable to the provision of that service,

is guilty of an offence.

(2) It is not an offence under this section to obtain a service mentioned in section 297(1) of the Copyright, Designs and Patents Act 1988 (c 48) (dishonestly obtaining a broadcasting … service provided from a place in the UK).

(3) A person guilty of an offence under this section shall be liable—

(a) on summary conviction, to imprisonment for a term not exceeding six months or to a fine not exceeding the statutory maximum, or to both;

(b) on conviction on indictment, to imprisonment for a term not exceeding five years or to a fine, or to both.

[3202]

NOTES

Commencement: 25 July 2003 (for the purpose of enabling network and service functions and spectrum functions to be carried out during the transitional period by the Director General of Telecommunications and the Secretary of State respectively) (see further s 408 and Sch 18 at **[3436]**, **[3460]**, and the Communications Act 2003 (Commencement No 1) Order 2003, SI 2003/1900 at **[3507]**); 29 December 2003 (for the purpose of enabling OFCOM to perform those functions) (see the Office of Communications Act 2002 (Commencement No 3) and Communications Act 2003 (Commencement No 2) Order 2003, SI 2003/3142 at **[3590]**).

Sub-s (2): words omitted repealed by the Copyright and Related Rights Regulations 2003, SI 2003/2498, reg 2(2), Sch 2; for savings and transitional provisions see regs 30–40 of those Regulations at **[2582B]–[2582L]**.

126 Possession or supply of apparatus etc for contravening s 125

(1) A person is guilty of an offence if, with an intention falling within subsection (3), he has in his possession or under his control anything that may be used—

(a) for obtaining an electronic communications service; or

(b) in connection with obtaining such a service.

(2) A person is guilty of an offence if—

(a) he supplies or offers to supply anything which may be used as mentioned in subsection (1); and

(b) he knows or believes that the intentions in relation to that thing of the person to whom it is supplied or offered fall within subsection (3).

(3) A person's intentions fall within this subsection if he intends—

(a) to use the thing to obtain an electronic communications service dishonestly;

(b) to use the thing for a purpose connected with the dishonest obtaining of such a service;

(c) dishonestly to allow the thing to be used to obtain such a service; or

(d) to allow the thing to be used for a purpose connected with the dishonest obtaining of such a service.

(4) An intention does not fall within subsection (3) if it relates exclusively to the obtaining of a service mentioned in section 297(1) of the Copyright, Designs and Patents Act 1988 (c 48).

(5) A person guilty of an offence under this section shall be liable—

(a) on summary conviction, to imprisonment for a term not exceeding six months or to a fine not exceeding the statutory maximum, or to both; and

(b) on conviction on indictment, to imprisonment for a term not exceeding five years or to a fine, or to both.

(6) In this section, references, in the case of a thing used for recording data, to the use of that thing include references to the use of data recorded by it.

[3203]

NOTES

Commencement: 25 July 2003 (for the purpose of enabling network and service functions and spectrum functions to be carried out during the transitional period by the Director General of Telecommunications and the Secretary of State respectively) (see further s 408 and Sch 18 at **[3436]**, **[3460]**, and the Communications Act 2003 (Commencement No 1) Order 2003, SI 2003/1900 at **[3507]**); 29 December 2003 (for the purpose of enabling OFCOM to perform those functions) (see the Office of Communications Act 2002 (Commencement No 3) and Communications Act 2003 (Commencement No 2) Order 2003, SI 2003/3142 at **[3590]**).

127 Improper use of public electronic communications network

(1) A person is guilty of an offence if he—

(a) sends by means of a public electronic communications network a message or other matter that is grossly offensive or of an indecent, obscene or menacing character; or

(b) causes any such message or matter to be so sent.

(2) A person is guilty of an offence if, for the purpose of causing annoyance, inconvenience or needless anxiety to another, he—

(a) sends by means of a public electronic communications network, a message that he knows to be false;

(b) causes such a message to be sent; or

(c) persistently makes use of a public electronic communications network.

(3) A person guilty of an offence under this section shall be liable, on summary conviction, to imprisonment for a term not exceeding six months or to a fine not exceeding level 5 on the standard scale, or to both.

(4) Subsections (1) and (2) do not apply to anything done in the course of providing a programme service (within the meaning of the Broadcasting Act 1990 (c 42)).

[3204]

NOTES

Commencement: 25 July 2003 (for the purpose of enabling network and service functions and spectrum functions to be carried out during the transitional period by the Director General of Telecommunications and the Secretary of State respectively) (see further s 408 and Sch 18 at **[3436]**, **[3460]**, and the Communications Act 2003 (Commencement No 1) Order 2003, SI 2003/1900 at **[3507]**); 29 December 2003 (for the purpose of enabling OFCOM to perform those functions) (see the Office of Communications Act 2002 (Commencement No 3) and Communications Act 2003 (Commencement No 2) Order 2003, SI 2003/3142 at **[3590]**).

Persistent misuse of network or service

128 Notification of misuse of networks and services

(1) Where OFCOM determine that there are reasonable grounds for believing that a person has persistently misused an electronic communications network or electronic communications services, they may give that person a notification under this section.

(2) A notification under this section is one which—

(a) sets out the determination made by OFCOM;

(b) specifies the use that OFCOM consider constitutes persistent misuse; and

(c) specifies the period during which the person notified has an opportunity of making representations about the matters notified.

(3) That period must not be less than the following—

(a) in an urgent case, seven days; and

(b) in any other case, one month.

(4) A case is an urgent case for the purposes of subsection (3) if OFCOM consider—

(a) that the misuse in question is continuing; and

(b) that the harm it causes makes it necessary for it to be stopped as soon as possible.

(5) For the purposes of this Chapter a person misuses an electronic communications network or electronic communications service if—

(a) the effect or likely effect of his use of the network or service is to cause another person unnecessarily to suffer annoyance, inconvenience or anxiety; or

(b) he uses the network or service to engage in conduct the effect or likely effect of which is to cause another person unnecessarily to suffer annoyance, inconvenience or anxiety.

(6) For the purposes of this Chapter the cases in which a person is to be treated as persistently misusing a network or service include any case in which his misuse is repeated on a sufficient number of occasions for it to be clear that the misuse represents—

(a) a pattern of behaviour or practice; or

(b) recklessness as to whether persons suffer annoyance, inconvenience or anxiety.

(7) For the purpose of determining whether misuse on a number of different occasions constitutes persistent misuse for the purposes of this Chapter, each of the following is immaterial—

(a) that the misuse was in relation to a network on some occasions and in relation to a service on others;

(b) that different networks or services were involved on different occasions; and

(c) that the persons who were or were likely to suffer annoyance inconvenience or anxiety were different on different occasions.

(8) If he considers that appropriate alternative means of dealing with it exists, the Secretary of State may by order provide that a use of a description specified in the order is not to be treated for the purposes of this Chapter as a misuse of an electronic communications network or electronic communications service.

[3205]

NOTES

Commencement: 25 July 2003 (for the purpose of enabling network and service functions and spectrum functions to be carried out during the transitional period by the Director General of Telecommunications and the Secretary of State respectively) (see further s 408 and Sch 18 at **[3436]**, **[3460]**, and the Communications Act 2003 (Commencement No 1) Order 2003, SI 2003/1900 at **[3507]**); 29 December 2003 (for the purpose of enabling OFCOM to perform those functions) (see the Office of Communications Act 2002 (Commencement No 3) and Communications Act 2003 (Commencement No 2) Order 2003, SI 2003/3142 at **[3590]**).

129 Enforcement notifications for stopping persistent misuse

(1) This section applies where—

(a) a person ("the notified misuser") has been given a notification under section 128;

(b) OFCOM have allowed the notified misuser an opportunity of making representations about the matters notified; and

(c) the period allowed for the making of the representations has expired.

(2) OFCOM may give the notified misuser an enforcement notification if they are satisfied—

(a) that he has, in one or more of the notified respects, persistently misused an electronic communications network or electronic communications service; and

(b) that he has not, since the giving of the notification, taken all such steps as OFCOM consider appropriate for—

(i) securing that his misuse is brought to an end and is not repeated; and

(ii) remedying the consequences of the notified misuse.

(3) An enforcement notification is a notification which imposes a requirement on the notified misuser to take all such steps for—

(a) securing that his misuse is brought to an end and is not repeated, and

(b) remedying the consequences of the notified misuse,

as may be specified in the notification.

(4) A decision of OFCOM to give an enforcement notification to a person must fix a reasonable period for the taking of the steps required by the notification.

(5) It shall be the duty of a person to whom an enforcement notification has been given to comply with it.

(6) That duty shall be enforceable in civil proceedings by OFCOM—

(a) for an injunction;

(b) for specific performance of a statutory duty under section 45 of the Court of Session Act 1988 (c 36); or

(c) for any other appropriate remedy or relief.

(7) References in this section to remedying the consequences of misuse include references to paying an amount to a person—

(a) by way of compensation for loss or damage suffered by that person; or

(b) in respect of annoyance, inconvenience or anxiety to which he has been put.

[3206]

NOTES

Commencement: 25 July 2003 (for the purpose of enabling network and service functions and spectrum functions to be carried out during the transitional period by the Director General of Telecommunications and the Secretary of State respectively) (see further s 408 and Sch 18 at **[3436]**, **[3460]**, and the Communications Act 2003 (Commencement No 1) Order 2003, SI 2003/1900 at **[3507]**); 29 December 2003 (for the purpose of enabling OFCOM to perform those functions) (see the Office of Communications Act 2002 (Commencement No 3) and Communications Act 2003 (Commencement No 2) Order 2003, SI 2003/3142 at **[3590]**).

130 Penalties for persistent misuse

(1) This section applies (in addition to section 129) where—

(a) a person ("the notified misuser") has been given a notification under section 128;
(b) OFCOM have allowed the notified misuser an opportunity of making representations about the matters notified; and
(c) the period allowed for the making of the representations has expired.

(2) OFCOM may impose a penalty on the notified misuser if he has, in one or more of the notified respects, persistently misused an electronic communications network or electronic communications service.

(3) OFCOM may also impose a penalty on the notified misuser if he has contravened a requirement of an enforcement notification given in respect of the notified misuse.

(4) The amount of a penalty imposed is to be such amount not exceeding [£50,000] as OFCOM determine to be—
(a) appropriate; and
(b) proportionate to the misuse in respect of which it is imposed.

(5) In making that determination OFCOM must have regard to—
(a) any representations made to them by the notified misuser;
(b) any steps taken by him for securing that his misuse is brought to an end and is not repeated; and
(c) any steps taken by him for remedying the consequences of the notified misuse.

(6) Where OFCOM impose a penalty on a person under this section, they shall—
(a) notify the person penalised; and
(b) in that notification, fix a reasonable period after it is given as the period within which the penalty is to be paid.

(7) A penalty imposed under this section—
(a) must be paid to OFCOM; and
(b) if not paid within the period fixed by them, is to be recoverable by them accordingly.

(8) It is to be possible for a person to be both liable for an offence under sections 125 to 127 and to have a penalty imposed on him under this section in respect of the same conduct.

(9) The Secretary of State may by order amend this section so as to substitute a different maximum penalty for the maximum penalty for the time being specified in subsection (4).

(10) No order is to be made containing provision authorised by subsection (9) unless a draft of the order has been laid before Parliament and approved by a resolution of each House. **[3207]**

NOTES

Commencement: 25 July 2003 (for the purpose of enabling network and service functions and spectrum functions to be carried out during the transitional period by the Director General of Telecommunications and the Secretary of State respectively) (see further s 408 and Sch 18 at **[3436]**, **[3460]**, and the Communications Act 2003 (Commencement No 1) Order 2003, SI 2003/1900 at **[3507]**); 29 December 2003 (for the purpose of enabling OFCOM to perform those functions) (see the Office of Communications Act 2002 (Commencement No 3) and Communications Act 2003 (Commencement No 2) Order 2003, SI 2003/3142 at **[3590]**).

Sub-s (4): sum in square brackets substituted for original sum "£5,000" by the Communications Act 2003 (Maximum Penalty for Persistent Misuse of Network or Service) Order 2006, SI 2006/1032, art 2, except in relation to penalties in respect of any misuse or contraventions which occurred before 6 April 2006.

Orders: the Communications Act 2003 (Maximum Penalty for Persistent Misuse of Network or Service) Order 2006, SI 2006/1032.

---

131 Statement of policy on persistent misuse

(1) It shall be the duty of OFCOM to prepare and publish a statement of their general policy with respect to the exercise of their powers under sections 128 to 130.

(2) OFCOM may from time to time revise that statement as they think fit.

(3) Where OFCOM make or revise their statement of policy under this section, they must publish that statement or (as the case may be) the revised statement in such manner as they consider appropriate for bringing it to the attention of the persons who, in their opinion, are likely to be affected by it.

(4) It shall be the duty of OFCOM, in exercising the powers conferred on them by sections 128 to 130, to have regard to the statement for the time being in force under this section.

[3208]

NOTES

Commencement: 25 July 2003 (for the purpose of enabling network and service functions and spectrum functions to be carried out during the transitional period by the Director General of Telecommunications and the Secretary of State respectively) (see further s 408 and Sch 18 at **[3436]**, **[3460]**, and the Communications Act 2003 (Commencement No 1) Order 2003, SI 2003/1900 at **[3507]**); 29 December 2003 (for the purpose of enabling OFCOM to perform those functions) (see the Office of Communications Act 2002 (Commencement No 3) and Communications Act 2003 (Commencement No 2) Order 2003, SI 2003/3142 at **[3590]**).

Powers to deal with emergencies

132 Powers to require suspension or restriction of a provider's entitlement

(1) If the Secretary of State has reasonable grounds for believing that it is necessary to do so—

(a) to protect the public from any threat to public safety or public health, or

(b) in the interests of national security,

he may, by a direction to OFCOM, require them to give a direction under subsection (3) to a person ("the relevant provider") who provides an electronic communications network or electronic communications service or who makes associated facilities available.

(2) OFCOM must comply with a requirement of the Secretary of State under subsection (1) by giving to the relevant provider such direction under subsection (3) as they consider necessary for the purpose of complying with the Secretary of State's direction.

(3) A direction under this section is—

(a) a direction that the entitlement of the relevant provider to provide electronic communications networks or electronic communications services, or to make associated facilities available, is suspended (either generally or in relation to particular networks, services or facilities); or

(b) a direction that that entitlement is restricted in the respects set out in the direction.

(4) A direction under subsection (3)—

(a) must specify the networks, services and facilities to which it relates; and

(b) except so far as it otherwise provides, takes effect for an indefinite period beginning with the time at which it is notified to the person to whom it is given.

(5) A direction under subsection (3)—

(a) in providing for the effect of a suspension or restriction to be postponed, may provide for it to take effect only at a time determined by or in accordance with the terms of the direction; and

(b) in connection with the suspension or restriction contained in the direction or with the postponement of its effect, may impose such conditions on the relevant provider as appear to OFCOM to be appropriate for the purpose of protecting that provider's customers.

(6) Those conditions may include a condition requiring the making of payments—

(a) by way of compensation for loss or damage suffered by the relevant provider's customers as a result of the direction; or

(b) in respect of annoyance, inconvenience or anxiety to which they have been put in consequence of the direction.

(7) Where OFCOM give a direction under subsection (3), they shall, as soon as practicable after doing so, provide that person with an opportunity of—

(a) making representations about the effect of the direction; and

(b) proposing steps for remedying the situation.

(8) If OFCOM consider it appropriate to do so (whether in consequence of any representations or proposals made to them under subsection (3) or otherwise), they may, without revoking it, at any time modify the terms of a direction under subsection (3) in such manner as they consider appropriate.

(9) If the Secretary of State considers it appropriate to do so, he may, by a direction to OFCOM, require them to revoke a direction under subsection (3).

(10) Where OFCOM modify or revoke a direction they have given under subsection (3), they may do so—

(a) with effect from such time as they may direct;
(b) subject to compliance with such requirements as they may specify; and
(c) to such extent and in relation to such networks, services or facilities, or parts of a network, service or facility, as they may determine.

(11) It shall be the duty of OFCOM to comply with—

(a) a requirement under subsection (9) to revoke a direction; and
(b) a requirement contained in that direction as to how they should exercise their powers under subsection (10) in the case of the required revocation.

[3209]

NOTES

Commencement: 25 July 2003 (for the purpose of enabling network and service functions and spectrum functions to be carried out during the transitional period by the Director General of Telecommunications and the Secretary of State respectively) (see further s 408 and Sch 18 at **[3436]**, **[3460]**, and the Communications Act 2003 (Commencement No 1) Order 2003, SI 2003/1900 at **[3507]**); 29 December 2003 (for the purpose of enabling OFCOM to perform those functions) (see the Office of Communications Act 2002 (Commencement No 3) and Communications Act 2003 (Commencement No 2) Order 2003, SI 2003/3142 at **[3590]**).

133 Enforcement of directions under s 132

(1) A person is guilty of an offence if he provides an electronic communications network or electronic communications service, or makes available any associated facility—

(a) while his entitlement to do so is suspended by a direction under section 132; or

(b) in contravention of a restriction contained in such a direction.

(2) A person guilty of an offence under subsection (1) shall be liable—

(a) on summary conviction, to a fine not exceeding the statutory maximum;

(b) on conviction on indictment, to a fine.

(3) The duty of a person to comply with a condition of a direction under section 132 shall be a duty owed to every person who may be affected by a contravention of the condition.

(4) Where a duty is owed by virtue of subsection (3) to a person—

(a) a breach of the duty that causes that person to sustain loss or damage; and

(b) an act which—
   (i) by inducing a breach of the duty or interfering with its performance, causes that person to sustain loss or damage, and
   (ii) is done wholly or partly for achieving that result,

shall be actionable at the suit or instance of that person.

(5) In proceedings brought against a person by virtue of subsection (4)(a) it shall be a defence for that person to show that he took all reasonable steps and exercised all due diligence to avoid contravening the condition in question.

(6) Sections 94 to 99 apply in relation to a contravention of conditions imposed by a direction under section 132 as they apply in relation to a contravention of conditions set under section 45.

[3210]

NOTES

Commencement: 25 July 2003 (for the purpose of enabling network and service functions and spectrum functions to be carried out during the transitional period by the Director General of Telecommunications and the Secretary of State respectively) (see further s 408 and Sch 18 at **[3436]**, **[3460]**, and the Communications Act 2003 (Commencement No 1) Order 2003, SI 2003/1900 at **[3507]**); 29 December 2003 (for the purpose of enabling OFCOM to perform those functions) (see the Office of Communications Act 2002 (Commencement No 3) and Communications Act 2003 (Commencement No 2) Order 2003, SI 2003/3142 at **[3590]**).

Restrictions in leases and licences

134 Restrictions in leases and licences

(1) This section applies where provision contained in a lease, licence or other agreement relating to premises has the effect of imposing on the occupier a prohibition or restriction under which his choice of—

(a) the person from whom he obtains electronic communications services, or particular electronic communications services, or

(b) the person through whom he arranges to be provided with electronic communications services, or particular electronic communications services,

is confined to a person with an interest in the premises, to a person selected by a person with such an interest or to persons who are one or the other.

(2) This section also applies where—

(a) provision contained in a lease for a year or more has the effect of imposing any other prohibition or restriction on the lessee with respect to an electronic communications matter; or

(b) provision contained in an agreement relating to premises to which a lease for a year or more applies has the effect of imposing a prohibition or restriction on the lessee with respect to such a matter.

(3) A provision falling within subsection (1) shall have effect—

(a) as if the prohibition or restriction applied only where the lessor, licensor or other party to the agreement has not given his consent to a departure from the requirements imposed by the prohibition or restriction; and

(b) as if the lessor, licensor or other party were required not to withhold that consent unreasonably.

(4) A provision falling within subsection (2)(a) or (b) shall have effect—

(a) in relation to things done inside a building occupied by the lessee under the lease, or

(b) for purposes connected with the provision to the lessee of an electronic communications service,

as if the prohibition or restriction applied only where the lessor has not given his consent in relation to the matter in question and as if the lessor were required not to withhold that consent unreasonably.

(5) Where (whether by virtue of this section or otherwise) a provision falling within subsection (1) or (2) imposes a requirement on a lessor, licensor or party to an agreement not unreasonably to withhold his consent—

(a) in relation to an electronic communications matter, or

(b) to the obtaining by the occupier of premises of an electronic communications service from or through a particular person,

the question whether the consent is unreasonably withheld has to be determined having regard to all the circumstances and to the principle that no person should unreasonably be denied access to an electronic communications network or to electronic communications services.

(6) OFCOM may by order provide for this section not to apply in the case of such provisions as may be described in the order.

(7) References in this section to electronic communications matters are references to—

(a) the provision of an electronic communications network or electronic communications service;

(b) the connection of electronic communications apparatus to a relevant electronic communications network or of any such network to another; and

(c) the installation, maintenance, adjustment, repair, alteration or use for purposes connected with the provision of such a network or service of electronic communications apparatus.

(8) In this section—

"alteration" has the same meaning as in the electronic communications code;

"lease" includes—

(a) a leasehold tenancy (whether in the nature of a head lease, sub-lease or under lease) and an agreement to grant such a tenancy, and

(b) in Scotland, a sub-lease and an agreement to grant a sub-lease,

and "lessor" and "lessee" are to be construed accordingly;

"relevant electronic communications network" means—

(a) a public electronic communications network that is specified for the purposes of this section in an order made by the Secretary of State; or
(b) an electronic communications network that is, or is to be, connected (directly or indirectly) to such a network.

(9) This section applies to provisions contained in leases, licences or agreements granted or entered into before the commencement of this section to the extent only that provision to that effect is contained in an order made by OFCOM.

(10) This section is not to be construed as affecting the operation of paragraph 2(3) of the electronic communications code (lessees etc bound by rights granted under code by owners).

(11) The consent of the Secretary of State is required for the making by OFCOM of an order under this section.

(12) Section 403 applies to the powers of OFCOM to make orders under this section.

(13) A statutory instrument containing an order made by OFCOM under this section shall be subject to annulment in pursuance of a resolution of either House of Parliament.

[3211]

NOTES

Commencement: 25 July 2003 (for the purpose of enabling network and service functions and spectrum functions to be carried out during the transitional period by the Director General of Telecommunications and the Secretary of State respectively) (see further s 408 and Sch 18 at **[3436]**, **[3460]**, and the Communications Act 2003 (Commencement No 1) Order 2003, SI 2003/1900 at **[3507]**); 29 December 2003 (for the purpose of enabling OFCOM to perform those functions) (see the Office of Communications Act 2002 (Commencement No 3) and Communications Act 2003 (Commencement No 2) Order 2003, SI 2003/3142 at **[3590]**).

Information provisions

135 Information required for purposes of Chapter 1 functions

(1) OFCOM may require a person falling within subsection (2) to provide them with all such information as they consider necessary for the purpose of carrying out their functions under this Chapter.

(2) The persons falling within this subsection are—
(a) a communications provider;
(b) a person who has been a communications provider;
(c) a person who makes, or has made, any associated facilities available to others;
(d) a person, other than a communications provider, to whom a universal service condition applies or has applied;
(e) a person who supplies electronic communications apparatus;
(f) a person not falling within the preceding paragraphs who appears to OFCOM to have information required by them for the purpose of carrying out their functions under this Chapter.

(3) The information that may be required by OFCOM under subsection (1) includes, in particular, information that they require for any one or more of the following purposes—
(a) ascertaining whether a contravention of a condition or other requirement set or imposed by or under this Chapter has occurred or is occurring;
(b) ascertaining or verifying the charges payable by a person under section 38;
(c) ascertaining whether a provision of a condition set under section 45 which is for the time being in force continues to be effective for the purpose for which it was made;
(d) ascertaining or verifying amounts payable by virtue of a condition falling within section 51(1)(d);
(e) making a designation in accordance with regulations made under section 66;
(f) carrying out a review under section 66 or 70;
(g) identifying markets and carrying out market analyses in accordance with, or for the purposes of, any provision of this Chapter;
(h) ascertaining whether a question has arisen that gives rise to their duty under section 105;
(i) considering a matter in exercise of that duty;

(j) statistical purposes connected with the carrying out of any of OFCOM's functions under this Chapter.

(4) A person required to provide information under this section must provide it in such manner and within such reasonable period as may be specified by OFCOM.

(5) The powers in this section are subject to the limitations in section 137.

[3212]

NOTES

Commencement: 25 July 2003 (for the purpose of enabling network and service functions and spectrum functions to be carried out during the transitional period by the Director General of Telecommunications and the Secretary of State respectively) (see further s 408 and Sch 18 at **[3436]**, **[3460]**, and the Communications Act 2003 (Commencement No 1) Order 2003, SI 2003/1900 at **[3507]**); 29 December 2003 (for the purpose of enabling OFCOM to perform those functions) (see the Office of Communications Act 2002 (Commencement No 3) and Communications Act 2003 (Commencement No 2) Order 2003, SI 2003/3142 at **[3590]**).

136 Information required for related purposes

(1) OFCOM may require—

(a) a communications provider, or

(b) a person who makes associated facilities available to others,

to provide OFCOM with all such information as they consider necessary for the purpose specified in subsection (2).

(2) That purpose is the carrying out—

(a) with a view to publication, and

(b) in the interest of the end-users of public electronic communications services,

of comparative overviews of the quality and prices of such services.

(3) OFCOM may also require—

(a) a communications provider, or

(b) a person who makes associated facilities available to others,

to provide them, for use for such statistical purposes as they think fit, with information relating to any electronic communications network, electronic communications service or associated facilities.

(4) A person required to provide information under this section must provide it in such manner and within such reasonable period as may be specified by OFCOM.

(5) The powers in this section are subject to the limitations in section 137.

[3213]

NOTES

Commencement: 25 July 2003 (for the purpose of enabling network and service functions and spectrum functions to be carried out during the transitional period by the Director General of Telecommunications and the Secretary of State respectively) (see further s 408 and Sch 18 at **[3436]**, **[3460]**, and the Communications Act 2003 (Commencement No 1) Order 2003, SI 2003/1900 at **[3507]**); 29 December 2003 (for the purpose of enabling OFCOM to perform those functions) (see the Office of Communications Act 2002 (Commencement No 3) and Communications Act 2003 (Commencement No 2) Order 2003, SI 2003/3142 at **[3590]**).

137 Restrictions on imposing information requirements

(1) This section limits the purposes for which, and manner in which, information may be required under sections 135 and 136.

(2) OFCOM are not to require the provision of information for the purpose of ascertaining whether a contravention of a general condition has occurred, or is occurring, unless—

(a) the requirement is imposed for the purpose of investigating a matter about which OFCOM have received a complaint;

(b) the requirement is imposed for the purposes of an investigation that OFCOM have decided to carry out into whether or not the general condition in question has been complied with;

(c) the condition in question is one which OFCOM have reason to suspect is one that has been or is being contravened; or

(d) the condition in question is one falling within section 51(1)(d).

(3) OFCOM are not to require the provision of information under section 135 or 136 except—

(a) by a demand for the information that describes the required information and sets out OFCOM's reasons for requiring it; and

(b) where the making of a demand for the information is proportionate to the use to which the information is to be put in the carrying out of OFCOM's functions.

(4) The reasons for requiring information for statistical purposes under section 135 or 136 must set out the statistical purposes for which the information is required.

(5) Except in the case of a demand made in the manner authorised by subsection (6), a demand for information required under section 135 or 136 must be contained in a notice served on the person from whom the information is required.

(6) In the case of information required by OFCOM for the purpose of ascertaining who is liable to charges under section 38, the demand may—

(a) be made by being published in such manner as OFCOM consider appropriate for bringing it to the attention of the persons who are described in the demand as the persons from whom the information is required; and

(b) take the form of a general demand for a person so described to provide information when specified conditions relevant to his liability to such charges are satisfied in his case.

[3214]

NOTES

Commencement: 25 July 2003 (for the purpose of enabling network and service functions and spectrum functions to be carried out during the transitional period by the Director General of Telecommunications and the Secretary of State respectively) (see further s 408 and Sch 18 at **[3436]**, **[3460]**, and the Communications Act 2003 (Commencement No 1) Order 2003, SI 2003/1900 at **[3507]**); 29 December 2003 (for the purpose of enabling OFCOM to perform those functions) (see the Office of Communications Act 2002 (Commencement No 3) and Communications Act 2003 (Commencement No 2) Order 2003, SI 2003/3142 at **[3590]**).

138 Notification of contravention of information requirements

(1) Where OFCOM determine that there are reasonable grounds for believing that a person is contravening, or has contravened, a requirement imposed under section 135 or 136, they may give that person a notification under this section.

(2) A notification under this section is one which—

(a) sets out the determination made by OFCOM;

(b) specifies the requirement and contravention in respect of which that determination has been made; and

(c) specifies the period during which the person notified has an opportunity of doing the things specified in subsection (3).

(3) Those things are—

(a) making representations about the matters notified; and

(b) complying with any notified requirement of which he remains in contravention.

(4) Subject to subsections (5) to (7), the period for doing those things must be the period of one month beginning with the day after the one on which the notification was given.

(5) OFCOM may, if they think fit, allow a longer period for doing those things either—

(a) by specifying a longer period in the notification; or

(b) by subsequently, on one or more occasions, extending the specified period.

(6) The person notified shall have a shorter period for doing those things if a shorter period is agreed between OFCOM and the person notified.

(7) The person notified shall also have a shorter period if—

(a) OFCOM have reasonable grounds for believing that the contravention is a repeated contravention;

(b) they have determined that, in those circumstances, a shorter period would be appropriate; and

(c) the shorter period has been specified in the notification.

(8) A notification under this section—

(a) may be given in respect of more than one contravention; and
(b) if it is given in respect of a continuing contravention, may be given in respect of any period during which the contravention has continued.

(9) Where a notification under this section has been given to a person in respect of a contravention of a requirement, OFCOM may give a further notification in respect of the same contravention of that requirement if, and only if—

(a) the contravention is one occurring after the time of the giving of the earlier notification;
(b) the contravention is a continuing contravention and the subsequent notification is in respect of so much of a period as falls after a period to which the earlier notification relates; or
(c) the earlier notification has been withdrawn without a penalty having been imposed in respect of the notified contravention.

(10) For the purposes of this section a contravention is a repeated contravention, in relation to a notification with respect to that contravention, if—

(a) a previous notification under this section has been given in respect of the same contravention or in respect of another contravention of the same requirement; and
(b) the subsequent notification is given no more than twelve months after the day of the making by OFCOM of a determination for the purposes of section 139(2) that the contravention to which the previous notification related did occur.

[3215]

NOTES

Commencement: 25 July 2003 (for the purpose of enabling network and service functions and spectrum functions to be carried out during the transitional period by the Director General of Telecommunications and the Secretary of State respectively) (see further s 408 and Sch 18 at **[3436]**, **[3460]**, and the Communications Act 2003 (Commencement No 1) Order 2003, SI 2003/1900 at **[3507]**); 29 December 2003 (for the purpose of enabling OFCOM to perform those functions) (see the Office of Communications Act 2002 (Commencement No 3) and Communications Act 2003 (Commencement No 2) Order 2003, SI 2003/3142 at **[3590]**).

139 Penalties for contravention of information requirements

(1) This section applies where—

(a) a person ("the notified person") has been given a notification under section 138;
(b) OFCOM have allowed the notified person an opportunity of making representations about the matters notified; and
(c) the period allowed for the making of the representations has expired.

(2) OFCOM may impose a penalty on the notified person if—

(a) they are satisfied that he has, in one or more of the respects notified, been in contravention of the requirement notified under section 138;
(b) he has not, during the period allowed under that section, complied with the notified requirement; and
(c) no proceedings for an offence under section 144 have been brought against the notified person in respect of the contravention.

(3) Where a notification under section 138 relates to more than one contravention, a separate penalty may be imposed in respect of each contravention.

(4) Where such a notification relates to a continuing contravention, no more than one penalty may be imposed in respect of the period of contravention specified in the notification.

(5) The amount of a penalty imposed under this section is to be such amount not exceeding £50,000 as OFCOM determine to be both—

(a) appropriate; and
(b) proportionate to the contravention in respect of which it is imposed.

(6) In making that determination OFCOM must have regard to—

(a) any representations made to them by the notified person; and
(b) any steps taken by him towards complying with the requirements contraventions of which have been notified to him under section 138.

(7) Where OFCOM impose a penalty on a person under this section, they shall—

(a) within one week of making their decision to impose the penalty, notify that person of that decision and of their reasons for that decision; and

(b) in that notification, fix a reasonable period after it is given as the period within which the penalty is to be paid.

(8) A penalty imposed under this section—

(a) must be paid to OFCOM; and

(b) if not paid within the period fixed by them, is to be recoverable by them accordingly.

(9) The Secretary of State may by order amend this section so as to substitute a different maximum penalty for the maximum penalty for the time being specified in subsection (5).

(10) No order is to be made containing provision authorised by subsection (9) unless a draft of the order has been laid before Parliament and approved by a resolution of each House. **[3216]**

NOTES

Commencement: 25 July 2003 (for the purpose of enabling network and service functions and spectrum functions to be carried out during the transitional period by the Director General of Telecommunications and the Secretary of State respectively) (see further s 408 and Sch 18 at **[3436]**, **[3460]**, and the Communications Act 2003 (Commencement No 1) Order 2003, SI 2003/1900 at **[3507]**); 29 December 2003 (for the purpose of enabling OFCOM to perform those functions) (see the Office of Communications Act 2002 (Commencement No 3) and Communications Act 2003 (Commencement No 2) Order 2003, SI 2003/3142 at **[3590]**).

140 Suspending service provision for information contraventions

(1) OFCOM may give a direction under this section to a person who is a communications provider or who makes associated facilities available ("the contravening provider") if they are satisfied—

(a) that he is or has been in serious and repeated contravention of requirements imposed under sections 135 and 136, or either of them;

(b) the requirements are not requirements imposed for purposes connected with the carrying out of OFCOM's functions in relation to SMP apparatus conditions;

(c) that an attempt, by the imposition of penalties under section 139 or the bringing of proceedings for an offence under section 144, to secure compliance with the contravened requirements has failed; and

(d) that the giving of the direction is appropriate and proportionate to the seriousness (when repeated as they have been) of the contraventions.

(2) A direction under this section is—

(a) a direction that the entitlement of the contravening provider to provide electronic communications networks or electronic communications services, or to make associated facilities available, is suspended (either generally or in relation to particular networks, services or facilities); or

(b) a direction that that entitlement is restricted in the respects set out in the direction.

(3) A direction under this section—

(a) must specify the networks, services and facilities to which it relates; and

(b) except so far as it otherwise provides, takes effect for an indefinite period beginning with the time at which it is notified to the person to whom it is given.

(4) A direction under this section—

(a) in providing for the effect of a suspension or restriction to be postponed, may provide for it to take effect only at a time determined by or in accordance with the terms of the direction; and

(b) in connection with the suspension or restriction contained in the direction or with the postponement of its effect, may impose such conditions on the contravening provider as appear to OFCOM to be appropriate for the purpose of protecting that provider's customers.

(5) Those conditions may include a condition requiring the making of payments—

(a) by way of compensation for loss or damage suffered by the contravening provider's customers as a result of the direction; or

(b) in respect of annoyance, inconvenience or anxiety to which they have been put in consequence of the direction.

(6) If OFCOM consider it appropriate to do so (whether or not in consequence of any representations or proposals made to them), they may revoke a direction under this section or modify its conditions—

(a) with effect from such time as they may direct;
(b) subject to compliance with such requirements as they may specify; and
(c) to such extent and in relation to such networks, services or facilities, or parts of a network, service or facility, as they may determine.

(7) For the purposes of this section there are repeated contraventions by a person of requirements imposed under sections 135 and 136, or either of them, to the extent that—
(a) in the case of a previous notification given to that person under section 138, OFCOM have determined for the purposes of section 139(2) that such a contravention did occur; and
(b) in the period of twelve months following the day of the making of that determination, one or more further notifications have been given to that person in respect of contraventions of such requirements;

and for the purposes of this subsection it shall be immaterial whether the notifications related to the same contravention or to different contraventions of the same or different requirements or of requirements under different sections.

[3217]

NOTES

Commencement: 25 July 2003 (for the purpose of enabling network and service functions and spectrum functions to be carried out during the transitional period by the Director General of Telecommunications and the Secretary of State respectively) (see further s 408 and Sch 18 at **[3436]**, **[3460]**, and the Communications Act 2003 (Commencement No 1) Order 2003, SI 2003/1900 at **[3507]**); 29 December 2003 (for the purpose of enabling OFCOM to perform those functions) (see the Office of Communications Act 2002 (Commencement No 3) and Communications Act 2003 (Commencement No 2) Order 2003, SI 2003/3142 at **[3590]**).

141 Suspending apparatus supply for information contraventions

(1) OFCOM may give a direction under this section to a person who supplies electronic communications apparatus ("the contravening supplier") if they are satisfied—
(a) that he is or has been in serious and repeated contravention of requirements imposed under section 135;
(b) that an attempt, by the imposition of penalties under section 139 or the bringing of proceedings for an offence under section 144, to secure compliance with the contravened requirements has failed; and
(c) that the giving of the direction is appropriate and proportionate to the seriousness (when repeated as they have been) of the contraventions.

(2) A direction under this section is—
(a) a direction to the contravening supplier to cease to act as a supplier of electronic communications apparatus (either generally or in relation to apparatus of a particular description); or
(b) a direction imposing such restrictions as may be set out in the direction on the supply by that supplier of electronic communications apparatus (either generally or in relation to apparatus of a particular description).

(3) A direction under this section takes effect, except so far as it otherwise provides, for an indefinite period beginning with the time at which it is notified to the person to whom it is given.

(4) A direction under this section—
(a) may provide for a prohibition or restriction to take effect only at a time determined by or in accordance with the terms of the direction; and
(b) in connection with a prohibition or restriction contained in the direction or with the postponement of its effect, may impose such conditions on the contravening supplier as appear to OFCOM to be appropriate for the purpose of protecting that supplier's customers.

(5) Those conditions may include a condition requiring the making of payments—
(a) by way of compensation for loss or damage suffered by the contravening supplier's customers as a result of the direction; or
(b) in respect of annoyance, inconvenience or anxiety to which they have been put in consequence of the direction.

(6) If OFCOM consider it appropriate to do so (whether or not in consequence of representations or proposals made to them), they may revoke a direction under this section or modify its conditions—

(a) with effect from such time as they may direct;
(b) subject to compliance with such requirements as they may specify; and
(c) to such extent and in relation to such apparatus or descriptions of apparatus as they may determine.

(7) For the purposes of this section contraventions by a person of requirements imposed under section 135 are repeated contraventions if—
(a) in the case of a previous notification given to that person under section 138, OFCOM have determined for the purposes of section 139(2) that such a contravention did occur; and
(b) in the period of twelve months following the day of the making of that determination, one or more further notifications have been given to that person in respect of contraventions of such requirements;

and for the purposes of this subsection it shall be immaterial whether the notifications related to the same contravention or to different contraventions of the same or different requirements. **[3218]**

NOTES

Commencement: 25 July 2003 (for the purpose of enabling network and service functions and spectrum functions to be carried out during the transitional period by the Director General of Telecommunications and the Secretary of State respectively) (see further s 408 and Sch 18 at **[3436]**, **[3460]**, and the Communications Act 2003 (Commencement No 1) Order 2003, SI 2003/1900 at **[3507]**); 29 December 2003 (for the purpose of enabling OFCOM to perform those functions) (see the Office of Communications Act 2002 (Commencement No 3) and Communications Act 2003 (Commencement No 2) Order 2003, SI 2003/3142 at **[3590]**).

142 Procedure for directions under ss 140 and 141

(1) Except in an urgent case, OFCOM are not to give a direction under section 140 or 141 unless they have—
(a) notified the contravening provider or contravening supplier of the proposed direction and of the conditions (if any) which they are proposing to impose by that direction;
(b) provided him with an opportunity of making representations about the proposals and of proposing steps for remedying the situation; and
(c) considered every representation and proposal made to them during the period allowed by them for the contravening provider or the contravening supplier to take advantage of that opportunity.

(2) That period must be one ending not less than one month after the day of the giving of the notification.

(3) As soon as practicable after giving a direction under section 140 or 141 in an urgent case, OFCOM must provide the contravening provider or contravening supplier with an opportunity of—
(a) making representations about the effect of the direction and of any of its conditions; and
(b) proposing steps for remedying the situation.

(4) A case is an urgent case for the purposes of this section if OFCOM—
(a) consider that it would be inappropriate, because the contraventions in question fall within subsection (5), to allow time, before giving a direction under section 140 or 141, for the making and consideration of representations; and
(b) decide for that reason to act in accordance with subsection (3), instead of subsection (1).

(5) The contraventions fall within this subsection if they have resulted in, or create an immediate risk of—
(a) a serious threat to the safety of the public, to public health or to national security;
(b) serious economic or operational problems for persons (apart from the contravening provider or contravening supplier) who are communications providers or persons who make associated facilities available; or
(c) serious economic or operational problems for persons who make use of electronic communications networks, electronic communications services or associated facilities.

(6) In this section—

"contravening provider" has the same meaning as in section 140; and
"contravening supplier" has the same meaning as in section 141.

[3219]

NOTES

Commencement: 25 July 2003 (for the purpose of enabling network and service functions and spectrum functions to be carried out during the transitional period by the Director General of Telecommunications and the Secretary of State respectively) (see further s 408 and Sch 18 at **[3436]**, **[3460]**, and the Communications Act 2003 (Commencement No 1) Order 2003, SI 2003/1900 at **[3507]**); 29 December 2003 (for the purpose of enabling OFCOM to perform those functions) (see the Office of Communications Act 2002 (Commencement No 3) and Communications Act 2003 (Commencement No 2) Order 2003, SI 2003/3142 at **[3590]**).

143 Enforcement of directions under ss 140 and 141

(1) A person is guilty of an offence if he provides an electronic communications network or electronic communications service, or makes available any associated facility—

(a) while his entitlement to do so is suspended by a direction under section 140; or
(b) in contravention of a restriction contained in such a direction.

(2) A person is guilty of an offence if he supplies electronic communications apparatus—

(a) while prohibited from doing so by a direction under section 141; or
(b) in contravention of a restriction contained in such a direction.

(3) A person guilty of an offence under this section shall be liable—

(a) on summary conviction, to a fine not exceeding the statutory maximum;
(b) on conviction on indictment, to a fine.

(4) Sections 94 to 99 apply in relation to a contravention of conditions imposed by a direction under section 140 or 141 as they apply in relation to a contravention of conditions set under section 45.

[3220]

NOTES

Commencement: 25 July 2003 (for the purpose of enabling network and service functions and spectrum functions to be carried out during the transitional period by the Director General of Telecommunications and the Secretary of State respectively) (see further s 408 and Sch 18 at **[3436]**, **[3460]**, and the Communications Act 2003 (Commencement No 1) Order 2003, SI 2003/1900 at **[3507]**); 29 December 2003 (for the purpose of enabling OFCOM to perform those functions) (see the Office of Communications Act 2002 (Commencement No 3) and Communications Act 2003 (Commencement No 2) Order 2003, SI 2003/3142 at **[3590]**).

144 Offences in connection with information requirements

(1) A person who fails to provide information in accordance with a requirement of OFCOM under section 135 or 136 is guilty of an offence and shall be liable—

(a) on summary conviction, to a fine not exceeding the statutory maximum;
(b) on conviction on indictment, to a fine.

(2) In proceedings against a person for an offence under subsection (1) it shall be a defence for that person to show—

(a) that it was not reasonably practicable for him to comply with the requirement within the period specified by OFCOM; but
(b) that he has taken all reasonable steps to provide the required information after the end of that period.

(3) A person is guilty of an offence if—

(a) in pursuance of any requirement under section 135 or 136, he provides any information that is false in any material particular; and
(b) at the time he provides it, he either knows it to be false or is reckless as to whether or not it is false.

(4) A person guilty of an offence under subsection (3) shall be liable—

(a) on summary conviction, to a fine not exceeding the statutory maximum;
(b) on conviction on indictment, to imprisonment for a term not exceeding two years or to a fine, or to both.

(5) Proceedings for an offence under subsection (1) may be brought in respect of a contravention by a person of a requirement imposed under section 135 or 136 only if—

(a) OFCOM have given the person a notification under section 138 in respect of that contravention;

(b) the period allowed under that section for doing the things mentioned in subsection (3) of that section has expired without the required information having been provided; and

(c) OFCOM have not imposed a financial penalty under section 139 in respect of that contravention.

[3221]

NOTES

Commencement: 25 July 2003 (for the purpose of enabling network and service functions and spectrum functions to be carried out during the transitional period by the Director General of Telecommunications and the Secretary of State respectively) (see further s 408 and Sch 18 at **[3436]**, **[3460]**, and the Communications Act 2003 (Commencement No 1) Order 2003, SI 2003/1900 at **[3507]**); 29 December 2003 (for the purpose of enabling OFCOM to perform those functions) (see the Office of Communications Act 2002 (Commencement No 3) and Communications Act 2003 (Commencement No 2) Order 2003, SI 2003/3142 at **[3590]**).

145 Statement of policy on information gathering

(1) It shall be the duty of OFCOM to prepare and publish a statement of their general policy with respect to—

(a) the exercise of their powers under sections 135 to 136; and

(b) the uses to which they are proposing to put information obtained under those sections.

(2) OFCOM may from time to time revise that statement as they think fit.

(3) Where OFCOM make or revise their statement of policy under this section, they must publish that statement or (as the case may be) the revised statement in such manner as they consider appropriate for bringing it to the attention of the persons who, in their opinion, are likely to be affected by it.

(4) It shall be the duty of OFCOM, in exercising the powers conferred on them by sections 135 to 144 to have regard to the statement for the time being in force under this section.

[3222]

NOTES

Commencement: 25 July 2003 (for the purpose of enabling network and service functions and spectrum functions to be carried out during the transitional period by the Director General of Telecommunications and the Secretary of State respectively) (see further s 408 and Sch 18 at **[3436]**, **[3460]**, and the Communications Act 2003 (Commencement No 1) Order 2003, SI 2003/1900 at **[3507]**); 29 December 2003 (for the purpose of enabling OFCOM to perform those functions) (see the Office of Communications Act 2002 (Commencement No 3) and Communications Act 2003 (Commencement No 2) Order 2003, SI 2003/3142 at **[3590]**).

146 Provision of information by OFCOM

(1) OFCOM must comply with a request made by a person for the purposes of this section—

(a) to notify the person whether or not a notification is required to be submitted by him under section 33;

(b) to notify the person whether a notification submitted by him for the purposes of that section satisfies the requirements of this Chapter;

(c) to provide the person with such information about his rights as may be necessary for the purpose of facilitating the negotiation by him of his right to network access; or

(d) to provide the person with such information as they consider necessary to enable the applicant to apply for a direction under section 106 to be made in his case.

(2) A request for the purposes of this section must be made in such manner as OFCOM may require.

(3) OFCOM are not required to comply with a request under this section if (without having been asked to do so) they have already given that person the notification or information for which he is asking.

(4) Any notification or information which under subsection (1) must be given or provided by OFCOM must be given or provided before the end of the period of one week beginning with the day on which the request for the notification or information was made to OFCOM.

[3223]

NOTES

Commencement: 25 July 2003 (for the purpose of enabling network and service functions and spectrum functions to be carried out during the transitional period by the Director General of Telecommunications and the Secretary of State respectively) (see further s 408 and Sch 18 at **[3436]**, **[3460]**, and the Communications Act 2003 (Commencement No 1) Order 2003, SI 2003/1900 at **[3507]**); 29 December 2003 (for the purpose of enabling OFCOM to perform those functions) (see the Office of Communications Act 2002 (Commencement No 3) and Communications Act 2003 (Commencement No 2) Order 2003, SI 2003/3142 at **[3590]**).

Abolition of telecommunications licensing etc

147 (*Repeals the Telecommunications Act 1984, ss 5–19, 27A–27L.*)

Local authority powers in relation to networks and services

148 Powers of local authorities in connection with networks

(1) A local authority may borrow money for the purpose of providing a public electronic communications network or public electronic communications service.

(2) A local authority may—

(a) provide a public electronic communications network part of which is outside their area; and

(b) provide a public electronic communications service even if some of the persons to whom they provide the service are outside their area.

(3) In this section, a "local authority" means—

(a) in relation to England, a London borough council or a district council;

(b) in relation to Wales, a county council or a county borough council;

(c) in Scotland, a council constituted under section 2 of the Local Government etc (Scotland) Act 1994 (c 39).

[3224]

NOTES

Commencement: 25 July 2003 (for the purpose of enabling network and service functions and spectrum functions to be carried out during the transitional period by the Director General of Telecommunications and the Secretary of State respectively) (see further s 408 and Sch 18 at **[3436]**, **[3460]**, and the Communications Act 2003 (Commencement No 1) Order 2003, SI 2003/1900 at **[3507]**); 29 December 2003 (for the purpose of enabling OFCOM to perform those functions) (see the Office of Communications Act 2002 (Commencement No 3) and Communications Act 2003 (Commencement No 2) Order 2003, SI 2003/3142 at **[3590]**).

Grants for networks and services in Northern Ireland

149 Grants by Department of Enterprise, Trade and Investment

(1) The Department of Enterprise, Trade and Investment may, in accordance with this section, make payments to persons engaged in, or in commercial activities connected with—

(a) the provision of electronic communications networks and electronic communications services in Northern Ireland; or

(b) improving the extent, quality and reliability of such networks or services.

(2) A payment shall not be made under this section unless in the opinion of the Department of Enterprise, Trade and Investment—

(a) the making of the payment is likely to achieve—

(i) one or more of the purposes set out in subsection (1); and

(ii) any other purposes prescribed by regulations made by that Department with the approval of the Department of Finance and Personnel; and

(b) the amount of the payment is reasonable having regard to all the circumstances.

(3) Payments under this section shall—

(a) be of such amounts, and

(b) be made subject to such conditions (including conditions as to repayment),

as the Department of Enterprise, Trade and Investment may determine.

(4) This section extends only to Northern Ireland.

[3225]

NOTES

Commencement: 25 July 2003 (for the purpose of enabling network and service functions and spectrum functions to be carried out during the transitional period by the Director General of Telecommunications and the Secretary of State respectively) (see further s 408 and Sch 18 at **[3436]**, **[3460]**, and the Communications Act 2003 (Commencement No 1) Order 2003, SI 2003/1900 at **[3507]**); 29 December 2003 (for the purpose of enabling OFCOM to perform those functions) (see the Office of Communications Act 2002 (Commencement No 3) and Communications Act 2003 (Commencement No 2) Order 2003, SI 2003/3142 at **[3590]**).

150 Grants by district councils

(1) This section applies where a district council in Northern Ireland consider that it would be for the benefit of their area—

(a) for a public electronic communications network or electronic communications service to be provided by a particular person;

(b) for facilities to be made available by a particular person for the purposes of, or in connection with, the provision of such a network or service; or

(c) for such a network or service that is being provided by a particular person, or for any such facilities that are being so made available by a particular person, to continue to be provided or made available.

(2) The district council may—

(a) undertake to pay to that person, and

(b) pay him,

whatever sums they think appropriate for, or towards, compensating him for losses sustained in the provision of the network or service or in making the facilities available.

(3) For the purposes of this section it is immaterial—

(a) in the case of a network, whether any part of the network is situated in the council's area; and

(b) in the case of a service or facility, whether any of the persons to whom the service or facility is provided or made available are in that area.

[3226]

NOTES

Commencement: 25 July 2003 (for the purpose of enabling network and service functions and spectrum functions to be carried out during the transitional period by the Director General of Telecommunications and the Secretary of State respectively) (see further s 408 and Sch 18 at **[3436]**, **[3460]**, and the Communications Act 2003 (Commencement No 1) Order 2003, SI 2003/1900 at **[3507]**); 29 December 2003 (for the purpose of enabling OFCOM to perform those functions) (see the Office of Communications Act 2002 (Commencement No 3) and Communications Act 2003 (Commencement No 2) Order 2003, SI 2003/3142 at **[3590]**).

Interpretation of Chapter 1

151 Interpretation of Chapter 1

(1) In this Chapter—

"the Access Directive" means Directive 2002/19/EC of the European Parliament and of the Council on access to, and interconnection of, electronic communications networks and associated facilities;

"access-related condition" means a condition set as an access-related condition under section 45;

"allocation" and "adoption", in relation to telephone numbers, and cognate expressions, are to be construed in accordance with section 56;

"apparatus market", in relation to a market power determination, is to be construed in accordance with section 46(9)(b);

"designated universal service provider" means a person who is for the time being designated in accordance with regulations under section 66 as a person to whom universal service conditions are applicable;

"electronic communications apparatus"—

(a) in relation to SMP apparatus conditions and in section 141, means apparatus that is designed or adapted for a use which consists of or includes the sending or receiving of communications or other signals (within the meaning of section 32) that are transmitted by means of an electronic communications network; and

(b) in all other contexts, has the same meaning as in the electronic communications code;

"the electronic communications code" has the meaning given by section 106(1);

"end-user", in relation to a public electronic communications service, means—

(a) a person who, otherwise than as a communications provider, is a customer of the provider of that service;

(b) a person who makes use of the service otherwise than as a communications provider; or

(c) a person who may be authorised, by a person falling within paragraph (a), so to make use of the service;

"the Framework Directive" means Directive 2002/21/EC of the European Parliament and of the Council on a common regulatory framework for electronic communications networks and services;

"general condition" means a condition set as a general condition under section 45;

"interconnection" is to be construed in accordance with subsection (2);

"market power determination" means—

(a) a determination, for the purposes of provisions of this Chapter, that a person has significant market power in an identified services market or an identified apparatus market; or

(b) a confirmation for such purposes of a market power determination reviewed on a further analysis under section 84 or 85;

"misuse", in relation to an electronic communications network or electronic communications service, is to be construed in accordance with section 128(5) and (8), and cognate expressions are to be construed accordingly;

"network access" is to be construed in accordance with subsection (3);

"persistent" and "persistently", in relation to misuse of an electronic communications network or electronic communications service, are to be construed in accordance with section 128(6) and (7);

"premium rate service" is to be construed in accordance with section 120(7);

"privileged supplier condition" means a condition set as a privileged supplier condition under section 45;

"provider", in relation to a premium rate service, is to be construed in accordance with section 120(9) to (12), and cognate expressions are to be construed accordingly;

"public communications provider" means—

(a) a provider of a public electronic communications network;

(b) a provider of a public electronic communications service; or

(c) a person who makes available facilities that are associated facilities by reference to a public electronic communications network or a public electronic communications service;

"public electronic communications network" means an electronic communications network provided wholly or mainly for the purpose of making electronic communications services available to members of the public;

"public electronic communications service" means any electronic communications service that is provided so as to be available for use by members of the public;

"regulatory authorities" is to be construed in accordance with subsection (5);

"relevant international standards" means—

(a) any standards or specifications from time to time drawn up and published in accordance with Article 17 of the Framework Directive;

(b) the standards and specifications from time to time adopted by—

(i) the European Committee for Standardisation;

(ii) the European Committee for Electrotechnical Standardisation; or

(iii) the European Telecommunications Standards Institute; and

(c) the international standards and recommendations from time to time adopted by—

(i) the International Telecommunication Union;
(ii) the International Organisation for Standardisation; or
(iii) the International Electrotechnical Committee;

"service interoperability" means interoperability between different electronic communications services;

"services market", in relation to a market power determination or market identification, is to be construed in accordance with section 46(8)(a);

"significant market power" is to be construed in accordance with section 78;

"SMP condition" means a condition set as an SMP condition under section 45, and "SMP services condition" and "SMP apparatus condition" are to be construed in accordance with subsections (8) and (9) of that section respectively;

"telephone number" has the meaning given by section 56(5);

"the Universal Service Directive" means Directive 2002/22/EC of the European Parliament and of the Council on universal service and users' rights relating to electronic communications networks and services;

"universal service condition" means a condition set as a universal service condition under section 45;

"the universal service order" means the order for the time being in force under section 65.

(2) In this Chapter references to interconnection are references to the linking (whether directly or indirectly by physical or logical means, or by a combination of physical and logical means) of one public electronic communications network to another for the purpose of enabling the persons using one of them to be able—

(a) to communicate with users of the other one; or
(b) to make use of services provided by means of the other one (whether by the provider of that network or by another person).

(3) In this Chapter references to network access are references to—

(a) interconnection of public electronic communications networks; or
(b) any services, facilities or arrangements which—
(i) are not comprised in interconnection; but
(ii) are services, facilities or arrangements by means of which a communications provider or person making available associated facilities is able, for the purposes of the provision of an electronic communications service (whether by him or by another), to make use of anything mentioned in subsection (4);

and references to providing network access include references to providing any such services, making available any such facilities or entering into any such arrangements.

(4) The things referred to in subsection (3)(b) are—

(a) any electronic communications network or electronic communications service provided by another communications provider;
(b) any apparatus comprised in such a network or used for the purposes of such a network or service;
(c) any facilities made available by another that are associated facilities by reference to any network or service (whether one provided by that provider or by another);
(d) any other services or facilities which are provided or made available by another person and are capable of being used for the provision of an electronic communications service.

(5) References in this Chapter to the regulatory authorities of member States are references to such of the authorities of the member States as have been notified to the European Commission as the regulatory authorities of those States for the purposes of the Framework Directive.

(6) For the purposes of this Chapter, where there is a contravention of an obligation that requires a person to do anything within a particular period or before a particular time, that contravention shall be taken to continue after the end of that period, or after that time, until that thing is done.

(7) References in this Chapter to remedying the consequences of a contravention include references to paying an amount to a person—

(a) by way of compensation for loss or damage suffered by that person; or
(b) in respect of annoyance, inconvenience or anxiety to which he has been put.

(8) In determining for the purposes of provisions of this Chapter whether a contravention is a repeated contravention for any purposes, a notification of a contravention under that provision shall be disregarded if it has been withdrawn before the imposition of a penalty in respect of the matters notified.

(9) For the purposes of this section a service is made available to members of the public if members of the public are customers, in respect of that service, of the provider of that service.

[3227]

NOTES

Commencement: 25 July 2003 (for the purpose of enabling network and service functions and spectrum functions to be carried out during the transitional period by the Director General of Telecommunications and the Secretary of State respectively) (see further s 408 and Sch 18 at **[3436]**, **[3460]**, and the Communications Act 2003 (Commencement No 1) Order 2003, SI 2003/1900 at **[3507]**); 29 December 2003 (for the purpose of enabling OFCOM to perform those functions) (see the Office of Communications Act 2002 (Commencement No 3) and Communications Act 2003 (Commencement No 2) Order 2003, SI 2003/3142 at **[3590]**).

CHAPTER 2
SPECTRUM USE

General functions relating to spectrum use

152 General functions of OFCOM in relation to radio spectrum

(*1*) *It shall be a function of OFCOM—*

(*a*) *to give such advice in relation to the use of the electro-magnetic spectrum for wireless telegraphy;*

(*b*) *to provide such other services; and*

(*c*) *to maintain such records;*

as they consider appropriate for the purpose of facilitating or managing the use of that spectrum for wireless telegraphy.

(*2*) *It shall be a function of OFCOM, in relation to the use of the electro-magnetic spectrum for wireless telegraphy—*

(*a*) *to give such further advice,*

(*b*) *to provide such other services, and*

(*c*) *to maintain such other records,*

as the Secretary of State may, for the purpose of securing compliance with the international obligations of the United Kingdom, require them to provide.

(*3*) *The advice, the other services and the records that OFCOM may give, provide or maintain under this section include advice, other services and records with respect to the use of the electro-magnetic spectrum at places outside the United Kingdom.*

(*4*) *The powers of OFCOM to carry out research, or to arrange for others to carry out research, are to be exercisable, in particular, for ascertaining, for the purpose of carrying out their functions under this section, information about—*

(*a*) *the demands for use of the electro-magnetic spectrum for wireless telegraphy in the United Kingdom;*

(*b*) *the effects, in the United Kingdom, of any such use of that spectrum;*

(*c*) *likely future developments in relation to those matters; and*

(*d*) *any other connected matters that OFCOM think relevant.*

(*5*) *OFCOM may make a grant to any person if, in their opinion, the making of the grant is likely to promote—*

(*a*) *the efficient use in the United Kingdom of the electro-magnetic spectrum for wireless telegraphy; or*

(*b*) *the efficient management of that use.*

(*6*) *A grant—*

(*a*) *may be made to a person holding a wireless telegraphy licence or a grant of recognised spectrum access under section 159 or to any other person; and*

(*b*) *is to be made on such terms and conditions as OFCOM consider appropriate;*

and those terms and conditions may include terms requiring the repayment of the grant in specified circumstances.

(*7*) *The consent of the Treasury is to be required—*

(*a*) *for the making of a grant under subsection (5); and*

(*b*) *for the terms and conditions on which such a grant is made.*

(*8*) *Where OFCOM are required to give advice or provide another service to a person under this section, they are to be entitled to make the giving of the advice or the provision of the other service conditional on the payment to them of such sums—*

(*a*) *as they may determine in advance; or*

(*b*) *as may be agreed between them and that person.*

(*9*) *In this section references to providing a service to a person include references to a service consisting in—*

(*a*) *the entry of that person's particulars in a register or other record kept by OFCOM for the purpose of carrying out their functions under this section; or*

(*b*) *the taking of steps for the purposes of determining whether to grant an application for an entry in a register or record so kept.*

[3228]

NOTES

Commencement: 25 July 2003 (sub-ss (1), (3), (9), for the purpose of enabling network and service functions and spectrum functions to be carried out during the transitional period by the Director General of Telecommunications and the Secretary of State respectively) (see further s 408 and Sch 18 at **[3436]**, **[3460]**, and the Communications Act 2003 (Commencement No 1) Order 2003, SI 2003/1900 at **[3507]**); 29 December 2003 (otherwise).

This section and ss 153–184 (Ch 2) repealed by the Wireless Telegraphy Act 2006, s 125(1), Sch 9, Pt 1, subject to transitional provisions and savings in s 124 of, Sch 8, Pt 1, paras 1–8, 15, 17, 22, 24 to, that Act at **[4230]**, **[4239]**.

153 United Kingdom Plan for Frequency Authorisation

(*1*) *It shall be the duty of OFCOM, from time to time as they think fit, to publish a document (to be known as "the United Kingdom Plan for Frequency Authorisation").*

(*2*) *The plan must set out—*

(*a*) *the frequencies that, in relation to the United Kingdom, have been allocated for particular purposes for wireless telegraphy and are available for assignment; and*

(*b*) *the purposes for which the different frequencies have been allocated.*

[3229]

NOTES

Commencement: 25 July 2003 (for the purpose of enabling network and service functions and spectrum functions to be carried out during the transitional period by the Director General of Telecommunications and the Secretary of State respectively) (see further s 408 and Sch 18 at **[3436]**, **[3460]**, and the Communications Act 2003 (Commencement No 1) Order 2003, SI 2003/1900 at **[3507]**); 29 December 2003 (for the purpose of enabling OFCOM to perform those functions) (see the Office of Communications Act 2002 (Commencement No 3) and Communications Act 2003 (Commencement No 2) Order 2003, SI 2003/3142 at **[3590]**).

Repealed as noted to s 152 at **[3228]**.

154 Duties of OFCOM when carrying out spectrum functions

(*1*) *It shall be the duty of OFCOM, in carrying out their functions under the enactments relating to the management of the radio spectrum, to have regard, in particular, to—*

(*a*) *the extent to which the electro-magnetic spectrum is available for use, or further use, for wireless telegraphy;*

(*b*) *the demand for use of that spectrum for wireless telegraphy; and*

(*c*) *the demand that is likely to arise in future for the use of that spectrum for wireless telegraphy.*

(*2*) *It shall also be their duty, in carrying out their functions under those enactments to have regard, in particular, to the desirability of promoting—*

(*a*) *the efficient management and use of the part of the electro-magnetic spectrum available for wireless telegraphy;*

(*b*) *the economic and other benefits that may arise from the use of wireless telegraphy;*

(*c*) *the development of innovative services; and*
(*d*) *competition in the provision of electronic communications services.*

(*3*) *In the application of this section to the functions of OFCOM under the enactments relating to the management of the radio spectrum other than section 2 of the Wireless Telegraphy Act 1998 (c 6) (exercise of power to prescribe wireless telegraphy licence fees), OFCOM may disregard such of the matters mentioned in the preceding subsections as appear to them—*

(*a*) *to be matters to which they are not required to have regard apart from this section; and*
(*b*) *to have no application to the case in question.*

(*4*) *Where it appears to OFCOM that any of their duties under this section conflict with one or more of their duties under sections 3 to 6, priority must be given to their duties under those sections.*

(*5*) *Where it appears to OFCOM that any of their duties under this section conflict with each other in a particular case, they must secure that the conflict is resolved in the manner they think best in the circumstances.*

[3230]

NOTES

Commencement: 25 July 2003 (for the purpose of enabling network and service functions and spectrum functions to be carried out during the transitional period by the Director General of Telecommunications and the Secretary of State respectively) (see further s 408 and Sch 18 at **[3436]**, **[3460]**, and the Communications Act 2003 (Commencement No 1) Order 2003, SI 2003/1900 at **[3507]**); 29 December 2003 (for the purpose of enabling OFCOM to perform those functions) (see the Office of Communications Act 2002 (Commencement No 3) and Communications Act 2003 (Commencement No 2) Order 2003, SI 2003/3142 at **[3590]**).

Repealed as noted to s 152 at **[3228]**.

155 Advisory service in relation to interference

(*1*) *It shall be a function of OFCOM to provide a service consisting in the giving of advice and assistance to persons complaining of interference with wireless telegraphy.*

(*2*) *In this section "interference", in relation to wireless telegraphy, has the same meaning as in the Wireless Telegraphy Act 1949 (c 54).*

[3231]

NOTES

Commencement: 29 December 2003.

Repealed as noted to s 152 at **[3228]**.

156 Directions with respect to the radio spectrum

(*1*) *The Secretary of State may by order give general or specific directions to OFCOM about the carrying out by OFCOM of their functions under the enactments relating to the management of the radio spectrum.*

(*2*) *The directions that may be given under this section include a direction requiring OFCOM to secure that such frequencies of the electro-magnetic spectrum as may be specified in the direction are kept available or become available—*

(*a*) *for such uses or descriptions of uses, or*
(*b*) *for such users or descriptions of users,*

as may be so specified.

(*3*) *The directions that may be given under this section include a direction requiring OFCOM to exercise their powers under the provisions mentioned in subsection (4)—*

(*a*) *in such cases,*
(*b*) *in such manner,*
(*c*) *subject to such restrictions and constraints, and*
(*d*) *with a view to achieving such purposes,*

as may be specified in the direction or as may be determined by the Secretary of State in accordance with the order.

(*4*) *Those provisions are—*

(*a*) *the proviso to section 1 of the Wireless Telegraphy Act 1949 (exemptions from requirement of wireless telegraphy licence); and*
(*b*) *sections 1 to 3A of the Wireless Telegraphy Act 1998 (c 6) (payments in respect of wireless telegraphy licences and grants of recognised spectrum access).*

(5) *This section is not to be construed as restricting the power of the Secretary of State under section 5, without the making of an order, to give a direction for any of the purposes for the time being specified in subsection (3) of that section.*

[3232]

NOTES

Commencement: 29 December 2003.
Repealed as noted to s 152 at **[3228]**.

157 Procedure for directions under s 156

(*1*) *An order containing a direction under section 156, if it is not one falling within subsection (2) or (3) of that section, must state the purpose for which the direction is given.*

(2) *Before making an order containing a direction under section 156, the Secretary of State must consult both—*
(*a*) *OFCOM; and*
(*b*) *such other persons as he thinks fit.*

(3) *Subsection (2) does not apply where the Secretary of State considers that the urgency of the case makes it inexpedient to carry out the consultation before making the order.*

(4) *Subject to subsection (5), no order is to be made containing provision authorised by section 156 unless a draft of the order has been laid before Parliament and approved by a resolution of each House.*

(5) *Subsection (4) does not apply where the Secretary of State considers either—*
(*a*) *before or in the course of the consultation required by subsection (2), or*
(*b*) *after the consultation and before or after a draft of the order has been laid before Parliament,*

that the urgency of the case is or has become such that he should make the order straight away.

(*6*) *Where under subsection (5) the Secretary of State makes an order containing a direction under section 156 without a draft of the order having been approved, the order shall cease to have effect at the end of the period of forty days beginning with the day on which it was made unless, before the end of that period, it has been approved by a resolution of each House of Parliament.*

(*7*) *For the purposes of subsection (6)—*
(*a*) *the order's ceasing to have effect is without prejudice to anything previously done, or to the making of a new order; and*
(*b*) *in reckoning the period of forty days no account shall be taken of any period during which Parliament is dissolved or prorogued or during which both Houses are adjourned for more than four days.*

[3233]

NOTES

Commencement: 29 December 2003.
Repealed as noted to s 152 at **[3228]**.

Reservation of spectrum for multiplex use

158 Special duty in relation to television multiplexes

(*1*) *This section applies where OFCOM, in exercise of their functions under the enactments relating to the management of the radio spectrum, have reserved frequencies for the broadcasting of television programmes.*

(2) *It shall be the duty of OFCOM, in the carrying out of their functions under those enactments, to exercise their powers so as to secure, so far as practicable, that the requirement of subsection (3) is satisfied.*

(3) That requirement is that sufficient capacity is made available on the reserved frequencies for ensuring, in the case of every licensed television multiplex service, that the qualifying services are broadcast by means of that multiplex service.

(4) In subsection (3) "licensed television multiplex service" means a television multiplex service the provision of which is authorised by a licence under Part 1 of the 1996 Act.

(5) In this section "qualifying service" and "television multiplex service" each has the same meaning as in Part 3 of this Act.

[3234]

NOTES

Commencement: 29 December 2003.
Repealed as noted to s 152 at **[3228]**.

Recognised spectrum access

159 Grant of recognised spectrum access

(1) This section applies where—

(a) a person is proposing to use or to continue to use a station or apparatus for wireless telegraphy;

(b) the circumstances of the use are circumstances specified for the purposes of this section in regulations made by OFCOM;

(c) that use does not require a wireless telegraphy licence but will involve the emission of electro-magnetic energy with a view to the reception of anything at places in the United Kingdom or in the territorial waters adjacent to the United Kingdom;

and for the purposes of this section it is immaterial whether the emissions are from a place within the United Kingdom or from a place outside the United Kingdom.

(2) On an application by that person, OFCOM may make a grant of recognised spectrum access in respect of any use by him of anything for wireless telegraphy that is specified in the grant.

(3) A grant of recognised spectrum access made to a person shall set out, by reference to such factors as OFCOM think fit (including, so far as they think fit, frequencies, times and places of reception and strength and type of signal), the respects in which the use of anything by that person for wireless telegraphy is recognised by the grant.

(4) A grant of recognised spectrum access to a person is made by giving him a notification containing the grant.

(5) A grant of recognised spectrum access may be made subject to such restrictions and conditions as OFCOM think fit, including, in particular, restrictions or conditions as to strength or type of signal, as to times of use and as to the sharing of frequencies.

(6) The restrictions and conditions of a grant of recognised spectrum access made to a person must not duplicate obligations already imposed on him by general conditions set under section 45.

(7) Where a grant of recognised spectrum access is made subject to restrictions and conditions, the restrictions and conditions must be set out in the notification by which the grant is made.

(8) Schedule 5 (which makes provision about the grant, revocation and modification of recognised spectrum access) shall have effect.

(9) Section 403 applies to the power of OFCOM to make regulations under subsection (1).

(10) Expressions used in this section and in the Wireless Telegraphy Act 1949 (c 54) have the same meanings in this section as in that Act.

[3235]

NOTES

Commencement: 29 December 2003.
Repealed as noted to s 152 at **[3228]**.

160 Effect of grant of recognised spectrum access

(*1*) *This section applies to the following functions of OFCOM—*

(*a*) *their functions under section 1 of the Wireless Telegraphy Act 1949 (c 54) (licensing of the use of the radio spectrum) with respect to the granting of wireless telegraphy licences;*

(*b*) *their functions under section 159 of this Act with respect to the making of grants of recognised spectrum access; and*

(*c*) *any of their other functions under the enactments relating to the management of the radio spectrum in the carrying out of which it is appropriate for them to have regard to—*

(*i*) *whether wireless telegraphy licences are in force; or*

(*ii*) *the terms, provisions or limitations of wireless telegraphy licences that are for the time being in force.*

(2) *In carrying out the functions to which this section applies it shall be the duty of OFCOM to take into account—*

(*a*) *the existence of any grant of recognised spectrum access that is for the time being in force, and*

(*b*) *the provisions imposing the restrictions and conditions subject to which the grant has effect,*

to the same extent as they would take into account a wireless telegraphy licence with terms, provisions or limitations making equivalent provision.

[3236]

NOTES

Commencement: 29 December 2003.
Repealed as noted to s 152 at **[3228]**.

161 (*Amends the Wireless Telegraphy Act 1998, s 1 at* **[4093]** *and inserts s 3A of that Act at* **[4096]**; *repealed as noted to s 152 at* **[3228]**.)

162 Conversion into and from wireless telegraphy licences

(*1*) *OFCOM may by regulations make provision for—*

(*a*) *the conversion, on the application of the licence holder, of a wireless telegraphy licence into a grant of recognised spectrum access; and*

(*b*) *the conversion, on the application of the holder of the grant, of a grant of recognised spectrum access into a wireless telegraphy licence.*

(2) *Section 403 applies to the power of OFCOM to make regulations under this section.*

[3237]

NOTES

Commencement: 29 December 2003.
Repealed as noted to s 152 at **[3228]**.

Crown use of the radio spectrum

163 Payments for use of radio spectrum by the Crown

(*1*) *The Secretary of State may, out of money provided by Parliament, make payments to OFCOM of such amounts as he considers appropriate in respect of—*

(*a*) *the establishment and use by or on behalf of the Crown, of a station for wireless telegraphy;*

(*b*) *the installation and use by or on behalf of the Crown, of apparatus for wireless telegraphy;*

(*c*) *any grant of recognised spectrum access made to the Crown.*

(*2*) *The payments made under this section shall be made at such times and, so far as made in relation to use, in relation to such periods as the Secretary of State considers appropriate.*

(*3*) *Expressions used in this section and in the Wireless Telegraphy Act 1949 (c 54) have the same meanings in this section as in that Act.*

[3238]

NOTES

Commencement: 29 December 2003.

Repealed as noted to s 152 at **[3228]**.

Limitations and exemptions applied to spectrum use

164 Limitations on authorised spectrum use

(1) If they consider it appropriate, for the purpose of securing the efficient use of the electro-magnetic spectrum, to impose limitations on the use of particular frequencies, OFCOM must make an order imposing the limitations.

(2) An order under this section may do one or both of the following—

(a) specify frequencies for the use of which OFCOM will grant or make only a limited number of wireless telegraphy licences and grants of recognised spectrum access; or

(b) specify uses for which, on specified frequencies, OFCOM will grant or make only a limited number of wireless telegraphy licences and grants of recognised spectrum access.

(3) Where OFCOM make an order under this section, it must set out the criteria which OFCOM will apply in determining in accordance with the order—

(a) the limit on the number of wireless telegraphy licences and grants of recognised spectrum access to be granted or made for the specified frequencies or uses;

(b) the persons to whom licences will be granted or grants of spectrum access made.

(4) OFCOM must satisfy themselves that any criteria set out by virtue of subsection (3) are—

(a) objectively justifiable in relation to the frequencies or uses to which they relate;

(b) not such as to discriminate unduly against particular persons or against a particular description of persons;

(c) proportionate to what they are intended to achieve; and

(d) in relation to what they are intended to achieve, transparent.

(5) It shall be the duty of OFCOM to exercise the following powers in accordance with the orders for the time being in force under this section—

(a) their powers under the Wireless Telegraphy Act 1949 and the Wireless Telegraphy Act 1998 (c 6) with respect to wireless telegraphy licences; and

(b) their powers under the Wireless Telegraphy Act 1998 and this Chapter with respect to grants of recognised spectrum access.

(6) OFCOM must keep under review any order for the time being in force under this section.

(7) It shall be the duty of OFCOM to make an order revoking or amending the provisions of an order under this section if, on reviewing it, they consider it necessary to do so for the purpose of securing the efficient use of the electromagnetic spectrum.

(8) An order under this section may make provision by reference to determinations which—

(a) are made from time to time by OFCOM in accordance with the provisions of such an order; and

(b) are published by them from time to time in such manner as may be provided for in such an order.

(9) Section 403 applies to the power of OFCOM to make an order under this section. **[3239]**

NOTES

Commencement: 25 July 2003 (for the purpose of enabling network and service functions and spectrum functions to be carried out during the transitional period by the Director General of Telecommunications and the Secretary of State respectively) (see further s 408 and Sch 18 at **[3436]**, **[3460]**, and the Communications Act 2003 (Commencement No 1) Order 2003, SI 2003/1900 at **[3507]**); 29 December 2003 (for the purpose of enabling OFCOM to perform those functions) (see the Office of Communications Act 2002 (Commencement No 3) and Communications Act 2003 (Commencement No 2) Order 2003, SI 2003/3142 at **[3590]**).

Repealed as noted to s 152 at **[3228]**.

Orders: the Wireless Telegraphy (Limitation of Number of Licences) Order 2003, SI 2003/1902 at **[3524]**; the Wireless Telegraphy (Limitation of Number of Concurrent Spectrum Access Licences) Order 2006, SI 2006/341; the Wireless Telegraphy (Limitation of Number of Spectrum Access Licences) Order 2006, SI 2006/1809.

165, 166 (*Amend the Wireless Telegraphy Act 1949, s 1 at* **[4001]** *and insert s 1AA of that Act at* **[4002]**; *repealed as noted to s 152 at* **[3228]**.)

Award and transfer of licences

167 (*Amends the Wireless Telegraphy Act 1998, s 3 at* **[4095]**; *repealed as noted to s 152 at* **[3228]**.)

168 Spectrum trading

(*1*) *OFCOM may by regulations authorise the transfer to another person by—*

(*a*) *the holder of a wireless telegraphy licence, or*

(*b*) *the holder of a grant of recognised spectrum access,*

of rights and obligations arising by virtue of such a licence or grant.

(*2*) *The transfers that may be authorised by regulations under this section are—*

(*a*) *such transfers of all or any of the rights and obligations under a licence or grant as have the effect that the rights and obligations of the person making the transfer become rights and obligations of the transferee to the exclusion of the person making the transfer;*

(*b*) *such transfers of all or any those rights and obligations as have the effect that the transferred rights and obligations become rights and obligations of the transferee while continuing, concurrently, to be rights and obligations of the person making the transfer; and*

(*c*) *transfers falling within either of the preceding paragraphs under which the rights and obligations that are acquired by the transferee take effect—*

(*i*) *if they are rights and obligations under a wireless telegraphy licence, as rights and obligations under a grant of recognised spectrum access; and*

(*ii*) *if they are rights and obligations under such a grant, as rights and obligations under a wireless telegraphy licence.*

(*3*) *Regulations authorising the transfer of rights and obligations under a wireless telegraphy licence or grant of recognised spectrum access may—*

(*a*) *authorise a partial transfer to be made by reference to such factors and apportionments, and to have effect in relation to such matters and periods, as may be described in the regulations, or as may be determined in accordance with them;*

(*b*) *by reference to such factors (including the terms and conditions of the licence or grant in question) as may be specified in or determined in accordance with the regulations, restrict the circumstances in which, the extent to which and the manner in which a transfer may be made;*

(*c*) *require the approval or consent of OFCOM for the making of a transfer;*

(*d*) *provide for a transfer to be effected by the surrender of a licence or grant of recognised spectrum access and the grant or making of a new one in respect of the transfer;*

(*e*) *confer power on OFCOM to direct that a transfer must not be made, or is to be made only after compliance with such conditions as OFCOM may impose in accordance with the regulations;*

(*f*) *authorise OFCOM to require the payment to them of such sums as may be determined by or in accordance with the regulations in respect of determinations made by OFCOM for the purposes of the regulations or in respect of an approval or consent given for those purposes;*

(*g*) *make provision for the giving of security (whether by the giving of deposits or otherwise) in respect of sums payable in pursuance of any regulations under this section;*

(*h*) *make provision as to the circumstances in which security given under such regulations is to be returned or may be retained;*

(*i*) *impose requirements as to the procedure to be followed for the making of a transfer and, in particular, as to the notification about a transfer that must be given to OFCOM, or must be published, both in advance of its being made and afterwards;*

(*j*) *impose requirements as to the records to be kept in connection with any transfer, and as to the persons to whom such records are to be made available;*

(*k*) *set out the matters to be taken into account in the making of determinations under regulations under this section.*

(*4*) *The transfer of rights and obligations under a wireless telegraphy licence or grant of recognised spectrum access shall be void except to the extent that it is made—*

(*a*) *in accordance with regulations under this section; or*

(*b*) *in accordance with a provision specified in subsection* (*5*).

(*5*) *That provision is a provision which—*

(*a*) *is contained in a wireless telegraphy licence granted before the commencement of this section or in the first or any subsequent renewal after the commencement of this section of a licence so granted; and*

(*b*) *allows the holder of the licence to confer the benefit of the licence on another in respect of any station or apparatus to which the licence relates.*

(*6*) *A transfer shall also be void if it is made in contravention of a direction given by OFCOM in exercise of a power conferred by regulations under this section.*

(*7*) *Section 403 applies to the power of OFCOM to make regulations under this section.*

[3240]

NOTES

Commencement: 29 December 2003.

Repealed as noted to s 152 at **[3228]**.

Regulations: the Wireless Telegraphy (Spectrum Trading) Regulations 2004, SI 2004/3154.

Variation and revocation of licences

169 Variation and revocation of wireless telegraphy licences

(*1*) ...

(*2*) *Nothing in this section is to apply in any case in which a notice under section 1E*(*1*) *of the Wireless Telegraphy Act 1949* (*c 54*) *was served before the commencement of this section.*

[3241]

NOTES

Commencement: 25 July 2003 (for the purpose of enabling network and service functions and spectrum functions to be carried out during the transitional period by the Director General of Telecommunications and the Secretary of State respectively) (see further s 408 and Sch 18 at **[3436]**, **[3460]**, and the Communications Act 2003 (Commencement No 1) Order 2003, SI 2003/1900 at **[3507]**); 29 December 2003 (for the purpose of enabling OFCOM to perform those functions) (see the Office of Communications Act 2002 (Commencement No 3) and Communications Act 2003 (Commencement No 2) Order 2003, SI 2003/3142 at **[3590]**).

Repealed as noted to s 152 at **[3228]**.

Sub-s (1): substitutes the Wireless Telegraphy Act 1949, s 1E at **[4007]**.

Wireless telegraphy register

170 Wireless telegraphy register

(*1*) *OFCOM may by regulations make provision for the establishment and maintenance of a register of relevant information.*

(*2*) *OFCOM are to include relevant information in the register if, and only if, it is relevant information of a description prescribed by regulations under this section.*

(*3*) *Information is relevant information for the purposes of subsection* (*1*) *if it relates to—*

(*a*) *the issue, renewal, transfer, variation or revocation of wireless telegraphy licences; or* (*b*) *the making, renewal, transfer, modification or revocation of grants of recognised spectrum access.*

(*4*) *Subject to such conditions (including conditions as to payment) as may be prescribed by regulations under this section, a register established by virtue of subsection (1) shall be open to inspection by the public.*

(*5*) *Section 403 applies to the power of OFCOM to make regulations under this section.* **[3242]**

NOTES

Commencement: 29 December 2003.
Repealed as noted to s 152 at **[3228]**.

Information requirements

171 (*Inserts the Wireless Telegraphy Act 1949, ss 13A, 13B at* **[4016]**, **[4017]**, *and amends s 14 of that Act at* **[4018]**; *repealed as noted to s 152 at* **[3228]**.)

Criminal proceedings etc

172 Contraventions of conditions for use of wireless telegraphy

(*1*) *Where OFCOM determine that there are reasonable grounds for believing that a person is contravening, or has contravened—*

(*a*) *a term, provision or limitation of a wireless telegraphy licence, or*
(*b*) *a term, provision or limitation of an exemption under the proviso to section 1(1) of the Wireless Telegraphy Act 1949 (c 54) (exemptions from licensing requirement),*

they may give that person a notification under this section.

(*2*) *A notification under this section is one which—*

(*a*) *sets out the determination made by OFCOM;*
(*b*) *specifies the term, provision or limitation, and the contravention, in respect of which that determination has been made; and*
(*c*) *specifies the period during which the person notified has an opportunity of doing the things specified in subsection (3).*

(*3*) *Those things are—*

(*a*) *making representations about the matters notified; and*
(*b*) *complying with any notified term, provision or limitation of which he remains in contravention.*

(*4*) *Subject to subsections (5) to (7), the period for doing those things must be the period of one month beginning with the day after the one on which the notification was given.*

(*5*) *OFCOM may, if they think fit, allow a longer period for doing those things either—*

(*a*) *by specifying a longer period in the notification; or*
(*b*) *by subsequently, on one or more occasions, extending the specified period.*

(*6*) *The person notified shall have a shorter period for doing those things if a shorter period is agreed between OFCOM and the person notified.*

(*7*) *The person notified shall also have a shorter period if—*

(*a*) *OFCOM have reasonable grounds for believing that the case is a case of repeated contravention;*
(*b*) *they have determined that, in those circumstances, a shorter period would be appropriate; and*
(*c*) *the shorter period has been specified in the notification.*

[3243]

NOTES

Commencement: 25 July 2003 (for the purpose of enabling network and service functions and spectrum functions to be carried out during the transitional period by the Director General of Telecommunications and the Secretary of State respectively) (see further s 408 and Sch 18 at **[3436]**, **[3460]**, and the Communications Act 2003 (Commencement No 1) Order 2003, SI 2003/1900 at **[3507]**);

29 December 2003 (for the purpose of enabling OFCOM to perform those functions) (see the Office of Communications Act 2002 (Commencement No 3) and Communications Act 2003 (Commencement No 2) Order 2003, SI 2003/3142 at **[3590]**).

Repealed as noted to s 152 at **[3228]**.

173 Meaning of "repeated contravention" in s 172

(1) For the purposes of section 172 a contravention is a repeated contravention, in relation to a notification with respect to that contravention, if—

- *(a) in the case of a contravention of a term, provision or limitation of a licence, it falls within subsection (2) or (3); or*
- *(b) in the case of a contravention of a term, provision or limitation of an exemption, it falls within subsection (4) or (5).*

(2) A contravention of a term, provision or limitation of a licence falls within this subsection if—

- *(a) a previous notification under section 172 has been given in respect of the same contravention or in respect of another contravention of a term, provision or limitation of the same licence;*
- *(b) the person who was given that notification subsequently took steps for remedying the notified contravention; and*
- *(c) the subsequent notification is given no more than twelve months after the day of the giving of the previous notification.*

(3) A contravention of a term, provision or limitation of a licence falls within this subsection if—

- *(a) the person concerned has been convicted of an offence under section 1(1) of the Wireless Telegraphy Act 1949 (c 54) in respect of the contravention to which the notification relates or in respect of another contravention of a term, provision or limitation of the same licence; and*
- *(b) the subsequent notification is given before the end of the period of twelve months from the contravention in respect of which that person was convicted of that offence.*

(4) A contravention of a term, provision or limitation of an exemption falls within this subsection if—

- *(a) a previous notification under section 172 has been given in respect of the same contravention or in respect of another contravention of the same term, provision or limitation;*
- *(b) the person who was given that notification subsequently took steps for remedying the notified contravention; and*
- *(c) the subsequent notification is given no more than twelve months after the day of the giving of the previous notification.*

(5) A contravention of a term, provision or limitation of an exemption falls within this subsection if—

- *(a) the person concerned has been convicted of an offence under section 1(1) of the Wireless Telegraphy Act 1949 (c 54) in respect of the contravention to which the notification relates or in respect of another contravention of the same term, provision or limitation; and*
- *(b) the subsequent notification is given before the end of the period of twelve months from the contravention in respect of which that person was convicted of that offence.*

(6) In calculating the periods of twelve months mentioned in subsections (3)(b) and (5)(b), the period between the institution of the criminal proceedings which led to the conviction and the conclusion of those proceedings shall be left out of account.

(7) For the purposes of subsection (6) criminal proceedings shall be taken to be concluded when no further appeal against conviction may be brought without the permission of the court and—

- *(a) in a case where there is no fixed period within which that permission can be sought, permission has been refused or has not been sought; or*
- *(b) in a case where there is a fixed period within which that permission can be sought, that permission has been refused or that period has expired without permission having been sought.*

(8) References in this section to remedying a contravention include references to each of the following—

(a) doing any thing the failure to do which, or the failure to do which within a particular period or before a particular time, constituted the whole or a part of the contravention;

(b) paying an amount to a person by way of compensation for loss or damage suffered by that person in consequence of the contravention;

(c) paying an amount to a person by way of compensation in respect of annoyance, inconvenience or anxiety to which he has been put in consequence of the contravention; and

(d) otherwise acting in a manner that constitutes an acknowledgement that the notified contravention did occur.

(9) References in this section to a contravention of a term, provision or limitation of a licence include a reference to a contravention of a term, provision or limitation contained in a previous licence of which the licence in question is a direct or indirect renewal.

[3244]

NOTES

Commencement: 25 July 2003 (for the purpose of enabling network and service functions and spectrum functions to be carried out during the transitional period by the Director General of Telecommunications and the Secretary of State respectively) (see further s 408 and Sch 18 at **[3436]**, **[3460]**, and the Communications Act 2003 (Commencement No 1) Order 2003, SI 2003/1900 at **[3507]**); 29 December 2003 (for the purpose of enabling OFCOM to perform those functions) (see the Office of Communications Act 2002 (Commencement No 3) and Communications Act 2003 (Commencement No 2) Order 2003, SI 2003/3142 at **[3590]**).

Repealed as noted to s 152 at **[3228]**.

174 Procedure for prosecutions of wireless telegraphy offences

(1) This section applies to proceedings against a person ("the defendant") for an offence under section 1 of the Wireless Telegraphy Act 1949 consisting in the contravention of—

(a) the terms, provisions or limitations of a wireless telegraphy licence; or

(b) the terms, provisions or limitations of an exemption under the proviso to section 1(1) of the Wireless Telegraphy Act 1949 (c 54) (exemptions from licensing requirement).

(2) Proceedings to which this section applies are not to be brought at any time after the coming into force of this section unless, before they are brought, OFCOM have—

(a) given the defendant a notification under section 172 in respect of the contravention to which the proceedings relate; and

(b) considered any representations about the matters notified which were made by the defendant within the period allowed under that section.

(3) Proceedings to which this section applies are not to be brought at any time after the coming into force of this section in respect of a contravention if—

(a) it is a contravention to which a notification given to that person under section 172 relates; and

(b) that person has, during the period allowed under that section, complied with the notified term, provision or limitation.

(4) Subsection (2) does not apply where OFCOM have certified that it would be inappropriate to follow the procedure in section 172 because of an immediate risk of—

(a) a serious threat to the safety of the public, to public health or to national security; or

(b) serious economic or operational problems for persons (other than the defendant) who—

(i) use stations or apparatus for wireless telegraphy; or

(ii) are communications providers or make associated facilities available.

(5) Where—

(a) proceedings to which this section applies are brought by virtue of subsection (4) without a notification having been given to the defendant, and

(b) the defendant is convicted in those proceedings of the offence under section 1 of the Wireless Telegraphy Act 1949,

the court, in determining how to deal with that person, shall have regard, in particular, to the matters specified in subsection (6).

(6) Those matters are—

(a) whether the defendant has ceased to be in contravention of the terms, provisions or limitations in question and (if so) when; and

(b) any steps taken by the defendant (whether before or after the commencement of the proceedings) for securing compliance with the obligations imposed on him by virtue of those terms, provisions or limitations.

(7) Notwithstanding anything in section 127 of the Magistrates' Courts Act 1980 (c 43) or Article 19 of the Magistrates' Courts (Northern Ireland) Order 1981 (SI 1981/1675 (NI 26)) (limitation on time for bringing summary proceedings) where—

(a) OFCOM give a notification under section 172 in respect of a contravention, and

(b) that notification is given before the end of six months after the day of the contravention,

the time for the bringing of proceedings for a summary offence in respect of that contravention shall be extended until the end of six months from the end of the period allowed, in the case of that notification, for doing the things mentioned in section 172(3) of this Act.

(8) In this section, "stations for wireless telegraphy" and "apparatus for wireless telegraphy" have the same meanings as in the Wireless Telegraphy Act 1949 (c 54).

[3245]

NOTES

Commencement: 25 July 2003 (for the purpose of enabling network and service functions and spectrum functions to be carried out during the transitional period by the Director General of Telecommunications and the Secretary of State respectively) (see further s 408 and Sch 18 at **[3436]**, **[3460]**, and the Communications Act 2003 (Commencement No 1) Order 2003, SI 2003/1900 at **[3507]**); 29 December 2003 (for the purpose of enabling OFCOM to perform those functions) (see the Office of Communications Act 2002 (Commencement No 3) and Communications Act 2003 (Commencement No 2) Order 2003, SI 2003/3142 at **[3590]**).

Repealed as noted to s 152 at **[3228]**.

175 Special procedure for contraventions by multiplex licence holders

(1) OFCOM may impose a penalty on a person if—

(a) that person is or has been in contravention in any respect of the terms, provisions or limitations of a general multiplex licence;

(b) the contravention relates to terms, provisions or limitations falling within section 1(2A)(b) or (c) of the Wireless Telegraphy Act 1949 (terms, provisions and limitations about service content);

(c) OFCOM have notified that person that it appears to them that those terms, provisions or limitations have been contravened in that respect; and

(d) that contravention is not one in respect of which proceedings for an offence under that Act have been brought against that person.

(2) Where OFCOM impose a penalty on a person under this section, they shall—

(a) notify that person of that decision and of their reasons for that decision; and

(b) in that notification, fix a reasonable period after it is given as the period within which the penalty is to be paid.

(3) A penalty imposed under this section—

(a) must be paid to OFCOM; and

(b) if not paid within the period fixed by them, is to be recoverable by them accordingly.

(4) No proceedings for an offence under the Wireless Telegraphy Act 1949 shall be commenced against a person in respect of a contravention in respect of which a penalty has been imposed by OFCOM under this section.

(5) For the purposes of this section a licence is a general multiplex licence, in relation to the time of a contravention, if—

(a) it is a wireless telegraphy licence containing terms, provisions or limitations by virtue of which the services for the purposes of which the use of the licensed station or apparatus is authorised are confined to, or are allowed to include, one or more multiplex services; and

(b) at that time, there is no licence under Part 1 or 2 of the 1996 Act in force in respect of a multiplex service to be broadcast using that station or apparatus.

(6) In this section "multiplex service" means—

(a) a service for broadcasting for general reception that consists in the packaging together of two or more services that are provided for inclusion together in that service by a combination of the relevant information in digital form; or

(b) a service provided with a view to its being a service falling within paragraph (a) but in the case of which only one service is for the time being comprised in digital form in what is provided.

[3246]

NOTES

Commencement: 29 December 2003.
Repealed as noted to s 152 at **[3228]**.

176 Amount of penalty under s 175

(1) The amount of a penalty imposed under section 175 is to be such amount, not exceeding the greater of the following, as OFCOM think fit, namely—

(a) £250,000; and

(b) 5 per cent of the relevant amount of gross revenue.

(2) In subsection (1) "the relevant amount of gross revenue" means the amount specified in section 177.

(3) The Secretary of State may by order amend this section so as to substitute a different amount for the amount for the time being specified in subsection (1)(a).

(4) No order is to be made containing provision authorised by subsection (3) unless a draft of the order has been laid before Parliament and approved by a resolution of each House.

[3247]

NOTES

Commencement: 29 December 2003.
Repealed as noted to s 152 at **[3228]**.

177 "Relevant amount of gross revenue" for the purposes of s 176

(1) The relevant amount of gross revenue for the purposes of section 176, in relation to a penalty imposed on a person, is—

(a) where the last accounting period of that person which falls before the contravention was a period of twelve months, the relevant part of his gross revenue for that period; and

(b) in any other case, the amount which, by making any appropriate apportionments or other adjustments of the relevant part of his gross revenue for the accounting period or periods mentioned in subsection (2), is computed to be the amount representing the annual rate for the relevant part of his gross revenues.

(2) The accounting period or periods referred to in subsection (1) are—

(a) every accounting period of his to end within the period of twelve months immediately preceding the contravention; and

(b) if there is no such accounting period, the accounting period of his which is current at the time of the contravention.

(3) In this section, a reference to the relevant part of a person's gross revenue, in relation to a contravention of the terms, provisions or limitations of a licence, is a reference to so much of his gross revenue as is attributable to the provision of the service to which that licence relates.

(4) For the purposes of this section—

(a) the gross revenue of a person for a period, and

(b) the extent to which a part of a person's gross revenue is attributable to the provision of any service,

shall be ascertained in accordance with such principles as may be set out in a statement made by OFCOM.

(5) Such a statement may provide for the amount of a person's gross revenue for an accounting period that is current when the amount falls to be calculated to be taken to be the

amount estimated by OFCOM, in accordance with the principles set out in the statement, to be the amount that will be his gross revenue for that period.

(*6*) *OFCOM may revise a statement made under subsection (4) from time to time.*

(*7*) *A statement made or revised under this section may set out different principles for different cases.*

(*8*) *Before making or revising a statement under this section, OFCOM must consult the Secretary of State and the Treasury.*

(*9*) *OFCOM must—*

(*a*) *publish the statement made under subsection (4) and every revision of it; and*

(*b*) *send a copy of the statement and of every such revision to the Secretary of State;*

and the Secretary of State must lay copies of the statement and of every such revision before each House of Parliament.

(*10*) *Section 13A of the Wireless Telegraphy Act 1949 (c 54) is to apply for the purpose of ascertaining the amount of a person's gross revenue for any period for the purposes of section 176 of this Act and this section as it applies for the purpose of obtaining information for statistical purposes about matters relating to the establishment, installation or use by that person of a station or apparatus.*

(*11*) *In this section—*

"accounting period", in relation to a person, means a period in respect of which accounts of the undertaking carried on by him are prepared or, if one such period is comprised in another, whichever of those periods is or is closest to a twelve month period; and

"gross revenue", in relation to a person, means the gross revenue of an undertaking carried on by that person.

[3248]

NOTES

Commencement: 29 December 2003.
Repealed as noted to s 152 at **[3228]**.

178 (*Amends the Wireless Telegraphy Act 1949, ss 11, 12 at* **[4013]**, **[4014]**; *repealed as noted to s 152 at* **[3228]**.)

179 Modification of penalties for certain wireless telegraphy offences

(*1*)–(*3*) …

(*4*) *This section only applies in relation to offences committed after the commencement of this section.*

[3249]

NOTES

Commencement: 18 September 2003.
Repealed as noted to s 152 at **[3228]**.
Sub-ss (1)–(3): amend the Wireless Telegraphy Act 1949, s 14 at **[4018]** and the Telecommunications Act 1984, s 79 at **[4044]**.

180 Fixed penalties for certain wireless telegraphy offences

Schedule 6 (which makes provision as respects fixed penalty notices for summary offences under the Wireless Telegraphy Act 1949 (c 54)) shall have effect.

[3250]

NOTES

Commencement: to be appointed.
Repealed as noted to s 152 at **[3228]**.

181 (*Outside the scope of this work.*)

182 Forfeiture etc of restricted apparatus

(1) Apparatus to which this section applies shall be liable to forfeiture if, immediately before being seized, it was in a person's custody or control in contravention of a prohibition imposed by an order under section 7 of the Wireless Telegraphy Act 1967 (*c 72*) (*restriction on dealings in and custody of certain apparatus*).

(2) This section applies to apparatus if it has been seized—

(*a*) *in pursuance of a warrant granted under section 15*(*1*) *of the Wireless Telegraphy Act 1949; or*

(*b*) *in the exercise of the power conferred by section 79*(*3*) *of the Telecommunications Act 1984* (*c 12*).

(3) Apparatus forfeited under this section is to be forfeited to OFCOM and may be disposed of by them in any manner they think fit.

(4) Schedule 7 (*which makes provision in relation to the seizure and forfeiture of apparatus*) *shall have effect.*

(5) The preceding provisions of this section and Schedule 7 apply only in relation to apparatus seized after the commencement of this section.

(6) Sections 80 and 81 of the Telecommunications Act 1984 (*c 12*) (*which make provision for forfeiture of apparatus*) *are not to apply in relation to apparatus seized after the commencement of this section.*

(7) …

[3251]

NOTES

Commencement: 29 December 2003.
Repealed as noted to s 152 at **[3228]**.
Sub-s (7): amends the Wireless Telegraphy Act 1967, s 7 at **[4029]**.

Construction of 1949 Act

183 (*Amends the Wireless Telegraphy Act 1949, s 19 at* **[4022]**; *repealed as noted to s 152 at* **[3228]**.)

184 Modification of definition of "wireless telegraphy"

(1) The Secretary of State may by order modify the definition of "wireless telegraphy" in section 19(*1*) *of the Wireless Telegraphy Act 1949 by substituting a different frequency for the frequency* (*at the passing of this Act, 3,000 GHz*) *that is for the time being specified in that definition.*

(2) No order is to be made containing provision authorised by this section unless a draft of the order has been laid before Parliament and approved by a resolution of each House.

[3252]

NOTES

Commencement: 18 September 2003.
Repealed as noted to s 152 at **[3228]**.

CHAPTER 3
DISPUTES AND APPEALS

Disputes

185 Reference of disputes to OFCOM

(1) This section applies in the case of a dispute relating to the provision of network access if it is—

(a) a dispute between different communications providers;

(b) a dispute between a communications provider and a person who makes associated facilities available;

(c) a dispute between different persons making such facilities available;
(d) a dispute relating to the subject-matter of a condition set under section 74(1) between a communications provider or person who makes associated facilities available and a person who (without being such a person) is a person to whom such a condition applies; or
(e) a dispute relating to the subject-matter of such a condition between different persons each of whom (without being a communications provider or a person who makes associated facilities available) is a person to whom such a condition applies.

(2) This section also applies in the case of any other dispute if—
(a) it relates to rights or obligations conferred or imposed by or under this Part or any of the enactments relating to the management of the radio spectrum that are not contained in this Part;
(b) it is a dispute between different communications providers; and
(c) it is not an excluded dispute.

(3) Any one or more of the parties to the dispute may refer it to OFCOM.

(4) A reference made under this section is to be made in such manner as OFCOM may require.

(5) The way in which a requirement under subsection (4)—
(a) is to be imposed, or
(b) may be withdrawn or modified,

is by a notice published in such manner as OFCOM consider appropriate for bringing the requirement, withdrawal or modification to the attention of the persons who, in their opinion, are likely to be affected by it.

(6) Requirements imposed under subsection (4) may make different provision for different cases.

(7) A dispute is an excluded dispute for the purposes of subsection (2) if it is about—
(a) obligations imposed on a communications provider by SMP apparatus conditions;
(b) contraventions of sections 125 to 127;
(c) obligations imposed on a communications provider by or under any of sections 128 to 131; or
(d) the operation in the case of a communications provider of section 134.

(8) For the purposes of this section—
(a) the disputes that relate to the provision of network access include disputes as to the terms or conditions on which it is or may be provided in a particular case; and
(b) the disputes that relate to an obligation include disputes as to the terms or conditions on which any transaction is to be entered into for the purpose of complying with that obligation.

[3253]

NOTES

Commencement: 25 July 2003 (for the purpose of enabling network and service functions and spectrum functions to be carried out during the transitional period by the Director General of Telecommunications and the Secretary of State respectively) (see further s 408 and Sch 18 at **[3436]**, **[3460]**, and the Communications Act 2003 (Commencement No 1) Order 2003, SI 2003/1900 at **[3507]**); 29 December 2003 (for the purpose of enabling OFCOM to perform those functions) (see the Office of Communications Act 2002 (Commencement No 3) and Communications Act 2003 (Commencement No 2) Order 2003, SI 2003/3142 at **[3590]**).

186 Action by OFCOM on dispute reference

(1) This section applies where a dispute is referred to OFCOM under and in accordance with section 185.

(2) OFCOM must decide whether or not it is appropriate for them to handle the dispute.

(3) Unless they consider—
(a) that there are alternative means available for resolving the dispute,
(b) that a resolution of the dispute by those means would be consistent with the Community requirements set out in section 4, and
(c) that a prompt and satisfactory resolution of the dispute is likely if those alternative means are used for resolving it,

their decision must be a decision that it is appropriate for them to handle the dispute.

(4) As soon as reasonably practicable after OFCOM have decided—

(a) that it is appropriate for them to handle the dispute, or

(b) that it is not,

they must inform each of the parties to the dispute of their decision and of their reasons for it.

(5) The notification must state the date of the decision.

(6) Where—

(a) OFCOM decide that it is not appropriate for them to handle the dispute, but

(b) the dispute is not resolved by other means before the end of the four months after the day of OFCOM's decision,

the dispute may be referred back to OFCOM by one or more of the parties to the dispute.

[3254]

NOTES

Commencement: 25 July 2003 (for the purpose of enabling network and service functions and spectrum functions to be carried out during the transitional period by the Director General of Telecommunications and the Secretary of State respectively) (see further s 408 and Sch 18 at **[3436]**, **[3460]**, and the Communications Act 2003 (Commencement No 1) Order 2003, SI 2003/1900 at **[3507]**); 29 December 2003 (for the purpose of enabling OFCOM to perform those functions) (see the Office of Communications Act 2002 (Commencement No 3) and Communications Act 2003 (Commencement No 2) Order 2003, SI 2003/3142 at **[3590]**).

187 Legal proceedings about referred disputes

(1) Where a dispute is referred or referred back to OFCOM under this Chapter, the reference is not to prevent—

(a) the person making it,

(b) another party to the dispute,

(c) OFCOM, or

(d) any other person,

from bringing, or continuing, any legal proceedings with respect to any of the matters under dispute.

(2) Nor is the reference or reference back to OFCOM under this Chapter of a dispute to prevent OFCOM from—

(a) giving a notification in respect of something that they have reasonable grounds for believing to be a contravention of any obligation imposed by or under any an enactment;

(b) exercising any of their other powers under any enactment in relation to a contravention of such an obligation; or

(c) taking any other step in preparation for or with a view to doing anything mentioned in the preceding paragraphs.

(3) If, in any legal proceedings with respect to a matter to which a dispute relates, the court orders the handling of the dispute by OFCOM to be stayed or sisted—

(a) OFCOM are required to make a determination for resolving the dispute only if the stay or sist is lifted or expires; and

(b) the period during which the stay or sist is in force must be disregarded in determining the period within which OFCOM are required to make such a determination.

(4) Subsection (1) is subject to section 190(8) and to any agreement to the contrary binding the parties to the dispute.

(5) In this section "legal proceedings" means civil or criminal proceedings in or before a court.

[3255]

NOTES

Commencement: 25 July 2003 (for the purpose of enabling network and service functions and spectrum functions to be carried out during the transitional period by the Director General of Telecommunications and the Secretary of State respectively) (see further s 408 and Sch 18 at **[3436]**, **[3460]**, and the Communications Act 2003 (Commencement No 1) Order 2003, SI 2003/1900 at **[3507]**);

29 December 2003 (for the purpose of enabling OFCOM to perform those functions) (see the Office of Communications Act 2002 (Commencement No 3) and Communications Act 2003 (Commencement No 2) Order 2003, SI 2003/3142 at **[3590]**).

188 Procedure for resolving disputes

(1) This section applies where—

(a) OFCOM have decided under section 186(2) that it is appropriate for them to handle a dispute; or

(b) a dispute is referred back to OFCOM under section 186(6).

(2) OFCOM must—

(a) consider the dispute; and

(b) make a determination for resolving it.

(3) The procedure for the consideration and determination of the dispute is to be the procedure that OFCOM consider appropriate.

(4) In the case of a dispute referred back to OFCOM under section 186(6), that procedure may involve allowing the continuation of a procedure that has already been begun for resolving the dispute by alternative means.

(5) Except in exceptional circumstances and subject to section 187(3), OFCOM must make their determination no more than four months after the following day—

(a) in a case falling within subsection (1)(a), the day of the decision by OFCOM that it is appropriate for them to handle the dispute; and

(b) in a case falling within subsection (1)(b), the day on which the dispute is referred back to them.

(6) Where it is practicable for OFCOM to make their determination before the end of the four month period, they must make it as soon in that period as practicable.

(7) OFCOM must—

(a) send a copy of their determination, together with a full statement of their reasons for it, to every party to the dispute; and

(b) publish so much of their determination as (having regard, in particular, to the need to preserve commercial confidentiality) they consider it appropriate to publish.

(8) The publication of information under this section must be in such manner as OFCOM consider appropriate for bringing it to the attention, to the extent that they consider appropriate, of members of the public.

[3256]

NOTES

Commencement: 25 July 2003 (for the purpose of enabling network and service functions and spectrum functions to be carried out during the transitional period by the Director General of Telecommunications and the Secretary of State respectively) (see further s 408 and Sch 18 at **[3436]**, **[3460]**, and the Communications Act 2003 (Commencement No 1) Order 2003, SI 2003/1900 at **[3507]**); 29 December 2003 (for the purpose of enabling OFCOM to perform those functions) (see the Office of Communications Act 2002 (Commencement No 3) and Communications Act 2003 (Commencement No 2) Order 2003, SI 2003/3142 at **[3590]**).

189 Disputes involving other member States

(1) This section applies where it appears to OFCOM that a dispute referred or referred back to them under this Chapter relates partly to a matter falling within the jurisdiction of the regulatory authorities of another member State.

(2) A dispute relates to matters falling within the jurisdiction of the regulatory authorities of another member State to the extent that—

(a) it relates to the carrying on of activities by one or both of the parties to the dispute in more than one member State or to activities carried on by different parties to the dispute in different member States; and

(b) the activities to which the dispute relates, so far as they are carried on in another member State, are carried on in the member State for which those authorities are the regulatory authorities.

(3) For the purposes of subsection (2) the activities that are carried on in a member State include anything done by means of an electronic communications network, or part of such a network, which is situated in that member State.

(4) Before taking any steps under this Chapter in relation to the reference or the dispute, OFCOM must consult the other regulatory authorities within whose jurisdiction the matter falls.

(5) It shall be the duty of OFCOM to secure that steps taken in relation to the reference or dispute (whether taken by them or by the other regulatory authorities) are, so far as practicable, agreed between OFCOM and those authorities.

(6) Accordingly, section 188 is to have effect in relation to the reference as if the period for making a determination which is specified in subsection (5) of that section were such period (if any) as may be agreed between—

(a) OFCOM; and
(b) the other regulatory authorities within whose jurisdiction the matter falls.

[3257]

NOTES

Commencement: 25 July 2003 (for the purpose of enabling network and service functions and spectrum functions to be carried out during the transitional period by the Director General of Telecommunications and the Secretary of State respectively) (see further s 408 and Sch 18 at **[3436]**, **[3460]**, and the Communications Act 2003 (Commencement No 1) Order 2003, SI 2003/1900 at **[3507]**); 29 December 2003 (for the purpose of enabling OFCOM to perform those functions) (see the Office of Communications Act 2002 (Commencement No 3) and Communications Act 2003 (Commencement No 2) Order 2003, SI 2003/3142 at **[3590]**).

190 Resolution of referred disputes

(1) Where OFCOM make a determination for resolving a dispute referred to them under this Chapter, their only powers are those conferred by this section.

(2) Their main power (except in the case of a dispute relating to rights and obligations conferred or imposed by or under the enactments relating to the management of the radio spectrum) is to do one or more of the following—

(a) to make a declaration setting out the rights and obligations of the parties to the dispute;
(b) to give a direction fixing the terms or conditions of transactions between the parties to the dispute;
(c) to give a direction imposing an obligation, enforceable by the parties to the dispute, to enter into a transaction between themselves on the terms and conditions fixed by OFCOM; and
(d) for the purpose of giving effect to a determination by OFCOM of the proper amount of a charge in respect of which amounts have been paid by one of the parties of the dispute to the other, to give a direction, enforceable by the party to whom the sums are to be paid, requiring the payment of sums by way of adjustment of an underpayment or overpayment.

(3) Their main power in the excepted case is just to make a declaration setting out the rights and obligations of the parties to the dispute.

(4) Nothing in this section prevents OFCOM from exercising the following powers in consequence of their consideration under this Chapter of any dispute—

(a) their powers under Chapter 1 of this Part to set, modify or revoke general conditions, universal service conditions, access related conditions, privileged supplier conditions or SMP conditions;
(b) their powers to vary, modify or revoke wireless telegraphy licences or grants of recognised spectrum access;
(c) their power to make, amend or revoke [regulations under section 8 or 45 of the Wireless Telegraphy Act 2006].

(5) In the case of a dispute referred back to OFCOM under section 186(6)—

(a) OFCOM may, in making their determination, take account of decisions already made by others in the course of an attempt to resolve the dispute by alternative means; and
(b) the determination made by OFCOM may include provision ratifying decisions so made.

(6) Where OFCOM make a determination for resolving a dispute, they may require a party to the dispute—

(a) to make payments to another party to the dispute in respect of costs and expenses incurred by that other party in consequence of the reference of the dispute to OFCOM, or in connection with it; and
(b) to make payments to OFCOM in respect of costs and expenses incurred by them in dealing with the dispute.

(7) OFCOM are not, under subsection (6)(b), to require payments to be made to them by a party to the dispute except—
(a) in a case where the dispute relates to the rights and obligations of the parties to the dispute under the enactments relating to the management of the radio spectrum; or
(b) where it appears to OFCOM that the reference of the dispute by that party was frivolous or vexatious or that that party has otherwise abused the right of reference conferred by this Chapter.

(8) A determination made by OFCOM for resolving a dispute referred or referred back to them under this Chapter binds all the parties to the dispute.

(9) Subsection (8) is subject to section 192.

[3258]

NOTES

Commencement: 25 July 2003 (for the purpose of enabling network and service functions and spectrum functions to be carried out during the transitional period by the Director General of Telecommunications and the Secretary of State respectively) (see further s 408 and Sch 18 at **[3436]**, **[3460]**, and the Communications Act 2003 (Commencement No 1) Order 2003, SI 2003/1900 at **[3507]**); 29 December 2003 (for the purpose of enabling OFCOM to perform those functions) (see the Office of Communications Act 2002 (Commencement No 3) and Communications Act 2003 (Commencement No 2) Order 2003, SI 2003/3142 at **[3590]**).

Sub-s (4): words in square brackets substituted by the Wireless Telegraphy Act 2006, s 123, Sch 7, paras 25, 27.

191 OFCOM's power to require information in connection with dispute

(1) Where a dispute has been referred or referred back to OFCOM under this Chapter, they may require any person to whom subsection (2) applies to provide them with all such information as they may require for the purpose of—
(a) deciding whether it is appropriate for them to handle the dispute;
(b) determining whether it is necessary for them to consult the regulatory authorities of another member State; or
(c) considering the dispute and making a determination for resolving it.

(2) This subsection applies to—
(a) a party to the dispute; and
(b) a person who is not a party to the dispute but appears to OFCOM to have information that is relevant to the matters mentioned in subsection (1)(a) to (c).

(3) A person required to provide information under this section must provide it in such manner and within such reasonable period as may be specified by OFCOM.

(4) In fixing the period within which information is to be provided in accordance with a requirement under this section OFCOM must have regard, in particular, to—
(a) their obligation to make a determination for resolving the dispute within the period specified in section 188;
(b) the nature of the dispute; and
(c) the information that is required.

(5) Sections 138 to 144 apply for the enforcement of a requirement under this section as they apply for the enforcement of requirements under section 135 or 136.

(6) In its application for the enforcement of this section, section 138 is to have effect as if it allowed OFCOM to specify such period of less than one month for doing the things mentioned in subsection (3) of that section as they consider appropriate for the purpose of enabling them to comply with an obligation of theirs to make a determination within a particular period.

[3259]

NOTES

Commencement: 25 July 2003 (for the purpose of enabling network and service functions and spectrum functions to be carried out during the transitional period by the Director General of

Telecommunications and the Secretary of State respectively) (see further s 408 and Sch 18 at **[3436]**, **[3460]**, and the Communications Act 2003 (Commencement No 1) Order 2003, SI 2003/1900 at **[3507]**); 29 December 2003 (for the purpose of enabling OFCOM to perform those functions) (see the Office of Communications Act 2002 (Commencement No 3) and Communications Act 2003 (Commencement No 2) Order 2003, SI 2003/3142 at **[3590]**).

Appeals

192 Appeals against decisions by OFCOM, the Secretary of State etc

(1) This section applies to the following decisions—

(a) a decision by OFCOM under this Part [or any of Parts 1 to 3 of the Wireless Telegraphy Act 2006] that is not a decision specified in Schedule 8;

(b) a decision (whether by OFCOM or another) to which effect is given by a direction, approval or consent given for the purposes of a provision of a condition set under section 45;

(c) a decision to which effect is given by the modification or withdrawal of such a direction, approval or consent;

(d) a decision by the Secretary of State to which effect is given by one of the following—

(i) a specific direction under section 5 that is not about the making of a decision specified in Schedule 8;

(ii) a restriction or condition set by regulations under section 109;

(iii) a direction to OFCOM under section 132;

(iv) a specific direction under [section 5 of the Wireless Telegraphy Act 2006] that is not about the making of a decision specified in Schedule 8.

(2) A person affected by a decision to which this section applies may appeal against it to the Tribunal.

(3) The means of making an appeal is by sending the Tribunal a notice of appeal in accordance with Tribunal rules.

(4) The notice of appeal must be sent within the period specified, in relation to the decision appealed against, in those rules.

(5) The notice of appeal must set out—

(a) the provision under which the decision appealed against was taken; and

(b) the grounds of appeal.

(6) The grounds of appeal must be set out in sufficient detail to indicate—

(a) to what extent (if any) the appellant contends that the decision appealed against was based on an error of fact or was wrong in law or both; and

(b) to what extent (if any) the appellant is appealing against the exercise of a discretion by OFCOM, by the Secretary of State or by another person.

(7) In this section and Schedule 8 references to a decision under an enactment—

(a) include references to a decision that is given effect to by the exercise or performance of a power or duty conferred or imposed by or under an enactment; but

(b) include references to a failure to make a decision, and to a failure to exercise a power or to perform a duty, only where the failure constitutes a failure to grant an application or to comply with any other form of request to make the decision, to exercise the power or to perform the duty;

and references in the following provisions of this Chapter to a decision appealed against are to be construed accordingly.

(8) For the purposes of this section and the following provisions of this Chapter a decision to which effect is given by the exercise or performance of a power or duty conferred or imposed by or under an enactment shall be treated, except where provision is made for the making of that decision at a different time, as made at the time when the power is exercised or the duty performed.

[3260]

NOTES

Commencement: 25 July 2003 (for the purpose of enabling network and service functions and spectrum functions to be carried out during the transitional period by the Director General of

Telecommunications and the Secretary of State respectively) (see further s 408 and Sch 18 at **[3436]**, **[3460]**, and the Communications Act 2003 (Commencement No 1) Order 2003, SI 2003/1900 at **[3507]**); 29 December 2003 (for the purpose of enabling OFCOM to perform those functions) (see the Office of Communications Act 2002 (Commencement No 3) and Communications Act 2003 (Commencement No 2) Order 2003, SI 2003/3142 at **[3590]**).

Sub-s (1): words in square brackets in paras (a), (d) substituted by the Wireless Telegraphy Act 2006, s 123, Sch 7, paras 25, 28.

193 Reference of price control matters to the Competition Commission

(1) Tribunal rules must provide in relation to appeals under section 192(2) relating to price control that the price control matters arising in that appeal, to the extent that they are matters of a description specified in the rules, must be referred by the Tribunal to the Competition Commission for determination.

(2) Where a price control matter is referred in accordance with Tribunal rules to the Competition Commission for determination, the Commission is to determine that matter—

(a) in accordance with the provision made by the rules;

(b) in accordance with directions given to them by the Tribunal in exercise of powers conferred by the rules; and

(c) subject to the rules and any such directions, using such procedure as the Commission consider appropriate.

(3) The provision that may be made by Tribunal rules about the determination of a price control matter referred to the Competition Commission in accordance with the rules includes provision about the period within which that matter is to be determined by that Commission.

(4) Where the Competition Commission determines a price control matter in accordance with Tribunal rules, they must notify the Tribunal of the determination they have made.

(5) The notification must be given as soon as practicable after the making of the notified determination.

(6) Where a price control matter arising in an appeal is required to be referred to the Competition Commission under this section, the Tribunal, in deciding the appeal on the merits under section 195, must decide that matter in accordance with the determination of that Commission.

(7) Subsection (6) does not apply to the extent that the Tribunal decides, applying the principles applicable on an application for judicial review, that the determination of the Competition Commission is a determination that would fall to be set aside on such an application.

(8) Section 117 of the Enterprise Act 2002 (c 40) (offences of supplying false or misleading information) shall have effect in relation to information supplied to the Competition Commission in connection with their functions under this section as it has effect in relation to information supplied to them in connection with their functions under Part 3 of that Act.

(9) For the purposes of this section an appeal relates to price control if the matters to which the appeal relates are or include price control matters.

(10) In this section "price control matter" means a matter relating to the imposition of any form of price control by an SMP condition the setting of which is authorised by—

(a) section 87(9);

(b) section 91; or

(c) section 93(3).

[3261]

NOTES

Commencement: 25 July 2003 (for the purpose of enabling network and service functions and spectrum functions to be carried out during the transitional period by the Director General of Telecommunications and the Secretary of State respectively) (see further s 408 and Sch 18 at **[3436]**, **[3460]**, and the Communications Act 2003 (Commencement No 1) Order 2003, SI 2003/1900 at **[3507]**); 29 December 2003 (for the purpose of enabling OFCOM to perform those functions) (see the Office of Communications Act 2002 (Commencement No 3) and Communications Act 2003 (Commencement No 2) Order 2003, SI 2003/3142 at **[3590]**).

194 Composition of Competition Commission for price control references

(1) The Secretary of State must appoint not less than three members of the Competition Commission for the purposes of references under section 193.

(2) In selecting a group to perform the Commission's functions in relation to a reference under section 193, the chairman of the Commission must select at least one, and not more than three, of the members appointed under this section to be members of the group.

[3262]

NOTES

Commencement: 25 July 2003 (for the purpose of enabling network and service functions and spectrum functions to be carried out during the transitional period by the Director General of Telecommunications and the Secretary of State respectively) (see further s 408 and Sch 18 at **[3436]**, **[3460]**, and the Communications Act 2003 (Commencement No 1) Order 2003, SI 2003/1900 at **[3507]**); 29 December 2003 (for the purpose of enabling OFCOM to perform those functions) (see the Office of Communications Act 2002 (Commencement No 3) and Communications Act 2003 (Commencement No 2) Order 2003, SI 2003/3142 at **[3590]**).

195 Decisions of the Tribunal

(1) The Tribunal shall dispose of an appeal under section 192(2) in accordance with this section.

(2) The Tribunal shall decide the appeal on the merits and by reference to the grounds of appeal set out in the notice of appeal.

(3) The Tribunal's decision must include a decision as to what (if any) is the appropriate action for the decision-maker to take in relation to the subject-matter of the decision under appeal.

(4) The Tribunal shall then remit the decision under appeal to the decision-maker with such directions (if any) as the Tribunal considers appropriate for giving effect to its decision.

(5) The Tribunal must not direct the decision-maker to take any action which he would not otherwise have power to take in relation to the decision under appeal.

(6) It shall be the duty of the decision-maker to comply with every direction given under subsection (4).

(7) In the case of an appeal against a decision given effect to by a restriction or condition set by regulations under section 109, the Tribunal must take only such steps for disposing of the appeal as it considers are not detrimental to good administration.

(8) In its application to a decision of the Tribunal under this section, paragraph 1(2)(b) of Schedule 4 to the Enterprise Act 2002 (c 40) (exclusion of commercial information from documents recording Tribunal decisions) is to have effect as if for the reference to the undertaking to which commercial information relates there were substituted a reference to any person to whom it relates.

(9) In this section "the decision-maker" means—

- (a) OFCOM or the Secretary of State, according to who took the decision appealed against; or
- (b) in the case of an appeal against—
  - (i) a direction, approval or consent given by a person other than OFCOM or the Secretary of State, or
  - (ii) the modification or withdrawal by such a person of such a direction, approval or consent,

that other person.

[3263]

NOTES

Commencement: 25 July 2003 (for the purpose of enabling network and service functions and spectrum functions to be carried out during the transitional period by the Director General of Telecommunications and the Secretary of State respectively) (see further s 408 and Sch 18 at **[3436]**, **[3460]**, and the Communications Act 2003 (Commencement No 1) Order 2003, SI 2003/1900 at **[3507]**); 29 December 2003 (for the purpose of enabling OFCOM to perform those functions) (see the Office of Communications Act 2002 (Commencement No 3) and Communications Act 2003 (Commencement No 2) Order 2003, SI 2003/3142 at **[3590]**).

196 Appeals from the Tribunal

(1) A decision of the Tribunal on an appeal under section 192(2) may itself be appealed.

(2) An appeal under this section—
(a) lies to the Court of Appeal or to the Court of Session; and
(b) must relate only to a point of law arising from the decision of the Tribunal.

(3) An appeal under this section may be brought by—
(a) a party to the proceedings before the Tribunal; or
(b) any other person who has a sufficient interest in the matter.

(4) An appeal under this section requires the permission of the Tribunal or of the court to which it is to be made.

(5) In this section references to a decision of the Tribunal include references to a direction given by it under section 195(4).

[3264]

NOTES

Commencement: 25 July 2003 (for the purpose of enabling network and service functions and spectrum functions to be carried out during the transitional period by the Director General of Telecommunications and the Secretary of State respectively) (see further s 408 and Sch 18 at **[3436]**, **[3460]**, and the Communications Act 2003 (Commencement No 1) Order 2003, SI 2003/1900 at **[3507]**); 29 December 2003 (for the purpose of enabling OFCOM to perform those functions) (see the Office of Communications Act 2002 (Commencement No 3) and Communications Act 2003 (Commencement No 2) Order 2003, SI 2003/3142 at **[3590]**).

Interpretation of Chapter 3

197 Interpretation of Chapter 3

(1) In this Chapter—
"network access" has the same meaning as in Chapter 1 of this Part;
"the Tribunal" means the Competition Appeal Tribunal; and
"Tribunal rules" means rules made under section 15 of the Enterprise Act 2002.

(2) References in this Chapter, in relation to a dispute, to the regulatory authorities of other member States are references to such of the authorities of the other member States as have been notified under the Framework Directive to the European Commission as the regulatory authorities of those States for the purposes of the matters to which the dispute relates.

(3) In this section "the Framework Directive" has the same meaning as in Chapter 1 of this Part.

[3265]

NOTES

Commencement: 25 July 2003 (for the purpose of enabling network and service functions and spectrum functions to be carried out during the transitional period by the Director General of Telecommunications and the Secretary of State respectively) (see further s 408 and Sch 18 at **[3436]**, **[3460]**, and the Communications Act 2003 (Commencement No 1) Order 2003, SI 2003/1900 at **[3507]**); 29 December 2003 (for the purpose of enabling OFCOM to perform those functions) (see the Office of Communications Act 2002 (Commencement No 3) and Communications Act 2003 (Commencement No 2) Order 2003, SI 2003/3142 at **[3590]**).

PART 3
TELEVISION AND RADIO SERVICES

CHAPTER 1
THE BBC, C4C THE WELSH AUTHORITY AND THE GAELIC MEDIA SERVICE

The BBC

198 Functions of OFCOM in relation to the BBC

(1) It shall be a function of OFCOM, to the extent that provision for them to do so is contained in—

(a) the BBC Charter and Agreement, and
(b) the provisions of this Act and of Part 5 of the 1996 Act,

to regulate the provision of the BBC's services and the carrying on by the BBC of other activities for purposes connected with the provision of those services.

(2) For the purposes of the carrying out of that function OFCOM—

(a) are to have such powers and duties as may be conferred on them by or under the BBC Charter and Agreement; and
(b) are entitled, to the extent that they are authorised to do so by the Secretary of State or under the terms of that Charter and Agreement, to act on his behalf in relation to that Charter and Agreement.

(3) The BBC must pay OFCOM such penalties in respect of contraventions by the BBC of provision made by or under—

(a) this Part, or
(b) the BBC Charter and Agreement,

as are imposed by OFCOM in exercise of powers conferred on them by that Charter and Agreement.

(4) The BBC are also to be liable to pay OFCOM such sums in respect of the carrying out by OFCOM of their functions in relation to the BBC as may be—

(a) agreed from time to time between the BBC and OFCOM; or
(b) (in default of agreement) fixed by the Secretary of State.

(5) The maximum penalty that may be imposed on the BBC on any occasion by OFCOM in exercise of a power conferred by virtue of the BBC Charter and Agreement is £250,000.

(6) The Secretary of State may by order substitute a different sum for the sum for the time being specified in subsection (5).

(7) No order is to be made containing provision authorised by subsection (6) unless a draft of the order has been laid before Parliament and approved by a resolution of each House.

(8) It shall be the duty of OFCOM to have regard to their functions under this section when carrying out their functions under the 1990 Act, the 1996 Act and this Part in relation to services provided by persons other than the BBC.

(9) In this section "the BBC's services" means such of the services provided by the BBC (excluding the services comprised in the World Service) as are of a description of service which, if provided by a BBC company, would fall to be regulated by OFCOM by virtue of section 211 or 245.

[3266]

NOTES

Commencement: 29 December 2003.

C4C

199 Functions of C4C

(1) The activities that C4C are able to carry on include any activities which appear to them—

(a) to be activities that it is appropriate for them to carry on in association with the carrying out of their primary functions; and
(b) to be connected, otherwise than merely in financial terms, with activities undertaken by them for the carrying out of those functions.

(2) C4C's primary functions are—

(a) securing the continued provision of Channel 4; and
(b) the fulfilment of the public service remit for that Channel under section 265.

(3), (4) …

(5) Schedule 9 (which makes provision for the approval by OFCOM, and for the enforcement, of arrangements made by C4C about the carrying on of their activities) shall have effect.

[3267]

NOTES

Commencement: 29 December 2003.
Sub-ss (3), (4): amend the Broadcasting Act 1990, s 24, Sch 3.

200 (*Amends the Broadcasting Act 1990, Sch 3, para 3* (*outside the scope of this work*).)

201 Deficits and surpluses of C4C

(1) …

(2) This section has effect in relation to a deficit or excess for a year ending after the commencement of this section.

[3268]

NOTES

Commencement: 29 December 2003.
Sub-s (1): repeals the Broadcasting Act 1990, ss 26, 27.

202 Borrowing limit for C4C

(1) The Secretary of State may by order provide for a limit on the borrowing that C4C is allowed to undertake.

(2) The order may fix the limit either—

(a) by specifying the sum which the outstanding borrowing of C4C must not at any time exceed; or

(b) by providing a method of determining the sum which that borrowing must not exceed.

(3) C4C are not to borrow money if the effect of the borrowing would be to cause the amount of their outstanding borrowing to be, or to remain, in excess of the limit (if any) that is for the time being in force.

(4) For the purposes of this section the amount of C4C's outstanding borrowing at any time is the aggregate amount outstanding at that time in respect of the principal of sums borrowed by them, but after allowing sums borrowed to repay existing loans to be applied for that purpose.

(5) Before making an order under this section, the Secretary of State must consult C4C.

(6) The consent of the Treasury is required for the making of an order under this section.

[3269]

NOTES

Commencement: 29 December 2003.
Orders: the Channel Four Television Corporation (Borrowing Limit) Order 2003, SI 2003/3176.

The Welsh Authority

203 Function of OFCOM in relation to the Welsh Authority

It shall be a function of OFCOM, to the extent that provision for them to do so is contained in this Act and Part 5 of the 1996 Act, to regulate the services provided by the Welsh Authority.

[3270]

NOTES

Commencement: 29 December 2003.

204 Welsh Authority's function of providing S4C and S4C Digital

(1) The Welsh Authority shall continue in existence with the substitution of the following function for their functions under section 57 of the 1990 Act.

(2) The Welsh Authority shall have the function of providing television programme services of high quality with a view to their being available for reception wholly or mainly by members of the public in Wales.

(3) The carrying out of that function—

(a) must include the continuing provision of the television broadcasting service known as Sianel Pedwar Cymru ("S4C"); and

(b) may include the continuing provision of the service provided in digital form and known as S4C Digital.

(4) The power of the Welsh Authority to provide S4C Digital includes a power to secure that arrangements are made and remain in force for it to be broadcast in digital form.

(5) It shall be the duty of the Welsh Authority to secure that S4C and S4C Digital each represents a public service for the dissemination of information, education and entertainment.

(6) The Welsh Authority may use part of the signals carrying S4C to provide—

(a) subtitling in relation to programmes included in the service; and

(b) other services which are ancillary to programmes included in S4C and which are directly related to their contents.

(7) In providing S4C Digital the Welsh Authority may also provide—

(a) assistance for disabled people in relation to programmes included in the service; and

(b) any other service (other than one mentioned in paragraph (a)) which is an ancillary service in relation to S4C Digital.

(8) The Secretary of State may by order modify this Act and such other enactments as he thinks fit for the purpose of—

(a) replacing the requirement of the Welsh Authority to provide S4C with a requirement to provide a service in digital form;

(b) requiring the Welsh Authority to secure that arrangements are made for that service and S4C Digital to be merged and provided as one service (also to be known as "S4C Digital"); and

(c) applying enactments relating to the provision of S4C or S4C Digital to the provision of the merged service.

(9) An order under subsection (8) may require the Welsh Authority to ensure that, from the coming into force of a requirement to provide a merged service in digital form until a time determined in the manner described in the order, the whole or a part of the merged service is also to be provided for broadcasting in analogue form.

(10) In this section "programme" does not include an advertisement.

[3271]

NOTES

Commencement: 29 December 2003.

205 Powers to provide other services

(1) The Welsh Authority are not, in the carrying out of their function under section 204, to provide any television programme service (apart from S4C and S4C Digital) unless—

(a) the service appears to them to satisfy the requirements of subsection (3); and

(b) the provision by them of the service has been approved by an order made by the Secretary of State.

(2) The functions of the Welsh Authority include the provision of services that are neither television programme services nor sound services but—

(a) are provided with a view to being made available for reception wholly or mainly by members of the public in Wales or otherwise to be received or used by persons in Wales;

(b) are services appearing to them to satisfy the requirements of subsection (3); and

(c) are services the provision of which by the Authority has been approved by an order made by the Secretary of State.

(3) A service provided under this section must be a public service of high quality for the dissemination of information, education or entertainment (or a combination of them) wholly or mainly to members of the public in Wales.

(4) The Welsh Authority are not to provide a television programme service under this section unless it is one the provision of which by them broadens the range of television programme services available for reception by members of the public in Wales.

(5) The Welsh Authority must ensure, in the case of every television programme service provided with the approval of the Secretary of State under this section, that a substantial proportion of the programmes included in the service consists of programmes in Welsh.

(6) An order under this section approving the provision of a service must set out—
- (a) the nature and other characteristics of the service that is approved; and
- (b) in the case of a service that is a television programme service, a public service remit for that service.

(7) In providing a service approved under this section the Welsh Authority may also provide—
- (a) assistance for disabled people in relation to programmes included in the service;
- (b) other services which are ancillary to programmes included in the service and which are directly related to their contents; and
- (c) any other service (other than one mentioned in paragraph (a) or (b)) which is an ancillary service in relation to so much of the service as is provided in digital form.

(8) A television programme service provided under this section in digital form is a qualifying service for the purposes of the 1996 Act.

(9) In this section "sound service" means a service which would fall to be regulated under section 245 if provided by an S4C company.

[3272]

NOTES

Commencement: 29 December 2003.

206 Other activities of Welsh Authority

(1) The activities that the Welsh Authority are able to carry on include activities which appear to them—
- (a) to be activities that it is appropriate for them to carry on in association with the carrying out of their function of providing S4C, S4C Digital or a service the provision of which is approved under section 205; and
- (b) to be connected, otherwise than merely in financial terms, with activities undertaken by them for the carrying out of that function.

(2) The approval of the Secretary of State is required for the carrying on by the Welsh Authority of activities authorised only by subsection (1).

(3) The approval of the Secretary of State—
- (a) must be contained in an order made by him; and
- (b) may be a general approval in relation to a description of activities or a specific approval in relation to particular activities.

(4) The activities capable of being authorised under subsection (1)—
- (a) do not include the provision of a licensable service; but
- (b) do include activities for securing the provision of such a service by an S4C company and other activities connected with the provision of such a service by such a company.

(5) The activities referred to in subsection (4)(b) include—
- (a) the formation of a company to provide a programme service;
- (b) the taking of steps by means of which a company that is providing such a service becomes an S4C company.

(6) …

(7) In this section "licensable service" means a service that would fall to be regulated under section 211 or 245 if provided by an S4C company.

(8) …

[3273]

NOTES

Commencement: 29 December 2003.
Sub-s (6): amends the Broadcasting Act 1990, Sch 6.
Sub-s (8): amends the Broadcasting Act 1990, s 57.

207 Welsh Authority finances

(1) The Welsh Authority must not, whether directly or indirectly, impose charges on persons—

(a) in respect of their reception or use in Wales of any of the Authority's public services;

(b) in respect of their reception in Wales of any service consisting in the provision of assistance for disabled people in relation to programmes included in any one or more of those services; or

(c) in respect of their reception in Wales of any service (other than one mentioned in paragraph (b)) which is an ancillary service in relation to any of the Authority's public services provided in digital form.

(2) It shall be unlawful to impose a charge in contravention of subsection (1).

(3) The power of the Welsh Authority to do anything that appears to them to be conducive or incidental to the carrying out of their functions includes power, subject to subsection (4), to borrow money.

(4) The Welsh Authority are not to borrow money except with the approval of the Secretary of State.

(5) The consent of the Treasury is to be required for the giving of an approval for the purposes of subsection (4).

(6) The Welsh Authority are to be liable to pay OFCOM such sums in respect of the carrying out by OFCOM of their functions in relation to the Authority as may be—

(a) agreed from time to time between the Authority and OFCOM; or

(b) (in default of agreement) fixed by the Secretary of State.

(7), (8) ...

(9) In this section references to the Welsh Authority's public services are references to the following—

(a) S4C;

(b) S4C Digital; and

(c) the services the provision of which by the Authority is authorised by or under section 205.

[3274]

NOTES

Commencement: 29 December 2003.
Sub-ss (7), (8): amend the Broadcasting Act 1990, ss 61, 61A.

The Gaelic Media Service

208 The Gaelic Media Service

(1) The body established for the purposes of section 183 of the 1990 Act (financing of programmes in Gaelic out of the Gaelic Television Fund) is hereby renamed Seirbheis nam Meadhanan Gàidhlig (the Gaelic Media Service).

(2) References in any instrument or other document to Comataidh Craolaidh Gaidhlig or to the Gaelic Broadcasting Committee are to be construed accordingly.

(3), (4) ...

[3275]

NOTES

Commencement: 29 December 2003.
Sub-ss (3), (4): amend the Broadcasting Act 1990, s 183.

209, 210 (*S 209 inserts the Broadcasting Act 1990, s 183A* (*outside the scope of this work*); *s 210 amends Sch 19 to that Act* (*outside the scope of this work*).)

CHAPTER 2
REGULATORY STRUCTURE FOR INDEPENDENT TELEVISION SERVICES

Preliminary

211 Regulation of independent television services

(1) It shall be a function of OFCOM to regulate the following services in accordance with this Act, the 1990 Act and the 1996 Act—

(a) services falling within subsection (2) that are provided otherwise than by the BBC or the Welsh Authority; and

(b) services falling within subsection (3) that are provided otherwise than by the BBC.

(2) The services referred to in subsection (1)(a) are—

(a) television broadcasting services that are provided from places in the United Kingdom with a view to their being broadcast otherwise than only from a satellite;

(b) television licensable content services that are provided by persons under the jurisdiction of the United Kingdom for the purposes of the Television without Frontiers Directive;

(c) digital television programme services that are provided by persons under the jurisdiction of the United Kingdom for the purposes of that Directive;

(d) restricted television services that are provided from places in the United Kingdom; and

(e) additional television services that are provided from places in the United Kingdom.

(3) The services referred to in subsection (1)(b) are—

(a) television multiplex services that are provided from places in the United Kingdom; and

(b) digital additional television services that are provided by persons under the jurisdiction of the United Kingdom for the purposes of the Television without Frontiers Directive.

[3276]

NOTES

Commencement: 29 December 2003.

212 Abolition of function of assigning television frequencies

The Secretary of State shall cease to have any function under the 1990 Act or the 1996 Act of assigning frequencies for the purposes of any of the following—

(a) services falling to be licensed under Part 1 of the 1990 Act;

(b) S4C; or

(c) television multiplex services falling to be licensed under Part 1 of the 1996 Act.

[3277]

NOTES

Commencement: 29 December 2003.

213 Abolition of licensing for local cable systems

On and after the television transfer date no licence shall be required under Part 2 of the 1990 Act for the provision of a local delivery service.

[3278]

NOTES

Commencement: 29 December 2003.

Channels 3 and 5

214 Digital Channel 3 and Channel 5 licences

(1) This section applies to the grant by OFCOM, at any time on or after the television transfer date, of a licence under Part 1 of the 1990 Act to provide a Channel 3 service or to provide Channel 5.

(2) The licence must—
(a) be a licence to provide the licensed service with a view to its being broadcast in digital form; and
(b) contain such condition (if any) requiring the provider of the service to ensure that the whole or a part of the service is also provided for broadcasting in analogue form as OFCOM consider appropriate.

(3) The conditions included in a licence by virtue of subsection (2)(b) must be such as to enable effect to be given to any directions given from time to time by the Secretary of State to OFCOM about the continuance of the provision of services in analogue form.

(4) Where the licence contains a condition falling within subsection (2)(b), it must also contain a condition that—
(a) the programmes (apart from the advertisements) that are included in the service provided in analogue form, and
(b) the times at which they are broadcast,
are to be the same as in the case of, or of the specified part of, the service provided for broadcasting in digital form.

(5) The licence—
(a) must be a licence which continues in force, from the time from which it takes effect, until the end of the licensing period beginning or current at that time; and
(b) shall be renewable, on one or more occasions, under section 216.

(6) For the purposes of subsection (5) a licensing period is—
(a) the period beginning with the commencement of this section and ending with the initial expiry date; or
(b) any subsequent period of ten years beginning with the end of the previous licensing period.

(7) The licence must contain the conditions that OFCOM consider appropriate for the purpose of performing their duty under section 263.

(8) The conditions of the licence must also include conditions prohibiting the imposition, whether directly or indirectly, of the following—
(a) charges on persons in respect of their reception in the United Kingdom of the licensed service;
(b) charges on persons in respect of their reception in the United Kingdom of any service consisting in the provision of assistance for disabled people in relation to programmes included in the licensed service; and
(c) charges on persons in respect of their reception in the United Kingdom of any service (other than one mentioned in paragraph (b)) which is an ancillary service in relation to so much of the licensed service as is provided in digital form.

(9) It shall be unlawful to impose a charge in contravention of a condition imposed under subsection (8).

[3279]

NOTES
Commencement: 29 December 2003.

215 Replacement of existing Channel 3 and Channel 5 licences

(1) It shall be the duty of OFCOM to make an offer under this section to every person who, when the offer is made, is the holder of a licence (an "existing licence")—
(a) to provide a Channel 3 service; or
(b) to provide Channel 5.

(2) The offer made to a person under this section—
(a) must be an offer to exchange his existing licence for a replacement licence; and

(b) must be made as soon as practicable after the television transfer date.

(3) The replacement licence offered must be one granted in accordance with the provisions of—

(a) Part 1 of the 1990 Act; and
(b) section 214 of this Act;

but sections 15 to 17A of the 1990 Act (award of licences) are not to apply in the case of the replacement licence.

(4) Subject to subsection (5), where OFCOM make an offer under this section to a person, the service which they are proposing to license by the replacement licence must be a service which—

(a) is provided with a view to its being broadcast in digital form; but
(b) subject to that and to any requirements of section 214, appears to OFCOM to be a service that is equivalent in all material respects to the service the provision of which in analogue form was authorised by the existing licence.

(5) An offer under this section may, to such extent as OFCOM think fit, propose the grant of a licence to provide a service for an area or at times which, though substantially the same as in the case of the existing licence, are not identical.

(6) The offer must propose the inclusion in the replacement licence of conditions as to the payment of amounts to OFCOM which require the payment of—

(a) the same amount in respect of each complete calendar year falling wholly or partly within the period for which the replacement licence is in force, and
(b) an amount equal to the same percentage of the qualifying revenue for each accounting period of the licence holder falling within that period,

as would have been payable under the existing licence had that licence continued in force until the end of the period for which the replacement licence is granted.

(7) That offer must also propose the conditions for allowing amounts paid for a period under the existing licence to be set off against liabilities for the same period arising under the replacement licence.

(8) An offer under this section must set out—

(a) the terms of the proposed replacement licence;
(b) the conditions on which OFCOM are proposing to grant the replacement licence;
(c) the period for which the offer is open;
(d) the date on which the proposed replacement licence will be granted if the offer is accepted;
(e) the time as from which it is proposed that that licence will take effect if the offer is accepted; and
(f) the time from which the existing licence will cease to have effect if the offer is not accepted.

(9) The times set out under subsection (8) must—

(a) in the case of the time set out under paragraph (e), be in the period of twelve months beginning with the television transfer date; and
(b) in the case of the time set out under paragraph (f), be in the period of eighteen months after the end of the period set out under paragraph (c) of that subsection.

(10) Where a person to whom an offer has been made under this section elects, by notification to OFCOM, to exchange his licence for the replacement licence offered to him—

(a) he is entitled, on the date set out in the offer, to be granted, in accordance with Part 1 of the 1990 Act and section 214 of this Act, a replacement licence under that Part in the terms, and on the conditions, so set out;
(b) the replacement licence shall come into force, and the existing licence cease to have effect, at the time specified in the offer, or such later time as OFCOM may, with the consent of that person, direct; and
(c) the service which he is authorised to provide by the replacement licence, so far as it is provided in digital form, shall be a qualifying service for the purposes of Part 1 of the 1996 Act.

(11) Where the person to whom an offer has been made under this section—

(a) does not elect, during the period for which the offer is open, to exchange the existing licence for the replacement licence, or
(b) rejects the offer before the end of that period,

the existing licence shall have effect as if the period for which it is to continue in force ended with the time specified in the offer for the purposes of subsection (8)(f).

(12) In this section "qualifying revenue" has the same meaning as in section 19 of the 1990 Act.

[3280]

NOTES

Commencement: 29 December 2003.

216 Renewal of Channel 3 and 5 licences

(1) The holder of—

(a) a licence to provide a Channel 3 service, or

(b) a licence to provide Channel 5,

may apply to OFCOM for the renewal of his licence for a period of ten years from the end of the licensing period current at the time of the application.

(2) An application for renewal may only be made in the period which—

(a) begins four years before the end of the current licensing period; and

(b) ends three months before the day that OFCOM have determined to be the day by which they would need to publish a tender notice if they were proposing to grant a fresh licence to take effect from the end of that period.

(3) A determination for the purposes of subsection (2)(b)—

(a) must be made at least one year before the day determined; and

(b) must be notified by OFCOM to every person who, at the time of the determination, holds a licence in respect of which there is right to apply for renewal under this section.

(4) Where OFCOM receive an application under this section for the renewal of a licence, they must—

(a) decide whether they will be renewing the licence;

(b) if they decide that they will be, determine in accordance with section 217 the financial terms on which the licence will be renewed; and

(c) notify the applicant of their decision and determination.

(5) Section 17(5) to (7) of the 1990 Act (suspect sources of funds) apply in relation to an applicant for a renewal under this section as they apply in relation to an applicant mentioned in section 17(5) of that Act, but as if references to the award of a licence were references to its renewal.

(6) OFCOM may decide not to renew the licence if they are not satisfied that the applicant (if his licence were renewed) would provide a service complying with the requirements imposed under Chapter 4 of this Part by conditions relating to—

(a) the public service remit for the licensed service;

(b) programming quotas;

(c) news and current affairs programmes; and

(d) programme production and regional programming.

(7) OFCOM may also decide not to renew the licence if they propose to grant a fresh licence for a service replacing the licensed service which would differ from the licensed service in—

(a) the area for which it would be provided; or

(b) the times of the day, or days of the week, between or on which it would be provided.

(8) In all cases in which—

(a) the applicant notifies OFCOM that he accepts the terms notified to him under subsection (4)(c), and

(b) they are not required or allowed by subsections (5) to (7) to refuse a renewal,

they must grant the renewal as soon as reasonably practicable.

(9) But OFCOM must not grant a renewal under this section more than eighteen months before the end of the licensing period from the end of which the renewal will take effect.

(10) Where a licence is renewed under this section, it must be renewed on the same terms and conditions, subject only to such modifications as are required to give effect, in accordance with the determination under subsection (4)(b), to the requirements imposed by section 217(4).

(11) Nothing in this section requires OFCOM, following the receipt of an application for the renewal of a licence—

(a) to make a decision or determination, or

(b) to take any other step under this section,

at any time after an order under section 230 has come into force preventing the renewal of the licence.

(12) For the purposes of this section a licensing period is—

(a) the period beginning with the commencement of this section and ending with the initial expiry date; or

(b) any subsequent period of ten years beginning with the end of the previous licensing period.

(13) In this section "tender notice" means a notice under section 15 of the 1990 Act.

[3281]

NOTES

Commencement: 29 December 2003.

217 Financial terms of licence renewed under s 216

(1) The determination under section 216(4)(b) must comprise—

(a) a determination of the amount which the holder of the renewed licence will be required by the conditions of that licence to pay to OFCOM in respect of the first complete calendar year falling within the renewal period; and

(b) a determination of the percentage of qualifying revenue for each accounting period of the licence holder falling within the renewal period which the holder of that licence will be required by those conditions to pay to OFCOM.

(2) The amount determined under subsection (1)(a) must be equal to the amount which, in OFCOM's opinion, would have been the cash bid of the licence holder were the licence (instead of being renewed) to be granted for the period of the renewal on an application made in accordance with section 15 of the 1990 Act.

(3) For the purposes of subsection (1)(b)—

(a) different percentages may be determined for different accounting periods; and

(b) the percentages that may be determined for an accounting period include a nil percentage.

(4) The renewed licence is required, as renewed, to include conditions requiring the licence holder to pay to OFCOM—

(a) in addition to any fees required to be paid by virtue of section 4(1)(b) of the 1990 Act, but

(b) instead of the amounts payable under the corresponding provision applicable under the conditions of the licence to the period before the renewal takes effect,

the amounts specified in subsection (5).

(5) Those amounts are—

(a) in respect of the first complete calendar year falling within the renewal period, the amount determined under subsection (1)(a);

(b) in respect of each subsequent year falling wholly or partly within the renewal period, that amount increased by the appropriate percentage; and

(c) in respect of each accounting period of the licence holder falling within the renewal period, an amount representing a specified percentage of qualifying revenue for that accounting period.

(6) The percentage specified for the purposes of subsection (5)(c) in respect of an accounting period must be the amount determined for that period under subsection (1)(b).

(7) In this section—

"the appropriate percentage" and "qualifying revenue" each has the same meaning as in section 19 of the 1990 Act; and "renewal period", in relation to a licence, means the period for which the licence is in force by reason of its renewal.

[3282]

NOTES

Commencement: 29 December 2003.

The public teletext service

218 Duty to secure the provision of a public teletext service

(1) OFCOM must do all that they can to secure the provision, in accordance with this Chapter and Part 1 of the 1996 Act, of a teletext service that is available nationwide.

(2) The service must consist of—

(a) a single teletext service provided in digital form with a view to its being broadcast by means of a television multiplex service; and

(b) for so long as Channel 4, S4C and one or more Channel 3 services are broadcast in analogue form, an analogue teletext service.

(3) The service, if licensed to do so in accordance with section 219, may continue to include an analogue teletext service after it is no longer required under subsection (2)(b) to include such a service.

(4) The analogue teletext service that must be or may be comprised in the public teletext service is a single additional television service that uses the combined spare capacity available for the provision of additional television services on the frequencies on which Channel 3 services, Channel 4 and S4C (or any of them) are broadcast in analogue form.

(5) For so long as the public teletext service must consist of both a teletext service provided in digital form and an analogue teletext service, OFCOM must secure that both services are provided by the same person.

(6) But nothing in this section—

(a) requires the contents of the two services comprised in the public teletext service to be the same;

(b) prevents the service from including different items for different parts of the United Kingdom or prevents the different items from being made available only in the parts of the United Kingdom for which they are included; or

(c) prevents the licence holder from making arrangements authorised by virtue of section 220 for the provision of the whole or a part of the public teletext service by another.

(7) OFCOM must exercise their powers—

(a) to make frequencies available for the purposes of Channel 3 services, Channel 4 and S4C; and

(b) to make determinations for the purposes of section 48(2)(b) of the 1990 Act (determinations of spare capacity),

in a manner that takes account of their duty under this section.

[3283]

NOTES

Commencement: 29 December 2003.

219 Licensing of the public teletext service

(1) The licence that is required for the purposes of section 13 of the 1990 Act in respect of the public teletext service is a licence under Part 1 of that Act complying with this section.

(2) The licence—

(a) must be a licence which continues in force, from the time from which it takes effect, until the end of the licensing period beginning or current at that time; and

(b) shall be renewable, on one or more occasions, under section 222.

(3) For the purposes of subsection (2) a licensing period is—

(a) the period beginning with the commencement of this section and ending with the initial expiry date; or
(b) any subsequent period of ten years beginning with the end of the previous licensing period.

(4) The licence must contain the conditions that OFCOM consider appropriate for the purpose of performing their duty under section 263.

(5) The conditions of the licence must also include conditions prohibiting the imposition, whether directly or indirectly, of any charges on persons in respect of their reception in the United Kingdom of the licensed service.

(6) It shall be unlawful to impose a charge in contravention of a condition imposed under subsection (5).

(7) The service authorised by a licence under this section, so far as it comprises a service provided in digital form, is a qualifying service for the purposes of Part 1 of the 1996 Act.

(8) Schedule 10 (which makes further provision about the award and grant of the licence for the public teletext service and about the conditions and enforcement of that licence) shall have effect.

[3284]

NOTES

Commencement: 29 December 2003 (for transitional provisions in relation to the existing licence (as referred to in s 221(1) of this Act) see the Office of Communications Act 2002 (Commencement No 3) and Communications Act 2003 (Commencement No 2) Order 2003, SI 2003/3142, art 8(1) at **[3597]**).

220 Delegation of provision of public teletext service

(1) The licence for the provision of the public teletext service may—
(a) include provision enabling the licence holder to authorise an eligible person to provide the whole or a part of the public teletext service on his behalf; and
(b) impose conditions subject to and in accordance with which the whole or a part of that service may be provided by a person authorised by the licence holder.

(2) The conditions of the licence to provide the public teletext service apply in relation to its provision by a person authorised to do so on the licence holder's behalf as they apply to its provision by the licence holder.

(3) A contravention of those conditions by a person so authorised shall be treated for the purposes of this Chapter and the 1990 Act as a contravention on the part of the licence holder.

(4) In this section "eligible person" means a person who is not a disqualified person under Part 2 of Schedule 2 to the 1990 Act in relation to the licence for the public teletext service.

[3285]

NOTES

Commencement: 29 December 2003 (for transitional provisions in relation to the existing licence (as referred to in s 221(1) of this Act) see the Office of Communications Act 2002 (Commencement No 3) and Communications Act 2003 (Commencement No 2) Order 2003, SI 2003/3142, art 8(1) at **[3597]**).

221 Replacement of existing public teletext provider's licence

(1) It shall be the duty of OFCOM to make an offer under this section to the person who, when the offer is made, is the holder of the licence to provide the existing service (the "existing licence").

(2) The offer made to a person under this section—
(a) must be an offer to exchange his existing licence for a replacement licence; and
(b) must be made as soon as practicable after the television transfer date.

(3) The replacement licence is to be one which is granted—
(a) for the purposes of section 218 of this Act; and
(b) in accordance with section 219 of this Act and the provisions of Part 1 of the 1990 Act;

but Part 1 of Schedule 10 to this Act is not to apply in the case of the replacement licence.

(4) Where OFCOM make an offer under this section, the service which they are proposing to license by or under the replacement licence must be a service which comprises both—

- (a) a service that appears to OFCOM to be equivalent in all material respects to the existing service; and
- (b) a service that appears to them to be equivalent in all material respects to the teletext service in digital form which that person is required to provide by virtue of section 30 of the 1996 Act.

(5) The offer must propose the inclusion in the replacement licence of conditions as to the payment of amounts to OFCOM which require the payment of—

- (a) the same amount in respect of each complete calendar year falling wholly or partly within the period for which the replacement licence is in force, and
- (b) an amount equal to the same percentage of the qualifying revenue for each accounting period of the licence holder falling within that period,

as would have been payable under the existing licence had that licence continued in force until the end of the period for which the replacement licence is granted.

(6) That offer must also propose conditions allowing amounts paid for a period under the existing licence to be set off against liabilities for the same period arising under the replacement licence.

(7) An offer under this section must set out—

- (a) the terms of the proposed replacement licence;
- (b) the conditions on which OFCOM are proposing to grant the replacement licence;
- (c) the period for which the offer is open;
- (d) the time as from which it is proposed the replacement licence will take effect if the offer is accepted; and
- (e) the time from which the existing licence will cease to have effect if the offer is not accepted.

(8) The times set out under subsection (7) must—

- (a) in the case of the time set out under paragraph (d), be in the period of twelve months beginning with the television transfer date; and
- (b) in the case of the time set out under paragraph (e), be in the period of eighteen months after the end of the period set out under paragraph (c) of that subsection.

(9) Where the person to whom an offer has been made under this section elects, by notification to OFCOM, to exchange his licence for the replacement licence offered to him—

- (a) he is entitled to be granted the replacement licence in the terms, and on the conditions, set out in the offer; and
- (b) the replacement licence shall come into force, and the existing licence cease to have effect, at the time specified in the offer, or such later time as OFCOM may, with the consent of that person, direct.

(10) Where the person to whom an offer has been made under this section—

- (a) does not elect, during the period for which the offer is open, to exchange the existing licence for the replacement licence, or
- (b) rejects the offer before the end of that period,

the existing licence shall have effect as if the period for which it is to continue in force ended with the time specified in the offer for the purposes of subsection (7)(e).

(11) In this section "the existing service" means the teletext service which—

- (a) is being provided immediately before the television transfer date on the combined spare capacity available for the provision of additional television services on frequencies on which Channel 3 services and Channel 4 are provided; and
- (b) is the service by reference to which the Independent Television Commission have discharged their duty under section 49(2) of the 1990 Act.

(12) In this section "qualifying revenue" means the revenue which would be qualifying revenue (within the meaning of section 52 of the 1990 Act) in relation to the holder of a licence to provide the analogue teletext service comprised in the public teletext service.

[3286]

NOTES

Commencement: 29 December 2003.

222 Renewal of public teletext licence

(1) The holder of the licence to provide the public teletext service may apply to OFCOM for the renewal of his licence for a period of ten years from the end of the licensing period current at the time of the application.

(2) An application for renewal may only be made in the period which—
- (a) begins four years before the end of the current licensing period; and
- (b) ends three months before the day that OFCOM have determined to be the day by which they would need to publish a tender notice if they were proposing to grant a fresh licence to take effect from the end of that period.

(3) A determination for the purposes of subsection (2)(b)—
- (a) must be made at least one year before the day determined; and
- (b) must be notified by OFCOM to the holder, at the time of the determination, of the licence to provide the public teletext service.

(4) Where OFCOM receive an application under this section for the renewal of a licence, they must—
- (a) decide whether they will be renewing the licence;
- (b) if they decide that they will be, determine in accordance with section 223 the financial terms on which the licence will be renewed; and
- (c) notify the applicant of their decision and determination.

(5) Section 17(5) to (7) of the 1990 Act (suspect sources of funds) apply in relation to an applicant for a renewal under this section as they apply in relation to an applicant mentioned in section 17(5) of that Act, but as if—
- (a) references to the award of a licence were references to its renewal; and
- (b) the reference in subsection (7)(a) to section 19(1) of that Act were a reference to paragraph 7 of Schedule 10.

(6) OFCOM may decide not to renew the licence if they are not satisfied that the applicant (if his licence were renewed) would provide a service complying with the requirements imposed under Chapter 4 of this Part by conditions relating to—
- (a) the public service remit for the public teletext service;
- (b) news; and
- (c) regional matters.

(7) OFCOM may also decide not to renew the licence if they propose to grant a fresh licence for the public teletext service which would differ in any material respect from the licensed service.

(8) In all cases in which—
- (a) the applicant notifies OFCOM that he accepts the terms notified to him under subsection (4)(c), and
- (b) they are not required or allowed by subsections (5) to (7) to refuse a renewal,

they must grant the renewal as soon as reasonably practicable.

(9) But OFCOM must not grant a renewal under this section more than eighteen months before the end of the licensing period from the end of which the renewal will take effect.

(10) Where a licence is renewed under this section, it must be renewed on the same terms and conditions subject only to such modifications as are required to give effect, in accordance with the determination under subsection (4)(b), to paragraph 7 of Schedule 10.

(11) Nothing in this section requires OFCOM, following the receipt of an application for the renewal of a licence—
- (a) to make a decision or determination, or
- (b) to take any other step under this section,

at any time after an order under section 230 has come into force preventing the renewal of the licence.

(12) For the purposes of this section a licensing period is—
- (a) the period beginning with the commencement of this section and ending with the initial expiry date; or
- (b) any subsequent period of ten years beginning with the end of the previous licensing period.

(13) In this section "tender notice" means a notice under paragraph 1 of Schedule 10.

[3287]

NOTES

Commencement: 29 December 2003.

223 Financial terms of licence renewed under s 222

(1) The determination under section 222(4)(b) must comprise—

(a) a determination of the amount which the holder of the renewed licence will be required by the conditions of that licence to pay to OFCOM in respect of the first complete calendar year falling within the renewal period;

(b) a determination of the percentage of qualifying revenue for each accounting period of the licence holder falling within the renewal period which he will be required by those conditions to pay to OFCOM.

(2) The amount determined under subsection (1)(a) must be equal to the amount which, in OFCOM's opinion, would have been the cash bid of the licence holder were the licence (instead of being renewed) to be granted for the period of the renewal on an application made in accordance with Part 1 of Schedule 10.

(3) For the purposes of subsection (1)(b)—

(a) different percentages may be determined for different accounting periods; and

(b) the percentages that may be determined for an accounting period include a nil percentage.

(4) In this section "renewal period", in relation to a licence, means the period for which the licence is in force by reason of its renewal.

(5) Part 3 of Schedule 10 applies for construing this section as it applies for construing that Schedule.

[3288]

NOTES

Commencement: 29 December 2003.

Meaning of initial expiry date

224 Meaning of "initial expiry date"

(1) Subject to any postponement under this section, the date which is the initial expiry date for the purposes of this Part is 31st December 2014.

(2) The Secretary of State may (on one or more occasions) by order postpone the initial expiry date.

(3) The Secretary of State's power to postpone the initial expiry date—

(a) is to be exercisable before 30th June 2013 only if he has fixed a date after 30th June 2013 as the date for digital switchover; and

(b) is not to be exercisable on or after 30th June 2013 if he has fixed 30th June 2013 or an earlier date as the date for digital switchover.

(4) Where the Secretary of State makes an order under this section at a time after he has fixed a date for digital switchover, the date to which the initial expiry date is postponed must be a date not less than eighteen months after the date for digital switchover.

(5) The Secretary of State must exercise his power to postpone the initial expiry date if it at any time appears to him that that date would otherwise fall within the period of eighteen months immediately following the date fixed for digital switchover.

(6) Where an order under this section extends a licensing period for which a licence has been granted in accordance with section 214 or 219, the 1990 Act and this Part shall have effect (subject to subsection (7)) as if the licence had originally been granted for the extended period.

(7) Where an order under this section extends the period for which a licence is to continue in force—

(a) that order shall not affect the earliest time at which an application for the renewal of that licence may be made in accordance with section 216(2)(a) or 222(2)(a);

(b) as soon as reasonably practicable after making the order, OFCOM must make such modification of any determination made by them in the case of that licence for the purposes of section 216(2)(b) or 222(2)(b) as they consider appropriate in consequence of the extension; and

(c) neither section 216(3)(a) nor section 222(3)(a) applies to the making of that modification.

(8) In this section a reference to the date for digital switchover is a reference to the date fixed by the Secretary of State for the purposes of this section as the date which appears to him, in consequence of directions given by him for the purposes of the conditions of the licences for the relevant public broadcasting services, to be the date after which none of those services will be broadcast to any significant extent in analogue form.

(9) In this section "the relevant public broadcasting service" means any of the following—

(a) the services comprised in Channel 3; and

(b) Channel 5.

[3289]

NOTES

Commencement: 29 December 2003.

Reviews relating to licensing of Channels 3 & 5 and teletext

225 Application for review of financial terms of replacement licences

(1) The holder of a replacement licence granted under section 215 or 221 may apply to OFCOM, at any time in the first or any subsequent review period, for a review of the financial terms on which that licence is held.

(2) For the purposes of this section the first review period is the period which—

(a) begins four years before the first notional expiry date; and

(b) ends with the day before the day that OFCOM have determined to be the one by which they would need to publish a tender notice if they were proposing to grant a fresh licence to take effect from the first notional expiry date.

(3) For the purposes of this section a subsequent review period in the case of a replacement licence is so much (if any) of the following period as falls before the end of the initial expiry date, namely, the period which—

(a) begins four years before a subsequent notional expiry date; and

(b) ends with the day before the day that OFCOM have determined to be the one by which they would need to publish a tender notice if they were proposing to grant a fresh licence to take effect from that notional expiry date.

(4) A determination for the purposes of subsection (2)(b) or (3)(b) in respect of a replacement licence—

(a) must be made at least one year before the day determined; and

(b) must be notified by OFCOM to the person who, at the time of the determination, holds the licence in question.

(5) No application under this section for a review of the financial terms on which a replacement licence is held is to be made—

(a) at any time when an application under section 226 for a review of those terms is pending; or

(b) at any time in the period of twelve months following the day on which a determination by OFCOM on such an application is notified to the licence holder.

(6) For the purposes of this section an application for a review under section 226 is pending from the time when the application is made until the end of the day on which OFCOM's determination on the review is notified to the licence holder.

(7) In this section—

"the first notional expiry date", in relation to a replacement licence, means the date with which (apart from this Act) the existing licence would have expired if not renewed;

"subsequent notional expiry date", in relation to a replacement licence, means—

(a) in a case in which an application by the licence holder for a review under this section was made during the review period beginning four years before the last notional expiry date, the tenth anniversary of the date on which OFCOM's determination on that review was notified to the licence holder; and

(b) in any other case, the tenth anniversary of the last notional expiry date;

"tender notice" means a notice under section 15(1) of the 1990 Act or (as the case may be) paragraph 1 of Schedule 10.

(8) In subsection (7) "existing licence" has the same meaning as in section 215 or (as the case may be) 221.

[3290]

NOTES

Commencement: 29 December 2003.

226 Application for review of financial terms in consequence of new obligations

(1) This section applies where an order is made under section 411 that brings section 272, 273 or 274 (or any two or more of them) into force for the purpose of including conditions in the regulatory regime for—

(a) a Channel 3 service;

(b) Channel 5; or

(c) the public teletext service.

(2) The holder of a licence in which conditions mentioned in section 272, 273 or 274 will fall to be included when the order comes into force may apply to OFCOM, at any time in the review period, for a review of the financial terms on which the licence is held.

(3) For the purposes of this section the review period in the case of an order under section 411 is the period which—

(a) begins with the day on which the order is made; and

(b) ends with the time at which, by virtue of the order, one or more of sections 272, 273 and 274 come into force in the case of the licence in question.

(4) If in the case of the same order there is more than one time falling within subsection (3)(b), the review period ends with the later or latest of them.

[3291]

NOTES

Commencement: 29 December 2003.

227 Reviews under ss 225 and 226

(1) This section applies where an application is made under section 225 or 226 for a review of the financial terms on which a licence is held.

(2) As soon as reasonably practicable after receiving the application, OFCOM must—

(a) determine the amount to be paid to them under the conditions of the licence for the first calendar year falling wholly or partly within the period under review to begin after the application date; and

(b) determine the percentage to be used for computing the payments to be made to them under those conditions in respect of each accounting period falling within the period under review to begin after that date.

(3) The amount determined under subsection (2)(a) must be equal to the amount which, in OFCOM's opinion, would have been the cash bid of the licence holder were the licence being granted afresh on an application made in accordance with—

(a) section 15 of the 1990 Act (licences for Channel 3 service or Channel 5); or

(b) paragraph 3 of Schedule 10 to this Act.

(4) The determination required by subsection (2)(b) is a determination of the percentage of qualifying revenue for each accounting period that is to be paid to OFCOM.

(5) For the purposes of subsection (2)(b)—

(a) different percentages may be determined for different accounting periods; and

(b) the percentages that may be determined for an accounting period include a nil percentage.

(6) In making their determinations on an application under section 226 OFCOM are to have regard, in particular, to any additional costs that are likely to be incurred by the licence holder in consequence of the commencement of so much of section 272, 273 or 274 (or any two or more of them) as is brought into force by the commencement order in question.

(7) References in this section to qualifying revenue for an accounting period are to be construed—

(a) in the case of the holder of a licence to provide a Channel 3 service or Channel 5, in accordance with section 19 of and Part 1 of Schedule 7 to the 1990 Act; and
(b) in the case of the holder of the licence to provide the public teletext service, in accordance with Part 3 of Schedule 10 to this Act.

(8) In this section—

"the application date", in relation to a review, means the date of the making under section 225 or 226 of the application for the review; and

"the period under review", in relation to a review of the financial terms of a licence, means so much of the period for which the licence will (if not renewed) continue in force after the application date.

[3292]

NOTES

Commencement: 29 December 2003.

228 Giving effect to reviews under ss 225 and 226

(1) As soon as reasonably practicable after making a determination under section 227 on an application under section 225 or 226, OFCOM must give a notification of their determination to the applicant.

(2) The notification must set out—

(a) the determination made by OFCOM;
(b) the modifications of the applicant's licence that are required to give effect to the determination;
(c) a date by which the applicant must notify OFCOM whether or not he accepts the determination and modifications; and
(d) a subsequent date by which the applicant's licence will cease to have effect if he does not.

(3) The modifications set out in accordance with subsection (2)(b) must secure that the amount falling to be paid under the conditions of the applicant's licence for each calendar year subsequent to that for which an amount has been determined in accordance with section 227(2)(a) is the amount so determined as increased by the appropriate percentage.

(4) In the case of a determination on an application under section 225, the date specified in accordance with subsection (2)(d) must not fall before whichever is the earlier of—

(a) the next notional expiry date after the application for the review; and
(b) the end of the licensing period in which that application was made.

(5) Where the applicant notifies OFCOM that he accepts the determination—

(a) his licence is to have effect with the modifications set out in OFCOM's notification; and
(b) all such adjustments by way of payment or repayment as may be necessary for giving effect to the modifications are to be made in respect of any payments already made for years or periods affected by the modifications.

(6) Where the applicant does not, before the date specified in accordance with paragraph (c) of subsection (2), notify OFCOM that he accepts the determination, his licence shall have effect as if the period for which it is to continue in force ended with the time specified in accordance with paragraph (d) of that subsection.

(7) Where the time at which a licence would cease to have effect in accordance with subsection (6) is the end of a licensing period, that subsection does not affect any rights of the licence holder with respect to the renewal of his licence from the end of that period.

(8) In this section—

"the appropriate percentage" has the same meaning as in section 19 of the 1990 Act;

"licensing period" means—

(a) the period beginning with the commencement of this section and ending with the initial expiry date; or
(b) any subsequent period of ten years beginning with the end of the previous licensing period;

"notional expiry date" means a first or subsequent notional expiry date within the meaning of section 225.

[3293]

NOTES

Commencement: 29 December 2003.

229 Report in anticipation of new licensing round

(1) OFCOM must, in anticipation of the end of each licensing period—
(a) prepare a report under this section; and
(b) submit it to the Secretary of State no later than thirty months before the end of that period.

(2) A report under this section must set out OFCOM's opinion on the effect of each of the matters mentioned in subsection (3) on the capacity of the holders of relevant licences to contribute, in the next licensing period, to the fulfilment of the purposes of public service television broadcasting in the United Kingdom at a cost to the licence holders that is commercially sustainable.

(3) Those matters are—
(a) the arrangements that (but for an order under section 230) would allow for the renewal of relevant licences from the end of the current licensing period; and
(b) the conditions included in the regulatory regimes for the services provided under relevant licences.

(4) A report under this section must also include the recommendations (if any) which OFCOM consider, in the light of the opinion set out in the report, should be made to the Secretary of State for the exercise by him of—
(a) his power under section 230; or
(b) any of the powers to make statutory instruments that are conferred on him by Chapter 4 of this Part.

(5) Where the Secretary of State makes an order under section 224 after receiving a report under this section in anticipation of the end of the licensing period that is extended by the order—
(a) he may require OFCOM to prepare a supplementary report in the light of the postponement of the beginning of the next licensing period; and
(b) it shall be the duty of OFCOM, within such period as may be specified by the Secretary of State, to prepare the required supplementary report and to submit it to him.

(6) In this section—

"licensing period" means—
(a) the period beginning with the commencement of this section and ending with the initial expiry date; or
(b) any subsequent period of ten years beginning with the end of the previous licensing period;

"relevant licence" means—
(a) a licence to provide a Channel 3 service;
(b) a licence to provide Channel 5; or
(c) the licence to provide the public teletext service.

[3294]

NOTES

Commencement: 29 December 2003.

230 Orders suspending rights of renewal

(1) This section applies where the Secretary of State has received and considered a report submitted to him by OFCOM under section 229.

(2) If—

(a) the report contains a recommendation by OFCOM for the making of an order under this section, or

(b) the Secretary of State considers, notwithstanding the absence of such a recommendation, that it would be appropriate to do so,

he may by order provide that licences for the time being in force that are of the description specified in the order are not to be renewable under section 216 or 222 from the end of the licensing period in which he received the report.

(3) An order under this section preventing the renewal of licences from the end of a licensing period must be made at least eighteen months before the end of that period.

(4) The Secretary of State is not to make an order under this section preventing the renewal of licences from the end of the initial licensing period unless he has fixed a date before the end of that period as the date for digital switchover.

(5) Where the Secretary of State postpones the date for digital switchover after making an order under this section preventing the renewal of licences from the end of the initial licensing period, the order shall have effect only if the date to which digital switchover is postponed falls before the end of that period.

(6) Subsection (5) does not affect the power of the Secretary of State to make another order under this section after postponing the date for digital switchover.

(7) An order under this section with respect to Channel 3 licences must be an order of one of the following descriptions—

(a) an order applying to every licence to provide a Channel 3 service;

(b) an order applying to every licence to provide a national Channel 3 service; or

(c) an order applying to every licence to provide a regional Channel 3 service.

(8) An order under this section does not affect—

(a) the person to whom a licence may be granted on an application made under section 15 of the 1990 Act or under paragraph 3 of Schedule 10 to this Act; or

(b) rights of renewal in respect of licences first granted so as to take effect from the beginning of a licensing period beginning after the making of the order, or from a subsequent time.

(9) No order is to be made containing provision authorised by this section unless a draft of the order has been laid before Parliament and approved by a resolution of each House.

(10) Subsection (8) of section 224 applies for construing references in this section to the date for digital switchover as it applies for the purposes of that section.

(11) In this section—

"initial licensing period" means the licensing period ending with the initial expiry date; and

"licensing period" has the same meaning as in section 229.

[3295]

NOTES

Commencement: 29 December 2003.

Replacement of Channel 4 licence

231 Replacement of Channel 4 licence

(1) On the commencement of this subsection—

(a) Channel 4 shall cease to be licensed under the licence in force for the purposes of section 24(3) of the 1990 Act immediately before the commencement of this subsection; and

(b) a licence granted for those purposes in accordance with the following provisions of this section shall come into force as the licence under which Channel 4 is licensed.

(2) It shall be the duty of OFCOM, as soon as practicable after the television transfer date—

(a) to prepare a draft of a licence under Part 1 of the 1990 Act to replace the licence that is likely to be in force for the purposes of section 24(3) of the 1990 Act when subsection (1) of this section comes into force;

(b) to notify C4C of the terms and conditions of the replacement licence they propose; and

(c) after considering any representations made by C4C, to grant such a replacement licence to C4C so that it takes effect in accordance with paragraph (b) of subsection (1) of this section.

(3) A replacement licence proposed or granted under this section—

(a) must be a licence to provide a service with a view to its being broadcast in digital form; and

(b) must contain such conditions (if any) requiring C4C to ensure that the whole or a part of Channel 4 is also provided for broadcasting in analogue form as OFCOM consider appropriate.

(4) The conditions included in a licence by virtue of subsection (3)(b) must be such as to enable effect to be given to any directions given from time to time by the Secretary of State to OFCOM about the continuance of the provision of services in analogue form.

(5) Where a replacement licence proposed or granted under this section contains a condition falling within subsection (3)(b), it must also contain a condition that—

(a) the programmes (apart from the advertisements) that are included in the service provided in analogue form, and

(b) the times at which they are broadcast,

are to be the same as in the case of, or of the specified part of, the service provided for broadcasting in digital form.

(6) The terms of a replacement licence proposed or granted under this section must provide for it to continue in force until the end of 2014.

(7) But—

(a) such a licence may be renewed, on one or more occasions, for such period as OFCOM may think fit in relation to the occasion in question; and

(b) the provisions of this section (apart from subsections (1), (2) and (6)) are to apply in the case of a licence granted by way of a renewal of a licence granted under this section as they apply in the case of the replacement licence.

(8) The conditions of a replacement licence proposed or granted under this section must include the conditions that OFCOM consider appropriate for the purpose of performing their duty under section 263.

(9) The conditions of such a licence must also include a condition prohibiting the imposition, whether directly or indirectly, of the following—

(a) charges on persons in respect of their reception in the United Kingdom of Channel 4;

(b) charges on persons in respect of their reception in the United Kingdom of any service consisting in the provision of assistance for disabled people in relation to programmes included in Channel 4; and

(c) charges on persons in respect of their reception in the United Kingdom of any service (other than one mentioned in paragraph (b)) which is an ancillary service in relation to so much of Channel 4 as is provided in digital form.

(10) It shall be unlawful to impose a charge in contravention of a condition falling within subsection (9).

[3296]

NOTES

Commencement: 29 December 2003 (sub-ss (2)(a), (b), (3)–(10)); 10 December 2004 (sub-s (2)(c)); 28 December 2004 (sub-s (1)).

Television licensable content services

232 Meaning of "television licensable content service"

(1) In this Part "television licensable content service" means (subject to section 233) any service falling within subsection (2) in so far as it is provided with a view to its availability for reception by members of the public being secured by one or [more] of the following means—

(a) the broadcasting of the service (whether by the person providing it or by another) from a satellite; …

[(aa) the broadcasting of the service (whether by that person or by another) by means of a radio multiplex service; or]

(b) the distribution of the service (whether by that person or by another) by any means involving the use of an electronic communications network.

(2) A service falls within this subsection if it—

(a) is provided (whether in digital or in analogue form) as a service that is to be made available for reception by members of the public; and

(b) consists of television programmes or electronic programme guides, or both.

(3) Where—

(a) a service consisting of television programmes, an electronic programme guide or both ("the main service") is provided by a person as a service to be made available for reception by members of the public, and

(b) that person provides the main service with other services or facilities that are ancillary to, or otherwise relate to, the main service and are also provided so as to be so available or in order to make a service so available,

subsection (1) has effect as if the main service and such of the other services or facilities as are relevant ancillary services and are not two-way services constituted a single service falling within subsection (2).

(4) Where a person providing the main service provides it with a facility giving access to another service, the other service shall also be taken for the purposes of this section as provided by that person with the main service only if what is comprised in the other service is something over which that person has general control.

(5) A service is a two-way service for the purposes of this section if it is provided by means of an electronic communications network and an essential feature of the service is that the purposes for which it is provided involve the use of that network, or a part of it, both—

(a) for the transmission of visual images or sounds (or both) by the person providing the service to users of the service; and

(b) for the transmission of visual images or sounds (or both) by those users for reception by the person providing the service or by other users of the service.

(6) In this section—

"electronic programme guide" means a service which consists of—

(a) the listing or promotion, or both the listing and the promotion, of some or all of the programmes included in any one or more programme services the providers of which are or include persons other than the provider of the guide; and

(b) a facility for obtaining access, in whole or in part, to the programme service or services listed or promoted in the guide;

"relevant ancillary service", in relation to the main service, means a service or facility provided or made available by the provider of the main service that consists of or gives access to—

(a) assistance for disabled people in relation to some or all of the programmes included in the main service;

(b) a service (apart from advertising) which is not an electronic programme guide but relates to the promotion or listing of programmes so included; or

(c) any other service (apart from advertising) which is ancillary to one or more programmes so included and relates directly to their contents.

[3297]

NOTES

Commencement: 29 December 2003.

Sub-s (1): word in square brackets substituted, word omitted from para (a) repealed and para (aa) inserted by the Television Licensable Content Services Order 2006, SI 2006/2131, art 2(1).

233 Services that are not television licensable content services

(1) A service is not a television licensable content service to the extent that it is provided with a view to its being broadcast by means of a [television multiplex service or a general multiplex service].

(2) A service is not a television licensable content service to the extent that it consists of a service the provision of which is authorised by—
(a) a licence to provide a television broadcasting service;
(b) the licence to provide the public teletext service; or
(c) a licence to provide additional television services.

(3) A service is not a television licensable content service to the extent that it is provided by means of an electronic communications service if—
(a) it forms part only of a service provided by means of that electronic communications service or is one of a number of services access to which is made available by means of a service so provided; and
(b) the service of which it forms part, or by which it may be accessed, is provided for purposes that do not consist wholly or mainly in making available television programmes or radio programmes (or both) for reception by members of the public.

(4) A service is not a television licensable content service if it is a two-way service (within the meaning of section 232).

(5) A service is not a television licensable content service if—
(a) it is distributed by means of an electronic communications network only to persons all of whom are on a single set of premises; and
(b) that network is wholly within those premises and is not connected to an electronic communications network any part of which is outside those premises.

(6) For the purposes of subsection (5)—
(a) a set of premises is a single set of premises if, and only if, the same person is the occupier of all the premises; and
(b) two or more vehicles are capable of constituting a single set of premises if, and only if, they are coupled together.

(7) A service is not a television licensable content service if it is provided for the purpose only of being received by persons who have qualified as users of the service by reason of being—
(a) persons who have a business interest in the programmes included in the service; or
(b) persons who are to receive the programmes for the purpose only of showing them to persons falling within sub-paragraph (a) or to persons all of whom are on the business premises of the person receiving them.

(8) For the purposes of subsection (7) a person has a business interest in programmes if he has an interest in receiving or watching them—
(a) for the purposes of a business carried on by him; or
(b) for the purposes of his employment.

(9) In this section—
"business premises", in relation to a person, means premises at or from which any business of that person is carried on;
. . .
"premises" includes a vehicle;
"vehicle" includes a vessel, aircraft or hovercraft.

(10) References in this section, in relation to a person, to a business include references to—
(a) any business or other activities carried on by a body of which he is a member and the affairs of which are managed by its members; and
(b) the carrying out of any functions conferred on that person, or on any such body, by or under any enactment.

[3298]

NOTES

Commencement: 29 December 2003.

Sub-s (1): words in square brackets substituted by the Television Licensable Content Services Order 2006, SI 2006/2131, art 2(2)(a).

Sub-s (9): words omitted repealed by SI 2006/2131, art 2(2)(b).

234 Modification of ss 232 and 233

(1) The Secretary of State may by order modify any of the provisions of section 232 or 233 if it appears to him appropriate to do so having regard to any one or more of the following—

(a) the protection which, taking account of the means by which the programmes and services are received or may be accessed, is expected by members of the public as respects the contents of television programmes;

(b) the extent to which members of the public are able, before television programmes are watched or accessed, to make use of facilities for exercising control, by reference to the contents of the programmes, over what is watched or accessed;

(c) the practicability of applying different levels of regulation in relation to different services;

(d) the financial impact for providers of particular services of any modification of the provisions of that section; and

(e) technological developments that have occurred or are likely to occur.

(2) The Secretary of State may also by order provide, in cases where it otherwise appears to him appropriate to do so, that a description of service specified in the order is not to be treated as a television licensable content service for the purposes of the provisions of this Act that are so specified.

(3) No order is to be made containing provision authorised by this section unless a draft of the order has been laid before Parliament and approved by a resolution of each House. **[3299]**

NOTES

Commencement: 29 December 2003.

Orders: the Television Licensable Content Services Order 2006, SI 2006/2131.

235 Licensing of television licensable content services

(1) The licence that is required for the purposes of section 13 of the 1990 Act in respect of a television licensable content service is a licence granted under Part 1 of that Act on an application complying with this section.

(2) An application for a licence to provide a television licensable content service—

(a) must be made in such manner,

(b) must contain such information about the applicant, his business and the service he proposes to provide, and

(c) must be accompanied by such fee (if any),

as OFCOM may determine.

(3) Where an application is made to OFCOM in accordance with subsection (2) for a licence to provide a television licensable content service, OFCOM are entitled to refuse the application only if—

(a) they are required to do so by section 3(3) of the 1990 Act (licences to be held only by fit and proper persons);

(b) they are required to do so by section 5 of the 1990 Act (restrictions on the holding of licences); or

(c) they are satisfied that, if the application were to be granted, the provision of the service would be likely to involve contraventions of—

(i) standards set under section 319 of this Act; or

(ii) the provisions of a code of practice in force under Part 5 of the 1996 Act (fairness).

(4) The provision of more than one television licensable content service shall require a separate licence under Part 1 of the 1990 Act to be granted and held in respect of each service.

(5) A single licence to provide a television licensable content service may authorise the provision of a service which consists (to any extent) of different programmes to be broadcast simultaneously, or virtually so.

(6) A licence to provide a television licensable content service shall continue in force until such time as it is surrendered or is revoked in accordance with any of the provisions of this Chapter or of the 1990 Act.

[(7) A licence to provide a television licensable content service must contain such conditions as OFCOM consider appropriate for requiring the licence holder—

(a) on entering into any agreement with the provider of a radio multiplex service for the provision of a television licensable content service to be broadcast by means of that multiplex service, to notify OFCOM—
   (i) of the identity of the radio multiplex service;
   (ii) of the period during which the service will be provided; and
   (iii) where under the agreement he will be entitled to the use of a specified amount of digital capacity, of that amount;

(b) when any such agreement is varied so far as it relates to any of the matters mentioned in paragraph (a)(i), (ii) or (iii), to notify OFCOM of the variation so far as relating to those matters; and

(c) where he is providing a television licensable content service to the provider of a radio multiplex service in accordance with such an agreement as is mentioned in paragraph (a) but intends to cease doing so, to notify OFCOM of that fact.]

[3300]

NOTES

Commencement: 29 December 2003.

Sub-s (7): added by the Television Licensable Content Services Order 2006, SI 2006/2131, art 3.

236 Direction to licensee to take remedial action

(1) This section applies if OFCOM are satisfied—

(a) that the holder of a licence to provide a television licensable content service has contravened a condition of the licence; and

(b) that the contravention can be appropriately remedied by the inclusion in the licensed service of a correction or a statement of findings (or both).

(2) OFCOM may direct the licence holder to include a correction or a statement of findings (or both) in the licensed service.

(3) A direction may require the correction or statement of findings to be in such form, and to be included in programmes at such time or times, as OFCOM may determine.

(4) OFCOM are not to give a person a direction under this section unless they have given him a reasonable opportunity of making representations to them about the matters appearing to them to provide grounds for the giving of the direction.

(5) Where the holder of a licence includes a correction or a statement of findings in the licensed service in pursuance of a direction under this section, he may announce that he is doing so in pursuance of such a direction.

(6) If OFCOM are satisfied that the inclusion of a programme in a television licensable content service involved a contravention of a condition of the licence to provide that service, they may direct the holder of the licence not to include that programme in that service on any future occasion.

(7) Where OFCOM—

(a) give a direction to a BBC company under subsection (2), or

(b) receive representations from a BBC company by virtue of subsection (4),

they must send a copy of the direction or representations to the Secretary of State.

(8) For the purposes of this section a statement of findings, in relation to a case in which OFCOM are satisfied that the holder of a licence has contravened the conditions of his licence, is a statement of OFCOM's findings in relation to that contravention.

[3301]

NOTES

Commencement: 29 December 2003.

237 Penalties for contravention of licence condition or direction

(1) If OFCOM are satisfied that the holder of a licence to provide a television licensable content service—

(a) has contravened a condition of the licence, or

(b) has failed to comply with a direction given by OFCOM under or by virtue of a provision of this Part, Part 1 of the 1990 Act or Part 5 of the 1996 Act,

they may serve on him a notice requiring him to pay them, within a specified period, a specified penalty.

(2) The amount of the penalty under this section must not exceed the maximum penalty given by subsection (3).

(3) The maximum penalty is whichever is the greater of—

(a) £250,000; and

(b) 5 per cent of the qualifying revenue for the licence holder's last complete accounting period falling within the period for which his licence has been in force ("the relevant period").

(4) In relation to a person whose first complete accounting period falling within the relevant period has not ended when the penalty is imposed, subsection (3) is to be construed as referring to 5 per cent of the amount which OFCOM estimate will be the qualifying revenue for that accounting period.

(5) Section 19(2) to (6) of the 1990 Act and Part 1 of Schedule 7 to that Act (calculation of qualifying revenue), with any necessary modifications, are to apply for the purposes of subsection (3) as they apply for the purposes of Part 1 of that Act.

(6) OFCOM are not to serve a notice on a person under subsection (1) unless they have given him a reasonable opportunity of making representations to them about the matters appearing to them to provide grounds for the service of the notice.

(7) Where OFCOM—

(a) serve a notice on a BBC company under subsection (1), or

(b) receive representations from a BBC company by virtue of subsection (6),

they must send a copy of the notice or representations to the Secretary of State.

(8) An exercise by OFCOM of their powers under subsection (1) does not preclude any exercise by them of their powers under section 236 in respect of the same contravention.

(9) The Secretary of State may by order substitute a different sum for the sum for the time being specified in subsection (3)(a).

(10) No order is to be made containing provision authorised by subsection (9) unless a draft of the order has been laid before Parliament and approved by a resolution of each House.

[3302]

NOTES

Commencement: 29 December 2003 (for effect see the Office of Communications Act 2002 (Commencement No 3) and Communications Act 2003 (Commencement No 2) Order 2003, SI 2003/3142, art 9 at **[3598]**).

238 Revocation of television licensable content service licence

(1) OFCOM must serve a notice under subsection (2) on the holder of a licence to provide a television licensable content service if they are satisfied—

(a) that the holder of the licence is in contravention of a condition of the licence or is failing to comply with a direction given by them under or by virtue of any provision of this Part, Part 1 of the 1990 Act or Part 5 of the 1996 Act; and

(b) that the contravention or failure, if not remedied, would justify the revocation of the licence.

(2) A notice under this subsection must—

(a) state that OFCOM are satisfied as mentioned in subsection (1);

(b) specify the respects in which, in their opinion, the licence holder is contravening the condition or failing to comply with the direction; and

(c) state that OFCOM will revoke the licence unless the licence holder takes, within such period as is specified in the notice, such steps to remedy the failure as are so specified.

(3) If, at the end of the period specified in a notice under subsection (2), OFCOM are satisfied—

(a) that the person on whom the notice was served has failed to take the steps specified in it, and

(b) that it is necessary in the public interest to revoke his licence,

they shall serve a notice on him revoking his licence.

(4) If OFCOM are satisfied in the case of a licence to provide a television licensable content service—

(a) that the holder of the licence has ceased to provide the licensed service, and

(b) that it is appropriate for them to do so,

they shall serve a notice on him revoking his licence.

(5) If OFCOM are satisfied—

(a) that the holder of a licence to provide a television licensable content service has provided them, in connection with his application for the licence, with information which was false in a material particular, or

(b) that, in connection with his application for the licence, the holder of such a licence withheld any material information with the intention of causing them to be misled,

they may serve a notice on him revoking his licence.

(6) A notice under this section revoking a licence to provide a television licensable content service takes effect as from the time when it is served on the licence holder.

(7) OFCOM are not to serve a notice on a person under this section unless they have given him a reasonable opportunity of making representations to them about the matters in respect of which it is served.

(8) Where OFCOM—

(a) serve a notice on a BBC company under this section, or

(b) receive representations from a BBC company by virtue of subsection (7),

they must send a copy of the notice or representations to the Secretary of State.

(9) Nothing in this section applies to the revocation of a licence in exercise of the power conferred by section 239.

[3303]

NOTES

Commencement: 29 December 2003.

239 Action against licence holders who incite crime or disorder

(1) OFCOM must serve a notice under subsection (2) on the holder of a licence to provide a television licensable content service if they are satisfied—

(a) that the holder of the licence has included in the service one or more programmes containing material likely to encourage or to incite the commission of crime, or to lead to disorder;

(b) that, in doing so, he has contravened conditions contained by virtue of Chapter 4 of this Part in the licence to provide that service; and

(c) that the contravention is such as to justify the revocation of the licence.

(2) A notice under this subsection must—

(a) state that OFCOM are satisfied as mentioned in subsection (1);

(b) specify the respects in which, in their opinion, the licence holder has contravened the condition mentioned in paragraph (b) of that subsection;

(c) state that OFCOM may revoke the licence after the end of the period of twenty-one days beginning with the day on which the notice is served on the licence holder; and

(d) inform the licence holder of his right to make representations to OFCOM within that period about the matters appearing to OFCOM to provide grounds for revoking the licence.

(3) The effect of a notice under subsection (2) shall be to suspend the licence as from the time when the notice is served on the licence holder until either—

(a) the revocation of the licence takes effect; or

(b) OFCOM decide not to revoke the licence.

(4) If, after considering any representations made to them by the licence holder within the period specified for the purposes of subsection (2)(c), OFCOM are satisfied that it is necessary in the public interest to revoke the licence, they shall serve a notice of revocation on the licence holder.

(5) The revocation of a licence by a notice under subsection (4) takes effect from such time as may be specified in the notice.

(6) A notice of revocation under subsection (4) must not specify a time for it to take effect that falls before the end of the period of twenty-eight days beginning with the day on which the notice is served on the licence holder.

[3304]

NOTES

Commencement: 29 December 2003.

240 Abolition of separate licences for certain television services

(1) The authorisations that are to be capable of being granted on or after the television transfer date by or under a licence under Part 1 of the 1990 Act do not include the authorisation of the provision, as such, of—

(a) any satellite television service (as defined, disregarding its repeal by this Act, in section 43(1) of the 1990 Act); or

(b) any licensable programme service (as defined, disregarding its repeal by this Act, in section 46(1) of that Act).

(2) Subsection (1) does not affect OFCOM's power, by means of a licence authorising the provision of a service falling within section 211(1), to authorise the provision of so much of any formerly regulated television service as is comprised in the licensed service.

(3) So much of any relevant existing licence as authorises the provision of a service which consists in or includes a television licensable content service—

(a) shall have effect, on and after the television transfer date, as a licence under Part 1 of the 1990 Act authorising the provision of the television licensable content service comprised in the licensed service;

(b) shall so have effect as a licence which, notwithstanding its terms and conditions, is to continue in force until such time as it is surrendered or is revoked in accordance with provisions of this Chapter or of the 1990 Act; and

(c) shall otherwise have effect as a licence on the same terms and conditions as those on which it had effect immediately before the television transfer date.

(4) It shall be the duty of OFCOM to exercise their power under section 3 of the 1990 Act to make such variations of any licence having effect in accordance with subsection (3) of this section as (after complying with subsection (4)(b) of that section) they consider appropriate for the purpose of performing their duty under section 263 of this Act.

(5) In this section—

"formerly regulated television service" means a service mentioned in subsection (1); and

"relevant existing licence", means any licence which—

(a) was granted by the Independent Television Commission under Part 1 of the 1990 Act before the television transfer date; and

(b) is in force immediately before the television transfer date as a licence authorising the provision of a formerly regulated service.

[3305]

NOTES

Commencement: 29 December 2003.

Television multiplex services

241 Television multiplex services

(1) Subject to the following provisions of this section, references in Part 1 of the 1996 Act to a multiplex service, other than those comprised in express references to a general multiplex service, shall have effect as references to any service ("a television multiplex service") which—

(a) falls within subsection (2); and

(b) is provided for broadcasting for general reception but otherwise than from a satellite.

(2) A service falls within this subsection if—

(a) it consists in the packaging together of two or more services which include at least one relevant television service and are provided for inclusion together in the service by a combination of the relevant information in digital form; or
(b) it is a service provided with a view to its being a service falling within paragraph (a) but is one in the case of which only one service is for the time being comprised in digital form in what is provided.

(3) The provision, at a time after the commencement of this section, of a television multiplex service the provision of which is not authorised by or under a licence under Part 1 of the 1996 Act is not to be an offence under section 13 of the 1990 Act.

(4) Accordingly, after the commencement of this section, a licence under Part 1 of the 1996 Act shall be required for the provision of a television multiplex service only in so far as it is required for the purposes of a limitation falling within subsection (5) that is contained in a wireless telegraphy licence, or is deemed to be so contained.

(5) A limitation falls within this subsection, in relation to a wireless telegraphy licence, if it provides that the only television multiplex services that are authorised to be broadcast using the station or apparatus to which the licence relates are those that are licensed under Part 1 of the 1996 Act.

(6) Where immediately before the coming into force of this section—
(a) a television multiplex service is licensed under Part 1 of the 1996 Act; and
(b) that service is one broadcast using a station or apparatus the use of which is authorised by a wireless telegraphy licence,

that wireless telegraphy licence shall be deemed to contain a limitation falling within subsection (5).

(7) In any case where a wireless telegraphy licence is deemed by virtue of subsection (6) to contain a limitation falling within subsection (5) and the person providing the television multiplex service in question—
(a) ceases to be licensed under Part 1 of the 1996 Act in respect of that service, or
(b) ceases to exist,

OFCOM may revoke the wireless telegraphy licence.

(8) Subsection (7) is not to be construed as restricting the powers of revocation exercisable apart from this section.

(9) In subsection (2) "relevant television service" means any of the following—
(a) any Channel 3 service in digital form;
(b) Channel 4 in digital form;
(c) Channel 5 in digital form;
(d) S4C Digital;
(e) any digital television programme service;
(f) the digital public teletext service.

[3306]

NOTES
Commencement: 29 December 2003.

242 (*Amends the Broadcasting Act 1996, s 12* (*outside the scope of this work*).)

243 Powers where frequencies reserved for qualifying services

(1) The Secretary of State may by order provide, in relation to the matters mentioned in subsection (2)—
(a) for any or all of the provisions of sections 7 to 16 and of sections 18 and 19 of the 1996 Act to have effect with the modifications specified in the order; and
(b) for provision made by the order to have effect in place of any or all of those provisions.

(2) Those matters are—
(a) licences under Part 1 of the 1996 Act, and
(b) the awarding and grant of such licences,

in a case in which the licence is, or is to be, a licence to provide a service for broadcasting on any one or more reserved frequencies.

(3) An order under this section may require OFCOM to include conditions falling within subsection (4) in any Broadcasting Act licence to provide a television multiplex service to be broadcast on a reserved frequency.

(4) Conditions falling within this subsection are conditions that OFCOM consider appropriate for securing that, in consideration for the making by any relevant public service broadcaster of such payments as are from time to time—

(a) agreed between the broadcaster and the holder of the licence to provide the television multiplex service, or

(b) in default of agreement, determined by OFCOM in accordance with the order,

the holder of that licence will use digital capacity reserved in accordance with conditions imposed under section 12 of the 1996 Act or any order under this section for the broadcasting of services provided by that broadcaster.

(5) Subsection (3) is not to be construed as restricting the provision that may be made under subsection (1).

(6) A frequency is a reserved frequency for the purposes of this section if it is one as respects which OFCOM have made a determination, in exercise of their functions under the enactments relating to the management of the radio spectrum, that the frequency should be reserved for the broadcasting of television multiplex services.

(7) In this section "relevant public service broadcaster" means any of the following—

(a) the holder of a licence to provide a Channel 3 service;

(b) C4C;

(c) the holder of a licence to provide Channel 5;

(d) the Welsh Authority;

(e) the public teletext provider.

[3307]

NOTES

Commencement: 29 December 2003.

Local digital television services

244 Local digital television services

(1) The Secretary of State may by order provide for—

(a) any of the provisions of this Part (apart from this section and the provisions relating exclusively to sound services), or

(b) any provision of Part 1 of the 1990 Act or of Part 1 of the 1996 Act (regulation of television services),

to have effect, in relation to services of such descriptions as may be set out in an order under this section, with such modifications as he considers necessary or appropriate for services of that description.

(2) The Secretary of State is not to make an order under this section in relation to a description of services except where—

(a) the description is of services to be provided in digital form with a view to their being included in a television multiplex service;

(b) the description is confined to services falling within one or both of subsections (3) and (4); and

(c) the Secretary of State is satisfied that the making of an order under this section in relation to that description of services will make possible, facilitate or encourage the provision of services so falling.

(3) Services fall within this subsection if they are—

(a) intended for reception only at a particular establishment or otherwise on particular premises; or

(b) provided for the purposes only of a particular event.

(4) Services fall within this subsection if the Secretary of State considers that they are services in relation to which all the following conditions are satisfied—

(a) they are intended for reception only within a particular area or locality;

(b) their provision meets, or would meet, the needs of the area or locality where they are received;

(c) their provision is or would be likely to broaden the range of television programmes available for viewing by persons living or working in that area or locality; and

(d) their provision is or would be likely to increase the number and range of the programmes about that area or locality that are available for such viewing, or to increase the number of programmes made in that area or locality that would be so available.

(5) Services shall be taken for the purposes of subsection (4) to meet the needs of an area or locality if, and only if—

(a) their provision brings social or economic benefits to the area or locality, or to different categories of persons living or working in that area or locality; or

(b) they cater for the tastes, interests and needs of some or all of the different descriptions of people living or working in the area or locality (including, in particular, tastes, interests and needs that are of special relevance in the light of the descriptions of people who do so live and work).

(6) In subsections (4) and (5), the references to persons living or working in an area or locality include references to persons undergoing education or training in that area or locality.

(7) An order under this section in relation to a description of services may, in particular, impose prohibitions or limitations on the inclusion of advertisements in services of that description and on the sponsorship of programmes included in the services.

(8) The power, by an order under this section, to make incidental, supplemental or consequential provision in connection with provision authorised by subsection (1) includes power to make incidental, supplemental or consequential provision modifying provisions of the 1990 Act, the 1996 Act or this Act that are not mentioned in that subsection.

(9) No order is to be made containing provision authorised by this section unless a draft of the order has been laid before Parliament and approved by a resolution of each House.

[3308]

NOTES

Commencement: 29 December 2003.

CHAPTER 3

REGULATORY STRUCTURE FOR INDEPENDENT RADIO SERVICES

Preliminary

245 Regulation of independent radio services

(1) It shall be a function of OFCOM to regulate the following services in accordance with this Act, the 1990 Act and the 1996 Act—

(a) services specified in subsection (2) that are provided from places in the United Kingdom and otherwise than by the BBC;

(b) services so specified that do not fall within paragraph (a) but are provided by a person, other than the BBC, whose principal place of business is in the United Kingdom.

(2) The services referred to in subsection (1)(a) are—

(a) sound broadcasting services to which subsection (3) applies;

(b) radio licensable content services;

(c) additional radio services;

(d) radio multiplex services;

(e) digital sound programme services;

(f) digital additional sound services.

(3) This subsection applies to a sound broadcasting service which—

(a) is provided with a view to its being broadcast otherwise than only from a satellite; and

(b) is a national service, local service or restricted service.

(4) For the purposes of this section—

(a) a service is a national service if it is a sound broadcasting service provided as mentioned in subsection (3)(a) with a view to its being broadcast for reception in any such minimum area of the United Kingdom as may be determined in accordance with section 98(2) of the 1990 Act;

(b) a service is a local service if it is a sound broadcasting service which (without being a national service) is provided as mentioned in subsection (3)(a) with a view to its being broadcast for reception in a particular area or locality in the United Kingdom; and

(c) a service is a restricted service if it is a sound broadcasting service provided as mentioned in subsection (3)(a) with a view to its being broadcast for reception—

(i) within a particular establishment in the United Kingdom or at another defined location in the United Kingdom; or

(ii) for the purposes of a particular event taking place within the United Kingdom.

(5) The services that are to be treated for the purposes of this section as provided from places in the United Kingdom include every radio licensable content service which would not fall to be so treated apart from this subsection but which—

(a) is provided with a view to its being broadcast from a satellite;

(b) is a service the broadcasting of which involves its transmission to the satellite by means of an electronic communications network from a place in the United Kingdom; and

(c) is not a service the provision of which is licensed or otherwise authorised under the laws of another EEA State.

(6) The services that are to be treated as so provided also include every service provided by a BBC company, a C4 company or an S4C company.

(7) A reference in subsection (4)(b) to an area of the United Kingdom does not include an area which comprises or includes the whole of England.

[3309]

NOTES

Commencement: 29 December 2003.

Modification: sub-s (4) is modified in its application to community radio services by the Community Radio Order 2004, SI 2004/1944, art 4, Schedule, Pt 2, paras 9, 10 at **[3625]**.

246 Abolition of function of assigning radio frequencies

The Secretary of State shall cease to have any function under the 1990 Act or the 1996 Act of assigning frequencies—

(a) for any of the purposes of Part 3 of the 1990 Act (regulation of radio services); or

(b) for the purposes of the provision of any radio multiplex services.

[3310]

NOTES

Commencement: 29 December 2003.

Radio licensable content services

247 Meaning of "radio licensable content services"

(1) In this Part "radio licensable content service" means (subject to section 248) any service falling within subsection (2) in so far as it is provided with a view to its availability for reception by members of the public being secured by one or both of the following means—

(a) the broadcasting of the service (whether by the person providing it or by another) from a satellite; or

(b) the distribution of the service (whether by that person or by another) by any means involving the use of an electronic communications network.

(2) A service falls within this subsection if it—

(a) consists of sound programmes; and

(b) is provided (whether in digital or in analogue form) as a service that is to be made available for reception by members of the public.

[3311]

NOTES

Commencement: 29 December 2003.

248 Services that are not radio licensable content services

(1) A service is not a radio licensable content service to the extent that—

(a) it is provided with a view to its being broadcast by means of a multiplex service;

(b) it is a sound broadcasting service to which subsection (3) of section 245 applies; or

(c) it is comprised in a television licensable content service.

(2) A service is not a radio licensable content service to the extent that it is provided by means of an electronic communications service if—

(a) it forms part only of a service provided by means of that electronic communications service or is one of a number of services access to which is made available by means of a service so provided; and

(b) the service of which it forms part, or by which it may be accessed, is provided for purposes that do not consist wholly or mainly in making available services of radio programmes or television programmes (or both) for reception by members of the public.

(3) A service is not a radio licensable content service if it is a two-way service.

(4) A service is a two-way service for the purposes of subsection (3) if it is provided by means of an electronic communications network and an essential feature of the service is that the purposes for which it is provided involve the use of that network, or a part of it, both—

(a) for the transmission of sounds by the person providing the service to users of the service; and

(b) for the transmission of sounds by those users for reception by the person providing the service or by other users of the service.

(5) A service is not a radio licensable content service if—

(a) it is distributed by means of an electronic communications network only to persons all of whom are on a single set of premises; and

(b) that network is wholly within those premises and is not connected to an electronic communications network any part of which is outside those premises.

(6) For the purposes of subsection (5)—

(a) a set of premises is a single set of premises if, and only if, the same person is the occupier of all the premises; and

(b) two or more vehicles are capable of constituting a single set of premises if, and only if, they are coupled together.

(7) A service is not a radio licensable content service if it is provided for the purpose only of being received by persons who have qualified as users of the service by reason of being—

(a) persons who have a business interest in the programmes included in the service; or

(b) persons who are to receive the programmes for the purpose only of allowing them to be listened to by persons falling within sub-paragraph (a) or by persons all of whom are on the business premises of the person receiving them.

(8) For the purposes of subsection (7) a person has a business interest in programmes if he has an interest in receiving or listening to them—

(a) for the purposes of a business carried on by him; or

(b) for the purposes of his employment.

(9) In this section—

"business premises", in relation to a person, means premises at or from which any business of that person is carried on;

"multiplex service" means a television multiplex service, a radio multiplex service or a general multiplex service;

"premises" includes a vehicle;

"vehicle" includes a vessel, aircraft or hovercraft.

(10) References in this section, in relation to a person, to a business include references to—

(a) any business or other activities carried on by a body of which he is a member and the affairs of which are managed by its members; and
(b) the carrying out of any functions conferred on that person, or on any such body, by or under any enactment.

[3312]

NOTES

Commencement: 29 December 2003.

249 Modification of ss 247 and 248

(1) The Secretary of State may by order modify any of the provisions of section 247 or 248 if it appears to him appropriate to do so having regard to any one or more of the following—
(a) the protection which is expected by members of the public as respects the contents of sound programmes;
(b) the practicability of applying different levels of regulation in relation to different services;
(c) the financial impact for providers of particular services of any modification of the provisions of that section; and
(d) technological developments that have occurred or are likely to occur.

(2) The Secretary of State may also by order provide, in cases where it otherwise appears to him appropriate to do so, that a description of service specified in the order is not to be treated as a radio licensable content service for the purposes of the provisions of this Act that are so specified.

(3) No order is to be made containing provision authorised by this section unless a draft of the order has been laid before Parliament and approved by a resolution of each House.

[3313]

NOTES

Commencement: 29 December 2003.

250 Licensing of radio licensable content services

(1) The licence that is required for the purposes of section 97 of the 1990 Act in respect of a radio licensable content service is a licence granted under Part 3 of that Act on an application complying with this section.

(2) An application for a licence under Part 3 of the 1990 Act to provide a radio licensable content service—
(a) must be made in such manner,
(b) must contain such information about the applicant, his business and the service he proposes to provide, and
(c) must be accompanied by such fee (if any),

as OFCOM may determine.

(3) Sections 109 to 111A of the 1990 Act (enforcement of licences) apply in relation to licences for radio licensable content services as they apply in relation to licences under Chapter 2 of Part 3 of the 1990 Act but with—
(a) the substitution of the word "or" for paragraph (b) of subsection (1) of section 110 (power to shorten licence period); and
(b) the omission of "(b)" in subsection (4) of that section and of subsection (5) of that section (which refer to the power disapplied by paragraph (a) of this subsection).

[3314]

NOTES

Commencement: 29 December 2003.

251 Abolition of separate licences for certain sound services

(1) The authorisations that are to be capable of being granted on or after the radio transfer date by or under a licence under Part 3 of the 1990 Act do not include the authorisation of the provision, as such, of—

(a) any satellite service (as defined, disregarding its repeal by this Act, in section 84(2)(b) of the 1990 Act); or
(b) any licensable sound programme service (as defined, disregarding its repeal by this Act, in section 112(1) of that Act).

(2) Subsection (1) does not affect OFCOM's power, by means of a licence authorising the provision of a service falling within section 245(1), to authorise the provision of so much of any formerly regulated radio service as is comprised in the licensed service.

(3) So much of any relevant existing licence as authorises the provision of a service which consists in or includes a radio licensable content service—
(a) shall have effect, on and after the radio transfer date, as a licence under Part 3 of the 1990 Act authorising the provision of the radio licensable content service comprised in the licensed service;
(b) shall so have effect as a licence which, notwithstanding its terms and conditions, is to continue in force until such time as it is surrendered or is revoked in accordance with provisions of the 1990 Act; and
(c) shall otherwise have effect as a licence on the same terms and conditions as those on which it had effect immediately before the radio transfer date.

(4) It shall be the duty of OFCOM to exercise their power under section 86 of the 1990 Act to make such variations of any licence having effect in accordance with subsection (3) of this section as (after complying with subsection (5)(b) of that section) they consider appropriate for the purpose of performing their duty under section 263 of this Act.

(5) In this section—
"formerly regulated radio service" means a service mentioned in subsection (1); and
"relevant existing licence" means any licence which—
(a) was granted by the Radio Authority under Part 3 of the 1990 Act before the radio transfer date; and
(b) is in force immediately before the radio transfer date as a licence authorising the provision of a formerly regulated service.

[3315]

NOTES
Commencement: 29 December 2003.

Licence periods etc

252 (*Amends the Broadcasting Act 1990, s 86 at* **[3028]**.)

253 Extension and modification of existing licences

(1) A person who immediately before the radio transfer date holds a pre-transfer national licence or a pre-transfer local licence is entitled, in accordance with the following provisions of this section, to apply to OFCOM for an extension of the licence.

(2) The period for which a licence may be extended on such an application is a period ending not more than four years after the end of the period for which it was granted originally or (if it has been renewed) for which it was last renewed.

(3) An application under subsection (1) may only be made in the period which—
(a) begins three years before the date on which the licence would otherwise expire; and
(b) ends three months before the day that OFCOM have determined to be the day by which they would need to publish a notice under section 98(1) or 104(1) of the 1990 Act if they were proposing to grant a fresh licence to take effect from that date.

(4) A determination for the purposes of subsection (3)(b)—
(a) must be made at least one year before the day determined; and
(b) must be notified by OFCOM to the person who holds the licence in question.

(5) An application under subsection (1)—
(a) must be made in such manner,
(b) must contain such information about the applicant, his business and the service he proposes to provide, and

(c) must be accompanied by such fee (if any),

as OFCOM may determine.

(6) If, on an application for an extension under subsection (1), OFCOM are satisfied as to the matters mentioned in subsection (7), they shall—

(a) modify the licence by extending the period for which the licence is to be in force by such period authorised by subsection (2) as they think fit; and

(b) make such other modifications as appear to them to be necessary for the purpose of securing that the provisions of the licence correspond to those that would be contained in a national sound broadcasting licence or (as the case may be) a local sound broadcasting licence granted after the radio transfer date.

(7) Those matters are—

(a) the ability of the licence holder to maintain the service for the period of the extension; and

(b) the likelihood of a contravention by the licence holder of a requirement imposed by—

(i) a condition included in the licence by virtue of section 106 of the 1990 Act; or

(ii) a condition of the licence varied in accordance with subsection (8).

(8) For the purposes of the modification under this section of a national licence, OFCOM—

(a) shall determine an amount which is to be payable to OFCOM by the licence holder in respect of the first complete calendar year falling within the period for which the licence is extended; and

(b) may, in relation to any accounting period of the licence holder during the period of the extension, modify a condition included in the licence in pursuance of section 102(1)(c) of the 1990 Act (additional payments to be made in respect of national licences) by specifying a different percentage of the qualifying revenue for that accounting period from that which was previously specified in the condition.

(9) The amount determined by OFCOM under subsection (8)(a) must be the amount which, in OFCOM's opinion, would have been the cash bid of the licence holder were the licence (instead of being extended) being granted afresh on an application made in accordance with section 98 of the 1990 Act.

(10) For the purposes of subsection (8)(b)—

(a) different percentages may be specified for different accounting periods; and

(b) the percentages that may be specified for an accounting period include a nil percentage.

(11) The modifications set out in accordance with subsection (6)(b) must secure—

(a) that the amount falling to be paid under the conditions of the licence for each calendar year subsequent to that for which an amount has been determined in accordance with subsection (8)(a) is the amount so determined as increased by the appropriate percentage; and

(b) that such adjustments as are appropriate are made as respects sums already paid in respect of any year or accounting period to which a modification under subsection (8) applies.

(12) Where OFCOM have granted a person's application under this section, the extensions and modifications take effect only if that person—

(a) has been notified by OFCOM of their proposals for modifications by virtue of subsection (6)(b) or (8)(b), and for the making of a determination under subsection (8)(a); and

(b) has consented to the extension on the terms proposed.

(13) In this section—

"the appropriate percentage" has the same meaning as in section 102 of the 1990 Act;

"national sound broadcasting licence" means a licence under Part 3 of the 1990 Act to provide a sound broadcasting service which, under subsection (4)(a) of section 245 is a national service for the purposes of that section;

"pre-transfer licence" means a licence which was granted under Part 3 of the 1990 Act before the radio transfer date and has not been modified under this section or renewed at any time on or after that date;

"pre-transfer local licence" means a pre-transfer licence which was granted as a local licence (within the meaning of Part 3 of the 1990 Act, as it had effect without the amendments made by this Act);

"pre-transfer national licence" means a pre-transfer licence granted or last renewed as a national licence (within the meaning of Part 3 of the 1990 Act, as it had effect without the amendments made by this Act).

[3316]

NOTES

Commencement: 2 January 2004 (for transitional provisions in relation to applications for extension of pre-transfer licences see s 406(6) of, and Sch 18, para 49 to, this Act at **[3434]**, **[3460]**).

254, 255 (*S 254 amends the Broadcasting Act 1990, s 104A at* **[3042]***; s 255 amends s 104B of the 1990 Act at* **[3043]**.)

Provision of simulcast radio services

256, 257 (*S 256 amends the Broadcasting Act 1996, s 41 and the Broadcasting Act 1990, s 126 (outside the scope of this work); s 257 amends the Broadcasting Act 1990, ss 98, 100 at* **[3033]**, **[3035]**, *and inserts s 100A of that Act at* **[3036]**.)

Multiplexes broadcasting sound programmes

258 Radio multiplex services

(1) Subject to the following provisions of this section, references in Part 2 of the 1996 Act to a radio multiplex service shall have effect as references to any service which—

(a) falls within subsection (2);

(b) is provided for broadcasting for general reception but otherwise than from a satellite; and

(c) is not a television multiplex service.

(2) A service falls within this subsection if—

(a) it consists in the packaging together (with or without other services) of two or more relevant sound services which are provided for inclusion together in that service by a combination of the relevant information in digital form; or

(b) it is a service provided with a view to its being a service falling within paragraph (a) but is one in the case of which only one relevant sound service is for the time being comprised in digital form in what is provided.

(3) The provision, at a time after the commencement of this section, of a radio multiplex service the provision of which is not authorised by or under a licence under Part 2 of the 1996 Act is not to be an offence under section 97 of the 1990 Act.

(4) Accordingly, after the commencement of this section, a licence under Part 2 of the 1996 Act shall be required for the provision of a radio multiplex service only in so far as it is required for the purposes of a limitation falling within subsection (5) which is contained in a wireless telegraphy licence, or is deemed to be so contained.

(5) A limitation falls within this subsection, in relation to a wireless telegraphy licence, if it provides that the only radio multiplex services that are authorised to be broadcast using the station or apparatus to which the licence relates are those that are licensed under Part 2 of the 1996 Act.

(6) Where immediately before the coming into force of this section—

(a) a radio multiplex service is licensed under Part 2 of the 1996 Act; and

(b) that service is one broadcast using a station or apparatus the use of which is authorised by a wireless telegraphy licence,

that wireless telegraphy licence shall be deemed to contain a limitation falling within subsection (5).

(7) In any case where a wireless telegraphy licence is deemed by virtue of subsection (6) to contain a limitation falling within subsection (5) and the person providing the radio multiplex service in question—

(a) ceases to be licensed under Part 2 of the 1996 Act in respect of that service, or

(b) ceases to exist,

OFCOM may revoke the wireless telegraphy licence.

(8) Subsection (7) is not to be construed as restricting the powers of revocation exercisable apart from this section.

(9) In subsection (2) "relevant sound service" means any of the following—
(a) a digital sound programme service;
(b) a simulcast radio service; and
(c) a digital additional sound service.

[3317]

NOTES

Commencement: 29 December 2003.

259–261 (*Amend the Broadcasting Act 1996, ss 54, 58, 60, 63, 72 (outside the scope of this work).*)

Community radio

262 Community radio

(1) The Secretary of State may by order provide for—
(a) any of the provisions of this Part (apart from this section and the provisions relating exclusively to television), or
(b) any provision of Part 3 of the 1990 Act or of Part 2 of the 1996 Act (regulation of radio services),

to have effect, in relation to services of such descriptions as may be set out in an order under this section, with such modifications as he considers necessary or appropriate for services of that description.

(2) The Secretary of State is not to make an order under this section in relation to a description of services unless—
(a) the description is of services to be provided primarily for the good of members of the public or of a particular community, rather than for commercial reasons; and
(b) he considers that the provision of services of that description confer, or would confer, significant benefits on the public or on the communities for which they are provided.

(3) An order under this section in relation to a description of services may, in particular, impose prohibitions or limitations on the inclusion of advertisements in services of that description and on the sponsorship of programmes included in the services.

(4) The power, by an order under this section, to make incidental, supplemental or consequential provision in connection with provision authorised by subsection (1) includes power to make incidental, supplemental or consequential provision modifying provisions of the 1990 Act, the 1996 Act or this Act that are not mentioned in that subsection.

(5) No order is to be made containing provision authorised by this section unless a draft of the order has been laid before Parliament and approved by a resolution of each House.

[3318]

NOTES

Commencement: 29 December 2003.
Orders: the Community Radio Order 2004, SI 2004/1944.

CHAPTER 4
REGULATORY PROVISIONS

Application of regulatory regimes

263 Application of regulatory regimes

(1) It shall be the duty of OFCOM, by exercising—

(a) their powers under the 1990 Act and the 1996 Act, and

(b) their powers under this Part,

to secure that the holder of every Broadcasting Act licence at all times holds his licence on the conditions which are for the time being included, under this Chapter and Chapter 5 of this Part, in the regulatory regime for the licensed service.

(2) It shall also be the duty of OFCOM to do all that they can to secure that the holder of every such licence complies, in relation to the licensed service, with the conditions so included in the regulatory regime for that service.

(3) Where—

(a) the licence for a Channel 3 service, for Channel 4, for Channel 5 or for the public teletext service ("the main service") authorises or requires a corresponding or additional service to be provided in analogue form, and

(b) the regulatory regime for the main service imposes obligations in relation to programmes and other items included in that service,

those obligations are to apply equally to programmes that are included in the analogue service without being included in the main service.

(4) The Secretary of State may by order provide for conditions which are included by virtue of a provision of this Act in the regulatory regime for any service to cease to be so included.

(5) No order is to be made containing provision authorised by subsection (4) unless a draft of the order has been laid before Parliament and approved by a resolution of each House.

(6) This section does not restrict OFCOM's powers and duties apart from this section to impose obligations by means of the inclusion of conditions in a Broadcasting Act licence.

[3319]

NOTES

Commencement: 29 December 2003.

The public service remit for television

264 OFCOM reports on the fulfilment of the public service remit

(1) It shall be the duty of OFCOM—

(a) as soon as practicable after the end of the period of twelve months beginning with the commencement of this section, and

(b) as soon as practicable after the end of each such subsequent period as may be selected by OFCOM for the purposes of this section,

to satisfy, for that period, the review and reporting obligations of subsection (3).

(2) The period selected by OFCOM for the purposes of subsection (1)(b) must be a period of not more than five years beginning with the end of the previous period for which OFCOM have satisfied those review and reporting obligations.

(3) The review and reporting obligations for a period are—

(a) an obligation to carry out a review of the extent to which the public service broadcasters have, during that period, provided relevant television services which (taking them all together over the period as a whole) fulfil the purposes of public service television broadcasting in the United Kingdom; and

(b) an obligation, with a view to maintaining and strengthening the quality of public service television broadcasting in the United Kingdom, to prepare a report on the matters found on the review.

(4) The purposes of public service television broadcasting in the United Kingdom are—

(a) the provision of relevant television services which secure that programmes dealing with a wide range of subject-matters are made available for viewing;

(b) the provision of relevant television services in a manner which (having regard to the days on which they are shown and the times of day at which they are shown) is likely to meet the needs and satisfy the interests of as many different audiences as practicable;

(c) the provision of relevant television services which (taken together and having regard to the same matters) are properly balanced, so far as their nature and subject-matters are concerned, for meeting the needs and satisfying the interests of the available audiences; and

(d) the provision of relevant television services which (taken together) maintain high general standards with respect to the programmes included in them, and, in particular with respect to—

(i) the contents of the programmes;

(ii) the quality of the programme making; and

(iii) the professional skill and editorial integrity applied in the making of the programmes.

(5) When—

(a) determining the extent to which any of the purposes of public service television broadcasting in the United Kingdom are fulfilled, and

(b) reviewing and reporting on that matter,

OFCOM must have regard to the desirability of those purposes being fulfilled in a manner that is compatible with subsection (6).

(6) A manner of fulfilling the purposes of public service television broadcasting in the United Kingdom is compatible with this subsection if it ensures—

(a) that the relevant television services (taken together) comprise a public service for the dissemination of information and for the provision of education and entertainment;

(b) that cultural activity in the United Kingdom, and its diversity, are reflected, supported and stimulated by the representation in those services (taken together) of drama, comedy and music, by the inclusion of feature films in those services and by the treatment of other visual and performing arts;

(c) that those services (taken together) provide, to the extent that is appropriate for facilitating civic understanding and fair and well-informed debate on news and current affairs, a comprehensive and authoritative coverage of news and current affairs in, and in the different parts of, the United Kingdom and from around the world;

(d) that those services (taken together) satisfy a wide range of different sporting and other leisure interests;

(e) that those services (taken together) include what appears to OFCOM to be a suitable quantity and range of programmes on educational matters, of programmes of an educational nature and of other programmes of educative value;

(f) that those services (taken together) include what appears to OFCOM to be a suitable quantity and range of programmes dealing with each of the following, science, religion and other beliefs, social issues, matters of international significance or interest and matters of specialist interest;

(g) that the programmes included in those services that deal with religion and other beliefs include—

(i) programmes providing news and other information about different religions and other beliefs;

(ii) programmes about the history of different religions and other beliefs; and

(iii) programmes showing acts of worship and other ceremonies and practices (including some showing acts of worship and other ceremonies in their entirety);

(h) that those services (taken together) include what appears to OFCOM to be a suitable quantity and range of high quality and original programmes for children and young people;

(i) that those services (taken together) include what appears to OFCOM to be a sufficient quantity of programmes that reflect the lives and concerns of different communities and cultural interests and traditions within the United Kingdom, and locally in different parts of the United Kingdom;

(j) that those services (taken together), so far as they include programmes made in the United Kingdom, include what appears to OFCOM to be an appropriate range and proportion of programmes made outside the M25 area.

(7) In carrying out a review under this section OFCOM must consider—

(a) the costs to persons providing relevant television services of the fulfilment of the purposes of public service television broadcasting in a manner compatible with subsection (6); and

(b) the sources of income available to each of them for meeting those costs.

(8) Every report under this section must—
(a) specify, and comment on, whatever changes appear to OFCOM to have occurred, during the period to which the report relates, in the extent to which the purposes of public service television broadcasting in the United Kingdom have been satisfied;
(b) specify, and comment on, whatever changes appear to OFCOM to have occurred, during that period, in the manner in which those purposes are fulfilled;
(c) set out the findings of OFCOM on their consideration of the matters mentioned in subsection (7) and any conclusions they have arrived at in relation to those findings; and
(d) set out OFCOM's conclusions on the current state of public service television broadcasting in the United Kingdom.

(9) In performing their duties under this section, OFCOM must have regard, in particular, to—
(a) every statement of programme or service policy which has been made by virtue of this Chapter by a public service broadcaster, or which is treated as such a statement;
(b) every equivalent statement of policy made by the BBC in pursuance of the BBC Charter and Agreement; and
(c) such matters arising at times before the coming into force of this section as OFCOM consider material.

(10) Every report prepared by OFCOM under this section must be published by them—
(a) as soon as practicable after its preparation is complete; and
(b) in such manner as they consider appropriate.

(11) The following are relevant television services for the purposes of this section—
(a) the television broadcasting services provided by the BBC;
(b) the television programme services that are public services of the Welsh Authority (within the meaning of section 207);
(c) every Channel 3 service;
(d) Channel 4;
(e) Channel 5;
(f) the public teletext service.

(12) The following are public service broadcasters for the purposes of this section—
(a) the BBC;
(b) the Welsh Authority;
(c) the providers of the licensed public service channels; and
(d) the public teletext provider.

(13) In this section—
"belief" means a collective belief in, or other adherence to, a systemised set of ethical or philosophical principles or of mystical or transcendental doctrines; and
"drama" includes contemporary and other drama in a variety of different formats.

[3320]

NOTES

Commencement: 25 July 2003 (for transitional provisions see the Communications Act 2003 (Commencement No 1) Order 2003, SI 2003/1900, art 4 at **[3510]**).

265 Public service remits of licensed providers

(1) The regulatory regime for every licensed public service channel, and for the public teletext service, includes a condition requiring the provider of the channel or service to fulfil the public service remit for that channel or service.

(2) The public service remit—
(a) for every Channel 3 service, and
(b) for Channel 5,
is the provision of a range of high quality and diverse programming.

(3) The public service remit for Channel 4 is the provision of a broad range of high quality and diverse programming which, in particular—
(a) demonstrates innovation, experiment and creativity in the form and content of programmes;
(b) appeals to the tastes and interests of a culturally diverse society;

(c) makes a significant contribution to meeting the need for the licensed public service channels to include programmes of an educational nature and other programmes of educative value; and

(d) exhibits a distinctive character.

(4) The public service remit for the public teletext service is the provision of a range of high quality and diverse text material.

(5) For so long as the public teletext service comprises both—

(a) an analogue teletext service, and

(b) a teletext service provided in digital form,

the conditions imposed under this section must require the public service remit of the public teletext service to be fulfilled separately in the case of each of those services.

[3321]

NOTES

Commencement: 28 December 2004.

266 Statements of programme policy

(1) The regulatory regime for every licensed public service channel includes a condition requiring the provider of the channel—

(a) as soon as practicable after the coming into force of this section and subsequently at annual intervals, to prepare a statement of programme policy; and

(b) to monitor his own performance in the carrying out of the proposals contained in the statements made in pursuance of the condition.

(2) The condition must require every statement of programme policy prepared in accordance with the condition to set out the proposals of the provider of the channel for securing that, during the following year—

(a) the public service remit for the channel will be fulfilled; and

(b) the duties imposed on the provider by virtue of sections 277 to 296 will be performed.

(3) The condition must also require every such statement to contain a report on the performance of the provider of the channel in the carrying out, during the period since the previous statement, of the proposals contained in that statement.

(4) The condition must also provide that every such statement—

(a) must be prepared having regard to guidance given by OFCOM;

(b) must be prepared taking account of the reports previously published by OFCOM under sections 264 and 358;

(c) must take special account of the most recent such reports;

(d) must be published by the provider of the channel in question as soon as practicable after its preparation is complete; and

(e) must be published in such manner as, having regard to any guidance given by OFCOM, the provider considers appropriate.

(5) In preparing guidance about the preparation of such a statement, OFCOM must have regard, in particular, to the matters which, in the light of the provisions of section 264(4) and (6), they consider should be included in statements of programme policy.

(6) It shall be the duty of OFCOM—

(a) from time to time to review the guidance for the time being in force for the purposes of this section; and

(b) to make such revisions of that guidance as they think fit.

(7) The conditions of a licence to provide a licensed public service channel may provide that a previous statement of policy made by the provider of the channel is to be treated for the purposes of this Part—

(a) as if it were a statement made in relation to such period as may be so specified; and

(b) were a statement of programme policy for the purposes of a condition imposed under this section.

(8) The reference in subsection (7) to a previous statement of policy is a reference to any statement made by the provider of the channel—

(a) whether before or after the commencement of this section, for the purposes of his application for a Broadcasting Act licence for the channel; or
(b) at any time before the commencement of this section, for any other purpose.

(9) A condition under subsection (7) cannot contain provision the effect of which is to postpone the time at which a licence holder is required to make the first statement of programme policy which (apart from that subsection) he is required to make in pursuance of a condition imposed under this section.

[3322]

NOTES

Commencement: 28 December 2004.

267 Changes of programme policy

(1) The regulatory regime for every licensed public service channel includes a condition requiring compliance with subsection (2) in the case of a statement of programme policy containing proposals for a significant change.

(2) This subsection requires the provider of the channel—
(a) to consult OFCOM before preparing the statement; and
(b) to take account, in the preparation of the statement, of any opinions expressed to the provider of the channel by OFCOM.

(3) A condition imposed under this section must further provide that, if it appears to OFCOM that a statement of programme policy has been prepared by the provider of the channel in contravention of a condition imposed under subsection (1), the provider is—
(a) to revise that statement in accordance with any directions given to him by OFCOM; and
(b) to publish a revision of the statement in accordance with any such directions only after the revision has been approved by OFCOM.

(4) A change is a significant change for the purposes of this section if it is a change as a result of which the channel would in any year be materially different in character from in previous years.

(5) In determining for the purposes of any condition under this section whether a change is a significant change—
(a) regard must be had to any guidance issued by OFCOM;
(b) the changes to be considered include any changes that, together with any proposed change for a particular year, would constitute a change occurring gradually over a period of not more than three years; and
(c) the previous years with which a comparison is to be made must be those immediately preceding the year in which the change is made, or in which the changes comprised in it began to occur.

(6) It shall be the duty of OFCOM—
(a) from time to time to review the guidance for the time being in force for the purposes of this section; and
(b) to make such revisions of that guidance as they think fit.

[3323]

NOTES

Commencement: 28 December 2004.

268 Statements of service policy by the public teletext provider

(1) The regulatory regime for the public teletext service includes a condition requiring the public teletext provider—
(a) as soon as practicable after the coming into force of this section and subsequently at annual intervals, to prepare a statement of service policy; and
(b) to monitor his own performance in the carrying out of the proposals contained in statements made in pursuance of the condition.

(2) The condition must require every statement of service policy prepared in accordance with the condition to set out the proposals of the public teletext provider for securing that, during the following year, the public service remit for the public teletext service will be fulfilled.

(3) The condition must also require every such statement to contain a report on the performance of the public teletext provider in the carrying out, during the period since the previous statement, of the proposals contained in that statement.

(4) The condition must provide that the proposals or report for a period in the course of which the public teletext service will comprise or has comprised both—

(a) an analogue teletext service, and
(b) a teletext service provided in digital form,

must deal separately with each of those services.

(5) The condition must also provide that every statement in pursuance of the condition—

(a) must be prepared having regard to guidance given by OFCOM;
(b) must be prepared taking account of the reports previously published by OFCOM under sections 264 and 358;
(c) must take special account of the most recent such reports;
(d) must be published by the public teletext provider as soon as practicable after its preparation is complete; and
(e) must be published in such manner as, having regard to any guidance given by OFCOM, that provider considers appropriate.

(6) In preparing guidance about the preparation of such a statement, OFCOM must have regard, in particular, to the matters which, in the light of the provisions of section 264(4) and (6), they consider should be included in statements of service policy by the public teletext provider.

(7) It shall be the duty of OFCOM—

(a) from time to time to review the guidance for the time being in force for the purposes of this section; and
(b) to make such revisions of that guidance as they think fit.

(8) The conditions of the licence to provide the public teletext service may provide that a previous statement of policy made by the public teletext provider is to be treated for the purposes of this Part—

(a) as if it were a statement made in relation to such period as may be so specified; and
(b) were a statement of service policy for the purposes of a condition imposed under this section.

(9) The reference in subsection (8) to a previous statement of policy is a reference to any statement made by the public teletext provider—

(a) whether before or after the commencement of this section, for the purposes of his application for a Broadcasting Act licence for the public teletext service or for the existing service (within the meaning of section 221); or
(b) at any time before the commencement of this section, for any other purpose.

(10) A condition under subsection (8) cannot contain provision the effect of which is to postpone the time at which a licence holder is required to make the first statement of service policy which (apart from that subsection) he is required to make in pursuance of a condition imposed under this section.

[3324]

NOTES

Commencement: 28 December 2004.

269 Changes of service policy

(1) The regulatory regime for the public teletext service includes a condition requiring compliance with subsection (2) in the case of a statement of service policy containing proposals for a significant change.

(2) This subsection requires the provider of the service—

(a) to consult OFCOM before preparing the statement; and
(b) to take account, in the preparation of the statement, of any opinions expressed to the provider of the service by OFCOM.

(3) A condition imposed under this section must further provide that, if it appears to OFCOM that a statement of service policy has been prepared by the public teletext provider in contravention of a condition imposed under subsection (1), that provider is—

(a) to revise that statement in accordance with any directions given to him by OFCOM; and
(b) to publish a revision of the statement in accordance with any such directions only after the revision has been approved by OFCOM.

(4) A change is a significant change for the purposes of this section if it is a change as a result of which the service would in any year be materially different in character from in previous years.

(5) In determining for the purposes of any condition under this section whether a change is a significant change—
(a) regard must be had to any guidance issued by OFCOM;
(b) the changes to be considered include any changes that, together with any proposed change for a particular year, would constitute a change occurring gradually over a period of not more than three years;
(c) the previous years with which a comparison is to be made must be those immediately preceding the year in which the change is made, or in which the changes comprised in it began to occur; and
(d) any change that is a significant change in relation to so much of the public teletext service as is provided in digital form or in relation to so much of it as is provided in analogue form is to be regarded as a significant change in relation to the whole service.

(6) It shall be the duty of OFCOM—
(a) from time to time to review the guidance for the time being in force for the purposes of this section; and
(b) to make such revisions of that guidance as they think fit.

[3325]

NOTES
Commencement: 28 December 2004.

270 Enforcement of public service remits

(1) This section applies if OFCOM are of the opinion that the provider of a licensed public service channel or the public teletext provider—
(a) has failed to fulfil the public service remit for that channel or the public teletext service; or
(b) has failed, in any respect, to make an adequate contribution towards the fulfilment of the purposes of public service television broadcasting in the United Kingdom.

(2) This section does not apply unless—
(a) OFCOM are of the opinion that the failure of the provider is serious and is not excused by economic or market conditions; and
(b) OFCOM determine that the situation requires the exercise of their powers under this section.

(3) In making a determination under subsection (2)(b), OFCOM must have regard, in particular, to—
(a) the public service remit of that provider;
(b) the statements of programme policy or statements of service policy made (or treated as made) by the provider under section 266 or 268;
(c) the record generally of the provider in relation to the carrying out of obligations imposed by conditions of licences under the 1990 Act and the 1996 Act (including past obligations);
(d) the effectiveness and efficiency of the provider in monitoring his own performance; and
(e) general economic and market conditions affecting generally the providers of television programme services or the providers of television multiplex services, or both of them.

(4) OFCOM shall have power to give directions to the provider to do one or both of the following—
(a) to revise the provider's latest statement of programme policy, or statement of service policy, in accordance with the directions; and
(b) to take such steps for remedying the provider's failure as OFCOM may specify in the direction as necessary for that purpose.

(5) A direction given under this section must set out—
(a) a reasonable timetable for complying with it; and
(b) the factors that will be taken into account by OFCOM in determining—
(i) whether or not a failure of the provider has been remedied; and
(ii) whether or not to exercise their powers under subsection (6).

(6) If OFCOM are satisfied—
(a) that the provider of a public service channel or the public teletext provider has failed to comply with a direction under this section,
(b) that that provider is still failing to fulfil the public service remit for that channel or service or adequately to contribute to the fulfilment of the purposes of public service television broadcasting in the United Kingdom, and
(c) that it would be both reasonable and proportionate to the seriousness of that failure to vary the provider's licence in accordance with this subsection,

OFCOM may, by notice to the provider, vary that licence so as to replace self-regulation with detailed regulation.

(7) For the purposes of subsection (6) a variation replacing self-regulation with detailed regulation is a variation which—
(a) omits the conditions imposed by virtue of sections 265 to 269; and
(b) replaces those conditions with such specific conditions as OFCOM consider appropriate for securing that the provider—
(i) fulfils the public service remit for his service; and
(ii) makes an adequate contribution towards the fulfilment of the purposes of public service television broadcasting in the United Kingdom.

(8) If, at any time following a variation in accordance with subsection (6) of a provider's licence, OFCOM consider that detailed regulation is no longer necessary, they may again vary the licence so as, with effect from such time as they may determine—
(a) to provide for the conditions required by virtue of sections 265 to 269 again to be included in the regulatory regime for the service provided by that provider; and
(b) to remove or modify some or all of the specific conditions inserted under that subsection.

(9) Before giving a direction under this section to a provider or exercising their power under this section to vary a provider's licence, OFCOM must consult that provider.

(10) In accordance with section 265(5), the reference in subsection (1) to a failure to fulfil the public service remit for the public teletext service includes a failure to fulfil that remit as respects only one of the services comprised in that service.

[3326]

NOTES

Commencement: 28 December 2004.

271 Power to amend public service remits

(1) The Secretary of State may by order modify any one or more of the following—
(a) the public service remit for any licensed public service channel or for the public teletext service;
(b) the purposes of public service television broadcasting in the United Kingdom (within the meaning given by subsection (4) of section 264);
(c) the matters to which OFCOM are to have regard under subsections (5) and (6) of that section.

(2) The Secretary of State is not to make an order under this section except where—
(a) OFCOM have made a recommendation for the making of such an order in their most recent report under section 229 or 264; or
(b) subsection (3) applies to the order.

(3) This subsection applies to an order if—
(a) it is made by the Secretary of State less than twelve months after the date on which he has received a report under section 229;
(b) he has considered that report; and
(c) he is satisfied that the making of the order is required, notwithstanding the absence of a recommendation by OFCOM, by circumstances or other matters which are dealt with in that report or which (in his opinion) should have been.

(4) Before including a recommendation for the making of an order under this section in a report under section 229 or 264, OFCOM must consult—

(a) members of the public in the United Kingdom;
(b) such public service broadcasters as they consider are likely to be affected if the Secretary of State gives effect to the recommendation they are proposing to make; and
(c) such of the other persons providing television and radio services as OFCOM consider appropriate.

(5) Before making an order under this section, the Secretary of State must consult the persons mentioned in subsection (6) about its terms (even if the order is the one recommended by OFCOM).

(6) Those persons are—

(a) OFCOM;
(b) such public service broadcasters as they consider are likely to be affected by the order; and
(c) such of the other persons providing television and radio services as he considers appropriate.

(7) No order is to be made containing provision authorised by this section unless a draft of the order has been laid before Parliament and approved by a resolution of each House.

(8) In this section "public service broadcaster" means any of the persons who are public service broadcasters for the purposes of section 264.

[3327]

NOTES

Commencement: 29 December 2003.

Must-offer obligations etc affecting public service television

272 Must-offer obligations in relation to networks

(1) The regulatory regime for—

(a) every licensed public service channel,
(b) the public teletext service, and
(c) every licensed television service added by order under section 64 to the list of must-carry services,

includes the conditions that OFCOM consider appropriate for securing the three objectives set out in this section (so far as they are not secured by provision made under section 243).

(2) The first objective is that the channel or other service, so far as it is provided in digital form, is at all times offered as available (subject to the need to agree terms) to be broadcast or distributed by means of every appropriate network.

(3) The second objective is that the person providing the channel or other service does his best to secure that arrangements are entered into, and kept in force, that ensure—

(a) that the channel or other service, so far as it is provided in digital form, is broadcast or distributed on appropriate networks; and
(b) that the broadcasting and distribution of the channel or other service, in accordance with those arrangements, result in its being available for reception, by means of appropriate networks, by as many members of its intended audience as practicable.

(4) The third objective is that the arrangements entered into and kept in force for the purpose of securing the second objective prohibit the imposition, for or in connection with the provision of an appropriate network, of any charge that is attributable (whether directly or indirectly) to the conferring of an entitlement to receive the channel or other service in question in an intelligible form by means of that network.

(5) The three objectives apply only in relation to times when the channel or other service in its digital form is included in the list of must-carry services in section 64.

(6) Conditions imposed under this section in relation to a channel or other service must, to such extent as OFCOM consider appropriate—

(a) require arrangements made or kept in force for the purpose of securing the second objective to apply in the case of every service which is an ancillary service by reference to the channel or other service in question as they apply to the channel or other service itself; and

(b) provide for the channel or other service to which the conditions apply to be treated, in relation to particular appropriate networks, as constituting such services comprised in or provided with that channel or other service as may be determined by OFCOM.

(7) In this section—

"appropriate network" means (subject to subsection (8)) an electronic communications network by means of which public electronic communications services are provided that are used by a significant number of end-users as their principal means of receiving television programmes;

"intended audience", in relation to a channel or other service, means—

(a) if the channel or other service is one provided only for a particular area or locality of the United Kingdom, members of the public in that area or locality;

(b) if the channel or other service is one provided for members of a particular community, members of that community; and

(c) in any other case, members of the public in the United Kingdom;

"licensed television service" means a service falling to be licensed under Part 1 of the 1990 Act or Part 1 of the 1996 Act.

(8) For the purposes of this section an electronic communications network is not an appropriate network in relation to so much of a channel or other service as is provided only for a particular area or locality of the United Kingdom unless it is a network by means of which electronic communications services are provided to persons in that area or locality

(9) In subsection (7) "public electronic communications service" and "end-user" each has the same meaning as in Part 2.

(10) An order under section 411 must not appoint a day for provisions of this section to come into force that falls less than six months after the day on which the order is made.

[3328]

NOTES

Commencement: to be appointed.

273 Must-offer obligations in relation to satellite services

(1) The regulatory regime for—

(a) every licensed public service channel,

(b) the public teletext service, and

(c) every other licensed television service specified for the purposes of this section in an order made by the Secretary of State,

includes the conditions that OFCOM consider appropriate for securing the three objectives set out in this section (so far as they are not secured by conditions imposed under section 272).

(2) The first objective is that the channel or other service, so far as it is provided in digital form, is at all times offered as available (subject to the need to agree terms) to be broadcast by means of every satellite television service that is available for reception by members of the public in the whole or a part of the United Kingdom.

(3) The second objective is that the person providing the channel or other service does his best to secure that arrangements are entered into, and kept in force, that ensure—

(a) that the channel or other service, so far as it is provided in digital form, is broadcast by means of satellite television services that are broadcast so as to be available for reception by members of the public in the United Kingdom; and

(b) that the broadcasting, in accordance with those arrangements, of the channel or other service by means of those satellite television services results in its being available for reception in an intelligible form and by means of those services by as many members of its intended audience as practicable.

(4) The third objective is that the arrangements entered into and kept in force for the purpose of securing the second objective prohibit the imposition, for or in connection with the provision of a satellite television service, of any charge that is attributable (whether directly or

indirectly) to the conferring of an entitlement to receive the channel or other service in question in an intelligible form by means of that service.

(5) The three objectives apply only in relation to a time when the channel or service is included, in its digital form, in the list of services that are must-provide services for the purposes of section 274.

(6) Conditions imposed under this section in relation to a channel or other service must, to such extent as OFCOM consider appropriate—

(a) require arrangements made or kept in force for the purpose of securing the second objective to apply in the case of every service which is an ancillary service by reference to the channel or other service in question as they apply to the channel or other service itself; and

(b) provide for the channel or other service to which the conditions apply to be treated, in relation to particular satellite television services, as constituting such services comprised in or provided with the channel or other service as may be determined by OFCOM.

(7) In this section—

"intended audience", in relation to a channel or other service, means—

(a) if the channel or other service is one provided only for a particular area or locality of the United Kingdom, members of the public in that area or locality;

(b) if the channel or other service is one provided for members of a particular community, members of that community; and

(c) in any other case, members of the public in the United Kingdom;

"licensed television service" means a service falling to be licensed under Part 1 of the 1990 Act or Part 1 of the 1996 Act; and

"satellite television service" means a service which—

(a) consists in or involves the broadcasting of television programme services from a satellite; and

(b) is used by a significant number of the persons by whom the broadcasts are received in an intelligible form as their principal means of receiving television programmes.

(8) An order under section 411 must not appoint a day for provisions of this section to come into force that falls less than six months after the day on which the order is made.

[3329]

NOTES

Commencement: to be appointed.

---

274 Securing reception of must-provide services in certain areas

(1) The regulatory regime for—

(a) every licensed public service channel,

(b) the public teletext service, and

(c) every licensed television service added by order under section 275 to the list of must-provide services,

includes the conditions that OFCOM consider appropriate for securing that arrangements satisfying the requirements of this section are entered into and maintained by all the persons who provide must-provide services.

(2) The conditions imposed on a person under this section may include the conditions that OFCOM consider appropriate for securing, in a case where—

(a) the persons providing must-provide services fail to enter into or maintain arrangements satisfying the requirements of this section, and

(b) OFCOM make and impose arrangements of their own instead,

that the person bound by the conditions is required to act in accordance with arrangements imposed by OFCOM.

(3) The arrangements that are to be entered into, or may be imposed, are arrangements that secure—

(a) that a facility for receiving each must-provide service is made available to every member of the intended audience for that service who is unable, without the use of that facility, to receive it in an intelligible form and free of charge;

(b) that the facility is one under which every such member of the intended audience for a must-provide service is entitled, free of charge, to receive in an intelligible form so much of a service broadcast from a satellite as includes that must-provide service;

(c) that the cost of making that facility available is shared, in appropriate proportions, by all the persons providing must-provide services;

(d) that procedures are established and maintained for dealing with complaints from persons claiming to be entitled, in accordance with the arrangements, to receive a service free of charge, and for resolving disputes about the existence or extent of such an entitlement;

(e) that the availability of those procedures is adequately publicised in accordance with guidance given from time to time by OFCOM.

(4) Arrangements entered into by the providers of must-provide services for the purposes of subsection (3), and any modifications of such arrangements made by the parties to them, are to have effect only if approved by OFCOM.

(5) Before imposing any arrangements for the purposes of a condition under subsection (2), OFCOM must consult all the persons who provide must-provide services.

(6) For the purposes of this section the reception of a service is not free of charge—

(a) if reception of the service is made conditional on the acceptance of an entitlement to receive another service in relation to which a charge is imposed (whether directly or indirectly);

(b) if a charge is made for or in connection with the provision of a service which is an ancillary service in relation to the service in question;

(c) if any consideration is required from the persons to whom it is made available for the provision of assistance for disabled people in respect of programmes included in the service; or

(d) if any other consideration is required to be given, by the person entitled to receive it, for or in connection with its provision or availability.

(7) A service is not prevented from being free of charge by a requirement to pay sums in accordance with regulations under section 365.

(8) The quality of reception that is required before someone is to be treated for the purposes of any conditions imposed under this section as able to receive a service in an intelligible form is to be determined by OFCOM.

(9) References in this section to a facility for receiving a must-provide service include references to—

(a) software to be used in giving effect to the entitlement to receive a must-provide service in an intelligible form, and

(b) apparatus to be used in associating apparatus capable of being used for receiving such a service, or for putting it into an intelligible form, with a person having such an entitlement,

but do not otherwise include references to apparatus.

(10) In this section—

"intended audience", in relation to a must-provide service, means—

(a) if the service is one provided only for a particular area or locality of the United Kingdom, members of the public in that area or locality;

(b) if the service is one provided for members of a particular community, members of that community; and

(c) in any other case, members of the public in the United Kingdom;

"licensed television service" means a service falling to be licensed under Part 1 of the 1990 Act or Part 1 of the 1996 Act;

"must-provide service" means a service for the time being included in the list of must-provide services in section 275.

(11) An order under section 411 must not appoint a day for provisions of this section to come into force that falls less than six months after the day on which the order is made.

[3330]

NOTES

Commencement: to be appointed.

275 Must-provide services for the purposes of s 274

(1) For the purposes of section 274 the list of must-provide services is as follows—

(a) every service of television programmes provided by the BBC so far as it is provided in digital form and is a service in relation to which OFCOM have functions;

(b) the Channel 3 services so far as provided in digital form;

(c) Channel 4 so far as provided in digital form;

(d) Channel 5 so far as provided in digital form;

(e) S4C Digital;

(f) the digital public teletext service.

(2) The Secretary of State may by order modify the list of must-provide services in subsection (1).

(3) In determining whether it is appropriate, by an order under subsection (2), to add a service to the list of must-provide services or to remove a service from that list, the Secretary of State must have regard, in particular, to—

(a) the public benefit to be secured by the addition of the service to the list, or by its retention in the list;

(b) the likely effect of the proposed modification as respects the costs to be borne, under arrangements entered into or imposed under section 274, by the persons who, after the coming into force of the modification, would have to be parties to those arrangements; and

(c) the extent to which that effect is proportionate to the benefit mentioned in paragraph (a).

[3331]

NOTES

Commencement: 29 December 2003.

276 Co-operation with the public teletext provider

(1) The regulatory regime for every Channel 3 service and for Channel 4 includes the conditions that OFCOM consider appropriate for securing that the provider of the service or channel grants access to the facilities mentioned in subsection (2)—

(a) to the public teletext provider; and

(b) to any person authorised by virtue of section 220 to provide the whole or a part of the public teletext service on his behalf.

(2) Those facilities are the facilities that are reasonably required by the public teletext provider or the authorised person for the purposes of, or in connection with, the provision of the public teletext service.

(3) A licence holder granting access to facilities in pursuance of a condition imposed under this section may require the public teletext provider or authorised person to pay a reasonable charge in respect of the facilities.

(4) In the event of a dispute, the amount of the charge is to be determined by OFCOM.

[3332]

NOTES

Commencement: 29 December 2003 (for transitional provisions in relation to the existing service (as defined in s 221(11) of this Act) see the Office of Communications Act 2002 (Commencement No 3) and Communications Act 2003 (Commencement No 2) Order 2003, SI 2003/3142, art 8(2) at **[3597]**).

Programming quotas for public service television

277 Programming quotas for independent productions

(1) The regulatory regime for every licensed public service channel includes the conditions that OFCOM consider appropriate for securing that, in each year, not less than 25 per cent of the total amount of time allocated to the broadcasting of qualifying programmes included in the channel is allocated to the broadcasting of a range and diversity of independent productions.

(2) In this section—

(a) a reference to qualifying programmes is a reference to programmes of such description as the Secretary of State may by order specify as describing the programmes that are to be qualifying programmes for the purposes of this section;

(b) a reference to independent productions is a reference to programmes of such description as the Secretary of State may by order specify as describing the programmes that are to be independent productions for the purposes of this section; and

(c) a reference to a range of independent productions is a reference to a range of such productions in terms of cost of acquisition as well as in terms of the types of programme involved.

(3) The Secretary of State may by order amend subsection (1) by substituting a different percentage for the percentage for the time being specified in that subsection.

(4) The Secretary of State may also by order provide for the regulatory regime for every licensed public service channel to include conditions falling within subsection (5), either instead of or as well as those falling within subsection (1).

(5) The conditions falling within this subsection are those that OFCOM consider appropriate for securing that, in each year, not less than the percentage specified in the order of the programming budget for that year for that channel is applied in the acquisition of independent productions.

(6) The power to make an order under subsection (4) includes power to provide that conditions that have previously ceased under such an order to be included in the regulatory regime for every licensed public service channel are again so included, in addition to or instead of the conditions already so included (apart from the exercise of that power) by virtue of this section.

(7) The Secretary of State is not to make an order for the regulatory regime of every licensed public service channel to include or exclude conditions falling within subsection (1) or conditions falling within subsection (5) unless—

(a) OFCOM have made a recommendation to him for those conditions to be included or excluded; and

(b) the order gives effect to that recommendation.

(8) The regulatory regime for every licensed public service channel also includes a condition requiring the provider of the channel to comply with directions given to him by OFCOM for the purpose of—

(a) carrying forward to one or more subsequent years determined in accordance with the direction any shortfall for any year in his compliance with the requirements of conditions imposed by virtue of subsection (1) or (4); and

(b) thereby increasing the percentage applicable for the purposes of those conditions to the subsequent year or years.

(9) For the purposes of conditions imposed by virtue of this section—

(a) the amount of the programming budget for a licensed public service channel for a year, and

(b) the means of determining the amount of that budget that is applied for any purpose,

are to be computed in accordance with such provision as may be set out in an order made by the Secretary of State, or as may be determined by OFCOM in accordance with such an order.

(10) The powers of the Secretary of State to make orders under this section do not include—

(a) power to specify different percentages for the purposes of subsection (1), or of a condition falling within subsection (5), for different regional Channel 3 services or for different national Channel 3 services; or

(b) power to make different provision for different licensed public service channels as to whether conditions falling within subsection (1) or conditions falling within subsection (5), or both, are included in the regulatory regimes for those services.

(11) Before making an order under this section the Secretary of State must consult OFCOM, the BBC and the Welsh Authority.

(12) No order is to be made containing provision authorised by this section unless a draft of the order has been laid before Parliament and approved by a resolution of each House.

(13) In this section—

"acquisition", in relation to a programme, includes commissioning and the acquisition of a right to include it in a service or to have it broadcast;

"programme" does not include an advertisement; and

"programming budget" means the budget for the production and acquisition of qualifying programmes.

[3333]

NOTES

Commencement: 29 December 2003.

278 Programming quotas for original productions

(1) The regulatory regime for every licensed public service channel includes the conditions that OFCOM consider appropriate for securing—

(a) that the time allocated, in each year, to the broadcasting of original productions included in that channel is no less than what appears to them to be an appropriate proportion of the total amount of time allocated to the broadcasting of all the programmes included in the channel; and

(b) that the time allocated to the broadcasting of original productions is split in what appears to them to be an appropriate manner between peak viewing times and other times.

(2) The proportion determined by OFCOM for the purposes of subsection (1)—

(a) must, in the case of each licensed public service channel, be such proportion as OFCOM consider appropriate for ensuring that the channel is consistently of a high quality; and

(b) may, for the purposes of paragraph (b) of that subsection, be expressed as the cumulative effect of two different minimum proportions, one applying to peak viewing times and the other to other times.

(3) A condition contained in a licence by virtue of this section may provide—

(a) that specified descriptions of programmes are to be excluded in determining the programmes a proportion of which is to consist of original productions;

(b) that, in determining for the purposes of the condition whether a programme is of a description of programmes excluded by virtue of paragraph (a), regard is to be had to any guidance prepared and published, and from to time revised, by OFCOM.

(4) Before imposing a condition under this section, OFCOM must consult the person on whom it is to be imposed.

(5) The requirement to consult is satisfied, in the case of the imposition of a condition by way of a variation of a licence, by compliance with section 3(4)(b) of the 1990 Act (obligation to give opportunity to make representations about variation).

(6) References in this section, in relation to a licensed public service channel, to original productions are references to programmes of such description as the Secretary of State may by order specify as describing the programmes that are to be original productions for the purposes of this section.

(7) The power to specify descriptions of programmes by order under subsection (6) includes power to confer such discretions on OFCOM as the Secretary of State thinks fit.

(8) Before making an order under this section the Secretary of State must consult OFCOM, the BBC and the Welsh Authority.

(9) No order is to be made containing provision authorised by this section unless a draft of the order has been laid before Parliament and approved by a resolution of each House.

(10) In this section—

"peak viewing time", in relation to a licensed public service channel, means a time that appears to OFCOM to be, or to be likely to be, a peak viewing time for that channel; and

"programme" does not include an advertisement.

(11) Before determining for the purposes of this section what constitutes a peak viewing time for a channel, OFCOM must consult the provider of the channel.

[3334]

NOTES

Commencement: 1 July 2004.
Orders: the Broadcasting (Original Productions) Order 2004, SI 2004/1652.

News provision etc on public service television

279 News and current affairs programmes

(1) The regulatory regime for every licensed public service channel includes the conditions that OFCOM consider appropriate for securing—

(a) that the programmes included in the channel include news programmes and current affairs programmes;
(b) that the news programmes and current affairs programmes included in the service are of high quality and deal with both national and international matters; and
(c) that the news programmes so included are broadcast for viewing at intervals throughout the period for which the channel is provided.

(2) That regime also includes the conditions that OFCOM consider appropriate for securing that, in each year—

(a) the time allocated to the broadcasting of news programmes included in the service, and
(b) the time allocated to the broadcasting of current affairs programmes so included,

each constitutes no less than what appears to OFCOM to be an appropriate proportion of the time allocated to the broadcasting of all the programmes included in the channel.

(3) It further includes the conditions that OFCOM consider appropriate for securing that the time allocated—

(a) to the broadcasting of news programmes included in the service, and
(b) to the broadcasting of current affairs programmes so included,

is, in each case, split in what appears to OFCOM to be an appropriate manner between peak viewing times and other times.

(4) The proportion determined by OFCOM for the purposes of subsection (2) may, for the purposes of subsection (3), be expressed as the cumulative effect of two different minimum proportions, one applying to peak viewing times and the other to other times.

(5) In this section "peak viewing time", in relation to a licensed public service channel, means a time determined by OFCOM to be, or to be likely to be, a peak viewing time for that channel.

(6) Before determining for the purposes of this section—

(a) the proportion of time to be allocated to the broadcasting of news programmes or current affairs programmes; or
(b) what constitutes a peak viewing time for a channel,

OFCOM must consult the provider of the channel or (as the case may be) the person who is proposing to provide it.

(7) The requirement to consult is satisfied, in the case of the imposition of a condition by way of a variation of a licence, by compliance with section 3(4)(b) of the 1990 Act (obligation to give opportunity to make representations about variation).

[3335]

NOTES

Commencement: 29 December 2003.

280 Appointed news providers for Channel 3

(1) The regulatory regime for every regional Channel 3 service includes the conditions that OFCOM consider appropriate for securing the nationwide broadcasting, on the regional Channel 3 services (taken together), of news programmes that are able to compete effectively with other television news programmes broadcast nationwide in the United Kingdom.

(2) The conditions imposed under this section must include a condition requiring the holder of a regional Channel 3 licence to do all that he can to ensure—

(a) that arrangements for the appointment of a single body corporate as the appointed news provider are maintained between all the holders of regional Channel 3 licences; and

(b) that, at all times while he is providing a regional Channel 3 service, there is in force an appointment made in accordance with those arrangements.

(3) The arrangements that are required to be maintained by virtue of conditions imposed under subsection (2) must provide—

(a) for the terms on which a body is appointed as the appointed news provider to include the terms appearing to OFCOM to be appropriate for securing that the body's finances are adequate, throughout the period of its appointment, to ensure that the Channel 3 news obligations are capable of being met; and

(b) for the approval of OFCOM to be required for the purposes of paragraph (a) to the terms on which an appointment is made.

(4) The conditions imposed under this section must include the conditions that OFCOM consider appropriate for securing that arrangements maintained between—

(a) the holders of regional Channel 3 licences, and

(b) the body which is the appointed news provider,

ensure that that body is subject to an obligation, enforceable by OFCOM, to provide OFCOM with all such information as they may require for the purpose of carrying out their functions.

(5) The conditions imposed under this section must include a condition requiring the news programmes included in a regional Channel 3 service—

(a) to be programmes provided by the body which is for the time being the appointed news provider for the purposes of this section; and

(b) to be so included in that service as to be broadcast simultaneously with the broadcasting of news programmes included, in accordance with conditions imposed under this subsection, in other regional Channel 3 services.

(6) Those conditions must also require the news programmes provided by the appointed news provider which, in accordance with a condition imposed under subsection (5), are included in a regional Channel 3 service to be programmes that are presented live.

(7) OFCOM—

(a) may issue guidance as to the terms that will satisfy requirements imposed by virtue of subsection (3)(a); and

(b) must have regard to guidance for the time being in force under this subsection when considering whether to give an approval for the purposes of provision made by virtue of subsection (3)(b).

(8) For the purposes of this section the Channel 3 news obligations are—

(a) the requirements of any conditions imposed in relation to regional Channel 3 services under section 279; and

(b) the nationwide broadcasting on the regional Channel 3 services (taken together) of news programmes that are able to compete effectively with other television news programmes broadcast nationwide in the United Kingdom.

(9) Conditions imposed under this section are not to require arrangements to make provision falling within subsection (3)(a) or (b) or (4) in relation to appointments made before the commencement of this section.

(10) …

[3336]

NOTES

Commencement: 29 December 2003.
Sub-s (10): repeals the Broadcasting Act 1990, s 32.

281 Disqualification from appointment as news provider

(1) The regulatory regime for every regional Channel 3 service includes the conditions that OFCOM consider appropriate for securing—

(a) that a body is not appointed as the appointed news provider if it falls within subsection (2); and

(b) that the appointment of a body as the appointed news provider ceases to have effect if it becomes a body falling within that subsection.

(2) A body falls within this subsection if—

(a) it is a disqualified person under Part 2 of Schedule 2 to the 1990 Act in relation to a Channel 3 licence; or

(b) there would be a contravention of Part 1 of Schedule 14 to this Act (whether by that body or by another person) if that body held a licence to provide a Channel 3 service, or held a licence to provide such a service for a particular area for which such a service is provided.

[(3) The reference in subsection (2)(a) to a body which is a disqualified person under Part 2 of Schedule 2 to the 1990 Act in relation to a Channel 3 licence includes a reference to a person who is disqualified by virtue of a disqualification order under section 145 of the 1996 Act.]

[3337]

NOTES

Commencement: 29 December 2003.

Sub-s (3): added by the Media Ownership (Local Radio and Appointed News Provider) Order 2003, SI 2003/3299, art 13(1).

282 Power to repeal or modify Channel 3 news provider provisions

(1) If it appears to the Secretary of State appropriate to do so, he may by order repeal or otherwise modify any of the provisions of section 280 or 281.

(2) Except in a case to which subsection (3) applies, the Secretary of State must consult OFCOM before making an order under this section.

(3) Consultation with OFCOM is not required if the order is confined to giving effect to recommendations by OFCOM that are contained in a report of a review under section 391.

(4) No order is to be made containing provision authorised by this section unless a draft of the order has been laid before Parliament and approved by a resolution of each House.

[3338]

NOTES

Commencement: 12 December 2003.

Orders: the Media Ownership (Local Radio and Appointed News Provider) Order 2003, SI 2003/3299 at **[3605]**.

283 News providers for Channel 5

(1) If it appears to the Secretary of State appropriate to do so, he may by order make provision requiring news programmes included in Channel 5 to be provided by a person appointed as a news provider in accordance with the order.

(2) An order under this section may make provision in relation to Channel 5 that corresponds, with such modifications as the Secretary of State thinks fit, to any provision made in relation to regional Channel 3 services by section 280 or 281.

(3) Subsection (2) applies irrespective of any repeal or other modification by an order under this Act of section 280 or 281.

(4) An order under this section may include provision for section 194A of the 1990 Act (application of Competition Act 1998 to Channel 3 news provision) to have effect (with such modifications as may be specified in the order) in relation to the appointment of a person as a news provider for Channel 5 as it has effect in relation to the appointment of a body as a news provider for Channel 3.

(5) The Secretary of State is not to make an order under this section for the imposition of obligations in relation to Channel 5 unless he is satisfied that Channel 5's share of the audience for television broadcasting services is broadly equivalent to that of the services comprising Channel 3.

(6) An order under this section must require a licence holder to have a reasonable opportunity of making representations to OFCOM before his licence is varied in pursuance of the order.

(7) Except in a case to which subsection (8) applies, the Secretary of State must consult OFCOM before making an order under this section.

(8) Consultation with OFCOM is not required if the order is confined to giving effect to recommendations by OFCOM that are contained in a report of a review under section 391.

(9) No order is to be made containing provision authorised by this section unless a draft of the order has been laid before Parliament and approved by a resolution of each House.

[3339]

NOTES

Commencement: 29 December 2003.

284 News provision on the public teletext service

(1) The regulatory regime for the public teletext service includes the conditions that OFCOM consider appropriate for securing—

(a) that the service includes what appears to OFCOM to be a suitable quantity and variety of news items; and

(b) that the news items included in the service are up to date and regularly revised.

(2) Conditions imposed under this section in relation to a time when the public teletext service comprises both—

(a) an analogue teletext service, and

(b) a teletext service provided in digital form,

must apply to both services but may make different provision for each of them.

[3340]

NOTES

Commencement: 29 December 2003.

Independent and regional productions and programmes for public service television

285 Code relating to programme commissioning

(1) The regulatory regime for every licensed public service channel includes the conditions that OFCOM consider appropriate for securing that the provider of the channel draws up and from time to time revises a code of practice setting out the principles he will apply when agreeing terms for the commissioning of independent productions.

(2) That regime also includes the conditions that OFCOM consider appropriate for securing that the provider of every licensed public service channel—

(a) at all times complies with a code of practice which has been drawn up by him by virtue of this section and is for the time being in force; and

(b) exercises his power to revise his code to take account of revisions from time to time of the guidance issued by OFCOM for the purposes of this section.

(3) The conditions imposed under this section must ensure that the code for the time being in force in the case of every licensed public service channel secures, in the manner described in guidance issued by OFCOM—

(a) that a reasonable timetable is applied to negotiations for the commissioning of an independent production and for the conclusion of a binding agreement;

(b) that there is what appears to OFCOM to be sufficient clarity, when an independent production is commissioned, about the different categories of rights to broadcast or otherwise to make use of or exploit the commissioned production that are being disposed of;

(c) that there is what appears to OFCOM to be sufficient transparency about the amounts to be paid in respect of each category of rights;

(d) that what appear to OFCOM to be satisfactory arrangements are made about the duration and exclusivity of those rights;

(e) that procedures exist for reviewing the arrangements adopted in accordance with the code and for demonstrating compliance with it;

(f) that those procedures include requirements for the monitoring of the application of the code and for the making of reports to OFCOM;

(g) that provision is made for resolving disputes arising in respect of the provisions of the code (by independent arbitration or otherwise) in a manner that appears to OFCOM to be appropriate.

(4) The conditions imposed under this section must also ensure that the drawing up or revision of a code by virtue of this section is in accordance with guidance issued by OFCOM as to—

(a) the times when the code is to be drawn up or reviewed with a view to revision;
(b) the consultation to be undertaken before a code is drawn up or revised; and
(c) the publication of every code or revised code.

(5) The provision that may be included in a condition imposed under this section includes—

(a) provision requiring a draft of a code or of any revision of a code to be submitted to OFCOM for approval;
(b) provision for the code or revision to have effect only if approved by OFCOM; and
(c) provision for a code or revision that is approved by OFCOM subject to modifications to have effect with those modifications.

(6) OFCOM—

(a) must issue and may from time to time revise guidance for the purposes of this section;
(b) must ensure that there is always guidance for those purposes in force;
(c) must, before issuing their guidance or revised guidance, consult the providers of licensed public service channels, persons who make independent productions (or persons appearing to OFCOM to represent them), the BBC and the Welsh Authority; and
(d) must publish their guidance or revised guidance in such manner as they think appropriate.

(7) Guidance issued by OFCOM for the purposes of this section must be general guidance and is not to specify particular terms to be included in agreements to which the guidance relates.

(8) Conditions imposed under this section requiring a code to be drawn up or approved may include transitional provision for treating a code drawn up before the imposition of the condition—

(a) as satisfying the requirements of that condition; and
(b) as a code approved by OFCOM for the purposes of conditions so imposed.

(9) In this section "independent production" has the same meaning as in section 277.

[3341]

NOTES

Commencement: 29 December 2003.

286 Regional programme-making for Channels 3 and 5

(1) The regulatory regime for every Channel 3 service includes the conditions (if any) that OFCOM consider appropriate in the case of that service for securing—

(a) that what appears to OFCOM to be a suitable proportion of Channel 3 programmes made in the United Kingdom are programmes made in the United Kingdom outside the M25 area;
(b) that the Channel 3 programmes that are made in the United Kingdom outside the M25 area (taken together) constitute what appears to OFCOM to be a suitable range of programmes;
(c) that what appears to OFCOM to be a suitable proportion of the expenditure of the providers of Channel 3 services on Channel 3 programmes made in the United Kingdom is referable to programme production at different production centres outside the M25 area; and
(d) that the different programme production centres to which that expenditure is referable constitute what appears to OFCOM to be a suitable range of such production centres.

(2) In the case of a national Channel 3 service, subsection (1) requires the inclusion of conditions in the licence for the service only where OFCOM consider, having regard to the nature of the service, that it would be appropriate for conditions falling within that subsection to be so included.

(3) The regulatory regime for Channel 5 includes the conditions that OFCOM consider appropriate for securing—

(a) that what appears to OFCOM to be a suitable proportion of the programmes made in the United Kingdom for viewing on that Channel are programmes made in the United Kingdom outside the M25 area;

(b) that the programmes for such viewing that are made in the United Kingdom outside the M25 area (taken together) constitute what appears to OFCOM to be a suitable range of programmes;

(c) that what appears to OFCOM to be a suitable proportion of the expenditure of the provider of Channel 5 on programmes made in the United Kingdom for viewing on that Channel is referable to programme production at different production centres outside the M25 area; and

(d) that the different programme production centres to which that expenditure is referable constitute what appears to OFCOM to be a suitable range of such production centres.

(4) Before imposing a condition under this section, OFCOM must consult the person on whom it is to be imposed.

(5) The requirement to consult is satisfied, in the case of the imposition of a condition by way of a variation of a licence, by compliance with section 3(4)(b) of the 1990 Act (obligation to give opportunity to make representations about variation).

(6) A proportion is not to be regarded by OFCOM as suitable for the purposes of a provision of this section if it constitutes less than a significant proportion of the programmes or expenditure in question.

(7) In this section—

"Channel 3 programmes" means programmes made for viewing on Channel 3 in more than one area for which regional Channel 3 services are provided, including any programme made for viewing on a national Channel 3 service other than a regional programme;

"expenditure", in relation to a programme, means—

(a) expenditure which constitutes an investment in or is otherwise attributable to the making of the programme; or

(b) expenditure on the commissioning or other acquisition of the programme or on the acquisition of a right to include it in a service or to have it broadcast;

"programme" does not include an advertisement; and

"regional programme" means a programme made with a view to its inclusion in a national Channel 3 service as a programme of particular interest to persons living within a particular area of the United Kingdom.

[3342]

NOTES

Commencement: 29 December 2003.

287 Regional programmes on Channel 3

(1) The regulatory regime for every regional Channel 3 service includes the conditions that OFCOM consider appropriate for securing—

(a) that what appears to OFCOM, in the case of that service, to be a sufficient amount of time is given in the programmes included in the service to what appears to them to be a suitable range of programmes (including regional news programmes) which are of particular interest to persons living within the area for which the service is provided;

(b) that the regional programmes included in the service are of high quality;

(c) that what appears to OFCOM, in the case of that service, to be a suitable proportion of the regional programmes included in the service consists of programmes made in that area;

(d) that the regional news programmes included in the service are broadcast for viewing at intervals throughout the period for which the service is provided and, in particular, at peak viewing times;

(e) that what appears to OFCOM, in the case of that service, to be a suitable proportion of the other regional programmes that are included in the service consists of programmes broadcast for viewing—

(i) at peak viewing times; and

(ii) at times immediately preceding or following those times.

(2) The regulatory regime for every local Channel 3 service includes the conditions that OFCOM consider appropriate for securing—

(a) that what appears to OFCOM, in the case of that service, to be a sufficient amount of time is given in the programmes included in the service to what appears to them to be a suitable range of local programmes;

(b) that, in the case of each part of an area or each community for which the service is provided, the range of local programmes is a range of programmes (including news programmes) which are of particular interest to persons living within that part of that area or to that community;

(c) that the local programmes included in the service are of high quality;

(d) that what appears to OFCOM, in the case of that service, to be a suitable proportion of the local programmes included in the service consists of programmes made in the area for which the service is provided;

(e) that the local news programmes included in the service are broadcast for viewing at intervals throughout the period for which the service is provided and, in particular, at peak viewing times;

(f) that what appears to OFCOM, in the case of that service, to be a suitable proportion of the other local programmes that are included in the service consists of programmes broadcast for viewing—

(i) at peak viewing times; and

(ii) at times immediately preceding or following those times.

(3) In the case of a local Channel 3 service, the conditions included in the regulatory regime for the service include conditions falling within subsection (1) to the extent only that it appears to OFCOM that the requirements of subsection (1) are not adequately met by conditions falling within subsection (2).

(4) In the case of a national Channel 3 service in the case of which OFCOM consider that it would be appropriate to impose conditions under this subsection, the regulatory regime for the service includes the conditions that OFCOM consider appropriate for securing—

(a) that what appears to OFCOM, in the case of that service, to be a sufficient amount of time is given in the programmes included in the service to what appears to them to be a suitable range of programmes (including regional news programmes) which are of particular interest to persons living within particular areas of the United Kingdom;

(b) that the regional programmes included in the service are of high quality;

(c) that what appears to OFCOM, in the case of that service, to be a suitable proportion of the regional programmes included in the service consists of programmes made in the area by reference to which they are regional programmes;

(d) that the regional news programmes included in the service are broadcast for viewing at intervals throughout the period for which the service is provided and, in particular, at peak viewing times;

(e) that what appears to OFCOM, in the case of that service, to be a suitable proportion of the other regional programmes that are included in the service consists of programmes broadcast for viewing—

(i) at peak viewing times; and

(ii) at times immediately preceding or following those times.

(5) Before imposing a condition under this section, OFCOM must consult the person on whom it is to be imposed.

(6) The requirement to consult is satisfied, in the case of the imposition of a condition by way of a variation of a licence, by compliance with section 3(4)(b) of the 1990 Act (obligation to give opportunity to make representations about variation).

(7) A proportion is not to be regarded by OFCOM as suitable for the purposes of a provision of this section if it constitutes less than a significant proportion of the programmes in question.

(8) In this section—

"local Channel 3 service" means a regional Channel 3 service the provision of which includes the provision (in pursuance of a determination under section 14(3) of the 1990 Act) of different programmes for different parts of an area or for different communities living within an area;

"local programme", in relation to a service provided for different parts of an area or for different communities, means a programme included in that service for any of the parts of that area or for any of those communities, and "local news programme" is to be construed accordingly;

"peak viewing time", in relation to a service, means a time determined by OFCOM to be, or to be likely to be, a peak viewing time for that service;

"programme" does not include an advertisement;

"regional programme"—

(a) in relation to a regional Channel 3 service, means a programme included in that service with a view to its being of particular interest to persons living within the area for which the service is provided;

(b) in relation to a national Channel 3 service, means a programme included in that service with a view to its being of particular interest to persons living within a particular area of the United Kingdom;

and "regional news programme" is to be construed accordingly.

[3343]

NOTES

Commencement: 29 December 2003.

288 Regional programme-making for Channel 4

(1) The regulatory regime for Channel 4 includes the conditions that OFCOM consider appropriate for securing—

(a) that what appears to OFCOM to be a suitable proportion of programmes made in the United Kingdom for viewing on Channel 4 are programmes made in the United Kingdom outside the M25 area;

(b) that the programmes for such viewing that are made in the United Kingdom outside the M25 area (taken together) constitute what appears to OFCOM to be a suitable range of programmes;

(c) that what appears to OFCOM to be a suitable proportion of the expenditure of C4C on programmes made in the United Kingdom for viewing on Channel 4 is referable to programme production at different production centres outside the M25 area; and

(d) that the different programme production centres to which that expenditure is referable constitute what appears to OFCOM to be a suitable range of such production centres.

(2) Before imposing a condition under this section, OFCOM must consult C4C.

(3) The requirement to consult is satisfied, in the case of the imposition of a condition by way of a variation of a licence, by compliance with section 3(4)(b) of the 1990 Act (obligation to give opportunity to make representations about variation).

(4) A proportion is not to be regarded by OFCOM as suitable for the purposes of a provision of this section if it constitutes less than a significant proportion of the programmes or expenditure in question.

(5) In this section—

"expenditure", in relation to a programme, means—

(a) expenditure which constitutes an investment in or is otherwise attributable to the making of the programme; or

(b) expenditure on the commissioning or other acquisition of the programme or on the acquisition of a right to include it in a service or to have it broadcast; and

"programme" does not include an advertisement.

[3344]

NOTES

Commencement: 29 December 2003.

289 Regional matters in the public teletext service

(1) The regulatory regime for the public teletext service includes the conditions that OFCOM consider appropriate for securing that the service includes what appears to them to be an appropriate proportion of material that is of particular interest to persons living in different parts of the United Kingdom.

(2) Conditions imposed under this section in relation to a time when the public teletext service comprises both—

(a) an analogue teletext service, and
(b) a teletext service provided in digital form,

must apply to both services but may make different provision for each of them.

[3345]

NOTES

Commencement: 29 December 2003.

Networking arrangements for Channel 3

290 Proposals for arrangements

(1) An application for a regional Channel 3 licence, in addition to being accompanied by the proposals mentioned in section 15(3)(b) of the 1990 Act, must be accompanied by the applicant's proposals for participating in networking arrangements.

(2) OFCOM may publish general guidance to applicants for regional Channel 3 licences as to the kinds of proposals which they are likely to consider satisfactory.

(3) The publication of guidance under subsection (2) is to be in such manner as OFCOM consider appropriate.

(4) Arrangements are networking arrangements for the purposes of this Part if they—

(a) apply to all the holders of regional Channel 3 licences;
(b) provide for programmes made, commissioned or acquired by or on behalf of one or more of the holders of such licences to be available for broadcasting in all regional Channel 3 services; and
(c) are made for the purpose of enabling regional Channel 3 services (taken as a whole) to be a nationwide system of services which is able to compete effectively with other television programme services provided in the United Kingdom.

[3346]

NOTES

Commencement: 29 December 2003.

291 Obligation as to making and continuance of approved arrangements

(1) The regulatory regime for every regional Channel 3 service includes the conditions that OFCOM consider appropriate for securing that the licence holder does all that he can to ensure that approved networking arrangements are in force whenever—

(a) the licence holder is providing the licensed service; and
(b) no networking arrangements imposed by OFCOM under section 292 are in force.

(2) In this section "approved networking arrangements" means networking arrangements which are for the time being approved by OFCOM in accordance with Schedule 11.

(3), (4) …

[3347]

NOTES

Commencement: 29 December 2003.
Sub-ss (3), (4): amend the Competition Act 1998, Sch 2, para 5.

292 OFCOM's power to impose arrangements

(1) This section applies on each occasion on which OFCOM—

(a) are proposing to award one or more regional Channel 3 licences; and
(b) for that purpose publish a notice under section 15(1) of the 1990 Act.

(2) OFCOM must—
(a) determine the date by which the holders of the licences awarded and all other regional Channel 3 providers (if any) must have entered into networking arrangements (the "networking date"); and
(b) set out that date in that notice.

(3) The networking date must be the date by which, in OFCOM's opinion, the networking arrangements must have been entered into if approved networking arrangements are to be fully in force before the persons awarded licences begin to provide their licensed services.

(4) If—
(a) no suitable networking arrangements exist by the networking date, or
(b) the suitable networking arrangements that exist at that date cease to apply to all regional Channel 3 providers on or after that date,

OFCOM may impose on all regional Channel 3 providers the networking arrangements that OFCOM consider appropriate.

(5) For the purposes of subsection (4) arrangements are suitable networking arrangements if it appears to OFCOM that they—
(a) have been submitted to them for approval or have been approved by them; and
(b) will be in force as approved networking arrangements when the persons awarded licences begin to provide their licensed services.

(6) Arrangements imposed under this section come into force on the date determined by OFCOM.

(7) The regulatory regime for every regional Channel 3 service includes the conditions that OFCOM consider appropriate for securing that the licence holder complies with the provisions of any networking arrangements imposed under this section.

(8) Where—
(a) networking arrangements are imposed under this section,
(b) other networking arrangements are entered into between the licence holders bound by the imposed arrangements, and
(c) the other arrangements entered into are approved by OFCOM,

the imposed arrangements shall cease to have effect on the coming into force of the other arrangements as approved networking arrangements.

(9) In this section—

"approved networking arrangements" has the same meaning as in section 291; and

"regional Channel 3 providers" means persons who will be licensed to provide regional Channel 3 services and will be providing such services when the licences to be awarded come into force.

[3348]

NOTES

Commencement: 29 December 2003.

293 Review of approved networking arrangements etc

(1) It shall be the duty of OFCOM from time to time to carry out general reviews of the networking arrangements (whether approved or imposed by OFCOM) that are in force.

(2) The first such review must be carried out no later than six months after the date on which the offers made under section 215(1) close or (if those offers close on different dates) the latest of those dates.

(3) Every subsequent review must be carried out no more than one year after the previous one.

(4) OFCOM may also, at any other time, carry out a review of whether those arrangements continue to satisfy one of the two competition tests set out in paragraph 6 of Schedule 11.

(5) If, on a review under this section, OFCOM are satisfied that modifications are required of the networking arrangements for the time being in force, they may—
- (a) require the holders of regional Channel 3 licences to give effect to the modifications proposed by OFCOM; or
- (b) in the case of arrangements imposed by OFCOM, make those modifications themselves.

(6) OFCOM must not exercise any of their powers under this Act or the 1990 Act so as to modify the requirements imposed on the holder of a regional Channel 3 licence by approved networking arrangements that are already in force except—
- (a) following a review under this section; or
- (b) with the consent of the licence holder.

(7) The regulatory regime for every Channel 3 service includes the conditions that OFCOM consider appropriate for securing that the licence holder does all that he can to ensure that modifications proposed by OFCOM under this section are given effect to.

(8) In this section "approved networking arrangements" has the same meaning as in section 291.

[3349]

NOTES

Commencement: 29 December 2003.

294 Supplemental provision about networking arrangements

(1) Schedule 11 (which makes provision about the approval of networking arrangements and the imposition or modification of such arrangements) shall have effect.

(2) The obligations arising under conditions imposed in accordance with sections 291 to 293 are subject to the rights of appeal conferred by that Schedule.

[3350]

NOTES

Commencement: 29 December 2003.

Special obligations for Channel 4

295 Involvement of C4 Corporation in programme-making

(1) The regulatory regime for Channel 4 includes a condition requiring C4C not to be involved, except to such extent as OFCOM may allow, in the making of programmes to be broadcast on Channel 4.

(2) In this section "programme" does not include an advertisement.

[3351]

NOTES

Commencement: 29 December 2003.

296 Schools programmes on Channel 4

(1) The regulatory regime for Channel 4 includes the conditions that OFCOM consider appropriate for securing that what appears to them to be a suitable proportion of the programmes which are included in Channel 4 are schools programmes.

(2) A licence under the 1990 Act to provide Channel 4 may also include conditions authorised by the following provisions of this section.

(3) The conditions authorised by this section include conditions requiring C4C—
- (a) to finance the production of schools programmes; and
- (b) to acquire schools programmes provided by other persons.

(4) The conditions authorised by this section include conditions requiring C4C to ensure that schools programmes on Channel 4—
- (a) are of high quality; and

(b) are suitable to meet the needs of schools throughout the United Kingdom.

(5) The conditions authorised by this section include conditions specifying the minimum number of hours in term time, or within normal school hours, that are to be allocated to the broadcasting of schools programmes on Channel 4.

(6) The conditions authorised by this section include conditions requiring C4C to provide such material for use in connection with the schools programmes broadcast by them as may be necessary to secure that effective use is made of those programmes in schools.

(7) The conditions authorised by this section include conditions requiring C4C from time to time to consult such persons who—

(a) are concerned with schools or with the production of schools programmes, or

(b) have an interest in schools or in the production of schools programmes,

as OFCOM think fit.

(8) Before imposing a condition under this section, OFCOM must consult C4C.

(9) The requirement to consult is satisfied, in the case of the imposition of a condition by way of a variation of a licence, by compliance with section 3(4)(b) of the 1990 Act (obligation to give opportunity to make representations about variation).

(10) In determining for the purposes of subsection (1) what proportion of the programmes included in Channel 4 should be schools programmes, OFCOM must take into account services, facilities and materials which C4C provide to schools, or make available for schools, otherwise than by the inclusion of programmes in Channel 4.

(11) …

(12) In this section "schools programmes" means programmes which are intended for use in schools.

[3352]

NOTES

Commencement: 29 December 2003.
Sub-s (11): repeals the Broadcasting Act 1990, s 34.

297 Channel 4 contribution towards national television archive

(1)–(3) …

(4) This section has effect in relation only to financial years beginning after the television transfer date.

[3353]

NOTES

Commencement: 29 December 2003.
Sub-ss (1)–(3): amend the Broadcasting Act 1990, s 185.

Special obligation for the public teletext provider

298 Conditions prohibiting interference with other services

The regulatory regime for the public teletext service includes the conditions that OFCOM consider appropriate for securing that the provision of so much of the public teletext service as is provided in analogue form does not cause interference with—

(a) the television broadcasting service or services on whose frequency or frequencies it is provided; or

(b) any other wireless telegraphy transmissions.

[3354]

NOTES

Commencement: 29 December 2003 (for transitional provisions in relation to the existing licence (as referred to in s 221(1) of this Act) see the Office of Communications Act 2002 (Commencement No 3) and Communications Act 2003 (Commencement No 2) Order 2003, SI 2003/3142, art 8(1) at **[3597]**).

Sporting and other events of national interest

299, 300 (*Amend the Broadcasting Act 1996, ss 97, 99, 101–103* (*outside the scope of this work*).)

301 Code relating to listed events

(1) …

(2) Where OFCOM are required to draw up a code by virtue of this section—

(a) they shall do so as soon as practicable after the commencement of this section; but

(b) the code shall have no effect in relation to any time before the commencement of section 300 of this Act.

[3355]

NOTES

Commencement: 29 December 2003.

Sub-s (1): substitutes the Broadcasting Act 1996, s 104(1).

302 (*Inserts the Broadcasting Act 1996, s 104ZA and amends s 105 of that Act* (*outside the scope of this work*).)

Television services for the deaf and visually impaired

303 Code relating to provision for the deaf and visually impaired

(1) It shall be the duty of OFCOM to draw up, and from time to time to review and revise, a code giving guidance as to—

(a) the extent to which the services to which this section applies should promote the understanding and enjoyment by—

(i) persons who are deaf or hard of hearing,

(ii) persons who are blind or partially-sighted, and

(iii) persons with a dual sensory impairment,

of the programmes to be included in such services; and

(b) the means by which such understanding and enjoyment should be promoted.

(2) The code must include provision for securing that every provider of a service to which this section applies ensures that adequate information about the assistance for disabled people that is provided in relation to that service is made available to those who are likely to want to make use of it.

(3) The code must also require that, from the fifth and tenth anniversaries of the relevant date, the obligations in subsections (4) and (5), respectively, must be fulfilled by reference to averages computed over each of the following—

(a) the twelve month period beginning with the anniversary in question; and

(b) every twelve month period ending one week after the end of the previous period for which an average fell to be computed.

(4) The obligation to be fulfilled from the fifth anniversary of the relevant date is that at least 60 per cent of so much of every service which—

(a) is a service to which this section applies, and

(b) has a relevant date after the passing of this Act,

as consists of programmes that are not excluded programmes must be accompanied by subtitling.

(5) The obligations to be fulfilled from the tenth anniversary of the relevant date are—

(a) that at least 90 per cent of so much of a Channel 3 service or of Channel 4 as consists of programmes that are not excluded programmes must be accompanied by subtitling;

(b) that at least 80 per cent of so much of every other service to which this section applies as consists of programmes that are not excluded programmes must be accompanied by subtitling;

(c) that at least 10 per cent of so much of every service to which this section applies as consists of programmes that are not excluded programmes must be accompanied by audio-description for the blind; and

(d) that at least 5 per cent of so much of every service to which this section applies as consists of programmes that are not excluded programmes must be presented in, or translated into, sign language.

(6) A reference in subsection (4) or in any paragraph of subsection (5) to excluded programmes is a reference to programmes of the description for the time being set out under subsection (7) in relation to that subsection or paragraph and also in relation to the service in question.

(7) The code must set out, in relation to subsection (4) and each of the paragraphs of subsection (5), the descriptions of programmes that OFCOM consider should be excluded programmes for the purposes of the requirement contained in that subsection or paragraph.

(8) In complying with subsection (7), OFCOM must have regard, in particular, to—

(a) the extent of the benefit which would be conferred by the provision of assistance for disabled people in relation to the programmes;
(b) the size of the intended audience for the programmes;
(c) the number of persons who would be likely to benefit from the assistance and the extent of the likely benefit in each case;
(d) the extent to which members of the intended audience for the programmes are resident in places outside the United Kingdom;
(e) the technical difficulty of providing the assistance; and
(f) the cost, in the context of the matters mentioned in paragraphs (a) to (e), of providing the assistance.

(9) The exclusions that may be set out in the code under subsection (7)—

(a) may include different descriptions of programmes in relation to different services to which this section applies; and
(b) in the case of a service which OFCOM are satisfied (having regard to the matters mentioned in subsection (8)) is a special case, may include all the programmes included in the service.

(10) The requirements that may be imposed by the code include, in particular—

(a) requirements on persons providing services to which this section applies to meet interim targets falling within subsection (11), from dates falling before an anniversary mentioned in subsection (3);
(b) requirements on persons providing such services to meet further targets from dates falling after the anniversary mentioned in subsection (5); and
(c) requirements with respect to the provision of assistance for disabled people in relation to excluded programmes, or in relation to a particular description of them.

(11) The interim targets mentioned in subsection (10)(a) are the targets with respect to the provision of assistance for disabled people which OFCOM consider it appropriate to impose as targets on the way to meeting the targets imposed in pursuance of subsection (3).

(12) This section applies to the following services—

(a) S4C Digital or any other television programme service provided by the Welsh Authority for broadcasting in digital form so as to be available for reception by members of the public;
(b) any licensed public service channel;
(c) a digital television programme service but not an electronic programme guide;
(d) a television licensable content service but not an electronic programme guide;
(e) a restricted television service.

(13) In this section—

"electronic programme guide" means a service which—

(a) is or is included in a television licensable content service or a digital television programme service; and
(b) consists of—
    (i) the listing or promotion, or both the listing and the promotion, of some or all of the programmes included in any one or more programme services the providers of which are or include persons other than the provider of the guide; and
    (ii) a facility for obtaining access, in whole or in part, to the programme service or services listed or promoted in the guide;

"programme" does not include an advertisement.

[3356]

NOTES

Commencement: 29 December 2003.

304 Procedure for issuing and revising code under s 303

(1) Before drawing up a code under section 303 or reviewing or revising it in pursuance of that section, OFCOM must consult—

(a) such persons appearing to them to represent the interests of persons falling within subsection (1)(a)(i), (ii) or (iii) of that section as OFCOM think fit; and

(b) such persons providing services to which that section applies as OFCOM think fit.

(2) OFCOM must publish the code drawn up under section 303, and every revision of it, in such manner as, having regard to the need to make the code or revision accessible to—

(a) persons who are deaf or hard of hearing,

(b) persons who are blind or partially sighted, and

(c) persons with a dual sensory impairment,

they consider appropriate.

[3357]

NOTES

Commencement: 29 December 2003.

305 Meaning of "relevant date" in s 303

(1) In relation to a service, the relevant date for the purposes of section 303 is—

(a) in a case to which any of subsections (2) to (4) applies, the date given by that subsection; and

(b) in any other case, the date (whether before or after the passing of this Act) when the provision of that service began or begins.

(2) In the case of a service the provision of which began before the television transfer date but which is not—

(a) a service provided by the Welsh Authority,

(b) a licensed public service channel, or

(c) a digital television programme service,

the relevant date is the date of the coming into force of this section.

(3) In the case of—

(a) a Channel 3 service the provision of which began before the date of the passing of this Act, and

(b) Channel 4 and S4C Digital,

the relevant date is 1st January 2000.

(4) In the case of Channel 5, so far as it consists of a service the provision of which began before the date of the passing of this Act, the relevant date is 1st January 1998.

(5) OFCOM may determine that a service provided by a person is to be treated for the purposes of section 303 and this section as a continuation of a service previously provided by him.

[3358]

NOTES

Commencement: 29 December 2003.

306 Power to modify targets in s 303

(1) Where it appears to the Secretary of State, in the case of services of a particular description, that the obligation specified in section 303(4) has been or is likely to be fulfilled in their case before the anniversary so specified, he may by order modify section 303 so as to do one or both of the following—

(a) increase the percentage so specified in relation to services of that description;

(b) substitute a different anniversary for the anniversary by which that obligation must be fulfilled in the case of such services.

(2) The Secretary of State may by order modify section 303 so as to do one or both of the following—

(a) substitute a later anniversary for the anniversary by which the obligations specified in subsection (5) of that section must be fulfilled;

(b) substitute a higher percentage for the percentage for the time being specified in any paragraph of that subsection.

(3) The provision that may be made by an order under this section includes—

(a) modifications for requiring the code to set out additional obligations to be fulfilled once the obligations previously required to be set out in the code have been fulfilled; and

(b) savings for the obligations previously set out in the code.

(4) Before making an order under this section the Secretary of State must consult OFCOM.

(5) No order is to be made containing provision authorised by this section unless a draft of the order has been laid before Parliament and approved by a resolution of each House.

[3359]

NOTES

Commencement: 29 December 2003.

307 Observance of code under s 303

(1) The regulatory regime for every service to which this section applies includes the conditions that OFCOM consider appropriate for securing that the code maintained by them under section 303 is observed in the provision of those services.

(2) This section applies to every service to which section 303 applies which is licensed by a Broadcasting Act licence.

[3360]

NOTES

Commencement: 29 December 2003.

308 Assistance for the visually impaired with the public teletext service

The regulatory regime for the public teletext service includes the conditions that OFCOM consider appropriate for securing, so far as it is reasonable and practicable, by the inclusion of features in that service, to do so, that persons with disabilities affecting their sight are able to make use of the service.

[3361]

NOTES

Commencement: 29 December 2003 (for transitional provisions in relation to the existing service (as defined in s 221(11) of this Act) see the Office of Communications Act 2002 (Commencement No 3) and Communications Act 2003 (Commencement No 2) Order 2003, SI 2003/3142, art 8(2) at **[3597]**).

Programming quotas for digital television programme services

309 Quotas for independent programmes

(1) The regulatory regime for every digital television programme service that is not comprised in a licensed public service channel includes the conditions that OFCOM consider appropriate for securing that, in each year, not less than 10 per cent of the total amount of time allocated to the broadcasting of qualifying programmes included in the service is allocated to the broadcasting of a range and diversity of independent productions.

(2) In subsection (1)—

(a) the reference to qualifying programmes is a reference to programmes of such description as the Secretary of State may by order specify as describing the programmes that are to be qualifying programmes for the purposes of that subsection;

(b) the reference to independent productions is a reference to programmes of such description as the Secretary of State may by order specify as describing the programmes that are to be independent productions for the purposes of that subsection; and

(c) the reference to a range of independent productions is a reference to a range of such productions in terms of cost of acquisition as well as in terms of the types of programme involved.

(3) The Secretary of State may by order amend subsection (1) by substituting a different percentage for the percentage for the time being specified in that subsection.

(4) Before making an order under this section the Secretary of State must consult OFCOM.

(5) No order is to be made containing provision authorised by this section unless a draft of the order has been laid before Parliament and approved by a resolution of each House.

(6) In this section "programme" does not include an advertisement.

[3362]

NOTES

Commencement: 29 December 2003.

Regulation of electronic programme guides

310 Code of practice for electronic programme guides

(1) It shall be the duty of OFCOM to draw up, and from time to time to review and revise, a code giving guidance as to the practices to be followed in the provision of electronic programme guides.

(2) The practices required by the code must include the giving, in the manner provided for in the code, of such degree of prominence as OFCOM consider appropriate to—

(a) the listing or promotion, or both the listing and promotion, for members of its intended audience, of the programmes included in each public service channel; and

(b) the facilities, in the case of each such channel, for members of its intended audience to select or access the programmes included in it.

(3) The practices required by the code must also include the incorporation of such features in electronic programme guides as OFCOM consider appropriate for securing that persons with disabilities affecting their sight or hearing or both—

(a) are able, so far as practicable, to make use of such guides for all the same purposes as persons without such disabilities; and

(b) are informed about, and are able to make use of, whatever assistance for disabled people is provided in relation to the programmes listed or promoted.

(4) Subject to subsection (5), in subsection (2) the reference to the public service channels is a reference to any of the following—

(a) any service of television programmes provided by the BBC in digital form so as to be available for reception by members of the public;

(b) any Channel 3 service in digital form;

(c) Channel 4 in digital form;

(d) Channel 5 in digital form;

(e) S4C Digital;

(f) the digital public teletext service.

(5) The Secretary of State may by order—

(a) add any programme service to the services for the time being specified in subsection (4) as public service channels; or

(b) delete a service from that subsection.

(6) Before making an order under subsection (5) the Secretary of State must consult OFCOM.

(7) In this section "intended audience", in relation to a service of any description, means—

(a) if the service is provided only for a particular area or locality of the United Kingdom, members of the public in that area or locality;

(b) if it is provided for members of a particular community, members of that community; and

(c) in any other case, members of the public in the United Kingdom.

(8) In this section "electronic programme guide" means a service which consists of—

(a) the listing or promotion, or both the listing and the promotion, of some or all of the programmes included in any one or more programme services the providers of which are or include persons other than the provider of the guide; and

(b) a facility for obtaining access, in whole or in part, to the programme service or services listed or promoted in the guide.

[3363]

NOTES

Commencement: 29 December 2003.

311 Conditions to comply with code under s 310

(1) The regulatory regime for every service consisting in or including an electronic programme guide includes whatever conditions (if any) OFCOM consider appropriate for securing that the code maintained by them under section 310 is observed in the provision of those services.

(2) In this section "electronic programme guide" has the same meaning as in section 310.

[3364]

NOTES

Commencement: 29 December 2003.

Character and coverage of radio services

312, 313 (*S 312 amends the Broadcasting Act 1990, s 106 at* **[3045]**; *s 313 inserts s 106ZA of that Act at* **[3046]**.)

314 Local content and character of local sound broadcasting services

(1) It shall be the duty of OFCOM to carry out their functions in relation to local sound broadcasting services in the manner that they consider is best calculated to secure—

(a) that programmes consisting of or including local material are included in such services but, in the case of each such service, only if and to the extent (if any) that OFCOM consider appropriate in that case; and

(b) that, where such programmes are included in such a service, what appears to OFCOM to be a suitable proportion of them consists of locally-made programmes.

(2) OFCOM must—

(a) draw up guidance as to how they consider the requirements of subsection (1)(a) and (b) should be satisfied; and

(b) have regard to that guidance in carrying out their functions in relation to local sound broadcasting services.

(3) The guidance may be different for different descriptions of services.

(4) OFCOM may revise the guidance from time to time.

(5) Before drawing up or revising the guidance, OFCOM must consult—

(a) such persons as appear to them to represent the interests of persons for whom local sound broadcasting services are or would be provided;

(b) persons holding licences to provide local sound broadcasting services or persons appearing to represent such persons, or both; and

(c) such other persons as they consider appropriate.

(6) OFCOM must publish the guidance and every revision of it in such manner as they consider appropriate.

(7) In this section—

"local material", in relation to a local sound broadcasting service, means material which is of particular interest—

(a) to persons living or working within the area or locality for which the service is provided;

(b) to persons living or working within a part of that area or locality; or

(c) to particular communities living or working within that area or locality or a part of it;

"locally-made", in relation to programmes included in a local sound broadcasting service, means made wholly or partly at premises in the area or locality for which that service is provided;

"material" includes news, information and other spoken material and music; and

"programme" does not include an advertisement.

(8) References in this section to persons living or working within an area or locality include references to persons undergoing education or training in that area or locality.

[3365]

NOTES

Commencement: 29 December 2003.

Modification: this section is modified in its application to community radio services by the Community Radio Order 2004, SI 2004/1944, art 4, Schedule, Pt 2, paras 9, 11 at **[3625]**.

315 (*Amends the Broadcasting Act 1996, s 54* (*outside the scope of this work*).)

Competition between licensed providers etc

316 Conditions relating to competition matters

(1) The regulatory regime for every licensed service includes the conditions (if any) that OFCOM consider appropriate for ensuring fair and effective competition in the provision of licensed services or of connected services.

(2) Those conditions must include the conditions (if any) that OFCOM consider appropriate for securing that the provider of the service does not—

(a) enter into or maintain any arrangements, or

(b) engage in any practice,

which OFCOM consider, or would consider, to be prejudicial to fair and effective competition in the provision of licensed services or of connected services.

(3) A condition imposed under this section may require a licence holder to comply with one or both of the following—

(a) a code for the time being approved by OFCOM for the purposes of the conditions; and

(b) directions given to him by OFCOM for those purposes.

(4) In this section—

"connected services", in relation to licensed services, means the provision of programmes for inclusion in licensed services and any other services provided for purposes connected with, or with the provision of, licensed services; and

"licensed service" means a service licensed by a Broadcasting Act licence.

[3366]

NOTES

Commencement: 29 December 2003.

317 Exercise of Broadcasting Act powers for a competition purpose

(1) This section applies to the following powers of OFCOM (their "Broadcasting Act powers")—

(a) their powers under this Part of this Act and under the 1990 Act and the 1996 Act to impose or vary the conditions of a Broadcasting Act licence;

(b) every power of theirs to give an approval for the purposes of provision contained in the conditions of such a licence;

(c) every power of theirs to give a direction to a person who is required to comply with it by the conditions of such a licence; and

(d) every power of theirs that is exercisable for the purpose of enforcing an obligation imposed by the conditions of such a licence.

(2) Before exercising any of their Broadcasting Act powers for a competition purpose, OFCOM must consider whether a more appropriate way of proceeding in relation to some or all of the matters in question would be under the Competition Act 1998 (c 41).

(3) If OFCOM decide that a more appropriate way of proceeding in relation to a matter would be under the Competition Act 1998, they are not, to the extent of that decision, to exercise their Broadcasting Act powers in relation to that matter.

(4) If OFCOM have decided to exercise any of their Broadcasting Act powers for a competition purpose, they must, on or before doing so, give a notification of their decision.

(5) A notification under subsection (4) must—

(a) be given to such persons, or published in such manner, as appears to OFCOM to be appropriate for bringing it to the attention of the persons who, in OFCOM's opinion, are likely to be affected by their decision; and

(b) must describe the rights conferred by subsection (6) on the persons affected by that decision.

(6) A person affected by a decision by OFCOM to exercise any of their Broadcasting Act powers for a competition purpose may appeal to the Competition Appeal Tribunal against so much of that decision as relates to the exercise of that power for that purpose.

(7) Sections 192(3) to (8), 195 and 196 apply in the case of an appeal under subsection (6) as they apply in the case of an appeal under section 192(2).

(8) The jurisdiction of the Competition Appeal Tribunal on an appeal under subsection (6) excludes—

(a) whether OFCOM have complied with subsection (2); and

(b) whether any of OFCOM's Broadcasting Act powers have been exercised in contravention of subsection (3);

and, accordingly, those decisions by OFCOM on those matters fall to be questioned only in proceedings for judicial review.

(9) For the purposes of this section a power is exercised by OFCOM for a competition purpose if the only or main reason for exercising it is to secure that the holder of a Broadcasting Act licence does not—

(a) enter into or maintain arrangements, or

(b) engage in a practice,

which OFCOM consider, or would consider, to be prejudicial to fair and effective competition in the provision of licensed services or of connected services.

(10) Nothing in this section applies to—

(a) the exercise by OFCOM of any of their powers under sections 290 to 294 or Schedule 11;

(b) the exercise by them of any power for the purposes of any provision of a condition included in a licence in accordance with any of those sections;

(c) the exercise by them of any power for the purpose of enforcing such a condition.

(11) In subsection (9) "connected services" and "licensed service" each has the same meaning as in section 316.

(12) References in this section to the exercise of a power include references to an exercise of a power in pursuance of a duty imposed on OFCOM by or under an enactment.

[3367]

NOTES

Commencement: 29 December 2003.

318 Review of powers exercised for competition purposes

(1) It shall be the duty of OFCOM, at such intervals as they consider appropriate, to carry out a review of so much of each of the following as has effect for a competition purpose—

(a) every code made or approved by them under or for the purposes of a broadcasting provision;

(b) the guidance issued by them under or for the purposes of broadcasting provisions; and

(c) every direction given by them under or for the purposes of a broadcasting provision.

(2) Before modifying or revoking, or withdrawing their approval from, anything which is subject to periodic review under this section, OFCOM must consult such persons as they consider appropriate.

(3) Subsection (2) applies irrespective or whether the modification, revocation or withdrawal is in consequence of a review under this section.

(4) For the purposes of this section a provision has effect for a competition purpose to the extent that its only or main purpose is to secure that the holder of a Broadcasting Act licence does not—

(a) enter into or maintain arrangements, or

(b) engage in a practice,

which OFCOM consider, or would consider, to be prejudicial to fair and effective competition in the provision of licensed services or of connected services.

(5) In this section "broadcasting provision" means—

(a) a provision of this Part of this Act, of the 1990 Act or of the 1996 Act, or

(b) any provision of a Broadcasting Act licence,

other than provision contained in any of sections 290 to 294 of this Act or Schedule 11 to this Act.

[3368]

NOTES

Commencement: 29 December 2003.

Programme and fairness standards for television and radio

319 OFCOM's standards code

(1) It shall be the duty of OFCOM to set, and from time to time to review and revise, such standards for the content of programmes to be included in television and radio services as appear to them best calculated to secure the standards objectives.

(2) The standards objectives are—

(a) that persons under the age of eighteen are protected;

(b) that material likely to encourage or to incite the commission of crime or to lead to disorder is not included in television and radio services;

(c) that news included in television and radio services is presented with due impartiality and that the impartiality requirements of section 320 are complied with;

(d) that news included in television and radio services is reported with due accuracy;

(e) that the proper degree of responsibility is exercised with respect to the content of programmes which are religious programmes;

(f) that generally accepted standards are applied to the contents of television and radio services so as to provide adequate protection for members of the public from the inclusion in such services of offensive and harmful material;

(g) that advertising that contravenes the prohibition on political advertising set out in section 321(2) is not included in television or radio services;

(h) that the inclusion of advertising which may be misleading, harmful or offensive in television and radio services is prevented;

(i) that the international obligations of the United Kingdom with respect to advertising included in television and radio services are complied with;

(j) that the unsuitable sponsorship of programmes included in television and radio services is prevented;

(k) that there is no undue discrimination between advertisers who seek to have advertisements included in television and radio services; and

(l) that there is no use of techniques which exploit the possibility of conveying a message to viewers or listeners, or of otherwise influencing their minds, without their being aware, or fully aware, of what has occurred.

(3) The standards set by OFCOM under this section must be contained in one or more codes.

(4) In setting or revising any standards under this section, OFCOM must have regard, in particular and to such extent as appears to them to be relevant to the securing of the standards objectives, to each of the following matters—

(a) the degree of harm or offence likely to be caused by the inclusion of any particular sort of material in programmes generally, or in programmes of a particular description;

(b) the likely size and composition of the potential audience for programmes included in television and radio services generally, or in television and radio services of a particular description;

(c) the likely expectation of the audience as to the nature of a programme's content and the extent to which the nature of a programme's content can be brought to the attention of potential members of the audience;

(d) the likelihood of persons who are unaware of the nature of a programme's content being unintentionally exposed, by their own actions, to that content;

(e) the desirability of securing that the content of services identifies when there is a change affecting the nature of a service that is being watched or listened to and, in particular, a change that is relevant to the application of the standards set under this section; and

(f) the desirability of maintaining the independence of editorial control over programme content.

(5) OFCOM must ensure that the standards from time to time in force under this section include—

(a) minimum standards applicable to all programmes included in television and radio services; and

(b) such other standards applicable to particular descriptions of programmes, or of television and radio services, as appear to them appropriate for securing the standards objectives.

(6) Standards set to secure the standards objective specified in subsection (2)(e) shall, in particular, contain provision designed to secure that religious programmes do not involve—

(a) any improper exploitation of any susceptibilities of the audience for such a programme; or

(b) any abusive treatment of the religious views and beliefs of those belonging to a particular religion or religious denomination.

(7) In setting standards under this section, OFCOM must take account of such of the international obligations of the United Kingdom as the Secretary of State may notify to them for the purposes of this section.

(8) In this section "news" means news in whatever form it is included in a service.

[3369]

NOTES

Commencement: 29 December 2003.

320 Special impartiality requirements

(1) The requirements of this section are—

(a) the exclusion, in the case of television and radio services (other than a restricted service within the meaning of section 245), from programmes included in any of those services of all expressions of the views or opinions of the person providing the service on any of the matters mentioned in subsection (2);

(b) the preservation, in the case of every television programme service, teletext service, national radio service and national digital sound programme service, of due impartiality, on the part of the person providing the service, as respects all of those matters;

(c) the prevention, in the case of every local radio service, local digital sound programme service or radio licensable content service, of the giving of undue prominence in the programmes included in the service to the views and opinions of particular persons or bodies on any of those matters.

(2) Those matters are—

(a) matters of political or industrial controversy; and

(b) matters relating to current public policy.

(3) Subsection (1)(a) does not require—

(a) the exclusion from television programmes of views or opinions relating to the provision of programme services; or
(b) the exclusion from radio programmes of views or opinions relating to the provision of programme services.

(4) For the purposes of this section—
(a) the requirement specified in subsection (1)(b) is one that (subject to any rules under subsection (5)) may be satisfied by being satisfied in relation to a series of programmes taken as a whole;
(b) the requirement specified in subsection (1)(c) is one that needs to be satisfied only in relation to all the programmes included in the service in question, taken as a whole.

(5) OFCOM's standards code shall contain provision setting out the rules to be observed in connection with the following matters—
(a) the application of the requirement specified in subsection (1)(b);
(b) the determination of what, in relation to that requirement, constitutes a series of programmes for the purposes of subsection (4)(a);
(c) the application of the requirement in subsection (1)(c).

(6) Any provision made for the purposes of subsection (5)(a) must, in particular, take account of the need to ensure the preservation of impartiality in relation to the following matters (taking each matter separately)—
(a) matters of major political or industrial controversy, and
(b) major matters relating to current public policy,

as well as of the need to ensure that the requirement specified in subsection (1)(b) is satisfied generally in relation to a series of programmes taken as a whole.

(7) In this section "national radio service" and "local radio service" mean, respectively, a sound broadcasting service which is a national service within the meaning of section 245 and a sound broadcasting service which is a local service within the meaning of that section.

[3370]

NOTES

Commencement: 29 December 2003.

---

321 Objectives for advertisements and sponsorship

(1) Standards set by OFCOM to secure the objectives mentioned in section 319(2)(a) and (g) to (j)—
(a) must include general provision governing standards and practice in advertising and in the sponsoring of programmes; and
(b) may include provision prohibiting advertisements and forms and methods of advertising or sponsorship (whether generally or in particular circumstances).

(2) For the purposes of section 319(2)(g) an advertisement contravenes the prohibition on political advertising if it is—
(a) an advertisement which is inserted by or on behalf of a body whose objects are wholly or mainly of a political nature;
(b) an advertisement which is directed towards a political end; or
(c) an advertisement which has a connection with an industrial dispute.

(3) For the purposes of this section objects of a political nature and political ends include each of the following—
(a) influencing the outcome of elections or referendums, whether in the United Kingdom or elsewhere;
(b) bringing about changes of the law in the whole or a part of the United Kingdom or elsewhere, or otherwise influencing the legislative process in any country or territory;
(c) influencing the policies or decisions of local, regional or national governments, whether in the United Kingdom or elsewhere;
(d) influencing the policies or decisions of persons on whom public functions are conferred by or under the law of the United Kingdom or of a country or territory outside the United Kingdom;
(e) influencing the policies or decisions of persons on whom functions are conferred by or under international agreements;

(f) influencing public opinion on a matter which, in the United Kingdom, is a matter of public controversy;

(g) promoting the interests of a party or other group of persons organised, in the United Kingdom or elsewhere, for political ends.

(4) OFCOM—

(a) shall, in relation to programme services, have a general responsibility with respect to advertisements and methods of advertising and sponsorship; and

(b) in the discharge of that responsibility may include conditions in any licence which is granted by them for any such service that enable OFCOM to impose requirements with respect to any of those matters that go beyond the provisions of OFCOM's standards code.

(5) OFCOM must, from time to time, consult the Secretary of State about—

(a) the descriptions of advertisements that should not be included in programme services; and

(b) the forms and methods of advertising and sponsorship that should not be employed in, or in connection with, the provision of such services.

(6) The Secretary of State may give OFCOM directions as to the matters mentioned in subsection (5); and it shall be the duty of OFCOM to comply with any such direction.

(7) Provision included by virtue of this section in standards set under section 319 is not to apply to, or to be construed as prohibiting the inclusion in a programme service of—

(a) an advertisement of a public service nature inserted by, or on behalf of, a government department; or

(b) a party political or referendum campaign broadcast the inclusion of which is required by a condition imposed under section 333 or by paragraph 18 of Schedule 12 to this Act.

(8) In this section "programme service" does not include a service provided by the BBC.

[3371]

NOTES

Commencement: 29 December 2003.

---

322 Supplementary powers relating to advertising

(1) The regulatory regime for each of the following—

(a) every television programme service licensed by a Broadcasting Act licence,

(b) the public teletext service, and

(c) every other teletext service so licensed that consists in an additional television service or a digital additional television service,

includes a condition requiring the person providing the service to comply with every direction given to him by OFCOM with respect to any of the matters mentioned in subsection (2).

(2) Those matters are—

(a) the maximum amount of time to be given to advertisements in any hour or other period;

(b) the minimum interval which must elapse between any two periods given over to advertisements;

(c) the number of such periods to be allowed in any programme or in any hour or day; and

(d) the exclusion of advertisements from a specified part of a licensed service.

(3) Directions under this section—

(a) may be either general or specific;

(b) may be qualified or unqualified; and

(c) may make different provision for different parts of the day, different days of the week, different types of programmes or for other differing circumstances.

(4) In giving a direction under this section, OFCOM must take account of such of the international obligations of the United Kingdom as the Secretary of State may notify to them for the purposes of this section.

[3372]

NOTES

Commencement: 29 December 2003.

323 Modification of matters to be taken into account under s 319

(1) The Secretary of State may by order modify the list of matters in section 319(4) to which OFCOM are to have regard when setting or revising standards.

(2) Before making an order under this section, the Secretary of State must consult OFCOM.

(3) No order is to be made containing provision authorised by subsection (1) unless a draft of the order has been laid before Parliament and approved by a resolution of each House. **[3373]**

NOTES

Commencement: 29 December 2003.

324 Setting and publication of standards

(1) Before setting standards under section 319, OFCOM must publish, in such manner as they think fit, a draft of the proposed code containing those standards.

(2) After publishing the draft code and before setting the standards, OFCOM must consult every person who holds a relevant licence and such of the following as they think fit—

- (a) persons appearing to OFCOM to represent the interests of those who watch television programmes;
- (b) persons appearing to OFCOM to represent the interests of those who make use of teletext services; and
- (c) persons appearing to OFCOM to represent the interests of those who listen to sound programmes.

(3) After publishing the draft code and before setting the standards, OFCOM must also consult—

- (a) the Welsh Authority, about so much of the draft code as relates to television programme services;
- (b) the BBC, about so much of the draft code as contains standards other than those for advertising or sponsorship; and
- (c) such of the persons mentioned in subsection (4) as OFCOM think fit, about so much of the draft code as contains standards for advertising or sponsorship.

(4) Those persons are—

- (a) persons appearing to OFCOM to represent the interests of those who will have to take account of the contents of the proposed standards for advertising or sponsorship;
- (b) bodies and associations appearing to OFCOM to be concerned with the application of standards of conduct in advertising; and
- (c) professional organisations appearing to OFCOM to be qualified to give relevant advice in relation to the advertising of particular products.

(5) If it appears to OFCOM that a body exists which represents the interests of a number of the persons who hold relevant licences, they may perform their duty under subsection (2) of consulting such persons, so far as it relates to the persons whose interests are so represented, by consulting that body.

(6) OFCOM may set standards under section 319 either—

- (a) in the terms proposed in a draft code published under subsection (1); or
- (b) with such modifications as OFCOM consider appropriate in the light of the consultation carried out as a result of subsections (2) to (5).

(7) Subsections (1) to (6) apply to a proposal by OFCOM to revise standards set under section 319 as they apply to a proposal to set such standards.

(8) Where OFCOM set standards under section 319, they must publish the code containing the standards in such manner as they consider appropriate for bringing it to the attention of the persons who, in their opinion, are likely to be affected by the standards.

(9) Where OFCOM revise standards set under section 319, they shall so publish the code containing the standards as revised.

(10) Where OFCOM publish a code under subsection (8) or (9), they shall send a copy of it—

(a) to the Secretary of State;

(b) except in the case of a code containing standards for advertising or sponsorship, to the BBC; and

(c) if the code relates to television programme services, to the Welsh Authority.

(11) A code (or draft code) contains standards for advertising or sponsorship for the purposes of this section to the extent that it sets standards under section 319 for securing any of the objectives mentioned in any of paragraphs (g) to (k) of subsection (2) of that section.

(12) In this section "relevant licence", in relation to a draft code, means—

(a) to the extent that the draft code relates to

(i) television programme services,

(ii) the public teletext service, or

(iii) an additional television service,

a licence under Part 1 of the 1990 Act (independent television services), under section 18 of the 1996 Act (digital television programme services) under section 25 of that Act (digital additional television services) or under section 219 of this Act; and

(b) to the extent that the draft code relates to radio programme services, any licence under Part 3 of the 1990 Act (independent radio services), under section 60 of the 1996 Act (digital sound programme service) or under section 64 of that Act (digital additional services).

[3374]

NOTES

Commencement: 29 December 2003.

325 Observance of standards code

(1) The regulatory regime for every programme service licensed by a Broadcasting Act licence includes conditions for securing—

(a) that standards set under section 319 are observed in the provision of that service; and

(b) that procedures for the handling and resolution of complaints about the observance of those standards are established and maintained.

(2) It shall be the duty of OFCOM themselves to establish procedures for the handling and resolution of complaints about the observance of standards set under section 319.

(3) OFCOM may from time to time make a report to the Secretary of State on any issues with respect to OFCOM's standards code which—

(a) have been identified by them in the course of carrying out their functions; and

(b) appear to them to raise questions of general broadcasting policy.

(4) The conditions of a licence which is granted by OFCOM for a programme service must, for the purpose of securing compliance—

(a) with OFCOM's standards code, so far as it relates to advertising and the sponsorship of programmes, and

(b) with any such requirements as are mentioned in section 321(4) which relate to advertising and sponsorship but go beyond that code,

include a condition requiring the licence holder to comply with every direction given to him by OFCOM with respect to any of the matters mentioned in subsection (5).

(5) Those matters are—

(a) the exclusion from the service of a particular advertisement, or its exclusion in particular circumstances;

(b) the descriptions of advertisements and methods of advertising to be excluded from the service (whether generally or in particular circumstances); and

(c) the forms and methods of sponsorship to be excluded from the service (whether generally or in particular circumstances).

(6) OFCOM's powers and duties under this section are not to be construed as restricting any power of theirs, apart from this section—

(a) to include conditions with respect to the content of programmes included in any service in the licence to provide that service; or

(b) to include conditions in a licence requiring the holder of a licence to comply with directions given by OFCOM or by any other person.

[3375]

NOTES

Commencement: 29 December 2003 (for transitional provisions see the Office of Communications Act 2002 (Commencement No 3) and Communications Act 2003 (Commencement No 2) Order 2003, SI 2003/3142, art 11 at **[3600]**).

326 Duty to observe fairness code

The regulatory regime for every programme service licensed by a Broadcasting Act licence includes the conditions that OFCOM consider appropriate for securing observance—

(a) in connection with the provision of that service, and

(b) in relation to the programmes included in that service,

of the code for the time being in force under section 107 of the 1996 Act (the fairness code).

[3376]

NOTES

Commencement: 29 December 2003.

327 Standards with respect to fairness

(1) Part 5 of the 1996 Act (functions of the Broadcasting Standards Commission which are transferred to OFCOM so far as they relate to codes of practice and complaints with respect to fairness and privacy) shall be amended as follows.

(2) No person shall be entitled to make a standards complaint under that Part at any time after the coming into force of this section, and no person shall be required to entertain any such complaint that is so made.

(3)–(5) ...

[3377]

NOTES

Commencement: 29 December 2003.

Sub-ss (3)–(5): amend the Broadcasting Act 1996, ss 115, 119, 120.

328 Duty to publicise OFCOM's functions in relation to complaints

(1) The regulatory regime for every programme service licensed by a Broadcasting Act licence includes the conditions that OFCOM consider appropriate for securing that—

(a) the procedures which, by virtue of section 325, are established and maintained for handling and resolving complaints about the observance of standards set under section 319, and

(b) their functions under Part 5 of the 1996 Act in relation to that service,

are brought to the attention of the public (whether by means of broadcasts or otherwise).

(2) Conditions included in a licence by virtue of subsection (1) may require the holder of the licence to comply with every direction given to him by OFCOM for the purpose mentioned in that subsection.

[3378]

NOTES

Commencement: 29 December 2003.

Power to proscribe unacceptable foreign television and radio services

329 Proscription orders

(1) Where—

(a) a foreign service to which this section applies comes to OFCOM's attention, and
(b) they consider that the service is unacceptable and should be the subject of an order under this section,

they must send a notification to the Secretary of State giving details of the service and their reasons for considering that an order should be made.

(2) A service is not to be considered unacceptable by OFCOM unless they are satisfied that—
(a) programmes containing objectionable matter are included in the service; and
(b) that the inclusion of objectionable matter in programmes so included is occurring repeatedly.

(3) Matter is objectionable for the purposes of subsection (2) only if—
(a) it offends against taste or decency;
(b) it is likely to encourage or to incite the commission of crime;
(c) it is likely to lead to disorder; or
(d) it is likely to be offensive to public feeling.

(4) Where the Secretary of State has received a notification under this section in the case of a service, he may make an order—
(a) identifying the service in such manner as he thinks fit; and
(b) proscribing it.

(5) The Secretary of State is not to make an order proscribing a service unless he is satisfied that the making of the order is—
(a) in the public interest; and
(b) compatible with the international obligations of the United Kingdom.

(6) The television and sound services to which this section applies are—
(a) television licensable content services provided otherwise than by broadcasting from a satellite;
(b) digital television programme services;
(c) digital additional television services;
(d) radio licensable sound services provided otherwise than by being broadcast from a satellite;
(e) digital sound programme services; and
(f) digital additional sound services.

(7) A service to which this section applies is a foreign service if it—
(a) is a service capable of being received in the United Kingdom for the provision of which no Broadcasting Act licence is either in force or required to be in force; but
(b) is also a service for the provision of which such a licence would be required—
(i) in the case of a service falling within subsection (6)(a) to (c), if the person providing it were under the jurisdiction of the United Kingdom for the purposes of the Television without Frontiers Directive; and
(ii) in any other case, if the person providing it provided it from a place in the United Kingdom or were a person whose principal place of business is in the United Kingdom.

[3379]

NOTES

Commencement: 29 December 2003.

330 Effect of proscription order

(1) This section applies where a service is for the time being proscribed by an order under section 329.

(2) The proscribed service is not to be included in—
(a) a multiplex service; or
(b) a cable package.

(3) In this section "multiplex service" means a television multiplex service, a radio multiplex service or a general multiplex service.

(4) In this section "cable package" means (subject to subsection (5)) a service by means of which programme services are packaged together with a view to their being distributed—
(a) by means of an electronic communications service;

(b) so as to be available for reception by members of the public in the United Kingdom; and
(c) without the final delivery of the programme services to the persons to whom they are distributed being by wireless telegraphy.

(5) Programme services distributed by means of an electronic communications service do not form part of a cable package if—
(a) the distribution of those services forms only part of a service provided by means of that electronic communications service; and
(b) the purposes for which the service of which it forms a part is provided do not consist wholly or mainly in making available television programmes or radio programmes (or both) for reception by members of the public.

[3380]

NOTES
Commencement: 29 December 2003.

331 Notification for enforcing proscription

(1) Where OFCOM determine that there are reasonable grounds for believing that there has been a contravention of section 330 in relation to a multiplex service or a cable package, they may give a notification under this section to—
(a) the provider of that multiplex service; or
(b) the person providing the cable package.

(2) A notification under this section is one which—
(a) sets out the determination made by OFCOM; and
(b) requires the person to whom it is given to secure that the proscribed service (so long as it remains proscribed) is not—
(i) included in the notified person's multiplex service, or
(ii) distributed as part of his cable package,
at any time more than seven days after the day of the giving of the notification.

(3) If it is reasonably practicable for a person to whom a notification is given under this section to secure that the proscribed service ceases to be included in that person's multiplex service, or to be distributed as part of his cable package, before the end of that seven days, then he must do so.

(4) It shall be the duty of a person to whom a notification is given under this section to comply with the requirements imposed by the notification and by subsection (3).

(5) That duty shall be enforceable in civil proceedings by OFCOM—
(a) for an injunction;
(b) for specific performance of a statutory duty under section 45 of the Court of Session Act 1988 (c 36); or
(c) for any other appropriate remedy or relief.

(6) In this section "cable package" and "multiplex service" each has the same meaning as in section 330.

[3381]

NOTES
Commencement: 29 December 2003.

332 Penalties for contravention of notification under s 331

(1) OFCOM may impose a penalty on a person who contravenes a requirement imposed on him by or under section 331.

(2) Before imposing a penalty on a person under this section OFCOM must give him a reasonable opportunity of making representations to them about their proposal to impose the penalty.

(3) The amount of the penalty imposed on a person is to be such amount not exceeding £5,000 as OFCOM determine to be—
(a) appropriate; and
(b) proportionate to the contravention in respect of which it is imposed.

(4) In making that determination OFCOM must have regard to—

(a) any representations made to them by the person notified under section 331; and

(b) any steps taken by him for complying with the requirements imposed on him under that section.

(5) Where OFCOM impose a penalty on a person under this section, they shall—

(a) notify the person penalised; and

(b) in that notification, fix a reasonable period after it is given as the period within which the penalty is to be paid.

(6) A penalty imposed under this section must be paid to OFCOM within the period fixed by them.

(7) The Secretary of State may by order amend this section so as to substitute a different maximum penalty for the maximum penalty for the time being specified in subsection (3).

(8) No order is to be made containing provision authorised by subsection (7) unless a draft of the order has been laid before Parliament and approved by a resolution of each House.

(9) For the purposes of this section there is a separate contravention in respect of every day on which the proscribed service is at any time included in a person's multiplex service or distributed as part of his cable package.

(10) In this section "multiplex service" and "cable package" each has the same meaning as in section 330.

[3382]

NOTES

Commencement: 29 December 2003.

Party political broadcasts on television and radio

333 Party political broadcasts

(1) The regulatory regime for every licensed public service channel, and the regulatory regime for every national radio service, includes—

(a) conditions requiring the inclusion in that channel or service of party political broadcasts and of referendum campaign broadcasts; and

(b) conditions requiring that licence holder to observe such rules with respect to party political broadcasts and referendum campaign broadcasts as may be made by OFCOM.

(2) The rules made by OFCOM for the purposes of this section may, in particular, include provision for determining—

(a) the political parties on whose behalf party political broadcasts may be made;

(b) in relation to each political party on whose behalf such broadcasts may be made, the length and frequency of the broadcasts; and

(c) in relation to each designated organisation on whose behalf referendum campaign broadcasts are required to be broadcast, the length and frequency of such broadcasts.

(3) Those rules are to have effect subject to sections 37 and 127 of the Political Parties, Elections and Referendums Act 2000 (c 41) (only registered parties and designated organisations to be entitled to party political broadcasts or referendum campaign broadcasts).

(4) Rules made by OFCOM for the purposes of this section may make different provision for different cases.

(5) Before making any rules for the purposes of this section, OFCOM must have regard to any views expressed by the Electoral Commission.

(6) In this section—

"designated organisation", in relation to a referendum, means a person or body designated by the Electoral Commission under section 108 of the Political Parties, Elections and Referendums Act 2000 (c 41) in respect of that referendum;

"national radio service" means a national service within the meaning of section 245 of this Act; and "referendum campaign broadcast" has the meaning given by section 127 of that Act. **[3383]**

NOTES

Commencement: 29 December 2003.

Monitoring of programmes

334 Retention and production of recordings

(1) The regulatory regime for every programme service licensed by a Broadcasting Act licence includes conditions imposing on the provider of the service—

(a) a requirement in respect of every programme included in the service to retain a recording of the programme in a specified form and for a specified period after its inclusion;

(b) a requirement to comply with any request by OFCOM to produce to them for examination or reproduction a recording retained in pursuance of the conditions in the licence; and

(c) a requirement, if the provider is able to do so, to comply with any request by OFCOM to produce to them a script or transcript of a programme included in the programme service.

(2) The period specified for the purposes of a condition under subsection (1)(a) must be—

(a) in the case of a programme included in a television programme service, a period not exceeding ninety days; and

(b) in the case of a programme included in a radio programme service, a period not exceeding forty-two days.

(3) For the purpose of maintaining supervision of the programmes included in programme services, OFCOM may themselves make and use recordings of those programmes or any part of them.

(4) Nothing in this Part is to be construed as requiring OFCOM, in the carrying out of their functions under this Part as respects programme services and the programmes included in them, to view or listen to programmes in advance of their being included in such services. **[3384]**

NOTES

Commencement: 29 December 2003.

International obligations

335 Conditions securing compliance with international obligations

(1) The regulatory regime for every service to which this section applies includes the conditions that OFCOM consider appropriate for securing that the relevant international obligations of the United Kingdom are complied with.

(2) In this section "relevant international obligations of the United Kingdom" means the international obligations of the United Kingdom which have been notified to OFCOM by the Secretary of State for the purposes of this section.

(3) This section applies to the following services—

(a) any Channel 3 service;

(b) Channel 4;

(c) Channel 5;

(d) the public teletext service;

(e) any television licensable content service;

(f) any digital television programme service;

(g) any additional television service;

(h) any digital additional television service;

(i) any restricted television service.

(4) The conditions included in any licence in accordance with the other provisions of this Chapter are in addition to any conditions included in that licence in pursuance of this section and have effect subject to them.

[3385]

NOTES

Commencement: 29 December 2003.

Government requirements for licensed services

336 Government requirements for licensed services

(1) If it appears to the Secretary of State or any other Minister of the Crown to be appropriate to do so in connection with any of his functions, the Secretary of State or that Minister may at any time by notice require OFCOM to give a direction under subsection (2).

(2) A direction under this subsection is a direction to the holders of the Broadcasting Act licences specified in the notice under subsection (1) to include an announcement so specified in their licensed services.

(3) The direction may specify the times at which the announcement is to be broadcast or otherwise transmitted.

(4) Where the holder of a Broadcasting Act licence includes an announcement in his licensed service in pursuance of a direction under this section, he may announce that he is doing so in pursuance of such a direction.

(5) The Secretary of State may, at any time, by notice require OFCOM to direct the holders of the Broadcasting Act licences specified in the notice to refrain from including in their licensed services any matter, or description of matter, specified in the notice.

(6) Where—

(a) OFCOM have given the holder of a Broadcasting Act licence a direction in accordance with a notice under subsection (5),

(b) in consequence of the revocation by the Secretary of State of such a notice, OFCOM have revoked such a direction, or

(c) such a notice has expired,

the holder of the licence in question may include in the licensed service an announcement of the giving or revocation of the direction or of the expiration of the notice, as the case may be.

(7) OFCOM must comply with every requirement contained in a notice under this section.

(8) The powers conferred by this section are in addition to any powers specifically conferred on the Secretary of State by or under this Act or any other enactment.

(9) In this section "Minister of the Crown" includes the Treasury.

[3386]

NOTES

Commencement: 29 December 2003.

Equal opportunities and training

337 Promotion of equal opportunities and training

(1) The regulatory regime for every service to which this section applies includes the conditions that OFCOM consider appropriate for requiring the licence holder to make arrangements for promoting, in relation to employment with the licence holder, equality of opportunity—

(a) between men and women; and

(b) between persons of different racial groups.

(2) That regime includes conditions requiring the licence holder to make arrangements for promoting, in relation to employment with the licence holder, the equalisation of opportunities for disabled persons.

(3) The regulatory regime for every service to which this section applies includes the conditions that OFCOM consider appropriate for requiring the licence holder to make arrangements for the training and retraining of persons whom he employs, in or in connection with—

(a) the provision of the licensed service; or
(b) the making of programmes to be included in that service.

(4) The conditions imposed by virtue of subsections (1) to (3) must contain provision, in relation to the arrangements made in pursuance of those conditions, requiring the person providing the service in question—

(a) to take appropriate steps to make those affected by the arrangements aware of them (including such publication of the arrangements as may be required in accordance with the conditions);
(b) from time to time, to review the arrangements; and
(c) from time to time (and at least annually) to publish, in such manner as he considers appropriate, his observations on the current operation and effectiveness of the arrangements.

(5) The conditions imposed by virtue of this section may include provision for treating obligations to make the arrangements mentioned in subsections (1) to (3), or to do anything mentioned in subsection (4), as discharged where a member of a group of companies to which the licence holder belongs—

(a) has made the required arrangements in relation to employment with the licence holder; or
(b) has done anything required by subsection (4) in relation to those arrangements.

(6) This section applies to a service if—

(a) it is a service the provision of which is authorised by a Broadcasting Act licence; and
(b) the requirements of both subsections (7) and (8) are satisfied in the case of that service.

(7) The requirements of this subsection are satisfied in the case of a service provided by a person if—

(a) that person employs, or is likely to employ, more than the threshold number of individuals in connection with the provision of licensed services; or
(b) the threshold number is exceeded by the aggregate number of individuals who are, or are likely to be, employed in that connection by members of a group of companies comprising that person and one or more other bodies corporate.

(8) The requirements of this subsection are satisfied in the case of a service if the licence authorising the provision of that service authorises either that service or another service authorised by that licence to be provided on a number of days in any year which exceeds the threshold number of days (whether or not the service is in fact provided on those days).

(9) In this section—

"disabled" has the same meaning as in the Disability Discrimination Act 1995 (c 50);

"licensed service", in relation to an employee or likely employee of a person, means a service the provision of which—

(a) by that person, or
(b) by a body corporate which is a member of the same group of companies as that person,

is authorised by a Broadcasting Act licence;

"racial group" has the same meaning as in the Race Relations Act 1976 (c 74) or, in Northern Ireland, the Race Relations (Northern Ireland) Order 1997 (SI 1997/869 (NI 6));

"the threshold number" means—

(a) in relation to individuals, twenty; and
(b) in relation to days, thirty-one.

(10) For the purposes of this section a person is a member of a group of companies to which a person licensed to provide a service belongs if, and only if, both of them are bodies corporate and either—

(a) one of them is controlled by the other; or
(b) both of them are controlled by the same person.

(11) In subsection (10) "controlled" has the same meaning as in Part 1 of Schedule 2 to the 1990 Act.

(12) The Secretary of State may, by order—

(a) amend subsection (1) by adding any other form of equality of opportunity that he considers appropriate;

(b) amend the definition of "the threshold number" in subsection (9).

(13) No order is to be made containing provision authorised by subsection (12) unless a draft of the order has been laid before Parliament and approved by a resolution of each House.

[3387]

NOTES

Commencement: 29 December 2003.

Corresponding rules for the BBC and Welsh Authority

338 Corresponding rules for the BBC and the Welsh Authority

Schedule 12 (which provides for the imposition on the BBC and the Welsh Authority of obligations corresponding to obligations included in the regulatory regime for licensed providers) shall have effect.

[3388]

NOTES

Commencement: 29 December 2003 (for certain purposes); 1 July 2004 (for certain purposes); to be appointed (otherwise).

Enforcement against the Welsh Authority

339 Review of fulfilment by Welsh Authority of public service remits

(1) The Secretary of State may carry out a review of the performance by the Welsh Authority of their duty to secure that each of the following public service remits—

(a) that for S4C;

(b) that for S4C Digital; and

(c) that for each of the television programme services provided by them with the approval of the Secretary of State under section 205,

is fulfilled in relation the services to which it applies.

(2) The first review carried out under this section—

(a) shall be a review relating to the period since the passing of this Act; and

(b) must not be carried out before the end of the period of five years beginning with the day of the passing of this Act.

(3) A subsequent review—

(a) shall be a review relating to the period since the end of the period to which the previous review related; and

(b) must not be carried out less than five years after the day of the publication of the report of the previous review.

(4) On a review under this section the Secretary of State—

(a) shall consult the National Assembly for Wales and the Welsh Authority on the matters under review; and

(b) shall have regard to their opinions when reaching his conclusions.

(5) The Secretary of State shall also consult such other persons as he considers are likely to be affected by whether, and in what manner, the Welsh Authority perform the duty mentioned in subsection (1).

(6) As soon as practicable after the conclusion of a review under this section the Secretary of State must publish a report of his conclusions.

[3389]

NOTES

Commencement: 29 December 2003.

340 Directions to Welsh Authority to take remedial action

(1) This section applies if the Secretary of State's conclusions on a review under section 339 include a finding—

(a) that the Welsh Authority has failed in any respect to perform their duty to secure that the public service remit for a service mentioned in that section is fulfilled; and

(b) that there is no reasonable excuse for the failure.

(2) The Secretary of State may give the Welsh Authority general or specific directions requiring them to take the steps that he considers will ensure that the Authority perform their duty properly in future.

(3) The Secretary of State is not to give a direction under this section unless a draft of the proposed direction has been laid before Parliament and approved by a resolution of each House.

(4) Before laying a proposed direction before Parliament, the Secretary of State must consult the Welsh Authority.

(5) It shall be the duty of the Welsh Authority to comply with every direction under this section.

[3390]

NOTES

Commencement: 29 December 2003.

341 Imposition of penalties on the Welsh Authority

(1) This section applies to the following requirements so far as they are imposed on the Welsh Authority in relation to services provided by them—

(a) the requirements imposed by or under paragraphs 7 and 8 of Schedule 12 (programme quotas);

(b) the requirements imposed by paragraph 9(1) and (3) of that Schedule (news and current affairs);

(c) the requirements imposed by paragraph 10 of that Schedule (code relating to programme commissioning) or by a direction under sub-paragraph (3)(d) of that paragraph;

(d) the requirement imposed by virtue of paragraph 12 of that Schedule to comply with standards set under section 319, so far as that requirement relates to standards set otherwise than for the purpose of securing the objectives set out in subsection (2)(c) or (d) of that section;

(e) the requirements imposed by paragraphs 14 and 16 of that Schedule (advertising or sponsorship) to comply with a direction under those paragraphs;

(f) the requirement imposed by paragraph 17 of that Schedule (observance of the fairness code);

(g) the requirement imposed by paragraph 19 of that Schedule (publicising complaints procedure);

(h) the requirement imposed by paragraph 20 of that Schedule (monitoring of programmes);

(i) the requirement imposed by paragraph 21 of that Schedule (international obligations) to comply with a direction under that paragraph;

(j) the requirement under paragraph 22 of that Schedule (assistance for disabled people) to comply with the code for the time being in force under section 303;

(k) the requirement to comply with a direction under section 119(1) of the 1996 Act (directions in respect of fairness matters).

(2) If OFCOM are satisfied that there has been a contravention of a requirement to which this section applies, they may serve on the Welsh Authority a notice requiring the Authority, within the specified period, to pay OFCOM a specified penalty.

(3) The amount of the penalty must not exceed £250,000.

(4) OFCOM are not to serve a notice on the Welsh Authority under this section unless they have given them a reasonable opportunity of making representations to OFCOM about the matters appearing to OFCOM to provide grounds for the service of the notice.

(5) An exercise by OFCOM of their powers under this section does not preclude any exercise by them of their powers under paragraph 15 of Schedule 12 in respect of the same contravention.

(6) The Secretary of State may by order substitute a different sum for the sum for the time being specified in subsection (3).

(7) No order is to be made containing provision authorised by subsection (6) unless a draft of the order has been laid before Parliament and approved by a resolution of each House.

[3391]

NOTES

Commencement: 29 December 2003.

342 (*Amends the Broadcasting Act 1990, Sch 6, para 13* (*outside the scope of this work*).)

343 Provision of information by Welsh Authority

(1) It shall be the duty of the Welsh Authority to comply with every direction given to them by OFCOM to provide OFCOM with information falling within subsection (2).

(2) The information that the Welsh Authority may be directed to provide is any information which OFCOM may reasonably require for the purposes of carrying out their functions in relation to the Welsh Authority under this Act, the 1990 Act or the 1996 Act.

(3) Information that is required to be provided by a direction under this section must be provided in such manner and at such times as may be required by the direction.

[3392]

NOTES

Commencement: 29 December 2003.

Enforcement of licence conditions

344 (*Amends the Broadcasting Act 1990, s 40* (*outside the scope of this work*) *and s 109 of that Act at* **[3047]**.)

345 Financial penalties imposable on licence holders

Schedule 13 (which modifies the maximum penalties that may be imposed on the holders of Broadcasting Act licences) shall have effect.

[3393]

NOTES

Commencement: 29 December 2003.

346 Recovery of fees and penalties

(1) This section applies to the following amounts—

(a) any amount payable to OFCOM under a Broadcasting Act licence;

(b) the amount of a penalty imposed by OFCOM under Part 1 or 3 of the 1990 Act, Part 1 or 2 of the 1996 Act or this Part of this Act.

(2) Every amount to which this section applies shall be recoverable by OFCOM as a debt due to them from the person obliged to pay it.

(3) The following liabilities—

(a) a person's liability to have a penalty imposed on him under Part 1 or 3 of the 1990 Act, Part 1 or 2 of the 1996 Act or this Part in respect of acts or omissions of his occurring while he was the holder of a Broadcasting Act licence, and

(b) a liability of a person as the holder of such a licence to pay an amount to which this section applies,

are not affected by that person's Broadcasting Act licence having ceased (for any reason) to be in force before the imposition of the penalty or the payment of that amount.

[3394]

NOTES

Commencement: 29 December 2003.

Broadcasting Act licence fees

347 Statement of charging principles

(1) OFCOM are not to fix a tariff under section 4(3) or 87(3) of the 1990 Act or under section 4(3) or 43(3) of the 1996 Act (tariffs for fees payable under Broadcasting Act licences for recovering OFCOM's costs) unless—

(a) at the time they do so, there is in force a statement of the principles that OFCOM are proposing to apply in fixing that tariff; and

(b) the tariff is fixed in accordance with those principles.

(2) Those principles must be such as appear to OFCOM to be likely to secure, on the basis of such estimates of the likely costs that it is practicable for them to make—

(a) that the aggregate amount of the Broadcasting Act licence fees that are required to be paid to OFCOM during a financial year is sufficient to enable them to meet, but does not exceed, the cost to them of the carrying out during that year of their functions relating to the regulation of broadcasting;

(b) that the requirement imposed by virtue of paragraph (a) is satisfied by the application to such fees of tariffs that are justifiable and proportionate to the matters in respect of which they are imposed; and

(c) that the relationship between meeting the cost of carrying out those functions and the tariffs applied to such fees is transparent.

(3) Before making or revising a statement of principles OFCOM must consult such of the persons who, in OFCOM's opinion, are likely to be affected by those principles as they think fit.

(4) The making or revision of a statement of principles for the purposes of this section has to be by the publication of the statement, or revised statement, in such manner as OFCOM consider appropriate for bringing it to the attention of the persons who, in their opinion, are likely to be affected by it.

(5) As soon as reasonably practicable after the end of each financial year, OFCOM must publish a statement setting out, for that year—

(a) the aggregate amount received by them during that year in respect of Broadcasting Act licence fees required to be paid during that year;

(b) the aggregate amount outstanding and likely to be paid or recovered in respect of Broadcasting Act licence fees that are required to be so paid; and

(c) the cost to OFCOM of the carrying out during that year of their functions relating to the regulation of broadcasting.

(6) Any deficit or surplus shown (after applying this subsection for all previous years) by a statement under subsection (5) shall be—

(a) carried forward; and

(b) taken into account in determining what is required to satisfy the requirement imposed by virtue of subsection (2)(a) in relation to the following year.

(7) References in this section to OFCOM's functions relating to the regulation of broadcasting do not include references to any of their functions in relation to the BBC or the Welsh Authority.

(8) In this section—

"Broadcasting Act licence fee" means a fee required to be paid to OFCOM in pursuance of conditions included in a Broadcasting Act licence under any of the following provisions—

(a) section 4(1)(b) or 87(1)(c) of the 1990 Act; or

(b) section 4(1)(b) or 43(1)(c) of the 1996 Act;

"financial year" means a period of twelve months ending with 31st March.

[3395]

NOTES

Commencement: 29 December 2003.

CHAPTER 5
MEDIA OWNERSHIP AND CONTROL

Restrictions on licence holders

348 Modification of disqualification provisions

(1)–(4) …

(5) The Secretary of State may by order make provision—

(a) for repealing paragraph 2 of Part 2 of Schedule 2 to the 1990 Act; or

(b) for making such other modifications of that paragraph and any enactment referring to it as he thinks fit.

(6) Before making an order under subsection (5) (other than one that is confined to giving effect to recommendations made by OFCOM in a report of a review under section 391), the Secretary of State must consult OFCOM.

(7) No order is to be made containing provision authorised by subsection (5) unless a draft of the order has been laid before Parliament and approved by a resolution of each House.

[3396]

NOTES

Commencement: 18 September 2003 (sub-ss (2), (3), (5)–(7)); 29 December 2003 (otherwise).

Sub-ss (1)–(4): amend the Broadcasting Act 1990, Sch 2, Pt 2 at **[3068]**.

349 (*Amends the Broadcasting Act 1990, Sch 2, Pt 2 at* **[3068]**, *the Local Government Act 1972, s 142 and the Local Government Act 1986, s 2* (*outside the scope of this work*).)

350 Relaxation of licence-holding restrictions

(1), (2) …

(3) Schedule 14 (which provides for the imposition of requirements which, in the case of Channel 3 services and certain radio services, replace those imposed by or under Parts 3 and 4 of Schedule 2 to the 1990 Act and requires approval for the holding of certain licences by religious bodies etc) shall have effect.

(4) The Secretary of State must not by order under section 411 appoint a day falling before the commencement day for paragraph 11 of Schedule 14 as the day for the coming into force of the repeal by this Act of any of the provisions of Parts 3 and 4 of Schedule 2 to the 1990 Act so far as they relate to the holding of licences for the provision of any local services (within the meaning of Part 3 of that Act).

(5) The Secretary of State must not by order under section 411 appoint a day falling before the commencement day for paragraph 12 of Schedule 14 as the day for the coming into force of the repeal by this Act of any of the provisions of Parts 3 and 4 of Schedule 2 to the 1990 Act so far as they relate to the holding of local digital sound programme licences or the provision of local digital sound programme services.

(6) In this section "the commencement day", in relation paragraph 11 or 12 of Schedule 14, means the day on which the first order to be made under that paragraph comes into force.

[3397]

NOTES

Commencement: 18 September 2003 (sub-s (3), certain purposes); 12 December 2003 (sub-s (3), certain purposes); 29 December 2003 (otherwise).

Sub-s (1): repeals the Broadcasting Act 1990, Sch 2, Pts 3–5.

Sub-s (2): amends the Broadcasting Act 1990, s 5 (outside the scope of this work) and s 88 of that Act at **[3030]**.

Changes of control

351 Changes of control of Channel 3 services

(1) The regulatory regime for every Channel 3 service provided by a body corporate includes—

(a) a condition requiring the licence holder to give OFCOM advance notification of any proposals known to the body that may give rise to a relevant change of control; and

(b) a condition requiring the licence holder to provide OFCOM, in such manner and at such times as they may reasonably require, with such information as they consider necessary for the purposes of exercising their functions under this section and section 352.

(2) OFCOM must carry out a review where—

(a) they receive notification, in accordance with a condition of a Channel 3 licence, of proposals that may give rise to a relevant change of control; or

(b) a relevant change of control takes place (whether or not that change has been previously notified to OFCOM).

(3) The review shall be a review of the effects or likely effects, in relation to the matters mentioned in subsections (4) to (7), of—

(a) the change to which the proposals may give rise; or

(b) the change that has taken place.

(4) The matters mentioned in this subsection are—

(a) the extent to which time available for broadcasting programmes included in the service is allocated to programmes of each of the following descriptions—

(i) original productions;

(ii) news programmes; and

(iii) current affairs programmes;

(b) the extent to which programmes of each of those descriptions that are included in the service are broadcast at peak viewing times.

(5) The matters mentioned in this subsection are—

(a) the extent to which Channel 3 programmes made in the United Kingdom that are included in the service are programmes made outside the M25 area;

(b) the range of Channel 3 programmes made in the United Kingdom outside that area that are included in the service;

(c) the extent to which the expenditure of the provider of the service on Channel 3 programmes is referable to programme production at different production centres outside the M25 area;

(d) the range of different such production centres to which that expenditure is referable.

(6) The matters mentioned in this subsection are—

(a) the quality and range of regional programmes included in the service;

(b) the quality and range of other programmes included in the service which contribute to the regional character of the service;

(c) the quality and range of the programmes made available by the licence holder for the purposes of inclusion in the nationwide system of services referred to in section 14(1) of the 1990 Act (nationwide Channel 3 service).

(7) The matters mentioned in this subsection are—

(a) the amount of time given, in the programmes included in the service—

(i) to regional programmes; and

(ii) to programmes included in the service which contribute to the regional character of the service;

(b) the proportion of regional programmes included in the service which are made within the area for which the service is provided;

(c) the extent of the use, in connection with the service, of the services of persons employed (whether by the licence holder or any other person) within that area;

(d) the extent to which managerial or editorial decisions relating to programmes to be included in the service are taken by persons so employed within that area.

(8) In relation to a national Channel 3 service, subsections (3) to (7) have effect as if—

(a) subsection (5) applied only where the service is subject to conditions imposed by virtue of a decision of OFCOM under section 286(2) or OFCOM otherwise consider, having regard to the nature of the service, that it is appropriate to consider the matters mentioned in that subsection;

(b) references to regional programmes were references to programmes which are regional programmes (within the meaning of section 287) in relation to that service and are included in it in accordance with a condition imposed under subsection (4)(a) of that section;

(c) references to the regional character of the service were references to the regional character of parts of the service;

(d) subsection (6)(c) of this section were omitted; and

(e) references, in relation to programmes such as are mentioned in paragraph (b), to the area for which the service is provided were references to the part of that area where the people are living to whom those programmes are likely to be of particular interest.

(9) Where OFCOM carry out a review under subsection (2), they must publish a report of that review—

(a) setting out their conclusions; and

(b) specifying any steps which they propose to take under section 352.

(10) In this section—

"Channel 3 programmes" and "expenditure" each has the same meaning as in section 286;

"original production" has the same meaning as in section 278;

"peak viewing time"—

(a) in relation to original productions, means a time determined by OFCOM for the purposes of section 278 to be a peak viewing time for the service in question; and

(b) in relation to news programmes or current affairs programmes, means a time so determined for the purposes of section 279;

"regional programme", in relation to a Channel 3 service, means (subject to subsection (8)) a programme (including a news programme) which is of particular interest—

(a) to persons living within the area for which the service is provided;

(b) to persons living within a part of that area; or

(c) to particular communities living within that area;

"relevant change of control" means a change in the persons having control over—

(a) a body holding the licence to provide a Channel 3 service; or

(b) any body which—

(i) is connected with a body holding such a licence; and

(ii) is involved, to a substantial extent, in the provision of the programmes included in the service provided under that licence, or is likely to become so involved.

(11) Expressions used in this section and in Part 1 of Schedule 2 to the 1990 Act (restrictions on licence holders) have the same meanings in this section as in that Part.

[3398]

NOTES

Commencement: 29 December 2003 (sub-ss (1)–(3), (4)(a)(ii), (iii), (b), (5)–(9), (10) (in part), (11)); 1 July 2004 (otherwise).

352 Action following review under s 351

(1) If, on a review under subsection (2) of section 351, it appears to OFCOM that the relevant change of control is or would be prejudicial to one or more of the matters mentioned in subsections (4) to (6) of that section, they shall vary the licence in accordance with subsection (2).

(2) The variation—

(a) must be made with a view to ensuring that the relevant change of control is not prejudicial to any of the matters so mentioned; and

(b) must be a variation for the inclusion in the licence of such conditions relating to any of those matters as they consider appropriate.

(3) If it appears to OFCOM, having regard to the matters mentioned in subsection (7) of section 351—

(a) that the proposed change of control would be prejudicial to the regional character of the service or (as the case may be) of any parts of it, or
(b) that the actual change of control is so prejudicial,

they may vary the licence so as to include in it such conditions relating to any of those matters as they consider appropriate.

(4) Subject to subsection (5), any new or varied condition imposed under this section in relation to any matter may be more onerous than the conditions relating to that matter having effect before the relevant change of control.

(5) A variation under this section must not provide for the inclusion of a new or varied condition in a licence unless the new condition, or the condition as varied, is one which (with any necessary modifications) would have been satisfied by the licence holder throughout the twelve months immediately before the relevant date.

(6) In subsection (5) "the relevant date" is the date of the relevant change of control or, if earlier, the date on which OFCOM exercise their powers under this section.

(7) A variation of a licence under this section shall be effected by the service of a notice of the variation on the licence holder.

(8) OFCOM are not to serve a notice of a variation under this section unless they have given the body on whom it is served a reasonable opportunity, after the publication of the report of the review under section 351, of making representations to them about the variation.

(9) Where, in a case of a proposed change of control, a notice varying a licence under this section is served before the change to which it relates takes place, the variation is not to take effect until the change takes place.

(10) A condition included in a licence by a variation under this section may be further varied by OFCOM either—
(a) with the consent of the licence holder; or
(b) in any other case, after complying with the requirements of section 3(4)(b) of the 1990 Act (variation after giving opportunity for representations by the licence holder).

(11) Expressions used in this section and section 351 have the same meanings in this section as in that.

[3399]

NOTES

Commencement: 29 December 2003.

353 Changes of control of Channel 5

(1) The regulatory regime for Channel 5 includes, in every case where it is provided by a body corporate—
(a) a condition requiring the licence holder to give OFCOM advance notification of any proposals known to the body that may give rise to a relevant change of control; and
(b) a condition requiring the licence holder to provide OFCOM, in such manner and at such times as they may reasonably require, with such information as they consider necessary for the purposes of exercising their functions under this section and section 354.

(2) OFCOM must carry out a review where—
(a) they receive notification, in accordance with a condition of the licence to provide Channel 5, of proposals that may give rise to a relevant change of control; or
(b) a relevant change of control takes place (whether or not that change has been previously notified to OFCOM).

(3) The review shall be a review of the effects or likely effects, in relation to the matters mentioned in subsections (4) and (5), of—
(a) the change to which the proposals may give rise; or
(b) the change that has taken place.

(4) The matters mentioned in this subsection are—
(a) the extent to which time available for broadcasting programmes included in Channel 5 is allocated to programmes of each of the following descriptions—

(i) original productions;
(ii) news programmes; and
(iii) current affairs programmes;

(b) the extent to which programmes of each of those descriptions that are included in that Channel are broadcast at peak viewing times.

(5) The matters mentioned in this subsection are—

(a) the extent to which programmes made in the United Kingdom that are included in the service are programmes made outside the M25 area;

(b) the range of programmes made in the United Kingdom outside that area that are included in Channel 5;

(c) the extent to which the expenditure of the provider of Channel 5 on programmes made in the United Kingdom is referable to programme production at different production centres outside the M25 area;

(d) the range of different such production centres to which that expenditure is referable.

(6) Where OFCOM carry out a review under subsection (2), they must publish a report of that review—

(a) setting out their conclusions; and

(b) specifying any steps which they propose to take under section 354.

(7) In this section—

"expenditure", in relation to a programme, means—

(a) expenditure which constitutes an investment in or is otherwise attributable to the making of the programme; or

(b) expenditure on the commissioning or other acquisition of the programme or on the acquisition of a right to include it in a service or to have it broadcast;

"original production" has the same meaning as in section 278;

"peak viewing time"—

(a) in relation to original productions, means a time determined by OFCOM for the purposes of section 278 to be a peak viewing time for Channel 5; and

(b) in relation to news programmes or current affairs programmes, means a time so determined for the purposes of section 279;

"relevant change of control" means a change in the persons having control over—

(a) a body holding a licence to provide Channel 5; or

(b) any body which—

(i) is connected with a body holding such a licence; and

(ii) is involved, to a substantial extent, in the provision of the programmes included in that channel, or is likely to become so involved.

(8) Expressions used in this section and in Part 1 of Schedule 2 to the 1990 Act (restrictions on licence holders) have the same meanings in this section as in that Part.

[3400]

NOTES

Commencement: 29 December 2003 (sub-ss (1)–(3), (4)(a)(ii), (iii), (b), (5), (6), (7) (in part), (8)); 1 July 2004 (otherwise).

354 Action following review under s 353

(1) If, on a review under subsection (2) of section 353, it appears to OFCOM that the relevant change of control is or would be prejudicial to one or more of the matters mentioned in subsections (4) and (5) of that section, they shall vary the licence in accordance with subsection (2).

(2) The variation—

(a) must be made with a view to ensuring that the relevant change of control is not prejudicial to any of the matters so mentioned; and

(b) must be a variation for the inclusion in the licence of such conditions relating to any of those matters as they consider appropriate.

(3) Subject to subsection (4), any new or varied condition imposed under this section in relation to any matter may be more onerous than the conditions relating to that matter having effect before the relevant change of control.

(4) A variation under this section must not provide for the inclusion of a new or varied condition in a licence unless the new condition, or the condition as varied, is one which (with any necessary modifications) would have been satisfied by the licence holder throughout the twelve months immediately before the relevant date.

(5) In subsection (4) "the relevant date" is the date of the relevant change of control or, if earlier, the date on which OFCOM exercise their powers under this section.

(6) A variation of a licence under this section shall be effected by the service of a notice of the variation on the licence holder.

(7) OFCOM are not to serve a notice of a variation under this section unless they have given the body on whom it is served a reasonable opportunity, after the publication of the report of the review under section 353, of making representations to them about the variation.

(8) Where, in a case of a proposed change of control, a notice varying a licence under this section is served before the change to which it relates takes place, the variation is not to take effect until the change takes place.

(9) A condition included in a licence by a variation under this section may be further varied by OFCOM either—

- (a) with the consent of the licence holder; or
- (b) in any other case, after complying with the requirements of section 3(4)(b) of the 1990 Act (variation after giving opportunity for representations by the licence holder).

(10) Expressions used in this section and section 353 have the same meanings in this section as in that.

[3401]

NOTES

Commencement: 29 December 2003.

355 Variation of local licence following change of control

(1) The regulatory regime for every local sound broadcasting service provided by a body corporate includes—

- (a) a condition requiring the licence holder to give OFCOM advance notification of any proposals known to it that may give rise to a relevant change of control; and
- (b) a condition requiring the licence holder to provide OFCOM, in such manner and at such times as they may reasonably require, with such information as they consider necessary for the purposes of exercising their functions under this section and section 356.

(2) OFCOM must carry out a review where—

- (a) they receive notification, in accordance with a condition of a local sound broadcasting licence, of proposals that may give rise to a relevant change of control; or
- (b) a relevant change of control takes place (whether or not that change has been previously notified to OFCOM).

(3) The review shall be a review of the effects or likely effects, in relation to the matters mentioned in subsection (4), of—

- (a) the change to which the proposals may give rise; or
- (b) the change that has taken place.

(4) Those matters are—

- (a) the quality and range of programmes included in the service;
- (b) the character of the service;
- (c) the extent to which OFCOM's duty under section 314 is performed in relation to the service.

(5) The matters to which OFCOM must have regard in determining for the purposes of this section the character of a local sound broadcasting service, include, in particular, the selection of spoken material and music in programmes included in the service.

(6) Where OFCOM carry out a review under subsection (2), they must publish a report of that review—

- (a) setting out their conclusions; and

(b) specifying any steps which they propose to take under section 356.

(7) In this section "relevant change of control" means a change in the persons having control over—

(a) a body holding the licence to provide a local sound broadcasting service; or

(b) any body which—

(i) is connected with a body holding such a licence; and

(ii) is involved, to a substantial extent, in the provision of the programmes included in the service provided under that licence, or is likely to become so involved.

(8) Expressions used in this section and in Schedule 2 to the 1990 Act (restrictions on licence holders) have the same meanings in this section as in that Schedule.

[3402]

NOTES

Commencement: 29 December 2003.

Modification: this section is modified in its application to community radio services by the Community Radio Order 2004, SI 2004/1944, art 4, Schedule, Pt 2, paras 9, 11 at **[3625]**.

356 Action following review under s 355

(1) If, on a review under section 355, it appears to OFCOM that the relevant change of control is or would be prejudicial to one or more of the matters mentioned in subsection (4) of that section, they must vary the local licence in accordance with subsection (2).

(2) The variation—

(a) must be made with a view to ensuring that the relevant change of control is not prejudicial to any of the matters so mentioned; and

(b) must be a variation for the inclusion in the licence of such conditions relating to any of those matters as they consider appropriate.

(3) Subject to subsection (4), any new or varied condition imposed under this section in relation to any matter may be more onerous than the conditions relating to that matter having effect before the relevant change of control.

(4) A variation under this section must not provide for the inclusion of any new or varied condition in a licence unless the new condition, or the condition as varied, is one which (with any necessary modifications) would have been satisfied by the licence holder throughout—

(a) the three months immediately before the relevant date; or

(b) such other three month period as has been notified under subsection (5).

(5) If OFCOM consider that the performance of the licence holder during the three month period immediately preceding the relevant date is not typical of his performance during the twelve months before the relevant date they—

(a) may determine that subsection (4) is to apply by reference to such other three month period falling within those twelve months as they may determine; and

(b) must notify any determination under this subsection to the licence holder.

(6) In subsection (4) "the relevant date" is the date of the relevant change of control or, if earlier, the date on which OFCOM exercise their powers under this section.

(7) A variation of a licence under this section shall be effected by the service of a notice of the variation on the licence holder.

(8) OFCOM are not to serve a notice of a variation under this section unless they have given the body on whom it is served a reasonable opportunity, after the publication of the report of the review under section 355, of making representations to them about the variation.

(9) Where, in a case of a proposed change of control, a notice varying a licence under this section is served before the change to which it relates takes place, the variation is not to take effect until that change takes place.

(10) A condition included in a licence by a variation under this section may be further varied by OFCOM either—

(a) with the consent of the licence holder; or

(b) in any other case, after complying with the requirements/n 86(5)(b) of the 1990 Act (variation after giving opportunity for representations by the licence holder).

(11) Expressions used in this section and section 355 have the same meanings in this section as in that.

[3403]

NOTES

Commencement: 29 December 2003.
Modification: this section is modified in its application to community radio services by the Community Radio Order 2004, SI 2004/1944, art 4, Schedule, Pt 2, paras 9, 11 at **[3625]**.

Meaning of control

357 Meaning of "control"

(1) …

(2) It shall be the duty of OFCOM to publish guidance setting out their intentions concerning the inclusion of particular matters in the matters that they will take into account when determining whether a person has control of a body, within the meaning of paragraph 1(3)(b) of Part 1 of Schedule 2 to the 1990 Act.

(3) OFCOM may from time to time revise the guidance issued by them under this section.

(4) OFCOM must publish the guidance and, where they revise it, the revised guidance in such manner as they consider appropriate for bringing it to the attention of the persons who, in their opinion, are likely to be affected by it.

[3404]

NOTES

Commencement: 29 December 2003.
Sub-s (1): amends the Broadcasting Act 1990, Sch 2, Pt 1 at **[3067]**.

CHAPTER 6
OTHER PROVISIONS ABOUT TELEVISION AND RADIO SERVICES

Annual report on television and radio

358 Annual factual and statistical report

(1) It shall be the duty of OFCOM—

(a) as soon as practicable after the end of the period of twelve months beginning with the commencement of this section, and

(b) as soon as practicable after the end of every subsequent period of twelve months,

to satisfy for that period the review and reporting requirements of this section.

(2) For any period those obligations are—

(a) to carry out a review of the provision of the television and radio services available for reception by members of the public in the United Kingdom during that period; and

(b) to prepare a factual and statistical report for that period on the provision of those services and on the state of the market in which they are provided.

(3) In carrying out a review for any period under this section, OFCOM must consider, in particular, each of the following—

(a) the extent to which programmes included during that period in television and radio services are representative of what OFCOM consider to be the principal genres for such programmes;

(b) the extent to which codes made by OFCOM under this Part or Part 4 or 5 of the 1996 Act (listed events and fairness) have been complied with during that period;

(c) the extent to which any guidance given by OFCOM under section 314 has been followed during that period;

(d) any trends appearing or operating during that period in the size and behaviour of the audience for radio and television services;

(e) the financial condition during that period of the market in which those services are provided and of the market in which programmes for such services are produced;

(f) what it is appropriate to achieve by conditions and duties under section 277 and paragraphs 1 and 7 of Schedule 12 and the effectiveness for that purpose of the conditions and duties for the time being in force;

(g) whether it would be appropriate to recommend to the Secretary of State that he exercises any of his powers under that section or those paragraphs;

(h) the extent to which work on independent productions (within the meaning of that section and those paragraphs) that are produced in the United Kingdom is done in a range of production centres outside the M25 area;

(i) any issues relating to intellectual property in programmes that have arisen or been of significance during that period;

(j) developments in technology that have occurred or become important during that period and are relevant to the provision, broadcasting or distribution of television and radio programmes;

(k) the availability during that period of persons with skills that are used or likely to be useful in connection with the provision of television and radio services and the production of programmes for inclusion in such services;

(l) the availability during that period of facilities for the provision of training in such skills.

(4) Every report under this section must set out OFCOM's findings on their consideration of the matters mentioned in subsection (3).

(5) Every report prepared by OFCOM under this section must be published by them—

(a) as soon as practicable after its preparation is complete; and

(b) in such manner as they consider appropriate.

(6) OFCOM's duties under this section are in addition to their duties under section 264. **[3405]**

NOTES

Commencement: 29 December 2003.

Community radio and local digital television

359 Grants to providers

(1) OFCOM may make such grants as they consider appropriate to the provider of any service of a description of service in relation to which provision is for the time being in force under section 262.

(2) The Secretary of State may by order provide that OFCOM may also make such grants as they consider appropriate to the provider of any service of a description of service in relation to which provision is for the time being in force under section 244.

(3) A grant made by virtue of this section may be made on such terms and conditions, and shall become repayable to OFCOM in such circumstances, as may be specified by OFCOM when making the grant.

(4) A person is not—

(a) by reason of the making to him of a grant by virtue of this section, or

(b) by reason of any terms or conditions (including any provisions for repayment) subject to which such a grant is or has been made to him,

to be a disqualified person by virtue of any provision of Schedule 2 to the 1990 Act in relation to a licence mentioned in subsection (5).

(5) Those licences are—

(a) a licence under Part 1 of the 1990 Act, or under Part 1 of the 1996 Act, which is granted in accordance with any provision made by an order under section 244 of this Act; and

(b) a licence under Part 3 of the 1990 Act, or under Part 2 of the 1996 Act, which is granted in accordance with any provision made by an order under section 262 of this Act.

(6) No order is to be made containing provision authorised by this section unless a draft of the order has been laid before Parliament and approved by a resolution of each House.

[3406]

NOTES

Commencement: 29 December 2003.

Supplemental provisions of Part 3

360 Amendments of the 1990 and 1996 Acts

(1), (2) …

(3) Schedule 15 (which makes minor and consequential amendments of the 1990 Act and the 1996 Act for purposes connected with the other provisions of this Chapter) shall have effect.

[3407]

NOTES

Commencement: 25 July 2003 (sub-s (3), certain purposes); 18 September 2003 (sub-s (3), certain purposes); 29 December 2003 (otherwise).

Sub-ss (1), (2): amend the Broadcasting Act 1990, s 201 at **[3063]**.

361 Meaning of "available for reception by members of the public"

(1) The services that are to be taken for the purposes of this Part to be available for reception by members of the public include (subject to subsection (2)) any service which—

(a) is made available for reception, or is made available for reception in an intelligible form, only to persons who subscribe to the service (whether for a period or in relation to a particular occasion) or who otherwise request its provision; but

(b) is a service the facility of subscribing to which, or of otherwise requesting its provision, is offered or made available to members of the public.

(2) A service is not to be treated as available for reception by members of the public if each of the three conditions set out in subsections (3) to (5) is satisfied.

(3) The first condition is that the service is confined to the provision of a facility—

(a) for the making by users of the service of individual selections of the material to be received; and

(b) for receiving whatever is selected.

(4) The second condition is that it is only in response to a selection made by a user of the service that anything (whether encrypted or not)—

(a) is broadcast from a satellite or by means of a multiplex service; or

(b) is otherwise transmitted by means of an electronic communications network.

(5) The third condition is that the individual selections that may be made do not include any that are limited to electing to be one of the recipients of material that is or has been offered for reception on the basis—

(a) that it is material selected by the provider of the service for the purpose of being made available for broadcasting or distribution simultaneously, or virtually so, to an audience consisting of users of the service; and

(b) that it will be broadcast or distributed simultaneously, or virtually so, to every member of the audience (if any) that consists of the users of the service who have elected to receive it.

(6) References in this section to members of the public are references to members of the public in, or in any area of, any one or more countries or territories (which may or may not include the United Kingdom).

(7) The Secretary of State may by order modify any of the provisions of this section if it appears to him appropriate to do so having regard to any one or more of the following—

(a) the protection which, taking account of the means by which the programmes and services are received or may be accessed, is expected by members of the public as respects the contents of television programmes or sound programmes;

(b) the extent to which members of the public are able, before television programmes are watched or accessed, to make use of facilities for exercising control, by reference to the contents of the programmes, over what is watched or accessed;

(c) the practicability of applying different levels of regulation in relation to different services;

(d) the financial impact for providers of particular services of any modification of the provisions of that section; and

(e) technological developments that have occurred or are likely to occur.

(8) No order is to be made containing provision authorised by subsection (7) unless a draft of the order has been laid before Parliament and approved by a resolution of each House.

(9) In this section "multiplex service" means a television multiplex service, a radio multiplex service or a general multiplex service.

[3408]

NOTES

Commencement: 25 July 2003.

362 Interpretation of Part 3

(1) In this Part—

"additional radio service" means an additional service within the meaning given by section 114(1) of the 1990 Act for the purposes of Part 3 of that Act;

"additional television service" (except in the expression "digital additional television service") means an additional service within the meaning given by section 48 of the 1990 Act for the purposes of Part 1 of the 1990 Act;

"analogue teletext service" is to be construed in accordance with section 218(4);

"ancillary service" has the same meaning as it has, by virtue of section 24(2) of the 1996 Act, in Part 1 of that Act;

"assistance for disabled people" means any of the following—

(a) subtitling;

(b) audio-description for the blind and partially sighted; and

(c) presentation in, or translation into, sign language;

"available for reception by members of the public" is to be construed in accordance with section 361;

"the BBC Charter and Agreement" means the following documents, or any one or more of them, so far as they are for the time being in force—

(a) a Royal Charter for the continuance of the BBC;

(b) supplemental Charters obtained by the BBC under such a Royal Charter;

(c) an agreement between the BBC and the Secretary of State entered into (whether before or after the passing of this Act) for purposes that include the regulation of activities carried on by the BBC;

"BBC company" means—

(a) a body corporate which is controlled by the BBC; or

(b) a body corporate in which the BBC or a body corporate controlled by the BBC is (to any extent) a participant;

"C4 company" means—

(a) a body corporate which is controlled by C4C; or

(b) a body corporate in which C4C or a body corporate controlled by C4C is (to any extent) a participant;

"Channel 3","Channel 4" and "Channel 5" each has the same meaning as in Part 1 of the 1990 Act (see section 71 of that Act);

"Channel 3 licence" means a licence to provide a Channel 3 service;

"a Channel 3 service" means a television broadcasting service comprised in Channel 3;

"digital additional sound service" means a digital additional service within the meaning given by section 63 of the 1996 Act for the purposes of Part 2 of that Act;

"digital additional television service" means a digital additional service within the meaning given by section 24(1) of the 1996 Act for the purposes of Part 1 of that Act;

"the digital public teletext service" means so much of the public teletext service as consists of a service provided in digital form;

"digital sound programme licence" and "digital sound programme service" each has the same meaning as in Part 2 of the 1996 Act (see sections 40 and 72 of that Act);

"digital television programme service" means a digital programme service within the meaning given by section 1(4) of the 1996 Act for the purposes of Part 1 of that Act;

"EEA State" means the United Kingdom or any other State that is a contracting party to the Agreement on the European Economic Area signed at Oporto on 22nd May 1992, as adjusted by the Protocol signed at Brussels on 17th March 1993, and "another EEA State" means an EEA State other than the United Kingdom;

"general multiplex service" means a multiplex service within the meaning of section 175 which is neither a television multiplex service nor a radio multiplex service;

"initial expiry date" has the meaning given by section 224;

"licensed public service channel" means any of the following services (whether provided for broadcasting in digital or in analogue form)—

(a) any Channel 3 service;
(b) Channel 4;
(c) Channel 5;

"local digital sound programme licence" and "local digital sound programme service" each has the same meaning as in Part 2 of the 1996 Act (see sections 60 and 72 of that Act);

"local radio multiplex licence" and "local radio multiplex service" each has the same meaning as in Part 2 of the 1996 Act (see sections 40 and 72 of that Act);

"local sound broadcasting licence" means a licence under Part 3 of the 1990 Act to provide a local sound broadcasting service;

"local sound broadcasting service" means a sound broadcasting service which, under subsection (4)(b) of section 245, is a local service for the purposes of that section;

"the M25 area" means the area the outer boundary of which is represented by the London Orbital Motorway (M25);

"national Channel 3 service" means a Channel 3 service provided between particular times of the day for more than one area for which regional Channel 3 services are provided;

"national digital sound programme service" has the same meaning as in Part 2 of the 1996 Act;

"national radio multiplex licence" and "national radio multiplex service" each has the same meaning as in Part 2 of the 1996 Act (see sections 40 and 72 of that Act);

"networking arrangements" has the meaning given by section 290;

"OFCOM's standards code" means any code or codes for the time being in force containing standards set by OFCOM under section 319 (whether originally or by way of any revision of any standards previously so set);

"provision", in relation to a service, is to be construed (subject to subsection (3)) in accordance with subsection (2), and cognate expressions are to be construed accordingly;

"the public teletext provider" means—

(a) subject to paragraph (b), the person holding the licence under section 219 to provide the public teletext service; and
(b) in relation to a time before the grant of the first licence to be granted under that section, the person holding the Broadcasting Act licence to provide the existing service (within the meaning of section 221);

"the public teletext service" means the service the provision of which is required to be secured in accordance with section 218;

"qualifying service" has the same meaning as in Part 1 of the 1996 Act (see section 2(2) of that Act);

"radio licensable content service" has the meaning given by section 247;

"radio multiplex service" has the same meaning as (by virtue of section 258 of this Act) it has in Part 2 of the 1996 Act;

"radio programme service" means any of the following—

(a) a service the provision of which is licensed under Part 3 of the 1990 Act;
(b) a digital sound programme service the provision of which is licensed under Part 2 of the 1996 Act;
(c) a digital additional sound service the provision of which is licensed under section 64 of the 1996 Act;

"regional Channel 3 licence" means a licence under Part 1 of the 1990 Act to provide a regional Channel 3 service;

"regional Channel 3 service" means a Channel 3 service provided for a particular area determined under section 14(2) of the 1990 Act;

"restricted television service" means any restricted service within the meaning given by section 42A of the 1990 Act for the purposes of Part 1 of that Act;

"S4C" and "S4C Digital" means the services so described in section 204(3);

"S4C company" means—

(a) a body corporate which is controlled by the Welsh Authority; or
(b) a body corporate in which that Authority or a body corporate controlled by that Authority is (to any extent) a participant;

"simulcast radio service" means any simulcast radio service within the meaning given by section 41(2) of the 1996 Act for the purposes of Part 2 of that Act;

"sound broadcasting service" has the same meaning as in Part 3 of the 1990 Act (see section 126 of that Act);

"standards objectives" has the meaning given by section 319(2);

"subtitling" means subtitling for the deaf or hard of hearing, whether provided by means of a teletext service or otherwise;

"television broadcasting service" means (subject to subsection (4)) a service which—
(a) consists in a service of television programmes provided with a view to its being broadcast (whether in digital or in analogue form);
(b) is provided so as to be available for reception by members of the public; and
(c) is not—
(i) a restricted television service;
(ii) a television multiplex service;
(iii) a service provided under the authority of a licence under Part 1 of the 1990 Act to provide a television licensable content service; or
(iv) a service provided under the authority of a licence under Part 1 of the 1996 Act to provide a digital television programme service;

"television licensable content service" has the meaning given by section 232 of this Act;

"television multiplex service" has meaning given by section 241(1) of this Act to a multiplex service within the meaning of Part 1 of the 1996 Act;

"television programme service" means any of the following—
(a) a television broadcasting service;
(b) a television licensable content service;
(c) a digital television programme service;
(d) a restricted television service;

"the Television without Frontiers Directive" means Council Directive 89/552/EEC on the Co-ordination of certain provisions laid down by law, regulation or administrative action in member States concerning the pursuit of television broadcasting activities, together with any modifications of that Directive by Directive 97/36/EC of the European Parliament and the Council;

"text service" means any teletext service or other service in the case of which the visual images broadcast or distributed by means of the service consist wholly or mainly of non-representational images.

(2) In the case of any of the following services—
(a) a television broadcasting service or sound broadcasting service,
(b) the public teletext service,
(c) a television licensable content service or radio licensable content service,
(d) a digital television programme service or digital sound programme service,
(e) a restricted television service,
(f) an additional television service or additional radio service,
(g) a digital additional television service or a digital additional sound service,

the person, and the only person, who is to be treated for the purposes of this Part as providing the service is the person with general control over which programmes and other services and facilities are comprised in the service (whether or not he has control of the content of individual programmes or of the broadcasting or distribution of the service).

(3) For the purposes of this Part—
(a) the provision of a service by the BBC does not include its provision by a BBC company;
(b) the provision of a service by C4C does not include its provision by a C4 company;
(c) the provision of a service by the Welsh Authority does not include its provision by an S4C company;

and, accordingly, control that is or is capable of being exercised by the BBC, C4C or the Welsh Authority over decisions by a BBC company, C4 company or S4C company about what is to be comprised in a service shall be disregarded for the purposes of subsection (2).

(4) References in this Part to a television broadcasting service do not include references to any text service.

(5) References in this Part to imposing a charge on a person in respect of his reception of a service in, or in a part of, the United Kingdom include references to imposing charges—

(a) for his use of the service at a place in the United Kingdom or in that part of it;
(b) for an entitlement of his to receive it at such place;
(c) for the use of a facility by means of which he exercises such an entitlement; or
(d) for the service's being made available for reception by him at such a place.

(6) In subsection (1) "controlled" and "participant" each has the same meaning as in Schedule 2 to the 1990 Act.

(7) In this section "non-representational images" means visual images which are neither still pictures nor comprised within sequences of visual images capable of being seen as moving pictures.

[3409]

NOTES

Commencement: 25 July 2003 (for transitional provisions in relation to the interpretation of sub-s (1) see the Communications Act 2003 (Commencement No 1) Order 2003, SI 2003/1900, art 6 at **[3512]**).

PART 4
LICENSING OF TV RECEPTION

363 Licence required for use of TV receiver

(1) A television receiver must not be installed or used unless the installation and use of the receiver is authorised by a licence under this Part.

(2) A person who installs or uses a television receiver in contravention of subsection (1) is guilty of an offence.

(3) A person with a television receiver in his possession or under his control who—

(a) intends to install or use it in contravention of subsection (1), or
(b) knows, or has reasonable grounds for believing, that another person intends to install or use it in contravention of that subsection,

is guilty of an offence.

(4) A person guilty of an offence under this section shall be liable, on summary conviction, to a fine not exceeding level 3 on the standard scale.

(5) Subsection (1) is not contravened by anything done in the course of the business of a dealer in television receivers solely for one or more of the following purposes—

(a) installing a television receiver on delivery;
(b) demonstrating, testing or repairing a television receiver.

(6) The Secretary of State may by regulations exempt from the requirement of a licence under subsection (1) the installation or use of television receivers—

(a) of such descriptions,
(b) by such persons,
(c) in such circumstances, and
(d) for such purposes,

as may be provided for in the regulations.

(7) Regulations under subsection (6) may make any exemption for which such regulations provide subject to compliance with such conditions as may be specified in the regulations.

[3410]

NOTES

Commencement: 1 April 2004.

364 TV licences

(1) A licence for the purposes of section 363 ("a TV licence")—

(a) may be issued by the BBC subject to such restrictions and conditions as the BBC think fit; and

(b) must be issued subject to such restrictions and conditions as the Secretary of State may require by a direction to the BBC.

(2) The matters to which the restrictions and conditions subject to which a TV licence may be issued may relate include, in particular—

(a) the description of television receivers that may be installed and used under the licence;
(b) the persons authorised by the licence to install and use a television receiver;
(c) the places where the installation and use of the television receiver is authorised by the licence;
(d) the circumstances in which the installation and use of such a receiver is so authorised;
(e) the purposes for which the installation and use of such a receiver is so authorised;
(f) the use of such receiver in a manner that causes, or may cause, interference (within the meaning of [the Wireless Telegraphy Act 2006]) with wireless telegraphy.

(3) The restrictions and conditions subject to which a TV licence may be issued do not include—

(a) a provision conferring a power of entry to any premises; or
(b) a provision prohibited by a direction to the BBC by the Secretary of State.

(4) A TV licence shall continue in force, unless previously revoked by the BBC, for such period as may be specified in the licence.

(5) The BBC may revoke or modify a TV licence, or the restrictions or conditions of such a licence—

(a) by a notice to the holder of the licence; or
(b) by a general notice published in such manner as may be specified in the licence.

(6) It shall be the duty of the BBC to exercise their power under subsection (5) to revoke or modify a TV licence, or any of its restrictions or conditions, if they are directed to do so by the Secretary of State.

(7) A direction by the Secretary of State under this section may be given either generally in relation to all TV licences (or all TV licences of a particular description) or in relation to a particular licence.

(8) A notice under subsection (5)(a) must be given—

(a) in the manner specified in the licence; or
(b) if no manner of service is so specified, in the manner authorised by section 394.

(9) For the purposes of the application, in relation to the giving of such a notice, of—

(a) section 394; and
(b) section 7 of the Interpretation Act 1978 (c 30) (service by post) in its application for the purposes of that section,

a person's proper address is any address where he is authorised by a TV licence to install or use a TV receiver or, if there is no such address, his last known address.

[3411]

NOTES

Commencement: 1 April 2004.

Sub-s (2): words in square brackets substituted by the Wireless Telegraphy Act 2006, s 123, Sch 7, paras 25, 29.

365 TV licence fees

(1) A person to whom a TV licence is issued shall be liable to pay—

(a) on the issue of the licence (whether initially or by way of renewal), and
(b) in such other circumstances as regulations made by the Secretary of State may provide,

such sum (if any) as may be provided for by any such regulations.

(2) Sums which a person is liable to pay by virtue of regulations under subsection (1) must be paid to the BBC and are to be recoverable by them accordingly.

(3) The BBC are entitled, in such cases as they may determine, to make refunds of sums received by them by virtue of regulations under this section.

(4) Regulations under this section may include provision—

(a) for the means by which an entitlement to a concession must be established; and

(b) for the payment of sums by means of an instalment scheme set out in the regulations.

(5) The reference to a concession in subsection (4) is a reference to any concession under which a person is, on the satisfaction of specified requirements—

(a) exempted from the liability to pay a sum in respect of a TV licence; or

(b) required to pay only a reduced sum in respect of such a licence.

(6) The consent of the Treasury shall be required for the making of any regulations under this section by the Secretary of State.

(7) Subject to subsection (8), sums received by the BBC by virtue of any regulations under this section must be paid into the Consolidated Fund.

(8) The BBC may retain, out of the sums received by them by virtue of regulations under this section, any sums they require for making refunds of sums so received.

[3412]

NOTES

Commencement: 1 April 2004.

Regulations: the Communications (Television Licensing) Regulations 2004, SI 2004/692.

366 Powers to enforce TV licensing

(1) If a justice of the peace, a sheriff in Scotland or a lay magistrate in Northern Ireland is satisfied by information on oath that there are reasonable grounds for believing—

(a) that an offence under section 363 has been or is being committed,

(b) that evidence of the commission of the offence is likely to be on premises specified in the information, or in a vehicle so specified, and

(c) that one or more of the conditions set out in subsection (3) is satisfied,

he may grant a warrant under this section.

(2) A warrant under this section is a warrant authorising any one or more persons authorised for the purpose by the BBC or by OFCOM—

(a) to enter the premises or vehicle at any time (either alone or in the company of one or more constables); and

(b) to search the premises or vehicle and examine and test any television receiver found there.

(3) Those conditions are—

(a) that there is no person entitled to grant entry to the premises or vehicle with whom it is practicable to communicate;

(b) that there is no person entitled to grant access to the evidence with whom it is practicable to communicate;

(c) that entry to the premises or vehicle will not be granted unless a warrant is produced;

(d) that the purpose of the search may be frustrated or seriously prejudiced unless the search is carried out by a person who secures entry immediately upon arriving at the premises or vehicle.

(4) A person is not to enter premises or a vehicle in pursuance of a warrant under this section at any time more than one month after the day on which the warrant was granted.

(5) The powers conferred by a warrant under this section on a person authorised by OFCOM are exercisable in relation only to a contravention or suspected contravention of a condition of a TV licence relating to interference with wireless telegraphy.

(6) A person authorised by the BBC, or by OFCOM, to exercise a power conferred by a warrant under this section may (if necessary) use such force as may be reasonable in the exercise of that power.

(7) Where a person has the power by virtue of a warrant under this section to examine or test any television receiver found on any premises, or in any vehicle, it shall be the duty—

(a) of a person who is on the premises or in the vehicle, and

(b) in the case of a vehicle, of a person who has charge of it or is present when it is searched, to give the person carrying out the examination or test all such assistance as that person may reasonably require for carrying it out.

(8) A person is guilty of an offence if he—

(a) intentionally obstructs a person in the exercise of any power conferred on that person by virtue of a warrant under this section; or

(b) without reasonable excuse, fails to give any assistance that he is under a duty to give by virtue of subsection (7).

(9) A person guilty of an offence under subsection (8) shall be liable, on summary conviction, to a fine not exceeding level 5 on the standard scale.

(10) In this section—

"interference", in relation to wireless telegraphy, has the same meaning as in [the Wireless Telegraphy Act 2006]; and

"vehicle" includes vessel, aircraft or hovercraft.

(11) In the application of this section to Scotland, the reference in subsection (1) to information on oath shall have effect as a reference to evidence on oath.

(12) In the application of this section to Northern Ireland, the reference in subsection (1) to a lay magistrate shall have effect, in relation to times before the coming into force of sections 9 and 10 of the Justice (Northern Ireland) Act 2002 (c 26), as a reference to a justice of the peace.

[3413]

NOTES

Commencement: 1 April 2004.

Sub-s (10): words in square brackets substituted by the Wireless Telegraphy Act 2006, s 123, Sch 7, paras 25, 30.

367 (*Amends the Wireless Telegraphy Act 1967, s 6 at* **[4028]**.)

368 Meanings of "television receiver" and "use"

(1) In this Part "television receiver" means any apparatus of a description specified in regulations made by the Secretary of State setting out the descriptions of apparatus that are to be television receivers for the purposes of this Part.

(2) Regulations under this section defining a television receiver may provide for references to such a receiver to include references to software used in association with apparatus.

(3) References in this Part to using a television receiver are references to using it for receiving television programmes.

(4) The power to make regulations under this section defining a television receiver includes power to modify subsection (3).

[3414]

NOTES

Commencement: 1 April 2004.

Regulations: the Communications (Television Licensing) Regulations 2004, SI 2004/692.

PART 5
COMPETITION IN COMMUNICATIONS MARKETS

CHAPTER 1
FUNCTIONS OF OFCOM UNDER COMPETITION LEGISLATION

369 Matters in relation to which OFCOM have competition functions

(1) In this Chapter references to communications matters are references to any one or more of the following—

(a) the provision of electronic communications networks;

(b) the provision of electronic communications services;

(c) the provision or making available of services or facilities which are provided or made available—
   (i) by means of, or in association with the provision (by the same person or another) of, an electronic communications network or electronic communications service; or
   (ii) for the purpose of facilitating the use of any such network or service (whether provided by the same person or another);

(d) apparatus used for providing or making available anything mentioned in the preceding paragraphs;

(e) broadcasting and related matters.

(2) The Secretary of State may by order make such amendments of subsection (1) as he may consider appropriate for the purpose of modifying the description of activities in respect of which any of the provisions of this Part—

(a) confer functions on OFCOM under Part 1 of the Competition Act 1998 (c 41) or relate to the carrying out by OFCOM of those functions; or

(b) confer functions on OFCOM under Part 4 of the Enterprise Act 2002 (c 40) or relate to the carrying out by OFCOM of those functions.

(3) No order is to be made containing provision authorised by this section unless a draft of the order has been laid before Parliament and approved by a resolution of each House.

[3415]

NOTES

Commencement: 25 July 2003 (sub-ss (1)(a)–(d), (2), (3), for the purpose of enabling network and service functions and spectrum functions to be carried out during the transitional period by the Director General of Telecommunications and the Secretary of State respectively); 29 December 2003 (otherwise) (for effect see the Communications Act 2003 (Commencement No 1) Order 2003, SI 2003/1900 at **[3507]** and the Office of Communications Act 2002 (Commencement No 3) and Communications Act 2003 (Commencement No 2) Order 2003, SI 2003/3142 at **[3590]**).

370 OFCOM's functions under Part 4 of the Enterprise Act 2002

(1) The functions to which subsection (2) applies shall be concurrent functions of OFCOM and the Office of Fair Trading.

(2) This subsection applies to the functions of the Office of Fair Trading under Part 4 of the Enterprise Act 2002 (market investigations) (other than sections 166 and 171) so far as relating to commercial activities connected with communications matters.

(3) So far as necessary for the purposes of, or in connection with, subsections (1) and (2), references in Part 4 of the Enterprise Act 2002 to the Office of Fair Trading (including references in provisions of that Act applied by that Part) shall be construed as including references to OFCOM except—

(a) in sections 166 and 171; and

(b) where the context otherwise requires.

(4) In subsection (2) the reference to activities connected with communications matters, so far as it is a reference to activities connected with any apparatus falling within paragraph (d) of section 369(1), includes a reference to—

(a) the supply and export of any such apparatus; and

(b) the production or acquisition of any such apparatus for supply or export.

(5) Before the Office of Fair Trading or OFCOM first exercises in relation to any matter functions which are exercisable concurrently by virtue of this section, that person shall consult the other.

(6) Neither the Office of Fair Trading nor OFCOM shall exercise in relation to any matter functions which are exercisable concurrently by virtue of this section if functions which are so exercisable have been exercised in relation to that matter by the other.

(7) It shall be the duty of OFCOM, for the purpose of assisting the Competition Commission in carrying out an investigation on a reference made to them by OFCOM by virtue of subsection (1), to give to the Commission—

(a) any information which is in OFCOM's possession and relates to matters falling within the scope of the investigation and—
   (i) is requested by the Commission for that purpose, or
   (ii) is information which, in OFCOM's opinion, it would be appropriate for that purpose to give to the Commission without any such request;

and

(b) any other assistance which the Commission may require, and which it is within OFCOM's power to give, in relation to any such matters,

and the Commission, for the purposes of carrying out any such investigation, shall take into account any information given to it for that purpose under this subsection.

(8) If any question arises as to whether, by virtue of this section, any functions fall to be, or are capable of being, carried out by OFCOM in relation to any particular case, that question shall be referred to and determined by the Secretary of State.

(9) No objection shall be taken to anything done under Part 4 of the Enterprise Act 2002 (c 40) by or in relation to OFCOM on the ground that it should have been done by or in relation to the Office of Fair Trading.

(10) Section 117 of the Enterprise Act 2002 (offences of supplying false or misleading information) as applied by section 180 of that Act shall have effect so far as relating to functions exercisable by OFCOM by virtue of this section as if the references in section 117(1)(a) and (2) to the Office of Fair Trading included references to OFCOM.

(11) Subject to subsection (12), section 3 does not apply in relation to anything done by OFCOM in the carrying out of their functions by virtue of this section.

(12) In the carrying out of any functions by virtue of this section OFCOM may nevertheless have regard to any of the matters in respect of which a duty is imposed by section 3(1) to (4) if it is a matter to which the Office of Fair Trading is entitled to have regard in the carrying out of those functions.

[3416]

NOTES

Commencement: 25 July 2003 (for the purpose of enabling network and service functions and spectrum functions to be carried out during the transitional period by the Director General of Telecommunications and the Secretary of State respectively) (see further s 408 and Sch 18 at **[3436]**, **[3460]**, and the Communications Act 2003 (Commencement No 1) Order 2003, SI 2003/1900 at **[3507]**); 29 December 2003 (for the purpose of enabling OFCOM to perform those functions) (see the Office of Communications Act 2002 (Commencement No 3) and Communications Act 2003 (Commencement No 2) Order 2003, SI 2003/3142 at **[3590]**).

371 OFCOM's functions under the Competition Act 1998

(1) The functions to which subsection (2) applies shall be concurrent functions of OFCOM and the Office of Fair Trading.

[(2) This subsection applies to the functions of the Office of Fair Trading under the provisions of Part 1 of the Competition Act 1998 (other than sections 31D(1) to (6), 38(1) to (6) and 51), so far as relating to—

(a) agreements, decisions or concerted practices of the kind mentioned in section 2(1) of that Act,

(b) conduct of the kind mentioned in section 18(1) of that Act,

(c) agreements, decisions or concerted practices of the kind mentioned in Article 81(1) of the treaty establishing the European Community, or

(d) conduct which amounts to abuse of the kind mentioned in Article 82 of the treaty establishing the European Community,

which relate to activities connected with communications matters.]

(3) So far as necessary for the purposes of, or in connection with, the provisions of subsections (1) and (2), references to the Office of Fair Trading in Part 1 of the Competition Act 1998 are to be read as including references to OFCOM, except—

(a) [in sections 31D(1) to (6), 38(1) to (6)], 51, 52(6) and (8) and 54; and

(b) where the context otherwise requires.

(4) In subsection (2), the reference to activities connected with communications matters, so far as it is a reference to activities connected with any apparatus falling within paragraph (d) of section 369(1), includes a reference to—

(a) the supply and export of any such apparatus; and

(b) the production or acquisition of any such apparatus for supply or export.

(5)–(7) …

(8) OFCOM may carry out, in respect of activities connected with communications matters and concurrently with the Office of Fair Trading, the functions of the Office of Fair Trading under any of paragraphs 3, 7, 19(3) and 36 to 39 of Schedule 13 to the Competition Act 1998 (transitional provisions).

(9) If any question arises as to whether, by virtue of this section, any functions fall to be, or are capable of being, carried out by OFCOM in relation to a particular case, that question shall be referred to and determined by the Secretary of State.

(10) No objection shall be taken to anything done under by or in relation to OFCOM under the Competition Act 1998 (c 41) on the ground that it should have been done by or in relation to the Office of Fair Trading.

(11) Subject to subsection (12), section 3 does not apply in relation to anything done by OFCOM in the carrying out of their functions by virtue of this section.

(12) In the carrying out of any functions by virtue of this section OFCOM may nevertheless have regard to any of the matters in respect of which a duty is imposed by section 3(1) to (4) if it is a matter to which the Office of Fair Trading is entitled to have regard in the carrying out of those functions.

[3417]

NOTES

Commencement: 25 July 2003 (for the purpose of enabling network and service functions and spectrum functions to be carried out during the transitional period by the Director General of Telecommunications and the Secretary of State respectively) (see further s 408 and Sch 18 at **[3436]**, **[3460]**, and the Communications Act 2003 (Commencement No 1) Order 2003, SI 2003/1900 at **[3507]**); 29 December 2003 (for the purpose of enabling OFCOM to perform those functions) (see the Office of Communications Act 2002 (Commencement No 3) and Communications Act 2003 (Commencement No 2) Order 2003, SI 2003/3142 at **[3590]**).

Sub-s (2): substituted by the Competition Act 1998 and Other Enactments (Amendment) Regulations 2004, SI 2004/1261, reg 5, Sch 2, para 11(1), (2)(a).

Sub-s (3): words in square brackets substituted by SI 2004/1261, reg 5, Sch 2, para 11(1), (2)(b).

Sub-ss (5)–(7): amend the Competition Act 1998, ss 54, 59, Sch 2.

372 (*Amends the Broadcasting Act 1990, s 194A* (*outside the scope of this work*).)

CHAPTER 2
MEDIA MERGERS

373–386 (*S 373 repeals the Fair Trading Act 1973, ss 57–62; ss 374–386 amend the Enterprise Act 2002, ss 44, 58, 59, 61, 105, 127, repeal s 69 of that Act, and insert ss 44A, 58A, 59A, 61A, 104A, 106A, 106B, 119A, 119B of that Act* (*outside the scope of this work*).)

Supplemental provisions of Chapter 2

387, 388 (*S 387 amends the Enterprise Act 2002, Sch 8* (*outside the scope of this work*); *s 388 amends the Competition Act 1998, Sch 7* (*outside the scope of this work*).)

389 Further provision in connection with media mergers

(1) Schedule 16 (which contains further amendments in connection with media mergers) shall have effect.

(2) Sections 276(2) and (3) and 277 of the Enterprise Act 2002 (c 40) (power to make transitional and consequential amendments etc) shall apply in relation to this Chapter of this Part of this Act and its related repeals as they apply in relation to that Act.

(3) For the avoidance of doubt, the power conferred by virtue of subsection (2) by applying section 277 of the Act of 2002 includes the power to modify that Act.

(4) Section 402 shall not apply in relation to any power to make an order which is exercisable by the Secretary of State by virtue of subsection (2).

[3418]

NOTES

Commencement: 29 December 2003.

PART 6
MISCELLANEOUS AND SUPPLEMENTAL

Annual report

390 Annual report on the Secretary of State's functions

(1) The Secretary of State must prepare and lay before Parliament regular reports on the carrying out by him of the functions to which this section applies.

(2) This section applies to the Secretary of State's functions under the following enactments—

(a) this Act;
(b) the Office of Communications Act 2002 (c 11);
(c) the enactments relating to the management of the radio spectrum so far as not comprised in this Act;
(d) the 1990 Act;
(e) the 1996 Act.

(3) The first report under this section must relate to the period which—

(a) begins with 19th March 2002 (the date of the passing of the Office of Communications Act 2002); and
(b) ends with the period of twelve months beginning with the first date to be appointed for the purposes of section 2 of this Act.

(4) Every subsequent report must relate to the period of twelve months beginning with the end of the period to which the previous report related.

(5) The obligation under this section to prepare and lay a report before Parliament is an obligation to do that as soon as reasonably practicable after the end of the period to which the report relates.

(6) Where a report for the purposes of this section relates to a period the whole or a part of which falls before the time when the whole of this Act is in force, the functions referred to in subsection (2) are to be taken as excluding all functions under the specified enactments that will have ceased to be functions of the Secretary of State when the whole of this Act is in force.

[3419]

NOTES

Commencement: 29 December 2003.

Review of media ownership

391 Review of media ownership

(1) It shall be the duty of OFCOM—

(a) to carry out regular reviews of the operation, taken together, of all the provisions to which this section applies; and
(b) to send a report on every such review to the Secretary of State.

(2) This section applies to—

(a) the provisions of Schedule 2 to the 1990 Act;
(b) the provision made by or under Schedule 14 to this Act;
(c) the provisions of sections 280 and 281 of this Act;
(d) whatever provision (if any) has been made under section 283 of this Act; and
(e) the provisions of Part 3 of the Enterprise Act 2002 (c 40) so far as they relate to intervention by the Secretary of State in connection with newspapers or other media enterprises.

(3) The first review must be carried out no more than three years after the commencement of this section, and subsequent reviews must be carried out at intervals of no more than three years.

(4) The report to the Secretary of State on a review must set out OFCOM's recommendations, in consequence of their conclusions on the review, for the exercise by the Secretary of State of—

(a) his power to make an order under section 348(5);
(b) his powers to make orders under Schedule 14;
(c) his powers under sections 282 and 283; and
(d) his powers under sections 44(11), 58(3) and 59(6A) of the Enterprise Act 2002 (media mergers).

(5) OFCOM must publish every report sent by them to the Secretary of State under this section in such manner as they consider appropriate for bringing it to the attention of persons who, in their opinion, are likely to be affected by it.

[3420]

NOTES

Commencement: 29 December 2003.

Guidelines as to penalties

392 Penalties imposed by OFCOM

(1) It shall be the duty of OFCOM to prepare and publish a statement containing the guidelines they propose to follow in determining the amount of penalties imposed by them under provisions contained in this Act or any other enactment apart from the Competition Act 1998 (c 41).

(2) OFCOM may from time to time revise that statement as they think fit.

(3) Where OFCOM make or revise their statement under this section, they must publish the statement or (as the case may be) the revised statement in such manner as they consider appropriate for bringing it to the attention of the persons who, in their opinion, are likely to be affected by it.

(4) Before publishing a statement or revised statement under this section OFCOM must consult both—
(a) the Secretary of State, and
(b) such other persons as they consider appropriate,
about the guidelines they are proposing to include in the statement.

(5) Before determining how to publish a statement or revised statement under this section OFCOM must consult the Secretary of State.

(6) It shall be the duty of OFCOM, in determining the amount of any penalty to be imposed by them under this Act or any other enactment (apart from the Competition Act 1998 (c 41)) to have regard to the guidelines contained in the statement for the time being in force under this section.

(7) References in this section to penalties imposed by OFCOM under provisions contained in this Act include references to penalties which the BBC is liable to pay to OFCOM by virtue of section 198(3).

[3421]

NOTES

Commencement: 29 December 2003.

Disclosure of information

393 General restrictions on disclosure of information

(1) Subject to the following provisions of this section, information with respect to a particular business which has been obtained in exercise of a power conferred by—
(a) this Act,
(b) …
(c) the 1990 Act, or
(d) the 1996 Act,
is not, so long as that business continues to be carried on, to be disclosed without the consent of the person for the time being carrying on that business.

(2) Subsection (1) does not apply to any disclosure of information which is made—
(a) for the purpose of facilitating the carrying out by OFCOM of any of their functions;
(b) for the purpose of facilitating the carrying out by any relevant person of any relevant function;
(c) for the purpose of facilitating the carrying out by the Comptroller and Auditor General of any of his functions;
(d) for any of the purposes specified in section 17(2)(a) to
(d) of the Anti-terrorism, Crime and Security Act 2001 (c 24) (criminal proceedings and investigations);
(e) for the purpose of any civil proceedings brought under or by virtue of this Act or any of the enactments or instruments mentioned in subsection (5); or
(f) for the purpose of securing compliance with an international obligation of the United Kingdom.

(3) Each of the following is a relevant person for the purposes of this section—
(a) a Minister of the Crown and the Treasury;
(b) the Scottish Executive;
(c) a Northern Ireland department;
(d) the Office of Fair Trading;
(e) the Competition Commission;
(f) the Consumer Panel;
(g) the Welsh Authority;
(h) a local weights and measures authority in Great Britain;
(i) any other person specified for the purposes of this subsection in an order made by the Secretary of State.

(4) The following are relevant functions for the purposes of this section—
(a) any function conferred by or under this Act;
(b) any function conferred by or under any enactment or instrument mentioned in subsection (5);
(c) any other function specified for the purposes of this subsection in an order made by the Secretary of State.

(5) The enactments and instruments referred to in subsections (2) and (4) are—
(a), (b) …
(c) the Wireless Telegraphy Act 1967 (c 72);
(d) the Trade Descriptions Act 1968 (c 29);
(e) the Fair Trading Act 1973 (c 41);
(f) the Consumer Credit Act 1974 (c 39);
(g) the Competition Act 1980 (c 21);
(h) the Telecommunications Act 1984 (c 12);
(i) the Consumer Protection Act 1987 (c 43);
(j) the 1990 Act;
(k) the 1996 Act;
(l) …
(m) the Competition Act 1998 (c 41);
(n) the Enterprise Act 2002 (c 40);
[(na) the Wireless Telegraphy Act 2006;]
(o) the Consumer Protection (Northern Ireland) Order 1987 (SI 1987/2049(NI 20));
(p) the Control of Misleading Advertisements Regulations 1988 (SI 1988/915).

(6) Nothing in this section—
(a) limits the matters that may be published under section 15, 26 or 390;
(b) limits the matters that may be included in, or made public as part of, a report made by OFCOM by virtue of a provision of this Act or the Office of Communications Act 2002 (c 11);
(c) prevents the disclosure of anything for the purposes of a report of legal proceedings in which it has been publicly disclosed;
(d) applies to information that has been published or made public as mentioned in paragraphs (a) to (c).

(7) Nothing in this section applies to information obtained in exercise of the powers conferred by section 196 of the 1990 Act (powers of entry and search).

(8) Information obtained by OFCOM in exercise of functions which are exercisable by them concurrently with the Office of Fair Trading under Part 1 of the Competition Act 1998 is subject to Part 9 of the Enterprise Act 2002, and not to the preceding provisions of this section.

(9) Section 18 of the Anti-terrorism, Crime and Security Act 2001 (c 24) (restriction on disclosure of information for overseas purposes) shall have effect in relation to a disclosure by virtue of subsection (2)(d) as it applies in relation to a disclosure in exercise of a power to which section 17 of that Act applies.

(10) A person who discloses information in contravention of this section is guilty of an offence and shall be liable—

(a) on summary conviction, to a fine not exceeding the statutory maximum;
(b) on conviction on indictment, to imprisonment for a term not exceeding two years or to a fine, or to both.

(11) No order is to be made containing provision authorised by subsection (3) or (4) unless a draft of the order has been laid before Parliament and approved by a resolution of each House.

(12) In this section "legal proceedings" means civil or criminal proceedings in or before any court, or proceedings before any tribunal established by or under any enactment.

[3422]

NOTES

Commencement: 25 July 2003 (sub-ss (1)(a), (b), (2)–(4), (5)(a)–(i), (l)–(p), (6)(a) (in part), (b)–(d), (8)–(12), for the purpose of enabling network and service functions and spectrum functions to be carried out during the transitional period by the Director General of Telecommunications and the Secretary of State respectively) (see further s 408 and Sch 18 at **[3436]**, **[3460]**, and the Communications Act 2003 (Commencement No 1) Order 2003, SI 2003/1900 at **[3507]**); 29 December 2003 (otherwise).

Sub-s (1): para (b) repealed by the Wireless Telegraphy Act 2006, s 125(1), Sch 9, Pt 1, subject to transitional provisions and savings in s 124 of, Sch 8, Pt 1, paras 1–8, 24 to, that Act at **[4230]**, **[4239]**, and previously read as follows:

"(b) the enactments relating to the management of the radio spectrum (so far as not contained in this Act),".

Sub-s (5): paras (a), (b), (l) repealed and para (na) inserted by the Wireless Telegraphy Act 2006, ss 123, 125(1), Sch 7, paras 25, 31, Sch 9, Pt 1, subject to transitional provisions and savings in s 124 of, Sch 8, Pt 1, paras 1–8, 24 to, that Act at **[4230]**, **[4239]**. Paras (a), (b), (l) previously read as follows:

"(a) the Wireless Telegraphy Act 1949 (c 54);
(b) the Marine, &c., Broadcasting (Offences) Act 1967 (c 41);
(l) the Wireless Telegraphy Act 1998 (c 6);".

Orders: the Communications Act 2003 (Maximum Penalty and Disclosure of Information) Order 2005, SI 2005/3469.

Notifications etc and electronic working

394 Service of notifications and other documents

(1) This section applies where provision made (in whatever terms) by or under an enactment specified in subsection (2) authorises or requires—

(a) a notification to be given to any person; or
(b) a document of any other description (including a copy of a document) to be sent to any person.

(2) Those enactments are—

(a) this Act;
(b) the Office of Communications Act 2002 (c 11);
(c) …
(d) Schedule 2 to the Telecommunications Act 1984 (c 12);
(e) the 1990 Act; and
(f) the 1996 Act.

(3) The notification or document may be given or sent to the person in question—

(a) by delivering it to him;
(b) by leaving it at his proper address; or
(c) by sending it by post to him at that address.

(4) The notification or document may be given or sent to a body corporate by being given or sent to the secretary or clerk of that body.

(5) The notification or document may be given or sent to a firm by being given or sent to—

(a) a partner in the firm; or
(b) a person having the control or management of the partnership business.

(6) The notification or document may be given or sent to an unincorporated body or association by being given or sent to a member of the governing body of the body or association.

(7) For the purposes of this section and section 7 of the Interpretation Act 1978 (c 30) (service of documents by post) in its application to this section, the proper address of a person is—

(a) in the case of body corporate, the address of the registered or principal office of the body;
(b) in the case of a firm, unincorporated body or association, the address of the principal office of the partnership, body or association;
(c) in the case of a person to whom the notification or other document is given or sent in reliance on any of subsections (4) to (6), the proper address of the body corporate, firm or (as the case may be) other body or association in question; and
(d) in any other case, the last known address of the person in question.

(8) In the case of—

(a) a company registered outside the United Kingdom,
(b) a firm carrying on business outside the United Kingdom, or
(c) an unincorporated body or association with offices outside the United Kingdom,

the references in subsection (7) to its principal office include references to its principal office within the United Kingdom (if any).

(9) In this section—

"document" includes anything in writing; and
"notification" includes notice;

and references in this section to giving or sending a notification or other document to a person include references to transmitting it to him and to serving it on him.

(10) This section has effect subject to section 395.

[3423]

NOTES

Commencement: 25 July 2003 (sub-ss (1), (2)(a)–(d), (3)–(10), for the purpose of enabling network and service functions and spectrum functions to be carried out during the transitional period by the Director General of Telecommunications and the Secretary of State respectively) (see further s 408 and Sch 18 at **[3436]**, **[3460]**, and the Communications Act 2003 (Commencement No 1) Order 2003, SI 2003/1900 at **[3507]**); 29 December 2003 (otherwise).

Sub-s (2): para (c) repealed by the Wireless Telegraphy Act 2006, s 125(1), Sch 9, Pt 1, subject to transitional provisions and savings in s 124 of, Sch 8, Pt 1, paras 1–8, 24 to, that Act at **[4230]**, **[4239]**, and previously read as follows:

"(c) the enactments relating to the management of the radio spectrum (so far as not contained in this Act),".

395 Notifications and documents in electronic form

(1) This section applies where—

(a) section 394 authorises the giving or sending of a notification or other document by its delivery to a particular person ("the recipient"); and
(b) the notification or other document is transmitted to the recipient—
   (i) by means of an electronic communications network; or
   (ii) by other means but in a form that nevertheless requires the use of apparatus by the recipient to render it intelligible.

(2) The transmission has effect for the purposes of the enactments specified in section 394(2) as a delivery of the notification or other document to the recipient, but only if the requirements imposed by or under this section are complied with.

(3) Where the recipient is OFCOM—

(a) they must have indicated their willingness to receive the notification or other document in a manner mentioned in subsection (1)(b);

(b) the transmission must be made in such manner and satisfy such other conditions as they may require; and
(c) the notification or other document must take such form as they may require.

(4) Where the person making the transmission is OFCOM, they may (subject to subsection (5)) determine—
(a) the manner in which the transmission is made; and
(b) the form in which the notification or other document is transmitted.

(5) Where the recipient is a person other than OFCOM—
(a) the recipient, or
(b) the person on whose behalf the recipient receives the notification or other document,

must have indicated to the person making the transmission the recipient's willingness to receive notifications or documents transmitted in the form and manner used.

(6) An indication to any person for the purposes of subsection (5)—
(a) must be given to that person in such manner as he may require;
(b) may be a general indication or one that is limited to notifications or documents of a particular description;
(c) must state the address to be used and must be accompanied by such other information as that person requires for the making of the transmission; and
(d) may be modified or withdrawn at any time by a notice given to that person in such manner as he may require.

(7) An indication, requirement or determination given, imposed or made by OFCOM for the purposes of this section is to be given, imposed or made by being published in such manner as they consider appropriate for bringing it to the attention of the persons who, in their opinion, are likely to be affected by it.

(8) Subsection (9) of section 394 applies for the purposes of this section as it applies for the purposes of that section.

[3424]

NOTES

Commencement: 25 July 2003 (for the purpose of enabling network and service functions and spectrum functions to be carried out during the transitional period by the Director General of Telecommunications and the Secretary of State respectively) (see further s 408 and Sch 18 at **[3436]**, **[3460]**, and the Communications Act 2003 (Commencement No 1) Order 2003, SI 2003/1900 at **[3507]**); 29 December 2003 (for the purpose of enabling OFCOM to perform those functions) (see the Office of Communications Act 2002 (Commencement No 3) and Communications Act 2003 (Commencement No 2) Order 2003, SI 2003/3142 at **[3590]**).

396 Timing and location of things done electronically

(1) The Secretary of State may by order make provision specifying, for the purposes of the enactments specified in section 394(2), the manner of determining—
(a) the times at which things done under those enactments by means of electronic communications networks are done; and
(b) the places at which such things are so done, and at which things transmitted by means of such networks are received.

(2) The provision made by subsection (1) may include provision as to the country or territory in which an electronic address is to be treated as located.

(3) An order made by the Secretary of State may also make provision about the manner of proving in any legal proceedings—
(a) that something done by means of an electronic communications network satisfies the requirements of the enactments specified in section 394(2) for the doing of that thing; and
(b) the matters mentioned in subsection (1)(a) and (b).

(4) An order under this section may provide for such presumptions to apply (whether conclusive or not) as the Secretary of State considers appropriate.

[3425]

NOTES

Commencement: 25 July 2003 (for the purpose of enabling network and service functions and spectrum functions to be carried out during the transitional period by the Director General of

Telecommunications and the Secretary of State respectively) (see further s 408 and Sch 18 at **[3436]**, **[3460]**, and the Communications Act 2003 (Commencement No 1) Order 2003, SI 2003/1900 at **[3507]**); 29 December 2003 (for the purpose of enabling OFCOM to perform those functions) (see the Office of Communications Act 2002 (Commencement No 3) and Communications Act 2003 (Commencement No 2) Order 2003, SI 2003/3142 at **[3590]**).

Other miscellaneous provisions

397 Purchase of Duchy of Lancaster land

(1) The Chancellor and Council of the Duchy of Lancaster may, if they think fit, agree with a person who provides a public electronic communications network for the sale, and absolutely make sale, for such sum of money as appears to them sufficient consideration for the same, of any land which—

(a) belongs to Her Majesty in right of the Duchy of Lancaster; and

(b) is land which that person seeks to acquire for, or in connection with, the provision of his network.

(2) In this section "public electronic communications network" has the same meaning as in Chapter 1 of Part 2.

[3426]

NOTES

Commencement: 25 July 2003 (for the purpose of enabling network and service functions and spectrum functions to be carried out during the transitional period by the Director General of Telecommunications and the Secretary of State respectively) (see further s 408 and Sch 18 at **[3436]**, **[3460]**, and the Communications Act 2003 (Commencement No 1) Order 2003, SI 2003/1900 at **[3507]**); 29 December 2003 (for the purpose of enabling OFCOM to perform those functions) (see the Office of Communications Act 2002 (Commencement No 3) and Communications Act 2003 (Commencement No 2) Order 2003, SI 2003/3142 at **[3590]**).

398 (*Repeals the Telecommunications Act 1984, ss 60, 61(1)–(6), 62, 63(1)–(4), 64–67, 69–71, 72(2), (4), (5), 73, 93, 97, and amends s 68 of that Act at* **[4041]**.)

Supplemental

399 Expenses

There shall be paid out of money provided by Parliament—

(a) any expenditure incurred by the Secretary of State for or in connection with the carrying out of any of his functions under this Act; and

(b) any increase attributable to this Act in the sums which are payable out of money so provided under any other Act.

[3427]

NOTES

Commencement: 25 July 2003 (for the purpose of enabling network and service functions and spectrum functions to be carried out during the transitional period by the Director General of Telecommunications and the Secretary of State respectively) (see further s 408 and Sch 18 at **[3436]**, **[3460]**, and the Communications Act 2003 (Commencement No 1) Order 2003, SI 2003/1900 at **[3507]**); 29 December 2003 (for the purpose of enabling OFCOM to perform those functions) (see the Office of Communications Act 2002 (Commencement No 3) and Communications Act 2003 (Commencement No 2) Order 2003, SI 2003/3142 at **[3590]**).

400 Destination of licence fees and penalties

(1) This section applies (subject to section 401) to the following amounts—

(a) an amount paid to OFCOM in respect of a penalty imposed by them under Chapter 1 of Part 2 (including a penalty imposed by virtue of section 191(5));

(b) so much of an amount paid to OFCOM under numbering conditions in respect of an allocation of telephone numbers as is an amount determined by reference to an indication given in response to an invitation such as is mentioned in section 58(5)(a);

(c) an amount paid to OFCOM in pursuance of an obligation imposed by or under [Chapter 1 or 2 of Part 2 of the Wireless Telegraphy Act 2006];
(d) an amount paid to OFCOM in respect of a penalty imposed by them under [section 42 of that Act];
(e) a cash bid amount paid to OFCOM under a Broadcasting Act licence for the first year falling within the period for which the licence is in force;
(f) an amount paid to OFCOM under such a licence for a subsequent year as the amount equal to a cash bid amount increased by the appropriate percentage;
(g) an amount paid to OFCOM under such a licence as an amount representing a percentage of relevant revenue for an accounting period;
(h) an amount paid to OFCOM in respect of a penalty imposed by them under Part 1 or 3 of the 1990 Act, Part 1 or 2 of the 1996 Act or Part 3 of this Act.

(2) Where OFCOM receive an amount to which this section applies, it must be paid into the appropriate Consolidated Fund; but this subsection does not apply to an amount which is required by OFCOM for making an adjustment in respect of an overpayment.

(3) The reference in subsection (2) to the payment of an amount into the appropriate Consolidated Fund—
(a) in the case of an amount received in respect of matters appearing to OFCOM to have no connection with Northern Ireland, is a reference to the payment of the amount into the Consolidated Fund of the United Kingdom;
(b) in the case of an amount received in respect of matters appearing to OFCOM to have a connection with Northern Ireland but no connection with the rest of the United Kingdom, is a reference to the payment of the amount into the Consolidated Fund of Northern Ireland; and
(c) in any other case, is a reference to the payment of the amount, in such proportions as OFCOM consider appropriate, into each of those Funds.

(4) OFCOM must, in respect of each financial year, prepare an account showing—
(a) the amounts to which this section applies that have been received by them during that year;
(b) the sums paid into the Consolidated Funds of the United Kingdom and Northern Ireland respectively under this section in respect of those amounts;
(c) the aggregate amount of the sums received by them during that year that is retained in accordance with a statement of principles under section 401 for meeting the costs of carrying out functions mentioned in subsection (4) of that section during that year;
(d) the aggregate amount that they estimate will fall to be so retained out of amounts due to them and likely to be paid or recovered; and
(e) the cost to OFCOM of carrying out during that year the functions in respect of which amounts are or are to be retained in accordance with such a statement.

(5) OFCOM must send that account to the Comptroller and Auditor General not later than the end of the month of November following the financial year to which it relates.

(6) The Comptroller and Auditor General must examine, certify and report on the account and lay copies of it, together with his report, before each House of Parliament.

(7) References in this section to penalties imposed by OFCOM under Part 3 of this Act include references to penalties which the BBC is liable to pay to OFCOM by virtue of section 198(3).

(8) In this section—

"the appropriate percentage" has the same meaning as in section 19 of the 1990 Act;

"cash bid amount" means an amount specified in a cash bid for a Broadcasting Act licence or the amount determined by OFCOM for the purposes of any provision of the 1990 Act or this Part to be what would have been the amount of a cash bid for a licence;

"financial year" has the same meaning as in the Schedule to the Office of Communications Act 2002 (c 11);

"numbering conditions" means conditions the setting of which is authorised by section 58 or 59; and

"relevant revenue" means any of the following—
(a) the amount which for the purposes of section 19, 52(1), 102(1) or 118 (1) of the 1990 Act is the amount of qualifying revenue for an accounting period;

(b) the amount which for the purposes of section 13(1) or 55(1) of the 1996 Act is the amount of multiplex revenue for an accounting period; or

(c) an amount which for the purposes of paragraph 7 of Schedule 10 to this Act is the amount of qualifying revenue for an accounting period.

[3428]

NOTES

Commencement: 29 December 2003.

Sub-s (1): words in square brackets in paras (c), (d) substituted by the Wireless Telegraphy Act 2006, s 123, Sch 7, paras 25, 32.

401 Power of OFCOM to retain costs of carrying out spectrum functions

(1) OFCOM have power to make a statement of the principles under which they may retain any or all of the amounts paid to them in pursuance of obligations imposed by or under [Chapter 1 or 2 of Part 2 of the Wireless Telegraphy Act 2006].

(2) Where such a statement of principles authorises the retention of an amount, OFCOM are not required to pay it into the appropriate Consolidated Fund in accordance with section 400.

(3) Principles contained in a statement made by OFCOM under this section must be such as appear to them to be likely to secure, on the basis of such estimates of the likely costs as it is practicable to make—

(a) that, on a year by year basis, the aggregate amount of the amounts retained by OFCOM does not exceed the amount required by OFCOM for meeting the annual cost to OFCOM of carrying out the functions mentioned in subsection (4);

(b) that the amounts retained by OFCOM are objectively justifiable and proportionate to the costs in respect of which they are retained; and

(c) that the relationship between meeting the cost of carrying out those functions and the amounts retained is transparent.

(4) Those functions are—

(a) OFCOM's functions under the enactments relating to the management of the radio spectrum except those specified in subsection (5); and

(b) the function of taking any steps that OFCOM consider it necessary to take—

(i) in preparation for the carrying out of any of the functions mentioned in paragraph (a) of this subsection; or

(ii) for the purpose of facilitating the carrying out of those functions or otherwise in connection with carrying them out.

(5) The excepted functions of OFCOM are—

(a) their functions under section 22(2);

[(b) their functions under section 1(1) and (2) of the Wireless Telegraphy Act 2006 so far as carried out in relation to the use of the electromagnetic spectrum at places outside the United Kingdom, and their functions under section 1(5);

(c) their functions under section 4 of that Act;

(d) their functions under section 7 of that Act;

(e) their functions under section 30 of that Act;

(f) their functions under sections 42 to 44 of that Act;

(g) any functions conferred on them under sections 47 to 49 of that Act; and]

(h) any function not falling within the preceding paragraphs in so far as the costs of carrying it out are met from payments made to OFCOM by virtue of section 28 [of this Act or section 1(8) of the Wireless Telegraphy Act 2006].

(6) A statement under this section may include provision which, for the purposes of the principles contained in the statement and of the preparation of accounts in accordance with section 400(4), requires an amount actually received in one year—

(a) to be treated as referable to costs incurred in that year and in one or more subsequent years; and

(b) to be brought into account, in each of those years, in accordance with an apportionment for which provision is made in the statement.

(7) A deficit or surplus shown (after applying this subsection for all previous years) by an account prepared under section 400(4) is to be carried forward and taken into account in determining what is required by OFCOM in relation to the following year for meeting the costs of carrying out the functions mentioned in subsection (4) of this section.

(8) A statement of principles under this section—
- (a) if it is expressed to apply for a limited period, does not apply to any amounts paid to OFCOM after the end of that period; and
- (b) in any event, does not apply to amounts paid to them after a withdrawal of the statement takes effect.

(9) OFCOM may revise a statement made under this section.

(10) The consent of the Treasury is required for the making, revision or withdrawal of a statement under this section.

(11) Where OFCOM make or revise a statement of this section they must publish so much of the statement or revised statement as appears to them necessary for demonstrating that the statement or revision complies with subsection (3).

[3429]

NOTES

Commencement: to be appointed.

Sub-s (1): words in square brackets substituted by the Wireless Telegraphy Act 2006, s 123, Sch 7, paras 25, 33(1), (2).

Sub-s (5): paras (b)–(g) and words in square brackets in para (h) substituted by the Wireless Telegraphy Act 2006, s 123, Sch 7, paras 25, 33(1), (3), (4).

402 Power of Secretary of State to make orders and regulations

(1) Every power conferred by this Act on the Secretary of State to make orders or regulations, other than the powers conferred by Schedule 4, is a power exercisable by statutory instrument.

(2) A statutory instrument containing an order or regulations made in exercise of any such power, other than—
- (a) an order under section 31 or 411,
- (b) …
- (c) any order that is required, by any provision of this Act, to be laid before Parliament and approved in draft,

shall be subject to annulment in pursuance of a resolution of either House of Parliament.

(3) Every power of the Secretary of State to make an order or regulations under this Act, other than an order under section 31 or 411 or an order made in exercise of a power conferred by Schedule 4, includes power—
- (a) to make different provision for different cases (including different provision in respect of different areas);
- (b) to make provision subject to such exemptions and exceptions as the Secretary of State thinks fit; and
- (c) to make such incidental, supplemental, consequential and transitional provision as the Secretary of State thinks fit.

[3430]

NOTES

Commencement: 25 July 2003 (for the purpose of enabling network and service functions and spectrum functions to be carried out during the transitional period by the Director General of Telecommunications and the Secretary of State respectively) (see further s 408 and Sch 18 at **[3436]**, **[3460]**, and the Communications Act 2003 (Commencement No 1) Order 2003, SI 2003/1900 at **[3507]**); 29 December 2003 (for the purpose of enabling OFCOM to perform those functions) (see the Office of Communications Act 2002 (Commencement No 3) and Communications Act 2003 (Commencement No 2) Order 2003, SI 2003/3142 at **[3590]**).

Sub-s (2): para (b) repealed by the Wireless Telegraphy Act 2006, s 125(1), Sch 9, Pt 1, subject to transitional provisions and savings in s 124 of, Sch 8, Pt 1, paras 1–8, 24 to, that Act at **[4230]**, **[4239]**, and previously read as follows:

"(b) an order containing a direction under section 156, or".

403 Regulations and orders made by OFCOM

(1) This section applies to any power of OFCOM to make regulations or to make an order or scheme if that power is one to which this section is expressly applied.

(2) The powers to which this section applies shall be exercisable by statutory instrument, and the Statutory Instruments Act 1946 (c 36) is to apply in relation to those powers as if OFCOM were a Minister of the Crown.

(3) Where an instrument made under a power to which this section applies falls to be laid before Parliament, OFCOM must, immediately after it is made, send it to the Secretary of State for laying by him.

(4) Before making any regulations or order under a power to which this section applies, OFCOM must—

(a) give a notice of their proposal to do so to such persons representative of the persons appearing to OFCOM to be likely to be affected by the implementation of the proposal as OFCOM think fit;

(b) publish notice of their proposal in such manner as they consider appropriate for bringing it to the attention of the persons who, in their opinion, are likely to be affected by it and are not given notice by virtue of paragraph (a); and

(c) consider any representations that are made to OFCOM, before the time specified in the notice.

(5) A notice for the purposes of subsection (4) must—

(a) state that OFCOM propose to make the regulations or order in question;

(b) set out the general effect of the regulations or order;

(c) specify an address from which a copy of the proposed regulations or order may be obtained; and

(d) specify a time before which any representations with respect to the proposal must be made to OFCOM.

(6) The time specified for the purposes of subsection (5)(d) must be no earlier than the end of the period of one month beginning with the day after the latest day on which the notice is given or published for the purposes of subsection (4).

(7) Every power of OFCOM to which this section applies includes power—

(a) to make different provision for different cases (including different provision in respect of different areas);

(b) to make provision subject to such exemptions and exceptions as OFCOM think fit; and

(c) to make such incidental, supplemental, consequential and transitional provision as OFCOM think fit.

(8) The Documentary Evidence Act 1868 (c 37) (proof of orders and regulations etc) shall have effect as if—

(a) OFCOM were included in the first column of the Schedule to that Act;

(b) OFCOM and persons authorised to act on their behalf were mentioned in the second column of that Schedule.

[3431]

NOTES

Commencement: 25 July 2003 (for the purpose of enabling network and service functions and spectrum functions to be carried out during the transitional period by the Director General of Telecommunications and the Secretary of State respectively) (see further s 408 and Sch 18 at **[3436]**, **[3460]**, and the Communications Act 2003 (Commencement No 1) Order 2003, SI 2003/1900 at **[3507]**); 29 December 2003 (for the purpose of enabling OFCOM to perform those functions) (see the Office of Communications Act 2002 (Commencement No 3) and Communications Act 2003 (Commencement No 2) Order 2003, SI 2003/3142 at **[3590]**).

---

404 Criminal liability of company directors etc

(1) Where an offence under any enactment to which this section applies is committed by a body corporate and is proved to have been committed with the consent or connivance of, or to be attributable to any neglect on the part of—

(a) a director, manager, secretary or other similar officer of the body corporate; or

(b) a person who was purporting to act in any such capacity;

he (as well as the body corporate) is guilty of that offence and shall be liable to be proceeded against and punished accordingly.

(2) Where an offence under any enactment to which this section applies—

(a) is committed by a Scottish firm, and

(b) is proved to have been committed with the consent or connivance of, or to be attributable to any neglect on the part of a partner of the firm,

he (as well as the firm) is guilty of that offence and shall be liable to be proceeded against and punished accordingly.

(3) In this section "director", in relation to a body corporate whose affairs are managed by its members, means a member of the body corporate.

(4) The enactments to which this section applies are every enactment contained in—

(a) this Act;

(b), (c) . . .

(d) the Wireless Telegraphy Act 1967 (c 72); or

(e) the Telecommunications Act 1984 (c 12).

(5) . . .

[3432]

NOTES

Commencement: 25 July 2003 (for the purpose of enabling network and service functions and spectrum functions to be carried out during the transitional period by the Director General of Telecommunications and the Secretary of State respectively) (see further s 408 and Sch 18 at **[3436]**, **[3460]**, and the Communications Act 2003 (Commencement No 1) Order 2003, SI 2003/1900 at **[3507]**); 29 December 2003 (for the purpose of enabling OFCOM to perform those functions) (see the Office of Communications Act 2002 (Commencement No 3) and Communications Act 2003 (Commencement No 2) Order 2003, SI 2003/3142 at **[3590]**).

Sub-s (4): paras (b), (c) repealed by the Wireless Telegraphy Act 2006, s 125(1), Sch 9, Pt 1, subject to transitional provisions and savings in s 124 of, Sch 8, Pt 1, paras 1–8, 24 to, that Act at **[4230]**, **[4239]**, and previously read as follows:

"(b) the Wireless Telegraphy Act 1949 (c 54);

(c) the Marine, &c., Broadcasting (Offences) Act 1967 (c 41);".

Sub-s (5): repeals the Wireless Telegraphy Act 1949, s 14(2).

405 General interpretation

(1) In this Act, except in so far as the context otherwise requires—

"the 1990 Act" means the Broadcasting Act 1990 (c 42);

"the 1996 Act" means the Broadcasting Act 1996 (c 55);

"access" is to be construed in accordance with subsection (4);

"apparatus" includes any equipment, machinery or device and any wire or cable and the casing or coating for any wire or cable;

"associated facility" has the meaning given by section 32;

"the BBC" means the British Broadcasting Corporation;

"body" (without more) means any body or association of persons, whether corporate or unincorporate, including a firm;

"broadcast" means broadcast by wireless telegraphy, and cognate expressions are to be construed accordingly;

"Broadcasting Act licence" means a licence under Part 1 or 3 of the 1990 Act or under Part 1 or 2 of the 1996 Act;

"business" includes any trade or profession;

"C4C" means the Channel Four Television Corporation;

"communications provider" means a person who (within the meaning of section 32(4)) provides an electronic communications network or an electronic communications service;

"the Consumer Panel" means the panel established under section 16;

"consumers" has the meaning given by subsection (5);

"Content Board" means the committee of OFCOM established and maintained under section 12;

"contravention" includes a failure to comply, and cognate expressions are to be construed accordingly;

"customers", in relation to a communications provider or a person who makes an associated facility available, means the following (including any of them whose use or potential use of the network, service or facility is for the purposes of, or in connection with, a business)—

(a) the persons to whom the network, service or facility is provided or made available in the course of any business carried on as such by the provider or person who makes it available;

(b) the persons to whom the communications provider or person making the facility available is seeking to secure that the network, service or facility is so provided or made available;

(c) the persons who wish to be so provided with the network or service, or to have the facility so made available, or who are likely to seek to become persons to whom the network, service or facility is so provided or made available;

"distribute", in relation to a service, does not include broadcast, and cognate expressions shall be construed accordingly;

"electronic communications network" and "electronic communications service" have the meanings given by section 32;

"enactment" includes any enactment comprised in an Act of the Scottish Parliament or in any Northern Ireland legislation;

"the enactments relating to the management of the radio spectrum" means—

[(a) the Wireless Telegraphy Act 2006; and

(g) the provisions of this Act so far as relating to that Act;]

"frequency" includes frequency band;

"holder", in relation to a Broadcasting Act licence, is to be construed in accordance with subsection (7), and cognate expressions are to be construed accordingly;

"information" includes accounts, estimates and projections and any document;

"intelligible" is to be construed in accordance with subsection (9);

"international obligation of the United Kingdom" includes any Community obligation and any obligation which will or may arise under any international agreement or arrangements to which the United Kingdom is a party;

"modification" includes omissions, alterations and additions, and cognate expressions are to be construed accordingly;

"OFCOM" means the Office of Communications;

"other member State" means a member State other than the United Kingdom;

"pre-commencement regulator" means any of the following—

(a) the Broadcasting Standards Commission;
(b) the Director General of Telecommunications;
(c) the Independent Television Commission;
(d) the Radio Authority;

"programme" includes an advertisement and, in relation to a service, anything included in that service;

"programme service" means—

(a) a television programme service;
(b) the public teletext service;
(c) an additional television service;
(d) a digital additional television service;
(e) a radio programme service; or
(f) a sound service provided by the BBC;

and expressions used in this definition and in Part 3 have the same meanings in this definition as in that Part;

"provide" and cognate expressions, in relation to an electronic communications network, electronic communications service or associated facilities, are to be construed in accordance with section 32(4);

"purposes of public service television broadcasting in the United Kingdom" shall be construed in accordance with subsection (4) of section 264 and subsections (5) and (6) of that section shall apply for the purposes of any provision of this Act referring to such purposes as they apply for the purposes of a report under that section;

"the radio transfer date" means the date on which the Radio Authority's functions under Part 3 of the 1990 Act and Part 2 of the 1996 Act are transferred under this Act to OFCOM;

"representation", in relation to a proposal or the contents of any notice or notification, includes an objection to the proposal or (as the case may be) to the whole or any part of those contents;

"subordinate legislation" means—

(a) any subordinate legislation, within the meaning of the Interpretation Act 1978 (c 30); or
(b) any statutory rules (within the meaning of the Statutory Rules (Northern Ireland) Order 1979 (SI 1979/1573 (NI 12));

"television and radio services" means—

(a) programme services apart from those provided by the BBC; and
(b) services provided by the BBC in relation to which OFCOM have functions;

"television programme" means any programme (with or without sounds) which—

(a) is produced wholly or partly to be seen on television; and
(b) consists of moving or still images or of legible text or of a combination of those things;

"the television transfer date" means the date on which the Independent Television Commission's functions under Part 1 of the 1990 Act and Part 1 of the 1996 Act are transferred under this Act to OFCOM;

"TV licence" means a licence for the purposes of section 363;

"the Welsh Authority" means the authority whose name is, by virtue of section 56(1) of the 1990 Act, Sianel Pedwar Cymru;

["wireless telegraphy" has the same meaning as in the Wireless Telegraphy Act 2006;

"wireless telegraphy licence" means a licence granted under section 8 of the Wireless Telegraphy Act 2006.]

(2) Any power under this Act to provide for the manner in which anything is to be done includes power to provide for the form in which it is to be done.

(3) References in this Act to OFCOM's functions under an enactment include references to their power to do anything which appears to them to be incidental or conducive to the carrying out of their functions under that enactment.

(4) References in this Act to access—

(a) in relation to an electronic communications network or electronic communications service, are references to the opportunity of making use of the network or service; and

(b) in relation to a programme service, are references to the opportunity of viewing in an intelligible form the programmes included in the service or (as the case may be) of listening to them in such a form.

(5) For the purposes of this Act persons are consumers in a market for a service, facility or apparatus, if they are—

(a) persons to whom the service, facility or apparatus is provided, made available or supplied (whether in their personal capacity or for the purposes of, or in connection with, their businesses);

(b) persons for whose benefit the service, facility or apparatus is provided, made available or supplied or for whose benefit persons falling within paragraph (a) arrange for it to be provided, made available or supplied;

(c) persons whom the person providing the service or making the facility available, or the supplier of the apparatus, is seeking to make into persons falling within paragraph (a) or (b); or

(d) persons who wish to become persons falling within paragraph (a) or (b) or who are likely to seek to become persons falling within one or both of those paragraphs.

(6) References in this Act to services in relation to which OFCOM have functions include references to any services in relation to which OFCOM are required to set standards under section 319.

(7) In this Act references, in relation to a time or a period, to the holder of a Broadcasting Act licence or of a particular description of such licence are references to the person who held that licence at that time or (as the case may be) to every person who held that licence for the whole or a part of that period.

(8) For the purposes of this Act the fact that a service is not in an intelligible form shall be disregarded, except where express provision is made to the contrary, in determining whether it has been provided—

(a) for general reception;

(b) for reception by particular persons; or

(c) for reception at a particular place or in a particular area.

(9) For the purposes of this Act something is not to be regarded as in an intelligible form if it cannot readily be understood without being decrypted or having some comparable process applied to it.

[3433]

NOTES

Commencement: 17 July 2003.

Sub-s (1): in definition "the enactments relating to the management of the radio spectrum", paras (a), (g) substituted for original paras (a)–(g), and definitions "wireless telegraphy" and "wireless telegraphy licence" substituted by the Wireless Telegraphy Act 2006, s 123, Sch 7, paras 25, 34.

406 Minor and consequential amendments, transitionals and repeals

(1) Schedule 17 (which provides for minor and consequential amendments in connection with the other provision made by this Act) shall have effect.

(2) The Secretary of State may by order make such consequential modifications of any enactment as—

(a) correspond to amendments of any other enactment that are made by Schedule 17; and

(b) appear to him to be appropriate in consequence of that provision of this Act.

(3) The Secretary of State may by order make any provision that he thinks fit for substituting a reference in any enactment or subordinate legislation to something defined for the purposes of this Act, or of any provisions contained in this Act, for a reference to something equivalent or similar that was defined for the purposes of the Telecommunications Act 1984 (c 12), or of provisions contained in that Act.

(4) The Secretary of State may by order make such further consequential modifications of—

(a) an enactment extending only to Scotland,

(b) an enactment extending only to Northern Ireland,

(c) a local enactment, or

(d) the provision of any subordinate legislation,

as appear to him to be appropriate in consequence of any provision of this Act.

(5) If it appears to the Secretary of State that a local enactment contains a provision which corresponds to a provision the effect of which is modified by an amendment in Schedule 17 of this Act of a listed provision, it shall be his duty to exercise his powers under this section to secure that a modification corresponding to that effected by that amendment is made to the local enactment.

(6) Schedule 18 (which contains transitional provisions in connection with the other provision made by this Act) shall have effect.

(7) Subject to the provisions of Schedule 18 and to the savings and commencement provisions set out in the notes to Schedule 19, the enactments and instruments specified in Schedule 19 (which include provisions that are spent or have ceased to be of any practical utility) are hereby repealed or revoked to the extent specified in the second column of that Schedule.

(8) In this section "local enactment" means—

(a) a local or personal Act;

(b) a public general Act relating only to London;

(c) an order or scheme made under an Act which has been confirmed by Parliament or brought into operation in accordance with special Parliamentary procedure;

(d) an enactment in a public general Act but amending a local enactment.

(9) In subsection (5) "listed provision" means the provisions of the following enactments—

(a) sections 11 and 14 of the London Overground Wires, etc Act 1933 (c xliv);

(b) section 7(6) of the London County Council (General Powers) Act 1949 (c lv);

(c) section 17(2) of the Lough Neagh and Lower Bann Drainage and Navigation Act (Northern Ireland) 1955 (c 15 (NI));

(d) section 17(4)(a) of the London County Council (General Powers) Act 1963 (c xvii);

(e) section 7(6) of the Greater London Council (General Powers) Act 1969 (c lii);

(f) section 20(1)(a) of the Thames Barrier and Flood Prevention Act 1972 (c xlv);

(g) section 32 of and paragraph 3(2)(b) of Schedule 2 and Part 10 of Schedule 7 to the Channel Tunnel Act 1987 (c 53);

(h) section 25(1) of the Norfolk and Suffolk Broads Act 1988 (c 4);

(i) section 5 of the London Local Authorities (No 2) Act 1990 (c xxx);

(j) paragraphs 1(c) and 16 of Schedule 2, paragraph 3(2)(c) of Schedule 4 and paragraph 21 of Schedule 7 to the Cardiff Bay Barrage Act 1993 (c 42);

(k) section 3(1) of the British Waterways Act 1995 (c i);

(l) paragraphs 6(4) and 15(4) of Schedule 6 and Part 4 of Schedule 15 to the Channel Tunnel Rail Link Act 1996 (c 61).

(10) This section has effect subject to section 408.

[3434]

NOTES

Commencement: this section is commenced as follows—

Sub-s (1): 25 July 2003 (certain purposes); 18 September 2003 (certain purposes); 29 December 2003 (certain purposes); 1 April 2004 (certain purposes).

Sub-ss (2)–(5), (8)–(10): 25 July 2003 (for the purpose of enabling network and service functions and spectrum functions to be carried out during the transitional period by the Director General of Telecommunications and the Secretary of State respectively); 29 December 2003 (for the purpose of transferring those functions to OFCOM).

Sub-s (6): see the Commencement note to Sch 18 at **[3460]**.

Sub-s (7): see the Commencement note to Sch 19 at **[3461]**.

Note: as to the transfer of network and service functions and spectrum functions during the transitional period, see s 408(6) of this Act at **[3436]**, the Communications Act 2003 (Commencement No 1) Order 2003, SI 2003/1900 at **[3507]**, and the Communications Act 2003 (Commencement No 2) Order 2003, SI 2003/3142 at **[3590]**.

Orders: the Communications Act 2003 (Consequential Amendments) Order 2003, SI 2003/2155; the Communications Act 2003 (Amendment of the Medicines (Monitoring of Advertising) Regulations 1994) Order 2003, SI 2003/3093; the Communications Act 2003 (Consequential Amendments No 2) Order 2003, SI 2003/3182; the Communications Act 2003 (Consequential Amendments) Order 2004, SI 2004/945.

407 Pre-consolidation amendments

(1) The Secretary of State may by order make such modifications of—

(a) …

(b) the enactments relating to broadcasting, and

(c) enactments referring to enactments falling within paragraph … (b),

as in his opinion facilitate, or are otherwise desirable in connection with, the consolidation of those enactments or any of them.

(2) No order is to be made under this section unless a Bill for repealing and re-enacting—

(a) the enactments modified by the order, or

(b) enactments relating to matters connected with the matters to which enactments modified by the order relate,

has been presented to either House of Parliament.

(3) An order under this section is not to come into force until immediately before the commencement of the Act resulting from that Bill.

(4) No order is to be made containing provision authorised by this section unless a draft of the order has been laid before Parliament and approved by a resolution of each House.

(5) In this section "the enactments relating to broadcasting" means—

(a) the 1990 Act;

(b) the 1996 Act;

(c) Part 3 of this Act; and

(d) the other provisions of this Act so far as relating to the 1990 Act, the 1996 Act or that Part.

[3435]

NOTES

Commencement: 18 September 2003.

Sub-s (1): para (a), and words "(a) or" in para (c) (omitted) repealed by the Wireless Telegraphy Act 2006, s 125(1), Sch 9, Pt 1, subject to transitional provisions and savings in s 124 of, Sch 8, Pt 1, paras 1–8, 24 to, that Act at **[4230]**, **[4239]**, and para (a) previously read as follows:

"(a) the enactments relating to the management of the radio spectrum,".

Orders: the Wireless Telegraphy (Pre-Consolidation Amendments) Order 2006, SI 2006/1391.

408 Transitional provision for anticipatory carrying out of functions

(1) This section applies where an order under section 411 bringing into force—

(a) a provision of Part 1, 2 or 6, or

(b) a provision of Chapter 1 of Part 5,

states that that provision is brought into force at a particular time for the purpose only of enabling specified networks and services functions, or specified spectrum functions, to be carried out during the transitional period by the Director General of Telecommunications or the Secretary of State.

(2) In relation to times falling in the transitional period, that provision is to have effect as if—

(a) references in that provision to OFCOM, and
(b) references to OFCOM inserted by that provision in any other enactment,

were references, in accordance with subsection (3), to the Director General of Telecommunications or to the Secretary of State.

(3) The references have effect—

(a) as references to the Director General of Telecommunications to the extent that the provision is brought into force for the purpose of enabling specified networks and services functions to be carried out; and
(b) as references to the Secretary of State, to the extent that the provision is brought into force for the purpose of enabling specified spectrum functions to be carried out.

(4) An order bringing a provision into force as mentioned in subsection (1) may include provision specifying the extent to which it is to be taken, for the purposes of subsection (3), to have been brought into force for the purpose of enabling particular functions to be carried out.

(5) In relation to times after the end of the transitional period for a provision which has been brought into force for enabling specified functions to be carried out by the Director General of Telecommunications or the Secretary of State, anything which—

(a) was done, during that period, by or in relation to that Director or the Secretary of State, and
(b) was so done for the purposes of, or in connection with, the carrying out of those functions,

is to have effect as if had been done by or in relation to OFCOM.

(6) In this section "the transitional period", in relation to a provision brought into force as mentioned in subsection (1) by an order under section 411, means the period which—

(a) begins with the time when it is so brought into force; and
(b) ends with the time from which that order, or a subsequent order under that section, brings the provision into force for the purpose of conferring on OFCOM the functions in question.

(7) In this section "networks and services functions" means any of the following functions of OFCOM under this Act—

(a) their functions under sections 24 and 25;
(b) their functions under Chapter 1 of Part 2;
(c) their functions under Chapter 3 of Part 2, except to the extent that those functions relate to—
  (i) disputes relating to rights or obligations conferred or imposed by or under the enactments relating to the management of the radio spectrum; or
  (ii) decisions made under those enactments;
(d) their functions under Chapter 1 of Part 5, except to the extent that those functions relate to broadcasting or related matters;
(e) their functions under Schedule 18 to this Act in relation to the abolition of licensing (within the meaning of that Schedule).

(8) In this section "spectrum functions" means—

(a) the functions under the enactments relating to the management of the radio spectrum which by virtue of this Act are conferred on OFCOM; and
(b) the functions conferred on OFCOM by so much of Chapter 3 of Part 2 as relates to the disputes and decisions mentioned in subsection (7)(c).

[3436]

NOTES

Commencement: 25 July 2003 (for the purpose of enabling network and service functions and spectrum functions to be carried out during the transitional period by the Director General of Telecommunications and the Secretary of State respectively) (see further s 408 and Sch 18 at **[3436]**, **[3460]**, and the Communications Act 2003 (Commencement No 1) Order 2003, SI 2003/1900 at **[3507]**); 29 December 2003 (for the purpose of enabling OFCOM to perform those functions) (see the Office of Communications Act 2002 (Commencement No 3) and Communications Act 2003 (Commencement No 2) Order 2003, SI 2003/3142 at **[3590]**).

Orders: the Communications Act 2003 (Commencement No 1) Order 2003, SI 2003/1900 at **[3507]**; the Office of Communications Act 2002 (Commencement No 3) and Communications Act 2003 (Commencement No 2) Order 2003, SI 2003/3142 at **[3590]**.

409 Modifications consequential on regulations implementing Directives

(1) This section applies if it appears to the Secretary of State that regulations under section 2 of the European Communities Act 1972 (c 68) for giving effect to Community obligations imposed by the Communications Directives have come into force before the passing of this Act.

(2) The Secretary of State may by order—

(a) repeal any relevant provision of this Act which appears to him to be unnecessary, or to have become spent, in consequence of the regulations;

(b) make such other modifications of the relevant provisions of this Act as he considers appropriate in consequence of the regulations;

(c) revoke provision made by the regulations; and

(d) make transitory or transitional provision in relation to anything done by or under the regulations.

(3) The Secretary of State's power under this section includes power to make consequential amendments of enactments not contained in this Act.

(4) In this section—

"the Communications Directives" means—

(a) the Access Directive, that is to say, Directive 2002/19/EC of the European Parliament and of the Council on access to, and interconnection of, electronic communications networks and associated facilities;

(b) the Authorisation Directive, that is to say, Directive 2002/20/EC of the European Parliament and of the Council on the authorisation of electronic communications networks and services;

(c) the Framework Directive, that is to say, Directive 2002/21/EC of the European Parliament and of the Council on a common regulatory framework for electronic communications networks and services;

(d) the Universal Service Directive, that is to say, Directive 2002/22/EC of the European Parliament and of the Council on universal service and users' rights relating to electronic communications networks and services;

"relevant provision of this Act" means a provision contained in—

(a) Part 1, 2 or 6; or

(b) Chapter 1 of Part 5.

(5) No order is to be made containing provision authorised by this section unless a draft of the order has been laid before Parliament and approved by a resolution of each House.

[3437]

NOTES

Commencement: to be appointed.

410 Application of enactments to territorial sea and other waters

(1) This section applies to—

(a) provision made by or under Part 2 of this Act;

(b) any provision of the enactments relating to the management of the radio spectrum that are not contained in that Part [or the Wireless Telegraphy Act 2006]; and

(c) any provision of Chapter 1 of Part 5 of this Act so far as it relates to a matter as respects which provision falling within paragraph (a) or (b) is made [or a matter as respects which the Wireless Telegraphy Act 2006 makes provision].

(2) Her Majesty may by Order in Council provide—

(a) for an area of the territorial sea to be treated, for the purposes of any provision to which this section applies, as if it were situated in such part of the United Kingdom as may be specified in the Order; and

(b) for jurisdiction with respect to questions arising in relation to the territorial sea under any such provision to be conferred on courts in a part of the United Kingdom so specified.

(3) An Order in Council under section 11 of the Petroleum Act 1998 (c 17) [or section 87 of the Energy Act 2004] (application of civil law to offshore installations etc) may make provision for treating—

(a) an installation with respect to which provision is made under that section and which is outside the territorial sea but in waters to which that section applies, and

(b) waters within 500 metres of the installation,

as if for the purposes of provisions to which this section applies, they were situated in such part of the United Kingdom as is specified in the Order.

(4) The jurisdiction conferred on a court by an Order in Council under this section is in addition to any jurisdiction exercisable apart from this section by that or any other court.

(5) Subsection (3) of section 402 applies to the power to make an Order in Council under this section as it applies to any power of the Secretary of State to make an order under this Act, but as if references in that subsection to the Secretary of State were references to Her Majesty in Council.

(6) A statutory instrument containing an Order in Council under this section shall be subject to annulment in pursuance of a resolution of either House of Parliament.

(7) In this section—

"installation" includes any floating structure or device maintained on a station by whatever means, and installations in transit;

"the territorial sea" means the territorial sea adjacent to the United Kingdom.

[3438]

NOTES

Commencement: 25 July 2003 (for the purpose of enabling network and service functions and spectrum functions to be carried out during the transitional period by the Director General of Telecommunications and the Secretary of State respectively) (see further s 408 and Sch 18 at **[3436]**, **[3460]**, and the Communications Act 2003 (Commencement No 1) Order 2003, SI 2003/1900 at **[3507]**); 29 December 2003 (for the purpose of enabling OFCOM to perform those functions) (see the Office of Communications Act 2002 (Commencement No 3) and Communications Act 2003 (Commencement No 2) Order 2003, SI 2003/3142 at **[3590]**).

Sub-s (1): words in square brackets in paras (b), (c) inserted by the Wireless Telegraphy Act 2006, s 123, Sch 7, paras 25, 35.

Sub-s (3): words in square brackets inserted by the Energy Act 2004, s 87(5).

411 Short title, commencement and extent

(1) This Act may be cited as the Communications Act 2003.

(2) This Act (except the provisions listed in subsection (3), which come into force on the passing of this Act) shall come into force on such day as the Secretary of State may by order appoint; and different days may be appointed under this subsection for different purposes.

(3) Those provisions are sections 31(1) to (4) and (6) and 405 and this section.

(4) An order under subsection (2) may include provision making such transitional or transitory provision, in addition to that made by Schedule 18, as the Secretary of State considers appropriate in connection with the bringing into force of any provisions of this Act; and the power to make transitional or transitory provision includes power to make—

(a) different provision for different cases (including different provision in respect of different areas);

(b) provision subject to such exemptions and exceptions as the Secretary of State thinks fit; and

(c) such incidental, supplemental and consequential provision as he thinks fit.

(5) This Act extends to Northern Ireland.

(6) Subject to subsection (7), Her Majesty may by Order in Council extend the provisions of this Act, with such modifications as appear to Her Majesty in Council to be appropriate, to any of the Channel Islands or to the Isle of Man.

(7) Subsection (6) does not authorise the extension to any place of a provision of this Act so far as it gives effect to an amendment of an enactment that is not itself capable of being extended there in exercise of a power conferred on Her Majesty in Council.

(8) Subsection (3) of section 402 applies to the power to make an Order in Council under this section as it applies to any power of the Secretary of State to make an order under this Act, but as if references in that subsection to the Secretary of State were references to Her Majesty in Council.

[3439]

NOTES

Commencement: 17 July 2003.

Orders: the Communications Act 2003 (Commencement No 1) Order 2003, SI 2003/1900 at **[3507]**; the Office of Communications Act 2002 (Commencement No 3) and Communications Act 2003 (Commencement No 2) Order 2003, SI 2003/3142 at **[3590]**; the Communications Act 2003 (Commencement No 3) Order 2004, SI 2004/3309.

Orders in Council: the Communications (Bailiwick of Guernsey) Order 2003, SI 2003/3195; the Communications (Jersey) Order 2003, SI 2003/3197; the Communications (Isle of Man) Order 2003, SI 2003/3198; the Communications (Bailiwick of Guernsey) Order 2004, SI 2004/307; the Broadcasting and Communications (Jersey) Order 2004, SI 2004/308; the Communications (Bailiwick of Guernsey) (No 2) Order 2004, SI 2004/715; the Broadcasting and Communications (Jersey) (No 2) Order 2004, SI 2004/716; the Broadcasting and Communications (Isle of Man) (No 2) Order 2004, SI 2004/718; the Broadcasting and Communications (Jersey) (No 3) Order 2004, SI 2004/1114; the Broadcasting and Communications (Isle of Man) (No 3) Order 2004, SI 2004/1115; the Communications (Bailiwick of Guernsey) (No 3) Order 2004, SI 2004/1116.

SCHEDULES

SCHEDULE 1
FUNCTIONS TRANSFERRED TO OFCOM

Section 2

Wireless telegraphy functions

1, 2. …

Functions in relation to the licensing etc of television services

3. The following functions of the Independent Television Commission are transferred to OFCOM—

   (a) the function of granting or awarding licences under Part 1 of the 1990 Act (independent television services) and Part 1 of the 1996 Act (digital television broadcasting);
   (b) the Commission's functions under those Parts in relation to, and to applications for, licences under either of those Parts;
   (c) the function of securing the provision of a nationwide system of television broadcasting services known as Channel 3;
   (d) the function of securing the provision of the television broadcasting service known as Channel 5.

Functions in relation to C4C

4. The functions conferred on the Independent Television Commission by or under section 23 of the 1990 Act and under Schedule 3 to that Act (appointment of members of C4C and related administrative functions) are transferred to OFCOM.

Functions in relation to the licensing of radio services

5. The following functions of the Radio Authority are transferred to OFCOM—

   (a) the function of granting or awarding licences under Part 3 of the 1990 Act (independent radio services) and Part 2 of the 1996 Act (digital sound broadcasting); and
   (b) the Authority's functions under those Parts in relation to licences granted or awarded under those Parts.

Functions in relation to the proscription of foreign satellite services

6. The functions of the Independent Television Commission and of the Radio Authority under section 177 of the 1990 Act (proscription of foreign satellite services) are transferred to OFCOM.

Functions in relation to Gaelic broadcasting

7. The functions of the Independent Television Commission under sections 183 and 184 of the 1990 Act and the functions of that Commission and of the Radio Authority under Schedule 19 to that Act (Gaelic broadcasting) are transferred to OFCOM.

Functions in relation to the national television archive

8. The functions of the Independent Television Commission under section 185 of the 1990 Act (maintenance of the national television archive) are transferred to OFCOM.

Warrants to enter and search premises to enforce broadcasting licences provisions

9. The functions of the Independent Television Commission and of the Radio Authority under section 196(1) of the 1990 Act (entry and search for the purposes of enforcing licensing provisions of the 1990 and 1996 Acts) are transferred to OFCOM.

Variation of existing Channel 3 and Channel 5 licences

10. Any power to vary licences which is conferred on the Independent Television Commission by an order under section 28 of the 1996 Act is transferred to OFCOM.

Reports for the purposes of the review of digital broadcasting

11. The functions of the Independent Television Commission and of the Radio Authority under sections 33 and 67 of the 1996 Act (reports to the Secretary of State for the purposes of his review of digital broadcasting) are transferred to OFCOM.

Functions in relation to reservation of digital capacity to the BBC

12. The function of the Secretary of State under section 49(4) of the 1996 Act (reserving digital capacity on a local radio multiplex service for the BBC) is transferred to OFCOM.

Functions in relation to listed events

13. The functions of the Independent Television Commission under Part 4 of the 1996 Act (functions in connection with listed events) are transferred to OFCOM.

Functions relating to fairness and privacy in broadcasting

14. The following functions of the Broadcasting Standards Commission under Part 5 of the 1996 Act are transferred to OFCOM—

(a) the Commission's function of drawing up and from time to time revising a code of practice under section 107 of that Act (codes of practice relation to fairness and privacy); and

(b) their functions in relation to fairness complaints under that Part.

[3440]

NOTES

Commencement: 29 December 2003 (paras 1(1)(a) except in relation to television licences, 1(1)(b)–(d), (2), (3), 2–14); 1 April 2004 (otherwise).

Paras 1, 2 repealed by the Wireless Telegraphy Act 2006, s 125(1), Sch 9, Pt 1, subject to transitional provisions and savings in s 124 of, Sch 8, Pt 1, paras 1–8, 24 to, that Act at **[4230]**, **[4239]**, and previously read as follows:

"1.—(1) Subject to sub-paragraphs (2) and (3), the functions of the Secretary of State under the following enactments are transferred to OFCOM—

(a) the Wireless Telegraphy Act 1949 (c 54);

(b) section 7 of the Wireless Telegraphy Act 1967 (c 72) (restriction on dealings in, and custody of, certain apparatus);
(c) Part 6 of the Telecommunications Act 1984 (c 12) (provisions relating to wireless telegraphy);
(d) the Wireless Telegraphy Act 1998 (c 6).

(2) The following functions remain functions of the Secretary of State—
(a) his functions under section 5 of the Wireless Telegraphy Act 1949 (misleading messages and interception and disclosure of wireless telegraphy messages);
(b) his functions under section 6 of that Act (regulations about apparatus on board ships etc);
(c) his functions under section 7 of that Act (powers as to wireless personnel).

(3) The functions of the Secretary of State under section 84 of the Telecommunications Act 1984 (approval of wireless telegraphy apparatus)—
(a) if an order made by the Secretary of State under subsection (8A) of that section is in force, shall be exercisable by him and by OFCOM in accordance with that order; and
(b) if there is no such order, shall be exercisable by OFCOM.

2.—(1) The functions of the Secretary of State under section 7A of the Marine, &c., Broadcasting (Offences) Act 1967 (c 41) (powers of enforcement of marine offences under that Act) shall (with the following exception) be exercisable concurrently by the Secretary of State and OFCOM.

(2) The exception is the functions of the Secretary of State under that section so far as they relate to powers exercisable by virtue of subsection (7) of that section.".

SCHEDULE 2
TRANSFER SCHEMES

Section 30

Contents of transfer scheme

1.—(1) A transfer scheme—
(a) shall set out the property, rights and liabilities to be transferred by the scheme; and
(b) may make incidental, supplemental, consequential and transitional provision in connection with the transfer of that property and of those rights and liabilities.

(2) The provisions of the scheme setting out the property, rights and liabilities to be transferred may do so in either or both of the following ways—
(a) by specifying them or describing them in particular; or
(b) by identifying them generally by reference to, or to a specific part of, an undertaking from which they are to be transferred.

(3) The property, rights and liabilities that are to be capable of being transferred by a transfer scheme include—
(a) property, rights and liabilities that would not otherwise be capable of being transferred or assigned by the person from whom they are transferred;
(b) property acquired and rights and liabilities arising in the period after the making of the scheme and before it comes into force;
(c) rights and liabilities arising subsequently in respect of matters occurring in that period;
(d) property situated anywhere in the United Kingdom or elsewhere and rights and liabilities under the law of any part of the United Kingdom or of any place outside the United Kingdom; and
(e) rights and liabilities under an enactment.

(4) The provision that may be made under sub-paragraph (1)(b) includes provision for the creation in favour of a pre-commencement regulator, the Secretary of State or OFCOM of rights or liabilities over or in respect of property transferred to OFCOM or property retained by a pre-commencement regulator or the Secretary of State.

(5) The transfers to which effect may be given by a transfer scheme, and the rights that may be created by means of such a scheme, include transfers that are to take effect, and rights that are to arise, in accordance with the scheme as if there were—
(a) no such requirement to obtain a person's consent or concurrence,
(b) no such liability in respect of any contravention of any other requirement, and
(c) no such interference with any interest or right,

as there would be, in the case of a transaction apart from this Act (whether under any enactment or agreement or otherwise), by reason of any provision having effect in relation to the terms on which a pre-commencement regulator or the Secretary of State is entitled or subject to any property, right or liability.

Effect of transfer scheme

2.—(1) Property transferred by a transfer scheme shall, on the coming into force of the scheme, vest in OFCOM without further assurance.

(2) Where any transfer scheme comes into force, any agreement made, transaction effected or other thing done by or in relation to the person from whom any transfers for which the scheme provides are made shall have effect, so far as necessary for the purposes of those transfers, as if—

(a) it had been made, effected or done by or in relation to OFCOM; and

(b) OFCOM were the same person in law as the person from whom the transfer is made.

(3) Accordingly, references in any agreement, document, process or instrument of any description to the person from whom anything is transferred by means of a transfer scheme shall have effect, so far as necessary for the purpose of giving effect to the transfer from the coming into force of the scheme, as references to OFCOM.

(4) Where any agreement, document, process or instrument of any description has effect, in relation to anything transferred by means of a transfer scheme, as referring (whether expressly or by implication)—

(a) to a member or to an officer of a pre-commencement regulator, or

(b) to an officer of the Secretary of State,

that agreement, document, process or instrument shall have effect so far as necessary for the purposes of the transfers effected by the scheme and in consequence of them, as referring instead to the person mentioned in sub-paragraph (5).

(5) That person is—

(a) the person nominated for the purposes of the transfer by OFCOM; or

(b) in default of a nomination, the member or employee of OFCOM who most closely corresponds to the member or officer originally referred to.

(6) Nothing in sub-paragraph (3) or (4) is to apply in relation to any reference in an enactment or in subordinate legislation.

Retrospective modification of a transfer scheme

3.—(1) If at any time after the coming into force of a transfer scheme it appears to the Secretary of State that it is appropriate to do so, he may by order provide for the scheme to be deemed to have come into force with such modifications (including modifications retrospective to the time of the coming into force of the scheme) as may be provided for in the order.

(2) The power under this paragraph to provide by order for the modification of a transfer scheme shall be exercisable for the purpose only of making provision that could have been made by the scheme.

(3) Before making an order under this paragraph the Secretary of State must consult OFCOM.

Compensation

4.—(1) Where, in consequence of any provision included in a transfer scheme, the interests, rights or liabilities of a third party are modified as mentioned in sub-paragraph (2), the third party is to be entitled to such compensation as may be just in respect of—

(a) any diminution in the value of any of his interests or rights, or

(b) any increase in the burden of his liabilities,

which is attributable to that modification.

(2) The modifications mentioned in sub-paragraph (1) are modifications by virtue of which—

(a) an interest of the third party in any property is transformed into, or replaced by—
(i) an interest in only part of that property; or
(ii) separate interests in different parts of that property;
(b) a right of the third party against any of the pre-commencement regulators or against the Secretary of State is transformed into, or replaced by, two or more rights which do not include a right which, on its own, is equivalent (disregarding the person against whom it is enforceable) to the right against that regulator or (as the case may be) against the Secretary of State; or
(c) a liability of the third party to any of the pre-commencement regulators or to the Secretary of State is transformed into, or replaced by, two or more separate liabilities at least one of which is a liability enforceable by a person other than the person by whom it was enforceable before being so transformed.

(3) Where—
(a) a third party would, apart from any provision of a transfer scheme, have become entitled to, or to exercise, any interest or right arising or exercisable in respect of the transfer or creation in accordance with such a scheme of any property, rights or liabilities, and
(b) the provisions of that scheme have the effect of preventing that person's entitlement to, or to exercise, that interest or right from arising on any occasion in respect of anything mentioned in paragraph (a), and
(c) provision is not made by a transfer scheme for securing that an entitlement to, or to exercise, that interest or right or an equivalent interest or right, is preserved or created so as to arise in respect of the first occasion when corresponding circumstances next occur after the coming into force of the transfers for which the scheme provides,

the third party is to be entitled to such compensation as may be just in respect of the extinguishment of the interest or right.

(4) A liability to pay compensation under this paragraph shall fall on the persons mentioned in sub-paragraph (5) who (as the case may be)—
(a) have interests in the whole or any part of the property affected by the modification in question,
(b) are subject to the rights of the person to be compensated which are affected by the modification in question,
(c) are entitled to enforce the liabilities of the person to be compensated which are affected by that modification, or
(d) benefit from the extinguishment of the entitlement mentioned in sub-paragraph (3),

and that liability shall be apportioned between those persons in such manner as may be appropriate having regard to the extent of their respective interests, rights or liabilities or the extent of the benefit they respectively obtain from the extinguishment.

(5) Those persons are the pre-commencement regulators and the Secretary of State.

(6) Sub-paragraph (4) shall have effect subject to so much of any transfer scheme (including the one that gives rise to the liability) as makes provision for the transfer of any liability under that sub-paragraph to OFCOM.

(7) Any dispute as to whether, or as to the person by whom, any compensation is to be paid under this paragraph, and any dispute as to the amount of compensation to be paid by a person, shall be referred to and determined—
(a) where the claimant requires the matter to be determined in England and Wales or in Northern Ireland, by an arbitrator appointed by the Lord Chancellor; or
(b) where the claimant requires the matter to be determined in Scotland, by an arbiter appointed by the Lord President of the Court of Session.

(8) In this paragraph "third party", in relation to provisions capable of giving rise to compensation under this paragraph, means any person other than—
(a) a pre-commencement regulator; and
(b) the Secretary of State.

Stamp duty

5.—(1) Stamp duty is not to be chargeable—
(a) on a transfer scheme; or
(b) on an instrument or agreement certified by the Secretary of State to the

Commissioners of Inland Revenue as made for the purposes of a transfer scheme, or as made for purposes connected with such a scheme.

(2) But a transfer scheme, or an instrument or agreement so certified, is to be treated as duly stamped only if—

(a) in accordance with section 12 of the Stamp Act 1891 (c 39) it has been stamped with a stamp denoting either that it is not chargeable to duty or that it has been duly stamped; or

(b) it is stamped with the duty to which it would be chargeable apart from this paragraph.

[Stamp duty land tax

5A.—(1) For the purposes of stamp duty land tax, a land transaction effected by, or for the purposes of, or for purposes connected with, a transfer scheme is exempt from charge.

(2) Relief under this paragraph must be claimed in a land transaction return or an amendment of such a return.

(3) In this paragraph—

"land transaction" has the meaning given by section 43(1) of the Finance Act 2003;

"land transaction return" has the meaning given by section 76(1) of that Act.]

Interpretation of Schedule

6. In this Schedule "transfer scheme" means a scheme made by a pre-commencement regulator or by the Secretary of State under section 30.

[3441]

NOTES

Commencement: 18 September 2003.

Para 5A: inserted by the Stamp Duty Land Tax (Consequential Amendment of Enactments) Regulations 2003, SI 2003/2867, reg 2, Schedule, Pt 1, para 33.

(*Sch 3 amends the Telecommunications Act 1984, Sch 2 at* **[4063]**.)

SCHEDULE 4
COMPULSORY PURCHASE AND ENTRY FOR EXPLORATORY PURPOSES

Section 118

Interpretation

1. In this Schedule—

"code operator" means a provider of an electronic communications network in whose case the electronic communications code is applied by a direction under section 106; and

"the operator's network", in relation to a code operator, means so much of the electronic communications network provided by the operator as is not excluded from the application of the electronic communications code under section 106(5).

General duties with respect to powers under Schedule

2. In exercising his powers under this Schedule it shall be the duty of the Secretary of State to have regard, in particular, to each of the following—

(a) the duties imposed on OFCOM by sections 3 and 4;

(b) the need to protect the environment and, in particular, to conserve the natural beauty and amenity of the countryside;

(c) the need to ensure that highways are not damaged or obstructed, and traffic not interfered with, to any greater extent than is reasonably necessary;

(d) the need to encourage the sharing of the use of electronic communications apparatus.

Compulsory purchase of land: England and Wales

3.—(1) Subject to sub-paragraph (2), the Secretary of State may authorise a code operator to purchase compulsorily any land in England and Wales which is required by the operator—

(a) for, or in connection with, the establishment or running of the operator's network; or

(b) as to which it can reasonably be foreseen that it will be so required.

(2) No order is to be made authorising a compulsory purchase under this paragraph by a code operator except with OFCOM's consent.

(3) This power to purchase land compulsorily includes power to acquire an easement or other right over land by the creation of a new right.

(4) The Acquisition of Land Act 1981 (c 67) is to apply to any compulsory purchase under this paragraph as if the code operator were a local authority within the meaning of that Act.

(5) The provisions of the Town and Country Planning Act 1990 (c 8) specified in sub-paragraph (6) have effect in relation to land acquired compulsorily by a code operator under this paragraph as they have effect in relation to land acquired compulsorily by statutory undertakers.

(6) Those provisions are—

(a) sections 238 to 240 (use and development of consecrated land and burial ground);

(b) section 241 (use and development of land for open spaces); and

(c) sections 271 to 274 (extinguishment of rights of way, and rights as to apparatus, of statutory undertakers).

(7) Where a code operator has acquired land under this paragraph, he must not dispose of that land, or of an interest or right in or over it, except with OFCOM's consent.

Compulsory purchase of land: Scotland

4.—(1) Subject to sub-paragraph (2), the Secretary of State may authorise a code operator to purchase compulsorily any land in Scotland which is required by the operator—

(a) for, or in connection with, the establishment or running of the operator's network; or

(b) as to which it can reasonably be foreseen that it will be so required.

(2) No order is to be made authorising a compulsory purchase under this paragraph except with OFCOM's consent.

(3) This power to purchase land compulsorily includes power to acquire a servitude or other right over land by the creation of a new right.

(4) The Acquisition of Land (Authorisation Procedure) (Scotland) Act 1947 (c 42) applies to any compulsory purchase under this paragraph as if—

(a) the code operator were a local authority within the meaning of that Act; and

(b) this paragraph had been in force immediately before the commencement of that Act.

(5) The provisions of the Town and Country Planning (Scotland) Act 1997 (c 8) specified in sub-paragraph (6) have effect in relation to land acquired compulsorily by a code operator under this paragraph as they have effect in relation to land acquired compulsorily by statutory undertakers.

(6) Those provisions are—

(a) section 197 (provisions as to churches and burial grounds);

(b) section 198 (use and development of land for open spaces); and

(c) sections 224 to 227 (extinguishment of rights of way, and rights as to apparatus, of statutory undertakers).

(7) Where a code operator has acquired land under this paragraph, he must not dispose of that land, or of any interest or right in or over it, except with OFCOM's consent.

Compulsory purchase of land: Northern Ireland

5.—(1) Where a code operator proposes to acquire, otherwise than by agreement, any land in Northern Ireland required by him—

(a) for, or in connection with, the establishment or running of the operator's network, or

(b) as to which it can reasonably be foreseen that it will be so required,

he may, with OFCOM's consent, apply to the Secretary of State for an order vesting that land in him.

(2) On such an application the Secretary of State is to have power to make such an order.

(3) This power to acquire land compulsorily includes power to acquire an easement or other right over land by the creation of a new right.

(4) Where a code operator has acquired land under this paragraph, he must not dispose of that land, or of any interest or right in or over it, except with OFCOM's consent.

(5) The following provisions—

(a) Schedule 6 to the Local Government Act (Northern Ireland) 1972 (c 9 (NI)) (acquisition of land by vesting order), and

(b) Schedule 8 to the Health and Personal Social Services (Northern Ireland) Order 1972 (SI 1972/1265 (NI 14)) (provisions as to inquiries),

have effect for the purposes of the acquisition of land by means of a vesting order under this paragraph as they have effect for the purposes of that Act and that Order but subject to the modifications set out in sub-paragraph (6).

(6) Those modifications are—

(a) for any reference to the Department substitute a reference to the Secretary of State;

(b) for any reference to the Act or Order in question substitute a reference to this Act;

(c) for any reference in Schedule 6 to the Local Government Act (Northern Ireland) 1972 to a council substitute a reference to the code operator;

(d) in paragraph 6(2) of that Schedule, for the words from "the fund" onwards substitute "funds of the code operator (in this Schedule referred to as "the compensation fund") and shall be discharged by payments made by the code operator"; and

(e) in paragraph 12(2) of that Schedule for "the clerk of the council" substitute "such person as may be designated for the purposes of this Schedule by the code operator".

(7) The enactments for the time being in force relating to the assessment of compensation in respect of land vested in a district council by an order made under Schedule 6 to the Local Government Act (Northern Ireland) 1972 are to apply, subject to any necessary modifications, in relation to land vested in a code operator by an order made under this paragraph.

(8) In this paragraph, "land" has the meaning assigned to it by section 45(1)(a) of the Interpretation Act (Northern Ireland) 1954 (c 33 (NI)).

Entry on land for exploratory purposes: England and Wales

6.—(1) A person—

(a) nominated by a code operator, and

(b) duly authorised in writing by the Secretary of State,

may, at any reasonable time, enter upon and survey land in England and Wales for the purpose of ascertaining whether the land would be suitable for use by the code operator for, or in connection with, the establishment or running of the operator's network.

(2) This paragraph does not apply in relation to land covered by buildings or used as a garden or pleasure ground.

(3) Sections 324(8) and 325(1) to (5), (8) and (9) of the Town and Country Planning Act 1990 (c 8) (supplementary provisions relating to powers of entry) have effect in relation to the power conferred by this paragraph—

(a) as they have effect in relation to the powers conferred by section 324 of that Act; but

(b) subject to the modifications set out in sub-paragraph (4).

(4) Those modifications are—

(a) in section 324(8) (power to search and bore for the purpose of ascertaining the nature of the subsoil or the presence of minerals) omit "or the presence of minerals therein"; and

(b) in section 325(1) (24 hours' notice to be given of an intended entry upon occupied land) for "24 hours" substitute "28 days".

(5) Where, in an exercise of the power conferred by this paragraph, any damage is caused to land or to chattels, the code operator must—

(a) make good the damage; or

(b) pay compensation in respect of the damage to every person interested in the land or chattels.

(6) Where, in consequence of an exercise of the power conferred by this paragraph, a person is disturbed in his enjoyment of land or chattels, the code operator must pay that person compensation in respect of the disturbance.

(7) Section 118 of the Town and Country Planning Act 1990 (c 8) (determination of disputes as to compensation) applies to any question of disputed compensation under this paragraph as it applies to such questions under Part 4 of that Act.

Entry on land for exploratory purposes: Scotland

7.—(1) A person—

(a) nominated by a code operator, and

(b) duly authorised in writing by the Secretary of State,

may, at any reasonable time, enter upon and survey any land in Scotland for the purpose of ascertaining whether the land would be suitable for use by the code operator for, or in connection with, the establishment or running of the operator's network.

(2) This paragraph does not apply in relation to land covered by buildings or used as a garden or pleasure ground.

(3) Sections 269(6) and 270(1) to (5), (8) and (9) of the Town and Country Planning (Scotland) Act 1997 (c 8) (supplementary provisions relating to powers of entry) have effect in relation to the power conferred by this paragraph—

(a) as they have effect in relation to the powers conferred by section 269 of that Act; but

(b) subject to the modifications set out in sub-paragraph (4).

(4) Those modifications are—

(a) in section 269(6) (power to search and bore for the purpose of ascertaining the nature of the subsoil or the presence of minerals), omit "or the presence of minerals therein"; and

(b) in section 270(1) (24 hours' notice to be given of an intended entry upon occupied land) for "24 hours" substitute "28 days".

(5) Where, in an exercise of the power conferred by this paragraph, damage is caused to land or to corporeal moveables, the code operator must—

(a) make good the damage; or

(b) pay compensation in respect of the damage to every person interested in the land or corporeal moveables.

(6) Where, in consequence of an exercise of the power conferred by this paragraph, a person is disturbed in his enjoyment of any land or corporeal moveables, the code operator must pay that person compensation in respect of the disturbance.

(7) A dispute arising under this paragraph—

(a) as to the effect of damage, or

(b) as to the amount of compensation,

must be determined by arbitration by a single arbiter appointed by agreement between the parties or, in default of an agreement, by the Secretary of State.

Entry on land for exploratory purposes: Northern Ireland

8.—(1) A person—

(a) nominated by a code operator, and

(b) duly authorised in writing by the Secretary of State,

may, at any reasonable time, enter upon and survey any land in Northern Ireland for the purpose of ascertaining whether the land would be suitable for use by the code operator for, or in connection with, the establishment or running of the operator's network.

(2) This paragraph does not apply in relation to land covered by buildings or used as a garden or pleasure ground.

(3) Subsections (2) to (5) and (8) of section 40 of the Land Development Values (Compensation) Act (Northern Ireland) 1965 (c 23 (NI)) (supplementary provisions relating to powers of entry) have effect in relation to the power of entry conferred by this paragraph—

(a) as they have effect in relation to the power conferred by that section; but

(b) subject to the modifications set out in sub-paragraph (4).

(4) Those modifications are—

(a) in section 40(2) (power to search and bore for the purpose of ascertaining the nature of the subsoil or the presence of minerals) omit "or the presence of minerals therein"; and

(b) in section 40(3)(b) (three days' notice to be given of an intended entry upon occupied land) for the word "three" substitute "twenty eight".

(5) Where, in an exercise of the power conferred by this paragraph, damage is caused to land or to chattels, the code operator must—

(a) make good the damage; or

(b) pay compensation in respect of the damage to every person interested in the land or chattels.

(6) Where, in consequence of an exercise of the power conferred by this paragraph, a person is disturbed in his enjoyment of any land or chattels, the code operator must pay that person compensation in respect of the disturbance.

(7) Section 31 of the Land Development Values (Compensation) Act (Northern Ireland) 1965 (determination of disputes as to compensation) applies to any question of disputed compensation under this paragraph as it applies to such questions under Part 3 of that Act.

Acquisition of land by agreement

9.—(1) For the purpose of the acquisition by agreement by a code operator of land in England and Wales, the provisions of Part 1 of the Compulsory Purchase Act 1965 (c 56) (so far as applicable), other than sections 4 to 8 (time limits, notices to treat etc) and section 31 (ecclesiastical property), apply as they apply for the purposes of that Act.

(2) For the purpose of the acquisition by agreement by a code operator of land in Scotland, section 109(2) of the Town and Country Planning (Scotland) Act 1972 (c 52) (incorporation of Lands Clauses Acts) applies, with any necessary modifications, for the purposes of this Act as it applies for the purposes of that Act.

(3) For the purpose of the acquisition by agreement by a code operator of land in Northern Ireland, the Lands Clauses Acts, except for sections 127 to 132 (sale of superfluous land) and sections 150 and 151 (access to the special Act) of the Lands Clauses Consolidation Act 1845 (c 18), apply as they apply for the purposes of those Acts.

[3442]

NOTES

Commencement: 25 July 2003 (for the purpose of enabling network and service functions and spectrum functions to be carried out during the transitional period by the Director General of Telecommunications and the Secretary of State respectively) (see further s 408 and Sch 18 at **[3436]**, **[3460]**, and the Communications Act 2003 (Commencement No 1) Order 2003, SI 2003/1900 at **[3507]**); 29 December 2003 (for the purpose of enabling OFCOM to perform those functions) (see the Office of Communications Act 2002 (Commencement No 3) and Communications Act 2003 (Commencement No 2) Order 2003, SI 2003/3142 at **[3590]**).

SCHEDULE 5
PROCEDURE FOR GRANTS OF RECOGNISED SPECTRUM ACCESS
Section 159

General procedure for applications

1.—(1) An application for a grant of recognised spectrum access shall be determined in accordance with procedures prescribed in regulations made by OFCOM.

(2) Section 403 applies to regulations made under this paragraph.

(3) The procedures must include provision for—

(a) time limits for dealing with applications for a grant of recognised spectrum access;

(b) requirements which must be met before a grant is made;

(c) the restrictions and conditions to which a grant may be made subject.

Information to be provided in connection with applications

2. The grounds on which a grant of recognised spectrum access may be refused by OFCOM include a failure by the applicant to provide information which OFCOM reasonably require in order to satisfy themselves that the applicant is able to comply with restrictions or conditions to which the grant may be made subject.

Notice of proposed refusal of application

3.—(1) Where OFCOM propose to refuse an application for a grant of recognised spectrum access, they shall give notice to the applicant—

(a) stating the reasons for their proposal; and

(b) specifying a period within which representations may be made about the proposal.

(2) That period must be a period ending not less than one month after the day of the giving of the notice.

Duration of grant

4. A grant of recognised spectrum access continues in force, unless previously revoked by OFCOM, for such period as may be specified in the notification by which the grant is made.

Revocation or modification

5. OFCOM may revoke or modify a grant of recognised spectrum access, or the restrictions or conditions to which such a grant is subject, by a notice to the person to whom the grant was made.

Notice of proposed revocation or modification

6.—(1) Where OFCOM propose to revoke or modify a grant of recognised spectrum access or a restriction or condition to which such a grant is subject, they shall give a notification to the holder of the grant—

(a) stating the reasons for their proposal; and

(b) specifying the period during which the person notified has an opportunity to do the things specified in sub-paragraph (2).

(2) Those things are—

(a) making representations about the proposal; and

(b) if the proposal is the result of a contravention of a restriction or condition of the grant, complying with it.

(3) Subject to sub-paragraphs (4) to (6), the period for doing those things must be the period of one month beginning with the day after the one on which the notification was given.

(4) OFCOM may, if they think fit, allow a longer period for doing those things either—
(a) by specifying a longer period in the notification; or
(b) by subsequently, on one or more occasions, extending the specified period.

(5) The person notified shall have a shorter period for doing those things if a shorter period is agreed between OFCOM and the person notified.

(6) The person notified shall also have a shorter period if—
(a) OFCOM have reasonable grounds for believing that the case is a case of serious and repeated contravention or an urgent case;
(b) they have determined that, in the circumstances, a shorter period would be appropriate; and
(c) the shorter period has been specified in the notification.

(7) A case is an urgent case if the failure to revoke or modify the grant will result in, or create an immediate risk of—
(a) a serious threat to the safety of the public, to public health or to national security; or
(b) serious economic or operational problems for persons, other than the person in contravention, who—
(i) use stations or apparatus for wireless telegraphy; or
(ii) are communications providers or make associated facilities available.

(8) For the purposes of this paragraph a contravention of a restriction or condition of a grant of recognised spectrum access is a repeated contravention, in relation to a proposal to revoke or modify the grant, if it falls within sub-paragraph (9).

(9) A contravention falls within this sub-paragraph if—
(a) a previous notification under sub-paragraph (1) has been given in respect of the same contravention or in respect of any other contravention of a restriction or condition of the same grant; and
(b) the subsequent notification under that sub-paragraph is given no more than twelve months after the day of the making by OFCOM of a determination for the purposes of sub-paragraph (10) that the contravention to which the previous notification related did occur.

(10) Where OFCOM have given a notification under sub-paragraph (1), they shall, within the period of one month beginning with the end of the period for the making of representations about the proposal contained in that notification—
(a) decide whether or not to revoke or modify the grant of recognised spectrum access in accordance with their proposal, or in accordance with that proposal but with modifications; and
(b) give the holder of the grant a notification of their decision.

(11) The notification under sub-paragraph (10)—
(a) must be given no more than one week after the making of the decision to which it relates; and
(b) must, in accordance with that decision, either revoke or modify the grant or withdraw the proposal for revocation or modification.

(12) Nothing in this paragraph is to apply to—
(a) a revocation or modification to be made at the request or with the consent of the holder of the grant; or
(b) a revocation or modification that appears to OFCOM to be necessary or expedient for the purpose of securing compliance with an international obligation of the United Kingdom.

(13) The reference in sub-paragraph (9) to a contravention of a restriction or condition of a grant includes a reference to a contravention of a restriction or condition contained in any previous grant of which the grant in question is a direct or indirect renewal.

Restriction on powers of revocation and modification

7.—(1) The conditions that OFCOM may include in a grant of recognised spectrum access include conditions restricting the exercise by them of their power to revoke or modify that grant.

(2) Those conditions include, in particular, conditions providing that the grant may not be revoked or modified except—

(*a*) *with the consent of the holder of the grant; or*
(*b*) *in such other circumstances, and on such grounds, as may be specified in the conditions.*

(*3*) *The circumstances or grounds—*
(*a*) *may relate to matters relevant for the purposes of any enactment (whether relating to wireless telegraphy or not); and*
(*b*) *may, in particular, be made dependent on the exercise of a statutory discretion under any enactment.*

(*4*) *Nothing in any condition included in a grant of recognised spectrum access shall restrict the power of OFCOM to revoke or modify a grant of recognised spectrum access if it appears to OFCOM to be necessary or appropriate to do so—*
(*a*) *in the interests of national security;*
(*b*) *in the interests of the safety of the public or public health; or*
(*c*) *for the purpose of securing compliance with any international obligation of the United Kingdom.*

Interpretation

8. In this Schedule, "stations for wireless telegraphy" and "apparatus for wireless telegraphy" each has the same meaning as in the Wireless Telegraphy Act 1949 (c 54).

[3443]

NOTES

Commencement: 29 December 2003.

This Schedule and Schs 6, 7 are repealed by the Wireless Telegraphy Act 2006, s 125(1), Sch 9, Pt 1, subject to transitional provisions and savings in s 124 of, Sch 8, Pt 1, paras 1–8, 24 to, that Act at **[4230]**, **[4239]**.

SCHEDULE 6
FIXED PENALTIES FOR WIRELESS TELEGRAPHY OFFENCES

Section 180

Offences to which this Schedule applies

1.—(1) This Schedule applies to an offence under the Wireless Telegraphy Act 1949 which—
(*a*) *is a summary offence; and*
(*b*) *is committed after the coming into force of section 180.*

(*2*) *Such an offence is referred to in this Schedule as a "relevant offence".*

Fixed penalties and fixed penalty notices

2.—(1) The fixed penalty for a relevant offence is such amount as may be prescribed in relation to that offence by regulations made by the Secretary of State.

(*2*) *The amount prescribed by regulations under sub-paragraph (1) is not to be more than 25 per cent of the maximum fine on summary conviction for the offence in question.*

(*3*) *In this Schedule "fixed penalty notice" means a notice offering the opportunity of the discharge of any liability to conviction of the offence to which the notice relates by payment of a fixed penalty in accordance with this Schedule.*

Issuing of fixed penalty notice

3.—(1) If OFCOM have reason to believe that a person has committed a relevant offence, they may send a fixed penalty notice to that person.

(*2*) *If a procurator fiscal receives a report that a person has committed a relevant offence in Scotland, he also shall have power to send a fixed penalty notice to that person.*

(*3*) *If an authorised person has, on any occasion, reason to believe that a person—*
(*a*) *is committing a relevant offence, or*

(b) has on that occasion committed a relevant offence,

he may hand that person a fixed penalty notice.

(4) In this paragraph "authorised person" means a person authorised by OFCOM, for the purposes of sub-paragraph (3), to issue fixed penalty notices on OFCOM's behalf.

(5) References in this Schedule to the person by whom a fixed penalty notice is issued, in relation to a notice handed to a person in accordance with sub-paragraph (3), are references to OFCOM.

Content of fixed penalty notice

4.—(1) A fixed penalty notice must—

(a) state the alleged offence;

(b) give such particulars of the circumstances alleged to constitute that offence as are necessary for giving reasonable information about it;

(c) state the fixed penalty for that offence;

(d) specify the relevant officer to whom the fixed penalty may be paid and the address at which it may be paid;

(e) state that proceedings against the person to whom it is issued cannot be commenced in respect of the offence until the end of the suspended enforcement period;

(f) state that such proceedings cannot be commenced if the penalty is paid within the suspended enforcement period;

(g) inform the person to whom it is issued of his right to ask to be tried for the alleged offence; and

(h) explain how that right may be exercised and the effect of exercising it.

(2) The suspended enforcement period for the purposes of this Schedule is—

(a) the period of one month beginning with the day after that on which the fixed penalty notice was issued; or

(b) such longer period as may be specified in the notice.

Withdrawal of fixed penalty notice

5. If it appears to a person who has issued a fixed penalty notice that it was wrongly issued—

(a) he may withdraw the notice by a further notice to the person to whom it was issued; and

(b) if he does so, the relevant officer must repay any amount paid in respect of the penalty.

Notification to person to whom payment is to be made

6. A person who issues or withdraws a fixed penalty notice shall send a copy of the notice or (as the case may be) of the notice of withdrawal to the relevant officer specified in the notice being issued or withdrawn.

Effect of fixed penalty notice

7.—(1) This paragraph applies if a fixed penalty notice is issued to a person ("the alleged offender").

(2) Proceedings for the offence to which the notice relates cannot be brought against the alleged offender until the person who issued the notice has been notified by the relevant officer specified in the notice that payment of the fixed penalty has not been made within the suspended enforcement period.

(3) If the alleged offender asks to be tried for the alleged offence—

(a) sub-paragraph (2) does not apply; and

(b) proceedings may be brought against him.

(4) Such a request must be made by a notice given by the alleged offender—

(a) in the manner specified in the fixed penalty notice; and

(*b*) *before the end of the suspended enforcement period.*

(5) *A request which is made in accordance with sub-paragraph* (3) *is referred to in this Schedule as a "request to be tried".*

Payment of fixed penalty

8.—(*1*) *If the alleged offender decides to pay the fixed penalty, he must pay it to the relevant officer specified in the notice.*

(2) *Payment of the penalty may be made by properly addressing, pre-paying and posting a letter containing the amount of the penalty* (*in cash or otherwise*).

(3) *Sub-paragraph* (4) *applies if a person—*
- (*a*) *claims to have made payment by that method; and*
- (*b*) *shows that his letter was posted.*

(4) *Unless the contrary is proved, payment is to be regarded as made at the time at which the letter would be delivered in the ordinary course of post.*

(5) *Sub-paragraph* (2) *is not to be read as preventing the payment of a penalty by other means.*

(6) *A letter is properly addressed for the purposes of sub-paragraph* (2) *if it is addressed in accordance with the requirements specified in the fixed penalty notice.*

Effect of payment

9. *If the fixed penalty specified in a fixed penalty notice is paid within the period specified in that notice, no proceedings for the offence to which that notice relates may be brought against the alleged offender.*

Service of statement and proof of service

10.—(*1*) *This paragraph applies to proceedings for a relevant offence.*

(2) *A certificate by OFCOM—*
- (*a*) *that a copy of a statement by a person authorised by OFCOM was included in, or given with, a fixed penalty notice,*
- (*b*) *that the notice was a notice with respect to the relevant offence, and*
- (*c*) *that that notice was issued to the accused on a date specified in the certificate,*

is evidence that a copy of the statement was served on the alleged offender by delivery to him on that date.

(3) *The statement is to be treated as properly served for the purposes of—*
- (*a*) *section 9 of the Criminal Justice Act 1967* (*c 80*) (*proof by written statement*), *and*
- (*b*) *section 1 of the Criminal Justice* (*Miscellaneous Provisions*) *Act* (*Northern Ireland*) *1968* (*c 28* (*NI*)) (*which contains corresponding provision for Northern Ireland*),

even though the manner of service is not authorised by subsection (*8*) *of either of those sections.*

(4) *Sub-paragraphs* (5) *and* (6) *apply to any proceedings in which service of a statement is proved by a certificate under this paragraph.*

(5) *For the purposes of—*
- (*a*) *section 9*(*2*)(*c*) *of the Criminal Justice Act 1967* (*copy of statement to be tendered in evidence to be served before hearing on other parties to the proceedings by or on behalf of the party proposing to tender it*), *and*
- (*b*) *section 1*(*2*)(*c*) *of the Criminal Justice* (*Miscellaneous Provisions*) *Act* (*Northern Ireland*) *1968* (*which contains corresponding provision for Northern Ireland*),

service of the statement is to be taken to have been effected by or on behalf of the prosecutor.

(6) *If the alleged offender makes a request to be tried—*
- (*a*) *section 9*(*2*)(*d*) *of the Criminal Justice Act 1967* (*time for objection*), *and*
- (*b*) *section 1*(*2*)(*d*) *of the Criminal Justice* (*Miscellaneous Provisions*) *Act* (*Northern Ireland*) *1968* (*which contains corresponding provision for Northern Ireland*),

are to apply with the substitution, for the reference to seven days from the service of the copy of the statement, of a reference to seven days beginning with the day after the one on which the request to be tried was made.

(7) *This paragraph does not extend to Scotland.*

Certificate about payment

11. *In any proceedings, a certificate—*

(*a*) *that payment of a fixed penalty was, or was not, received by the relevant officer specified in the fixed penalty notice by a date specified in the certificate, or*

(*b*) *that a letter containing an amount sent by post in payment of a fixed penalty was marked as posted on a date specified in the certificate,*

shall, if the certificate purports to be signed by that officer, be evidence (and in Scotland sufficient evidence) of the facts stated.

Regulations

12. *The Secretary of State may by regulations make provision as to any matter incidental to the operation of this Schedule, and in particular—*

(*a*) *for prescribing any information or further information to be provided in a notice, notification, certificate or receipt;*

(*b*) *for prescribing the duties of relevant officers and the information to be supplied to and by them.*

Interpretation

13. *In this Schedule "relevant officer" means—*

(*a*) *in relation to England and Wales, the [designated officer for the magistrates' court];*

(*b*) *in relation to Scotland, the clerk of court; and*

(*c*) *in relation to Northern Ireland, the clerk of petty sessions.*

[3444]

NOTES

Commencement: to be appointed.

Repealed as noted to Sch 5 at **[3443]**.

Para 13: words in square brackets substituted by the Courts Act 2003 (Consequential Provisions) Order 2005, SI 2005/886, art 2, Schedule, para 95.

SCHEDULE 7
SEIZURE AND FORFEITURE OF APPARATUS

Section 182

Application of Schedule

1.—(1) This Schedule applies to restricted apparatus seized, after the coming into force of this Schedule—

(*a*) *in pursuance of a warrant granted under section 15(1) of the Wireless Telegraphy Act 1949 (c 54); or*

(*b*) *in the exercise of the power conferred by section 79(3) of the Telecommunications Act 1984 (c 12).*

(2) *Apparatus is restricted apparatus for the purposes of this Schedule if custody or control of apparatus of any class or description to which it belongs is for the time being restricted by an order under section 7 of the Wireless Telegraphy Act 1967 (c 72).*

Notice of seizure

2.—(1) OFCOM must give notice of the seizure of the restricted apparatus to every person who, to their knowledge, was at the time of the seizure the owner or one of the owners of the apparatus.

(2) The notice must set out the grounds of the seizure.

(3) Where there is no proper address for the purposes of the service of a notice under sub-paragraph (1) in a manner authorised by section 394, the requirements of that subparagraph shall be satisfied by the publication of a notice of the seizure (according to the part of the United Kingdom where the seizure took place) in the London, Edinburgh or Belfast Gazette.

(4) Apparatus may be condemned or taken to have been condemned under this Schedule only if the requirements of this paragraph have been complied with in the case of that apparatus.

Notice of claim

3. A person claiming that the restricted apparatus is not liable to forfeiture must give written notice of his claim to OFCOM.

4.—(1) A notice of claim must be given within one month after the day of the giving of the notice of seizure.

(2) A notice of claim must specify—

(a) the name and address of the claimant; and

(b) in the case of a claimant who is outside the United Kingdom, the name and address of a solicitor in the United Kingdom who is authorised to accept service of process and to act on behalf of the claimant.

(3) Service of process upon a solicitor so specified is to be taken to be proper service upon the claimant.

Condemnation

5. The restricted apparatus is to be taken to have been duly condemned as forfeited if—

(a) by the end of the period for the giving of a notice of claim in respect of the apparatus, no such notice has been given to OFCOM; or

(b) a notice of claim is given which does not comply with the requirements of paragraphs 3 and 4.

6.—(1) Where a notice of claim in respect of the restricted apparatus is duly given in accordance with paragraphs 3 and 4, OFCOM may take proceedings for the condemnation of that apparatus by the court.

(2) In any such proceedings—

(a) if the court finds that the apparatus was liable to forfeiture at the time of seizure, it must condemn the apparatus as forfeited unless cause is shown why it should not; and

(b) if the court finds that the apparatus was not liable to forfeiture at that time, or cause is shown why it should not be forfeited, the court must order the return of the apparatus to the person appearing to the court to be entitled to it.

(3) If OFCOM decide not to take proceedings for condemnation in a case in which a notice of claim has been so given, they must return the apparatus to the person appearing to them to be the owner of the apparatus, or to one of the persons appearing to them to be the owners of it.

(4) Apparatus required to be returned in accordance with sub-paragraph (3) must be returned as soon as reasonably practicable after the decision not to take proceedings for condemnation.

(5) OFCOM's decision whether to take such proceedings must be taken as soon as reasonably practicable after the receipt of the notice of claim.

7. Where the restricted apparatus is condemned or taken to have been condemned as forfeited, the forfeiture is to have effect as from the time of the seizure.

Proceedings for condemnation by court

8. Proceedings for condemnation are civil proceedings and may be instituted—

- *(a) in England or Wales, either in the High Court or in a magistrates' court;*
- *(b) in Scotland, either in the Court of Session or in the sheriff court;*
- *(c) in Northern Ireland, either in the High Court or in a court of summary jurisdiction.*

9. Proceedings for the condemnation of restricted apparatus instituted in a magistrates' court in England or Wales, in the sheriff court in Scotland or in a court of summary jurisdiction in Northern Ireland may be so instituted—

- *(a) in any such court having jurisdiction in a place where an offence under section 7 of the Wireless Telegraphy Act 1967 (c 72) involving that apparatus was committed;*
- *(b) in any such court having jurisdiction in proceedings for such an offence;*
- *(c) in any such court having jurisdiction in the place where the claimant resides or, if the claimant has specified a solicitor under paragraph 4, in the place where that solicitor has his office; or*
- *(d) in any such court having jurisdiction in the place where that apparatus was seized or to which it was first brought after being seized.*

10.—(1) In proceedings for condemnation that are instituted in England and Wales or Northern Ireland, the claimant or his solicitor must make his oath that the seized apparatus was, or was to the best of his knowledge and belief, the property of the claimant at the time of the seizure.

(2) In proceedings for condemnation instituted in the High Court—

- *(a) the court may require the claimant to give such security for the costs of the proceedings as may be determined by the court; and*
- *(b) the claimant must comply with any such requirement.*

(3) If a requirement of this paragraph is not complied with, the court shall give judgement for OFCOM.

11.—(1) In the case of proceedings for condemnation instituted in a magistrates' court in England or Wales, either party may appeal against the decision of that court to the Crown Court.

(2) In the case of proceedings for condemnation instituted in a court of summary jurisdiction in Northern Ireland, either party may appeal against the decision of that court to the county court.

(3) This paragraph does not affect any right to require the statement of a case for the opinion of the High Court.

12. Where an appeal has been made (whether by case stated or otherwise) against the decision of the court in proceedings for the condemnation of restricted apparatus, that apparatus is to be left with OFCOM pending the final determination of the matter.

Disposal of unclaimed property

13.—(1) This paragraph applies where a requirement is imposed by or under this Schedule for apparatus to be returned to a person.

(2) If the apparatus is still in OFCOM's possession after the end of the period of twelve months beginning with the day after the requirement to return it arose, OFCOM may dispose of it in any manner they think fit.

(3) OFCOM may exercise their power under this paragraph to dispose of apparatus only if it is not practicable at the time when the power is exercised to dispose of the apparatus by returning it immediately to the person to whom it is required to be returned.

Provisions as to proof

14. In proceedings arising out of the seizure of restricted apparatus, the fact, form and manner of the seizure is to be taken, without further evidence and unless the contrary is shown, to have been as set forth in the process.

15. In any proceedings, the condemnation by a court of restricted apparatus as forfeited may be proved by the production of either—

(a) the order or certificate of condemnation; or

(b) a certified copy of the order purporting to be signed by an officer of the court by which the order or certificate was made or granted.

Special provisions as to certain claimants

16.—(1) This paragraph applies for the purposes of a claim to the restricted apparatus, and of proceedings for its condemnation.

(2) Where, at the time of the seizure, the apparatus is—

(a) the property of a body corporate,

(b) the property of two or more partners, or

(c) the property of more than five persons,

the oath required by paragraph 10 to be taken by the claimant, and any other thing required by this Schedule or by rules of court to be done by the owner of the apparatus, may be done by a person falling within sub-paragraph (3) or by a person authorised to act on his behalf.

(3) The persons falling within this sub-paragraph are—

(a) where the owner is a body corporate, the secretary or some duly authorised officer of that body;

(b) where the owners are in partnership, any one or more of the owners;

(c) where there are more than five owners and they are not in partnership, any two or more of the owners acting on behalf of themselves and any of their co-owners who are not acting on their own behalf.

Saving for owner's rights

17. Neither the imposition of a requirement by or under this Schedule to return apparatus to a person nor the return of apparatus to a person in accordance with such a requirement affects—

(a) the rights in relation to that apparatus of any other person; or

(b) the right of any other person to enforce his rights against the person to whom it is returned.

[3445]

NOTES

Commencement: 29 December 2003.
Repealed as noted to Sch 5 at **[3443]**.

SCHEDULE 8
DECISIONS NOT SUBJECT TO APPEAL

Section 192

Prosecutions and civil proceedings

1. A decision to institute, bring or carry on any criminal or civil proceedings.

2. A decision (other than one under section 119) to take preliminary steps for the purpose of enabling any such proceedings to be instituted.

This Act

3. A decision relating to the making or revision of a statement under section 38.

4. A decision required to be published in a notification under section 44(4).

5. A decision given effect to by an order under section 55.

6. A decision given effect to by regulations under section 66.

7. A decision given effect to by regulations under section 71.

8. A decision required to be published in a notification under section 108(4).

9. A decision given effect to by an order under section 122.

10. A decision relating to the making or revision of a statement under section 131.

11. A decision given effect to by an order under section 134(6).

12. A decision relating to the making or revision of a statement under section 145.

13–36. …

[Wireless Telegraphy Act 2006

37. A decision relating to the publication of the United Kingdom Plan for Frequency Authorisation.

38. A decision in exercise of the functions conferred on OFCOM by section 1 as to—
(a) the services, records and advice to be provided, maintained or given by them;
(b) the research to be carried out or the arrangements made for carrying it out; or
(c) the making or terms of any grant.

39. A decision under section 4 or 7.

40. A decision given effect to—
(a) by regulations under section 8(3), 12, 14, 18, 21, 23, 27, 30, 45 or 54 or paragraph 1 of Schedule 1 or paragraph 1 of Schedule 2;
(b) by an order under section 29 or 62.

41. A decision relating to the recovery of a sum payable to OFCOM under section 15 or 24.

42. A decision given effect to by regulations under section 31 and any decision under any such regulations.

43. A decision relating to the making or revision of a statement under—
(a) section 34, or
(b) section 44.

44. A decision to impose a penalty under section 42(1).

45. A decision for the purposes of section 59.

46. A decision relating to an authority under section 62(5).]

[3446]

NOTES

Commencement: 25 July 2003 (for the purpose of enabling network and service functions and spectrum functions to be carried out during the transitional period by the Director General of Telecommunications and the Secretary of State respectively) (see further s 408 and Sch 18 at **[3436]**, **[3460]**, and the Communications Act 2003 (Commencement No 1) Order 2003, SI 2003/1900 at **[3507]**); 29 December 2003 (for the purpose of enabling OFCOM to perform those functions) (see the Office of Communications Act 2002 (Commencement No 3) and Communications Act 2003 (Commencement No 2) Order 2003, SI 2003/3142 at **[3590]**).

Paras 13–36: repealed by the Wireless Telegraphy Act 2006, s 125(1), Sch 9, Pt 1, subject to transitional provisions and savings in s 124 of, Sch 8, Pt 1, paras 1–8, 24 to, that Act at **[4230]**, **[4239]**, and previously read as follows:

"13. A decision relating to the publication of the United Kingdom Plan for Frequency Authorisation.

14. A decision in exercise of the functions conferred on OFCOM by section 152 as to—
(a) the services, records and advice to be provided, maintained or given by them;
(b) the research to be carried out or the arrangements made for carrying it out; or
(c) the making or terms of any grant.

15. A decision under section 155.

16. A decision under section 158.

17. A decision given effect to by regulations under section 159.

18. A decision given effect to by regulations under section 162.

19. A decision given effect to by an order under section 164.

20. A decision given effect to by regulations under section 168.

21. A decision given effect to by regulations under section 170 and any decision under any such regulations.

22. A decision to impose a penalty under section 175(1).

23. A decision relating to the making or revision of a statement under section 177.

24. A decision given effect to by regulations under paragraph 1 of Schedule 5.

25. A decision under any provision of Schedule 6.

26. A decision under any provision of Schedule 7.

Wireless Telegraphy Act 1949

27. A decision given effect to by regulations under the proviso to section 1(1) of the Wireless Telegraphy Act 1949 (c 54).

28. A decision given effect to by regulations under section 1D(3) of that Act.

29. A decision given effect to by regulations under section 3 of that Act.

30. A decision given effect to by regulations under section 10 of that Act.

31. A decision relating to the making or revision of a statement under section 13B of that Act.

32. A decision for the purposes of section 15 of that Act.

Wireless Telegraphy Act 1998

33. A decision given effect to by regulations under section 1 of the Wireless Telegraphy Act 1998 (c 6).

34. A decision given effect to by regulations under section 3 of that Act.

35. A decision given effect to by regulations under section 3A of that Act.

36. A decision relating to the recovery of a sum payable to OFCOM under section 4A of that Act.".

Paras 37–46: added, together with preceding cross-heading, by the Wireless Telegraphy Act 2006, s 123, Sch 7, paras 25, 36.

SCHEDULE 9
ARRANGEMENTS ABOUT CARRYING ON OF C4C'S ACTIVITIES

Section 199

Notification of requirement to submit proposals

1.—(1) It shall be the duty of OFCOM to give a notification under this paragraph to C4C—

(a) as soon as practicable after the commencement of this Schedule; and

(b) as soon as practicable in the last twelve months preceding each date on which the replacement licence granted in accordance with section 231 would expire if not renewed.

(2) A notification under this paragraph is one requiring C4C to submit proposals to OFCOM in accordance with this Schedule for the relevant licence period.

(3) A notification under this paragraph must specify the period within which C4C must submit their proposals.

(4) The period specified under sub-paragraph (3) must be a period ending not less than three months after the day of the giving of the notification.

Submission of proposed arrangements

2.—(1) This paragraph applies where C4C have received a notification under paragraph 1.

(2) C4C must, within the period set out in the notification, submit proposals to OFCOM for the arrangements under which they are proposing to secure, so far as reasonably practicable, that all significant risks that their other activities will have an adverse effect on the carrying out, during the relevant licence period, of their primary functions are—

(a) identified;
(b) evaluated; and
(c) properly managed.

(3) The proposals must include proposals for the arrangements that C4C consider appropriate for securing the transparency objectives during the relevant licence period.

(4) For the purposes of this Schedule the transparency objectives are—

(a) an appropriate financial and organisational separation between the activities of C4C that relate to the carrying out of their primary functions and their other activities; and
(b) an appropriate degree of transparency in financial and other reporting where resources are shared between separated activities or where there is some other financial or practical connection between otherwise separated activities.

(5) The matters to which the proposals submitted under this paragraph may relate include, in particular, the procedures and other practices to be followed by C4C in the case of—

(a) the initiation and management of new ventures;
(b) the exercise of particular powers;
(c) the assessment of risks;
(d) the imposition of charges; and
(e) the keeping of records.

(6) The determination of what is appropriate for the purposes of sub-paragraphs (3) and (4) is not to be confined to a determination of what is appropriate for securing the matters mentioned in sub-paragraph (2).

(7) The arrangements proposed by C4C must contain provision for compliance with the arrangements to be checked regularly by a person appointed in accordance with that provision.

(8) That person must be a person other than the person for the time being holding an appointment for the purposes of paragraph 12(2) of Schedule 3 to the 1990 Act (C4C's auditor).

Consideration and approval of proposals

3.—(1) OFCOM must consider every proposal or revised proposal submitted to them by C4C under paragraph 2 or this paragraph and may do one of the following—

(a) approve the proposed arrangements;
(b) approve them with such modifications as they may notify to C4C;
(c) require C4C to submit revised proposals in accordance with directions given by OFCOM.

(2) Before—

(a) making modifications of proposed arrangements for the purpose of approving them, or
(b) requiring the submission of revised proposals,

OFCOM must consult C4C.

Duration of approval and modification of arrangements

4.—(1) Arrangements approved under this Schedule are to remain in force (subject to the following provisions of this paragraph) throughout the licence period to which they relate.

(2) The arrangements for the time being approved under this Schedule for any licence period may be modified, by agreement between OFCOM and C4C, at any time during the licence period for which they apply.

(3) OFCOM may carry out a review of the arrangements for the time being approved under this Schedule.

(4) The reviews that may be carried out under this paragraph in any one licence period are confined to either—

(a) one review relating to all the arrangements; or
(b) two reviews carried out at separate times as follows—
  (i) one (whether the first or second) relating to the arrangements for securing the transparency objectives; and
  (ii) the other relating to other matters.

(5) On a review under this paragraph, OFCOM may require C4C to submit proposals for modifying the arrangements for the time being approved under this Schedule so far as they relate to the matters under review.

(6) Paragraph 3 applies where proposals are submitted to OFCOM under sub-paragraph (5) as it applies where they are submitted under paragraph 2.

Publication of approved arrangements

5.—(1) OFCOM must publish all arrangements approved by them under this Schedule.

(2) The publication of anything under this paragraph must be in such manner as OFCOM consider appropriate for bringing it to the attention of members of the public.

Duty of C4C to act in accordance with the approved arrangements

6. It shall be the duty of C4C to act in accordance with the arrangements for the time being in force under this Schedule.

Enforcement of duties

7.—(1) This paragraph applies to—

(a) every duty of C4C under this Schedule to submit proposals to OFCOM; and
(b) the duty imposed on C4C by paragraph 6.

(2) Each of those duties shall be enforceable in civil proceedings by OFCOM—

(a) for an injunction;
(b) for specific performance of a statutory duty under section 45 of the Court of Session Act 1988 (c 36); or
(c) for any other appropriate remedy or relief.

Penalty for contravention of the arrangements

8.—(1) OFCOM may impose a penalty on C4C if C4C have contravened—

(a) a requirement of this Schedule to submit proposals to OFCOM;
(b) a requirement of arrangements for the time being approved under this Schedule.

(2) The amount of the penalty must not exceed 3 per cent of C4C's qualifying revenue for their last complete accounting period before the contravention.

(3) Before imposing a penalty on C4C under this paragraph OFCOM must give C4C a reasonable opportunity of making representations to OFCOM about their proposal to impose the penalty.

(4) Where OFCOM impose a penalty on C4C under this paragraph, they shall—

(a) notify C4C; and
(b) in that notification, fix a reasonable period after it is given as the period within which the penalty is to be paid.

(5) In the case of a continuing contravention—

(a) separate penalties may be imposed in respect of different periods during which the contravention continues;
(b) the notification of the penalty must specify the period in respect of which the penalty is imposed; and
(c) the reference in sub-paragraph (2) to the last complete accounting period before the contravention is a reference to the last complete accounting period before the end of the period in respect of which the penalty is imposed.

(6) A penalty imposed under this paragraph must be paid to OFCOM within the period fixed by them.

(7) Section 19(2) to (6) of the 1990 Act and Part 1 of Schedule 7 to that Act (calculation of qualifying revenue), with any necessary modifications, have effect in relation to C4C for the purposes of this paragraph as they have effect in relation to the holder of a Channel 3 licence for the purposes of Part 1 of that Act.

OFCOM's duty to take account of need to support C4C's primary functions

9. In exercising their powers under this Schedule OFCOM must have regard, in particular, to the need to secure, so far as practicable, that all significant risks that C4C's other activities will have an adverse effect on the carrying out of their primary functions are—

(a) identified;
(b) evaluated; and
(c) properly managed.

Interpretation of Schedule

10. In this Schedule—

"arrangements" means arrangements about the procedures and other practices to be followed by C4C and about other matters connected with the carrying on by them of any of their activities;

"licence period" means—

(a) the period for which the replacement licence is granted to C4C in accordance with section 231; or
(b) any subsequent period for which it is renewed;

"primary functions" is to be construed in accordance with section 199(2);

"relevant licence period"—

(a) in relation to the first notification to be given under paragraph 1, the licence period mentioned in paragraph (a) of the definition of that period; and
(b) in relation to any other such notification, the first licence period to begin after the giving of the notification;

"transparency objectives" is to be construed in accordance with paragraph 2(4).

[3447]

NOTES

Commencement: 29 December 2003.

SCHEDULE 10
LICENSING THE PUBLIC TELETEXT SERVICE

Section 219

PART 1
APPLICATIONS FOR AND AWARD OF LICENCE

Notice of proposal to grant licence

1.—(1) Where OFCOM propose to grant a licence to provide the public teletext service they must publish a notice stating that they are proposing to do so.

(2) The notice must—

(a) specify the digital capacity which is available for the public teletext service on television multiplex services;
(b) specify whether the licence will require the public teletext service to comprise a service to be provided for broadcasting in analogue form;
(c) invite applications for the licence;
(d) specify the closing date for applications;
(e) specify the fee payable on the making of an application for the licence; and
(f) specify the percentage of qualifying revenue for each accounting period of the licence holder which OFCOM have determined to be the percentage of that revenue that will have to be paid to them.

(3) Where the licence is to comprise an analogue teletext service the notice must specify—

(a) the television broadcasting service or services on whose frequency or frequencies the services are to be provided; and

(b) the extent and nature of the spare capacity which is to be allocated by the licence.

(4) For the purposes of sub-paragraph (2)(f)—

(a) different percentages may be determined and specified for different accounting periods; and

(b) the percentages that may be determined and specified for an accounting period include a nil percentage.

(5) A notice under this paragraph is to be published in such manner as OFCOM consider appropriate.

Guidance as to applications

2.—(1) When publishing a notice under paragraph 1, OFCOM must publish with it some general guidance to applicants about what is likely to make proposals relating to the matters mentioned in paragraph 3(1)(c) to (e) acceptable to them.

(2) Guidance published under this paragraph must include examples.

Applications for the licence

3.—(1) An application made in response to a notice under paragraph 1 must be accompanied by—

(a) the fee specified in the notice as payable on the making of the application;

(b) a technical plan complying with sub-paragraph (2);

(c) the applicant's proposals for providing, or securing the provision of, a service that fulfils the public service remit for the public teletext service;

(d) the applicant's proposals for including news items in the service and for securing that the news items included in the service are up to date and regularly revised;

(e) the applicant's proposals for the inclusion in the service of material that is of particular interest to persons living in different parts of the United Kingdom;

(f) the applicant's cash bid in respect of the licence; and

(g) such information as OFCOM may reasonably require about the matters mentioned in sub-paragraph (3).

(2) The technical plan must indicate—

(a) the nature of the public teletext service which the applicant is proposing to provide; and

(b) the nature of any services the provision of which, in accordance with proposals made by another person, would be secured by the applicant in accordance with provision made under section 220.

(3) The matters about which OFCOM may require information under sub-paragraph (1)(g) are—

(a) the applicant's present financial position; and

(b) his projected financial position during the period for which the licence would be in force.

(4) At any time after receiving an application under this Schedule and before disposing of it, OFCOM may require the applicant to furnish additional information about any one or more of the following—

(a) the matters that must be indicated in the technical plan;

(b) the applicant's proposals with respect to the matters mentioned in sub-paragraph (1)(c) to (e); and

(c) the matters mentioned in sub-paragraph (3).

(5) Any information to be furnished to OFCOM under this paragraph must be in such form, and must be verified, in such manner as they may require.

Notice inviting public representations

4.—(1) As soon as reasonably practicable after the date specified in a notice under paragraph 1 as the closing date for applications, OFCOM must publish—

(a) the name of every person who has made an application to them in response to their notice;

(b) particulars of the technical plan submitted by each applicant;

(c) the proposals submitted by each applicant with respect to the matters mentioned in paragraph 3(1)(c) to (e);

(d) such other information connected with each application as OFCOM consider appropriate; and

(e) a notice under sub-paragraph (2).

(2) The notice required by this paragraph is one that—

(a) invites representations to be made to OFCOM with respect to the other matters published under this paragraph; and

(b) specifies the manner in which, and the time by which, such representations have to be made.

(3) Publication of any information or notice under this paragraph is to be in such manner as OFCOM consider appropriate.

Determination of applications

5.—(1) This paragraph applies where, in response to a notice under paragraph 1, a person has made an application for a licence to provide the public teletext service.

(2) OFCOM must not proceed to consider whether to award the applicant the licence in accordance with the following provisions of this paragraph unless it appears to them—

(a) that the applicant's technical plan, in so far as it involves the use of an electronic communications network, contains proposals that are acceptable to them;

(b) that the applicant's proposals with respect to the matters mentioned in paragraph 3(1)(c) to (e) are acceptable to them; and

(c) that the services proposed to be provided under the licence would be capable of being maintained throughout the period for which the licence would be in force.

(3) In determining whether it appears to them as mentioned in sub-paragraph (2), OFCOM must take account of any representations made to them in response to the invitation published under paragraph 4.

(4) Sections 17 and 17A of the 1990 Act (award of licence to highest cash bidder and financial conditions) apply in relation to a licence to provide the public teletext service as they apply in relation to a Channel 3 licence, but with the modifications set out in sub-paragraphs (5) and (6).

(5) In the application of section 17 of the 1990 Act in accordance with sub-paragraph (4)—

(a) any reference to an applicant is to be construed as a reference to an applicant in whose case it appears to OFCOM as mentioned in sub-paragraph (2);

(b) the provisions of subsection (4) down to the end of paragraph (b) are to be omitted;

(c) in subsection (7)(a), the reference to section 19(1) of the 1990 Act is to be construed as a reference to paragraph 7 of this Schedule;

(d) subsection (12) shall have effect with the substitution of the following paragraph for paragraph (b)—

"(b) the name of every other applicant in whose case it appeared to OFCOM as mentioned in paragraph 5(2) of Schedule 10 to the Communications Act 2003;"

(e) in subsection (14), the references to a notice under section 15(1) of the 1990 Act and a notice under Part 1 of that Act shall each have effect as a reference to a notice under paragraph 1 of this Schedule.

(6) In the application of section 17A of the 1990 Act in accordance with sub-paragraph (4)—

(a) the reference in subsection (1)(b) to section 15(3)(g) of the 1990 Act shall have effect as a reference to paragraph 3(1)(g) of this Schedule; and

(b) the reference in subsection (3) to a notice under section 15(1) of the 1990 Act shall have effect as a reference to a notice under paragraph 1 of this Schedule.

Revocation of award

6.—(1) This paragraph applies if, at any time after a licence to provide the public teletext service has been awarded to a person, but before it has come into force—

(a) that person indicates to OFCOM that he does not intend to provide, or secure the provision of, the licensed service; or

(b) OFCOM have, for any other reason, reasonable grounds for believing that the licensed service will not be provided once the licence has come into force.

(2) OFCOM must revoke the licence by serving a notice of revocation on the person to whom it was awarded.

(3) OFCOM may then award the licence again in accordance with section 17 of the 1990 Act (as applied by paragraph 5 of this Schedule) as if the person whose licence is revoked had not made an application.

(4) Sub-paragraph (3) has effect subject to subsection (14) of section 17 of the 1990 Act (as so applied) (re-publication of invitation to make applications) as if the reference in that subsection to the following provisions of Part 1 of that Act included a reference to that sub-paragraph.

(5) Before acting under sub-paragraphs (2) and (3) in a case falling within subparagraph (1)(b), OFCOM must serve a notice on the person awarded the licence stating their grounds for believing that the licensed service will not be provided once the licence has come into force.

(6) Where such a notice is required to be given, OFCOM must not revoke the licence unless they have given the person to whom it was awarded a reasonable opportunity of making representations to them about the matters by reference to which they are proposing to revoke it.

(7) In the case of a licence to provide a service that must comprise both—

(a) an analogue teletext service, and

(b) a teletext service provided in digital form,

the references in sub-paragraphs (1) and (5) to the licensed service are references to one or both of those services.

[3448]

NOTES

Commencement: 29 December 2003 (for transitional provisions in relation to the existing licence (as referred to in s 221(1) of this Act) see the Office of Communications Act 2002 (Commencement No 3) and Communications Act 2003 (Commencement No 2) Order 2003, SI 2003/3142, art 8(1) at **[3597]**).

PART 2
CONDITIONS AND ENFORCEMENT OF LICENCE

Payments to be made in respect of the public teletext service

7.—(1) A licence to provide the public teletext service must include conditions requiring the licence holder to pay the following amounts to OFCOM (in addition to any fees required to be so paid by virtue of section 4(1)(b) of the 1990 Act)—

(a) a specified amount in respect of the first complete calendar year falling within the licence period;

(b) in respect of each subsequent year falling wholly or partly within the licence period, that amount increased by the appropriate percentage;

(c) in respect of each accounting period of his falling within the licence period, an amount representing a specified percentage of qualifying revenue for that accounting period.

(2) The amount specified for the purposes of sub-paragraph (1)(a) must be—

(a) in the case of the replacement licence under section 221, the amount proposed in accordance with subsection (5)(a) of that section;

(b) in the case of a licence renewed under section 222, the amount determined under section 223(1)(a); and

(c) in any other case, the amount specified in the licence holder's cash bid.

(3) The percentage specified for the purposes of sub-paragraph (1)(c) in respect of an accounting period must be—

- (a) in the case of the replacement licence under section 221, nil;
- (b) in the case of a licence renewed under section 222, the percentage determined under section 223(1)(b); and
- (c) in any other case, the percentage determined and specified for the purposes of paragraph 1(2)(f) of this Schedule.

(4) A licence to provide the public teletext service may also include conditions—

- (a) enabling OFCOM to estimate before the beginning of an accounting period the amount due for that period by virtue of any condition imposed under this paragraph; and
- (b) requiring the licence holder to pay the estimated amount by monthly instalments throughout that period.

(5) Such a licence may, in particular, include conditions—

- (a) authorising OFCOM to revise an estimate on one or more occasions;
- (b) requiring them to alter the amounts of the instalments payable by the licence holder to take account of the revised estimate;
- (c) providing for the adjustment of an overpayment or underpayment.

(6) This paragraph has effect subject to sections 225 and 226 and to the requirement in section 221(5)(b).

(7) In this paragraph "the appropriate percentage" has the same meaning as in section 19 of the 1990 Act.

Corrections and statements of findings by the public teletext provider

8.—(1) Section 40 of the 1990 Act (power to direct correction or a statement of findings) shall have effect in relation to the public teletext service as it has effect in relation to a Channel 3 service but as if the references in subsection (4) to a programme were references to an item.

(2) OFCOM's powers by virtue of this paragraph in relation to any matter are not affected by any prior exercise by them in relation to that matter of their powers under either or both of paragraphs 9 and 10.

Enforcement of the licence for the public teletext service

9.—(1) If OFCOM are satisfied that the holder of the licence to provide the public teletext service has—

- (a) contravened a condition of the licence, or
- (b) failed to comply with a direction given to him by OFCOM under or by virtue of a provision of the 1990 Act, the 1996 Act or Part 3 of this Act,

they may serve on him a notice requiring him to pay a specified financial penalty to them.

(2) The maximum amount which a person may be required to pay by way of a penalty under this paragraph is 5 per cent of the qualifying revenue for his last complete accounting period.

(3) Where an accounting period by reference to which the maximum amount of a penalty falls to be calculated has not ended when the penalty is imposed, the amount taken into account in respect of that period is to be the amount estimated by OFCOM.

(4) OFCOM are not to serve a notice under this paragraph on any person unless they have given him a reasonable opportunity of making representations to them about the matters complained of.

(5) A notice requiring a person to pay a penalty under this paragraph must specify the period within which it is to be paid.

Power to shorten licence period

10.—(1) If OFCOM are satisfied that the holder of the licence to provide the public teletext service has—

(a) contravened a condition of the licence, or
(b) failed to comply with a direction given to him by OFCOM under or by virtue of any provision of the 1990 Act, the 1996 Act or Part 3 of this Act,

they may serve on him a notice reducing the period for which the licence is to be in force by a specified period not exceeding two years.

(2) OFCOM are not to serve a notice under this paragraph on any person unless they have given him a reasonable opportunity of making representations to them about the matters in respect of which it is served.

(3) Where a licence is due to expire on a particular date by virtue of a notice served on a person under this paragraph, OFCOM may, on the application of that person, revoke that notice by a further notice served on him at any time before that date.

(4) OFCOM may exercise their power under sub-paragraph (3) only if they are satisfied that, since the date of the earlier notice, the conduct of the licence holder in relation to the operation of the licensed service has been such as to justify the revocation of that notice.

Revocation for contravention of condition or direction

11. Section 42 of the 1990 Act (revocation for contravention) shall apply in relation to the licence to provide the public teletext service as it applies in relation to a licence to provide a Channel 3 service.

Penalty on revocation

12.—(1) Where OFCOM revoke the licence to provide the public teletext service (whether under paragraph 6 or a provision of the 1990 Act or 1996 Act), they must serve on the licence holder a notice requiring him to pay a specified financial penalty to them.

(2) The maximum amount which a person may be required to pay by way of a penalty under this paragraph is the maximum given by sub-paragraphs (3) and (4).

(3) In a case where the licence is revoked under paragraph 6 or the penalty is imposed before the end of the first complete accounting period of the licence holder to begin in the licence period, the maximum penalty is whichever is the greater of—

(a) £500,000; and
(b) 7 per cent of the amount which OFCOM estimate would have been the qualifying revenue for the first complete accounting period of the licence holder falling within the period for which the licence would have been in force.

(4) In any other case, the maximum penalty is whichever is the greater of—

(a) £500,000; and
(b) 7 per cent of the qualifying revenue for the last complete accounting period of the licence holder falling within the licence period.

(5) A notice requiring a person to pay a penalty under this paragraph must specify the period within which it is to be paid.

(6) A financial penalty that must be paid by virtue of this paragraph by a body of any description shall also be recoverable—

(a) as a debt due to OFCOM from the person who controls the body; or
(b) if two or more persons control it, as a debt due jointly and severally from them all.

(7) Sub-paragraph (6) is in addition to the provision for the recovery of penalties contained in section 346, but the amount recovered in respect of any one penalty must not exceed the full amount of that penalty.

(8) References in this paragraph to a person controlling a body are references to his controlling it within the meaning of Schedule 2 to the 1990 Act.

Power to modify penalties in paragraph 12

13.—(1) The Secretary of State may by order substitute a different sum for the sum for the time being specified in paragraph 12(3)(a) or (4)(a).

(2) No order is to be made containing provision authorised by this paragraph unless a draft of the order has been laid before Parliament and approved by a resolution of each House.
[3449]

NOTES

Commencement: 29 December 2003 (for transitional provisions in relation to the existing licence (as referred to in s 221(1) of this Act) see the Office of Communications Act 2002 (Commencement No 3) and Communications Act 2003 (Commencement No 2) Order 2003, SI 2003/3142, art 8(1) at **[3597]**).

PART 3
INTERPRETATION OF SCHEDULE

14. In this Schedule "licence period", in relation to a licence, means the period for which the licence is in force.

15.—(1) For the purposes of this Schedule the qualifying revenue for an accounting period of the holder of a licence to provide the public teletext service consists of the aggregate of all the following amounts—

(a) the amounts received or to be received by a person mentioned in sub-paragraph (2) in consideration of the inclusion in the licensed service in that period of advertisements or other items; and

(b) the amounts received or to be received by such a person in respect of the provision of the service from—

(i) a person authorised by the licence holder to provide the whole or a part of the licensed service; or

(ii) a person who is a connected person in relation to a person so authorised.

(2) Those persons are—

(a) the licence holder; or

(b) a person who is a connected person in relation to the licence holder without being a person authorised by the licence holder to provide the whole or a part of the licensed service.

(3) Part 1 of Schedule 7 to the 1990 Act applies for determining qualifying revenue for the purposes of this Schedule as it applies for the purposes of Part 1 of that Act.

(4) Where, in the case of the licence to provide the public teletext service—

(a) the first complete accounting period of the licence holder to fall within the licence period does not begin at the same time as the licence period, or

(b) the last complete accounting period of his to fall within the licence period does not end at the same time as the licence period,

references in this Schedule to an accounting period of the licence holder include references to such part of the accounting period preceding the first complete accounting period, or (as the case may be) following the last complete accounting period, as falls within the licence period.

(5) In this paragraph "connected person" has the same meaning as in Schedule 2 to the 1990 Act.
[3450]

NOTES

Commencement: 29 December 2003 (for transitional provisions in relation to the existing licence (as referred to in s 221(1) of this Act) see the Office of Communications Act 2002 (Commencement No 3) and Communications Act 2003 (Commencement No 2) Order 2003, SI 2003/3142, art 8(1) at **[3597]**).

SCHEDULE 11
APPROVAL, IMPOSITION AND MODIFICATION OF NETWORKING ARRANGEMENTS

Sections 291 and 294

Application of Schedule

1.—(1) This Schedule applies where OFCOM's approval of networking arrangements entered into by the holders of regional Channel 3 licences is required—

(a) for the purposes of conditions included in regional Channel 3 licences in accordance with section 291; or
(b) in order for networking arrangements made by OFCOM to cease to have effect in accordance with section 292.

(2) This Schedule also has effect as respects—
(a) the imposition by OFCOM under section 292 of networking arrangements;
(b) the modification of such arrangements following a review under section 293; and
(c) the making of proposals for modifications of networking arrangements following such a review.

Approval required for modifications

2.—(1) Where networking arrangements are approved by OFCOM for purposes mentioned in paragraph 1(1), those arrangements are not to be modified unless OFCOM have approved the modifications in accordance with this Schedule.

(2) This paragraph does not apply to modifications proposed by OFCOM under section 293.

Procedure for giving approval

3.—(1) This paragraph applies where arrangements or modifications are submitted to OFCOM for their approval.

(2) OFCOM must publish a description of the arrangements or modifications that have been submitted.

(3) The publication must be in such manner as OFCOM consider appropriate for bringing the matters published to the attention of the persons who, in OFCOM's opinion, are likely to be affected by the arrangements or modifications.

(4) After allowing a reasonable time after the publication for the making of representations, OFCOM must consider the arrangements or modifications and decide whether or not to approve them.

Decision of OFCOM whether or not to approve arrangements or modifications

4.—(1) The decision made by OFCOM under paragraph 3(4) has to be one of the following—
(a) a decision to approve the arrangements or modifications unconditionally;
(b) a decision to give a conditional approval to the arrangements or modifications;
(c) a decision to refuse approval.

(2) A conditional approval is one that has effect only if effect is given, in relation to the proposed arrangements or modifications, to changes proposed by OFCOM.

(3) Before deciding to give a conditional approval, OFCOM must consult every holder of a regional Channel 3 licence about the changes they are proposing.

(4) When OFCOM have made their decision, they must prepare a report setting out—
(a) their decision; and
(b) their reasons for that decision.

(5) OFCOM must publish the report and send a copy of it to—
(a) the Office of Fair Trading; and
(b) every person to whom the relevant arrangements will apply, or do apply.

(6) The relevant arrangements are—
(a) the arrangements for which approval has been sought; or
(b) the arrangements which are the subject of the modifications for which approval has been sought.

Notification of decisions on imposition of arrangements

5.—(1) Where OFCOM impose arrangements they must prepare and publish a report setting out details of the imposed arrangements.

(2) Where OFCOM carry out a review under section 293, they must prepare and publish a report setting out—
- (a) their conclusions on the review;
- (b) their reasons for those conclusions; and
- (c) the modifications (if any) that they are proposing, or intend to make, following the review.

(3) OFCOM must send a copy of a report prepared under this paragraph to—
- (a) the Office of Fair Trading; and
- (b) every person to whom the relevant arrangements will apply or do apply.

(4) The relevant arrangements are—
- (a) the arrangements which are imposed; or
- (b) the arrangements which are the subject of the modifications proposed by OFCOM or to be made by them.

Competition tests applying to OFCOM's decisions

6.—(1) OFCOM must not—
- (a) approve arrangements or modifications,
- (b) impose arrangements or modify imposed arrangements, or
- (c) propose modifications following a review under section 293,

unless they are satisfied that the arrangements, or the arrangements as proposed to be modified, satisfy the first or second competition test.

(2) Before making a decision about whether a competition test is satisfied OFCOM must consult the Office of Fair Trading.

(3) Arrangements satisfy the first competition test if they do not have as their object or effect the prevention, restriction or distortion of competition within the United Kingdom.

(4) Arrangements satisfy the second competition test if—
- (a) they do have such an object or effect; but
- (b) they would satisfy the criteria set out in section 9 of the Competition Act 1998 (c 41) (agreements contributing to improving the production or distribution of goods or to promoting technical or economic progress).

(5) For the purposes of the second competition test, arrangements imposed by OFCOM and modifications of such arrangements are to be treated as if they were given effect to by an agreement between undertakings.

(6) In determining whether arrangements or modified arrangements would satisfy either of the competition tests, OFCOM must act with a view to securing that there is no inconsistency between—
- (a) the principles they apply and the decision they reach; and
- (b) any principles or decisions referred to in sub-paragraph (7).

(7) Those principles and decisions are—
- (a) the principles laid down by the Treaty establishing the European Community and the European Court, and any decisions of that Court, that are relevant to the construction of Article 81 of that Treaty; and
- (b) any decisions under Part 1 of the Competition Act 1998, and any decisions of a court in the United Kingdom, that are relevant to the construction of a provision of that Act that is equivalent to the provisions of this Schedule imposing the competition tests.

(8) In the case of a conditional approval, the requirements of this paragraph have to be satisfied in relation to the arrangements or modified arrangements as they will be after giving effect to the changes proposed by OFCOM.

(9) In this paragraph, the "European Court" includes a court attached to the European Court.

Other matters to be taken into account

7.—(1) OFCOM must not—
- (a) approve arrangements or modifications,
- (b) impose arrangements or modify imposed arrangements, or

(c) propose modifications following a review under section 293,

unless they consider that the arrangements, or the arrangements as proposed to be modified, are satisfactory.

(2) OFCOM's consideration under sub-paragraph (1) must include consideration of the following two factors.

(3) The first factor is whether the arrangements, or the arrangements as proposed to be modified, represent a satisfactory means of achieving the purpose set out in section 290(4)(c).

(4) The second factor is the likely effect of the arrangements, or the arrangements as modified, on the ability of the persons who will be or are the holders of regional Channel 3 licences, or of any of them, to maintain the quality and range of—

(a) regional programmes included in regional Channel 3 services; and
(b) the other programmes included in such services which contribute to the regional character of the services.

(5) In this paragraph "regional programme", in relation to a regional Channel 3 service, means a programme (including a news programme) which is of particular interest—

(a) to persons living within the area for which the service is provided;
(b) to persons living within a part of that area; or
(c) to particular communities living within that area.

Duty to refuse approval in certain cases

8.—(1) This paragraph applies to a decision by OFCOM—

(a) to approve arrangements or modifications;
(b) to impose arrangements or to modify imposed arrangements; or
(c) to propose modifications following a review under section 293.

(2) OFCOM must not make that decision if it appears to them that the arrangements, or the arrangements as proposed to be modified, would be likely to be prejudicial to the ability of holders of regional Channel 3 licences, or of any of them, to comply with—

(a) their public service remits;
(b) conditions imposed on them under section 286;
(c) conditions imposed on them under section 287; or
(d) conditions imposed on them under section 352.

Appeals against decisions relating to competition test

9.—(1) A person holding a regional Channel 3 licence may appeal to the Tribunal against the following decisions by OFCOM—

(a) a decision on how to dispose of an application for the approval of arrangements or modifications;
(b) a decision to impose arrangements or to modify imposed arrangements; or
(c) a decision to propose modifications following a review under section 293.

(2) An appeal can be made only by sending the Tribunal a notice of appeal within the period specified, in relation to the decision appealed against, in Tribunal rules.

(3) The notice of appeal must set out the grounds of appeal.

(4) The only grounds on which an appeal may be brought are—

(a) that OFCOM have wrongly decided that a competition test is or is not satisfied in relation to arrangements or modifications submitted to them for approval;
(b) that a competition test is not satisfied in the case of arrangements proposed by OFCOM;
(c) that provisions contained in arrangements proposed by OFCOM for satisfying a competition test are not required for that purpose;
(d) that the requirement to satisfy a competition test should be discharged in a different manner from that in which it would be satisfied in accordance with arrangements proposed by OFCOM.

(5) In sub-paragraph (4) "arrangements proposed by OFCOM" means—

(a) arrangements or modified arrangements as they will have effect after giving effect to changes proposed by OFCOM in giving a conditional approval;
(b) arrangements imposed by them;

(c) imposed arrangements as modified by them;
(d) arrangements as modified by proposals made by OFCOM following a review under section 293.

(6) The holder of a regional Channel 3 licence is not required by the conditions of his licence to take steps for giving effect to a decision of OFCOM at any time when an appeal under this Schedule against that decision is pending.

Decisions on an appeal

10.—(1) Appeals to the Tribunal under paragraph 9 are to be disposed of in accordance with this paragraph.

(2) The Tribunal shall decide the appeal on the merits and by reference to the grounds of appeal set out in the notice of appeal.

(3) The Tribunal shall decide what (if any) is the appropriate decision for OFCOM to have made in relation to the matters to which those grounds relate.

(4) The Tribunal shall then either—
(a) confirm OFCOM's decision; or
(b) remit the matter to OFCOM with such directions (if any) as the Tribunal considers appropriate for giving effect to its decision.

(5) The Tribunal must not direct OFCOM to take any action which they would not otherwise have had power to take in relation to the matter under appeal.

(6) It shall be the duty of OFCOM to comply with every direction given to them under sub-paragraph (4).

(7) In its application to a decision of the Tribunal under this paragraph, paragraph 1(2)(b) of Schedule 4 to the Enterprise Act 2002 (c 40) (exclusion of commercial information from documents recording Tribunal decisions) is to have effect as if for the reference to the undertaking to which commercial information relates there were substituted a reference to the person to whom such information relates.

Appeals against decisions of the Tribunal

11.—(1) A decision of the Tribunal on an appeal under paragraph 9 may itself be appealed.

(2) An appeal under this paragraph—
(a) lies to the Court of Appeal or to the Court of Session; and
(b) must relate only to a point of law arising from the decision of the Tribunal.

(3) An appeal under this paragraph may be brought by a party to the proceedings before the Tribunal.

(4) An appeal under this paragraph requires the permission of the Tribunal or of the court to which it is to be made.

(5) In this paragraph references to a decision of the Tribunal include references to a direction given by it under paragraph 10(4).

Information for OFCOM

12.—(1) OFCOM may by notice require a person—
(a) to produce to them such documents specified or described in the notice, or
(b) to furnish them with such other information so specified or described,

as they consider necessary in order to determine for the purposes of section 293 or this Schedule whether the competition tests are satisfied.

(2) A requirement imposed by a notice under this paragraph has to be complied with by producing the document, or by furnishing the required information, at the time and place specified in the notice.

(3) If the requirement is one for the furnishing of information otherwise than by the production of a document, the information must be furnished in the manner specified in the notice.

(4) The only documents that a person is required to produce by a notice under this paragraph are those that are in his custody or under his control—
(a) at the time of the notice; or
(b) at a time between that time and the time when the notice must be complied with.

Enforcement of information provisions

13.—(1) The court may, on an application by OFCOM, enquire into whether any person ("the defaulter") has refused or otherwise failed, without reasonable excuse, to comply with a requirement contained in a notice under paragraph 12.

(2) An application under sub-paragraph (1) shall include details of the possible failure which OFCOM consider has occurred.

(3) In enquiring into a case under sub-paragraph (1), the court shall hear—
(a) any witness who may be produced against or on behalf of the defaulter; and
(b) any statement which may be offered in defence.

(4) Sub-paragraphs (5) and (6) apply where the court is satisfied, after hearing any witnesses and statements as mentioned in sub-paragraph (3), that the defaulter has refused or failed, without reasonable excuse, to comply with the requirement contained in the notice under paragraph 12.

(5) The court may punish the defaulter as it would have been able to punish him had he been guilty of contempt of court.

(6) Where the defaulter is a body corporate, the power of the court to punish the defaulter includes power to punish a director or officer of the body corporate.

(7) Where the defaulter is a partnership constituted under the law of Scotland, the power of the court to punish the defaulter includes power to punish a member of the partnership.

(8) A person is guilty of an offence if he intentionally alters, suppresses or destroys a document which he has been required to produce by a notice under paragraph 12.

(9) A person is guilty of an offence if—
(a) he supplies information to OFCOM in purported compliance with a notice given to him under paragraph 12;
(b) the information is false or misleading in a material respect; and
(c) he knows that it is false or misleading in a material respect or is reckless as to whether it is false or misleading in a material respect.

(10) A person is guilty of an offence if—
(a) he supplies information to another person knowing that the information is to be used for complying with a notice under paragraph 12;
(b) the information is false or misleading in a material respect; and
(c) he knows that it is false or misleading in a material respect or is reckless as to whether it is false or misleading in a material respect.

(11) A person guilty of an offence under this paragraph shall be liable—
(a) on summary conviction, to a fine not exceeding the statutory maximum;
(b) on conviction on indictment, to imprisonment for a term not exceeding two years or to a fine, or to both.

(12) In this paragraph "the court" means—
(a) in relation to England and Wales, the High Court;
(b) in relation to Scotland, the Court of Session; and
(c) in relation to Northern Ireland, the High Court or a judge of the High Court.

Confidentiality and defamation

14.—(1) When publishing a report prepared under paragraph 4 or 5, OFCOM must have regard to the need to exclude from the publication, so far as practicable, the matters which are confidential in accordance with sub-paragraphs (2) and (3).

(2) A matter is confidential under this sub-paragraph if—
(a) it relates specifically to the affairs of a particular body; and
(b) publication of that matter would or might, in OFCOM's opinion, seriously and prejudicially affect the interests of that body.

(3) A matter is confidential under this sub-paragraph if—
(a) it relates to the private affairs of an individual; and
(b) publication of that matter would or might, in OFCOM's opinion, seriously and prejudicially affect the interests of that individual.

(4) For the purposes of the law of defamation absolute privilege attaches to every report prepared under paragraph 4 or 5.

Interpretation of Schedule

15. In this Schedule—
"competition test" is to be construed in accordance with paragraph 6;
"the Tribunal" means the Competition Appeal Tribunal; and
"Tribunal rules" means rules made under section 15 of the Enterprise Act 2002 (c 40).
[3451]

NOTES

Commencement: 29 December 2003.

SCHEDULE 12
CORRESPONDING OBLIGATIONS OF THE BBC AND WELSH AUTHORITY

Section 338

PART 1
THE BBC

Quotas for independent productions

1.—(1) It shall be the duty of the BBC to secure that, in each year, not less than 25 per cent of the total amount of time allocated to the broadcasting of qualifying programmes included in the television broadcasting services provided by the BBC is allocated to the broadcasting of a range and diversity of independent productions.

(2) In this paragraph—
(a) a reference to qualifying programmes is a reference to programmes of such description as the Secretary of State may by order specify as describing the programmes that are to be qualifying programmes for the purposes of this paragraph;
(b) a reference to independent productions is a reference to programmes of such description as the Secretary of State may by order specify as describing the programmes that are to be independent productions for the purposes of this paragraph; and
(c) a reference to a range of independent productions is a reference to a range of such productions in terms of cost of acquisition as well as in terms of the types of programme involved.

(3) The Secretary of State may by order amend sub-paragraph (1) by substituting a different percentage for the percentage for the time being specified in that sub-paragraph.

(4) The Secretary of State may also by order provide for the BBC to have the duty set out in sub-paragraph (5), either instead of or as well as the one set out in sub-paragraph (1).

(5) That duty is a duty to secure that, in each year, not less than the percentage specified in the order of the programming budget for that year for the television broadcasting services provided by the BBC is applied in the acquisition of independent productions.

(6) The power to make an order under sub-paragraph (4) includes power to provide that the BBC are again to be subject to a duty to which they have previously ceased to be subject by virtue of such an order, in addition to or instead of the duty to which they are subject (apart from the exercise of that power) by virtue of this paragraph.

(7) The Secretary of State is not to make an order for the BBC to be or to cease to be subject to the duty mentioned in sub-paragraph (1) or (5) unless—
(a) OFCOM have made a recommendation to him that the BBC should be subject to that duty, or should cease to be subject to it; and

(b) the order gives effect to that recommendation.

(8) Where television broadcasting services are designated by or under the BBC Charter and Agreement—

(a) as services that must be treated separately for the purposes of the duty imposed by sub-paragraph (1) or a duty imposed under sub-paragraph (4), or

(b) as services that must be included in a group of services that must be taken together for the purposes of such a duty,

that duty is to have effect in accordance with sub-paragraph (9).

(9) A duty having effect in accordance with this sub-paragraph is to have effect as if (instead of applying to all the television broadcasting services provided by the BBC, taken together) it applied separately—

(a) in relation to each service that is required to be treated separately; and

(b) in relation to each group of services that are required to be taken together.

(10) The BBC must comply with directions given to them by OFCOM for the purpose of—

(a) carrying forward to one or more subsequent years determined in accordance with the direction any shortfall for any year in their compliance with the duties imposed by virtue of sub-paragraph (1) or (4); and

(b) thereby increasing the percentage applicable for the purposes of those duties to the subsequent year or years.

(11) For the purposes of this paragraph—

(a) the amount of the programming budget for a year, and

(b) the means of determining the amount of that budget that is applied for any purpose,

are to be computed in accordance with such provision as may be set out in an order made by the Secretary of State, or as may be determined by OFCOM in accordance with such an order.

(12) Before making an order under this paragraph the Secretary of State must consult OFCOM and the BBC.

(13) No order is to be made containing provision authorised by this paragraph unless a draft of the order has been laid before Parliament and approved by a resolution of each House.

(14) In this paragraph—

"acquisition", in relation to a programme, includes commissioning and acquiring a right to include it in a service or to have it broadcast; and

"programming budget" means the budget for the production and acquisition of qualifying programmes.

Duty to publicise complaints procedures etc

2.—(1) It shall be the duty of the BBC to make arrangements for securing that the matters mentioned in sub-paragraph (2) are brought to the attention of the public (whether by means of broadcasts or otherwise).

(2) Those matters are—

(a) OFCOM's functions under Part 5 of the 1996 Act in relation to services provided by the BBC; and

(b) any procedures established by OFCOM or the BBC for the handling and resolution of complaints about the observance by the BBC of standards set under section 319.

[3452]

NOTES

Commencement: 29 December 2003.

PART 2
THE WELSH AUTHORITY

Public service remits of the Welsh Authority services

3.—(1) It shall be the duty of the Welsh Authority to secure that the public service remits for each of their public television services is fulfilled.

(2) The public service remit for S4C is the provision of a broad range of high quality and diverse programming in a service in which—

(a) a substantial proportion of the programmes consists of programmes in Welsh;
(b) the programmes broadcast for viewing between 6:30 PM and 10:00 PM on every day of the week consist mainly of programmes in Welsh; and
(c) the programmes that are not in Welsh are normally programmes which are being, have been or are to be broadcast on Channel 4.

(3) The public service remit for S4C Digital is the provision of a broad range of high quality and diverse programming in a service in which a substantial proportion of the programmes consists of programmes in Welsh.

(4) The public service remit for a television programme service provided by the Welsh Authority with the approval of the Secretary of State under section 205 is the remit set out in the order approving the provision of the service.

(5) The Secretary of State may by order modify sub-paragraphs (2) and (3).

(6) Before making an order specifying or modifying the public service remit for any of the Welsh Authority's public television services, the Secretary of State must consult—

(a) the Authority; and
(b) where the order relates to the inclusion in any service of programmes that are not in Welsh, C4C.

(7) An order modifying the public service remit for S4C or S4C Digital must not contain provision inconsistent with a requirement that each service must—

(a) represent a public service for the dissemination of information, education and entertainment; and
(b) include programmes a substantial proportion of which consists of programmes in Welsh.

(8) No order is to be made containing provision authorised by sub-paragraph (5) unless a draft of the order has been laid before Parliament and approved by a resolution of each House.

Statements of programme policy

4.—(1) It shall be the duty of the Welsh Authority—

(a) as soon as practicable after the coming into force of this paragraph, and subsequently at annual intervals, to prepare a statement of programme policy; and
(b) to monitor their own performance in the carrying out of the proposals contained in statements made under this paragraph.

(2) Every statement of programme policy prepared under this paragraph must set out the Welsh Authority's proposals for securing that, during the following year—

(a) the public service remit for each of their public television services to be provided during that year will be fulfilled; and
(b) the Welsh Authority's duties under the provisions of this Schedule will be performed.

(3) Every such statement must contain a report on the performance of the Welsh Authority in the carrying out during the period since the previous statement of the proposals contained in that previous statement.

(4) When preparing such a statement, the Welsh Authority must consider—

(a) any guidance by OFCOM that is in force for the purposes of section 266; and
(b) any reports previously published by OFCOM under section 264 or 358.

(5) Every such statement must be published by the Welsh Authority as soon as practicable after its preparation is complete.

(6) OFCOM may direct that any statement of policy which—

(a) was made by the Welsh Authority before the coming into force of this paragraph, and
(b) is specified in the direction,

is to be treated for the purposes of this Act as if it were a statement made in relation to such period as may be so specified in pursuance of this paragraph.

(7) A direction under sub-paragraph (6) cannot contain provision the effect of which is to postpone the time at which the Welsh Authority would otherwise be required to make its first statement of programme policy.

Must-offer obligations in relation to networks and satellite services

5.—(1) It shall be the duty of the Welsh Authority to ensure that each of their public digital services is at all times offered as available (subject to the need to agree terms)—

(a) to be broadcast or distributed by means of every appropriate network; and

(b) to be broadcast by means of every satellite television service that is available for reception by members of the public in Wales.

(2) It shall be the duty of the Welsh Authority to do their best to secure that arrangements are entered into, and kept in force, that ensure—

(a) that each of their public digital services is broadcast or distributed on appropriate networks; and

(b) that the broadcasting and distribution of each of their public digital services, in accordance with those arrangements, result in the service being available for reception, by means of appropriate networks, by as many members of its intended audience as practicable.

(3) It shall be the duty of the Welsh Authority to do their best to secure that arrangements are entered into, and kept in force, that ensure—

(a) that each of their public digital services is broadcast by means of satellite television services that are broadcast so as to be available for reception by members of the public in Wales; and

(b) that the broadcasting, in accordance with those arrangements, of each of the Authority's public digital services by means of satellite television services results in its being available for reception in an intelligible form and by means of those services by as many members of its intended audience as practicable.

(4) The Welsh Authority must secure that the arrangements entered into and kept in force for the purposes of sub-paragraphs (2) and (3) prohibit the imposition, for or in connection with the provision of an appropriate network or a satellite television service, of any charge that is attributable (whether directly or indirectly) to the conferring of an entitlement to receive each of the Authority's public digital services in an intelligible form by means of that network or service.

(5) OFCOM may, by a direction to the Welsh Authority, require arrangements made or kept in force for the purposes of sub-paragraphs (2) or (3) to apply in the case of every service which is an ancillary service by reference to one of their public digital services as they apply to the service itself.

(6) For the purposes of this paragraph a public digital service of the Welsh Authority is to be treated, in relation to particular appropriate networks and satellite television services, as constituting such services comprised in or provided with that public digital service—

(a) as may be determined by agreement between the Welsh Authority and OFCOM; or

(b) in default of agreement, as may be directed by OFCOM.

(7) This paragraph—

(a) so far as it relates to the broadcasting or distribution of any of the Welsh Authority's public digital services by means of appropriate networks, applies only in relation to times when that service is included in the list of must-carry services in section 64; and

(b) so far as it relates to the broadcasting of such a public digital service by means of a satellite television service, applies only in relation to times when that service is included in the list of must-provide services in section 275.

(8) In this paragraph—

"appropriate network" means an electronic communications network by means of which public electronic communications services are provided that are used by a significant number of end-users in Wales as their principal means of receiving television programmes;

"intended audience", in relation to a public digital service of the Welsh Authority, means—

(a) if the service is one provided only for a particular area or locality of Wales, members of the public in that area or locality;

(b) if the service is one provided for members of a particular community, members of that community; and

(c) in any other case, members of the public in Wales;

"public digital service", in relation to the Welsh Authority, means any of their public television services so far as it is provided in digital form; and "satellite television service" means a service which—

(a) consists in or involves the broadcasting of television programme services from a satellite; and

(b) is used by a significant number of the persons by whom the broadcasts are received in an intelligible form as their principal means of receiving television programmes.

(9) For the purposes of this paragraph an electronic communications network is not an appropriate network in relation to so much of a channel or other service as is provided only for a particular area or locality of Wales unless it is a network by means of which electronic communications services are provided to persons in that area or locality

(10) In sub-paragraph (8) "public electronic communications service" and "end-user" each has the same meaning as in Chapter 1 of Part 2.

(11) An order under section 411 must not appoint a day for provisions of this paragraph to come into force that falls less than six months after the day on which the order is made.

Supply of services by satellite in certain areas

6. It shall be the duty of the Welsh Authority—

(a) to join with the providers of other must-provide services in entering into and maintaining arrangements satisfying the requirements of section 274; and

(b) to comply with the requirements of any arrangements imposed by OFCOM for the purposes of conditions under subsection (2) of that section.

Programming quotas for independent productions

7.—(1) It shall be the duty of the Welsh Authority to secure that, in each year, not less than 25 per cent of the total amount of time allocated to the broadcasting of qualifying programmes included in their designated public services (taken together) is allocated to the broadcasting of a range and diversity of independent productions.

(2) In this paragraph—

(a) a reference to qualifying programmes is a reference to programmes of such description as the Secretary of State may by order specify as describing the programmes that are to be qualifying programmes for the purposes of this paragraph;

(b) a reference to independent productions is a reference to programmes of such description as the Secretary of State may by order specify as describing the programmes that are to be independent productions for the purposes of this paragraph; and

(c) a reference to a range of independent productions is a reference to a range of such productions in terms of cost of acquisition as well as in terms of the types of programme involved.

(3) The Secretary of State may by order amend sub-paragraph (1) by substituting a different percentage for the percentage for the time being specified in that sub-paragraph.

(4) The Secretary of State may also by order provide for the Welsh Authority to have the duty set out in sub-paragraph (5), either instead of or as well as the one set out in subparagraph (1).

(5) That duty is a duty to secure that, in each year, not less than the percentage specified in the order of the programming budget for that year for the designated public services (taken together) is applied in the acquisition of independent productions.

(6) The power to make an order under sub-paragraph (4) includes power to provide that the Welsh Authority are again to be subject to a duty to which they have previously ceased to be subject by virtue of such an order, in addition to or instead of the duty to which they are subject (apart from the exercise of that power) by virtue of this paragraph.

(7) The Secretary of State is not to make an order for the Welsh Authority to be or to cease to be subject to the duty mentioned in sub-paragraph (1) or (5) unless—

(a) OFCOM have made a recommendation to him that the Authority should be subject to that duty, or should cease to be subject to it; and

(b) the order gives effect to that recommendation.

(8) The Welsh Authority must comply with directions given to them by OFCOM for the purpose of—

(a) carrying forward to one or more subsequent years determined in accordance with the direction any shortfall for any year in their compliance with the duties imposed by virtue of sub-paragraph (1) or (4); and

(b) thereby increasing the percentage applicable for the purposes of those duties to the subsequent year or years.

(9) For the purposes of this paragraph—

(a) the amount of the programming budget for a year, and

(b) the means of determining the amount of that budget that is applied for any purpose,

are to be computed in accordance with such provision as may be set out in an order made by the Secretary of State, or as may be determined by OFCOM in accordance with such an order.

(10) Before making an order under this paragraph the Secretary of State must consult OFCOM, the BBC and the Welsh Authority.

(11) No order is to be made containing provision authorised by this paragraph unless a draft of the order has been laid before Parliament and approved by a resolution of each House.

(12) The services that are designated public services for the purposes of this paragraph are—

(a) S4C;

(b) S4C Digital; and

(c) any of the Welsh Authority's other public television services which is designated for the purposes of this paragraph by the order under section 205 approving its provision.

(13) In this paragraph—

"acquisition", in relation to a programme, includes commissioning and acquiring a right to include it in a service or to have it broadcast;

"programme" does not include an advertisement; and

"programming budget" means the budget for the production and acquisition of qualifying programmes.

Programme quotas for original productions

8.—(1) It shall be the duty of the Welsh Authority, in relation to their designated public services (taken together) to secure—

(a) that the time allocated, in each year, to the broadcasting of original productions included in those services is no less than the proportion fixed under sub-paragraph (2) of the total amount of time allocated to the broadcasting of all the programmes included in those services; and

(b) that the time allocated to the broadcasting of original productions is split in the manner so fixed between peak viewing times and other times.

(2) The fixing for the purposes of sub-paragraph (1) of a proportion or manner of splitting allocated time is to be—

(a) by agreement between the Welsh Authority and OFCOM; or

(b) in default of agreement, by a direction given by OFCOM to the Authority fixing the proportion or manner according to whatever OFCOM consider appropriate for ensuring that the service is consistently of a high quality.

(3) The agreement or direction may, for the purposes of sub-paragraph (1)(b), fix a proportion for the purposes of sub-paragraph (1)(a) in terms of the cumulative effect of two different minimum proportions, one applying to peak viewing times and the other to other times.

(4) The agreement or direction may provide that specified descriptions of programmes are to be excluded in determining the programmes a proportion of which is to constitute original productions.

(5) It may also provide that, in determining whether a programme is of a description of programmes excluded by an agreement or direction by virtue of sub-paragraph (4), regard is to be had to any guidance prepared and published, and from to time revised, by OFCOM.

(6) References in this paragraph, in relation to the designated public services of the Welsh Authority, to original productions are references to programmes of such description as

the Secretary of State may by order specify as describing the programmes that are to be original productions for the purposes of this paragraph.

(7) The power to specify descriptions of programmes by order under sub-paragraph (6) includes power to confer such discretions on OFCOM as the Secretary of State thinks fit.

(8) Before making an order under this paragraph the Secretary of State must consult OFCOM, the BBC and the Welsh Authority.

(9) No order is to be made containing provision authorised by this paragraph unless a draft of the order has been laid before Parliament and approved by a resolution of each House.

(10) The services that are designated public services for the purposes of this paragraph are—

(a) S4C;

(b) S4C Digital; and

(c) any of the Welsh Authority's other public television services which is designated for the purposes of this paragraph by the order under section 205 approving its provision.

(11) In this paragraph—

"peak viewing time", in relation to the designated public services of the Welsh Authority, means a time that is determined in accordance with sub-paragraph (12) to be a peak viewing time for one or more of those services; and

"programme" does not include an advertisement.

(12) The determination for the purposes of this paragraph of peak viewing times is to be—

(a) by agreement between the Welsh Authority and OFCOM; or

(b) in default of agreement, by a direction given by OFCOM to the Authority determining those times.

News and current affairs programmes

9.—(1) It shall be the duty of the Welsh Authority, in relation to their designated public services, to secure—

(a) that the programmes included in each service include news programmes and current affairs programmes;

(b) that the news programmes and current affairs programmes included in each service deal with both national and international matters; and

(c) that the news programmes so included are broadcast for viewing at intervals throughout the period for which the service is provided.

(2) It shall be the duty of the Welsh Authority, in relation to each of their designated public services, to ensure that the news programmes and current affairs programmes included in each service are of high quality.

(3) It shall also be the duty of the Welsh Authority, in relation to each of their designated public services, to secure that in each year—

(a) the time allocated to the broadcasting of news programmes included in the service, and

(b) the time allocated to the broadcasting of current affairs programmes so included,

each constitutes no less than the proportion fixed under sub-paragraph (5) of the time allocated to the broadcasting of all the programmes included in the service.

(4) It is the further duty of the Welsh Authority, in relation to each of their designated public services, to secure that the time allocated—

(a) to the broadcasting of news programmes included in the service, and

(b) to the broadcasting of current affairs programmes so included,

is, in each case, split, in the manner fixed under sub-paragraph (5), between peak viewing times and other times.

(5) The fixing for the purposes of sub-paragraph (3) or (4) of a proportion or manner of splitting allocated time is to be—

(a) by agreement between the Welsh Authority and OFCOM; or

(b) in default of agreement, by a direction given by OFCOM to the Authority fixing the proportion or manner according to whatever OFCOM consider appropriate.

(6) The agreement or direction may, for the purposes of sub-paragraph (4), fix a proportion for the purposes of sub-paragraph (3) in terms of the cumulative effect of two different minimum proportions, one applying to peak viewing times and the other to other times.

(7) The services that are designated public services for the purposes of this paragraph are—

- (a) S4C;
- (b) S4C Digital; and
- (c) any of the Welsh Authority's other public television services which is designated for the purposes of this paragraph by the order under section 205 approving its provision.

(8) In this paragraph "peak viewing time", in relation to a service, means a time that is determined in accordance with sub-paragraph (9) to be a peak viewing time for that service.

(9) The determination for the purposes of this paragraph of a peak viewing time is to be—

- (a) by agreement between the Welsh Authority and OFCOM; or
- (b) in default of agreement, by a direction given by OFCOM to the Authority determining that time.

Code relating to programme commissioning

10.—(1) It shall be the duty of the Welsh Authority to draw up and from time to time revise a code of practice setting out the principles that are to be applied when they or an S4C company are for a relevant purpose agreeing terms for the commissioning of independent productions.

(2) A relevant purpose is a purpose connected with the provision by the Welsh Authority or an S4C company of a programme service.

(3) It shall also be the duty of the Welsh Authority—

- (a) at all times to comply with the code of practice which is for the time being in force under this paragraph;
- (b) to take all reasonable steps for securing that the code is complied with by S4C companies;
- (c) to exercise their power to revise that code to take account of revisions from time to time of the guidance issued by OFCOM for the purposes of this paragraph; and
- (d) to comply with such directions as may be given to the Authority by OFCOM for securing that they properly perform their duties under paragraphs (a) and (b).

(4) The code for the time being in force under this paragraph must be such as to secure, in the manner described in guidance issued by OFCOM—

- (a) that a reasonable timetable is applied to negotiations for the commissioning of an independent production and for the conclusion of a binding agreement;
- (b) that there is sufficient clarity when an independent production is commissioned about the different categories of rights to broadcast or otherwise to make use of or exploit the commissioned production that are being disposed of;
- (c) that there is sufficient transparency about the amounts to be paid in respect of each category of rights;
- (d) that satisfactory arrangements are made about the duration and exclusivity of those rights;
- (e) that procedures exist for reviewing the arrangements adopted in accordance with the code and for demonstrating compliance with it;
- (f) that those procedures include requirements for the monitoring of the application of the code and for the making of reports to OFCOM;
- (g) that provision is made for resolving disputes arising in respect of the provisions of the code (by independent arbitration or otherwise) in a manner that appears to OFCOM to be appropriate.

(5) The Welsh Authority must also ensure that the drawing up or revision of a code by virtue of this paragraph is in accordance with guidance issued by OFCOM as to—

- (a) the times when the code is to be drawn up or reviewed with a view to revision;
- (b) the consultation to be undertaken before a code is drawn up or revised;
- (c) the publication of every code or revised code.

(6) The Welsh Authority must submit to OFCOM for approval a draft of—

(a) every code that is required to be drawn up under this paragraph; and
(b) every revision made by that Authority of such a code.

(7) A code drawn up by the Welsh Authority or a revision of such a code—
(a) is to have effect for the purposes of this paragraph only if approved by OFCOM; and
(b) if approved by OFCOM subject to modifications, is to have effect with those modifications.

(8) OFCOM—
(a) must issue and may from time to time revise guidance for the purposes of this paragraph;
(b) must ensure that there is always guidance for those purposes in force;
(c) must, before issuing their guidance or revised guidance, consult the providers of licensed public service channels, persons who make independent productions (or persons appearing to OFCOM to represent them), the BBC and the Welsh Authority; and
(d) must publish their guidance or revised guidance in such manner as they think appropriate.

(9) Guidance issued by OFCOM for the purposes of this paragraph must be general guidance and is not to specify particular terms to be included in agreements to which the guidance relates.

(10) OFCOM may by a direction to the Welsh Authority specify that a code which—
(a) was drawn up by the Authority before the commencement of this paragraph, and
(b) is identified in the direction,
is to be treated as drawn up in pursuance of this paragraph and approved by OFCOM.

(11) In this paragraph "independent production" has the same meaning as in paragraph 7.

Co-operation with the public teletext provider

11.—(1) The Welsh Authority must grant access to the public teletext provider to the facilities that are reasonably required by him for the purposes of, or in connection with, the provision of the public teletext service.

(2) The Welsh Authority may require the public teletext provider to pay a reasonable charge in respect of facilities access to which is granted under this paragraph.

(3) In the event of a dispute, the amount of the charge is to be determined by OFCOM.

Programme standards

12. It shall be the duty of the Welsh Authority in relation to their public television services to observe the standards set under section 319.

13. It shall be the duty of the Welsh Authority to comply with a direction given to them by OFCOM with respect to the establishment of procedures for the handling and resolution of complaints about the observance by the Authority of standards set under section 319.

14.—(1) It shall be the duty of the Welsh Authority to comply with directions given to them by OFCOM with respect to any of the matters mentioned in sub-paragraph (2).

(2) Those matters are—
(a) the exclusion from any of the Authority's public television services of a particular advertisement, or its exclusion in particular circumstances;
(b) the descriptions of advertisements and methods of advertising to be excluded from the services so provided (whether generally or in particular circumstances); and
(c) the methods of sponsorship to be excluded from those services (whether generally or in particular circumstances).

15.—(1) This paragraph applies if OFCOM are satisfied—
(a) that the Welsh Authority have failed in any respect to perform any of their duties under paragraphs 12 to 14; and
(b) that the failure can be appropriately remedied by the inclusion in any or all of the Authority's public television services of a correction or a statement of findings.

(2) OFCOM may direct the Welsh Authority to include a correction or a statement of findings (or both) in any one or more of their public television services.

(3) A direction may require the correction or statement of findings to be in such form, and to be included in programmes at such time or times, as OFCOM may determine.

(4) OFCOM are not to give a direction under this paragraph unless they have given the Welsh Authority a reasonable opportunity of making representations to them about the matters appearing to OFCOM to provide grounds for the giving of the direction.

(5) Where the Welsh Authority include a correction or a statement of findings in any of their public television services in pursuance of a direction under this paragraph, the Authority may announce that they are doing so in pursuance of such a direction.

(6) For the purposes of this paragraph a statement of findings, in relation to a case in which OFCOM are satisfied that the Welsh Authority have failed to perform a duty imposed on them under paragraphs 12 to 14, is a statement of OFCOM's findings in relation to that failure.

Directions with respect to advertising

16.—(1) The Welsh Authority must comply with directions given to them by OFCOM with respect to any of the matters mentioned in sub-paragraph (2).

(2) Those matters are—
- (a) the maximum amount of time to be given to advertisements in any hour or other period;
- (b) the minimum interval which must elapse between any two periods given over to advertisements;
- (c) the number of such periods to be allowed in any programme or in any hour or day; and
- (d) the exclusion of advertisements from a specified part of S4C or S4C Digital.

(3) Directions under this paragraph—
- (a) may be either general or specific;
- (b) may be qualified or unqualified; and
- (c) may make different provision for different parts of the day, different days of the week, different types of programmes or for other differing circumstances.

(4) In giving a direction under this paragraph, OFCOM shall take account of such of the international obligations of the United Kingdom as the Secretary of State may notify to them for the purposes of this paragraph.

Fairness standards

17. It shall be the duty of the Welsh Authority to secure the observance—
- (a) in connection with the provision of their public television services, and
- (b) in relation to the programmes included in those services,

of the code for the time being in force under section 107 of the 1996 Act (the fairness code).

Party political broadcasts

18.—(1) It shall be the duty of the Welsh Authority to include—
- (a) party political broadcasts, and
- (b) referendum campaign broadcasts,

in every designated public service of theirs.

(2) The Welsh Authority must prepare, publish and from time to time review and revise their policy with respect to—
- (a) party political broadcasts and referendum campaign broadcasts; and
- (b) the manner in which they propose to perform their duty under sub-paragraph (1).

(3) The Welsh Authority's policy may, in particular, include provision for determining—
- (a) the political parties on whose behalf party political broadcasts may be made;
- (b) in relation to each political party on whose behalf such broadcasts may be made, the length and frequency of the broadcasts; and

(c) in relation to each designated organisation on whose behalf referendum campaign broadcasts are required to be broadcast, the length and frequency of such broadcasts.

(4) That policy is to have effect subject to sections 37 and 127 of the Political Parties, Elections and Referendums Act 2000 (c 41) (only registered parties and designated organisations to be entitled to party political broadcasts or referendum campaign broadcasts).

(5) In preparing or revising their policy with respect to the inclusion of party political broadcasts or referendum campaign broadcasts in their designated public services, the Welsh Authority must have regard to—

(a) any views expressed for the purposes of this paragraph by the Electoral Commission; and

(b) any rules made by OFCOM under section 333.

(6) The services that are designated public services for the purposes of this paragraph are—

(a) S4C;

(b) S4C Digital; and

(c) any of the Welsh Authority's other public television services which is designated for the purposes of this paragraph by the order under section 205 approving its provision.

(7) In this paragraph—

"designated organisation", in relation to a referendum, means a person or body designated by the Electoral Commission under section 108 of the Political Parties, Elections and Referendums Act 2000 in respect of that referendum; and

"referendum campaign broadcast" has the meaning given by section 127 of that Act.

Duty to publicise complaints procedures etc

19.—(1) It shall be the duty of the Welsh Authority to make arrangements for securing that the matters mentioned in sub-paragraph (2) are brought to the attention of the public (whether by means of broadcasts or otherwise).

(2) Those matters are—

(a) OFCOM's functions under Part 5 of the 1996 Act in relation to services provided by the Welsh Authority; and

(b) any procedures established by OFCOM or the Authority for the handling and resolution of complaints about the observance by the Authority of standards set under section 319.

Monitoring of programmes

20.—(1) It shall be the duty of the Welsh Authority—

(a) in respect of every programme included in any of their public television services, to retain a recording of the programme in the form, and for the period, specified by OFCOM;

(b) to comply with any request to produce such recordings to OFCOM for examination or reproduction; and

(c) to comply, to the extent that they are able to do so, with any request to produce to OFCOM a script or transcript of a programme included in any of their public television services.

(2) The period specified for the purposes of sub-paragraph (1)(a) must be a period not exceeding ninety days.

Compliance with international obligations

21.—(1) OFCOM may give the Welsh Authority such directions as OFCOM consider appropriate for securing that all relevant international obligations are complied with.

(2) It shall be the duty of the Authority to comply with a direction under this paragraph.

(3) Before giving a direction under this paragraph, OFCOM must consult the Authority.

(4) In this paragraph "relevant international obligations" means the international obligations of the United Kingdom which have been notified to OFCOM by the Secretary of State for the purposes of this paragraph.

Services for the deaf and visually impaired

22. It shall be the duty of the Welsh Authority to observe the code for the time being in force under section 303 in the provision of—

(a) S4C Digital; and
(b) so much of any of the Welsh Authority's other public television services as is provided in digital form.

Equality of opportunity

23.—(1) It shall be the duty of the Welsh Authority to make such arrangements as they consider appropriate for promoting, in relation to employment with the Authority, equality of opportunity—

(a) between men and women; and
(b) between persons of different racial groups.

(2) It shall be the duty of the Welsh Authority to make arrangements for promoting, in relation to employment with the Authority, the equalisation of opportunities for disabled persons.

(3) The Welsh Authority shall also make such arrangements as they consider appropriate for the training and retraining of persons whom they employ in or in connection with—

(a) the provision of one or more of their public services; or
(b) the making of programmes to be included in one or more of those services.

(4) The Welsh Authority—

(a) shall take all such steps as they consider appropriate for making persons affected by any arrangements made in pursuance of sub-paragraphs (1) to (3) aware of the arrangements (including the publication of the arrangements in such manner as they think fit);
(b) shall review the arrangements from time to time; and
(c) shall, from time to time (and at least annually), publish, in such manner as they consider appropriate, their observations on the current operation and effectiveness of the arrangements.

(5) Before making any arrangements in pursuance of any of sub-paragraphs (1) to (3) or determining the manner in which they will comply with sub-paragraph (4), the Welsh Authority must consult OFCOM.

(6) In this paragraph—

"disabled" has the same meaning as in the Disability Discrimination Act 1995 (c 50);

"racial group" has the same meaning as in the Race Relations Act 1976 (c 74) or, in Northern Ireland, the Race Relations (Northern Ireland) Order 1997 (SI 1997/869 (NI 6)).

(7) The Secretary of State may by order amend sub-paragraph (1) by adding any other form of equality of opportunity that he considers appropriate to that sub-paragraph.

(8) No order is to be made containing provision authorised by sub-paragraph (7) unless a draft of the order has been laid before Parliament and approved by a resolution of each House.

Meaning of Welsh Authority's public services

24.—(1) In this Part of this Schedule, references to the Welsh Authority's public services are references to the following—

(a) S4C;
(b) S4C Digital; and
(c) the services the provision of which by the Authority is authorised by or under section 205.

(2) References in this Schedule to a public television service of the Welsh Authority are references to any public service of the Authority which is a television programme service. **[3453]**

NOTES

Commencement: 29 December 2003 (paras 3, 4, 7, 9–24); 1 July 2004 (para 8); to be appointed (otherwise).

Orders: the Broadcasting (Original Productions) Order 2004, SI 2004/1652.

SCHEDULE 13
FINANCIAL PENALTIES UNDER THE BROADCASTING ACTS

Section 345

PART 1
BROADCASTING ACT 1990

1–4. …

Additional television services licences

5.—(1) …

(2) This paragraph applies in relation to a failure to comply with a condition or direction only if it is one occurring after the commencement of this paragraph.

Revocation of national sound broadcasting licence

6.—(1), (2) …

(3) This paragraph applies only in a case of a revocation in relation to which—

(a) the notice required by section 101(2) of the 1990 Act, or

(b) the notice revoking the licence,

is served after the commencement of this paragraph.

Licences for analogue sound services

7.—(1), (2) …

(3) This paragraph applies in relation to a failure to comply with a condition or direction only if it is one occurring after the commencement of this paragraph.

Additional radio services licences

8.—(1) …

(2) This paragraph applies in relation to a failure to comply with a condition or direction only if it is one occurring after the commencement of this paragraph.

Power to amend penalties under the 1990 Act

9.—(1) The Secretary of State may by order amend any of the provisions of the 1990 Act specified in sub-paragraph (2) by substituting a different sum for the sum for the time being specified in that provision.

(2) Those provisions are—

(a) section 18(3B)(a) and (3C)(a);

(b) section 42B(3A)(a);

(c) section 101(3B)(a) and (3C)(a);

(d) section 110(1B)(a) and (3).

(3) No order is to be made under this paragraph unless a draft of the order has been laid before Parliament and approved by a resolution of each House.

[3454]

NOTES

Commencement: 29 December 2003.
Paras 1–4: amend the Broadcasting Act 1990, ss 18, 41, 42B.
Para 5: sub-para (1) amends the Broadcasting Act 1990, s 55 at **[3022]**.
Para 6: sub-paras (1), (2) amend the Broadcasting Act 1990, s 101 at **[3037]**.
Para 7: sub-paras (1), (2) amend the Broadcasting Act 1990, s 110 at **[3048]**.
Para 8: sub-para (1) amends the Broadcasting Act 1990, s 120 at **[3058]**.

(*Sch 13, Pt 2 amends the Broadcasting Act 1996* (*outside the scope of this work*).)

SCHEDULE 14
MEDIA OWNERSHIP RULES

Section 350

PART 1
CHANNEL 3 SERVICES

Ban on newspaper proprietors holding Channel 3 licences

1.—(1) A person is not to hold a licence to provide a Channel 3 service if—
- (a) he runs a national newspaper which for the time being has a national market share of 20 per cent or more; or
- (b) he runs national newspapers which for the time being together have a national market share of 20 per cent or more.

(2) A person is not to hold a licence to provide a regional Channel 3 service if—
- (a) he runs a local newspaper which for the time being has a local market share of 20 per cent or more in the coverage area of the service; or
- (b) he runs local newspapers which for the time being together have a local market share of 20 per cent or more in that coverage area.

(3) For the purposes of this paragraph, where there is a licence to provide a Channel 3 service, each of the following shall be treated as holding that licence—
- (a) the actual licence holder; and
- (b) every person connected with the actual licence holder.

Restrictions on participation

2.—(1) A person who is—
- (a) the proprietor of a national newspaper which for the time being has a national market share of 20 per cent or more, or
- (b) the proprietor of national newspapers which for the time being together have a national market share of 20 per cent or more,

is not to be a participant with more than a 20 per cent interest in a body corporate which is the holder of a licence to provide a Channel 3 service.

(2) A person who is the holder of a licence to provide a Channel 3 service is not to be a participant with more than a 20 per cent interest in a body corporate which is a relevant national newspaper proprietor.

(3) A body corporate is not to be a participant with more than a 20 per cent interest in a body corporate which holds a licence to provide a Channel 3 service if the first body corporate is one in which a relevant national newspaper proprietor is a participant with more than a 20 per cent interest.

(4) A restriction imposed by this paragraph on participation in a body corporate which is the holder of a Channel 3 licence applies equally to participation in a body corporate which controls the holder of such a licence.

(5) Any restriction on participation imposed by this paragraph—
- (a) on the proprietor of a newspaper, or

(b) on the holder of a licence,

is to apply as if he and every person connected with him were one person.

(6) In this paragraph "a relevant national newspaper proprietor" means a person who runs—

(a) a national newspaper which for the time being has a national market share of 20 per cent or more; or
(b) national newspapers which for the time being together have a national market share of 20 per cent or more.

National and local newspapers and their respective national and local market shares

3.—(1) In this Part of this Schedule references to a national or local newspaper are references to a national or local newspaper circulating wholly or mainly in the United Kingdom or in a part of the United Kingdom.

(2) Where a newspaper is published in different regional editions on the same day, OFCOM have the power to determine whether those regional editions should be treated for the purposes of this Part of this Schedule as constituting—

(a) one national newspaper;
(b) two or more local newspapers; or
(c) one national newspaper and one or more local newspapers.

(3) In the case of a newspaper which would otherwise be neither a national nor a local newspaper for the purposes of this Part of this Schedule, OFCOM have the power to determine, if they consider it appropriate to do so in the light of—

(a) its circulation and influence in the United Kingdom, or
(b) its circulation or influence in a part of the United Kingdom,

that the newspaper is to be treated as a national or as a local newspaper for such of those purposes as they may determine.

(4) For the purposes of this Part of this Schedule, the national market share of a national newspaper at any time is the percentage of the total number of copies of all national newspapers sold in the United Kingdom in the relevant six months which is represented by the total number of copies of that newspaper sold in the United Kingdom in that six months.

(5) For the purposes of this Part of this Schedule, the local market share of a local newspaper in any area at any time is the percentage of the total number of copies of all local newspapers sold in that area in the relevant six months which is represented by the total number of copies of that newspaper sold in that area in that six months.

(6) In sub-paragraphs (4) and (5) "the relevant six months" means the six months ending with the last whole calendar month to end before the time in question.

(7) For the purposes of sub-paragraphs (4) and (5), the number of copies of a newspaper sold in the United Kingdom, or in a particular area, during any period may be taken to be such number as is estimated by OFCOM—

(a) in such manner, or
(b) by reference to such statistics prepared by any other person,

as they think fit.

(8) In relation to a newspaper which is distributed free of charge (rather than sold), references in this paragraph to the number of copies sold include references to the number of copies distributed.

Construction of references to running a newspaper

4. For the purposes of this Part of this Schedule a person runs a national or local newspaper if—

(a) he is the proprietor of the newspaper; or
(b) he controls a body which is the proprietor of the newspaper.

Coverage area for a Channel 3 service

5. For the purposes of this Part of this Schedule the coverage area for a Channel 3 service is the area that is determined by OFCOM to be the area of the United Kingdom within which

that service is capable of being received at a level satisfying such technical standards as may have been laid down by them for the purposes of this paragraph.

Power to amend Part 1 of Schedule

6. The Secretary of State may by order repeal or otherwise modify any of the restrictions imposed by this Part of this Schedule.

[3455]

NOTES

Commencement: 29 December 2003.

PART 2
RADIO MULTIPLEX SERVICES

Restriction on holding of national radio multiplex licences

7. A person is not to hold more than one national radio multiplex licence at the same time.

Restriction on holding of local radio multiplex licences

8.—(1) A person is not to hold any two local radio multiplex licences at the same time where the [protected area] of one of the licensed services overlaps with the [protected area] of the other in a way that means that the potential audience for one of them is or includes at least half the potential audience of the other.

(2) …

(3) Where a person is in contravention of this paragraph in respect of the holding by him of local radio multiplex licences, that contravention is to be disregarded in relation to any time if—

(a) he held those licences immediately before the commencement of this paragraph;
(b) his holding of those licences immediately before the commencement of this paragraph was not in contravention of paragraph 11(4) of Part 3 of Schedule 2 to the 1990 Act; and
(c) there has not been a relevant change of circumstances between the commencement of this paragraph and that time.

(4) There is a relevant change of circumstances in the case of the person in contravention if another person becomes the holder of the two pre-commencement licences in relation to which the contravention arises.

(5) In sub-paragraph (4) "pre-commencement licence", in relation to a person and a time, means a local radio multiplex licence held by him immediately before the commencement of this paragraph and still held by him at that time.

[(6) In this paragraph, in relation to a local radio multiplex service—

"potential audience" means the persons who have attained the age of 15 years and reside within the protected area for that multiplex service; and

"the protected area" means—

(a) subject to paragraph (b), the area or locality specified in a notice published under section 50(1) of the 1996 Act as that in which that multiplex service is to be available; or
(b) if different from that area or locality, the area or locality specified in the relevant licence as that in which that multiplex service is to be available.

(7) In sub-paragraph (6), "the relevant licence" means the local radio multiplex licence under which the multiplex service concerned is authorised to be provided.]

Connected persons rules etc

9. For the purposes of this Part of this Schedule, where there is a licence to provide a radio multiplex service, each of the following shall be treated as holding that licence—

(a) the actual licence holder; and

(b) every person connected with the actual licence holder.

Power to amend Part 2 of Schedule

10. The Secretary of State may by order repeal or otherwise modify any of the restrictions imposed by this Part of this Schedule.

[3456]

NOTES

12 December 2003 (para 10); 29 December 2003 (otherwise).

Para 8: words in square brackets in sub-para (1) substituted, sub-para (2) repealed, and sub-paras (6), (7) added, by the Media Ownership (Local Radio and Appointed News Provider) Order 2003, SI 2003/3299, art 14.

Orders: the Media Ownership (Local Radio and Appointed News Provider) Order 2003, SI 2003/3299 at **[3605]**.

PART 3
LOCAL SOUND PROGRAMME SERVICES

Restriction on holding of local sound broadcasting licences

11.—(1) The Secretary of State may by order impose—

(a) requirements prohibiting the holding at the same time by the same person, in the circumstances described in the order, of more than the number of local sound broadcasting licences that is determined in the manner set out in the order;

(b) requirements prohibiting a person from holding even one local sound broadcasting licence in the circumstances described in the order.

(2) The circumstances by reference to which a person may be prohibited under subparagraph (1) from holding a local sound broadcasting licence, and the factors that may be used for determining the number of such licences that he may hold, include, in particular—

(a) whether and to what extent the coverage areas of different services provided by that person under different local sound broadcasting licences would overlap;

(b) the sizes of the potential audiences for those services and the times when those services would be made available;

(c) whether and to what extent members of the potential audiences for those services would also be members of the potential audiences for services provided under local sound broadcasting licences held by other persons;

(d) in a case in which members of potential audiences for services so provided by that person would also be members of the potential audiences for services so provided by other persons—

(i) the number of those other persons;

(ii) the coverage areas of their services;

(iii) the sizes of the potential audiences for their services; and

(iv) the times when their services are or will be made available;

(e) whether that person runs one or more national newspapers, and their national market share;

(f) whether and to what extent the whole or a part of the coverage area for a service for which that person would hold a local sound broadcasting licence is or includes an area in which one or more local newspapers run by him is circulating, and the newspapers' local market share;

(g) whether and to what extent the whole or a part the coverage area for which that person would hold a local sound broadcasting licence is or is included in the coverage area of a regional Channel 3 service for which he also holds a licence.

(3) For the purposes of this paragraph the coverage area for a service provided under a local sound broadcasting licence or a Channel 3 licence is the area in the United Kingdom within which that service is capable of being received at a level satisfying such technical standards as may have been laid down by OFCOM for the purposes of the provisions of an order under this paragraph.

Restriction applying to local digital sound programme services

12.—(1) The Secretary of State may by order impose requirements, on persons holding local digital sound programme licences, prohibiting the provision by the same person, in the circumstances described in the order, of more than the number of local digital sound programme services that is determined in the manner set out in the order.

(2) The circumstances by reference to which a person may be prohibited under subparagraph (1) from providing a local digital sound programme service, and the factors that may be used for determining the number of such services that he may provide, include, in particular—

- (a) whether and to what extent the coverage areas of different local digital sound programme services provided by that person would overlap;
- (b) the capacity used by those services on the relevant multiplexes;
- (c) the sizes of the potential audiences for those services and the times when those services would be made available;
- (d) whether and to what extent members of the potential audiences for those services would also be members of the potential audiences for local digital sound programme services provided by other persons;
- (e) in a case in which members of the potential audiences for the services provided by that person would also be members of the potential audiences for local digital sound programme services provided by other persons—
  - (i) the number of those other persons;
  - (ii) the coverage areas of their services;
  - (iii) the capacity used by their services on the relevant multiplexes;
  - (iv) the sizes of the potential audiences for their services; and
  - (v) the times when their services are or will be made available.

(3) For the purposes of this paragraph the coverage area for a service provided under a local digital sound programme licence is the area in the United Kingdom within which the relevant multiplex is capable of being received at a level satisfying such technical standards as may have been laid down by OFCOM for the purposes of the provisions of an order under this paragraph.

(4) In this paragraph "the relevant multiplex", in relation to a service provided under a local digital sound programme licence, means the local radio multiplex service in which the service provided under that licence is or is to be included.

(5) For the purposes of this paragraph a person who holds a licence to provide local digital sound programme services provides such a service if, and only if—

- (a) the service is one provided by him and is included in a local radio multiplex service for which he holds a local radio multiplex licence; or
- (b) under a contract between that person and a person who holds a licence to provide a local radio multiplex service, the person holding the licence to provide the radio multiplex service is required to include that local digital sound programme service in that multiplex service.

Powers supplemental to powers under paragraphs 11 and 12

13.—(1) An order under paragraph 11 or 12 may make provision for treating—

- (a) persons who are connected with a person who holds a licence,
- (b) persons who are associates of a person who holds a licence or of a person who is connected with a person who holds a licence, and
- (c) persons who (whether alone or together with such persons as may be described in the order) participate in a body which holds a licence or is treated as doing so by virtue of paragraph (a) or (b),

as if each of them were also a holder of the licence for the purposes of a requirement imposed under that paragraph.

(2) An order under paragraph 12 may make provision for treating—

- (a) persons who are connected with a person who provides a local digital sound programme service,
- (b) persons who are associates of a person who provides such a service or of a person who is connected with a person who provides such a service, and
- (c) persons who (whether alone or together with such persons as may be described in the order) participate in a body who provides such a service or is treated as doing so by virtue of paragraph (a) or (b),

as if each of them were also a person providing the service for the purposes of a requirement imposed under that paragraph.

(3) An order under paragraph 11 or 12 may also make provision for treating—

(a) persons who are connected with each other,

(b) persons who are associates of each other, and

(c) persons who (whether alone or together with such persons as may be described in the order) participate in a body,

as if they and such other persons who are connected with, associates of or participators in any of them as may be described in the order were the same person for the purposes of a requirement imposed under that paragraph.

(4) An order under paragraph 11 may make provision—

(a) as to the circumstances in which a newspaper is to be treated as a national newspaper or a local newspaper for the purposes of a requirement imposed under that paragraph;

(b) as to the person or persons who are to be treated for any such purposes as running a newspaper;

(c) as to the determination for any such purposes of the area within which a local newspaper is circulating; and

(d) as to what is to constitute the national market share or local market share of any newspaper or of a number of newspapers taken together;

and provision made by virtue of this paragraph may apply, with or without modifications, any of the provisions of paragraph 3 or 4 of this Schedule.

(5) Power to make provision with respect to any matter by any order under paragraph 11 or 12 includes power—

(a) to make provision with respect to that matter by reference to the making or giving by OFCOM, in accordance with the order, of any determination, approval or consent; and

(b) to confer such other discretions on OFCOM as the Secretary of State thinks fit.

(6) Sub-paragraph (5) of paragraph 12 applies for the purposes of this paragraph as it applies for the purposes of that paragraph.

Transitional provision for orders under paragraphs 11 and 12

14.—(1) This paragraph applies where—

(a) immediately after the coming into force of an order under paragraph 11 or 12, a person ("the person in contravention") is in contravention, in any respect, of a requirement imposed under that paragraph; and

(b) immediately before the coming into force of the order, that person—

(i) held one or more relevant licences; but

(ii) was not, in that respect, in contravention of a requirement imposed under that paragraph.

(2) This paragraph does not apply in the case of the first order to be made under paragraph 11 or 12 if the person in contravention was, immediately before the coming into force of the order, in contravention, in relation to one or more of the relevant licences, of a requirement imposed under Part 3 or 4 of Schedule 2 to the 1990 Act.

(3) In sub-paragraphs (1) and (2) the reference to a relevant licence is—

(a) in relation to the coming into force of an order under paragraph 11, a local sound broadcasting licence; and

(b) in relation to the coming into force of an order under paragraph 12, a local digital sound programme licence.

(4) The contravention mentioned in sub-paragraph (1)(a), to the extent that it arises by reason of the coming into force of the order, is to be disregarded (in the case of the person in contravention) in relation to any time which falls—

(a) after the coming into force of the order; and

(b) before there is a relevant change of circumstances.

(5) Where the contravention is one arising under paragraph 11 in the case of a person who held one or more local sound broadcasting licences immediately before the coming into force of the order, there is a relevant change of circumstances if—

(a) another person becomes the holder of any of those licences, otherwise than in consequence of a transaction under which the person in contravention ceases to be a holder of the licence; or
(b) the person in contravention becomes the holder of another local sound broadcasting licence.

(6) A change of circumstances is not a relevant change of circumstances by virtue of sub-paragraph (5)(b) unless the licence of which the person in contravention becomes the holder is one the holding of which, with the holding of licences already held by him, would (apart from sub-paragraph (4)) constitute a contravention of a requirement imposed under paragraph 11.

(7) Where the contravention is one arising under paragraph 12 in the case of a person who, under a local digital sound programme licence, was providing one or more local digital sound programme services immediately before the coming into force of the order, there is a relevant change of circumstances if—
(a) another person becomes the holder of that licence, otherwise than in consequence of a transaction under which the person in contravention ceases to be a holder of the licence; or
(b) the person in contravention becomes the provider of another local digital sound programme service provided under that licence.

(8) A change of circumstances is not a relevant change of circumstances by virtue of sub-paragraph (7)(b) unless the service of which the person in contravention becomes the provider is one the provision of which, with the services already provided by him, would (apart from sub-paragraph (4)) constitute a contravention of a requirement imposed under paragraph 12.

(9) For the purposes of this paragraph, in its application in relation to a contravention of a requirement imposed under paragraph 11 or 12—
(a) references to holding a licence or providing a local digital sound programme service are to be construed in accordance with the provision having effect for the purposes of that requirement; and
(b) the persons who are taken to be holding a local digital sound programme licence immediately before the coming into force of the order include every person who at that time would, in accordance with that provision, be treated as providing local digital sound programme services that were being provided at that time under that licence.

[3457]

NOTES

Commencement: 29 December 2003.

Orders: the Media Ownership (Local Radio and Appointed News Provider) Order 2003, SI 2003/3299 at **[3605]**; the Community Radio Order 2004, SI 2004/1944 at **[3618]**.

PART 4
RELIGIOUS BODIES ETC

Approval required for religious bodies etc to hold licences

15.—(1) A person mentioned in paragraph 2(1) of Part 2 of Schedule 2 to the 1990 Act (religious bodies etc) is not to hold a Broadcasting Act licence not mentioned in paragraph 2(1A) of that Part unless—
(a) OFCOM have made a determination in his case as respects a description of licences applicable to that licence; and
(b) that determination remains in force.

(2) OFCOM are to make a determination under this paragraph in a person's case and as respects a particular description of licence if, and only if, they are satisfied that it is appropriate for that person to hold a licence of that description.

(3) OFCOM are not to make a determination under this paragraph except on an application made to them for the purpose.

(4) OFCOM must publish guidance for persons making applications to them under this paragraph as to the principles that they will apply when determining for the purposes of sub-paragraph (2) what is appropriate.

(5) OFCOM must have regard to guidance for the time being in force under subparagraph (4) when making determinations under this paragraph.

(6) OFCOM may revise any guidance under sub-paragraph (4) by publishing their revisions of it.

(7) The publication of guidance under sub-paragraph (4), or of any revisions of it, is to be in whatever manner OFCOM consider appropriate.

Power to amend Part 4 of Schedule

16. The Secretary of State may by order repeal or otherwise modify the restriction imposed by this Part of this Schedule.

[3458]

NOTES

Commencement: 18 September 2003 (for transitional provisions see the Communications Act 2003 (Commencement No 1) Order 2003, SI 2003/1900, art 5 at **[3511]**).

PART 5
SUPPLEMENTAL PROVISIONS OF SCHEDULE

Procedure for orders

17.—(1) Before making an order under any provision of this Schedule (other than one that is confined to giving effect to recommendations made by OFCOM in a report of a review under section 391), the Secretary of State must consult OFCOM.

(2) No order is to be made containing provision authorised by any provision of this Schedule unless a draft of the order has been laid before Parliament and approved by a resolution of each House.

Interpretation of Schedule

18.—(1) Part 1 of Schedule 2 to the 1990 Act applies for construing this Schedule as it applies for construing Part 2 of that Schedule.

(2) References in this paragraph to an area overlapping another include references to its being the same as, or lying wholly inside, the other area.

[3459]

NOTES

18 September 2003 (para 17, for the purposes of Sch 14, para 16 to this Act); 12 December 2003 (para 17, otherwise); 29 December 2003 (otherwise).

(Sch 15, Pt 1 amends the Broadcasting Act 1990 at **[3015]–[3073]***, and in so far as the amendments are relevant to this work, they have been incorporated at the appropriate place; Sch 15, Pt 2 amends the Broadcasting Act 1996 (outside the scope of this work); Sch 16 outside the scope of this work; Sch 17 contains minor and consequential amendments, and in so far as these are relevant to this work, they have been incorporated at the appropriate place.)*

SCHEDULE 18
TRANSITIONAL PROVISIONS

Section 406

General

1.—(1) This paragraph applies where, at any time before the coming into force of a transfer made by virtue of section 2—

(a) any subordinate legislation has been made in the carrying out of the transferred functions by the person from whom the transfer is made; or

(b) any other thing has been done by or in relation to that person for the purposes of or in connection with the carrying out of those functions.

(2) The subordinate legislation or other thing—

(a) is to have effect, on and after the coming into force of the transfer, and so far as necessary for its purposes, as if it had been made or done by or in relation to OFCOM; and

(b) in the case of subordinate legislation to which section 403 applies when it is made by OFCOM, shall so have effect as if made in accordance with the requirements of that section.

(3) Where any subordinate legislation, direction, authorisation or notice has effect in accordance with this paragraph—

(a) so much of it as authorises or requires anything to be done by or in relation to the person from whom the transfer is made is to have effect in relation to times after the coming into force of the transfer as if it authorised or required that thing to be done by or in relation to OFCOM; and

(b) other references in the subordinate legislation, direction, authorisation or notice to the person from whom the transfer is made are to have effect, in relation to such times, as references to OFCOM.

Steps taken in anticipation of passing or coming into force of Act

2.—(1) This paragraph applies where the Secretary of State or OFCOM is or are required—

(a) by a provision of this Act, or

(b) by virtue of an amendment made by this Act,

to take steps before exercising a power or performing a duty.

(2) The requirement is capable of being satisfied by the taking of the steps in anticipation of effect being given to the provision by virtue of which the power or duty is—

(a) conferred or imposed on the Secretary of State or OFCOM; or

(b) transferred to OFCOM.

(3) For the purposes of sub-paragraph (2) it is immaterial—

(a) that the provision by virtue of which the power or duty is conferred, imposed or transferred had not been enacted, or had not come into force, when the steps were taken; and

(b) in the case of steps taken before the enactment of that provision, that the provision the effect of which was anticipated was modified before being enacted.

(4) In relation to provisions brought into force as mentioned in subsection (1) of section 408 for the purpose of enabling specified functions to be carried out by the Director or the Secretary of State—

(a) this paragraph has effect in relation to steps taken by the Director or the Secretary of State as it has in relation to steps taken by OFCOM; and

(b) subsection (5) of that section applies in relation to steps taken by the Director or the Secretary of State in anticipation of effect being given to those provisions as it would apply to anything done by the Director or the Secretary of State for the purposes of, or in connection with, the carrying out of those functions.

(5) Where a requirement is satisfied by virtue of this paragraph by steps taken in anticipation of effect being given to a provision—

(a) representations made to or other things done in relation to OFCOM, or the Director or the Secretary of State, in consequence of the taking of those steps, and

(b) any requirements framed by reference to the time at which those steps were taken,

are to have effect as if the provision in question had come into force before those steps were taken.

Savings for agreements referring to the termination of a 1984 Act licence

3.—(1) This paragraph applies where a term or condition of an agreement in force immediately before the abolition of licensing provides—

(a) for the agreement, or a provision of it, to cease to have effect,

(b) for the agreement to become capable of being terminated,

(c) for a requirement to pay or repay an amount (whether liquidated or unliquidated) to arise under the agreement, or to arise earlier than it would otherwise have arisen,
(d) for a security to become enforceable, or
(e) for rights or obligations of a person under the agreement to be different or to be modified,

if a person (whether or not a party to the agreement) ceases to hold a licence under section 7 of the 1984 Act, or ceases to do so in a manner or in circumstances described in the agreement.

(2) Where a person ceases to hold a licence in consequence of the provisions of this Act removing the requirement to hold a licence under section 7 of the 1984 Act—
(a) the term or condition is not to apply; and
(b) the rights and obligations of the parties to the agreement are to be the same (subject to the following sub-paragraphs) as they would have been had the person in question continued to hold such a licence.

(3) In relation to times after the abolition of licensing, that term or condition is to have effect as if the reference in that term or condition—
(a) to a person's ceasing to hold a licence under section 7 of the 1984 Act, or
(b) to his ceasing to do so in a particular manner or particular circumstances,

were a reference to his becoming subject to a direction under this Act by virtue of which he is prohibited from providing the whole or a part of an electronic communications network or electronic communications service.

(4) In sub-paragraph (3) the reference to a person's becoming subject to a direction by virtue of which he is prohibited from providing the whole or a part of an electronic communications network or electronic communications service—
(a) does not include a reference to his becoming subject to a direction imposing a prohibition for a fixed period of less than eighteen months or to a direction that will have to be revoked if not confirmed; but
(b) except in the case of a direction imposing a prohibition for such a fixed period, does include a reference to the confirmation of a direction that would otherwise have had to be revoked.

(5) This paragraph does not apply in the case of a term or condition of an agreement if, on an application to the court by one or both of the parties to the agreement, the court directs—
(a) that this paragraph is not to apply; or
(b) that it is to apply with such modifications, or subject to the payment of such compensation, as the court may specify in the direction.

(6) In determining whether to give a direction under sub-paragraph (5) or what modifications or compensation to specify in such a direction the court must have regard to the following—
(a) whether either or both of the parties to the agreement contemplated the abolition of the licensing requirements of the 1984 Act when they entered into the agreement; and
(b) the extent (if any) to which the provisions of this paragraph represent what it would have been reasonable for the parties to have agreed had they both known at that time what provision was to be made by this Act and when it was to come into force.

(7) For the purposes of this paragraph—
(a) references to ceasing to hold a licence include references to its expiring or being revoked; and
(b) references to a licence under section 7 of the 1984 Act include references to a licence under that section of a particular description.

(8) In this paragraph "the court" means the High Court or the Court of Session.

(9) This paragraph has effect subject to paragraph 14.

Saving for agreements with special provision for 1984 Act licence holders

4.—(1) This paragraph applies in a case to which paragraph 3 does not apply and in which a term or condition of an agreement in force immediately before the abolition of licensing provides for rights or obligations of a person ("the contracting party") under the agreement to be different or to be modified according to whether or not he or another person (whether or not a party to the agreement)—

(a) is or has become the holder of a licence under section 7 of the 1984 Act; or

(b) is or has become the holder of such a licence in a manner or in circumstances described in the agreement.

(2) In relation to times after the abolition of licensing, that term or condition is to have effect as if the rights and obligations to which the contracting party is entitled or subject under the agreement were, except in a case falling within sub-paragraph (3), those for which the agreement provides in relation to a case in which the person in question—

(a) is or has become the holder of such a licence; or

(b) is or has become the holder of such a licence in that manner or in those circumstances.

(3) The excepted case is where that person is subject to a direction under this Act by virtue of which he is prohibited from providing the whole or a part of an electronic communications network or electronic communications service.

(4) In sub-paragraph (3) the reference to a person's being subject to a direction by virtue of which he is prohibited from providing the whole or a part of an electronic communications network or electronic communications service—

(a) does not include a reference to his being subject to a direction imposing a prohibition for a fixed period of less than eighteen months or to a direction that will have to be revoked if not confirmed; but

(b) except in the case of a direction imposing a prohibition for such a fixed period, does include a reference to his being subject to a direction which would have had to be revoked if not confirmed but which has been confirmed.

(5) This paragraph does not apply in the case of a term or condition of an agreement if, on an application to the court by one or both of the parties to the agreement, the court directs—

(a) that this paragraph is not to apply; or

(b) that it is to apply with such modifications, or subject to the payment of such compensation, as the court may specify in the direction.

(6) In determining whether to give a direction under sub-paragraph (5) or what modifications or compensation to specify in such a direction the court must have regard to the following—

(a) whether either or both of the parties to the agreement contemplated the abolition of the licensing requirements of the 1984 Act when they entered into the agreement; and

(b) the extent (if any) to which the provisions of this paragraph represent what it would have been reasonable for the parties to have agreed had they both known at that time what provision was to be made by this Act and when it was to come into force.

(7) For the purposes of this paragraph references to a licence under section 7 of the 1984 Act include references to a licence under that section of a particular description.

(8) In this paragraph "the court" means the High Court or the Court of Session.

General saving for agreements conditional on certain Broadcasting Act licences

5.—(1) This paragraph has effect where an agreement in force immediately before the coming into force of a provision of this Act removing a requirement for a relevant Broadcasting Act licence provides—

(a) for the agreement to cease to have effect, or

(b) for it to be capable of being terminated,

if a party to the agreement ceases to hold a relevant Broadcasting Act licence of a particular description, or so ceases in a manner described in the agreement.

(2) In this paragraph "relevant Broadcasting Act licence" means—

(a) a licence under Part 1 of the 1990 Act to provide a satellite television service or a licensable programme service;

(b) a licence under that Part to provide the service mentioned in section 49(2) of that Act;

(c) a licence under Part 2 of that Act to provide a local delivery service; or

(d) a licence under Part 3 of that Act to provide a formerly regulated radio service (within the meaning of section 251 of this Act).

(3) The agreement is not to cease to have effect, or to be capable of being terminated, by reason only of the coming into force of the provisions of this Act under which the requirement for the licence is removed.

(4) In relation to times after the commencement of the provision of this Act removing the requirement for a licence to provide a satellite television service or a licensable programme service, a reference to such a licence in the provision of the agreement in question is to have effect as a reference to a licence granted or having effect as if granted as a licence to provide a television licensable content service.

(5) In relation to times after the commencement of the provision of this Act removing the requirement for a licence to provide the service mentioned in section 49(2) of the 1990 Act, a reference to such a licence in the provision of the agreement in question is to have effect as a reference to a licence to provide the public teletext service.

(6) In relation to times after the commencement of the provision of this Act removing the requirement for a licence to provide a licensable sound programme service, a reference to such a licence in the provision of the agreement in question is to have effect as a reference to a licence to provide a radio licensable content service.

(7) References in this paragraph to a provision having effect if a person ceases to hold a licence include references—

(a) to a provision having effect if a licence of his expires without being renewed; and
(b) to a provision having effect if his licence is revoked.

(8) Expressions used in this paragraph and in Part 3 of this Act have the same meanings in this paragraph as in that Part.

Orders under Part 2 of the Deregulation and Contracting Out Act 1994

6. …

Pre-commencement proposals relating to universal service matters

7.—(1) Where a proposal for the designation of a person as a universal service provider has been confirmed under regulation 4(10) of the Electronic Communications (Universal Service) Regulations 2003 (SI 2003/33), the designation is to have effect after the commencement of section 66 of this Act as a designation in accordance with regulations under that section.

(2) Where in any person's case a proposal to set a condition has been confirmed under regulation 4(10) or 5(4) of those regulations, that condition is to have effect after the commencement of that section as a condition set by OFCOM under section 45 of this Act and applied to that person.

(3) Where an appeal under regulation 6 of those regulations against a decision under them has been brought but not concluded before the commencement of section 192 of this Act—

(a) that appeal is to be stayed or sisted as from the commencement of the section; but
(b) the appellant is to have a new right of appeal under the section against the decision (as it has effect by virtue of this paragraph) as if—
    (i) it were the corresponding decision made by OFCOM under Chapter 1 of Part 2 of this Act; and
    (ii) it had been made immediately after the commencement of the section.

(4) Tribunal rules (within the meaning of Chapter 3 of Part 2 of this Act) may, in relation to an appeal stayed or sisted under sub-paragraph (3), make transitional provision for requiring steps taken and things done for the purposes of that appeal to be taken into account, to the extent set out in the rules, in the case of an appeal brought by virtue of paragraph (b) of that sub-paragraph.

Local loop notifications

8.—(1) This paragraph applies where, as a result of a market power determination made by OFCOM for the purposes of a provision of Chapter 1 of Part 2 of this Act, they conclude that a person who is for the time being LLU notified is no longer a person falling to be so notified.

(2) OFCOM must give a notification of their conclusion to—
(a) the Secretary of State; and
(b) the notified person.

(3) On receiving a notification under sub-paragraph (2) the Secretary of State must withdraw the LLU notification of the person in question.

(4) For the purposes of this paragraph a person is LLU notified if he is a person who, for the purposes of Regulation (EC) No 2887/2000 of the European Parliament and of the Council on unbundled access to the local loop, is notified to the European Commission as having significant market power in an identified market, and "LLU notification" shall be construed accordingly.

(5) Section 192 applies to a decision by OFCOM to give a notification under this paragraph as it applies to a decision by them under Part 2 of this Act.

Conditions relating to premium rate services and conditions corresponding to SMP or access-related conditions

9.—(1) This paragraph applies where OFCOM give a continuation notice to the holder of a licence granted under section 7 of the 1984 Act.

(2) A continuation notice is a notice that a provision contained in a condition of the licence is to have effect, after the abolition of licensing—
(a) to the extent specified in the notice; and
(b) subject to such modifications (if any) as may be so specified.

(3) OFCOM are not to give a continuation notice except to the extent that they consider that provision to which it will give effect, as modified by the notice, ("the continued provision")—
(a) regulates the provision of premium rate services; or
(b) falls within sub-paragraph (4).

(4) The continued provision falls within this sub-paragraph in so far as it corresponds to provision of one or more of the following descriptions—
(a) provision that OFCOM have power to include in SMP conditions;
(b) provision authorised by section 73(2) or (4) for inclusion in access-related conditions;
(c) provision relating to matters mentioned in Article 16 of the Universal Service Directive or Article 7 of the Access Directive.

(5) A continuation notice relating to provision corresponding to anything that OFCOM have power to include in SMP conditions—
(a) may identify the market by reference to which an SMP condition replacing the provision would have to be set; and
(b) in so far as the provision corresponds to anything that OFCOM have power to include only in SMP apparatus conditions, must do so.

(6) OFCOM are not to give a continuation notice relating to provision corresponding to anything that OFCOM have power to include only in SMP apparatus conditions except to the extent that it has effect in relation to the supply of electronic communications apparatus of a description supplied in the market identified in the notice as the market by reference to which SMP conditions replacing the continued provision would have to be set.

(7) The modifications for which a continuation notice may provide—
(a) must be confined to modifications for the purpose of securing that the provision to which they relate continues to have effect for so long as the notice is in force; but
(b) in the case of provision which is expressed to impose a requirement to be met before the abolition of licensing, may include a modification under which that requirement must continue to be met for so long as the notice remains in force.

(8) Notwithstanding any repeal or revocation made by this Act—
(a) the continued provision,
(b) every provision made by a direction, determination or consent given or made for the purposes of the continued provision, and
(c) so far as necessary for giving effect to anything mentioned in paragraph (a) or (b), every provision made by or under the licence under the 1984 Act that is not so mentioned,

are to remain in force for so long as the continuation notice is in force.

(9) A continuation notice shall cease to have effect if OFCOM give a notice to that effect to the holder of the licence.

(10) Where the continued provision is one that OFCOM have power to include only in an SMP apparatus condition, it shall be their duty, as soon as reasonably practicable after giving the continuation notice—

- (a) to carry out an analysis of the market which, under sub-paragraph (5), is identified in that notice;
- (b) to take all other steps necessary for enabling them to decide whether or not to set an SMP apparatus condition by reference to that market for the purpose of replacing the continued provision; and
- (c) to decide whether or not to exercise their power to set such a condition for that purpose.

(11) In the case of every other continued provision falling within sub-paragraph (4), it shall be OFCOM's duty, as soon as reasonably practicable after giving the continuation notice—

- (a) to take all steps necessary for enabling them to decide whether or not to set a condition of any other description under Chapter 1 of Part 2 of this Act for the purpose of replacing the continued provision; and
- (b) to decide whether or not to exercise their power to set a condition under that Chapter for that purpose.

(12) It shall be the duty of OFCOM—

- (a) as soon as reasonably practicable after making a decision required by sub-paragraph (10) or (11), but
- (b) in a case where that decision is a decision to set a condition, not before the coming into force of that condition,

to give a notice under sub-paragraph (9) with respect to the continuation notice.

(13) The duties imposed by sub-paragraphs (10) to (12) apply only where OFCOM have not previously given a notice under sub-paragraph (9) with respect to the continuation notice in question.

(14) This paragraph has effect in the case of a licence granted under section 7 of the 1984 Act to persons of a particular class as if—

- (a) references to the holder of that licence were references to the members of that class; and
- (b) the manner in which a continuation notice or notice under sub-paragraph (9) is to be given to members of that class were by its publication in such manner as, in OFCOM's opinion, is appropriate for bringing it to the attention of the members of that class who are affected by the notice.

(15) Section 192 applies to a decision by OFCOM to give a notice under this paragraph as it applies to a decision by them under Part 2 of this Act.

(16) In this paragraph "Access Directive", "electronic communications apparatus", "the provision of premium rate services", "SMP condition", "SMP apparatus condition" and "Universal Service Directive" each has the same meaning as in Chapter 1 of Part 2 of this Act.

Pre-commencement proposals relating to market power determinations

10.—(1) Sub-paragraph (2) has effect where a proposal for—

- (a) the identification of a market,
- (b) the making of a market power determination, or
- (c) the setting of conditions by reference to a proposal for a market power determination,

has been confirmed under regulation 8 of the Electronic Communications (Market Analysis) Regulations 2003 (SI 2003/330).

(2) If, at any time after the commencement of section 45, OFCOM—

- (a) are satisfied that a procedure has been followed in relation to the proposal that satisfies the requirements of Article 7 of the Framework Directive, and
- (b) publish a notification to that effect in such manner as they consider appropriate for bringing it to the attention of the persons who, in their opinion, are likely to be affected by the proposal,

the proposal (with such modifications, if any, as are specified in the notification) is to have effect, from the publication of the notification, in accordance with sub-paragraph (3).

(3) The proposal is to have effect as follows—

(a) in the case of a proposal for identifying a market, as an identification of a services market in accordance with and for the purposes of section 79 of this Act;

(b) in the case of a proposal for the making of a market power determination, as a market power determination made in accordance with and for the purposes of Chapter 1 of Part 2 of this Act; and

(c) in the case of a proposal for setting conditions, as if the conditions were SMP services conditions set under section 45 of this Act and applied to the same person as the condition in the proposal.

(4) Where an appeal under regulation 11 of those regulations against a decision under them has been brought but not concluded before the commencement of section 192 of this Act—

(a) that appeal is to be stayed or sisted as from the commencement of the section; but

(b) the appellant is to have a new right of appeal under the section against the decision (as it has effect by virtue of this paragraph) as if—

(i) it were the corresponding decision made by OFCOM under Chapter 1 of Part 2 of this Act; and

(ii) it had been made immediately after the commencement of the section.

(5) Tribunal rules (within the meaning of Chapter 3 of Part 2 of this Act) may, in relation to an appeal stayed or sisted under sub-paragraph (4), make transitional provision for requiring steps taken and things done for the purposes of that appeal to be taken into account, to the extent set out in the rules, in the case of an appeal brought by virtue of paragraph (b) of that sub-paragraph.

(6) Section 192 applies to a decision by OFCOM to publish a notification under this paragraph as it applies to a decision by them under Part 2 of this Act.

(7) In this paragraph "the Framework Directive" has the same meaning as in Chapter 1 of Part 2 of this Act.

Savings for licence conditions relating to accounting

11.—(1) This paragraph applies where a licence granted under section 7 of the 1984 Act contains conditions which impose requirements with respect to—

(a) the keeping of accounts or financial information; or

(b) the provision of accounts and financial information to the Director.

(2) OFCOM may give a notice to the holder of the licence as respects so much of those conditions as relates to—

(a) the keeping of accounts for a period current at the time of the abolition of licensing; and

(b) the provision of accounts and financial information in relation to any such period or in relation to periods ending before the abolition of licensing.

(3) In the case of a licence granted otherwise than to a particular person, a notice under this paragraph may be given to the licence holders by being published in such manner as OFCOM consider appropriate for bringing it to their attention.

(4) Notwithstanding any repeal or revocation made by this Act—

(a) the licence under the 1984 Act is to continue in force to the extent that it imposes requirements as respects which a notice has been given under this paragraph; but

(b) those requirements, so far as they require the provision of accounts or information to the Director, are to have effect in relation to times after the abolition of licensing, as requirements to provide the accounts or information to OFCOM.

(5) Section 192 applies to a decision by OFCOM to give a notice under this paragraph as it applies to a decision by them under Part 2 of this Act.

Charges under Telecommunications Act licences

12.—(1) Where any amount is required by a licence under section 7 of the 1984 Act to be paid to the Director in respect of a period beginning before the abolition of licensing, that liability is to have effect after the abolition of licensing as a liability to pay to OFCOM so much of that amount as does not relate to times after the abolition of licensing.

(2) For the purpose of determining how much of an amount payable to the Director relates to times after the abolition of licensing, an apportionment is to be made according to how much of that period had expired before the abolition of licensing.

Enforcement of breaches of licence conditions

13.—(1) This paragraph applies to—
(a) any provision to which effect is given, after the abolition of licensing, by a continuation notice under paragraph 9;
(b) conditions in respect of which notices under paragraph 11 have been given;
(c) liabilities under paragraph 12; and
(d) conditions of a licence under section 7 of the 1984 Act requiring compliance by the licence holder with directions given by the Director under regulation 6 of the Telecommunications (Interconnection) Regulations 1997 (SI 1997/2931).

(2) Notwithstanding any repeal or revocation made by this Act, after the abolition of licensing, OFCOM are, for the purpose of enforcing anything to which this paragraph applies, to have all the enforcement powers previously exercisable by the Director under the 1984 Act.

(3) Those powers are to be exercisable in accordance with this paragraph irrespective of whether the contraventions occurred before or after the abolition of licensing.

(4) For the purpose of exercising those powers, references to the likelihood that a person will again be in contravention of a condition include references to whether he will be in contravention of any equivalent obligation imposed—
(a) by section 38 of this Act;
(b) by conditions set under section 45 of this Act; or
(c) by directions under section 190 of this Act.

(5) OFCOM are not to exercise any powers conferred by virtue of this paragraph if they consider that the exercise of those powers would be incompatible with the requirements of the Directives.

(6) In this paragraph "enforcement powers" includes—
(a) the Director's powers under sections 16 to 18 and 53 of the 1984 Act; and
(b) in the case of a licence issued to a particular person, every power of his under the licence to require information for the purpose of computing the amount of the liability to a charge.

(7) In this paragraph "the Directives" means the Authorisation Directive or any of the following Directives (as defined in Chapter 1 of Part 2 of this Act)—
(a) the Access Directive;
(b) the Framework Directive;
(c) the Universal Service Directive.

(8) In sub-paragraph (7) "the Authorisation Directive" means Directive 2002/20/EC of the European Parliament and of the Council on the authorisation of electronic communications networks and services.

Saving for agreements having effect by reference to licensing regime

14.—(1) This paragraph has effect where an agreement entered into for the purposes of a condition of a licence under section 7 of the 1984 Act has effect immediately before the abolition of licensing subject to a provision which entitles a party to it to terminate the agreement if he or another party ceases to be a Schedule 2 public operator.

(2) The right of termination is not to be exercisable by reason of the effect of the coming into force of any provision of this Act if—
(a) a general condition,
(b) an access-related condition, or
(c) a provision made by or having effect as if made under an SMP condition,

imposes requirements on one or both of the parties to the agreement that correspond to those for the purposes of which the agreement was originally entered into.

(3) In any such case, the agreement shall have effect in relation to times after the abolition of licensing as if references in the agreement to a Schedule 2 public operator were references to the provider of a public electronic communications network.

(4) In this paragraph "Schedule 2 public operator" has the same meaning as in Schedule 1 to the Telecommunications (Licence Modifications) (Standard Schedules) Regulations 1999 (SI 1999/2450).

(5) Expressions used in this paragraph and in Chapter 1 of Part 2 of this Act have the same meanings in this paragraph as in that Chapter.

Fees for approvals for the purposes of licence conditions

15.—(1) This paragraph has effect where a general condition set under section 45 of this Act requires apparatus to be approved by reference to a standard previously designated for the purposes of section 24(6) of the 1984 Act.

(2) The Secretary of State may by order provide for the charging of fees in respect of the giving of approvals for the purposes of the condition.

(3) Fees charged under this paragraph are be paid to the person giving the approvals and, to the extent authorised by the Secretary of State, may be retained by that person.

(4) To the extent that they are not retained by that person, the fees must be paid into the Consolidated Fund.

(5) Any order made under section 24(13) of the 1984 Act that is in force immediately before the coming into force of the repeal of section 24 of that Act shall have effect after the coming into force of the repeal as an order made under this paragraph.

Allocated telephone numbers

16.—(1) Where immediately before the abolition of licensing telephone numbers are allocated to a person holding a licence under section 7 of the 1984 Act for the purposes of the conditions of that licence, those numbers shall be treated, after the abolition of licensing as allocated to that person for the purposes of general conditions such as are mentioned in section 58 of this Act.

(2) An allocation having effect by virtue of sub-paragraph (1) may be withdrawn by OFCOM at any time, but only in accordance with section 61 of this Act.

(3) An allocation shall only continue to have effect in accordance with this paragraph for so long as the person to whom the allocation was made for the purposes of the licence conditions is a communications provider.

(4) The power by virtue of section 58 for general conditions to make provision for the making of periodic payments in respect of the allocation of telephone numbers shall be exercisable, at any time after the coming into force of that section, in relation to an allocation having effect by virtue of this paragraph as it has effect in relation to an allocation made under that section.

(5) Expressions used in this paragraph and in Chapter 1 of Part 2 of this Act have the same meanings in this paragraph as in that Chapter.

Electronic communications code

17.—(1) Sub-paragraph (2) applies where, immediately before the coming into force of section 106 of this Act, the telecommunications code set out in Schedule 2 to the 1984 Act applies to a person by virtue of the provisions of his licence under section 7 of that Act.

(2) That person shall be treated after the commencement of section 106 of this Act as a person in whose case the electronic communications code applies by virtue of a direction given by OFCOM.

(3) The deemed direction shall be assumed to be one given in relation to so much of any electronic communications network as—

(a) was included immediately before the commencement of section 106 of this Act in the telecommunication system which was the operator's system for the purposes of the application of the code; or

(b) which would have been so included if it had been being provided at that time.

(4) So much of the code in Schedule 2 to the 1984 Act as has effect immediately before the commencement of Schedule 3 to this Act—

(a) in relation to telecommunication apparatus, or

(b) in relation a telecommunication system,

is to have effect after the commencement of that Schedule in relation to so much of the apparatus or system as is electronic communications apparatus or the operator's network for the purposes of the application of that Schedule to this Act by virtue of this paragraph or section 106(3)(b) of this Act.

(5) A right which for the purposes of the code in Schedule 2 to the 1984 Act has effect immediately before the commencement of Schedule 3 to this Act as conferred for purposes connected with the provision of a telecommunication service is to have effect after the commencement of that Schedule as conferred for the purposes of the corresponding electronic communications service.

(6) Any agreement which, immediately before the repeal of the provisions contained in section 10(3A) and (3B) of the 1984 Act or section 189 of the 1990 Act, is a relevant agreement for the purposes of those provisions shall be deemed in relation to times after the coming into force of that repeal to be a relevant agreement for the purposes of paragraph 29 of the electronic communications code.

(7) In this paragraph "the electronic communications code" has the same meaning as in Chapter 1 of Part 2 of this Act.

Saving for guarantees of liabilities of telecommunications code operators

18.—(1) his paragraph applies where, immediately before the abolition of licensing, a person holding a licence under section 7 of the 1984 Act ("the operator")—

(a) is a person to whom the telecommunications code applies in respect of the running of a telecommunications system by him ("the operator's system"); and

(b) in pursuance of a condition of his licence imposed for the purpose of securing that sufficient funds are available to meet code-related liabilities specified in the licence, is a party to any guarantee arrangements.

(2) Arrangements are guarantee arrangements for the purposes of this paragraph if they are arrangements under which a person (the "guarantor") is obliged, in circumstances specified in the arrangements, to make payments in respect of a failure by the operator to meet a code-related liability specified in the licence.

(3) The guarantor's obligation to make payments under the guarantee arrangements is not to arise by reason only of the abolition of licensing.

(4) In relation to times after the abolition of licensing, the guarantee arrangements are to have effect, notwithstanding the operator's licence having ceased to have effect on the abolition of licensing and subject to sub-paragraph (7), as if the following references continued to have effect—

(a) references in those arrangements to the code-related liabilities specified in the licence; and

(b) (subject to sub-paragraph (5)(a)) references, for the purposes of any provision identifying the circumstances in which payments are to be made under the arrangements, to events specified in the licence.

(5) In relation to such times, those arrangements are also to have effect—

(a) as if references (directly or indirectly) to the revocation, or to the expiration without renewal, of the operator's licence were references to his becoming subject to a direction by virtue of which he is prohibited from providing the whole or a part of his network; and

(b) as if references to the telecommunications code were references to the electronic communications code.

(6) In sub-paragraph (5) the reference to a person's becoming subject to a direction by virtue of which he is prohibited from providing the whole or a part of an electronic communications network—

(a) does not include a reference to his becoming subject to a direction imposing a prohibition for a fixed period of less than eighteen months or to a direction that will have to be revoked if not confirmed; but

(b) except in the case of a direction imposing a prohibition for such a fixed period, does include a reference to the confirmation of a direction that would otherwise have had to be revoked.

(7) The guarantor is not to be liable in respect of any liability arising in connection with or as a result of activities carried on after the abolition of licensing except in so far as those activities are activities carried on for the purposes of providing the operator's network.

(8) In this paragraph "code-related liabilities", in relation to the operator, means liabilities arising or incurred by him—

(a) by reason of the application to him of the telecommunications code;
(b) by reason of its ceasing to apply to him; or
(c) otherwise in respect of activities carried on by him in connection with running the operator's system.

(9) In this paragraph—

"the electronic communications code" has the same meaning as in Chapter 1 of Part 2 of this Act;

"the operator's network" means so much of any electronic communications network provided by the operator as is a network in relation to which the electronic communications code applies in the operator's case by virtue of paragraph 17(3)(a) of this Schedule;

"the telecommunications code" means the code set out in Schedule 2 to the 1984 Act (as it had effect immediately before the abolition of licensing).

Compulsory purchase

19. Where—

(a) a compulsory purchase order made under section 34 or 35 of the 1984 Act,
(b) a vesting order, or an application for a vesting order, made under section 36 of that Act, or
(c) an authorisation given by the Secretary of State under section 37, 38 or 39 of that Act,

is effective immediately before the commencement of Schedule 4 to this Act, it is to have effect after the commencement of that Schedule as if made or given under that Schedule.

Notices under section 1D of the Wireless Telegraphy Act 1949

20. …

Notices under regulations under section 3 of the Wireless Telegraphy Act 1998

21. …

Disputes about interconnection

22.—(1) Where—

(a) before the revocation by this Act of the Telecommunications (Interconnection) Regulations 1997 (SI 1997/2931) a dispute was referred to the Director under regulation 6 of those regulations, and
(b) that dispute has not been resolved when the revocation comes into force,

Chapter 3 of Part 2 of this Act (except sections 189 and 190) is to have effect as if that dispute were a dispute which, immediately after the commencement of section 185 of this Act, was referred to OFCOM under that section.

(2) Where a dispute—

(a) has arisen or arises about anything occurring or existing before the time when the revocation of those regulations comes into force ("the relevant time"),
(b) relates to matters disputes about which would (before that time) have been referable to the Director under regulation 6,
(c) is neither a dispute which was referred to him before that time nor a dispute arising after that time which is referable to OFCOM under section 185, and
(d) is referred to OFCOM after that time either during the transitional period or in a

case in which OFCOM are satisfied that the circumstances that prevented the making of a reference before the end of that period are exceptional,

sub-paragraph (1) is to have effect as if the dispute were a dispute arising before the relevant time in the case of which a reference to the Director had been made under regulation 6 before that time.

(3) Where OFCOM make a determination for resolving a dispute falling to be resolved in accordance with sub-paragraph (1) or (2)—

(a) their powers on making that determination are to be those which would have been exercisable by the Director under those regulations (instead of those under Chapter 3 of Part 2);

(b) conditions of a licence under section 7 of the 1984 Act requiring compliance with directions given by the Director under regulation 6 of those regulations are to continue to have effect as if they also applied to directions given by OFCOM by virtue of paragraph (a); and

(c) paragraph 13 of this Schedule has effect as if the reference in sub-paragraph (1)(d) to directions given by the Director under that regulation included a reference to directions given by OFCOM by virtue of paragraph (a) of this sub-paragraph.

(4) But OFCOM are not to give a direction by virtue of sub-paragraph (3)(a) containing provision which they would have no power to include in—

(a) a condition set under Chapter 1 of Part 2 of this Act; or

(b) a direction under section 190.

(5) Where the Director gave a direction under regulation 6 of those regulations at any time before the coming into force of their revocation, the direction is to continue, after the revocation comes into force, to have effect (and be enforceable in accordance with paragraph 13 of this Schedule) to the extent that it is continued in force under this paragraph.

(6) The direction is continued in force under this paragraph only where OFCOM have at any time after the passing of this Act given notice to the persons to whom it applies that it is continued in force.

(7) OFCOM are to give such a notice only if they consider that the direction makes provision corresponding to that which they have power to include in—

(a) conditions set under Chapter 1 of Part 2 of this Act; or

(b) directions under section 190.

(8) OFCOM may at any time by notice to the person to whom it applies revoke (in whole or in part) a direction which—

(a) was given by virtue of sub-paragraph (3)(a); or

(b) is a direction to which a notice under sub-paragraph (6) relates.

(9) Where a direction which OFCOM have power to revoke under sub-paragraph (8) makes provision corresponding to anything that OFCOM have power to include in a condition set under Chapter 1 of Part 2 of this Act, it shall be their duty, as soon as reasonably practicable after giving the direction or as the case may be the notice under sub-paragraph (6)—

(a) to take all steps necessary for enabling them to decide whether or not to set such a condition for the purpose of replacing the direction; and

(b) to decide whether or not to exercise their power to set a condition under that Chapter for that purpose.

(10) It shall be the duty of OFCOM—

(a) as soon as reasonably practicable after making a decision required by subparagraph (9), but

(b) in a case where that decision is a decision to set a condition, not before the coming into force of that condition,

to give a notice under sub-paragraph (8) revoking the direction in question.

(11) The duties imposed by sub-paragraphs (9) and (10) apply only where OFCOM have not previously revoked the direction in question.

(12) Section 192 applies to a decision by OFCOM to give a notice under this paragraph as it applies to a decision by them under Part 2 of this Act.

(13) In this paragraph "transitional period" means the period which is the transitional period (within the meaning of section 408) in relation to this paragraph.

Appeals against wireless telegraphy and telecommunications decisions

23.—(1) This paragraph applies where—

(a) a decision was made before the commencement of section 192;

(b) the decision has effect after the commencement of a provision of this Act as a decision made by OFCOM, or is a decision not to do something which (if done) would so have had effect; and

(c) the decision is one against which an appeal was or could have been brought under—

(i) …

(ii) section 46B of the 1984 Act.

(2) If no such appeal has been brought before the commencement of section 192 of this Act, that section applies to the decision as it applies to decisions by OFCOM under Part 2 of this Act … , but as if that section had been in force when the decision was made.

(3) If an appeal under … section 46B of the 1984 Act—

(a) has been brought against the decision, but

(b) has not been concluded before the commencement of section 192 of this Act,

the court in which it was brought may stay or sist the appeal as from the commencement of that section of this Act.

(4) If the court stays or sists the appeal under sub-paragraph (3), the appellant is to have a new right of appeal under section 192 against the decision as if (subject to sub-paragraph (7)) it were a decision to which that section applies that had been made immediately after the commencement of that section.

(5) Tribunal rules (within the meaning of Chapter 3 of Part 2 of this Act) may, in relation to an appeal stayed or sisted under sub-paragraph (3), make transitional provision—

(a) for requiring steps taken and things done for the purposes of that appeal to be taken into account, to the extent set out in the rules, in the case of an appeal brought by virtue of sub-paragraph (4); and

(b) for enabling the Tribunal in an appeal under sub-paragraph (4) to give directions to OFCOM as to the carrying out of functions of theirs that are the same as or correspond to those in the course of carrying out which the maker of the appealed decision made that decision.

(6) If, in a case falling within sub-paragraph (3), the court does not stay or sist the appeal—

(a) it must determine the appeal in the manner in which the Tribunal is required under section 195 of this Act to determine an appeal under section 192; but

(b) its powers on determining the appeal include a power to give directions to OFCOM as to the carrying out of any functions of theirs that correspond to those in the course of which the appealed decision was made.

(7) On an appeal brought or continued under this paragraph against a decision, the court or the Tribunal, in determining what was the appropriate action for the maker of the decision to take, must determine that question according to the law in force at the time when the decision was made.

Section 94 of the Telecommunications Act 1984

24.—(1) Subject to sub-paragraph (2), provisions of Schedule 17 to this Act amending section 94 of the 1984 Act do not affect—

(a) the continuation, after the coming into force of the amendment, of any duty of a person previously given a direction under that section to give effect to it; or

(b) the power of the Secretary of State after the amendment comes into force to make grants under subsection (6) of that section to such a person.

(2) A direction under that section which was given to the Director before the relevant transfer date shall have effect in relation to times on and after that date as if it were a direction to OFCOM.

(3) In sub-paragraph (2) "the relevant transfer date" means the date of the coming into force of the provisions of Schedule 17 to this Act substituting "OFCOM" for "the Director" in section 94(8) of the 1984 Act.

Competition Commission: specialist panel members

25. The persons who—

(a) have been appointed as members of the Competition Commission by the Secretary of State under section 13(10) of the 1984 Act, and

(b) hold office immediately before the date on which section 194 comes into force,

shall continue to hold office as members of the Competition Commission as if they had been appointed to that office by the Secretary of State under section 194(1).

Transitory amendments to telecommunications terms in Broadcasting Act 1990

26.—(1) This paragraph has effect, in the case of each of the provisions of the 1990 Act to which it applies, in relation to times between—

(a) the commencement of Chapter 1 of Part 2 of this Act; and

(b) the commencement of so much of this Act (apart from this paragraph) as amends or repeals that provision.

(2) The provisions of the 1990 Act set out in sub-paragraph (3) shall have effect (subject to sub-paragraph (4)) as if—

(a) for every reference to a telecommunication system there were substituted a reference to an electronic communications network; and

(b) for references to running such a system there were substituted references to providing it.

(3) Those provisions of the 1990 Act are—

(a) section 46 (licensable programme services);

(b) section 51(1)(a) (procedures for consideration of applications for additional services licences);

(c) section 72 (local delivery services);

(d) section 75 (procedures for consideration of applications for local delivery licences);

(e) section 112 (licensable sound programme services);

(f) section 117(1)(a) (procedures for consideration of applications for additional services licences);

(g) section 181 (apparatus deemed to be apparatus for wireless telegraphy).

(4) Sections 46(2) (licensable programme services), 112(2) (licensable sound programme services) and 201(2) (programme services) of the 1990 Act shall each have effect as if for paragraph (b) there were substituted—

"(b) a service which satisfies the conditions in section 233(5) of the Communications Act 2003;".

(5) In sections 48 and 114 of the 1990 Act (additional services), references to electronic signals shall have effect as references to signals within the meaning of section 32 of this Act.

(6) Section 75(2) of the 1990 Act (consultation with relevant licensing authorities) shall have effect as if in paragraph (b) for the words "would be required to be licensed" there were substituted "is a system which (but for repeals made by the Communications Act 2003) would have been required to be licensed".

(7) In section 181 of the 1990 Act (apparatus deemed to be apparatus for wireless telegraphy), "connected"—

(a) shall continue to be construed in accordance (notwithstanding its repeal) with section 4 of the 1984 Act; but

(b) shall be so construed as if, in that section of the 1984 Act, a reference to an electronic communications network were substituted for every reference to a telecommunication system.

(8) Part 5 of Schedule 2 to the 1990 Act (restriction on holding of licences by operators of public telecommunication systems) and the Broadcasting (Restrictions on the Holding of Licences) Order 1991 (SI 1991/1176) shall have effect as if references to a national public telecommunications operator were references to a person who provides an electronic communications network so as to make it available for use by members of the public in the whole, or substantially the whole, of the United Kingdom.

Activities of the Welsh Authority

27.—(1) No approval shall be required under section 205 for the continued provision after the commencement of that section of any service that was being provided by the Welsh Authority immediately before the commencement of that section.

(2) Where any activities are being carried on immediately before the commencement of section 206 by the Welsh Authority, no approval is required under that section in respect of the continued carrying on of the activities by the Authority.

(3) Where any activities are being carried on immediately before the commencement of section 206 by an S4C company, no approval is required under that section in respect of the carrying on after that commencement by that company or another S4C company of those activities.

Gaelic Broadcasting

28. The persons who are members of Comataidh Craolaidh Gaidhlig immediately before the date on which section 208 comes into force—

(a) shall continue to hold office as members of Seirbheis nam Meadhanan Gàidhlig as if they had been appointed to that office by OFCOM;
(b) shall hold and vacate office in accordance with the terms of their appointment by the ITC;
(c) shall hold office for the period for which they were appointed by the ITC; and
(d) after the end of that period, shall be eligible for re-appointment as members of Seirbheis nam Meadhanan Gàidhlig.

29.—(1) The continuance in force of the Multiplex Licence (Broadcasting of Programmes in Gaelic) Order 1996 (SI 1996/2758) made under section 32 of the 1996 Act is not affected by the amendment of that section by Schedule 15 to this Act.

(2) But in relation to times after the television transfer date, that order shall have effect as if—

(a) the reference in that order to the ITC were a reference to OFCOM; and
(b) the reference to the application of section 28 of the 1996 Act to a frequency were omitted.

Pre-transfer Broadcasting Act licences

30.(1) Subject to any express provision made by this Act in relation to a particular description of Broadcasting Act licence, neither—

(a) the transfer from a pre-commencement regulator to OFCOM of the function of granting or awarding such licences or of any other power exercisable in relation to such licences, nor
(b) any other modification by or by virtue of this Act of the power to grant or award such licences or of a provision having effect in relation to such licences,

shall affect the continuing validity of a licence by or under which the provision of a service is authorised immediately before the coming into force of the transfer or modification.

(2) Accordingly, such a licence shall continue to have effect, after the coming into force of the transfer or modification—

(a) on the same terms and conditions and for the same period as it would have done if this Act had not been passed; but
(b) as if, in relation to times after the coming into force of any relevant transfer of functions to OFCOM, every reference in the licence to a pre-commencement regulator were a reference to OFCOM.

(3) Sub-paragraph (2) is subject to the following provisions of this Act—

(a) those under which a licence is to have effect as if the period for which it is granted were the period determined under this Act; and
(b) those under which the conditions of a licence fall to be varied for the purpose of imposing a condition required by this Act.

(4) Anything done at any time before the relevant transfer date under or for the purposes of enforcing any provision of a Broadcasting Act licence is to have effect in relation to times on or after that date—

(a) to the extent that it was done by or in relation to the ITC or Radio Authority, and
(b) so far as necessary for preserving its effect or for facilitating the taking of further action by OFCOM,

as a thing done by or in relation to OFCOM.

(5) In sub-paragraph (4) "relevant transfer date"—
(a) in relation to licences under Part 1 of the 1990 Act or Part 1 of the 1996 Act, means the television transfer date; and
(b) in relation to licences under Part 3 of the 1990 Act or Part 2 of the 1996 Act, means the radio transfer date.

Channels 3 and 5

31. A determination made by the ITC under or for the purposes of section 14 or 28 of the 1990 Act (Channels 3 and 5) is to have effect on and after the television transfer date as a determination under that section by OFCOM.

Saving pending replacement of licences for Channels 3 and 5 and the public teletext service

32.—(1) The regulatory regime for a Channel 3 service, and that for Channel 5 and the existing teletext service, shall not include the self-regulation conditions in any case in which the service or (as the case may be) Channel 5 is provided under a licence granted before the television transfer date.

(2) In sub-paragraph (1) "the self-regulation conditions" means the conditions which (apart from that sub-paragraph) are included by virtue of sections 265 to 269 of this Act in the regulatory regime for Channel 3 services, for Channel 5 and for the public teletext service.

(3) In relation to a licence granted before the television transfer date for a Channel 3 service, Channel 5 or the existing teletext service, section 263 shall have effect as if the reference in subsection (3)(a) of that section to a corresponding or additional service to be provided in analogue form were a reference to a corresponding or additional service to be provided in digital form.

(4) In this paragraph "the existing teletext service" means the existing service within the meaning of section 221 of this Act.

Digital additional licences

33.—(1) This paragraph applies where immediately before the coming into force of section 242 of this Act a person holds a digital additional services licence under Part 1 of the 1996 Act in respect of a digital sound programme service and with a view to the inclusion of the broadcasting of that service by means of a television multiplex service licensed under Part 1 of the 1996 Act.

(2) The licence is to have effect on and after the coming into force of section 242 of this Act as if it were a national digital sound programme licence or (as the case may be) were comprised in any national digital sound programme licence already held by the licence holder for the service in question.

(3) Where a licence has effect in accordance with this paragraph, it shall not (to the extent that it so has effect) authorise the broadcasting of the digital sound programme service in question by means of a radio multiplex service.

(4) In this paragraph—
"digital additional services licence" has the same meaning as in Part 1 of the 1996 Act; and
"national digital sound programme licence" has the same meaning as in Part 2 of that Act.

Programme quotas

34. Any order which—

(a) was made under section 16(5)(a) of the 1990 Act (definitions of "qualifying programmes" and "independent productions"), and

(b) is in force immediately before the commencement of sections 277 and 309 of this Act and paragraphs 1 and 7 of Schedule 12 to this Act,

is to have effect in relation to times after the commencement of those sections and those paragraphs as an order made in exercise of the corresponding powers conferred by those sections and those paragraphs.

Continuity in relation to appointed news provider

35. Where a body holds an appointment for the purposes of section 31(2) of the 1990 Act immediately before the date of the commencement of section 280 of this Act—

(a) that appointment shall have effect in relation to times on and after that date as an appointment for the purposes of arrangements entered into in accordance with conditions imposed under section 280 of this Act;

(b) the arrangements under which that appointment was made shall have effect in relation to such times as arrangements so entered into; and

(c) so much of the appointment or arrangements, or of any agreement to which the body is a party, as makes provision by reference to the body's ceasing to be nominated under section 32 of the 1990 Act shall have effect in relation to such times as if references to ceasing to be so nominated were references to becoming a body falling within section 281(2) of this Act.

Networking arrangements

36.—(1) Where arrangements approved for the purposes of section 39 of the 1990 Act (networking arrangements) are in force immediately before the commencement of section 291 of this Act, those arrangements are to have effect for the purposes of this Act, and of any conditions imposed under that section of this Act, as approved networking arrangements.

(2) For the purposes of proceedings in relation to a report under Schedule 4 to the 1990 Act at any time after the commencement of Schedule 11 to this Act, that report is to have effect as if it were a report under that Schedule to this Act.

Determination of qualifying revenue

37.—(1) A statement of the ITC that is for the time being in force immediately before the television transfer date for the purposes of—

(a) Schedule 7 to the 1990 Act (statement of principles for determining qualifying revenue), or

(b) Schedule 1 to the 1996 Act (corresponding statement for the purposes of that Act,

is to have effect on and after that date as a statement by OFCOM.

(2) On and after the television transfer date a determination by the ITC under paragraph 2 of Part 1 of either of those Schedules is to have effect as a determination under that paragraph by OFCOM, and sub-paragraph (2) of that paragraph is to have effect accordingly.

Rules for political broadcasts

38. Where—

(a) rules made by the ITC for the purposes of section 36 of the 1990 Act (party political broadcasts on Channel 3, Channel 4 or Channel 5), or

(b) rules made by the Radio Authority for the purposes of section 107 of the 1990 Act (party political broadcasts on national radio services),

are in force immediately before the commencement of section 333 of this Act, those rules are to have effect after its commencement as rules made by OFCOM for the purposes of that section of this Act.

Functions under section 88 of the 1990 Act

39. A requirement imposed or notice given before the radio transfer date by the Radio Authority under section 88 of the 1990 Act (restriction on holding of licences) is to have effect on and after that date as if it were imposed or given by OFCOM.

Notices under section 94 of the 1990 Act

40. A notice given by the Secretary of State or any other Minister of the Crown under section 94 of the 1990 Act (government control over licensed services) is to have effect on and after the radio transfer date as a notice given to OFCOM under section 336 of this Act.

Programme standards: television

41.—(1) This paragraph applies as respects times on or after the television transfer date and before the first coming into force, in the case of the holder of a licence under Part 1 of the 1990 Act or Part 1 of the 1996 Act, of conditions imposed under section 325 of this Act.

(2) Sections 6 to 12 of the 1990 Act (general provisions about the content of licensed services) are to have effect in the case of that licence holder as if references in those sections to the ITC were references to OFCOM.

(3) A code drawn up by the ITC under section 6, 7 or 9 of the 1990 Act is to have effect as if it had been drawn up by OFCOM.

Programme standards: radio

42.—(1) This paragraph applies as respects times on or after the radio transfer date and before the first coming into force, in the case of the holder of a licence under Part 3 of the 1990 Act or Part 2 of the 1996 Act, of conditions imposed under section 325 of this Act.

(2) Sections 90 to 96 of the 1990 Act (general provisions about the content of licensed services) are to have effect as if references in those sections to the Radio Authority were references to OFCOM.

(3) A code drawn up by the Radio Authority under section 90, 91 or 93 of the 1990 Act is to have effect as if it had been drawn up by OFCOM.

Standards code

43.—(1) In relation to any time after the commencement of section 319 of this Act, a code in force immediately before its commencement as a code drawn up under section 6, 7, 9, 90, 91 or 93 of the 1990 Act or section 108 of the 1996 Act is to have effect (subject to sub-paragraphs (2) and (3)) as if it were a code issued by OFCOM for the purpose of setting standards under section 319 of this Act.

(2) A code under the 1990 Act shall have effect by virtue of sub-paragraph (1) in relation only to the following—

(a) in the case of the codes under sections 6, 7 and 9, services the provision of which is authorised by licences under Part 1 of the 1990 Act and S4C; and

(b) in the case of the codes under sections 90, 91 and 93, services the provision of which is authorised by licences under Part 3 of that Act.

(3) In the case of the code under section 108 of the 1996 Act, the code shall have effect by virtue of sub-paragraph (1)—

(a) in relation only to services provided by the BBC or the Welsh Authority; and

(b) to the extent only that it contains provision that applies to those services and, in the case of services provided by the Welsh Authority, relates to matters other than advertising and impartiality.

Local and national radio licences

44.—(1) Section 103 of the 1990 Act (restriction on changes of control affecting holders of national licences) is to apply in relation to a pre-transfer national licence as it applies in relation to a national licence within the meaning of Part 3 of the 1990 Act.

(2) Anything done by or in relation to the Radio Authority under any of sections 98 to 102 or 103A of the 1990 Act, so far as it has been done—

(a) before the radio transfer date, and
(b) for the purposes of, or in connection with, the grant or renewal of a pre-transfer national licence,

is to have effect for the purposes of, and in connection with, the grant or renewal of a licence at times on or after that date as if done by or in relation to OFCOM in connection with or for the purposes of the grant or renewal of national licence (within the meaning of Part 3 of that Act).

(3) Anything done by or in relation to the Radio Authority under any of sections 104 to 105 of the 1990 Act, so far as it has been done—

(a) before the radio transfer date, and
(b) for the purposes of, or in connection with, the grant or renewal of a pre-transfer local licence,

is to have effect for the purposes of, and in connection with, the grant or renewal of a licence at times on or after that date as if done by or in relation to OFCOM in connection with, or for the purposes of, the grant or renewal of local licence (within the meaning of Part 3 of that Act).

(4) In this paragraph "pre-transfer local licence" and "pre-transfer national licence" each has the same meaning as in section 253 of this Act.

Section 111B of the 1990 Act

45.—(1) Section 111B of the 1990 Act (power to suspend satellite services) is to have effect in relation to a licence to provide a formerly regulated radio service (within the meaning of section 251) as it applies in relation to a licence to provide a radio licensable content service, but as if the reference in subsection (1)(b) of that section to a condition included in the licence in pursuance of the provisions there mentioned included a reference to a condition included in the licence in pursuance of section 90(1)(a) of that Act.

(2) In relation to any time falling—

(a) on or after the radio transfer date, and
(b) before the first coming into force, in the case of the holder of a licence under Part 3 of the 1990 Act or Part 2 of the 1996 Act, of conditions imposed under section 325 of this Act,

section 111B of the 1990 Act is to have effect in relation to a licence to provide a radio licensable content service as if the reference in subsection (1)(b) of section 111B of that Act to a condition included in the licence in pursuance of the provisions there mentioned were a reference to a condition included in the licence in pursuance of section 90(1)(a) of that Act.

Section 185 of the 1990 Act

46.—(1) A determination or nomination made for the purposes of section 185 of the 1990 Act (the national television archive) by the ITC is to have effect on and after the television transfer date as a determination or nomination made by OFCOM.

(2) Sub-paragraph (1) applies in the case of a determination so far only as it relates to a financial year beginning on or after the television transfer date.

Section 28 of the 1996 Act

47.—(1) The repeal by this Act of section 28 of the 1996 Act does not affect any power to vary a licence under Part 1 of the 1990 Act which is—

(a) conferred on the ITC by an order under that section; and
(b) transferred to OFCOM by this Act.

(2) Nor does it affect so much of any order under that section in force immediately before the repeal as—

(a) modifies section 16 of the 1996 Act in its application in relation to the renewal of a licence first granted before the television transfer date; or

(b) imposes a prohibition on the use of digital capacity reserved before that date;

but so much of any such prohibition as requires the consent of the ITC for the use of any digital capacity shall have effect after the television transfer date as if the consent required were OFCOM's consent.

(3) Sub-paragraph (1) only saves the power so far as it is exercisable in relation to a licence granted before the television transfer date.

Section 48 of the 1996 Act

48. Subsections (4) to (6) of section 48 of the 1996 Act (reservations of capacity for national radio multiplex licences to independent national broadcasters) are to apply in relation to conditions included in pursuance of that section in licences granted before the radio transfer date as they apply in relation to conditions included in licences by virtue of the amendments of that section made by this Act.

Applications for extension of pre-transfer licences

49.—(1) Section 253(4)(a) does not prevent the determination by OFCOM of a day falling less than one year after the making of the determination where—

(a) OFCOM consider that the day by which they would need to publish a notice is a day which is not more than 15 months after the commencement date; and

(b) the determination of that day is made as soon as practicable after the commencement date.

(2) Where the day determined by OFCOM for the purposes of paragraph (b) of section 253(3) is a day in the period of three months beginning with the day after the determination, that paragraph shall have effect as if for the words "three months before" there were substituted "on".

(3) In this paragraph, the "commencement date" is the date on which section 253 comes into force.

Applications for renewal of licences under 1990 Act and 1996 Act

50.—(1) A provision set out in sub-paragraph (2) does not prevent the determination by OFCOM of a date falling less than one year after the making of the determination where—

(a) OFCOM consider that the relevant date for the purposes of the section in question is a date which is not more than 15 months after the commencement date; and

(b) the determination of the relevant date is made as soon as practicable after the commencement date.

(2) Those provisions are—

(a) section 53(12) of the 1990 Act;

(b) section 103A(12) of the 1990 Act;

(c) section 104A(14) of the 1990 Act;

(d) section 16(12A) of the 1996 Act;

(e) section 58(12A) of the 1996 Act.

(3) An application which is made before the commencement date in accordance with a provision set out in sub-paragraph (5) shall be treated after that date as if it had been made in accordance with that provision as amended by this Act.

(4) Where, in a case where a provision set out in sub-paragraph (5) applies, the relevant date for the purposes of the section in question is a date in the period of three months beginning with—

(a) the commencement date, or

(b) the day after the day on which the relevant date is determined,

that provision shall have effect as if the words "the day falling three months before" were omitted.

(5) Those provisions are—
- (a) section 53(2) of the 1990 Act;
- (b) section 103A(2) of the 1990 Act;
- (c) section 104A(3) of the 1990 Act;
- (d) section 16(3) of the 1996 Act;
- (e) section 58(3) of the 1996 Act.

(6) In this paragraph, the "commencement date", in relation to any provision set out in sub-paragraph (2) or (5) is the date on which the provision of Schedule 15 inserting or amending that provision comes into force.

Listed events rules

51.—(1) Subject to sub-paragraph (2), Part 4 of the 1996 Act (sporting and other events of national interest) is to have effect in relation to times on or after the television transfer date as if anything done before that date by or in relation to the ITC had been done by or in relation to OFCOM.

(2) The code drawn up by the ITC under section 104 of the 1996 Act (code of guidance as to the operation of Part 4) and in force immediately before the commencement of section 301 of this Act is to continue to have effect (notwithstanding the substitutions made by that section of this Act)—
- (a) until the code drawn up by OFCOM under that section comes into force; but
- (b) in relation to times on or after the transfer date and before the coming into force of OFCOM's code, as if references in section 104(2) of that Act and in the code to the ITC were references to OFCOM.

(3) If a provision of sections 300 to 302 of this Act comes into force before the television transfer date, a reference to OFCOM in an amendment made by that provision is to be construed in relation to times before that date as a reference to the ITC.

(4) On the date on which section 300 of this Act comes into force, the Secretary of State shall revise the list maintained for the purposes of Part 4 of the 1996 Act in order to allocate each event which is a listed event on that date either to Group A or to Group B.

(5) Where—
- (a) the events listed in the list in force immediately before the Secretary of State revises it under sub-paragraph (4) are treated, for any of the purposes of the code in force under section 104 of the 1996 Act at that time, as divided into two categories, and
- (b) the Secretary of State's revision under that sub-paragraph makes the same division,

section 97(2) of the 1996 Act shall not apply in relation to that revision of that list.

(6) In this paragraph "the transfer date" is the date on which paragraph 13 of Schedule 1 comes into force.

Complaints to the Broadcasting Standards Commission

52.—(1) On and after the transfer to OFCOM under this Act of the functions of the Broadcasting Standards Commission under Part 5 of the 1996 Act, that Part is to have effect in relation to a fairness complaint made to, but not disposed of by, the Commission before the transfer as if—
- (a) anything done, or treated as done, by or in relation to the Commission for the purposes of, or in connection with, that complaint had been done by or in relation OFCOM; and
- (b) those functions had been functions of OFCOM at the time when it was done.

(2) Where immediately before the commencement of section 327 of this Act a licence to provide a licensed service (within the meaning of Part 5 of the 1996 Act) contains a condition included in that licence by virtue of section 119(7) of that Act (conditions requiring compliance with BSC directions), that condition is to have effect on and after the coming into force of section 327 of this Act as a condition requiring the licence holder to comply with directions given to him by OFCOM.

(3) In this paragraph "fairness complaint" has the same meaning as in Part 5 of the 1996 Act.

Codes of practice drawn up by the Broadcasting Standards Commission

53. The code of practice drawn up by the Broadcasting Standards Commission under section 107 of the 1996 Act (code in respect of unjust and unfair treatment and infringements of privacy) is to have effect on and after the transfer under this Act to OFCOM of the Commission's functions under Part 5 of that Act as if it were the code required to be drawn up under that section by OFCOM.

Media ownership provisions

54.—(1) Part 4 of Schedule 14 to this Act is to have effect—

(a) in relation to times before the television transfer date as if references to OFCOM were, in relation to licences under Part 1 of the 1990 Act or Part 1 of the 1996 Act, references to the ITC; and

(b) in relation to times before the radio transfer date as if references to OFCOM were, in relation to licences under Part 3 of the 1990 Act or Part 2 of the 1996 Act, references to the Radio Authority.

(2) A determination by the ITC or the Radio Authority under paragraph 2(2) of Part 2 of Schedule 2 to the 1990 Act which is in force immediately before the commencement of Part 4 of Schedule 14 to this Act is to have effect on and after its commencement as a determination under paragraph 15 of that Schedule to this Act.

(3) Any guidance issued by the ITC and the Radio Authority under paragraph 2(3) of Part 2 of Schedule 2 to the 1990 Act and in force immediately before the commencement of Part 4 of Schedule 14 to this Act is to have effect on and after its commencement as guidance published under paragraph 15(4) of that Schedule to this Act.

(4) Anything done under paragraph 15 of Schedule 14 by the ITC or the Radio Authority which is in force immediately before the relevant transfer date is to have effect on and after that date as if done under that paragraph by OFCOM.

(5) The following powers under enactments in force before the relevant transfer date shall be exercisable by OFCOM at all times on or after that date in relation to a pre commencement contravention of a requirement imposed by or under Parts 3 to 5 of Schedule 2 to the 1990 Act—

(a) all the powers and duties of the ITC under section 5 of the 1990 Act and section 5 of the 1996 Act;

(b) all the powers and duties of the Radio Authority under section 88 of the 1990 Act and section 44 of the 1996 Act; and

(c) all the other powers and duties of the ITC or the Radio Authority in relation to contraventions of conditions imposed under section 5 or 88 of the 1990 Act or section 5 or 44 of the 1996 Act.

(6) For the purpose of determining whether anything occurring after the relevant transfer date is a pre-commencement contravention of a requirement imposed by or under Parts 3 to 5 of Schedule 2 to the 1990 Act, references in those Parts of that Schedule to the ITC or to the Radio Authority are to be construed as including references to OFCOM.

(7) In this paragraph—

"pre-commencement contravention" means a contravention of a requirement which occurred before the coming into force of the repeal by this Act of the provision by or under which the requirement was imposed; and

"the relevant transfer date"—

(a) in relation to the ITC, means the television transfer date; and

(b) in relation to the Radio Authority, means the radio transfer date.

TV licences

55. …

Functions under the Enterprise Act 2002

56.—(1) This section has effect in so far as, at any time before the coming into force of section 370 of this Act, anything has been done or is treated as done by or in relation to the Director for the purposes of, or in connection with, the carrying out of any of his functions under the Enterprise Act 2002 (c 40).

(2) That thing is to have effect on and after that date, and OFCOM may carry out their functions and continue anything begun by that Director, as if—

(a) that thing had been done by or in relation to OFCOM for the purposes of, or in connection with, their functions under that Act by virtue of that section; and
(b) the provisions conferring those functions on OFCOM had been in force at the time it was done.

(3) Sub-paragraph (1) does not apply to anything that could not be done by or in relation to OFCOM for the purposes of, or in connection with, the carrying out of their functions under the Enterprise Act 2002 (c 40).

(4) Where, by virtue of sub-paragraph (3), sub-paragraph (1) does not apply to something, that thing is to have effect instead as if done by or in relation to the Office of Fair Trading.

Functions under the Competition Act 1998

57.—(1) This paragraph applies in so far as, at any time before the coming into force of section 371 of this Act, anything has been done by or in relation to the Director for the purposes of, or in connection with, the carrying out of any of his functions under the Competition Act 1998 (c 41).

(2) That thing is to have effect on and after that date, and OFCOM may carry out their functions and continue anything begun by that Director, as if—

(a) that thing had been done by or in relation to OFCOM for the purposes of, or in connection with, their functions under that Act by virtue of that section; and
(b) the provisions conferring those functions on OFCOM had been in force at the time it was done.

(3) Sub-paragraph (1) does not apply to anything that could not be done by or in relation to OFCOM for the purposes of, or in connection with, the carrying out of their functions under the Competition Act 1998.

(4) Where, by virtue of sub-paragraph (3), sub-paragraph (1) does not apply to something, that thing is to have effect instead as if done by or in relation to the Office of Fair Trading.

58.—(1) Where any regulations made under section 54(4) of the Competition Act 1998 (regulations about concurrent functions of regulators and the Office of Fair Trading) are in force at the coming into force of section 371 of this Act, those regulations—

(a) shall, from that time have effect in relation to functions exercisable concurrently by virtue of section 371 of this Act as they have effect in relation to functions exercisable concurrently by virtue of Part 2 of Schedule 10 to the Competition Act 1998; but
(b) shall so have effect subject to any amendments or revocations coming into force at or after that time.

(2) Where, at any time before the coming into force of section 371, anything has been done by or in relation to the Director under or for the purposes of any regulations made under section 54(4) of the Competition Act 1998 that thing is to have effect, so far as necessary for the purposes of paragraph 57 of this Schedule, as if done by or in relation to OFCOM.

Newspaper mergers

59.—(1) Chapter 2 of Part 5 and any related repeals shall, subject to sub-paragraph (2), not apply in relation to—

(a) a transfer of a newspaper or of newspaper assets (within the meaning given by section 57(2) of the Fair Trading Act 1973 (c 41)) which has been made before the coming into force of section 373 of this Act; or

(b) a proposed transfer of a newspaper or of newspaper assets in relation to which an application for the consent of the Secretary of State under section 58 of the Act of 1973 has been made before the coming into force of section 373 of this Act.

(2) Chapter 2 of Part 5 and any related repeals shall apply in relation to a proposed transfer of a newspaper or of newspaper assets if—

(a) an application for the consent of the Secretary of State under section 58 of the Act of 1973 has been made;

(b) the application is expressed to depend on the operation of subsection (3) or (4) of that section;

(c) no consent is given by the Secretary of State under subsection (3) or (4) of that section; and

(d) no further application has been made for the consent of the Secretary of State under that section before the coming into force of section 373 of this Act.

60. Chapter 2 of Part 5 and any related repeals shall apply in relation to any transfer of a newspaper or of newspaper assets which is proposed (and not made) before the coming into force of section 373 of this Act and in relation to which no application has been made for the consent of the Secretary of State under section 58 of the Act of 1973 before the coming into force of that section.

61. References in paragraphs 59 and 60 to Chapter 2 of Part 5 do not include references to subsections (2) to (4) of section 389 (powers to make transitional and consequential amendments etc).

62.—(1) The Secretary of State may, instead of any or all of the conditions attached to a consent given by him (or treated as so given) under section 58 of the Fair Trading Act 1973 (c 41)), accept undertakings under this paragraph to take, or refrain from taking, action specified or described in the undertakings.

(2) If, and so far as, the Secretary of State accepts an undertaking under this paragraph instead of a condition, that condition shall cease to have effect.

(3) In deciding whether to accept an undertaking under this paragraph, the Secretary of State may, in particular, consult the Office of Fair Trading and OFCOM.

(4) An undertaking under this paragraph—

(a) shall come into force when accepted;

(b) may be varied or superseded by another undertaking; and

(c) may be released by the Secretary of State.

(5) The Secretary of State shall, as soon as reasonably practicable, consider any representations received by him in relation to varying or releasing an undertaking under this paragraph.

(6) Paragraph 10 of Schedule 7 to the Enterprise Act 2002 (c 40) (order-making power where final undertakings not fulfilled) shall apply in relation to an undertaking under this paragraph as it applies in relation to an undertaking under paragraph 9 of that Schedule to that Act but as if—

(a) in sub-paragraph (2) the words from "for any" to "66(6)" were omitted; and

(b) sub-paragraph (3) were omitted.

(7) The following provisions of the Enterprise Act 2002 (c 40) shall apply in relation to an undertaking under this paragraph or an order made by virtue of sub-paragraph (6) as they apply in relation to an undertaking under paragraph 9 of Schedule 7 to that Act or (as the case may be) an order under paragraph 10 of that Schedule to that Act—

(a) section 90 and Schedule 10 (procedural requirements for certain undertakings and orders);

(b) section 91 (register of undertakings and orders);

(c) section 92 (duty of OFT to monitor undertakings and orders);

(d) section 93 (further role of OFT in relation to undertakings and orders); and

(e) section 94 (rights to enforce undertakings and orders).

(8) Section 402 of this Act shall not apply in relation to the power of the Secretary of State to make an order which is exercisable by virtue of sub-paragraph (6) but supplementary provisions of Part 3 of the Enterprise Act 2002 which relate to the making of an order under paragraph 10 of Schedule 7 to that Act shall apply in relation to the making of an order by virtue of sub-paragraph (6).

(9) Section 402 of this Act shall not apply in relation to the power of the Secretary of State to make an order under section 91(6)(a) of the Enterprise Act 2002 as applied by virtue of sub-paragraph (7)(b) above but supplementary provisions of Part 3 of the Enterprise Act 2002 which relate to the making of an order under section 91(6)(a) of that Act shall apply in relation to the making of an order under that provision as applied by virtue of sub-paragraph (7)(b) above.

Orders in Council under section 6 of the Continental Shelf Act 1964

63. …

Interpretation of Schedule

64. In this Schedule—

"the 1984 Act" means the Telecommunications Act 1984 (c 12);

"the abolition of licensing" means the coming into force of the repeal by this Act of section 7 of the 1984 Act;

"the Director" means the Director General of Telecommunications;

"the ITC" means the Independent Television Commission.

[3460]

NOTES

Commencement: 25 July 2003 (para 30; paras 1–4, 7–19, 22–26, 56–58, 63, 64 for the purpose of enabling network and service functions and spectrum functions to be carried out during the transitional period by the Director General of Telecommunications and the Secretary of State respectively) (see further s 408 and Sch 18 at **[3436]**, **[3460]**, and the Communications Act 2003 (Commencement No 1) Order 2003, SI 2003/1900 at **[3507]**); 18 September 2003 (para 54(1)–(4); para 21 for the purpose of enabling network and service functions and spectrum functions to be carried out during the transitional period by the Director General of Telecommunications and the Secretary of State respectively); 29 December 2003 (paras 5, 6, 20, 27–29, 31–53, 54(5)–(7), 59–62; paras 1–4, 7–19, 21–26, 56–58, 63, 64 for the purpose of enabling OFCOM to perform those functions) (see the Office of Communications Act 2002 (Commencement No 3) and Communications Act 2003 (Commencement No 2) Order 2003, SI 2003/3142 at **[3590]**); 1 April 2004 (otherwise).

Paras 6, 20, 21, 55, 63: repealed by the Wireless Telegraphy Act 2006, s 125(1), Sch 9, Pt 1, subject to transitional provisions and savings in s 124 of, Sch 8, Pt 1, paras 1–8, 24, 25 to, that Act at **[4230]**, **[4239]**, and previously read as follows:

"6.—(1) This paragraph applies where, immediately before functions under the Wireless Telegraphy Act 1949 (c 54) are transferred under this Act to OFCOM, an order is in force with respect to those functions under Part 2 of the Deregulation and Contracting Out Act 1994 (c 40).

(2) The order is to have effect in relation to times after the transfer—

(a) as if made in exercise of the power conferred by virtue of section 1(7) in relation to such of the functions of OFCOM under that Act of 1949 as are specified in the order;

(b) as if any power conferred on the Secretary of State by that order to authorise the exercise by a person of functions under that Act of 1949 were conferred on OFCOM; and

(c) as if an authorisation given by the Secretary of State in exercise of that power were an authorisation given under that order by OFCOM.

20.—(1) This paragraph applies to procedures set out in a notice given by the Secretary of State under section 1D of the Wireless Telegraphy Act 1949 (c 54) and in force immediately before the commencement of sub-paragraph (4) of paragraph 8 of Schedule 17 to this Act.

(2) In relation to times after the commencement of that sub-paragraph, the procedures are to have effect as if prescribed by OFCOM by regulations under section 1D(3) of the Wireless Telegraphy Act 1949 (c 54).

(3) So much of any notice having effect in accordance with this paragraph as authorises or requires anything to be done by or in relation to the Secretary of State is to have effect in relation to times after the commencement of paragraph 8 of Schedule 17 to this Act as if it authorised or required that thing to be done by or in relation to OFCOM.

21.—(1) This paragraph applies to procedures set out in a notice issued by the Secretary of State under regulations under section 3 of the Wireless Telegraphy Act 1998 (c 6) and in force immediately before the commencement of section 167 of this Act.

(2) In relation to times after the commencement of section 167 of this Act, the procedures are to have effect as if prescribed by OFCOM by regulations under section 3 of that Act.

(3) So much of any notice having effect in accordance with this paragraph as authorises or requires anything to be done by or in relation to the Secretary of State is to have effect in relation to times after the commencement of section 167 of this Act as if it authorised or required that thing to be done by or in relation to OFCOM.

55. A television licence granted under the Wireless Telegraphy Act 1949 (c 54) before the coming into force of section 363 of this Act is to have effect after the commencement of that section as a licence for the purposes of that section.

63. If an Order in Council made, or having effect as if made, in exercise of a power conferred by virtue of section 6 of the Continental Shelf Act 1964 (c 29) is in force immediately before the commencement of section 410 of this Act in relation to provisions of—

(a) the Wireless Telegraphy Act 1949 (c 54), or

(b) the Wireless Telegraphy Act 1998 (c 6),

that Order is to have effect after the commencement of section 410 of this Act as an Order in Council made in exercise of the powers conferred by that section of this Act.".

Para 23: words omitted from sub-paras (1)–(3) repealed by the Wireless Telegraphy Act 2006, s 125(1), Sch 9, Pt 1, subject to transitional provisions and savings in s 124 of, Sch 8, Pt 1, paras 1–8, 23, 24 to, that Act at **[4230]**, **[4239]**, and sub-paras (1)–(3) prior to the amendments made by the 2006 Act read as follows:

"(1) This paragraph applies where—

(a) a decision was made before the commencement of section 192;

(b) the decision has effect after the commencement of a provision of this Act as a decision made by OFCOM, or is a decision not to do something which (if done) would so have had effect; and

(c) the decision is one against which an appeal was or could have been brought under—

(i) section 1F of the Wireless Telegraphy Act 1949 (c 54); or

(ii) section 46B of the 1984 Act.

(2) If no such appeal has been brought before the commencement of section 192 of this Act, that section applies to the decision as it applies to decisions by OFCOM under Part 2 of this Act (or that Act of 1949), but as if that section had been in force when the decision was made.

(3) If an appeal under section 1F of that Act of 1949 or section 46B of the 1984 Act—

(a) has been brought against the decision, but

(b) has not been concluded before the commencement of section 192 of this Act,

the court in which it was brought may stay or sist the appeal as from the commencement of that section of this Act.".

SCHEDULE 19
REPEALS

Section 406

(1) ENACTMENTS

Short title and chapter	*Extent of repeal*
Telegraph Act 1899 (c 38)	The whole Act.
Wireless Telegraphy Act 1949 (c 54)	In section 1—
	(a) subsection (1A);
	(b) in subsection (4), the words "other than a television licence" and the words from "; and a television licence" onwards;
	(c) subsections (6) and (7).
	Section 1D(1), (2), (7) and (8).
	Section 1F.
	Section 2.
	In section 3(1), the words after paragraph (d) from "and different" to "classes of case:".
	Section 9.
	In section 10(2), the words after paragraph (b).

Short title and chapter	*Extent of repeal*
	In section 11(1)— (a) paragraph (i) of the proviso; (b) in paragraph (ii) of the proviso the words ", and paragraph (i) of this proviso shall not apply".
	Section 14(1A)(e), (2) and (3)(b).
	Section 15(4)(c) and the word "or" immediately preceding it.
	Section 19(2A) and (9).
	Schedule 2.
Army Act 1955 (3 & 4 Eliz. 2 c 18)	In section 44B(5), the definition of "telecommunication system" and the word "and" immediately preceding it.
Air Force Act 1955 (3 & 4 Eliz. 2 c 19)	In section 44B(5), the definition of "telecommunication system" and the word "and" immediately preceding it.
Naval Discipline Act 1957 (c 53)	In section 29B(5), the definition of "telecommunication system" and the word "and" immediately preceding it.
Opencast Coal Act 1958 (c 69)	In section 45(3), the word "a" before "telecommunication apparatus".
Continental Shelf Act 1964 (c 29)	Section 6.
Parliamentary Commissioner Act 1967 (c 13)	In Schedule 2, the entries relating to the Broadcasting Standards Commission and the Office of the Director General of Telecommunications.
Marine, &c., Broadcasting (Offences) Act 1967 (c 41)	Section 6(2) and (7).
Wireless Telegraphy Act 1967 (c 72)	Section 4.
	In section 7(5), paragraph (b) and the word "or" immediately preceding it.
Fair Trading Act 1973 (c 41)	Sections 57 to 62.
	In section 93B— (a) in subsection (1)(b), the words "the Telecommunications Act 1984 or"; (b) in subsection (5), the words "section 13B of the Telecommunications Act 1984 or".
House of Commons Disqualification Act 1975 (c 24)	In Part 2 of Schedule 1, the entries relating to— (a) the Broadcasting Standards Commission; (b) Comataidh Craolaidh Gaidhlig; (c) the Independent Television Commission; (d) the Radio Authority.
	In Part 3 of Schedule 1, the entry relating to the Director General of Telecommunications.
Northern Ireland Assembly Disqualification Act 1975 (c 25)	In Part 2 of Schedule 1, the entries relating to— (a) the Broadcasting Standards Commission; (b) the Independent Television Commission; (c) the Radio Authority;

Short title and chapter	*Extent of repeal*
	(d) the Tribunal established under Part 2 of the Wireless Telegraphy Act 1949.
	In Part 3 of Schedule 1, the entries relating—
	(a) the Director General of Telecommunications;
	(b) to a Director of the successor company within the meaning of Part 5 of the Telecommunications Act 1984.
Welsh Development Agency Act 1975 (c 70)	In section 19(11), the definition of "appropriate authority".
British Telecommunications Act 1981 (c 38)	In section 88—
	(a) in subsection (1), the words from ", and the special" to "Schedule 5,";
	(b) in subsection (2), the words "and 5".
	In Schedule 4, paragraphs 2 to 18, 21 and 22.
	In Schedule 5, paragraphs 1 and 3 to 22.
Acquisition of Land Act 1981 (c 67)	In section 28, paragraph (f).
Telecommunications Act 1984 (c 12)	Sections 1 to 30.
	Sections 34 to 49.
	In section 50, subsections (2) to (6A).
	Sections 51 to 55.
	Section 60.
	Section 61(1) to (6).
	Section 62.
	Section 63(1) to (4).
	Sections 64 to 67.
	Sections 69 to 71.
	In section 72—
	(a) in subsection (1), the words from the beginning to "this Act," and the words "and development land tax";
	(b) subsections (2), (4) and (5).
	Section 73.
	Sections 80 and 81.
	Section 88.
	Section 90.
	In section 91—
	(a) in subsection (2), the words "or section 80(9)(b) above" and the words "for an offence or (as the case may be) for the forfeiture of any apparatus under that section";
	(b) in subsection (4), the words "and in section 80(9)(b) above".
	Section 92(4).
	Section 93.
	Sections 95 to 97.
	In section 98(9), the words "and 'telecommunication apparatus'".

Short title and chapter	*Extent of repeal*
	In section 101—
	(a) in subsection (2)(a), the words "or transferred";
	(b) subsection (4).
	Section 102.
	In section 104—
	(a) in subsection (1), the words "2, 27L 60(1) or (3), 69(2) or" and ", or paragraph 1 of Schedule 5,";
	(b) subsection (3).
	In section 106(1), the definitions of—
	(a) "commercial activities connected with telecommunications";
	(b) "consumer", "monopoly situation", "practice" and "supply";
	(c) "the Director";
	(d) "directory information service";
	(e) "disabled person" and "disabled";
	(f) "public telecommunications operator";
	(g) "public telecommunications system";
	(h) "telecommunication apparatus ";
	(i) "telecommunication service";
	(j) "telecommunications operator ";
	(k) "telecommunication system";
	(l) "transitional period".
	Section 107(1), (2) and (4).
	In section 109—
	(a) subsections (2) and (3);
	(b) in subsection (4), the words "and the special transitional provisions with respect to patents for inventions and registered designs contained in Schedule 6 to this Act";
	(c) subsections (5) to (7).
	Schedule 1.
	In Schedule 2—
	(a) in paragraph 1(1), the words from "'telecommunications apparatus' includes any apparatus" onwards;
	(b) in paragraph 9(2), the words "section 11(1) of this Act,";
	(c) in paragraph 10(2)(b), the words "(within the meaning of section 6 of this Act)";
	(d) in paragraph 27(1), the words "section 109(2) or (3) of or".
	In Schedule 4, paragraphs 2, 3, 12, 16, 28(2), 40, 55(1) and (7), 65, 80(1), 86(1), 89(5) and 90.
	In Schedule 5—
	(a) paragraphs 1 to 7;

Short title and chapter	*Extent of repeal*
	(b) paragraph 8(2) and (4);
	(c) paragraphs 9 to 14;
	(d) paragraphs 16 to 29;
	(e) paragraphs 31 to 33;
	(f) paragraph 35;
	(g) paragraphs 38 to 42;
	(h) paragraph 47;
	(i) in paragraph 48, in sub-paragraph (1), the words "Part 1 of the Industry Act 1972 and" and in sub-paragraph (2), the words "Part 1 of the Industry Act 1972 or";
	(j) paragraphs 49 to 51.
	Schedule 6.
Companies Consolidation (Consequential Provisions) Act 1985 (c 9)	In Schedule 2, the entries relating to sections 60(3), 61(4), 66, 70 and 73(1) of and Schedule 5 to the Telecommunications Act 1984.
Surrogacy Arrangements Act 1985 (c 49)	Section 3(6).
Interception of Communications Act 1985 (c 56)	Schedule 2.
Housing Act 1985 (c 68)	Section 298(1).
Airports Act 1986 (c 31)	Section 62(8).
Insolvency Act 1986 (c 45)	In Schedule 2A, paragraph 10(1)(a).
Consumer Protection Act 1987 (c 43)	In Schedule 4, in paragraph 9(1), the words "28(6) and".
Channel Tunnel Act 1987 (c 53)	In Part 10 of Schedule 7, paragraph 1(2).
Income and Corporation Taxes Act 1988 (c 1)	In Schedule 29, in the Table in paragraph 32, the entries relating to sections 62(7) and 72(4) of the Telecommunications Act 1984.
Legal Aid Act 1988 (c 34)	In Schedule 5, paragraph 11.
Copyright, Designs and Patents Act 1988 (c 48)	In section 69(2), the word "or" at the end of paragraph (b).
	In Schedule 2, the word "or" at the end of paragraph 17(2)(b).
	In Schedule 7, paragraph 27.
Housing Act 1988 (c 50)	In Part 2 of Schedule 10, paragraph 19.
Electricity Act 1989 (c 29)	In Schedule 4, in paragraph 12, the definitions of "public telecommunications operator" and of "telecommunication apparatus", "telecommunication system" and "the telecommunications code".
Companies Act 1989 (c 40)	In Schedule 18, paragraph 28.
	In Schedule 20, paragraph 2.
Planning (Consequential Provisions) Act 1990 (c 11)	In Schedule 2, paragraph 63.
Courts and Legal Services Act 1990 (c 41)	In Schedule 10, paragraph 8.
Broadcasting Act 1990 (c 42)	Sections 1 and 2.
	In section 4(3), the words from "and the amount" onwards.
	In section 5—
	(a) subsection (6A)(a);
	(b) subsection (6B).

Short title and chapter	*Extent of repeal*
	Sections 6 to 12.
	In section 15(3), paragraphs (c) to (e).
	In section 16— (a) subsections (2) and (3); (b) in subsection (4), the words from "; and in applying" onwards; (c) subsections (5) to (8).
	Section 20.
	Section 21A.
	In section 24, subsections (4) to (6).
	Sections 25 to 27.
	In section 29— (a) in subsection (2), paragraph (b) and the word "and" immediately preceding it; (b) subsection (3).
	Sections 30 to 36.
	Sections 38 and 39.
	In section 42A, paragraph (b) and the word "and" immediately preceding it.
	Chapters 3 and 4 of Part 1.
	Section 48(5).
	In section 50— (a) in subsection (1)(b)(ii), the words "(subject to the approval of the Secretary of State)"; (b) subsection (7).
	Section 51(2) and (7).
	In section 53(4), the words "before the relevant date".
	Section 54(2).
	In section 56(1)(b), the words ", and have the functions conferred by,".
	Section 57.
	Section 59.
	Section 60(1) to (3) and (6).
	In section 61A— (a) subsection (1); (b) in subsection (2) the words "on or after the notified date"; (c) subsections (5) and (6).
	Section 62.
	Section 65.
	In section 66A(2), paragraphs (c) and (d).
	Sections 68 to 70.
	In section 71(1)— (a) in the definition of "Channel 3", the words "by the Commission";

Short title and chapter	*Extent of repeal*
	(b) the definitions of "the Commission", "licensable programme service" and "satellite television service".
	Part 2.
	Sections 83 and 84.
	In section 85, subsections (3) and (4).
	In section 87—
	(a) in subsection (2)(b), sub-paragraph (ii) and the word "or" immediately preceding it;
	(b) in subsection (3), the words from "and the amount" onwards.
	In section 88—
	(a) subsection (6A)(a); and
	(b) subsection (6B).
	Section 89(2).
	Sections 90 to 96.
	In section 98(3)(a), the word "both" and sub-paragraph (ii) and the word "and" immediately preceding it.
	In section 99(1)(a), the word "both" and sub-paragraph (ii) and the word "and" immediately preceding it.
	In section 103A—
	(a) in subsection (3), the words "before the relevant date", paragraph (a) and, in paragraph;
	(b) the words "in any other case";
	(c) in subsection (8), the words from "(whether because" to "any other reason)";
	(d) subsection (10);
	(e) in subsection (11), the definition of "simulcast radio service".
	In section 104A(5), at the end of paragraph (a), the word "and".
	In section 104B—
	(a) subsection (1)(b);
	(b) subsections (6) and (7).
	In section 106(1), the words from ", except" onwards.
	Sections 106A to 108.
	Section 110(7).
	Sections 112 and 113.
	Section 114(5).
	In section 116(1)(b)(iii), the words "(subject to the approval of the Secretary of State)".
	Section 117(2) and (7).
	Section 119(2).
	Section 122 to 125.

Short title and chapter	*Extent of repeal*
	In section 126(1), the definitions of "assigned frequency", "the Authority" and "licensable sound programme service".
	Section 134.
	In section 177(6), the definition of "relevant foreign satellite service".
	Section 180(2) and (3).
	Section 181.
	In section 183—
	(a) in subsection (3), the words ", which shall be called" onwards;
	(b) subsection (3A);
	(c) subsections (6) and (7).
	In section 185(5), the definition of "the Commission".
	Section 186.
	Section 187(1) and (2).
	In section 188(2), paragraphs (b), (d) and (e).
	Sections 189 to 191.
	In section 196—
	(a) in subsection (1)(a), the words ", 82";
	(b) subsection (2).
	Section 197.
	Section 199(1) to (4) and (6).
	In section 201(1), the words "under this Act".
	In section 202—
	(a) in subsection (1), the definition of "telecommunication system ";
	(b) in subsection (2)(b), the words "1" and "8";
	(c) in subsection (5)(a), the words "for general reception, or".
	Schedule 1.
	In Part 1 of Schedule 2—
	(a) in paragraph 1(1), the definitions of "coverage area", of "digital programme service", of "local delivery licence" and "local delivery service", of "local digital sound programme service" and "national digital sound programme service", of "local radio multiplex service" and "national radio multiplex service" and of "television multiplex service";
	(b) paragraph 1(8);
	(c) paragraph 3A;
	(d) paragraph 3B;
	(e) paragraph 4.
	In Part 2 of Schedule 2—
	(a) paragraph 1(1)(a) and (b);

Short title and chapter	Extent of repeal
	(b) in paragraph 1(1)(j)(i), the words "(a), (b) or";
	(c) paragraph 1(2) and (3);
	(d) in paragraph 5A(1)(a), the words "granted by the Commission";
	(e) paragraph 5A(1)(b) and the word "and" immediately preceding it;
	(f) in paragraph 5A(2), the words "granted by the Authority";
	(g) paragraph 5A(3).
	Parts 3 to 5 of Schedule 2.
	Schedule 4.
	Schedule 5.
	In Schedule 6—
	(a) paragraph 2(1);
	(b) in paragraph 13(2), the words from "and shall include" onwards.
	Schedule 8.
	Schedule 12.
	In Schedule 18—
	(a) in Part 1, paragraphs 1(4) to (6), 2(1) and (3) and 4;
	(b) in Part 2, paragraphs 1(d) and 5.
	In Schedule 19—
	(a) in paragraph 8(c), the words "and (where the expenses relate to the Commission's functions in connection with sound programmes) the Radio Authority";
	(b) in paragraph 11(4), the words "or the Radio Authority" and "or, as the case may be, the Authority".
	In Schedule 20—
	(a) paragraph 9;
	(b) paragraph 24(c)(ii);
	(c) paragraph 38;
	(d) paragraph 54.
	In Schedule 22—
	(a) paragraphs 1 to 3;
	(b) in paragraph 4, the words "and 45";
	(c) paragraph 5.
New Roads and Street Works Act 1991 (c 22)	In Schedule 4, in paragraph 7(4), the definitions of "telecommunication apparatus" and "telecommunication system".
	In Schedule 6, in paragraph 7(4), the definitions of "telecommunication apparatus" and "telecommunication system".
Taxation of Chargeable Gains Act 1992 (c 12)	In Schedule 10, paragraph 7.
Charities Act 1992 (c 41)	In section 60(10), the definition of "telecommunication apparatus".

Short title and chapter	*Extent of repeal*
Competition and Service (Utilities) Act 1992 (c 43)	Sections 1 to 10.
	Section 49.
	In Schedule 1, paragraphs 1, 2, 3(b) and 4.
Carriage of Goods by Sea Act 1992 (c 50)	In section 5(1), the definition of "telecommunication system" and the word "and" immediately preceding it.
Tribunals and Inquiries Act 1992 (c 53)	In Part 1 of Schedule 1, the entry at paragraph 45 relating to wireless telegraphy.
Judicial Pensions and Retirement Act 1993 (c 8)	Section 26(8)(a).
	In Schedule 5, the entry relating to the President of the tribunal established under section 9 of the Wireless Telegraphy Act 1949.
	In Schedule 6, paragraph 58.
	In Schedule 7, paragraph 5(5)(xxxii).
Leasehold Reform, Housing and Urban Development Act 1993 (c 28)	In Part 2 of Schedule 20, paragraph 19(1).
Cardiff Bay Barrage Act 1993 (c 42)	In Schedule 4, in paragraph 3(2), the words following paragraph (c).
	In Schedule 7, paragraph 21(10).
Local Government (Wales) Act 1994 (c 19)	In Schedule 16, paragraph 72.
Vehicle Excise and Registration Act 1994 (c 22)	In Schedule 3, paragraph 3(a)(i).
Criminal Justice and Public Order Act 1994 (c 33)	Section 92.
Deregulation and Contracting Out Act 1994 (c 40)	Section 8.
	In Schedule 4, paragraph 3(a).
Criminal Procedure (Consequential Provisions) (Scotland) Act 1995 (c 40)	In Schedule 4, paragraph 48(2) and (3).
Criminal Procedure (Scotland) Act 1995 (c 46)	In Schedule 9, the entry relating to the Wireless Telegraphy Act 1949.
Arbitration Act 1996 (c 23)	In Schedule 3, paragraph 7.
Broadcasting Act 1996 (c 55)	Section 1(1A) to (3).
	Section 2(1), (6) and (7).
	In section 4(3), the words from "and the amount" onwards.
	Section 5(7)(a).
	Section 6.
	In section 11(5), the words from "not exceeding" onwards.
	Section 12(7).
	In section 16(6), the words "before the relevant date".
	Section 18(5) and (6).
	Section 19(2) and (4) to (10).
	Sections 20 to 22.
	Section 25(5) and (6).
	Section 28.
	In section 29(2), the word "59,".

Short title and chapter	Extent of repeal
	Sections 30 and 31.
	In section 33(3)(c), the words "or II".
	Section 34.
	Section 38.
	In section 39(1), the definitions of "the Commission" and "qualifying teletext service".
	In section 40(4), the words "provided on a frequency or frequencies assigned to the Authority under section 45(1)".
	In section 43— (a) in subsection (2)(b), sub-paragraph (ii) and the word "or" immediately preceding it; (b) in subsection (3), the words from "and the amount" onwards.
	Section 44(7)(a).
	Section 45.
	In section 46(1), paragraph (e).
	Section 47(4).
	Section 54(7).
	In section 56(1)(a)(i), the words "to which the licence relates".
	In section 58— (a) subsection (5); (b) in subsection (6), the words "before the relevant date".
	In section 60, subsections (7) to (10).
	In section 61, subsections (3) and (4).
	Section 68.
	Section 71.
	In section 72(1), the definition of "the Authority".
	Sections 74 to 76.
	Sections 78 and 79.
	Section 80(2).
	Sections 82 to 84.
	Section 86(3).
	Sections 87 to 90.
	Section 91.
	Section 93.
	In section 95, subsections (3) to (7).
	In section 97(3)(b), the words "by the Commission" and "by them".
	In section 104(4)(d), the words "by the Commission" and "by them".
	In section 105(1), the definitions of "the Commission" and "live".
	Section 106.
	In section 107— (a) subsection (2);

Short title and chapter	*Extent of repeal*
	(b) in subsection (4)(a), the words "or regulatory".
	Sections 108 and 109.
	In section 110—
	(a) subsection (2);
	(b) in subsection (3), the words from "; and in exercising" onwards;
	(c) in subsection (4), the definition of "a standards complaint" and the word "and" immediately preceding it.
	Sections 112 and 113.
	In section 114—
	(a) in subsection (1), the words "or a standards complaint";
	(b) in subsection (2), the words "or a standards complaint" and in paragraph (b) the words ", in the case of a fairness complaint,".
	In section 115—
	(a) in subsection (2), paragraph (c);
	(b) in subsection (3), paragraph (b) and the word "and" immediately preceding it.
	Section 116.
	In section 118, the words "or a standards complaint".
	In section 119—
	(a) in subsection (3), paragraph (c);
	(b) in subsection (8), the words "or standards complaint" and in paragraph (c) the words ", a regulatory body";
	(c) in subsection (9), the words "or standards complaint" and ", 113(1)";
	(d) subsection (12).
	In section 120(1), the words "or a standards complaint".
	Sections 122 to 129.
	In section 130—
	(a) in subsection (1), in the definition of "licensed service", the words from ", subject to" to "125(6),";
	(b) the definitions in that subsection of "the appropriate regulatory body", "the BSC", "financial year", "local delivery service", "regulatory body", "sexual conduct" and "standards complaint";
	(c) in subsection (2), paragraph (b) and the word "and" immediately preceding it.
	Section 142.
	Section 143(3) and (4).
	Section 144(5).

Short title and chapter	*Extent of repeal*
	In section 145(8), the definition of "the relevant authority". In Schedule 2, paragraphs 1(2)(d) to (f), 4, 5, 6(3), 10 and 11. Schedule 3. Schedule 4. In Schedule 8, paragraph 4. In Schedule 10, paragraphs 1, 3 to 6, 8, 11 to 14, 16, 18 to 20, 22 to 25, 26(a)(ii) and (b) and 27(a).
Channel Tunnel Rail Link Act 1996 (c 61)	In Part 4 of Schedule 15, in paragraph 1(2), the definitions of "telecommunications code", "telecommunications operator" and "operator", "telecommunication apparatus", "telecommunications code system" and "telecommunication system".
Telecommunications (Fraud) Act 1997 (c 4)	The whole Act.
Planning (Consequential Provisions) (Scotland) Act 1997 (c 11)	In Schedule 2, paragraph 37.
Wireless Telegraphy Act 1998 (c 6)	In section 1(1), the words "other than a television licence as defined in section 1(7) of that Act". In section 1(3)— (a) paragraph (a); (b) in paragraph (b) the words from "or provide" to "the Secretary of State"; (c) paragraph (d) and the word "and" immediately preceding it. In section 3— (a) in subsection (1), the words "or determined by him under" and paragraph (a) and the word "and" immediately after it; (b) subsection (2); (c) in subsection (3), paragraph (h) and the word "and" immediately preceding it. Section 5. Schedule 1.
Petroleum Act 1998 (c 17)	In Schedule 4— (a) in paragraph 2(3), the words "section 6 (wireless telegraphy) and"; (b) paragraph 19.
Competition Act 1998 (c 41)	In Schedule 1, paragraph 3. In Schedule 7— (a) paragraph 2(1)(d)(iii); (b) in paragraph 19A(9), in the definition of "merger reference group", the words "section 59 of the Fair Trading Act 1973 (c 41)," and in the definition of "special reference group" paragraphs (b) and (f) and the word "or" at the end of paragraph (m).

Short title and chapter	*Extent of repeal*
	In Schedule 7A, in paragraph 1, in the definition of "merger investigation", the words "section 59 of the Fair Trading Act 1973 (c 41),".
	In Schedule 10— (a) paragraph 2(1) to (6), (8) and (9); (b) paragraph 9(2) to (4) and (6).
	In Schedule 12, paragraph 14(3).
	In Schedule 13, paragraph 35(2)(a).
Regional Development Agencies Act 1998 (c 45)	In Schedule 6, paragraph 16(1).
Access to Justice Act 1999 (c 22)	In Schedule 4, paragraph 26.
Electronic Communications Act 2000 (c 7)	Sections 11 and 12.
Regulation of Investigatory Powers Act 2000 (c 23)	Section 18(12)(e).
	In Schedule 4, paragraph 3.
Postal Services Act 2000 (c 26)	In Schedule 7, paragraph 3(2)(g).
Freedom of Information Act 2000 (c 36)	In Part 6 of Schedule 1, the entries relating to— (a) the Broadcasting Standards Commission; (b) the Independent Television Commission; (c) the Radio Authority; (d) the Scottish Advisory Committee on Telecommunications; (e) the Welsh Advisory Committee on Telecommunications.
	In Part 7 of Schedule 1, the entry relating to the Northern Ireland Advisory Committee on Telecommunications.
Countryside and Rights of Way Act 2000 (c 37)	In section 45(1), the definitions of "telecommunications code" and "telecommunications code system".
Transport Act 2000 (c 38)	In Schedule 8, paragraph 14(2).
	In Schedule 9, paragraph 3(2)(e).
Political Parties, Elections and Referendums Act 2000 (c 41)	Section 11(1) and (2).
	In Schedule 12, in paragraph 4, sub-paragraphs (1) to (5) and in sub-paragraph (7) the definitions of "the 1990 Act", "licence", "licensed" and "the licensing body".
	In Schedule 21, paragraph 8.
Criminal Justice and Police Act 2001 (c 16)	In the table in section 1(1), the entry relating to section 43(1)(b) of the Telecommunications Act 1984.
Anti-terrorism, Crime and Security Act 2001 (c 24)	In Schedule 4, paragraph 29.
Office of Communications Act 2002 (c 11)	Section 2.
	Sections 4 to 6.
	In the Schedule, paragraphs 1(4), 8(5), 17(8) and (9) and 20.
Tobacco Advertising and Promotion Act 2002 (c 36)	Section 12(4).
Enterprise Act 2002 (c 40)	In section 22(3)(a), the words "69(1),".
	In section 33(3)(a), the words "69(1),".

Short title and chapter	*Extent of repeal*
	In section 46(1)(a), the words "69(1),".
	In section 62(4), the words "section 69(1) or".
	In section 67(1)(b), the words from "which" to "or 33".
	In section 68(2)(c), the words from "which", where it occurs for the second time, to "or 33".
	Section 69.
	In section 121—
	(a) in subsection (1), the words ", Part V of the Fair Trading Act 1973 (c 41)";
	(b) in subsection (2), paragraph (b) and the word "or" at the end of the paragraph;
	(c) in subsection (4)(c), sub-paragraph (i), the word "and" at the end of the sub-paragraph and, in sub-paragraph (ii), the words "in any other case,";
	(d) in subsection (8), the words ", Part V of the Act of 1973";
	(e) subsection (10).
	In section 136—
	(a) in subsection (7), paragraph (a) and the word "and" immediately preceding paragraph (g);
	(b) in subsection (8), the words "the Director of Telecommunications,".
	Section 168(3)(a), (4)(a) and (5)(d).
	In Schedule 9, paragraphs 1 and 16.
	In Schedule 25, paragraphs 13(2) to (8), 24(2) to (6), (8) and (9) and 34.
Income Tax (Earnings and Pensions) Act 2003 (c 1)	In section 320(7), paragraph (d).
European Parliament (Representation) Act 2003 (c 7)	In section 12(4), in the definition of "programme services", the words from "(including" to "local delivery services".

Note

1. …
2. The repeal of section 63 of the Telecommunications Act 1984 (c 12) does not affect the power of the Secretary of State or the Treasury to acquire or subscribe for securities of the successor company or of any subsidiary of the successor company other than pursuant to an enactment.
3. …
4. The repeal of paragraph 20 of Schedule 5 to the Telecommunications Act 1984 shall be disregarded for the purposes of Schedule 18 to this Act.
5. The repeals of sections 27A to 27L and in section 50 of the Telecommunications Act 1984 and the repeal of sections 1 to 10 of the Competition and Service Utilities Act 1992 do not have effect in relation to any dispute or other matter referred to the Director General of Telecommunications before the coming into force of the repeals.
6. The repeals of sections 26 and 27 of the 1990 Act have effect subject to section 201(2) of this Act.

(2) INSTRUMENTS

Title and number	*Extent of revocation*
Planning (Northern Ireland) Order 1991 (SI 1991/1220 (NI 11))	Article 104(5).
Electricity (Northern Ireland) Order 1992 (SI 1992/231 (NI 1))	In Schedule 4, in paragraph 1(1), the definitions of "public telecommunications operator" and of "telecommunication apparatus", "telecommunication system" and "the telecommunications code".
Telecommunications (Single Emergency Call Number) Regulations 1992 (SI 1992/2875)	The whole regulations.
Roads (Northern Ireland) Order 1993 (SI 1993/3160 (NI 15))	In Article 2(2), the definitions of "telecommunication apparatus", "the telecommunications code" and "telecommunications code system".
Airports (Northern Ireland) Order 1994 (SI 1994/426 (NI 1))	Article 12(7).
Street Works (Northern Ireland) Order 1995 (SI 1995/3210 (NI 19))	In Schedule 2, in paragraph 7(4), the definitions of "telecommunication apparatus" and "telecommunication system".
Gas (Northern Ireland) Order 1996 (SI 1996/275 (NI 2))	In Schedule 3, in paragraph 1, the definitions of "public telecommunications operator" and of "telecommunication apparatus", "telecommunication system" and "the telecommunications code".
Race Relations (Northern Ireland) Order 1997 (SI 1997/869 (NI 6))	Paragraphs 4 and 9 of Schedule 2.
Telecommunications (Voice Telephony) Regulations 1997 (SI 1997/1886)	The whole regulations.
Telecommunications (Interconnection) Regulations 1997 (SI 1997/2931)	The whole regulations.
Telecommunications (Open Network Provision and Leased Lines) Regulations 1997 (SI 1997/2932)	The whole regulations.
Telecommunications (Open Network Provision) (Voice Telephony) Regulations 1998 (SI 1998/1580)	The whole regulations.
Telecommunications (Licence Modification) (Standard Schedules) Regulations 1999 (SI 1999/2450)	The whole regulations.
Telecommunications (Licence Modification) (Fixed Voice Telephony and International Facilities Operator Licences) Regulations 1999 (SI 1999/2451)	The whole regulations.
Telecommunications (Licence Modification) (Mobile Public Telecommunications Operators) Regulations 1999 (SI 1999/2452)	The whole regulations.
Telecommunications (Licence Modification) (British Telecommunications plc) Regulations 1999 (SI 1999/2453)	The whole regulations.
Telecommunications (Licence Modification) (Cable and Local Delivery Operator Licences) Regulations 1999 (SI 1999/2454)	The whole regulations.
Telecommunications (Licence Modification) (Kingston Communications (Hull) PLC) Regulations 1999 (SI 1999/2455)	The whole regulations.

Title and number	Extent of revocation
Telecommunications (Interconnection) (Carrier Pre-section) Regulations 1999 (SI 1999/3448)	The whole regulations.
Telecommunications (Interconnection) (Number Portability, etc) Regulations 1999 (SI 1999/3449)	The whole regulations.
Telecommunications (Licence Modification) (Satellite Operator Licences) Regulations 2000 (SI 2000/1711)	The whole regulations.
Telecommunications (Licence Modification) (Regional Public Access Mobile Radio Operator Licences) Regulations 2000 (SI 2000/1712)	The whole regulations.
Telecommunications (Licence Modification) (Amendment) Regulations 2000 (SI 2000/1713)	The whole regulations.
Telecommunications (Licence Modification) (Mobile Data Operator Licences) Regulations 2000 (SI 2000/1714)	The whole regulations.
Telecommunications (Licence Modification) (Paging Operator Licences) Regulations 2000 (SI 2000/1715)	The whole regulations.
Telecommunications (Services for Disabled Persons) Regulations 2000 (SI 2000/2410)	The whole regulations.
Telecommunications (Licence Modifications) (Amendment No 2) Regulations 2000 (SI 2000/2998)	The whole regulations.
Telecommunications (Licence Modifications) (Amendment) Regulations 2001 (SI 2001/2495)	The whole regulations.

[3461]–[3463]

NOTES

Commencement: 25 July 2003 and 18 September 2003 (in part, for the purpose of enabling network and service functions and spectrum functions to be carried out during the transitional period by the Director General of Telecommunications and the Secretary of State respectively) (see further s 408 and Sch 18 at **[3436]**, **[3460]**, and the Communications Act 2003 (Commencement No 1) Order 2003, SI 2003/1900 at **[3507]**); 29 December 2003 (in part, and in part for the purpose of enabling OFCOM to perform the network and service functions and spectrum functions) (see the Office of Communications Act 2002 (Commencement No 3) and Communications Act 2003 (Commencement No 2) Order 2003, SI 2003/3142 at **[3590]**); 1 April 2004 (in part); to be appointed (otherwise).

Notes 1, 3: repealed by the Wireless Telegraphy Act 2006, s 125(1), Sch 9, Pt 1, subject to transitional provisions and savings in s 124 of, Sch 8, Pt 1, paras 1–8, 24, to, that Act at **[4230]**, **[4239]**, and previously read as follows:

"1. These repeals, so far as they relate to appeals to the tribunal established under section 9 of the Wireless Telegraphy Act 1949 (c 54), have effect in relation only to appeals against decisions made after the coming into force of section 192.

3. The repeals of sections 80 and 81 of the Telecommunications Act 1984 do not apply in relation to apparatus seized before the coming into force of the repeal.".

It is understood that the entry relating to the repeal of words in the Enterprise Act 2002, s 136(8) should actually read "Director General of Telecommunications".

MARINE, &C, BROADCASTING (OFFENCES) (PRESCRIBED AREAS OF THE HIGH SEAS) ORDER 1990

(SI 1990/2503)

NOTES

Made: 8 December 1990.

Authority: Marine, &c, Broadcasting (Offences) Act 1967, s 2A(1), (5).

Commencement: 1 January 1991.

1 Citation and commencement

This Order may be cited as the Marine, &c, Broadcasting (Offences) (Prescribed Areas of the High Seas) Order 1990 and shall come into force on 1st January 1991.

[3464]

2 Interpretation

In this Order—

"co-ordinates" means co-ordinates of latitude and longitude on European Datum (First Adjustment 1950); and

"nautical mile" means a nautical mile of 1,852 metres.

[3465]

3 The prescribed areas of the high seas

The areas of the high seas prescribed for the purposes of section 2A of the Marine, &c, Broadcasting (Offences) Act 1967 shall be the areas described in the Schedule hereto.

[3466]

SCHEDULE
PRESCRIBED AREAS OF THE HIGH SEAS

Article 3

The following are the areas to which article 3 of this Order applies—

(A) the area bounded by loxodromes and arcs joining the following co-ordinates:—

(1) 50° 49'31"N 01° 15'53"E
south westward and westward following the seaward limit of the territorial sea adjacent to France to:

(2) 49° 55'23"N 02° 03'12"W
thence following the seaward limit of arcs drawn 12 nautical miles around the Bailiwick of Guernsey measured from the territorial sea baseline to:

(3) 49° 18'18"N 02° 56'09"W
thence westward following the seaward limit of the territorial sea adjacent to France to:

(4) 49° 00'00"N 03° 53'45"W
thence westward to:

(5) 49° 00'00"N 07° 00'00"W
thence northward to:

(6) 51° 53'58"N 07° 00'00"W
thence eastward and northward following the seaward limit of the territorial sea adjacent to the Republic of Ireland and Northern Ireland to:

(7) 54° 27'54"N 05° 04'35"W
thence eastward following the seaward limit of the territorial sea adjacent to Great Britain to:

(8) 54° 26'05"N 04° 52'01"W
thence following the seaward limit of arcs drawn 12 nautical miles around the Isle of Man measured from the territorial sea baseline to:

(9) 54° 27'18"N 04° 01'22"W
thence southward and eastward following the seaward limit of the territorial sea adjacent to Great Britain to the co-ordinates referred to at paragraph (1) above; and

(B) the area bounded by loxodromes and arcs joining the following co-ordinates:—

(10) 55° 26'39"N 06° 34'38"W
thence westward following the seaward limit of the territorial sea adjacent to Northern Ireland and the Republic of Ireland to:

(11) 55° 25'45"N 08° 00'00"W
thence northward to:

(12) 56° 40'00"N 08° 00'00"W
thence westward to:

(13) 56° 40'00"N 09° 00'00"W
thence northward to:

(14) 57° 45'35"N 09° 00'00"W
thence northward following the seaward limit of the territorial sea adjacent to Great Britain to:

(15) 57° 54’02”N 09° 00’00”W
thence northward to:
(16) 59° 00’00”N 09° 00’00”W
thence north eastward to:
(17) 61° 05’00”N 02° 00’00”W
thence eastward to:
(18) 61° 05’00”N 01° 00’00”E
thence southward to:
(19) 56° 00’00”N 01° 00’00”E
thence eastward to:
(20) 56° 00’00”N 05° 00’00”E
thence southward to:
(21) 53° 33’43”N 05° 00’00”E
thence southward and westward following the seaward limit of the territorial sea adjacent to the Netherlands, Belgium and France to:
(22) 51° 12’01”N 01° 53’20”E
thence northward, westward and southward following the seaward limit of the territorial sea adjacent to Great Britain to the co-ordinates referred to at paragraph (10) above.

[3467]

BROADCASTING ACT 1990 (INDEPENDENT RADIO SERVICES: EXCEPTIONS) ORDER 1990

(SI 1990/2536)

NOTES

Made: 12 December 1990.
Authority: Broadcasting Act 1990, ss 97(2), 200.
Commencement: 1 January 1991.

1—(1) This Order may be cited as the Broadcasting Act 1990 (Independent Radio Services: Exceptions) Order 1990 and shall come into force on 1st January 1991.

(2) In this Order “the 1990 Act” means the Broadcasting Act 1990.

[3468]

2—(1) Section 97(1) of the 1990 Act (by which any person who provides any independent radio service without being authorised to do so by or under a licence under Part III of that Act is guilty of an offence) shall not apply to the services or descriptions of services which are specified in paragraph (2) below.

(2) The services and descriptions of services referred to in paragraph (1) above are—

(a) any independent radio service, as defined by section 84(1) of the 1990 Act, provided under and in accordance with Schedule 11 to the 1990 Act;

(b) any independent radio service, as so defined,—

(i) which is provided for reception at a place or places in the United Kingdom provided that no such place is a dwelling-house (within the meaning of section 202(1) of the 1990 Act),

(ii) which is so provided for the purpose of its being heard there either by members of the public or by a group of persons some or all of whom do not have a business interest in hearing it,

(iii) which does not include any advertisement, and

(iv) in respect of which no payment is made either directly or indirectly for its provision by the persons by whom it is heard; and

(c) any independent radio service, as so defined, consisting only of sounds sent by means of [an electronic communications network provided by a person who is a provider of a public electronic communications network] and who is not licensed to provide a local delivery service, as defined by section 72 of the 1990 Act.

[3469]

NOTES

Para (2): words in square brackets in sub-para (c) substituted by the Communications Act (Consequential Amendments) Order 2003, SI 2003/2155, art 3(1), Sch 1, Pt 5, para 30.

BROADCASTING ACT 1990 (INDEPENDENT TELEVISION SERVICES: EXCEPTIONS) ORDER 1990

(SI 1990/2537)

NOTES

Made: 12 December 1990.
Authority: Broadcasting Act 1990, ss 13(2), 200.
Commencement: 1 January 1991.

1—(1) This Order may be cited as the Broadcasting Act 1990 (Independent Television Services: Exceptions) Order 1990 and shall come into force on 1st January 1991.

(2) In this Order "the 1990 Act" means the Broadcasting Act 1990.

[3470]

2—(1) Section 13(1) of the 1990 Act (by which any person who provides any service falling within section 2(1)(a) or (b) of that Act without being authorised to do so by or under a licence under Part I of that Act is guilty of an offence) shall not apply to the services or descriptions of services which are specified in paragraph (2) below.

(2) The services and descriptions of services referred to in paragraph (1) above are—

(a) any television programme service, as defined by section 2(4) of the 1990 Act, provided under and in accordance with the provisions of Schedule 11 to the 1990 Act; and

(b) any television programme service, as so defined,—

(i) which is provided for reception at a place or places in the United Kingdom provided that no such place is a dwelling-house (within the meaning of section 202(1) of the 1990 Act),

(ii) which is so provided for the purposes of its being presented there either to members of the public or to a group of persons some or all of whom do not have a business interest in hearing or seeing it,

(iii) which does not include any advertisement, and

(iv) in respect of which no payment is made either directly or indirectly for its provision by the persons to whom it is presented.

[3471]–[3475]

BROADCASTING (INDEPENDENT PRODUCTIONS) ORDER 1991

(SI 1991/1408)

NOTES

Made: 18 June 1991.
Authority: Broadcasting Act 1990, s 16(5).
Commencement: 1 January 1993.

1 Citation, commencement and interpretation

(1) This Order may be cited as the Broadcasting (Independent Productions) Order 1991 and shall come into force on 1st January 1993.

(2) In this Order—

"the 1990 Act" means the Broadcasting Act 1990;

"programme" does not include an advertisement or any separate item whose duration is two minutes or less;

"relevant broadcaster" means, subject to [paragraph (5)] below, the person who provides the [television programme service] in which a percentage of qualifying programmes must be independent productions and "relevant [television programme service]" means that service; and

["television programme service" has the same meaning as in Part I of the 1990 Act.]

(3) For the purposes of this Order a programme may be treated as being made by a particular person or persons notwithstanding that more than 75 per cent of the duration of the programme includes images or images and sounds which have been provided by some person other than that person or those persons provided that—

(a) the images or images and sounds so provided are not broadcast live; and

(b) changes of substance (whether by means of editing or otherwise) have been made to such images or images and sounds.

[(4) For the purposes of this Order, a programme shall not be prevented from being treated as having been commissioned by a broadcaster by reason only of the fact that it was intended to be first shown commercially in cinemas.

(5) In the application of articles 2(1) and 3(6A) below to a regional Channel 3 service, references to the relevant broadcaster shall include references to the holder of another regional Channel 3 licence or any person acting on behalf of the holders of such licences.]

[3476]

NOTES

Para (2): in definition "relevant broadcaster" words in square brackets substituted, and definition "television programme service" substituted, for original definition "television broadcasting service", by the Broadcasting (Independent Productions) (Amendment) Order 2003, SI 2003/1672, arts 2, 4(a), 6.

Paras (4), (5): added by SI 2003/1672, arts 2, 4(b).

2 Meaning of "qualifying programmes"

(1) In section 16(2)(h) of the 1990 Act, the expression "qualifying programmes" means, subject to [paragraph (2)] below, all the programmes included in the relevant [television programme service] which fall within any of the following descriptions of programmes, namely—

(a) a programme which has been made either by the relevant broadcaster or by a person commissioned by him;

(b) a programme which has been made by the relevant broadcaster together with any other person or by a person commissioned by the relevant broadcaster together with any other person, provided that not less than 25 per cent of the actual cost of the production of the programme has been borne or provided by the relevant broadcaster; and

(c) a programme including images or images and sounds which have been provided by a person other than the relevant broadcaster or a person commissioned by him where—

  (i) the images or images and sounds so provided consist of live coverage of an event;

  (ii) they do not exceed 75 per cent of the duration of the programme, and

  (iii) the remainder of the programme (including any sound commentary added to those images or images and sounds) has been made by the relevant broadcaster or a person commissioned by him.

(2) In section 16(2)(h) of the 1990 Act the expression "qualifying programme" shall not include any programme which falls within any of the following descriptions, namely—

(a) a programme which has previously been shown in substantially the same form on the relevant [television programme service];

(b) a programme which consists, wholly or mainly, of news;

(c) a programme constituting part of a series of programmes which—

  (i) consist, wholly or mainly, of news or items relevant to news,

  (ii) are presented live, and

  (iii) are usually shown on at least four days in each of the weeks when they are shown;

(d) a programme provided by or on behalf of the Open University or Open College; and

(e) a broadcast on behalf of a political party or any statement by a Minister of the Crown within the meaning of the Ministers of the Crown Act 1975 [or by the Scottish Ministers].

(3), (4) ...

[3477]

NOTES

Para (1): words in square brackets substituted by the Broadcasting (Independent Productions) (Amendment) Order 2003, SI 2003/1672, arts 2, 5(a), 6(1).

Para (2): in sub-para (a) words in square brackets substituted by SI 2003/1672, arts 2, 6(1); in sub-para (e) words in square brackets added by the Scotland Act 1998 (Consequential Modifications) (No 2) Order 1999, SI 1999/1820, art 4, Sch 2, Pt II, para 147.

Paras (3), (4): revoked by SI 2003/1672, arts 2, 5(b).

3 Meaning of "independent productions"

(1) In section 16(2)(h) of the 1990 Act the expression "independent productions" means any programme which—

(a) falls within the definition of "qualifying programmes" specified in article 2 above;

(b) in the case of a programme to which sub-paragraph (a) or (b) of article 2(1) above applies, has been made by an independent producer (as defined by paragraph (4) below) or, in the case of a programme to which sub-paragraph (c) of that provision applies, has been made, as respects that part of the programme referred to in paragraph (iii) of that sub-paragraph by an independent producer;

(c) has been made in pursuance of a contract which complies, where appropriate, with the condition specified in paragraph (2) below, and

(d) has not been made in the circumstances specified in paragraph (3) below.

(2) The condition referred to in paragraph (1)(c) above is that any contractual obligations between a broadcaster and a producer which concern, directly or indirectly, the making of programmes (but not in respect of the use made of them) and which are capable of remaining in force for a period in excess of five years shall provide either side with the right to terminate those obligations at intervals of not more than five years (but without prejudice to any rights in respect of obligations that had not been discharged at the date of termination).

(3) The circumstances referred to in paragraph (1)(d) above are those where a broadcaster has required, otherwise than in pursuance of any contractual obligation arising from an earlier agreement that remains in force, the person to whom the contract to make the programme has been granted to agree, as a condition on which that contract is granted, to use the production facilities of that broadcaster or not to use the production facilities of some other broadcaster.

In this paragraph the reference to the production facilities of a broadcaster means—

(a) any premises or equipment which may be used to make a programme and which are owned or leased by that broadcaster or are otherwise under his control; and

(b) any person who is employed by, or has contractual obligations with, that broadcaster in connection with the making of programmes except any person who is employed, or has contractual obligations, to be seen or heard (or both) on programmes.

(4) In this article "independent producer" means a producer—

(a) who is not an employee (whether or not on temporary leave of absence) of a broadcaster;

(b) who[, subject to paragraph (4A) below,] does not have a shareholding greater than [25 per cent] in a broadcaster; and

[(c) which is not a body corporate in which any one [UK broadcaster] has a shareholding greater than 25 per cent or in which any two or more [UK broadcasters] together have an aggregate shareholding greater than 50 per cent.]

[(4A) A shareholding greater than 25 per cent which a producer has in a broadcaster shall not have the effect that the producer is not an independent producer if—

(a) the producer is incorporated under the laws of a state for the time being bound by the agreement on the European Economic Area signed at Oporto on 2 May 1992 or has his principal place of business in such a state; and

(b) the television services which the broadcaster provides are provided exclusively for reception in states which are not for the time being bound by that agreement and are not received directly or indirectly in any state which is for the time being bound by that agreement.

In applying sub-paragraph (a) above no regard shall be had to persons connected with the producer by virtue of paragraph (5) below or to the state under the laws of which a person so connected is incorporated or the state in which a person so connected has his principal place of business.]

(5) In paragraph (4) above [and in paragraph (4A) above except as otherwise indicated], any reference to a broadcaster or producer includes a reference to a person connected with, respectively, a broadcaster or producer.

For these purposes the following persons shall be treated as connected with, respectively, a broadcaster or producer, namely—

(a) a person who controls the broadcaster or, as the case may be, producer;

(b) an associate of the broadcaster or, as the case may be, producer or of a person falling within sub-paragraph (a) above; and

(c) a body which is controlled by the broadcaster or, as the case may be, producer or by an associate of the broadcaster or, as the case may be, producer.

In this paragraph "associate" has the same meaning as in Schedule 2 to the 1990 Act, except that paragraph 1(2) of Part I of that Schedule shall not apply so as to construe the meaning of that word in relation to a producer (but not a broadcaster) in the context of sub-paragraph (a) of paragraph (4) above only.

[(6) In paragraphs (4) and (4A) above, any reference however expressed to a person, or to two or more persons, having a shareholding in a body corporate greater than a percentage specified in that paragraph is a reference to the person or persons—

(a) holding or being beneficially entitled to more than the specified percentage of shares in that body, or

(b) possessing more than the specified percentage of voting power in that body.

For the purposes of this paragraph a person holds or is beneficially entitled to shares, or possesses voting power, in a body corporate whether he does so or is so entitled alone or jointly with one or more other persons and whether he does so or is so entitled directly or through one or more nominees.]

[(6A) For the purposes of this article, where a programme has been made by a producer (whether on his own or together with any other person) who would not, apart from this paragraph, be treated as an independent producer in relation to his part in the making of that programme, he shall be so treated if—

(a) he was commissioned to make the programme (whether on his own or together with any other person) by the relevant broadcaster,

(b) he was an independent producer when he was so commissioned,

(c) the relevant broadcaster so commissioned him in good faith in the expectation that he would be an independent producer when he performed his part in the making of the programme, and

(d) the programme was made within 2 years of the date on which he was so commissioned.

In this paragraph, any reference to a programme, in relation to a programme to which sub-paragraph (c) of article 2(1) above applies, is to that part of the programme referred to in paragraph (iii) of that sub-paragraph.

(6B) For the purposes of paragraph (6A) above, a producer is commissioned to make a programme on the date on which he becomes subject to a contractual obligation to make that programme (whether on his own or with another person) regardless whether that obligation is subsequently varied in any particular or supplemented by any further contractual provisions relating to the making of the programme.]

(7) In this article—

"broadcaster" means, subject to paragraph (5) above, a person who provides a television service (that is to say a service providing to members of the public images or images and sounds for reception on television receiving apparatus, whether provided by broadcasting or by other means) whether in the United Kingdom or elsewhere [but does not include a person who provides, in the United Kingdom or elsewhere, only a teletext service or any other service consisting wholly or mainly of visual images which are neither still pictures nor comprised within sequences of visual images capable of being seen as moving pictures, whether provided by broadcasting or by other means;]

"control" has the same meaning as in Schedule 2 to the 1990 Act; …

"producer" means, subject to paragraph (5) above, a person by whom the arrangements necessary for—

(i) the making of a programme, or

(ii) in the case of a programme to which article 2(1)(c) above applies, part of a programme[, and]

["UK broadcaster" means any broadcaster who provides a television service intended for reception in, or in any area in, the United Kingdom (whether or not that service is also intended for reception elsewhere)], are undertaken.

[3478]–[3481]

NOTES

Para (4): words in first pair of square brackets in sub-para (b) inserted and words in second pair of square brackets in sub-para (b), and the whole of sub-para (c), substituted by the Broadcasting (Independent Productions) (Amendment) Order 1995, SI 1995/1925, art 2(1), (2); words in square brackets in sub-para (c) substituted by the Broadcasting (Independent Productions) (Amendment) Order 2003, SI 2003/1672, arts 2, 3(a).

Para (4A): inserted by SI 1995/1925, art 2(3).

Para (5): words in square brackets inserted by SI 1995/1925, art 2(4).

Para (6): substituted by SI 1995/1925, art 2(5).

Paras (6A), (6B): inserted by SI 2003/1672, arts 2, 3(b).

Para (7): in definition "broadcaster" words in square brackets inserted by SI 1995/1925, art 2(6); word omitted from definition "control" revoked, and in definition "producer" word in brackets inserted, and definition "UK broadcaster" inserted, by SI 2003/1672, arts 2, 3(c).

INDEPENDENT ANALOGUE BROADCASTERS (RESERVATION OF DIGITAL CAPACITY) ORDER 1996

(SI 1996/2760)

NOTES

Made: 30 October 1996.

Authority: Broadcasting Act 1990, s 200; Broadcasting Act 1996, s 28(3), (6).

Commencement: 20 November 1996.

ARRANGEMENT OF ARTICLES

PART I
PRELIMINARY

PART II
THE C3/C4 MULTIPLEX LICENCE

PART III
THE C5/S4C MULTIPLEX LICENCE

PART I
PRELIMINARY

1 Citation, commencement and interpretation

(1) This Order may be cited as the Independent Analogue Broadcasters (Reservation of Digital Capacity) Order 1996 and shall come into force on 20th November 1996.

(2) In this Order—
- (a) "the 1990 Act" means the Broadcasting Act 1990;
- (b) "the 1996 Act" means the Broadcasting Act 1996;
- (c) "the C3/C4 multiplex licence" means the licence to provide a multiplex service on the frequency designated by the Secretary of State, pursuant to section 28(2) of the 1996 Act, as one of the frequencies to which section 28 applies and in relation to which 48.5 per cent of the digital capacity is reserved for the Channel 3 companies, 48.5 per cent for Channel Four and 3 per cent for the public teletext provider;
- (d) "the C5/S4C multiplex licence" means the licence to provide a multiplex service on the frequency designated by the Secretary of State, pursuant to section 28(2) of the 1996 Act, as one of the frequencies to which section 28 applies and in relation to which 50 per cent of the digital capacity is reserved for the holder of the Channel 5 licence throughout the United Kingdom and 50 per cent of the digital capacity is reserved for the Welsh Authority for the purposes of broadcasts which may be received wholly or mainly in Wales;
- (e) "acquisition" includes acquisition on hire or loan;
- (f) "Channel Four" means the Channel Four Television Corporation;
- (g) "the Channel 3 companies" means the holders of national or regional Channel 3 licences; and
- (h) "controlled" shall be construed in accordance with Part I of Schedule 2 to the 1990 Act; and
- [(i) in Part II, "qualifying company" has the same meaning as in section 24(6) of the 1990 Act and in Part III, "qualifying company" has the same meaning as in section 57(1B) of the 1990 Act].

(3) For the purposes of any provision of this Order which refers to a body corporate controlled by two or more persons taken together, the persons in question shall not be regarded as controlling the body corporate by virtue of sub-paragraph 2(h) unless they are acting together in concert.

[3482]

NOTES

Para (2): sub-para (i) substituted by the Independent Analogue Broadcasters (Reservation of Digital Capacity) (Amendment) Order 1999, SI 1999/1996, art 2.

PART II
THE C3/C4 MULTIPLEX LICENCE

2 Disapplication of 1996 Act

Sections 7, 8, 9 and 10 of the 1996 Act shall not apply to the C3/C4 multiplex licence except as provided in articles 3 and 4, which shall have effect in place of those provisions.

[3483]

3 Applications for the licence

(1) Where the Commission propose to grant the C3/C4 multiplex licence, they shall publish, in such manner as they consider appropriate, a notice—

(a) inviting an application for the licence and specifying the closing date for such an application;

(b) specifying the frequency on which the service is to be provided and the area or areas in the United Kingdom in which the frequency is to be available;

(c) stating that no percentage of multiplex revenue would be payable by the applicant in pursuance of section 13 of the 1996 Act if he were granted the licence, and

(d) containing general guidance as to requirements to be met by proposals as to the matters referred to in paragraphs (i) and (ii) of sub-paragraph (2)(a) and in sub-paragraph (2)(e), and such other general guidance as they consider appropriate.

(2) An application for the C3/C4 multiplex licence may be made only by a body corporate controlled by the Channel 3 companies and Channel Four taken together and must be in writing and accompanied by—

(a) a technical plan relating to the service which the applicant proposes to provide and indicating—

(i) the proposed coverage area of the service,

(ii) the timetable in accordance with which that coverage would be achieved, and

(iii) the technical means by which it would be achieved;

(b) the applicant's proposals as to the number of digital programme services to be broadcast, as to the characteristics of each of those services and as to the areas in which they would be provided;

(c) the applicant's proposals as to the timetable in accordance with which the broadcasting of each of those services would begin;

(d) the applicant's proposals as to the broadcasting of digital additional services;

(e) the applicant's proposals for promoting or assisting the acquisition, by persons in the proposed coverage area of the service, of equipment capable of receiving all the multiplex services available in that area;

(f) the applicant's proposals for the broadcasting and reception of the Channel 3 services and Channel 4 in digital form and of the qualifying teletext service;

(g) such information as the Commission may reasonably require as to the applicant's present financial position and his projected financial position during the period for which the licence would be in force; and

(h) such other information as the Commission may reasonably require for the purpose of considering the application.

(3) At any time after receiving such an application and before determining it, the Commission may require the applicant to furnish additional information under paragraph (2).

(4) Any information to be furnished to the Commission under paragraphs (2) and (3) shall, if they so require, be in such form or verified in such manner as they may specify.

(5) The Commission shall, as soon as reasonably practicable after the date specified under paragraph (1) as the closing date for an application, publish in such manner as they consider appropriate—

(a) the name of the person who has made that application to them;

(b) the proposals submitted by him under sub-paragraph (2)(b); and

(c) such other information connected with his application as the Commission consider appropriate.

[3484]

4 Award of licence

(1) Where an application for the C3/C4 multiplex licence has been duly made to the Commission in accordance with article 3(2), they may only (subject to sections 3(3) and 5(1) of the 1996 Act) refuse the application if they are not satisfied that—

(a) the proposed service would comply with the requirements specified in article 3(1);

(b) the applicant would be able to maintain that service throughout the period for which the licence would be in force;

(c) the applicant would not charge viewers for the reception of any qualifying service; or

(d) the arrangements proposed for the broadcasting of the qualifying teletext service would meet the reasonable requirements of the public teletext provider in relation to the provision of that service.

(2) Where the Commission have awarded the C3/C4 multiplex licence to any person in accordance with this article, they shall, as soon as reasonably practicable after awarding the licence—

(a) publish in such manner as they consider appropriate—

(i) the name of the person to whom the licence has been awarded, and

(ii) such other information as the Commission consider appropriate; and

(b) grant the licence to that person.

[3485]

5 Modifications of 1996 Act

(1) Sections 11, 12, 13 and 16 of the 1996 Act shall apply to the C3/C4 multiplex licence with the omissions and modifications set out in this article.

(2) Section 11 of the 1996 Act shall apply to the C3/C4 multiplex licence with the omission of section 11(3)(b) and (4).

(3) Section 12 of the 1996 Act shall apply to the C3/C4 multiplex licence with the following modifications:—

(a) as if the references in section 12 to sections 7(4)(b), (c), (d), (e) and (f) were references to sub-paragraphs (a), (b), (c), (d) and (e) of article 3(2), and

(b) with the omission of section 12(1)(f).

(4) The C3/C4 multiplex licence shall also include such conditions as appear to the Commission to be appropriate for securing the broadcasting of the Channel 3 services and Channel 4 in digital form and of the qualifying teletext service.

(5) Section 13(1) of the 1996 Act shall apply to the C3/C4 multiplex licence as if it had been granted in pursuance of a notice under section 7(1) of that Act.

(6) Sections 13(2) and (3) of the 1996 Act shall not apply to the C3/C4 multiplex licence.

(7) Section 16 of the 1996 Act shall apply to the C3/C4 multiplex licence with the following modifications—

(a) as if the references to section 7(1) were references to article 3(1) and the references to paragraph (f) of section 7(1) were references to sub-paragraph (c) of article 3(1);

(b) as if the reference to section 7(2)(b) were omitted;

(c) as if the references to section 7(4)(b) and (f) were references to sub-paragraphs (a) and (e) of article 3(2);

(d) as if section 16(8) were omitted and replaced by—

"On the grant of such an application the Commission may, with the consent of the Secretary of State, and shall if so required by him, specify a percentage as the percentage of multiplex revenue for each accounting period of his that will be payable by the applicant in pursuance of section 13(1) during the period for which the licence is to be renewed."; and

(e) as if section 16(9) were omitted.

[3486]

6 Variation of Channel 3 and Channel 4 licences

(1) The Commission shall vary the licences under which the Channel 3 services and Channel 4 are provided in analogue form so as to include such conditions as appear to the Commission to be appropriate for imposing on the holders of such licences, in specified circumstances, an obligation to provide the relevant qualifying service and such other consequential and transitional provisions as the Commission may consider appropriate.

(2) The Commission shall also include such conditions in any other licence under which the corresponding analogue service is subsequently provided.

(3) The Commission may further vary any licence under which any Channel 3 service is provided by including such transitional provisions as they may determine exempting the holder of that licence from providing his qualifying service during such hours of the day as they may specify throughout any part of the area for which that service is provided for a period not exceeding two years beginning on the date of the variation.

[3487]

7 Use of digital capacity

The holder of the C3/C4 multiplex licence shall not, without the prior consent of the Commission, use any of the digital capacity reserved for the Channel 3 companies and Channel Four by direction of the Secretary of State to the Commission under section 28(2)(b)(ii) of the 1996 Act for the broadcasting of any digital programme services or digital additional services provided under licences which are not held by any of the Channel 3 companies, or by any body corporate controlled by a Channel 3 company, or by more than one of the Channel 3 companies taken together, or by a qualifying company controlled by Channel Four.

[3488]

PART III
THE C5/S4C MULTIPLEX LICENCE

8 Applications for the licence

(1) The notice published by the Commission under section 7(1) of the 1996 Act in respect of the C5/S4C multiplex licence shall, in addition to the matters set out in that section, specify the amount of digital capacity reserved in accordance with a direction of the Secretary of State to the Commission under section 28(2)(b)(ii) of the 1996 Act for the broadcasting of Channel 5 in digital form and of S4C Digital on the frequency on which the multiplex service is to be provided.

(2) A application made in pursuance of the notice referred to in paragraph (1) shall, in addition to the matters set out in section 7(4) of the 1996 Act, be accompanied by the applicant's proposals for the broadcasting of Channel 5 in digital form and of S4C Digital.

(3) Where an application for the C5/S4C multiplex licence has been duly made to the Commission in accordance with section 7 of the 1996 Act and with paragraph (2), they may, without prejudice to section 8 of the 1996 Act, refuse the application if they are not satisfied that the applicant would not charge viewers for the reception of any qualifying service.

[3489]

[9 Conditions attaching to the licence

(1) The C5/S4C multiplex licence shall include, in addition to the conditions referred to in section 12(1) of the 1996 Act, such conditions as appear to be appropriate to the Commission for securing that, in consideration of the making of such payments as are specified in paragraph (2) below, the holder of the C5/S4C multiplex licence will use the digital capacity specified in the direction of the Secretary of State referred to in article 8(1) for the broadcasting of services provided by the holder of the Channel 5 licence and by—

(a) the Welsh Authority, or
(b) the Welsh Authority and one or more qualifying companies which either is or are controlled by the Welsh Authority.

(2) The payments referred to in paragraph (1) above are—

(a) payments made by the holder of the Channel 5 licence, and
(b) payments made by either—
 (i) the Welsh Authority, or
 (ii) the Welsh Authority and one or more qualifying companies which either is or are controlled by the Welsh Authority,

as are from time to time agreed between each of them respectively and the holder of the C5/S4C multiplex licence or (in default of agreement) determined by the Commission.]

[3490]

NOTES

Substituted by the Independent Analogue Broadcasters (Reservation of Digital Capacity) (Amendment) Order 1999, SI 1999/1996, art 3.

10 Variation of Channel 5 licence

(1) The Commission shall vary the licence under which Channel 5 is provided in analogue form so as to include such conditions as appear to the Commission to be appropriate for imposing on the holder of that licence, in specified circumstances, an obligation to provide his qualifying service and such other consequential and transitional provisions as the Commission may consider appropriate.

(2) The Commission shall also include such conditions in any other licence under which Channel 5 is subsequently provided in analogue form.

[3491]

LISTED EVENTS (PRESCRIBED MULTIPLIER) ORDER 1997

(SI 1997/1333)

NOTES

Made: 19 May 1997.
Authority: Broadcasting Act 1996, s 104(2)(b).
Commencement: 10 June 1997.

1 This Order may be cited as the Listed Events (Prescribed Multiplier) Order 1997 and shall come into force on 10th June 1997.

[3492]

2 The prescribed multiplier for the purposes of section 102(3) of the Broadcasting Act 1996 shall be one.

[3493]

BROADCASTING (TECHNICAL SERVICES) ORDER 1997

(SI 1997/1856)

NOTES

Made: 29 July 1997.
Authority: Broadcasting Act 1996, s 24(3)(b).
Commencement: 20 August 1997.

1 This Order may be cited as the Broadcasting (Technical Services) Order 1997 and shall come into force on 20th August 1997.

[3494]

2 The services specified for the purposes of section 24(3)(b) of the Broadcasting Act 1996 are those consisting of the transmission of [electronic signals (as defined for the purposes of section 48 of the Broadcasting Act 1990)] by means of which access to programmes or other information included in digital programme services or digital additional services is controlled so that only those viewers who are authorised to receive such programmes and information do so, and which are required to be offered to all holders of licences under Part I of the Broadcasting Act 1996 in accordance with regulation 11(1)(a) of the Advanced Television Services Regulations 1996.

[3495]–[3498]

NOTES

Words in square brackets substituted by the Communications Act (Consequential Amendments) Order 2003, SI 2003/2155, art 3(1), Sch 1, Pt 5, para 40.

BROADCASTING DIGITAL TERRESTRIAL SOUND (TECHNICAL SERVICE) ORDER 1998

(SI 1998/685)

NOTES

Made: 10 March 1998.
Authority: Broadcasting Act 1996, s 63(3)(b).

Commencement: 2 April 1998.

1 Citation and commencement

This Order may be cited as the Broadcasting Digital Terrestrial Sound (Technical Service) Order 1998 and shall come into force on 2nd April 1998.

[3499]

2 Meaning of technical service

The service specified for the purpose of section 63(3)(b) of the Broadcasting Act 1996 is that consisting of the transmission of [electronic signals (as defined for the purposes of section 114 of the Broadcasting Act 1990)] by means of which access to programmes or other information included in digital sound programme services[, television licensable content services] or digital additional services is controlled so that only those persons who are authorised to receive such programmes and information do so.

[3500]–[3504]

NOTES

Words in first pair of square brackets substituted by the Communications Act (Consequential Amendments) Order 2003, SI 2003/2155, art 3(1), Sch 1, Pt 5, para 42; words in second pair of square brackets inserted by the Broadcasting Digital Terrestrial Sound (Technical Service) Order 2006, SI 2006/2793, art 2.

OFFICE OF COMMUNICATIONS (MEMBERSHIP) ORDER 2002

(SI 2002/2956)

NOTES

Made: 29 November 2002.
Authority: Office of Communications Act 2002, s 1(7).
Commencement: 24 December 2002.

1 This Order may be cited as the Office of Communications (Membership) Order 2002 and shall come into force on 24th December 2002.

[3505]

NOTES

Commencement: 24 December 2002.

2 The number specified in section 1(2) of the Office of Communications Act 2002 as the maximum membership for the Office of Communications shall be nine.

[3506]

NOTES

Commencement: 24 December 2002.

COMMUNICATIONS ACT 2003 (COMMENCEMENT NO 1) ORDER 2003

(SI 2003/1900)

NOTES

Made: 17 July 2003.
Authority: Communications Act 2003, ss 408(1), (4), 411(2), (4).

ARRANGEMENT OF ARTICLES

1 Citation and interpretation

(1) This Order may be cited as the Communications Act 2003 (Commencement No 1) Order 2003.

(2) In this Order—

"the Act" means the Communications Act 2003;

"the transitionally commenced provisions" means—

the provisions of the Act brought into force by article 2(1) of this Order, other than those contained in sections 264 and 360 to 362, Schedule 15 and paragraph 30 of Schedule 18;

the provisions of the Act brought into force by article 2(2) of this Order contained in—

section 152 and 167,
paragraphs 18, 149 and 150 of Schedule 17,
paragraph 21 of Schedule 18, and
Schedule 19; and

"the transitional period" means the period provided for by section 408(6) of the Act.

[3507]

2 Commencement

(1) The provisions of the Act set out in Schedule 1 hereto shall, subject to the exceptions set out therein, come into force on 25th July 2003.

(2) The provisions of the Act set out in Schedule 2 hereto shall come into force on 18th September 2003.

[3508]

3 Transitional provisions: the transitionally commenced provisions

(1) The transitionally commenced provisions are brought into force by this Order on 25th July 2003 or (as the case may be) 18th September 2003 for the purpose only of enabling the networks and services functions and the spectrum functions under those provisions to be carried out during the transitional period by the Director General of Telecommunications and the Secretary of State respectively.

(2) …

[3509]

NOTES

Para (2): revoked by the Office of Communications Act 2002 (Commencement No 3) and Communications Act 2003 (Commencement No 2) Order 2003, SI 2003/3142, art 1(3).

4 Transitional provisions: section 264 of the Act

(1) This article shall have effect for the interpretation of section 264 of the Act.

(2) In relation to times before the coming into force of section 207 of the Act, the reference to the television programme services that are public services of the Welsh Authority shall be taken to be a reference to S4C and S4C Digital.

(3) In relation to times before the coming into force of section 266 of the Act, references to statements of programme policy shall be taken to include references to any statement made by the provider of a licensed public service channel for the purposes of his application for a

licence under Part 1 of the 1990 Act for the channel or for any other purpose connected with the performance of his obligations under that licence.

(4) In relation to times before the coming into force of section 268 of the Act, references to statements of service policy shall be taken to include references to any statement made by the public teletext provider for the purposes of his application for a licence under Part 1 of the 1990 Act for the public teletext service or for any other purpose connected with the performance of his obligations under that licence.

[3510]

5 Transitional provisions: section 348 of, and Part 4 of Schedule 14 to, the Act

(1) In relation to times before the coming into force of section 350(2) of the Act, sections 5 and 88 of the 1990 Act and sections 5 and 44 of the 1996 Act (restrictions on holding licences) shall have effect as if, in paragraph (b) of subsection (1) of each of those sections, the reference to any requirements imposed by or under Parts 3 to 5 of Schedule 2 to the 1990 Act included a reference to any requirements imposed by or under Part 4 of Schedule 14 to the Act.

(2) In relation to times before the coming into force of the relevant amending provision, each of sections 5(7)(c) and 88(7)(c) of the 1990 Act and sections 5(8)(c) and 44(8)(c) of the 1996 Act shall have effect as if the reference to any requirement imposed by or under Schedule 2 to the 1990 Act included a reference to any requirement imposed by or under Part 4 of Schedule 14 to the Act.

(3) In paragraph (2) above, in relation to each provision of the 1990 or 1996 Act mentioned there, "the relevant amending provision" means the following provision of Schedule 15 to the Act, that is to say—

- (a) in the case of section 5(7)(c) of the 1990 Act, paragraph 3(7);
- (b) in the case of section 88(7)(c) of that Act, paragraph 35(7);
- (c) in the case of section 5(8)(c) of the 1996 Act, paragraph 78(6);
- (d) in the case of section 44(8)(c) of that Act, paragraph 104(6).

[3511]

6 Transitional provisions: section 362(1) of the Act

(1) This article shall have effect for the interpretation of section 362(1) of the Act.

(2) In relation to times before the coming into force of section 241(1) of the Act, "television multiplex service" means a multiplex service within the meaning of Part 1 of the 1996 Act.

(3) In relation to times before the coming into force of section 258(1) of the Act, "radio multiplex service" shall have the same meaning as it has in Part 2 of the 1996 Act.

(4) In relation to times before the grant of the first licence under section 219 of the Act—

- (a) "the public teletext provider" means the person who holds the additional services licence (within the meaning of Part 1 of the 1990 Act) which relates to the teletext service referred to in subsection (2) of section 49 of the 1990 Act;
- (b) "the public teletext service" means the teletext service referred to in that subsection and the qualifying teletext service within the meaning of Part 1 of the 1996 Act; and
- (c) "the digital public teletext service" means the qualifying teletext service within the meaning of Part 1 of the 1996 Act.

[3512]

SCHEDULE 1
PROVISIONS COMING INTO FORCE ON 25TH JULY 2003

Article 2(1)

Section 1(3) (except for the words "including borrow money") and (5)(c) to the extent only that those provisions are to be taken for the purposes of section 408(3) of the Act to be brought into force for the purpose of enabling networks and services functions to be carried out.

Section 4.

Section 5 to the extent only that it is to be taken for the purposes of section 408(3) of the Act to be brought into force for the purpose of enabling networks and services functions to be carried out.

Sections 24 and 25.

Section 26, except for paragraph (d) of subsection (2).

Section 32 to 55.

Sections 56 to 63, except in respect of any number which is used as an internet domain name, an internet address or an address or identifier incorporating either an internet domain name or an internet address, including an email address.

Sections 64 to 119, 125 to 151, 153, 154, 164 to 166, 169, 172 to 174, 178, 183, 185 to 197 and 264.

Section 360(3) in respect of the provisions of Schedule 15 set out in this Schedule.

Section 361 and 362.

Section 369, except for paragraph (e) of subsection (1).

Sections 370 and 371.

Section 393, except for—
paragraphs (c) and (d) of subsection (1);
paragraphs (j) and (k) of subsection (5);
paragraph (a) of subsection (6) in its application to sections 15 and 390;
subsection (7).

Section 394, except for paragraphs (e) and (f) of subsection (2).

Sections 395 to 399 and 402 to 404.

Section 406, except for—
subsection (1) in respect of the provisions of Schedule 17 not set out in this Schedule;
subsection (6) in respect of the provisions of Schedule 18 not set out in this Schedule;
subsection (7) in respect of the provisions of Schedule 19 not set out in this Schedule.

Sections 408 and 410.

Schedules 3, 4 and 8.

In Schedule 15, paragraphs 20(1) and (2)(a) and 52(1) and (2)(a).

In Schedule 17—
paragraphs 1 to 5, 8(1), (3), (6), (8) and (10), 10, 14(1), (2), (3)(b) and (4)(a), 16, 19 to 31, 38, 40 to 47, 51 to 60, 63, 71, 72(1) to (3), (5) and (6), 75, 77 to 82, 84 to 90, 94 to 128, 129(1) and (3), 130, 131, 134 to 144, 152 to 158, 160, 162, 163, 165, 166(1), (2) and (3)(b), 168 to 170, 174(1), (2), (4), (6) and (7) and 175;
paragraph 8(9), except in respect of the repeal of the words in section 1D(8) of the Wireless Telegraphy Act 1949 from "A notice under this section" to "affected by them";
paragraph 9, except in respect of the new subsection (2A) in subparagraph (3);
paragraph 11, except in respect of the new subsection (4A) in subparagraph (4);
paragraph 37, except in respect of the new subsection (11B) in subparagraph (5);
paragraph 70, except for the purpose of the giving of directions to any person to whom directions could not be given on 24th July 2003;
paragraph 73, except in respect of the new subsection (1B);
paragraph 147, except for the words "or of grant of recognised spectrum access" in subsection (1) of the new section 2, paragraph (b) of that subsection and the word "or" preceding that paragraph;
paragraph 150, except in respect of subsection (3) of the new section 6.

In Schedule 18, paragraphs 1 to 4, 7 to 19, 22 to 26, 30, 56 to 58, 63 and 64.

In Schedule 19 —
the entries for—
Telegraph Act 1899
Wireless Telegraphy Act 1949, sections 1D(1), (2) and (7), 1F, 3(1), 9, 10(2), 11(1), 14, 15(4)(c) and 19(9) and Schedule 2
Wireless Telegraphy Act 1949, section 1D(8) in respect of the words "and a reference to such notice shall also be published in the London, Edinburgh and Belfast Gazettes"
Army Act 1955
Air Force Act 1955
Naval Discipline Act 1957

Opencast Coal Act 1958
Continental Shelf Act 1964
Marine, &c., Broadcasting (Offences) Act 1967
British Telecommunications Act 1981
Acquisition of Land Act 1981
Telecommunications Act 1984, sections 2 to 53, 60 to 73, 92 to 98, 101(2)(a), 102, 104, 107 and 109 and Schedules 2 to 6
Telecommunications Act 1984, section 106(1), except in respect of the definition of "the Director"
Companies Consolidation (Consequential Provisions) Act 1985
Surrogacy Arrangements Act 1985
Interception of Communications Act 1985
Housing Act 1985
Airports Act 1986
Insolvency Act 1986
Consumer Protection Act 1987
Channel Tunnel Act 1987
Income and Corporation Taxes Act 1988
Legal Aid Act 1988
Copyright, Designs and Patents Act 1988, Schedule 7
Housing Act 1988
Electricity Act 1989
Companies Act 1989, Schedule 18
Planning (Consequential Provisions) Act 1990
Courts and Legal Services Act 1990
New Roads and Street Works Act 1991
Taxation of Chargeable Gains Act 1992
Charities Act 1992
Competition and Service (Utilities) Act 1992, except in respect of paragraph 3(b) of Schedule 1
Carriage of Goods by Sea Act 1992
Tribunals and Inquiries Act 1992
Judicial Pensions and Retirement Act 1993
Leasehold Reform, Housing and Urban Development Act 1993
Cardiff Bay Barrage Act 1993
Local Government (Wales) Act 1994
Vehicle Excise and Registration Act 1994
Criminal Justice and Public Order Act 1994
Deregulation and Contracting Out Act 1994, Schedule 4
Arbitration Act 1996
Channel Tunnel Rail Link Act 1996
Telecommunications (Fraud) Act 1997
Wireless Telegraphy Act 1998, section 1(3)
Wireless Telegraphy Act 1998, Schedule 1 in respect of paragraphs 2 and 3
Petroleum Act 1998
Competition Act 1998, Schedule 7, paragraph 2 and Schedules 10 and 13
Regional Development Agencies Act 1998
Access to Justice Act 1999
Electronic Communications Act 2000
Regulation of Investigatory Powers Act 2000
Countryside and Rights of Way Act 2000
Transport Act 2000, Schedule 8
Criminal Justice and Police Act 2001
Enterprise Act 2002, sections 136 and 168, Schedule 9 and Schedule 25, paragraph 13
Income Tax (Earnings and Pensions) Act 2003;

notes 1, 2, 4 and 5;

the entries for all of the instruments specified except the Race Relations (Northern Ireland) Order 1997.

[3513]

SCHEDULE 2

PROVISIONS COMING INTO FORCE ON 18TH SEPTEMBER 2003

Article 2(2)

Sections 5 (so far as not already in force), 28 to 30, 152(1), (3) and (9), 167, 179, 181, 184 and 348(2), (3) and (5) to (7).

Section 350(3) in respect of the provisions of Schedule 14 set out in this Schedule.

Section 360(3) in respect of the provisions of Schedule 15 set out in this Schedule.

Section 406(1), (6) and (7) in respect of the provisions of Schedules 17, 18 and 19 set out in this Schedule.

Section 407.

Schedule 2.

In Schedule 14, Part 4 and paragraph 17 so far as that paragraph relates to paragraph 16 of that Schedule.

In Schedule 15, paragraph 53(1) and (4).

In Schedule 17—

paragraphs 7, 18, 32, 33, 70 (so far as not already in force) and 149;

paragraph 150 in respect of subsection (3) of the new section 6, except for the words "or 3A".

In Schedule 18, paragraphs 21 and 54(1) to (4).

In Schedule 19, the entry for section 3 of the Wireless Telegraphy Act 1998.

[3514]

ADVANCED TELEVISION SERVICES REGULATIONS 2003

(SI 2003/1901)

NOTES

Made: 17 July 2003.
Authority: European Communities Act 1972, s 2(2).
Commencement: 25 July 2003.

ARRANGEMENT OF REGULATIONS

1 Citation and commencement

These Regulations may be cited as the Advanced Television Services Regulations 2003 and shall come into force on 25th July 2003.

[3515]

NOTES

Commencement: 25 July 2003.

2 Revocation and saving

(1) Save as provided in paragraph (2), the Advanced Television Services Regulations 1996 and the Advanced Television Services (Amendment) Regulations 1996 are hereby revoked.

(2) Regulations 1, 3, 6, 8(1), 9, 14, 15, 16 and 17 of, and Schedule 2 to, the Advanced Television Services Regulations 1996 shall remain in force in respect of television sets (within the meaning of regulation 6 thereof) and consumer equipment (within the meaning of regulation 9 thereof) which (in either case) were put on the market in any member State before 25th July 2003; and references in those Regulations to "the Director" shall be treated

as references to the Office of Communications from the time (or from the first time if there is more than one) at which the transitional period provided for in section 408 of the Communications Act 2003 ends in respect of a function to be carried on by the Director thereunder.

[3516]

NOTES

Commencement: 25 July 2003.

3 Interpretation

In these Regulations—

"analogue television set" means a television set which can receive and display analogue television signals;

"conditional access service" means a service which is provided over a conditional access system;

"conditional access system" has the meaning given by section 75(3) of the Communications Act 2003;

"digital television set" means a television set with an integrated decoder of digital television signals;

"electronic communications network" has the meaning given by section 32 of the Communications Act 2003;

"electronic communications service" has the meaning given by section 32 of the Communications Act 2003;

"public electronic communications network" has the meaning given by section 151(1) of the Communications Act 2003;

"rent out" in relation to any television set or other equipment means the first supplying of that set or equipment pursuant to the making of a rental agreement, and "offer for rent" and "expose for rent" ' shall be construed accordingly;

"sell" includes transfer by means of conditional sale or hire purchase, and "offer for sale" and "expose for sale" shall be construed accordingly;

"television programme" means any programme (with or without sounds) which—

(a) is produced wholly or partly to be seen on television; and

(b) consists of moving or still images or of legible text or of any combination of those things; and

"wide-screen television service" means a television service that consists wholly or partially of programmes produced and edited to be displayed with a [width-height ratio] of 16:9.

[3517]

NOTES

Commencement: 25 July 2003.

In definition "wide-screen television service" words in square brackets substituted by the Advanced Television Services (Amendment) Regulations 2003, SI 2003/2750, reg 2.

4 Wide-Screen Television Services

(1) Any person providing (within the meaning of section 32(4)(a) of the Communications Act 2003) a public electronic communications network established to distribute digital television services shall have a duty to ensure that it is capable of distributing wide-screen television services and television programmes.

(2) Any person who receives and redistributes television services or television programmes to the public shall have a duty to redistribute in wide-screen format all television services and television programmes he receives in that format.

(3) The duties in paragraphs (1) and (2) shall be enforced as if they were conditions set under section 45 of the Communications Act 2003.

[3518]

NOTES

Commencement: 25 July 2003.

5 The Common Scrambling Algorithm and the transmission of unscrambled images

(1) No person shall sell or rent out or otherwise make available, or offer or expose for sale or rent or otherwise for making available, any equipment to which this regulation applies unless that equipment possesses the capability—

(a) to allow the descrambling of signals according to the common European scrambling algorithm as administered by the European Telecommunications Standards Institute (ETSI); and

(b) to display television programmes that have been transmitted unscrambled: save that if the equipment is rented, this regulation applies only if the rentee is in compliance with the relevant rental agreement.

(2) This regulation applies to all consumer equipment intended for the reception of digital television signals and capable of descrambling such signals, except equipment which was put on the market in any member State before 25th July 2003.

[3519]

NOTES

Commencement: 25 July 2003.

6 Interoperability for analogue television sets

(1) No person shall sell or rent out, or offer or expose for sale or rent, an analogue television set to which this regulation applies unless it is fitted with at least one standardised open interface socket permitting the simple connection of peripherals.

(2) This regulation applies to any analogue television set with an integral viewing screen of visible diagonal greater than 42cm, except a television set which was put on the market in any member State before 25th July 2003.

(3) In this regulation—

"a standardised open interface socket" means an interface that would be recognised as such in all member States;

"peripherals" includes additional decoders and digital receivers.

[3520]

NOTES

Commencement: 25 July 2003.

7 Interoperability for digital television sets

(1) No person shall sell or rent out, or offer or expose for sale or rent, a digital television set to which this regulation applies unless it is fitted with at least one standardised open interface socket that permits the—

(a) simple connection of peripherals; and

(b) passage of all the elements of a digital television signal.

(2) This regulation applies to any digital television set with an integral viewing screen of visible diagonal greater than 30cm, except a television set which was put on the market in any member State before 25th July 2003.

(3) In this regulation—

"a standardised open interface socket" means an interface that would be recognised as such in all member States or conforms to an industry-wide specification;

"digital television signal" includes information relating to interactive and conditionally accessed services.

[3521]

NOTES

Commencement: 25 July 2003.

8 Enforcement

The Schedule to these Regulations shall have effect for the purposes of enforcement of regulations 5, 6 and 7.

[3522]

NOTES

Commencement: 25 July 2003.

SCHEDULE
ENFORCEMENT OF REGULATIONS 5, 6 AND 7

Regulation 8

Enforcement of the relevant provisions

1. This Schedule shall have effect for the purposes of providing for the enforcement of regulations 5(1), 6(1) and 7(1), and in this Schedule, each such provision is hereinafter referred to as a "relevant provision".

Enforcement authorities

2.—(1) It shall be the duty of the following authorities to enforce the relevant provisions—

(a) in Great Britain, a local weights and measures authority; and

(b) in Northern Ireland, the Department of Enterprise, Trade and Investment.

(2) The Secretary of State may enforce the relevant provisions.

(3) In this Schedule—

"enforcement authority" means any person who is, pursuant to the provisions of this paragraph, authorised to enforce the relevant provisions; and

"local weights and measures authority" has the meaning given by section 69 of the Weights and Measures Act 1985.

Test purchases

3.—(1) An enforcement authority shall have the power, for the purposes of ascertaining whether any equipment which is required to comply with a relevant provision does in fact so comply, to make, or authorise an officer of that authority to make, any purchase of equipment.

(2) Where—

(a) any equipment purchased pursuant to this paragraph by or on behalf of an enforcement authority is submitted to a test;

(b) the test leads to the bringing of forfeiture proceedings in respect of that equipment or equipment of the same description pursuant to paragraph 7 or 8 below; and

(c) the enforcement authority is requested to do so and it is practicable for that authority to comply with the request,

the enforcement authority shall allow the person from whom the equipment was purchased or any person who is a party to the proceedings or has an interest in any equipment to which the notice relates to have the apparatus tested.

(3) In this paragraph, "purchase" includes, where equipment is only available to rent, renting, and where consumer equipment capable of descrambling digital television signals is only made available by a method otherwise than by way of sale or rent, obtaining such equipment by that method, and cognate expressions shall be construed accordingly.

Powers of search etc

4.—(1) Subject to paragraph 5 below, a duly authorised officer of an enforcement authority may at any reasonable hour and on production, if required, of his credentials exercise any of the powers conferred by the following provisions of this paragraph.

(2) The officer may, for the purposes of ascertaining whether there has been a contravention of a relevant provision—

(a) inspect any equipment and enter any premises other than premises occupied only as a person's residence; or

(b) examine any procedure connected with the production of any equipment.

(3) If the officer has reasonable grounds for suspecting that there has been breach of a relevant provision, he may for the purpose of ascertaining (by testing or otherwise) whether there has been any such breach, or for the purposes of bringing proceedings for forfeiture under paragraph 8 or 9, seize and detain any equipment.

(4) The officer may seize and detain—

(a) any document, record or information or any other thing which he has reasonable grounds for believing may be required—

(i) as evidence in proceedings for forfeiture under paragraph 8 or 9; or

(ii) by the authorities of a member State other than the United Kingdom for the purposes of the exercise of their functions with regard to the Universal Service Directive;

(b) any equipment which he has reasonable grounds for suspecting may be liable to be forfeited.

(5) The officer may, for the purposes of the exercise of his powers under subparagraph (3) or (4) above to seize any equipment, any document, record or information or any other thing—

(a) require any person having authority to do so to open any container; and

(b) himself open or break open any such container where a requirement made under subparagraph (a) above in relation to the container has not been complied with.

(6) In this paragraph, "Universal Service Directive" means Directive 2002/22/EC of the European Parliament and of the Council on universal service and users' rights relating to electronic communications networks and services.

Provisions supplemental to paragraph 4

5.—(1) An officer seizing any equipment, document, record or information or any other thing under paragraph 4 above shall inform the person from whom it is seized that such equipment, document, record or information or other thing has been so seized.

(2) If a justice of the peace—

(a) is satisfied by any written information on oath that there are reasonable grounds for believing either—

(i) that any equipment, document, record or information or any other thing which any officer has power to inspect under paragraph 4 above is on any premises (which may be premises occupied only as a person's residence) and that such inspection is likely to disclose evidence that there has been a contravention of a relevant provision; or

(ii) that such a contravention has taken place, is taking place or is about to take place on any premises; and

(b) is also satisfied by any such information either—

(i) that admission to the premises has been or is likely to be refused and that notice of an intention to apply for a warrant under this subparagraph has been given to the occupier; or

(ii) that an application for admission, or the giving of such a notice, would defeat the object of the entry or that the premises are unoccupied or that the occupier is temporarily absent and it might defeat the object of the entry to await his return,

the justice may by warrant under his hand, which shall continue in force for one month, authorise any officer of an enforcement authority to enter the premises, if need be by force.

(3) An officer entering any premises by virtue of paragraph 4 above or a warrant under subparagraph (2) of this paragraph may take with him such other persons and such equipment as may appear to him to be necessary.

(4) On leaving any premises which a person is authorised to enter by a warrant under subparagraph (2) of this paragraph, that person shall, if the premises are unoccupied or the occupier is temporarily absent, leave the premises as effectively secured against trespassers as he found them.

(5) Where any equipment seized by an officer under paragraph 4 above is submitted to a test, the officer shall inform the person mentioned in subparagraph (1) of this paragraph of the result of the test and, if—

(a) proceedings are brought in respect of a contravention of a relevant provision for the forfeiture of the equipment concerned; and

(b) the officer is requested to do so and it is practicable to comply with the request,

the officer shall allow any person who is a party to the proceedings or has an interest in the equipment to have the equipment tested.

(6) In the application of this paragraph to Scotland, the reference in subparagraph (2) above to a justice of the peace shall include a reference to a sheriff and the references to written information on oath shall be construed as references to evidence on oath.

(7) In the application of this paragraph to Northern Ireland, the references in subparagraph (2) above to any information on oath shall be construed as references to any complaint on oath.

Exception from paragraphs 4 and 5

6. Nothing in paragraph 4 or 5 above shall be taken to authorise the taking of any action in relation to any equipment which has been sold or rented out or otherwise made available as the case may be to any person who has physically taken delivery of the equipment; but—

(a) this is without prejudice to the taking of any other action authorised by this Schedule in relation to such equipment by an enforcement authority or an officer of such authority; and

(b) nothing in this Schedule shall prevent a person to whom equipment has been sold, rented out or otherwise made available from taking any action or bringing any proceedings which he might otherwise take or bring.

Appeals against detention of equipment

7.—(1) Any person having an interest in any equipment, document, record, information or other thing, which is for the time being detained under any provision of this Schedule by an enforcement authority or by an officer of such an authority, may apply for an order requiring such item to be released to him or to another person.

(2) An application under this paragraph may be made—

(a) to any magistrates' court in which proceedings for forfeiture have been brought in England and Wales or Northern Ireland; or

(b) where no such proceedings have been brought, by way of complaint to a magistrates' court.

(3) On an application under this paragraph to a magistrates' court, an order requiring equipment to be released shall be made only if the court is satisfied—

(a) that proceedings for the forfeiture of the equipment under paragraph 8 or 9 have not been brought, or, having been brought, have been concluded without the equipment being forfeited; and

(b) where no such proceedings have been brought, that more than six months have elapsed since the equipment was seized.

(4) Subparagraphs (1) to (3) apply to Scotland with the substitution for references to the magistrates' court of references to the sheriff; and application to the sheriff is by way of summary application.

(5) Any person aggrieved by an order made under this paragraph by a magistrates' court in England and Wales or Northern Ireland, or by a decision of such a court not to make such an order, may appeal against that order or decision—

(a) in England and Wales, to the Crown Court;

(b) in Northern Ireland, to the county court;

and an order so made may contain such provision as appears to the court appropriate for delaying the coming into force of the order pending the making and determination of any appeal (including any application under section 111 of the Magistrates' Courts Act 1980 or article 146 of the Magistrates' Courts (Northern Ireland) Order 1981.

(6) In Scotland appeal shall lie—

(a) to the sheriff principal from the decision of the sheriff; and

(b) with leave of the sheriff principal, to the Court of Session from the decision of the sheriff principal.

Proceedings in England and Wales or Northern Ireland for forfeiture

8.—(1) Where in England and Wales or Northern Ireland any equipment has been seized and detained by an officer of an enforcement authority pursuant to paragraph 4, an officer of that authority may apply to a justice of the peace [acting in] the [local justice area] in which the equipment was seized (referred to below in this paragraph as the relevant [local justice area]) to initiate proceedings for forfeiture of the equipment under this paragraph.

(2) An application under this paragraph must be made within the period of six months beginning with the date on which the equipment to which it relates was seized.

(3) A justice of the peace to whom an application under this paragraph is made may issue a summons to any person appearing to him to be the owner of or otherwise interested in any equipment to which the application relates requiring him to appear on a day specified in the summons before a magistrates' court [acting in the relevant local justice area] to show cause why the equipment should not be forfeited.

(4) In addition to the person summoned, any other person claiming to be the owner of or otherwise interested in any equipment to which an application under this paragraph relates shall be entitled to appear before the court on the day specified in the summons to show cause why it should not be forfeited.

(5) Where any equipment is brought before a magistrates' court in proceedings under this paragraph the court can only order forfeiture to the enforcement authority if—

(a) the court is satisfied that the equipment contravenes the relevant provision;

(b) any person summoned under subparagraph (3) appears before the court, or service of the summons is proved; and

(c) the court is satisfied that there is no good reason why it should not order forfeiture.

(6) Where in any proceedings under this paragraph an order is made for the forfeiture of any equipment, any person who appeared, or who was entitled to appear, to show cause against the making of the order may appeal to the Crown Court.

(7) No order for the forfeiture of any equipment made under this paragraph shall take effect—

(a) until the end of the period of twenty-one days after the day on which the order is made; or

(b) if appeal proceedings are brought in respect of the order within that period (whether by way of appeal to the Crown Court or by way of case stated for the opinion of the High Court), until the conclusion of those proceedings.

(8) If a magistrates' court does not order forfeiture of any equipment brought before it in proceedings under this paragraph the court may if it thinks fit order the person on whose application the proceedings were initiated to pay such costs as the court thinks reasonable to any person who has appeared before the court to show cause why the equipment should not be forfeited; and costs ordered to be paid under this subparagraph shall be enforceable as a civil debt.

(9) Any equipment ordered to be forfeited under this paragraph may be disposed of by the enforcement authority concerned in such manner as it thinks fit.

(10) This paragraph has effect notwithstanding anything in section 140 of the Magistrates' Courts Act 1980 or article 58 of the Magistrates' Courts (Northern Ireland) Order 1981 (disposal of non-pecuniary forfeitures).

(11) In the application of this paragraph to Northern Ireland references to a [local justice area] shall be read as references to a petty sessions district.

(12) This paragraph applies to England and Wales and Northern Ireland only.

Proceedings for forfeiture in Scotland

9.—(1) Where in Scotland any equipment has been seized and detained by an officer of an enforcement authority pursuant to paragraph 4 above, the enforcement authority may apply to the sheriff for forfeiture of the equipment under this paragraph.

(2) An application to the sheriff under subparagraph (1) shall be made by summary application and must be made within the period of six months beginning with the date on which the equipment to which it relates was seized.

(3) Where an application is made under this paragraph and the sheriff is satisfied that the equipment breaches the relevant provision, the sheriff shall order the equipment to be forfeited to the enforcement authority concerned, unless cause is shown why the equipment should not be forfeited.

(4) Any equipment ordered to be forfeited under this paragraph may be disposed of by the enforcement authority concerned in such manner as it thinks fit.

(5) This paragraph applies to Scotland only.

Power of the court to require matter to be remedied

10.—(1) Where an application is made for the forfeiture of any equipment in respect of any matters which appear to the court or sheriff as the case may be to be matters which it is in the power of any person to remedy who appears or who is entitled to appear to show cause why such equipment should not be forfeited, the court or sheriff may, instead of ordering the equipment to be forfeited, order him, within such time as may be fixed by the order, to take such steps as may be specified in the order for remedying the said matters.

(2) The time fixed by an order under subparagraph (1) may be extended or further extended by order of the court or sheriff on an application made before the end of that time as originally fixed or as extended under this subparagraph as the case may be.

Recovery of expenses of enforcement

11.—(1) This paragraph applies where a court or sheriff as the case may be makes an order under paragraph 8, 9 or 10.

(2) The court or sheriff may (in addition to any other order it may make as to costs) order the person appearing to be the owner of or otherwise interested in the equipment or from whom the equipment was seized, to reimburse the enforcement authority for any expenditure which has been or may be incurred by that authority—

(a) in investigating the contravention, and, without prejudice to the generality of the foregoing, in having the equipment tested; or

(b) in connection with any seizure or detention of the equipment by or on behalf of the authority.

Application in England and Wales of certain provisions of the Police and Criminal Evidence Act 1984

12.—(1) Whilst nothing in these Regulations shall be taken as providing that a contravention of a relevant provision constitutes a criminal offence, sections 15, 16, 20 and 21 of the Police and Criminal Evidence Act 1984 shall apply to the exercise by an officer of an enforcement authority of the powers conferred by this Schedule as they apply to a constable.

(2) This paragraph applies to England and Wales only.

Application in Northern Ireland of certain provisions of the Police and Criminal Evidence (Northern Ireland) Order 1989

13.—(1) Whilst nothing in these Regulations shall be taken as providing that a contravention of a relevant provision constitutes a criminal offence, articles 17, 18, 22 and 23 of the Police and Criminal Evidence (Northern Ireland) Order 1989 shall apply to the exercise by an officer of an enforcement authority of the powers conferred by this Schedule as they apply to a constable.

(2) This paragraph applies to Northern Ireland only.

Interpretation

14. In this Schedule—

"document, record or information" includes any computer disk or other electronic, magnetic or electromagnetic means upon which the document, record or information is or is reasonably believed to be stored;

"equipment" means—

(a) in relation to the enforcement of regulation 5, consumer equipment capable of descrambling digital television signals;

(b) in relation to the enforcement of regulation 6, an analogue television set;

(c) in relation to the enforcement of regulation 7, a digital television set;

"forfeiture" means forfeiture under paragraph 7 above, and "forfeited" shall be construed accordingly; and

"premises" includes any place and, in particular, includes—

(a) any vehicle, vessel, aircraft or hovercraft;

(b) any offshore installation; and

(c) any tent or movable structure,

and in this definition, "offshore installation" has the meaning given to it in Great Britain by regulation 3 of the Offshore Installations and Pipeline Works (Management and

Administration) Regulations 1995 and in Northern Ireland by regulation 3 of the Offshore Installations and Pipeline Works (Management and Administration) Regulations (Northern Ireland) 1995.

[3523]

NOTES

Commencement: 25 July 2003.

Para 8: words in square brackets in sub-paras (1), (3), (11) substituted by the Courts Act 2003 (Consequential Provisions) (No 2) Order 2005, SI 2005/617, art 2, Schedule, para 218.

WIRELESS TELEGRAPHY (LIMITATION OF NUMBER OF LICENCES) ORDER 2003

(SI 2003/1902)

NOTES

Made: 17 July 2003.

Authority: Communications Act 2003, s 164(1)–(3).

Commencement: 25 July 2003.

ARRANGEMENT OF ARTICLES

1 Citation and commencement

This Order may be cited as the Wireless Telegraphy (Limitation of Number of Licences) Order 2003 and shall come into force on 25th July 2003.

[3524]

NOTES

Commencement: 25 July 2003.

2 Interpretation

... In this Order—

["OFCOM" means the Office of Communications;]

"the Radio Regulations" means the 2001 edition of the Radio Regulations made under Article 13 of the Constitution of the International Telecommunication Union; and

"wireless telegraphy licence" means any licence granted under section 1 of the Wireless Telegraphy Act 1949 other than a television licence as defined in section 1(7) of that Act.

[3525]

NOTES

Commencement: 25 July 2003.

Reference to "(1)" (omitted) revoked and definition "OFCOM" substituted for original definition "RA" by the Wireless Telegraphy (Limitation of Number of Licences) (Amendment) Order 2006, SI 2006/2786, art 2, Schedule, para 1.

3 Wireless telegraphy licences to be limited in number

[OFCOM] will grant only a limited number of wireless telegraphy licences at the frequencies and for the uses specified in Part 1 of each of Schedules 1 to 11 to this Order.

[3526]

NOTES

Commencement: 25 July 2003.

Word in square brackets substituted by the Wireless Telegraphy (Limitation of Number of Licences) (Amendment) Order 2006, SI 2006/2786, art 2, Schedule, para 2.

4 Criteria for limiting the number of wireless telegraphy licences

... [OFCOM] shall in relation to the frequencies and uses set out in Part 1 of each of Schedules 1 to 11—

(a) apply the criteria relating to the persons to whom wireless telegraphy licences may be granted specified in Part 2 of the Schedule concerned;

(b) apply the criteria limiting the number of wireless telegraphy licences specified in Part 3 of the Schedule concerned; and

(c) take into account the ability of each applicant for a wireless telegraphy licence to meet the licence terms, provisions and limitations applying to that wireless telegraphy licence,

in determining the limit on the number of wireless telegraphy licences to be granted and the persons to whom wireless telegraphy licences will be granted.

[3527]

NOTES

Commencement: 25 July 2003.

Reference to "(1)" (omitted) revoked and word in square brackets substituted by the Wireless Telegraphy (Limitation of Number of Licences) (Amendment) Order 2006, SI 2006/2786, art 2, Schedule, para 3.

SCHEDULE 1
BROADCASTING

Articles 3 and 4

PART 1
FREQUENCIES ALLOCATED TO BROADCASTING USE

Transmission of Terrestrial UHF Analogue TV Services and Digital TV Multiplexes

470.0–854.0 MHz

Transmission of National and Local Radio Broadcasting Services

148.5–283.5 kHz (LW)

526.5–1605.5 kHz (MW)

87.5–108.0 MHz (FM)

217.5–230.0 MHz (T-DAB)

[Community Radio

148.5–283.5 kHz (LW)

526.5–1605.5 kHz (MW)

87.5–108.0 MHz (FM)

217.5–230.0 MHz (T-DAB)]

Restricted Radio Services Transmission (Class A—Freely Radiating)

Restricted Radio Services Transmission (Class B—Radiating Cable)

Restricted Radio Services Transmission (Class C[—Freely] Radiating Very Low Power)

526.5–1605.5 kHz

87.5–108.0 MHz

[3528]

NOTES

Commencement: 25 July 2003.

Entry "Community Radio", and word in square brackets in entry beginning "Restricted Radio Services Transmission (Class C" inserted by the Wireless Telegraphy (Limitation of Number of Licences) (Amendment) Order 2006, SI 2006/2786, art 2, Schedule, para 4.

PART 2
CRITERIA RELATING TO PERSONS TO WHOM WIRELESS TELEGRAPHY LICENCES MAY BE GRANTED

1. The frequencies are assigned only to the British Broadcasting Corporation (BBC) and persons who possess one of the following Broadcasting Act licences:

(a) Terrestrial Analogue TV Services under Part I of the Broadcasting Act 1990 or under Part III of the Broadcasting Act 1996;

(b) Digital TV Multiplexes under Part I of the Broadcasting Act 1996;

(c) Terrestrial National and Local Analogue Radio Broadcasting Services under Part III of the Broadcasting Act 1990;

(d) Digital Radio Multiplexes under Part II of the Broadcasting Act 1996; …

(e) Restricted Radio Services Transmission (Class A, B and C) under Part III of the Broadcasting Act 1990[; and

(f) Community Radio Licence under Section 262 of the Communications Act 2003].

[3529]

NOTES

Commencement: 25 July 2003.

Word omitted from para (d) revoked, and para (f) and word immediately preceding it inserted by the Wireless Telegraphy (Limitation of Number of Licences) (Amendment) Order 2006, SI 2006/2786, art 2, Schedule, para 5.

PART 3
CRITERIA LIMITING NUMBER OF WIRELESS TELEGRAPHY LICENCES

2. The availability of wireless telegraphy licences is limited at these frequencies by the technical frequency assignment criteria set out in the Technical Frequency Assignment Criteria for Television and Sound Broadcasting published by [OFCOM].

3. Applicants must undertake to use the assigned frequencies solely for the transmission and reception of signals as part of the broadcasting service as defined in Article 1.38 of the Radio Regulations.

[3530]–[3533]

NOTES

Commencement: 25 July 2003.

Para 2: word in square brackets substituted by the Wireless Telegraphy (Limitation of Number of Licences) (Amendment) Order 2006, SI 2006/2786, art 2, Schedule, para 6.

(*Sch 2 revoked by the Wireless Telegraphy* (*Limitation of Number of Licences*) (*Amendment*) *Order 2006, SI 2006/2786, art 2, Schedule, para 7.*)

SCHEDULE 3
PROGRAMME MAKING AND SPECIAL EVENTS

Articles 3 and 4

[PART 1
FREQUENCIES ALLOCATED TO PROGRAMME MAKING AND SPECIAL EVENTS USE

Programme Making and Special Events Fixed Site

47.5–86.9 MHz	1488–1525 MHz	10.3–12.5 GHz
139.5–224.5 MHz	2025–2690 MHz	24.25–24.5 GHz
425.3–862.0 MHz	3400–8500 MHz	48.0–48.4 GHz

Programme Making and Special Events Link

47.5–86.9 MHz	1488–1525 MHz	10.3–12.5 GHz
139.5–224.5 MHz	2025–2690 MHz	24.25–24.5 GHz
425.3–862.0 MHz	3400–8500 MHz	48.0–48.4 GHz

Programme Making and Special Events Low Power

47.5–86.9 MHz	1488–1525 MHz	10.3–12.5 GHz
139.5–224.5 MHz	2025–2690 MHz	24.25–24.5 GHz
425.3–862.0 MHz	3400–8500 MHz	48.0–48.4 GHz

UK Wireless Microphone (Annual)
UK Wireless Microphone (Biennial)

175.1–176.7 MHz	199.6–200.7 MHz	216.0–216.9 MHz
191.8–193.1 MHz	208.2–209.1 MHz	854.2–862.0 MHz]

[3534]

NOTES

Commencement: 25 July 2003.

Substituted by the Wireless Telegraphy (Limitation of Number of Licences) (Amendment) Order 2006, SI 2006/2786, art 2, Schedule, para 8.

PART 2
CRITERIA RELATING TO PERSONS TO WHOM WIRELESS TELEGRAPHY LICENCES MAY BE GRANTED

1. None.

[3535]

NOTES

Commencement: 25 July 2003.

PART 3
CRITERIA LIMITING NUMBER OF WIRELESS TELEGRAPHY LICENCES

2. The [availability] of wireless telegraphy licences at these frequencies is limited by the technical frequency assignment criteria set out in Technical Frequency Assignment Criteria [and] Programme Making and Special Events published by [OFCOM].

3. All applications for licences are considered (and the technical frequency assignment criteria applied) in the order of receipt of each correctly completed application form except for the UK Wireless Microphone (Annual) Licence and the UK Wireless Microphone (Biennial) Licence for which the technical frequency assignment criteria do not limit the number of licences.

[3536]–[3539]

NOTES

Commencement: 25 July 2003.

Para 2: words in square brackets substituted by the Wireless Telegraphy (Limitation of Number of Licences) (Amendment) Order 2006, SI 2006/2786, art 2, Schedule, para 9.

(*Sch 4 revoked by the Wireless Telegraphy* (*Limitation of Number of Licences*) (*Amendment*) *Order 2006, SI 2006/2786, art 2, Schedule, para 10.*)

SCHEDULE 5
[FIXED LINKS]

Articles 3 and 4

NOTES

Schedule heading substituted by the Wireless Telegraphy (Limitation of Number of Licences) (Amendment) Order 2006, SI 2006/2786, art 2, Schedule, para 11.

PART 1
FREQUENCIES ALLOCATED TO FIXED … LINKS USE

Point-to-Point Fixed Links

1350–1517 MHz	12.75–13.25 GHz	24.50–26.50 GHz
3600–4200 MHz	…	31.80–33.40 GHz
5925–6425 MHz	14.50–15.35 GHz	37.00–39.50 GHz
6425–7125 MHz	17.70–19.70 GHz	51.40–52.60 GHz
7425–7900 MHz	22.00–23.60 GHz	55.78–57.00 GHz
		[64.00–66.00 GHz]

[Point-to-Point Security CCTV Services

31.00–31.80 GHz]

[Self Co-ordinated Links

65.00 GHz]

Scanning Telemetry

457.50–464.00 MHz

[3540]

NOTES

Commencement: 25 July 2003.

Words omitted from Part heading revoked, in entry "Point-to-Point Fixed Links" reference omitted revoked and reference in square brackets inserted, entry "Point-to-Point Security CCTV Services" substituted, and entry "Self Co-ordinated Links" inserted by the Wireless Telegraphy (Limitation of Number of Licences) (Amendment) Order 2006, SI 2006/2786, art 2, Schedule, para 12.

PART 2
CRITERIA RELATING TO PERSONS TO WHOM WIRELESS TELEGRAPHY LICENCES MAY BE GRANTED

1. An applicant cannot be a person whose entitlement to provide electronic communications networks or electronic communications services, or to make associated facilities available is suspended or restricted under the Communications Act 2003.

[3541]

NOTES

Commencement: 25 July 2003.

PART 3
CRITERIA LIMITING NUMBER OF WIRELESS TELEGRAPHY LICENCES

[2. Except in the case of Self Co-ordinated Links, the availability of wireless telegraphy licences is limited at these frequencies by the technical frequency assignment criteria set out in the OFCOM publications applying to the frequencies concerned.]

3. All applications for licences are considered (and the technical frequency assignment criteria applied) in the order of receipt of each correctly completed application form.

4. Applicants must undertake to use the assigned frequencies solely for the transmission and reception of signals as part of the "fixed service" as defined in Article 1.20 of the Radio Regulations.

[3542]

NOTES

Commencement: 25 July 2003.

Para 2: substituted by the Wireless Telegraphy (Limitation of Number of Licences) (Amendment) Order 2006, SI 2006/2786, art 2, Schedule, para 13.

SCHEDULE 6
SATELLITE SERVICES

Articles 3 and 4

[PART 1
FREQUENCIES OF OPERATION FOR SATELLITE SERVICES

Satellite (Permanent Earth Station)

3600–4200 MHz

5150–5250 MHz

5725–7075 MHz

10.70–11.70 GHz

12.50–13.25 GHz

13.75–14.50 GHz

17.30–20.20 GHz

27.05–30.00 GHz

Satellite (Earth Station—Non-Geostationary)

137–138 MHz	5150–5250 MHz	17.30–18.40 GHz
149–149.9 MHz	5725–7075 MHz	19.70–20.20 GHz
2025–2110 MHz	10.70–11.70 GHz	27.50–30.00 GHz
2200–2290 MHz	12.50–13.25 GHz	
3600–4200 MHz	13.75–14.50 GHz	

Satellite (Earth Station—Non-Fixed Satellite Service)

All frequency bands available for Satellite Services as defined within the United Kingdom Frequency Allocation Table (excluding those specified for the Fixed Satellite Service).

Satellite (Transportable Earth Station)

Satellite (Transportable Very Small Aperture Terminal)

14.00–14.50 GHz

Satellite (Earth Station Network)

12.50–12.75 GHz

14.00–14.50 GHz

19.70–20.20 GHz

29.50–30.00 GHz

Satellite (Aircraft Earth Station)

Satellite (Earth Station on Board Vessel)

Satellite (Earth Station on Train)

14.00–14.25 GHz (Earth to Space)]

[3543]

NOTES

Commencement: 25 July 2003.

Substituted by the Wireless Telegraphy (Limitation of Number of Licences) (Amendment) Order 2006, SI 2006/2786, art 2, Schedule, para 14.

PART 2
CRITERIA RELATING TO PERSONS TO WHOM WIRELESS TELEGRAPHY LICENCES MAY BE GRANTED

1. An applicant cannot be a person whose entitlement to provide electronic communications networks or electronic communications services, or to make associated facilities available is suspended or restricted under the Communications Act 2003.

[3544]

NOTES

Commencement: 25 July 2003.

PART 3
CRITERIA LIMITING NUMBER OF WIRELESS TELEGRAPHY LICENCES

[2. The availability of Satellite (Permanent Earth Station) Licences, Satellite (Earth Station—Non-Geostationary) Licences, Satellite (Earth Station—Non-fixed Satellite Service) Licences, Satellite (Transportable Earth Station) Licences, Satellite (Aircraft Earth Station), Satellite (Earth Station on Board Vessel), Satellite (Earth Station on Train) and Satellite (Earth Station Network) Licences is limited at any particular location at these frequencies by the relevant technical frequency assignment criteria set out in OFCOM publications.]

3. All applications for licences are considered (and any technical frequency assignment criteria applied) in the order of receipt of each correctly completed application form.

[3545]

NOTES

Commencement: 25 July 2003.

Para 2: substituted by the Wireless Telegraphy (Limitation of Number of Licences) (Amendment) Order 2006, SI 2006/2786, art 2, Schedule, para 15.

SCHEDULE 7
MARITIME

Articles 3 and 4

PART 1
FREQUENCIES ALLOCATED TO MARITIME USE

Coastal Station Radio [(UK)]

156.00–163.00 MHz

Coastal Station Radio (Marina)

[157.025 MHz (Ship)

157.850 MHz (Ship and Coastal Station Radio)

161.425 MHz (Ship and Coastal Station Radio)

161.625 MHz (Coastal Station Radio)]

Coastal Station Radio (International)

156.00–162.05 MHz

Coastal Station Radio [(International)] (Training School)

This licence is used for non-operational training purposes and the equipment radiates minimum power confined to the building or site. The licence is therefore only for use at frequencies that are allocated to the Coastal Station Radio to agreed specifications.

Differential Global Positioning System

[283.5–315.0 kHz

1606.5–4000 kHz]

Ship Portable Radio

121.5 MHz	156.00–162.05 MHz	406.0–406.1 MHz
121.5 and 123.1 MHz	243.0 MHz	1645.5–1646.5 MHz

[Maritime Navigational Aids and Radar

283.5–315.0 kHz

2900–3100 MHz

9300–9500 MHz

Automatic Identification System

156.525 MHz

161.975 MHz

162.025 MHz]

Maritime Radio (Suppliers and Demonstration)

283.5–315.0 kHz	243.0 MHz	467.575 MHz
[415.0–526.5 kHz]	406.0–406.1 MHz	467.5375 MHz
1606.5–27500 kHz	457.525 MHz	467.5625 MHz
121.5 MHz	457.5375 MHz	1626.5–1660.5 MHz
121.65 MHz	457.55 MHz	(with associated
121.5 and 123.1 MHz	457.5625 MHz	downlink frequencies:
156.00–163.0 MHz	457.575 MHz	1525–1559 MHz)
162.4375–162.4625 MHz	467.525 MHz	2900–3100 MHz
163.0125–163.03125 MHz	467.550 MHz	9200–9500 MHz

Ship Radio

415–526.5 kHz	[457.525 MHz]	467.575 MHz
1605–27500 kHz	457.5375 MHz	467.5375 MHz
121.5 MHz	457.55 MHz	[467.5625 MHz]
121.5 and 123.1 MHz	[457.5625 MHz]	2900–3100 MHz
156.00–162.05 MHz	457.575 MHz	9300–9500 MHz
243.0 MHz	467.525 MHz	1626.5–1660.5 MHz (with associated downlink
406.0–406.1 MHz	467.550 MHz	frequencies: 1525–1559 MHz)

[3546]

NOTES

Commencement: 25 July 2003.

Words in first and third pairs of square brackets inserted, and other words and references in square brackets substituted by the Wireless Telegraphy (Limitation of Number of Licences) (Amendment) Order 2006, SI 2006/2786, art 2, Schedule, para 16.

PART 2
CRITERIA RELATING TO PERSONS TO WHOM WIRELESS TELEGRAPHY LICENCES MAY BE GRANTED

1. An applicant who intends to operate on international channels must possess a Maritime Radio Operators Certificate of Competence (including a valid Authority to Operate) issued by the Maritime and Coastguard Agency on behalf of the Secretary of State.

2. An applicant for a Coastal Station Radio [(UK)] Licence must intend to use the assigned frequency solely to communicate with vessels on commercial matters using a private maritime channel and port operation and control.

3. An applicant for a Coastal Station Radio (Marina) Licence must be a yacht club, marina or similar organisation and must undertake to transmit solely for the purpose of communications concerning the movement and berthing of pleasure craft and to control races.

4. An applicant for a Coastal Station Radio (International) Licence must be intending to operate ports or harbours for port operations and ship movements.

5. An applicant for a Ship Radio Licence must be the owner or operator of a British-registered vessel as required by Part 1 of the Merchant Shipping Act 1995.

6. An applicant for a Maritime Radio (Navigational Aids and Radar) Licence [or an Automatic Identification System Licence] must have an official position in the operation of ports or harbours, and be responsible for ship movement or coastal surveillance.

7. An applicant for a Maritime Radio (Suppliers and Demonstration) Licence must be engaged in the manufacture, development, repair or supply of maritime radio equipment.

[3547]

NOTES

Commencement: 25 July 2003.

Paras 2, 6: words in square brackets inserted by the Wireless Telegraphy (Limitation of Number of Licences) (Amendment) Order 2006, SI 2006/2786, art 2, Schedule, para 17.

PART 3
CRITERIA LIMITING NUMBER OF WIRELESS TELEGRAPHY LICENCES

[8. Applicants must undertake to use the assigned frequencies solely for the transmission and reception of signals as part of the maritime mobile, (including satellite) and radio navigation services as defined in Article 1 of the Radio Regulations.]

9. The availability of the Coastal Station Radio [(UK)] Licence, Coastal Station Radio (Marina) Licence, Coastal Station Radio (International) Licence and Differential Global Positioning System Licence is limited in any particular location at these frequencies by the technical frequency assignment criteria set out in [Coastal Station Radio OFCOM information booklet published by OFCOM].

[9A. The availability of Automatic Identification System Licences is limited in any particular location at these frequencies by the availability of time slots.]

10. All applications for licences are considered (and any technical frequency assignment criteria applied) in the order of receipt of each correctly completed application form.

[3548]

NOTES

Commencement: 25 July 2003.

Para 8: substituted by the Wireless Telegraphy (Limitation of Number of Licences) (Amendment) Order 2006, SI 2006/2786, art 2, Schedule, para 18(a).

Para 9: word in first pair of square brackets inserted and words in second pair of square brackets substituted by SI 2006/2786, art 2, Schedule, para 18(b).

Para 9A: inserted by SI 2006/2786, art 2, Schedule, para 18(c).

SCHEDULE 8
AERONAUTICAL

Articles 3 and 4

PART 1
FREQUENCIES ALLOCATED TO AERONAUTICAL USE

Aircraft

…

2850–3025 kHz	17900–17970 kHz	5350–5470 MHz
3400–3500 kHz	21924–22000 kHz	9300–9500 MHz
4650–4700 kHz	117.975–137.000 MHz	13250–13400 MHz
5480–5680 kHz	… , 243 and 406–406.1 MHz	15500–15700 MHz
6525–6685 kHz	960–1215 MHz	
8815–8965 kHz	1626.5–1660.5 MHz	
[10005–10100 kHz]	…	
11275–11400 kHz	1525–1559 MHz …	
13260–13360 kHz	4200–4400 MHz	

[Aircraft (Transportable)

117.975–137.000 MHz]

[Aeronautical Ground Station (Air Traffic/Ground Movement Control)

[Aeronautical Ground Station (Air/Ground Communications Services)

Aeronautical Ground Station (Airfield Flight Information Service)

117.975–137.000 MHz]

Aeronautical Ground Station (General Aviation)

129.900 MHz, 130.100 MHz, 130.125 MHz, 130.400 MHz (Glider Ground Station (Standard))

129.975 (Glider Ground Station (Common Field Frequency))

122.475 MHz (Balloon Ground Station)

130.525 MHz, 129.900 MHz (Parachute Ground Station)

129.825 MHz (Microlight Ground Station)

118.675 MHz (Hang Gliders/Paragliders)

…

[Aeronautical Ground Station (Fire)

121.600 MHz]

Aeronautical Ground Station (High Frequency)

2850–3025 kHz	6524–6685 kHz	13260–13360 kHz
3400–3500 kHz	8815–8965 kHz	17900–17970 kHz
4650–4700 kHz	10005–10100 kHz	21924–22000 kHz
5480–5680 kHz	11275–11400 kHz	

Aeronautical Ground Station (Offshore Platform)

117.975–137.000 MHz]

[Aeronautical Navigation Aid Stations

255.0–495 kHz	108.000–117.975 MHz
505–526.5 kHz	328.6–335.4 MHz
74.8–75.2 MHz	960–1215 MHz
	5000–5250 MHz]

[Aeronautical Radar

1030 MHz	2700–3100 MHz

1090 MHz
1215–1350 MHz
9000–9200 MHz
9300–9500 MHz
15400–15700 MHz]

[Aeronautical Ground Station (Operations Controls)
117.975–137.000 MHz]

[3549]

NOTES

Commencement: 25 July 2003.

Words omitted revoked, and words in square brackets substituted and inserted by the Wireless Telegraphy (Limitation of Number of Licences) (Amendment) Order 2006, SI 2006/2786, art 2, Schedule, para 19.

PART 2
CRITERIA RELATING TO PERSONS TO WHOM WIRELESS TELEGRAPHY LICENCES MAY BE GRANTED

Aircraft Licence (including Aircraft (Transportable))

1. An applicant must undertake to use the radio equipment in an aircraft or similar airborne apparatus.

2. An applicant must possess a Flight Radiotelephony Operators Certificate of Competence issued by the Secretary of State under Article 21 of the Air Navigation Order 2000. This is issued by the Civil Aviation Authority (CAA) on behalf of the Secretary of State.

3. An applicant who is a glider pilot and who undertakes to operate only on the nominated glider frequencies is exempt from the requirement in paragraph 2 of Part 2 of this Schedule.

[Aeronautical Ground Station (Air Traffic/Ground Movement Control)]

4. An applicant must be in an official position in an air traffic control capacity.

5. An applicant must prove that the equipment he intends to use under an Aeronautical Ground Station Air Traffic/Ground Movement Control Licence is an aeronautical [communications] installation assessed as fit for purpose under the Air Navigation Order 2000 by the Civil Aviation Authority's Air Traffic Safety Standards Department.

[Aeronautical Ground Station (Air/Ground Communication Services)]

6. …

7. An applicant must prove that the equipment he intends to use under an [Aeronautical Ground Station (Air/Ground Communication Services) Licence] is an aeronautical [communications] installation assessed as fit for purpose under the Air Navigation Order 2000 by the Civil Aviation Authority's Air Traffic Safety Standards Department.

[Aeronautical Ground Station (Airfield Flight Information Service)]

8. An applicant must prove that the equipment he intends to use under an [Aeronautical Ground Station (Airfield Flight Information Service) Licence] is an aeronautical [communications] installation assessed as fit for purpose under the Air Navigation Order 2000 by the Civil Aviation Authority's Air Traffic Safety Standards Department.

[Aeronautical Ground Station (General Aviation)

8A. An applicant must prove that the equipment he intends to use under an Aeronautical Ground Station (General Aviation) Licence is an aeronautical communications installation assessed as fit for purpose under the Air Navigation Order 2005 by the Civil Aviation Authority's Air Traffic Standards Department.

Aeronautical Ground Station (High Frequency)

8B. An applicant must undertake to use the assigned frequencies solely for the purposes of communication with aircraft.

8C. An applicant must prove that the equipment he intends to use under an Aeronautical Ground Station (High Frequency) Licence is an aeronautical communications installation assessed as fit for purpose under the Air Navigation Order 2005 by the Civil Aviation Authority's Air Traffic Standards Department.

Aeronautical Ground Station (Offshore Platform)

8D. An applicant must be an offshore platform operator and must undertake to use the assigned frequencies solely for the purposes of communication with aircraft as well as emergency mobile ground stations and airport vehicles within the confines of aerodromes authorised by the CAA.

8E. An applicant must prove that the equipment he intends to use under an Aeronautical Ground Station (Offshore Platform) Licence is an aeronautical communications installation assessed as fit for purpose under the Air Navigation Order 2005 by the Civil Aviation Authority's Air Traffic Standards Department.

Aeronautical Navigational Aid Stations
Aeronautical Radar

8F. An applicant must prove that the equipment he intends to use under an Aeronautical Navigational Aid Stations Licence or an Aeronautical Radar Licence is an aeronautical navigation installation assessed as fit for purpose under the Air Navigation Order 2005 by the Civil Aviation Authority's Air Traffic Standards Department.

Aeronautical Ground Station (Operations Control)

8G. An applicant must undertake to use the assigned frequencies solely for the purposes of operation control, where "operation control" means the exercise of authority over the initiation, continuation, or diversion of a flight in the interest of safety of the aircraft and the regularity and efficiency of the flight.

8H. An applicant must prove that the equipment he intends to use under an Aeronautical Ground Station (Operations Control) Licence is an aeronautical communications installation assessed as fit for purpose under the Air Navigation Order 2005 by the Civil Aviation Authority's Air Traffic Standards Department.]

...

9. ...

[3550]

NOTES

Commencement: 25 July 2003.

Paras 4, 5, 7, 8: words in square brackets substituted by the Wireless Telegraphy (Limitation of Number of Licences) (Amendment) Order 2006, SI 2006/2786, art 2, Schedule, para 20(a)–(c), (e)–(g).

Para 6: revoked by SI 2006/2786, art 2, Schedule, para 20(d).

Paras 8A–8H: inserted, together with preceding cross-headings, by SI 2006/2786, art 2, Schedule, para 20(h).

Para 9: revoked, together with preceding cross-heading, by SI 2006/2786, art 2, Schedule, para 20(i).

PART 3
CRITERIA LIMITING NUMBER OF WIRELESS TELEGRAPHY LICENCES

[10. The availability of the Aeronautical Ground Station (Air Traffic/Ground Movement Control) Licence, Aeronautical Ground Station (Air/Ground Communication Service) Licence, Aeronautical Ground Station (General Aviation) Licence, Aeronautical Ground Station (High Frequency) Licence, and Aeronautical Ground Station (Offshore Platform) Licence is limited in any particular location at these frequencies by the technical frequency assignment criteria set out in Aeronautical Wireless Telegraphy Act Radio Licences (Including Technical Frequency Assignment Criteria) published by OFCOM.]

11. All applications for licences are considered (and any technical frequency assignment criteria applied) in the order of receipt of each correctly completed application form.

12. Applicants must undertake to use the assigned frequencies [solely] for the transmission and reception of signals as part of the "[aeronautical mobile service, aeronautical mobile-satellite service and the aeronautical radio navigation service]" as defined in Article 1 of the Radio Regulations.

[3551]

NOTES

Commencement: 25 July 2003.

Para 10: substituted by the Wireless Telegraphy (Limitation of Number of Licences) (Amendment) Order 2006, SI 2006/2786, art 2, Schedule, para 21(a).

Para 12: words in square brackets substituted by SI 2006/2786, art 2, Schedule, para 21(b).

SCHEDULE 9
AMATEUR RADIO

Articles 3 and 4

[PART 1
FREQUENCIES ALLOCATED TO AMATEUR RADIO USE

Amateur Radio Foundation

0.1357–0.1378 MHz	14.00–14.350 MHz	50.00–52.00 MHz
1.810–2.000 MHz	18.068–18.168 MHz	70.00–70.50 MHz
3.500–3.800 MHz	21.000–21.450 MHz	144.0–146.0 MHz
7.000–7.200 MHz	24.890–24.990 MHz	430.0–440.0 MHz

Amateur Radio Intermediate

0.1357–0.1378 MHz	28.000–29.700 MHz	5755–5765 MHz
1.810–2.000 MHz	50.000–52.000 MHz	5820–5850 MHz
3.500–3.800 MHz	70.00–70.50 MHz	1000–10125 MHz
7.000–7.200 MHz	144.0–146.00 MHz	10225–10500 MHz
10.100–10.150 MHz	430.0–440.0 MHz	24000–24250 MHz
14.000–14.350 MHz	1240–1325 MHz	47000–47200 MHz
18.068–18.168 MHz	2310–2450 MHz	75500–81000 MHz
21.000–21.450 MHz	3400–3475 MHz	142000–144000 MHz
24.890–24.990 MHz	5650–5680 MHz	248000–250000 MHz

Amateur Radio Full

0.1357–0.1378 MHz	28.000–29.700 MHz	5755–5765 MHz
1.810 MHz-2.000 MHz	50.00–52.00 MHz	5820–5850 MHz
3.500–3.800 MHz	70.00–70.50 MHz	10000–10125 MHz
7.000–7.200 MHz	144.0–146.0 MHz	10225–10500 MHz
10.100–10.150 MHz	430.0–440.0 MHz	24000–24250 MHz
14.000–14.350 MHz	1240–1325 MHz	47000–47200 MHz
18.068–18.168 MHz	2310–2450 MHz	75500–81000 MHz
21.000–21.450 MHz	3400–3475 MHz	122250–123000 MHz
24.890–24.990 MHz	5650–5680 MHz	134000–141000 MHz
		142000–144000 MHz
		241000–25000 MHz]

[3552]

NOTES

Commencement: 25 July 2003.

Substituted by the Wireless Telegraphy (Limitation of Number of Licences) (Amendment) Order 2006, SI 2006/2786, art 2, Schedule, para 22.

PART 2
CRITERIA RELATING TO PERSONS TO WHOM WIRELESS TELEGRAPHY LICENCES MAY BE GRANTED

Amateur Radio Foundation

1. An applicant must possess a valid pass certificate for the Foundation Amateur Radio Examination or equivalent examination.

Amateur Radio Intermediate …

2. An applicant must possess:
   (a) a valid pass certificate for the … Foundation Amateur Radio Examination or equivalent examination; [and]
   (b) a valid pass certificate for the … Intermediate Radio Amateur Examination or equivalent [examination.]
   (c) …

[Amateur Radio Full

3. An applicant must possess—
   (a) a valid pass certificate for the Intermediate and Full Radio Amateur Examination or equivalent examination; or
   (b) a valid pass certificate for the City and Guilds Institute 7307-Radio Amateur Examination or equivalent examination.]

5. …

[3553]

NOTES

Commencement: 25 July 2003.

Para 2: words omitted revoked, word in square brackets in sub-para (a) inserted, and word in square brackets in sub-para (b) substituted, by the Wireless Telegraphy (Limitation of Number of Licences) (Amendment) Order 2006, SI 2006/2786, art 2, Schedule, para 23(a)–(c).

Para 3: substituted, together with preceding cross-heading, for original paras 3, 4, by SI 2006/2786, art 2, Schedule, para 23(d).

Para 5: revoked by SI 2006/2786, art 2, Schedule, para 23(e).

PART 3
CRITERIA LIMITING NUMBER OF WIRELESS TELEGRAPHY LICENCES

6. None.

[3554]

NOTES

Commencement: 25 July 2003.

SCHEDULE 10
[SCIENCE AND TECHNOLOGY]

Articles 3 and 4

NOTES

Schedule heading substituted by the Wireless Telegraphy (Limitation of Number of Licences) (Amendment) Order 2006, SI 2006/2786, art 2, Schedule, para 24.

PART 1
FREQUENCIES ALLOCATED TO [SCIENCE AND TECHNOLOGY] USE

1. Frequencies assigned to a Non-Operational Development Licence and Non-Operational Temporary [Use] Licence will be suitable for the particular type of product being developed.

[Ground Probing Radar

150–4000 MHz]

[3555]

NOTES

Commencement: 25 July 2003.

Words in square brackets in Part heading substituted, and other words in square brackets inserted by the Wireless Telegraphy (Limitation of Number of Licences) (Amendment) Order 2006, SI 2006/2786, art 2, Schedule, para 25.

PART 2
CRITERIA RELATING TO PERSONS TO WHOM WIRELESS TELEGRAPHY LICENCES MAY BE GRANTED

Non-Operational Development

2. Applicants must be seeking authority to use spectrum on a non-commercial, non-permanent basis to build innovative spectrum apparatus or equipment or undertake academic or scientific research.

Non-Operational Temporary [Use]

3. Applicants must be seeking authority to use spectrum on a non-commercial, non-permanent basis to trial a new system or radio concept or demonstrate a new system or radio concept.

[Ground Probing Radar

4. An applicant cannot be a person whose entitlement to provide electronic communications networks or electronic communications services, or to make associated facilities available is suspended or restricted under the Communications Act 2003.]

[3556]

NOTES

Commencement: 25 July 2003.

Words in square brackets inserted by the Wireless Telegraphy (Limitation of Number of Licences) (Amendment) Order 2006, SI 2006/2786, art 2, Schedule, para 26.

PART 3
CRITERIA LIMITING NUMBER OF WIRELESS TELEGRAPHY LICENCES

4. The availability of [Non-Operational Development Licences and Non-Operational Temporary Use Licences] is limited in any particular location on a case by case basis depending upon the nature of the product being developed and the technical frequency assignment criteria which are appropriate for the frequencies which the product will use.

[5. Applications for Ground Probing Radar Licences are considered in the order of receipt of each correctly completed application form.]

[3557]

NOTES

Commencement: 25 July 2003.

Para 4: words in square brackets substituted by the Wireless Telegraphy (Limitation of Number of Licences) (Amendment) Order 2006, SI 2006/2786, art 2, Schedule, para 27(a).

Para 5: inserted by SI 2006/2786, art 2, Schedule, para 27(b).

SCHEDULE 11
... BUSINESS RADIO

Articles 3 and 4

NOTES

Word omitted revoked by the Wireless Telegraphy (Limitation of Number of Licences) (Amendment) Order 2006, SI 2006/2786, art 2, Schedule, para 28.

[PART 1
FREQUENCIES ALLOCATED TO BUSINESS RADIO USE

Business Radio (National and Regional)

Business Radio (On-Site Speech and Data Systems)

Business Radio (Suppliers)

Business Radio (UK General)

Business Radio (Wide Area Speech and Data Systems)

55.75–87.50 MHz

137.95–215.30 MHz

425.0–462.50 MHz

Business Radio (On-Site Local Communications Systems)

137.95–215.30 MHz

425.0–462.50 MHz

Business Radio (IR2008 Data)

55.75–87.50 MHz

137.95–215.30 MHz

425.0–462.50 MHz

Business Radio (Wide Area Distress Alarm Systems)

137.95–215.30

Business Radio (Self-Select)

26.225–26.9325 MHz

48.968750–49.493750MHz

425.0–462.5 MHz

Business Radio (On-Site One-Way Paging and Speech Systems)

425.0–462.5 MHz

Business Radio (Wide Area One-Way Paging and Speech Systems)

137.96250–153.48750

425.0–462.5 MHz

Business Radio (On-Site Hospital Paging and Emergency Speech Systems)

31.71250–31.78750 MHz

48.968750–49.493750 MHz

159.63125–164.20625 MHz

Public Safety and Emergency Services Radio

171.59375–171.60625 MHz	450–470 MHz	4800–4900 MHz
173.9875–174.4125 MHz	862–863 MHz	8340–8460 MHz

380–395 MHz	1668–1798 MHz	10.25–10.46 GHz
410–412 MHz	2302–2380 MHz	24.05–24.15 GHz
420–422 MHz	3442–3475 MHz	50.2–51.4 GHz

Business Radio (Common Base Station)

55.75–87.5 MHz	165–173 MHz	425–449 MHz
157–165 MHz	177–192 MHz	

Business Radio (Remote Meter Reading Operator (National Shared)

Business Radio (Remote Meter Reading Operator (Regional Shared)

183.5–184.5 MHz]

[3558]

NOTES

Commencement: 25 July 2003.

Substituted by the Wireless Telegraphy (Limitation of Number of Licences) (Amendment) Order 2006, SI 2006/2786, art 2, Schedule, para 29.

[PART 2
CRITERIA RELATING TO PERSONS TO WHOM WIRELESS TELEGRAPHY LICENCES MAY BE GRANTED

1A. An applicant for a Business Radio (Common Base Station) Licence or a Business Radio (Remote Meter Reading Operator) Licence cannot be a person whose entitlement to provide electronic communications networks or electronic communications services, or to make associated facilities available is suspended or restricted under the Communications Act 2003.

Business Radio (On-Site Hospital Paging and Emergency Speech Systems)

2. An applicant must be engaged in the management of a hospital or medical practice.

Business Radio (Suppliers)

3. An applicant must be engaged in the hire, supply or demonstration of private business radio equipment.

Public Safety and Emergency Services Radio

4. An applicant must be engaged in activities related to public safety.]

[3559]

NOTES

Commencement: 25 July 2003.

Substituted by the Wireless Telegraphy (Limitation of Number of Licences) (Amendment) Order 2006, SI 2006/2786, art 2, Schedule, para 30.

PART 3
CRITERIA LIMITING NUMBER OF WIRELESS TELEGRAPHY LICENCES

6. Applicants for licences must undertake to operate under any licence granted solely for the purposes of private business radio.

[7. The availability of licences (save in respect of the Business Radio (Suppliers) Licence, the Business Radio (UK General) Licence and the Business Radio (Self-Select Licence)) is limited in any particular location at these frequencies by the technical assignment criteria set out in Business Radio Technical Frequency Assignment Criteria published by OFCOM.]

8. All applications for licences are considered (and any technical frequency assignment criteria applied) in the order of receipt of each correctly completed application form.

[3560]

NOTES

Commencement: 25 July 2003.

Para 7: substituted by the Wireless Telegraphy (Limitation of Number of Licences) (Amendment) Order 2006, SI 2006/2786, art 2, Schedule, para 31.

ELECTRONIC COMMUNICATIONS (UNIVERSAL SERVICE) ORDER 2003

(SI 2003/1904)

NOTES

Made: 17 July 2003.

Authority: Communications Act 2003, s 65.

Commencement: 25 July 2003.

1 Citation and Commencement

This Order may be cited as the Electronic Communications (Universal Service) Order 2003 and shall come into force on 25th July 2003.

[3561]

NOTES

Commencement: 25 July 2003.

2 Interpretation

In this Order—

"the Act" means the Communications Act 2003;

"disability" has the same meaning as in section 1 of the Disability Discrimination Act 1995;

"network termination point" means the physical point at which a subscriber is provided with access to a public electronic communications network and in the case of electronic communications networks involving switching or routing, the network termination point is identified by means of a specific electronic communications network address, which may be linked to a subscriber's number or name;

"publicly available telephone service" means a service available to the public for originating and receiving national and international calls and access to emergency services through a telephone number or numbers in a national or international telephone numbering plan, and may, where relevant, also include one or more of the following—

- (a) the provision of operator assistance,
- (b) directory enquiry facilities,
- (c) directories,
- (d) the provision of public pay telephones,
- (e) the provision of service under special terms,
- (f) the provision of specific facilities for end-users with a disability or with special social needs, and
- (g) the provision of non-geographic services;

"public pay telephone" means a telephone available to the general public, for the use of which the means of payment may include one or more of the following:

- (a) coins;
- (b) credit or debit cards; and
- (c) pre-payment cards, including cards for use with dialling codes;

"public telephone network" means an electronic communications network which is used to provide publicly available telephone services and supports the transfer between network termination points of speech communications, and also other forms of communications, such as facsimile and data;

"relay service" means a service which:

- (a) provides facilities for the receipt and translation of voice messages into text and text into voice messages, and the conveyance of that text or voice message to the textphone of subscribers of a person providing a publicly available telephone service; and

(b) has been approved as a text relay service by OFCOM;

"subscriber" means any person who is a party to a contract with the provider of a public electronic communications service for the supply of such service; and

"textphone" means an integrated terminal incorporating an alphanumeric keyboard and means of displaying text, intended for connection to the public telephone network for the sole or primary purpose of supporting live telephone conversations between two or more individuals.

[3562]

NOTES

Commencement: 25 July 2003.

3 Universal service obligations

The extent to which the things falling within section 65(2) of the Act must be provided, made available or supplied throughout the United Kingdom is set out in the Schedule to this Order.

[3563]

NOTES

Commencement: 25 July 2003.

4 Guidance on the pricing of universal service obligations

The matters set out in the Schedule should be offered at prices that are:

(a) affordable for all end-users; and

(b) uniform throughout the United Kingdom, unless OFCOM have determined that there is clear justification for not doing so.

[3564]

NOTES

Commencement: 25 July 2003.

SCHEDULE

Article 3

Publicly available telephone services

1.—(1) At least one designated universal service provider shall meet all reasonable requests by end-users for connection at a fixed location to the public telephone network and for access to publicly available telephone services at a fixed location.

(2) The connection referred to in sub-paragraph (1) shall be capable of allowing end-users to make and receive local, national and international telephone calls, facsimile communications and data communications, at data rates that are sufficient to permit functional Internet access, taking into account prevailing technologies used by the majority of subscribers and technological feasibility.

(3) Access to a publicly available telephone service in accordance with subparagraph (1) shall continue to be provided in the event of non-payment of bills for the use of that service, unless the provider of the service has first taken adequate measures regarding interruption to, or disconnection of the service.

Directories

2.—(1) At least one comprehensive directory shall be made available to end-users in a form approved by OFCOM, whether printed or electronic, or both, and it shall be updated at least once a year.

(2) This directory shall comprise, subject to the provisions of the [Privacy and Electronic Communications (EC Directive) Regulations 2003], the details of all subscribers of publicly available telephone services and their telephone numbers, including fixed and mobile telephone numbers.

Directory Enquiry Facilities

3.—(1) At least one comprehensive telephone directory enquiry facility shall be made available to end-users, including users of public pay telephones.

(2) This facility shall comprise, subject to the provisions of the [Privacy and Electronic Communications (EC Directive) Regulations 2003], the details of all subscribers of publicly available telephone services and their telephone numbers, including fixed and mobile telephone numbers.

Public pay telephones

4.—(1) Public pay telephones shall be provided to meet the reasonable needs of end-users in terms of geographical coverage, the number of telephones and the quality of public electronic communication services.

(2) It shall be possible to make emergency calls from public pay telephones using the single European emergency call number "112" and the UK emergency call number "999", free of charge and without the use of coins or cards.

Billing, payment and tariff options

5.—(1) Facilities, methods of billing and methods of accepting payment for electronic communications services that enable subscribers to monitor and control their expenditure in relation to the use of those services shall be provided to subscribers of services provided by designated universal service providers.

(2) Appropriate tariff options and packages that depart from those provided under normal commercial conditions shall be made available by designated universal service providers to the subscribers of their services who are on low incomes or have special social needs.

Special measures for end-users with a disability

6.—(1) Special measures shall be taken to ensure access to and affordability of publicly available telephone services for end-users with a disability equivalent to those enjoyed by other end-users.

(2) The measures to be taken for the purposes of sub-paragraph (1) shall include:

(a) provision of access to the directory information facilities provided for the purposes of paragraph 3 in a form appropriate to meet the needs of end-users with a disability who are unable to use a telephone directory in a form in which it is generally available to other end-users;

(b) provision of priority fault repair services to end-users with a disability as is necessary to ensure access to publicly available telephone services by such end-users;

(c) provision of, and the provision of access to, relay services for end-users with a disability where required to ensure access to publicly available telephone services by such end-users;

(d) methods of billing and methods of accepting payment for publicly available telephone services in an appropriate format for subscribers with a disability, including provision for such subscribers to nominate a third party to handle their billing issues; and

(e) accessibility and functionality of the public pay telephones to be provided for the purposes of paragraph 4 for use by end-users with a disability, including the adequate provision of textphone facilities.

[3565]

NOTES

Commencement: 25 July 2003.

Paras 2, 3: in sub-para (2) words in square brackets substituted by the Privacy and Electronic Communications (EC Directive) Regulations 2003, SI 2003/2426, reg 35(1) (for effect and transitional provisions see regs 35(2), 36, Sch 2, para 5 to those Regulations at **[1085]**, **[1086]**, **[1088]**).

ELECTRONIC COMMUNICATIONS CODE (CONDITIONS AND RESTRICTIONS) REGULATIONS 2003

(SI 2003/2553)

NOTES

Made: 2 October 2003.
Authority: Communications Act 2003, ss 109(1), (3), 402(3)(a), (b), (c).
Commencement: 23 October 2003.

ARRANGEMENT OF REGULATIONS

1 Citation and commencement

These Regulations may be cited as the Electronic Communications Code (Conditions and Restrictions) Regulations 2003 and shall come into force on 23rd October 2003.

[3566]

NOTES

Commencement: 23 October 2003.

2 Interpretation

(1) Unless the contrary intention appears, expressions used in these Regulations which are used in Schedule 2 to the Telecommunications Act 1984 have the same meanings as in that Schedule.

(2) In these Regulations—

"the Act" means the Communications Act 2003;

"appropriate authority" means—

(a) in relation to England and Wales, a relevant authority within the meaning of section 49(6) of the New Roads and Street Works Act 1991;

(b) in relation to Scotland, a person to whom notice would be required to be given by section 108(6) of the New Roads and Street Works Act 1991; and

(c) in relation to Northern Ireland, a relevant authority within the meaning of article 7(5) of the Street Works (Northern Ireland) Order 1995;

"area of special scientific interest" means, in relation to Great Britain, any area in respect of which notice has been given under section 28(1) of the Wildlife and Countryside Act 1981 or, in relation to Northern Ireland, any area in respect of which a declaration has been made under article 24(1) of the Nature Conservation and Amenity Lands (Northern Ireland) Order 1985;

"authorised area" has, in relation to Great Britain, the meaning given by section 6(9) of the Electricity Act 1989 and, in relation to Northern Ireland, the meaning given by article 3 of the Electricity (Northern Ireland) Order 1992;

"the Broads" means the area in which the Broads Authority established under section 1 of the Norfolk and Suffolk Broads Act 1988 exercises powers of development control;

"carriageway" has the meanings given—

(a) in relation to England and Wales, by section 329 of the Highways Act 1980;

(b) in relation to Scotland, by section 151 of the Roads (Scotland) Act 1984; and

(c) in relation to Northern Ireland, by article 2(2) of the Roads (Northern Ireland) Order 1993;

and additionally means, in relation to a street to which vehicles have access, that part of the street which is primarily intended to carry vehicles;

"code operator" means a person in whose case the electronic communications code is applied by a direction under section 106(3)(a) of the Act;

"conservation area" means—

(a) in relation to England and Wales, any area designated as a conservation area under sections 69 and 70 of the Planning (Listed Buildings and Conservation Areas) Act 1990;

(b) in relation to Scotland, any area designated as a conservation area under section 61 of the Planning (Listed Buildings and Conservation Areas) (Scotland) Act 1997; and

(c) in relation to Northern Ireland, any area designated as a conservation area under article 50 of the Planning (Northern Ireland) Order 1991;

"Countryside Council for Wales" means the body known as the Countryside Council for Wales and established by section 128 of the Environmental Protection Act 1990;

"electricity supplier" means, in relation to an area in which a code operator has installed or proposes to install any electronic communications apparatus, the person who is the holder of a licence granted (in Great Britain) under section 6(1) of the Electricity Act 1989 or (in Northern Ireland) under article 10(1) of the Electricity (Northern Ireland) Order 1992;

"emergency organisation" means any of the police, fire, ambulance and coastguard services and any other organisation which, in the normal course of its activities, may be called upon in an emergency to undertake tasks necessary for—

(a) the preservation of life,

(b) the prevention or treatment of injury or disease,

(c) the protection of public health, or

(d) national defence or the protection of national security;

"English Nature" means the body known as English Nature and established by section 128 of the Environmental Protection Act 1990;

"footway" has the meanings given—

(a) in relation to England and Wales, by section 329 of the Highways Act 1980;

(b) in relation to Scotland, by section 151 of the Roads (Scotland) Act 1984; and

(c) in relation to Northern Ireland, by article 2 of the Roads (Northern Ireland) Order 1993;

and additionally means, in relation to a street to which vehicles have access, that part of the street which is not primarily intended to carry vehicles;

"a high load grid route" is a route included in the records of routes suitable for the transport of high abnormal loads maintained by the Secretary of State;

"highway authority" means, in relation to England and Wales, the highway authority as defined in section 1 of the Highways Act 1980 and, in relation to Northern Ireland, the Department for Regional Development;

"limestone pavement area" means an area designated as such by an order made under section 34(2) of the Wildlife and Countryside Act 1981;

"local nature reserve" means an area designated as such under section 21(1) of the National Parks and Access to the Countryside Act 1949;

"marine nature reserve" means, in relation to Great Britain, an area designated as such under section 36(1) of the Wildlife and Countryside Act 1981 and, in relation to Northern Ireland, an area designated as such under article 20(1) of the Nature Conservation and Amenity Lands (Northern Ireland) Order 1985;

"national nature reserve" means any land declared to be a national nature reserve under section 35(1) of the Wildlife and Countryside Act 1981 by—

(a) English Nature, in England;

(b) Scottish Natural Heritage, in Scotland; or

(c) the Countryside Council for Wales, in Wales;

and in Northern Ireland means any land declared to be a national nature reserve under article 18(1) of the Nature Conservation and Amenity Lands (Northern Ireland) Order 1985;

"national park" means—

(a) any area in England and Wales designated and confirmed as such under section 5(3) of the National Parks and Access to the Countryside Act 1949;

(b) any area in Scotland designated as such by an order made under section 6(2) of the National Parks (Scotland) Act 2000; or

(c) any area in Northern Ireland designated as such under article 12(1) of the Nature Conservation and Amenity Lands (Northern Ireland) Order 1985;

"national scenic area" means any area designated as such under section 262C of the Town and Country Planning (Scotland) Act 1972;

"natural heritage area" means any area designated as such under section 6(2) of the Natural Heritage (Scotland) Act 1991;

"the New Forest" means the area defined by section 1(1) of the New Forest Act 1964;

"OFCOM" means the Office of Communications as established by section 1 of the Office of Communications Act 2002;

"planning authority" means—

(a) in relation to England, a local planning authority within the meaning of section 1(1) or (2) of the Town and Country Planning Act 1990;

(b) in relation to Wales, a local planning authority within the meaning of section 1(1B) or (2) of the Town and Country Planning Act 1990;

(c) in relation to Scotland, a planning authority within the meaning of section 1 of the Town and Country Planning (Scotland) Act 1997 or a national park authority designated as a planning authority by an order made under section 10(1) of the National Parks (Scotland) Act 2000; and

(d) in relation to Northern Ireland, the Department of the Environment.

"relevant undertaker" has the meaning given by paragraph 23(10) of Schedule 2 to the Telecommunications Act 1984 and additionally includes any undertaker engaged in the supply of gas, electricity, water, heat or the disposal of sewage;

"responsible authority"—

(a) in relation to England and Wales, has the meaning given by section 90(4) of the New Roads and Street Works Act 1991;

(b) in relation to Scotland, has the meaning given by section 194(4) of that Act; and

(c) in Northern Ireland, has the meaning given by article 49(4) of the Street Works (Northern Ireland) Order 1995;

"roads authority" has the meaning given by section 151(1) of the Roads (Scotland) Act 1984;

"road works authority" has the meaning given by section 108(1) of the New Roads and Street Works Act 1991;

"Scottish Natural Heritage" means the body known as Scottish Natural Heritage and established by section 1 of the Natural Heritage (Scotland) Act 1991;

"service line" means any line placed or intended to be placed for the purposes of providing any electronic communications service to the occupier from time to time of any land, as distinct from a line placed or intended to be placed for the general purposes of any electronic communications network;

"service line distribution point" means the point at which any line placed or intended to be placed for the general purposes of any electronic communications network is connected to any service line;

"site of special scientific interest" means an area in respect of which a notification has been given under section 28(1) of the Wildlife and Countryside Act 1981;

"statutory list of buildings" means—

(a) in relation to England and Wales, the list of buildings of special architectural or historic interest compiled or approved under section 1(1) of the Planning (Listed Buildings and Conservation Areas) Act 1990;

(b) in relation to Scotland, the list compiled under section 1(1) of the Planning (Listed Buildings and Conservation Areas) (Scotland) Act 1997; or

(c) in relation to Northern Ireland, the list compiled under article 42 of the Planning (Northern Ireland) Order 1991;

"street authority" has, in relation to England and Wales, the meaning given by section 49 of the New Roads and Street Works Act 1991 and, in relation to Northern Ireland, the meaning given by article 7(1) of the Street Works (Northern Ireland) Order 1995;

"traffic authority" has, in relation to England and Wales, the meaning given by section 121A of the Road Traffic Regulation Act 1984 and, in relation to Northern Ireland, means the Department for Regional Development.

[3567]

NOTES

Commencement: 23 October 2003.

3 General conditions

(1) A code operator shall consult—

(a) highway authorities or, in Scotland, roads authorities to ensure that any works involving the breaking up of maintainable highways or public roads do not undermine or unduly disturb the highway authorities' or roads authorities' work;

(b) planning authorities in relation to the installation of electronic communications apparatus, including installation in a local nature reserve; and

(c) relevant undertakers with a view to avoiding the disruption of the services provided by those undertakers.

(2) A code operator shall ensure that any electronic communications apparatus installed underground is installed at such a depth that it will not interfere with the use of the land (as at the date of the installation), unless the occupier and any other person having a legal interest in that land have consented.

(3) A code operator, when installing any electronic communications apparatus, shall, so far as reasonably practicable, minimise—

(a) the impact on the visual amenity of properties, in particular buildings on the statutory list of buildings;

(b) any potential hazards posed by work carried out in installing the apparatus or by apparatus once installed; and

(c) interference with traffic.

(4) A code operator, where practicable, shall share the use of electronic communications apparatus.

(5) A code operator shall install the minimum practicable number of items of electronic communications apparatus consistent with the intended provision of electronic communications services and allowing for an estimate of growth in demand for such services.

[3568]

NOTES

Commencement: 23 October 2003.

4 Lines

(1) A code operator shall install all lines underground unless—

(a) the line is flown from a pole in an area where service lines are already flown from poles;

(b) the line is—

(i) affixed to and lying on the exterior surface of a building or other permanent structure and is either used as a service line or terminates at a service line distribution point;

(ii) a service line flown from the eaves of one building or other permanent structure to those of another where the distance between them is less than 8 metres; or

(iii) a feeder cable connecting equipment for the provision of services by wireless telegraphy;

and is neither affixed to a building shown as grade 1 or category A in the statutory list of buildings nor located in a conservation area;

(c) the line is attached to or supported by poles or pylons which are used in connection with the transport of electricity at a nominal voltage of at least 6000 volts;

(d) the line is installed for the purpose of providing a temporary electronic communications network under regulation 15; or

(e) it is not in all the circumstances reasonably practicable to do so.

(2) A code operator shall ensure that any lines installed over the carriageway of—

(a) a maintainable highway or, in Scotland, a public road are placed at least 5.5 metres above the surface of the highway or road; and

(b) a maintainable highway or, in Scotland, a public road which is a high load grid route are placed at least 6.5 metres above the surface of the highway or road.

(3) If requested by any person to relocate a line which is already installed above the ground, a code operator must relocate that line unless—

(a) he determines either that the request is unreasonable or that the person making the request will not pay the costs of the relocation; and

(b) he notifies that person of that determination within 56 days of the receipt of the request.

[3569]

NOTES

Commencement: 23 October 2003.

5 Installation of electronic communications apparatus

(1) A code operator must give one calendar month's notice, in writing, to the planning authority for the area in question where—

(a) he has not previously installed electronic communications apparatus in the area and is intending to install electronic communications apparatus, other than lines, in that area; or

(b) he intends to install a cabinet, box, pillar, pedestal or similar apparatus for the installation of which he is not required to obtain planning permission under the Town and Country Planning Act 1990.

(2) The notice to be given under paragraph (1) must state the code operator's intention to install electronic communications apparatus and must describe that apparatus and identify the location where it is proposed to install it.

(3) Where a code operator has given notice under paragraph (1), the planning authority may, within one calendar month of the receipt of that notice, give the code operator written notice of conditions with which the planning authority wishes him to comply in respect of the installation of the apparatus, but he is not obliged to comply with those conditions to the extent that they are unreasonable in all the circumstances.

(4) A code operator is exempt from paragraph (1) if—

(a) the electronic communications apparatus he intends to install is to be installed inside a building or other permanent structure;

(b) the apparatus is to be installed for the purpose of providing a temporary electronic communications network under regulation 15; or

(c) the apparatus he intends to install is to be attached to or supported by poles or pylons which are used for the transport of electricity at a nominal voltage of at least 6000 volts.

(5) Where a code operator installs electronic communications apparatus underground in a maintainable highway or a street or, in Scotland, a public road or a road he shall place that apparatus in the verge or footway rather than the carriageway unless it is not reasonably practicable to do so.

[3570]

NOTES

Commencement: 23 October 2003.

6 Conservation areas

(1) In conservation areas, electronic communications apparatus installed by a code operator shall be installed underground unless the conditions in paragraph (2) are met or unless it is—

(a) a line flown between poles or pylons which are used for the transport of electricity at a nominal voltage of at least 6000 volts;

(b) a replacement pole or replacement line, the installation of which does not increase the environmental impact of the apparatus located in the area compared with the apparatus as it was before the replacement;

(c) a service line flown from a pole where that pole was installed prior to the area being designated as a conservation area;

(d) a service line—

(i) which is flown from a building or other permanent structure in an area where there are already service lines flown from buildings or other permanent structures or poles, and

(ii) which does not, by reason of its installation, increase the environmental impact of the apparatus located in the area compared with the apparatus as it was before the service line was installed;

(e) a service line—

(i) which is affixed to and lying on the exterior surface of a building or other permanent structure, and

(ii) which does not, by reason of its installation, increase the environmental impact of the apparatus located in the area compared with the apparatus as it was before the service line was installed;

(f) apparatus which forms part of emergency works where the code operator has provided the planning authority with an expected date of completion and a statement of the grounds for the need to execute the works; or

(g) apparatus which forms part of a temporary electronic communications network which the code operator is providing under regulation 15.

(2) Electronic communications apparatus installed by a code operator in a conservation area is not required to be installed underground where a code operator has given the planning authority written notice and—

(a) the planning authority has not objected in writing to the installation of the apparatus within 56 days of the notice being given; or

(b) if the planning authority has previously objected to the installation of the apparatus, it has given written notice of the withdrawal of its objection; or

(c) in Great Britain, the Secretary of State, after consulting with the planning authority, so directs.

(3) The notice to be given under paragraph (2) must state the code operator's intention to install electronic communications apparatus and must describe that apparatus and identify the location where it is proposed to install it.

(4) For the purposes of paragraph (1), the environmental impact of apparatus is to be assessed having regard, in particular, to—

(a) its visual impact on the landscape,

(b) its effect on plant and animal life, and

(c) its impact on the visual amenity of properties.

[3571]

NOTES

Commencement: 23 October 2003.

7 Listed buildings and ancient monuments

(1) A code operator may install electronic communications apparatus in proximity to a building shown as grade 1 or category A in the statutory list of buildings only if he gives written notice to the planning authority and—

(a) the planning authority has not objected in writing to the installation of the apparatus within 56 days of the notice being given; or

(b) if the planning authority has previously objected, it has given written notice of the withdrawal of its objection; or

(c) in Great Britain, the Secretary of State, after consulting with the planning authority, so directs.

(2) The notice to be given under paragraph (1) must state the code operator's intention to install electronic communications apparatus and must describe that apparatus and identify the location where it is proposed to install it.

(3) A code operator is exempt from paragraph (1) if—

(a) the apparatus is to be installed for the purpose of providing a temporary electronic communications network under regulation 15; or

(b) he is undertaking emergency works and he has provided the planning authority with an expected date of completion and a statement of the grounds for the need to execute the works.

[3572]

NOTES

Commencement: 23 October 2003.

8 Protected areas

(1) When a code operator intends to install electronic communications apparatus in—

(a) a national park, the Broads, the New Forest or a limestone pavement area he must give written notice to the planning authority;

(b) a national nature reserve, site of special scientific interest, area of special scientific interest or marine nature reserve he must give written notice to—

(i) English Nature, in England;

(ii) Scottish Natural Heritage, in Scotland;

(iii) the Countryside Council for Wales, in Wales; or

(iv) the planning authority, in Northern Ireland (in the case of a national nature reserve, area of special scientific interest or marine nature reserve);

(c) a natural heritage area or national scenic area he must give written notice to Scottish Natural Heritage; or

(d) any land which the National Trust or the National Trust for Scotland has notified the code operator that it owns, or holds any interest in, he must give written notice to its relevant regional office.

(2) The notice to be given under paragraph (1) must state the code operator's intention to install electronic communications apparatus and must describe that apparatus and identify the location where it is proposed to install it.

(3) Where a code operator has given notice under paragraph (1), he may install the electronic communications apparatus only if—

(a) within 56 days the person notified has not objected in writing; or

(b) if the person notified has previously objected, he has given written notice of the withdrawal of his objection; or

(c) in Great Britain, the Secretary of State, after consulting with the person notified, so directs;

and only if he also complies with any direction given to him by the Secretary of State, or, in Northern Ireland, the Department of the Environment, requiring him to give written notice to and consider representations from any other person exercising functions specified in that direction.

(4) A code operator shall not be required to give notice under paragraph (1) where the electronic communications apparatus to be installed is—

(a) a service line—

(i) which is affixed to and lying on the exterior surface of a building or other permanent structure, and

(ii) which does not, by reason of its installation, increase the environmental impact of the apparatus located in the area compared with the apparatus as it was before the service line was installed;

(b) a replacement pole or replacement line the installation of which does not increase the environmental impact of the apparatus located in the area compared with the apparatus as it was before the replacement;

(c) a replacement line in an existing conduit, if the installation of the replacement line does not entail enlarging the conduit or altering its position;

(d) apparatus required for the provision of a temporary electronic communications network under regulation 15; or

(e) apparatus which forms part of emergency works, where the code operator has provided the person who would otherwise be notified under paragraph (1) with an expected date of completion and a statement of the grounds for the need to execute the works.

(5) For the purposes of paragraph (4), the environmental impact of apparatus is to be assessed having regard, in particular, to—

(a) its visual impact on the landscape,

(b) its effect on plant and animal life, and

(c) its impact on the visual amenity of properties.

[3573]

NOTES

Commencement: 23 October 2003.

9 Use of conduits

Where electronic communications apparatus is to be installed underground in—

(a) a part of a maintainable highway or, in Scotland, a public road which is paved, or

(b) a street or, in Scotland, a road which the code operator has been notified by the street authority or the road works authority is to be paved, or

(c) the verge of any street or, in Scotland, road,

it shall be installed in conduits unless it is not reasonably practicable to do so.

[3574]

NOTES

Commencement: 23 October 2003.

10 Maintenance and the safety of apparatus

(1) A code operator shall inspect and maintain his electronic communications apparatus, other than apparatus installed underground or inside a building or other permanent structure, so as to ensure that it will not cause injury to any person or damage to property.

(2) A code operator who receives a report that any electronic communications apparatus of his, wherever installed, is in a dangerous state shall investigate that report and, if necessary, make the apparatus safe.

(3) A code operator shall inform the highway authority or, in Scotland, the roads authority of the arrangements he has made to comply with paragraph (1).

[3575]

NOTES

Commencement: 23 October 2003.

11 Records of apparatus

(1) A code operator shall keep accurate records of where all his electronic communications apparatus that is installed in or under a maintainable highway or street or, in Scotland, a public road or a road, is located.

(2) The duty to keep records in paragraph (1) shall apply only in respect of apparatus located in Scotland and Wales and shall not apply in respect of any apparatus installed prior to the date on which these Regulations come into force.

(3) The records shall be in the form of route plans based on Ordnance Survey map backgrounds on an appropriate scale for the density development in the area concerned.

(4) Where a person who has reasonable grounds to inspect any records kept pursuant to paragraph (1) makes a request to inspect them, a code operator shall make them available for that purpose as soon as practicable and, in any case, within one month of the request being made.

[3576]

NOTES

Commencement: 23 October 2003.

12 Duty to retain and allow inspection of existing records

(1) A code operator shall retain all his records created prior to the date on which these Regulations come into force of where his electronic communications apparatus installed in or under a maintainable highway or street or, in Scotland, a public road or a road is located.

(2) Where a person who has reasonable grounds to inspect any records kept pursuant to paragraph (1) makes a request to inspect them, a code operator shall make them available for that purpose as soon as practicable and, in any case, within one month of the request being made.

[3577]

NOTES

Commencement: 23 October 2003.

13 Duty to make staff available

A code operator shall make trained staff available, as soon as practicable after a reasonable request made by a relevant undertaker, a highway authority or, in Scotland, a roads authority, to indicate, on site, the location and nature of electronic communications apparatus of his installed in or under a maintainable highway or street or, in Scotland, a public road or a road.

[3578]

NOTES

Commencement: 23 October 2003.

14 Arrangements with electricity suppliers

(1) Before a code operator exercises any rights under the electronic communications code in an authorised area, he shall use his best endeavours to enter into an agreement with any relevant electricity supplier as to the engineering principles to be adopted and the allocation and apportionment of costs which arise—

(a) when the code operator installs and keeps installed electronic communications apparatus in proximity to plant which is already installed and which is the responsibility of the electricity supplier; or

(b) when the electricity supplier gives notice to the code operator that it proposes to install plant in proximity to any of the code operator's apparatus which is already installed.

(2) A code operator shall not install electronic communications apparatus which is—

(a) of such a nature, or

(b) in such a position, as adversely to affect any plant of an electricity supplier which is already installed.

[3579]

NOTES

Commencement: 23 October 2003.

15 Provision of a temporary electronic communications network

(1) A code operator who provides any electronic communications service for a limited period at the site of a public or private event or at a construction site may install lines and poles on or above the ground, subject to the condition that—

(a) as soon as practicable the planning authority is given a reasonable estimate of the date by which the lines and poles will be removed; and

(b) the lines and poles are removed within a reasonable time after the end of the event or after the work on the construction site is complete.

(2) A code operator who provides any electronic communications service required for use in dealing with an emergency by an emergency organisation may install lines and poles on or above the ground, subject to the condition that the lines and poles are removed within a reasonable time after they cease to be required.

[3580]

NOTES

Commencement: 23 October 2003.

16 Funds for meeting liabilities

(1) A code operator must—

(a) ensure that sufficient funds are available to meet the specified liabilities which—

(i) arise on or before the date on which a relevant event occurs, or

(ii) may arise at any time during the liability period,

from the exercise of rights conferred upon the code operator by paragraph 9 of the electronic communications code;

(b) on 1st April each year, provide OFCOM with the certificate the requirements of which are set out in paragraphs (2) to (6) inclusive unless he has not previously exercised any rights conferred by the electronic communications code; and

(c) where he has not previously exercised any rights conferred by the electronic communications code and intends to exercise such rights for the first time, provide OFCOM with the said certificate two weeks before he exercises such rights to install any apparatus.

(2) The certificate shall be signed by—

(a) the director or the company secretary, in the case of a company;

(b) a member, in the case of a body corporate the conduct of the management of which is vested in its members;

(c) a member of the management committee, in the case of a body (whether or not incorporated) not falling within subparagraph (a), (b) or (d);

(d) one of the partners, in the case of a partnership;

(e) the code operator himself, in the case of an individual;

and, in a case falling within subparagraph (a), (b) or (c), shall be approved by a resolution of the board, the body corporate or the management committee, as the case may be.

(3) The certificate shall state that in the reasonable opinion of—

(a) the board, in the case of a company;

(b) the body corporate, in the case of a body corporate the conduct of the management of which is vested in its members;

(c) the management committee, in the case of a body (whether or not incorporated) not falling within subparagraph (a), (b) or (d);

(d) the partner signing the certificate, in the case of a partnership; or

(e) the code operator himself, in the case of an individual;

the code operator has fulfilled his duty under paragraph (1).

(4) In a case falling within subparagraph (a), (b) or (c) of paragraph (3), the board, the body corporate or the management committee, as the case may be, shall not make the statement in paragraph (3) unless it has first made appropriate enquiries into whether the code operator has fulfilled its duty under paragraph (1).

(5) The certificate shall state—

(a) the amount of the funds which have been provided for, and

(b) the systems and processes which enabled the board, the body corporate, the management committee, the partner or the code operator himself as the case may be, to form the opinion referred to in paragraph (3).

(6) The certificate shall be accompanied by copies of any insurance policy, bond, guarantee or other instrument which will provide the funds in paragraph (1)(a).

(7) Where OFCOM are not satisfied that a code operator has discharged his duty under paragraph (1) they may—

(a) direct that code operator to take such steps as they consider appropriate for the purpose of securing that sufficient funds are available to meet the specified liabilities; and

(b) publish details of any direction under subparagraph (a).

(8) Where OFCOM give a direction under paragraph (7)(a), the code operator shall comply with it.

(9) A code operator shall inform OFCOM in writing immediately if he becomes aware of any circumstance which causes him to be unable to fulfil his duty under paragraph (1).

(10) In this regulation—

"board" means the board of directors of a company;

"liability period" means the period commencing on the occurrence of a relevant event and ending on the third anniversary thereof;

"management committee" means the group of individuals in which the conduct of the management of a body of persons, other than a company, a partnership or a body corporate the conduct of the management of which is vested in its members, is vested;

a "relevant event" occurs if—

(a) a code operator becomes subject to a direction under the Act by virtue of which he is prohibited from providing the electronic communications network for the purposes of the provision of which the electronic communications code was applied to him by a direction under section 106(3)(a) of the Act;

(b) a code operator ceases to provide an electronic communications network;

(c) a code operator is deemed to be unable to pay his debts;

(d) a code operator enters into administration, receivership or liquidation;

(e) any person takes action for the voluntary winding-up, dissolution, bankruptcy or sequestration of a code operator;

(f) an administrator, receiver, trustee or similar officer of a code operator, or of all or any material part of the revenues and assets of that operator, is appointed;

(g) any order is made for the compulsory winding-up, dissolution, bankruptcy or sequestration of a code operator;

"specified liabilities" are—

(a) liabilities, including liabilities for the payment of indemnities in respect of costs or expenses incurred, arising under the New Roads and Street Works Act 1991 or, in Northern Ireland, the Street Works (Northern Ireland) Order 1995 towards—

(i) any appropriate authority, traffic authority or responsible authority;

(ii) any other person having the authority to execute works in, or having apparatus in, a street or, in Scotland, a road;

(iii) any concessionaire within the meaning of section 1 of that Act of 1991 or, in the case of Northern Ireland, within the meaning of article 23(1) of the Roads (Northern Ireland) Order 1993;

(b) any other costs or expenses reasonably incurred by any appropriate authority or responsible authority in making good any damage caused by the installation or removal of electronic communications apparatus, whether such damage occurs before or after a relevant event;

(c) any other costs or expenses reasonably incurred by any appropriate authority or responsible authority after a relevant event occurs in removing any electronic communications apparatus—

(i) which is installed under, over, along or across a street;

(ii) which is not, or is no longer, used for the purposes of any electronic communications network and in relation to which there is no reasonable likelihood that it will be so used; and

(iii) the removal of which is desirable having regard to any harm it may cause to other persons or property or to the visual amenity of land or buildings in proximity to which the apparatus is installed.

(11) A code operator shall, for the purposes of this regulation, be deemed to be unable to pay its debts if—

(a) where it is a company registered under the enactments relating to companies for the time being in force in the United Kingdom, it satisfies any of the requirements in section 123 of the Insolvency Act 1986, except that, for the purposes of this regulation, the figure of "£750" in section 123 of that Act, or such other sum as may be specified from time to time pursuant to section 416 of that Act, shall be replaced by "£250,000";

(b) where it is a company which is not so registered, it satisfies any of the requirements in section 222, 223 or 224 of the Insolvency Act 1986, except that, for the purposes of this regulation, the figure of "£750" in section 222 of that Act, or such other sum as may be specified from time to time pursuant to section 417 of that Act, shall be replaced by "£250,000";

(c) where it is a partnership—

(i) it satisfies any of the requirements in section 222, 223 or 224 of the Insolvency Act 1986 (as modified by paragraphs 4 and 5 of Part I of Schedule 3 to the Insolvent Partnerships Order 1994), except that for the purposes of this regulation the figure of "£750" in section 222 of that Act, or such other sum as may be specified from time to time pursuant to section 417 of that Act, shall be replaced by "£250,000";

(ii) it is apparently insolvent within the meaning of section 7 of the Bankruptcy (Scotland) Act 1985, except that for the purposes of this regulation the figure of "£750" in section 7 of that Act, or such other sum as may be specified from time to time by any enactment which amends section 7, shall be replaced by "£250,000"; or

(iii) it satisfies any of the requirements in article 186, 187 or 188 of the Insolvency (Northern Ireland) Order 1989 (as modified by paragraphs 4, 5 and 6 of Part I of Schedule 3 to the Insolvent Partnerships Order (Northern Ireland) 1995), except that for the purposes of this regulation the figure of "£750" in article 186 of the Order of 1989, or such other sum as may be specified from time to time pursuant to article 362(1)(a) of that Order, shall be replaced by "£250,000";

(d) where he is an individual—

(i) he satisfies either of the requirements in section 268(1) of the Insolvency Act 1986 and the debt, or the aggregate amount of the debts, that he owes is equal to or more than £250,000;

(ii) he is apparently insolvent within the meaning of section 7 of the Bankruptcy (Scotland) Act 1985, except that for the purposes of this regulation the figure of "£750" in section 7 of that Act, or such other sum as may be specified from time to time by any enactment amending section 7, shall be replaced by "£250,000"; or

(iii) he satisfies either of the requirements in article 242(1) of the Insolvency (Northern Ireland) Order 1989 and the debt, or the aggregate amount of the debts, that he owes is equal to or more than £250,000.

(12) In the definition of "relevant event" in paragraph (10), the reference to a code operator's becoming subject to a direction by virtue of which he is prohibited from providing the electronic communications network for the purposes of the provision of which the electronic communications code was applied to him—

(a) does not include a reference to his becoming subject to a direction which will have to be revoked if not confirmed, but

(b) does include a reference to the confirmation of a direction which would otherwise have had to be revoked.

[3581]

NOTES

Commencement: 23 October 2003.

17 Production of guidelines

(1) A code operator shall co-operate with planning authorities and with highway authorities or, in Scotland, roads authorities in the production of guidelines on the manner in which code operators should conduct the installation, including the positioning, of—

(a) cabinets, boxes, pillars, pedestals and other similar apparatus installed above the ground;

(b) lines and service line distribution points affixed to and lying on the exterior surface of buildings or other permanent structures; and

(c) apparatus installed on or above the ground in proximity to a building notified by the planning authority to the code operator as being on the statutory list of buildings.

(2) A code operator shall comply with the guidelines referred to in paragraph (1) from the date on which they come into effect.

(3) A code operator shall provide OFCOM with a copy of the guidelines referred to in paragraph (1).

[3582]

NOTES

Commencement: 23 October 2003.

18 Transitional provision

In relation to times before an order made under section 411 of the Act brings sections 106 to 119 inclusive of the Act into force for the purpose of conferring on OFCOM the functions contained in those sections, references to OFCOM in these Regulations are to be treated as references to the Director General of Telecommunications.

[3583]

NOTES

Commencement: 23 October 2003.

DISSOLUTION OF THE INDEPENDENT BROADCASTING AUTHORITY ORDER 2003

(SI 2003/2554)

NOTES

Made: 2 October 2003.
Authority: Broadcasting Act 1990, s 127(3), (6).
Commencement: 2 October 2003.

1 This Order may be cited as the Dissolution of the Independent Broadcasting Authority Order 2003.

[3584]

NOTES

Commencement: 2 October 2003.

2 The Independent Broadcasting Authority are hereby dissolved with effect from 2nd October 2003.

[3585]

NOTES

Commencement: 2 October 2003.

ELECTRONIC COMMUNICATIONS (NETWORKS AND SERVICES) (PENALTIES) (RULES FOR CALCULATION OF TURNOVER) ORDER 2003

(SI 2003/2712)

NOTES

Made: 22 October 2003.
Authority: Communications Act 2003, ss 97(3)(a), 402(3)(a).
Commencement: 27 October 2003.

1 Citation and commencement

This Order may be cited as the Electronic Communications (Networks and Services) (Penalties) (Rules for Calculation of Turnover) Order 2003 and shall come into force on 27th October 2003.

[3586]

NOTES

Commencement: 27 October 2003.

2 Interpretation

In this Order:

"the Act" means the Communications Act 2003; and

"notified provider" has the same meaning as in section 96 of the Act.

[3587]

NOTES

Commencement: 27 October 2003.

3 Rules for Calculation of turnover for the purposes of section 97

The rules for the calculation of turnover of a notified provider's relevant business for a relevant period for the purposes of section 97 of the Act shall be the rules set out in the Schedule to this Order.

[3588]

NOTES

Commencement: 27 October 2003.

SCHEDULE

RULES FOR CALCULATION OF TURNOVER FOR PURPOSES OF SECTION 97

Rule 3

General rules

1. The turnover of a notified provider shall be calculated in conformity with accounting practices and principles which are generally accepted in the United Kingdom.

2. The turnover of a notified provider shall be limited to the amounts derived by that provider from the relevant business after deduction of sales rebates, value added tax and other taxes directly related to turnover.

3. When a notified provider's relevant business consists of two or more undertakings that each prepare accounts then the turnover shall be calculated by adding together the turnover of each, save that no account shall be taken of any turnover resulting from the supply of goods or the provision of services between them.

Rules about aids granted to a notified provider

4. Any aid (within the meaning of Article 87 of the EC Treaty) granted by a public body to a notified provider which relates to one of that provider's ordinary activities shall be included in the calculation of turnover if the notified provider is himself the recipient of the aid and if the aid is directly linked to the carrying out by that provider of the relevant business.

[3589]

NOTES

Commencement: 27 October 2003.

OFFICE OF COMMUNICATIONS ACT 2002 (COMMENCEMENT NO 3) AND COMMUNICATIONS ACT 2003 (COMMENCEMENT NO 2) ORDER 2003

(SI 2003/3142)

NOTES

Made: 8 December 2003.

Authority: Office of Communications Act 2002, s 7(2); Communications Act 2003, ss 408(6)(b), 411(2), (4).

ARRANGEMENT OF ARTICLES

1 Citation, interpretation and revocation

(1) This Order may be cited as the Office of Communications Act 2002 (Commencement No 3) and Communications Act 2003 (Commencement No 2) Order 2003.

(2) In this Order—

"the 1949 Act" means the Wireless Telegraphy Act 1949;

"the 1990 Act" means the Broadcasting Act 1990;

"the 1996 Act" means the Broadcasting Act 1996;

"BSC" means the Broadcasting Standards Commission;

"the first commencement order" means the Communications Act 2003 (Commencement No 1) Order 2003;

"ITC" means the Independent Television Commission;

"the principal Act" means the Communications Act 2003;

"television licence" and "television receiver" have the meanings provided by section 1(7) of the 1949 Act; and

"the transitionally commenced provisions" has the same meaning as in the first commencement order.

(3) Article 3(2) of the first commencement order is revoked.

[3590]

2 Commencement on 12th December 2003

Section 282 of and paragraphs 10 and 17 of Schedule 14 to the principal Act shall come into force on 12th December 2003.

[3591]

3 Commencement on 29th December 2003

(1) Paragraph 12 of the Schedule to the Office of Communications Act 2002 and the provisions of the principal Act set out in Schedule 1 hereto shall, subject to the exceptions set out therein and to paragraph (3) below, come into force on 29th December 2003.

(2) The transitionally commenced provisions are brought into force by this Order on 29th December 2003 for the purpose of conferring the networks and services functions and the spectrum functions on OFCOM.

(3) Section 2 of, and paragraph 1(1)(a) of Schedule 1 and paragraphs 6 and 15 of Schedule 17 to, the principal Act shall not come into force on 29th December 2003 to the extent that the 1949 Act applies in respect of television licences and television receivers; and until those provisions are further brought into force by article 4 below on 1st April 2004—

(a) the 1949 Act shall continue to apply in respect of television licences and television receivers as it applies immediately before 29th December 2003,

(b) the reference to section 1(7) of the 1949 Act in section 1(1) of the Wireless Telegraphy Act 1998 shall be construed accordingly,

(c) the reference to the enactments relating to the management of the radio spectrum in section 394(2)(c) of the principal Act shall be construed in respect of television licences and television receivers as a reference to those enactments as they apply immediately before 29th December 2003, and

(d) section 15 of the 1949 Act shall apply in respect of television licences and television receivers as if references therein to the Secretary of State included references to OFCOM, save that in respect of television licences and television receivers, OFCOM may do under the said section 15 only those things which they will be able to do under section 366 of the principal Act when it comes into force on 1st April 2004.

[3592]

4 Subsequent commencement

(1) Section 253 of the principal Act shall come into force on 2nd January 2004.

[(1A) Section 367 of the principal Act shall come into force on 9th March 2004 for the purposes of enabling regulations to be made under section 6(1) of the Wireless Telegraphy Act 1967 as amended by that section.]

(2) The provisions of the principal Act set out in Schedule 2 hereto shall come into force on 1st April 2004.

(3) …

[(4) The following provisions of the principal Act shall come into force on 1st July 2004—

(a) section 278;

(b) sections 351 and 353 (so far as not already in force); and

(c) paragraph 8 of Schedule 12.]

[3593]

NOTES

Para (1A): inserted by the Office of Communications Act 2002 (Commencement No 3) and Communications Act 2003 (Commencement No 2) (Amendment No 2) Order 2004, SI 2004/697, art 2(1), (2).

Para (3): revoked by the Office of Communications Act 2002 (Commencement No 3) and Communications Act 2003 (Commencement No 2) (Amendment No 3) Order 2004, SI 2004/1492, art 2.

Para (4): added by the Office of Communications Act 2002 (Commencement No 3) and Communications Act 2003 (Commencement No 2) (Amendment) Order 2004, SI 2004/545, art 2(1), (2).

5 Transitional provision: advisory bodies under Telecommunications Act 1984, section 54

If, upon the repeal of section 54 of the Telecommunications Act 1984 on 29th December 2003, any of the advisory bodies established thereunder has not ceased to exist by virtue of an order under section 31(5) of the principal Act, subsections (7) and (8) of the said section 54 shall continue to have effect in respect of that body until it ceases to exist as if the reference to the Director in subsection (7) were a reference to OFCOM and the reference thereto in subsection (8) were omitted.

[3594]

6 Transitional provisions: Independent Television Commission, Radio Authority and Broadcasting Standards Commission

(1) In any period between the repeal of section 1 of and Schedule 1 to the 1990 Act on 29th December 2003 and the day on which the ITC ceases to exist by virtue of an order under section 31(4) of the principal Act—

(a) the ITC—

(i) shall continue in existence only for one or more of the purposes specified in this paragraph or for any purpose connected with the making or coming into force of a scheme under section 30 of the principal Act, and

(ii) in that period shall consist of a chairman appointed by the Secretary of State and, if the Secretary of State thinks fit, such one or more other persons as he may appoint as members of the ITC;

(b) the said section 1 (except for subsection (2)(b)) and, subject to the following subparagraphs, Schedule 1 (except for paragraph 2(3) and in paragraph 9(1) the words "shall appoint a secretary and" and "other") and any definitions relevant to their interpretation the repeal of which is brought into force on 29th December 2003 shall continue to have effect during that period for those purposes;

(c) the ITC shall prepare a statement of accounts and annual report for the period beginning on 1st January 2003 and ending with 28th December 2003;

(d) Schedule 1 to the 1990 Act shall have effect for the purposes of the accounts and report referred to in subparagraph (c) above as if any reference to "financial year" or "year" were a reference to the period referred to in that subparagraph;

(e) the ITC shall prepare a statement of accounts in respect of the period of twelve months beginning on 29th December in any year; and

(f) Schedule 1 to the 1990 Act shall have effect for the purposes of any accounts referred to in subparagraph (e) above as if any reference to the "financial year" or "year" were a reference to the period referred to in that subparagraph.

(2) In any period between the repeal of section 83 of and Schedule 8 to the 1990 Act on 29th December 2003 and the day on which the Radio Authority ceases to exist by virtue of an order under section 31(4) of the principal Act—

(a) the Authority—

(i) shall continue in existence only for one or more of the purposes specified in this paragraph or for any purpose connected with the making or coming into force of a scheme under section 30 of the principal Act, and

(ii) in that period shall consist of a chairman appointed by the Secretary of State and, if the Secretary of State thinks fit, such one or more other persons as he may appoint as members of the Authority;

(b) the said section 83 (except for subsection (2)(b)) and, subject to the following subparagraphs, Schedule 8 (except for the words "shall appoint a secretary and" and "other" in paragraph 9(1)) and any definitions relevant to their interpretation the repeal of which is brought into force on 29th December 2003 shall continue to have effect during that period for those purposes;

(c) the Authority shall prepare a statement of accounts and annual report for the period beginning on 1st January 2003 and ending with 28th December 2003;

(d) Schedule 8 to the 1990 Act shall have effect for the purposes of the accounts and report referred to in subparagraph (c) above as if any reference to "financial year" or "year" were a reference to the period referred to in that subparagraph;

(e) the Authority shall prepare a statement of accounts in respect of the period of twelve months beginning on 29th December in any year; and

(f) Schedule 8 to the 1990 Act shall have effect for the purposes of any accounts referred to in subparagraph (e) above as if any reference to the "financial year" or "year" were a reference to the period referred to in that subparagraph.

(3) In any period between the repeal of sections 106, 121 and 125 of and Schedule 3 to the 1996 Act on 29th December 2003 and the day on which the BSC ceases to exist by virtue of an order under section 31(4) of the principal Act—

(a) the BSC—

(i) shall continue in existence only for one or more of the purposes specified in this paragraph or for any purpose connected with the making or coming into force of a scheme under section 30 of the principal Act, and

(ii) in that period shall consist of a chairman appointed by the Secretary of State and, if the Secretary of State thinks fit, such one or more other persons as he may appoint as members of the BSC;

(b) the said sections 106 (except for the words from "or" in subsection (2)(b) to the end of subsection (2)), 121 and, subject to the following subparagraphs, 125 and Schedule 3 and any definitions relevant to their interpretation the repeal of which is brought into force on 29th December 2003 shall continue to have effect during that period for those purposes;

(c) the BSC shall prepare a statement of accounts and annual report for the period beginning on 1st April 2003 and ending with 28th December 2003;

(d) section 125 of and Schedule 3 to the 1996 Act shall have effect for the purposes of the accounts and report referred to in subparagraph (c) above as if—

(i) any reference to "financial year" or "year" were a reference to the period referred to in that subparagraph, and

(ii) any reference to a person providing a licensed service were a reference to a person providing such a service immediately before 29th December 2003;

(e) the BSC shall prepare a statement of accounts in respect of the period of twelve months beginning on 29th December in any year; and

(f) section 125 of and Schedule 3 to the 1996 Act shall have effect for the purposes of any accounts referred to in subparagraph (e) above as if—
  (i) any reference to the "financial year" or "year" were a reference to the period referred to in that subparagraph, and
  (ii) any reference to a person providing a licensed service were a reference to a person providing such a service immediately before 29th December 2003.

[3595]

7 Transitional provision: section 199 of the principal Act

In relation to any period between the commencement of section 199 of the principal Act and the commencement of section 265 of that Act, the reference in subsection (2)(b) of section 199 to "the public service remit for that Channel under section 265" shall have effect, notwithstanding any repeal brought into force by this Order, as if the public service remit for Channel Four consisted of the requirements to be complied with by that Channel which are specified in subsection (1) and paragraphs (a) and (b) of subsection (2) of section 25 of the 1990 Act.

[3596]

8 Transitional provisions: section 221 of the principal Act

(1) Sections 219, 220 and 298 of and Schedule 10 to the principal Act shall not apply in relation to the existing licence referred to in section 221(1) thereof.

(2) Sections 276 and 308 of and paragraph 21(4) of Schedule 15 to the principal Act shall not apply in relation to the existing service as defined in section 221(11) thereof.

[3597]

9 Transitional provision: section 237 of the principal Act

Section 237 of the principal Act applies in relation to a contravention of a condition of a licence or a failure to comply with a direction only if it is one occurring after the commencement of that section.

[3598]

10 Transitional provisions: existing legislation

(1) The repeal of sections 45(5) to (6A) and 47(8) to (9A) of the 1990 Act shall not affect the operation of section 41 of that Act, as applied by those provisions, in relation to any matter arising before the coming into force of those repeals.

(2) In the period beginning with the transfer of functions from the ITC to OFCOM on 29th December 2003 in accordance with the provisions of the principal Act brought into force by this Order and ending immediately before section 299(1) of the principal Act is brought into force by this Order on 30th June 2004, for the reference to "the Commission" in section 97(2)(c) of the 1996 Act there shall be substituted a reference to "OFCOM".

(3) In relation to any time between the commencement of the repeal of section 2 of the 1990 Act on 29th December 2003 and the commencement of the repeal of section 181 of that Act on 1st April 2004, section 181 shall have effect as if the definition of "television broadcasting service" in subsection (4) were—

> ""television broadcasting service" means a television broadcasting service within the meaning of Part 3 of the Communications Act 2003, whether provided by the holder of a licence under Part 1 of this Act or by the BBC or the Welsh Authority."

(4) In relation to any time between the commencement of the repeal of section 2 of the 1990 Act on 29th December 2003 and the coming into force of any revocation of regulation 3 of the Wireless Telegraphy (Television Licence Fees) Regulations 1997, the reference in that regulation to "television programme services" as defined by section 2(4) of the 1990 Act shall be read as if it were a reference to such services as defined by section 362 of the principal Act.

[3599]

11 Transitional provision: complaints to Broadcasting Standards Commission

(1) This article shall apply to a standards complaint made to, but not disposed of by, the BSC before the transfer to OFCOM on 29th December 2003, in accordance with the provisions of the principal Act brought into force by this Order, of the functions of the BSC under Part 5 of the 1996 Act.

(2) The standards complaint shall be treated as if—

(a) anything done, or treated as done, by or in relation to the BSC for the purposes of, or in connection with, that complaint had been done by or in relation to OFCOM; and

(b) those functions had been functions of OFCOM at the time when it was done.

(3) The procedure for the handling and resolution of complaints established by OFCOM under section 325 of the principal Act shall apply in relation to anything remaining to be done for the purposes of, or in connection with, the complaint.

(4) In exercising their functions in relation to the complaint, OFCOM shall apply any relevant provisions of the code maintained by the BSC under section 108 of the 1996 Act immediately before 29th December 2003.

(5) In this article, "standards complaint" has the same meaning as in Part 5 of the 1996 Act, notwithstanding any repeal brought into force by this Order.

[3600]

SCHEDULE 1
PROVISIONS OF THE COMMUNICATIONS ACT 2003 COMING INTO FORCE ON 29TH DECEMBER 2003

Article 3(1)

The following sections so far as not already in force: 1, 26, 31, 56 to 63, 152, 350, 360, 369, 393 and 394.

Section 2, except as provided in article 3(3) of this Order.

Sections 3, 6 to 23, 27, 120 to 124, 155 to 163, 168, 170, 171, 175 to 177, 182 and 198 to 230.

Section 231, except for subsection (1) and paragraph (c) of subsection (2).

Sections 232 to 252, 254 to 263, 271, 275 to 277, 279 to 281 and 283 to 298.

Section 299(2).

Sections 301 to 337.

Section 338 in respect of the provisions of Schedule 12 set out in this Schedule.

Sections 339 to 349.

Section 351, except for subparagraph (i) in subsection (4)(a), the definition of "original production" in subsection (10) and paragraph (a) of the definition of "peak viewing time" in subsection (10).

Section 352.

Section 353, except for subparagraph (i) in subsection (4)(a), the definition of "original production" in subsection (7) and paragraph (a) of the definition of "peak viewing time" in subsection (7).

Sections 354 to 359, 372 to 392 and 400.

Section 406(1), (6) and (7) in respect of the provisions of Schedules 17, 18 and 19 set out in this Schedule.

In Schedule 1—

paragraph 1(1)(a), except as provided in article 3(3) of this Order;
paragraph 1(1)(b) to (d), (2) and (3);
paragraphs 2 to 14.

Schedules 5, 7 and 9 to 11.

In Schedule 12, paragraphs 1 to 4, 7 and 9 to 24.

Schedule 13.

Schedules 14 and 15 (so far as not already in force).

Schedule 16.

In Schedule 17—

the following paragraphs so far as not already in force: 8, 9, 11, 14, 37, 72, 73, 129, 147, 150, 166 and 174;

paragraphs 12, 13, 17, 34 to 36, 39, 48 to 50, 61, 62, 64 to 69, 74, 76, 83, 91 to 93, 132, 145, 146, 148, 151, 161(1) and (3), 164, 167 and 171 to 173;
paragraphs 6(1), (2) and (4) to (7) and 15, except as provided in article 3(3) of this Order.

In Schedule 18—
paragraphs 5, 6, 20, 27 to 29, 31 to 53 and 59 to 62;
paragraph 54 (so far as not already in force).

In Schedule 19—
the entries for—
Wireless Telegraphy Act 1949, section 1D(8) (so far as not already in force);
Parliamentary Commissioner Act 1967;
Wireless Telegraphy Act 1967, section 7(5);
Fair Trading Act 1973;
House of Commons Disqualification Act 1975;
Northern Ireland Assembly Disqualification Act 1975;
Welsh Development Agency Act 1975;
Telecommunications Act 1984, except in respect of sections 1 and 55 and Schedule 1;
Copyright, Designs and Patents Act 1988 (so far as not already in force);
Companies Act 1989 (so far as not already in force);
Broadcasting Act 1990, except in respect of sections 180 and 181 and Schedule 18;
Competition and Service (Utilities) Act 1992 (so far as not already in force);
Deregulation and Contracting Out Act 1994 (so far as not already in force);
Criminal Procedure (Consequential Provisions) (Scotland) Act 1995;
Broadcasting Act 1996;
Planning (Consequential Provisions) (Scotland) Act 1997;
Wireless Telegraphy Act 1998, sections 3 and 5;
Competition Act 1998 (so far as not already in force);
Freedom of Information Act 2000, except in respect of the entries relating to the Broadcasting Standards Commission, the Independent Television Commission and the Radio Authority;
Transport Act 2000 (so far as not already in force);
Political Parties, Elections and Referendums Act 2000;
Anti-terrorism, Crime and Security Act 2001;
Office of Communications Act 2002;
Tobacco Advertising and Promotion Act 2002;
Enterprise Act 2002 (so far as not already in force);
European Parliament (Representation) Act 2003;
note 3;
the entry for the Race Relations (Northern Ireland) Order 1997.

[3601]

SCHEDULE 2
PROVISIONS OF THE COMMUNICATIONS ACT 2003 COMING INTO FORCE ON 1ST APRIL 2004

Article 4(2)

[Section 2] (so far as not already in force).

[Sections 363 to 366, 367 (so far as not already in force) and 368.]

Section 406(1) and (7) in respect of the provisions of Schedules 17 and 19 set out in this Schedule.

Section 406(6) (so far as not already in force).

Schedule 1 (so far as not already in force).

…

In Schedule 17—
the following paragraphs so far as not already in force: 6, 15 and 161;
paragraphs 133(1) and (3) and 159.

Schedule 18 (so far as not already in force).

In Schedule 19, the entries for—
Wireless Telegraphy Act 1949 (so far as not already in force);

Wireless Telegraphy Act 1967 (so far as not already in force);
Broadcasting Act 1990 (so far as not already in force);
Criminal Procedure (Scotland) Act 1995;
Wireless Telegraphy Act 1998 (so far as not already in force).

[3602]

NOTES

Words in first pair of square brackets substituted, and entry omitted revoked, by the Office of Communications Act 2002 (Commencement No 3) and Communications Act 2003 (Commencement No 2) (Amendment) Order 2004, SI 2004/545, art 2(1), (3)(a), (c).

Entry "Sections 363 to 366, 367 (so far as not already in force) and 368" substituted by the Office of Communications Act 2002 (Commencement No 3) and Communications Act 2003 (Commencement No 2) (Amendment No 2) Order 2004, SI 2004/697, art 2(1), (3).

TELEPHONE NUMBER EXCLUSION (DOMAIN NAMES AND INTERNET ADDRESSES) ORDER 2003

(SI 2003/3281)

NOTES

Made: 15 December 2003.
Authority: Communications Act 2003, s 56(7).
Commencement: 29 December 2003.

1 Citation and commencement

This Order may be cited as the Telephone Number Exclusion (Domain Names and Internet Addresses) Order 2003 and shall come into force on 29th December 2003.

[3603]

NOTES

Commencement: 29 December 2003.

2 Exclusion

Any number which is used as—

(a) an internet domain name;
(b) an internet address; or
(c) an address or identifier incorporating either an internet domain name or an internet address, including an email address,

shall be excluded from treatment as a telephone number for the purposes of Chapter 1 of Part 2 of the Communications Act 2003.

[3604]

NOTES

Commencement: 29 December 2003.

MEDIA OWNERSHIP (LOCAL RADIO AND APPOINTED NEWS PROVIDER) ORDER 2003

(SI 2003/3299)

NOTES

Made: 17 December 2003.
Authority: Communications Act 2003, ss 282(1), 402(3), Sch 14, paras 10–13.
Commencement: 29 December 2003.

ARRANGEMENT OF ARTICLES

PART 1
GENERAL PROVISIONS

PART 2
REQUIREMENTS APPLYING TO LOCAL SOUND BROADCASTING LICENCES

PART 3
REQUIREMENTS APPLYING TO LOCAL DIGITAL SOUND PROGRAMME SERVICES

PART 1
GENERAL PROVISIONS

1 Citation and commencement

(1) This Order may be cited as the Media Ownership (Local Radio and Appointed News Provider) Order 2003.

(2) This Order comes into force on 29th December 2003.

[3605]

NOTES

Commencement: 29 December 2003.

2 Interpretation of the Order

(1) In this Order—

"the 1990 Act" means the Broadcasting Act 1990;
"the 1996 Act" means the Broadcasting Act 1996; and
"the 2003 Act" means the Communications Act 2003.

(2) Expressions used in this Order and in Part 3 of the 2003 Act have the same meanings in this Order as they have in that Part.

[3606]

NOTES

Commencement: 29 December 2003.

[2A Community radio licences

Nothing in this Order shall apply in respect of—

(a) any local sound broadcasting service that is a community radio service, as defined by article 2(1) of the Community Radio Order 2004, or
(b) any licence to provide such a service.]

[3607]

NOTES
Commencement: 20 July 2004.
Inserted by the Community Radio Order 2004, SI 2004/1944, art 5.

3 Connected persons

(1) For the purposes of this Order—
(a) any person connected with a person who holds a licence shall be treated as if he also were a holder of that licence, and
(b) any person connected with a person who provides a local digital sound programme service shall be treated as if he also were providing that service,
and references to a person becoming the holder of a licence, or beginning to provide a service, shall be construed accordingly.

(2) References in this article to a person being connected with any other person shall be construed in accordance with Part 1 of Schedule 2 to the 1990 Act.

(3) But a person shall not be treated as holding a local sound broadcasting licence or a local digital sound programme licence, or providing a local digital sound programme service, merely because he is the director of a body corporate which holds the licence or (as the case may be) provides the service.

[3608]

NOTES
Commencement: 29 December 2003.

PART 2
REQUIREMENTS APPLYING TO LOCAL SOUND BROADCASTING LICENCES

4 Interpretation of Part 2

(1) In this Part, "potential audience" means, in relation to a local sound broadcasting service or a regional Channel 3 service, the persons who have attained the age of 15 years and reside within the coverage area for that service.

(2) For the purposes of this Part, two local sound broadcasting licences overlap if (but only if) the potential audience of the service provided under either of those licences includes 50 per cent or more of the potential audience of the service provided under the other licence.

(3) For the purposes of this Part, the coverage area for a service provided under a local sound broadcasting licence or a regional Channel 3 licence is the area in the United Kingdom within which that service is capable of being received at a level satisfying such technical standards as have been laid down by OFCOM for the purposes of this Part.

(4) Paragraphs 3 and 4 of Part 1 of Schedule 14 to the 2003 Act (which contain provisions concerning local and national newspapers and their market shares and provisions for the construction of references to running a newspaper) apply for the purposes of this Part of this Order as they apply for the purposes of that Part of that Schedule.

[3609]

NOTES
Commencement: 29 December 2003.

5 Restriction on holding more than two overlapping licences

(1) A person ("the relevant person") who holds at least two local sound broadcasting licences may not hold a further such licence ("the further licence") in any case where, if he were to do so, the conditions in paragraph (2) would be satisfied in relation to any licence held by him ("the licence in question") at the time immediately after he became the holder of the further licence.

(2) The conditions are that—

(a) the licence in question overlaps with any two other local sound broadcasting licences held by the relevant person which also overlap with each other;

(b) one of the licences mentioned in sub-paragraph (a) is the further licence; and

(c) the limit on concentration is contravened in the case of the licence in question.

(3) For the purposes of paragraph (2), the limit on concentration is contravened in the case of the licence in question if the first total represents more than 55 per cent of the second total.

(4) The first total is the aggregate number of points attributable (according to the table in article 8) to—

(a) the licence in question; and

(b) any other local sound broadcasting licences held by the relevant person and of a description mentioned in the first column of the table in article 8.

(5) The second total is the aggregate number of points attributable to the licence in question and all other local sound broadcasting licences of a description mentioned in the first column of the table in article 8 (regardless of who holds them).

[3610]

NOTES

Commencement: 29 December 2003.

6 Cross-media ownership

(1) A person ("the relevant person") may not hold a local sound broadcasting licence ("the relevant licence") in any case where, if he were to do so, then, at the time immediately after he became the holder of the relevant licence—

(a) he would be a person of a description falling within paragraph (2); and

(b) the conditions in paragraph (3) would be satisfied in relation to any licence that he holds ("the licence in question").

(2) The descriptions of persons referred to in paragraph (1) are—

(a) a person who runs a local newspaper which has a local market share of 50 per cent or more in the coverage area of the service provided under the licence in question;

(b) a person who runs local newspapers which together have a local market share of 50 per cent or more in that coverage area;

(c) a person who holds the licence to provide any regional Channel 3 service where at least 50 per cent of the potential audience of the service provided under the licence in question reside within the coverage area for that regional Channel 3 service.

(3) The conditions are that—

(a) the licence in question overlaps with any two other local sound broadcasting licences which also overlap with each other (regardless of who holds the other licences);

(b) one of the licences mentioned in sub-paragraph (a) is the relevant licence; and

(c) the limit on concentration is contravened in the case of the licence in question.

(4) For the purposes of paragraph (3), the limit on concentration is contravened in the case of the licence in question if the first total represents more than 45 per cent of the second total.

(5) The first total is the aggregate number of points attributable (according to the table in article 8) to—

(a) the licence in question; and

(b) any other local sound broadcasting licences held by the relevant person and of a description mentioned in the first column of the table in article 8.

(6) The second total is the aggregate number of points attributable to the licence in question and all other local sound broadcasting licences of a description mentioned in the first column of the table in article 8 (regardless of who holds them).

(7) Where—

(a) any person holds any local sound broadcasting licence which overlaps with any two other local sound broadcasting licences (regardless of who holds the other licences) which also overlap with each other,

(b) that person becomes a person of a description mentioned in paragraph (2) while he is the holder of such a licence, and

(c) at the time immediately after he becomes a person of that description, the condition in paragraph (3)(c) is satisfied in relation to any such licence that he holds,

that person may not then hold a local sound broadcasting licence in respect of which that condition is satisfied, taking, for the purposes of this paragraph, the references in paragraphs (2) to (6) to the licence in question to be references to the licence held by him mentioned in sub-paragraph (a) or (if there is more than one) each such licence in turn, and the reference in paragraph (5)(b) to the relevant person to be a reference to the person mentioned in sub-paragraph (a).

[3611]

NOTES

Commencement: 29 December 2003.

7 Application of articles 5 and 6 to changes in coverage area of local sound broadcasting services

(1) Where—

(a) a person (in this paragraph, "the relevant person") holds any local sound broadcasting licence which overlaps with any two other local sound broadcasting licences held by him which also overlap with each other,

(b) the coverage area for the service provided under any of the licences mentioned in sub-paragraph (a) changes at any time while the relevant person is the holder of that licence, and

(c) at the time immediately after that change takes effect, the condition in article 5(2)(c) is satisfied in relation to any of those licences,

the relevant person may not then hold the licence or (as the case may be) licences in respect of which that condition is satisfied, taking, for the purposes of this paragraph, the references in article 5 to the licence in question to be references to each licence such as is mentioned in sub-paragraph (a) in turn, and the reference in article 5(4)(b) to the relevant person to be a reference to the relevant person referred to in this paragraph.

(2) Where—

(a) a person of a description mentioned in article 6(2) (in this paragraph, "the relevant person") holds any local sound broadcasting licence which overlaps with any two other local sound broadcasting licences (regardless of who holds the other licences) which also overlap with each other,

(b) the coverage area for the service provided under any such licence changes at any time while the relevant person is its holder, and

(c) at the time immediately after that change takes effect, the condition in article 6(3)(c) is satisfied in relation to any such licence,

the relevant person may not then hold the licence or (as the case may be) licences in respect of which that condition is satisfied, taking, for the purposes of this paragraph, the references in article 6 to the licence in question to be references to the licence held by him mentioned in sub-paragraph (a) or (if there is more than one) each such licence in turn, and the reference in article 6(5)(b) to the relevant person to be a reference to the relevant person referred to in this paragraph.

[3612]

NOTES

Commencement: 29 December 2003.

8 Table referred to in articles 5 and 6

The table is as follows, and in the table—

(a) references to "the service in question" are references to the service provided under the licence that is the licence in question for the purposes of article 5 or 6 (as the case may require); and

(b) the number of points attributable to each licence of a description mentioned in an entry in the first column of the table is the number of points shown in the corresponding entry in the second column.

Description of licence	Number of points
The licence in question	4 points
Each local sound broadcasting licence under which is provided a service whose potential audience includes 75 per cent or more of the potential audience of the service in question	4 points
Each local sound broadcasting licence under which is provided a service whose potential audience includes at least 25 per cent of, but less than 75 per cent of, the potential audience of the service in question	2 points
Each local sound broadcasting licence under which is provided a service whose potential audience includes at least 5 per cent of, but less than 25 per cent of, the potential audience of the service in question	1 point

[3613]

NOTES

Commencement: 29 December 2003.

9 Prohibition on holding a local sound broadcasting licence, holding a Channel 3 licence, and running a local newspaper

No one person may at the same time—

(a) hold a local sound broadcasting licence ("the licence in question"); and

(b) hold the licence to provide any regional Channel 3 service the potential audience of which includes at least 50 per cent of the potential audience of the service provided under the licence in question; and

(c) run—

(i) a local newspaper which has a local market share of 50 per cent or more in the coverage area for the service provided under the licence in question, or

(ii) local newspapers which together have a local market share of 50 per cent or more in that coverage area.

[3614]

NOTES

Commencement: 29 December 2003.

PART 3
REQUIREMENTS APPLYING TO LOCAL DIGITAL SOUND PROGRAMME SERVICES

10 Interpretation of Part 3

(1) In this Part, "potential audience" means, in relation to a local radio multiplex service, the persons who have attained the age of 15 years and reside within the protected area for that service.

(2) For the purposes of this Part, a person who holds a licence to provide local digital sound programme services provides such a service if, and only if—

(a) the service is one provided by him and is included in a local radio multiplex service for which he holds a local radio multiplex licence; or

(b) under a contract between that person and a person who holds a licence to provide a local radio multiplex service, the person holding the licence to provide the radio multiplex service is required to include that local digital sound programme service in that multiplex service.

(3) In this Part, "the protected area" means, in relation to a local radio multiplex service—

(a) subject to sub-paragraph (b), the area or locality specified in a notice published under section 50(1) of the 1996 Act as that in which that multiplex service is to be available, or

(b) if different from that area or locality, the area or locality specified in the relevant licence as that in which that multiplex service is to be available,

and in this paragraph, "the relevant licence" means the local radio multiplex licence under which the multiplex service concerned is authorised to be provided.

[3615]

NOTES

Commencement: 29 December 2003.

11 Local digital sound programme services

(1) A person ("the relevant person") who provides local digital sound programme services under the authority of a local digital sound programme licence may not provide a further such service ("the further service") in any case where, if he did so, there would be a contravention of paragraph (2) at the time immediately after he began providing the further service.

(2) This paragraph is contravened if—

(a) the relevant person is already providing the threshold number, or more than that number, of local digital sound programme services; and

(b) the number of points attributable (according to Table 1 below) to local digital sound programme services provided by the relevant person in the market area of the relevant multiplex service represents more than 55 per cent of the total number of points attributable (according to Table 2) to all local digital sound programme services provided in that market area, whether by the relevant person or by any other person.

(3) For the purposes of paragraph (2), the threshold number of local digital sound programme services is four such services, comprising significant services or intermittent services (or any combination of significant services and intermittent services) that are included—

(a) in the relevant multiplex service; or

(b) in any other local radio multiplex service which overlaps with the relevant multiplex service, or in any two or more local radio multiplex services which so overlap, taking the number of significant or intermittent services in those multiplex services together; or

(c) in the relevant multiplex service and in one or more other local radio multiplex services such as are mentioned in sub-paragraph (b), taking the number of significant or intermittent services in those multiplex services together;

and for the purposes of this paragraph, two local radio multiplex services overlap if (but only if) the potential audience of either of those services includes 50 per cent or more of the potential audience of the other service.

(4) Subject to paragraph (5), in this article, "the relevant multiplex service" means the local radio multiplex service in which the further service is or is proposed to be included.

(5) In the case of a local radio multiplex service by means of different parts of which different selections of local digital sound programme services are made available for reception in different areas, any reference, in relation to a local digital sound programme service, to a local radio multiplex service is a reference to that part of that multiplex service in which that programme service is or is proposed to be included; and references to the market area, the potential audience and the protected area of such a multiplex service shall be construed accordingly.

(6) For the purposes of this article, a local digital sound programme service is provided in the market area of the relevant multiplex service if its provision is, or is to be, by means of its inclusion in that multiplex service or in any other local radio multiplex service the potential audience of which includes at least 5 per cent of the potential audience of the relevant multiplex service.

(7) The Tables referred to in paragraph (2)(b) are as follows, and the number of points attributable to services provided by the relevant person shall be calculated according to Table 1, and the total number of points attributable to all local digital sound programme services provided in the market area of the relevant multiplex, whether by the relevant person or by

any other person, shall be calculated according to Table 2, where the number of points attributable to each service of a description mentioned in an entry in the first column of a Table is the number of points shown in the corresponding entry in the second or third column (as the case may require) of that Table.

TABLE 1
NUMBER OF POINTS ATTRIBUTABLE TO SERVICES PROVIDED BY THE RELEVANT PERSON

Description of service	*Significant services*	*Intermittent services*
The further service	4	4
For each local digital sound programme service included in the relevant multiplex service	4	4
For each such service included in any other local radio multiplex service whose potential audience includes 75 per cent or more of the potential audience of the relevant multiplex service	4	4
For each such service included in any other local radio multiplex service whose potential audience includes at least 25 per cent, but less than 75 per cent, of the potential audience of the relevant multiplex service	2	2
For each such service included in any other local radio multiplex service whose potential audience includes at least 5 per cent, but less than 25 per cent, of the potential audience of the relevant multiplex service	1	1

TABLE 2
NUMBER OF POINTS ATTRIBUTABLE TO SERVICES WHETHER PROVIDED BY THE RELEVANT PERSON OR BY ANY OTHER PERSON

Description of service	*Significant services*	*Intermittent services*
The further service	4	0
For each local digital sound programme service included in the relevant multiplex service	4	0
For each such service included in any other local radio multiplex service whose potential audience includes 75 per cent or more of the potential audience of the relevant multiplex service	4	0

Description of service	*Significant services*	*Intermittent services*
For each such service included in any other local radio multiplex service whose potential audience includes at least 25 per cent, but less than 75 per cent, of the potential audience of the relevant multiplex service	2	0
For each such service included in any other local radio multiplex service whose potential audience includes at least 5 per cent, but less than 25 per cent, of the potential audience of the relevant multiplex service	1	0

(8) In this article, "significant service" and "intermittent service" mean, respectively, a local digital sound programme service determined by OFCOM to be a significant service or an intermittent service, in accordance with article 12.

[3616]

NOTES

Commencement: 29 December 2003.

12 "Significant" and "intermittent" services

(1) For the purposes of applying article 11, OFCOM shall determine, in the case of every local digital sound programme service falling to be considered for those purposes, whether that service is a "significant service", or is an "intermittent service", or is neither a significant service nor an intermittent service; and any such determination shall be made in accordance with the following provisions of this article.

(2) OFCOM—

(a) shall determine a local digital sound programme service to be a significant service if it appears to them to be broadcast for at least 126 hours every week over a period of at least three months, or to be proposed to be so broadcast; and

(b) may determine a local digital sound programme service to be a significant service if it appears to them to be broadcast for more than 100 hours every week over a period of at least three months, or to be proposed to be so broadcast.

(3) OFCOM—

(a) shall determine a local digital sound programme service to be an intermittent service if it does not appear to them to be a significant service, but appears to them to be broadcast for more than 72 hours in any period of three months, or to be proposed to be so broadcast; and

(b) may determine a service to be an intermittent service if it does not appear to them to be a significant service, but appears to them to be broadcast for more than 50 hours in any period of three months, or to be proposed to be so broadcast.

(4) As soon as reasonably practicable after making a determination under this article in the case of any local digital sound programme service, OFCOM must notify the person who holds the local digital sound programme licence under which that service is or is to be provided of their determination.

[3617]

NOTES

Commencement: 29 December 2003.

13, 14 ((*Pt 4*) *amends the Communications Act 2003, s 281, Sch 14, Pt 2 at* **[3337]**, **[3456]** *and the Broadcasting Act 1996, s 145* (*outside the scope of this work*).)

COMMUNITY RADIO ORDER 2004

(SI 2004/1944)

NOTES

Made: 19 July 2004.
Authority: Communications Act 2003, ss 262, 402(3), Sch 14, paras 11, 13.
Commencement: 20 July 2004.

ARRANGEMENT OF ARTICLES

1 Citation and commencement

(1) This Order may be cited as the Community Radio Order 2004.

(2) This Order shall come into force on the day after the day on which it is made.
[3618]

NOTES

Commencement: 20 July 2004.

2 Interpretation

(1) In this Order—

"the 1990 Act" means the Broadcasting Act 1990;
"the 2003 Act" means the Communications Act 2003;
"community" means—
(a) the persons who live or work or undergo education or training in a particular area or locality, or
(b) persons who (whether or not they fall within paragraph (a)) have one or more interests or characteristics in common;
"community radio licence" means a licence under Part 3 of the 1990 Act (as it has effect by virtue of this Order) to provide a community radio service;
"community radio service" means a local service having the characteristics set out in article 3;
"coverage area" means, in relation to a service provided under a local sound broadcasting licence, the area in the United Kingdom within which that service is capable of being received at a level satisfying such technical standards as have been laid down by OFCOM for the purposes of Part 2 of the Media Ownership (Local Radio and Appointed News Provider) Order 2003 in relation to such a service;
"local authority" has the meaning given in paragraph 1(1) of Part 1 of Schedule 2 to the 1990 Act;
"local service", "national service" and "restricted service" each has the meaning given in section 245(4) of the 2003 Act;
"potential audience" means, in relation to any local service, the persons who reside within the coverage area for that service;
"social enterprise" means a business which has as its primary objective the support of one or more projects of a social nature (rather than the production of a financial profit);
"social gain" has the meaning given by paragraph (2).

(2) In relation to a community radio service, "social gain" means the achievement, in respect of individuals or groups of individuals in the community that the service is intended to serve, or in respect of other members of the public, of the following objectives—

(a) the provision of sound broadcasting services to individuals who are otherwise underserved by such services,

(b) the facilitation of discussion and the expression of opinion,

(c) the provision (whether by means of programmes included in the service or otherwise) of education or training to individuals not employed by the person providing the service, and

(d) the better understanding of the particular community and the strengthening of links within it,

and may also include the achievement of other objectives of a social nature and, in particular, those mentioned in paragraph (3).

(3) Those objectives are—

(a) the delivery of services provided by local authorities and other services of a social nature and the increasing, and wider dissemination, of knowledge about those services and about local amenities;

(b) the promotion of economic development and of social enterprises;

(c) the promotion of employment;

(d) the provision of opportunities for the gaining of work experience;

(e) the promotion of social inclusion;

(f) the promotion of cultural and linguistic diversity;

(g) the promotion of civic participation and volunteering.

(4) For the purposes of this Order, two local sound broadcasting licences overlap if (but only if) the potential audience of the service provided under either of those licences includes 50 per cent or more of the potential audience of the service provided under the other licence.

(5) In this Order, in relation to any service which is intended to serve more than one community, any reference to the community which that service is intended to serve shall be taken to include a reference to every such community.

(6) In this Order, one person shall be treated as being connected with another person if he would be so treated for the purposes of Schedule 2 to the 1990 Act.

[3619]

NOTES

Commencement: 20 July 2004.

3 Characteristics of community radio services

(1) It is a characteristic of community radio services that they are local services provided primarily—

(a) for the good of members of the public, or of particular communities, and

(b) in order to deliver social gain,

rather than primarily for commercial reasons or for the financial or other material gain of the individuals involved in providing the service.

(2) It is a characteristic of every community radio service that it is intended primarily to serve one or more communities (whether or not it also serves other members of the public).

(3) It is a characteristic of every community radio service that the person providing the service—

(a) does not do so in order to make a financial profit by so doing, and

(b) uses any profit that is produced in the provision of the service wholly and exclusively for securing or improving the future provision of the service, or for the delivery of social gain to members of the public or the community that the service is intended to serve.

(4) It is a characteristic of every community radio service that members of the community it is intended to serve are given opportunities to participate in the operation and management of the service.

(5) It is a characteristic of every community radio service that, in respect of the provision of that service, the person providing the service makes himself accountable to the community that the service is intended to serve.

[3620]

NOTES
Commencement: 20 July 2004.

4 Application of broadcasting legislation

The provisions of the 1990 Act and the 2003 Act shall have effect in relation to a community radio service with the modifications set out in the Schedule.

[3621]

NOTES
Commencement: 20 July 2004.

5 (*Inserts the Media Ownership* (*Local Radio and Appointed News Provider*) *Order 2003, SI 2003/3299, art 2A at* **[3607]**.)

6 Disqualified persons

(1) In addition to the modifications made by article 4 of, and the Schedule to, this Order, Part 2 of Schedule 2 to the Broadcasting Act 1990 shall have effect in relation to community radio licences as if the persons who are disqualified persons by virtue of that Part of that Schedule included, in relation to such licences, any person falling within paragraph (2).

(2) Those persons are—

(a) any person who is not a body corporate;

(b) any body corporate falling within paragraph (3); and

(c) any C4 company or S4C company that would not otherwise be a disqualified person by virtue of paragraph (3).

(3) A body corporate falls within this paragraph if—

(a) that body holds at least one relevant Broadcasting Act licence, or

(b) that body is connected with a person who holds one or more such licences.

(4) In this article, a relevant Broadcasting Act licence is a Broadcasting Act licence which is not a licence to provide one of the following services—

(a) a community radio service;

(b) a digital sound programme service;

(c) a restricted service;

(d) a radio licensable content service;

(e) a restricted television service;

(f) a television licensable content service.

[3622]

NOTES
Commencement: 20 July 2004.

7 Restrictions on holding of community radio licences

(1) No body corporate may hold more than one community radio licence at any one time.

(2) For the purposes of this article, any body corporate which is connected with another such body which holds such a licence shall be treated as if it also were a holder of that licence.

[3623]

NOTES
Commencement: 20 July 2004.

SCHEDULE
MODIFICATION OF LEGISLATION IN RELATION TO COMMUNITY RADIO SERVICES

Article 4

PART 1
MODIFICATIONS TO THE BROADCASTING ACT 1990

1. The modifications to the Broadcasting Act 1990 referred to in article 4 are the modifications set out in this Part.

Licences

2. Section 86(3) (which makes provision as to the duration of certain licences) shall have effect as if, for the words "local or national service or to provide an additional service", there were substituted the words "community radio service", and as if, for the word "twelve", there was substituted the word "five".

Applications for Licences

3. Section 104 (which makes provision as to the giving of notice of proposals to grant licences, and as to the content of applications) shall have effect as if—

(a) in subsection (1), for the word "local" there were substituted the words "community radio", and in paragraph (b) of that subsection, for the words from "the area" to the end, there were substituted the words "any areas or localities in the United Kingdom in relation to which no applications may be made";

(b) in subsection (2)(b)—

(i) in sub-paragraph (i), for the words "living in the area or locality for which it would be provided" there were substituted the words "comprising the relevant community", and the word "and" following that sub-paragraph were omitted;

(ii) in sub-paragraph (ii), for the words "living in that area or locality;" there were substituted the words "comprising that community,"; and

(iii) after sub-paragraph (ii), there was added—

"(iii) broaden the range of local services provided in the area or locality in which the proposed service would be provided, and

(iv) be of a nature or have a content distinct from that of any local service the licence for which would overlap with that for the proposed service;";

(c) after subsection (2)(b), there was added—

"(ba) evidence that the provision of the service will result in the delivery of significant social gain to the public or the relevant community;";

(d) in subsection (2)(c)—

(i) in sub-paragraph (i), after the words "projected financial position", there were added the words "(with regard, in particular, to the number and nature of any persons from whom he proposes to receive the income required to provide the proposed service and the proportion of that income that he proposes to receive from each of those persons)"; and

(ii) in sub-paragraph (ii), after the word "service", there was added—

", and—

(iii) as to the effect that the provision of the service would be likely to have on the economic viability of any other local service;";

(e) in subsection (3) after the words "subsection (2)(b)," there was added "(ba),"; and

(f) in subsection (4)—

(i) after "(2)(b)" there were added the words "or (ba)", and

(ii) for the word "local" there were substituted the words "community radio".

Renewal of Local Licences and Special Application Procedure

4. Sections 104A (renewal of local licences) and 104B (special application procedure) shall not have effect.

Grant of Licences

5.—(1) Section 105 (which makes provision as to the matters to which OFCOM are required to have regard in determining whether, and to whom, to grant local licences) shall have effect as if the provision made by that section were re-numbered as subsection (1) of that section, and as if, in that provision—

(a) for the words "local licence" there were substituted the words "community radio licence";

(b) in paragraph (b), for the words from "living in the area or locality for which the service would be provided" there were substituted the words "comprising the relevant community";

(c) in paragraph (c), for the word "for", in the first place where it occurs, there was substituted the word "in", and for the words "cater for tastes" to the end there were substituted the words "be of a nature or have a content distinct from that of any other local service the licence for which would overlap with the licence for the proposed service";

(d) the word "and" immediately before paragraph (d) was omitted, and after the word "service" in that paragraph there were added the following paragraphs—

"(e) the extent to which the provision of any such proposed service would result in the delivery of social gain to the public or the relevant community;

(f) the provision that each of the applicants proposes to make in order to render himself accountable to the relevant community in respect of the provision of the proposed service;

(g) the provision that each of the applicants proposes to make to allow for access by members of the relevant community to the facilities to be used for the provision of the service and for their training in the use of those facilities".

(2) Also, that section shall have effect as if the following subsections were added at the end—

"(2) OFCOM shall not grant a community radio licence to any applicant who proposes to receive from—

(a) any one person, or

(b) from any one person and any other persons connected with him, taken together,

more than 50 per cent of the income that would be required in each financial year of the applicant to provide the proposed service in that year.

(3) Where OFCOM have published a notice under section 104(1), in the case of a proposal of theirs to grant a licence to provide a community radio service, they shall, in determining—

(a) whether, or to whom, to grant the licence in question, and

(b) if they grant it, the terms on which it is granted,

have regard to the need to ensure that any service provided under that licence does not prejudice unduly the economic viability of any other local service.

(4) Accordingly, and without prejudice to the generality of subsection (3)—

(a) OFCOM shall not grant a licence to provide a community radio service in any case where the licence, if granted, would overlap with another local licence for a service, other than a community radio service, the potential audience of which includes no more than 50,000 persons who have attained the age of 15 years;

(b) every licence to provide a community radio service that overlaps with any other local licence the potential audience of which includes more than 50,000 persons who have attained the age of 15 years, but no more than 150,000 such persons, must contain such conditions as appear to OFCOM to be appropriate for prohibiting—

(i) the inclusion in that service of any remunerated advertisement, and

(ii) the sponsorship of any programmes included in that service; and

(c) every licence to provide a community radio service, other than a licence to provide a service such as falls within paragraph (b) above, must contain the conditions mentioned in subsection (5).

(5) Subject to subsection (6), the conditions are those that appear to OFCOM to be appropriate, in the case of the community radio licence in question, for ensuring that the amount of such of the relevant income for that licence as is attributable to any arrangements for—

(a) the inclusion in the service provided under that licence of any remunerated advertisement, or

(b) the sponsorship of any programmes included in that service,

does not, in any financial year of the licence holder, exceed such proportion of the total relevant income for that licence in that year as may be specified in those conditions.

(6) Any condition imposed by OFCOM pursuant to subsection (4)(c) must specify such proportion of that total relevant income as—

(a) appears to OFCOM to be likely to secure the result that—

(i) the inclusion in the service provided under that licence of remunerated advertisements, and

(ii) the sponsorship of programmes included in that service,

do not prejudice unduly the economic viability of any other local service; and

(b) is such as to secure that 50 per cent of that income, or some lesser proportion of it, is attributable to the arrangements mentioned in subsection (5)(a) and (b).

(7) In this section—

"relevant income", in relation to any community radio licence, means any payment or other financial benefit (whether direct or indirect) attributable to the provision of the service under that licence which any relevant person has received, will receive or is or will be entitled to receive in the financial year in question;

"relevant person", in relation to a community radio licence, means the holder of that licence and every person who is connected with him; and

"remunerated advertisement", in relation to a service provided under a community radio licence, means any advertisement included in that service for which any relevant person has received, will receive or is or will be entitled to receive, any payment or other financial benefit (whether direct or indirect) in consideration for so including it.

(8) Any reference in this section to sponsorship does not include a reference to any payment made, or other financial benefit (whether direct or indirect) conferred, by a person for purposes that are wholly or mainly philanthropic in nature.".

Character and Coverage of Services

6. Section 106 (requirements as to character and coverage of national and local services) shall have effect as if—

(a) in subsection (1), for the words "national or local", there were substituted the words "community radio";

(b) in subsection (1A)—

(i) in paragraph (b), for the words from "living in" to the end there were substituted the words "comprising the relevant community";

(ii) paragraph (c) and the word "or" following it were omitted;

(iii) in paragraph (d), the words ", in the case of a local licence," were omitted and for the words "living in that area or locality" there were substituted the words "comprising that community"; and

(iv) after the word "departure" in that paragraph there were added—

";

(e) that the departure would not be prejudicial to the access by members of that community to the facilities used for the provision of the service and for training in the use of those facilities; or

(f) that the departure would not be prejudicial to the delivery of social gain resulting from the provision of the service provided under that licence";

(c) in subsection (1B), for the word "local" there were substituted the words "community radio", and after that subsection there were added—

";

(1C) Without prejudice to the generality of subsection (1), a community radio licence shall include such conditions as appear to OFCOM to be appropriate for securing that the holder of the licence does not enter into, or remain subject to, any arrangement if an effect of that arrangement is to allow another holder of a Broadcasting

Act licence or the BBC or the Welsh Authority to exercise an undue influence over the nature and content of the programmes included in the service provided under that licence.

(1D) In subsection (1C), "arrangement" includes any agreement or arrangement with one or more other persons, whether or not it is, or is intended to be, legally enforceable.";

(d) for subsection (2), there was substituted the following subsection—

"(2) Without prejudice to the generality of the provisions in subsections (1) to (1D), a community radio licence shall include such conditions as OFCOM consider are appropriate to ensure that the licence holder provides the service described in the application for that licence.";

(e) in subsection (4), for the word "local" there were substituted the words "community radio";

(f) in subsections (4), (5) and (6), for the words "locality for which", wherever they occur, there were substituted the words "locality in which";

(g) in subsection (7), for the word "local" there were substituted the words "community radio", and for the words "living and working in the area or locality" there were substituted the words "comprising the relevant community".

Definitions Applicable in Part 3

7. Section 126 (interpretation of Part 3) shall have effect as if—

(a) after the definition of "cash bid" there were added—

""community" means—

(a) the persons who live or work or undergo education or training in a particular area or locality, or

(b) persons who (whether or not they fall within paragraph (a)) have one or more interests or characteristics in common;

"community radio licence" means a licence to provide a community radio service;

"community radio service" has the meaning given in article 2(1) of the Community Radio Order 2004;

"coverage area" means, in relation to a service provided under a local sound broadcasting licence, the area in the United Kingdom within which that service is capable of being received at a level satisfying such technical standards as have been laid down by OFCOM for the purposes of OFCOM for the purposes of Part 2 of the Media Ownership (Local Radio and Appointed News Provider) Order 2003 in relation to such a service;"

(b) after the definition of "local service", "national service" and "restricted service", there were added—

""overlap" shall be construed in accordance with article 2(4) of the Community Radio Order 2004;

"potential audience" has the meaning given in article 2(1) of the Community Radio Order 2004;" and

(c) after the definition of "radio transfer date", there were added—

""relevant community" means, in relation to a community radio service, the community or communities which that service is intended to serve;".

Disqualified Persons

8.—(1) In Part 2 of Schedule 2 (persons who are disqualified from holding certain Broadcasting Act licences), paragraphs 1(1)(f) (individual who is an officer of a political body etc) and 3 (certain publicly-funded bodies) shall not have effect.

(2) In paragraph 4 of that Part of that Schedule (persons disqualified on grounds that they are subject to undue influence), sub-paragraph (1)(a) shall have effect as if for the words "relevant body" there were substituted "person", and sub-paragraph (2) (meaning of "relevant body") were omitted.

[3624]

NOTES

Commencement: 20 July 2004.

PART 2
MODIFICATIONS TO THE COMMUNICATIONS ACT 2003

9. The modifications to the Communications Act 2003 referred to in article 4 are the modifications set out in this Part.

Regulation by OFCOM of Independent Radio Services

10. Section 245 shall have effect as if, in subsection (4)(b), after the words "United Kingdom;" the following paragraph was added—

"(ba) a service is a community radio service if it is a local service having the characteristics set out in article 3 of the Community Radio Order 2004;".

Provisions that Do Not Have Effect

11. Sections 314 (character and content of services), 355 and 356 (variation of licences following change of control) shall not have effect.

[3625]

NOTES

Commencement: 20 July 2004.

OFFICE OF COMMUNICATIONS (MEMBERSHIP) ORDER 2005

(SI 2005/2718)

NOTES

Made: 29 September 2005.
Authority: Office of Communications Act 2002, s 1(7).
Commencement: 26 October 2005.

1 This Order may be cited as the Office of Communications (Membership) Order 2005 and shall come into force on 26th October 2005.

[3625A]

NOTES

Commencement: 26 October 2005.

2 The number specified in section 1(2) of the Office of Communications Act 2002 as the maximum membership for the Office of Communications shall be ten.

[3625B]

NOTES

Commencement: 26 October 2005.

EUROPEAN AGREEMENT CONCERNING PROGRAMME EXCHANGES BY MEANS OF TELEVISION FILMS

Strasbourg, 15 December 1958

(European Treaty Series No 27 (1971))

The Governments signatory hereto, being Members of the Council of Europe,

Considering that the aim of the Council of Europe is to achieve a greater unity between its Members;

Considering that it is important in the interests of European cultural and economic unity that programmes may be exchanged by means of television films between the member countries of the Council of Europe as freely as possible;

Considering that national legislations allow different conclusions as regards the legal nature of television films and as regards the rights which they grant in respect of such films;

Considering that it is necessary to resolve the difficulties arising from this situation;

Having regard to Article 20 of the Berne Convention for the Protection of Literary and Artistic Works, by the terms of which the Governments of the countries of the Union reserve to themselves the right to enter into special arrangements which do not embody stipulations contrary to that Convention,

Have agreed as follows—

Article 1

In the absence of any contrary or special stipulation within the meaning of Article 4 of the present Agreement, a broadcasting organisation under the jurisdiction of a country which is a Party to this Agreement has the right to authorise in the other countries which are Parties thereto the exploitation for television of television films of which it is the maker.

[3626]

Article 2

1. All visual or sound and visual recordings intended for television shall be deemed to be television films within the meaning of the present Agreement.

2. A broadcasting organisation shall be deemed to be the maker if it has taken the initiative in, and responsibility for, the making of a television film.

[3627]

Article 3

1. If the television film has been made by a maker other than the one defined in Article 2, paragraph 2, the latter is entitled, in the absence of contrary or special stipulations within the meaning of Article 4, to transfer to a broadcasting organisation the right provided in Article 1.

2. The provision contained in the preceding paragraph applies only if the maker and the broadcasting organisation are under the jurisdiction of countries which are Parties to the present Agreement.

[3628]

Article 4

By "contrary or special stipulation" is meant any restrictive condition agreed between the maker and persons who contribute to the making of the television film.

[3629]

Article 5

This Agreement shall not affect the following rights, which shall be entirely reserved—

(a) any moral right recognised in relation to films;
(b) the copyright in literary, dramatic or artistic works from which the television film is derived,
(c) the copyright in a musical work, with or without words, accompanying a television film;
(d) the copyright in films other than television films;
(e) the copyright in the exploitation of television films otherwise than on television.

[3630]

Article 6

1. This Agreement shall be open to signature by the Members of the Council of Europe, who may accede to it either by—

(a) signature without reservation in respect of ratification; or
(b) signature with reservation in respect of ratification, followed by the deposit of an instrument of ratification.

2. Instruments of ratification shall be deposited with the Secretary-General of the Council of Europe.

[3631]

Article 7

1. This Agreement shall enter into force thirty days after the date on which three Members of the Council shall, in accordance with Article 6 thereof, have signed it without reservation in respect of ratification or shall have ratified it.

2. In the case of any Member of the Council who shall subsequently sign the Agreement without reservation in respect of ratification or who shall ratify it, the Agreement shall enter into force thirty days after the date of such signature or deposit of the instrument of ratification.

[3632]

Article 8

1. After this Agreement has come into force, any country which is not a Member of the Council of Europe may accede to it, subject to the prior approval of the Committee of Ministers of the Council of Europe.

2. Such accession shall be effected by the deposit of an instrument of accession with the Secretary-General of the Council of Europe, and shall take effect thirty days after the date of deposit.

[3633]

Article 9

Signature without reservation in respect of ratification, ratification or accession shall imply full acceptance of all the provisions of this Agreement.

[3634]

Article 10

The Secretary-General of the Council of Europe shall notify Members of the Council, the Governments of any countries which may have acceded to this Agreement and the Director of the Bureau of the International Union for the protection of literary and artistic works—

(a) of the date of entry into force of this Agreement and the names of any Members of the Council which have become Parties thereto;

(b) of the deposit of any instruments of accession in accordance with Article 8 of the present Agreement;

(c) of any declaration or notification received in accordance with Articles 11 and 12 thereof.

[3635]

Article 11

1. This Agreement shall apply to the metropolitan territories of the Contracting Parties.

2. Any Contracting Party may, at the time of signature, ratification or accession, or at any later date, declare by notice addressed to the Secretary-General of the Council of Europe that this Agreement shall apply to any territory or territories mentioned in the said declaration and for whose international relations it is responsible.

3. Any declaration made in accordance with the preceding paragraph may, in respect of any territory mentioned in such a declaration, be withdrawn under the conditions laid down in Article 12 of this Agreement.

[3636]

Article 12

1. This Agreement shall remain in force for an unlimited period.

2. Any Contracting Party may denounce this Agreement at one year's notice by notification to this effect to the Secretary-General of the Council of Europe.

[3637]

In witness whereof, the undersigned, being duly authorised thereto, have signed this Agreement.

Done at Paris, this 15th day of December 1958, in English and French, both texts being equally authoritative, in a single copy, which shall remain in the archives of the Council of Europe and of which the Secretary-General shall send certified copies to each of the signatory and acceding Governments and to the Director of the International Bureau for the Protection of Literary and Artistic Works.

EUROPEAN AGREEMENT ON THE PROTECTION OF TELEVISION BROADCASTS

Strasbourg, 22 June 1960

(European Treaty Series No 87 (1961))

The Governments signatory hereto, being Members of the Council of Europe,

Considering that the object of the Council is to achieve a greater unity between its Members;

Considering that exchanges of television programmes between the countries of Europe are calculated to further the achievement of that object;

Considering that these exchanges are hampered by the fact that the majority of television organisations are at present powerless to restrain the re-broadcasting, fixation or public performance of their broadcasts, whereas the organisers of musical or dramatic performances or the like, and the promoters of sports meetings, make their consent to broadcasting to other countries conditional upon an undertaking that the relays will not be used for purposes other than private viewing;

Considering that the international protection of television broadcasts will in no way affect any rights of third parties in these broadcasts;

Considering that the problem is one of some urgency, in view of the installations and links now being brought into service throughout Europe, which are such as to make it easy from the technical point of view for European television organisations to exchange their programmes;

Considering that, pending the conclusion of a potentially universal Convention on "neighbouring rights" at present in contemplation, it is fitting to conclude a regional Agreement restricted in scope to television broadcasts and of limited duration,

Have agreed as follows—

Article 1

Broadcasting organisations constituted in the territory and under the laws of a Party to this Agreement or transmitting from such territory shall enjoy, in respect of all their television broadcasts—

1. in the territory of all Parties to this Agreement, the right to authorise or prohibit—
   (a) the re-broadcasting of such broadcasts;
   (b) the diffusion of such broadcasts to the public by wire;
   (c) the communication of such broadcasts to the public by means of any instrument for the transmission of signs, sounds or images;
   (d) any fixation of such broadcasts or still photographs thereof, and any reproduction of such a fixation; and
   (e) re-broadcasting, wire diffusion or public performance with the aid of the fixations or reproductions referred to in sub-paragraph (d) of this paragraph, except where the organisation in which the right vests has authorised the sale of the said fixations or reproductions to the public;

2. in the territory of any other Party to this Agreement, the same protection as that other Party may extend to organisations constituted in its territory and under its laws or transmitting from its territory, where such protection is greater than that provided for in paragraph 1 above.

[3638]

Article 2

1. [Subject to paragraph 2 of Article 1, and Articles 13 and 14, the protection provided for in paragraph 1 of Article 1 shall last not less than a period of twenty years from the end of the year in which the broadcast took place.]

2. …

[3639]

NOTES

Para 1: substituted by Art 1 of the Protocol to this Agreement.
Para 2: deleted by Art 1 of the Protocol to this Agreement.

Article 3

1. Parties to this Agreement, by making a declaration as provided in Article 10, and in respect of their own territory, may—

[(a) withhold the protection provided for in sub-paragraph 1(b) of Article 1 as regards broadcasting organisations constituted in their territory or transmitting from such territory, and restrict the exercise of such protection, as regards broadcasts by broadcasting organisations constituted in the territory of another Party to this Agreement or transmitting from such territory, to a percentage of the transmissions by such organisations, which shall not be less than 50% of the average weekly duration of the broadcasts of each of these organisations.]

(b) withhold the protection provided for in sub-paragraph 1(c) of Article 1, where the communication is not to a paying audience within the meaning of their domestic law;

(c) withhold the protection provided for in sub-paragraph 1(d) of Article 1, where the fixation or reproduction of the fixation is made for private use, or solely for educational purposes;

(d) withhold the protection provided for in sub-paragraphs 1(d) and (e) of Article 1, in respect of still photographs or reproductions of such photographs;

[(e) without prejudice to sub-paragraph 1(a) of this Article, withhold all protection provided for in this Agreement from television broadcasts by broadcasting organisations constituted in their territory and under their laws or transmitting from such territory, where such broadcasts enjoy protection under their domestic law.]

(f) restrict the operation of this Agreement to broadcasting organisations constituted in the territory and under the laws of a Party to this Agreement and also transmitting from the territory of such Party.

2. It shall be open to the aforesaid Parties, in respect of their own territory, to provide exceptions to the protection of television broadcasts—

(a) for the purpose of reporting current events, in respect of the rebroadcasting, fixation or reproduction of the fixation, wire diffusion or public performance of short extracts from a broadcast which itself constitutes the whole or part of the event in question;

(b) in respect of the making of ephemeral fixations of television broadcasts by a broadcasting organisation by means of its own facilities and for its own broadcasts.

[3. The aforesaid Parties may, in respect of their own territory, provide for a body with jurisdiction over cases where the right of diffusion to the public by wire referred to in sub-paragraph 1(b) of Article 1, or the right of communication to the public referred to in sub-paragraph 1(c) of Article 1, has been unreasonably refused or granted on unreasonable terms by the broadcasting organisation in which the said right vests.]

[3640]

NOTES

Para 1: sub-paras (a), (e) substituted by Art 2 of the Protocol to this Agreement.
Para 3: substituted by Art 2 of the Protocol to this Agreement.

Article 4

1. Fixations of a broadcast in which protection under this Agreement subsists, or still photographs thereof, as well as reproductions of such photographs, made in a territory to which this Agreement does not apply and imported into the territory of a Party to this Agreement where they would be unlawful without the consent of the broadcasting organisation in which the right vests, shall be liable to seizure in the latter territory.

2. The provisions of the last preceding paragraph shall apply to the importation into the territory of a Party to this Agreement of still photographs of a broadcast in which protection

under this Agreement subsists and of reproductions of such photographs, where such photographs or reproductions are made in the territory of another Party to this Agreement by virtue of sub-paragraph 1(d) of Article 3.

3. Seizure shall be effected in accordance with the domestic law of each Party to this Agreement.

4. No Party to this Agreement shall be required to provide protection in respect of still photographs, or the reproduction of such photographs, of broadcasts made by a broadcasting organisation constituted in the territory and under the laws of another Party to this Agreement or transmitting from such territory, if the said other Party has availed itself of the reservation provided for in sub-paragraph 1(d) of Article 3.

[3641]

Article 5

The protection afforded by this Agreement shall apply both in relation to the visual element and in relation to the sound element of a television broadcast. It shall not affect the sound element when broadcast separately.

[3642]

Article 6

1. The protection provided for in Article 1 shall not affect any rights in respect of a television broadcast that may accrue to third parties, such as authors, performers, film makers, manufacturers of phonographic records or organisers of entertainments.

2. It shall likewise be without prejudice to any protection of television broadcasts that may be accorded apart from this Agreement.

[3643]

Article 7

1. This Agreement shall be open to signature by the Members of the Council of Europe, who may become Parties to it either by

(a) signature without reservation in respect of ratification; or

(b) signature with reservation in respect of ratification, followed by the deposit of an instrument of ratification.

2. Instruments of ratification shall be deposited with the Secretary-General of the Council of Europe.

[3644]

Article 8

1. This Agreement shall enter into force one month after the date on which three Members of the Council of Europe shall, in accordance with Article 7 thereof, have signed it without reservation in respect of ratification or shall have ratified it.

2. In the case of any Member of the Council of Europe who shall subsequently sign the Agreement without reservation in respect of ratification or who shall ratify it, the Agreement shall enter into force one month after the date of such signature or deposit of the instrument of ratification.

[3645]

Article 9

1. After this Agreement has come into force, any European Government which is not a Member of the Council of Europe or any non-European Government having political ties with a Member of the Council of Europe may accede to it, subject to the prior approval of the Committee of Ministers of the Council of Europe.

2. Such accession shall be effected by the deposit of an instrument of accession with the Secretary-General of the Council of Europe and shall take effect one month after the date of deposit.

[3646]

Article 10

Signature, ratification or accession shall imply full acceptance of all the provisions of this Agreement; provided always that any country may declare, at the time of signature or of deposit of its instrument of ratification or accession, that it intends to avail itself of one or more of the options in paragraph 1 of Article 3 above.

[3647]

Article 11

The Secretary-General of the Council of Europe shall notify Members of the Council, the Governments of any countries which may have acceded to this Agreement and the Director of the Bureau of the International Union for the Protection of Literary and Artistic Works—

(a) of any signatures, together with any reservations as to ratification, of the deposit of instruments of ratification and of the date of entry into force of this Agreement;

(b) of the deposit of any instruments of accession in accordance with Article 9;

(c) of any declaration or notification received in accordance with Articles 12, 13 or 14;

(d) of any decision of the Committee of Ministers taken in pursuance of paragraph 2 of Article 12.

[3648]

Article 12

1. This Agreement shall apply to the metropolitan territories of the Parties.

2. Any Party may, at the time of signature, of the deposit of its instrument of ratification or accession, or at any later date, declare by notice addressed to the Secretary-General of the Council of Europe that this Agreement shall extend to any or all of the territories for whose international relations it is responsible.

3. Any Government which has made a declaration under paragraph 2 of this Article extending this Agreement to any territory for whose international relations it is responsible may denounce the Agreement separately in respect of that territory in accordance with Article 14 thereof.

[3649]

Article 13

[1. This Agreement shall remain in force indefinitely.

[2. Nevertheless, as from 1 January 1990, no State may remain or become a Party to this Agreement unless it is also a Party to the International Convention for the Protection of Performers, Producers of Phonograms and Broadcasting Organisations, signed in Rome on 26 October 1961.]]

[3650]

NOTES

Substituted by Art 3 of the Protocol to this Agreement.
Para 2: substituted by Art 1 of the Additional Protocol to the Protocol to this Agreement.

Article 14

Any Contracting Party may denounce this Agreement by giving one year's notice to that effect to the Secretary-General of the Council of Europe.

[3651]

In witness whereof, the undersigned, being duly authorised thereto, have signed this Agreement.

Done at Strasbourg, this 22nd day of June, 1960, in English and French, both texts being equally authoritative, in a single copy, which shall remain in the archives of the Council of Europe and of which the Secretary-General shall send certified copies to each of the signatory and acceding Governments and to the Director of the Bureau of the International Union for the Protection of Literary and Artistic Works.

PROTOCOL TO THE EUROPEAN AGREEMENT ON THE PROTECTION OF TELEVISION BROADCASTS

Strasbourg, 22 January 1965

(European Treaty Series No 69 (1965))

The member States of the Council of Europe, signatory hereto,

Considering the desirability of amending the European Agreement on the Protection of Television Broadcasts, signed at Strasbourg on 22nd June 1960, hereinafter referred to as "the Agreement";

Considering that the International Convention for the Protection of Performers, Producers of Phonograms and Broadcasting Organisations, signed in Rome on 26th October 1961, entered into force on 18th May 1964,

Have agreed as follows—

Article 1

(*Substitutes para 1 of Art 2 of the Agreement at* **[3639]** *and deletes para 2 thereof.*)

Article 2

1–3. (*Substitutes paras 1(a), (e), 3 of Art 3 of the Agreement at* **[3640]**.)

4. Any State which in accordance with Article 10 of the Agreement has, before the entry into force of this Protocol, availed itself of the option in sub-paragraph 1(a) of Article 3 of the Agreement may, notwithstanding anything in paragraph 1 of the present Article, maintain the application of such option.

[3652]

Article 3

(*Substitutes Art 13 of the Agreement at* **[3650]**.)

Article 4

1. The Governments signatory to the Agreement and the Governments having acceded thereto may become Parties to this Protocol by the procedure laid down in Article 7 or Article 9 of the Agreement, according to whether they are member States of the Council of Europe or not.

2. This Protocol shall enter into force one month after the date on which all the Parties to the Agreement have signed this Protocol without reservation in respect of ratification, or deposited their instrument of ratification or accession in accordance with the provisions of the preceding paragraph.

3. As from the date on which this Protocol enters into force, no State may become a Party to the Agreement without becoming also a Party to this Protocol.

[3653]

Article 5

The Secretary-General of the Council of Europe shall notify member States of the Council, other States Parties to the Agreement, and the Director of the Bureau of the International Union for the Protection of Literary and Artistic Works of any signature of this Protocol, together with any reservations as to ratification, and of the deposit of any instrument of ratification of the Protocol or of accession to it, and of the date referred to in paragraph 2 of Article 4 of this Protocol.

[3654]

In witness whereof the undersigned, being duly authorised thereto, have signed this Protocol.

Done at Strasbourg, this 22nd day of January 1965 in English and French, both texts being equally authoritative, in a single copy which shall remain deposited in the archives of the Council of Europe. The Secretary-General of the Council of Europe shall transmit certified copies to each of the signatory and acceding States.

EUROPEAN AGREEMENT FOR THE PREVENTION OF BROADCASTS TRANSMITTED FROM STATIONS OUTSIDE NATIONAL TERRITORIES

Strasbourg, 22 January 1965

(European Treaty Series No 53 (1972))

The member States of the Council of Europe signatory hereto,

Considering that the aim of the Council of Europe is to achieve a greater unity between its Members;

Considering that the Radio Regulations annexed to the International Telecommunication Convention prohibit the establishment and use of broadcasting stations on board ships, aircraft or any other floating or airborne objects outside national territories;

Considering also the desirability of providing for the possibility of preventing the establishment and use of broadcasting stations on objects affixed to or supported by the bed of the sea outside national territories;

Considering the desirability of European collaboration in this matter,

Have agreed as follows—

Article 1

This Agreement is concerned with broadcasting stations which are installed or maintained on board ships, aircraft, or any other floating or airborne objects and which, outside national territories, transmit broadcasts intended for reception or capable of being received, wholly or in part, within the territory of any Contracting Party, or which cause harmful interference to any radio-communication service operating under the authority of a Contracting Party in accordance with the Radio Regulations.

[3655]

Article 2

1. Each Contracting Party undertakes to take appropriate steps to make punishable as offences, in accordance with its domestic law, the establishment or operation of broadcasting stations referred to in Article 1, as well as acts of collaboration knowingly performed.

2. The following shall, in relation to broadcasting stations referred to in Article 1, be acts of collaboration—

(a) the provision, maintenance or repairing of equipment;
(b) the provision of supplies;
(c) the provision of transport for, or the transporting of, persons, equipment or supplies;
(d) the ordering or production of material of any kind, including advertisements, to be broadcast;
(e) the provision of services concerning advertising for the benefit of the stations.

[3656]

Article 3

Each Contracting Party shall, in accordance with its domestic law, apply the provisions of this Agreement in regard to—

(a) its nationals who have committed any act referred to in Article 2 on its territory, ships, or aircraft, or outside national territories on any ships, aircraft or any other floating or airborne object;
(b) non-nationals who, on its territory, ships or aircraft, or on board any floating or airborne object under its jurisdiction have committed any act referred to in Article 2.

[3657]

Article 4

Nothing in this Agreement shall be deemed to prevent a Contracting Party—

(a) from also treating as punishable offences acts other than those referred to in Article 2 and also applying the provisions concerned to persons other than those referred to in Article 3;
(b) from also applying the provisions of this Agreement to broadcasting stations installed or maintained on objects affixed to or supported by the bed of the sea.

[3658]

Article 5

The Contracting Parties may elect not to apply the provisions of this Agreement in respect of the services of performers which have been provided elsewhere than on the stations referred to in Article 1.

[3659]

Article 6

The provisions of Article 2 shall not apply to any acts performed for the purpose of giving assistance to a ship or aircraft or any other floating or airborne object in distress or of protecting human life.

[3660]

Article 7

No reservation may be made to the provisions of this Agreement.

[3661]

Article 8

1. This Agreement shall be open to signature by the member States of the Council of Europe, which may become Parties to it either by—
   (a) signature without reservation in respect of ratification or acceptance, or
   (b) signature with reservation in respect of ratification or acceptance followed by ratification or acceptance.

2. Instruments of ratification or acceptance shall be deposited with the Secretary-General of the Council of Europe.

[3662]

Article 9

1. This Agreement shall enter into force one month after the date on which three member States of the Council shall, in accordance with the provisions of Article 8, have signed the Agreement without reservation in respect of ratification or acceptance, or shall have deposited their instrument of ratification or acceptance.

2. As regards any member State which shall subsequently sign the Agreement without reservation in respect of ratification or acceptance or which shall ratify or accept it, the Agreement shall enter into force one month after the date of such signature or the date of deposit of the instrument of ratification or acceptance.

[3663]

Article 10

1. After this Agreement has entered into force, any Member or Associate Member of the International Telecommunication Union which is not a Member of the Council of Europe may accede to it subject to the prior agreement of the Committee of Ministers.

2. Such accession shall be effected by depositing with the Secretary-General of the Council of Europe an instrument of accession which shall take effect one month after the date of its deposit.

[3664]

Article 11

1. Any Contracting Party may, at the time of signature or when depositing its instrument of ratification, acceptance or accession, specify the territory or territories to which this Agreement shall apply.

2. Any Contracting Party may, when depositing its instrument of ratification, acceptance or accession or at any later date, by declaration addressed to the Secretary-General of the Council of Europe, extend this Agreement to any other territory or territories specified in the declaration and for whose international relations it is responsible or on whose behalf it is authorised to give undertakings.

3. Any declaration made in pursuance of the preceding paragraph may, in respect of any territory mentioned in such declaration, be withdrawn according to the procedure laid down in Article 12 of this Agreement.

[3665]

Article 12

1. This Agreement shall remain in force indefinitely.

2. Any Contracting Party may, in so far as it is concerned, denounce this Agreement by means of a notification addressed to the Secretary-General of the Council of Europe.

3. Such denunciation shall take effect six months after the date of receipt by the Secretary-General of such notification.

[3666]

Article 13

The Secretary-General of the Council of Europe shall notify the member States of the Council and the Government of any State which has acceded to this Agreement, of—

(a) any signature without reservation in respect of ratification or acceptance;
(b) any signature with reservation in respect of ratification or acceptance;
(c) any deposit of an instrument of ratification, acceptance or accession;
(d) any date of entry into force of this Agreement in accordance with Articles 9 and 10 thereof;
(e) any declaration received in pursuance of paragraphs 2 and 3 of Article 11;
(f) any notification received in pursuance of the provisions of Article 12 and the date on which denunciation takes effect.

[3667]

In witness whereof the undersigned, being duly authorised thereto, have signed this Agreement.

Done at Strasbourg, this 22nd day of January 1965 in English and French, both texts being equally authoritative, in a single copy which shall remain deposited in the archives of the Council of Europe. The Secretary General of the Council of Europe shall transmit certified copies to each of the signatory and acceding States.

ADDITIONAL PROTOCOL TO THE PROTOCOL TO THE EUROPEAN AGREEMENT ON THE PROTECTION OF TELEVISION BROADCASTS

Strasbourg, 14 January 1974

(European Treaty Series No 47 (1975))

The member States of the Council of Europe, signatory hereto,

Considering the desirability of extending the duration of the European Agreement on the Protection of Television Broadcasts and the Protocol to this Agreement for the benefit of States which are not yet Parties to the International Convention for the Protection of Performers, Producers of Phonograms and Broadcasting Organisations, signed in Rome on 26 October 1961,

Have agreed as follows—

Article 1

(*Substitutes para 2 of Art 3 of the Protocol to the Agreement.*)

Article 2

1. The States signatory to the Agreement and the Protocol thereto may become Parties to this Additional Protocol in accordance with the procedure laid down in Article 7 of the Agreement.

2. The States having acceded to the Agreement and to the Protocol may become Parties to this Additional Protocol by the deposit of an instrument of accession with the Secretary General of the Council of Europe.

[3668]

Article 3

1. This Additional Protocol shall enter into force one month after the date on which all the Parties to the Agreement and the Protocol have signed this Additional Protocol without reservation in respect of ratification, or have deposited their instrument of ratification or accession in conformity with the provisions of Article 2.

2. After the date of entry into force of this Additional Protocol, no State may become a Party to the Agreement and the Protocol without becoming also a Party to this Additional Protocol.

[3669]

Article 4

The Secretary General of the Council of Europe shall notify member States of the Council, other Contracting Parties to the Agreement and the Director General of the World Intellectual Property Organisation of any signature of this Additional Protocol, together with any reservations as to ratification, and of the deposit of any instrument of ratification of the Additional Protocol or of accession to it, and of the date referred to in paragraph 1 of Article 3 of this Additional Protocol.

[3670]

In witness whereof the undersigned, being duly authorised thereto, have signed this Additional Protocol.

Done at Strasbourg, this 14th day of January 1974, in the English and French languages, both texts being equally authoritative, in a single copy which shall remain deposited in the archives of the Council of Europe. The Secretary General of the Council of Europe shall transmit certified copies to each of the signatory and acceding States.

SIGNATURES AND RATIFICATIONS

State	*Date of signature*	*Date of deposit of instrument of ratification*
Belgium	14 January 1974*	30 November 1974
Cyprus	14 January 1974*	25 April 1974
Denmark	19 September 1974	—
France	17 June 1974	—
Germany, Federal Republic of†	14 January 1974*	21 November 1974
Luxembourg	26 February 1974*	
Norway	19 September 1974	—
Sweden	1 April 1974	—
Turkey	24 April 1974*	
United Kingdom	15 March 1974	—

[3671]

ACCESSION

	Date of deposit of instrument of accession
Spain	2 August 1974

* With reservation in respect of ratification or acceptance.

† Applies to Land Berlin.

[3672]

CONVENTION FOR THE PROTECTION OF INDIVIDUALS WITH REGARD TO AUTOMATIC PROCESSING OF PERSONAL DATA

Strasbourg, 28 January 1981

(European Treaty Series No 86 (1990))

The member States of the Council of Europe, signatory hereto,

Considering that the aim of the Council of Europe is to achieve greater unity between its members, based in particular on respect for the rule of law, as well as human rights and fundamental freedoms;

Considering that it is desirable to extend the safeguards for everyone's rights and fundamental freedoms, and in particular the right to the respect for privacy, taking account of the increasing flow across frontiers of personal data undergoing automatic processing;

Reaffirming at the same time their commitment to freedom of information regardless of frontiers;

Recognising that it is necessary to reconcile the fundamental values of the respect for privacy and the free flow of information between peoples,

Have agreed as follows—

CHAPTER I
GENERAL PROVISIONS

Article 1

Object and purpose

The purpose of this convention is to secure in the territory of each Party for every individual, whatever his nationality or residence, respect for his rights and fundamental freedoms, and in particular his right to privacy, with regard to automatic processing of personal data relating to him ("data protection").

[3673]

Article 2

Definitions

For the purposes of this convention—

(a) "personal data" means any information relating to an identified or identifiable individual ("data subject");

(b) "automated data file" means any set of data undergoing automatic processing;

(c) "automatic processing" includes the following operations if carried out in whole or in part by automated means: storage of data, carrying out of logical and/or arithmetical operations on those data, their alteration, erasure, retrieval or dissemination;

(d) "controller of the file" means the natural or legal person, public authority, agency or any other body who is competent according to the national law to decide what should be the purpose of the automated data file, which categories of personal data should be stored and which operations should be applied to them.

[3674]

Article 3

Scope

1. The Parties undertake to apply this convention to automated personal data files and automatic processing of personal data in the public and private sectors.

2. Any State may, at the time of signature or when depositing its instrument of ratification, acceptance, approval or accession, or at any later time, give notice by a declaration addressed to the Secretary General of the Council of Europe—

(a) that it will not apply this convention to certain categories of automated personal data files, a list of which will be deposited. In this list it shall not include, however, categories of automated data files subject under its domestic law to data protection provisions. Consequently, it shall amend this list by a new declaration whenever additional categories of automated personal data files are subjected to data protection provisions under its domestic law;

(b) that it will also apply this convention to information relating to groups of persons, associations, foundations, companies, corporations and any other bodies consisting directly or indirectly of individuals, whether or not such bodies possess legal personality;

(c) that it will also apply this convention to personal data files which are not processed automatically.

3. Any State which has extended the scope of this convention by any of the declarations provided for in sub-paragraph 2(b) or (c) above may give notice in the said declaration that such extensions shall apply only to certain categories of personal data files, a list of which will be deposited.

4. Any Party which has excluded certain categories of automated personal data files by a declaration provided for in sub-paragraph 2(a) above may not claim the application of this convention to such categories by a Party which has not excluded them.

5. Likewise, a Party which has not made one or other of the extensions provided for in sub-paragraphs 2(b) and (c) above may not claim the application of this convention on these points with respect to a Party which has made such extensions.

6. The declarations provided for in paragraph 2 above shall take effect from the moment of the entry into force of the convention with regard to the State which has made them if they have been made at the time of signature or deposit of its instrument of ratification, acceptance, approval or accession, or three months after their receipt by the Secretary General of the Council of Europe if they have been made at any later time. These declarations may be withdrawn, in whole or in part, by a notification addressed to the Secretary General of the Council of Europe. Such withdrawals shall take effect three months after the date of receipt of such notification.

[3675]

CHAPTER II
BASIC PRINCIPLES FOR DATA PROTECTION

Article 4

Duties of the Parties

1. Each Party shall take the necessary measures in its domestic law to give effect to the basic principles for data protection set out in this chapter.

2. These measures shall be taken at the latest at the time of entry into force of this convention in respect of that Party.

[3676]

Article 5

Quality of data

Personal data undergoing automatic processing shall be—

(a) obtained and processed fairly and lawfully;

(b) stored for specified and legitimate purposes and not used in a way incompatible with those purposes;

(c) adequate, relevant and not excessive in relation to the purposes for which they are stored;

(d) accurate and, where necessary, kept up to date;

(e) preserved in a form which permits identification of the data subjects for no longer than is required for the purpose for which those data are stored.

[3677]

Article 6

Special categories of data

Personal data revealing racial origin, political opinions or religious or other beliefs, as well as personal data concerning health or sexual life, may not be processed automatically unless domestic law provides appropriate safeguards. The same shall apply to personal data relating to criminal convictions.

[3678]

Article 7

Data security

Appropriate security measures shall be taken for the protection of personal data stored in automated data files against accidental or unauthorised destruction or accidental loss as well as against unauthorised access, alteration or dissemination.

[3679]

Article 8

Additional safeguards for the data subject

Any person shall be enabled—

(a) to establish the existence of an automated personal data file, its main purposes, as well as the identity and habitual residence or principal place of business of the controller of the file;

(b) to obtain at reasonable intervals and without excessive delay or expense confirmation of whether personal data relating to him are stored in the automated data file as well as communication to him of such data in an intelligible form;

(c) to obtain, as the case may be, rectification or erasure of such data if these have been processed contrary to the provisions of domestic law giving effect to the basic principles set out in Articles 5 and 6 of this convention;

(d) to have a remedy if a request for confirmation or, as the case may be, communication, rectification or erasure as referred to in paragraphs (b) and (c) of this article is not complied with.

[3680]

Article 9

Exceptions and restrictions

1. No exception to the provisions of Articles 5, 6 and 8 of this convention shall be allowed except within the limits defined in this article.

2. Derogation from the provisions of Articles 5, 6 and 8 of this convention shall be allowed when such derogation is provided for by the law of the Party and constitutes a necessary measure in a democratic society in the interests of—

(a) protecting State security, public safety, the monetary interests of the State or the suppression of criminal offences;

(b) protecting the data subject or the rights and freedoms of others.

3. Restrictions on the exercise of the rights specified in Article 8, paragraphs (b), (c) and (d), may be provided by law with respect to automated personal data files used for statistics or for scientific research purposes when there is obviously no risk of an infringement of the privacy of the data subjects.

[3681]

Article 10

Sanctions and remedies

Each Party undertakes to establish appropriate sanctions and remedies for violations of provisions of domestic law giving effect to the basic principles for data protection set out in this chapter.

[3682]

Article 11

Extended protection

None of the provisions of this chapter shall be interpreted as limiting or otherwise affecting the possibility for a Party to grant data subjects a wider measure of protection than that stipulated in this convention.

[3683]

CHAPTER III
TRANSBORDER DATA FLOWS

Article 12

Transborder flows of personal data and domestic law

1. The following provisions shall apply to the transfer across national borders, by whatever medium, of personal data undergoing automatic processing or collected with a view to their being automatically processed.

2. A Party shall not, for the sole purpose of the protection of privacy, prohibit or subject to special authorisation transborder flows of personal data going to the territory of another Party.

3. Nevertheless, each Party shall be entitled to derogate from the provisions of paragraph 2—

(a) in so far as its legislation includes specific regulations for certain categories of personal data or of automated personal data files, because of the nature of those data or those files, except where the regulations of the other Party provide an equivalent protection;

(b) when the transfer is made from its territory to the territory of a non-Contracting State through the intermediary of the territory of another Party, in order to avoid such transfers resulting in circumvention of the legislation of the Party referred to at the beginning of this paragraph.

[3684]

CHAPTER IV
MUTUAL ASSISTANCE

Article 13

Co-operation between Parties

1. The Parties agree to render each other mutual assistance in order to implement this convention.

2. For that purpose—

(a) each Party shall designate one or more authorities, the name and address of each of which it shall communicate to the Secretary General of the Council of Europe;

(b) each Party which has designated more than one authority shall specify in its communication referred to in the previous sub-paragraph the competence of each authority.

3. An authority designated by a Party shall at the request of an authority designated by another Party—

(a) furnish information on its law and administrative practice in the field of data protection;

(b) take, in conformity with its domestic law and for the sole purpose of protection of privacy, all appropriate measures for furnishing factual information relating to specific automatic processing carried out in its territory, with the exception however of the personal data being processed.

[3685]

Article 14

Assistance to data subjects resident abroad

1. Each Party shall assist any person resident abroad to exercise the rights conferred by its domestic law giving effect to the principles set out in Article 8 of this convention.

2. When such a person resides in the territory of another Party he shall be given the option of submitting his request through the intermediary of the authority designated by that Party.

3. The request for assistance shall contain all the necessary particulars, relating *inter alia* to—

(a) the name, address and any other relevant particulars identifying the person making the request;
(b) the automated personal data file to which the request pertains, or its controller;
(c) the purpose of the request.

[3686]

Article 15

Safeguards concerning assistance rendered by designated authorities

1. An authority designated by a Party which has received information from an authority designated by another Party either accompanying a request for assistance or in reply to its own request for assistance shall not use that information for purposes other than those specified in the request for assistance.

2. Each Party shall see to it that the persons belonging to or acting on behalf of the designated authority shall be bound by appropriate obligations of secrecy or confidentiality with regard to that information.

3. In no case may a designated authority be allowed to make under Article 14, paragraph 2, a request for assistance on behalf of a data subject resident abroad, of its own accord and without the express consent of the person concerned.

[3687]

Article 16

Refusal of requests for assistance

A designated authority to which a request for assistance is addressed under Articles 13 or 14 of this convention may not refuse to comply with it unless—

(a) the request is not compatible with the powers in the field of data protection of the authorities responsible for replying;
(b) the request does not comply with the provisions of this convention;
(c) compliance with the request would be incompatible with the sovereignty, security or public policy (*ordre public*) of the Party by which it was designated, or with the rights and fundamental freedoms of persons under the jurisdiction of that Party.

[3688]

Article 17

Costs and procedures of assistance

1. Mutual assistance which the Parties render each other under Article 13 and assistance they render to data subjects abroad under Article 14 shall not give rise to the payment of any costs or fees other than those incurred for experts and interpreters. The latter costs or fees shall be borne by the Party which has designated the authority making the request for assistance.

2. The data subject may not be charged costs or fees in connection with the steps taken on his behalf in the territory of another Party other than those lawfully payable by residents of that Party.

3. Other details concerning the assistance relating in particular to the forms and procedures and the languages to be used, shall be established directly between the Parties concerned.

[3689]

CHAPTER V
CONSULTATIVE COMMITTEE

Article 18

Composition of the committee

1. A Consultative Committee shall be set up after the entry into force of this convention.

2. Each Party shall appoint a representative to the committee and a deputy representative. Any member State of the Council of Europe which is not a Party to the convention shall have the right to be represented on the committee by an observer.

3. The Consultative Committee may, be unanimous decision, invite any non-member State of the Council of Europe which is not a Party to the convention to be represented by an observer at a given meeting.

[3690]

Article 19

Functions of the committee

The Consultative Committee—

(a) may make proposals with a view to facilitating or improving the application of the convention;

(b) may make proposals for amendment of this convention in accordance with Article 21;

(c) shall formulate its opinion on any proposal for amendment of this convention which is referred to it in accordance with Article 21, paragraph 3;

(d) may, at the request of a Party, express an opinion on any question concerning the application of this convention.

[3691]

Article 20

Procedure

1. The Consultative Committee shall be convened by the Secretary General of the Council of Europe. Its first meeting shall be held within twelve months of the entry into force of this convention. It shall subsequently meet at least once every two years and in any case when one-third of the representatives of the Parties request its convocation.

2. A majority of representatives of the Parties shall constitute a quorum for a meeting of the Consultative Committee.

3. After each of its meetings, the Consultative Committee shall submit to the Committee of Ministers of the Council of Europe a report on its work and on the functioning of the convention.

4. Subject to the provisions of this convention, the Consultative Committee shall draw up its own Rules of Procedure.

[3692]

CHAPTER VI
AMENDMENTS

Article 21

Amendments

1. Amendments to this convention may be proposed by a Party, the Committee of Ministers of the Council of Europe or the Consultative Committee.

2. Any proposal for amendment shall be communicated by the Secretary General of the Council of Europe to the member States of the Council of Europe and to every non-member State which has acceded to or has been invited to accede to this convention in accordance with the provisions of Article 23.

3. Moreover, any amendment proposed by a Party or the Committee of Ministers shall be communicated to the Consultative Committee, which shall submit to the Committee of Ministers its opinion on that proposed amendment.

4. The Committee of Ministers shall consider the proposed amendment and any opinion submitted by the Consultative Committee and may approve the amendment.

5. The text of any amendment approved by the Committee of Ministers in accordance with paragraph 4 of this article shall be forwarded to the Parties for acceptance.

6. Any amendment approved in accordance with paragraph 4 of this article shall come into force on the thirtieth day after all Parties have informed the Secretary General of their acceptance thereof.

[3693]

CHAPTER VII
FINAL CLAUSES

Article 22

Entry into force

1. This convention shall be open for signature by the member States of the Council of Europe. It is subject to ratification, acceptance or approval. Instruments of ratification, acceptance or approval shall be deposited with the Secretary General of the Council of Europe.

2. This convention shall enter into force on the first day of the month following the expiration of a period of three months after the date on which five member States of the Council of Europe have expressed their consent to be bound by the convention in accordance with the provisions of the preceding paragraph.

3. In respect of any member State which subsequently expresses its consent to be bound by it, the convention shall enter into force on the first day of the month following the expiration of a period of three months after the date of the deposit of the instrument of ratification, acceptance or approval.

[3694]

Article 23

Accession by non-member States

1. After the entry into force of this convention, the Committee of Ministers of the Council of Europe may invite any State not a member of the Council of Europe to accede to this convention by a decision taken by the majority provided for in Article 20.d of the Statute of the Council of Europe and by the unanimous vote of the representatives of the Contracting States entitled to sit on the committee.

2. In respect of any acceding State, the convention shall enter into force on the first day of the month following the expiration of a period of three months after the date of deposit of the instrument of accession with the Secretary General of the Council of Europe.

[3695]

Article 24

Territorial clause

1. Any State may at the time of signature or when depositing its instrument of ratification acceptance, approval or accession, specify the territory or territories to which this convention shall apply.

2. Any State may at any later date, by a declaration addressed to the Secretary General of the Council of Europe, extend the application of this convention to any other territory specified in the declaration. In respect of such territory the convention shall enter into force on the first day of the month following the expiration of a period of three months after the date of receipt of such declaration by the Secretary General.

3. Any declaration made under the two preceding paragraphs may, in respect of any territory specified in such declaration, be withdrawn by a notification addressed to the Secretary General. The withdrawal shall become effective on the first day of the month following the expiration of a period of six months after the date of receipt of such notification by the Secretary General.

[3696]

Article 25

Reservations

No reservation may be made in respect of the provisions of this convention.

[3697]

Article 26

Denunciation

1. Any Party may at any time denounce this convention by means of a notification addressed to the Secretary General of the Council of Europe.

2. Such denunciation shall become effective on the first day of the month following the expiration of a period of six months after the date of receipt of the notification by the Secretary General.

[3698]

Article 27

Notifications

The Secretary General of the Council of Europe shall notify the member States of the Council and any State which has acceded to this convention of—

(a) any signature;
(b) the deposit of any instrument of ratification, acceptance, approval or accession;
(c) any date of entry into force of this convention in accordance with Articles 22, 23 and 24;
(d) any other act, notification or communication relating to this convention.

[3699]

In witness whereof the undersigned, being duly authorised thereto, have signed this Convention.

Done at Strasbourg, the 28th day of January 1981, in English and in French, both texts being equally authoritative, in a single copy which shall remain deposited in the archives of the Council of Europe. The Secretary General of the Council of Europe shall transmit certified copies to each member State of the Council of Europe and to any State invited to accede to this Convention.

SIGNATURES AND RATIFICATIONS

State	*Date of signature*	*Date of deposit of instrument of ratification*
Austria	28 Jan 1981	30 Mar 1988
Belgium	7 May 1982	
Cyprus	25 July 1986	
Denmark	28 Jan 1981	23 Oct 1989
France	28 Jan 1981	24 Mar 1983
Germany, Federal. Republic of	28 Jan 1981	19 June 1985
Greece	17 Feb 1983	
Iceland	27 Sept 1982	
Ireland, Republic of	18 Dec 1986	25 Apr 1990
Italy	2 Feb 1983	
Luxembourg	28 Jan 1981	10 Feb 1988
Netherlands	21 Jan 1988	
Norway	13 Mar 1981	20 Feb 1984
Portugal	14 May 1981	
Spain	28 Jan 1982	31 Jan 1984
Sweden	28 Jan 1981	29 Sept 1982
Turkey	28 Jan 1981	
United Kingdom	14 May 1981	26 Aug 1987

RESERVATIONS AND DECLARATIONS

AUSTRIA

On ratifying the Convention the Government of Austria made the following declarations—

Article 2(c)

The Republic of Austria takes the assumption that the term "dissemination" covers the terms "communication" and "making available" used in section 3 paragraphs 9 and 10 of the amendment to the Austrian Data Protection Act, Federal Law Gazette No 370/1986.

Article 5(e)

The Republic of Austria takes the assumption that this requirement is fully met by the stipulation of the Austrian Data Protection Act concerning the deletion of data upon application by the data subject.

Article 9(2)

The Republic of Austria takes the assumption that the contents of the phrase "provided for by the law of the Party" contained in the introductory sentence of Article 9(2) of the Convention conforms to the contents of the phrase "in accordance with the law" contained in Article 8(2) of the European Convention on Human Rights, and that it is therefore in agreement with the Convention if under the Austrian basic right to data protection it is admissible to restrict such basic right only if provided for by the law.

Furthermore, the Republic of Austria takes the assumption that, in its scope, the restriction in the interest of the "monetary interests of the State" as provided for in Article 9(2)a of the Convention in conjunction with the restriction under paragraph 2(b) corresponds to the restriction in the interest of the "economic well-being of the country" contained in Article 8(2) of the European Convention on Human Rights.

In accordance with Article 3(2)b it is hereby notified that Austria will also apply this Convention to information relating to groups of persons, associations, foundations, companies, corporations or any other bodies consisting directly or indirectly of individuals whether or not such bodies possess legal personality (legal persons or associations of persons within the meaning of section 3(2), Data Protection Act).

DENMARK

On ratifying the Convention the Government of Denmark made the following declaration—

Article 24, paragraph 1

The Convention shall not apply to the Faroe Islands and Greenland.

FRANCE

On signing the Convention the Government of France made the following declaration—

The Government of the French Republic declares that in Article 9, paragraph 2(a) it interprets the phrase "Sécurité de l'Etat" as meaning "Sûreté de l'Etat" and the phrase "Sûreté publique" as meaning "Sécurité publique".

(Declaration contained in a letter registered at the Secretariat General on 16 May 1983)

The Government of the French Republic wishes to make the following complementary declaration—

> "In accordance with the provisions of Article 3, paragraph 2, sub-paragraph c, it will also apply the present Convention to personal data files which are not processed automatically.".

GERMANY, FEDERAL REPUBLIC OF

On signing the Convention the Government of the Federal Republic of Germany made the following declaration—

On the occasion of this signature of the Convention for the protection of individuals with regard to automatic processing of personal data, I have the honour to declare on behalf of the Federal Republic of Germany that the Federal Republic of Germany, following upon the examination which it has commenced, will, if necessary, when depositing its instrument of ratification, make declarations of interpretation with regard to specific provisions of the Convention and in particular Article 8 and Article 12, paragraphs 2 and 3.

On ratifying the Convention the Government of the Federal Republic of Germany made the following declarations—

Article 8, paragraph b—

"The Federal Republic of Germany starts from the assumption that a request for information pursuant to Article 8, paragraph b, cannot be complied with if the data subject is unable adequately to specify his request."

Article 12, paragraph 2—

"The Federal Republic of Germany, with reference to paragraph 67, sub-paragraph 5, of the Explanatory Report to the Convention for the Protection of Individuals with regard to Automatic Processing of Personal Data, starts from the assumption that Article 12, paragraph 2, leaves a Party at liberty to lay down, in its domestic data protection law, provisions which do not permit, in particular cases, the transfer of personal data, in consideration of the interests of the data subject that warrant protection."

Article 24, paragraph 1—

"The Convention shall also apply to Land Berlin, with effect from the date on which it enters into force for the Federal Republic of Germany."

IRELAND, REPUBLIC OF

On ratifying the Convention the Government of the Republic of Ireland made the following declarations—

The Government of Ireland wish to make a declaration in accordance with Article 3(2)(a) of the Convention for the Protection of Individuals with regard to Automatic Processing of Personal Data to the effect that the Convention will not apply to the following categories of automated personal data files, which are set out at Section 1(4) of the Data Protection Act 1988, to wit—

(a) personal data that in the opinion of the Minister for Justice or the Minister for Defence are, or at any time, were, kept for the purpose of safeguarding the security of the State;
(b) personal data consisting of information that the person keeping the data is required by law to make available to the public;
(c) personal data kept by an individual and concerned only with the management of his personal, family or household affairs or kept by an individual only for recreational purposes.

ITALY

On signing the Convention the Government of Italy made the following declaration—

"The Italian Government declares, under Article 3, paragraph 2(a), of the Convention for the Protection of Individuals with Regard to Automatic Processing of Personal Data, that it will not apply the present Convention to the automated Centres of the police, which are governed by national law and are not subject to any domestic rules on data protection."

LUXEMBOURG

On ratifying the Convention the Government of Luxembourg made the following declaration—

Article 3, paragraph 2(a)

The Grand Duchy of Luxembourg declares that it avails itself of the right, within the limits of Article 3(2)(a) of the Convention, not to apply the Convention—

(a) to data banks which, by virtue of a law or regulation are accessible to the public;
(b) to data banks which exclusively contain data relating to the owner of the data bank;
(c) to data banks which have been set up for public international law institutions.

NORWAY

On ratifying the Convention the Government of Norway made the following declarations—

Article 3, paragraph 2a—

"The Convention shall not apply to private personal registers which are not utilised in the private sector or by societies or foundations."

Article 3, paragraph 2b—

"The rules of the Convention shall also be applied to information on associations or foundations."

Article 24, paragraph 1—

"The Convention will not be made applicable to Svalbard."

UNITED KINGDOM

On signing the Convention the Government of the United Kingdom made the following declaration—

"The Government of the United Kingdom of Great Britain and Northern Ireland may wish to make formal declarations at the time of ratification, in particular in accordance with the provisions of Article 3 of the Convention."

On ratifying the Convention the Government of the United Kingdom made the following declarations—

Article 3, paragraph 2, subparagraph (a)

"… the Convention will not be applied to the following categories of automated personal data files—

(a) payroll and pensions: personal data held only for calculating employment remuneration or pensions, or paying deductions from same;

(b) accounts and transaction records: personal data held only for keeping accounts or records of transactions;

(c) information publicly available by law: personal data which must be publicly available under an enactment."

Article 24, paragraph 1—

"… in addition to the United Kingdom of Great Britain and Northern Ireland the Convention shall also apply to the Bailiwick of Jersey and the Bailiwick of Guernsey."

[3700]–[3701]

DIRECTIVE OF THE EUROPEAN PARLIAMENT AND OF THE COUNCIL

of 9 March 1999

on radio equipment and telecommunications terminal equipment and the mutual recognition of their conformity

(1999/5/EC)

NOTES

Date of publication in OJ: OJ L191, 7.4.1999, p 10.

THE EUROPEAN PARLIAMENT AND THE COUNCIL OF THE EUROPEAN UNION,

Having regard to the Treaty establishing the European Community, and in particular Article 100a,

Having regard to the proposal from the Commission,[1]

Having regard to the opinion of the Economic and Social Committee,[2]

Acting in accordance with the procedure laid down in Article 189b of the Treaty,[3] in the light of the joint text approved by the Conciliation Committee on 8 December 1998,

(1) Whereas the radio equipment and telecommunications terminal equipment sector is an essential part of the telecommunications market, which is a key element of the economy in the Community; whereas the directives applicable to the telecommunications terminal equipment sector are no longer capable of accommodating the expected changes in the sector caused by new technology, market developments and network legislation;

(2) Whereas in accordance with the principles of subsidiarity and proportionality referred to in Article 3b of the Treaty, the objective of creating an open competitive single market for telecommunications equipment cannot be sufficiently achieved by the Member States and can therefore be better achieved by the Community; whereas this Directive does not go beyond what is necessary to achieve this aim;

(3) Whereas Member States may rely upon Article 36 of the Treaty to exclude certain classes of equipment from this Directive;

(4) Whereas Directive 98/13/EC[4] consolidated the provisions relating to telecommunications terminal equipment and satellite earth station equipment, including measures for the mutual recognition of their conformity;

(5) Whereas that Directive does not cover a substantial proportion of the radio equipment market;

(6) Whereas dual-use goods are subject to the Community regime of export controls introduced by Council Regulation (EC) No 3381/94;[5]

(7) Whereas the broad scope of this Directive requires new definitions of the expressions "radio equipment" and "telecommunications terminal equipment"; whereas a regulatory regime aimed at the development of a single market for radio equipment and telecommunications terminal equipment should permit investment, manufacture and sale to take place at the pace of technology and market developments;

(8) Whereas, given the increasing importance of telecommunications terminal equipment and networks using radio transmission besides equipment connected through wired links, any rules governing the manufacturing, marketing and use of radio equipment and telecommunications terminal equipment should cover both classes of such equipment;

(9) Whereas Directive 98/10/EC of the European Parliament and of the Council of 26February 1998 on the application of open network provision (ONP) to voice telephony and on universal service for telecommunications in a competitive environment[6] calls on national regulatory authorities to ensure the publication of details of technical interface specifications for network access for the purpose of ensuring a competitive market for the supply of terminal equipment;

(10) Whereas the objectives of Council Directive 73/23/EEC of 19 February 1973 on the harmonisation of the laws of the Member States relating to electrical equipment designed for use within certain voltage limits[7] are sufficient to cover radio equipment and telecommunications terminal equipment, but with no lower voltage limit applying;

(11) Whereas the electromagnetic compatibility related protection requirements laid down by Council Directive 89/336/EEC of 3 May 1989 on the approximation of the laws of Member States relating to electromagnetic compatibility[8] are sufficient to cover radio equipment and telecommunications terminal equipment;

(12) Whereas Community law provides that obstacles to the free movement of goods within the Community, resulting from disparities in national legislation relating to the marketing of products, can only be justified where any national requirements are necessary and proportionate; whereas, therefore, the harmonisation of laws must be limited to those requirements necessary to satisfy the essential requirements relating to radio equipment and telecommunications terminal equipment;

(13) Whereas the essential requirements relevant to a class of radio equipment and telecommunications terminal equipment should depend on the nature and the needs of that class of equipment; whereas these requirements must be applied with discernment in order not to inhibit technological innovation or the meeting of the needs of a free-market economy;

(14) Whereas care should be taken that radio equipment and telecommunications terminal equipment should not represent an avoidable hazard to health;

(15) Whereas telecommunications are important to the well-being and employment of people with disabilities who represent a substantial and growing proportion of the population of Europe; whereas radio equipment and telecommunications terminal equipment should therefore in appropriate cases be designed in such a way that disabled people may use it without or with only minimal adaptation;

(16) Whereas radio equipment and telecommunications terminal equipment can provide certain functions required by emergency services;

(17) Whereas some features may have to be introduced on the radio equipment and telecommunications terminal equipment in order to prevent the infringement of personal data and privacy of the user and of the subscriber and/or the avoidance of fraud;

(18) Whereas in some cases interworking via networks with other apparatus within the meaning of this Directive and connection with interfaces of the appropriate type throughout the Community may be necessary;

(19) Whereas it should therefore be possible to identify and add specific essential requirements on user privacy, features for users with a disability, features for emergency services and/or features for avoidance of fraud;

(20) Whereas it is recognised that in a competitive market, voluntary certification and marking schemes developed by consumer organisations, manufacturers, operators and other industry actors contribute to quality and are a useful means of improving consumers' confidence in telecommunications products and services; whereas Member States may support such schemes; whereas such schemes should be compatible with the competition rules of the Treaty;

(21) Whereas unacceptable degradation of service to persons other than the user of radio equipment and telecommunications terminal equipment should be prevented; whereas manufacturers of terminals should construct equipment in a way which prevents networks from suffering harm which results in such degradation when used under normal operating conditions; whereas network operators should construct their networks in a way that does not oblige manufacturers of terminal equipment to take disproportionate measures to prevent networks from being harmed; whereas the European Telecommunications Standards Institute (ETSI) should take due account of this objective when developing standards concerning access to public networks;

(22) Whereas effective use of the radio spectrum should be ensured so as to avoid harmful interference; whereas the most efficient possible use, according to the state of the art, of limited resources such as the radio frequency spectrum should be encouraged;

(23) Whereas harmonised interfaces between terminal equipment and telecommunications networks contribute to promoting competitive markets both for terminal equipment and network services;

(24) Whereas, however, operators of public telecommunications networks should be able to define the technical characteristics of their interfaces, subject to the competition rules of the Treaty; whereas, accordingly, they should publish accurate and adequate technical specifications of such interfaces so as to enable manufacturers to design telecommunications terminal equipment which satisfies the requirements of this Directive;

(25) Whereas, nevertheless, the competition rules of the Treaty and Commission Directive 88/301/EEC of 16 May 1988 on competition in the markets in telecommunications terminal equipment[9] establish the principle of equal, transparent and non-discriminatory treatment of all technical specifications having regulatory implications; whereas therefore it is the task of the Community and the Member States, in consultation with the economic players, to ensure that the regulatory framework created by this Directive is fair;

(26) Whereas it is the task of the European standardisation organisations, notably ETSI, to ensure that harmonised standards are appropriately updated and drafted in a way which allows for unambiguous interpretation; whereas maintenance, interpretation and implementation of harmonised standards constitute very specialised areas of increasing technical complexity; whereas those tasks require the active participation of experts drawn from amongst the economic players; whereas in some circumstances it may be necessary to provide more urgent interpretation of or corrections to harmonised standards than is possible through the normal procedures of the European standardisation organisations operating in conformity with Directive 98/34/EC of 22 June 1998 of the European Parliament and of the Council laying down a procedure for the provision of information in the field of technical standards and regulations and of rules on information society services;[10]

(27) Whereas it is in the public interest to have harmonised standards at European level in connection with the design and manufacture of radio equipment and telecommunications terminal equipment; whereas compliance with such harmonised standards gives rise to a presumption of conformity to the essential requirements; whereas other means of demonstrating conformity to the essential requirements are permitted;

(28) Whereas the assignment of equipment class identifiers should draw on the expertise of CEPT/ERC and of the relevant European standards bodies in radio matters; whereas other forms of cooperation with those bodies is to be encouraged where possible;

(29) Whereas, in order to enable the Commission to monitor market control effectively, the Member States should provide the relevant information concerning types of interfaces, inadequate or incorrectly applied harmonised standards, notified bodies and surveillance authorities;

(30) Whereas notified bodies and surveillance authorities should exchange information on radio equipment and telecommunications terminal equipment with a view to efficient surveillance of the market; whereas such cooperation should make the utmost use of electronic means; whereas, in particular, such cooperation should enable national authorities to be informed about radio equipment placed on their market operating in frequency bands not harmonised in the Community;

(31) Whereas manufacturers should notify Member States of their intention to place radio equipment on the market using frequency bands whose use is not harmonised throughout the Community; whereas Member States therefore need to put in place procedures for such notification; whereas such procedures should be proportionate and should not constitute a conformity assessment procedure additional to those provided for in Annexes IV

or V; whereas it is desirable that those notification procedures should be harmonised and preferably implemented by electronic means and one-stop-shopping;

(32) Whereas radio equipment and telecommunications terminal equipment which complies with the relevant essential requirements should be permitted to circulate freely; whereas such equipment should be permitted to be put into service for its intended purpose; whereas the putting into service may be subject to authorisations on the use of the radio spectrum and the provision of the service concerned;

(33) Whereas, for trade fairs, exhibitions, etc, it must be possible to exhibit radio equipment and telecommunications terminal equipment which does not conform to this Directive; whereas, however, interested parties should be properly informed that such equipment does not conform and cannot be purchased in that condition; whereas Member States may restrict the putting into service, including the switching on, of such exhibited radio equipment for reasons related to the effective and appropriate use of the radio spectrum, avoidance of harmful interference or matters relating to public health;

(34) Whereas radio frequencies are allocated nationally and, to the extent that they have not been harmonised, remain within the exclusive competence of the Member States; whereas it is necessary to include a safeguard provision permitting Member States, in conformity with Article 36 of the Treaty, to prohibit, restrict or require the withdrawal from its market of radio equipment which has caused, or which it reasonably considers will cause, harmful interference; whereas interference with nationally allocated radio frequencies constitutes a valid ground for Member States to take safeguard measures;

(35) Whereas manufacturers are liable for damage caused by defective apparatus according to the provisions of Council Directive 85/374/EEC;[11] whereas without prejudice to any liability on the part of the manufacturer, any person who imports apparatus into the Community for sale in the course of his business is liable according to that Directive; whereas the manufacturer, his authorised representative or the person responsible for placing the apparatus on the Community market is liable according to the rules of the law of contractual or non-contractual liability in the Member States;

(36) Whereas the measures which are appropriate to be taken by the Member States or the Commission where apparatus declared to be compliant with the provisions of this Directive causes serious damage to a network or harmful radio interference shall be determined in accordance with the general principles of Community law, in particular, the principles of objectivity, proportionality and non-discrimination;

(37) Whereas on 22 July 1993 the Council adopted Decision 93/465/EEC concerning the modules for the various phases of the conformity assessment procedures and the rules for the affixing and the use of EC conformity marking which are intended to be used in the technical harmonisation directives;[12] whereas the applicable conformity assessment procedures should preferably be chosen from among the available modules laid down by that Decision;

(38) Whereas Member States may request that notified bodies they designate and their surveillance authorities be accredited according to appropriate European standards;

(39) Whereas it is appropriate that compliance of radio equipment and telecommunications terminal equipment with the requirements of Directives 73/23/EEC and 89/336/EEC may be demonstrated using the procedures specified in those Directives where the apparatus is within their scope; whereas, as a result, the procedure provided for in Article 10(1) of Directive 89/336/EEC may be used where the application of harmonised standards gives rise to a presumption of conformity with the protection requirements; whereas the procedure provided for in Article 10[13] may be used where the manufacturer has not applied harmonised standards or where no such standards exist;

(40) Whereas Community undertakings should have effective and comparable access to third countries' markets and enjoy treatment in third countries similar to that offered in the Community to undertakings owned wholly, controlled through majority ownership or effectively controlled by nationals of the third countries concerned;

(41) Whereas it is desirable to establish a committee bringing together parties directly involved in the implementation of regulation of radio equipment and telecommunications terminal equipment, in particular the national conformity assessment bodies and national bodies responsible for market surveillance, in order to assist the Commission in achieving a harmonised and proportionate application of the provisions so as to meet the needs of the market and the public at large; whereas representatives of telecommunications operators, users, consumers, manufacturers and service providers should be consulted where appropriate;

(42) Whereas a modus vivendi between the European Parliament, the Council and the Commission concerning the implementing measures for acts adopted in accordance with the procedure laid down in Article 189b of the Treaty was concluded on 20 December 1994;[14]

(43) Whereas the Commission should keep under review the implementation and practical application of this and other relevant directives and take steps to ensure coordination

of the application of all relevant directives in order to avoid disturbance to telecommunications equipment which affects the health of humans or is harmful to property;

(44) Whereas the functioning of this Directive should be reviewed in due course in the light of the development of the telecommunications sector and of experience gained from application of the essential requirements and the conformity assessment procedures provided for in this Directive;

(45) Whereas it is necessary to ensure that with the introduction of changes to the regulatory regime there is a smooth transition from the previous regime in order to avoid disruption to the market and legal uncertainty;

(46) Whereas this Directive replaces Directive 98/13/EC, which should accordingly be repealed; whereas Directives 73/23/EEC and 89/336/EEC will no longer apply to apparatus within the scope of this Directive, with the exception of protection and safety requirements and certain conformity assessment procedures,

NOTES

1 OJ C 248, 14.8.1997, p 4.
2 OJ C 73, 9.3.1998, p 10.
3 Opinion of the European Parliament of 29 January 1998 (OJ C 56, 23.2.1998, p 27), Council common position of 8 June 1998 (OJ C 227, 20.7.1998, p 37) and Decision of the European Parliament of 6 October 1998 (OJ C 328, 26.10.1998, p 32). Decision of the Council of 25 January 1999 and Decision of the European Parliament of 10 February 1999.
4 OJ L 74, 12.3.1998, p 1.
5 OJ L 367, 31.12.1994, p 1.
6 OJ L 101, 1.4.1998, p 24.
7 OJ L 77, 26.3.1973, p 29. Directive as amended by Directive 93/68/EEC (OJ L 220, 30.8.1993, p 1).
8 OJ L 139, 23.5.1989, p 19. Directive as last amended by Directive 93/68/EEC.
9 OJ L 131, 27.5.1988, p 73. Directive as amended by Directive 94/46/EC (OJ L 268, 19.10.1994, p 15).
10 OJ L 204, 21.7.1998, p 37. Directive as amended by Directive 98/48/EC (OJ L 217, 5.8.1998, p 18).
11 OJ L 210, 7.8.1985, p 29.
12 OJ L 220, 30.8.1993, p 23.
13 OJ L 220, 30.8.1993, p 23.
14 OJ C 102, 4.4.1996, p 1.

HAVE ADOPTED THIS DIRECTIVE—

CHAPTER I
GENERAL ASPECTS

Article 1

Scope and aim

1. This Directive establishes a regulatory framework for the placing on the market, free movement and putting into service in the Community of radio equipment and telecommunications terminal equipment.

2. Where apparatus as defined in Article 2(a) incorporates, as an integral part, or as an accessory—

(a) a medical device within the meaning of Article 1 of Council Directive 93/42/EEC of 14 June 1993 concerning medical devices,[1] or

(b) an active implantable medical device within the meaning of Article 1 of Council Directive 90/385/EEC of 20 June 1990 on the approximation of the laws of the Member States relating to active implantable medical devices,[2]

the apparatus shall be governed by this Directive, without prejudice to the application of Directives 93/42/EEC and 90/385/EEC to medical devices and active implantable medical devices, respectively.

3. Where apparatus constitutes a component or a separate technical unit of a vehicle within the meaning of Council Directive 72/245/EEC[3] relating to the radio interference (electromagnetic compatibility) of vehicles or a component or a separate technical unit of a vehicle within the meaning of Article 1 of Council Directive 92/61/EEC of 30 June 1992 relating to the type-approval of two or three-wheel motor vehicles, the apparatus shall be governed by this Directive without prejudice to the application of Directive 72/245/EEC or of Directive 92/61/EEC respectively.

4. This Directive shall not apply to equipment listed in Annex I.

5. This Directive shall not apply to apparatus exclusively used for activities concerning public security, defence, State security (including the economic wellbeing of the State in the case of activities pertaining to State security matters) and the activities of the State in the area of criminal law.

[3702]

NOTES

1 OJ L169, 12.7.1993, p 1.

2 OJ L152, 6.7.1972, p 15. Directive as last amended by Commission Directive 95/54/EC (OJ L266, 8.11.1995, p 1).

3 OJ L225, 10.8.1992, p 72. Directive as amended by the 1994 Act of Accession.

Article 2

Definitions

For the purpose of this Directive the following definitions shall apply:

(a) "apparatus" means any equipment that is either radio equipment or telecommunications terminal equipment or both;

(b) "telecommunications terminal equipment" means a product enabling communication or a relevant component thereof which is intended to be connected directly or indirectly by any means whatsoever to interfaces of public telecommunications networks (that is to say, telecommunications networks used wholly or partly for the provision of publicly available telecommunications services);

(c) "radio equipment" means a product, or relevant component thereof, capable of communication by means of the emission and/or reception of radio waves utilising the spectrum allocated to terrestrial/space radiocommunication;

(d) "radio waves" means electromagnetic waves of frequencies from 9 kHz to 3 000 GHz, propagated in space without artificial guide;

(e) "interface" means

(i) a network termination point, which is a physical connection point at which a user is provided with access to public telecommunications network, and/or

(ii) an air interface specifying the radio path between radio equipment and their technical specifications;

(f) "equipment class" means a class identifying particular types of apparatus which under this Directive are considered similar and those interfaces for which the apparatus is designed. Apparatus may belong to more than one equipment class;

(g) "technical construction file" means a file describing the apparatus and providing information and explanations as to how the applicable essential requirements have been implemented;

(h) "harmonised standard" means a technical specification adopted by a recognised standards body under a mandate from the Commission in conformity with the procedures laid down in Directive 98/34/EC for the purpose of establishing a European requirement, compliance with which is not compulsory.

(i) "harmful interference" means interference which endangers the functioning of a radionavigation service or of other safety services or which otherwise seriously degrades, obstructs or repeatedly interrupts a radio-communications service operating in accordance with the applicable Community or national regulations.

[3703]

Article 3

Essential requirements

1. The following essential requirements are applicable to all apparatus:

(a) the protection of the health and the safety of the user and any other person, including the objectives with respect to safety requirements contained in Directive 73/23/EEC, but with no voltage limit applying;

(b) the protection requirements with respect to electro-magnetic compatibility contained in Directive 89/336/EEC.

2. In addition, radio equipment shall be so constructed that it effectively uses the spectrum allocated to terrestrial/space radio communication and orbital resources so as to avoid harmful interference.

3. In accordance with the procedure laid down in Article 15, the Commission may decide that apparatus within certain equipment classes or apparatus of particular types shall be so constructed that—

(a) it interworks via networks with other apparatus and that it can be connected to interfaces of the appropriate type throughout the Community; and/or that
(b) it does not harm the network or its functioning nor misuse network resources, thereby causing an unacceptable degradation of service; and/or that
(c) it incorporates safeguards to ensure that the personal data and privacy of the user and of the subscriber are protected; and/or that
(d) it supports certain features ensuring avoidance of fraud; and/or that
(e) it supports certain features ensuring access to emergency services; and/or that
(f) it supports certain features in order to facilitate its use by users with a disability.

[3704]

Article 4

Notification and publication of interface specifications

1. Member States shall notify the interfaces which they have regulated to the Commission insofar as the said interfaces have not been notified under the provisions of Directive 98/34/EC. After consulting the committee in accordance with the procedure set out in Article 15, the Commission shall establish the equivalence between notified interfaces and assign an equipment class identifier, details of which shall be published in the *Official Journal of the European Communities.*

2. Each Member State shall notify to the Commission the types of interface offered in that State by operators of public telecommunications networks. Member States shall ensure that such operators publish accurate and adequate technical specifications of such interfaces before services provided through those interfaces are made publicly available, and regularly publish any updated specifications. The specifications shall be in sufficient detail to permit the design of telecommunications terminal equipment capable of utilising all services provided through the corresponding interface. The specifications shall include, *inter alia,* all the information necessary to allow manufacturers to carry out, at their choice, the relevant tests for the essential requirements applicable to the telecommunications terminal equipment. Member States shall ensure that those specifications are made readily available by the operators.

[3705]

Article 5

Harmonised standards

1. Where apparatus meets the relevant harmonised standards or parts thereof whose reference numbers have been published in the *Official Journal of the European Communities,* Member States shall presume compliance with those of the essential requirements referred to in Article 3 as are covered by the said harmonised standards or parts thereof.

2. Where a Member State or the Commission considers that conformity with a harmonised standard does not ensure compliance with the essential requirements referred to in Article 3 which the said standard is intended to cover, the Commission or the Member State concerned shall bring the matter before the committee.

3. In the case of shortcomings of harmonised standards with respect to the essential requirements, the Commission may, after consulting the committee and in accordance with the procedure laid down in Article 14, publish in the *Official Journal of the European Communities* guidelines on the interpretation of harmonised standards or the conditions under which compliance with that standard raises a presumption of conformity. After consultation of the committee and in accordance with the procedure laid down in Article 14, the Commission may withdraw harmonised standards by publication of a notice in the *Official Journal of the European Communities.*

[3706]

Article 6

Placing on the market

1. Member States shall ensure that apparatus is placed on the market only if it complies with the appropriate essential requirements identified in Article 3 and the other relevant

provisions of this Directive when it is properly installed and maintained and used for its intended purpose. It shall not be subject to further national provisions in respect of placing on the market.

2. In taking a decision regarding the application of essential requirements under Article 3(3), the Commission shall determine the date of application of the requirements. If it is determined that an equipment class needs to comply with particular essential requirements under Article 3(3), any apparatus of the equipment class in question which is first placed on the market before the date of application of the Commission's determination can continue to be placed on the market for a reasonable period. Both the date of application and the period shall be determined by the Commission in accordance with the procedure laid down in Article 14.

3. Member States shall ensure that the manufacturer or the person responsible for placing the apparatus on the market provides information for the user on the intended use of the apparatus, together with the declaration of conformity to the essential requirements. Where it concerns radio equipment, such information shall be sufficient to identify on the packaging and the instructions for use of the apparatus the Member States or the geographical area within a Member State where the equipment is intended to be used and shall alert the user by the marking on the apparatus referred to in Annex VII, paragraph 5, to potential restrictions or requirements for authorisation of use of the radio equipment in certain Member States. Where it concerns telecommunications terminal equipment, such information shall be sufficient to identify interfaces of the public telecommunications networks to which the equipment is intended to be connected. For all apparatus such information shall be prominently displayed.

4. In the case of radio equipment using frequency bands whose use is not harmonised throughout the Community, the manufacturer or his authorised representative established within the Community or the person responsible for placing the equipment on the market shall notify the national authority responsible in the relevant Member State for spectrum management of the intention to place such equipment on its national market.

This notification shall be given no less than four weeks in advance of the start of placing on the market and shall provide information about the radio characteristics of the equipment (in particular frequency bands, channel spacing, type of modulation and RF-power) and the identification number of the notified body referred to in Annex IV or V.

[3707]

Article 7

Putting into service and right to connect

1. Member States shall allow the putting into service of apparatus for its intended purpose where it complies with the appropriate essential requirements identified in Article 3 and the other relevant provisions of this Directive.

2. Not withstanding paragraph 1, and without prejudice to conditions attached to authorisations for the provision of the service concerned in conformity with Community law, Member States may restrict the putting into service of radio equipment only for reasons related to the effective and appropriate use of the radio spectrum, avoidance of harmful interference or matters relating to public health.

3. Without prejudice to paragraph 4, Member States shall ensure that operators of public telecommunications networks do not refuse to connect telecommunications terminal equipment to appropriate interfaces on technical grounds where that equipment complies with the applicable requirements of Article 3.

4. Where a Member State considers that apparatus declared to be compliant with the provisions of this Directive causes serious damage to a network or harmful radio interference or harm to the network or its functioning, the operator may be authorised to refuse connection, to disconnect such apparatus or to withdraw it from service. The Member States shall notify each such authorisation to the Commission, which shall convene a meeting of the committee for the purpose of giving its opinion on the matter. After the committee has been consulted, the Commission may initiate the procedures referred to in Article 5(2) and (3). The Commission and the Member States may also take other appropriate measures.

5. In case of emergency, an operator may disconnect apparatus if the protection of the network requires the equipment to be disconnected without delay and if the user can be offered, without delay and without costs for him, an alternative solution. The operator shall immediately inform the national authority responsible for the implementation of paragraph 4 and Article 9.

[3708]

Article 8

Free movement of apparatus

1. Member States shall not prohibit, restrict or impede the placing on the market and putting into service in their territory of apparatus bearing the CE marking referred to in Annex VII, which indicates its conformity with all provisions of this Directive, including the conformity assessment procedures set out in Chapter II. This shall be without prejudice to Articles 6(4), 7(2) and 9(5).

2. At trade fairs, exhibitions, demonstrations, etc, Member States shall not create any obstacles to the display of apparatus which does not comply with this Directive, provided that a visible sign clearly indicates that such apparatus may not be marketed or put into service until it has been made to comply.

3. Where the apparatus is subject to other directives which concern other aspects and also provide for the affixing of the CE marking, the latter shall indicate that such apparatus also fulfils the provisions of those other directives. However, should one or more of those directives allow the manufacturer, during a transitional period, to choose which arrangements to apply, the CE marking shall indicate that the apparatus fulfils the provisions only of those directives applied by the manufacturer. In this case, the particulars of those directives, as published in the *Official Journal of the European Communities,* must be given in the documents, notices or instructions required by those directives and accompanying such products.

[3709]

Article 9

Safeguards

1. Where a Member State ascertains that apparatus within the scope of this Directive does not comply with the requirements of this Directive, it shall take all appropriate measures in its territory to withdraw the apparatus from the market or from service, prohibit its placing on the market or putting into service or restrict its free movement.

2. The Member State concerned shall immediately notify the Commission of any such measures indicating the reasons for its decision and whether non-compliance is due to:
- (a) incorrect application of the harmonised standards referred to in Article 5(1);
- (b) shortcomings in the harmonised standards referred to in Article 5(1);
- (c) failure to satisfy the requirements referred to in Article 3 where the apparatus does not meet the harmonised standards referred to in Article 5(1).

3. If the measures referred to in paragraph 1 are attributed to incorrect application of the harmonised standards referred to in Article 5(1) or to a failure to satisfy the requirements referred to in Article 3 where the apparatus does not meet the harmonised standards referred to in Article 5(1), the Commission shall consult the parties concerned as soon as possible. The Commission shall forthwith inform the Member States of its findings and of its opinion as to whether the measures are justified, within two months of notification of the said measures to the Commission.

4. Where the decision referred to in paragraph 1 is attributed to shortcomings in the harmonised standards referred to in Article 5(1), the Commission shall bring the matter before the committee within two months. The committee shall deliver an opinion in accordance with the procedure laid down in Article 14. After such consultation, the Commission shall inform the Member States of its findings and of its opinion as to whether the action by the Member State is justified. If it finds that the action is justified it shall forthwith initiate the procedure referred to in Article 5(2).

5.
- (a) Notwithstanding the provisions of Article 6, a Member State may, acting in conformity with the Treaty, and in particular Articles 30 and 36 thereof, adopt any appropriate measures with a view to—
  - (i) prohibiting or restricting the placing on its market, and/or
  - (ii) requiring the withdrawal from its market,

of radio equipment, including types of radio equipment, which has caused or which it reasonably considers will cause harmful interference, including interference with existing or planned services on nationally allocated frequency bands.
- (b) Where a Member State takes measures in accordance with subparagraph (a) it shall immediately inform the Commission of the said measures, specifying the reasons for adopting them.

6. When a Member State notifies the Commission of a measure referred to in paragraph 1 or 5 the Commission shall in turn inform other Member States and consult the committee on the matter.

Where, after such consultation, the Commission considers that:

— the measure is justified, it shall immediately so inform the Member State which took the initiative and the other Member States,

— the measure is unjustified, it shall immediately so inform the Member State and request it to withdraw the measure.

7. The Commission shall maintain a record of the cases notified by Member States, which shall be made available to them on request.

[3710]

CHAPTER II
CONFORMITY ASSESSMENT

Article 10

Conformity assessment procedures

1. The conformity assessment procedures identified in this Article shall be used to demonstrate the compliance of the apparatus with all the relevant essential requirements identified in Article 3.

2. At the choice of the manufacturer, compliance of the apparatus with the essential requirements identified in Article 3(l)(a) and (b) may be demonstrated using the procedures specified in Directive 73/23/EEC and Directive 89/336/EEC respectively, where the apparatus is within the scope of those Directives, as an alternative to the procedures laid out below.

3. Telecommunications terminal equipment which does not make use of the spectrum allocated to terrestrial/space radio communication and receiving parts of radio equipment shall be subject to the procedures described in any one of Annexes II, IV or V at the choice of the manufacturer.

4. Where a manufacturer has applied the harmonised standards referred to in Article 5(1), radio equipment not within the scope of paragraph 3 shall be subject to the procedures described in any one of Annexes III, IV or V at the choice of the manufacturer.

5. Where a manufacturer has not applied or has only applied in part the harmonised standards referred to in Article 5(1), radio equipment not within the scope of paragraph 3 of this Article shall be subject to the procedures described in either of Annexes IV or V at the choice of the manufacturer.

6. Records and correspondence relating to the conformity assessment procedures referred to in paragraphs 2 to 5 shall be in an official language of the Member State where the procedure will be carried out, or in a language accepted by the notified body involved.

[3711]

Article 11

Notified bodies and surveillance authorities

1. Member States shall notify the Commission of the bodies which they have designated to carry out the relevant tasks referred to in Article 10. Member States shall apply the criteria laid down in Annex VI in determining the bodies to be designated.

2. Member States shall notify the Commission of the authorities established within their territory which are to carry out the surveillance tasks related to the operation of this Directive.

3. The Commission shall publish a list of the notified bodies, together with their identification numbers and the tasks for which they have been notified, in the *Official Journal of the European Communities*. The Commission shall also publish a list of surveillance authorities in the *Official Journal of the European Communities*. Member States shall provide the Commission with all information necessary to keep these lists up to date.

[3712]

CHAPTER III
CE CONFORMITY MARKING AND INSCRIPTIONS

Article 12
CE marking

1. Apparatus complying with all relevant essential requirements shall bear the EC conformity marking referred to in Annex VII. It shall be affixed under the responsibility of the manufacturer, his authorised representative within the Community or the person responsible for placing the apparatus on the market.

Where the procedures identified in Annex III, IV or V are used, the marking shall be accompanied by the identification number of the notified body referred to in Article 11(1). Radio equipment shall in addition be accompanied by the equipment class identifier where such identifier has been assigned. Any other marking may be affixed to the equipment provided that the visibility and legibility of the EC marking is not thereby reduced.

2. No apparatus, whether or not it complies with the relevant essential requirements, may bear any other marking which is likely to deceive third parties as to the meaning and form of the EC marking specified in Annex VII.

3. The competent Member State shall take appropriate action against any person who has affixed a marking not in conformity with paragraphs 1 and 2. If the person who affixed the marking is not identifiable, appropriate action may be taken against the holder of the apparatus at the time when non-compliance was discovered.

4. Apparatus shall be identified by the manufacturer by means of type, batch and/or serial numbers and by the name of the manufacturer or the person responsible for placing the apparatus on the market.

[3713]

CHAPTER IV
THE COMMITTEE

[Article 13

Constitution of the Committee

1. The Commission shall be assisted by the Telecommunications Conformity Assessment and Market Surveillance Committee (TCAM), hereinafter referred to as 'the Committee'.

2. The Committee shall adopt its rules of procedure.]

[3714]

NOTES

Substituted, together with Art 14, by European Parliament and Council Regulation 1882/2003/EC, Annex I(16).

[Article 14

Advisory committee procedure

1. The Committee shall be consulted on the matters covered by Articles 5, 6(2), 7(4), 9(4) and Annex VII(5).

2. The Commission shall consult the Committee periodically on the surveillance tasks relating to the application of this Directive, and, where appropriate, issue guidelines on this matter.

3. Articles 3 and 7 of Decision 1999/468/EC[1] shall apply, having regard to the provisions of Article 8 thereof.

4. The Commission shall periodically consult the representatives of the telecommunications networks providers, the consumers and the manufacturers. It shall keep the Committee regularly informed of the outcome of such consultations.]

[3715]

NOTES

[1] OJ L184, 17.7.1999, p 23.

Substituted as noted to Art 13 at **[3714]**.

[Article 15

Regulatory committee procedure

1. The procedure laid down in paragraph 2 shall apply in respect of the matters covered by Articles 3(3) and 4(1).

2. Where reference is made to this Article, Articles 5 and 7 of Decision 1999/468/EC[1] shall apply, having regard to he provision of Article 8 thereof.

The period laid down in Article 5(6) of Decision 1999/468/EC shall be set at three months.

3. The Committee shall adopt its rules of procedure.]

[3716]

NOTES

[1] OJ L184, 17.7.1999, p 23.

Substituted by European Parliament and Council Regulation 1882/2003/EC, Annex III(85).

CHAPTER V
FINAL AND TRANSITIONAL PROVISIONS

Article 16

Third countries

1. Member States may inform the Commission of any general difficulties encountered, *de jure* or *de facto,* by Community undertakings with respect to placing on the market in third countries, which have been brought to their attention.

2. Whenever the Commission is informed of such difficulties, it may, if necessary, submit proposals to the Council for an appropriate mandate for negotiation of comparable rights for Community undertakings in these third countries. The Council shall decide by qualified majority.

3. Measures taken pursuant to paragraph 2 shall be without prejudice to the obligations of the Community and of the Member States under relevant international agreements.

[3717]

Article 17

Review and reporting

The Commission shall review the operation of this Directive and report thereon to the European Parliament and to the Council, on the first occasion not later than 7 October 2000 18 months after the entry into force of this Directive and every third year thereafter. The report shall cover progress on drawing up the relevant standards, as well as any problems that have arisen in the course of implementation. The report shall also outline the activities of the committee, assess progress in achieving an open competitive market for apparatus at Community level and examine how the regulatory framework for the placing on the market and putting into service of apparatus should be developed to—

(a) ensure that a coherent system is achieved at Community level for all apparatus;
(b) allow for convergence of the telecommunications, audiovisual and information technology sectors;
(c) enable harmonisation of regulatory measures at international level.

It shall in particular examine whether essential requirements are still necessary for all categories of apparatus covered and whether the procedures contained in Annex IV, third paragraph, are proportionate to the aim of ensuring that the essential requirements are met for apparatus covered by that Annex. Where necessary, further measures may be proposed in the report for full implementation of the aim of the Directive.

[3718]

Article 18

Transitional provisions

1. Standards under Directive 73/23/EEC or 89/336/EEC whose references have been published in the *Official Journal of the European Communities* may be used as the basis for a

presumption of conformity with the essential requirements referred to in Article 3(1)(a) and Article 3(1)(b). Common technical regulations under Directive 98/13/EC whose references have been published in the *Official Journal of the European Communities* may be used as the basis for a presumption of conformity with the other relevant essential requirements referred to in Article 3. The Commission shall publish a list of references to those standards in the *Official Journal of the European Communities* immediately after this Directive enters into force.

2. Member States shall not impede the placing on the market and putting into service of apparatus which is in accordance with the provisions in Directive 98/13/EC or rules in force in their territory and was placed on the market for the first time before this Directive entered into force or at the latest two years after this Directive entered into force.

3. Apart from the essential requirements referred to in Article 3(1), the Member States may request to continue, for a period of up to 30 months following the date referred to in the first sentence of Article 19(1), and in conformity with the provisions of the Treaty, to require telecommunications terminal equipment not to be capable of causing unacceptable deterioration of a voice telephony service accessible within the framework of the universal service as defined in Directive 98/10/EC.

The Member State shall inform the Commission of the reasons for requesting a continuation of such a requirement, the date by which the service concerned will no longer need the requirement, and the measures envisaged in order to meet this deadline. The Commission shall consider the request taking into account the particular situation in the Member State and the need to ensure a coherent regulatory environment at Community level, and shall inform the Member State whether it deems that the particular situation in that Member State justifies a continuation and, if so, until which date such continuation is justified.

[3719]

Article 19

Transposition

1. Member States shall not later than 7 April 2000 adopt and publish the laws, regulations and administrative provisions necessary to comply with this Directive. They shall forthwith inform the Commission thereof. They shall apply these provisions as from 8 April 2000.

When Member States adopt these measures, they shall contain a reference to this Directive or shall be accompanied by such reference on the occasion of their official publication. The methods of making such a reference shall be laid down by Member States.

2. Member States shall inform the Commission of the main provisions of domestic law which they adopt in the field covered by this Directive.

[3720]

Article 20

Repeal

1. (*Repeals Directive 98/13/EC.*)

2. This Directive is not a specific directive within the meaning of Article 2(2) of Directive 89/336/EEC. The provisions of Directive 89/336/EEC shall not apply to apparatus falling within the scope of this Directive, with the exception of the protection requirements in Article 4 and Annex III and the conformity assessment procedure in Article 10(1) and (2) of, and Annex I to, Directive 89/336/EEC, as from 8 April 2000.

3. The provisions of Directive 73/23/EEC shall not apply to apparatus falling within the scope of this Directive, with the exceptions of the objectives with respect to safety requirements in Article 2 and Annex I and the conformity assessment procedure in Annex III, Section B, and Annex IV to Directive 73/23/EEC, as from 8 April 2000.

[3721]

Article 21

Entry into force

This Directive shall enter into force on the day of its publication in the *Official Journal of the European Communities.*

[3722]

Article 22

Addressees

This Directive is addressed to the Member States.

[3723]

Done at Brussels, 9 March 1999.

ANNEX I
EQUIPMENT NOT COVERED BY THIS DIRECTIVE AS REFERRED TO IN ARTICLE 1(4)

1. Radio equipment used by radio amateurs within Article 1, definition 53, of the International Telecommunications Union (ITU) radio regulations unless the equipment is available commercially.

Kits of components to be assembled by radio amateurs and commercial equipment modified by and for the use of radio amateurs are not regarded as commercially available equipment.

2. Equipment falling within the scope of Council Directive 96/98/EC of 20 December 1996 on marine equipment.[1]

3. Cabling and wiring.

4. Receive only radio equipment intended to be used solely for the reception of sound and TV broadcasting services.

5. Products, appliances and components within the meaning of Article 2 of Council Regulation (EEC) No 3922/91 of 16 December 1991 on the harmonisation of technical requirements and administrative procedures in the field of civil aviation.[2]

6. Air-traffic-management equipment and systems within the meaning of Article 1 of Council Directive 93/65/EEC of 19 July 1993 on the definition and use of compatible technical specifications for the procurement of air-traffic-management equipment and systems.[3]

[3724]

NOTES

1 OJ L46, 17.2.1997, p 25.

2 OJ L373, 31.12.1991, p 4. Regulation as amended by Commission Regulation 2176/96/EC (OJ L291, 14.11.1996, p 15).

3 OJ L187, 29.7.1993, p 52. Directive as last amended by Commission Directive 97/15/EC (OJ L95, 10.4.1997, p 16).

ANNEX II
CONFORMITY ASSESSMENT PROCEDURE REFERRED TO IN ARTICLE 10(3)

MODULE A (INTERNAL PRODUCTION CONTROL)

1. This module describes the procedure whereby the manufacturer or his authorised representative established within the Community, who carries out the obligations laid down in point 2, ensures and declares that the products concerned satisfy the requirements of this Directive that apply to them. The manufacturer or his authorised representative established within the Community must affix the CE marking to each product and draw up a written declaration of conformity.

2. The manufacturer must establish the technical documentation described in point 4 and he or his authorised representative established within the Community must keep it for a period ending at least 10 years after the last product has been manufactured at the disposal of the relevant national authorities of any Member State for inspection purposes.

3. Where neither the manufacturer nor his authorised representative is established within the Community, the obligation to keep the technical documentation available is the responsibility of the person who places the product on the Community market.

4. The technical documentation must enable the conformity of the product with the essential requirements to be assessed. It must cover the design, manufacture and operation of the product, in particular—
   — a general description of the product,
   — conceptual design and manufacturing drawings and schemes of components, sub-assemblies, circuits, etc,
   — descriptions and explanations necessary for the understanding of said drawings and schemes and the operation of the product,
   — a list of the standards referred to in Article 5, applied in full or in part, and descriptions and explanations of the solutions adopted to meet the essential requirements of the Directive where such standards referred to in Article 5 have not been applied or do not exist,
   — results of design calculations made, examinations carried out, etc,
   — test reports.

5. The manufacturer or his authorised representative must keep a copy of the declaration of conformity with the technical documentation.

6. The manufacturer must take all measures necessary in order that the manufacturing process ensures compliance of the manufactured products with the technical documentation referred to in point 2 and with the requirements of this Directive that apply to them.

[3725]

ANNEX III
CONFORMITY ASSESSMENT PROCEDURE REFERRED TO IN ARTICLE 10(4)

(INTERNAL PRODUCTION CONTROL PLUS SPECIFIC APPARATUS TESTS)[1]

This Annex consists of Annex II, plus the following supplementary requirements:

For each type of apparatus, all essential radio test suites must be carried out by the manufacturer or on his behalf. The identification of the test suites that are considered to be essential is the responsibility of a notified body chosen by the manufacturer except where the test suites are defined in the harmonised standards. The notified body must take due account of previous decisions made by notified bodies acting together.

The manufacturer or his authorised representative established within the Community or the person responsible for placing the apparatus on the market must declare that these tests have been carried out and that the apparatus complies with the essential requirements and must affix the notified body's identification number during the manufacturing process.

[3726]

NOTES

[1] Annex based on Module A with additional requirements appropriate to the sector.

ANNEX IV
CONFORMITY ASSESSMENT PROCEDURE REFERRED TO IN ARTICLE 10(5)

(TECHNICAL CONSTRUCTION FILE)

This Annex consists of Annex III plus the following supplementary requirements:

The technical documentation described in point 4 of Annex II and the declaration of conformity to specific radio test suites described in Annex III must form a technical construction file.

The manufacturer, his authorised representative established within the Community or the person responsible for placing the apparatus on the market, must present the file to one or more notified bodies, each of the notified bodies must be informed of others who have received the file.

The notified body must review the file and if it is considered that it has not been properly demonstrated that the requirements of the Directive have been met, the notified body may issue an opinion to the manufacturer, his representative or the person responsible for placing the apparatus on the market and must inform the other notified bodies who have received the file accordingly. Such an opinion must be given within four weeks of receipt of the file by the notified body. On receipt of this opinion, or after the end of the four-week period, the apparatus may be placed on the market, without prejudice to Articles 6(4) and 9(5).

The manufacturer or his authorised representative established within the Community or the person responsible for placing the apparatus on the market must keep the file for a period ending at least 10 years after the last apparatus has been manufactured at the disposal of the relevant national authorities of any Member States for inspection.

[3727]

ANNEX V
CONFORMITY ASSESSMENT PROCEDURE REFERRED TO IN ARTICLE 10

FULL QUALITY ASSURANCE

1. Full quality assurance is the procedure whereby the manufacturer who satisfies the obligations of point 2 ensures and declares that the products concerned satisfy the requirements of the Directive that apply to them. The manufacturer must affix the marks referred to in Article 12(1) to each product and draw up a written declaration of conformity.

2. The manufacturer must operate an approved quality system for design, manufacture and final product inspection and testing as specified in point 3 and must be subject to surveillance as specified in point 4.

3. Quality system

3.1. The manufacturer must lodge an application for assessment of his quality system with a notified body.

The application must include:
— all relevant information for the products envisaged,
— the quality system's documentation.

3.2. The quality system must ensure compliance of the products with the requirements of the Directive that apply to them. All the elements, requirements and provisions adopted by the manufacturer must be documented in a systematic and orderly manner in the form of written policies, procedures and instructions. This quality system documentation must ensure a common understanding of the quality policies and procedures such as quality programmes, plans, manuals and records.

It must contain in particular an adequate description of:
— the quality objectives and the organisational structure, responsibilities and powers of the management with regard to design and product quality,
— the technical specifications, including the harmonised standards and technical regulations as well as relevant test specifications that will be applied and, where the standards referred to in Article 5(1) will not be applied in full, the means that will be used to ensure that the essential requirements of the Directive that apply to the products will be met,
— the design control and design verification techniques, processes and systematic actions that will be used when designing the products pertaining to the product category covered,
— the corresponding manufacturing, quality control and quality assurance techniques, processes and systematic actions that will be used,
— the examinations and tests that will be carried out before, during and after manufacture, and the frequency with which they will be carried out, as well as the results of the tests carried out before manufacture where appropriate,
— the means by which it is ensured that the test and examination facilities respect the appropriate requirements for the performance of the necessary test,
— the quality records, such as inspection reports and test data, calibration data, qualification reports of the personnel concerned, etc,
— the means to monitor the achievement of the required design and product quality and the effective operation of the quality system.

3.3. The notified body must assess the quality system to determine whether it satisfies the requirements referred to in point 3.2. It must presume compliance with these requirements in respect of quality systems that implement the relevant harmonised standard.

The notified body must assess in particular whether the quality control system ensures conformity of the products with the requirements of the Directive in the light of the relevant documentation supplied in respect of points 3.1 and 3.2 including, where relevant, test results supplied by the manufacturer.

The auditing team must have at least one member experienced as an assessor in the product technology concerned. The evaluation procedure must include an assessment visit to the manufacturer's premises.

The decision must be notified to the manufacturer. The notification must contain the conclusions of the examination and the reasoned assessment decision.

3.4. The manufacturer must undertake to fulfil the obligations arising out of the quality system as approved and to uphold it so that it remains adequate and efficient.

The manufacturer or his authorised representative must keep the notified body that has approved the quality system informed of any intended updating of the quality system.

The notified body must evaluate the modifications proposed and decide whether the amended quality system will still satisfy the requirements referred to in point 3.2 or whether a reassessment is required.

It must notify its decision to the manufacturer. The notification must contain the conclusions of the examination and the reasoned assessment decision.

4. EC surveillance under the responsibility of the notified body

4.1. The purpose of surveillance is to make sure that the manufacturer duly fulfils the obligations arising out of the approved quality system.

4.2. The manufacturer must allow the notified body access for inspection purposes to the locations of design, manufacture, inspection and testing, and storage and must provide it with all necessary information, in particular—

— the quality system documentation,
— the quality records as foreseen by the design part of the quality system, such as results of analyses, calculations, tests, etc,
— the quality records as foreseen by the manufacturing part of the quality system, such as inspection reports and test data, calibration data, qualification reports of the personnel concerned, etc.

4.3. The notified body must carry out audits at reasonable intervals to make sure that the manufacturer maintains and applies the quality system and must provide an audit report to the manufacturer.

4.4. Additionally, the notified body may pay unexpected visits to the manufacturer. At the time of such visits, the notified body may carry out tests or have them carried out in order to check the proper functioning of the quality system where necessary; it must provide the manufacturer with a visit report and, if a test has been carried out, with a test report.

5. The manufacturer must, for a period ending at least 10 years after the last product has been manufactured, keep at the disposal of the national authorities—

— the documentation referred to in the second indent of point 3.1,
— the updating referred to in the second paragraph of point 3.4,
— the decisions and reports from the notified body which are referred to in the final paragraph of point 3.4 and in points 4.3 and 4.4.

6. Each notified body must make available to the other notified bodies the relevant information concerning quality system approvals including references to the product(s) concerned, issued and withdrawn.

[3728]

ANNEX VI
MINIMUM CRITERIA TO BE TAKEN INTO ACCOUNT BY MEMBER STATES WHEN DESIGNATING NOTIFIED BODIES IN ACCORDANCE WITH ARTICLE 11(1)

1. The notified body, its director and the staff responsible for carrying out the tasks for which the notified body has been designated must not be a designer, manufacturer, supplier or installer of radio equipment or telecommunications terminal equipment, or a network operator or a service provider, nor the authorised representative of any of such parties. They must be independent and not become directly involved in the design, construction, marketing or maintenance of radio equipment or telecommunications terminal equipment, nor represent the parties engaged in these activities. This does not preclude the possibility of exchanges of technical information between the manufacturer and the notified body.

2. The notified body and its staff must carry out the tasks for which the notified body has been designated with the highest degree of professional integrity and technical competence

and must be free from all pressures and inducements, particularly financial, which might influence their judgement or the results of any inspection, especially from persons or groups of persons with an interest in such results.

3. The notified body must have at its disposal the necessary staff and facilities to enable it to perform properly the administrative and technical work associated with the tasks for which it has been designated.

4. The staff responsible for inspections must have:

— sound technical and professional training,
— satisfactory knowledge of the requirements of the tests or inspections that are carried out and adequate experience of such tests or inspections,
— the ability to draw up the certificates, records and reports required to authenticate the performance of the inspections.

5. The impartiality of inspection staff must be guaranteed. Their remuneration must not depend on the number of tests or inspections carried out nor on the results of such inspections.

6. The notified body must take out liability insurance unless its liability is assumed by the Member State in accordance with national law, or the Member State itself is directly responsible.

7. The staff of the notified body is bound to observe professional secrecy with regard to all information gained in carrying out its tasks (except *vis-à-vis* the competent administrative authorities of the Member State in which its activities are carried out) under this Directive or any provision of national law giving effect thereto.

[3729]

ANNEX VII
MARKING OF EQUIPMENT REFERRED TO IN ARTICLE 12(1)

1. The CE conformity marking must consist of the initials "CE" taking the following form—

If the CE marking is reduced or enlarged, the proportions given in the above graduated drawing must be respected.

2. The CE marking must have a height of at least 5 mm except where this is not possible on account of the nature of the apparatus.

3. The CE marking must be affixed to the product or to its data plate. Additionally it must be affixed to the packaging, if any, and to the accompanying documents.

4. The CE marking must be affixed visibly, legibly and indelibly.

5. The equipment class identifier must take a form to be decided by the Commission in accordance with the procedure laid down in Article 14.

Where appropriate it must include an element intended to provide information to the user that the apparatus makes use of radio frequency bands where their use is not harmonised throughout the Community.

It must have the same height as the initials "CE".

JOINT DECLARATION OF THE EUROPEAN PARLIAMENT, THE COUNCIL AND THE COMMISSION

The European Parliament, the Council and the Commission recognise the importance of the requirement relating to the prevention of harm to the network or its functioning which causes an unacceptable degradation of service taking into account in particular the need to safeguard the interests of the consumer.

Therefore, they note that the Commission will carry out a continuous assessment of the situation in order to evaluate whether that risk occurs frequently and, in such a case, to find an appropriate solution in the framework of the Committee acting in accordance with the procedure laid down in Article 15.

Such a solution will, where appropriate, consist of the systematic application of the essential requirement provided for in Article 3(3)(b).

Furthermore, the European Parliament, the Council and the Commission state that the procedure described above applies without prejudice to the possibilities foreseen in Article 7(5) and to the development of voluntary certification and marking schemes to prevent either the degradation of service or any harm to the network.

[3730]

CONVENTION RELATING TO THE DISTRIBUTION OF PROGRAMME-CARRYING SIGNALS TRANSMITTED BY SATELLITE

Brussels, May 21, 1974

THE CONTRACTING STATES,

Aware that the use of satellites for the distribution of programme-carrying signals is rapidly growing both in volume and geographical coverage;

Concerned that there is no world-wide system to prevent distributors from distributing programme-carrying signals transmitted by satellite which were not intended for those distributors, and that this lack is likely to hamper the use of satellite communications;

Recognising, in this respect, the importance of the interests of authors, performers, producers of phonograms and broadcasting organisations;

Convinced that an international system should be established under which measures would be provided to prevent distributors from distributing programme-carrying signals transmitted by satellite which were not intended for those distributors;

Conscious of the need not to impair in any way international agreements already in force, including the International Telecommunication Convention and the Radio Regulations annexed to that Convention, and in particular in no way to prejudice wider acceptance of the Rome Convention of October 26, 1961, which affords protection to performers, producers of phonograms and broadcasting organisations,

HAVE AGREED AS FOLLOWS—

Article 1

For the purposes of this Convention—

(i) "signal" is an electronically-generated carrier capable of transmitting programmes;
(ii) "programme" is a body of live or recorded material consisting of images, sounds or both, embodied in signals emitted for the purpose of ultimate distribution;
(iii) "satellite" is any device in extraterrestrial space capable of transmitting signals;
(iv) "emitted signal" or "signal emitted" is any programme-carrying signal that goes to or passes through a satellite;
(v) "derived signal" is a signal obtained by modifying the technical characteristics of the emitted signal, whether or not there have been one or more intervening fixations;
(vi) "originating organisation" is the person or legal entity that decides what programme the emitted signals will carry;
(vii) "distributor" is the person or legal entity that decides that the transmission of the derived signals to the general public or any section thereof should take place;
(viii) "distribution" is the operation by which a distributor transmits derived signals to the general public or any section thereof.

[3731]

Article 2

(1) Each Contracting State undertakes to take adequate measures to prevent the distribution on or from its territory of any programme-carrying signal by any distributor for whom the signal emitted to or passing through the satellite is not intended. This obligation

shall apply where the originating organisation is a national of another Contracting State and where the signal distributed is a derived signal.

(2) In any Contracting State in which the application of the measures referred to in paragraph (1) is limited in time, the duration thereof shall be fixed by its domestic law. The Secretary-General of the United Nations shall be notified in writing of such duration at the time of ratification, acceptance or accession, or if the domestic law comes into force or is changed thereafter, within six months of the coming into force of that law or of its modification.

(3) The obligation provided for in paragraph (1) shall not apply to the distribution of derived signals taken from signals which have already been distributed by a distributor for whom the emitted signals were intended.

[3732]

Article 3

This Convention shall not apply where the signals emitted by or on behalf of the originating organisation are intended for direct reception from the satellite by the general public.

[3733]

Article 4

No Contracting State shall be required to apply the measures referred to in Article 2(1) where the signal distributed on its territory by a distributor for whom the emitted signal is not intended—

(i) carries short excerpts of the programme carried by the emitted signal, consisting of reports of current events, but only to the extent justified by the informatory purpose of such excerpts, or

(ii) carries, as quotations, short excerpts of the programme carried by the emitted signal, provided that such quotations are compatible with fair practice and are justified by the informatory purpose of such quotations, or

(iii) carries, where the said territory is that of a Contracting State regarded as a developing country in conformity with the established practice of the General Assembly of the United Nations, a programme carried by the emitted signal, provided that the distribution is solely for the purpose of teaching, including teaching in the framework of adult education, or scientific research.

[3734]

Article 5

No Contracting State shall be required to apply this Convention with respect to any signal emitted before this Convention entered into force for that State.

[3735]

Article 6

This Convention shall in no way be interpreted to limit or prejudice the protection secured to authors, performers, producers of phonograms, or broadcasting organisations, under any domestic law or international agreement.

[3736]

Article 7

This Convention shall in no way be interpreted as limiting the right of any Contracting State to apply its domestic law in order to prevent abuses of monopoly.

[3737]

Article 8

(1) Subject to paragraphs (2) and (3), no reservation to this Convention shall be permitted.

(2) Any Contracting State whose domestic law, on May 21, 1974, so provides may, by a written notification deposited with the Secretary-General of the United Nations, declare that, for its purposes, the words "where the originating organisation is a national of another Contracting State" appearing in Article 2(1) shall be considered as if they were replaced by the words "where the signal is emitted from the territory of another Contracting State."

(3)

(a) Any Contracting State which, on May 21, 1974, limits or denies protection with respect to the distribution of programme-carrying signals by means of wires, cable or other similar communications channels to subscribing members of the public may, by a written notification deposited with the Secretary-General of the United Nations, declare that, to the extent that and as long as its domestic law limits or denies protection, it will not apply this Convention to such distributions.

(b) Any State that has deposited a notification in accordance with subparagraph (a) shall notify the Secretary-General of the United Nations in writing, within six months of their coming into force, of any changes in its domestic law whereby the reservation under that subparagraph becomes inapplicable or more limited in scope.

[3738]

Article 9

(1) This Convention shall be deposited with the Secretary-General of the United Nations. It shall be open until March 31, 1975, for signature by any State that is a member of the United Nations, any of the Specialised Agencies brought into relationship with the United Nations, or the International Atomic Energy Agency, or is a party to the Statute of the International Court of Justice.

(2) This Convention shall be subject to ratification or acceptance by the signatory States. It shall be open for accession by any State referred to in paragraph (1).

(3) Instruments of ratification, acceptance or accession shall be deposited with the Secretary-General of the United Nations.

(4) It is understood that, at the time a State becomes bound by this Convention, it will be in a position in accordance with its domestic law to give effect to the provisions of the Convention.

[3739]

Article 10

(1) This Convention shall enter into force three months after the deposit of the fifth instrument of ratification, acceptance or accession.

(2) For each State ratifying, accepting or acceding to this Convention after the deposit of the fifth instrument of ratification, acceptance or accession, this Convention shall enter into force three months after the deposit of its instrument.

[3740]

Article 11

(1) Any Contracting State may denounce this Convention by written notification deposited with the Secretary-General of the United Nations.

(2) Denunciation shall take effect twelve months after the date on which the notification referred to in paragraph (1) is received.

[3741]

Article 12

(1) This Convention shall be signed in a single copy in English, French, Russian and Spanish, the four texts being equally authentic.

(2) Official texts shall be established by the Director-General of the United Nations Educational, Scientific and Cultural Organisation and the Director General of the World Intellectual Property Organisation, after consultation with the interested Governments, in the Arabic, Dutch, German, Italian and Portuguese languages.

(3) The Secretary-General of the United Nations shall notify the States referred to in Article 9(1), as well as the Director-General of the United Nations Educational, Scientific and Cultural Organisation, the Director General of the World Intellectual Property Organisation, the Director-General of the International Labour Office and the Secretary-General of the International Telecommunication Union, of—

(i) signatures to this Convention;

(ii) the deposit of instruments of ratification, acceptance or accession;

(iii) the date of entry into force of this Convention under Article 10(1);

(iv) the deposit of any notification relating to Article 2(2) or Article 8(2) or (3), together with its text;
(v) the receipt of notifications of denunciation.

(4) The Secretary-General of the United Nations shall transmit two certified copies of this Convention to all States referred to in Article 9(1).

[3742]–[4000]

PART VI
TELECOMMUNICATIONS

WIRELESS TELEGRAPHY ACT 1949

(1949 c 54)

ARRANGEMENT OF SECTIONS

PART I

Regulation of Wireless Telegraphy

PART II

Special provisions as to interference

PART III

Supplemental

An Act to amend the law relating to wireless telegraphy

[30 July 1949]

PART I

Regulation of Wireless Telegraphy

1 Licensing of wireless telegraphy

(*1*) *No person shall establish or use any station for wireless telegraphy or instal or use any apparatus for wireless telegraphy except under the authority of a licence in that behalf [granted under this section [by OFCOM] and any person] who establishes or uses any*

PART VI TELECOMMUNICATIONS

station for wireless telegraphy or instals or uses any apparatus for wireless telegraphy except under and in accordance with such a licence shall be guilty of an offence under this Act:

[Provided that OFCOM may by regulations] exempt from the provisions of this subsection the establishment, installation or use of stations for wireless telegraphy or wireless telegraphy apparatus of such classes or descriptions as may be specified in the regulations, either absolutely or subject to such terms, provisions and limitations as may be so specified.

[(1AA) Subsection (1) shall not apply to the use of a television receiver (within the meaning of Part 4 of the Communications Act 2003) for receiving a television programme or to the installation of a television receiver for use solely for that purpose.]

[(1A) ...]

(2) A licence granted under this section (hereafter in this Act referred to as a wireless telegraphy licence) may be issued subject to such terms, provisions and [limitations [as OFCOM think fit,] including] in particular in the case of a licence to establish a station, limitations as to the position and nature of the station, the purpose for which, the circumstances in which, and the persons by whom the station may be used, and the apparatus which may be installed or used therein, and, in the case of any other licence, limitations as to the apparatus which may be installed or used, and the places where, the purposes for which, the circumstances in which and the persons by whom the apparatus may be used.

[(2A) Those terms, provisions and limitations may also include, in particular—

(a) terms, provisions and limitations as to strength or type of signal, as to times of use and as to the sharing of frequencies;

(b) terms, provisions or limitations imposing prohibitions on the transmission or broadcasting of particular matters by the holder of the licence; and

(c) terms or provisions requiring the transmission or broadcasting of particular matters by that person.

(2B) A licence under this section may be granted either—

(a) in relation to a particular station or particular apparatus; or

(b) in relation to any station or apparatus falling within a description specified in the licence;

and such a description may be expressed by reference to such factors (including factors confined to the manner in which it is established, installed or used) as OFCOM think fit.

(2C) The terms, provisions and limitations of a licence granted under this section to a person must not duplicate obligations already imposed on him by general conditions set under section 45 of the Communications Act 2003.]

(3) A wireless telegraphy licence shall, unless previously [revoked by OFCOM], continue in force for such period as may be specified in the licence.

(4) A wireless telegraphy licence [...] may be revoked, or the terms, provisions or limitations thereof varied, by a [notice in writing from OFCOM served by them] on the holder of the licence or by a general notice applicable to licences of the class to which the licence in question belongs published in such manner as may be specified in the licence [...]

(5) Where a wireless telegraphy licence has expired or has been revoked, it shall be the duty of the person to whom the licence was issued, and of every other person in whose possession or under whose control the licence may be, to cause the licence to be [surrendered to OFCOM if required by them to do so], and any person who without reasonable excuse fails or refuses to comply with the provisions of this subsection shall be guilty of an offence under this Act:

Provided that this subsection shall not apply to a licence relating solely to apparatus not designed or adapted for emission (as opposed to reception).

(6), [(7)] ...

[4001]

NOTES

Whole Act repealed by the Wireless Telegraphy Act 2006, s 125(1), Sch 9, Pt 1, subject to transitional provisions and savings in s 124 of, Sch 8, Pt 1, paras 1–8, 10–13, 24 to, that Act at **[4230]**, **[4239]**.

Sub-s (1): words in first (outer) pair of square brackets substituted by the Broadcasting Act 1990, s 180(1), Sch 18, Pt I, para 1; words in second (inner) and third pairs of square brackets substituted by the Communications Act 2003, s 406(1), Sch 17, para 6(1), (2), subject to transitional provisions in s 406(6) of, and Sch 18, para 55 to, that Act at **[3434]**, **[3460]**.

Sub-s (1AA): inserted by the Communications Act 2003, s 406(1), Sch 17, para 6(1), (3), subject to transitional provisions in s 406(6) of, and Sch 18, para 55 to, that Act at **[3434]**, **[3460]**.

Sub-s (1A): inserted by the Deregulation (Wireless Telegraphy) Order 1996, SI 1996/1864, art 3; repealed by the Communications Act 2003, s 406(7), Sch 19(1), subject to transitional provisions in s 406(6) of, and Sch 18, para 55 to, that Act at **[3434]**, **[3460]**.

Sub-s (2): words in first (outer) pair of square brackets substituted by the Broadcasting Act 1990, s 180(1), Sch 18, Pt I, para 1; words in second (inner) pair of square brackets substituted by the Communications Act 2003, s 406(1), Sch 17, para 6(1), (4), subject to transitional provisions in s 406(6) of, and Sch 18, para 55 to, that Act at **[3434]**, **[3460]**.

Sub-s (2A)–(2C): inserted by the Communications Act 2003, s 165; for effect see s 406(6), Sch 18, para 55 to that Act at **[3434]**, **[3460]**.

Sub-ss (3), (5): words in square brackets substituted by the Communications Act 2003, s 406(1), Sch 17, para 6(1), (5), (7), subject to transitional provisions in s 406(6) of, and Sch 18, para 55 to, that Act at **[3434]**, **[3460]**.

Sub-s (4): words omitted originally inserted by the Broadcasting Act 1990, s 180(1), Sch 18, Pt I, para 1, and repealed by the Communications Act 2003, s 406(7), Sch 19(1), subject to transitional provisions in s 406(6) of, and Sch 18, para 55 to, that Act at **[3434]**, **[3460]**; words in square brackets substituted by the Communications Act 2003, s 406(1), Sch 17, para 6(1), (6), subject to transitional provisions as noted above.

Sub-s (6): repealed by the Communications Act 2003, s 406(7), Sch 19(1), subject to transitional provisions in s 406(6) of, and Sch 18, para 55 to, that Act at **[3434]**, **[3460]**.

Sub-s (7): added by the Broadcasting Act 1990, s 180(1), Sch 18, Pt I, para 1; repealed by the Communications Act 2003, s 406(7), Sch 19(1), subject to transitional provisions in s 406(6) of, and Sch 18, para 55 to, that Act at **[3434]**, **[3460]**.

Functions of the Secretary of State: the functions of the Secretary of State under this section in so far as they relate to programme making may be exercised by, or by employees of, such person (if any) as may be authorised in that behalf by the Secretary of State; see the Contracting Out (Functions relating to Wireless Telegraphy) Order 1996, SI 1996/2290.

Regulations: the Wireless Telegraphy (Reciprocal Exemption of European Radio Amateurs) Regulations 1988, SI 1988/2090 at **[4273]**; the Wireless Telegraphy Apparatus (Receivers) (Exemption) Regulations 1989, SI 1989/123 at **[4278]**; the Wireless Telegraphy Apparatus (Citizens' Band European Users) (Exemption) Regulations 1989, SI 1989/943 at **[4284]**; the Wireless Telegraphy (Testing and Development Under Suppressed Radiation Conditions) (Exemption) Regulations 1989, SI 1989/1842 at **[4292]**; the Wireless Telegraphy (Exemption) Regulations 2003, SI 2003/74 at **[4384]**; the Wireless Telegraphy (Automotive Short Range Radar) (Exemption) Regulations 2005, SI 2005/353; the Wireless Telegraphy (Automotive Short Range Radar) (Exemption) (No 2) Regulations 2005, SI 2005/1585; the Wireless Telegraphy (Radio Frequency Identification Equipment) (Exemption) Regulations 2005, SI 2005/3471.

PART VI TELECOMMUNICATIONS

[1AA Exemption from need for wireless telegraphy licence

(*1*) *If OFCOM are satisfied that the condition in subsection* (*2*) *is satisfied as respects the use of stations or apparatus of any particular description, they shall make regulations under section 1 of this Act exempting the establishment, installation and use of any station or apparatus of that description from the prohibition in that section.*

(*2*) *That condition is that the use of stations or apparatus of that description is not likely to involve any undue interference with wireless telegraphy.*]

[4002]

NOTES

Repealed as noted to s 1 at **[4001]**.

Commencement: 25 July 2003 (for the purpose of enabling network and service functions and spectrum functions to be carried out during the transitional period by the Director General of Telecommunications and the Secretary of State respectively) (see further s 408 of, and Sch 18 to, that Act at **[3436]**, **[3460]**, and the Communications Act 2003 (Commencement No 1) Order 2003, SI 2003/1900 at **[3507]**); 29 December 2003 (for the purpose of enabling OFCOM to perform those functions) (see the Office of Communications Act 2002 (Commencement No 3) and Communications Act 2003 (Commencement No 2) Order 2003, SI 2003/3142 at **[3590]**).

Inserted by the Communications Act 2003, s 166; for transitional provisions and effect see s 406(6) of, and Sch 18, para 55 to, that Act at **[3434]**, **[3460]**.

[1A Offence of keeping wireless telegraphy station or apparatus available for unauthorised use

Any person who has any station for wireless telegraphy or apparatus for wireless telegraphy in his possession or under his control and either—

(*a*) *intends to use it in contravention of section 1 of this Act; or* (*b*) *knows, or has reasonable cause to believe, that another person intends to use it in contravention of that section,*

shall be guilty of an offence.]

[4003]

NOTES

Repealed as noted to s 1 at **[4001]**.
Inserted by the Broadcasting Act 1990, s 168.

[1B Offence of allowing premises to be used for purpose of unlawful broadcasting

(*1*) *A person who is in charge of any premises which are used for making an unlawful broadcast, or for sending signals for the operation or control of any apparatus used for the purpose of making an unlawful broadcast from any other place, shall be guilty of an offence if—*

(*a*) *he knowingly causes or permits the premises to be so used; or*

(*b*) *having reasonable cause to believe that the premises are being so used, he fails to take such steps as are reasonable in the circumstances of the case to prevent the premises from being so used.*

(*2*) *For the purposes of this section a person is in charge of any premises if he—*

(*a*) *is the owner or occupier of the premises; or*

(*b*) *has, or acts or assists in, the management or control of the premises.*

(*3*) *For the purposes of this section a broadcast is unlawful if—*

(*a*) *it is made by means of the use of any station for wireless telegraphy or apparatus for wireless telegraphy in contravention of section 1 of this Act; or*

(*b*) *the making of the broadcast contravenes any provision of the Marine, &c, Broadcasting* (*Offences*) *Act 1967.*

(*4*) *In this section—*

"broadcast" has the same meaning as in the Marine, &c, Broadcasting (*Offences*) *Act 1967;*

"premises" includes any place and, in particular, includes—

(*a*) *any vehicle, vessel or aircraft; and*

(*b*) *any structure or other object* (*whether movable or otherwise and whether on land or otherwise*)*.]*

[4004]

NOTES

Repealed as noted to s 1 at **[4001]**.
Inserted by the Broadcasting Act 1990, s 169.

[1C Prohibition of acts facilitating unauthorised broadcasting

(*1*) *If a person—*

(*a*) *does any of the acts mentioned in subsection* (*2*) *in relation to a broadcasting station by which unauthorised broadcasts are made, and*

(*b*) *if any knowledge or belief or any circumstances is or are specified in relation to the act, does it with that knowledge or belief or in those circumstances,*

he shall be guilty of an offence.

(*2*) *The acts referred to in subsection* (*1*) *are—*

(*a*) *participating in the management, financing, operation or day-to-day running of the station knowing, or having reasonable cause to believe, that unauthorised broadcasts are made by the station;*

(*b*) *supplying, installing, repairing or maintaining any wireless telegraphy apparatus or any other item knowing, or having reasonable cause to believe, that the apparatus or other item is to be, or is, used for the purpose of facilitating the operation or day-to-day running of the station and that unauthorised broadcasts are made by the station;*

(*c*) *rendering any other service to any person knowing, or having reasonable cause to believe, that the rendering of that service to that person will facilitate the operation or day-to-day running of the station and that unauthorised broadcasts are so made;*

(*d*) *supplying a film or sound recording knowing, or having reasonable cause to believe, that an unauthorised broadcast of the film or recording is to be so made;*
(*e*) *making a literary, dramatic or musical work knowing, or having reasonable cause to believe, that an unauthorised broadcast of the work is to be so made;*
(*f*) *making an artistic work knowing, or having reasonable cause to believe, that an unauthorised broadcast including that work is to be so made;*
(*g*) *doing any of the following acts, namely—*
  (*i*) *participating in an unauthorised broadcast made by the station, being actually present as an announcer, as a performer or one of the performers concerned in an entertainment given, or as the deliverer of a speech;*
  (*ii*) *advertising, or inviting another to advertise, by means of an unauthorised broadcast made by the station; or*
  (*iii*) *publishing the times or other details of any unauthorised broadcasts made by the station or (otherwise than by publishing such details) publishing an advertisement of matter calculated to promote the station (whether directly or indirectly),*

knowing, or having reasonable cause to believe, that unauthorised broadcasts are made by the station.

(*3*) *In any proceedings against a person for an offence under this section consisting in the supplying of any thing or the rendering of any service, it shall be a defence for him to prove that he was obliged, under or by virtue of any enactment, to supply that thing or render that service.*

[(4) The cases in which a person is to be taken for the purposes of this section as advertising by means of a broadcast include any case in which he causes or allows it to be stated, suggested or implied that entertainment included in the broadcast—
(*a*) *has been supplied by him; or*
(*b*) *is provided wholly or partly at his expense.]*

(*5*) *Section 46 of the Consumer Protection Act 1987 shall have effect for the purpose of construing references in this section to the supply of any thing as it has effect for the purpose of construing references in that Act to the supply of any goods.*

(*6*) *In this section—*

"broadcast" has the same meaning as in the Marine, &c, Broadcasting (Offences) Act 1967;

"broadcasting station" means any business or other operation (whether or not in the nature of a commercial venture) which is engaged in the making of broadcasts;

"film", "sound recording", "literary, dramatic or musical work" and "artistic work" have the same meaning as in Part I of the Copyright, Designs and Patents Act 1988;

"speech" includes lecture, address and sermon; and

"unauthorised broadcast" means a broadcast made by means of the use of a station for wireless telegraphy or wireless telegraphy apparatus in contravention of section 1 of this Act.]

[4005]

NOTES

Repealed as noted to s 1 at **[4001]**.

Inserted by the Broadcasting Act 1990, s 170.

Sub-s (4): substituted by the Communications Act 2003, s 406(1), Sch 17, para 7; for effect and transitional provisions, see ss 363, 406(6) of, and Sch 18, para 55 to, that Act at **[3410]**, **[3434]**, **[3460]**).

[1D Procedures for the grant of licences providing a telecommunications service

(*1*), (*2*) ...

[(3) An application for a grant of a wireless telegraphy licence shall be determined in accordance with procedures prescribed in regulations made by OFCOM.]

(*4*) *The procedures [must include provision for] time-limits for dealing with the grant of licences, requirements which must be met for the grant of a licence, and particulars of the terms, provisions and limitations to which licences which may be issued are to be subject.*

[(4A) The time limits fixed for the purposes of subsection (4) in relation to any application made after the coming into force of this subsection must require a decision on the application to be made, notified to the applicant and published—
(*a*) *in the case of an application for a licence relating to a frequency allocated in*

accordance with the United Kingdom Plan for Frequency Authorisation, not more than six weeks after the day of the receipt of the application; and

(*b*) *in any other case, as soon as possible after the receipt of the application.*

(4B) The period of six weeks specified in subsection (4A)(a) may be extended by OFCOM where it appears to them necessary to do so—

(*a*) *for the purpose of enabling the requirements of any international agreement relating to frequencies or to orbital positions or to satellite Co-ordination to be complied with; or*

(*b*) *in a case where a determination falls to be made as to which of a number of applicants is the more or most suitable to be licensed, for the purpose of securing that the procedure for the making of that determination is fair, reasonable, open and transparent.*

(4C) That period shall not be extended by virtue of subsection (4B)(b) by more than eight months.]

(5) Where the person applying for a licence fails to provide any information which [OFCOM] reasonably [require] in order to satisfy [themselves] that the applicant is able to comply with the terms, provisions and limitations in the licence [OFCOM] may refuse to grant the licence.

(6) Where [OFCOM] [propose] to refuse a licence [they] shall give to the person applying for the licence the reasons for the proposed refusal and shall specify a period of not less than [one month] within which representations with respect to the proposed refusal may be made.

(7), (8) …]

[(9) In imposing terms, provisions or limitations of a wireless telegraphy licence, OFCOM shall impose only those that they are satisfied are—

(*a*) *objectively justifiable in relation to the networks and services to which they relate;*

(*b*) *not such as to discriminate unduly against particular persons or against a particular description of persons;*

(*c*) *proportionate to what they are intended to achieve; and*

(*d*) *in relation to what they are intended to achieve, transparent.]*

[4006]

NOTES

Repealed as noted to s 1 at **[4001]**.

Inserted, together with s 1E, by the Telecommunications (Licensing) Regulations 1997, SI 1997/2930, reg 4(2).

Sub-ss (1), (2), (7), (8): repealed by the Communications Act 2003, s 406(1), (7), Sch 17, para 8(1), (3), (9), Sch 19(1); for transitional provisions and effect see ss 363, 406(6) of, and Sch 18, paras 20, 55 to, that Act at **[3410]**, **[3434]**, **[3460]**.

Sub-ss (3), (9): substituted by the Communications Act 2003, s 406(1), Sch 17, para 8(1), (4), (10); for transitional provisions and effect see ss 363, 406(6) of, and Sch 18, paras 20, 55 to, that Act at **[3410]**, **[3434]**, **[3460]**.

Sub-ss (4A)–(4C): inserted by the Communications Act 2003, s 406(1), Sch 17, para 8(1), (6); for transitional provisions and effect see ss 363, 406(6) of, and Sch 18, paras 20, 55 to, that Act at **[3410]**, **[3434]**, **[3460]**.

Sub-ss (4), (5), (6): words in square brackets substituted by the Communications Act 2003, s 406(1), Sch 17, para 8(1), (2), (5), (7), (8); for transitional provisions and effect see ss 363, 406(6) of, and Sch 18, paras 20, 55 to, that Act at **[3410]**, **[3434]**, **[3460]**.

Regulations: the Wireless Telegraphy (Licensing Procedures) Regulations 2006, SI 2006/2785 at **[4565]**.

[1E Variation or revocation of a licence

(1) Where OFCOM propose to vary or revoke a wireless telegraphy licence, they shall give the person holding the licence a notification under this subsection—

(*a*) *stating the reasons for the proposed variation or revocation; and*

(*b*) *specifying the period during which the person notified has an opportunity to do the things specified in subsection (2).*

(2) Those things are—

(*a*) *making representations about the proposal; and*

(*b*) *if the proposal is the result of a contravention of a term, provision or limitation of the licence, complying with that term, provision or limitation.*

(3) Subject to subsections (4) to (6), the period for doing those things must be the period of one month beginning with the day after the one on which the notification was given.

(4) OFCOM may, if they think fit, allow a longer period for doing those things either—

(a) by specifying a longer period in the notification; or

(b) by subsequently, on one or more occasions, extending the specified period.

(5) The person notified shall have a shorter period for doing those things if a shorter period is agreed between OFCOM and the person notified.

(6) The person notified shall also have a shorter period if—

(a) OFCOM have reasonable grounds for believing that the case is a case of serious and repeated contravention or an urgent case;

(b) they have determined that, in the circumstances, a shorter period would be appropriate; and

(c) the shorter period has been specified in the notification.

(7) A case is an urgent case if the failure to vary or revoke the licence will result in, or create an immediate risk of—

(a) a serious threat to the safety of the public, to public health or to national security; or

(b) serious economic or operational problems for persons, other than the person in contravention, who—

(i) use stations or apparatus for wireless telegraphy; or

(ii) are communications providers or make associated facilities available.

(8) Subsection (1) does not apply to a proposal to vary or revoke a licence if the proposal is made at the request or with the consent of the licence holder.

(9) For the purposes of this section a contravention of a term, provision or limitation of a licence is a repeated contravention, in relation to a proposal to vary or revoke a licence, if it falls within subsection (10).

(10) A contravention falls within this subsection if—

(a) a previous notification under subsection (1) has been given in respect of the same contravention or in respect of another contravention of a term, provision or limitation of the same licence; and

(b) the subsequent notification under that subsection is given no more than twelve months after the day of the making by OFCOM of a determination for the purposes of subsection (11) that the contravention to which the previous notification related did occur.

(11) Where OFCOM have given a notification under subsection (1), they shall, within the period of one month beginning with the end of the period for the making of representations about the proposal contained in that notification—

(a) decide whether or not to vary or revoke the licence in accordance with their proposal, or in accordance with that proposal but with modifications; and

(b) give the person holding the licence a notification of their decision.

(12) The notification under subsection (11)—

(a) must be given no more than one week after the making of the decision to which it relates; and

(b) must, in accordance with that decision, either vary or revoke the licence or withdraw the proposal for a variation or revocation.

(13) The reference in subsection (10) to a contravention of a term, provision or limitation of the same licence includes a reference to a contravention of a term, provision or limitation contained in a previous licence of which the licence in question is a direct or indirect renewal.

(14) In this section, "communications provider" and "associated facility" have the same meaning as in the Communications Act 2003.]

[4007]

NOTES

Repealed as noted to s 1 at **[4001]**.

Commencement: 25 July 2003 (for the purpose of enabling network and service functions and spectrum functions to be carried out during the transitional period by the Director General of Telecommunications and the Secretary of State respectively) (see further s 408 of, and Sch 18 to, that Act at **[3436]**, **[3460]**, and the Communications Act 2003 (Commencement No 1) Order 2003, SI 2003/1900 at **[3507]**); 29 December 2003 (for the purpose of enabling OFCOM to perform those functions) (see the

Office of Communications Act 2002 (Commencement No 3) and Communications Act 2003 (Commencement No 2) Order 2003, SI 2003/3142 at **[3590]**).

Inserted as noted to s 1D at **[4006]**; substituted by the Communications Act 2003, s 169, except in any case in which a notice was served before 25 July 2003; for transitional provisions and effect see ss 363, 406(6) of, and Sch 18, para 55 to, that Act at **[3410]**, **[3434]**, **[3460]**.

1F, 2 *(S 1F originally inserted by the Telecommunications (Appeals) Regulations 1999, SI 1999/3180, reg 4(1), (3); repealed, together with s 2, by the Communications Act 2003, s 406(7), Sch 19(1); for transitional provisions and effect see ss 363, 406(6) of, and Sch 18, paras 23, 55 to, that Act at* **[3410]**, **[3434]**, **[3460]**.)

3 Regulations as to wireless telegraphy

(*1*) *[OFCOM may make regulations—]*

(*a*) *prescribing the things which are to be done or are not to be done in connection with the use of any station for wireless telegraphy or wireless telegraphy apparatus, and, in particular, requiring the use of any such station or apparatus to cease on the demand in that behalf of any such persons as may be prescribed by or under the regulations;*

(*b*) *imposing on the person to whom a wireless telegraphy licence is issued with respect to any station for wireless telegraphy or wireless telegraphy apparatus, or who is in possession or control of any station for wireless telegraphy or wireless telegraphy apparatus, obligations as to permitting and facilitating the inspection of the station and apparatus, as to the condition in which the station and apparatus are to be kept and, in the case of a station or apparatus for the establishment, installation or use of which a wireless telegraphy licence is necessary, as to the production of the licence, or of such other evidence of the licensing of the station or apparatus as may be prescribed by the regulations;*

(*c*) *where sums are or may become due from the person to whom a wireless telegraphy licence is issued after the issue or renewal thereof, requiring that person to keep and produce such accounts and records as may be specified in the regulations; and*

(*d*) *requiring the person to whom a wireless telegraphy licence authorising the establishment or use of a station has been issued to exhibit at the station such notices as may be specified in the regulations,*

…

Provided that nothing in any such regulations shall require any person to concede any form of right of entry into a private dwellinghouse for the purpose of permitting or facilitating the inspection of any apparatus not designed or adapted for emission (as opposed to reception).

(2) *Any person who contravenes any regulations made under this section, or causes or permits any station for wireless telegraphy or wireless telegraphy apparatus to be used in contravention of any such regulations, shall be guilty of an offence under this Act.*

[(2A) The approval of the Secretary of State is required for the making by OFCOM of any regulations under this section.

(*2B*) *A statutory instrument containing regulations made by OFCOM under this section shall be subject to annulment in pursuance of a resolution of either House of Parliament.]*

[4008]

NOTES

Repealed as noted to s 1 at **[4001]**.

Sub-s (1): words in square brackets substituted, and words omitted repealed, by the Communications Act 2003, s 406(1), (7), Sch 17, para 9(1), (2), Sch 19(1); for transitional provisions and effect see ss 363, 406(6) of, and Sch 18, para 55 to, that Act at **[3410]**, **[3434]**, **[3460]**.

Sub-ss (2A), (2B): inserted by the Communications Act 2003, s 406(1), Sch 17, para 9(1), (3); for transitional provisions and effect see ss 363, 406(6) of, and Sch 18, para 55 to, that Act at **[3410]**, **[3434]**, **[3460]**.

Regulations: the Wireless Telegraphy (Content of Transmission) Regulations 1988, SI 1988/47; the Wireless Telegraphy Apparatus (Citizens' Band European Users) (Exemption) Regulations 1989, SI 1989/943 at **[4284]**; the Wireless Telegraphy (Testing and Development Under Suppressed Radiation Conditions) (Exemption) Regulations 1989, SI 1989/1842 at **[4292]**; the Wireless Telegraphy (Exemption) Regulations 2003, SI 2003/74 at **[4384]**; the Wireless Telegraphy (Inspection and Restrictions on Use of Exempt Stations and Apparatus) Regulations 2005, SI 2005/3481.

3A, 4 *(S 3A inserted by the Telecommunications Act 1984, s 74; repealed, together with s 4, by the Wireless Telegraphy Act 1998, s 7, Sch 1, para 2, Sch 2, Pt I.)*

5 Misleading messages and interception and disclosure of messages

[(1)] Any person who—

(*a*) *by means of wireless telegraphy, sends or attempts to send, any message which, to his knowledge, is false or misleading and is, to his knowledge, likely to prejudice the efficiency of any safety of life service or endanger the safety of any person or of any vessel, aircraft or vehicle, and, in particular, any message which, to his knowledge, falsely suggests that a vessel or aircraft is in distress or in need of assistance or is not in distress or not in need of assistance; or*

(*b*) *otherwise than under [under the authority of a designated person], either—*

(*i*) *uses any wireless telegraphy apparatus with intent to obtain information as to the contents, sender or addressee of any message (whether sent by means of wireless telegraphy or not) [of which neither the person using the apparatus nor a person on whose behalf he is acting is an intended recipient]; or*

(*ii*) *except in the course of legal proceedings or for the purpose of any report thereof, discloses any information as to the contents, sender or addressee of any such message, being information which would not have come to his knowledge but for the use of wireless telegraphy apparatus by him or by another person, shall be guilty of an offence under this Act.*

[(2) The conduct in relation to which a designated person may give a separate authority for the purposes of this section shall not, except where he believes the conduct to be necessary on grounds falling within subsection (5) of this section, include—

(*a*) *any conduct which, if engaged in without lawful authority, constitutes an offence under section 1(1) or (2) of the Regulation of Investigatory Powers Act 2000;*

(*b*) *any conduct which, if engaged in without lawful authority, is actionable under section 1(3) of that Act;*

(*c*) *any conduct which is capable of being authorised by an authorisation or notice granted by any person under Chapter II of Part I of that Act (communications data);*

(*d*) *any conduct which is capable of being authorised by an authorisation granted by any person under Part II of that Act (surveillance etc).*

(3) A designated person shall not exercise his power to give a separate authority for the purposes of this section except where he believes—

(*a*) *that the giving of his authority is necessary on grounds falling within subsection (4) or (5) of this section; and*

(*b*) *that the conduct authorised by him is proportionate to what is sought to be achieved by that conduct.*

(4) A separate authority for the purposes of this section is necessary on grounds falling within this subsection if it is necessary—

(*a*) *in the interests of national security;*

(*b*) *for the purpose of preventing or detecting crime (within the meaning of the Regulation of Investigatory Powers Act 2000) or of preventing disorder;*

(*c*) *in the interests of the economic well-being of the United Kingdom;*

(*d*) *in the interests of public safety;*

(*e*) *for the purpose of protecting public health;*

(*f*) *for the purpose of assessing or collecting any tax, duty, levy or other imposition, contribution or charge payable to a government department; or*

(*g*) *for any purpose (not falling within paragraphs (a) to (f)) which is specified for the purposes of this subsection by regulations made by the Secretary of State.*

(5) A separate authority for the purposes of this section is necessary on grounds falling within this subsection if it is not necessary on grounds falling within subsection (4)(a) or (c) to (g) but is necessary for purposes connected with—

(*a*) *the issue of licences under this Act;*

(*b*) *the prevention or detection of anything which constitutes interference with wireless telegraphy; or*

(*c*) *the enforcement of any enactment contained in this Act or of any enactment not so contained that relates to such interference.*

(6) The matters to be taken into account in considering whether the requirements of subsection (3) of this section are satisfied in the case of the giving of any separate authority for the purposes of this section shall include whether what it is thought necessary to achieve by the authorised conduct could reasonably be achieved by other means.

(7) A separate authority for the purposes of this section must be in writing and under the hand of—

- *(a) the Secretary of State;*
- *[(aa) in the case of an authority given by the Scottish Ministers (by virtue of provision made under section 63 of the Scotland Act 1998), a member of the Scottish Executive;]*
- *(b) one of the Commissioners of Customs and Excise; or*
- *(c) a person not falling within paragraph (a) or (b) who is designated for the purposes of this subsection by regulations made by the Secretary of State.*

(8) A separate authority for the purposes of this section may be general or specific and may be given—

- *(a) to such person or persons, or description of persons,*
- *(b) for such period, and*
- *(c) subject to such restrictions and limitations,*

as the designated person thinks fit.

(9) No regulations shall be made under subsection (4)(g) unless a draft of them has first been laid before Parliament and approved by a resolution of each House.

(10) For the purposes of this section the question whether conduct is capable of being authorised under Chapter II of Part I of the Regulation of Investigatory Powers Act 2000 or under Part II of that Act shall be determined without reference—

- *(a) to whether the person whose conduct it is is a person on whom any power or duty is or may be conferred or imposed by or under Chapter II of Part I or Part II of that Act; or*
- *(b) to whether there are grounds for believing that the requirements for the grant of an authorisation or the giving of a notice under Chapter II of Part I or Part II of that Act are satisfied.*

(11) References in this section to a separate authority for the purposes of this section are references to any authority for the purposes of this section given otherwise than by way of the issue or renewal of a warrant, authorisation or notice under Part I or II of the Regulation of Investigatory Powers Act 2000.

(12) In this section "designated person" means—

- *(a) the Secretary of State;*
- *(b) the Commissioners of Customs and Excise; or*
- *(c) any other person designated for the purposes of this section by regulations made by the Secretary of State.]*

[4009]

NOTES

Repealed as noted to s 1 at **[4001]**.

Sub-s (1): numbered as such, and words in square brackets substituted, by the Regulation of Investigatory Powers Act 2000, s 73(1), (2).

Sub-ss (2)–(6), (8)–(12): added by the Regulation of Investigatory Powers Act 2000, s 73(3).

Sub-s (7): added by the Regulation of Investigatory Powers Act 2000, s 73(3); para (aa) inserted by the Scotland Act 1998 (Transfer of Functions to the Scottish Ministers etc) (No 2) Order 2000, SI 2000/3253, art 4(1), Sch 3, Pt I, paras 1, 2.

Functions under sub-s (1): in so far as these are exercisable in or as regards Scotland, see the Scotland Act 1998 (Functions Exercisable in or as Regards Scotland) Order 1999, SI 1999/1748, art 3, Sch 1, para 1, and the Scottish Ministers, see the Scotland Act 1998 (Transfer of Functions to the Scottish Ministers etc) Order 1999, SI 1999/1750, art 2, Sch 1.

Regulations: the Wireless Telegraphy (Interception and Disclosure of Messages) (Designation) Regulations 2003, SI 2003/3104 at **[4430]**.

6 Territorial extent of preceding provisions

(1) Subject to the provisions of this section, the preceding provisions of this Part of this Act shall apply—

- *(a) to all stations and apparatus in or over, or for the time being in or over, the United Kingdom or the territorial waters adjacent thereto; and*
- *(b) subject to any limitations which the [Secretary of State] may by regulations*

determine, to all stations and apparatus on board any … ship or … aircraft which is registered in the United Kingdom but is not for the time being in or over the United Kingdom or the said territorial waters; and

(*c*) *subject to any limitations which the [Secretary of State] may by regulations determine, to all apparatus which is not in or over the United Kingdom or the said territorial waters but was released from within the United Kingdom or the said territorial waters, or from any … ship or … aircraft which is registered in the United Kingdom,*

and, without prejudice to the liability of any other person, in the event of any contravention of the said preceding provisions or of any regulations made thereunder occurring in relation to any station or apparatus on board or released from any vessel or aircraft, the captain or person for the time being in charge of the vessel or aircraft shall be guilty of an offence under this Act:

Provided that the captain or person for the time being in charge of a vessel or aircraft shall not be guilty of any offence under this Act by reason of any contravention of the said provisions or regulations occurring in relation to apparatus on board the vessel or aircraft if the contravention consists of the use by a passenger on board the ship or aircraft of apparatus not designed or adapted for emission (as opposed to reception) which is not part of the wireless telegraphy apparatus, if any, of the ship or aircraft.

(2) *The [Secretary of State] may make regulations for regulating the use, on board any [ship or aircraft which, not being registered in the United Kingdom, is registered in a country other than the United Kingdom, the Isle of Man or any of the Channel Islands while that ship or aircraft is] within the limits of the United Kingdom and the territorial waters adjacent thereto, of wireless telegraphy apparatus on board the ship or aircraft, and such regulations may provide for the punishment of persons contravening the regulations by [a maximum fine for each offence of an amount not exceeding level 5 on the standard scale, … or of a lesser amount] and for the forfeiture of any wireless telegraphy apparatus in respect of which an offence under such regulations is committed; but, save as aforesaid [or by virtue of an Order in Council under subsection (3) of this section], nothing in this Part of this Act shall operate so as to impose any prohibition or restriction on persons using wireless telegraphy apparatus on board any [such ship or aircraft as aforesaid].*

(*3*) *His Majesty may by Order in Council direct that any reference in this section to any … ship or aircraft registered in the United Kingdom shall be construed as including a reference to any … ship or aircraft registered in the Isle of Man, in any of the Channel Islands, or in any colony, British protectorate or British protected state, or registered under the law of any other country or territory outside the United Kingdom which is for the time being administered by His Majesty's Government in the United Kingdom.*

[(4) …]

[4010]

NOTES

Repealed as noted to s 1 at **[4001]**.

Sub-s (1): words in square brackets substituted by virtue of the Post Office Act 1969, s 3, and the Ministry of Posts and Telecommunications (Dissolution) Order 1974, SI 1974/691, art 2; words omitted repealed by the Wireless Telegraphy Act 1967, s 9(2).

Sub-s (2): words in first pair of square brackets substituted by virtue of the Post Office Act 1969, s 3, and SI 1974/691, art 2; words in second and fifth pairs of square brackets substituted, and words in fourth pair of square brackets inserted, by the Wireless Telegraphy Act 1967, s 9(3); words in third pair of square brackets substituted by the Criminal Justice Act 1982, s 50(1), words omitted therein repealed by the Statute Law (Repeals) Act 1993.

Sub-s (3): words omitted repealed by the Wireless Telegraphy Act 1967, s 9(2).

Sub-s (4): added by the Criminal Justice Act 1982, s 50(1); repealed by the Fines and Penalties (Northern Ireland) Order 1984, SI 1984/703 (NI), art 19(2), Sch 7.

Regulations: the Wireless Telegraphy (Visiting Ships and Aircraft) Regulations 1998, SI 1998/2970 at **[4328]**.

7 Powers of [Secretary of State] as to wireless personnel

(*1*) *The [Secretary of State] may hold examinations to determine the competence of the persons examined to fill positions in connection with the operation of stations for wireless telegraphy or wireless telegraphy apparatus and may issue to persons successful at such examinations certificates of competence of such types as he may from time to time determine.*

(2) *The [Secretary of State] may issue to such persons as he thinks fit authorities in writing authorising the persons to whom the authorities are issued to fill such positions in*

connection with the operation of stations for wireless telegraphy or wireless telegraphy apparatus as may be specified in the respective authorities, being positions for the holding of which the possession of such an authority is, under wireless telegraphy licences granted under this Act or under any licences granted under any corresponding law of any part of His Majesty's dominions, a necessity or a qualification.

(3) The [Secretary of State], if it appears to him that there are sufficient grounds so to do, may at any time suspend any authority granted under the last preceding subsection with a view to the revocation thereof, and where he so suspends an authority, the provisions of the First Schedule to this Act shall have effect.

(4) Where any authority granted under subsection (2) of this section has ceased to be in force or has been suspended, it shall be the duty of the person to whom the authority was issued, and of every other person in whose possession or under whose control the authority may be, to cause the authority to be surrendered to the [Secretary of State] if required by the [Secretary of State] so to do, and any person who without reasonable excuse fails or refuses to comply with the provisions of this subsection shall be guilty of an offence under this Act.

(5) The [Secretary of State] may charge to persons applying to take part in any examination under this section, and to applicants for, or for copies of, any certificate or authority issued under this section, such fees, if any, as he may determine.

[4011]

NOTES

Repealed as noted to s 1 at **[4001]**.

Words in square brackets substituted by virtue of the Post Office Act 1969, s 3, and the Ministry of Posts and Telecommunications (Dissolution) Order 1974, SI 1974/691, art 2.

8 (*Repealed by the Post Office Act 1969, s 137(1), Sch 8, Pt I.*)

PART II

Special provisions as to interference

9 (*Repealed by the Communications Act 2003, s 406(7), Sch 17, para 10, Sch 19(1), in relation to decisions made after the coming into force of s 192 of that Act; for transitional provisions and effect see ss 363, 406(1), (6), (7) of, and Sch 18, para 55, Sch 19(1), Note 1 to, that Act at* **[3410]**, **[3434]**, **[3460]**, **[3461]**.)

10 Regulations as to radiation of electro-magnetic energy, etc

(1) [OFCOM may make regulations for either or both of the following purposes—]

- *(a) for prescribing the requirements to be complied with in the case of any apparatus to which this section applies if the apparatus is to be used;*
- *(b) for prescribing the requirements to be complied with in the case of any apparatus to which this section applies if the apparatus is to be sold otherwise than for export, or offered or advertised for sale otherwise than for export, or let on hire or offered or advertised for letting on hire, by any person who in the course of business manufactures, assembles or imports such apparatus.*

(2) [The requirements prescribed under subsection (1) shall be such as OFCOM think fit] for the purpose of ensuring that the use of the apparatus does not cause undue interference with wireless telegraphy, and may in particular include—

- *(a) requirements as to the maximum intensity of electro-magnetic energy of any specified frequencies which may be radiated in any direction from the apparatus while it is being used; and*
- *(b) in the case of an apparatus the power for which is supplied from electric lines, requirements as to the maximum electro-magnetic energy of any specified frequencies which may be injected into those lines by the apparatus,*

…

(3) The apparatus to which this section applies shall be such apparatus as may be specified in the regulations made thereunder, being apparatus generating, or designed to generate, or liable to generate fortuitously, electro-magnetic energy at frequencies of not more than three million megacycles per second …

The references in this subsection to apparatus include references to any form of electric line, and other references in this Act to apparatus shall be construed accordingly.

(4) It shall not be unlawful for any person to use any apparatus to which this section applies or to sell any such apparatus or offer or advertise it for sale or let it on hire or offer or advertise it for letting on hire by reason only that it does not comply with the requirements applicable under any regulations made under this section, but the non-compliance shall be a ground for the giving of a notice under the next succeeding section or under section twelve of this Act, as the case may be.

[(4A) The approval of the Secretary of State is required for the making by OFCOM of any regulations under this section.

(4B) A statutory instrument containing regulations made by OFCOM under this section shall be subject to annulment in pursuance of a resolution of either House of Parliament.]

[4012]

NOTES

Repealed as noted to s 1 at **[4001]**.

Sub-s (1): words in square brackets substituted by the Communications Act 2003, s 406(1), Sch 17, para 11(1), (2); for transitional provisions and effect see ss 363, 406(6) of, and Sch 18, para 55 to, that Act at **[3410]**, **[3434]**, **[3460]**.

Sub-s (2): words in square brackets substituted, and words omitted repealed, by the Communications Act 2003, s 406(1), (7), Sch 17, para 11(1), (3), Sch 19(1); for transitional provisions and effect see ss 363, 406(6) of, and Sch 18, para 55 to, that Act at **[3410]**, **[3434]**, **[3460]**.

Sub-s (3): words omitted repealed by the Wireless Telegraphy Act 1967, s 10(2).

Sub-ss (4A), (4B): added by the Communications Act 2003, s 406(1), Sch 17, para 11(1), (4); for transitional provisions and effect see ss 363, 406(6) of, and Sch 18, para 55 to, that Act at **[3410]**, **[3434]**, **[3460]**.

Regulations: the Wireless Telegraphy (Control of Interference from Ignition Apparatus) Regulations 1952, SI 1952/2023; the Wireless Telegraphy (Control of Interference from Electro-Medical Apparatus) Regulations 1963, SI 1963/1895; the Wireless Telegraphy (Control of Interference from Radio-Frequency Heating Apparatus) Regulations 1971, SI 1971/1675 at **[4241]**; the Wireless Telegraphy (Control of Interference from Ignition Apparatus) Regulations 1973, SI 1973/1217 at **[4250]**; the Wireless Telegraphy (Control of Interference from Household Appliances, Portable Tools, etc) Regulations 1978, SI 1978/1267 at **[4256]**; the Wireless Telegraphy (Control of Interference from Fluorescent Lighting Apparatus) Regulations 1978, SI 1978/1268 at **[4262]**; the Wireless Telegraphy (Control of Interference from Citizens' Band Radio Apparatus) Regulations 1982, SI 1982/635 at **[4268]**.

11 Enforcement of regulations as to use of apparatus

(1) [If OFCOM are of the opinion—]

- *(a) that any apparatus does not comply with the requirements applicable to it under regulations made for the purpose specified in paragraph (a) of subsection (1) of the last preceding section; and*
- *(b) that either—*
  - *(i) the use of the apparatus is likely to cause undue interference with any wireless telegraphy used for the purposes of any safety of life service or for any purpose on which the safety of any person or of any vessel, aircraft or vehicle may depend; or*
  - *(ii) the use of the apparatus is likely to cause undue interference with any other wireless telegraphy and in fact has caused or is causing such interference in a case where [they consider] that all reasonable steps to minimize interference have been taken in relation to the station or apparatus receiving the telegraphy,*

[OFCOM may] serve on the person in whose possession the apparatus is a notice in writing requiring that, after a date fixed by the notice, not being less than twenty-eight days from the date of the service thereof, the apparatus shall not be used, whether by the person to whom the notice is given or otherwise, [or, if OFCOM think fit] so to frame the notice, shall only be used in such manner, at such times and in such circumstances as may be specified in the notice:

Provided that—

- *(i) …*
- *(ii) [if OFCOM are satisfied] that the use of the apparatus in question is likely to cause undue interference with any wireless telegraphy used for the purposes of any safety of life service or for any purpose on which the safety of any person or of any vessel, aircraft or vehicle may depend, the date to be fixed by the notice may be the date of the service thereof, …*

PART VI TELECOMMUNICATIONS

(2) A notice under subsection (1) of this section may be revoked or varied by a subsequent [notice in writing from OFCOM served by them] on the person in whose possession the apparatus then is:

Provided that where a notice under this subsection has the effect of imposing any additional restrictions on the use of the apparatus, the provisions of subsection (1) of this section relating to the coming into force of notices shall apply in relation to the notice as if it had been a notice served under the said subsection (1).

[(2A) Where an appeal with respect to a notice under this section is pending—

(a) proceedings for an offence of contravening that notice (whether instituted before or after the bringing of the appeal) shall be stayed until the appeal has been finally determined; and

(b) any such proceedings shall be discharged if the notice is set aside in consequence of the appeal;

but this subsection does not affect proceedings in which a person has been convicted at a time when there was no pending appeal.

(2B) For the purposes of this section an appeal under section 192 of the Communications Act 2003 with respect to a notice under this section or a further appeal relating to the decision on such an appeal is pending unless—

(a) that appeal has been brought to a conclusion or withdrawn and there is no further appeal pending in relation to the decision on the appeal; or

(b) no further appeal against a decision made on the appeal or on any such further appeal may be brought without the permission of the court and—

(i) in a case where there is no fixed period within which that permission can be sought, that permission has been refused or has not been sought; or

(ii) in a case where there is a fixed period within which that permission can be sought, that permission has been refused or that period has expired without permission having been sought.

(2C) No proceedings for an offence of contravening a notice under this section may be commenced in Scotland—

(a) until the time during which an appeal against such a notice may be brought has expired; or

(b) where such an appeal has been brought, until that appeal has been determined.

(2D) Such proceedings in Scotland must be commenced within six months of—

(a) where no appeal has been brought, the time referred to in paragraph (a) of subsection (2C); and

(b) where an appeal has been brought and determined, the date of that determination.]

(7) Any person who, knowing that a [notice from OFCOM under this section] is in force with respect to any apparatus, used that apparatus, or causes or permits it to be used, in contravention of the notice, shall be guilty of an offence under this Act.

[4013]

NOTES

Repealed as noted to s 1 at **[4001]**.

Sub-s (1): words in square brackets substituted, and words omitted repealed in relation to any notice served after 25 July 2003, by the Communications Act 2003, ss 178(1)(a), 406(1), (7), Sch 17, para 12(1), (2), Sch 19(1); for transitional provisions and effect see ss 363, 406(6) of, and Sch 18, para 55 to, that Act at **[3410]**, **[3434]**, **[3460]**.

Sub-ss (2), (7): words in square brackets substituted by the Communications Act 2003, s 406(1), Sch 17, para 12(1), (3), (4); for transitional provisions see s 406(6) of, and Sch 18, para 55 to, that Act at **[3434]**, **[3460]**.

Sub-ss (2A)–(2D): substituted, for original sub-ss (3)–(6), by the Communications Act 2003, s 178(1)(b) in relation to any notice served after 25 July 2003; for transitional provisions and effect see ss 363, 406(6) of, and Sch 18, para 55 to, that Act at **[3410]**, **[3434]**, **[3460]**.

12 Enforcement of regulations as to sales, etc, by manufacturers and others

(1) [If OFCOM are of the opinion] that any apparatus does not comply with the requirements applicable to it under regulations made for the purpose specified in paragraph (b) of subsection (1) of section ten of this Act, [OFCOM] may serve on any person who has manufactured, assembled or imported the apparatus in the course of business a

notice in writing prohibiting him from selling the apparatus, otherwise than for export, or offering or advertising it for sale, otherwise than for export, or letting it on hire or offering or advertising it for letting on hire.

[(1A) Where an appeal with respect to a notice under subsection (1) of this section is pending—

(a) proceedings for an offence of contravening that notice (whether instituted before or after the bringing of the appeal) shall be stayed until the appeal has been finally determined; and

(b) any such proceedings shall be discharged if the notice is set aside in consequence of the appeal;

but this subsection does not affect proceedings in which a person has been convicted at a time when there was no pending appeal.

(1B) For the purposes of this section any appeal under section 192 of the Communications Act 2003 with respect to a notice under this section or a further appeal relating to the decision on that appeal is pending unless—

(a) that appeal has been brought to a conclusion or withdrawn and there is no further appeal pending in relation to the decision; or

(b) no further appeal against any decision made on the appeal or on any such further appeal may be brought without the permission of the court and—

(i) in a case where there is no fixed period within which that permission can be sought, that permission has been refused or has not been sought; or

(ii) in a case where there is a fixed period within which that permission can be sought, that permission has been refused or that period has expired without permission having been sought.

(1C) No proceedings for an offence of contravening a notice under this section may be commenced in Scotland—

(a) until the time during which an appeal against such a notice may be brought has expired; or

(b) where such an appeal has been brought, until that appeal has been determined.

(1D) Such proceedings in Scotland must be commenced within six months of—

(a) where no appeal has been brought, the time referred to in paragraph (a) of subsection (1C); and

(b) where an appeal has been brought and determined, the date of that determination.]

(5) Where a notice has been served under subsection (1) of this section, the person on whom the notice has been served shall, if he contravenes the provisions of the notice without the notice having been previously revoked [by OFCOM, be guilty of an offence.]

[4014]

NOTES

Repealed as noted to s 1 at **[4001]**.

Sub-ss (1), (5): words in square brackets substituted by the Communications Act 2003, s 406(1), Sch 17, para 13, subject to transitional provisions in s 406(6) of, and Sch 18, para 55 to, that Act at **[3434]**, **[3460]**.

Sub-ss (1A)–(1D): substituted, for original sub-ss (2)–(4), by the Communications Act 2003, s 178(2).

12A (*Inserted by the Telecommunications Act 1984, s 78; repealed by the Electromagnetic Compatibility Regulations 1992, SI 1992/2372, reg 2(1).*)

13 Deliberate interference

(1) Any person who uses any apparatus for the purpose of interfering with any wireless telegraphy shall be guilty of an offence under this Act.

(2) This section shall apply whether or not the apparatus in question is wireless telegraphy apparatus or apparatus to which any of the preceding provisions of this Part of this Act apply, and whether or not any notice under section eleven or section twelve of this Act has been given with respect to the apparatus, or, if given, has been varied or revoked.

[4015]

NOTES

Repealed as noted to s 1 at **[4001]**.

PART VI TELECOMMUNICATIONS

PART III

Supplemental

[13A Information requirements

(1) Subject to the following provisions of this section, OFCOM may require a person who is using or has established, installed or used a station or apparatus for wireless telegraphy to provide OFCOM with all such information relating to—

- (*a*) *the establishment, installation or use of the station or apparatus, and*
- (*b*) *any related matters,*

as OFCOM may require for statistical purposes.

(2) *OFCOM are not to require the provision of information under this section except—*

- (*a*) *by a demand for the information that sets out OFCOM's reasons for requiring the information and the statistical purposes for which it is required, and*
- (*b*) *where the making of a demand for that information is proportionate to the use to which the information is to be put in the carrying out of OFCOM's functions.*

(3) A demand for information required under this section must be contained in the notice served on the person from whom the information is required.

(4) A person required to provide information under this section must provide it in such manner and within such reasonable period as may be specified by OFCOM.

(5) A person who fails to provide information in accordance with a requirement of OFCOM under this section is guilty of an offence.

(6) In proceedings against a person for an offence under subsection (1) it shall be a defence for that person to show—

- (*a*) *that it was not reasonably practicable for him to comply with the requirement within the period specified by OFCOM; but*
- (*b*) *that he has taken all reasonable steps to provide the required information after the end of that period.*

(7) A person is guilty of an offence if—

- (*a*) *in pursuance of any requirement under this section, he provides information that is false in any material particular, and*
- (*b*) *at the time he provides it, he either knows it to be false or is reckless as to whether or not it is false.]*

[4016]

NOTES

Repealed as noted to s 1 at **[4001]**.
Commencement: 29 December 2003.
Inserted, together with s 13B, by the Communications Act 2003, s 171(1).

[13B Statement of policy on information gathering

(1) It shall be the duty of OFCOM to prepare and publish a statement of their general policy with respect to—

- (*a*) *the exercise of their powers under section 13A, and*
- (*b*) *the uses to which they are proposing to put information obtained under that section.*

(2) *OFCOM may from time to time revise that statement as they think fit.*

(3) Where OFCOM make or revise their statement of policy under this section, they must publish that statement or (as the case may be) the revised statement in such manner as they consider appropriate for bringing it to the attention of the persons who, in their opinion, are likely to be affected by it.

(4) It shall be the duty of OFCOM, in exercising the powers conferred on them by section 13A, to have regard to the statement for the time being in force under this section.]

[4017]

NOTES

Repealed as noted to s 1 at **[4001]**.
Commencement: 29 December 2003.

Inserted as noted to s 13A at **[4016]**.

14 Penalties and legal proceedings

[(1) Any person committing—

[[(aa) any offence under section 1(1) of this Act consisting in the establishment or use of a station for wireless telegraphy, or the installation or use of wireless telegraphy apparatus, for the purpose of making a broadcast (within the meaning of section 9 of the Marine, &c, Broadcasting (Offences) Act 1967 (c 41));

(ab) any offence under section 1A of this Act where the relevant contravention of section 1 would constitute an offence falling within paragraph (aa);]

(ac) any offence under section 1B or 1C of this Act;]

[(a) any offence under section 5(1)(a) of this Act; or]

(b) any offence under section 13 of this Act;

shall be liable on summary conviction to imprisonment for a term not exceeding six months or a fine not exceeding the statutory maximum or both, or on conviction on indictment to imprisonment for a term not exceeding two years or a fine or both.

(1A) Any person committing—

(a) any offence under section 1(1) of this Act consisting in the installation or use, otherwise than under and in accordance with a wireless telegraphy licence, of any apparatus not designed or adapted for emission (as opposed to reception); or

[(aa) any offence under section 1A of this Act committed in relation to any wireless telegraphy apparatus not designed or adapted for emission (as opposed to reception);]

(b) any offence under section 3(2) of this Act consisting in a contravention, in relation to any such apparatus, of any regulations made under that section; or

(c) any offence under section 11(7) or 12(5) of this Act involving or consisting in a contravention of a notice [from OFCOM] in relation to any apparatus, not being apparatus the use of which is likely to cause undue interference with any wireless telegraphy used for the purpose of any safety of life service or any purpose on which the safety of any person or of any vessel, aircraft or vehicle may depend; or

(d) any offence under section 1(5) or 7(4) of this Act; or

(e) …

[(ea) any offence under section 13A(1) of this Act; or]

(f) any offence under this Act which is an offence under section 5 or 8(2) of the Wireless Telegraphy Act 1967 (failure to comply with notices under Part I of that Act, giving false information, etc);

shall be liable on summary conviction to a fine not exceeding level 3 on the standard scale.

[(1AA) A person committing—

(a) an offence under section 1(1) of this Act other than—

(i) one which falls within subsection (1)(aa), or

(ii) one which falls within subsection (1A)(a), or

(b) an offence under section 1A of this Act other than—

(i) one which falls within subsection (1)(ab), or

(ii) one which falls within subsection (1A)(aa),

shall be liable, on summary conviction, to imprisonment for a term not exceeding six months or to a fine not exceeding level 5 on the standard scale, or to both.]

(1B) Any person committing—

(a) …

(b) any offence under section 11(7) of this Act other than one within subsection (1A)(c) of this section;

shall be liable on summary conviction to imprisonment for a term not exceeding three months or to a fine not exceeding level 5 on the standard scale, or both.

(1C) Any person committing any other offence under this Act shall be liable on summary conviction to a fine not exceeding level 5 on the standard scale.]

(2) …

[[(3) Where a person is convicted of—

(a) an offence under this Act consisting in any contravention of any of the provisions of Part I of this Act in relation to any station for wireless telegraphy or any

PART VI TELECOMMUNICATIONS

wireless telegraphy apparatus (including an offence under section 1B or 1C of this Act) or in the use of any apparatus for the purpose of interfering with any wireless telegraphy;

(*b*) ...

(*c*) *any offence under the Marine, &c, Broadcasting (Offences) Act 1967; or*

(*d*) *any offence under this Act which is an offence under section 7 of the Wireless Telegraphy Act 1967 (whether as originally enacted or as substituted by section 77 of the Telecommunications Act 1984),*

the court may, in addition to any other penalty, order such of the following things to be forfeited to [OFCOM] as the court considers appropriate, that is to say—

(i) any vehicle, vessel or aircraft, or any structure or other object, which was used in connection with the commission of the offence;

(ii) any wireless telegraphy apparatus or other apparatus in relation to which the offence was committed or which was used in connection with the commission of it;

(iii) any wireless telegraphy apparatus or other apparatus not falling within paragraph (ii) above which was, at the time of the commission of the offence, in the possession or under the control of the person convicted of the offence and was intended to be used (whether or not by that person) in connection with the making of any broadcast or other transmission that would contravene section 1 of this Act or any provision of the Marine, &c, Broadcasting (Offences) Act 1967.

(*3AA*) *The power conferred by virtue of subsection (3)(a) above does not apply in a case where the offence is any such offence as is mentioned in subsection (1A)(a) or (aa) above.*

(*3AB*) *References in subsection (3)(ii) or (iii) above to apparatus other than wireless telegraphy apparatus include references to—*

(*a*) *recordings;*

(*b*) *equipment designed or adapted for use—*

(*i*) *in making recordings; or*

(*ii*) *in reproducing from recordings any sounds or visual images; and*

(*c*) *equipment not falling within paragraphs (a) and (b) above but connected, directly or indirectly, to wireless telegraphy apparatus.]*

(*3A*) *Without prejudice to the operation of subsection (3) of this section in relation to any other apparatus, where a person is convicted of an offence under this Act involving restricted apparatus, the court shall order the apparatus to be forfeited to [OFCOM] unless the accused or any person claiming to be the owner of or otherwise interested in the apparatus shows cause why the apparatus should not be forfeited.*

Apparatus is restricted apparatus for the purposes of this subsection if custody or control of apparatus of any class or description to which it belongs is for the time being restricted by an order under section 7 of the Wireless Telegraphy Act 1967.

(*3B*) *Apparatus may be ordered to be forfeited under this section notwithstanding that it is not the property of the person by whom the offence giving rise to the forfeiture was committed, and any apparatus ordered to be forfeited under this section may be disposed of by [OFCOM] in such manner as [they think] fit.*

(*3C*) *Subsections (3) to (3B) of this section have effect notwithstanding anything in section 140 of the Magistrates' Courts Act 1980 or Article 58 of the Magistrates' Courts (Northern Ireland) Order 1981.*

(*3D*) *The court by whom any apparatus is ordered to be forfeited under this section may also order the person by whom the offence giving rise to the forfeiture was committed not to dispose of that apparatus except by delivering it up to [OFCOM] within forty-eight hours of being so required by [them].*

(*3E*) *If a person against whom an order is made under subsection (3D) of this section contravenes that order or fails to deliver up the apparatus to [OFCOM] as required he shall be guilty of a further offence under this Act which, for the purpose of determining the appropriate penalty in accordance with the provisions of this section relating to penalties[, shall be treated as an offence committed under the same provision, and at the same time,] as the offence for which the forfeiture was ordered.]*

(*4*), (*5*) ...

(*6*) *Without prejudice to the right to bring separate proceedings for contraventions of this Act taking place on separate occasions, a person who is convicted of an offence under this Act consisting in the use of any station or apparatus, or in a failure or refusal to cause any licence or authority to be surrendered, shall, where the use, or failure or refusal continues after the conviction, be deemed to commit a separate offence in respect of every day on which the use, failure or refusal so continues.*

(7) Nothing in the preceding provisions of this section shall limit any right of any person to bring civil proceedings in respect of the doing or apprehended doing of anything rendered unlawful by any provision of this Act [or section 7 of the Wireless Telegraphy Act 1967], and, without prejudice to the generality of the preceding words, compliance with the provisions of this Act [or section 7 of the Wireless Telegraphy Act 1967] contraventions of which are declared to be offences under this Act shall be enforceable by civil proceedings by the Crown [or by OFCOM] for an injunction or for any other appropriate relief.

[In the application of this section to Scotland for the words from "civil proceedings" to "appropriate relief" there shall be substituted "civil proceedings by the Advocate General for Scotland, or by OFCOM, for an interdict or for any other appropriate remedy or relief".]

[(8), (9) ...]

[4018]

NOTES

Repealed as noted to s 1 at **[4001]**.

Sub-s (1): substituted, together with sub-ss (1A)–(1C), for original sub-s (1), by the Telecommunications Act 1984, s 75, Sch 3, para 1; paras (aa)–(ac) inserted by the Broadcasting Act 1990, s 172(1), (2); paras (aa), (ab) substituted by the Communications Act 2003, s 179(1), (4), in relation to offences committed after 18 September 2003, and para (a) substituted by s 406(1) of, and Sch 17, para 14(1), (2) to, that Act.

Sub-s (1A): substituted, together with sub-ss (1), (1B), (1C), for original sub-s (1), by the Telecommunications Act 1984, s 75, Sch 3, para 1; para (aa) inserted by the Broadcasting Act 1990, s 172(1), (3); words in square brackets in para (c) substituted, para (e) repealed, and para (ea) inserted, by the Communications Act 2003, ss 171(2), 406(1), (7), Sch 17, para 14(1), (3), Sch 19(1).

Sub-s (1AA): inserted by the Communications Act 2003, s 179(2), (4) in relation to offences committed after 18 September 2003.

Sub-s (1B): substituted, together with sub-ss (1), (1A), (1C), for original sub-s (1), by the Telecommunications Act 1984, s 75, Sch 3, para 1; para (a) repealed by the Broadcasting Act 1990, s 203(3), Sch 21; words "to imprisonment for a term not exceeding three months or" and ", or both" repealed, in relation to England and Wales, by the Criminal Justice Act 2003, s 332, Sch 37, Pt 9, as from a day to be appointed.

Sub-s (1C): substituted, together with sub-ss (1)–(1B), for original sub-s (1), by the Telecommunications Act 1984, s 75, Sch 3, para 1.

Sub-s (2): repealed by the Communications Act 2003, s 406(7), Sch 19(1).

Sub-s (3): substituted, together with sub-ss (3AA), (3BB), for sub-s (3) (as previously substituted by the Telecommunications Act 1984, s 82) by the Broadcasting Act 1990, s 172(4); para (b) repealed, and words in square brackets substituted, by the Communications Act 2003, s 406(1), (7), Sch 17, para 14(1), (4), Sch 19(1).

Sub-ss (3AA), (3AB): substituted, together with sub-s (3), for sub-s (3) (as previously substituted by the Telecommunications Act 1984, s 82), by the Broadcasting Act 1990, s 172(4).

Sub-ss (3A)–(3D): substituted, together with sub-s (3E), for original sub-s (3), by the Telecommunications Act 1984, s 82; words in square brackets substituted by the Communications Act 2003, s 406(1), Sch 17, para 14(1), (5)–(7).

Sub-s (3E): substituted, together with sub-ss (3A)–(3D), for original sub-s (3), by the Telecommunications Act 1984, s 82; words in square brackets substituted by the Broadcasting Act 1990, s 172(5).

Sub-ss (4), (5): repealed by the Post Office Act 1969, s 137(1), Sch 8.

Sub-s (7): words in first and second pairs of square brackets inserted by the Wireless Telegraphy (Pre-Consolidation Amendments) Order 2006, SI 2006/1391, art 2, Schedule, paras 1, 2; words in third pair of square brackets inserted, and word in fourth pair of square brackets substituted, by the Communications Act 2003, s 406(1), Sch 17, para 14(1), (8).

Sub-ss (8), (9): added by the Telecommunications Act 1984, s 75, Sch 3, para 2; repealed by the Statute Law (Repeals) Act 1993.

15 Entry and search of premises, etc

(1) If, in England, Wales or Northern Ireland, a justice of the peace, or, in Scotland, the sheriff, is satisfied by information on oath that there is reasonable ground for suspecting that an offence under this Act [or under the Marine, &c, Broadcasting (Offences) Act 1967] has been or is being committed, and that evidence of the commission of the offence is to be found on any premises specified in the information, or in any vehicle, vessel or aircraft so specified, he may grant a search warrant [authorising] [any constable or any person or persons authorised for the purpose by OFCOM or the Secretary of State] to enter, at any time within [three months] from the date of the warrant, the premises specified in the information or, as the case may be, the vehicle, vessel or aircraft so specified and any premises upon which it

may be, and to search the premises, or, as the case may be, the vehicle, vessel or aircraft, and to examine and test any apparatus found on the premises, vessel, vehicle or aircraft.

[(1A) Where a person authorised by OFCOM or the Secretary of State is authorised by a warrant under subsection (1) to enter any premises, he is to be entitled to exercise that warrant alone or to exercise it accompanied by one or more constables.]

(2) If, in England, Wales or Northern Ireland, a justice of the peace, or, in Scotland, the sheriff, is satisfied upon an application supported by sworn evidence—

- *(a) that there is reasonable ground for believing that, on any specified premises or in any specified vessel, aircraft or vehicle, apparatus to which section ten of this Act applies is to be found which does not comply with the requirements applicable to it under regulations made under that section; and*
- *(b) that it is necessary to enter those premises, or that vessel, aircraft or vehicle, for the purpose of obtaining such information as will [enable OFCOM to decide] whether or not to serve a notice under section eleven or section twelve of this Act; and*
- *(c) that access to the premises, vessel, aircraft or vehicle for the purpose of obtaining such information as aforesaid has, within fourteen days before the date of the application to the justice or sheriff, been demanded by a person authorised in that [behalf by OFCOM and producing] sufficient documentary evidence of his identity and authority, but has been refused,*

the justice or sheriff may issue a written authorisation under his hand empowering any person or persons authorised in that [behalf by OFCOM, with] or without any constables, to enter the premises or, as the case may be, the vessel, aircraft or vehicle and any premises on which it may be and to search the premises, vessel, aircraft or vehicle with a view to discovering whether any such apparatus as aforesaid is situate thereon or therein, and, if he finds or they find any such apparatus thereon, or therein, to examine and test it with a view to obtaining such information as aforesaid:

Provided that an authorisation shall not be issued under this subsection unless either—

- *(i) it is shown to the justice or sheriff [that OFCOM are satisfied] that there is reasonable ground for believing that the use of the apparatus in question is likely to cause undue interference with any wireless telegraphy used for the purposes of any safety of life service or any purpose on which the safety of any person or of any vessel, aircraft or vehicle may depend; or*
- *(ii) it is shown to the justice or sheriff that not less than seven days' notice of the demand for access was served on the occupier of the premises, or, as the case may be, the person in possession or the person in charge of the vessel, aircraft or vehicle, and that the demand was made at a reasonable hour and was unreasonably refused.*

[(2A) Without prejudice to any power exercisable by him apart from this subsection, a person authorised by the Secretary of State or (as the case may be) by [OFCOM] to exercise any power conferred by this section may use reasonable force, if necessary, in the exercise of that power.]

(3) Where under this section a person has a right to examine and test any apparatus on any premises or in any vessel, aircraft or vehicle, it shall be the duty of any person who is on the premises, or is in charge of, or in or in attendance on, the vessel, aircraft or vehicle, to give him any such assistance as he may reasonably require in the examination or testing of the apparatus.

(4) Any person who—

- *(a) [intentionally] obstructs any person in the exercise of the powers conferred on him under this section; or*
- *(b) [without reasonable excuse] fails or refuses to give to any such person any assistance which he is under this section under a duty to give to him; …*
- *(c) …*

shall be guilty of an offence under this Act …

[4019]

NOTES

Repealed as noted to s 1 at **[4001]**.

Sub-s (1): words in first pair of square brackets inserted, and word in second pair of square brackets substituted, by the Broadcasting Act 1990, ss 173(1), 180(1), Sch 18, Pt I, para 3; words in third pair of square brackets substituted by the Communications Act 2003, s 406(1), Sch 17, para 15(1), (2), subject to transitional provisions in s 406(6) of, and Sch 18, para 55 to, that Act at **[3434]**, **[3460]**; words in fourth pair of square brackets substituted in relation to England and Wales, for original words "one month", by the Serious Organised Crime and Police Act 2005, s 174(1), Sch 16, para 3.

Sub-s (1A): inserted by the Communications Act 2003, s 406(1), Sch 17, para 15(1), (3), subject to transitional provisions in s 406(6) of, and Sch 18, para 55 to, that Act at **[3434]**, **[3460]**.

Sub-s (2): words in square brackets substituted by the Communications Act 2003, s 406(1), Sch 17, para 15(1), (4), subject to transitional provisions in s 406(6) of, and Sch 18, para 55 to, that Act at **[3434]**, **[3460]**.

Sub-s (2A): inserted by the Broadcasting Act 1990, s 173(3); word in square brackets substituted by the Communications Act 2003, s 406(1), Sch 17, para 15(1), (5), subject to transitional provisions in s 406(6) of, and Sch 18, para 55 to, that Act at **[3434]**, **[3460]**.

Sub-s (4): words in square brackets inserted by the Telecommunications Act 1984, s 92(2); para (c) and preceding word repealed by the Communications Act 2003, s 406(7), Sch 19(1); final words omitted repealed by the Post Office Act 1969, s 137(1), Sch 8, Pt II.

16 Regulations and orders

(1) Any Order in Council under this Act may be revoked or varied by a subsequent Order in Council.

[(1A) Section 403 of the Communications Act 2003 (procedure for regulations and orders made by OFCOM) applies to every power of OFCOM to make regulations under a provision of this Act.]

(2) [Any power conferred on the Secretary of State] by any of the provisions of this Act to make regulations shall be exercisable by statutory instrument, and any statutory instrument made in the exercise of any of the said powers[, other than one containing regulations a draft of which has been approved for the purposes of section 5(9),] shall be subject to annulment in pursuance of a resolution of either House of Parliament.

[4020]

NOTES

Repealed as noted to s 1 at **[4001]**.

Sub-s (1A): inserted by the Communications Act 2003, s 406(1), Sch 17, para 16(1), (2), subject to transitional provisions in s 406(6) of, and Sch 18, para 55 to, that Act at **[3434]**, **[3460]**.

Sub-s (2): words in first pair of square brackets substituted by the Communications Act 2003, s 406(1), Sch 17, para 16(1), (3), subject to transitional provisions in s 406(6) of, and Sch 18, para 55 to, that Act at **[3434]**, **[3460]**; words in second pair of square brackets inserted by the Regulation of Investigatory Powers Act 2000, s 73(4).

17 Financial provisions

(1) … any fines imposed for offences under this Act, shall be paid into the Exchequer.

(2) …

[4021]

NOTES

Repealed as noted to s 1 at **[4001]**.

Sub-s (1): words omitted repealed by the Post Office Act 1961, s 28(1), Schedule.

Sub-s (2): repealed by the Transfer of Functions (Local Government, etc) (Northern Ireland) Order 1973, SR & O (NI) 1973/256, art 3, Sch 2.

18 *(Repealed by the Post Office Act 1969, s 137(1), Sch 8, Pt I.)*

19 Interpretation

(1) In this Act, except where the context otherwise requires, the expression "wireless telegraphy" means the emitting or receiving, over paths which are not provided by any material substance constructed or arranged for that purpose, of electro-magnetic energy of a frequency not exceeding three million megacycles a second, being energy which either—

- *(a) serves for the conveying of messages, sound or visual images (whether the messages, sound or images are actually received by any person or not), or for the actuation or control of machinery or apparatus; or*
- *(b) is used in connection with the determination of position, bearing, or distance, or for the gaining of information as to the presence, absence, position or motion of any object or of any objects of any class,*

and references to stations for wireless telegraphy and apparatus for wireless telegraphy or wireless telegraphy apparatus shall be construed as references to stations and apparatus for the emitting or receiving as aforesaid of such electro-magnetic energy as aforesaid:

…

(2) *In this Act, the expression "station for wireless telegraphy" includes the wireless telegraphy apparatus of a ship or aircraft, and the expression "electric line" has the same meaning as in [the Electricity Act 1989].*

[(2AA) In this Act "OFCOM" means the Office of Communications.]

[(2A) …]

(3) Any reference in this Act to the emission of electro-magnetic energy, or to emission (as opposed to reception), shall be construed as including a reference to the deliberate reflection of electro-magnetic energy by means of any apparatus designed or specially adapted for that purpose, whether the reflection is continuous or intermittent.

(4) In this Act, the expression "interference," in relation to wireless telegraphy, means the prejudicing by any emission or reflection of electro-magnetic energy of the fulfilment of the purposes of the telegraphy (either generally or in part, and, without prejudice to the generality of the preceding words, as respects all, or as respects any, of the recipients or intended recipients of any message, sound or visual image intended to be conveyed by the telegraphy), and the expression "interfere" shall be construed accordingly.

[(5) Interference with any wireless telegraphy is not to be regarded as undue for the purposes of this Act unless it is also harmful.

(5A) For the purposes of this Act interference is harmful if—

(a) it creates dangers, or risks of danger, in relation to the functioning of any service provided by means of wireless telegraphy for the purposes of navigation or otherwise for safety purposes; or

(b) it degrades, obstructs or repeatedly interrupts anything which is being broadcast or otherwise transmitted—

(i) by means of wireless telegraphy; and

(ii) in accordance with a licence under this Act, regulations under the proviso to section 1(1) of this Act or a grant of recognised spectrum access under Chapter 2 of Part 2 of the Communications Act 2003 or otherwise lawfully.]

(6) Any reference in this Act to the sending or the conveying of messages includes a reference to the making of any signal or the sending or conveying of any warning or information, and any reference to the reception of messages shall be construed accordingly.

(7) In this Act, the expressions "ship" and "vessel" have the [same meaning as "ship" in the Merchant Shipping Act 1995].

(8) References in this Act to apparatus on board a ship or vessel include references to apparatus on a kite or captive balloon flown from a ship or vessel.

(9) …

(10) Any reference in this Act to any enactment shall, except so far as the context otherwise requires, be construed as a reference to that enactment as amended by or under any other enactment, including this Act.

[4022]

NOTES

Repealed as noted to s 1 at **[4001]**.

Sub-s (1): words omitted repealed by the Cable and Broadcasting Act 1984, s 57(2), Sch 6.

Sub-s (2): words in square brackets substituted by the Electricity Act 1989, s 112(1), Sch 16, para 6.

Sub-s (2AA): inserted by the Communications Act 2003, s 406(1), Sch 17, para 17, subject to transitional provisions in s 406(6) of, and Sch 18, para 55 to, that Act at **[3434]**, **[3460]**.

Sub-s (2A): inserted by the Broadcasting Act 1990, s 180(1), Sch 18, Pt I, para 4; repealed by the Communications Act 2003, s 406(7), Sch 19(1), subject to transitional provisions in s 406(6) of, and Sch 18, para 55 to, that Act at **[3434]**, **[3460]**.

Sub-ss (5), (5A): substituted for original sub-s (5) by the Communications Act 2003, s 183.

Sub-s (7): words in square brackets substituted by the Merchant Shipping Act 1995, s 314(2), Sch 13, para 24.

Sub-s (9): repealed by the Communications Act 2003, s 406(7), Sch 19(1), subject to transitional provisions in s 406(6) of, and Sch 18, para 55 to, that Act at **[3434]**, **[3460]**.

20 Short title and extent

(1) *This Act may be cited as the Wireless Telegraphy Act 1949.*

(2) *It is hereby declared that this Act extends to Northern Ireland.*

(3) *His Majesty may by Order in Council direct that all or any of the provisions of this Act shall extend to the Isle of Man or any of the Channel Islands with such adaptations and modifications, if any, as may be specified in the Order.*

[4023]

NOTES

Repealed as noted to s 1 at **[4001]**.

Orders: the Wireless Telegraphy (Isle of Man) Order 1952, SI 1952/1899; the Wireless Telegraphy (Channel Islands) Order 1952, SI 1952/1900; the Wireless Telegraphy (Channel Islands) Order 1967, SI 1967/1279; the Wireless Telegraphy (Channel Islands) Order 1969, SI 1969/1369; the Wireless Telegraphy (Isle of Man) Order 1969, SI 1969/1371; the Wireless Telegraphy (Guernsey) Order 1994, SI 1994/1064; the Wireless Telegraphy (Isle of Man) Order 1995, SI 1995/268; the Wireless Telegraphy (Isle of Man) Order 1998, SI 1998/1510; the Wireless Telegraphy (Guernsey) Order 1998, SI 1998/1511; the Wireless Telegraphy (Jersey) Order 1998, SI 1998/1512; the Communications (Bailiwick of Guernsey) Order 2003, SI 2003/3195; the Wireless Telegraphy (Jersey) Order 2003, SI 2003/3196; the Communications (Jersey) Order 2003, SI 2003/3197; the Communications (Isle of Man) Order 2003, SI 2003/3198; the Communications (Bailiwick of Guernsey) Order 2004, SI 2004/307; the Broadcasting and Communications (Jersey) Order 2004, SI 2004/308; the Broadcasting and Communications (Isle of Man) Order 2004, SI 2004/309.

SCHEDULES

FIRST SCHEDULE
PROCEDURE IN RELATION TO SUSPENSION AND REVOCATION OF AUTHORITIES TO WIRELESS PERSONNEL

Section 7

1. *The [Secretary of State] shall, on suspending the authority, serve on the person to whom it was issued a notice informing him of the suspension, of the grounds thereof and of his rights under the subsequent provisions of this Schedule, and further informing him that if he does not avail himself of those rights the [Secretary of State] may revoke the authority:*

Provided that where it appears to the [Secretary of State] that it is not reasonably practicable to serve the notice on the said person, the [Secretary of State], in lieu of serving the notice on him, shall take such steps, by advertisement or otherwise, to bring the notice to his knowledge as appear to the [Secretary of State] to be reasonable in the circumstances.

2.—(1) *If, within such time and in such manner as may be specified in the notice, the person to whom the authority was issued requests that the question whether the authority should be revoked or the suspension thereof continued or terminated should be referred to an advisory committee, the [Secretary of State], unless he terminates the suspension, shall refer that question to an advisory committee accordingly.*

(2) *Every such advisory committee shall consist of three persons appointed by the [Secretary of State], of whom one shall be an independent chairman selected by the [Secretary of State] and two shall be persons nominated respectively by such body or bodies representing employers of wireless operators and such association or associations representing wireless operators as seem to the [Secretary of State] to be appropriate for the purpose.*

(3) *Where a question is referred to an advisory committee under this paragraph, the committee shall inquire into the matter, shall consider any representations made by the person to whom the authority was issued, and shall then make a report to the [Secretary of State] stating the facts as found by them and the action which, in their opinion, ought to be taken as respects the revocation of the authority or the continuation or termination of the suspension thereof, and the [Secretary of State] shall consider the report.*

(4) *After considering the report of the advisory committee or, as the case may be, on the expiration of the time referred to in sub-paragraph (1) of this paragraph without the person to*

whom the authority was issued having required in the manner therein referred to that the question should be referred to an advisory committee, the [Secretary of State] shall, as he thinks fit, either revoke the authority, or terminate the suspension thereof, or continue the suspension thereof for such period as he thinks fit.

(5) Where the [Secretary of State] revokes the authority or continues the suspension thereof, he shall, if requested so to do by the person to whom the authority was issued, inform him of the opinion which the advisory committee expressed as to the action which ought to be taken as respects the revocation of the authority or the continuation or termination of the suspension thereof.

[3.—(1) The Secretary of State is to pay—
(a) the expenses incurred by an advisory committee under this Schedule, to the extent determined by him; and
(b) such sums as he may determine in respect of the expenses of the members of the committee.]

(2) The approval of the Treasury shall be requisite to a determination under head (a) of the foregoing sub-paragraph and that of the Minister for the Civil Service to a determination under head (b) of that sub-paragraph.]

[4024]

NOTES

Repealed as noted to s 1 at **[4001]**.

Paras 1, 2: words in square brackets substituted by virtue of the Post Office Act 1969, s 3, and the Ministry of Posts and Telecommunications (Dissolution) Order 1974, SI 1974/691, art 2.

Para 3: substituted by the Communications Act 2003, s 406(1), Sch 17, para 18; for transitional provisions and effect see ss 363, 406(6) of, and Sch 18, para 55 to, that Act at **[3410]**, **[3434]**, **[3460]**.

(Sch 2 repealed by the Communications Act 2003, s 406(7), Sch 19(1); for transitional provisions and effect see s 406(6), (7), of, and Sch 18, para 55, Sch 19(1), Note 1 to, that Act.)

WIRELESS TELEGRAPHY ACT 1967

(1967 c 72)

ARRANGEMENT OF SECTIONS

PART I
INFORMATION AS TO SALE AND HIRE OF TELEVISION SETS

PART II
MISCELLANEOUS

PART III
GENERAL

An Act to enable the Postmaster General to obtain information as to the sale and hire of television receiving sets; to enable him to prohibit the manufacture or importation of certain wireless telegraphy apparatus; to make provision for requiring applicants for vehicle excise licences to give information about such apparatus installed in vehicles; to make miscellaneous amendments in the Wireless Telegraphy Act 1949; and for connected purposes

[27 July 1967]

PART I
INFORMATION AS TO SALE AND HIRE OF TELEVISION SETS

1 (*Repealed by the Deregulation (Wireless Telegraphy) Order 1996, SI 1996/1864, art 4(1).*)

2 Notification and recording of transactions

(1) [Subject to subsections (1A) and (2) of this section, every television dealer who, after the end of twenty-eight days from the date on which he became such a dealer]—

- (a) sells a television set by retail;
- (b) lets a television set on hire or hire-purchase; or
- (c) arranges for a television set to be sold or let as aforesaid to any person by another television dealer,

shall, in relation to that sale or letting, give to [the BBC] a notification containing the particulars specified in Part I of the Schedule to this Act and make a record of the particulars specified in Part II of that Schedule.

[(1A) Subsection (1) of this section shall not apply to a television dealer in whose case the following conditions are satisfied, that is to say—

- (a) that he is such a dealer by reason only that he sells or lets, or holds himself out as willing to sell or let, television sets in pursuance of arrangements made by another television dealer; and
- (b) that all payments of or towards the price or by way of rent in respect of any television set sold or let by him are received or collected on his behalf by the dealer who arranged for the sale or letting to be made.

(1B) A television dealer in whose case the conditions specified in subsection (1A) of this section cease to be satisfied shall be treated for the purposes of subsection (1) of this section as having become a television dealer when those conditions ceased to be satisfied in his case.]

(2) In relation to any sale or letting as respects which [subsection (1) of this section] is required to be complied with by the dealer who arranges for the sale or letting to be made, the other dealer concerned—

- (a) shall not be required to comply with that subsection; but
- (b) shall, unless all payments of or towards the price or by way of rent in respect of the sale or letting are to be received or collected on his behalf by the first-mentioned dealer, make a record of the particulars specified in Part III of the Schedule to this Act.

(3) Any notification to be given to [the BBC] under this section shall be in the prescribed form and shall be given to [them] within twenty-eight days from the date of the sale or letting to which it relates; and any such notification to be given by any dealer shall be given to [the BBC] at such address as [they] may have directed by a notice in writing given to that dealer or, if no such notice has been given, at the prescribed address.

(4) Any record under this section may be made either in the prescribed form or in any other form which enables the matters recorded to be readily ascertained by any person to whom the record is produced for inspection; and any matter required to be recorded by virtue of Part II or Part III of the Schedule to this Act shall be recorded within the time specified in relation thereto in that Part of the Schedule.

(5) Any record made under this section by any person shall be kept at a place at which he carries on business and, unless he previously ceases to be a television dealer, shall be preserved by him—

(a) if it relates to a sale and the price is not payable by instalments, for twelve months from the date of the sale;
(b) if it relates to a sale and the price is payable by instalments or to a letting, for twelve months from the date when the last instalment or payment of rent is due.

(6) The person having charge of any place where records are kept under this section shall at any time during normal business hours, if so required by a person duly authorised in that behalf by [the BBC], produce the records for inspection.

(7) The [Secretary of State] may by regulations amend or delete any provision of the Schedule to this Act or add any further provision thereto.

[4025]

NOTES

Sub-s (1): words in first pair of square brackets substituted by the Deregulation (Wireless Telegraphy) Order 1996, SI 1996/1864, art 4(2), words in second pair of square brackets substituted by the Broadcasting Act 1990, s 180(4), Sch 18, Pt II, paras 1(b), 3.
Sub-ss (1A), (1B): inserted by SI 1996/1864, art 4(3).
Sub-s (2): words in square brackets substituted by SI 1996/1864, art 4(4).
Sub-ss (3), (6): words in square brackets substituted by the Broadcasting Act 1990, s 180(4), Sch 18, Pt II, paras 1(b), 3.
Sub-s (7): words in square brackets substituted by virtue of the Post Office Act 1969, s 3, and the Ministry of Posts and Telecommunications (Dissolution) Order 1974, SI 1974/691.
Regulations: the Wireless Telegraphy Act 1967 (Prescribed Forms etc) Regulations 1979, SI 1979/563.

3 Power to call for additional information

(1) [The BBC] may by notice in writing require a television dealer to furnish to [them], at the specified address and within twenty-eight days from the date of the notice, a statement containing the following information—
(a) whether, in the case of any specified credit-sale contract, hire contract or hire-purchase contract made after the expiration of twenty-eight days from the appointed day, any instalment of the price or payment of rent will fall to be received or collected by him from the buyer or hirer after the date of the notice;
(b) if so, the present or last-known address of the buyer or hirer.

(2) …

(3) In this section "credit-sale contract" means a contract for the sale of a television set by retail on terms providing for the price to be paid by instalments, "hire contract" means a contract for the letting of a television set on hire, "hire-purchase contract" means a contract for the letting of a television set on hire-purchase and "specified" means specified in the notice in question.

[4026]

NOTES

Sub-s (1): words in square brackets substituted by the Broadcasting Act 1990, s 180(4), Sch 18, Pt II, paras 1(c), 4.
Sub-s (2): repealed by the Broadcasting Act 1990, s 203(3), Sch 21.

4 (*Repealed by the Communications Act 2003, s 406(7), Sch 19(1).*)

5 Offences and enforcement

(1) Any person who—
(a) without reasonable excuse, fails to comply with, or with any notice given under, any of the foregoing provisions of this Part of this Act; or
(b) in purported compliance therewith—
(i) knowingly or recklessly furnishes any information which is false in a material particular; or
(ii) makes or causes to be made or knowingly allows to be made any record which he knows to be false in a material particular,

shall be guilty of [an offence under this section].

[(1A) A person who commits an offence under this section is liable on summary conviction to a fine not exceeding level 3 on the standard scale.]

(2) …

(3) Summary proceedings in England, Wales or Northern Ireland for an offence under this section may be taken on behalf of [the BBC] at any time within six months from the date on which evidence sufficient in [their] opinion to justify the proceedings comes to [their] knowledge:

Provided that proceedings shall not be so taken more than three years after the commission of the offence.

(4) Summary proceedings in Scotland for an offence under this section shall not be commenced after the expiration of three years from the commission of the offence, but subject to the foregoing limitation, and notwithstanding anything in [section 331 of the Criminal Procedure (Scotland) Act 1975], such proceedings may be commenced at any time within six months after the date on which evidence sufficient in the opinion of the Lord Advocate to justify the proceedings comes to his knowledge or, where such evidence was reported to him by [the BBC], within six months after the date on which it came to the knowledge of [the BBC]; and [subsection (3) of the said section 331] shall apply for the purposes of this subsection as it applies for the purposes of that section.

(5) For the purpose of subsections (3) and (4) of this section, a certificate of [the BBC] or the Lord Advocate, as the case may be, as to the date on which such evidence as aforesaid came to [their or] his knowledge shall be conclusive evidence of that fact.

[(6) Sections 97 and 98 of the Wireless Telegraphy Act 2006 (provision for entry and search of premises) apply in relation to an offence under this section as they apply in relation to an offence under that Act (other than an offence under Part 4 or section 111).]

[4027]

NOTES

Sub-s (1): words in square brackets substituted by the Wireless Telegraphy Act 2006, s 123, Sch 7, para 2(1), (2).

Sub-ss (1A), (6): inserted by the Wireless Telegraphy Act 2006, s 123, Sch 7, para 2(1), (3), (4).

Sub-s (2): repealed by the Broadcasting Act 1990, s 203(3), Sch 21.

Sub-s (3): words in square brackets substituted by the Broadcasting Act 1990, s 180(4), Sch 18, Pt II, paras 1(e), 6(a).

Sub-s (4): words in first and fourth pairs of square brackets substituted by virtue of the Criminal Procedure (Consequential Provisions) (Scotland) Act 1995, s 460(1)(b); words in second and third pairs of square brackets substituted by the Broadcasting Act 1990, s 180, Sch 18, Pt II, para 1(e).

Sub-s (5): words in first pair of square brackets substituted, and words in second pair of square brackets inserted, by the Broadcasting Act 1990, s 180(4), Sch 18, Pt II, paras 1(e), 6(b).

Lord Advocate: as to the transfer of certain powers of the Lord Advocate, see the Transfer of Functions (Lord Advocate and Secretary of State) Order 1999, SI 1999/678, and the Transfer of Functions (Lord Advocate and Advocate General for Scotland) Order 1999, SI 1999/679.

6 Interpretation of Part I

(1) In this Part of this Act—

"appointed day" means such day as the [Secretary of State] may by order appoint;

["the BBC" means the British Broadcasting Corporation;]

"prescribed" means prescribed by regulations made by the [Secretary of State] [after consultation with the BBC];

["television dealer" means a person of any description specified in regulations made by the Secretary of State setting out the descriptions of persons who are to be television dealers for the purposes of this Part;

"television set" means any apparatus of a description specified in regulations made by the Secretary of State setting out the descriptions of apparatus that are to be television sets for the purposes of this Part].

[(1A) Regulations under subsection (1) defining a television set may provide for references to such a set to include references to software used in association with apparatus.]

(2) In this Part of this Act references to sale by retail do not include references to such sales by auction unless the auctioneer is selling as principal; and references to letting on hire or hire-purchase do not include references to letting as aforesaid for the purpose of re-sale or re-letting.

(3) For the purposes of this Part of this Act a television set is sold or let on hire or hire-purchase when the contract of sale or, as the case may be, the contract of hire or hire-purchase is made.

[4028]

NOTES

Sub-s (1): words in square brackets in definition "appointed day" and words in first pair of square brackets in definition "prescribed" substituted by virtue of the Post Office Act 1969, s 3, and the Ministry of Posts and Telecommunications (Dissolution) Order 1974, SI 1974/691; definition "the BBC" and words in second pair of square brackets in definition "prescribed" inserted by the Broadcasting Act 1990, ss 180(4), 203(1), Sch 18, Pt II, para 7, Sch 20, para 9; definitions "television dealer" and "television set" substituted for definitions "television dealer", "television programme" and "television set" (as inserted by the Cable and Broadcasting Act 1984, s 57(1), Sch 5, para 17) by the Communications Act 2003, s 367(1),(2).

Sub-s (1A): inserted by the Communications Act 2003, s 367(1), (3).

Orders: the Wireless Telegraphy Act 1967 (Appointed Day) Order 1967, SI 1967/1691.

Regulations: the Wireless Telegraphy Act 1967 (Prescribed Forms etc) Regulations 1979, SI 1979/563.

PART II
MISCELLANEOUS

[7 Restriction on dealings in and custody of certain apparatus

(1) This section applies to wireless telegraphy apparatus and to any apparatus designed or adapted for use in connection with wireless telegraphy apparatus.

(2) Where it appears to [OFCOM] to be expedient to do so for the purpose of preventing or reducing the risk of interference with wireless telegraphy, [they] may make an order applying restrictions under this section in relation to apparatus to which this section applies of any class or description specified in the order.

(3) Any of the following actions in relation to any such apparatus is subject to restriction under this section—

- *(a) manufacture (whether or not for sale);*
- *(b) selling or offering for sale, letting on hire or offering to let on hire, or indicating (whether by display of the apparatus or by any form of advertisement) one's willingness to sell or let on hire;*
- *(c) having in one's custody or control; and*
- *(d) importation.*

(4) An order under this section shall specify such of the actions subject to restriction under this section as are restricted by the order in the case of apparatus of any class or description specified in the order.

(5) Any action for the time being restricted by an order under this section in the case of any apparatus is prohibited by this section—

- *(a) save with the authority of [OFCOM] and subject to compliance with any terms and conditions attached by [OFCOM] to that authority; …*
- *(b) …*

(6) An authority given by [OFCOM] for the purposes of this section in the case of apparatus of any class or description specified in an order under this section may be limited—

- *(a) to such of the actions restricted by the order; and*
- *(b) to such subsidiary class or description of apparatus within the class or description specified in the order;*

as may be specified in the authority.

(7) Any terms or conditions attached by [OFCOM] to any authority under this section for manufacture or importation may relate to a period after, as well as to the time of, or a period before, the manufacture or importation.

(8) [OFCOM's] authority may be given, and any terms or conditions may be attached to it, either generally by means of a notice in the London Gazette or by an instrument in writing issued to each person authorised to do, in relation to apparatus of any class or description to which an order under this section relates, anything for the time being restricted by the order; and any such notice published in the London Gazette shall also be published in the Edinburgh Gazette and the Belfast Gazette.

(9) [OFCOM] shall not make any order under this section or give any authority for the purposes of this section or attach any term or condition to any such authority, unless [OFCOM] [are satisfied] that the order, authority, term or condition in question is compatible

with the international obligations of the United Kingdom; and where any statutory instrument containing such an order or any notice or instrument in writing giving such an authority or attaching any term or condition to such an authority contains a statement that [OFCOM] [are so satisfied], that statement shall be evidence (and, in Scotland, sufficient evidence) of that fact.

(10) Where the importation of apparatus of any class or description to which this section applies is for the time being restricted by an order under this section, a person commissioned by the Commissioners of Customs and Excise may require any person having custody or control of any apparatus of that class or description which is being or has been imported to furnish proof that the importation of the apparatus is or was not unlawful by virtue of this section; and if such proof is not furnished to the satisfaction of those Commissioners the apparatus shall be deemed, unless the contrary is proved, to be prohibited goods, and shall be liable to forfeiture under the Customs and Excise Management Act 1979.

(11) Any person who—

(a) takes any action within subsection (3)(a) or (b) above in relation to any apparatus in contravention of subsection (5) above; or

(b) without reasonable excuse has any apparatus in his custody or control in contravention of that subsection; or

(c) contravenes or fails to comply with any terms or conditions attached to any authority given by [OFCOM] for the purposes of this section (whatever the action to which that authority relates);

shall, without prejudice to any liability to a penalty which he may have incurred under the Act of 1979 mentioned above, be guilty of an offence under the principal Act.

[(11A) Section 403 of the Communications Act 2003 (procedure for regulations and orders made by OFCOM) applies to the power of OFCOM to make an order under this section.

(11B) The approval of the Secretary of State is required for the making by OFCOM of an order under this section.

(11C) A statutory instrument containing an order made by OFCOM under this section shall be subject to annulment in pursuance of a resolution of either House of Parliament.

(11D) In this section "OFCOM" means the Office of Communications.]

(12) For the avoidance of doubt, it is hereby declared that in this section "manufacture" includes construction by any method and the assembly of component parts.]

[4029]

NOTES

Repealed, together with ss 8–10, 12, by the Wireless Telegraphy Act 2006, s 125(1), Sch 9, Pt 1, subject to transitional provisions and savings in s 124 of, Sch 8, Pt 1, paras 1–8, 24 to, that Act at **[4230]**, **[4239]**.

Substituted by the Telecommunications Act 1984, s 77(1).

Sub-ss (2), (6)–(9), (11): words in square brackets substituted by the Communications Act, s 406(1), Sch 17, para 37(1)–(4).

Sub-s (5): words in square brackets substituted, and words omitted repealed, by the Communications Act, ss 182(7), 406(1), (7), Sch 17, para 37(1), (3), Sch 19(1).

Sub-ss (11A)–(11D): inserted by the Communications Act 2003, s 406(1), Sch 17, para 37(1), (5).

Orders: the Wireless Telegraphy (Control of Interference from Videosenders) Order 1998, SI 1998/722 at **[4318]**; the Wireless Telegraphy (Citizens' Band and Amateur Apparatus) (Various Provisions) Order 1998, SI 1998/2531 at **[4321]**; the Wireless Telegraphy (Cordless Telephone Apparatus) (Restriction and Marking) Order 1999, SI 1999/2934.

8 Provisions for securing enforcement of s 1(1) of principal Act in relation to vehicles

(1) The power [of the Secretary of State under section 7(1) of the Vehicle Excise and Registration Act 1994 to specify] the declaration to be made and particulars to be furnished by a person applying for a licence under that Act in respect of a vehicle shall include power to require the declaration and particulars to extend to any matters relevant for the enforcement of section 1(1) of the principal Act in respect of any apparatus for wireless telegraphy installed in the vehicle; and the appropriate authority shall accordingly not be required to issue a licence under [the Vehicle Excise and Registration Act 1994] the applicant fails to comply with [a requirement imposed] by virtue of this subsection.

(2) If any person, in furnishing any information for the purpose of [a requirement imposed] by virtue of subsection (1) of this section, makes any statement which he knows to

be false in a material particular, or recklessly makes any statement which is false in a material particular, he shall be guilty of an offence under the principal Act.

(3) Subsection (2) of this section shall have effect to the exclusion of any provision for corresponding purposes [contained in the Vehicle Excise and Registration Act 1994].

(4) …

[4030]

NOTES

Repealed as noted to s 7 at **[4029]**.

Sub-s (1): words in first and third pairs of square brackets substituted by the Communications Act 2003, s 406(1), Sch 17, para 38(1), (2); words in second pair of square brackets substituted by the Vehicle Excise and Registration Act 1994, s 63, Sch 3, para 3.

Sub-s (2): words in square brackets substituted by the Communications Act 2003, s 406(1), Sch 17, para 38(1), (3).

Sub-s (3): words in square brackets substituted by the Vehicle Excise and Registration Act 1994, s 63, Sch 3, para 3.

Sub-s (4): repealed by the Vehicle Excise and Registration Act 1994, s 65, Sch 5, Pt I.

9 Amendments as to territorial extent of Part I of principal Act

(1) …

(2) The references in paragraphs (b) and (c) of subsection (1) of the said section 6 to any British seagoing ship or British aircraft which is registered in the United Kingdom shall be construed as references to any ship or aircraft which is so registered; …

(3) …

(4) Regulations under subsection (2) of the said section 6 may make different provision for different cases or for ships or aircraft registered in different countries.

(5) The provisions of subsections (2) and (3) of this section shall have effect as from the expiration of the period of one month beginning with the day on which this Act is passed.

[4031]

NOTES

Repealed as noted to s 7 at **[4029]**.

Sub-s (1): repealed by the Territorial Sea Act 1987, s 3(4), Sch 2.

Sub-s (2): words omitted amend the Wireless Telegraphy Act 1949, s 6 at **[4010]**.

Sub-s (3): repealed in part by the Telecommunications Act 1984, s 109(6), Sch 7, Pt IV; remainder amends the Wireless Telegraphy Act 1949, s 6 at **[4010]**.

10 Amendments as to scope and territorial extent of Part II of principal Act

(1) The provisions of this section shall have effect for the purposes of Part II of the principal Act (which makes provision as to interference with wireless telegraphy).

(2) The apparatus which may be specified in regulations under section 10 of the principal Act shall include wireless telegraphy apparatus; …

(3) Section 6 of the principal Act shall have effect as if any reference therein to the preceding provisions of Part I of that Act included a reference to the provisions of any regulations made under section 10 and the provisions of sections 11, 12 and 13 of that Act.

[4032]

NOTES

Repealed as noted to s 7 at **[4029]**.

Sub-s (2): words omitted amend the Wireless Telegraphy Act 1949, s 10 at **[4012]**.

11 *(Repealed by the Telecommunications Act 1984, s 109(6), Sch 7, Pt IV.)*

12 Enforcement of principal Act

(1) For the purposes of any offence under the principal Act committed within the seaward limits referred to in section 9(1) of this Act but not within the United Kingdom, proceedings for that offence may be taken, and the offence may for all incidental purposes be treated as having been committed, in any place in the United Kingdom.

(2) *For the purpose of the enforcement of the principal Act, a member of a police force shall have in any area of the sea within the seaward limits aforesaid all the powers, protection and privileges which he has in the area for which he acts as constable.*

(3) *In the application of this section to Northern Ireland, the following subsection shall be substituted for subsection (2)—*

> "(2) *For the purpose of the enforcement of the principal Act, a [member of the Police Service of Northern Ireland] shall have in any area of the sea within the seaward limits aforesaid all the powers, protection and privileges which he has in Northern Ireland.*"

[4033]

NOTES

Repealed as noted to s 7 at **[4029]**.

Sub-s (3): words in square brackets substituted by the Police (Northern Ireland) Act 2000, s 78(2)(c).

PART III
GENERAL

13 Regulations and orders

(1) Any power to make regulations [under Part 1 of] this Act shall be exercisable by statutory instrument.

(2) A statutory instrument made in the exercise of any such power shall be subject to annulment in pursuance of a resolution of either House of Parliament.

(3) Regulations under this Act may make different provision for different classes of case.

(4) Any Order in Council under this Act may be revoked or varied by a subsequent Order in Council …

[4034]

NOTES

Sub-s (1): words in square brackets substituted by the Communications Act 2003, s 406(1), Sch 17, para 39.

Sub-s (4): words ", and any order under section 7 of this Act may be revoked or varied by a subsequent order under that section" (omitted) repealed by the Wireless Telegraphy Act 2006, s 125(1), Sch 9, Pt 1, subject to transitional provisions and savings in s 124 of, Sch 8, Pt 1, paras 1–8, 24 to that Act at **[4230]**, **[4239]**.

Orders in Council: the Wireless Telegraphy (Channel Islands) Order 1969, SI 1969/1369; the Wireless Telegraphy (Isle of Man) Order 1981, SI 1981/1113; the Wireless Telegraphy (Isle of Man) Order 1995, SI 1995/268.

14 (*Sub-s (1) repealed by the Post Office Act 1969, s 141, Sch 11, Pt II; sub-s (2) repealed by the Vehicle Excise and Registration Act 1994, s 65, Sch 5, Pt I.*)

15 Short title, citation, interpretation and extent

(1) This Act may be cited as the Wireless Telegraphy Act 1967.

(2), (3) …

(4) Any reference in this Act to any enactment shall, except so far as the context otherwise requires, be construed as a reference to that enactment as amended by or under any other enactment, including any enactment contained in this Act.

(5) It is hereby declared that this Act extends to Northern Ireland.

(6) Her Majesty may by Order in Council direct that all or any of the provisions of this Act shall extend to the Isle of Man or … to any of the Channel Islands with such exceptions, adaptations and modifications as may be specified in the Order.

[4035]

NOTES

Sub-ss (2), (3): repealed by the Wireless Telegraphy Act 2006, s 125(1), Sch 9, Pt 1, subject to transitional provisions and savings in s 124 of, Sch 8, Pt 1, paras 1–8, 24 to, that Act at **[4230]**, **[4239]**, and previously read as follows:

"(2) The Wireless Telegraphy Acts 1949 and 1955 and this Act may be cited together as the Wireless Telegraphy Acts 1949 to 1967.

(3) In this Act "the principal Act" means the Wireless Telegraphy Act 1949, and "wireless telegraphy", "wireless telegraphy apparatus", "apparatus for wireless telegraphy" and "interference" have the same meanings respectively as in that Act.".

Sub-s (6): words ", except for section 7 of this Act," (omitted) repealed by the Wireless Telegraphy Act 2006, s 125(1), Sch 9, Pt 1, subject to transitional provisions and savings in s 124 of, Sch 8, Pt 1, paras 1–8, 24 to, that Act at **[4230]**, **[4239]**.

Orders in Council: the Wireless Telegraphy (Channel Islands) Order 1967, SI 1967/1279; the Wireless Telegraphy (Channel Islands) Order 1969, SI 1969/1369; the Wireless Telegraphy (Isle of Man) Order 1981, SI 1981/1113; the Wireless Telegraphy (Isle of Man) Order 1995, SI 1995/268.

SCHEDULE

Section 2

NOTIFICATIONS AND RECORDS

PART I
PARTICULARS TO BE NOTIFIED

1. The date of the sale or letting.

2. The name and address of the buyer or hirer.

[3. The address of the premises where the set is to be installed.

4. Whether the set is designed for reception in colour.

5. The name, address and registration number of the dealer selling or letting the set.]

[4036]

NOTES

Paras 3–5: substituted for original paras 3–7 by the Wireless Telegraphy Act 1967 (Prescribed Forms etc) Regulations 1979, SI 1979/563, reg 7(1).

PART II
PARTICULARS TO BE RECORDED BY NOTIFYING DEALER

Within 28 days from the date of the sale or letting

1. The date of the sale or letting.

2. The name and address of the buyer or hirer.

[3. The address of the premises where the set is to be installed.

4. Whether the set is designed for reception in colour.

5. The name, address and registration number of the dealer selling or letting the set.]

[4037]

NOTES

Paras 3–5: substituted for original paras 3–8 by the Wireless Telegraphy Act 1967 (Prescribed Forms etc) Regulations 1979, SI 1979/563, reg 7(2).

NOTIFICATIONS AND PARTICULARS

PART III
PARTICULARS TO BE RECORDED BY OTHER DEALER

Within 28 days from the date of the sale or letting

1. The date of the sale or letting.

2. The name and address of the buyer or hirer.

3. The name and address of the dealer who arranged the sale or letting.

4. The address (if known) of the premises where the set is [to be installed].

5. Whether the set is designed for reception in colour.

6, 7. …

[4038]

NOTES

Para 4: words in square brackets substituted by the Wireless Telegraphy Act 1967 (Prescribed Forms etc) Regulations 1979, SI 1979/563, reg 7(3).

Paras 6, 7: repealed by SI 1979/563, reg 7(3).

TELECOMMUNICATIONS ACT 1984

(1984 c 12)

ARRANGEMENT OF SECTIONS

PART I
INTRODUCTORY

PART III
OTHER FUNCTIONS OF DIRECTOR

PART V
TRANSFER OF UNDERTAKING OF BRITISH TELECOMMUNICATIONS

Vesting of property etc of British Telecommunications in a company nominated by the Secretary of State

Miscellaneous and supplemental

PART VI
PROVISIONS RELATING TO WIRELESS TELEGRAPHY

Amendment and enforcement of Wireless Telegraphy Acts

Approvals

Marking etc of apparatus

Miscellaneous and supplemental

PART VII
MISCELLANEOUS AND SUPPLEMENTAL

Miscellaneous

Supplemental

An Act to provide for the appointment and functions of a Director General of Telecommunications; to abolish British Telecommunications' exclusive privilege with respect to telecommunications and to make new provision with respect to the provision of telecommunication services and certain related services; to make provision, in substitution for the Telegraph Acts 1863 to 1916 and Part IV of the Post Office Act 1969, for the matters there dealt with and related matters; to provide for the vesting of property, rights and liabilities of British Telecommunications in a company nominated by the Secretary of State and the subsequent dissolution of British Telecommunications; to make provision with respect to the finances of that company; to amend the Wireless Telegraphy Acts 1949 to

1967, to make further provision for facilitating enforcement of those Acts and otherwise to make provision with respect to wireless telegraphy apparatus and certain related apparatus; to give statutory authority for the payment out of money provided by Parliament of expenses incurred by the Secretary of State in providing a radio interference service; to increase the maximum number of members of British Telecommunications pending its dissolution; and for connected purposes

[12 April 1984]

PART I
INTRODUCTORY

1 The Director General of Telecommunications

(1) The Secretary of State shall appoint an officer to be known as the Director General of Telecommunications (in this Act referred to as "the Director") for the purpose of performing the functions assigned or transferred to the Director by or under this Act.

(2) An appointment of a person to hold office as the Director shall not be for a term exceeding five years; but previous appointment to that office shall not affect eligibility for re-appointment.

(3) The Director may at any time resign his office as the Director by notice in writing addressed to the Secretary of State; and the Secretary of State may remove any person from that office on the ground of incapacity or misbehaviour.

(4) Subject to subsections (2) and (3) above, the Director shall hold and vacate office as such in accordance with the terms of his appointment.

(5) The Director may appoint such staff as he may think fit, subject to the approval of the Treasury as to numbers and as to terms and conditions of service.

(6) There shall be paid out of money provided by Parliament the remuneration of, and any travelling or other allowances payable under this Act to, the Director and any staff of the Director, any sums payable under this Act to or in respect of the Director and any expenses duly incurred by the Director or by any of his staff [in consequence of the provisions of—

(a) this Act;

(b) the Telecommunications (Open Network Provision) (Voice Telephony) Regulations 1998; or

(c) the Telecommunications (Data Protection and Privacy) Regulations 1999.]

(7) The provisions of Schedule 1 to this Act shall have effect with respect to the Director.

[4039]

NOTES

Repealed by the Communications Act 2003, s 406(7), Sch 19(1), as from a day to be appointed.

The Director General of Telecommunications: on such a day as may be appointed under the Communications Act 2003, s 31(4)(a) at **[3108]**, the office of the Director is abolished. As to the transfer of the Director's functions, etc, see s 2 of the 2003 Act at **[3079]**.

Sub-s (6): words in square brackets substituted by the Telecommunications (Data Protection and Privacy) Regulations 1999, SI 1999/2093, reg 3(3), Sch 1, Pt II, para 1.

2–46, 46A, 46B *(Ss 2–30, 34–46B repealed by the Communications Act 2003, ss 147, 406(1), (7), Sch 17, para 63(1), Sch 19(1); ss 31–33 outside the scope of this work.)*

PART III
OTHER FUNCTIONS OF DIRECTOR

47–54 *(Ss 47–49, 51–53 repealed by the Communications Act 2003, s 406(7), Sch 19(1) (for effect see Sch 17, para 63(2), (3) of that Act); s 50 repealed in part by the Enterprise Act 2002, ss 168(9), 278, Sch 9, Pt 2, para 16(1), (6), Sch 25, para 13(1), (8)(a), Sch 26, remainder repealed by the Communications Act 2003, s 406(7), Sch 19(1); s 54 repealed by the Communications Act 2003, s 406(7), Sch 19(1), for transitional provisions in relation to advisory bodies, see the Office of Communications Act 2002 (Commencement No 3) and Communications Act 2003 (Commencement No 2) Order 2003, SI 2003/3142, art 5 at* **[3594]**.)

55 Annual and other reports

(1) The Director shall, as soon as practicable after the end of the year 1984 and of each subsequent calendar year, make to the Secretary of State a report on—

(a) his activities during that year; and

(b) the Commission's activities during that year so far as relating to references made by him.

(2) Every such report shall include—

(a) a general survey of developments, during the year to which it relates, in respect of matters falling within the scope of the Director's functions (including, in particular, those affecting small businesses or persons who are disabled or of pensionable age); and

(b) the reports which the advisory bodies established under section 54(1) or (4) above make to him on their activities during that year.

(3) The Secretary of State shall lay a copy of every report made by the Director under subsection (1) above before each House of Parliament, and shall arrange for every such report to be published in such manner as he may consider appropriate.

(4) The Director may also prepare such other reports as appear to him to be expedient with respect to such matters as are mentioned in subsection (2) above and may arrange for any such report to be published in such manner as he may consider appropriate.

(5) In making any report under this section the Director shall have regard to the need for excluding, so far as that is practicable, the matters specified in section 8(2)(a) and (b) above. **[4040]**

NOTES

Repealed by the Communications Act 2003, s 406(7), Sch 19(1), as from a day to be appointed.

56–59 ((*Pt IV) Repealed by the Cable and Broadcasting Act 1984, s 57(2), Sch 6.*)

PART V
TRANSFER OF UNDERTAKING OF BRITISH TELECOMMUNICATIONS

Vesting of property etc of British Telecommunications in a company nominated by the Secretary of State

60–67 (*Ss 60, 61(1)–(6), 62, 63(1)–(4), 64–67 repealed by the Communications Act 2003, ss 398(1), (2)(a)–(e), 406(7), Sch 19(1), for effect in relation to the repeal of s 63(1)–(4) see s 406(7) of, and Sch 19(1), Note 2 to, that Act at* **[3434]**, **[3461]**; *ss 61(7), 63(5) repealed by the Finance Act 1988, s 148, Sch 14, Pt XI.*)

68 Liability of Secretary of State in respect of liabilities vesting in successor company

(1) This section applies where—

(a) a resolution has been passed, in accordance with the [Insolvency Act 1986], for the voluntary winding up of the successor company, otherwise than merely for the purpose of reconstruction or amalgamation with another company; or

(b) without any such resolution having been passed beforehand, an order has been made for the winding up of the successor company by the court under that Act.

(2) The Secretary of State shall become liable on the commencement of the winding up to discharge any outstanding liability of the successor company [for the payment of pensions] which vested in that company by virtue of section 60 above.

(3) Any sums required by the Secretary of State for discharging any liability imposed on him by this section shall be paid out of money provided by Parliament.

(4) Where the Secretary of State makes a payment to any person in discharge of what appears to him to be a liability imposed on him by this section, he shall thereupon become a creditor of the successor company to the extent of the amount paid, his claim being treated for the purposes of the winding up as a claim in respect of the original liability.

(5) Any sums received by the Secretary of State in respect of any claim made by virtue of subsection (4) above in the winding up of the successor company shall be paid into the Consolidated Fund.

(6) The reference in subsection (2) above to the commencement of the winding up is a reference—

(a) in a case within subsection (1)(a) above, to the passing of the resolution; and
(b) in a case within subsection (1)(b) above, to the making of the order.

[4041]

NOTES

Sub-s (1): words in square brackets substituted by the Insolvency Act 1986, s 439(2), Sch 14.
Sub-s (2): words in square brackets inserted by the Communications Act 2003, s 398(1)(3).

69 (*Repealed by the Communications Act 2003, ss 398(1), (2)(f), 406(7), Sch 19(1).*)

Miscellaneous and supplemental

70, 71 (*Repealed by the Communications Act 2003, ss 398(1), (2)(f), 406(7), Sch 19(1).*)

72 Tax provisions

(1) … the successor company shall be treated for all purposes of corporation tax … as if it were the same person as British Telecommunications.

(2) …

[(3) Where, in the discharge of any liability which is vested in the successor company by this Act, the successor company makes payments—

(a) to an occupational pension scheme,

(b) with a view to the provision of benefits authorised under Chapter 3 of Part 4 of the Finance Act 2004, and

(c) for persons who are employees of the Post Office,

the Taxes Acts shall have effect in relation to those payments as if those persons were employees of the successor company and in this subsection expressions which are used in Part 4 of the Finance Act 2004 have the same meanings as in that Part.]

(4), (5) …

[4042]

NOTES

Sub-s (1): words omitted repealed by the Communications Act 2003, s 406(7), Sch 19(1).
Sub-ss (2), (4), (5): repealed by the Communications Act 2003, ss 398(1), (2)(g), 406(7), Sch 19(1).
Sub-s (3): substituted by the Taxation of Pension Schemes (Consequential Amendments) Order 2006, SI 2006/745, art 2.

73 (*Repealed by the Communications Act 2003, ss 398(1), (2)(h), 406(7), Sch 19(1).*)

PART VI
PROVISIONS RELATING TO WIRELESS TELEGRAPHY

NOTES

Pt VI (ss 74–92) repealed by the Wireless Telegraphy Act 2006, s 125(1), Sch 9, Pt 1, subject to transitional provisions and savings in s 124 of, Sch 8, Pt 1, paras 1–8, 24 to, that Act at **[4230]**, **[4239]**.

Amendments and enforcement of Wireless Telegraphy Acts

74 (*Repealed as noted at the beginning of this Part (previously repealed by the Wireless Telegraphy Act 1998, s 7, Sch 2, Pt I).*)

75 Alteration of penalties and mode of trial for certain offences under the 1949 Act

(1) The following offences under the 1949 Act shall be triable on indictment as well as summarily, that is to say—

(a) any offence under section 5(a) of that Act (sending false or misleading messages likely to prejudice the efficiency of any safety of life service, etc); and

(b) any offence under section 13 of that Act (using any apparatus for the purpose of interfering with wireless telegraphy).

(2) Schedule 3 to this Act shall have effect for the purpose of—

(a) incorporating the amendment made by subsection (1) above and certain other amendments made as respects Great Britain by the Criminal Justice Act 1982 in the text of section 14 of the 1949 Act (which gives the penalties for offences under that Act) as that section has effect both in Great Britain and in Northern Ireland; and

(b) making certain other amendments of that section as it so has effect;

and for other connected purposes.

(3) Nothing in this section or in any provision of Schedule 3 to this Act—

(a) shall affect the mode of trial in proceedings for an offence commenced before the date on which this section comes into force; or

(b) shall render a person liable in respect of an offence committed before that date to a punishment more severe than the punishment applicable in the case of that offence immediately before that date;

but except as provided above in this subsection the provisions of section 14 of the 1949 Act, as amended by Schedule 3 to this Act and by section 82 below, shall have effect in relation to any conviction on or after that date of an offence under that Act.

[4043]

NOTES

Repealed as noted at the beginning of this Part.

76–78 *(Repealed as noted at the beginning of this Part (s 76 previously repealed by virtue of the Police and Criminal Evidence Act 1984, s 26(1), and s 78 previously repealed by the Electromagnetic Compatibility Regulations 1992, SI 1992/2372, reg 2(1)).)*

79 Seizure of apparatus and other property used in committing certain offences under the 1949 Act

(1) This section applies to—

(a) any indictable offence under the 1949 Act;

(b) any offence under section 1(1) of that Act other than one consisting in the installation or use, otherwise than under and in accordance with a wireless telegraphy licence, of any apparatus not designed or adapted for emission (as opposed to reception);

[(bza) any offence under section 1A of that Act other than one where the relevant contravention of section 1 of that Act would constitute an offence so consisting;]

[(ba) any offence under section 5(b) of that Act;

(bb) any offence under the Marine, &c, Broadcasting (Offences) Act 1967;] and

(c) any offence under section 7 of the 1967 Act.

(2) Where—

(a) a search warrant is granted under section 15(1) of the 1949 Act (entry and search of premises, etc); and

(b) the suspected offence (or any of the suspected offences) is an offence to which this section applies;

the warrant may authorise [any person authorised by [OFCOM] to exercise the power conferred by this subsection] to seize and detain, for the purposes of any relevant proceedings, any apparatus or other thing found in the course of the search carried out in pursuance of the warrant which appears to him ... to have been used in connection with or to be evidence of the commission of any such offence.

(3) If a constable or any person authorised by [OFCOM] to exercise the power conferred by this subsection has reasonable grounds to suspect that an offence to which this section applies has been or is being committed, he may seize and detain, for the purposes of

any relevant proceedings, any apparatus or other thing which appears to him to have been used in connection with or to be evidence of the commission of any such offence.

(4) Nothing in this section shall prejudice any power to seize or detain property which is exercisable by a constable apart from this section.

[(4A) Without prejudice to any power exercisable by him apart from this subsection, a person authorised by [OFCOM] to exercise any power conferred by this section may use reasonable force, if necessary, in the exercise of that power.]

(5) Any person who intentionally obstructs any person in the exercise of the power conferred on him under subsection (3) above shall be guilty of an offence under the 1949 Act.

(6) References in this section to relevant proceedings are references to—

- *(a) any proceedings for an offence to which this section applies; and*
- *(b) any proceedings for forfeiture under [Schedule 7 to the Communications Act 2003].*

[4044]

NOTES

Repealed as noted at the beginning of this Part.

Sub-s (1): para (bza) inserted by the Communications Act 2003, s 179(3); (4) in relation to offences committed after 18 September 2003; paras (ba), (bb) inserted by the Broadcasting Act 1990, s 173(4).

Sub-s (2): words in first (outer) pair of square brackets substituted, and words omitted repealed, by the Broadcasting Act 1990, ss 173(5), 203(3), Sch 21; word in second (inner) pair of square brackets substituted by the Communications Act 2003, s 406(1), Sch 17, para 64.

Sub-ss (3), (6): words in square brackets substituted by the Communications Act 2003, s 406(1), Sch 17, paras 64, 65.

Sub-s (4A): inserted by the Broadcasting Act 1990, s 173(6); word in square brackets substituted by the Communications Act 2003, s 406(1), Sch 17, para 64.

80–82 *(Repealed as noted at the beginning of this Part (ss 80, 81 previously repealed by the Communications Act 2003, s 406(7), Sch 19(1), except in relation to apparatus seized before 29 December 2003).)*

83 Disposal of apparatus and other property seized by virtue of section 79

(1) Any property seized by a person authorised by [OFCOM] in pursuance of a warrant under section 15(1) of the 1949 Act or in exercise of the power conferred by section 79(3) above may be detained—

- *(a) until the end of the period of six months beginning with the date of the seizure; or*
- *(b) if proceedings for an offence to which section 79 above applies involving that property or proceedings for forfeiture of that property under [Schedule 7 to the Communications Act 2003] are instituted within that period, until the conclusion of those proceedings.*

(2) After the end of the period for which its detention is authorised by virtue of subsection (1) above, any such property which—

- *(a) remains in the possession of [OFCOM]; and*
- *(b) has not been ordered to be forfeited under section 14 of the 1949 Act (which includes provision for forfeiture of wireless telegraphy apparatus used in the commission of certain offences) or under [Schedule 7 to the Communications Act 2003];*

shall be dealt with in accordance with the following provisions of this section (and references in those provisions to the relevant property are references to any property to which this subsection applies).

(3) [OFCOM] shall take reasonable steps to deliver the relevant property to any person appearing to [them] to be its owner.

(4) Where the relevant property remains in the possession of [OFCOM] after the end of the period of one year immediately following the end of the period for which its detention is authorised by subsection (1) above, [OFCOM] may dispose of it in such manner as [they think] fit.

(5) The delivery of the relevant property in accordance with subsection (3) above to any person appearing to [OFCOM] to be its owner shall not affect the right of any other person to

take legal proceedings against the person to whom it is delivered or against anyone subsequently in possession of the property for the recovery of the property.

[4045]

NOTES

Repealed as noted at the beginning of this Part.
Words in square brackets substituted by the Communications Act 2003, s 406(1), Sch 17, paras 64, 66.

Approvals

84 Approval of wireless telegraphy apparatus etc

(1) Where any of the following instruments, namely—

(a) any licence granted under section 1 of the 1949 Act (licensing of wireless telegraphy),

(b) any regulations made under that section,

(c) any regulations made under section 10 of that Act (regulations as to radiation of electro-magnetic energy etc),

(d) any order made under section 7 of the 1967 Act (restriction on dealings in and custody of certain apparatus), or

(e) any authority given for the purposes of that section,

contains any provision which is framed by reference to relevant apparatus for the time being approved under this section for the purposes of that instrument, such apparatus may be approved for those purposes by the [relevant authority].

In this subsection "relevant apparatus" means wireless telegraphy apparatus or apparatus designed or adapted for use in connection with wireless telegraphy apparatus.

(2) A person applying for an approval under this section may be required by the [relevant authority] to comply with such requirements as the [relevant authority] may think appropriate; and those requirements may include a requirement to satisfy some other person with respect to any matter.

(3) An approval under this section may apply either to particular apparatus or to any apparatus of a description specified in the approval, and may so apply either for the purposes of a particular instrument falling within any of paragraphs (a) to (e) of subsection (1) above or for the purposes of instruments falling within any of those paragraphs of a description so specified.

(4) An approval under this section may specify conditions which must be complied with if the approval is to apply for any purposes specified in the approval, to any apparatus which is so specified or is of a description so specified, and any such condition may impose on the person to whom the approval is given a requirement from time to time to satisfy any person with respect to any matter.

(5) The [relevant authority] may at any time vary or withdraw any approval given by [the relevant authority] under this section.

(6) A person appointed by the [relevant authority] may exercise any function conferred on the [relevant authority] by the preceding provisions of this section to such extent and subject to such conditions as may be specified in the appointment.

(7) The [relevant authority] may by order provide for the charging of fees in respect of the exercise of any function in pursuance of this section by or on behalf of the [relevant authority]; and an appointment under subsection (6) above may authorise the person appointed to retain any fees received by him in pursuance of any such order.

(8) Nothing in subsection (7) above shall preclude a person (not being the [relevant authority] or a person acting on [the relevant authority's] behalf) by whom any matter falls to be determined for the purposes of any requirement imposed in pursuance of subsection (2) or (4) above from charging any fee in respect of the carrying out of any test or other assessment made by him.

[(8A) Subject to subsection (8B), in this section "the relevant authority" means—

(a) in such cases as may be specified in an order made by the Secretary of State, the Secretary of State, and

(b) in any other case, OFCOM.

(8B) Where an application for the purposes of this section is made to the Secretary of State or OFCOM and it appears to the person to whom it is made that it should have been made to the other—

(a) that person shall refer the application to the other, and

(b) the application shall be proceeded with as if made to the person to whom it is referred.]

(9) Any sums received by the Secretary of State under this section shall be paid into the Consolidated Fund.

[4046]

NOTES

Repealed as noted at the beginning of this Part.

Previously repealed, in relation to any equipment that is either radio equipment or telecommunications terminal equipment or both, by the Radio Equipment and Telecommunications Terminal Equipment Regulations 2000, SI 2000/730, reg 1(3).

Sub-ss (1), (2), (5)–(8): words in square brackets substituted by the Communications Act 2003, s 406(1), Sch 17, para 67(1)–(4).

Sub-ss (8A), (8B): inserted by the Communications Act 2003, s 406(1), Sch 17, para 67(1), (5).

Orders: the Wireless Telegraphy Apparatus Approval and Examination Fees Order 1997, SI 1997/3050 at **[4308]**; the Wireless Telegraphy (Citizens' Band and Amateur Apparatus) (Various Provisions) Order 1998, SI 1998/2531 at **[4321]**; the Wireless Telegraphy (Exemption) Regulations 2003, SI 2003/74 at **[4384]**.

Marking etc of apparatus

85 Information etc to be marked on or to accompany apparatus

(1) Where it appears to [OFCOM] expedient that any description of relevant apparatus should be marked with or accompanied by any information or instruction relating to the apparatus or its installation or use, [OFCOM] may by order—

(a) impose requirements for securing that relevant apparatus of that description is so marked or accompanied, and

(b) regulate or prohibit the supply of any such apparatus with respect to which the requirements are not complied with;

and the requirements may extend to the form and manner in which the information or instruction is given.

(2) An order under this section may, in the case of apparatus supplied in circumstances where the information or instruction required by the order would not be conveyed until after delivery, require the whole or part thereof to be also displayed near the apparatus.

(3) Where an order under this section is in force with respect to relevant apparatus of any description, any person who, in the course of any trade or business, supplies or offers to supply relevant apparatus of that description in contravention of the order shall, subject to section 87 below, be guilty of an offence and liable on summary conviction to a fine not exceeding level 5 on the standard scale.

(4) For the purposes of this section a person exposing relevant apparatus for supply or having such apparatus in his possession for supply shall be deemed to offer to supply it.

(5) In this section and section 86 below—

(a) "relevant apparatus" means wireless telegraphy apparatus or apparatus designed or adapted for use in connection with wireless telegraphy apparatus; and

(b) "supply" shall [have the same meaning as it has in Part II of the Consumer Protection Act 1987].

[4047]

NOTES

Repealed as noted at the beginning of this Part.

Sub-s (1): words in square brackets substituted by the Communications Act 2003, s 406(1), Sch 17, para 64.

Sub-s (5): words in square brackets in para (b) substituted by the Consumer Protection Act 1987, s 48(1), Sch 4, para 9(1).

Orders: the Wireless Telegraphy (Citizens' Band and Amateur Apparatus) (Various Provisions) Order 1998, SI 1998/2531 at **[4321]**; the Wireless Telegraphy (Cordless Telephone Apparatus) (Restriction and Marking) Order 1999, SI 1999/2934.

86 Information etc to be given in advertisements

(1) Where it appears to [OFCOM] expedient that any description of advertisements of relevant apparatus should contain or refer to any information relating to the apparatus or its installation or use, [OFCOM] may by order impose requirements as to the inclusion of the information, or an indication of the means by which it may be obtained, in advertisements of that description.

(2) An order under this section may specify the form and manner in which any information or indication required by the order is to be included in advertisements of any description.

(3) Where an advertisement of any relevant apparatus which is to be supplied in the course of any trade or business fails to comply with any requirement imposed under this section, any person who publishes the advertisement shall, subject to section 87 below, be guilty of an offence and liable on summary conviction to a fine not exceeding level 5 on the standard scale.

(4) Section 85(5) above applies for the purposes of this section; and in this section "advertisement" includes a catalogue, a circular and a price list.

[4048]

NOTES

Repealed as noted at the beginning of this Part.

Sub-s (1): words in square brackets substituted by the Communications Act 2003, s 406(1), Sch 17, para 64.

87 Offences under section 85 or 86 due to default of third person

(1) Where the commission by any person of an offence under section 85 or 86 above is due to the act or default of some other person, that other person shall be guilty of the offence; and a person may be charged with and convicted of the offence by virtue of this subsection whether or not proceedings are taken against the first-mentioned person.

(2) In any proceedings for an offence under either of those sections it shall, subject to subsection (3) below, be a defence for the person charged to prove that he took all reasonable steps and exercised all due diligence to avoid committing the offence.

(3) Where the defence provided by subsection (2) above involves an allegation that the commission of the offence was due to the act or default of another person, the person charged shall not, without leave of the court, be entitled to rely on that defence unless, within a period ending seven clear days before the hearing, he has served on the prosecutor a notice in writing giving such information identifying or assisting in the identification of that other person as was then in his possession.

(4) In any proceedings for an offence under section 86 above it shall be a defence for the person charged to prove that he is a person whose business it is to publish or arrange for the publication of advertisements and that he received the advertisement for publication in the ordinary course of business and did not know and had no reason to suspect that its publication would amount to an offence under that section.

[4049]

NOTES

Repealed as noted at the beginning of this Part.

Miscellaneous and supplemental

88–90 (*Repealed as noted at the beginning of this Part* (*ss 88, 90 previously repealed by the Communications Act 2003, s 406(1), (7), Sch 17, para 68, Sch 19(1), and s 89 previously repealed by the Statute Law (Repeals) Act 2004, Sch 1, Pt 5*).)

91 Construction of references to conclusion of proceedings

(1) Where proceedings for an offence [to which section 79 above applies or for the forfeiture of any apparatus under Schedule 7 to the Communications Act 2003] have been terminated by any decision of a description against which an appeal will lie (whether by way

of case stated or otherwise and whether with or without leave), those proceedings shall not be regarded as concluded for the purposes of section 83(1)(b) above—

(*a*) *until the end of the ordinary time for appeal against that decision, if no appeal proceedings in respect of it are brought within that time; or*

(*b*) *if any such proceedings are so brought, until the conclusion of the appeal proceedings.*

(2) *Subsection (1) above shall apply for determining, for the purposes of paragraph (b) of that subsection ..., when any appeal proceedings are concluded as it applies for determining when original proceedings ... are concluded.*

(3) *References in subsection (1) above, as it applies in relation to any proceedings, to a decision terminating those proceedings, include references to any verdict, sentence, finding or order which puts an end to those proceedings.*

(4) *References in this section ... to appeal proceedings include references to an application for leave to appeal.*

[4050]

NOTES

Repealed as noted at the beginning of this Part.

Sub-s (1): words in square brackets substituted by the Communications Act 2003, s 406(1), Sch 17, para 69.

Sub-ss (2), (4): words omitted repealed by the Communications Act 2003, s 406(7), Sch 19(1).

92 Interpretation of Part VI and minor amendments

(*1*) *In this Part—*

"the 1949 Act" means the Wireless Telegraphy Act 1949;

"the 1967 Act" means the Wireless Telegraphy Act 1967; and

"wireless telegraphy", "wireless telegraphy apparatus", "emission" and "interference" have the same meanings as in the 1949 Act.

(*2*)–(*4*) ...

[4051]

NOTES

Repealed as noted at the beginning of this Part.

Sub-s (2): amends the Wireless Telegraphy Act 1949, s 15 at **[4019]**.

Sub-s (3): repealed by the Cable and Broadcasting Act 1984, s 57(2), Sch 6.

Sub-s (4): repealed by the Communications Act 2003, s 406(7), Sch 19(1).

PART VII
MISCELLANEOUS AND SUPPLEMENTAL

Miscellaneous

93 (*Repealed by the Communications Act 2003, ss 398(1), (4)(a), 406(7), Sch 19(1).*)

94 Directions in the interests of national security etc

(1) The Secretary of State may, after consultation with a person to whom this section applies, give to that person such directions of a general character as appear to the Secretary of State to be [necessary] in the interests of national security or relations with the government of a country or territory outside the United Kingdom.

(2) If it appears to the Secretary of State to be [necessary] to do so in the interests of national security or relations with the government of a country or territory outside the United Kingdom, he may, after consultation with a person to whom this section applies, give to that person a direction requiring him (according to the circumstances of the case) to do, or not to do, a particular thing specified in the direction.

[(2A) The Secretary of State shall not give a direction under subsection (1) or (2) unless he believes that the conduct required by the direction is proportionate to what is sought to be achieved by that conduct.]

PART VI TELECOMMUNICATIONS

(3) A person to whom this section applies shall give effect to any direction given to him by the Secretary of State under this section notwithstanding any other duty imposed on him by or under [Part 1 or Chapter 1 of Part 2 of the Communications Act 2003 and, in the case of a direction to a provider of a public electronic communications network, notwithstanding that it relates to him in a capacity other than as the provider of such a network].

(4) The Secretary of State shall lay before each House of Parliament a copy of every direction given under this section unless he is of opinion that disclosure of the direction is against the interests of national security or relations with the government of a country or territory outside the United Kingdom, or the commercial interests of any person.

(5) A person shall not disclose, or be required by virtue of any enactment or otherwise to disclose, anything done by virtue of this section if the Secretary of State has notified him that the Secretary of State is of the opinion that disclosure of that thing is against the interests of national security or relations with the government of a country or territory outside the United Kingdom, or the commercial interests of some other person.

(6) The Secretary of State may, with the approval of the Treasury, make grants to [providers of public electronic communications networks] for the purpose of defraying or contributing towards any losses they may sustain by reason of compliance with the directions given under this section.

(7) There shall be paid out of money provided by Parliament any sums required by the Secretary of State for making grants under this section.

(8) This section applies to [OFCOM and to providers of public electronic communications networks.]

[4052]

NOTES

Sub-ss (1)–(3), (6), (8): words in square brackets substituted by the Communications Act 2003, s 406(1), Sch 17, para 70(1)–(3), (5)–(7), subject to transitional provisions in s 406(6) of, and Sch 18, para 24 to, that Act at **[3434]**, **[3460]**.

Sub-s (2A): inserted by the Communications Act 2003, s 406(1), Sch 17, para 70(1), (4), subject to transitional provisions in s 406(6) of, and Sch 18, para 24 to, that Act at **[3434]**, **[3460]**.

95–97 (*Repealed by the Communications Act 2003, ss 398(1), (4)(b), 406(7), Sch 19(1).*)

98 Use of certain conduits for telecommunication purposes

(1) The functions of an authority with control of a relevant conduit shall include the power—

- (a) to carry out, or to authorise another person to carry out, any works in relation to that conduit for or in connection with the installation, maintenance, adjustment, repair or alteration of [electronic communications apparatus];
- (b) to keep [electronic communications apparatus] installed in that conduit or to authorise any other person to keep [electronic communications apparatus] so installed;
- (c) to authorise any person to enter that conduit to inspect [electronic communications apparatus] kept installed there;
- (d) to enter into agreements, on such terms (including terms as to the payments to be made to the authority) as it thinks fit, in connection with the doing of anything authorised by or under this section; and
- (e) to carry on an ancillary business consisting in the making and carrying out of such agreements.

(2) Where any enactment or subordinate legislation expressly or impliedly imposes any limitation on the use to which a relevant conduit may be put, that limitation shall not have effect so as to prohibit the doing of anything authorised by or under this section.

(3) Where the doing by an authority with control of a public sewer of anything authorised by this section would, apart from this subsection, constitute a contravention of any obligation imposed (whether by virtue of any conveyance or agreement or otherwise) on the authority, the doing of that thing shall not constitute such a contravention to the extent that it consists in, or in authorising, the carrying out of works or inspections, or keeping of apparatus, wholly inside a public sewer.

(4) Subject to subsections (2) and (3) above, subsection (1) above is without prejudice to the rights of any person with an interest in land on, under or over which a relevant conduit is situated.

(5) Without prejudice to subsections (1) to (4) above, the Secretary of State may by order provide for any local Act under or in accordance with which any conduits (whether or not relevant conduits) are kept installed in streets to be amended in such manner as appears to him requisite or expedient for securing—

(a) that there is power for those conduits to be used for [the purposes of any electronic communications network or of any electronic communications service];

(b) that the terms (including terms as to payment) on which those conduits are used for those purposes are reasonable; and

(c) that the use of those conduits for those purposes is not unreasonably inhibited (whether directly or indirectly) by reason of the terms of any consent, licence or agreement which has been given, granted or made in relation to any of those conduits for the purposes of that Act.

(6) In this section "relevant conduit" means—

(a) any conduit which, whether or not it is itself an electric line, is maintained by an electricity authority for the purpose of enclosing, surrounding or supporting such a line, including where such a conduit is connected to any box, chamber or other structure (including a building) maintained by an electricity authority for purposes connected with the conveyance, transmission or distribution of electricity, that box, chamber or structure; or

(b) a water main or any other conduit maintained by a water authority for the purpose of conveying water from one place to another; or

(c) a public sewer; or

(d) a culvert which is a designated watercourse within the meaning of the Drainage (Northern Ireland) Order 1973.

(7) In this section a reference to the authority with control of a relevant conduit—

(a) in relation to a conduit or structure falling within paragraph (a) or (b) of subsection (6) above, shall be construed as a reference to the authority by whom the conduit or structure is maintained;

(b) in relation to a public sewer, shall be construed, subject to subsection (8) below, as a reference to the [person] in whom the sewer is vested; and

(c) in relation to a culvert falling within paragraph (d) of subsection (6) above, shall be construed as a reference to the Department of Agriculture for Northern Ireland.

(8) Where—

(a) the functions of an authority with control of a public sewer are, in pursuance of any enactment, discharged on its behalf by [another person], and

(b) the [other person] is authorised by the authority with control of the sewer to act on its behalf for the purposes of the matters referred to in subsection (1) above,

this section shall have effect in relation to that sewer as if any reference to the authority with control of the sewer included, to such extent as may be necessary for the [other person] so to act, a reference to the [other person].

(9) In this section—

"alteration", "street" … have the same meanings as in Schedule 2 to this Act;

"conduit" includes a tunnel or subway;

"electric line"—

(a) in Great Britain, has the same meaning as in [the Electricity Act 1989]; and

(b) in Northern Ireland, has the same meaning as in the [Electricity (Northern Ireland) Order 1992];

"electricity authority" means [a person authorised by a licence under Part I of the Electricity Act 1989 to [supply or participate in the transmission of]] or [a person authorised by a licence under Part II of the Electricity (Northern Ireland) Order 1992 to transmit or supply electricity];

"public sewer"—

(a) in England and Wales, has the same meaning as in the Public Health Act 1936;

(b) in Scotland, means any sewer which is vested in [Scottish Water]; and

(c) in Northern Ireland, means a sewer as defined in the Water and Sewerage Services (Northern Ireland) Order 1973;

[…]

PART VI TELECOMMUNICATIONS

"subordinate legislation" means any subordinate legislation within the meaning of the Interpretation Act 1978 or any instrument, as defined in section 1 of the Interpretation Act (Northern Ireland) 1954;

"water authority"—

[(a) in England and Wales, means the [Environment Agency] or a water undertaker;]

(b) in Scotland, [means Scottish Water]; and

(c) in Northern Ireland, means the Department of the Environment for Northern Ireland;

"water main"—

[(a) in England and Wales, means a water main [or resource main within the meaning of the Water Industry Act 1991];]

(b) in Scotland, means a main within the meaning of the Water (Scotland) Act 1980; and

(c) in Northern Ireland, means a main within the meaning of the Water and Sewerage Services (Northern Ireland) Order 1973.

[4053]

NOTES

Sub-s (1): words in square brackets substituted by the Communications Act 2003, s 406(1), Sch 17, para 71(1), (2).

Sub-s (5): for the word "streets" there is substituted the word "roads", in relation to Scotland only, by the Roads (Scotland) Act 1984, s 156(1), Sch 9, para 92(1), (3)(a); words in square brackets in para (a) substituted by the Communications Act 2003, s 406(1), Sch 17, para 71(1), (3).

Sub-ss (7), (8): words in square brackets substituted by the Water Act 1989, s 190(1), Sch 25, para 68(a), (b).

Sub-s (9): in definition beginning "alteration", words omitted repealed by the Communications Act 2003, s 406(7), Sch 19(1), and for the word "street" there is substituted the word "road", in relation to Scotland only, by the Roads (Scotland) Act 1984, s 156(1), Sch 9, para 92(1), (3)(b); in definition "electric line" words in first pair of square brackets substituted by the Electricity Act 1989, s 112(1), Sch 16, para 29(1) and words in second pair of square brackets substituted by the Electricity (Northern Ireland) Order 1992, SI 1992/231 (NI 1), art 95(1), Sch 12, para 28(a); in definition "electricity authority" words in first (outer) pair of square brackets substituted by the Electricity Act 1989, s 112(1), Sch 16, para 29(2), words in second (inner) pair of square brackets substituted by the Energy Act 2004, s 143(1), Sch 19, para 2, and words in third pair of square brackets substituted by SI 1992/231 (NI 1), art 95(1), Sch 12, para 28(b); in definition "public sewer" words in square brackets substituted by the Water Industry (Scotland) Act 2002 (Consequential Modifications) Order 2004, SI 2004/1822, art 2, Schedule, Pt 1, para 12(a); definition "sewerage authority" (omitted) inserted by the Local Government etc (Scotland) Act 1994, s 180(1), Sch 13, para 133(1), (3), repealed by SI 2004/1822, art 2, Schedule, Pt 1, para 12(b); in definition "water authority", para (a) substituted by the Water Act 1989, s 190, Sch 25, para 68(c)(i), words in square brackets therein substituted by the Environment Act 1995 (Consequential Amendments) Regulations 1996, SI 1996/593, reg 2, Sch 1, and in para (b) words in square brackets substituted by SI 2004/1822, art 2, Schedule, Pt 1, para 12(c); in definition "water main", para (a) substituted by the Water Act 1989, s 190, Sch 25, para 68(c)(ii), and words in square brackets therein substituted by the Water Consolidation (Consequential Provisions) Act 1991, s 2, Sch 1, para 38(1).

99, 100 (*S 99 repealed in part by the Postal Services Act 2000, s 127(6), Sch 9; remainder repealed by the Postal Services Act 2000 (Consequential Modifications No 1) Order 2001, SI 2001/1149, art 3(2), Sch 2; s 100 ceased to have effect on the dissolution of British Telecommunications on 6 September 1994 (see SI 1994/2162).*)

Supplemental

101 General restrictions on disclosure of information

(1) Subject to the following provisions of this section, no information with respect to any particular business which—

(a) has been obtained under or by virtue of the provisions of this Act […]; and

(b) relates to the private affairs of any individual or to any particular business,

shall during the lifetime of that individual or so long as that business continues to be carried on, be disclosed without the consent of that individual or the person for the time being carrying on that business.

(2) Subsection (1) above does not apply to any disclosure of information which is made—

(a) for the purpose of facilitating the performance of any functions assigned … to the Secretary of State [or OFCOM by or under this Act …];

(b) for the purpose of facilitating the performance of any functions of any Minister, any Northern Ireland department, the head of any such department, [the Office of Fair Trading][, the Commission] [, the Water Services Regulation Authority,] [the Gas and Electricity Markets Authority] [the Director General of Electricity Supply for Northern Ireland] [or the Director General of Gas for Northern Ireland] [the Office of Rail Regulation][, OFCOM][, the Civil Aviation Authority] or a local weights and measures authority in Great Britain under any of the enactments [or subordinate legislation] specified in subsection (3) below;

[(bb) for the purpose of facilitating the carrying out by the Comptroller and Auditor General of any of his functions under any enactment;]

(c) in connection with the investigation of any criminal offence or for the purposes of any criminal proceedings;

(d) for the purpose of any civil proceedings brought under or by virtue of this Act or any of the enactments [or subordinate legislation] specified in subsection (3) below; or

(e) in pursuance of a Community obligation.

(3) The enactments [or subordinate legislation] referred to in subsection (2) above are—

(a) the Trade Descriptions Act 1968;
(b) the 1973 Act;
(c) the Consumer Credit Act 1974;
(d), (e) …
(f) the Estate Agents Act 1979; …
(g) the 1980 Act;
[(h) the Consumer Protection Act 1987]
[(i) the Consumer Protection (Northern Ireland) Order 1987]
[(i) the Control of Misleading Advertisements Regulations 1988]
[(j) the Water Act 1989] [the Water Industry Act 1991 or any of the other consolidation Acts (within the meaning of section 206 of that Act of 1991)][, or the Water Act 2003]
[(k) the Electricity Act 1989]
[(l) the Electricity (Northern Ireland) Order 1992]
[(ll) the Gas (Northern Ireland) Order 1996;]
[(m) the Railways Act 1993]
[(n) the Competition Act 1998]
[(o) Part I of the Transport Act 2000]
[(p) the Enterprise Act 2002]
[(q) the Communications Act 2003 …]
[(r) the Railways Act 2005.]

(4) …

(5) Any person who discloses any information in contravention of this section shall be guilty of an offence and liable—

(a) on summary conviction, to a fine not exceeding the statutory maximum;
(b) on conviction on indictment, to imprisonment for a term not exceeding two years or to a fine or to both.

[(6) Information obtained by [OFCOM] in the exercise of functions which are exercisable concurrently with [the Office of Fair Trading] under Part I of the Competition Act 1998 is subject to [Part 9 of the Enterprise Act 2002 (Information)] and not to subsections (1) to (5) of this section.]

[4054]

NOTES

Sub-s (1): words "(except Part 6)" omitted from square brackets, inserted by the Communications Act 2003, s 406(1), Sch 17, para 72(1), (2) and repealed by the Wireless Telegraphy Act 2006, s 125(1), Sch 9, Pt 1, subject to transitional provisions and savings in s 124 of, Sch 8, Pt 1, paras 1–8, 24 to, that Act at **[4230]**, **[4239]**.

Sub-s (2): in para (a), first words omitted repealed, and words in square brackets substituted, by the Communications Act 2003, s 406(1), (7), Sch 17, para 72(1), (3), Sch 19(1); words "(except functions assigned by or under Part 6)" omitted from square brackets in para (a), repealed by the Wireless Telegraphy Act 2006, s 125(1), Sch 9, Pt 1, subject to transitional provisions and savings in s 124 of, Sch 8, Pt 1, paras 1–8, 24 to, that Act at **[4230]**, **[4239]**; in para (b) words in first pair of square brackets substituted by the Enterprise Act 2002, s 278(1), Sch 25, para 13(1), (9)(a), words in second pair of square brackets inserted by the Competition Act 1998 (Competition Commission) Transitional, Consequential and Supplemental Provisions Order 1999, SI 1999/506, art 18(b), words in third pair of square brackets inserted by the Water Act 1989, s 190(1), Sch 25, para 68(2)(a), and substituted by the

PART VI TELECOMMUNICATIONS

Water Act 2003, s 101(1), Sch 7, Pt 2, para 23(a), words in fourth pair of square brackets inserted by the Electricity Act 1989, s 112(1), Sch 16, para 29(1), (3)(a), and substituted by virtue of the Utilities Act 2000, s 3(2), words in fifth pair of square brackets inserted by the Electricity (Northern Ireland) Order 1992, SI 1992/231 (NI 1), art 95(1), Sch 12, para 29(a), words in sixth pair of square brackets inserted by the Gas (Northern Ireland) Order 1996, SI 1996/275, art 71(1), Sch 6, words in seventh pair of square brackets inserted by the Railways Act 1993, s 152(1), Sch 12, para 13(1), substituted by the Railways and Transport Safety Act 2003, s 16(5), Sch 2, para 19(g), subject to savings in s 16(5) of, and Sch 3 to, that Act, word in eighth pair of square brackets substituted by the Communications Act 2003, s 406(1), Sch 17, para 72(1), (4), words in ninth pair of square brackets inserted by the Transport Act 2000 (Consequential Amendments) Order 2001, SI 2001/4050, art 2, Schedule, Pt IV, para 17(a), and words in final pair of square brackets inserted by the Control of Misleading Advertisements Regulations 1988, SI 1988/915, reg 7(6)(f)(i); para (bb) inserted by the Competition and Service (Utilities) Act 1992, s 56(6), Sch 1, para 3(a); words in square brackets in para (d) inserted by the Control of Misleading Advertisements Regulations 1988, SI 1988/915, reg 7(6)(f)(i).

Sub-s (3): words in first pair of square brackets inserted by SI 1988/915, reg 7(6)(f)(ii); paras (d), (e) repealed by the Competition Act 1998, ss 54(3), 74(3), Sch 10, Pt IV, para 9(1), (7), Sch 14, Pt I; word omitted from para (f) repealed, and para (h) added, by the Consumer Protection Act 1987, s 48(1), (3), Sch 4, para 9(2), Sch 5; first para (i) inserted by the Consumer Protection (Northern Ireland) Order 1987, SI 1987/2049 (NI 20), art 35(1), Sch 3, para 6; second para (i) inserted by SI 1988/915, reg 7(6)(f); para (j) added by the Water Act 1989, s 190(1), Sch 25, para 68(2)(b), words in first pair of square brackets therein inserted by the Water Consolidation (Consequential Provisions) Act 1991, s 2(1), Sch 1, para 38(2), words in second pair of square brackets therein inserted by the Water Act 2003, s 101(1), Sch 7, Pt 2, para 23(b); para (k) added by the Electricity Act 1989, s 112(1), Sch 16, para 29(1), (3)(b); para (l) added by SI 1992/231 (NI 1), art 95(1), Sch 12, para 29(b); para (ll) inserted by the Gas (Northern Ireland) Order 1996, SI 1996/275, art 71(1), Sch 6; para (m) added by the Railways Act 1993, s 152(1), Sch 12, para 13(2); para (n) added by the Competition Act 1998, s 54(3), Sch 10, Pt IV, para 9(1), (7)(b); para (o) added by SI 2001/4050, art 2, Schedule, Pt IV, para 17(b); para (p) added by the Enterprise Act 2002, s 278(1), Sch 25, para 13(1), (9)(b); para (q) added by the Communications Act 2003, s 406(1), Sch 17, para 72(1), (5), and words "(excluding the provisions of that Act which are enactments relating to the management of the radio spectrum within the meaning of that Act)" (omitted) repealed by the Wireless Telegraphy Act 2006, s 125(1), Sch 9, Pt 1, subject to transitional provisions and savings in s 124 of, Sch 8, Pt 1, paras 1–8, 24 to, that Act at **[4230]**, **[4239]**; para (r) added by the Railways Act 2005, s 59(1), Sch 12, para 7.

Sub-s (4): repealed by the Communications Act 2003, s 406(1), (7), Sch 17, para 72(1), (6), Sch 19(1).

Sub-s (6): added by the Competition Act 1998, s 54(3), Sch 10, para 9(8); word in first pair of square brackets substituted by the Communications Act 2003, s 406(1), Sch 17, para 72(1), (7); words in second and third pairs of square brackets substituted by the Enterprise Act 2002, s 278(1), Sch 25, para 13(1), (9)(c).

102 (*Repealed by the Communications Act 2003, s 406(7), Sch 19(1).*)

103 Summary proceedings

[(1)] Proceedings for any offence under this Act which is punishable on summary conviction may be commenced at any time within twelve months next after the commission of the offence.

[(2) Subsection (1) above shall not apply for the purposes of an offence under any provision of the Enterprise Act 2002 as applied by virtue of section 13B above.]

[4055]

NOTES

Sub-s (1) numbered as such and sub-s (2) added by the Enterprise Act 2002, s 278(1), Sch 25, para 13(1), (10).

104 Orders and schemes

(1) Any power of the Secretary of State to make an order or a scheme under this Act shall be exercisable by statutory instrument subject, except in the case of an order under section … 110(5) … to annulment in pursuance of a resolution of either House of Parliament.

[(1A) Section 403 of the Communications Act 2003 (procedure for regulations and orders made by OFCOM) applies to every power of OFCOM to make an order under a provision of this Act.

(1B), (1C) …]

(2) Any order or scheme under this Act may make different provision with respect to different cases or descriptions of case.

(3) …

[4056]

NOTES

Sub-s (1): words omitted repealed by the Communications Act 2003, s 406(7), Sch 19(1).

Sub-s (1A): inserted by the Communications Act 2003, s 406(1), Sch 17, para 73.

Sub-ss (1B), (1C): inserted by the Communications Act 2003, s 406(1), Sch 17, para 73; repealed by the Wireless Telegraphy Act 2006, s 125(1), Sch 9, Pt 1, subject to transitional provisions and savings in s 124 of, Sch 8, Pt 1, paras 1–8, 24 to, that Act at **[4230]**, **[4239]**, and previously read as follows:

"(1B) The approval of the Secretary of State is required for the making by OFCOM of an order under section 85 or 86 above.

(1C) A statutory instrument containing an order made by OFCOM under section 85 or 86 above shall be subject to annulment in pursuance of a resolution of either House of Parliament.".

Sub-s (3): repealed by the Communications Act 2003, s 406(7), Sch 19(1).

105 Financial provisions

There shall be paid out of money provided by Parliament any administrative expenses incurred by the Secretary of State in consequence of the provisions of this Act and any increase attributable to this Act in the sums payable out of money so provided under any other Act.

[4057]

106 General interpretation

(1) In this Act, unless the context otherwise requires—

"the 1973 Act" means the Fair Trading Act 1973;

"the 1980 Act" means the Competition Act 1980;

"the 1981 Act" means the British Telecommunications Act 1981;

"the appointed day" has the meaning given by section 2 above;

.....

"the Commission" means the [Competition Commission];

.....

"the excepted liabilities" has the meaning given by section 60(2) above;

"modifications" includes additions, alterations and omissions and cognate expressions shall be construed accordingly;

["OFCOM" means the Office of Communications;]

.....

"the successor company" and "the transfer date" have the meanings given by section 60(1) above;

.....

(2), (3) …

(4) Any power conferred on the Secretary of State by this Act to give a direction if it appears to him to be requisite or expedient to do so in the interests of national security or relations with the government of a country or territory outside the United Kingdom includes power to give the direction if it appears to him to be requisite or expedient to do so in order—

(a) to discharge, or facilitate the discharge of, an obligation binding on Her Majesty's Government in the United Kingdom by virtue of it being a member of an international organisation or a party to an international agreement;

(b) to attain, or facilitate the attainment of, any other objects the attainment of which is, in the Secretary of State's opinion, requisite or expedient in view of Her Majesty's Government in the United Kingdom being a member of such an organisation or a party to such an agreement; or

(c) to enable Her Majesty's Government in the United Kingdom to become a member of such an organisation or a party to such an agreement.

(5) For the purposes of any licence granted, approval given or order made under this Act any description or class may be framed by reference to any circumstances whatsoever.

[4058]

NOTES

Sub-s (1): definitions omitted repealed, and definition "OFCOM" inserted, by the Communications Act 2003, s 406(1), (7), Sch 17, para 74, Sch 19(1); in definition "the Commission" words in square brackets substituted by the Competition Act 1998 (Competition Commission) Transitional, Consequential and Supplemental Provisions Order 1999, SI 1999/506, art 18(a).

Sub-ss (2), (3): repealed by the Statute Law (Repeals) Act 1993.

107 *(Sub-ss (1), (2), (4) repealed by the Communications Act 2003, s 406(7), Sch 19(1); sub-s (3) repealed by the Petroleum Act 1998, ss 50, 51(1), Sch 4, para 19(b), Sch 5, Pt I.)*

108 Extension to the Isle of Man and the Channel Islands

Her Majesty may by Order in Council direct that any of the provisions of this Act specified in the Order shall extend to the Isle of Man or any of the Channel Islands with such exceptions, adaptations and modifications as may be so specified.

[4059]

NOTES

Orders: the Telecommunications Act 1984 (Isle of Man) Order 1984, SI 1984/861; the Wireless Telegraphy (Guernsey) Order 1994, SI 1994/1064; the Wireless Telegraphy (Isle of Man) Order 1995, SI 1995/268; the Wireless Telegraphy (Jersey) Order 2003, SI 2003/3196; the Broadcasting and Communications (Jersey) Order 2004, SI 2004/308.

109 Amendments, transitional provisions and repeals

(1) The enactments mentioned in Schedule 4 to this Act shall have effect subject to the amendments there specified (being minor amendments or amendments consequential on the preceding provisions of this Act).

(2), (3) …

(4) The general transitional provisions and savings contained in Schedule 5 to this Act … shall have effect; but those provisions and savings are without prejudice to sections 16 and 17 of the Interpretation Act 1978 (effect of repeals).

(5)–(7) …

[4060]

NOTES

Sub-ss (2), (3), (5)–(7): repealed by the Communications Act 2003, s 406(7), Sch 19(1).
Sub-s (4): words omitted repealed by the Communications Act 2003, s 406(7), Sch 19(1).

110 Short title, commencement and extent

(1) This Act may be cited as the Telecommunications Act 1984.

(2) The following provisions of this Act, namely—
sections 2 to 4;
Parts II to IV;
sections 93 to 95;
sections 97 to 99;
sections 101 to 103;
section 106;
section 109(1) and Schedule 4;
section 109(2), (3) and (7);
Part I of Schedule 5 and section 109(4) so far as relating to that Part; and
Part I of Schedule 7 and section 109(6) so far as relating to that Part,
shall come into force on the appointed day.

(3) The following provisions of this Act, namely—
Part V;
Part II of Schedule 5 and Schedule 6 and section 109(4) so far as relating to that Part and that Schedule; and
Part II of Schedule 7 and section 109(6) so far as relating to that Part,
shall come into force on the transfer date.

(4) Part III of Schedule 7 and section 109(6) so far as relating to that Part shall come into force on the dissolution of British Telecommunications.

(5) Subject to subsections (2) and (4) above, this Act shall come into force on such day as the Secretary of State may by order appoint; and different days may be so appointed for different provisions or for different purposes.

(6) This Act extends to Northern Ireland.

[4061]

NOTES

Orders: the Telecommunications Act 1984 (Appointed Day) (No 1) Order 1984, SI 1984/749; the Telecommunications Act 1984 (Appointed Day) (No 2) Order 1984, SI 1984/876.

SCHEDULES

SCHEDULE 1
DIRECTOR GENERAL OF TELECOMMUNICATIONS

Section 1

1. *There shall be paid to the Director such remuneration, and such travelling and other allowances, as the Secretary of State with the approval of the Treasury may determine.*

2. *In the case of any such holder of the office of the Director as may be determined by the Secretary of State with the approval of the Treasury, there shall be paid such pension, allowance or gratuity to or in respect of him on his retirement or death, or such contributions or payments towards provision for such a pension, allowance or gratuity as may be so determined.*

3. *If, when any person ceases to hold office as the Director, it appears to the Secretary of State with the approval of the Treasury that there are special circumstances which make it right that he should receive compensation, there may be paid to him a sum by way of compensation of such amount as may be so determined.*

4, 5. …

6. *The Director shall have an official seal for the authentication of documents required for the purposes of his functions.*

7. *The Documentary Evidence Act 1868 shall have effect as if the Director were included in the first column of the Schedule to that Act, as if the Director and any person authorised to act on behalf of the Director were mentioned in the second column of that Schedule, and as if the regulations referred to in that Act included any document issued by the Director or by any such person.*

8. *Anything authorised or required by or under this Act or any other enactment to be done by the Director, other than the making of a statutory instrument, may be done by any member of the staff of the Director who is authorised generally or specially in that behalf by the Director.*

[4062]

NOTES

Repealed by the Communications Act 2003, s 406(7), Sch 19(1), as from a day to be appointed.

Para 4: repealed by the Parliamentary and Health Service Commissioners Act 1987, s 10(2), Sch 2.

Para 5: amends the House of Commons Disqualification Act 1975, Sch 1, Pt III, and the Northern Ireland Assembly Disqualification Act 1975, Sch 1, Pt III.

By the Transfer of Functions (Treasury and Minister for the Civil Service) Order 1995, SI 1995/269, arts 3, 5(2), Schedule, para 12, the functions of the Treasury under paras 1–3 of this Schedule were transferred to the Minister for the Civil Service with effect from 1 April 1995, and accordingly the references to the Treasury in those paragraphs are to be taken as if they were references to the Minister for the Civil Service.

SCHEDULE 2
THE TELECOMMUNICATIONS CODE

Section 10

ARRANGEMENT OF PARAGRAPHS

Interpretation of code

1.—(1) In this code, except in so far as the context otherwise requires—

"agriculture" and "agricultural"—

(a) in England and Wales, have the same meanings as in the Highways Act 1980;

(b) in Scotland, have the same meanings as in the Town and Country Planning (Scotland) Act 1972; and

(c) in Northern Ireland, have the same meanings as in the Agriculture Act (Northern Ireland) 1949;

"alter", "alteration" and "altered" shall be construed in accordance with sub-paragraph (2) below;

"bridleway" and "footpath"—

(a) in England and Wales, have the same meanings as in the Highways Act 1980;

(b) in Scotland, have the same meanings as in Part III of the Countryside (Scotland) Act 1967; and

(c) in Northern Ireland, mean a way over which the public have, by virtue of the Access to the Countryside (Northern Ireland) Order 1983, a right of way on horseback and on foot, respectively;

["conduit" includes a tunnel, subway, tube or pipe;

"conduit system" means a system of conduits provided so as to be available for use by providers of electronic communications networks for the purposes of the provision by them of their networks;]

"the court" means, without prejudice to any right of appeal conferred by virtue of paragraph 25 below or otherwise—

(a) in relation to England and Wales and Northern Ireland, the county court; and

(b) in relation to Scotland, the sheriff;

["electronic communications apparatus" means—

(a) any apparatus (within the meaning of the Communications Act 2003) which is designed or adapted for use in connection with the provision of an electronic communications network;

(b) any apparatus (within the meaning of that Act) that is designed or adapted for a use which consists of or includes the sending or receiving of communications or other signals that are transmitted by means of an electronic communications network;

(c) any line;
(d) any conduit, structure, pole or other thing in, on, by or from which any electronic communications apparatus is or may be installed, supported, carried or suspended;

and references to the installation of electronic communications apparatus are to be construed accordingly;

"electronic communications network" has the same meaning as in the Communications Act 2003, and references to the provision of such a network are to be construed in accordance with the provisions of that Act;

"electronic communications service" has the same meaning as in the Communications Act 2003, and references to the provision of such a service are to be construed in accordance with the provisions of that Act;]

"emergency works" in relation to the operator or a relevant undertaker for the purposes of paragraph 23 below, means works the execution of which at the time it is proposed to execute them is requisite in order to put an end to, or prevent, the arising of circumstances then existing or imminent which are likely to cause—
(a) danger to persons or property,
(b) the interruption of any service provided by [the operator's network] or, as the case may be, interference with the exercise of any functions conferred or imposed on the undertaker by or under any enactment; or
(c) substantial loss to the operator or, as the case may be, the undertaker,

and such other works as in all the circumstances it is reasonable to execute with those works;

["line" means any wire, cable, tube, pipe or similar thing (including its casing or coating) which is designed or adapted for use in connection with the provision of any electronic communications network or electronic communications service;]

"maintainable highway"—
(a) [in England and Wales, means a maintainable highway within the meaning of Part III of the New Roads and Street Works Act 1991] other than one which is a footpath[, bridleway or restricted byway] that crosses, and forms part of, any agricultural land or any land which is being brought into use for agriculture; and
(b) in Northern Ireland, means a [road within the meaning of the Roads (Northern Ireland) Order 1993];

["the operator" means—
(a) where the code is applied in any person's case by a direction under section 106 of the Communications Act 2003, that person; and
(b) where it applies by virtue of section 106(3)(b) of that Act, the Secretary of State or (as the case may be) the Northern Ireland department in question;

"the operator's network" means—
(a) in relation to an operator falling within paragraph (a) of the definition of "operator", so much of any electronic communications network or conduit system provided by that operator as is not excluded from the application of the code under section 106(5) of the Communications Act 2003; and
(b) in relation to an operator falling within paragraph (b) of that definition, the electronic communications network which the Secretary of State or the Northern Ireland department is providing or proposing to provide;]

["public road" means a public road within the meaning of [Part IV of the New Roads and Street Works Act 1991] other than one which is a footpath or a bridleway that crosses, and forms part of, any agricultural land or any land which is being brought into use for agriculture;]

"railway" includes a light railway;

["restricted byway" has the same meaning as in Part 2 of the Countryside and Rights of Way Act 2000;]

["road" has [the same meaning as in Part III of the New Roads and Street Works Act 1991];]

["signal" has the same meaning as in section 32 of the Communications Act 2003;]

"the statutory purposes" means the purposes of [the provision of the operator's network];

"street" has [the same meaning as in Part III of the New Roads and Street Works Act 1991] [or, in Northern Ireland, the Street Works (Northern Ireland) Order 1995];

"structure" does not include a building;

.....

(2) In this code, references to the alteration of any apparatus include references to the moving, removal or replacement of the apparatus.

PART VI TELECOMMUNICATIONS

(3) In relation to any land which, otherwise than in connection with a street on that land, is divided horizontally into different parcels, the references in this code to a place over or under the land shall have effect in relation to each parcel as not including references to any place in a different parcel.

[(3A) References in this code to the provision of a conduit system include references to establishing or maintaining such a system.]

(4), (5) ...

[4063]

NOTES

Sub-para (1): definitions "conduit", "conduit system", "electronic communications apparatus", "electronic communications network", "electronic communications service" and "signal" inserted, words in square brackets in definitions "emergency works" and "the statutory purposes" substituted, definition "line" substituted, definitions "the operator" and "the operator's network" substituted, for original definitions "the operator" and "the operator's system", and definition "telecommunications apparatus" (omitted) repealed, by the Communications Act 2003, ss 106(2), 406(7), Sch 3, paras 1–3, Sch 19(1), subject to transitional provisions in s 406(6) of, and Sch 18, paras 17, 64 to, that Act at **[3434]**, **[3460]**; definition "maintainable highway" repealed, in relation to Scotland only, by the Roads (Scotland) Act 1984, s 156(1), Sch 9, para 92(4)(a)(i), words in first pair of square brackets substituted by the New Roads and Street Works Act 1991, s 168(1), Sch 8, Pt IV, para 113, words in second pair of square brackets substituted by the Restricted Byways (Application and Consequential Amendment of Provisions) Regulations 2006, SI 2006/1177, reg 2, Schedule, Pt I, and words in third pair of square brackets substituted by the Street Works (Northern Ireland) Order 1995, SI 1995/3210, art 60(1), Sch 3, para 9(a)(i); definitions "public road" and "road" inserted, in relation to Scotland only, by the Roads (Scotland) Act 1984, s 156(1), Sch 9, para 92(4)(a)(ii), words in square brackets therein substituted by the New Roads and Street Works Act 1991, s 168(1), Sch 8, Pt IV, para 113; definition "restricted byway" inserted, in relation to England and Wales, by SI 2006/1177, reg 2, Schedule, Pt I; definition "street" repealed, in relation to Scotland only, by the Roads (Scotland) Act 1984, s 156(1), Sch 9, para 92(4)(a)(i), words in square brackets inserted by the Street Works (Northern Ireland) Order 1995, SI 1995/3210, art 60(1), Sch 3, para 9(a)(ii).

Sub-para (3): for the word "street" there is substituted the word "road", in relation to Scotland only, by the Roads (Scotland) Act 1984, s 156(1), Sch 9, para 92(4)(b).

Sub-para (3A): inserted by the Communications Act 2003, s 106(2), Sch 3, paras 1, 4, subject to transitional provisions in s 406(6) of, and Sch 18, paras 17, 64 to, that Act.

Sub-para (4): repealed by the New Roads and Street Works Act 1991, s 168(1), (2), Sch 8, Pt IV, para 113, Sch 9.

Sub-para (5): repealed by the Roads (Scotland) Act 1984, s 156(1), Sch 9, para 92(4)(d), and the Street Works (Northern Ireland) Order 1995, SI 1995/3210, art 60(2), Sch 4.

Agreement required to confer right to execute works etc

2.—(1) The agreement in writing of the occupier for the time being of any land shall be required for conferring on the operator a right for the statutory purposes—

(a) to execute any works on that land for or in connection with the installation, maintenance, adjustment, repair or alteration of [electronic communications apparatus]; or

(b) to keep [electronic communications apparatus] installed on, under or over that land; or

(c) to enter that land to inspect any apparatus kept installed (whether on, under or over that land or elsewhere) for the purposes of the operator's [network].

(2) A person who is the owner of the freehold estate in any land or is a lessee of any land shall not be bound by a right conferred in accordance with sub-paragraph (1) above by the occupier of that land unless—

(a) he conferred the right himself as occupier of the land; or

(b) he has agreed in writing to be bound by the right; or

(c) he is for the time being treated by virtue of sub-paragraph (3) below as having so agreed; or

(d) he is bound by the right by virtue of sub-paragraph (4) below.

(3) If a right falling within sub-paragraph (1) above has been conferred by the occupier of any land for purposes connected with the provision, to the occupier from time to time of that land, of any [electronic communications services] and—

(a) the person conferring the right is also the owner of the freehold estate in that land or is a lessee of the land under a lease for a term of a year or more, or

(b) in a case not falling within paragraph (a) above, a person owning the freehold estate in the land or a lessee of the land under a lease for a term of a year or more has agreed in writing that his interest in the land should be bound by the right,

then, subject to paragraph 4 below, that right shall (as well as binding the person who conferred it) have effect, at any time when the person who conferred it or a person bound by it under sub-paragraph (2)(b) or (4) of this paragraph is the occupier of the land, as if every person for the time being owning an interest in that land had agreed in writing to the right being conferred for the said purposes and, subject to its being exercised solely for those purposes, to be bound by it.

(4) In any case where a person owning an interest in land agrees in writing (whether when agreeing to the right as occupier or for the purposes of sub-paragraph (3)(b) above or otherwise) that his interest should be bound by a right falling within sub-paragraph (1) above, that right shall (except in so far as the contrary intention appears) bind the owner from time to time of that interest and also—

- (a) the owner from time to time of any other interest in the land, being an interest created after the right is conferred and not having priority over the interest to which the agreement relates; and
- (b) any other person who is at any time in occupation of the land and whose right to occupation of the land derives (by contract or otherwise) from a person who at the time the right to occupation was granted was bound by virtue of this sub-paragraph.

(5) A right falling within sub-paragraph (1) above shall not be exercisable except in accordance with the terms (whether as to payment or otherwise) subject to which it is conferred; and, accordingly, every person for the time being bound by such a right shall have the benefit of those terms.

(6) A variation of a right falling within sub-paragraph (1) above or of the terms on which such a right is exercisable shall be capable of binding persons who are not parties to the variation in the same way as, under sub-paragraphs (2), (3) and (4) above, such a right is capable of binding persons who are not parties to the conferring of the right.

(7) It is hereby declared that a right falling within sub-paragraph (1) above is not subject to the provisions of any enactment requiring the registration of interests in, charges on or other obligations affecting land.

(8) In this paragraph and paragraphs 3 and 4 below—

- (a) references to the occupier of any land shall have effect—
  - (i) in relation to any footpath[, bridleway or restricted byway] that crosses and forms part of any agricultural land or any land which is being brought into use for agriculture, as references to the occupier of that land;
  - (ii) in relation to any [street or, in Scotland, road] (not being such a footpath[, bridleway or restricted byway]), [as references—

    in England and Wales or Northern Ireland, to the street managers within the meaning of Part III of the New Roads and Street Works Act 1991 [or the Street Works (Northern Ireland) Order 1995], and in Scotland, to the road managers within the meaning of Part IV of that Act; and]
  - (iii) in relation to any land (not being a [street or, in Scotland, road]) which is unoccupied, as references to the person (if any) who for the time being exercises powers of management or control over the land or, if there is no such person, to every person whose interest in the land would be prejudicially affected by the exercise of the right in question;
- (b) "lease" includes any leasehold tenancy (whether in the nature of a head lease, sub-lease or underlease) and any agreement to grant such a tenancy but not a mortgage by demise or sub-demise and "lessee" shall be construed accordingly; and
- (c) references to the owner of a freehold estate shall, in relation to land in Scotland, have effect as references to the person—
  - (i) who is infeft proprietor of the land; or
  - (ii) who has right to the land but whose title thereto is not complete; or
  - (iii) in the case of land subject to a heritable security constituted by ex facie absolute disposition, who is the debtor in the security, except where the creditor is in possession of the land,

  other than a person having a right as a superior only.

PART VI TELECOMMUNICATIONS

(9) Subject to paragraphs 9(2) and 11(2) below, this paragraph shall not require any person to give his agreement to the exercise of any right conferred by any of paragraphs 9 to 12 below.

[4064]

NOTES

Sub-paras (1), (3): words in square brackets substituted by the Communications Act 2003, s 106(2), Sch 3, paras 1, 5(a), (b), (d), subject to transitional provisions in s 406(6) of, and Sch 18, paras 17, 64 to, that Act at **[3434]**, **[3460]**.

Sub-para (8): in para (a), words in first and third pairs of square brackets substituted by the Restricted Byways (Application and Consequential Amendment of Provisions) Regulations 2006, SI 2006/1177, reg 2, Schedule, Pt I; words "(which for this purpose shall be deemed to extend to Northern Ireland)" repealed, in relation to Scotland only, by the Roads (Scotland) Act 1984, s 156(1), Sch 9, para 92(4)(e), and substituted by the words in fifth (inner) pair of square brackets by the Street Works (Northern Ireland) Order 1995, SI 1995/3210, art 60(1), Sch 3, para 9(b); words in other pairs of square brackets substituted by the New Roads and Street Works Act 1991, s 168(1), Sch 8, Part IV, para 114.

Agreement required for obstructing access etc

3.—(1) A right conferred in accordance with paragraph 2 above or by paragraph 9, 10 or 11 below to execute any works on any land, to keep [electronic communications apparatus] installed on, under or over any land or to enter any land shall not be exercisable so as to interfere with or obstruct any means of entering or leaving any other land unless the occupier for the time being of the other land conferred, or is otherwise bound by, a right to interfere with or obstruct that means of entering or leaving the other land.

(2) The agreement in writing of the occupier for the time being of the other land shall be required for conferring any right for the purposes of sub-paragraph (1) above on the operator.

(3) The references in sub-paragraph (1) above to a means of entering or leaving any land include references to any means of entering or leaving the land provided for use in emergencies.

(4) Sub-paragraphs (2) to (7) of paragraph 2 above except sub-paragraph (3) shall apply (subject to the following provisions of this code) in relation to a right falling within sub-paragraph (1) above as they apply in relation to a right falling within paragraph 2(1)above.

(5) Nothing in this paragraph shall require the person who is the occupier of, or owns any interest in, any land which is a street or to which paragraph 11 below applies to agree to the exercise of any right on any other land.

[4065]

NOTES

Sub-para (1): words in square brackets substituted by the Communications Act 2003, s 106(2), Sch 3, paras 1, 5(a), subject to transitional provisions in s 406(6) of, and Sch 18, paras 17, 64 to, that Act at **[3434]**, **[3460]**.

Sub-para (5): for the word "street" there is substituted the word "road", in relation to Scotland only, by the Roads (Scotland) Act 1984, s 156(1), Sch 9, para 92(4)(f).

Effect of rights and compensation

4.—(1) Anything done by the operator in exercise of a right conferred in relation to any land in accordance with paragraph 2 or 3 above shall be deemed to be done in exercise of a statutory power except as against—

(a) a person who, being the owner of the freehold estate in that land or a lessee of the land, is not for the time being bound by the right; or
(b) a person having the benefit of any covenant or agreement which has been entered into as respects the land under any enactment and which, by virtue of that enactment, binds or will bind persons deriving title or otherwise claiming under the covenantor or, as the case may be, a person who was a party to the agreement.

(2) Where a right has been conferred in relation to any land in accordance with paragraph 2 or 3 above and anything has been done in exercise of that right, any person who, being the occupier of the land, the owner of the freehold estate in the land or a lessee of the

land, is not for the time being bound by the right shall have the right to require the operator to restore the land to its condition before that thing was done.

(3) Any duty imposed by virtue of sub-paragraph (2) above shall, to the extent that its performance involves the removal of any [electronic communications apparatus] from any land, be enforceable only in accordance with paragraph 21 below.

(4) Where—

(a) on a right in relation to any land being conferred or varied in accordance with paragraph 2 above, there is a depreciation in the value of any relevant interest in the land, and

(b) that depreciation is attributable to the fact that paragraph 21 below will apply to the removal from the land, when the owner for the time being of that interest becomes the occupier of the land, of any [electronic communications apparatus] installed in pursuance of that right,

the operator shall pay compensation to the person who, at the time the right is conferred or, as the case may be, varied, is the owner of that relevant interest; and the amount of that compensation shall be equal (subject to sub-paragraph (9) below) to the amount of the depreciation.

(5) In sub-paragraph (4) above "relevant interest", in relation to land subject to a right conferred or varied in accordance with paragraph 2 above, means any interest in respect of which the following two conditions are satisfied at the time the right is conferred or varied, namely—

(a) the owner of the interest is not the occupier of the land but may become the occupier of the land by virtue of that interest; and

(b) the owner of the interest becomes bound by the right or variation by virtue only of paragraph 2(3) above.

(6) Any question as to a person's entitlement to compensation under sub-paragraph (4) above, or as to the amount of any compensation under that sub-paragraph, shall, in default of agreement, be referred to and determined by the Lands Tribunal; and sections 2 and 4 of the Land Compensation Act 1961 (procedure and costs before Lands Tribunal) shall apply, with the necessary modifications, in relation to any such determination.

(7) A claim to compensation under sub-paragraph (4) above shall be made by giving the operator notice of the claim and specifying in that notice particulars of—

(a) the land in respect of which the claim is made;

(b) the claimant's interest in the land and, so far as known to the claimant, any other interests in the land;

(c) the right or variation in respect of which the claim is made; and

(d) the amount of the compensation claimed;

and such a claim shall be capable of being made at any time before the claimant becomes the occupier of the land in question, or at any time in the period of three years beginning with that time.

(8) For the purposes of assessing any compensation under sub-paragraph (4) above, rules (2) to (4) set out in section 5 of the Land Compensation Act 1961 shall, subject to any necessary modifications, have effect as they have effect for the purposes of assessing compensation for the compulsory acquisition of any interest in land.

(9) Without prejudice to the powers of the Lands Tribunal in respect of the costs of any proceedings before the Tribunal by virtue of this paragraph, where compensation is payable under sub-paragraph (4) above there shall also be payable, by the operator to the claimant, any reasonable valuation or legal expenses incurred by the claimant for the purposes of the preparation and prosecution of his claim for that compensation.

(10) Subsections (1) to (3) of section 10 of the Land Compensation Act 1973 (compensation in respect of mortgages, [trusts of land] and settled land) shall apply in relation to compensation under sub-paragraph (4) above as they apply in relation to compensation under Part I of that Act.

(11) In the application of this paragraph to Scotland—

(a) for any reference to the Lands Tribunal there is substituted a reference to the Lands Tribunal for Scotland and for any reference to costs there is substituted a reference to expenses;

(b) for the reference in sub-paragraph (6) above to sections 2 and 4 of the Land Compensation Act 1961 there is substituted a reference to sections 9 and 11 of the Land Compensation (Scotland) Act 1963;

(c) for the reference in sub-paragraph (8) above to section 5 of the Land Compensation Act 1961 there is substituted a reference to section 12 of the Land Compensation (Scotland) Act 1963;

(d) for the reference in sub-paragraph (10) above to subsections (1) to (3) of section 10 of the Land Compensation Act 1973 there is substituted a reference to subsections (1) and (2) of section 10 of the Land Compensation (Scotland) Act 1973.

(12) In the application of this paragraph to Northern Ireland—

(a) for any reference to the Lands Tribunal there is substituted a reference to the Lands Tribunal for Northern Ireland;

(b) for the references in sub-paragraphs (6) and (8) above to sections 2, 4 and 5 of the Land Compensation Act 1961 there are substituted references to Articles 4, 5 and 6 of the Land Compensation (Northern Ireland) Order 1982, respectively;

(c) for the references in sub-paragraph (10) above to subsections (1) to (3) of section 10 of the Land Compensation Act 1973 and to Part I of that Act there are substituted references to paragraphs (1) to (3) of Article 13 of the Land Acquisition and Compensation (Northern Ireland) Order 1973 and to Part II of that Order, respectively.

[4066]

NOTES

Sub-paras (3), (4): words in square brackets substituted by the Communications Act 2003, s 106(2), Sch 3, paras 1, 5(a), subject to transitional provisions in s 406(6) of, and Sch 18, paras 17, 64 to, that Act at **[3434]**, **[3460]**.

Sub-para (10): words in square brackets substituted by the Trusts of Land and Appointment of Trustees Act 1996, s 25(1), Sch 3, para 22.

Power to dispense with the need for required agreement

5.—(1) Where the operator requires any person to agree for the purposes of paragraph 2 or 3 above that any right should be conferred on the operator, or that any right should bind that person or any interest in land, the operator may give a notice to that person of the right and of the agreement that he requires.

(2) Where the period of 28 days beginning with the giving of a notice under sub-paragraph (1) above has expired without the giving of the required agreement, the operator may apply to the court for an order conferring the proposed right, or providing for it to bind any person or any interest in land, and (in either case) dispensing with the need for the agreement of the person to whom the notice was given.

(3) The court shall make an order under this paragraph if, but only if, it is satisfied that any prejudice caused by the order—

(a) is capable of being adequately compensated for by money; or

(b) is outweighed by the benefit accruing from the order to the persons whose access to [an electronic communications network or to electronic communications services] will be secured by the order;

and in determining the extent of the prejudice, and the weight of that benefit, the court shall have regard to all the circumstances and to the principle that no person should unreasonably be denied access to [an electronic communications network or to electronic communications services].

(4) An order under this paragraph made in respect of a proposed right may, in conferring that right or providing for it to bind any person or any interest in land and in dispensing with the need for any person's agreement, direct that the right shall have effect with such modifications, be exercisable on such terms and be subject to such conditions as may be specified in the order.

(5) The terms and conditions specified by virtue of sub-paragraph (4) above in an order under this paragraph, shall include such terms and conditions as appear to the court appropriate for ensuring that the least possible loss and damage is caused by the exercise of the right in respect of which the order is made to persons who occupy, own interests in or are from time to time on the land in question.

(6) For the purposes of proceedings under this paragraph in a county court in England and Wales or Northern Ireland, section 63(1) of the County Courts Act 1984 and Article 33(1)

of the County Courts (Northern Ireland) Order 1980 (assessors) shall have effect as if the words "on the application of any party" were omitted; and where an assessor is summoned, or, in Northern Ireland, appointed, by virtue of this sub-paragraph—

(a) he may, if so directed by the judge, inspect the land to which the proceedings relate without the judge and report on the land to the judge in writing; and

(b) the judge may take the report into account in determining whether to make an order under this paragraph and what order to make.

...

(7) Where an order under this paragraph, for the purpose of conferring any right or making provision for a right to bind any person or any interest in land, dispenses with the need for the agreement of any person, the order shall have the same effect and incidents as the agreement of the person the need for whose agreement is dispensed with and accordingly (without prejudice to the foregoing) shall be capable of variation or release by a subsequent agreement.

[4067]

NOTES

Sub-para (3): words in square brackets substituted by the Communications Act 2003, s 106(2), Sch 3, paras 1, 5(c), subject to transitional provisions in s 406(6) of, and Sch 18, paras 17, 64 to, that Act at **[3434]**, **[3460]**.

Sub-para (6): words omitted spent.

Acquisition of rights in respect of apparatus already installed

6.—(1) The following provisions of this paragraph apply where the operator gives notice under paragraph 5(1) above to any person and—

(a) that notice requires that person's agreement in respect of a right which is to be exercisable (in whole or in part) in relation to [electronic communications apparatus] already kept installed on, under or over the land in question, and

(b) that person is entitled to require the removal of that apparatus but, by virtue of paragraph 21 below, is not entitled to enforce its removal.

(2) The court may, on the application of the operator, confer on the operator such temporary rights as appear to the court reasonably necessary for securing that, pending the determination of any proceedings under paragraph 5 above or paragraph 21 below, the service provided by the operator's [network] is maintained and the apparatus properly adjusted and kept in repair.

(3) In any case where it is shown that a person with an interest in the land was entitled to require the removal of the apparatus immediately after it was installed, the court shall, in determining for the purposes of paragraph 5 above whether the apparatus should continue to be kept installed on, under or over the land, disregard the fact that the apparatus has already been installed there.

[4068]

NOTES

Sub-paras (1), (2): words in square brackets substituted by the Communications Act 2003, s 106(2), Sch 3, paras 1, 5(a), (d), subject to transitional provisions in s 406(6) of, and Sch 18, paras 17, 64 to, that Act at **[3434]**, **[3460]**.

Court to fix financial terms where agreement dispensed with

7.—(1) The terms and conditions specified by virtue of sub-paragraph (4) of paragraph 5 above in an order under that paragraph dispensing with the need for a person's agreement, shall include—

(a) such terms with respect to the payment of consideration in respect of the giving of the agreement, or the exercise of the rights to which the order relates, as it appears to the court would have been fair and reasonable if the agreement had been given willingly and subject to the other provisions of the order; and

(b) such terms as appear to the court appropriate for ensuring that that person and persons from time to time bound by virtue of paragraph 2(4) above by the rights to which the order relates are adequately compensated (whether by the payment of such consideration or otherwise) for any loss or damage sustained by them in consequence of the exercise of those rights.

(2) In determining what terms should be specified in an order under paragraph 5 above for requiring an amount to be paid to any person in respect of—

(a) the provisions of that order conferring any right or providing for any right to bind any person or any interest in land, or

(b) the exercise of any right to which the order relates,

the court shall take into account the prejudicial effect (if any) of the order or, as the case may be, of the exercise of the right on that person's enjoyment of, or on any interest of his in, land other than the land in relation to which the right is conferred.

(3) In determining what terms should be specified in an order under paragraph 5 above for requiring an amount to be paid to any person, the court shall, in a case where the order is made in consequence of an application made in connection with proceedings under paragraph 21 below, take into account, to such extent as it thinks fit, any period during which that person—

(a) was entitled to require the removal of any [electronic communications apparatus] from the land in question, but

(b) by virtue of paragraph 21 below, was not entitled to enforce its removal;

but where the court takes any such period into account, it may also take into account any compensation paid under paragraph 4(4) above.

(4) The terms specified by virtue of sub-paragraph (1) above in an order under paragraph 5 above may provide—

(a) for the making of payments from time to time to such persons as may be determined under those terms; and

(b) for questions arising in consequence of those terms (whether as to the amount of any loss or damage caused by the exercise of a right or otherwise) to be referred to arbitration or to be determined in such other manner as may be specified in the order.

(5) The court may, if it thinks fit—

(a) where the amount of any sum required to be paid by virtue of terms specified in an order under paragraph 5 above has been determined, require the whole or any part of any such sum to be paid into court;

(b) pending the determination of the amount of any such sum, order the payment into court of such amount on account as the court thinks fit.

(6) Where terms specified in an order under paragraph 5 above require the payment of any sum to a person who cannot be found or ascertained, that sum shall be paid into court.

[4069]

NOTES

Sub-para (3): words in square brackets substituted by the Communications Act 2003, s 106(2), Sch 3, paras 1, 5(a), subject to transitional provisions in s 406(6) of, and Sch 18, paras 17, 64 to, that Act at **[3434]**, **[3460]**.

Notices and applications by potential subscribers

8.—(1) Where—

(a) it is reasonably necessary for the agreement of any person to the conferring of any right, or to any right's binding any person or any interest in land, to be obtained by the operator before another person ("the potential subscriber") may be afforded access to the operator's [network], and

(b) the operator has not given a notice or (if he has given a notice) has not made an application in respect of that right under paragraph 5 above,

the potential subscriber may at any time give a notice to the operator requiring him to give a notice or make an application under paragraph 5 above in respect of that right.

(2) At any time after notice has been given to the operator under sub-paragraph (1) above, the operator may apply to the court to have the notice set aside on the ground that the conditions mentioned in that sub-paragraph are not satisfied on the ground that, even if the agreement were obtained, the operator would not afford the potential subscriber access to the operator's [network] and could not be required to afford him access to that [network].

(3) Subject to any order of the court made in or pending any proceedings under sub-paragraph (2) above, if at any time after the expiration of the period of 28 days beginning with the giving to the operator of a notice under sub-paragraph (1) above the operator has not complied with the notice, the potential subscriber may himself, on the operator's behalf, give the required notice and (if necessary) make an application under paragraph 5 above or, as the case may be, make the required application.

(4) The court may, on an application made by virtue of sub-paragraph (3) above, give such directions as it thinks fit—

(a) with respect to the separate participation of the operator in the proceedings to which the application gives rise, and

(b) requiring the operator to provide information to the court.

(5) A covenant, condition or agreement which would have the effect of preventing or restricting the taking by any person as a potential subscriber of any step under this paragraph shall be void to the extent that it would have that effect.

(6) Nothing in this paragraph shall be construed as requiring the operator to reimburse the potential subscriber for any costs incurred by the potential subscriber in or in connection with the taking of any step under this paragraph on the operator's behalf.

[4070]

NOTES

Sub-paras (1), (2): words in square brackets substituted by the Communications Act 2003, s 106(2), Sch 3, paras 1, 5(d), subject to transitional provisions in s 406(6) of, and Sch 18, paras 17, 64 to, that Act at **[3434]**, **[3460]**.

Street works

9.—(1) The operator shall, for the statutory purposes, have the right to do any of the following things, that is to say—

(a) install [electronic communications apparatus], or keep [electronic communications apparatus] installed, under, over, [in, on,] along or across [a street or, in Scotland, a road];

(b) inspect, maintain, adjust, repair or alter any [electronic communications apparatus] so installed; and

(c) execute any works requisite for or incidental to the purposes of any works falling within paragraph (a) or (b) above, including for those purposes the following kinds of works, that is to say—

(i) breaking up or opening [a street or, in Scotland, a road];

(ii) tunnelling or boring under [a street or, in Scotland, a road]; and

(iii) breaking up or opening a sewer, drain or tunnel;

…

(2) This paragraph has effect subject to … paragraph 3 above and the following provisions of this code, and the rights conferred by this paragraph shall not be exercisable [in a street which is not a maintainable highway or, in Scotland, a road which is not a public road] without either the agreement required by paragraph 2 above or an order of the court under paragraph 5 above dispensing with the need for that agreement.

(3) …

[4071]

NOTES

Sub-para (1): words in first and second pairs of square brackets in para (a), and words in square brackets in sub-para (b), substituted by the Communications Act 2003, s 106(2), Sch 3, paras 1, 5(a), subject to transitional provisions in s 406(6) of, and Sch 18, paras 17, 64 to, that Act at **[3434]**, **[3460]**; in para (a), words in third pair of square brackets inserted, words in fourth pair of square brackets substituted, words in square brackets in para (c) substituted, and words omitted repealed, by the New Roads and Street Works Act 1991, s 168(1), (2), Sch 8, Pt IV, para 115(2), Sch 9.

Sub-para (2): words omitted repealed by the Communications Act 2003, s 406(7), Sch 19, subject to transitional provisions in s 406(6) of, and Sch 18, paras 17, 64 to, that Act at **[3434]**, **[3460]**; words in square brackets substituted by the New Roads and Street Works Act 1991, s 168(1), (2), Sch 8, Pt IV, para 115(3).

Sub-para (3): repealed by the Street Works (Northern Ireland) Order 1995, SI 1995/3210, art 60(2), Sch 4.

Power to fly lines

10.—(1) Subject to paragraph 3 above and the following provisions of this code, where any [electronic communications apparatus] is kept installed on or over any land for the purposes of the operator's [network], the operator shall, for the statutory purposes, have the right to install and keep installed lines which—

(a) pass over other land adjacent to or in the vicinity of the land on or over which that apparatus is so kept;
(b) are connected to that apparatus; and
(c) are not at any point in the course of passing over the other land less than 3 metres above the ground or within 2 metres of any building over which they pass.

(2) Nothing in sub-paragraph (1) above shall authorise the installation or keeping on or over any land of—

(a) any [electronic communications apparatus] used to support, carry or suspend a line installed in pursuance of that sub-paragraph; or
(b) any line which by reason of its position interferes with the carrying on of any business … carried on on that land.

[(3) In this paragraph "business" includes a trade, profession or employment and includes any activity carried on by a body of persons (whether corporate or unincorporate).]
[4072]

NOTES

Sub-para (1): words in square brackets substituted by the Communications Act 2003, s 106(2), Sch 3, paras 1, 5(a), (d), subject to transitional provisions in s 406(6) of, and Sch 18, paras 17, 64 to, that Act at **[3434]**, **[3460]**.

Sub-para (2): words in square brackets substituted, and words omitted repealed, by the Communications Act 2003, ss 106(2), 406(7), Sch 3, paras 1, 5(a), Sch 19(1), subject to transitional provisions in s 406(6) of, and Sch 18, paras 17, 64 to, that Act at **[3434]**, **[3460]**.

Sub-para (3): added by the Communications Act 2003, s 106(2), Sch 3, paras 1, 6, subject to transitional provisions in s 406(6) of, and Sch 18, paras 17, 64 to, that Act at **[3434]**, **[3460]**.

Tidal waters etc

11.—(1) Subject to paragraph 3 above and the following provisions of this code, the operator shall have the right for the statutory purposes—

(a) to execute any works (including placing any buoy or seamark) on any tidal water or lands for or in connection with the installation, maintenance, adjustment, repair or alteration of [electronic communications apparatus];
(b) to keep [electronic communications apparatus] installed on, under or over tidal water or lands; and
(c) to enter any tidal water or lands to inspect any [electronic communications apparatus] so installed.

(2) A right conferred by this paragraph shall not be exercised in relation to any land in which a Crown interest, within the meaning of paragraph 26 below, subsists unless agreement to the exercise of the right in relation to that land has been given, in accordance with sub-paragraph (3) of that paragraph, in respect of that interest.

(3) Before executing any works in exercise of a right conferred by this paragraph the operator (not being the Secretary of State) shall submit a plan of the proposed works to the Secretary of State for the Secretary of State's approval.

(4) Sub-paragraph (3) above shall not apply to the execution of any emergency works, but as soon as practicable after commencing any emergency works on any tidal water or lands the operator (not being the Secretary of State) shall submit a plan of those works to the Secretary of State for the Secretary of State's approval.

(5) As soon as reasonably practicable after a plan is submitted to him under sub-paragraph (3) or (4) above the Secretary of State shall, after consulting such authorities exercising functions in relation to the tidal water or lands in question as it appears to him appropriate to consult, consider whether to approve it; and, if he does approve it, he may do so subject to such modifications and conditions and on such terms as he thinks fit.

(6) The Secretary of State shall not approve a plan submitted to him under sub-paragraph (3) or (4) above unless he is satisfied that adequate arrangements have been made

for compensating any persons appearing to him to be owners of interests in the tidal water or lands in question for any loss or damage sustained by those persons in consequence of the execution of the works to which the plan relates.

(7) If—

(a) the operator (not being the Secretary of State) executes any works in exercise of a right conferred by this paragraph, but

(b) those works are executed otherwise than in accordance with a plan approved by the Secretary of State (including, in the case of emergency works, where works already commenced are not approved) or a condition on which any approval of the Secretary of State is given is or has been contravened,

the Secretary of State may by notice require the operator to execute such remedial works as the Secretary of State thinks appropriate having regard to the terms and conditions of any approval that he has given and, if those works are not executed in accordance with the notice, may execute them himself at the operator's expense.

(8) Where, as the result—

(a) of the failure of the operator (not being the Secretary of State) reasonably to maintain any [electronic communications apparatus] kept installed for the purposes of the operator's [network] on, under or over any tidal water or lands, or

(b) of the abandonment by the operator of any such apparatus,

it appears to the Secretary of State that any remedial works should be executed, he may by notice require the operator to execute those works and, if those works are not executed in accordance with the notice, may execute them himself at the operator's expense.

(9) The Secretary of State shall have power for the purposes of exercising his functions (other than as the operator) under this paragraph, and of determining whether to exercise those functions, to cause a survey or examination to be carried out, at the operator's expense, of any works or apparatus or of the site or proposed site of any works or apparatus.

(10) Where the Secretary of State is authorised by this paragraph to do any thing at the operator's expense, the expenses incurred by the Secretary of State in or in connection with the doing of that thing shall be recoverable by the Secretary of State from the operator in any court of competent jurisdiction.

(11) In this paragraph—

"remedial works" includes any works of repair or restoration, the alteration of any apparatus and any works to restore the site of any apparatus to its original condition;

"tidal water or lands" includes any estuary or branch of the sea, the shore below mean high water springs and the bed of any tidal water.

[4073]

NOTES

Sub-paras (1), (8): words in square brackets substituted by the Communications Act 2003, s 106(2), Sch 3, paras 1, 5(a), (d), subject to transitional provisions in s 406(6) of, and Sch 18, paras 17, 64 to, that Act at **[3434]**, **[3460]**.

Linear obstacles

12.—(1) Subject to the following provisions of this code, the operator shall, for the statutory purposes, have the right in order to cross any relevant land with a line, to install and keep the line and other [electronic communications apparatus] on, under or over that land and—

(a) to execute any works on that land for or in connection with the installation, maintenance, adjustment, repair or alteration of that line or the other [electronic communications apparatus]; and

(b) to enter on that land to inspect the line or the other apparatus.

(2) A line installed in pursuance of any right conferred by this paragraph need not cross the relevant land in question by a direct route or by the shortest route from the point at which the line enters that land, but it shall not cross that land by any route which, in the horizontal plane, exceeds the said shortest route by more than 400 metres.

(3) [Electronic communications apparatus] shall not be installed in pursuance of any right conferred by this paragraph in any position on the relevant land in which it interferes with traffic on the railway, canal or tramway on that land.

(4) The operator shall not execute any works on any land in pursuance of any right conferred by this paragraph unless—

(a) he has given the person with control of the land 28 days' notice of his intention to do so; or

(b) the works are emergency works.

(5) A notice under sub-paragraph (4) above shall contain a plan and section of the proposed works or (in lieu of a plan and section) any description of the proposed works (whether or not in the form of a diagram) which the person with control of the land has agreed to accept for the purposes of this sub-paragraph.

(6) If, at any time before a notice under sub-paragraph (4) above expires, the person with control of the land gives the operator notice of objection to the works, the operator shall be entitled to execute the works only—

(a) if, within the period of 28 days beginning with the giving of the notice of objection, neither the operator nor that person has given notice to the other requiring him to agree to an arbitrator to whom the objection may be referred under paragraph 13 below; or

(b) in accordance with an award made on such a reference; or

(c) to the extent that the works have at any time become emergency works.

(7) If the operator exercises any power conferred by this paragraph to execute emergency works on any land, he shall, as soon as reasonably practicable after commencing those works, give the person with control of the land a notice identifying the works and containing—

(a) a statement of the reason why the works are emergency works; and

(b) either the matters which would be required to be contained in a notice under sub-paragraph (4) above with respect to those works or, as the case may require, a reference to an earlier notice under that sub-paragraph with respect to those works.

(8) If within the period of 28 days beginning with the giving of a notice under sub-paragraph (7) above the person to whom that notice was given gives a notice to the operator requiring him to pay compensation, the operator shall be liable to pay that person compensation in respect of loss or damage sustained in consequence of the carrying out of the emergency works in question; and any question as to the amount of that compensation shall, in default of agreement, be referred to arbitration under paragraph 13 below.

(9) If the operator commences the execution of any works in contravention of any provision of this paragraph, he shall be guilty of an offence and liable on summary conviction to a fine not exceeding level 3 on the standard scale.

(10) In this paragraph "relevant land" means land which is used wholly or mainly either as a railway, canal or tramway or in connection with a railway, canal or tramway on that land, and a reference to the person with control of any such land is a reference to the person carrying on the railway, canal or tramway undertaking in question.

[4074]

NOTES

Sub-paras (1), (3): words in square brackets substituted by the Communications Act 2003, s 106(2), Sch 3, paras 1, 5(a), subject to transitional provisions in s 406(6) of, and Sch 18, paras 17, 64 to, that Act at **[3434]**, **[3460]**.

Arbitration in relation to linear obstacles

13.—(1) Any objection or question which, in accordance with paragraph 12 above, is referred to arbitration under this paragraph shall be referred to the arbitration of a single arbitrator appointed by agreement between the parties concerned or, in default of agreement, by the President of the Institution of Civil Engineers.

(2) Where an objection under paragraph 12 above is referred to arbitration under this paragraph the arbitrator shall have the power—

(a) to require the operator to submit to the arbitrator a plan and section in such form as the arbitrator may think requisite for those purposes;

(b) to require the observations on any such plan or section of the person who objects to the works to be submitted to the arbitrator in such form as the arbitrator may think requisite for those purposes;

(c) to direct the operator or that person to furnish him with such information and to comply with such other requirements as the arbitrator may think requisite for those purposes;
(d) to make an award requiring modifications to the proposed works and specifying the terms on which and the conditions subject to which the works may be executed; and
(e) to award such sum as the arbitrator may determine in respect of one or both of the following matters, that is to say—
(i) compensation to the person who objects to the works in respect of loss or damage sustained by that person in consequence of the carrying out of the works, and
(ii) consideration payable to that person for the right to carry out the works.

(3) Where a question as to compensation in respect of emergency works is referred to arbitration under this paragraph, the arbitrator—
(a) shall have the power to direct the operator or the person who requires the payment of compensation to furnish him with such information and to comply with such other requirements as the arbitrator may think requisite for the purposes of the arbitration; and
(b) shall award to the person requiring the payment of compensation such sum (if any) as the arbitrator may determine in respect of the loss or damage sustained by that person in consequence of the carrying out of the emergency works in question.

(4) The arbitrator may treat compliance with any requirement made in pursuance of sub-paragraph (2)(a) to (c) or (3)(a) above as a condition of his making an award.

(5) In determining what award to make on a reference under this paragraph, the arbitrator shall have regard to all the circumstances and to the principle that no person should unreasonably be denied access to [an electronic communications network or to electronic communications services].

(6) For the purposes of the making of an award under this paragraph—
(a) the references in sub-paragraphs (2)(e) and (3)(b) above to loss shall, in relation to a person carrying on a railway, canal or tramway undertaking, include references to any increase in the expenses of carrying on that undertaking; and
(b) the consideration mentioned in sub-paragraph (2)(e) above shall be determined on the basis of what would have been fair and reasonable if the person who objects to the works had given his authority willingly for the works to be executed on the same terms and subject to the same conditions (if any) as are contained in the award.

(7) In the application of this paragraph to Scotland, the reference to an arbitrator shall have effect as a reference to an arbiter and the arbiter may and, if so directed by the Court of Session, shall state a case for the decision of that Court on any question of law arising in the arbitration.

(8) …

[4075]

NOTES

Sub-para (5): words in square brackets substituted by the Communications Act 2003, s 106(2), Sch 3, paras 1, 5(c), subject to transitional provisions in s 406(6) of, and Sch 18, paras 17, 64 to, that Act at **[3434]**, **[3460]**.

Sub-para (8): repealed by the Arbitration Act 1996, s 107(2), Sch 4.

Alteration of apparatus crossing a linear obstacle

14.—(1) Without prejudice to the following provisions of this code, the person with control of any relevant land may, on the ground that any [electronic communications apparatus] kept installed on, under or over that land for the purposes of the operator's [network] interferes, or is likely to interfere, with—
(a) the carrying on of the railway, canal or tramway undertaking carried on by that person, or
(b) anything done or to be done for the purposes of that undertaking,

give notice to the operator requiring him to alter that apparatus.

(2) The operator shall within a reasonable time and to the reasonable satisfaction of the person giving the notice comply with a notice under sub-paragraph (1) above unless before the expiration of the period of 28 days beginning with the giving of the notice he gives a counter-notice to the person with control of the land in question specifying the respects in which he is not prepared to comply with the original notice.

(3) Where a counter-notice has been given under sub-paragraph (2) above the operator shall not be required to comply with the original notice but the person with control of the relevant land may apply to the court for an order requiring the alteration of any [electronic communications apparatus] to which the notice relates.

(4) The court shall not make an order under this paragraph unless it is satisfied that the order is necessary on one of the grounds mentioned in sub-paragraph (1) above and in determining whether to make such an order the court shall also have regard to all the circumstances and to the principle that no person should unreasonably be denied access to [an electronic communications network or to electronic communications services].

(5) An order under this paragraph may take such form and be on such terms as the court thinks fit and may impose such conditions and may contain such directions to the operator or the person with control of the land in question as the court thinks necessary for resolving any difference between the operator and that person and for protecting their respective interests.

(6) In this paragraph references to relevant land and to the person with control of such land have the same meaning as in paragraph 12 above.

[4076]

NOTES

Sub-paras (1), (3), (4): words in square brackets substituted by the Communications Act 2003, s 106(2), Sch 3, paras 1, 5(a), (c), (d), subject to transitional provisions in s 406(6) of, and Sch 18, paras 17, 64 to, that Act at **[3434]**, **[3460]**.

Use of certain conduits

15.—(1) Nothing in the preceding provisions of this code shall authorise the doing of anything inside a relevant conduit without the agreement of the authority with control of that conduit.

(2) The agreement of the authority with control of a public sewer shall be sufficient in all cases to confer a right falling within any of the preceding provisions of this code where the right is to be exercised wholly inside that sewer.

(3) In this paragraph—

(a) "relevant conduit" and "public sewer" have the same meanings as in section 98 of this Act; and

(b) a reference to the authority with control of a relevant conduit shall be construed in accordance with subsections (7) and (8) of that section.

[4077]

Compensation for injurious affection to neighbouring land etc

16.—(1) Where a right conferred by or in accordance with any of the preceding provisions of this code is exercised, compensation shall be payable by the operator under section 10 of the Compulsory Purchase Act 1965 (compensation for injurious affection to neighbouring land etc) as if that section had effect in relation to injury caused by the exercise of such a right as it has effect in relation to injury caused by the execution of works on land that has been compulsorily purchased.

(2) Sub-paragraph (1) above shall not confer any entitlement to compensation on any person in respect of the exercise of a right conferred in accordance with paragraph 2 or 3 above, if that person conferred the right or is bound by it by virtue of paragraph 2(2)(b) or (d) above, but, save as aforesaid, the entitlement of any person to compensation under this paragraph shall be determined irrespective of his ownership of any interest in the land where the right is exercised.

(3) Compensation shall not be payable on any claim for compensation under this paragraph unless the amount of the compensation exceeds £50.

(4) In the application of this paragraph to Scotland—

(a) for any reference in sub-paragraph (1) to section 10 of the Compulsory Purchase Act 1965 there is substituted a reference to section 6 of the Railway Clauses Consolidation (Scotland) Act 1845.

(b) for the reference in that sub-paragraph to land that has been compulsorily purchased there is substituted a reference to land that has been taken or used for the purpose of a railway;

(c) any question as to a person's entitlement to compensation by virtue of that sub-paragraph, or as to the amount of that compensation, shall, in default of agreement, be determined by the Lands Tribunal for Scotland.

(5) In the application of this paragraph to Northern Ireland—

(a) for any reference in sub-paragraph (1) to section 10 of the Compulsory Purchase Act 1965 there is substituted a reference to Article 18 of the Land Compensation (Northern Ireland) Order 1982;

(b) any question as to a person's entitlement to compensation by virtue of sub-paragraph (1) above, or as to the amount of that compensation, shall, in default of agreement, be determined by the Lands Tribunal for Northern Ireland.

[4078]

Objections to overhead apparatus

17.—(1) This paragraph applies where the operator has completed the installation for the purposes of the operator's [network] of any [electronic communications apparatus] the whole or part of which is at a height of 3 metres or more above the ground.

(2) At any time before the expiration of the period of 3 months beginning with the completion of the installation of the apparatus a person who is the occupier of or owns an interest in—

(a) any land over or on which the apparatus has been installed, or

(b) any land the enjoyment of which, or any interest in which, is, because of the nearness of the land to the land on or over which the apparatus has been installed, capable of being prejudiced by the apparatus,

may give the operator notice of objection in respect of that apparatus.

(3) No notice of objection may be given in respect of any apparatus if the apparatus—

(a) replaces any [electronic communications apparatus] which is not substantially different from the new apparatus; and

(b) is not in a significantly different position.

(4) Where a person has both given a notice under this paragraph and applied for compensation under any of the preceding provisions of this code, the court—

(a) may give such directions as it thinks fit for ensuring that no compensation is paid until any proceedings under this paragraph have been disposed of, and

(b) if the court makes an order under this paragraph, may provide in that order for some or all of the compensation otherwise payable under this code to that person not to be so payable, or, if the case so requires, for some or all of any compensation paid under this code to that person to be repaid to the operator.

(5) At any time after the expiration of the period of 2 months beginning with the giving of a notice of objection but before the expiration of the period of 4 months beginning with the giving of that notice, the person who gave the notice may apply to the court to have the objection upheld.

(6) Subject to sub-paragraph (7) below, the court shall uphold the objection if the apparatus appears materially to prejudice the applicant's enjoyment of, or interest in, the land in right of which the objection is made and the court is not satisfied that the only possible alterations of the apparatus will—

(a) substantially increase the cost or diminish the quality of the service provided by the operator's [network] to persons who have, or may in future have, access to it, or

(b) involve the operator in substantial additional expenditure (disregarding any expenditure occasioned solely by the fact that any proposed alteration was not adopted originally or, as the case may be, that the apparatus has been unnecessarily installed), or

(c) give to any person a case at least as good as the applicant has to have an objection under this paragraph upheld.

PART VI TELECOMMUNICATIONS

(7) The court shall not uphold the objection if the applicant is bound by a right of the operator falling within paragraph 2 or 3(1) above to install the apparatus and it appears to the court unreasonable, having regard to the fact that the applicant is so bound and the circumstances in which he became so bound, for the applicant to have given notice of objection.

(8) In considering the matters specified in sub-paragraph (6) above the court shall have regard to all the circumstances and to the principle that no person should unreasonably be denied access to [an electronic communications network or to electronic communications services].

(9) If it upholds an objection under this paragraph the court may by order—

(a) direct the alteration of the apparatus to which the objection relates;

(b) authorise the installation (instead of the apparatus to which the objection relates), in a manner and position specified in the order, of any apparatus so specified;

(c) direct that no objection may be made under this paragraph in respect of any apparatus the installation of which is authorised by the court.

(10) The court shall not make any order under this paragraph directing the alteration of any apparatus or authorising the installation of any apparatus unless it is satisfied either—

(a) that the operator has all such rights as it appears to the court appropriate that he should have for the purpose of making the alteration or, as the case may be, installing the apparatus, or

(b) that—

(i) he would have all those rights if the court, on an application under paragraph 5 above, dispensed with the need for the agreement of any person, and

(ii) it would be appropriate for the court, on such an application, to dispense with the need for that agreement;

and, accordingly, for the purposes of dispensing with the need for the agreement of any person to the alteration or installation of any apparatus, the court shall have the same powers as it would have if an application had been duly made under paragraph 5 above for an order dispensing with the need for that person's agreement.

(11) For the purposes of sub-paragraphs (6)(c) and (10) above, the court shall have power on an application under this paragraph to give the applicant directions for bringing the application to the notice of such other interested persons as it thinks fit.

[4079]

NOTES

Sub-paras (1), (3), (6), (8): words in square brackets substituted by the Communications Act 2003, s 106(2), Sch 3, paras 1, 5(a), (c), (d), subject to transitional provisions in s 406(6) of, and Sch 18, paras 17, 64 to, that Act at **[3434]**, **[3460]**.

Obligation to affix notices to overhead apparatus

18.—(1) Where the operator has for the purposes of the operator's [network] installed any [electronic communications apparatus] the whole or part of which is at a height of 3 metres or more above the ground, the operator shall, before the expiration of the period of 3 days beginning with the completion of the installation, in a secure and durable manner affix a notice—

(a) to every major item of apparatus installed; or

(b) if no major item of apparatus is installed, to the nearest major item of [electronic communications apparatus] to which the apparatus that is installed is directly or indirectly connected.

(2) A notice affixed under sub-paragraph (1) above shall be affixed in a position where it is reasonably legible and shall give the name of the operator and an address in the United Kingdom at which any notice of objection may be given under paragraph 17 above in respect of the apparatus in question; and any person giving such a notice at that address in respect of that apparatus shall be deemed to have been furnished with that address for the purposes of [paragraph 24(2A)(a)] below.

(3) If the operator contravenes the requirements of this paragraph he shall be guilty of an offence and liable on summary conviction to a fine not exceeding level 2 on the standard scale.

(4) In any proceedings for an offence under this paragraph it shall be a defence for the person charged to prove that he took all reasonable steps and exercised all due diligence to avoid committing the offence.

[4080]

NOTES

Sub-paras (1), (2): words in square brackets substituted by the Communications Act 2003, ss 106(2), 406(1), Sch 3, paras 1, 5(a), (d), Sch 17, para 75, subject to transitional provisions in s 406(6) of, and Sch 18, paras 17, 64 to, that Act at **[3434]**, **[3460]**.

Tree lopping

19.—(1) Where any tree overhangs any street and, in doing so, either—

(a) obstructs or interferes with the working of any [electronic communications apparatus] used for the purposes of the operator's [network], or

(b) will obstruct or interfere with the working of any [electronic communications apparatus] which is about to be installed for those purposes,

the operator may by notice to the occupier of the land on which the tree is growing require the tree to be lopped so as to prevent the obstruction or interference.

(2) If within the period of 28 days beginning with the giving of the notice by the operator, the occupier of the land on which the tree is growing gives the operator a counter-notice objecting to the lopping of the tree, the notice shall have effect only if confirmed by an order of the court.

(3) If at any time a notice under sub-paragraph (1) above has not been complied with and either—

(a) a period of 28 days beginning with the giving of the notice has expired without a counter-notice having been given, or

(b) an order of the court confirming the notice has come into force,

the operator may himself cause the tree to be lopped as mentioned in sub-paragraph (1) above.

(4) Where the operator lops a tree in exercise of the power conferred by sub-paragraph (3) above he shall do so in a husband-like manner and in such a way as to cause the minimum damage to the tree.

(5) Where—

(a) a notice under sub-paragraph (1) above is complied with either without a counter-notice having been given or after the notice has been confirmed, or

(b) the operator exercises the power conferred by sub-paragraph (3) above,

the court shall, on an application made by a person who has sustained loss or damage in consequence of the lopping of the tree or who has incurred expenses in complying with the notice, order the operator to pay that person such compensation in respect of the loss, damage or expenses as it thinks fit.

[4081]

NOTES

Sub-para (1): for the word "street" there is substituted the word "road", in relation to Scotland only, by the Roads (Scotland) Act 1984, s 156(1), Sch 9, para 92(4)(j); words in square brackets substituted by the Communications Act 2003, s 106(2), Sch 3, paras 1, 5(a), (d), subject to transitional provisions in s 406(6) of, and Sch 18, paras 17, 64 to, that Act at **[3434]**, **[3460]**.

Power to require alteration of apparatus

20.—(1) Where any [electronic communications apparatus] is kept installed on, under or over any land for the purposes of the operator's [network], any person with an interest in that land or adjacent land may (notwithstanding the terms of any agreement binding that person) by notice given to the operator require the alteration of the apparatus on the ground that the alteration is necessary to enable that person to carry out a proposed improvement of the land in which he has an interest.

(2) Where a notice is given under sub-paragraph (1) above by any person to the operator, the operator shall comply with it unless he gives a counter-notice under this subparagraph within the period of 28 days beginning with the giving of the notice.

(3) Where a counter-notice is given under sub-paragraph (2) above to any person, the operator shall make the required alteration only if the court on an application by that person makes an order requiring the alteration to be made.

(4) The court shall make an order under this paragraph for an alteration to be made only if, having regard to all the circumstances and the principle that no person should unreasonably be denied access to [an electronic communications network or to electronic communications services], it is satisfied—

(a) that the alteration is necessary as mentioned in sub-paragraph (1) above; and
(b) that the alteration will not substantially interfere with any service [which is or is likely to be provided using] the operator's [network].

(5) The court shall not make an order under this paragraph for the alteration of any apparatus unless it is satisfied either—

(a) that the operator has all such rights as it appears to the court appropriate that he should have for the purpose of making the alteration, or
(b) that—
    (i) he would have all those rights if the court, on an application under paragraph 5 above, dispensed with the need for the agreement of any person, and
    (ii) it would be appropriate for the court, on such an application, to dispense with the need for that agreement;

and, accordingly, for the purposes of dispensing with the need for the agreement of any person to the alteration of any apparatus, the court shall have the same powers as it would have if an application had been duly made under paragraph 5 above for an order dispensing with the need for that person's agreement.

(6) For the purposes of sub-paragraph (5) above, the court shall have power on an application under this paragraph to give the applicant directions for bringing the application to the notice of such other interested persons as it thinks fit.

(7) An order under this paragraph may provide for the alteration to be carried out with such modifications, on such terms and subject to such conditions as the court thinks fit, but the court shall not include any such modifications, terms or conditions in its order without the consent of the applicant, and if such consent is not given may refuse to make an order under this paragraph.

(8) An order made under this paragraph on the application of any person shall, unless the court otherwise thinks fit, require that person to reimburse the operator in respect of any expenses which the operator incurs in or in connection with the execution of any works in compliance with the order.

(9) In sub-paragraph (1) above "improvement" includes development and change of use.
[4082]

NOTES

Sub-paras (1), (4): words in square brackets substituted by the Communications Act 2003, s 106(2), Sch 3, paras 1, 5(a), (c), (d), 7, subject to transitional provisions in s 406(6) of, and Sch 18, paras 17, 64 to, that Act at **[3434]**, **[3460]**.

Restriction on right to require the removal of apparatus

21.—(1) Where any person is for the time being entitled to require the removal of any of the operator's [electronic communications apparatus] from any land (whether under any enactment or because that apparatus is kept on, under or over that land otherwise than in pursuance of a right binding that person or for any other reason) that person shall not be entitled to enforce the removal of the apparatus except, subject to sub-paragraph (12) below, in accordance with the following provisions of this paragraph.

(2) The person entitled to require the removal of any of the operator's [electronic communications apparatus] shall give a notice to the operator requiring the removal of the apparatus.

(3) Where a person gives a notice under sub-paragraph (2) above and the operator does not give that person a counter-notice within the period of 28 days beginning with the giving of the notice, that person shall be entitled to enforce the removal of the apparatus.

(4) A counter-notice given under sub-paragraph (3) above to any person by the operator shall do one or both of the following, that is to say—

(a) state that that person is not entitled to require the removal of the apparatus;

(b) specify the steps which the operator proposes to take for the purpose of securing a right as against that person to keep the apparatus on the land.

(5) Those steps may include any steps which the operator could take for the purpose of enabling him, if the apparatus is removed, to re-install the apparatus; and the fact that by reason of the following provisions of this paragraph any proposed re-installation is only hypothetical shall not prevent the operator from taking those steps or any court or person from exercising any function in consequence of those steps having been taken.

(6) Where a counter-notice is given under sub-paragraph (3) above to any person, that person may only enforce the removal of the apparatus in pursuance of an order of the court; and, where the counter-notice specifies steps which the operator is proposing to take to secure a right to keep the apparatus on the land, the court shall not make such an order unless it is satisfied—

(a) that the operator is not intending to take those steps or is being unreasonably dilatory in the taking of those steps; or

(b) that the taking of those steps has not secured, or will not secure, for the operator as against that person any right to keep the apparatus installed on, under or over the land or, as the case may be, to re-install it if it is removed.

(7) Where any person is entitled to enforce the removal of any apparatus under this paragraph (whether by virtue of sub-paragraph (3) above or an order of the court under sub-paragraph (6) above), that person may, without prejudice to any method available to him apart from this sub-paragraph for enforcing the removal of that apparatus, apply to the court for authority to remove it himself; and, on such an application, the court may, if it thinks fit, give that authority.

(8) Where any apparatus is removed by any person under an authority given by the court under sub-paragraph (7) above, any expenses incurred by him in or in connection with the removal of the apparatus shall be recoverable by him from the operator in any court of competent jurisdiction; and in so giving an authority to any person the court may also authorise him, in accordance with the directions of the court, to sell any apparatus removed under the authority and to retain the whole or a part of the proceeds of sale on account of those expenses.

(9) Any [electronic communications apparatus] kept installed on, under or over any land shall (except for the purposes of this paragraph and without prejudice to paragraphs 6(3) and 7(3) above) be deemed, as against any person who was at any time entitled to require the removal of the apparatus, but by virtue of this paragraph not entitled to enforce its removal, to have been lawfully so kept at that time.

(10) Where this paragraph applies (whether in pursuance of an enactment amended by Schedule 4 to this Act or otherwise) in relation to [electronic communications apparatus] the alteration of which some person ("the relevant person") is entitled to require in consequence of the stopping up, closure, change or diversion of any street or the extinguishment or alteration of any public right of way—

(a) the removal of the apparatus shall constitute compliance with a requirement to make any other alteration;

(b) a counter-notice under sub-paragraph (3) above may state (in addition to, or instead of, any of the matters mentioned in sub-paragraph (4) above) that the operator requires the relevant person to reimburse him in respect of any expenses which he incurs in or in connection with the making of any alteration in compliance with the requirements of the relevant person;

(c) an order made under this paragraph on an application by the relevant person in respect of a counter-notice containing such a statement shall, unless the court otherwise thinks fit, require the relevant person to reimburse the operator in respect of any expenses which he so incurs; and

(d) sub-paragraph (8) above shall not apply.

(11) References in this paragraph to the operator's [electronic communications apparatus] include references to [electronic communications apparatus] which (whether or not vested in the operator) is being, is to be or has been used for the purposes of the operator's [network].

(12) A person shall not, under this paragraph, be entitled to enforce the removal of any apparatus on the ground only that he is entitled to give a notice under paragraph 11, 14, 17 or

PART VI TELECOMMUNICATIONS

20 above; and this paragraph is without prejudice to paragraph 23 below and to the power to enforce an order of the court under the said paragraph 11, 14, 17 or 20.

[4083]

NOTES

Sub-paras (1), (2), (9)–(11): words in square brackets substituted by the Communications Act 2003, s 106(2), Sch 3, paras 1, 5(a), (d), subject to transitional provisions in s 406(6) of, and Sch 18, paras 17, 64 to, that Act at **[3434]**, **[3460]**.

Sub-para (10): for the word "street" there is substituted the word "road", in relation to Scotland only, by the Roads (Scotland) Act 1984, s 156(1), Sch 9, para 92(4)(k).

Abandonment of apparatus

22. Without prejudice to the preceding provisions of this code, where the operator has a right conferred by or in accordance with this code for the statutory purposes to keep [electronic communications apparatus] installed on, under or over any land, he is not entitled to keep that apparatus so installed if, at a time when the apparatus is not, or is no longer, used for the purposes of the operator's [network], there is no reasonable likelihood that it will be so used.

[4084]

NOTES

Words in square brackets substituted by the Communications Act 2003, s 106(2), Sch 3, paras 1, 5(a), (d), subject to transitional provisions in s 406(6) of, and Sch 18, paras 17, 64 to, that Act at **[3434]**, **[3460]**.

Undertaker's works

23.—(1) The following provisions of this paragraph apply where a relevant undertaker is proposing to execute any undertaker's works which involve or are likely to involve a temporary or permanent alteration of any [electronic communications apparatus] kept installed on, under or over any land for the purposes of the operator's [network].

(2) The relevant undertaker shall, not less than 10 days before the works are commenced, give the operator a notice specifying the nature of the undertaker's works, the alteration or likely alteration involved and the time and place at which the works will be commenced.

(3) Sub-paragraph (2) above shall not apply in relation to any emergency works of which the relevant undertaker gives the operator notice as soon as practicable after commencing the works.

(4) Where a notice has been given under sub-paragraph (2) above by a relevant undertaker to the operator, the operator may within the period of 10 days beginning with the giving of the notice give the relevant undertaker a counter-notice which may state either—

(a) that the operator intends himself to make any alteration made necessary or expedient by the proposed undertaker's works; or

(b) that he requires the undertaker in making any such alteration to do so under the supervision and to the satisfaction of the operator.

(5) Where a counter-notice given under sub-paragraph (4) above states that the operator intends himself to make any alteration—

(a) the operator shall (subject to sub-paragraph (7) below) have the right, instead of the relevant undertaker, to execute any works for the purpose of making that alteration; and

(b) any expenses incurred by the operator in or in connection with the execution of those works and the amount of any loss or damage sustained by the operator in consequence of the alteration shall be recoverable by the operator from the undertaker in any court of competent jurisdiction.

(6) Where a counter-notice given under sub-paragraph (4) above states that any alteration is to be made under the supervision and to the satisfaction of the operator—

(a) the relevant undertaker shall not make the alteration except as required by the notice or under sub-paragraph (7) below; and

(b) any expenses incurred by the operator in or in connection with the provision of that supervision and the amount of any loss or damage sustained by the operator in consequence of the alteration shall be recoverable by the operator from the undertaker in any court of competent jurisdiction.

(7) Where—

(a) no counter-notice is given under sub-paragraph (4) above, or

(b) the operator, having given a counter-notice falling within that sub-paragraph, fails within a reasonable time to make any alteration made necessary or expedient by the proposed undertaker's works or, as the case may be, unreasonably fails to provide the required supervision,

the relevant undertaker may himself execute works for the purpose of making the alteration or, as the case may be, may execute such works without the supervision of the operator; but in either case the undertaker shall execute the works to the satisfaction of the operator.

(8) If the relevant undertaker or any of his agents—

(a) executes any works without the notice required by sub-paragraph (2) above having been given, or

(b) unreasonably fails to comply with any reasonable requirement of the operator under this paragraph,

he shall, subject to sub-paragraph (9) below, be guilty of an offence and liable on summary conviction to a fine which—

(i) if the service provided by the operator's [network] is interrupted by the works or failure, shall not exceed level 4 on the standard scale; and

(ii) if that service is not so interrupted, shall not exceed level 3 on the standard scale.

(9) Sub-paragraph (8) above does not apply to a Northern Ireland department.

(10) In this paragraph—

"relevant undertaker" means—

(a) any person (including a local authority) authorised by any Act (whether public general or local) or by any order or scheme made under or confirmed by any Act to carry on—

(i) any railway, tramway, road transport, water transport, canal, inland navigation, dock, harbour, pier or lighthouse undertaking; [or]

(ii), (iii) . . .

(b) any person (apart from the operator) to whom this code is applied [by a direction under section 106 of the Communications Act 2003]; and

(c) any person to whom this paragraph is applied by any Act amended by or under or passed after this Act;

"undertaker's works" means—

(a) in relation to a relevant undertaker falling within paragraph (a) of the preceding definition, any works which that undertaker is authorised to execute for the purposes of, or in connection with, the carrying on by him of the undertaking mentioned in that paragraph;

(b) in relation to a relevant undertaker falling within paragraph (b) of that definition, any works which that undertaker is authorised to execute by or in accordance with any provision of this code; and

(c) in relation to a relevant undertaker falling within paragraph (c) of that definition, the works for the purposes of which this paragraph is applied to that undertaker.

(11) The application of this paragraph by virtue of paragraph (c) of each of the definitions in sub-paragraph (10) above to any person for the purposes of any works shall be without prejudice to its application by virtue of paragraph (a) of each of those definitions to that person for the purposes of any other works.

[4085]

NOTES

Sub-para (1), (8): words in square brackets substituted by the Communications Act 2003, s 106(2), Sch 3, paras 1, 5(a), (d), subject to transitional provisions in s 406(6) of, and Sch 18, paras 17, 64 to, that Act at **[3434]**, **[3460]**.

Sub-para (10): in definition "relevant undertaker" word in square brackets in para (a)(i) inserted, and para (a)(iii) repealed, by the Water Act 1989, s 190(1), (3), Sch 25, para 68(3), Sch 27, Pt I; para (a)(ii) repealed by the Electricity Act 1989, s 112(4), Sch 18 (it is assumed that word "or" in para (a)(i) is also repealed); words in square brackets in para (b) substituted by the Communications Act 2003, s 106(2), Sch 3, paras 1, 8, subject to transitional provisions in s 406(6) of, and Sch 18, paras 17, 64 to, that Act at **[3434]**, **[3460]**.

PART VI TELECOMMUNICATIONS

Notices under code

24.—(1) Any notice required to be given by the operator to any person for the purposes of any provision of this code must be in a form approved by [OFCOM] as adequate for indicating to that person the effect of the notice and of so much of this code as is relevant to the notice and to the steps that may be taken by that person under this code in respect of that notice.

[(2) A notice required to be given to any person for the purposes of any provision of this code is not to be sent to him by post unless it is sent by a registered post service or by recorded delivery.

(2A) For the purposes, in the case of such a notice, of section 394 of the Communications Act 2003 and the application of section 7 of the Interpretation Act 1978 in relation to that section, the proper address of a person is—

(a) if the person to whom the notice is to be given has furnished the person giving the notice with an address for service under this code, that address; and

(b) only if he has not, the address given by that section of the Act of 2003.]

(5) If it is not practicable, for the purposes of giving any notice under this code, after reasonable inquiries to ascertain the name and address—

(a) of the person who is for the purposes of any provision of this code the occupier of any land, or

(b) of the owner of any interest in any land,

a notice may be given under this code by addressing it to a person by the description of "occupier" of the land (describing it) or, as the case may be, "owner" of the interest (describing both the interest and the land) and by delivering it to some person on the land or, if there is no person on the land to whom it can be delivered, by affixing it, or a copy of it, to some conspicuous object on the land.

(6) In any proceedings under this code a certificate [issued by OFCOM] and stating that a particular form of notice has been approved by [them] as mentioned in sub-paragraph (1) above shall be conclusive evidence of the matter certified.

[4086]

NOTES

Sub-paras (1), (6): words in square brackets substituted by the Communications Act 2003, s 106(2), Sch 3, paras 1, 9(1), (3), subject to transitional provisions in s 406(6) of, and Sch 18, paras 17, 64 to, that Act at **[3434]**, **[3460]**.

Sub-paras (2), (2A): substituted, for original sub-paras (2)–(4), by the Communications Act 2003, s 106(2), Sch 3, paras 1, 9(2), subject to transitional provisions in s 406(6) of, and Sch 18, paras 17, 64 to, that Act at **[3434]**, **[3460]**.

Appeals in Northern Ireland

25. Article 60 of the County Courts (Northern Ireland) Order 1980 (ordinary appeals from the county court in civil cases) shall apply in relation to any determination of the court in Northern Ireland under this code in like manner as it applies in relation to any decree of the court made in the exercise of the jurisdiction conferred by Part III of that Order.

[4087]

Application to the Crown

26.—(1) This code shall apply in relation to land in which there subsists, or at any material time subsisted, a Crown interest as it applies in relation to land in which no such interest subsists.

(2) In this paragraph "Crown interest" means an interest which belongs to Her Majesty in right of the Crown or of the Duchy of Lancaster or to the Duchy of Cornwall or to a Government department or which is held in trust for Her Majesty for the purposes of a Government department and, without prejudice to the foregoing, includes any interest which belongs to Her Majesty in right of Her Majesty's Government in Northern Ireland or to a Northern Ireland department or which is held in trust for Her Majesty for the purposes of a Northern Ireland department.

(3) An agreement required by this code to be given in respect of any Crown interest subsisting in any land shall be given by the appropriate authority, that is to say—

(a) in the case of land belonging to Her Majesty in right of the Crown, the Crown Estate Commissioners or, as the case may require, the government department having the management of the land in question;

(b) in the case of land belonging to Her Majesty in right of the Duchy of Lancaster, the Chancellor of that Duchy;

(c) in the case of land belonging to the Duchy of Cornwall, such person as the Duke of Cornwall, or the possessor for the time being of the Duchy of Cornwall, appoints;

(d) in the case of land belonging to Her Majesty in right of Her Majesty's Government in Northern Ireland, the Northern Ireland department having the management of the land in question;

(e) in the case of land belonging to a government department or a Northern Ireland department or held in trust for Her Majesty for the purposes of a government department or a Northern Ireland department, that department;

and if any question arises as to what authority is the appropriate authority in relation to any land that question shall be referred to the Treasury, whose decision shall be final.

(4) Paragraphs 12(9) and 18(3) above shall not apply where this code [applies in the case of the Secretary of State or a Northern Ireland department by virtue of section 106(3)(b) of the Communications Act 2003].

[4088]

NOTES

Sub-para (4): words in square brackets substituted by the Communications Act 2003, s 106(2), Sch 3, paras 1, 10, subject to transitional provisions in s 406(6) of, and Sch 18, paras 17, 64 to, that Act at **[3434]**, **[3460]**.

Savings for and exclusion of certain remedies etc

27.—(1) Except in so far as provision is otherwise made by virtue of … Schedule 4 to this Act, this code shall not authorise the contravention of any provision made by or under any enactment passed before this Act.

(2) The provisions of this code, except paragraphs 8(5) and 21 and sub-paragraph (1) above, shall be without prejudice to any rights or liabilities arising under any agreement to which the operator is a party.

(3) Except as provided under the preceding provisions of this code, the operator shall not be liable to compensate any person for, or be subject to any other liability in respect of, any loss or damage caused by the lawful exercise of any right conferred by or in accordance with this code.

(4) The ownership of any property shall not be affected by the fact that it is installed on or under, or affixed to, any land by any person in exercise of a right conferred by or in accordance with this code.

[4089]

NOTES

Sub-para (1): words omitted repealed by the Communications Act 2003, s 406(7), Sch 19(1), subject to transitional provisions in s 406(6) of, and Sch 18, paras 17, 64 to, that Act at **[3434]**, **[3460]**.

Application of code to existing systems

28.—(1) Subject to the following provisions of this paragraph, references in this code to [electronic communications apparatus] installed on, under or over any land include references to[electronic communications apparatus] so installed before this code comes into force.

(2) Without prejudice to sub-paragraph (1) above, any line or other apparatus lawfully installed before this code comes into force which if this code had come into force could have been installed under paragraph 12 of this code shall (subject to sub-paragraph (6) below) be treated for the purposes of this code as if it had been so installed.

(3) Any consent given (or deemed to have been given) for the purposes of any provision of the Telegraph Acts 1863 to 1916 before this code comes into force shall—

(a) have effect after this code comes into force as an agreement given for the purposes of this code, and

(b) so have effect, to any extent that is necessary for ensuring that the same persons are bound under this code as were bound by the consent, as if it were an agreement to confer a right or, as the case may require, to bind any interest in land of the person who gave (or is deemed to have given) the consent.

(4) Where by virtue of sub-paragraph (3) above any person is bound by any right, that right shall not be exercisable except on the same terms and subject to the same conditions as the right which, by virtue of the giving of the consent, was exercisable before this code comes into force; and where under any enactment repealed by this Act those terms or conditions included a requirement for the payment of compensation or required the determination of any matter by any court or person, the amount of the compensation or, as the case may be, that matter shall be determined after the coming into force of this code in like manner as if this Act had not been passed.

(5) A person shall not be entitled to compensation under any provision of this code if he is entitled to compensation in respect of the same matter by virtue of sub-paragraph (4)above.

(6) Neither this code nor the repeal by this Act of any provision of the Telegraph Acts 1863 to 1916 (which contain provisions confirming or continuing in force certain agreements) shall prejudice any rights or liabilities (including any rights or liabilities transferred by virtue of section 60 of this Act) which arise at any time under any agreement which was entered into before this code comes into force and relates to the installation, maintenance, adjustment, repair, alteration or inspection of any [electronic communications apparatus] or to keeping any such apparatus installed on, under or over any land.

(7) Any person who before the coming into force of this code has—

(a) given a notice ("the Telegraph Acts notice") under or for the purposes of any provision of the Telegraph Acts 1863 to 1916 to any person, or

(b) made an application under or for the purposes of any such provision (including, in particular, an application for any matter to be referred to any court or person),

may give a notice to the person to whom the Telegraph Acts notice was given or, as the case may be, to every person who is or may be a party to the proceedings resulting from the application stating that a specified step required to be taken under or for the purposes of this code, being a step equivalent to the giving of the Telegraph Acts notice or the making of the application, and any steps required to be so taken before the taking of that step should be treated as having been so taken.

(8) A notice may be given under sub-paragraph (7) above with respect to an application notwithstanding that proceedings resulting from the application have been commenced.

(9) Where a notice has been given to any person under sub-paragraph (7) above, that person may apply to the court for an order setting aside the notice on the ground that it is unreasonable in all the circumstances to treat the giving of the Telegraph Acts notice or the making of the application in question as equivalent to the taking of the steps specified in the notice under that sub-paragraph; but unless the court sets aside the notice under that sub-paragraph the steps specified in the notice shall be treated as having been taken and any proceedings already commenced shall be continued accordingly.

(10) Where before this code comes into force anything has, in connection with the exercise by the operator of any power conferred on him by the Telegraph Acts 1863 to 1916, been done under or for the purposes of the street works code contained in the Public Utilities Street Works Act 1950, that thing shall, in so far as it could have been done in connection with the exercise of any power conferred by this code, have effect under sub-paragraph (7) above, as if it had been done in connection with the power conferred by this code.

(11) In relation to anything done under section 5 of Schedule 3 to the Water Act 1945 or section 5 of Schedule 4 to the Water (Scotland) Act 1980 before the coming into force of this code, the preceding provisions of this paragraph shall have effect, so far as the context permits, as if references to the Telegraph Act 1863 to 1916 included references to that section.

(12) References in this paragraph to the coming into force of this code shall have effect as references to the time at which the code comes into force in relation to the operator.

[4089A]

NOTES

Sub-paras (1), (6): words in square brackets substituted by the Communications Act 2003, s 106(2), Sch 3, paras 1, 5(a), subject to transitional provisions in s 406(6) of, and Sch 18, paras 17, 64 to, that Act at **[3434]**, **[3460]**.

[Effect of agreements concerning sharing of apparatus

29.—(1) This paragraph applies where—

(a) this code has been applied by a direction under section 106 of the Communications Act 2003 in a person's case;

(b) this code expressly or impliedly imposes a limitation on the use to which electronic communications apparatus installed by that person may be put or on the purposes for which it may be used; and

(c) that person is a party to a relevant agreement or becomes a party to an agreement which (after he has become a party to it) is a relevant agreement.

(2) The limitation is not to preclude—

(a) the doing of anything in relation to that apparatus, or

(b) its use for particular purposes,

to the extent that the doing of that thing, or the use of the apparatus for those purposes, is in pursuance of the agreement.

(3) This paragraph is not to be construed, in relation to a person who is entitled or authorised by or under a relevant agreement to share the use of apparatus installed by another party to the agreement, as affecting any consent requirement imposed (whether by a statutory provision or otherwise) on that person.

(4) In this paragraph—

"consent requirement", in relation to a person, means a requirement for him to obtain consent or permission to or in connection with—

(a) the installation by him of apparatus; or

(b) the doing by him of any other thing in relation to apparatus the use of which he is entitled or authorised to share;

"relevant agreement" means an agreement in relation to electronic communications apparatus which—

(a) relates to the sharing by different parties to the agreement of the use of that apparatus; and

(b) is an agreement that satisfies the requirements of sub-paragraph (5);

"statutory provision" means a provision of an enactment or of an instrument having effect under an enactment.

(5) An agreement satisfies the requirements of this sub-paragraph if—

(a) every party to the agreement is a person in whose case this code applies by virtue of a direction under section 106 of the Communications Act 2003; or

(b) one or more of the parties to the agreement is a person in whose case this code so applies and every other party to the agreement is a qualifying person.

(6) A person is a qualifying person for the purposes of sub-paragraph (5) if he is either—

(a) a person who provides an electronic communications network without being a person in whose case this code applies; or

(b) a designated provider of an electronic communications service consisting in the distribution of a programme service by means of an electronic communications network.

(7) In sub-paragraph (6)—

"designated" means designated by an order made by the Secretary of State;

"programme service" has the same meaning as in the Broadcasting Act 1990.]

[4090]

NOTES

Commencement: 25 July 2003 (for the purpose of enabling network and service functions and spectrum functions to be carried out during the transitional period by the Director General of Telecommunications and the Secretary of State respectively) (see further s 408 and Sch 18 at **[3436]**, **[3460]**, and the Communications Act 2003 (Commencement No 1) Order 2003, SI 2003/1900 at **[3507]**);

29 December 2003 (for the purpose of enabling OFCOM to perform those functions) (see the Office of Communications Act 2002 (Commencement No 3) and Communications Act 2003 (Commencement No 2) Order 2003, SI 2003/3142 at **[3590]**).

Added by the Communications Act 2003, s 106(2), Sch 3, paras 1, 11, subject to transitional provisions in s 406(6) of, and Sch 18, paras 17, 64 to, that Act at **[3434]**, **[3460]**.

SCHEDULE 3
PENALTIES AND MODE OF TRIAL UNDER THE WIRELESS TELEGRAPHY ACT 1949

Section 75

1, 2. …

3. The following provisions shall not apply where a person is convicted of an offence under the 1949 Act [or the Marine, &c, Broadcasting (Offences) Act 1967]—

[(a) section 143 of the Powers of Criminal Courts (Sentencing) Act 2000 (which gives the convicting court in England and Wales power to deprive a person convicted of an offence of property used etc for purposes of crime); and]

(b) [Part II of the Proceeds of Crime (Scotland) Act 1995] and [Article 11 of the Criminal Justice (Northern Ireland) Order 1994] (which give the convicting court in Scotland and Northern Ireland respectively power corresponding to the power under [that section]).

[4091]

NOTES

Para 1: amends the Wireless Telegraphy Act 1949, s 14 at **[4018]**.

Para 2: repealed by the Statute Law (Repeals) Act 1993.

Para 3: words in first pair of square brackets inserted by the Wireless Telegraphy (Pre-Consolidation Amendments) Order 2006, SI 2006/1391, art 2, Schedule, para 4; para (a), and words in third pair of square brackets in para (b), substituted by the Powers of Criminal Courts (Sentencing) Act 2000, s 165(1), Sch 9, para 92; in para (b) words in first pair of square brackets substituted by the Criminal Procedure (Consequential Provisions) (Scotland) Act 1995, s 5, Sch 4, para 48(1), (4), words in second pair of square brackets substituted by the Criminal Justice (Northern Ireland) Order 1994, SI 1994/2795 (NI 15), art 26(1), Sch 2, para 10.

(*Sch 4 outside the scope of this work.*)

SCHEDULE 5
GENERAL TRANSITIONAL PROVISIONS AND SAVINGS

Section 109

((Pt I) para 8(1), (3) repealed by the Broadcasting Act 1990, s 203(3), Sch 21; para 15 repealed, in relation to England and Wales, by the Local Government Finance (Repeals, Savings and Consequential Amendments) Order 1990, SI 1990/776, art 3, Sch 1; remainder repealed by the Communications Act 2003, s 406(7), Sch 19(1).)

PART II
PROVISIONS AND SAVINGS COMING INTO FORCE ON TRANSFER DATE

20–33. …

34.—(1) For the purposes of authorising the making, in relation to employees of the successor company or any of its subsidiaries, of provision corresponding to that authorised to be made, in relation to employees of British Telecommunications or any of its subsidiaries, by section 4 of the 1981 Act, that section shall have effect as if—

(a) any reference to the Post Office or to employees of, persons employed by or employment by the Post Office were a reference to British Telecommunications or to employees of, persons employed by or employment by British Telecommunications; and

(b) any reference to a relevant body or to employees of, persons employed by or employment by a relevant body were a reference to the successor company or any subsidiary of the successor company or to employees of, persons employed by or employment by the successor company or any such subsidiary.

(2) Nothing in sub-paragraph (1) above shall be taken as prejudicing the operation of section 84 of the 1981 Act as originally enacted.

35. …

36.—(1) Except as otherwise provided by the foregoing provisions of this Part of this Schedule (whether expressly or by necessary implication), any agreement made, transaction effected or other thing done by, to or in relation to British Telecommunications which is in force or effective immediately before the transfer date shall have effect as from that date as if made, effected or done by, to or in relation to the successor company, in all respects as if the successor company were the same person, in law, as British Telecommunications, and accordingly references to British Telecommunications—

(a) in any agreement (whether or not in writing) and in any deed, bond or instrument;
(b) in any process or other document issued, prepared or employed for the purpose of any proceeding before any court or other tribunal or authority; and
(c) in any other document whatsoever (other than an enactment) relating to or affecting any property, right or liability of British Telecommunications which vests by virtue of section 60 of this Act in the successor company,

shall be taken as from the transfer date as referring to the successor company.

(2) Nothing in sub-paragraph (1) above shall be taken as applying in relation to the deed of covenant by virtue of which the excepted liabilities subsist.

37.—(1) It is hereby declared for the avoidance of doubt that—

(a) the effect of section 60 of this Act in relation to any contract of employment with British Telecommunications in force immediately before the transfer date is merely to modify the contract (as from that date) by substituting the successor company as the employer (and not to terminate the contract or vary it in any other way); and
(b) that section is effective to vest the rights and liabilities of British Telecommunications under any agreement or arrangement for the payment of pensions, allowances or gratuities in the successor company along with all other rights and liabilities of British Telecommunications;

and accordingly for the purposes of any such agreement or arrangement (as it has effect by virtue of paragraph 36 above in relation to employment with the successor company or with a wholly owned subsidiary of that company) any period of employment with British Telecommunications shall count as employment with the successor company or (as the case may be) with a wholly owned subsidiary of that company.

(2) Nothing in sub-paragraph (1) above shall be taken as applying in relation to the excepted liabilities or to the deed of covenant by virtue of which those liabilities subsist.

38–42. …

43. Nothing in this Act shall affect the operation of any order made under section 33 of the 1981Act before the transfer date or any duty imposed by subsection (3) of that section to amend any order so made.

44. Nothing in this Act shall affect the operation of section 56 of the 1981 Act in relation to any records of British Telecommunications which become records of the successor company on the transfer date or any records kept by British Telecommunications for the purposes of paragraph 39 above.

45. Where by virtue of anything done before the transfer date, any enactment amended by Schedule 4 to this Act has effect (whether or not as so amended) in relation to British Telecommunications, then, on and after that date, that enactment shall have effect in relation to the successor company as if that company were the same person, in law, as British Telecommunications.

46.—(1) Section 6(2) of the Commonwealth Telegraph Act 1949 shall continue to have effect with the modifications made by section 34(1) of the 1981 Act and, subject to that, shall have effect as if references which include references to British Telecommunications, in paragraph (c) and sub-paragraphs (iv), (v) and (vi) of paragraph (d), included references to the successor company.

(2) The power to make regulations conferred on the Secretary of State by section 49 of the Post Office Act 1969 shall include power to make such regulations as appear to him to be requisite for securing that persons to whom that section applies, and persons claiming in right of them, are not adversely affected in the matter of pension rights by reason only that—

(a) in consequence of the 1981 Act, they ceased to be employed by the Post Office; or

(b) in consequence of section 60 of this Act, they cease to be employed by British Telecommunications.

47. ...

48.—(1) Where an asset, or the right to receive an asset, vests in the successor company by virtue of section 60 of this Act, then for the purposes of Part I of the Industry Act 1972 and Part II of the Industrial Development Act 1982—

(a) so much of any expenditure incurred by British Telecommunications in providing that asset as is approved capital expenditure (of any description relevant for the purposes of regional development grant) in respect of which no payment of regional development grant has been made to British Telecommunications shall be treated as having been incurred by the successor company and not only by British Telecommunications; and

(b) where the asset itself vests in the successor company by virtue of section 60 of this Act, it shall be treated as a new asset if it would have fallen to be so treated if it had remained vested in British Telecommunications.

(2) In this paragraph "regional development grant" means a grant under Part I of the Industry Act 1972 or Part II of the Industrial Development Act 1982 and "approved capital expenditure" has the same meaning as it has for the purposes of the provisions relating to regional development grant.

49–51. ...

[4092]

NOTES

Paras 20–29, 31–33, 35, 38–42, 47, 49–51: repealed by the Communications Act 2003, s 406(7), Sch 19(1); for effect in relation to para 20 see s 406(7) of, and Sch 19(1), Note 4 to, that Act.

Para 30: repealed by the Broadcasting Act 1990, s 203(3), Sch 21.

Para 48: words omitted repealed by the Communications Act 2003, s 406(7), Sch 19(1).

(Sch 6 repealed by the Communications Act 2003, s 406(7), Sch 19(1); Sch 7 contains repeals.)

WIRELESS TELEGRAPHY ACT 1998

(1998 c 6)

ARRANGEMENT OF SECTIONS

An Act to make provision about the grant of, and sums payable in respect of, licences under the Wireless Telegraphy Act 1949 other than television licences, and about the promotion of the efficient use and management of the electro-magnetic spectrum for wireless telegraphy; and for connected purposes

[18 March 1998]

1 Charges for wireless telegraphy licences

(*1*) *In this Act—*

[(a) references to a grant of recognised spectrum access are references to a grant made under section 159 of the Communications Act 2003 (recognised spectrum access); and

(b)] "wireless telegraphy licence" means any licence under the Wireless Telegraphy Act 1949 ...

(2) On the issue [of a wireless telegraphy licence or the making of a grant of recognised spectrum access and, where regulations under this section so provide, subsequently at such times during the term of the licence or grant and such times in respect of its variation, modification or revocation, as may be prescribed by the regulations, there shall be paid to OFCOM by the person to whom the licence is issued or the grant made]—

(a) such sums as may be prescribed by the regulations, or

(b) if the regulations so provide, such sums (whether on [the issue of the licence or the making of the grant] or subsequently) as [OFCOM] may in the particular case determine.

(3) Regulations under this section—

(a) ...

(b) may confer exemptions from provisions of the regulations ... in particular cases,

(c) may provide for sums paid to be refunded, in whole or in part, in such cases as may be specified in the regulations or in such cases as [OFCOM think] fit, ...

(d) ...

(4) Where sums will or may become payable under regulations under this section subsequently to the issue [of a licence or the making of a grant of recognised spectrum access, OFCOM may, on the issue of the licence or the making of the grant,] require such security to be given, by way of deposit or otherwise, for the payment of the sums which will or may become payable as [they think] fit.

(5) Regulations under this section shall not apply in relation to any licence granted in accordance with regulations under section 3 [or any grant of recognised spectrum access made in accordance with regulations under section 3A].

(6) Any regulations under section 2(1) of the Wireless Telegraphy Act 1949 which—

(a) relate to wireless telegraphy licences within the meaning of this Act, and

(b) are in force immediately before the commencement of this section,

shall be taken to have been made under this section; and accordingly may be amended or revoked by regulations under this section.

(7) Any reference in a wireless telegraphy licence granted before the commencement of this section to section 2(1) of the Wireless Telegraphy Act 1949 shall be construed, in relation to any time after that commencement, as a reference to this section.

[4093]

NOTES

Whole Act repealed by the Wireless Telegraphy Act 2006, s 125(1), Sch 9, Pt 1, subject to transitional provisions and savings in s 124 of, Sch 8, Pt 1, paras 1–8, 24 to, that Act at **[4230]**, **[4239]**.

Sub-s (1): para (a) inserted and para (b) numbered as such, and words omitted repealed, by the Communications Act 2003, ss 161(1), (2)(a), 406(7), Sch 19(1).

Sub-ss (2), (4): words in square brackets substituted by the Communications Act 2003, ss 161(1), (2)(b), (c), 406(1), Sch 17, paras 145, 146(a), (c).

Sub-s (3): words omitted repealed, and words in square brackets substituted, by the Communications Act 2003, s 406(1), (7), Sch 17, para 146(b), Sch 19(1).

Sub-s (5): words in square brackets added by the Communications Act 2003, s 406(1), Sch 17, para 146(d).

Regulations: the Wireless Telegraphy (Licence Charges) Regulations 2005, SI 2005/1378 at **[4543]**.

[2 Matters to be taken into account

(1) This section applies where OFCOM exercise any of their powers under section 1 to prescribe sums payable in respect of any description of wireless telegraphy licence or of grant of recognised spectrum access, other than a power to prescribe sums payable where—

PART VI TELECOMMUNICATIONS

(*a*) *a wireless telegraphy licence is varied or revoked at the request or with the consent of the licence holder, or*

(*b*) *a grant of recognised spectrum access is varied or revoked at the request or with the consent of the holder of the grant.*

(*2*) *OFCOM may, if they think fit in the light (in particular) of the matters to which they are required to have regard under section 154 of the Communications Act 2003, prescribe sums which would be greater than those that would be necessary for the purposes of recovering costs incurred by them in connection with functions under the enactments relating to the management of the radio spectrum.*

(*3*) *In this section—*

"the enactments relating to the management of the radio spectrum" has the same meaning as in the Communications Act 2003,

"prescribe" means prescribe by regulations or determine in accordance with regulations.]

[4094]

NOTES

Repealed as noted to s 1 at **[4093]**.

Commencement: 25 July 2003 (except in so far as it relates to the words "or of grant of recognised spectrum access" in sub-s (1), and sub-s (1)(b) and word "or" immediately preceding it, and for the purpose of enabling network and service functions and spectrum functions to be carried out during the transitional period by the Director General of Telecommunications and the Secretary of State respectively) (see further s 408 of, and Sch 18 to, that Act at **[3436]**, **[3460]**, and the Communications Act 2003 (Commencement No 1) Order 2003, SI 2003/1900 at **[3507]**); 29 December 2003 (otherwise).

Substituted by the Communications Act 2003, s 406(1), Sch 17, para 147.

Regulations: the Wireless Telegraphy (Licence Charges) Regulations 2005, SI 2005/1378 at **[4543]**.

3 Bidding for licences

(*1*) *Having regard to the desirability of promoting the optimal use of the electro-magnetic spectrum, [OFCOM] may by regulations provide that, in such cases as may be specified in ... the regulations, applications for the grant of wireless telegraphy licences must be made in accordance with a procedure which—*

(*a*) ...

(*b*) *involves the making by the applicant of a bid specifying an amount which he is willing to pay to [OFCOM] in respect of the licence.*

(2) ...

(*3*) *Regulations under this section may make provision with respect to the grant of the licences to which they apply and the terms, provisions and limitations subject to which such licences are issued and may, in particular—*

[(a) require the applicant's bid to specify the amount he is willing to pay;

(aa) require that amount to be expressed—

(i) as a cash sum;

(ii) as a sum determined by reference to a variable (such as income attributable wholly or in part to the holding of the licence);

(iii) as a combination of the two; or

(iv) (at the applicant's choice) in any one of the ways falling within the preceding sub-paragraphs that is authorised by the regulations;

(ab) require that amount to be expressed in terms of—

(i) the making of a single payment;

(ii) the making of periodic payments;

(iii) a combination of the two; or

(iv) (at the applicant's choice) in any one of the ways falling within the preceding sub-paragraphs that is authorised by the regulations;]

(*b*) *specify requirements (such as, for example, technical or financial requirements, requirements relating to fitness to hold the licence and requirements intended to restrict the holding of two or more wireless telegraphy licences by any one person) which must be met by applicants for a licence,*

(*c*) *require any such applicant to pay a deposit to [OFCOM],*

(*d*) *specify circumstances in which such a deposit is, or is not, to be refundable,*

(*e*) *specify matters to be taken into account by [OFCOM] (in addition to the bids made in accordance with the prescribed procedure) in deciding whether, or to whom, to grant a licence,*

(*f*) *specify the other terms, provisions and limitations subject to which [a licence to which the regulations apply] is to be issued, [and]*
(*g*) *make any provision referred to in section 1(3), ...*
(*h*) ...

[(4) Regulations under this section are not to be construed as binding OFCOM to grant a licence on the completion of the procedure provided for in the regulations except in such circumstances as may be provided for in the regulations.]

[(5) A wireless telegraphy licence granted in accordance with regulations under this section shall specify either—
(*a*) *the sum or sums which in consequence of the bids made are, in accordance with the regulations, to be payable in respect of the licence; or*
(*b*) *the method for determining that sum or those sums;*
and that sum or those sums shall be paid to OFCOM by the person to whom the licence is granted in accordance with the terms of the licence.]

[(5A) In determining the sum or sums payable in respect of a wireless telegraphy licence, regard may be had to bids made for other wireless telegraphy licences and for grants of recognised spectrum access.

(5B) Regulations under this section may provide that where a person—
(*a*) *makes an application for a licence in accordance with a procedure provided for by such regulations, but*
(*b*) *subsequently refuses the licence applied for,*
that person shall make such payments to OFCOM as may be determined in accordance with the regulations by reference to bids made for the licence.

(6) Subsection (4) of section 1 is to apply in relation to sums that will or may become payable under regulations under this section subsequently to the grant of a wireless telegraphy licence as it applies to sums that will or may become payable under regulations under that section.]

(7) Section 1(2) of the Wireless Telegraphy Act 1949 (powers of [OFCOM] in relation to grant of licences) and regulations under section 3 of that Act (regulations as to wireless telegraphy) shall have effect subject to regulations under this section.

(8) In this section "grant", in relation to a licence, includes renewal.

[4095]

NOTES

Repealed as noted to s 1 at **[4093]**.

Sub-s (1): words in square brackets substituted, and words omitted repealed, by the Communications Act 2003, ss 167(1), (2)(a), 406(1), (7), Sch 17, para 145, Sch 19(1), subject to transitional provisions in s 406(6) of, and Sch 18, para 21 to, that Act at **[3434]**, **[3460]**.

Sub-s (2): repealed by the Communications Act 2003, ss 167(1), (2)(b), 406(7), Sch 19(1), subject to transitional provisions in s 406(6) of, and Sch 18, para 21 to, that Act at **[3434]**, **[3460]**.

Sub-s (3): paras (a)–(ab) substituted, for original para (a), words in square brackets in paras (c), (e), and words in first pair of square brackets in para (f), substituted, word in second pair of square brackets in para (f) inserted, and words omitted repealed, by the Communications Act 2003, ss 167(1), (3), 406(1), (7), Sch 17, para 145, Sch 19(1), subject to transitional provisions in s 406(6) of, and Sch 18, para 21 to, that Act at **[3434]**, **[3460]**.

Sub-ss (4), (5): substituted by the Communications Act 2003, ss 167(1), (4), (5), subject to transitional provisions in s 406(6) of, and Sch 18, para 21 to, that Act at **[3434]**, **[3460]**.

Sub-ss (5A)–(6): substituted, for original sub-s (6), by the Communications Act 2003, ss 167(1), (6), subject to transitional provisions in s 406(6) of, and Sch 18, para 21 to, that Act at **[3434]**, **[3460]**.

Sub-s (7): words in square brackets substituted by the Communications Act 2003, s 406(1), Sch 17, para 145.

Regulations: the Wireless Telegraphy (Third Generation Licences) Regulations 1999, SI 1999/3162; the Wireless Telegraphy (Broadband Fixed Wireless Access Licences) Regulations 2000, SI 2000/2039 at **[4363]**; the Wireless Telegraphy (Broadband Fixed Wireless Access Licences) Regulations 2001, SI 2001/3193; the Wireless Telegraphy (Public Fixed Wireless Access Licences) Regulations 2002, SI 2002/1911 at **[4370]**; the Wireless Telegraphy (Licence Award) Regulations 2006, SI 2006/338; the Wireless Telegraphy (Licence Award) (No 2) Regulations 2006, SI 2006/1806.

[3A Bidding for grants of recognised spectrum access

(1) Having regard to the desirability of promoting the optimal use of the electromagnetic spectrum, OFCOM may by regulations provide that, in such cases as may be specified in the regulations, applications for grants of recognised spectrum access must be made in

accordance with a procedure which involves the making by the applicant of a bid specifying an amount which he is willing to pay to OFCOM in respect of the grant.

(2) Regulations under this section may make provision with respect to the grants to which they apply and the restrictions and conditions subject to which such grants are made.

(3) The regulations may, in particular—

(a) require the applicant's bid to specify the amount which he is willing to pay;

(b) require that amount to be expressed—

(i) as a cash sum;

(ii) as a sum determined by reference to a variable (such as income attributable wholly or in part to the use of wireless telegraphy to which the grant relates);

(iii) as a combination of the two; or

(iv) (at the applicant's choice) in any one of the ways falling within the preceding sub-paragraphs that is authorised by the regulations;

(c) require that amount to be expressed in terms of—

(i) the making of a single payment;

(ii) the making of periodic payments;

(iii) a combination of the two; or

(iv) (at the applicant's choice) in any one of the ways falling within the preceding sub-paragraphs that is authorised by the regulations;

(d) specify requirements (such as, for example, technical or financial requirements, requirements relating to the use of wireless telegraphy to which the grant relates and requirements intended to restrict the holding of two or more grants of recognised spectrum access by any one person) which must be met by applicants for a grant;

(e) require any such applicant to pay a deposit to OFCOM;

(f) specify circumstances in which such a deposit is, or is not, to be refundable;

(g) specify matters to be taken into account by OFCOM (in addition to the bids made in accordance with the prescribed procedure) in deciding whether, or to whom, to make a grant of recognised spectrum access;

(h) specify the other restrictions and conditions subject to which a grant to which the regulations apply is to be made; and

(i) make any provision referred to in section 1(3).

(4) Regulations under this section are not to be construed as binding OFCOM to make a grant on the completion of the procedure provided for in the regulations except in such circumstances as may be provided for in the regulations.

(5) A grant of recognised spectrum access made in accordance with regulations under this section shall specify either—

(a) the sum or sums which in consequence of the bids made are, in accordance with the regulations, to be payable in respect of the grant; or

(b) the method for determining that sum or those sums;

and that sum or those sums shall be paid to OFCOM by the person to whom the grant is made in accordance with the conditions of the grant.

(6) In determining the sum or sums payable in respect of a grant, regard may be had to bids made for other grants of recognised spectrum access and for wireless telegraphy licences.

(7) Regulations under this section may provide that where a person—

(a) makes an application for a grant of recognised spectrum access in accordance with a procedure provided for by such regulations, but

(b) subsequently refuses the grant applied for,

that person shall make such payments to OFCOM as may be determined in accordance with the regulations by reference to bids made for the grant.

(8) Subsection (4) of section 1 is to apply in relation to sums that will or may become payable under regulations under this section subsequently to the making of a grant of recognised spectrum access as it applies to sums that will or may become payable under regulations under that section.]

[4096]

NOTES

Repealed as noted to s 1 at **[4093]**.
Commencement: 29 December 2003.
Inserted by the Communications Act 2003, s 161(1), (3).

4 Restriction on revocation or variation of licences

(*1*) *[OFCOM] may include in any wireless telegraphy licence terms restricting the exercise by [them] of [their] power under section 1(4) of the Wireless Telegraphy Act 1949 to revoke or vary the licence.*

(*2*) *The terms that may be included in a wireless telegraphy licence by virtue of subsection (1) include, in particular, terms providing that the licence may not be revoked or varied except with the consent of the licence holder or in such other circumstances and on such grounds as may be specified in the licence.*

(*3*) *Any such circumstances or grounds may relate to matters relevant for the purposes of any other enactment (and may, in particular, be dependent on the exercise of a statutory discretion under any other enactment).*

(*4*) *A wireless telegraphy licence containing any terms included in the licence by virtue of subsection (1) may also provide that regulations made under section 3 of the Wireless Telegraphy Act 1949—*

- (*a*) *shall not apply in relation to any station or apparatus to which the licence relates, or*
- (*b*) *shall apply in relation to any such station or apparatus to such an extent only, or subject to such modifications, as may be specified in the licence.*

(*5*) *Notwithstanding any terms or provisions included in a wireless telegraphy licence in accordance with this section, [OFCOM] may at any time by a notice in writing served on the holder of the licence, revoke the licence or vary its terms, provisions or limitations, if it appears to [them] to be requisite or expedient to do so—*

- (*a*) *in the interests of national security, or*
- [(*b*) *for the purpose of securing compliance with an international obligation of the United Kingdom (within the meaning of the Communications Act 2003).]*

[4097]

NOTES

Repealed as noted to s 1 at **[4093]**.
Sub-s (1): words in square brackets substituted by the Communications Act 2003, s 406(1), Sch 17, paras 145, 148(1), (2).
Sub-s (5): words in square brackets substituted by the Communications Act 2003, s 406(1), Sch 17, paras 145, 148(1), (3); para (b) substituted by the Wireless Telegraphy (Pre-Consolidation Amendments) Order 2006, SI 2006/1391, art 2, Schedule, para 5.

[4A Recovery of sums payable to OFCOM

Where any sum is required to be paid to OFCOM—

- (*a*) *under any provision of this Act,*
- (*b*) *in pursuance of any provision of regulations under this Act, or*
- (*c*) *by virtue of any terms or conditions contained by virtue of this Act in a wireless telegraphy licence, or in a grant of recognised spectrum access,*

that sum shall be so paid to them as soon as it becomes due in accordance with that provision, or those terms or conditions, and if not paid is to be recoverable by them accordingly.]

[4098]

NOTES

Repealed as noted to s 1 at **[4093]**.
Commencement: 18 September 2003 (for the purpose of enabling network and service functions and spectrum functions to be carried out during the transitional period by the Director General of Telecommunications and the Secretary of State respectively) (see further s 408 of, and Sch 18 to, that Act at **[3436]**, **[3460]**, and the Communications Act 2003 (Commencement No 1) Order 2003, SI 2003/1900 at **[3507]**); 29 December 2003 (for the purpose of enabling OFCOM to perform those functions) (see the Office of Communications Act 2002 (Commencement No 3) and Communications Act 2003 (Commencement No 2) Order 2003, SI 2003/3142 at **[3590]**).

Inserted by the Communications Act 2003, s 406(1), Sch 17, para 149(1), except in relation to a sum that first became payable before 18 September 2003.

5 (*Repealed by the Communications Act 2003, s 406(7), Sch 19(1).*)

[6 Regulations

(1) Section 403 of the Communications Act 2003 (procedure for regulations and orders made by OFCOM) applies to every power of OFCOM to make regulations under a provision of this Act.

(2) Subsections (4) to (6) of that section shall not apply in any case in which it appears to OFCOM that by reason of the urgency of the matter it is inexpedient to publish a notice in accordance with subsection (4)(b) of that section.

(3) Subsections (4) to (6) of that section shall not apply in the case of any regulations under section 3 or 3A modifying previous regulations under that section in a case not falling within subsection (2) if it appears to OFCOM—

- *(a) that the modifications would not adversely affect the interests of any person or otherwise put him in a worse position or, as regards someone else, put him at a disadvantage, and*
- *(b) in so far as the modifications affect a procedure that has already begun, that no person would have acted differently had the modifications come into force before the procedure began.]*

[4099]

NOTES

Repealed as noted to s 1 at **[4093]**.

Commencement: 25 July 2003 (in so far as it relates to sub-ss (1), (2), and for the purpose of enabling network and service functions and spectrum functions to be carried out during the transitional period by the Director General of Telecommunications and the Secretary of State respectively); 18 September 2003 (in so far as it relates to sub-s (3), except for the words "or 3A", and for the purpose of enabling network and service functions and spectrum functions to be carried out during the transitional period by the Director General of Telecommunications and the Secretary of State respectively); 29 December 2003 (otherwise).

Substituted by the Communications Act 2003, s 406(1), Sch 17, para 150.

7 Minor and consequential amendments and repeals

Schedule 1 (minor and consequential amendments) and Schedule 2 (repeals and revocations) shall have effect.

[4100]

NOTES

Repealed as noted to s 1 at **[4093]**.

8 Interpretation

In this Act—

["grant of recognised spectrum access" means a grant of recognised spectrum access made under section 159 of the Communications Act 2003;

"OFCOM" means the Office of Communications;]

"wireless telegraphy" has the same meaning as in the Wireless Telegraphy Act 1949;

"wireless telegraphy licence" has the meaning given by section 1;

[and references in this Act to the issue of a wireless telegraphy licence or the making of a grant of recognised spectrum access include references to the issue of such a licence, or the making of a grant of such access, by way of renewal of a previous licence or grant.]

[4101]

NOTES

Repealed as noted to s 1 at **[4093]**.

Words in square brackets inserted by the Communications Act 2003, s 406(1), Sch 17, para 151.

9 Extent and application

(1) This Act extends to Northern Ireland.

(2) The provisions capable of being extended to the Isle of Man or any of the Channel Islands under section 20(3) of the Wireless Telegraphy Act 1949 include the provisions of this Act amending that Act.

(3) Her Majesty may by Order in Council direct that all or any of the other provisions of this Act shall extend to the Isle of Man or any of the Channel Islands with such adaptations and modifications, if any, as may be specified in the Order.

[4102]

NOTES

Repealed as noted to s 1 at **[4093]**.

Orders in Council: the Wireless Telegraphy (Isle of Man) Order 1998, SI 1998/1510; the Wireless Telegraphy (Guernsey) Order 1998, SI 1998/1511; the Wireless Telegraphy (Jersey) Order 1998, SI 1998/1512.

10 Short title and commencement

(1) This Act may be cited as the Wireless Telegraphy Act 1998.

(2) This Act shall come into force at the end of the period of three months beginning with the day on which it is passed.

[4103]

(Sch 1 repealed by the Communications Act 2003, s 406(7), Sch 19(1); Sch 2 contains repeals and revocations; repealed as noted to s 1 at **[4093]**.*)*

PART VI TELECOMMUNICATIONS

MOBILE TELEPHONES (RE-PROGRAMMING) ACT 2002

(2002 c 31)

An Act to create offences in respect of unique electronic equipment identifiers of mobile wireless communications devices

[24 July 2002]

1 Re-programming mobile telephone etc

(1) A person commits an offence if—

(a) he changes a unique device identifier, *or*

(b) he interferes with the operation of a unique device identifier

[(c) he offers or agrees to change, or interfere with the operation of, a unique device identifier, or

(d) he offers or agrees to arrange for another person to change, or interfere with the operation of, a unique device identifier.]

(2) A unique device identifier is an electronic equipment identifier which is unique to a mobile wireless communications device.

(3) But a person does not commit an offence under this section if—

(a) he is the manufacturer of the device, or

(b) he does the act mentioned in subsection (1) with the written consent of the manufacturer of the device.

(4) A person guilty of an offence under this section is liable—

(a) on summary conviction, to imprisonment for a term not exceeding 6 months or to a fine not exceeding the statutory maximum or to both, or

(b) on conviction on indictment, to imprisonment for a term not exceeding 5 years or to a fine or to both.

[4104]

NOTES

Commencement: 4 October 2002.

Sub-s (1): word in italics in para (a) repealed and paras (c), (d) inserted by the Violent Crime Reduction Act 2006, ss 62, 65, Sch 5, as from a day to be appointed.

2 Possession or supply of anything for re-programming purposes

(1) A person commits an offence if—

(a) he has in his custody or under his control anything which may be used for the purpose of changing or interfering with the operation of a unique device identifier, and

(b) he intends to use the thing unlawfully for that purpose or to allow it to be used unlawfully for that purpose.

(2) A person commits an offence if—

(a) he supplies anything which may be used for the purpose of changing or interfering with the operation of a unique device identifier, and

(b) he knows or believes that the person to whom the thing is supplied intends to use it unlawfully for that purpose or to allow it to be used unlawfully for that purpose.

(3) A person commits an offence if—

(a) he offers to supply anything which may be used for the purpose of changing or interfering with the operation of a unique device identifier, and

(b) he knows or believes that the person to whom the thing is offered intends if it is supplied to him to use it unlawfully for that purpose or to allow it to be used unlawfully for that purpose.

(4) A unique device identifier is an electronic equipment identifier which is unique to a mobile wireless communications device.

(5) A thing is used by a person unlawfully for a purpose if in using it for that purpose he commits an offence under section 1.

(6) A person guilty of an offence under this section is liable—

(a) on summary conviction, to imprisonment for a term not exceeding 6 months or to a fine not exceeding the statutory maximum or to both, or

(b) on conviction on indictment, to imprisonment for a term not exceeding 5 years or to a fine or to both.

[4105]

NOTES

Commencement: 4 October 2002.

3 Citation etc

(1) This Act may be cited as the Mobile Telephones (Re-programming) Act 2002.

(2) Sections 1 and 2 come into force in accordance with provision made by the Secretary of State by order made by statutory instrument.

(3) This Act extends to Northern Ireland.

[4106]

NOTES

Commencement: 24 July 2002.

WIRELESS TELEGRAPHY ACT 2006

(2006 c 36)

ARRANGEMENT OF SECTIONS

PART I
GENERAL PROVISION ABOUT RADIO SPECTRUM

Radio spectrum functions of OFCOM

Reservation of spectrum for multiplex use

PART 2
REGULATION OF RADIO SPECTRUM

CHAPTER 1
WIRELESS TELEGRAPHY LICENCES

Licensing of wireless telegraphy

Charges etc

CHAPTER 2
GRANTS OF RECOGNISED SPECTRUM ACCESS

Making of grants

Charges etc

CHAPTER 3
MANAGEMENT OF RADIO SPECTRUM

General

Wireless telegraphy register

Statistical information

CHAPTER 4
ENFORCEMENT

Unauthorised use etc

Procedures for contraventions

CHAPTER 5
MISCELLANEOUS

Regulations about wireless telegraphy

Misuse of wireless telegraphy

Miscellaneous

PART 3
REGULATION OF APPARATUS

Undue interference

Penalties and proceedings

Saving

Interpretation

PART 6
GENERAL

Fixed penalties

Entry, search and seizure

Disposal and forfeiture

Enforcement, proceedings etc

Disclosure of information

Notifications etc and electronic working

An Act to consolidate enactments about wireless telegraphy

[8 November 2006]

PART 1
GENERAL PROVISION ABOUT RADIO SPECTRUM

Radio spectrum functions of OFCOM

1 General functions

(1) It is a function of OFCOM—

(a) to give such advice in relation to the use of the electromagnetic spectrum for wireless telegraphy,

(b) to provide such other services, and

(c) to maintain such records,

as they consider appropriate for the purpose of facilitating or managing the use of the spectrum for wireless telegraphy.

(2) It is a function of OFCOM, in relation to the use of the electromagnetic spectrum for wireless telegraphy—

(a) to give such further advice,

(b) to provide such other services, and

(c) to maintain such other records,

as the Secretary of State may require for the purpose of securing compliance with the international obligations of the United Kingdom.

(3) The advice, other services and records that OFCOM may give, provide or maintain under this section include advice, other services and records with respect to the use of the electromagnetic spectrum at places outside the United Kingdom.

(4) The powers of OFCOM under Part 1 of the Communications Act 2003 (c 21) to carry out research, or to arrange for others to carry out research, are to be exercisable, in particular, for ascertaining, for the purpose of carrying out OFCOM's functions under this section, information about—

(a) the demands for use of the electromagnetic spectrum for wireless telegraphy in the United Kingdom;

(b) the effects, in the United Kingdom, of any such use of the spectrum;

(c) likely future developments in relation to those matters; and

(d) any other connected matters that OFCOM think relevant.

(5) OFCOM may make a grant to any person if, in their opinion, the making of the grant is likely to promote—

(a) the efficient use in the United Kingdom of the electromagnetic spectrum for wireless telegraphy; or

(b) the efficient management of that use.

(6) A grant—

(a) may be made to a person holding a wireless telegraphy licence or a grant of recognised spectrum access or to any other person; and

(b) is to be made on such terms and conditions as OFCOM consider appropriate;

and the terms and conditions may include terms requiring the repayment of the grant in specified circumstances.

(7) The consent of the Treasury is required—

(a) for the making of a grant under subsection (5); and

(b) for the terms and conditions on which such a grant is made.

(8) Where OFCOM are required to give advice or provide another service to a person under this section, they may make the giving of the advice or the provision of the other service conditional on the payment to them of such sums—

(a) as they may determine in advance; or

(b) as may be agreed between them and that person.

(9) In this section references to providing a service to a person include references to a service consisting in—

(a) the entry of that person's particulars in a register or other record kept by OFCOM for the purpose of carrying out their functions under this section; or

(b) the taking of steps for the purposes of determining whether to grant an application for an entry in a register or record so kept.

[4107]

NOTES

Commencement: 8 February 2007.

2 United Kingdom Plan for Frequency Authorisation

(1) OFCOM must, from time to time as they think fit, publish a plan ("the United Kingdom Plan for Frequency Authorisation").

(2) The plan must set out—

(a) in relation to the United Kingdom, the frequencies that—

(i) have been allocated for particular wireless telegraphy purposes, and

(ii) are available for assignment; and

(b) the purposes for which the different frequencies have been allocated.

[4108]

NOTES

Commencement: 8 February 2007.

3 Duties of OFCOM when carrying out functions

(1) In carrying out their radio spectrum functions, OFCOM must have regard, in particular, to—

(a) the extent to which the electromagnetic spectrum is available for use, or further use, for wireless telegraphy;

(b) the demand for use of the spectrum for wireless telegraphy; and

(c) the demand that is likely to arise in future for the use of the spectrum for wireless telegraphy.

(2) In carrying out those functions, they must also have regard, in particular, to the desirability of promoting—

(a) the efficient management and use of the part of the electromagnetic spectrum available for wireless telegraphy;
(b) the economic and other benefits that may arise from the use of wireless telegraphy;
(c) the development of innovative services; and
(d) competition in the provision of electronic communications services.

(3) Subsection (4) has effect in the case of OFCOM's radio spectrum functions, other than their functions under sections 13 and 22.

(4) In the application of this section to those functions, OFCOM may disregard such of the matters mentioned in subsections (1) and (2) as appear to them—

(a) to be matters to which they are not required to have regard apart from this section; and
(b) to have no application to the case in question.

(5) Where it appears to OFCOM that a duty under this section conflicts with one or more of their duties under sections 3 to 6 of the Communications Act 2003 (c 21), priority must be given to their duties under those sections.

(6) Where it appears to OFCOM that a duty under this section conflicts with another in a particular case, they must secure that the conflict is resolved in the manner they think best in the circumstances.

[4109]

NOTES

Commencement: 8 February 2007.

4 Advisory service in relation to interference

It is a function of OFCOM to provide a service consisting in the giving of advice and assistance to persons complaining of interference with wireless telegraphy.

[4110]

NOTES

Commencement: 8 February 2007.

5 Directions of Secretary of State

(1) The Secretary of State may by order give general or specific directions to OFCOM about the carrying out by them of their radio spectrum functions.

(2) An order under this section may require OFCOM to secure that such frequencies of the electromagnetic spectrum as may be specified in the order are kept available or become available—

(a) for such uses or descriptions of uses, or
(b) for such users or descriptions of users,

as may be so specified.

(3) An order under this section may require OFCOM to exercise their powers under the provisions mentioned in subsection (4)—

(a) in such cases,
(b) in such manner,
(c) subject to such restrictions and constraints, and
(d) with a view to achieving such purposes,

as may be specified in, or determined by the Secretary of State in accordance with, the order.

(4) The provisions are—

(a) section 8(3);
(b) sections 12 to 14; and
(c) sections 21 to 23.

(5) This section does not restrict the Secretary of State's power under section 5 of the Communications Act 2003 (c 21) (directions in respect of networks and spectrum functions).

[4111]

NOTES

Commencement: 8 February 2007.

6 Procedure for directions

(1) An order under section 5 must state the purpose for which a direction is given, unless it falls within section 5(2) or (3).

(2) Before making an order under section 5, the Secretary of State must consult—

(a) OFCOM; and

(b) such other persons as he thinks fit.

(3) Subsection (2) does not apply where the Secretary of State considers that the urgency of the case makes it inexpedient to consult before making the order.

(4) No order is to be made under section 5 unless a draft of the order has been laid before Parliament and approved by a resolution of each House.

(5) But subsection (4) does not apply where—

(a) before or in the course of the consultation required by subsection (2), or

(b) after the consultation and before or after a draft of the order has been laid before Parliament,

the Secretary of State considers that the urgency of the case is or has become such that he should make the order straight away.

(6) Where under subsection (5) the Secretary of State makes an order under section 5 without a draft of the order having been approved, the order ceases to have effect at the end of the period of forty days beginning with the day on which it was made unless, before the end of that period, it has been approved by a resolution of each House of Parliament.

(7) For the purposes of subsection (6)—

(a) the order's ceasing to have effect is without prejudice to anything previously done, or to the making of a new order; and

(b) in reckoning the period of forty days no account is to be taken of any period during which Parliament is dissolved or prorogued or during which both Houses are adjourned for more than four days.

[4112]

NOTES

Commencement: 8 February 2007.

Reservation of spectrum for multiplex use

7 Special duty in relation to television multiplexes

(1) This section applies where OFCOM, in the exercise of their radio spectrum functions, have reserved frequencies for the broadcasting of television programmes.

(2) OFCOM must, in carrying out those functions, exercise their powers so as to secure, so far as practicable, that the requirement in subsection (3) is satisfied.

(3) The requirement is that sufficient capacity is made available on the reserved frequencies for ensuring, in the case of every licensed television multiplex service, that the qualifying services are broadcast by means of that multiplex service.

(4) "Licensed television multiplex service" means a television multiplex service the provision of which is authorised by a licence under Part 1 of the Broadcasting Act 1996 (c 55).

(5) "Qualifying service" and "television multiplex service" each has the same meaning as in Part 3 of the Communications Act 2003 (c 21).

[4113]

NOTES

Commencement: 8 February 2007.

PART 2
REGULATION OF RADIO SPECTRUM

CHAPTER 1
WIRELESS TELEGRAPHY LICENCES

Licensing of wireless telegraphy

8 Licences and exemptions

(1) It is unlawful—

(a) to establish or use a wireless telegraphy station, or

(b) to instal or use wireless telegraphy apparatus,

except under and in accordance with a licence (a "wireless telegraphy licence") granted under this section by OFCOM.

(2) Subsection (1) does not apply to—

(a) the use of a television receiver (within the meaning of Part 4 of the Communications Act 2003) for receiving a television programme; or

(b) the installation of a television receiver for use solely for that purpose.

(3) OFCOM may by regulations exempt from subsection (1) the establishment, installation or use of wireless telegraphy stations or wireless telegraphy apparatus of such classes or descriptions as may be specified in the regulations, either absolutely or subject to such terms, provisions and limitations as may be so specified.

(4) If OFCOM are satisfied that the condition in subsection (5) is satisfied as respects the use of stations or apparatus of a particular description, they must make regulations under subsection (3) exempting the establishment, installation and use of a station or apparatus of that description from subsection (1).

(5) The condition is that the use of stations or apparatus of that description is not likely to involve undue interference with wireless telegraphy.

[4114]

NOTES

Commencement: 8 February 2007.

9 Terms, provisions and limitations

(1) A wireless telegraphy licence may be granted subject to such terms, provisions and limitations as OFCOM think fit.

(2) In the case of a licence to establish a station, the limitations may, in particular, include limitations as to—

(a) the position and nature of the station;

(b) the purpose for which, the circumstances in which and the persons by whom the station may be used;

(c) the apparatus that may be installed or used in the station.

(3) In the case of any other licence, the limitations may, in particular, include limitations as to—

(a) the apparatus that may be installed or used;

(b) the places where, the purposes for which, the circumstances in which and the persons by whom the apparatus may be used.

(4) The terms, provisions and limitations may also include, in particular—

(a) terms, provisions and limitations as to strength or type of signal, as to times of use and as to the sharing of frequencies;

(b) terms, provisions or limitations imposing prohibitions on the transmission or broadcasting of particular matters by the holder of the licence;

(c) terms or provisions requiring the transmission or broadcasting of particular matters by that person.

(5) A wireless telegraphy licence may be granted—

(a) in relation to a particular station or particular apparatus; or

(b) in relation to any station or apparatus falling within a description specified in the licence;

and such a description may be expressed by reference to such factors (including factors confined to the manner in which it is established, installed or used) as OFCOM think fit.

(6) The terms, provisions and limitations of a wireless telegraphy licence granted to a person must not duplicate obligations already imposed on him by general conditions set under section 45 of the Communications Act 2003 (c 21) (power of OFCOM to set conditions in relation to electronic communications networks and services).

(7) In imposing terms, provisions or limitations on a wireless telegraphy licence, OFCOM may impose only those that they are satisfied are—

(a) objectively justifiable in relation to the networks and services to which they relate;

(b) not such as to discriminate unduly against particular persons or against a particular description of persons;

(c) proportionate to what they are intended to achieve; and

(d) in relation to what they are intended to achieve, transparent.

(8) This section has effect subject to regulations under section 14.

[4115]

NOTES

Commencement: 8 February 2007.

10 Procedure

Schedule 1 (which makes provision about the grant, revocation and variation of wireless telegraphy licences) has effect.

[4116]

NOTES

Commencement: 8 February 2007.

11 Surrender of licence

(1) Where a wireless telegraphy licence has expired or has been revoked, it is the duty of—

(a) the person to whom the licence was granted, and

(b) any other person in whose possession or under whose control the licence may be,

to cause it to be surrendered to OFCOM if required by them to do so.

(2) Subsection (1) does not apply to a licence that relates solely to receiving apparatus.

(3) A person commits an offence if—

(a) he has a duty under subsection (1) to cause a wireless telegraphy licence to be surrendered to OFCOM; and

(b) without reasonable excuse he fails or refuses to do so.

(4) A person who commits an offence under this section is liable on summary conviction to a fine not exceeding level 3 on the standard scale.

[4117]

NOTES

Commencement: 8 February 2007.

Charges etc

12 Charges for grant of licence

(1) A person to whom a wireless telegraphy licence is granted must pay to OFCOM—

(a) on the grant of the licence, and
(b) if regulations made by OFCOM so provide, subsequently at such times during its term and such times in respect of its variation or revocation as may be prescribed by the regulations,

the sums described in subsection (2).

(2) The sums are—
(a) such sums as OFCOM may prescribe by regulations, or
(b) if regulations made by OFCOM so provide, such sums (whether on the grant of the licence or subsequently) as OFCOM may determine in the particular case.

(3) Regulations under this section may—
(a) confer exemptions from provisions of the regulations in particular cases; and
(b) provide for sums paid to be refunded, in whole or in part, in such cases as may be specified in the regulations or in such cases as OFCOM think fit.

(4) On the grant of a licence in respect of which sums will or may subsequently become payable under regulations under this section, OFCOM may require such security to be given, by way of deposit or otherwise, for the payment of those sums as they think fit.

(5) Regulations under this section do not apply in relation to a licence granted in accordance with regulations under section 14.

[4118]

NOTES

Commencement: 8 February 2007.

13 Matters taken into account

(1) This section applies where OFCOM exercise a power under section 12 to prescribe sums payable in respect of wireless telegraphy licences, other than a power to prescribe sums payable where a licence is varied or revoked at the request or with the consent of the holder of the licence.

(2) OFCOM may, if they think fit in the light (in particular) of the matters to which they must have regard under section 3, prescribe sums greater than those necessary to recover costs incurred by them in connection with their radio spectrum functions.

(3) "Prescribe" means prescribe by regulations or determine in accordance with regulations.

[4119]

NOTES

Commencement: 8 February 2007.

14 Bidding for licences

(1) Having regard to the desirability of promoting the optimal use of the electromagnetic spectrum, OFCOM may by regulations provide that, in such cases as may be specified in the regulations, applications for wireless telegraphy licences must be made in accordance with a procedure that involves the making by the applicant of a bid specifying an amount that he is willing to pay to OFCOM in respect of the licence.

(2) The regulations may make provision with respect to—
(a) the grant of the licences to which they apply; and
(b) the terms, provisions and limitations subject to which such licences are granted.

(3) The regulations may, in particular—
(a) require the applicant's bid to specify the amount he is willing to pay;
(b) require that amount to be expressed—
  (i) as a cash sum;
  (ii) as a sum determined by reference to a variable (such as income attributable wholly or in part to the holding of the licence);
  (iii) as a combination of the two; or
  (iv) (at the applicant's choice) in any one of the ways falling within sub-paragraphs (i) to (iii) that is authorised by the regulations;
(c) require that amount to be expressed in terms of—

(i) the making of a single payment;
(ii) the making of periodic payments;
(iii) a combination of the two; or
(iv) (at the applicant's choice) any one of the ways falling within sub-paragraphs (i) to (iii) that is authorised by the regulations;

(d) specify requirements (for example, technical or financial requirements, requirements relating to fitness to hold the licence and requirements intended to restrict the holding of two or more wireless telegraphy licences by any one person) which must be met by applicants for a licence;

(e) require an applicant to pay a deposit to OFCOM;

(f) specify circumstances in which a deposit is, or is not, to be refundable;

(g) specify matters to be taken into account by OFCOM (in addition to the bids made in accordance with the procedure provided for in the regulations) in deciding whether, or to whom, to grant a licence;

(h) specify the other terms, provisions and limitations subject to which a licence to which the regulations apply is to be granted;

(i) make any provision referred to in section 12(3).

(4) Regulations do not require OFCOM to grant a wireless telegraphy licence on the completion of the procedure provided for in the regulations, except in such circumstances as may be provided for in the regulations.

(5) A wireless telegraphy licence granted in accordance with the regulations must specify—

(a) the sum or sums which in consequence of the bids made are, in accordance with the regulations, to be payable in respect of the licence; or

(b) the method for determining that sum or those sums;

and that sum or those sums must be paid to OFCOM by the person to whom the licence is granted in accordance with the terms of the licence.

(6) In determining the sum or sums payable in respect of a wireless telegraphy licence, regard may be had to bids made for other wireless telegraphy licences and for grants of recognised spectrum access.

(7) The regulations may provide that where a person—

(a) applies for a licence in accordance with a procedure provided for in the regulations, but

(b) subsequently refuses the licence applied for,

that person must make such payments to OFCOM as may be determined in accordance with the regulations by reference to bids made for the licence.

(8) Section 12(4) applies in relation to sums that will or may become payable under regulations under this section after the grant of a wireless telegraphy licence as it applies in relation to sums that will or may become payable under regulations under section 12.

[4120]

NOTES

Commencement: 8 February 2007.

15 Recovery

(1) This section applies in the case of a sum which is to be paid to OFCOM—

(a) under any provision of sections 12 to 14;

(b) in pursuance of any provision of any regulations under those sections; or

(c) because of any terms contained as a result of those sections in a wireless telegraphy licence.

(2) The sum must be paid to OFCOM as soon as it becomes due in accordance with that provision or those terms and, if it is not paid, it is to be recoverable by them accordingly.

[4121]

NOTES

Commencement: 8 February 2007.

16 Regulations

(1) In its application to the powers of OFCOM to make regulations under sections 12 to 14, section 122 is subject to the following provisions of this section.

(2) Subsections (4) to (6) of section 122 do not apply in any case in which it appears to OFCOM that by reason of the urgency of the matter it is inexpedient to publish a notice in accordance with section 122(4)(b).

(3) Subsections (4) to (6) of section 122 do not apply in the case of any regulations under section 14 modifying previous regulations under section 14 in a case not falling within subsection (2) of this section, if it appears to OFCOM—

(a) that the modifications would not adversely affect the interests of any person or otherwise put him in a worse position or, as regards someone else, put him at a disadvantage; and

(b) in so far as the modifications affect a procedure that has already begun, that no person would have acted differently had the modifications come into force before the procedure began.

[4122]

NOTES

Commencement: 8 February 2007.

17 Sections 12 to 16: interpretation

References in sections 12 to 16 to the grant of a wireless telegraphy licence include references to the grant of a licence by way of renewal of a previous licence.

[4123]

NOTES

Commencement: 8 February 2007.

CHAPTER 2
GRANTS OF RECOGNISED SPECTRUM ACCESS

Making of grants

18 Grant of recognised spectrum access

(1) This section applies where—

(a) a person is proposing to use or to continue to use a wireless telegraphy station or wireless telegraphy apparatus;

(b) the circumstances of the use are circumstances specified for the purposes of this section in regulations made by OFCOM;

(c) that use does not require a wireless telegraphy licence but will involve the emission of electromagnetic energy with a view to the reception of anything at places in the United Kingdom or in UK territorial sea.

(2) For the purposes of this section it is immaterial whether the emissions are from a place within the United Kingdom or from a place outside the United Kingdom.

(3) On an application by that person, OFCOM may make a grant of recognised spectrum access in respect of any use by him of anything for wireless telegraphy that is specified in the grant.

(4) A grant of recognised spectrum access made to a person shall set out, by reference to such factors as OFCOM think fit (including, so far as they think fit, frequencies, times and places of reception and strength and type of signal), the respects in which the use of anything by that person for wireless telegraphy is recognised by the grant.

(5) A grant of recognised spectrum access to a person is made by giving him a notification containing the grant.

(6) A grant of recognised spectrum access may be made subject to such restrictions and conditions as OFCOM think fit, including, in particular, restrictions or conditions as to strength or type of signal, as to times of use and as to the sharing of frequencies.

(7) The restrictions and conditions of a grant of recognised spectrum access made to a person must not duplicate obligations already imposed on him by general conditions set under section 45 of the Communications Act 2003 (c 21) (power of OFCOM to set conditions in relation to electronic communications networks and services).

(8) Where a grant of recognised spectrum access is made subject to restrictions and conditions, the restrictions and conditions must be set out in the notification by which the grant is made.

[4124]

NOTES

Commencement: 8 February 2007.

19 Procedure

Schedule 2 (which makes provision about the making, revocation and modification of grants of recognised spectrum access) has effect.

[4125]

NOTES

Commencement: 8 February 2007.

20 Effect of grant of recognised spectrum access

(1) This section applies to—

(a) OFCOM's functions under sections 8 and 9 with respect to the granting of wireless telegraphy licences;

(b) their functions under section 18 with respect to the making of grants of recognised spectrum access; and

(c) any of their other radio spectrum functions in the carrying out of which it is appropriate for them to have regard to—

(i) whether wireless telegraphy licences are in force, or

(ii) the terms, provisions or limitations of wireless telegraphy licences that are in force.

(2) In carrying out those functions, OFCOM must take into account—

(a) the existence of any grant of recognised spectrum access that is in force, and

(b) the provisions imposing the restrictions and conditions subject to which such a grant has effect,

to the same extent as they would take into account a wireless telegraphy licence with terms, provisions or limitations making equivalent provision.

[4126]

NOTES

Commencement: 8 February 2007.

Charges etc

21 Charges for grant of recognised spectrum access

(1) A person to whom a grant of recognised spectrum access is made must pay to OFCOM—

(a) on the making of the grant, and

(b) if regulations made by OFCOM so provide, subsequently at such times during its term and such times in respect of its modification or revocation as may be prescribed by the regulations,

the sums described in subsection (2).

(2) The sums are—

(a) such sums as OFCOM may prescribe by regulations, or

(b) if regulations made by OFCOM so provide, such sums (whether on the making of the grant or subsequently) as OFCOM may determine in the particular case.

(3) Regulations under this section may—

(a) confer exemptions from provisions of the regulations in particular cases; and
(b) provide for sums paid to be refunded, in whole or in part, in such cases as may be specified in the regulations or in such cases as OFCOM think fit.

(4) On the making of a grant of recognised spectrum access in respect of which sums will or may subsequently become payable under regulations under this section, OFCOM may require such security to be given, by way of deposit or otherwise, for the payment of those sums as they think fit.

(5) Regulations under this section do not apply in relation to a grant of recognised spectrum access made in accordance with regulations under section 23.

[4127]

NOTES

Commencement: 8 February 2007.

22 Matters taken into account

(1) This section applies where OFCOM exercise a power under section 21 to prescribe sums payable in respect of grants of recognised spectrum access, other than a power to prescribe sums payable where a grant is modified or revoked at the request or with the consent of the holder of the grant.

(2) OFCOM may, if they think fit in the light (in particular) of the matters to which they must have regard under section 3, prescribe sums greater than those necessary to recover costs incurred by them in connection with their radio spectrum functions.

(3) "Prescribe" means prescribe by regulations or determine in accordance with regulations.

[4128]

NOTES

Commencement: 8 February 2007.

23 Bidding for grants

(1) Having regard to the desirability of promoting the optimal use of the electromagnetic spectrum, OFCOM may by regulations provide that, in such cases as may be specified in the regulations, applications for grants of recognised spectrum access must be made in accordance with a procedure that involves the making by the applicant of a bid specifying an amount that he is willing to pay to OFCOM in respect of the grant.

(2) The regulations may make provision with respect to—
(a) the grants to which they apply; and
(b) the restrictions and conditions subject to which such grants are made.

(3) The regulations may, in particular—
(a) require the applicant's bid to specify the amount he is willing to pay;
(b) require that amount to be expressed—
  (i) as a cash sum;
  (ii) as a sum determined by reference to a variable (such as income attributable wholly or in part to the use of wireless telegraphy to which the grant relates);
  (iii) as a combination of the two; or
  (iv) (at the applicant's choice) in any one of the ways falling within sub-paragraphs (i) to (iii) that is authorised by the regulations;
(c) require that amount to be expressed in terms of—
  (i) the making of a single payment;
  (ii) the making of periodic payments;
  (iii) a combination of the two; or
  (iv) (at the applicant's choice) any one of the ways falling within sub-paragraphs (i) to (iii) that is authorised by the regulations;
(d) specify requirements (for example, technical or financial requirements, requirements relating to the use of wireless telegraphy to which the grant relates and requirements intended to restrict the holding of two or more grants of recognised spectrum access by any one person) which must be met by applicants for a grant;

PART VI TELECOMMUNICATIONS

(e) require an applicant to pay a deposit to OFCOM;
(f) specify circumstances in which a deposit is, or is not, to be refundable;
(g) specify matters to be taken into account by OFCOM (in addition to the bids made in accordance with the procedure provided for in the regulations) in deciding whether, or to whom, to make a grant of recognised spectrum access;
(h) specify the other restrictions and conditions subject to which a grant to which the regulations apply is to be made;
(i) make any provision referred to in section 21(3).

(4) Regulations do not require OFCOM to make a grant of recognised spectrum access on the completion of the procedure provided for in the regulations, except in such circumstances as may be provided for in the regulations.

(5) A grant of recognised spectrum access made in accordance with the regulations must specify—
(a) the sum or sums which in consequence of the bids made are, in accordance with the regulations, to be payable in respect of the grant; or
(b) the method for determining that sum or those sums;
and that sum or those sums must be paid to OFCOM by the person to whom the grant is made in accordance with the terms of the grant.

(6) In determining the sum or sums payable in respect of a grant, regard may be had to bids made for other grants of recognised spectrum access and for wireless telegraphy licences.

(7) The regulations may provide that where a person—
(a) applies for a grant of recognised spectrum access in accordance with a procedure provided for in the regulations, but
(b) subsequently refuses the grant applied for,
that person must make such payments to OFCOM as may be determined in accordance with the regulations by reference to bids made for the grant.

(8) Section 21(4) applies in relation to sums that will or may become payable under regulations under this section after the making of a grant of recognised spectrum access as it applies in relation to sums that will or may become payable under regulations under section 21.

[4129]

NOTES

Commencement: 8 February 2007.

24 Recovery

(1) This section applies in the case of a sum which is to be paid to OFCOM—
(a) under any provision of sections 21 to 23;
(b) in pursuance of any provision of any regulations under those sections; or
(c) because of any conditions contained as a result of those sections in a grant of recognised spectrum access.

(2) The sum must be paid to OFCOM as soon as it becomes due in accordance with that provision or those conditions and, if it is not paid, it is to be recoverable by them accordingly.

[4130]

NOTES

Commencement: 8 February 2007.

25 Regulations

(1) In its application to the powers of OFCOM to make regulations under sections 21 to 23, section 122 is subject to the following provisions of this section.

(2) Subsections (4) to (6) of section 122 do not apply in any case in which it appears to OFCOM that by reason of the urgency of the matter it is inexpedient to publish a notice in accordance with section 122(4)(b).

(3) Subsections (4) to (6) of section 122 do not apply in the case of any regulations under section 23 modifying previous regulations under section 23 in a case not falling within subsection (2) of this section, if it appears to OFCOM—

(a) that the modifications would not adversely affect the interests of any person or otherwise put him in a worse position or, as regards someone else, put him at a disadvantage; and

(b) in so far as the modifications affect a procedure that has already begun, that no person would have acted differently had the modifications come into force before the procedure began.

[4131]

NOTES

Commencement: 8 February 2007.

26 Sections 21 to 25: interpretation

References in sections 21 to 25 to the making of a grant of recognised spectrum access include references to the making of a grant by way of renewal of a previous grant.

[4132]

NOTES

Commencement: 8 February 2007.

CHAPTER 3
MANAGEMENT OF RADIO SPECTRUM

General

27 Conversion into and from wireless telegraphy licences

OFCOM may by regulations make provision for—

(a) the conversion, on the application of the licence holder, of a wireless telegraphy licence into a grant of recognised spectrum access; and

(b) the conversion, on the application of the holder of the grant, of a grant of recognised spectrum access into a wireless telegraphy licence.

[4133]

NOTES

Commencement: 8 February 2007.

28 Payments by the Crown

(1) The Secretary of State may, out of money provided by Parliament, make payments to OFCOM of such amounts as he considers appropriate in respect of—

(a) the establishment and use, by or on behalf of the Crown, of a wireless telegraphy station;

(b) the installation and use, by or on behalf of the Crown, of wireless telegraphy apparatus;

(c) any grant of recognised spectrum access made to the Crown.

(2) The payments made under this section are to be made—

(a) at such times, and

(b) so far as made in relation to use, in relation to such periods,

as the Secretary of State considers appropriate.

[4134]

NOTES

Commencement: 8 February 2007.

29 Limitations on authorised spectrum use

(1) If they consider it appropriate to impose limitations on the use of particular frequencies for the purpose of securing the efficient use of the electromagnetic spectrum, OFCOM must make an order imposing the limitations.

(2) An order under this section may do one or both of the following—

(a) specify frequencies for the use of which OFCOM will grant or make only a limited number of wireless telegraphy licences and grants of recognised spectrum access; or

(b) specify uses for which, on specified frequencies, OFCOM will grant or make only a limited number of wireless telegraphy licences and grants of recognised spectrum access.

(3) Where OFCOM make an order under this section, it must set out the criteria which OFCOM will apply in determining in accordance with the order—

(a) the limit on the number of wireless telegraphy licences and grants of recognised spectrum access to be granted or made for the specified frequencies or uses;

(b) the persons to whom licences will be granted or grants of recognised spectrum access made.

(4) OFCOM must satisfy themselves that any criteria set out as a result of subsection (3) are—

(a) objectively justifiable in relation to the frequencies or uses to which they relate;

(b) not such as to discriminate unduly against particular persons or against a particular description of persons;

(c) proportionate to what they are intended to achieve; and

(d) in relation to what they are intended to achieve, transparent.

(5) OFCOM must exercise—

(a) their powers under Chapter 1 of this Part with respect to wireless telegraphy licences, and

(b) their powers under Chapter 2 of this Part with respect to grants of recognised spectrum access,

in accordance with the orders for the time being in force under this section.

(6) OFCOM must keep under review any order for the time being in force under this section.

(7) OFCOM must make an order revoking or amending the provisions of an order under this section if, on reviewing it, they consider it necessary to do so for the purpose of securing the efficient use of the electromagnetic spectrum.

(8) An order under this section may make provision by reference to determinations which—

(a) are made from time to time by OFCOM in accordance with the provisions of such an order; and

(b) are published by them from time to time in such manner as may be provided for in such an order.

[4135]

NOTES

Commencement: 8 February 2007.

30 Spectrum trading

(1) OFCOM may by regulations authorise the transfer to another person by—

(a) the holder of a wireless telegraphy licence, or

(b) the holder of a grant of recognised spectrum access,

of rights and obligations arising as a result of such a licence or grant.

(2) The transfers that may be so authorised are—

(a) transfers of all or any of the rights and obligations under a licence or grant such that the rights and obligations of the person making the transfer become rights and obligations of the transferee to the exclusion of the person making the transfer;

(b) transfers of all or any of those rights and obligations such that the transferred rights and obligations become rights and obligations of the transferee while continuing, concurrently, to be rights and obligations of the person making the transfer; and

(c) transfers falling within either of paragraphs (a) and (b) under which the rights and obligations that are acquired by the transferee take effect—

(i) if they are rights and obligations under a wireless telegraphy licence, as rights and obligations under a grant of recognised spectrum access; and

(ii) if they are rights and obligations under a grant of recognised spectrum access, as rights and obligations under a wireless telegraphy licence.

(3) Regulations authorising the transfer of rights and obligations under a wireless telegraphy licence or a grant of recognised spectrum access may—

(a) authorise a partial transfer—

(i) to be made by reference to such factors and apportionments, and

(ii) to have effect in relation to such matters and periods,

as may be described in, or determined in accordance with, the regulations;

(b) by reference to such factors (including the terms and conditions of the licence or grant in question) as may be specified in or determined in accordance with the regulations, restrict the circumstances in which, the extent to which and the manner in which a transfer may be made;

(c) require the approval or consent of OFCOM for the making of a transfer;

(d) provide for a transfer to be effected by the surrender of a wireless telegraphy licence or grant of recognised spectrum access and the grant or making of a new one in respect of the transfer;

(e) confer power on OFCOM to direct that a transfer must not be made, or is to be made only after compliance with such conditions as OFCOM may impose in accordance with the regulations;

(f) authorise OFCOM to require the payment to them of such sums as may be determined by or in accordance with the regulations—

(i) in respect of determinations made by OFCOM for the purposes of the regulations, or

(ii) in respect of an approval or consent given for those purposes;

(g) make provision for the giving of security (whether by the giving of deposits or otherwise) in respect of sums payable in pursuance of any regulations under this section;

(h) make provision as to the circumstances in which security given under such regulations is to be returned or may be retained;

(i) impose requirements as to the procedure to be followed for the making of a transfer and, in particular, as to the notification about a transfer that must be given to OFCOM, or must be published, both in advance of its being made and afterwards;

(j) impose requirements as to the records to be kept in connection with any transfer, and as to the persons to whom such records are to be made available;

(k) set out the matters to be taken into account in the making of determinations under regulations under this section.

(4) The transfer of rights and obligations under a wireless telegraphy licence or grant of recognised spectrum access is void except to the extent that it is made—

(a) in accordance with regulations under this section; or

(b) in accordance with a provision falling within subsection (5).

(5) The provision is one which—

(a) is contained in a wireless telegraphy licence granted before 29th December 2003 or in the first or any subsequent renewal on or after that date of a licence so granted; and

(b) allows the holder of the licence to confer the benefit of the licence on another in respect of any station or apparatus to which the licence relates.

(6) A transfer is also void if it is made in contravention of a direction given by OFCOM in exercise of a power conferred by regulations under this section.

[4136]

NOTES

Commencement: 8 February 2007.

Wireless telegraphy register

31 Wireless telegraphy register

(1) OFCOM may by regulations make provision for the establishment and maintenance of a register of relevant information.

(2) OFCOM may include relevant information in the register if, and only if, it is relevant information of a description prescribed by regulations under this section.

(3) Information is relevant information for the purposes of subsection (1) if it relates to—

(a) the grant, renewal, transfer, variation or revocation of wireless telegraphy licences; or

(b) the making, renewal, transfer, modification or revocation of grants of recognised spectrum access.

(4) Subject to such conditions (including conditions as to payment) as may be prescribed by regulations under this section, a register established by virtue of subsection (1) is to be open to inspection by the public.

[4137]

NOTES

Commencement: 8 February 2007.

Statistical information

32 Statistical information

(1) OFCOM may require a person who is using or has established, installed or used a wireless telegraphy station or wireless telegraphy apparatus to provide OFCOM with all such information relating to—

(a) the establishment, installation or use of the station or apparatus, and

(b) any related matters,

as OFCOM may require for statistical purposes.

(2) Subsection (1) has effect subject to the following provisions of this section.

(3) OFCOM may not require the provision of information under this section except—

(a) by a demand for information that sets out OFCOM's reasons for requiring the information and the statistical purposes for which it is required; and

(b) where the making of a demand for that information is proportionate to the use to which the information is to be put in the carrying out of OFCOM's functions.

(4) A demand for information required under this section must be contained in a notice given to the person from whom the information is required.

(5) A person required to give information under this section must provide it in such manner and within such reasonable period as may be specified by OFCOM.

[4138]

NOTES

Commencement: 8 February 2007.

33 Failure to provide information etc

(1) A person commits an offence if he fails to provide information in accordance with a requirement of OFCOM under section 32.

(2) In proceedings against a person for an offence under subsection (1) it is a defence for the person to show—

(a) that it was not reasonably practicable for him to comply with the requirement within the period specified by OFCOM; but

(b) that he has taken all reasonable steps to provide the required information after the end of that period.

(3) A person who commits an offence under subsection (1) is liable on summary conviction to a fine not exceeding level 3 on the standard scale.

(4) A person commits an offence if—

(a) in pursuance of a requirement under section 32, he provides information that is false in any material particular; and

(b) at the time he provides it, he knows it to be false or is reckless as to whether or not it is false.

(5) A person who commits an offence under subsection (4) is liable on summary conviction to a fine not exceeding level 5 on the standard scale.

[4139]

NOTES

Commencement: 8 February 2007.

34 Statement of policy

(1) OFCOM must prepare and publish a statement of their general policy with respect to—

(a) the exercise of their powers under section 32; and

(b) the uses to which they are proposing to put information obtained under that section.

(2) OFCOM may from time to time revise that statement as they think fit.

(3) Where OFCOM make a statement under this section (or revise it), they must publish the statement (or the revised statement) in such manner as they consider appropriate for bringing it to the attention of persons who, in their opinion, are likely to be affected by it.

(4) OFCOM must, in exercising their powers under section 32, have regard to the statement for the time being in force under this section.

[4140]

NOTES

Commencement: 8 February 2007.

CHAPTER 4 ENFORCEMENT

Unauthorised use etc

35 Unauthorised use etc of wireless telegraphy station or apparatus

(1) A person commits an offence if he contravenes section 8.

(2) A person who commits an offence under this section consisting in the establishment or use of a wireless telegraphy station, or the installation or use of wireless telegraphy apparatus, for the purpose of making a broadcast is liable—

(a) on summary conviction, to imprisonment for a term not exceeding 12 months or to a fine not exceeding the statutory maximum or to both;

(b) on conviction on indictment, to imprisonment for a term not exceeding two years or to a fine or to both.

(3) In the application of subsection (2) to Scotland or Northern Ireland the reference to 12 months is to be read as a reference to six months.

(4) A person who commits an offence under this section consisting in the installation or use of receiving apparatus is liable on summary conviction to a fine not exceeding level 3 on the standard scale.

(5) A person who commits an offence under this section other than one falling within subsection (2) or (4) is liable on summary conviction to imprisonment for a term not exceeding 51 weeks or to a fine not exceeding level 5 on the standard scale or to both.

(6) In the application of subsection (5) to Scotland or Northern Ireland the reference to 51 weeks is to be read as a reference to six months.

(7) In this section "broadcast" has the same meaning as in Part 5.

[4141]

NOTES

Commencement: 8 February 2007.

36 Keeping available for unauthorised use

(1) A person who has a wireless telegraphy station or wireless telegraphy apparatus in his possession or under his control commits an offence if—

(a) he intends to use it in contravention of section 8; or
(b) he knows, or has reasonable cause to believe, that another person intends to use it in contravention of that section.

(2) A person who commits an offence under this section where the relevant contravention of section 8 would constitute an offence to which section 35(2) applies is liable—

(a) on summary conviction, to imprisonment for a term not exceeding 12 months or to a fine not exceeding the statutory maximum or to both;
(b) on conviction on indictment, to imprisonment for a term not exceeding two years or to a fine or to both.

(3) In the application of subsection (2) to Scotland or Northern Ireland the reference to 12 months is to be read as a reference to six months.

(4) A person who commits an offence under this section in relation to receiving apparatus is liable on summary conviction to a fine not exceeding level 3 on the standard scale.

(5) A person who commits an offence under this section other than one falling within subsection (2) or (4) is liable on summary conviction to imprisonment for a term not exceeding 51 weeks or to a fine not exceeding level 5 on the standard scale or to both.

(6) In the application of subsection (5) to Scotland or Northern Ireland the reference to 51 weeks is to be read as a reference to six months.

[4142]

NOTES

Commencement: 8 February 2007.

37 Allowing premises to be used for unlawful broadcasting

(1) A person who is in charge of premises that are used for unlawful broadcasting commits an offence if—

(a) he knowingly causes or permits the premises to be so used; or
(b) he has reasonable cause to believe that the premises are being so used but fails to take such steps as are reasonable in the circumstances of the case to prevent them from being so used.

(2) A person who commits an offence under this section is liable—

(a) on summary conviction, to imprisonment for a term not exceeding 12 months or to a fine not exceeding the statutory maximum or to both;
(b) on conviction on indictment, to imprisonment for a term not exceeding two years or to a fine or to both.

(3) In the application of subsection (2) to Scotland or Northern Ireland the reference to 12 months is to be read as a reference to six months.

(4) For the purposes of this section a person is in charge of premises if—

(a) he is the owner or occupier of the premises; or
(b) he has, or acts or assists in, the management or control of the premises.

(5) For the purposes of this section premises are used for unlawful broadcasting if they are used—

(a) for making an unlawful broadcast; or
(b) for sending signals for the operation or control of apparatus used for the purpose of making an unlawful broadcast from another place.

(6) For the purposes of this section a broadcast is unlawful if—

(a) it is made by means of the use of a wireless telegraphy station or wireless telegraphy apparatus in contravention of section 8; or
(b) the making of the broadcast contravenes a provision of Part 5.

(7) In this section—

"broadcast" has the same meaning as in Part 5;

"premises" includes any place and, in particular, includes—

(a) a vehicle, ship or aircraft; and

(b) a structure or other object (whether movable or not, and whether on land or not).

[4143]

NOTES

Commencement: 8 February 2007.

38 Facilitating unauthorised broadcasting

(1) This section applies in the case of a broadcasting station from which unauthorised broadcasts are made.

(2) A person commits an offence if—

(a) he participates in the management, financing, operation or day-to-day running of the broadcasting station knowing, or having reasonable cause to believe, that unauthorised broadcasts are made by the station;

(b) he supplies, instals, repairs or maintains wireless telegraphy apparatus or any other item knowing, or having reasonable cause to believe—

(i) that the apparatus or other item is to be, or is, used for the purpose of facilitating the operation or day-to-day running of the broadcasting station, and

(ii) that unauthorised broadcasts are made by the station;

(c) he renders any other service to a person knowing, or having reasonable cause to believe—

(i) that the rendering of the service to the person will facilitate the operation or day-to-day running of the broadcasting station, and

(ii) that unauthorised broadcasts are made by the station;

(d) he supplies a film or sound recording knowing, or having reasonable cause to believe, that an unauthorised broadcast of it is to be made by the broadcasting station;

(e) he makes a literary, dramatic or musical work knowing, or having reasonable cause to believe, that an unauthorised broadcast of it is to be made by the broadcasting station;

(f) he makes an artistic work knowing, or having reasonable cause to believe, that an unauthorised broadcast including that work is to be made by the broadcasting station;

(g) he participates in an unauthorised broadcast made by the broadcasting station knowing, or having reasonable cause to believe, that unauthorised broadcasts are made by the station;

(h) he advertises, or invites another to advertise, by means of an unauthorised broadcast made by the broadcasting station knowing, or having reasonable cause to believe, that unauthorised broadcasts are made by the station;

(i) he publishes the times or other details of unauthorised broadcasts made by the broadcasting station, or (otherwise than by publishing such details) publishes an advertisement of matter calculated to promote the station (whether directly or indirectly), knowing, or having reasonable cause to believe, that unauthorised broadcasts are made by the station.

(3) For the purposes of this section a person participates in a broadcast only if he is actually present—

(a) as an announcer;

(b) as a performer or one of the performers concerned in an entertainment given; or

(c) as the deliverer of a speech.

(4) The cases in which a person is to be taken for the purposes of this section as advertising by means of a broadcast include any case in which he causes or allows it to be stated, suggested or implied that entertainment included in the broadcast—

(a) has been supplied by him; or

(b) is provided wholly or partly at his expense.

(5) In proceedings for an offence under this section consisting in supplying a thing or rendering a service, it is a defence for the defendant to prove that he was obliged, under or by virtue of any enactment, to supply the thing or render the service.

(6) A person who commits an offence under this section is liable—

(a) on summary conviction, to imprisonment for a term not exceeding 12 months or to a fine not exceeding the statutory maximum or to both;
(b) on conviction on indictment, to imprisonment for a term not exceeding two years or to a fine or to both.

(7) In the application of subsection (6) to Scotland or Northern Ireland the reference to 12 months is to be read as a reference to six months.

(8) In this section—
"broadcast" has the same meaning as in Part 5;
"broadcasting station" means a business or other operation (whether or not in the nature of a commercial venture) that is engaged in the making of broadcasts;
"unauthorised broadcast" means a broadcast made by means of the use of a wireless telegraphy station or wireless telegraphy apparatus in contravention of section 8.

[4144]

NOTES

Commencement: 8 February 2007.

Procedures for contraventions

39 Contravention of terms, etc

(1) Where OFCOM determine that there are reasonable grounds for believing that a person is contravening, or has contravened—
(a) a term, provision or limitation of a wireless telegraphy licence, or
(b) a term, provision or limitation of an exemption under section 8(3),
they may give that person a notification under this section.

(2) A notification under this section—
(a) sets out the determination made by OFCOM;
(b) specifies the term, provision or limitation, and the contravention, in respect of which that determination has been made; and
(c) specifies the period during which the person notified has an opportunity of doing the things specified in subsection (3).

(3) The things are—
(a) making representations about the matters notified; and
(b) complying with any notified term, provision or limitation of which he remains in contravention.

(4) Subject to subsections (5) to (7), the period for doing those things must be the period of one month beginning with the day after the one on which the notification was given.

(5) OFCOM may, if they think fit, allow a longer period for doing those things—
(a) by specifying a longer period in the notification; or
(b) by subsequently, on one or more occasions, extending the specified period.

(6) The person notified has a shorter period for doing those things if a shorter period is agreed between OFCOM and the person notified.

(7) The person notified also has a shorter period if—
(a) OFCOM have reasonable grounds for believing that the case is a case of repeated contravention;
(b) they have determined that, in those circumstances, a shorter period would be appropriate; and
(c) the shorter period has been specified in the notification.

[4145]

NOTES

Commencement: 8 February 2007.

40 Repeated contravention

(1) For the purposes of section 39 a contravention is a repeated contravention, in relation to a notification with respect to that contravention, if—

(a) in the case of a contravention of a term, provision or limitation of a wireless telegraphy licence, it falls within subsection (2) or (3); or

(b) in the case of a contravention of a term, provision or limitation of an exemption under section 8(3), it falls within subsection (4) or (5).

(2) A contravention of a term, provision or limitation of a wireless telegraphy licence falls within this subsection if—

(a) a previous notification under section 39 has been given in respect of the same contravention or in respect of another contravention of a term, provision or limitation of the same licence;

(b) the person who was given that notification subsequently took steps for remedying the notified contravention; and

(c) the subsequent notification is given no more than 12 months after the day of the giving of the previous notification.

(3) A contravention of a term, provision or limitation of a wireless telegraphy licence falls within this subsection if—

(a) the person concerned has been convicted of an offence under section 35 in respect of the contravention to which the notification relates or in respect of another contravention of a term, provision or limitation of the same licence; and

(b) the subsequent notification is given before the end of the period of 12 months from the contravention in respect of which that person was convicted of that offence.

(4) A contravention of a term, provision or limitation of an exemption falls within this subsection if—

(a) a previous notification under section 39 has been given in respect of the same contravention or in respect of another contravention of the same term, provision or limitation;

(b) the person who was given that notification subsequently took steps for remedying the notified contravention; and

(c) the subsequent notification is given no more than 12 months after the day of the giving of the previous notification.

(5) A contravention of a term, provision or limitation of an exemption falls within this subsection if—

(a) the person concerned has been convicted of an offence under section 35 in respect of the contravention to which the notification relates or in respect of another contravention of the same term, provision or limitation; and

(b) the subsequent notification is given before the end of the period of 12 months from the contravention in respect of which that person was convicted of that offence.

(6) In calculating the periods of 12 months mentioned in subsections (3)(b) and (5)(b), the period between the institution of the criminal proceedings which led to the conviction and the conclusion of those proceedings is to be left out of account.

(7) For the purposes of subsection (6) criminal proceedings are taken to be concluded when no further appeal against conviction may be brought without the permission of the court and—

(a) in a case where there is no fixed period within which that permission can be sought, permission has been refused or has not been sought; or

(b) in a case where there is a fixed period within which that permission can be sought, that permission has been refused or that period has expired without permission having been sought.

(8) References to remedying a contravention include references to—

(a) doing any thing the failure to do which, or the failure to do which within a particular period or before a particular time, constituted the whole or a part of the contravention;

(b) paying an amount to a person by way of compensation for loss or damage suffered by that person in consequence of the contravention;

(c) paying an amount to a person by way of compensation in respect of annoyance, inconvenience or anxiety to which he has been put in consequence of the contravention;

(d) otherwise acting in a manner that constitutes an acknowledgement that the notified contravention did occur.

PART VI TELECOMMUNICATIONS

(9) References to a contravention of a term, provision or limitation of a wireless telegraphy licence include references to a contravention of a term, provision or limitation contained in a previous licence of which the licence in question is a direct or indirect renewal. **[4146]**

NOTES

Commencement: 8 February 2007.

41 Procedure for prosecutions

(1) This section applies to proceedings against a person ("the defendant") for an offence under section 35 consisting in the contravention of—

- (a) the terms, provisions or limitations of a wireless telegraphy licence; or
- (b) the terms, provisions or limitations of an exemption under section 8(3).

(2) Proceedings to which this section applies are not to be brought unless, before they are brought, OFCOM have—

- (a) given the defendant a notification under section 39 in respect of the contravention to which the proceedings relate; and
- (b) considered any representations about the matters notified which were made by the defendant within the period allowed under that section.

(3) Proceedings to which this section applies are not to be brought against a person in respect of a contravention if—

- (a) it is a contravention to which a notification given to that person under section 39 relates; and
- (b) that person has, during the period allowed under that section, complied with the notified term, provision or limitation.

(4) Subsection (2) does not apply where OFCOM have certified that it would be inappropriate to follow the procedure in section 39 because of an immediate risk of—

- (a) a serious threat to the safety of the public, to public health or to national security; or
- (b) serious economic or operational problems for persons (other than the defendant) who—
  - (i) use wireless telegraphy stations or wireless telegraphy apparatus; or
  - (ii) are communications providers or make associated facilities available.

(5) Where—

- (a) proceedings to which this section applies are as a result of subsection (4) brought without a notification having been given to the defendant, and
- (b) the defendant is convicted in those proceedings of the offence under section 35,

the court, in determining how to deal with that person, must have regard, in particular, to the matters specified in subsection (6).

(6) The matters are—

- (a) whether the defendant has ceased to be in contravention of the terms, provisions or limitations in question and (if so) when; and
- (b) any steps taken by the defendant (whether before or after the commencement of the proceedings) for securing compliance with the obligations imposed on him by virtue of those terms, provisions or limitations.

(7) Where—

- (a) OFCOM give a notification under section 39 in respect of a contravention, and
- (b) that notification is given before the end of six months after the day of the contravention,

the time for the bringing of proceedings for a summary offence in respect of that contravention shall be extended until the end of six months from the end of the period allowed, in the case of that notification, for doing the things mentioned in section 39(3).

(8) Subsection (7) has effect notwithstanding anything in—

- (a) section 127 of the Magistrates' Courts Act 1980 (c 43) (limitation on time for bringing summary proceedings), or
- (b) Article 19 of the Magistrates' Courts (Northern Ireland) Order 1981 (SI 1981/1675 (NI 26)) (equivalent provision for Northern Ireland).

[4147]

NOTES

Commencement: 8 February 2007.

42 Special procedure for contraventions by multiplex licence holders

(1) OFCOM may impose a penalty on a person if—

(a) that person is or has been in contravention in any respect of the terms, provisions or limitations of a general multiplex licence;

(b) the contravention relates to terms, provisions or limitations falling within section 9(4)(b) or (c);

(c) OFCOM have notified that person that it appears to them that those terms, provisions or limitations have been contravened in that respect; and

(d) that contravention is not one in respect of which proceedings for an offence under this Chapter have been brought against that person.

(2) Where OFCOM impose a penalty on a person under this section, they must—

(a) notify that person of that decision and of their reasons for that decision; and

(b) in that notification, fix a reasonable period after it is given as the period within which the penalty is to be paid.

(3) A penalty imposed under this section—

(a) must be paid to OFCOM; and

(b) if not paid within the period fixed by them, is to be recoverable by them accordingly.

(4) No proceedings for an offence under this Chapter may be commenced against a person in respect of a contravention in respect of which a penalty has been imposed by OFCOM under this section.

(5) A licence is a general multiplex licence, in relation to the time of a contravention, if—

(a) it is a wireless telegraphy licence containing terms, provisions or limitations as a result of which the services for the purposes of which the use of the licensed station or apparatus is authorised are confined to, or are allowed to include, one or more multiplex services; and

(b) at that time, there is no licence under Part 1 or 2 of the Broadcasting Act 1996 (c 55) in force in respect of a multiplex service to be broadcast using that station or apparatus.

(6) "Multiplex service" means—

(a) a service for broadcasting for general reception consisting in the packaging together of two or more services that are provided for inclusion together in that service by a combination of the relevant information in digital form; or

(b) a service provided with a view to its being a service falling within paragraph (a) but in the case of which only one service is for the time being comprised in digital form in what is provided.

[4148]

NOTES

Commencement: 8 February 2007.

43 Amount of penalty under section 42

(1) The amount of a penalty imposed under section 42 is to be such amount as OFCOM think fit.

(2) But the amount of the penalty may not exceed the greater of—

(a) £250,000; and

(b) 5 per cent of the relevant amount of gross revenue.

(3) In subsection (2) "the relevant amount of gross revenue" means the amount specified in section 44.

(4) The Secretary of State may by order amend this section so as to substitute a different amount for the amount for the time being specified in subsection (2)(a).

(5) No order is to be made containing provision authorised by subsection (4) unless a draft of the order has been laid before Parliament and approved by a resolution of each House.

[4149]

NOTES

Commencement: 8 February 2007.

44 Relevant amount of gross revenue

(1) The relevant amount of gross revenue for the purposes of section 43, in relation to a penalty imposed on a person, is—

(a) where the last accounting period of that person which falls before the contravention was a period of 12 months, the relevant part of his gross revenue for that period; and

(b) in any other case, the amount which, by making any appropriate apportionments or other adjustments of the relevant part of his gross revenue for the accounting period or periods mentioned in subsection (2), is computed to be the amount representing the annual rate for the relevant part of his gross revenue.

(2) The accounting period or periods referred to in subsection (1) are—

(a) every accounting period of his to end within the period of 12 months immediately preceding the contravention; and

(b) if there is no such accounting period, the accounting period of his which is current at the time of the contravention.

(3) A reference to the relevant part of a person's gross revenue, in relation to a contravention of the terms, provisions or limitations of a licence, is a reference to so much of his gross revenue as is attributable to the provision of the service to which that licence relates.

(4) For the purposes of this section—

(a) the gross revenue of a person for a period, and

(b) the extent to which a part of a person's gross revenue is attributable to the provision of any service,

is to be ascertained in accordance with such principles as may be set out in a statement made by OFCOM.

(5) Such a statement may provide for the amount of a person's gross revenue for an accounting period that is current when the amount falls to be calculated to be taken to be the amount estimated by OFCOM, in accordance with the principles set out in the statement, to be the amount that will be his gross revenue for that period.

(6) OFCOM may revise a statement made under subsection (4) from time to time.

(7) A statement made or revised under this section may set out different principles for different cases.

(8) Before making or revising a statement under this section, OFCOM must consult the Secretary of State and the Treasury.

(9) OFCOM must—

(a) publish the statement made under subsection (4) and every revision of it; and

(b) send a copy of the statement and of every such revision to the Secretary of State;

and the Secretary of State must lay copies of the statement and of every such revision before each House of Parliament.

(10) Sections 32 and 33 are to apply for the purpose of ascertaining the amount of a person's gross revenue for any period for the purposes of section 43 and this section as they apply for the purpose of obtaining information for statistical purposes about matters relating to the establishment, installation or use by that person of a wireless telegraphy station or wireless telegraphy apparatus.

(11) In this section—

"accounting period", in relation to a person, means a period in respect of which accounts of the undertaking carried on by him are prepared or, if one such period is comprised in another, whichever of those periods is or is closest to a 12 month period;

"gross revenue", in relation to a person, means the gross revenue of an undertaking carried on by that person.

[4150]

NOTES
Commencement: 8 February 2007.

CHAPTER 5
MISCELLANEOUS

Regulations about wireless telegraphy

45 Regulations

(1) OFCOM may make regulations prescribing the things that are to be done, or not done, in connection with the use of a wireless telegraphy station or wireless telegraphy apparatus.

(2) Regulations under subsection (1) may, in particular, require the use of a wireless telegraphy station or wireless telegraphy apparatus to cease on the demand of such persons as may be prescribed by or under the regulations.

(3) OFCOM may make regulations imposing on a person—

(a) to whom a wireless telegraphy licence relating to a wireless telegraphy station or wireless telegraphy apparatus is granted, or

(b) who is in possession or control of such a station or such apparatus,

the obligations mentioned in subsection (4).

(4) The obligations are—

(a) obligations as to permitting and facilitating the inspection of the station or apparatus;

(b) obligations as to the condition in which the station or apparatus is to be kept;

(c) in the case of a station or apparatus for the establishment, installation or use of which a wireless telegraphy licence is necessary, obligations as to the production of the licence, or of such other evidence of the licensing of the station or apparatus as may be prescribed by the regulations.

(5) OFCOM may make regulations requiring the holder of a wireless telegraphy licence in respect of which sums are or may become due after the grant of the licence, or after its renewal, to keep and produce such accounts and records as may be specified in the regulations.

(6) OFCOM may make regulations requiring the holder of a wireless telegraphy licence authorising the establishment or use of a wireless telegraphy station to exhibit at the station such notices as may be specified in the regulations.

(7) Regulations under this section have effect subject to regulations under section 14.

(8) Nothing in regulations under this section requires a person to concede any form of right of entry into a private dwelling-house for the purpose of permitting or facilitating the inspection of receiving apparatus.

(9) The approval of the Secretary of State is required for the making by OFCOM of regulations under this section.

(10) A statutory instrument containing regulations made by OFCOM under this section is subject to annulment in pursuance of a resolution of either House of Parliament.

[4151]

NOTES
Commencement: 8 February 2007.

46 Offences

(1) A person commits an offence if—

(a) he contravenes regulations made under section 45; or

(b) he causes or permits a wireless telegraphy station or wireless telegraphy apparatus to be used in contravention of regulations made under that section.

PART VI TELECOMMUNICATIONS

(2) A person who commits an offence under this section consisting in a contravention, in relation to receiving apparatus, of regulations made under section 45 is liable on summary conviction to a fine not exceeding level 3 on the standard scale.

(3) A person who commits an offence under this section other than one falling within subsection (2) is liable on summary conviction to a fine not exceeding level 5 on the standard scale.

[4152]

NOTES

Commencement: 8 February 2007.

Misuse of wireless telegraphy

47 Misleading messages

(1) A person commits an offence if, by means of wireless telegraphy, he sends or attempts to send a message to which this section applies.

(2) This section applies to a message which, to the person's knowledge—

(a) is false or misleading; and

(b) is likely to prejudice the efficiency of a safety of life service or to endanger the safety of a person or of a ship, aircraft or vehicle.

(3) This section applies in particular to a message which, to the person's knowledge, falsely suggests that a ship or aircraft—

(a) is in distress or in need of assistance; or

(b) is not in distress or not in need of assistance.

(4) A person who commits an offence under this section is liable—

(a) on summary conviction, to imprisonment for a term not exceeding 12 months or to a fine not exceeding the statutory maximum or to both;

(b) on conviction on indictment, to imprisonment for a term not exceeding two years or to a fine or to both.

(5) In the application of subsection (4) to Scotland or Northern Ireland the reference to 12 months is to be read as a reference to six months.

[4153]

NOTES

Commencement: 8 February 2007.

48 Interception and disclosure of messages

(1) A person commits an offence if, otherwise than under the authority of a designated person—

(a) he uses wireless telegraphy apparatus with intent to obtain information as to the contents, sender or addressee of a message (whether sent by means of wireless telegraphy or not) of which neither he nor a person on whose behalf he is acting is an intended recipient, or

(b) he discloses information as to the contents, sender or addressee of such a message.

(2) A person commits an offence under this section consisting in the disclosure of information only if the information disclosed by him is information that would not have come to his knowledge but for the use of wireless telegraphy apparatus by him or by another person.

(3) A person does not commit an offence under this section consisting in the disclosure of information if he discloses the information in the course of legal proceedings or for the purpose of a report of legal proceedings.

(4) A person who commits an offence under this section is liable on summary conviction to a fine not exceeding level 5 on the standard scale.

(5) "Designated person" means—

(a) the Secretary of State;

(b) the Commissioners for Her Majesty's Revenue and Customs; or

(c) any other person designated for the purposes of this section by regulations made by the Secretary of State.

[4154]

NOTES

Commencement: 8 February 2007.

49 Interception authorities

(1) The conduct in relation to which a designated person may give an interception authority is not to include conduct falling within subsection (2), except where he believes that the conduct is necessary on grounds falling within subsection (5).

(2) Conduct falls within this subsection if it is—

(a) conduct that, if engaged in without lawful authority, constitutes an offence under section 1(1) or (2) of the Regulation of Investigatory Powers Act 2000 (c 23);
(b) conduct that, if engaged in without lawful authority, is actionable under section 1(3) of that Act;
(c) conduct that is capable of being authorised by an authorisation or notice granted under Chapter 2 of Part 1 of that Act (communications data); or
(d) conduct that is capable of being authorised by an authorisation granted under Part 2 of that Act (surveillance etc).

(3) A designated person may not exercise his power to give an interception authority except where he believes—

(a) that the giving of his authority is necessary on grounds falling within subsection (4) or (5); and
(b) that the conduct authorised by him is proportionate to what is sought to be achieved by that conduct.

(4) An interception authority is necessary on grounds falling within this subsection if it is necessary—

(a) in the interests of national security;
(b) for the purpose of preventing or detecting crime or of preventing disorder;
(c) in the interests of the economic well-being of the United Kingdom;
(d) in the interests of public safety;
(e) for the purpose of protecting public health;
(f) for the purpose of assessing or collecting a tax, duty, levy or other imposition, contribution or charge payable to a government department; or
(g) for any purpose (not falling within paragraphs (a) to (f)) that is specified for the purposes of this subsection by regulations made by the Secretary of State.

(5) An interception authority is necessary on grounds falling within this subsection if it is not necessary on grounds falling within subsection (4)(a) or (c) to (g) but is necessary for purposes connected with—

(a) the grant of wireless telegraphy licences;
(b) the prevention or detection of anything that constitutes interference with wireless telegraphy; or
(c) the enforcement of—
 (i) any provision of this Part (other than Chapter 2 and sections 27 to 31) or Part 3, or
 (ii) any enactment not falling within sub-paragraph (i) that relates to interference with wireless telegraphy.

(6) The matters to be taken into account in considering whether the requirements of subsection (3) are satisfied in the case of the giving of an interception authority include whether what it is thought necessary to achieve by the authorised conduct could reasonably be achieved by other means.

(7) An interception authority must be in writing and under the hand of—

(a) the Secretary of State;
(b) one of the Commissioners for Her Majesty's Revenue and Customs; or
(c) a person not falling within paragraph (a) or (b) who is designated for the purposes of this subsection by regulations made by the Secretary of State.

(8) An interception authority may be general or specific and may be given—

(a) to such person or persons, or description of persons,

(b) for such period, and
(c) subject to such restrictions and limitations,

as the designated person thinks fit.

(9) No regulations may be made under subsection (4)(g) unless a draft of them has first been laid before Parliament and approved by a resolution of each House.

(10) For the purposes of this section the question whether a person's conduct is capable of being authorised under Chapter 2 of Part 1 of the Regulation of Investigatory Powers Act 2000 (c 23) or under Part 2 of that Act is to be determined without reference—

(a) to whether the person is someone upon whom a power or duty is or may be conferred or imposed by or under that Chapter or that Part; or
(b) to whether there are grounds for believing that the requirements for the grant of an authorisation or the giving of a notice under that Chapter or that Part are satisfied.

(11) References in this section to an interception authority are references to an authority for the purposes of section 48 given otherwise than by way of the issue or renewal of a warrant, authorisation or notice under Part 1 or 2 of the Regulation of Investigatory Powers Act 2000.

(12) In this section—

"crime" has the meaning given by section 81(2)(a) of the Regulation of Investigatory Powers Act 2000 (c 23);

"designated person" has the same meaning as in section 48.

[4155]

NOTES

Commencement: 8 February 2007.

Miscellaneous

50 Apparatus on foreign-registered ships etc

(1) The Secretary of State may make regulations for regulating the use, on board a foreign-registered ship or aircraft while it is within the limits of the United Kingdom and UK territorial sea, of wireless telegraphy apparatus on board the ship or aircraft.

(2) The regulations may provide—

(a) for the punishment of persons contravening the regulations by a fine;
(b) for the forfeiture of any wireless telegraphy apparatus in respect of which an offence under the regulations is committed.

(3) The maximum fine for each offence under the regulations is—

(a) an amount not exceeding level 5 on the standard scale; or
(b) a lesser amount.

(4) The regulations may make different provision for ships or aircraft registered in different countries.

(5) Except as provided by this section or in consequence of an Order in Council under section 119(3), nothing in sections 8 to 11, 35 to 38, 45 to 49, 105 and 119 operates so as to impose any prohibition or restriction on persons using wireless telegraphy apparatus on board a foreign-registered ship or aircraft.

(6) A foreign-registered ship or aircraft is one that—

(a) is not registered in the United Kingdom; and
(b) is registered in a country other than the United Kingdom, the Isle of Man or any of the Channel Islands.

[4156]

NOTES

Commencement: 8 February 2007.

51 Apparatus in vehicles

(1) This section applies to the power of the Secretary of State under section 7(1) of the Vehicle Excise and Registration Act 1994 (c 22) to specify—

(a) the declaration to be made, and
(b) the particulars to be furnished,

by a person applying for a vehicle licence (within the meaning of that Act).

(2) The power of the Secretary of State includes power to require that the declaration and particulars extend to any matters relevant for the enforcement of section 8 of this Act in respect of any wireless telegraphy apparatus installed in the vehicle.

(3) Accordingly, the Secretary of State is not required to issue a vehicle licence under the Vehicle Excise and Registration Act 1994 where the applicant fails to comply with a requirement imposed because of subsection (2).

(4) A person commits an offence if in providing information that he is required to provide because of subsection (2)—
(a) he makes a statement that he knows to be false in a material particular; or
(b) he recklessly makes a statement that is false in a material particular.

(5) A person who commits an offence under subsection (4) is liable on summary conviction to a fine not exceeding level 3 on the standard scale.

(6) Where subsection (4) applies, it applies instead of section 45 of the Vehicle Excise and Registration Act 1994 (c 22) (false or misleading declarations and information).

[4157]

NOTES

Commencement: 8 February 2007.

52 Wireless personnel

(1) The Secretary of State may—
(a) hold examinations to determine the competence of the persons examined to fill positions in connection with the operation of wireless telegraphy stations or wireless telegraphy apparatus;
(b) issue certificates of competence to persons successful in such examinations.

(2) The certificates of competence are to be of such types as the Secretary of State may from time to time determine.

(3) The Secretary of State may issue written authorities to such persons as he thinks fit authorising them to fill such positions in connection with the operation of wireless telegraphy stations or wireless telegraphy apparatus as may be specified in the authority.

(4) The positions that may be so specified are positions for the holding of which the possession of an authority under subsection (3) is a necessity or a qualification under—
(a) a wireless telegraphy licence granted under this Act, or
(b) a licence granted under a corresponding law of a country or territory under the sovereignty of Her Majesty.

(5) If it appears to the Secretary of State that there are sufficient grounds to do so, he may at any time suspend an authority under subsection (3) with a view to its revocation.

(6) Schedule 3 has effect where an authority is suspended under subsection (5).

(7) The Secretary of State may charge such fees, if any, as he may determine—
(a) to persons applying to take part in an examination under this section;
(b) to applicants for, or for copies of, a certificate or authority issued under this section.

[4158]

NOTES

Commencement: 8 February 2007.

53 Surrender of authority

(1) Where an authority under section 52(3) has ceased to be in force or has been suspended, it is the duty of—
(a) the person to whom the authority was issued, and
(b) any other person in whose possession or under whose control the authority may be,

to cause it to be surrendered to the Secretary of State if required by the Secretary of State to do so.

(2) A person commits an offence if—

(a) he has a duty under subsection (1) to cause an authority under section 52(3) to be surrendered to the Secretary of State, and

(b) without reasonable excuse he fails or refuses to do so.

(3) A person who commits an offence under subsection (2) is liable on summary conviction to a fine not exceeding level 3 on the standard scale.

[4159]

NOTES

Commencement: 8 February 2007.

PART 3
REGULATION OF APPARATUS

Undue interference

54 Regulations about use and sale etc of apparatus

(1) OFCOM may make regulations prescribing the requirements to be complied with in the case of apparatus specified in the regulations, if the apparatus is to be used.

(2) OFCOM may make regulations prescribing the requirements to be complied with in the case of apparatus specified in the regulations, if the apparatus is to be—

(a) sold otherwise than for export,

(b) offered or advertised for sale otherwise than for export, or

(c) let on hire, or offered or advertised for letting on hire,

by a person who manufactures, assembles or imports such apparatus in the course of business.

(3) The requirements prescribed under subsection (1) or (2) are to be such requirements as OFCOM think fit for the purpose of ensuring that the use of the apparatus does not cause undue interference with wireless telegraphy.

(4) In particular, the requirements may include—

(a) requirements as to the maximum intensity of electromagnetic energy of specified frequencies that may be radiated in any direction from the apparatus while it is being used;

(b) in the case of apparatus the power for which is supplied from electric lines, requirements as to the maximum electromagnetic energy of specified frequencies that may be injected into those lines by the apparatus.

(5) The apparatus which may be specified in the regulations under subsection (1) or (2) is apparatus which generates, or is designed to generate, or is liable to generate fortuitously, electromagnetic energy at frequencies not exceeding 3,000 gigahertz.

(6) In a case where apparatus does not comply with the requirements applicable to it under regulations made under subsection (1) or (2), a person does not act unlawfully only because—

(a) he uses the apparatus, or

(b) he sells it, or offers or advertises it for sale, or lets it on hire or offers or advertises it for letting on hire.

But the non-compliance is a ground for the giving of a notice under section 55 or 56.

(7) The approval of the Secretary of State is required for the making by OFCOM of regulations under this section.

(8) A statutory instrument containing regulations made by OFCOM under this section is subject to annulment in pursuance of a resolution of either House of Parliament.

[4160]

NOTES

Commencement: 8 February 2007.

55 Enforcement: use of apparatus

(1) This section applies where, in the opinion of OFCOM—

(a) apparatus does not comply with the requirements applicable to it under regulations made under section 54(1); and

(b) the first or second condition is satisfied in relation to the apparatus.

(2) The first condition is that the use of the apparatus is likely to cause undue interference with wireless telegraphy used—

(a) for the purposes of a safety of life service; or

(b) for a purpose on which the safety of a person, or of a ship, aircraft or vehicle, may depend.

(3) The second condition is that—

(a) the use of the apparatus is likely to cause undue interference with wireless telegraphy other than wireless telegraphy falling within subsection (2);

(b) the use of the apparatus in fact has caused, or is causing, such interference; and

(c) the case is one where OFCOM consider that all reasonable steps to minimise interference have been taken in relation to the wireless telegraphy station or wireless telegraphy apparatus receiving the telegraphy interfered with.

(4) OFCOM may give a notice in writing to the person in possession of the apparatus—

(a) prohibiting the use of the apparatus after a date fixed by the notice, whether by the person to whom the notice is given or otherwise; or

(b) (if OFCOM think fit so to frame the notice) prohibiting the use of the apparatus after a date fixed by the notice except in such way, at such times and in such circumstances as the notice may specify.

(5) The date fixed by a notice under subsection (4) must be not less than 28 days from the date on which the notice is given.

(6) But if OFCOM are satisfied that the use of the apparatus in question is likely to cause such undue interference as is described in subsection (2), the date fixed by a notice under subsection (4) may be the date on which the notice is given.

(7) A notice under subsection (4) may be revoked or varied by a subsequent notice in writing from OFCOM given to the person who is then in possession of the apparatus.

(8) Where a notice under subsection (7) has the effect of imposing additional restrictions on the use of the apparatus, the provisions of this section about the coming into force of notices apply in relation to the notice as if it were a notice under subsection (4).

[4161]

NOTES

Commencement: 8 February 2007.

56 Enforcement: sale etc of apparatus

(1) This section applies where, in the opinion of OFCOM, apparatus does not comply with the requirements applicable to it under regulations made under section 54(2).

(2) OFCOM may give a notice in writing to the person who, in the course of business, has manufactured, assembled or imported the apparatus, prohibiting him from—

(a) selling the apparatus otherwise than for export;

(b) offering or advertising it for sale otherwise than for export; or

(c) letting it on hire, or offering or advertising it for letting on hire.

[4162]

NOTES

Commencement: 8 February 2007.

57 Appeal against notice under section 55 or 56 etc

(1) Where an appeal with respect to a notice under section 55 (or section 56) is pending—

(a) proceedings for an offence under section 58(1) (or section 58(4)) relating to that notice, whether instituted before or after the bringing of the appeal, are to be stayed until the appeal has been finally determined; and

PART VI TELECOMMUNICATIONS

(b) the proceedings are to be discharged if the notice is set aside in consequence of the appeal.

(2) But subsection (1) does not affect proceedings in which a person has been convicted at a time when there was no pending appeal.

(3) For the purposes of this section an appeal under section 192 of the Communications Act 2003 (c 21) with respect to a notice under section 55 (or section 56) or a further appeal relating to the decision on such an appeal is pending unless—

(a) that appeal has been brought to a conclusion or withdrawn and there is no further appeal pending in relation to the decision on the appeal; or

(b) no further appeal against a decision made on the appeal or on any such further appeal may be brought without the permission of the court and—

(i) in a case where there is no fixed period within which that permission can be sought, that permission has been refused or has not been sought, or

(ii) in a case where there is a fixed period within which that permission can be sought, that permission has been refused or that period has expired without permission having been sought.

(4) No proceedings for an offence under section 58(1) (or section 58(4)) relating to a notice under section 55 (or section 56) may be commenced in Scotland—

(a) until the time during which an appeal against such a notice may be brought has expired; or

(b) where such an appeal has been brought, until that appeal has been determined.

(5) Proceedings in Scotland for such an offence must be commenced—

(a) where no appeal has been brought, within six months of the time referred to in subsection (4)(a); and

(b) where an appeal has been brought and determined, within six months of the date of that determination.

[4163]

NOTES

Commencement: 8 February 2007.

58 Contravening notice under section 55 or 56

(1) A person commits an offence if—

(a) he uses apparatus, or causes or permits apparatus to be used, knowing that a notice under section 55 is in force with respect to it; and

(b) the use of the apparatus contravenes the notice.

(2) A person who commits an offence under subsection (1) is liable on summary conviction—

(a) if the offence is one that falls within subsection (6), to a fine not exceeding level 5 on the standard scale;

(b) otherwise, to a fine not exceeding level 3 on the standard scale.

(3) In the application of subsection (2) to Scotland or Northern Ireland, paragraph (a) has effect as if for the words "to a fine not exceeding level 5 on the standard scale" there were substituted "to imprisonment for a term not exceeding three months or to a fine not exceeding level 5 on the standard scale or to both".

(4) A person commits an offence if he contravenes the provisions of a notice given to him under section 56 (unless the notice has previously been revoked by OFCOM).

(5) A person who commits an offence under subsection (4) is liable on summary conviction—

(a) if the offence is one that falls within subsection (6), to a fine not exceeding level 5 on the standard scale;

(b) otherwise, to a fine not exceeding level 3 on the standard scale.

(6) An offence falls within this subsection if it involves or consists in a contravention of a notice under section 55 or 56 in relation to apparatus the use of which is likely to cause undue interference with wireless telegraphy used—

(a) for the purpose of a safety of life service; or

(b) for a purpose on which the safety of a person, or of a ship, aircraft or vehicle, may depend.

[4164]

NOTES

Commencement: 8 February 2007.

59 Entry and search of premises etc

(1) A justice of the peace may issue an authorisation under this section if he is satisfied, on an application supported by sworn evidence, that—

(a) there is reasonable ground for believing that there is to be found, on specified premises or in a specified ship, aircraft or vehicle, apparatus that does not comply with the requirements applicable to it under regulations made under section 54;

(b) it is necessary to enter those premises, or that ship, aircraft or vehicle, for the purpose of obtaining information that will enable OFCOM to decide whether or not to give a notice under section 55 or 56; and

(c) within the period of 14 days before the date of the application to the justice, access to the premises, ship, aircraft or vehicle for the purpose of obtaining such information—

(i) has been demanded by a person authorised for the purpose by OFCOM, who has produced sufficient documentary evidence of his identity and authority; but

(ii) has been refused.

(2) But the justice may not issue an authorisation unless the first or second condition is fulfilled as regards the application.

(3) The first condition is that it is shown to the justice that OFCOM are satisfied that there is reasonable ground for believing that the use of the apparatus in question is likely to cause undue interference with wireless telegraphy used—

(a) for the purposes of a safety of life service; or

(b) for a purpose on which the safety of a person, or of a ship, aircraft or vehicle, may depend.

(4) The second condition is that it is shown to the justice that—

(a) at least seven days before the demand was made, notice that access would be demanded was given to the occupier of the premises or (as the case may be) the person in possession or the person in charge of the ship, aircraft or vehicle;

(b) the demand for access was made at a reasonable hour; and

(c) it was unreasonably refused.

(5) An authorisation under this section is an authorisation empowering a person or persons authorised for the purpose by OFCOM, with or without constables—

(a) to enter the premises or (as the case may be) the ship, aircraft or vehicle and any premises on which it may be;

(b) to search the premises, ship, aircraft or vehicle with a view to discovering whether apparatus falling within subsection (1)(a) is there;

(c) if he or they find such apparatus there, to examine and test it with a view to obtaining the information mentioned in subsection (1)(b).

(6) An authorisation under this section must be in writing and signed by the justice.

(7) A person authorised by OFCOM to exercise a power conferred by this section may if necessary use reasonable force in the exercise of the power.

(8) Subsection (7) does not affect any power exercisable by the person apart from that subsection.

(9) Where under this section a person has a right to examine and test apparatus on premises or in a ship, aircraft or vehicle, any person who—

(a) is on the premises, or

(b) is in charge of, or in or in attendance on, the ship, aircraft or vehicle,

must give him whatever assistance he may reasonably require in the examination or testing of the apparatus.

(10) A reference in this section to a justice of the peace is to be read—

(a) in Scotland, as a reference to a sheriff;

PART VI TELECOMMUNICATIONS

(b) in Northern Ireland, as a reference to a lay magistrate.

[4165]

NOTES

Commencement: 8 February 2007.

60 Obstruction and failure to assist

(1) A person commits an offence if—

(a) he intentionally obstructs a person in the exercise of the powers conferred on him under section 59; or

(b) he fails or refuses, without reasonable excuse, to give to such a person any assistance which, under that section, he is under a duty to give to him.

(2) A person who commits an offence under this section is liable on summary conviction to a fine not exceeding level 5 on the standard scale.

[4166]

NOTES

Commencement: 8 February 2007.

61 Sections 54 to 60: interpretation

References in sections 54 to 60 to apparatus include references to any form of electric line.

[4167]

NOTES

Commencement: 8 February 2007.

Restriction orders

62 Restriction orders

(1) This section applies to wireless telegraphy apparatus and to apparatus designed or adapted for use in connection with wireless telegraphy apparatus.

(2) Where it appears to OFCOM to be expedient to do so for the purpose of preventing or reducing the risk of interference with wireless telegraphy, they may make an order (a "restriction order") imposing restrictions in relation to apparatus to which this section applies of a class or description specified in the order.

(3) The restrictions may relate to the following actions—

(a) the manufacture of apparatus (whether or not for sale);

(b) selling apparatus or offering it for sale;

(c) letting apparatus on hire or offering to let it on hire;

(d) indicating (whether by displaying apparatus or by any form of advertisement) willingness to sell apparatus or to let it on hire;

(e) having custody or control of apparatus;

(f) the importation of apparatus.

(4) A restriction order must specify, in the case of apparatus of any class or description specified in the order, what actions are restricted by it.

(5) An action for the time being restricted by a restriction order is prohibited by this section unless—

(a) an authority given by OFCOM relates to it; and

(b) it complies with any terms and conditions that OFCOM attach to the authority.

(6) The approval of the Secretary of State is required for the making by OFCOM of an order under this section.

(7) A statutory instrument containing an order made by OFCOM under this section is subject to annulment in pursuance of a resolution of either House of Parliament.

[4168]

NOTES
Commencement: 8 February 2007.

63 Authorities

(1) An authority given by OFCOM under section 62(5) in the case of apparatus of a class or description specified in a restriction order may be limited—
(a) to such of the actions restricted by the order as may be specified in the authority;
(b) to such subsidiary class or description of apparatus, falling within the class or description specified in the order, as may be specified in the authority.

(2) Terms or conditions attached by OFCOM to an authority under section 62(5) for the manufacture or importation of apparatus may relate to a period after, as well as to the time of, or a period before, the manufacture or importation.

(3) An authority under section 62(5) may be given, and terms or conditions may be attached to it—
(a) generally by means of a notice published in the London, Edinburgh and Belfast Gazettes; or
(b) by an instrument in writing issued to each person authorised to do, in relation to apparatus of a class or description to which a restriction order relates, any action for the time being restricted by the order.

[4169]

NOTES
Commencement: 8 February 2007.

64 Compatibility with international obligations

(1) OFCOM may not—
(a) make a restriction order,
(b) give an authority under section 62(5), or
(c) attach a term or condition to such an authority,

unless they are satisfied that the order, authority, term or condition is compatible with the international obligations of the United Kingdom.

(2) Where—
(a) a statutory instrument containing a restriction order, or
(b) a notice or instrument in writing giving an authority under section 62(5), or attaching a term or condition to such an authority,

contains a statement that OFCOM are satisfied as mentioned in subsection (1), the statement is evidence of that fact (and, in Scotland, sufficient evidence of it).

[4170]

NOTES
Commencement: 8 February 2007.

65 Powers of Commissioners for Her Majesty's Revenue and Customs

(1) This section applies where the importation of apparatus of a particular class or description is for the time being restricted by a restriction order.

(2) An officer of Revenue and Customs may require a person with custody or control of apparatus of that class or description which is being or has been imported to provide proof that the importation of the apparatus is or was not unlawful by virtue of section 62.

(3) If the proof required under subsection (2) is not provided to the satisfaction of the Commissioners for Her Majesty's Revenue and Customs, the apparatus is to be treated, unless the contrary is proved, as being prohibited goods, within the meaning of the Customs and Excise Management Act 1979 (c 2), and is liable to forfeiture under that Act.

[4171]

NOTES
Commencement: 8 February 2007.

66 Offences

(1) A person commits an offence if—

(a) he takes any action falling within section 62(3)(a) to (d) in relation to apparatus in contravention of section 62(5); or

(b) without reasonable excuse he has apparatus in his custody or control in contravention of section 62(5).

(2) A person commits an offence if he contravenes or fails to comply with any terms or conditions attached to an authority given by OFCOM under section 62(5) (whatever the action to which the authority relates).

(3) A person who commits an offence under this section is liable on summary conviction to a fine not exceeding level 5 on the standard scale.

(4) This section does not affect any liability to a penalty that may have been incurred under the Customs and Excise Management Act 1979 (c 2).

[4172]

NOTES

Commencement: 8 February 2007.

67 Restriction orders: interpretation

In sections 62 to 66—

"manufacture" includes construction by any method and the assembly of component parts;

"restriction order" has the meaning given by section 62.

[4173]

NOTES

Commencement: 8 February 2007.

Deliberate interference

68 Deliberate interference

(1) A person commits an offence if he uses apparatus for the purpose of interfering with wireless telegraphy.

(2) This section applies—

(a) whether or not the apparatus in question is wireless telegraphy apparatus;

(b) whether or not it is apparatus specified in regulations under section 54;

(c) whether or not a notice under section 55 or 56 has been given with respect to it, or, if given, has been varied or revoked.

(3) A person who commits an offence under this section is liable—

(a) on summary conviction, to imprisonment for a term not exceeding 12 months or to a fine not exceeding the statutory maximum or to both;

(b) on conviction on indictment, to imprisonment for a term not exceeding two years or to a fine or to both.

(4) In the application of subsection (3) to Scotland or Northern Ireland the reference to 12 months is to be read as a reference to six months.

[4174]

NOTES

Commencement: 8 February 2007.

PART 4
APPROVAL OF APPARATUS ETC

Approval of apparatus

69 Approval of apparatus

(1) This section applies where an instrument falling within subsection (2) contains provision framed by reference to relevant apparatus for the time being approved under this section for the purposes of that instrument.

(2) The instruments are—
(a) wireless telegraphy licences granted under section 8;
(b) regulations made under section 8(3);
(c) regulations made under section 54;
(d) restriction orders made under section 62;
(e) authorities given under section 62(5).

(3) The relevant authority may approve relevant apparatus for the purposes of such an instrument.

(4) The relevant authority may require a person applying for an approval under this section to comply with such requirements as the relevant authority may think appropriate; and those requirements may include a requirement to satisfy some other person with respect to a particular matter.

(5) An approval under this section may apply—
(a) to particular apparatus or to apparatus of a description specified in the approval;
(b) for the purposes of a particular instrument or for the purposes of instruments that are of a description specified in the approval.

(6) An approval under this section may specify conditions that must be complied with if the approval is to apply to apparatus specified in the approval (or to apparatus of a description so specified) for purposes specified in the approval.

(7) A condition so specified may impose on the person to whom the approval is given a requirement to satisfy a person from time to time with respect to a particular matter.

(8) The relevant authority may at any time vary or withdraw an approval given by the relevant authority under this section.

[4175]

NOTES
Commencement: 8 February 2007.

70 Approvals: supplementary

(1) A person appointed by the relevant authority may exercise a function conferred on the relevant authority by section 69 to such extent and subject to such conditions as may be specified in the appointment.

(2) The relevant authority may by order provide for the charging of fees in respect of the exercise of a function in pursuance of section 69 by or on behalf of the relevant authority.

(3) Section 128 of the Finance Act 1990 (c 29) (power to provide for repayment of fees etc) applies in relation to the power under subsection (2) to make an order as it applies in relation to any power to make such an order conferred before that Act was passed.

(4) An appointment under subsection (1) may authorise the person appointed to retain any fees received by him in pursuance of an order under subsection (2).

(5) Nothing in subsection (2) precludes a person (not being the relevant authority or a person acting on behalf of the relevant authority) by whom a matter falls to be determined for the purposes of a requirement imposed in pursuance of section 69(4) or (7) from charging a fee in respect of the carrying out of a test or other assessment made by him.

(6) Any sums received by the Secretary of State under this section shall be paid into the Consolidated Fund.

[4176]

NOTES

Commencement: 8 February 2007.

71 The relevant authority

(1) In sections 69 and 70 "the relevant authority" means (subject to subsection (2))—

(a) in such cases as may be specified in an order made by the Secretary of State, the Secretary of State; and

(b) in any other case, OFCOM.

(2) Where an application for the purposes of section 69 is made to the Secretary of State or OFCOM and it appears to the person to whom it is made that it should have been made to the other—

(a) that person is to refer the application to the other; and

(b) the application is to be proceeded with as if made to the person to whom it is referred.

[4177]

NOTES

Commencement: 8 February 2007.

Marking etc of apparatus

72 Information etc on or with apparatus

(1) This section applies where it appears to OFCOM to be expedient that relevant apparatus of a particular description should be marked with or accompanied by particular information or instruction relating to—

(a) the apparatus; or

(b) its installation or use.

(2) OFCOM may by order—

(a) impose requirements for securing that relevant apparatus of that description is so marked or accompanied; and

(b) regulate or prohibit the supply of such relevant apparatus in cases where the requirements are not complied with.

(3) The requirements imposed by the order may extend to the form and manner in which the information or instruction is given.

(4) In the case of apparatus supplied in circumstances where the required information or instruction would not be conveyed until after delivery, an order under this section may require the whole or part of the information or instruction to be also displayed near the apparatus.

(5) The approval of the Secretary of State is required for the making by OFCOM of an order under this section.

(6) A statutory instrument containing an order made by OFCOM under this section is subject to annulment in pursuance of a resolution of either House of Parliament.

[4178]

NOTES

Commencement: 8 February 2007.

73 Information etc in advertisements

(1) This section applies where it appears to OFCOM to be expedient that a particular description of advertisements for relevant apparatus should contain or refer to particular information relating to—

(a) the apparatus; or

(b) its installation or use.

(2) OFCOM may by order impose requirements as to the inclusion in advertisements of that description of—

(a) that information; or
(b) an indication of the means by which that information may be obtained.

(3) An order under this section may specify the form and manner in which the information or indication required by the order is to be included in a particular description of advertisements.

(4) The approval of the Secretary of State is required for the making by OFCOM of an order under this section.

(5) A statutory instrument containing an order made by OFCOM under this section is subject to annulment in pursuance of a resolution of either House of Parliament.

[4179]

NOTES
Commencement: 8 February 2007.

74 Offences

(1) A person commits an offence if in the course of a trade or business he supplies, or offers to supply, apparatus in contravention of an order under section 72.

(2) A person is to be treated as offering to supply apparatus if—
(a) he exposes apparatus for supply, or
(b) he has apparatus in his possession for supply.

(3) A person who publishes an advertisement for apparatus to be supplied in the course of a trade or business commits an offence if the advertisement fails to comply with a requirement imposed by an order under section 73.

(4) A person who commits an offence under subsection (1) or (3) is liable on summary conviction to a fine not exceeding level 5 on the standard scale.

(5) Proceedings for an offence under this section may be commenced at any time within the period of 12 months beginning with the day after the commission of the offence.

[4180]

NOTES
Commencement: 8 February 2007.

75 Default of third person

(1) Where the commission by one person ("A") of an offence under section 74(1) or (3) is due to the act or default of another ("B"), B also commits the offence; and B may be charged with and convicted of the offence by virtue of this subsection whether or not proceedings are taken against A.

(2) In proceedings for an offence under section 74(1) or (3) it is a defence for the defendant to prove that he took all reasonable steps and exercised all due diligence to avoid committing the offence.

(3) A person may not rely on a defence under subsection (2) which involves an allegation that the commission of the offence was due to the act or default of another person unless—
(a) at least seven clear days before the hearing he has given to the prosecutor a notice in writing giving such information identifying or assisting in the identification of the other person as was then in his possession; or
(b) the court grants him leave.

(4) In proceedings for an offence under section 74(3) it is a defence for the defendant to prove that—
(a) at the time of the alleged offence he was a person whose business it was to publish or arrange for the publication of advertisements;
(b) he received the advertisement for publication in the ordinary course of business; and
(c) he did not know and had no reason to suspect that publication of the advertisement would amount to an offence under that subsection.

[4181]

NOTES

Commencement: 8 February 2007.

Interpretation

76 Part 4: interpretation

In this Part—

"advertisement" includes a catalogue, a circular and a price list;

"relevant apparatus" means wireless telegraphy apparatus or apparatus designed or adapted for use in connection with wireless telegraphy apparatus.

[4182]

NOTES

Commencement: 8 February 2007.

PART 5
PROHIBITION OF BROADCASTING FROM SEA OR AIR

Prohibitions

77 Broadcasting from ships and aircraft

(1) It is unlawful—

(a) in the case of any ship or aircraft, to make a broadcast from it while it is in or over the United Kingdom or external waters; or

(b) in the case of a British-registered ship or British-registered aircraft, to make a broadcast from it while it is not in or over the United Kingdom or external waters.

(2) If a broadcast is made from a ship in contravention of subsection (1), an offence is committed by—

(a) the owner of the ship;

(b) the master of the ship; and

(c) a person who operates, or participates in the operation of, the apparatus by means of which the broadcast is made.

(3) If a broadcast is made from an aircraft in contravention of subsection (1), an offence is committed by—

(a) the operator of the aircraft;

(b) the commander of the aircraft; and

(c) a person who operates, or participates in the operation of, the apparatus by means of which the broadcast is made.

(4) A person commits an offence if he procures a broadcast to be made in contravention of subsection (1).

(5) In this section—

"master", in relation to a ship, includes any other person (except a pilot) who has command or charge of the ship;

"operator", in relation to an aircraft, means the person who at the relevant time has the management of the aircraft.

[4183]

NOTES

Commencement: 8 February 2007.

78 Broadcasting from marine structures etc

(1) This section applies to—

(a) tidal waters in the United Kingdom;

(b) external waters;

(c) waters in a designated area.

(2) It is unlawful to make a broadcast from—

(a) a structure, other than a ship, that is affixed to, or supported by, the bed of waters to which this section applies, or

(b) any other object in those waters.

(3) Subsection (2) does not apply by virtue of paragraph (b) to a broadcast made from a ship or aircraft.

(4) A person commits an offence if he operates, or participates in the operation of, apparatus by means of which a broadcast is made in contravention of subsection (2).

(5) A person commits an offence if he procures a broadcast to be made in contravention of subsection (2).

[4184]

NOTES

Commencement: 8 February 2007.

79 Broadcasting from prescribed areas of high seas

(1) It is unlawful—

(a) to make a broadcast that is capable of being received in the United Kingdom, or

(b) to make a broadcast that causes interference with any wireless telegraphy in the United Kingdom,

from a ship (other than a British-registered ship) while it is within a prescribed area of the high seas.

(2) If a broadcast is made in contravention of subsection (1), an offence is committed by—

(a) the owner of the ship from which the broadcast is made;

(b) the master of the ship; and

(c) a person who operates, or participates in the operation of, apparatus by means of which the broadcast is made.

(3) A person commits an offence if he procures a broadcast to be made in contravention of subsection (1).

(4) The making of a broadcast does not contravene subsection (1) if it is shown to have been authorised under the law of a country or territory outside the United Kingdom.

(5) "Prescribed" means prescribed for the purposes of this section by an order made by the Secretary of State.

[4185]

NOTES

Commencement: 8 February 2007.

80 Acts connected with broadcasting

(1) A British person commits an offence if he operates, or participates in the operation of, apparatus by means of which a broadcast is made—

(a) from a ship (other than a British-registered ship) while it is on the high seas;

(b) from an aircraft (other than a British-registered aircraft) while it is on or over the high seas;

(c) from a structure (other than a ship) that is affixed to, or supported by, the bed of the high seas; or

(d) from an object on the high seas (other than a structure falling within paragraph (c), a ship or an aircraft).

(2) Subsection (1) does not apply—

(a) by virtue of paragraph (a), to a broadcast made in contravention of section 79(1);

(b) by virtue of paragraph (c) or (d), to a broadcast made from a structure or other object in waters in a designated area.

(3) A person commits an offence if he procures a broadcast to be made as mentioned in subsection (1).

[4186]

NOTES
Commencement: 8 February 2007.

81 Management of station

(1) A person commits an offence if, from anywhere in the United Kingdom or external waters, he participates in the management, financing, operation or day-to-day running of a broadcasting station by which broadcasts are made—

(a) in contravention of section 77(1), 78(2) or 79(1); or
(b) as mentioned in section 80(1)(a).

(2) In this section "broadcasting station" means a business or other operation (whether or not in the nature of a commercial venture) that is engaged in the making of broadcasts.

[4187]

NOTES
Commencement: 8 February 2007.

82 Facilitating broadcasting from ships or aircraft

(1) A person commits an offence if he provides a ship or aircraft to another, or agrees to do so, knowing, or having reasonable cause to believe, that broadcasts are to be made from it—

(a) in contravention of section 77(1); or
(b) while it is on or over the high seas.

(2) A person commits an offence if—

(a) he carries wireless telegraphy apparatus in a ship or aircraft, or agrees to do so, or
(b) he supplies wireless telegraphy apparatus to a ship or aircraft, or instals such apparatus in a ship or aircraft,

knowing, or having reasonable cause to believe, that by means of the apparatus broadcasts are to be made from the ship or aircraft as mentioned in subsection (1).

(3) A person commits an offence if—

(a) he supplies goods or materials—
  (i) for the operation or maintenance of a ship or aircraft,
  (ii) for the operation or maintenance of wireless telegraphy apparatus installed in a ship or aircraft, or
  (iii) for the sustenance or comfort of the persons on board a ship or aircraft,
(b) he carries by water or air goods or persons to or from a ship or aircraft, or
(c) he engages a person as an officer or one of the crew of a ship or aircraft,

knowing, or having reasonable cause to believe, that broadcasts are made, or are to be made, from the ship or aircraft as mentioned in subsection (1).

(4) In proceedings for an offence under this section consisting in carrying goods or persons to or from a ship or aircraft, it is a defence for the defendant to prove—

(a) that the ship or aircraft was, or was believed to be, wrecked, stranded or in distress, and that the goods or persons were carried for the purpose of—
  (i) preserving the ship or aircraft, or its cargo or equipment, or
  (ii) saving the lives of persons on board the ship or aircraft; or
(b) that a person on board the ship or aircraft was, or was believed to be, hurt, injured or ill, and that the goods or persons were carried for the purpose of securing that he received the necessary surgical or medical advice and attendance.

(5) The reference in subsection (4)(a) to persons carried for the purpose of saving lives is not to be read as excluding the persons whose lives were to be saved.

(6) The reference in subsection (4)(b) to persons carried for the purpose of securing that advice and attendance were received is not to be read as excluding the person who was (or was believed to be) hurt, injured or ill.

(7) In proceedings for an offence under this section consisting in carrying a person ("A") to or from a ship or aircraft, it is a defence for the defendant to prove that A was visiting the ship or aircraft for the purpose of exercising or performing a power or duty conferred or imposed on A by law.

(8) This section is subject to section 86.

[4188]

NOTES

Commencement: 8 February 2007.

83 Facilitating broadcasting from structures etc

(1) A person commits an offence if he instals wireless telegraphy apparatus on or in a structure or other object, or supplies such apparatus for installation on or in a structure or other object, knowing, or having reasonable cause to believe, that by means of the apparatus broadcasts are to be made from it—

(a) in contravention of section 78(2); or

(b) while it is on the high seas.

(2) A person commits an offence if, in the case of a structure or other object—

(a) he supplies goods or materials—

(i) for its maintenance,

(ii) for the operation or maintenance of wireless telegraphy apparatus installed in or on it, or

(iii) for the sustenance or comfort of the persons in or on it,

(b) he carries goods or persons to or from it by water or air, or

(c) he engages a person to render services in or on it,

knowing, or having reasonable cause to believe, that broadcasts are made, or are to be made, from the structure or other object as mentioned in subsection (1).

(3) In proceedings for an offence under this section consisting in carrying goods or persons to or from a structure or other object, it is a defence for the defendant to prove—

(a) that it was, or was believed to be, unsafe, and that the goods or persons were carried for the purpose of saving the lives of persons in or on it; or

(b) that a person in or on it was, or was believed to be, hurt, injured or ill, and that the goods or persons were carried for the purpose of securing that he received the necessary surgical or medical advice and attendance.

(4) The reference in subsection (3)(a) to persons carried for the purpose of saving lives is not to be read as excluding the persons whose lives were to be saved.

(5) The reference in subsection (3)(b) to persons carried for the purpose of securing that advice and attendance were received is not to be read as excluding the person who was (or was believed to be) hurt, injured or ill.

(6) In proceedings for an offence under this section consisting in carrying a person ("A") to or from a structure or other object, it is a defence for the defendant to prove that A was visiting it for the purpose of exercising or performing a power or duty conferred or imposed on A by law.

(7) In this section references to a structure or other object do not include references to a ship or aircraft.

(8) This section is subject to section 86.

[4189]

NOTES

Commencement: 8 February 2007.

84 Maintaining or repairing apparatus

(1) A person commits an offence if he repairs or maintains wireless telegraphy apparatus knowing, or having reasonable cause to believe, that by means of it broadcasts are made, or are to be made—

(a) in contravention of section 77(1), 78(2) or 79(1); or

(b) as mentioned in section 80(1).

(2) This section is subject to section 86.

[4190]

PART VI TELECOMMUNICATIONS

NOTES

Commencement: 8 February 2007.

85 Acts relating to broadcast material

(1) A person commits an offence if—

(a) he supplies a film or sound recording knowing, or having reasonable cause to believe, that an unlawful broadcast is to be made of it;

(b) he makes a literary, dramatic or musical work knowing, or having reasonable cause to believe, that an unlawful broadcast is to be made of it;

(c) he makes an artistic work knowing, or having reasonable cause to believe, that it is to be included in an unlawful television broadcast;

(d) he participates in an unlawful broadcast;

(e) he advertises by means of an unlawful broadcast or invites another to advertise by means of an unlawful broadcast that is to be made;

(f) he publishes the times or other details of unlawful broadcasts that are to be made, or (otherwise than by publishing such details) publishes an advertisement of matter calculated to promote (whether directly or indirectly) the interests of a business whose activities consist in or include the operation of a station from which unlawful broadcasts are or are to be made.

(2) An unlawful broadcast is a broadcast made—

(a) in contravention of section 77(1), 78(2) or 79(1); or

(b) as mentioned in section 80(1).

(3) A person participates in a broadcast only if he is actually present—

(a) as an announcer;

(b) as a performer or one of the performers concerned in an entertainment given; or

(c) as the deliverer of a speech.

(4) The cases in which a person is to be taken for the purposes of this section as advertising by means of a broadcast include any case in which he causes or allows it to be stated, suggested or implied that entertainment included in the broadcast—

(a) has been supplied by him; or

(b) is provided wholly or partly at his expense.

(5) For the purposes of this section advertising by means of a broadcast takes place not only where the broadcast is made but also wherever it is received.

(6) This section is subject to section 86.

[4191]

NOTES

Commencement: 8 February 2007.

86 Facilitation offences: territorial scope

(1) A person who does an act mentioned in section 82, 83, 84 or 85 does not commit an offence under that section unless condition A, B, C, D or E is satisfied.

(2) Condition A is satisfied if he does the act in the United Kingdom or external waters.

(3) Condition B is satisfied if he does the act in a British-registered ship or British-registered aircraft while it is not in or over the United Kingdom or external waters.

(4) Condition C is satisfied if, in a case where—

(a) neither condition A nor condition B is satisfied, but

(b) the broadcasts in question are made, or are to be made, from a structure or other object (which is not a ship or aircraft) in waters in a designated area,

he does the act on that structure or other object within those waters.

(5) Condition D is satisfied if, in a case where—

(a) neither condition A nor condition B is satisfied, but

(b) the broadcasts in question are made, or are to be made, from a ship in contravention of section 79(1), he does the act in that ship within an area of the high seas that is prescribed for the purposes of section 79.

(6) Condition E is satisfied if—

(a) he is a British person; and

(b) he does the act on or over the high seas.

[4192]

NOTES

Commencement: 8 February 2007.

87 Procuring person to commit offence abroad

A person commits an offence if he procures, in the United Kingdom, another person to do, outside the United Kingdom, anything that would have constituted an offence under sections 82 to 85 had the other person done it in the United Kingdom.

[4193]

NOTES

Commencement: 8 February 2007.

Enforcement

88 Enforcement officers

(1) For the purposes of sections 89 to 92 enforcement officers are—

(a) persons authorised by the Secretary of State or OFCOM to exercise the powers conferred by sections 89 and 90;

(b) police officers;

(c) commissioned officers of Her Majesty's armed forces;

(d) officers of Revenue and Customs; and

(e) other persons who are British sea-fishery officers by virtue of section 7(1) of the Sea Fisheries Act 1968 (c 77).

(2) A reference in sections 89 to 92, in relation to an enforcement officer, to an assistant is a reference to a person assigned to assist the enforcement officer in his duties.

(3) In this section "armed forces" means the Royal Navy, the Royal Marines, the regular army and the regular air force, and a reserve or auxiliary force of any of those services that has been called out on permanent service or embodied.

[4194]

NOTES

Commencement: 8 February 2007.

89 Enforcement powers

(1) If conditions A and B are satisfied in the case of a ship, structure or other object, an enforcement officer may, with or without assistants, exercise the powers mentioned in subsection (4) in relation to it.

(2) Condition A is satisfied if the enforcement officer has reasonable grounds for suspecting that—

(a) an offence under this Part has been or is being committed by the making of a broadcast—

(i) from a ship, structure or other object in external waters or in tidal waters in the United Kingdom, or

(ii) from a British-registered ship while it is on the high seas;

(b) an offence under section 78 has been or is being committed by the making of a broadcast from a structure or other object in waters in a designated area; or

(c) an offence under section 79 has been or is being committed by the making of a broadcast from a ship.

(3) Condition B is satisfied if a written authorisation has been issued by the Secretary of State or OFCOM for the exercise of the powers mentioned in subsection (4) in relation to that ship, structure or other object.

(4) The powers are—

(a) to board and search the ship, structure or other object;

(b) to seize and detain it, and any apparatus or other thing found in the course of the search that appears to him—

(i) to have been used, or to have been intended to be used, in connection with the commission of the suspected offence, or

(ii) to be evidence of the commission of the suspected offence;

(c) to arrest and search any person who he has reasonable grounds to suspect has committed or is committing an offence under this Part if—

(i) the person is on board the ship, structure or other object, or

(ii) the officer has reasonable grounds for suspecting that the person was on board at, or shortly before, the time when the officer boarded the object;

(d) to arrest any person—

(i) who assaults him, or an assistant of his, while exercising any of the powers mentioned in this subsection, or

(ii) who intentionally obstructs him, or an assistant of his, in the exercise of any of those powers;

(e) to require any person on board the ship, structure or other object to produce any documents or other items that are in his custody or possession and are or may be evidence of the commission of an offence under this Part;

(f) to require any such person to do anything for the purpose of—

(i) enabling any apparatus or other thing to be rendered safe and, in the case of a ship, enabling the ship to be taken to a port, or

(ii) facilitating in any other way the exercise of any of the powers mentioned in this subsection;

(g) to use reasonable force, if necessary, in exercising any of those powers.

(5) In subsection (4)(a) to (c) and (e) a reference to the ship, structure or other object includes a reference to a ship's boat, or other vessel, used from it.

[4195]

NOTES

Commencement: 8 February 2007.

90 Enforcement powers: facilitation offences

(1) Subsection (2) applies if—

(a) a written authorisation has been issued by the Secretary of State or OFCOM under section 89(3) for the exercise of the powers mentioned in section 89(4) in relation to a ship, structure or other object, and

(b) an enforcement officer has reasonable grounds for suspecting that an offence under section 82, 83, 84 or 85 has been or is being committed in connection with the making of a broadcast from that ship, structure or other object.

(2) The enforcement officer may, with or without assistants, exercise the powers mentioned in section 89(4) in relation to any ship, structure or other object which he has reasonable grounds to suspect has been or is being used in connection with the commission of the offence referred to in subsection (1)(b).

(3) Subsection (4) applies if—

(a) an enforcement officer has reasonable grounds for suspecting that an offence under section 82, 83, 84 or 85 has been or is being committed in connection with the making of a broadcast from a ship, structure or other object, but

(b) no written authorisation has been issued under section 89(3) for the exercise of the powers mentioned in section 89(4) in relation to that ship, structure or other object.

(4) The enforcement officer may, with or without assistants, exercise the powers mentioned in section 89(4) in relation to any ship, structure or other object which he has reasonable grounds to suspect has been or is being used in connection with the commission of the offence referred to in subsection (3)(a).

(5) Subsection (4) only applies if a written authorisation under this subsection has been issued by the Secretary of State or OFCOM for the exercise of those powers in relation to that ship, structure or other object.

[4196]

NOTES

Commencement: 8 February 2007.

91 Exercise of powers

(1) Except as provided in subsections (2) and (3), the powers mentioned in section 89(4) may be exercised only in tidal waters in the United Kingdom or in external waters.

(2) The powers may in addition—

(a) in the case of a suspected offence under this Part committed in a British-registered ship while it is on the high seas, be exercised in relation to the ship on the high seas;

(b) in the case of a suspected offence under section 78 committed on a structure or other object within waters in a designated area, be exercised in relation to the structure or other object within those waters;

(c) in the case of a suspected offence under section 79 committed in a ship within an area of the high seas prescribed for the purposes of that section, be exercised in relation to the ship within that area of the high seas.

(3) Subsection (2) does not apply so far as the powers are exercisable by virtue of a written authorisation issued by OFCOM.

[4197]

NOTES

Commencement: 8 February 2007.

92 Further provisions

(1) A person commits an offence if—

(a) he assaults an enforcement officer, or an assistant of his, while he is exercising any of the powers conferred by section 89 or 90;

(b) he intentionally obstructs an enforcement officer, or an assistant of his, in the exercise of any of those powers; or

(c) he fails or refuses, without reasonable excuse, to comply with such a requirement as is mentioned in section 89(4)(e) or (f).

(2) Neither an enforcement officer nor an assistant of his is liable in civil or criminal proceedings for anything done in purported exercise of any of the powers conferred by section 89 or 90 if the court is satisfied that the act was done in good faith and that there were reasonable grounds for doing it.

(3) Nothing in sections 89 to 91 or this section affects the exercise of any powers exercisable apart from those sections.

(4) A reference in sections 89 to 91 or this section, in relation to an enforcement officer's assistant, to the exercise of any of the powers mentioned in section 89(4) is a reference to the exercise by the assistant of any of those powers on behalf of the officer.

[4198]

NOTES

Commencement: 8 February 2007.

Penalties and proceedings

93 Penalties and proceedings

(1) A person who commits an offence under this Part is liable—

(a) on summary conviction, to imprisonment for a term not exceeding 12 months or to a fine not exceeding the statutory maximum or to both;

PART VI TELECOMMUNICATIONS

(b) on conviction on indictment, to imprisonment for a term not exceeding two years or to a fine or to both.

(2) In the application of subsection (1) to Scotland or Northern Ireland the reference to 12 months is to be read as a reference to six months.

(3) Proceedings in England and Wales for an offence under this Part may be brought only—

(a) by OFCOM; or

(b) by or with the consent of the Secretary of State or the Director of Public Prosecutions.

(4) Proceedings in Northern Ireland for an offence under this Part may be brought only—

(a) by OFCOM; or

(b) by or with the consent of the Secretary of State or the Advocate General for Northern Ireland.

(5) Summary proceedings in Scotland for an offence under this Part may be commenced at any time within the period of two years beginning with the day after the commission of the offence.

[4199]

NOTES

Commencement: 8 February 2007.

Saving

94 Saving for certain broadcasts

Nothing in this Part makes it unlawful to do anything under and in accordance with a wireless telegraphy licence, or to procure anything to be so done.

[4200]

NOTES

Commencement: 8 February 2007.

Interpretation

95 Part 5: interpretation

(1) In this Part—

"British-registered" means registered in the United Kingdom, the Isle of Man or any of the Channel Islands;

"broadcast" means a broadcast by wireless telegraphy of sounds or visual images intended for general reception (whether or not the sounds or images are actually received by anyone), but does not include a broadcast consisting in a message or signal sent in connection with navigation or for the purpose of securing safety;

"designated area" has the meaning given by section 1(7) of the Continental Shelf Act 1964 (c 29);

"external waters" means the whole of the sea adjacent to the United Kingdom that is within the seaward limits of UK territorial sea;

"the high seas" means seas that are not within the seaward limits of UK territorial sea or of the territorial waters adjacent to a country or territory outside the United Kingdom.

(2) For the purposes of this Part references to a "British person" are references to—

(a) a British citizen, a British overseas territories citizen, a British National (Overseas) or a British Overseas citizen;

(b) a person who under the British Nationality Act 1981 (c 61) is a British subject; or

(c) a British protected person within the meaning given by section 50(1) of that Act.

[4201]

NOTES

Commencement: 8 February 2007.

PART 6
GENERAL

Fixed penalties

96 Fixed penalties for summary offences

Schedule 4 (which makes provision as respects fixed penalty notices for certain summary offences) has effect.

[4202]

NOTES

Commencement: 8 February 2007.

Entry, search and seizure

97 Powers of entry and search

(1) A justice of the peace may grant a search warrant under this section if he is satisfied by information on oath that—

(a) there is reasonable ground for suspecting that an offence under this Act, other than an offence under Part 4 or section 111, has been or is being committed; and

(b) evidence of the commission of the offence is to be found on premises specified in the information, or in a vehicle, ship or aircraft so specified.

(2) A search warrant under this section is a warrant empowering a constable or any person or persons authorised for the purpose by OFCOM or the Secretary of State—

(a) to enter, at any time within the relevant period, the premises specified in the information or (as the case may be) the vehicle, ship or aircraft so specified and any premises on which it may be;

(b) to search the premises, vehicle, ship or aircraft;

(c) to examine and test any apparatus found there.

(3) In subsection (2) "the relevant period" means the period of three months beginning with the day after the date of the warrant.

(4) In the application of subsection (3) to Scotland or Northern Ireland the reference to three months is to be read as a reference to one month.

(5) Where a person authorised by OFCOM or the Secretary of State is empowered by a search warrant under this section to enter any premises, he is to be entitled to exercise that warrant alone or to exercise it accompanied by one or more constables.

(6) A person authorised by OFCOM or the Secretary of State to exercise a power conferred by this section may if necessary use reasonable force in the exercise of the power.

(7) Subsection (6) does not affect any power exercisable apart from that subsection by a person so authorised.

(8) Where under this section a person has a right to examine and test apparatus on premises or in a ship, aircraft or vehicle, any person who—

(a) is on the premises, or

(b) is in charge of, or in or in attendance on, the ship, aircraft or vehicle,

must give him whatever assistance he may reasonably require in the examination or testing of the apparatus.

(9) In this section—

(a) a reference to a justice of the peace is to be read, in Scotland, as a reference to a sheriff and, in Northern Ireland, as a reference to a lay magistrate;

(b) a reference to information on oath is to be read, in Northern Ireland, as a reference to complaint on oath.

[4203]

NOTES

Commencement: 8 February 2007.

98 Obstruction and failure to assist

(1) A person commits an offence if—

(a) he intentionally obstructs a person in the exercise of the powers conferred on him under section 97; or

(b) he fails or refuses, without reasonable excuse, to give to such a person any assistance which, under that section, he is under a duty to give to him.

(2) A person who commits an offence under this section is liable on summary conviction to a fine not exceeding level 5 on the standard scale.

[4204]

NOTES

Commencement: 8 February 2007.

99 Powers of seizure

(1) This section applies to—

(a) an indictable offence under this Act, other than an offence under section 111;

(b) an offence under section 35, other than one consisting in the installation or use of receiving apparatus;

(c) an offence under section 36, other than one where the relevant contravention of section 8 would constitute an offence consisting in the use of receiving apparatus;

(d) an offence under section 48;

(e) an offence under section 66.

(2) Where—

(a) a search warrant is granted under section 97, and

(b) the suspected offence (or any of the suspected offences) is an offence to which this section applies,

the warrant may authorise a person authorised by OFCOM to exercise the power conferred by this subsection to seize and detain, for the purposes of any relevant proceedings, any apparatus or other thing found in the course of the search carried out in pursuance of the warrant that appears to him to be a relevant item.

(3) If a constable or a person authorised by OFCOM to exercise the power conferred by this subsection has reasonable grounds to suspect that an offence to which this section applies has been or is being committed, he may seize and detain, for the purposes of any relevant proceedings, any apparatus or other thing that appears to him to be a relevant item.

(4) A person authorised by OFCOM to exercise a power conferred by this section may if necessary use reasonable force in the exercise of the power.

(5) Subsection (4) does not affect any power exercisable by the person so authorised apart from that subsection.

(6) Nothing in this section affects any power to seize or detain property that is exercisable by a constable apart from this section.

(7) In this section—

"relevant item" means an item that—

(a) was used in connection with an offence to which this section applies; or

(b) is evidence of the commission of such an offence;

"relevant proceedings" means—

(a) proceedings for an offence to which this section applies; or

(b) proceedings for condemnation under Schedule 6.

[4205]

NOTES

Commencement: 8 February 2007.

100 Obstruction

(1) A person commits an offence if he intentionally obstructs a person in the exercise of the power conferred on him under section 99(3).

(2) A person who commits an offence under this section is liable on summary conviction to a fine not exceeding level 5 on the standard scale.

[4206]

NOTES

Commencement: 8 February 2007.

Disposal and forfeiture

101 Detention and disposal of property

(1) This section applies to property seized by a person authorised by OFCOM—
- (a) in pursuance of a warrant under section 97; or
- (b) in the exercise of the power conferred by section 99(3).

(2) The property may be detained—
- (a) until the end of the period of six months beginning with the date of seizure; or
- (b) if proceedings for an offence to which section 99 applies involving that property or proceedings under Schedule 6 for condemnation of that property as forfeited are instituted within that period, until the conclusion of those proceedings.

(3) Subsections (4) to (6) apply in the case of property so detained which, after the end of the period authorised by subsection (2)—
- (a) remains in the possession of OFCOM; and
- (b) has not been ordered to be forfeited under Schedule 5 or condemned as forfeited under Schedule 6.

(4) OFCOM must take reasonable steps to deliver the property to the person who appears to them to be its owner.

(5) If the property remains in the possession of OFCOM after the end of one year immediately following the end of the period of detention authorised by subsection (2), OFCOM may dispose of it in such manner as they think fit.

(6) The delivery of the property in accordance with subsection (4) to the person who appears to OFCOM to be its owner does not affect the right of any other person to take legal proceedings for the recovery of the property—
- (a) against the person to whom the property is so delivered; or
- (b) against any person subsequently in possession of the property.

[4207]

NOTES

Commencement: 8 February 2007.

102 Section 101: conclusion of proceedings

(1) This section applies to—
- (a) proceedings for an offence to which section 99 applies;
- (b) proceedings under Schedule 6 for the condemnation of apparatus as forfeited.

(2) Where proceedings to which this section applies are terminated by an appealable decision, they are not to be regarded as concluded for the purposes of section 101(2)(b)—
- (a) until the end of the ordinary time for appeal against the decision, if no appeal in respect of the decision is brought within that time; or
- (b) if an appeal in respect of the decision is brought within that time, until the conclusion of the appeal.

(3) Subsection (2) applies for determining, for the purposes of paragraph (b) of that subsection, when proceedings on an appeal are concluded as it applies for determining when the original proceedings are concluded.

(4) References in subsection (2) to a decision which terminates proceedings include references to a verdict, sentence, finding or order that puts an end to the proceedings.

(5) An appealable decision is a decision of a description against which an appeal will lie, whether by way of case stated or otherwise and whether with or without permission.

(6) References to an appeal include references to an application for permission to appeal. **[4208]**

NOTES

Commencement: 8 February 2007.

103 Forfeiture on conviction

Schedule 5 (which makes provision in relation to forfeiture on conviction) has effect. **[4209]**

NOTES

Commencement: 8 February 2007.

104 Forfeiture etc of restricted apparatus

(1) Apparatus to which this section applies is liable to forfeiture if, immediately before being seized, it was in a person's custody or control in contravention of section 62(5).

(2) This section applies to apparatus if it has been seized—

(a) in pursuance of a warrant granted under section 97; or

(b) in the exercise of the power conferred by section 99(3).

(3) Apparatus forfeited under this section is to be forfeited to OFCOM and may be disposed of by them in any manner they think fit.

(4) Schedule 6 (which makes provision in relation to the seizure and forfeiture of apparatus) has effect. **[4210]**

NOTES

Commencement: 8 February 2007.

Enforcement, proceedings etc

105 Offences relating to ships or aircraft

(1) This section applies if an offence is committed under any of sections 11, 35 to 38, 46 to 48, 58 and 68.

(2) Where the offence is committed in relation to a station or apparatus on board or released from a ship or aircraft, the captain or person for the time being in charge of the ship or aircraft is guilty of the offence (as well as anyone who is guilty of it apart from this subsection).

(3) This section does not apply where the offence consists in the use by a passenger on board the ship or aircraft of receiving apparatus that is not part of the wireless telegraphy apparatus, if any, of the ship or aircraft. **[4211]**

NOTES

Commencement: 8 February 2007.

106 Continuing offences

(1) This section applies where—

(a) a person is convicted of an offence under Part 2 or 3 consisting in—

(i) the use of a wireless telegraphy station or wireless telegraphy apparatus, or

(ii) a failure or refusal to cause a wireless telegraphy licence or an authority under section 52(3) to be surrendered; and

(b) the use, or the failure or refusal, continues after the conviction.

(2) The person is to be treated as committing a separate offence in respect of every day on which the use, or the failure or refusal, so continues.

(3) Subsection (2) does not affect the right to bring separate proceedings for contraventions of this Act taking place on separate occasions.

[4212]

NOTES

Commencement: 8 February 2007.

107 Proceedings and enforcement

(1) Proceedings for—

(a) an offence under Part 2, 3 or 6 (other than an offence under section 111) that is committed in UK territorial sea, or

(b) an offence under Part 5,

may be taken, and the offence may for all incidental purposes be treated as having been committed, in any place in the United Kingdom.

(2) For the purpose of the enforcement of any provision falling within subsection (3), a member of a police force has in any area of the sea within the seaward limits of UK territorial sea all the powers, protection and privileges which he has in the area for which he acts as constable.

(3) The provisions are—

(a) sections 8 to 11, 32 to 38 and 45 to 53;

(b) Part 3;

(c) Part 5;

(d) sections 97 to 100, 103, 105 and 106 and Schedule 5.

(4) In the application of this section to Northern Ireland, subsection (2) has effect with the substitution—

(a) for the words "a police force" of the words "the Police Service of Northern Ireland", and

(b) for the words "the area for which he acts as constable" of the words "Northern Ireland".

[4213]

NOTES

Commencement: 8 February 2007.

108 Civil proceedings

(1) Where the doing of a thing is rendered unlawful by Part 2 or 3, and it is also an offence under this Act, the fact that it is such an offence does not limit a person's right to bring civil proceedings in respect of the doing or apprehended doing of that thing.

(2) Without prejudice to the generality of subsection (1), compliance with a provision of Part 2 or 3 contravention of which is an offence under this Act is enforceable in civil proceedings by the Crown, or by OFCOM, for an injunction or for any other appropriate relief.

(3) In the application of this section to Scotland, subsection (2) has effect as if for the words from "civil proceedings" to the end there were substituted "civil proceedings by the Advocate General for Scotland, or by OFCOM, for an interdict or for any other appropriate relief or remedy".

[4214]

NOTES

Commencement: 8 February 2007.

109 Fines in Scotland

(1) Fines imposed in respect of offences falling within subsection (2) are to be paid into the Consolidated Fund.

(2) The offences are offences committed in Scotland under—

(a) Part 2;

(b) Part 3;

(c) section 98;
(d) section 100;
(e) paragraph 5 of Schedule 5.

[4215]

NOTES
Commencement: 8 February 2007.

110 Criminal liability of company directors etc

(1) Where an offence under this Act is committed by a body corporate and is proved to have been committed with the consent or connivance of, or to be attributable to any neglect on the part of—

(a) a director, manager, secretary or other similar officer of the body corporate, or
(b) a person who was purporting to act in any such capacity,

he (as well as the body corporate) is guilty of that offence and is liable to be proceeded against and punished accordingly.

(2) Where an offence under this Act—

(a) is committed by a Scottish firm, and
(b) is proved to have been committed with the consent or connivance of, or to be attributable to any neglect on the part of a partner of the firm,

he (as well as the firm) is guilty of that offence and is liable to be proceeded against and punished accordingly.

(3) "Director", in relation to a body corporate whose affairs are managed by its members, means a member of the body corporate.

[4216]

NOTES
Commencement: 8 February 2007.

Disclosure of information

111 General restrictions

(1) Information with respect to a particular business which has been obtained in exercise of a power conferred by this Act is not, so long as that business continues to be carried on, to be disclosed without the consent of the person for the time being carrying on that business.

(2) Subsection (1) has effect subject to the following provisions of this section.

(3) Subsection (1) does not apply to any disclosure of information which is made—

(a) for the purpose of facilitating the carrying out by OFCOM of any of their functions;
(b) for the purpose of facilitating the carrying out by any relevant person of any relevant function;
(c) for the purpose of facilitating the carrying out by the Comptroller and Auditor General of any of his functions;
(d) for any of the purposes specified in section 17(2)(a) to (d) of the Anti-terrorism, Crime and Security Act 2001 (c 24) (criminal proceedings and investigations);
(e) for the purpose of any civil proceedings brought under or because of this Act or any of the enactments or instruments mentioned in subsection (6); or
(f) for the purpose of securing compliance with an international obligation of the United Kingdom.

(4) The following are relevant persons—

(a) a Minister of the Crown and the Treasury;
(b) the Scottish Executive;
(c) a Northern Ireland department;
(d) the Office of Fair Trading;
(e) the Competition Commission;
(f) the Consumer Panel;
(g) the Welsh Authority;

(h) a local weights and measures authority in Great Britain;
(i) any other person specified for the purposes of this subsection in an order made by the Secretary of State.

(5) The following are relevant functions—
(a) any function conferred by or under this Act;
(b) any function conferred by or under any enactment or instrument mentioned in subsection (6);
(c) any other function specified for the purposes of this subsection in an order made by the Secretary of State.

(6) The enactments and instruments referred to in subsections (3) and (5) are—
(a) the Wireless Telegraphy Act 1967 (c 72);
(b) the Trade Descriptions Act 1968 (c 29);
(c) the Fair Trading Act 1973 (c 41);
(d) the Consumer Credit Act 1974 (c 39);
(e) the Competition Act 1980 (c 21);
(f) the Telecommunications Act 1984 (c 12);
(g) the Consumer Protection Act 1987 (c 43);
(h) the Broadcasting Act 1990 (c 42);
(i) the Broadcasting Act 1996 (c 55);
(j) the Competition Act 1998 (c 41);
(k) the Enterprise Act 2002 (c 40);
(l) the Communications Act 2003 (c 21);
(m) the Consumer Protection (Northern Ireland) Order 1987 (SI 1987/2049 (NI 20));
(n) the Control of Misleading Advertisements Regulations 1988 (SI 1988/915).

(7) Nothing in this section—
(a) limits the matters that may be published under section 15, 26 or 390 of the Communications Act 2003;
(b) limits the matters that may be included in, or made public as part of, a report made by OFCOM because of a provision of the Office of Communications Act 2002 (c 11) or the Communications Act 2003;
(c) prevents the disclosure of anything for the purposes of a report of legal proceedings in which it has been publicly disclosed;
(d) applies to information that has been published or made public as mentioned in paragraphs (a) to (c).

(8) Section 18 of the Anti-terrorism, Crime and Security Act 2001 (c 24) (restriction on disclosure of information for overseas purposes) has effect in relation to a disclosure because of subsection (3)(d) as it has effect in relation to a disclosure in exercise of a power to which section 17 of that Act applies.

(9) A person commits an offence if he discloses information in contravention of this section.

(10) A person who commits an offence under subsection (9) is liable—
(a) on summary conviction, to a fine not exceeding the statutory maximum;
(b) on conviction on indictment, to imprisonment for a term not exceeding two years or to a fine or to both.

(11) No order is to be made containing provision authorised by subsection (4) or (5) unless a draft of the order has been laid before Parliament and approved by a resolution of each House.

(12) In this section—
"the Consumer Panel" means the panel established under section 16 of the Communications Act 2003 (c 21);
"enactment" has the same meaning as in the Communications Act 2003;
"legal proceedings" means civil or criminal proceedings in or before any court, or proceedings before any tribunal established by or under any enactment;
"the Welsh Authority" means the authority whose name is, by virtue of section 56(1) of the Broadcasting Act 1990 (c 42), Sianel Pedwar Cymru.

[4217]

NOTES
Commencement: 8 February 2007.

PART VI TELECOMMUNICATIONS

Notifications etc and electronic working

112 Service of documents

(1) This section applies where provision made (in whatever terms) by or under this Act authorises or requires—

- (a) a notification to be given to any person; or
- (b) a document of any other description (including a copy of a document) to be sent to any person.

(2) The notification or document may be given or sent to the person in question—

- (a) by delivering it to him;
- (b) by leaving it at his proper address; or
- (c) by sending it by post to him at that address.

(3) The notification or document may be given or sent to a body corporate by being given or sent to the secretary or clerk of that body.

(4) The notification or document may be given or sent to a firm by being given or sent to—

- (a) a partner in the firm; or
- (b) a person having the control or management of the partnership business.

(5) The notification or document may be given or sent to an unincorporated body or association by being given or sent to a member of the governing body of the body or association.

(6) For the purposes of this section and section 7 of the Interpretation Act 1978 (c 30) (service of documents by post) in its application to this section, the proper address of a person is—

- (a) in the case of a body corporate, the address of the registered or principal office of the body;
- (b) in the case of a firm, unincorporated body or association, the address of the principal office of the partnership, body or association;
- (c) in the case of a person to whom the notification or other document is given or sent in reliance on any of subsections (3) to (5), the proper address of the body corporate, firm or (as the case may be) other body or association in question; and
- (d) in any other case, the last known address of the person in question.

(7) In the case of—

- (a) a company registered outside the United Kingdom,
- (b) a firm carrying on business outside the United Kingdom, or
- (c) an unincorporated body or association with offices outside the United Kingdom,

the references in subsection (6) to its principal office include references to its principal office within the United Kingdom (if any).

(8) In this section—

"document" includes anything in writing; and

"notification" includes notice;

and references to giving or sending a notification or other document to a person include references to transmitting it to him and to serving it on him.

(9) This section has effect subject to section 113.

[4218]

NOTES

Commencement: 8 February 2007.

113 Documents in electronic form

(1) This section applies where—

- (a) section 112 authorises the giving or sending of a notification or other document by its delivery to a particular person ("the recipient"); and
- (b) the notification or other document is transmitted to the recipient—
  - (i) by means of an electronic communications network; or
  - (ii) by other means but in a form that nevertheless requires the use of apparatus by the recipient to render it intelligible.

(2) For the purposes of subsection (1), something is not to be regarded as in an intelligible form if it cannot be readily understood without being decrypted or having some comparable process applied to it.

(3) The transmission has effect for the purposes of this Act as a delivery of the notification or other document to the recipient, but only if the requirements imposed by or under this section are complied with.

(4) Where the recipient is OFCOM—
- (a) they must have indicated their willingness to receive the notification or other document in a manner mentioned in subsection (1)(b);
- (b) the transmission must be made in such manner and satisfy such other conditions as they may require; and
- (c) the notification or other document must take such form as they may require.

(5) Where the person making the transmission is OFCOM, they may (subject to subsection (6)) determine—
- (a) the manner in which the transmission is made; and
- (b) the form in which the notification or other document is transmitted.

(6) Where the recipient is a person other than OFCOM—
- (a) the recipient, or
- (b) the person on whose behalf the recipient receives the notification or other document,

must have indicated to the person making the transmission the recipient's willingness to receive notifications or documents transmitted in the form and manner used.

(7) An indication to any person for the purposes of subsection (6)—
- (a) must be given to that person in such manner as he may require;
- (b) may be a general indication or one that is limited to notifications or documents of a particular description;
- (c) must state the address to be used and must be accompanied by such other information as that person requires for the making of the transmission; and
- (d) may be modified or withdrawn at any time by a notice given to that person in such manner as he may require.

(8) An indication, requirement or determination given, imposed or made by OFCOM for the purposes of this section is to be given, imposed or made by being published in such manner as they consider appropriate for bringing it to the attention of the persons who, in their opinion, are likely to be affected by it.

(9) Section 112(8) applies for the purposes of this section as it applies for the purposes of section 112.

[4219]

NOTES

Commencement: 8 February 2007.

---

114 Timing and location of things done electronically

(1) The Secretary of State may by order make provision specifying, for the purposes of this Act, the manner of determining—
- (a) the times at which things done under this Act by means of electronic communications networks are done; and
- (b) the places at which such things are so done, and at which things transmitted by means of such networks are received.

(2) The provision made by subsection (1) may include provision as to the country or territory in which an electronic address is to be treated as located.

(3) An order made by the Secretary of State may also make provision about the manner of proving in any legal proceedings—
- (a) that something done by means of an electronic communications network satisfies the requirements of this Act for the doing of that thing; and
- (b) the matters mentioned in subsection (1)(a) and (b).

(4) An order under this section may provide for such presumptions to apply (whether conclusive or not) as the Secretary of State considers appropriate.

[4220]

PART VI TELECOMMUNICATIONS

NOTES

Commencement: 8 February 2007.

Interpretation

115 General interpretation

(1) In this Act—

"artistic work" has the meaning given by section 4(1) of the Copyright, Designs and Patents Act 1988 (c 48);

"associated facility" has the meaning given by section 32 of the Communications Act 2003 (c 21);

"broadcast" (except in sections 35 to 38 and Part 5), means broadcast by wireless telegraphy, and cognate expressions are to be construed accordingly;

"business" includes a trade or profession;

"communications provider" has the same meaning as in the Communications Act 2003;

"contravention" includes a failure to comply, and cognate expressions are to be construed accordingly;

"electric line" has the meaning given by section 64(1) of the Electricity Act 1989 (c 29);

"electronic communications network" and "electronic communications service" have the meaning given by section 32 of the Communications Act 2003;

"emission", in relation to electromagnetic energy, is to be construed in accordance with subsection (2);

"the enactments relating to the management of the radio spectrum" has the meaning given by section 405 of the Communications Act 2003;

"film" has the meaning given by section 5B(1) of the Copyright, Designs and Patents Act 1988 (c 48);

"frequency" includes frequency band;

"grant of recognised spectrum access" means a grant made under section 18;

"information" includes accounts, estimates and projections and any document;

"interfere" and "interference", in relation to wireless telegraphy, are to be construed in accordance with subsection (3);

"international obligation of the United Kingdom" includes any Community obligation and any obligation which will or may arise under any international agreement or arrangements to which the United Kingdom is party;

"literary, dramatic or musical work" has the same meaning as in Part 1 of the Copyright, Designs and Patents Act 1988;

"modification" includes omissions, alterations and additions, and cognate expressions are to be construed accordingly;

"OFCOM" means the Office of Communications;

"radio spectrum functions", in relation to OFCOM, means their functions under the enactments relating to the management of the radio spectrum;

"receiving apparatus" means wireless telegraphy apparatus that is not designed or adapted for emission (as opposed to reception);

"ship" includes every description of vessel used in navigation;

"sound recording" has the meaning given by section 5A(1) of the Copyright, Designs and Patents Act 1988;

"speech" includes lecture, address and sermon;

"supply", in relation to any item, is to be construed in accordance with subsection (6);

"UK territorial sea" means the territorial sea adjacent to the United Kingdom;

"wireless telegraphy" is to be construed in accordance with section 116;

"wireless telegraphy apparatus" is to be construed in accordance with section 117;

"wireless telegraphy licence" means a licence granted under section 8;

"wireless telegraphy station" is to be construed in accordance with section 117.

(2) A reference in this Act to the emission of electromagnetic energy, or to emission (as opposed to reception), includes a reference to the deliberate reflection (whether continuous or intermittent) of electromagnetic energy by means of apparatus designed or specially adapted for the purpose.

(3) For the purposes of this Act, wireless telegraphy is interfered with if the fulfilment of the purposes of the telegraphy is prejudiced (either generally or in part and, in particular, as

respects all, or as respects any, of the recipients or intended recipients of a message, sound or visual image intended to be conveyed by the telegraphy) by an emission or reflection of electromagnetic energy.

(4) Interference with any wireless telegraphy is not to be regarded as undue for the purposes of this Act unless it is also harmful.

(5) For the purposes of this Act interference is harmful if—

- (a) it creates dangers, or risks of danger, in relation to the functioning of any service provided by means of wireless telegraphy for the purposes of navigation or otherwise for safety purposes; or
- (b) it degrades, obstructs or repeatedly interrupts anything which is being broadcast or otherwise transmitted—
  - (i) by means of wireless telegraphy; and
  - (ii) in accordance with a wireless telegraphy licence, regulations under section 8(3) or a grant of recognised spectrum access or otherwise lawfully.

(6) Section 46 of the Consumer Protection Act 1987 (c 43) has effect for the purpose of construing references in this Act to the supply of any thing as it has effect for the purpose of construing references in that Act to the supply of goods.

(7) In this Act (except Part 5) a reference to the sending or conveying of a message includes a reference to the making of a signal or the sending or conveying of a warning or information, and a reference to the reception of a message is to be construed accordingly.

(8) A reference in this Act to apparatus on board a ship includes a reference to apparatus on a kite or captive balloon flown from a ship.

[4221]

NOTES

Commencement: 8 February 2007.

116 "Wireless telegraphy"

(1) In this Act "wireless telegraphy" means the emitting or receiving, over paths that are not provided by any material substance constructed or arranged for the purpose, of energy to which subsection (2) applies.

(2) This subsection applies to electromagnetic energy of a frequency not exceeding 3,000 gigahertz that—

- (a) serves for conveying messages, sound or visual images (whether or not the messages, sound or images are actually received by anyone), or for operating or controlling machinery or apparatus; or
- (b) is used in connection with determining position, bearing or distance, or for gaining information as to the presence, absence, position or motion of an object or of a class of objects.

(3) The Secretary of State may by order modify the definition of "wireless telegraphy" by substituting a different frequency for the frequency that is for the time being specified in subsection (2).

(4) No order is to be made containing provision authorised by subsection (3) unless a draft of the order has been laid before Parliament and approved by a resolution of each House.

[4222]

NOTES

Commencement: 8 February 2007.

117 "Wireless telegraphy apparatus" and "wireless telegraphy station"

(1) In this Act "wireless telegraphy apparatus" means apparatus for the emitting or receiving, over paths that are not provided by any material substance constructed or arranged for the purpose, of energy to which section 116(2) applies.

(2) In this Act "wireless telegraphy station"—

- (a) means a station for the emitting or receiving, over paths that are not provided by any material substance constructed or arranged for the purpose, of energy to which section 116(2) applies; and

(b) includes the wireless telegraphy apparatus of a ship or aircraft.

[4223]

NOTES

Commencement: 8 February 2007.

Extent and application

118 Extent

(1) Subject to subsection (2), this Act extends to Northern Ireland.

(2) An amendment, repeal or revocation made by this Act has the same extent as the enactment or other instrument amended, repealed or revoked.

(3) Her Majesty may by Order in Council extend the provisions of this Act, with such modifications as appear to Her Majesty to be appropriate, to the Isle of Man or any of the Channel Islands.

(4) But subsection (3) does not authorise the extension of sections 62 to 67 to any of the Channel Islands.

(5) Section 121(3) applies to the power to make an Order in Council under this section as it applies to a power of the Secretary of State to make an order under this Act, but as if references in section 121(3) to the Secretary of State were references to Her Majesty in Council.

(6) The provisions capable of being extended outside the United Kingdom under—

(a) section 15(6) of the Wireless Telegraphy Act 1967 (c 72),
(b) section 204(6) of the Broadcasting Act 1990 (c 42),
(c) section 12(4) of the Intelligence Services Act 1994 (c 13),
(d) section 315(2) of the Merchant Shipping Act 1995 (c 21),
(e) section 150(4) of the Broadcasting Act 1996 (c 55), or
(f) section 411(6) of the Communications Act 2003 (c 21),

include any amendment of those provisions made by this Act.

[4224]

NOTES

Commencement: 8 February 2007.

119 Territorial application

(1) The provisions mentioned in subsection (2) apply to—

(a) all stations and apparatus in or over, or for the time being in or over, the United Kingdom or UK territorial sea;
(b) subject to any limitations that the Secretary of State may by regulations determine, all stations and apparatus on board a ship or aircraft that is registered in the United Kingdom but is not for the time being in or over the United Kingdom or UK territorial sea; and
(c) subject to any limitations that the Secretary of State may by regulations determine, all apparatus not itself in or over the United Kingdom or UK territorial sea but released—
 (i) from within the United Kingdom or UK territorial sea, or
 (ii) from a ship or aircraft that is registered in the United Kingdom.

(2) The provisions are—

(a) sections 8 to 11, 35 to 38, 45 to 49, 55 to 58 and 68; and
(b) regulations under section 54.

(3) Her Majesty may by Order in Council direct that a reference in subsection (1) to a ship or aircraft registered in the United Kingdom is to be construed as including a reference to a ship or aircraft—

(a) registered in the Isle of Man, in any of the Channel Islands or in a colony; or
(b) registered under the law of any other country or territory outside the United Kingdom that is for the time being administered by Her Majesty's Government in the United Kingdom.

(4) For the purposes of paragraph 4(3) of Schedule 2 to the Interpretation Act 1978 (c 30) (meaning of "colony" in existing enactments), subsection (3) is to be treated as if contained in an Act passed before the commencement of that Act.

[4225]

NOTES

Commencement: 8 February 2007.

120 Territorial sea and other waters

(1) Her Majesty may by Order in Council provide—

(a) for an area of UK territorial sea to be treated, for the purposes of any provision of this Act, as if it were situated in such part of the United Kingdom as may be specified in the Order; and

(b) for jurisdiction with respect to questions arising in relation to UK territorial sea under any such provision to be conferred on courts in a part of the United Kingdom so specified.

(2) An Order in Council under section 11 of the Petroleum Act 1998 (c 17) (application of civil law to offshore installations etc) or section 87 of the Energy Act 2004 (c 20) (application of civil law to renewable energy installations etc) may make provision for treating—

(a) an installation with respect to which provision is made under that section and which is outside UK territorial sea but in waters to which that section applies, and

(b) waters within 500 metres of the installation,

as if, for the purposes of any provision of this Act, they were situated in such part of the United Kingdom as is specified in the Order.

(3) The jurisdiction conferred on a court by an Order in Council under this section is in addition to any jurisdiction exercisable apart from this section by that or any other court.

(4) Section 121(3) applies to the power to make an Order in Council under this section as it applies to any power of the Secretary of State to make an order under this Act, but as if references in section 121(3) to the Secretary of State were references to Her Majesty in Council.

(5) A statutory instrument containing an Order in Council under this section is subject to annulment in pursuance of a resolution of either House of Parliament.

(6) "Installation" includes any floating structure or device maintained on a station by whatever means, and installations in transit.

[4226]

NOTES

Commencement: 8 February 2007.

Supplemental

121 Orders and regulations made by Secretary of State

(1) Every power conferred by this Act on the Secretary of State to make orders or regulations is exercisable by statutory instrument.

(2) A statutory instrument containing an order or regulations made in exercise of such a power, other than—

(a) an order under section 5,

(b) regulations under section 49(4)(g),

(c) an order under section 111,

(d) an order under section 116, or

(e) an order under paragraph 26 or 27 of Schedule 8,

is subject to annulment in pursuance of a resolution of either House of Parliament.

(3) Every power of the Secretary of State to make an order or regulations under this Act includes power—

(a) to make different provision for different cases (including different provision in respect of different areas);

(b) to make provision subject to such exemptions and exceptions as the Secretary of State thinks fit; and

(c) to make such incidental, supplemental, consequential and transitional provision as the Secretary of State thinks fit.

[4227]

NOTES

Commencement: 8 February 2007.

122 Orders and regulations made by OFCOM

(1) This section applies to every power of OFCOM to make regulations or an order under this Act.

(2) Those powers are exercisable by statutory instrument, and the Statutory Instruments Act 1946 (c 36) is to apply in relation to those powers as if OFCOM were a Minister of the Crown.

(3) Where an instrument made under such a power falls to be laid before Parliament, OFCOM must, immediately after it is made, send it to the Secretary of State for laying by him.

(4) Before making any regulations or order under such a power, OFCOM must—

(a) give a notice of their proposal to do so to such persons representative of the persons appearing to OFCOM to be likely to be affected by the implementation of the proposal as OFCOM think fit;

(b) publish notice of their proposal in such manner as they consider appropriate for bringing it to the attention of the persons who, in their opinion, are likely to be affected by it and are not given notice by virtue of paragraph (a); and

(c) consider any representations that are made to OFCOM, before the time specified in the notice.

(5) A notice for the purposes of subsection (4) must—

(a) state that OFCOM propose to make the regulations or order in question;

(b) set out the general effect of the regulations or order;

(c) specify an address from which a copy of the proposed regulations or order may be obtained; and

(d) specify a time before which any representations with respect to the proposal must be made to OFCOM.

(6) The time specified for the purposes of subsection (5)(d) must be no earlier than the end of the period of one month beginning with the day after the latest day on which the notice is given or published for the purposes of subsection (4).

(7) Every power of OFCOM to make regulations or an order under this Act includes power—

(a) to make different provision for different cases (including different provision in respect of different areas);

(b) to make provision subject to such exemptions and exceptions as OFCOM think fit; and

(c) to make such incidental, supplemental, consequential and transitional provision as OFCOM think fit.

[4228]

NOTES

Commencement: 8 February 2007.

123 Consequential amendments

Schedule 7 (consequential amendments) has effect.

[4229]

NOTES

Commencement: 8 February 2007.

124 Transitional provisions, savings and transitory modifications

Schedule 8 (transitional provisions, savings and transitory modifications) has effect.

[4230]

NOTES

Commencement: 8 February 2007.

125 Repeals and revocations

(1) The enactments mentioned in Part 1 of Schedule 9 are repealed to the extent specified.

(2) The instruments mentioned in Part 2 of that Schedule are revoked to the extent specified.

[4231]

NOTES

Commencement: 8 February 2007.

126 Short title and commencement

(1) This Act may be cited as the Wireless Telegraphy Act 2006.

(2) This Act comes into force at the end of the period of three months beginning with the day on which it is passed.

[4232]

NOTES

Commencement: 8 February 2007.

SCHEDULE 1
PROCEDURE FOR WIRELESS TELEGRAPHY LICENCES

Section 10

General procedure for applications

1(1) An application for a grant of a wireless telegraphy licence is to be determined in accordance with procedures prescribed in regulations made by OFCOM.

(2) The procedures must include provision for—

(a) time limits for dealing with the granting of licences;

(b) requirements that must be met for the grant of a licence;

(c) particulars of the terms, provisions and limitations to which a licence may be made subject.

Time limits

2(1) The time limits fixed for the purposes of paragraph 1(2) must require a decision on the application to be made, notified to the applicant and published—

(a) in the case of an application for a licence relating to a frequency allocated in accordance with the United Kingdom Plan for Frequency Authorisation, not more than six weeks after the day of the receipt of the application; and

(b) in any other case, as soon as possible after the receipt of the application.

(2) The period of six weeks specified in sub-paragraph (1)(a) may be extended by OFCOM where it appears to them necessary to do so—

(a) for the purpose of enabling the requirements of any international agreement relating to frequencies, to orbital positions or to satellite co-ordination to be complied with; or

(b) in a case where a determination falls to be made as to which of a number of applicants is the more or most suitable to be licensed, for the purpose of securing that the procedure for the making of that determination is fair, reasonable, open and transparent.

(3) The period may not be extended by virtue of sub-paragraph (2)(b) by more than eight months.

Information to be provided in connection with applications

3 The grounds on which a licence may be refused by OFCOM include a failure by the applicant to provide information which OFCOM reasonably require in order to satisfy themselves that the applicant is able to comply with terms, provisions or limitations to which the licence may be made subject.

Proposed refusal

4 Where OFCOM propose to refuse a licence they must—

(a) give to the applicant the reasons for the proposed refusal;

(b) specify a period of not less than one month within which representations about the proposed refusal may be made.

Duration

5 A wireless telegraphy licence continues in force, unless previously revoked by OFCOM, for such period as may be specified in the licence.

Revocation or variation

6 OFCOM may revoke a wireless telegraphy licence or vary its terms, provisions or limitations—

(a) by a notice in writing given to the holder of the licence; or

(b) by a general notice applicable to licences of the class to which the licence belongs, published in such way as may be specified in the licence.

Notification of proposed revocation or variation

7(1) Where OFCOM propose to revoke or vary a wireless telegraphy licence, they must give the person holding the licence a notification under this sub-paragraph—

(a) stating the reasons for the proposed revocation or variation; and

(b) specifying the period during which the person notified has an opportunity to do the things specified in sub-paragraph (2).

(2) The things are—

(a) making representations about the proposal; and

(b) if the proposal is the result of a contravention of a term, provision or limitation of the licence, complying with that term, provision or limitation.

(3) Subject to sub-paragraphs (4) to (6), the period for doing those things must be the period of one month beginning with the day after the one on which the notification was given.

(4) OFCOM may, if they think fit, allow a longer period for doing those things—

(a) by specifying a longer period in the notification; or

(b) by subsequently, on one or more occasions, extending the specified period.

(5) The person notified has a shorter period for doing those things if a shorter period is agreed between OFCOM and the person notified.

(6) The person notified also has a shorter period if—

(a) OFCOM have reasonable grounds for believing that the case is urgent or a case of serious and repeated contravention;

(b) they have determined that, in the circumstances, a shorter period would be appropriate; and

(c) the shorter period has been specified in the notification.

(7) A case is urgent if the failure to revoke or vary the licence will result in, or create an immediate risk of—

(a) a serious threat to the safety of the public, to public health or to national security; or

(b) serious economic or operational problems for persons, other than the person in contravention, who—

(i) use wireless telegraphy stations or wireless telegraphy apparatus; or

(ii) are communications providers or make associated facilities available.

(8) A contravention of a term, provision or limitation of a licence is a repeated contravention, in relation to a proposal to revoke or vary a licence, if it falls within sub-paragraph (9).

(9) A contravention falls within this sub-paragraph if—

(a) a previous notification under sub-paragraph (1) has been given in respect of the same contravention or in respect of another contravention of a term, provision or limitation of the same licence; and

(b) the subsequent notification under that sub-paragraph is given no more than 12 months after the day of the making by OFCOM of a determination for the purposes of sub-paragraph (10) that the contravention to which the previous notification related did occur.

(10) Where OFCOM have given a notification under sub-paragraph (1), they must, within the period of one month beginning with the end of the period for the making of representations about the proposal contained in that notification—

(a) decide whether or not to revoke or vary the licence in accordance with their proposal, or in accordance with that proposal but with modifications; and

(b) give the person holding the licence a notification of their decision.

(11) The notification under sub-paragraph (10)—

(a) must be given no more than one week after the making of the decision to which it relates; and

(b) must, in accordance with that decision, either revoke or vary the licence or withdraw the proposal for a revocation or variation.

(12) Nothing in this paragraph applies to a proposal to revoke or vary a licence if the proposal is made at the request or with the consent of the holder of the licence.

(13) The reference in sub-paragraph (9) to a contravention of a term, provision or limitation of the same licence includes a reference to a contravention of a term, provision or limitation contained in a previous licence of which the licence in question is a direct or indirect renewal.

Restriction on powers of revocation and variation

8(1) The terms that OFCOM may include in a wireless telegraphy licence include terms restricting the exercise by them of their power to revoke or vary the licence.

(2) The terms that may be included because of sub-paragraph (1) include, in particular, terms providing that the licence may not be revoked or varied except—

(a) with the consent of the holder of the licence; or

(b) in such other circumstances and on such grounds as may be specified in the licence.

(3) The circumstances or grounds may relate to matters relevant for the purposes of any other enactment (and may, in particular, be dependent on the exercise of a statutory discretion under any other enactment).

(4) A licence containing terms included because of sub-paragraph (1) may also provide that regulations made under section 45—

(a) do not apply in relation to a station or apparatus to which the licence relates; or

(b) apply in relation to such a station or such apparatus to such extent only, or subject to such modifications, as may be specified in the licence.

(5) Despite any term or provision included in a wireless telegraphy licence in accordance with this paragraph, OFCOM may at any time by giving the holder of the licence a notice in writing revoke the licence or vary its terms, provisions or limitations, if it appears to OFCOM to be necessary or expedient to do so—

(a) in the interests of national security; or

(b) for the purpose of securing compliance with an international obligation of the United Kingdom.

[4233]

NOTES

Commencement: 8 February 2007.

SCHEDULE 2
PROCEDURE FOR GRANTS OF RECOGNISED SPECTRUM ACCESS

Section 19

General procedure for applications

1(1) An application for a grant of recognised spectrum access is to be determined in accordance with procedures prescribed in regulations made by OFCOM.

(2) The procedures must include provision for—

(a) time limits for dealing with applications for a grant of recognised spectrum access;
(b) requirements which must be met before a grant is made;
(c) the restrictions and conditions to which a grant may be made subject.

Information to be provided in connection with applications

2 The grounds on which a grant of recognised spectrum access may be refused by OFCOM include a failure by the applicant to provide information which OFCOM reasonably require in order to satisfy themselves that the applicant is able to comply with restrictions or conditions to which the grant may be made subject.

Notice of proposed refusal of application

3(1) Where OFCOM propose to refuse an application for a grant of recognised spectrum access, they must give notice to the applicant—

(a) stating the reasons for their proposal; and
(b) specifying a period within which representations may be made about the proposal.

(2) The period must be a period ending not less than one month after the day of the giving of the notice.

Duration of grant

4 A grant of recognised spectrum access continues in force, unless previously revoked by OFCOM, for such period as may be specified in the notification by which the grant is made.

Revocation or modification

5 OFCOM may revoke or modify a grant of recognised spectrum access, or the restrictions or conditions to which such a grant is subject, by a notice to the person to whom the grant was made.

Notice of proposed revocation or modification

6(1) Where OFCOM propose to revoke or modify a grant of recognised spectrum access or a restriction or condition to which such a grant is subject, they must give a notification to the holder of the grant—

(a) stating the reasons for their proposal; and
(b) specifying the period during which the person notified has an opportunity to do the things specified in sub-paragraph (2).

(2) The things are—

(a) making representations about the proposal; and
(b) if the proposal is the result of a contravention of a restriction or condition of the grant, complying with it.

(3) Subject to sub-paragraphs (4) to (6), the period for doing those things must be the period of one month beginning with the day after the one on which the notification was given.

(4) OFCOM may, if they think fit, allow a longer period for doing those things—
(a) by specifying a longer period in the notification; or
(b) by subsequently, on one or more occasions, extending the specified period.

(5) The person notified has a shorter period for doing those things if a shorter period is agreed between OFCOM and the person notified.

(6) The person notified also has a shorter period if—
(a) OFCOM have reasonable grounds for believing that the case is urgent or a case of serious and repeated contravention;
(b) they have determined that, in the circumstances, a shorter period would be appropriate; and
(c) the shorter period has been specified in the notification.

(7) A case is urgent if the failure to revoke or modify the grant will result in, or create an immediate risk of—
(a) a serious threat to the safety of the public, to public health or to national security; or
(b) serious economic or operational problems for persons, other than the person in contravention, who—
(i) use wireless telegraphy stations or wireless telegraphy apparatus; or
(ii) are communications providers or make associated facilities available.

(8) A contravention of a restriction or condition of a grant of recognised spectrum access is a repeated contravention, in relation to a proposal to revoke or modify the grant, if it falls within sub-paragraph (9).

(9) A contravention falls within this sub-paragraph if—
(a) a previous notification under sub-paragraph (1) has been given in respect of the same contravention or in respect of any other contravention of a restriction or condition of the same grant; and
(b) the subsequent notification under that sub-paragraph is given no more than 12 months after the day of the making by OFCOM of a determination for the purposes of sub-paragraph (10) that the contravention to which the previous notification related did occur.

(10) Where OFCOM have given a notification under sub-paragraph (1), they must, within the period of one month beginning with the end of the period for the making of representations about the proposal contained in that notification—
(a) decide whether or not to revoke or modify the grant of recognised spectrum access in accordance with their proposal, or in accordance with that proposal but with modifications; and
(b) give the holder of the grant a notification of their decision.

(11) The notification under sub-paragraph (10)—
(a) must be given no more than one week after the making of the decision to which it relates; and
(b) must, in accordance with that decision, either revoke or modify the grant or withdraw the proposal for revocation or modification.

(12) Nothing in this paragraph is to apply to—
(a) a revocation or modification to be made at the request or with the consent of the holder of the grant; or
(b) a revocation or modification that appears to OFCOM to be necessary or expedient for the purpose of securing compliance with an international obligation of the United Kingdom.

(13) The reference in sub-paragraph (9) to a contravention of a restriction or condition of the same grant includes a reference to a contravention of a restriction or condition contained in any previous grant of which the grant in question is a direct or indirect renewal.

Restriction on powers of revocation and modification

7(1) The conditions that OFCOM may include in a grant of recognised spectrum access include conditions restricting the exercise by them of their power to revoke or modify the grant.

(2) Those conditions include, in particular, conditions providing that the grant may not be revoked or modified except—

(a) with the consent of the holder of the grant; or

(b) in such other circumstances and on such grounds as may be specified in the conditions.

(3) The circumstances or grounds may relate to matters relevant for the purposes of any enactment, whether relating to wireless telegraphy or not (and may, in particular, be made dependent on the exercise of a statutory discretion under any enactment).

(4) Nothing in a condition included in a grant of recognised spectrum access restricts the power of OFCOM to revoke or modify a grant of recognised spectrum access, if it appears to OFCOM to be necessary or appropriate to do so—

(a) in the interests of national security;

(b) in the interests of the safety of the public or public health; or

(c) for the purpose of securing compliance with an international obligation of the United Kingdom.

(5) "Enactment" has the same meaning as in the Communications Act 2003 (c 21).

[4234]

NOTES

Commencement: 8 February 2007.

SCHEDULE 3
SUSPENSION AND REVOCATION OF AUTHORITIES ISSUED TO WIRELESS PERSONNEL

Section 52

Notice of suspension

1(1) On suspending the authority, the Secretary of State must give the person to whom the authority under section 52(3) was issued a notice—

(a) informing him of the suspension, of the grounds of the suspension and of his rights under this Schedule;

(b) further informing him that if he does not avail himself of those rights the Secretary of State may revoke the authority.

(2) Sub-paragraph (3) applies where it appears to the Secretary of State that it is not reasonably practicable to give the notice to the person to whom the authority was issued.

(3) The Secretary of State must take such steps, by advertisement or otherwise, to bring the notice to the person's knowledge as appear to the Secretary of State to be reasonable in the circumstances.

Reference to advisory committee

2(1) The person to whom the authority was issued may request that the question whether the authority should be revoked, or its suspension continued or terminated, be referred to an advisory committee.

(2) The request is to be made within such period and in such manner as may be specified in the notice under paragraph 1.

(3) Where a request is made under sub-paragraph (1) the Secretary of State must, unless he terminates the suspension, refer the question to an advisory committee.

(4) For the purposes of this Schedule an advisory committee is a committee consisting of three persons appointed by the Secretary of State.

(5) The three persons appointed are to be—

(a) an independent chairman selected by the Secretary of State;
(b) a person nominated by such body or bodies representing employers of wireless operators as seem to the Secretary of State to be appropriate for the purpose;
(c) a person nominated by such association or associations representing wireless operators as seem to the Secretary of State to be appropriate for the purpose.

(6) Where a question is referred to an advisory committee under this paragraph, the committee must—
(a) inquire into the matter, and
(b) consider any representations made by the person to whom the authority was issued,

and then make a report to the Secretary of State.

(7) The report is to state—
(a) the facts as found by the committee, and
(b) the action that, in their opinion, ought to be taken as respects the revocation of the authority or the continuation or termination of its suspension.

(8) The Secretary of State is to consider the report.

Decision by Secretary of State

3(1) Sub-paragraph (2) applies—
(a) after the Secretary of State has considered the report of the advisory committee; or
(b) if no request for a reference to an advisory committee has been made within the period and in the manner referred to in paragraph 2(2), on the expiry of that period.

(2) The Secretary of State must (as he thinks fit)—
(a) revoke the authority;
(b) terminate the suspension of the authority; or
(c) continue the suspension for such period as he thinks fit.

(3) Sub-paragraph (4) applies where the Secretary of State revokes the authority or continues its suspension.

(4) The Secretary of State must, if requested to do so by the person to whom the authority was issued, inform him of the opinion expressed by the advisory committee as to the action that ought to be taken as respects—
(a) the revocation of the authority; or
(b) the continuation or termination of its suspension.

Payment of expenses

4 The Secretary of State is to pay—
(a) the expenses incurred by an advisory committee under this Schedule, to the extent determined by him; and
(b) such sums as he may determine in respect of the expenses of the members of the committee.

[4235]

NOTES

Commencement: 8 February 2007.

SCHEDULE 4
FIXED PENALTIES

Section 96

Offences to which this Schedule applies

1(1) This Schedule applies to an offence under this Act (other than Part 4) which is a summary offence.

(2) Such an offence is referred to in this Schedule as a "relevant offence".

Fixed penalties and fixed penalty notices

2(1) The fixed penalty for a relevant offence is such amount as may be prescribed in relation to that offence by regulations made by the Secretary of State.

(2) The amount prescribed by regulations under sub-paragraph (1) is not to be more than 25 per cent of the maximum fine on summary conviction for the offence in question.

(3) In this Schedule "fixed penalty notice" means a notice offering the opportunity of the discharge of any liability to conviction of the offence to which the notice relates by payment of a fixed penalty in accordance with this Schedule.

Issuing of fixed penalty notice

3(1) If OFCOM have reason to believe that a person has committed a relevant offence, they may send a fixed penalty notice to that person.

(2) If a procurator fiscal receives a report that a person has committed a relevant offence in Scotland, he also has power to send a fixed penalty notice to that person.

(3) If an authorised person has, on any occasion, reason to believe that a person—

- (a) is committing a relevant offence, or
- (b) has on that occasion committed a relevant offence,

he may hand that person a fixed penalty notice.

(4) "Authorised person" means a person authorised by OFCOM, for the purposes of sub-paragraph (3), to issue fixed penalty notices on OFCOM's behalf.

(5) References in this Schedule to the person by whom a fixed penalty notice is issued, in relation to a notice handed to a person in accordance with sub-paragraph (3), are references to OFCOM.

Content of fixed penalty notice

4(1) A fixed penalty notice must—

- (a) state the alleged offence;
- (b) give such particulars of the circumstances alleged to constitute that offence as are necessary for giving reasonable information about it;
- (c) state the fixed penalty for that offence;
- (d) specify the relevant officer to whom the fixed penalty may be paid and the address at which it may be paid;
- (e) state that proceedings against the person to whom it is issued cannot be commenced in respect of the offence until the end of the suspended enforcement period;
- (f) state that such proceedings cannot be commenced if the penalty is paid within the suspended enforcement period;
- (g) inform the person to whom it is issued of his right to ask to be tried for the alleged offence; and
- (h) explain how that right may be exercised and the effect of exercising it.

(2) The suspended enforcement period for the purposes of this Schedule is—

- (a) the period of one month beginning with the day after that on which the fixed penalty notice was issued; or
- (b) such longer period as may be specified in the notice.

Withdrawal of fixed penalty notice

5 If it appears to a person who has issued a fixed penalty notice that it was wrongly issued—

- (a) he may withdraw the notice by a further notice to the person to whom it was issued; and
- (b) if he does so, the relevant officer must repay any amount paid in respect of the penalty.

Notification to person to whom payment is to be made

6 A person who issues (or withdraws) a fixed penalty notice must send a copy of the notice (or of the notice of withdrawal) to the relevant officer specified in the notice being issued (or withdrawn).

Effect of fixed penalty notice

7(1) This paragraph applies if a fixed penalty notice is issued to a person ("the alleged offender").

(2) Proceedings for the offence to which the notice relates cannot be brought against the alleged offender until the person who issued the notice has been notified by the relevant officer specified in the notice that payment of the fixed penalty has not been made within the suspended enforcement period.

(3) If the alleged offender asks to be tried for the alleged offence—
- (a) sub-paragraph (2) does not apply; and
- (b) proceedings may be brought against him.

(4) Such a request must be made by a notice given by the alleged offender—
- (a) in the manner specified in the fixed penalty notice; and
- (b) before the end of the suspended enforcement period.

(5) A request made in accordance with sub-paragraph (3) is referred to in this Schedule as a "request to be tried".

Payment of fixed penalty

8(1) If the alleged offender decides to pay the fixed penalty, he must pay it to the relevant officer specified in the notice.

(2) Payment of the penalty may be made by properly addressing, pre-paying and posting a letter containing the amount of the penalty (in cash or otherwise).

(3) Sub-paragraph (4) applies if a person—
- (a) claims to have made payment by that method; and
- (b) shows that his letter was posted.

(4) Unless the contrary is proved, payment is to be regarded as made at the time at which the letter would be delivered in the ordinary course of post.

(5) Sub-paragraph (2) does not prevent the payment of a penalty by other means.

(6) A letter is properly addressed for the purposes of sub-paragraph (2) if it is addressed in accordance with the requirements specified in the fixed penalty notice.

Effect of payment

9 If the fixed penalty specified in a fixed penalty notice is paid within the period specified in that notice, no proceedings for the offence to which that notice relates may be brought against the alleged offender.

Service of statement and proof of service

10(1) This paragraph applies to proceedings for a relevant offence.

(2) A certificate by OFCOM—
- (a) that a copy of a statement by a person authorised by OFCOM was included in, or given with, a fixed penalty notice,
- (b) that the notice was a notice with respect to the relevant offence, and
- (c) that that notice was issued to the accused on a date specified in the certificate,

is evidence that a copy of the statement was served on the alleged offender by delivery to him on that date.

(3) The statement is to be treated as properly served for the purposes of—

(a) section 9 of the Criminal Justice Act 1967 (c 80) (proof by written statement), and

(b) section 1 of the Criminal Justice (Miscellaneous Provisions) Act (Northern Ireland) 1968 (c 28 (NI)) (corresponding provision for Northern Ireland),

even though the manner of service is not authorised by subsection (8) of either of those sections.

(4) Sub-paragraphs (5) and (6) apply to any proceedings in which service of a statement is proved by a certificate under this paragraph.

(5) For the purposes of—

(a) section 9(2)(c) of the Criminal Justice Act 1967 (copy of statement to be tendered in evidence to be served before hearing on other parties to the proceedings by or on behalf of the party proposing to tender it), and

(b) section 1(2)(c) of the Criminal Justice (Miscellaneous Provisions) Act (Northern Ireland) 1968 (corresponding provision for Northern Ireland),

service of the statement is to be taken to have been effected by or on behalf of the prosecutor.

(6) If the alleged offender makes a request to be tried—

(a) section 9(2)(d) of the Criminal Justice Act 1967 (time for objection), and

(b) section 1(2)(d) of the Criminal Justice (Miscellaneous Provisions) Act (Northern Ireland) 1968 (corresponding provision for Northern Ireland),

are to apply with the substitution, for the reference to seven days from the service of the copy of the statement, of a reference to seven days beginning with the day after the one on which the request to be tried was made.

(7) This paragraph does not extend to Scotland.

Certificate about payment

11 In any proceedings, a certificate—

(a) that payment of a fixed penalty was, or was not, received by the relevant officer specified in the fixed penalty notice by a date specified in the certificate, or

(b) that a letter containing an amount sent by post in payment of a fixed penalty was marked as posted on a date specified in the certificate,

is evidence (and in Scotland sufficient evidence) of the facts stated, if the certificate purports to be signed by that officer.

Regulations

12 The Secretary of State may by regulations make provision as to any matter incidental to the operation of this Schedule, and in particular—

(a) for prescribing any information or further information to be provided in a notice, notification, certificate or receipt;

(b) for prescribing the duties of relevant officers and the information to be supplied to and by them.

Interpretation

13 In this Schedule "relevant officer" means—

(a) in relation to England and Wales, the designated officer for the magistrates' court;

(b) in relation to Scotland, the clerk of court; and

(c) in relation to Northern Ireland, the clerk of petty sessions.

[4236]

NOTES

Commencement: 8 February 2007.

SCHEDULE 5
FORFEITURE ON CONVICTION

Section 103

Power to order forfeiture

1(1) Where a person is convicted of a relevant offence, the court may, as well as imposing any other penalty, order to be forfeited to OFCOM such of the things mentioned in sub-paragraph (2) as the court considers appropriate.

(2) The things are—

(a) any vehicle, ship or aircraft, or any structure or other object, that was used in connection with the commission of the offence;
(b) any wireless telegraphy apparatus or other apparatus in relation to which the offence was committed;
(c) any wireless telegraphy apparatus or other apparatus that was used in connection with the commission of the offence;
(d) any wireless telegraphy apparatus or other apparatus (not falling within paragraph (b) or (c)) that—
  (i) was in the possession or under the control of the person convicted of the offence at the time he committed it, and
  (ii) was intended to be used (whether or not by that person) in connection with the making of a broadcast or other transmission that would contravene section 8 or any provision of Part 5.

(3) References in sub-paragraph (2)(b) to (d) to apparatus other than wireless telegraphy apparatus include references to—

(a) recordings;
(b) equipment designed or adapted for use—
  (i) in making recordings, or
  (ii) in reproducing sounds or visual images from recordings;
(c) any other equipment that is connected, directly or indirectly, to wireless telegraphy apparatus.

(4) A relevant offence is—

(a) an offence under Chapter 4 or 5 of Part 2 consisting in a contravention of any provision of that Part in relation to a wireless telegraphy station or wireless telegraphy apparatus (including an offence under section 37 or 38);
(b) an offence under section 66;
(c) an offence under section 68;
(d) an offence under Part 5.

(5) But the following are not relevant offences—

(a) an offence under section 35 consisting in the installation or use of receiving apparatus;
(b) an offence under section 36 committed in relation to receiving apparatus;
(c) an offence under section 51(4).

Forfeiture in relation to restricted apparatus

2(1) Where a person is convicted of an offence under Part 2, 3 or 6 involving restricted apparatus, the court must order the apparatus to be forfeited to OFCOM unless the defendant or a person who claims to be the owner of, or otherwise interested in, the apparatus shows cause why it should not be forfeited.

(2) This paragraph does not affect the operation of paragraph 1 in relation to apparatus that is not restricted apparatus.

(3) Apparatus is restricted apparatus if custody or control of apparatus of any class or description to which it belongs is for the time being restricted by a restriction order under section 62.

Property of third parties

3 Apparatus may be ordered to be forfeited under paragraph 1 or 2 even if it is not the property of the person by whom the offence giving rise to the forfeiture was committed.

Disposal of apparatus

4 Apparatus ordered to be forfeited under paragraph 1 or 2 may be disposed of by OFCOM in such manner as they think fit.

Delivery to OFCOM

5(1) A court that orders apparatus to be forfeited under paragraph 1 or 2 may also order the person by whom the offence giving rise to the forfeiture was committed not to dispose of it except by delivering it up to OFCOM within 48 hours of being so required by them.

(2) A person against whom an order is made under sub-paragraph (1) commits a further offence if—
- (a) he contravenes the order; or
- (b) he fails to deliver up the apparatus to OFCOM as required.

(3) An offence under sub-paragraph (2) is punishable as if it were committed under the same provision, and at the same time, as the offence for which the forfeiture was ordered.

Provisions as to disposal of property disapplied

6 Section 140 of the Magistrates' Courts Act 1980 (c 43) and Article 58 of the Magistrates' Courts (Northern Ireland) Order 1981 (SI 1981/1675 (NI 26)) (under which magistrates sell or dispose of forfeited property) do not apply in relation to apparatus ordered to be forfeited under paragraph 1 or 2.

Provisions as to deprivation of property disapplied

7 The following provisions (under which a court convicting a person of an offence has power to deprive him of property used etc for purposes of crime) do not apply where a person is convicted of an offence under Part 2, 3 or 5—
- (a) section 143 of the Powers of Criminal Courts (Sentencing) Act 2000 (c 6);
- (b) Part 2 of the Proceeds of Crime (Scotland) Act 1995 (c 43);
- (c) Article 11 of the Criminal Justice (Northern Ireland) Order 1994 (SI 1994/2795 (NI 15)).

[4237]

NOTES

Commencement: 8 February 2007.

SCHEDULE 6
SEIZURE AND FORFEITURE OF RESTRICTED APPARATUS

Section 104

Application of Schedule

1(1) This Schedule applies to restricted apparatus seized—
- (a) in pursuance of a warrant granted under section 97; or
- (b) in the exercise of the power conferred by section 99(3).

(2) Apparatus is restricted apparatus for the purposes of this Schedule if custody or control of apparatus of any class or description to which it belongs is for the time being restricted by a restriction order under section 62.

Notice of seizure

2(1) OFCOM must give notice of the seizure of the restricted apparatus to every person who, to their knowledge, was at the time of the seizure the owner or one of the owners of the apparatus.

(2) The notice must set out the grounds of the seizure.

(3) Where there is no proper address for the purposes of the service of a notice under sub-paragraph (1) in a manner authorised by section 112, the requirements of that sub-paragraph shall be satisfied by the publication of a notice of the seizure in the London, Edinburgh or Belfast Gazette (according to the part of the United Kingdom where the seizure took place).

(4) Apparatus may be condemned or taken to have been condemned under this Schedule only if the requirements of this paragraph have been complied with in the case of that apparatus.

Notice of claim

3 A person claiming that the restricted apparatus is not liable to forfeiture must give written notice of his claim to OFCOM.

4(1) A notice of claim must be given within one month after the day of the giving of the notice of seizure.

(2) A notice of claim must specify—

(a) the name and address of the claimant; and

(b) in the case of a claimant who is outside the United Kingdom, the name and address of a solicitor in the United Kingdom who is authorised to accept service of process and to act on behalf of the claimant.

(3) Service of process upon a solicitor so specified is to be taken to be proper service upon the claimant.

Condemnation

5 The restricted apparatus is to be taken to have been duly condemned as forfeited if—

(a) by the end of the period for the giving of a notice of claim in respect of the apparatus, no notice of claim has been given to OFCOM; or

(b) a notice of claim is given which does not comply with the requirements of paragraphs 3 and 4.

6(1) Where a notice of claim in respect of the restricted apparatus is duly given in accordance with paragraphs 3 and 4, OFCOM may take proceedings for the condemnation of the apparatus by the court.

(2) In such proceedings—

(a) if the court finds that the apparatus was liable to forfeiture at the time of seizure, it must condemn the apparatus as forfeited unless cause is shown why it should not; and

(b) if the court finds that the apparatus was not liable to forfeiture at that time, or cause is shown why it should not be forfeited, the court must order the return of the apparatus to the person appearing to the court to be entitled to it.

(3) If OFCOM decide not to take proceedings for condemnation in a case in which a notice of claim has been so given, they must return the apparatus to the person appearing to them to be the owner of the apparatus, or to one of the persons appearing to them to be the owners of it.

(4) Apparatus required to be returned in accordance with sub-paragraph (3) must be returned as soon as reasonably practicable after the decision not to take proceedings for condemnation.

(5) OFCOM's decision whether to take such proceedings must be taken as soon as reasonably practicable after the receipt of the notice of claim.

7 Where the restricted apparatus is condemned or taken to have been condemned as forfeited, the forfeiture is to have effect as from the time of the seizure.

Proceedings for condemnation by court

8 Proceedings for condemnation are civil proceedings and may be instituted—

(a) in England or Wales, in the High Court or in a magistrates' court;
(b) in Scotland, in the Court of Session or in the sheriff court;
(c) in Northern Ireland, in the High Court or in a court of summary jurisdiction.

9 Proceedings for the condemnation of restricted apparatus instituted in a magistrates' court in England or Wales, in the sheriff court in Scotland or in a court of summary jurisdiction in Northern Ireland may be so instituted—

(a) in a court having jurisdiction in a place where an offence under section 66 involving that apparatus was committed;
(b) in a court having jurisdiction in proceedings for such an offence;
(c) in a court having jurisdiction in the place where the claimant resides or, if the claimant has specified a solicitor under paragraph 4, in the place where that solicitor has his office; or
(d) in a court having jurisdiction in the place where that apparatus was seized or to which it was first brought after being seized.

10(1) In proceedings for condemnation that are instituted in England and Wales or Northern Ireland, the claimant or his solicitor must make his oath that the seized apparatus was, or was to the best of his knowledge and belief, the property of the claimant at the time of the seizure.

(2) In proceedings for condemnation instituted in the High Court—

(a) the court may require the claimant to give such security for the costs of the proceedings as may be determined by the court; and
(b) the claimant must comply with such a requirement.

(3) If a requirement of this paragraph is not complied with, the court must give judgment for OFCOM.

11(1) In the case of proceedings for condemnation instituted in a magistrates' court in England or Wales, either party may appeal against the decision of that court to the Crown Court.

(2) In the case of proceedings for condemnation instituted in a court of summary jurisdiction in Northern Ireland, either party may appeal against the decision of that court to the county court.

(3) This paragraph does not affect any right to require the statement of a case for the opinion of the High Court.

12 Where an appeal has been made (whether by case stated or otherwise) against the decision of the court in proceedings for the condemnation of restricted apparatus, the apparatus is to be left with OFCOM pending the final determination of the matter.

Disposal of unclaimed property

13(1) This paragraph applies where a requirement is imposed by or under this Schedule for apparatus to be returned to a person.

(2) If the apparatus is still in OFCOM's possession after the end of the period of 12 months beginning with the day after the requirement to return it arose, OFCOM may dispose of it in any manner they think fit.

(3) OFCOM may exercise their power under this paragraph to dispose of apparatus only if it is not practicable at the time when the power is exercised to dispose of the apparatus by returning it immediately to the person to whom it is required to be returned.

Provisions as to proof

14 In proceedings arising out of the seizure of restricted apparatus, the fact, form and manner of the seizure is to be taken, without further evidence and unless the contrary is shown, to have been as set forth in the process.

15 In any proceedings, the condemnation by a court of restricted apparatus as forfeited may be proved by the production of—

(a) the order or certificate of condemnation; or

(b) a certified copy of the order purporting to be signed by an officer of the court by which the order or certificate was made or granted.

Special provisions as to certain claimants

16(1) This paragraph applies for the purposes of—
(a) a claim to the restricted apparatus; and
(b) proceedings for its condemnation.

(2) Where at the time of the seizure the apparatus is—
(a) the property of a body corporate,
(b) the property of two or more partners, or
(c) the property of more than five persons,

the oath required by paragraph 10 to be taken by the claimant, and any other thing required by this Schedule or by rules of court to be done by the owner of the apparatus, may be done by a person falling within sub-paragraph (3) or by a person authorised to act on his behalf.

(3) The persons are—
(a) where the owner is a body corporate, the secretary or some duly authorised officer of that body;
(b) where the owners are in partnership, any one or more of the owners;
(c) where there are more than five owners and they are not in partnership, any two or more of the owners acting on behalf of themselves and any of their co-owners who are not acting on their own behalf.

Saving for owner's rights

17 Neither the imposition of a requirement by or under this Schedule to return apparatus to a person nor the return of apparatus to a person in accordance with such a requirement affects—
(a) the rights in relation to that apparatus of any other person; or
(b) the right of any other person to enforce his rights against the person to whom it is returned.

[4238]

NOTES
Commencement: 8 February 2007.

(*Sch 7 contains consequential amendments which, in so far as relevant to this work, have been incorporated at the appropriate place.*)

SCHEDULE 8
TRANSITIONAL PROVISIONS, SAVINGS AND TRANSITORY MODIFICATIONS
Section 124

PART 1
TRANSITIONAL PROVISIONS AND SAVINGS

General provisions

1 The substitution of provisions of this Act for provisions repealed or revoked by it does not affect the continuity of the law.

2 Anything done, or having effect as if done, under or for the purposes of a provision repealed by this Act (including subordinate legislation so made or having effect as if so made), and in force or effective immediately before the commencement of this Act, has effect after that commencement as if done under or for the purposes of the corresponding provision of this Act.

3 A reference (express or implied) in this Act or another enactment, or in an instrument or document, to a provision of this Act is (so far as the context permits) to be read as (according

PART VI TELECOMMUNICATIONS

to the context) being or including a reference to the corresponding provision repealed by this Act, in relation to times, circumstances or purposes in relation to which the repealed provision had effect.

4(1) A reference (express or implied) in an enactment, or in an instrument or document, to a provision repealed by this Act is (so far as the context permits) to be read as (according to the context) being or including a reference to the corresponding provision of this Act, in relation to times, circumstances and purposes in relation to which that corresponding provision has effect.

(2) In particular, where a power conferred by an Act is expressed to be exercisable in relation to enactments contained in Acts passed before or in the same Session as the Act conferring the power, the power is also exercisable in relation to provisions of this Act that reproduce such enactments.

5 Paragraphs 1 to 4 have effect in place of section 17(2) of the Interpretation Act 1978 (c 30) (but do not affect the application of any other provision of that Act).

6 Paragraphs 2 and 4(1) do not apply to an Order in Council to which paragraph 24(1) applies.

General rule for old savings

7(1) The repeal by this Act of an enactment previously repealed subject to savings does not affect the continued operation of those savings.

(2) The repeal by this Act of a saving on the previous repeal of an enactment does not affect the saving in so far as it remains capable of having effect.

Use of existing forms etc

8 A reference to an enactment repealed by this Act which is contained in a document made, served or issued on or after the commencement of that repeal is to be read, except so far as a contrary intention appears, as referring or, as the context may require, including a reference to the corresponding provision of this Act.

Regulatory Reform Act 2001 (c 6)

9(1) This paragraph has effect during the period of two years beginning with the day on which this Act is passed for the purposes of the making of an order under section 1 of the 2001 Act in relation to a provision of this Act that reproduces a provision repealed or revoked by this Act.

(2) The law contained in such a provision of this Act is legislation for the purposes of section 1 of the 2001 Act if, at the time the order is made, the corresponding repealed or revoked provision would have been legislation for those purposes had it not been repealed or revoked.

(3) No order under section 1 of the 2001 Act may be made, in relation to a provision of this Act, if the corresponding repealed provision was amended otherwise than merely for consequential or incidental purposes—

- (a) by an Act passed not more than two years before the day on which the order is made, or
- (b) by subordinate legislation made not more than two years before that day.

(4) Sub-paragraph (3) does not prevent an order under section 1 of the 2001 Act re-enacting without substantive amendment the provision of this Act that reproduces the repealed provision which was so amended.

(5) Sub-paragraph (3) does not affect the operation of section 1(4) of the 2001 Act in relation to any amendment made to this Act.

(6) The 2001 Act is the Regulatory Reform Act 2001.

Contracted-out functions under section 1 of the Wireless Telegraphy Act 1949

10 An order under Part 2 of the Deregulation and Contracting Out Act 1994 (c 40) which is in force immediately before the commencement of this Act and, by virtue of paragraph 6 of Schedule 18 to the Communications Act 2003 (c 21), has effect as if made by virtue of section 1(7) of that Act shall, so long as the order remains in force, continue to have that effect by virtue of this paragraph.

Wireless telegraphy licences granted before 18th June 1998

11(1) This paragraph has effect in relation to wireless telegraphy licences granted before 18th June 1998 (the date on which section 1 of the Wireless Telegraphy Act 1998 (c 6) came into force).

(2) Where this paragraph has effect, section 12 is the provision of this Act which, for the purposes of paragraph 4(1) of this Schedule, corresponds to section 2(1) of the Wireless Telegraphy Act 1949 (c 54).

Procedures treated as prescribed by regulations made by OFCOM

12(1) Sub-paragraph (2) applies where, immediately before the commencement of this Act, procedures have effect, by virtue of paragraph 20(2) or 21(2) of Schedule 18 to the Communications Act 2003 (c 21), as if prescribed by OFCOM by regulations under—

(a) section 1D(3) of the Wireless Telegraphy Act 1949, or
(b) section 3 of the Wireless Telegraphy Act 1998.

(2) In relation to times after the commencement of this Act, the procedures are to have effect as if prescribed by OFCOM by regulations under—

(a) paragraph 1 of Schedule 1, or
(b) section 14.

(3) A notice under—

(a) section 1D of the Wireless Telegraphy Act 1949, or
(b) regulations under section 3 of the Wireless Telegraphy Act 1998,

which is in force immediately before the commencement of this Act and, by virtue of paragraph 20 or 21 of Schedule 18, has effect as if it authorised or required a thing to be done by or in relation to OFCOM shall, so long as it remains in force, continue to have that effect by virtue of this paragraph.

Tribunal established under section 9 of the Wireless Telegraphy Act 1949

13 The repeal by this Act of sections 11 and 12 of the Wireless Telegraphy Act 1949 does not affect the continued operation of section 11 or 12 (without the amendments made in those sections by section 178 of the Communications Act 2003) in relation to a notice under section 11(1) or (2) or section 12(1) that is served before 25th July 2003.

References to Postmaster General etc

14 The repeal by this Act of part of section 3(1)(ii) of the Post Office Act 1969 (c 48) is not to affect the continued operation of section 3(1)(ii) in relation to a provision of regulations or a licence where the regulations were made or the licence was granted under the Wireless Telegraphy Act 1949 before 1st October 1969 (the day on which functions of the Postmaster General were transferred to the Minister).

Procedure for prosecutions

15(1) This paragraph has effect in relation to prosecutions to which section 41 of this Act applies.

(2) The restrictions on the bringing of proceedings which are imposed by section 41(2) and (3) do not have effect in relation to proceedings started before 25th July 2003 (the date on which section 174 of the Communications Act 2003 (c 21) came into force).

PART VI TELECOMMUNICATIONS

Penalties for certain offences triable either way

16 In relation to an offence committed before the commencement of section 282(3) of the Criminal Justice Act 2003 (c 44), the references in the following provisions to periods of imprisonment of 12 months are to be read as references to periods of imprisonment of six months—

(a) section 35(2);

(b) section 36(2);

(c) section 37(2);

(d) section 38(6);

(e) section 47(4);

(f) section 68(3);

(g) section 93(1).

Penalties for offences: unauthorised use of wireless telegraphy station etc

17 In relation to an offence committed before 18th September 2003 (the date on which section 179 of the Communications Act 2003 came into force), each of sections 35(5) and 36(5) is to have effect as if for the words from "is liable" to the end there were substituted

"is liable—

(a) on summary conviction, to imprisonment for a term not exceeding six months or to a fine not exceeding the statutory maximum or to both;

(b) on conviction on indictment, to imprisonment for a term not exceeding two years or to a fine or to both."

18 In relation to an offence committed on or after 18th September 2003 but before the commencement of section 281(5) of the Criminal Justice Act 2003, the references in the following provisions to periods of imprisonment of 51 weeks are to be read as references to periods of imprisonment of six months—

(a) section 35(5);

(b) section 36(5).

Penalties for offences: contravening notice under section 55 or 56

19 In relation to an offence committed before the commencement of section 280 of the Criminal Justice Act 2003, section 58(2) has effect as if in paragraph (a) for the words "to a fine not exceeding level 5 on the standard scale" there were substituted "to imprisonment for a term not exceeding three months or to a fine not exceeding level 5 on the standard scale or to both".

Fixed penalties for wireless telegraphy offences

20 Schedule 4 to this Act does not apply to offences committed before the day which is the relevant commencement date for the purposes of paragraph 27 of this Schedule.

Powers of seizure

21 In relation to an offence committed before 18th September 2003 (the date on which section 179 of the Communications Act 2003 (c 21) came into force), section 99(1) of this Act has effect with the omission of paragraph (c).

Forfeiture etc of restricted apparatus

22 Nothing in section 104 of, and Schedule 6 to, this Act applies in relation to apparatus seized before 29th December 2003 (the date on which section 182 of the Communications Act 2003 came into force).

Appeals of wireless telegraphy decisions

23 The repeals made by this Act do not affect the continued operation of paragraph 23(2) of Schedule 18 to the Communications Act 2003 as regards decisions against which an appeal could have been brought under section 1F of the Wireless Telegraphy Act 1949 (c 54).

Orders in Council: section 118

24(1) An Order in Council made under a provision that is repealed by this Act and re-enacted in section 118(3) continues to have effect despite the repeal of that provision.

(2) An Order in Council made under section 118(3) may amend or revoke an Order in Council continued in effect by sub-paragraph (1).

Orders in Council: continental shelf

25(1) This paragraph applies in the case of an Order in Council which, as a result of paragraph 63 of Schedule 18 to the Communications Act 2003 (provision relating to Orders in Council under section 6 of the Continental Shelf Act 1964 (c 29)), has effect, immediately before the commencement of this Act, as if made under section 410 of the Communications Act 2003.

(2) An Order in Council to which this paragraph applies is to have effect, after the commencement of this Act, as an Order in Council made in exercise of the powers conferred by section 120.

[4239]

NOTES

Commencement: 8 February 2007.

PART 2
TRANSITORY MODIFICATIONS

Justice (Northern Ireland) Act 2002 (c 26)

26(1) This paragraph applies if paragraph 25 of Schedule 7 to the Justice (Northern Ireland) Act 2002 has not come into force before the commencement of this Act.

(2) Until the relevant commencement date, section 93(4)(b) has effect as if for "the Advocate General for Northern Ireland" there were substituted "the Attorney General for Northern Ireland".

(3) The relevant commencement date is—
- (a) if an order has been made before the commencement of this Act appointing a day after that commencement as the day for the coming into force of paragraph 25 of Schedule 7 to the Justice (Northern Ireland) Act 2002 (c 26), the day so appointed;
- (b) otherwise, such day as the Secretary of State may by order appoint.

Communications Act 2003 (c 21)

27(1) This paragraph applies if—
- (a) section 180 of the Communications Act 2003, and
- (b) Schedule 6 to that Act,

have not come into force before the commencement of this Act.

(2) Until the relevant commencement date, this Act has effect with the omission of—
- (a) section 96, and
- (b) Schedule 4.

(3) The relevant commencement date is—
- (a) if an order has been made before the commencement of this Act appointing a day after that commencement as the day for the coming into force of the provisions mentioned in sub-paragraph (1), the day so appointed;

(b) otherwise, such day as the Secretary of State may by order appoint.

Power to make transitional provision

28 Section 121(3) of this Act does not apply to an order made by the Secretary of State under paragraph 26 or 27, but—

(a) an order under paragraph 26 may make such provision as may be made by an order under section 89(1) of the Justice (Northern Ireland) Act 2002 in connection with the coming into force of a provision of that Act, and

(b) an order under paragraph 27 may make such provision as, by virtue of section 411(4) of the Communications Act 2003, is authorised to be made by an order under section 411(2) of that Act.

Saving for old transitional provisions

29(1) This paragraph applies to any transitional or transitory provision or saving ("the transitional provision") made in connection with the coming into force of any provision of the Justice (Northern Ireland) Act 2002 or the Communications Act 2003 mentioned in sub-paragraph (1) of paragraph 26 or 27 ("the old enactment").

(2) If the old enactment is in force before the commencement of the provision of this Act reproducing its effect ("the corresponding provision of this Act"), the transitional provision is to continue to have effect (so far as capable of doing so) in relation to the corresponding provision of this Act.

(3) Sub-paragraph (4) applies if—

(a) sub-paragraph (2) does not apply, but

(b) before the commencement of this Act an order has been made appointing a day for the coming into force of the old enactment.

(4) The transitional provision is to have effect from the date so appointed in relation to the corresponding provision of this Act.

[4240]

NOTES

Commencement: 8 February 2007.

(*Sch 9 contains repeals and revocations which, in so far as relevant to this work, have been incorporated at the appropriate place.*)

WIRELESS TELEGRAPHY (CONTROL OF INTERFERENCE FROM RADIO-FREQUENCY HEATING APPARATUS) REGULATIONS 1971

(SI 1971/1675)

NOTES

Made: 14 October 1971.
Authority: Wireless Telegraphy Act 1949, s 10.
Commencement: 21 October 1972.

ARRANGEMENT OF REGULATIONS

1 Citation and Commencement

These Regulations may be cited as the Wireless Telegraphy (Control of Interference from Radio-Frequency Heating Apparatus) Regulations 1971, and shall come into operation on 21st October 1972.

[4241]

NOTES

These Regulations are revoked, in so far as they impose electromagnetic compatibility requirements on relevant apparatus which is to be supplied or taken into service and used for the purpose for which it was intended, by the Electromagnetic Compatibility Regulations 2005, SI 2005/281, reg 2(2), Sch 1 at **[4433]**, **[4536]**.

2 Interpretation

(*1*) *In these Regulations, except so far as the contrary is provided or the context otherwise requires, the following expressions have the meanings hereby respectively assigned to them—*

"the Act" means the Wireless Telegraphy Act 1949;

"the British Islands" means the area comprised by the United Kingdom, the Channel Islands, and the Isle of Man;

"radio-frequency heating apparatus" means apparatus, not being electro-medical apparatus, scientific apparatus, or arc-welding apparatus, which is designed to produce a heating effect by the use of radio-frequency energy and which, or any part of which, generates or is liable to generate electro-magnetic energy at frequencies of three million megahertz or less when it is in operation, and includes any switchgear or controlling apparatus forming part of or directly associated with that apparatus and any induction cables, attachment, electrodes and connecting leads used or designed to be used with that apparatus;

"kilohertz" has the same meaning as kilocycles per second, i e one thousand cycles per second;

"megahertz" has the same meaning as megacycles per second, i e one million cycles per second;

"electric supply lines" means electric lines for transmitting electric power to a radio-frequency heating apparatus;

"terminal voltage" means the radio-frequency voltage present between each electric supply line terminal of a radio-frequency heating apparatus and the screening of the measuring apparatus referred to in Regulation 5;

expressions used in Schedule 2 have the meanings respectively assigned to them in Part 1 of Schedule 2;

and other expressions have the same meaning as they have in the Act.

(2) *The Interpretation Act 1889 applies for the interpretation of these Regulations as it applies for the interpretation of an Act of Parliament.*

[4242]

NOTES

Revoked as noted to reg 1 at **[4241]**.
Interpretation Act 1889: see now the Interpretation Act 1978.

3 Requirements

When any radio-frequency heating apparatus is used in the British Islands on or after the 21st October 1972 it shall comply with the following requirements for the purposes of section 10 of the Act—

(*a*) *the field strength of electro-magnetic energy radiated in any direction from the apparatus, as measured and computed in accordance with Regulation 5 shall not exceed the limits specified in columns 1 and 2 of Schedule 1 at any frequency within the range from 150 kilohertz to 1000 megahertz, but if the apparatus causes undue interference with any wireless telegraphy used for the purposes of any*

PART VI TELECOMMUNICATIONS

safety of life service or for any purpose on which the safety of any person or of any vessel, aircraft or vehicle may depend, the limits specified in columns 1 and 4 of Schedule 1 shall apply, and

(*b*) *the terminal voltage, as measured and computed in accordance with Regulation 5 shall not exceed the limits specified in columns 1 and 3 of Schedule 1 at any frequency within the range from 150 kilohertz to 30megahertz but if the apparatus causes undue interference with any wireless telegraphy used for the purposes of any safety of life service, or for any purpose on which the safety of any person or of any vessel, aircraft or vehicle may depend, the limits specified in columns 1 and 5 of Schedule 1 shall apply.*

[4243]

NOTES

Revoked as noted to reg 1 at **[4241]**.

4 *Any radio-frequency heating apparatus which obtains its electric power from any supply to which dwelling houses are not also directly connected is exempt from the provisions of Schedule 1 Columns 3 and 5.*

[4244]

NOTES

Revoked as noted to reg 1 at **[4241]**.

5 Field strength and terminal voltage measurement

(*1*) *For the purpose of measuring and computing the field strength of the electro-magnetic energy and the terminal voltage at frequencies exceeding 150 kilohertz but not exceeding 1000 megahertz the radio-frequency heating apparatus shall be tested by means of measuring apparatus of the description and having the physical and electrical characteristics and performance set out in British Standard 727 : 1967, Section 1, Pages 9–13.*

(*2*) *The tests for field strength shall be made by the method and under the conditions set out in Part 2 of Schedule 2 and the tests for terminal voltage shall be made by the method and under the conditions set out in Part 3 of Schedule 2.*

(*3*) *The said field strength and terminal voltage shall be computed as provided in Parts 2 and 3 of Schedule 2 from the readings afforded by the measuring apparatus while the radio-frequency heating apparatus is operating.*

[4245]

NOTES

Revoked as noted to reg 1 at **[4241]**.

SCHEDULES

Regulations 3 and 4

SCHEDULE 1

The limits of field strength and terminal voltage shall be as follows—

Col 1		Col 2	Col 3	Col 4	Col 5
Frequency Range in MHz		*Maximum radiated field strength in microvolts per metre*	*Maximum terminal voltage in microvolts*	*For protection of safety of life services*	
Exceeding	*Not Exceeding*			*Maximum radiated field strength in microvolts per metre*	*Maximum terminal voltage in microvolts*
13.533	13.533	300,000	5,000,000		
13.553	13.567	unlimited	unlimited		
13.567	13.587	300,000	5,000,000		
26.957	27.283	unlimited	unlimited		
83.996	84.004	3,000,000			
167.992	168.008	3,000,000			
886	906	1,000,000			

For all other frequencies in the ranges specified below, the limits of field strength and terminal voltage shall be as follows—

Col 1		Col 2	Col 3	Col 4	Col 5
0.15	0.2	50	3,000	15	1,000
0.2	0.285	50	2,000	15	650
0.285	0.49	250	2,000	80	650
0.49	0.5	50	2,000	15	650
0.5	1.605	50	1,000	15	350
1.605	3.95	250	1,000	80	350
3.95	30.00	50	1,000	15	350
30.00	470.00	30		10	
470.00	1,000.00	100		35	

[4246]

NOTES

Revoked as noted to reg 1 at **[4241]**.

SCHEDULE 2

Regulation 5

PART 1

DEFINITION OF EXPRESSIONS USED IN THE SCHEDULE

Voltage and e.m.f.

References to the voltage or e.m.f. of a sinewave are references to its effective or root mean square value.

Decibel (abbreviated dB)

A unit of transmission giving the ratio of two powers.

If P_1 and P_2 represent two values of power, and n the number of decibels representing their ratio—

$$n = 10 \log_{10}\left(\frac{P_1}{P_2}\right)$$

If the two powers are dissipated in equal resistive impedances, their ratio in decibels may be expressed by—

$$n = 20 \log_{10}\left(\frac{V_1}{V_2}\right)$$

where V_1, V_2 are the voltages across the two resistive impedances.

Terminal voltage calibration constant

The number of decibels that must be added to the reading of the measuring apparatus, when a measurement of terminal voltage is made as prescribed, to give the terminal voltage in decibels above 1 microvolt.

Field strength calibration constant

The number of decibels that must be added to the reading of the measuring apparatus, when a measurement of field-strength is made as prescribed, to give the value of field-strength in decibels above 1 microvolt per metre.

[4247]

NOTES

Revoked as noted to reg 1 at **[4241]**.

PART 2
METHOD AND CONDITIONS OF MEASURING FIELD-STRENGTH

1. General

Where a radio-frequency heating apparatus is being tested for the purpose of this regulation it shall so far as is consistent with the following provisions of this Part of this Schedule, be tested under its normal conditions of installation.

2. Attachments and load

The radio-frequency heating apparatus must be tested in complete working form with its work circuit connected. The load employed for the test shall be similar to that which was being treated at the time of the alleged interference, and the electrodes and cables shall be disposed in the manner of their normal use.

3. Other electrical apparatus to be disconnected

All other electrical apparatus which is installed in proximity to the radio-frequency heating apparatus, and which in operation could appreciably affect the result of the test, shall be switched off or otherwise prevented from being energised by complete or partial electrical disconnection.

4. Conditions for measurement

The measuring set receiver shall be connected with an appropriate source of electric power. The receiver shall be tuned to the frequency, as indicated by the tuning dial calibrations, at which it is desired to test, and its gain shall be set, in accordance with the relevant instruction manual, to that used when the measuring set was calibrated.

5. Input connexion of measuring apparatus, and distance and height of aerial

(1) The receiver shall be connected to the aerial mentioned in British Standard 727 : 1967 clause 11.1.2, page 13 or the aerial and feeder mentioned in British Standard 727 : 1967 clause 11.2.1 page 13 (as the case may be).

(2) The distance between the aerial of the measuring apparatus and the nearest point on the boundary of the premises in which the radio-frequency heating apparatus is installed shall not be greater than 100 metres for measurement in the frequency range 0.15 megahertz up to and including 30 megahertz, and 30 metres for higher frequencies up to and including 1000 megahertz.

(3) For the frequency range 0.15 megahertz up to and including 30 megahertz the aerial shall be supported in a vertical plane and be rotatable about a vertical axis. The lowest point of the loop shall be 1 metre above the ground.

(4) For higher frequencies up to and including 1000 megahertz the centre of the aerial shall be supported at a height of not less than 2.8 metres and not more than 3.2 metres above the ground. Measurements shall be made in each case with the measuring aerial horizontal and vertical. When the aerial is used in the horizontal plane it shall be orientated in that plane for maximum output on the measuring set.

6. Adjustment of radio-frequency heating apparatus

For the purpose of the main test in paragraph 8 of this Part of this Schedule the radio-frequency heating apparatus shall be switched on, and adjusted to deliver its rated output power into the work load.

7. Making the measurement

(1) The measuring receiver shall be adjusted and operated in accordance with the relevant instruction manual. The field-strength shall be observed over the whole of the work cycle of the radio-frequency heating apparatus and the highest value, subject to the provisions of paragraph 9 of this Part of this Schedule, shall be taken.

(2) The frequency at which a test is being made shall be measured by means of a frequency meter incorporating a crystal controlled frequency standard having an inherent error of measurement not greater than one part in one hundred thousand.

The frequency shall be measured over the load range from the lowest power normally used to maximum power.

8. Tests

A set of tests shall be made in each case as follows—

- *(a) A check test while the radio-frequency heating apparatus is not operating;*
- *(b) A main test;*
- *(c) A further check test as mentioned in (a).*

9. If a click (as opposed to a buzz of appreciable duration) is heard in the monitoring loudspeaker or earphones at any time when any switchgear or controlling apparatus of the radio-frequency heating apparatus is operating, then provided that not more than one further click is heard during the period of two seconds immediately following the first, the readings of the measuring apparatus appearing within that period of two seconds shall be disregarded for the purpose of these Regulations.

10. Interpretation of results

The field-strength expressed in decibels above 1 microvolt per metre will be given by the sum of: (a) the reading(s) of the attenuator(s), (b) the field-strength calibration constant (if any) appropriate to the frequency at which the measurement is being made, and (c) the reading of the indicating meter of the valve-voltmeter, if calibrated in decibels. If the result obtained is x decibels, the field strength expressed in microvolts per metre is given by the antilog to the base 10 of

$$\frac{x}{20}$$

11. If the maximum reading obtained on any main test exceeds the maximum reading obtained on either of the check tests made next before or next after that main test by at least 10 dB, the readings obtained on that main test are to be regarded as not materially affected by extraneous noise or signals. Otherwise the readings obtained on that main test are to be regarded as materially affected by extraneous noise or signals, and the results of that main test shall be disregarded for the purpose of these Regulations.

[4248]

NOTES

Revoked as noted to reg 1 at **[4241]**.

PART VI TELECOMMUNICATIONS

PART 3
METHOD AND CONDITIONS OF MEASURING TERMINAL VOLTAGE

1. General

(1) Where a radio-frequency heating apparatus is being tested for the purpose of this regulation, it shall be connected with an appropriate source of electric power.

(2) The radio-frequency heating apparatus shall be tested under its normal conditions of installation with a work load similar to that being treated at the time of the complaint.

(3) The measurement of terminal voltage shall be made at any convenient point within the boundaries of the user's premises but as near to the boundary as practicable.

2. Connexions to be made to the electric supply line terminals of the radio-frequency heating apparatus and the input terminals of the measuring set.

The following connexions shall be made—

The electric supply line terminal of the radio-frequency heating apparatus which is the terminal being tested shall be connected through the isolation capacitor C and the 1450 ohm resistor shown in Fig 1. An inductor L shall be connected between the input terminal of the measuring set and the screening of the measuring set.

The impedance of the capacitor C at the frequency of measurement shall be less than 10 ohms. The impedance of the inductor L at the frequency of measurement shall be greater than 1000 ohms.

3. Tests

A set of tests as mentioned in sub-paragraphs (a), (b) and (c) of paragraph 8 of Part 2 of this Schedule shall be made in each case with the receiver of the testing apparatus connected with one of the electric supply line terminals of the radio-frequency heating apparatus and another set or other sets of tests as mentioned in those sub-paragraphs shall be made with the receiver of the testing apparatus connected with the other or each of the others of such terminals.

4. Paragraph 9 of Part 2 of this Schedule shall apply.

5. Interpretation of results

The terminal voltage, expressed in decibels above 1 microvolt, will be given by the sum of: (a) the reading(s) of the attenuator(s), (b) the terminal voltage calibration constant (if any) appropriate to the frequency at which the measurement is being made, (c) the reading of the indicating meter of the valve-voltmeter, if calibrated in decibels and (d) 30 decibels to take into account the loss in the measuring circuit shown in Fig 1. If the result obtained is x decibels, the voltage expressed in microvolts is given by the antilog to the base 10 of

$$\frac{x}{20}$$

6. Paragraph 11 of Part 2 of this Schedule shall apply.

FIG 1. CIRCUIT FOR R.F. VOLTAGE MEASUREMENT ON SUPPLY MAINS

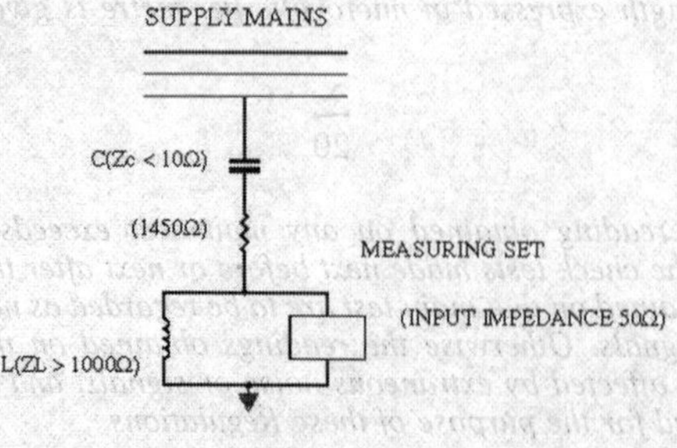

[4249]

NOTES

Revoked as noted to reg 1 at **[4241]**.

WIRELESS TELEGRAPHY (CONTROL OF INTERFERENCE FROM IGNITION APPARATUS) REGULATIONS 1973

(SI 1973/1217)

NOTES

Made: 11 July 1973.
Authority: Wireless Telegraphy Act 1949, s 10.
Commencement: 1 October 1973.

ARRANGEMENT OF REGULATIONS

1 Citation and Commencement

These Regulations may be cited as the Wireless Telegraphy (Control of Interference from Ignition Apparatus) Regulations 1973, and shall come into operation on 1st October 1973.

[4250]

2 Interpretation

(1) In these Regulations, except so far as the contrary is provided or the context otherwise requires, the following expressions have the meanings hereby respectively assigned to them—

"ignition apparatus" means equipment assembled for the purpose of providing and conveying electrical energy for igniting gas or vapour in an internal combustion engine;

"suppressor" means a piece of equipment designed to reduce the field-strength of the electro-magnetic energy radiated from the apparatus to which it is fitted when that apparatus is being used, and references to "suppressors" include references to a single suppressor;

"the British Islands" means the area comprised by the United Kingdom, the Channel Islands, and the Isle of Man;

"megahertz (MHz)" has the same meaning as megacycles per second, i e one million cycles per second;

and other expressions have the same meaning as they have in the Wireless Telegraphy Act 1949.

(2) The Interpretation Act 1889 applies to the interpretation of these Regulations as it applies to the interpretation of an Act of Parliament.

[4251]

NOTES

Interpretation Act 1889: see now the Interpretation Act 1978.

3 Assemblers and Importers

(1) This Regulation applies to ignition apparatus forming part of an internal combustion engine other than an engine which forms part of an aircraft.

(2) The requirement referred to in Regulation 5 shall be complied with in the case of any ignition apparatus to which this Regulation applies if, on or after the date on which these Regulations come into operation, that apparatus is, as being part of a vehicle, vessel or engine, to be sold otherwise than for export, or offered or advertised for sale otherwise than for export, or let on hire or offered or advertised for letting on hire, by any person who in the British Islands in the course of business assembles such apparatus as part of a vehicle, vessel

or engine, or who in the course of business imports into the British Islands such apparatus already assembled as part of a vehicle, vessel or engine.

[4252]

4 Users

(1) This Regulation applies to:—

(a) ignition apparatus forming part of an internal combustion engine other than an engine which forms part of an aircraft or of a foreign vessel, except ignition apparatus which is proved by the person using it to have been assembled as part of a vehicle, vessel or engine before the date on which these Regulations come into operation; and

(b) apparatus which includes one or more components designed to form part of the ignition apparatus of an internal combustion engine, and which is assembled for the purpose of testing or demonstrating the operation of one or more of those components, and which when used involves sudden changes of current in a high-voltage circuit.

(2) The requirement referred to in Regulation 5 shall be complied with in the case of any apparatus to which this Regulation applies, if the apparatus is to be used within the British Islands or the territorial waters adjacent thereto:—

(a) on land, or

(b) on the sea or in any estuary within one hundred metres of any moored vessel or on the landward side of a line one hundred metres to seaward of low water mark, or

(c) on any water, other than the sea or an estuary—

provided that the use of any apparatus referred to in sub-paragraph (a) of paragraph (1) of this Regulation shall be deemed to comply with the said requirement if the person using the apparatus establishes:—

(i) that suppressors were fitted to the apparatus by the manufacturer or builder of the vehicle, vessel or engine of which the apparatus forms part or by the importer of that vehicle, vessel or engine into the British Islands, and

(ii) that the suppressors so fitted remained fitted to the apparatus at the time of the use, or that suppressors having equivalent electrical characteristics had been correctly fitted to the apparatus at that time in substitution for those fitted as aforesaid, and in either case that the suppressors were then in good electrical and mechanical repair and condition, and

(iii) that the apparatus at the time of the use consisted of the same components as those which were fitted at the time when the vehicle, vessel or engine was manufactured or built, or that any components which had been substituted for those components had equivalent electrical characteristics and had been correctly fitted.

[4253]

5 Requirement

(1) The requirement hereinbefore referred to is that the apparatus shall be so designed, constructed, assembled and installed, and that such precautions shall be taken in relation to it (by means of the fitting of suppressors or otherwise) as to ensure that the field-strength, at any distance of not less than ten metres from the apparatus when it is used, as measured and computed in accordance with paragraph 5(3) and the Schedule hereto, of the electro-magnetic energy radiated at forty megahertz and at any frequency up to seventy-five megahertz does not exceed fifty microvolts per metre and at any frequency between seventy-five and two hundred and fifty megahertz does not exceed fifty microvolts per metre at seventy-five megahertz rising linearly with frequency to one hundred and twenty microvolts per metre at two hundred and fifty megahertz.

(2) For the purpose of this Regulation the apparatus shall be deemed to meet these requirements over the whole frequency range of forty to two hundred and fifty megahertz if it meets them at the following discrete frequencies; forty-five, sixty-five, ninety, one hundred and fifty, one hundred and eighty, and two hundred and twenty megahertz. To avoid interference from transmissions operating on these discrete frequencies each frequency shall be subject to a tolerance of plus or minus five megahertz.

(3) For the purpose of Regulation 3 the apparatus shall be deemed to meet these requirements if measurements for the purpose of type-approval and production conformity in type-approved equipment are carried out in accordance with the procedures set out in paragraphs 3.6 and 3.7 respectively of British Standard 833:1970.

(4) For the purpose of measuring and computing the field-strength of such electro-magnetic energy, the apparatus shall be tested by means of measuring apparatus of the description and having the physical and electrical characteristics and performance set out in Section 1 of British Standard 727:1967 "Specification for Radio-Interference Measuring Apparatus for the Frequency Range 0.015 MHz to 1000 MHz", except that where the apparatus forms part of the engine of a road vehicle measuring apparatus having the physical and electrical characteristics and performance set out in Section 2 of British Standard 727:1967 may be used. The tests shall be made by the method and under the conditions set out in the Schedule hereto.

[4254]

SCHEDULE
DETAILS OF MEASURING SITE AND TEST PROCEDURE

Regulation 5

1. Measuring Site

The site to be used for testing for the purpose of Regulation 5 shall conform to the specification set out in paragraph 3.2 of British Standard 833:1970 "Specification for Radio Interference Limits and Measurements for the Electrical Ignition Systems of Internal Combustion Engines".

2. Test Procedure

(1) The test shall be carried out in accordance with the procedures set out in paragraphs 3.3, 3.4 and 3.5 of British Standard 833:1970.

(2) Where ignition apparatus is being tested for the purpose of Regulation 3, it shall be tested as installed in the engine. If the engine is to form part of a vehicle, vessel or equipment which is to be sold or let on hire by the assembler or importer, the test shall be made with the engine installed in the vehicle, vessel or equipment.

(3) Where ignition apparatus is being tested for the purpose of Regulation 4, it shall be tested under normal conditions of installation. Where apparatus mentioned in Regulation 4(1)(b) is being tested for the purpose of that Regulation it shall be tested under normal conditions of installation and use.

[4255]

WIRELESS TELEGRAPHY (CONTROL OF INTERFERENCE FROM HOUSEHOLD APPLIANCES, PORTABLE TOOLS ETC) REGULATIONS 1978

(SI 1978/1267)

NOTES

Made: 23 August 1978.
Authority: Wireless Telegraphy Act 1949, s 10.
Commencement: 1 November 1979 (in relation to lighting dimmers); 1 April 1979 (remaining purposes).

1—(1) These Regulations may be cited as the Wireless Telegraphy (Control of Interference from Household Appliances, Portable Tools etc) Regulations 1978.

(2) These Regulations shall come into operation on 1st April 1979 except that insofar as these Regulations apply to any lighting dimmer these Regulations shall come into operation on 1st November 1979.

[4256]

NOTES

These Regulations are revoked, in so far as they impose electromagnetic compatibility requirements on relevant apparatus which is to be supplied or taken into service and used for the purpose for which it was intended, by the Electromagnetic Compatibility Regulations 2005, SI 2005/281, reg 2(2), Sch 1 at **[4433]**, **[4536]**.

2—(1) In these Regulations—

["BS800: 1983" means the British Standard Specification for radio interference limits and measurements for household appliances, portable tools and other electrical equipment causing similar types of interference, BS800: 1983 published on 31st May 1983;]

["BS800: 1988" means the British Standard Specification for Limits and methods of measurement of radio interference characteristics of household electrical appliances, portable tools and similar electrical apparatus, BS800: 1988, published on 31st October 1988;]

["the Directive" means Council Directive No 76/889/EEC as amended by Commission Directive No 87/308/EEC;]

"lighting dimmer" means any electronic device which controls the light output of an electric lamp ...

(2) The Interpretation Act 1889 applies for the interpretation of these Regulations as it applies for the interpretation of an Act of Parliament.

[4257]

NOTES

Revoked as noted to reg 1 at **[4256]**.

Para (1): definition "BS800: 1983" substituted for original definition "BS800: 1977" and in definition "lighting dimmer" words omitted revoked by the Wireless Telegraphy (Control of Interference from Household Appliances, Portable Tools etc) (Amendment) Regulation 1985, SI 1985/808, reg 3(a), (c); definition "BS800: 1988" inserted and definition "the Directive" substituted by the Wireless Telegraphy (Control of Interference from Household Appliances, Portable Tools etc) (Amendment) Regulations 1989, SI 1989/562, reg 3.

Interpretation Act 1889: see now the Interpretation Act 1978.

3 These Regulations apply to any household appliance or portable tool or other electrical equipment specified in paragraph 1.1 of the Annex to the Directive ... except any such equipment as is excluded from the scope of the Directive by any provision of that Annex and in these Regulations any equipment to which these Regulations apply is referred to as "apparatus".

[4258]

NOTES

Revoked as noted to reg 1 at **[4256]**.

Words omitted revoked by the Wireless Telegraphy (Control of Interference from Household Appliances, Portable Tools etc) (Amendment) Regulations 1989, SI 1989/562, reg 4.

4—(1) The requirements of Regulation 6 below shall be complied with in the case of any apparatus which is sold otherwise than for export, or offered or advertised for sale otherwise than for export, or let on hire or offered or advertised for letting on hire, by any person who in the course of business manufactures, assembles or imports apparatus.

(2) In the case of any apparatus which, by virtue of paragraph (1) above is required to comply with the requirements of Regulation 6 below there shall be a statement (however expressed) either on the apparatus or in an accompanying document to the effect that the apparatus complies with those requirements:

Provided that such a statement shall not be required in the case of any apparatus in relation to which use is made of a mark or certificate issued by a body notified by a member State to the Commission and to the Secretary of State in accordance with Article 3.2 of the Directive.

[4259]

NOTES

Revoked as noted to reg 1 at **[4256]**.

5—(1) The requirements of Regulation 6 below [as originally specified or as subsequently amended] shall, subject to paragraph (2) below, be complied with if any apparatus is used by any person unless it—

(a) complied with the said requirements at the date of its manufacture, assembly or importation; and

(*b*) *is maintained in reasonable working order; and*

(*c*) *is not likely to cause undue interference with any wireless telegraphy used for the purposes of any safety of life service or for any purpose on which the safety of any person or of any vessel, aircraft or vehicle may depend.*

(2) *The provisions of paragraph* (*1*) *above shall not apply to the use of apparatus which is sold or let on hire before the date of the coming into force of these Regulations by a person who in the course of business manufactures, assembles or imports such apparatus and which is not likely to cause undue interference with any wireless telegraphy.*

[4260]

NOTES

Revoked as noted to reg 1 at **[4256]**.

Para (1): words in square brackets inserted by the Wireless Telegraphy (Control of Interference from Household Appliances, Portable Tools etc) (Amendment) Regulations 1989, SI 1989/562, reg 5.

[6—(*1*) *Subject to paragraph* (*2*) *below, the apparatus shall be measured in the manner prescribed by clauses 6 and 7 of BS800: 1983 or of BS800: 1988 and shall comply with the relevant limits of interference prescribed in clause 4 of BS800: 1983 or of BS800: 1988, as the case may be, and, in relation to the testing of the apparatus and the limits of interference thereof, the apparatus shall comply with any other relevant procedures, requirements and specifications set out in BS800: 1983 or BS800: 1988, as the case may be.*

(*2*) *On and after 1st January 1990, apparatus which, by virtue of Regulation 4*(*1*)*, is required to comply with Regulation 6, shall comply only with the relevant procedures, requirements and specifications of BS800: 1988 and, in so far as such apparatus is concerned, the references to BS800: 1983 in paragraph* (*1*) *above shall not apply.]*

[4261]

PART VI TELECOMMUNICATIONS

NOTES

Revoked as noted to reg 1 at **[4256]**.

Substituted by the Wireless Telegraphy (Control of Interference from Household Appliances, Portable Tools etc) (Amendment) Regulations 1989, SI 1989/562, reg 6.

7 (*Introduces the Schedule which contains revocations; revoked as noted to reg 1 at* **[4256]**.)

WIRELESS TELEGRAPHY (CONTROL OF INTERFERENCE FROM FLUORESCENT LIGHTING APPARATUS) REGULATIONS 1978

(SI 1978/1268)

NOTES

Made: 23 August 1978.

Authority: Wireless Telegraphy Act 1949, s 10.

Commencement: 1 January 1979.

1 *These Regulations may be cited as the Wireless Telegraphy* (*Control of Interference from Fluorescent Lighting Apparatus*) *Regulations 1978 and shall come into operation on 1st January 1979.*

[4262]

NOTES

These Regulations are revoked, in so far as they impose electromagnetic compatibility requirements on relevant apparatus which is to be supplied or taken into service and used for the purpose for which it was intended, by the Electromagnetic Compatibility Regulations 2005, SI 2005/281, reg 2(2), Sch 1 at **[4433]**, **[4536]**.

2 *In these Regulations—*

["BS5394: 1983" means the British Standard Specification for radio interference limits and measurements for luminaires using tubular fluorescent lamps and fitted with starters. BS5394: 1983 published on 31 May 1985;]

["BS5394: 1988" means the British Standard Specification for Limits and methods of measurement of radio interference characteristics of fluorescent lamps and luminaires, BS5394: 1988, published on 29th July 1988;]

["the Directive" means Council Directive No 76/890/EEC as amended by Commission Directive No 87/310/EEC;]

"fluorescent lighting apparatus" means any fluorescent lighting apparatus of which a luminaire forms a part;

"luminaire" means apparatus which forms, or is designed to form, part of any fluorescent lighting apparatus, which is fitted with a starter and which conveys electricity to a tubular fluorescent lamp and includes any apparatus which supports, fixes or protects the lamp.

[4263]

NOTES

Revoked as noted to reg 1 at **[4262]**.

Definition "BS5394: 1983" substituted for original definition "BS5394: Part 1 1976" by the Wireless Telegraphy (Control of Interference from Fluorescent Lighting Apparatus) (Amendment) Regulations 1985, SI 1985/807, reg 3(a); definition "BS5394: 1988" inserted and definition "the Directive" substituted by the Wireless Telegraphy (Control of Interference from Fluorescent Lighting Apparatus) (Amendment) Regulations 1989, SI 1989/561, reg 3.

3 The Interpretation Act 1889 applies for the interpretation of these Regulations as it applies for the interpretation of an Act of Parliament.

[4264]

NOTES

Revoked as noted to reg 1 at **[4262]**.

Interpretation Act 1889: see now the Interpretation Act 1978.

4—(1) The requirements of Regulation 6 below shall be complied with in the case of any luminaire, other than a luminaire which bears, or has affixed to it a label which bears, the words "unsuppressed luminaire for use in non-residential areas", which is sold otherwise than for export, or offered or advertised for sale otherwise than for export, or let on hire or offered or advertised for letting on hire, by any person who in the course of business manufactures, assembles or imports luminaires.

(2) In the case of any luminaire which, by virtue of paragraph (1) above, is required to comply with the requirements of Regulation 6 below there shall be a statement (however expressed) either on the luminaire or in an accompanying document to the effect that the luminaire complies with those requirements:

Provided that such a statement shall not be required in the case of any luminaire in relation to which use is made of a mark or certificate issued by a body notified by a member State to the Commission and to the Secretary of State in accordance with Article 3.2 of the Directive.

[4265]

NOTES

Revoked as noted to reg 1 at **[4262]**.

5 The requirements of Regulation 6 below [as originally specified or as subsequently amended] shall be complied with in the case of any fluorescent lighting apparatus used within 15 metres of residential accommodation of any kind unless—

(a) the fluorescent lighting apparatus is used on premises which are isolated from the electrical supply to the said residential accommodation by means of a transformer or like apparatus; or

(b) the luminaire complied with the said requirements at the date of its manufacture, assembly or importation and is maintained in reasonable working order and the fluorescent lighting apparatus is not likely to cause undue interference with any wireless telegraphy used for the purposes of any safety of life service or for any purpose on which the safety of any person or any vessel, aircraft or vehicle may depend; or

(*c*) *the fluorescent lighting apparatus was sold or let on hire before the date of the coming into force of these Regulations by a person who in the course of business manufactures, assembles or imports such apparatus and the fluorescent lighting apparatus is not likely to cause undue interference with any wireless telegraphy.*

[4266]

NOTES

Revoked as noted to reg 1 at **[4262]**.

Words in square brackets inserted by the Wireless Telegraphy (Control of Interference from Fluorescent Lighting Apparatus) (Amendment) Regulations 1989, SI 1989/561, reg 4.

[6—(1) Subject to paragraph (3) below, the insertion loss of a luminaire within the meaning of clause 3.5 of BS5394: 1983 or clause 3 of BS5394: 1988 as measured by the method prescribed in clause 5 of BS5394: 1983 or clause 5, 6 or 7 of BS5394: 1988, as the case may be, shall not be less than the minimum values relevant to that luminaire prescribed in clause 4 of BS5394: 1983 or of BS5394: 1988, as the case may be (being values which are related to the frequencies at which the fluorescent lighting apparatus generates electro-magnetic energy).

(2) The relevant procedures, requirements and specifications set out in BS5394: 1983 or BS5394: 1988, as the case may be, shall be complied with in the testing of a luminaire and the determination of the minimum values of insertion loss thereof.

(3) On and after 1st January 1990, luminaires which, by virtue of Regulation 4(1), are required to comply with Regulation 6, shall comply only with the relevant procedures, requirements and specifications of BS5394: 1988 and, in so far as such luminaires are concerned, the references to BS5394: 1983 in paragraphs (1) and (2) above shall not apply.]

[4267]

NOTES

Revoked as noted to reg 1 at **[4262]**.

Substituted by the Wireless Telegraphy (Control of Interference from Fluorescent Lighting Apparatus) (Amendment) Regulations 1989, SI 1989/561, reg 5.

PART VI TELECOMMUNICATIONS

WIRELESS TELEGRAPHY (CONTROL OF INTERFERENCE FROM CITIZENS' BAND RADIO APPARATUS) REGULATIONS 1982

(SI 1982/635)

NOTES

Made: 4 May 1982.

Authority: Wireless Telegraphy Act 1949, s 10.

Commencement: 10 June 1982.

1 These Regulations may be cited as the Wireless Telegraphy (Control of Interference from Citizens' Band Radio Apparatus) Regulations 1982 and shall come into operation on 10th June 1982.

[4268]

NOTES

These Regulations are revoked, in so far as they impose electromagnetic compatibility requirements on relevant apparatus which is to be supplied or taken into service and used for the purpose for which it was intended, by the Electromagnetic Compatibility Regulations 2005, SI 2005/281, reg 2(2), Sch 1 at **[4433]**, **[4536]**.

2 In these Regulations—

"CB apparatus" means Citizens' Band Radio apparatus, that is to say, wireless telegraphy apparatus designed or adapted for the purpose of transmitting or receiving spoken messages on the frequency channels specified in paragraph 1.3 of the relevant specification;

["relevant specification" means Performance Specification MPT 1321, as amended, published in April 1981.]

[4269]

NOTES

Revoked as noted to reg 1 at **[4268]**.

Definition "relevant specification" substituted by the Wireless Telegraphy (Control of Interference from Citizens' Band Radio Apparatus) (Amendment) Regulations 1988, SI 1988/1216, reg 3.

3 The requirements specified in the Schedule to these Regulations shall be complied with in the case of any CB apparatus which is sold otherwise than for export, or offered or advertised for sale otherwise than for export, or let on hire or offered or advertised for letting on hire, by any person who in the course of business manufactures, assembles or imports CB apparatus.

[4270]

NOTES

Revoked as noted to reg 1 at **[4268]**.

4 Any CB apparatus which, by virtue of Regulation 3, is required to comply with the requirements specified in the Schedule to these Regulations, shall, in order to show that it does so comply, be marked in accordance with paragraph 1.6 of the relevant specification.

[4271]

NOTES

Revoked as noted to reg 1 at **[4268]**.

SCHEDULE
REQUIREMENTS TO BE COMPLIED WITH IN THE CASE OF CB APPARATUS REFERRED TO IN REGULATION 3

Regulation 3

1.—(1) In this Schedule—

"adjacent channel power", "carrier power", "frequency deviation" and "frequency error" have the meanings respectively assigned to them by paragraphs 4.4.1., 4.2.1., 4.3.1. and 4.1.1. of the relevant specification;

"BS 4727: Part 3: Group 01: 1971" means the British Standard Glossary of Electrotechnical, Power, Telecommunication, Electronics, Lighting and Colour Terms Part 3 Group 01 (General telecommunication and electronics terminology) published in August 1971;

"carrier frequency", "frequency modulation", "modulation" and "phase modulation" have the meanings assigned to them by BS 4727: Part 3: Group 01: 1971;

"spurious emissions" has the meaning assigned to it by paragraph 4.5.1. or (as the case may be) 5.1.1. of the relevant specification.

(2) Where reference is made in this Schedule to the measurement of any of the characteristics of CB apparatus, the reference is to measurement carried out under the conditions specified in Chapters 2 and 3 of the relevant specification, accurate within the tolerance specified in Chapter 6 of the relevant specification and following tests carried out in accordance with Chapter 7 of the relevant specification.

2. The modulation of the CB apparatus shall be frequency modulation or phase modulation.

3. The frequency error of the CB apparatus shall be that specified in paragraph 4.1.3. of the relevant specification when measured by the method described in paragraph 4.1.2. of the relevant specification.

4. The carrier power of the CB apparatus shall not exceed that specified in paragraph 4.2.4. of the relevant specification when measured by the method described in paragraphs 4.2.2. and 4.2.3. of the relevant specification.

5. The frequency deviation of the CB apparatus shall not exceed that specified in paragraph 4.3.3. of the relevant specification when measured by the method described in paragraph 4.3.2.2. of the relevant specification.

6. The adjacent channel power of the CB apparatus shall not exceed that specified in paragraph 4.4.3. of the relevant specification when measured by the method described in paragraph 4.4.2. of the relevant specification using the equipment described in paragraph 4.4.4. of the relevant specification.

7.—(1) In the case of CB apparatus designed or adapted for emission the power of spurious emissions shall not exceed that specified in paragraph 4.5.4. of the relevant specification when measured by the methods described in paragraphs 4.5.2. and 4.5.3. of the relevant specification.

(2) *In the case of CB apparatus designed or adapted for reception the power of spurious emissions shall not exceed that specified in paragraph 5.1.4. of the relevant specification when measured by the method described in paragraph 5.1.2. or 5.1.3.* (*as the case may be*) *of the relevant specification.*

8. In the case of CB apparatus which is designed or adapted for the purpose of transmitting or receiving spoken messages on more than one of the frequency channels specified in paragraph 1.3. of the relevant specification, there shall be the separation specified in paragraph 1.1. of the relevant specification between adjacent channel carrier frequencies.

9. The CB apparatus shall not be capable of transmitting or receiving digital signals except digital signals designed solely for the purpose of identifying or selecting a particular station or for indicating the end of a transmission.

[4272]

NOTES

Revoked as noted to reg 1 at **[4268]**.

WIRELESS TELEGRAPHY (RECIPROCAL EXEMPTION OF EUROPEAN RADIO AMATEURS) REGULATIONS 1988

(SI 1988/2090)

NOTES

Made: 29 November 1988.
Authority: Wireless Telegraphy Act 1949, s 1.
Commencement: 1 January 1989.

1 Citation and Commencement

These Regulations may be cited as the Wireless Telegraphy (Reciprocal Exemption of European Radio Amateurs) Regulations 1988 and shall come into force on 1st January 1989.

[4273]

2 Interpretation

In these Regulations—

“amateur service” and “amateur-satellite service” have the same meanings as they have in the 1982 edition of the Radio Regulations, as revised in 1985, 1986 and 1988, annexed to the International Telecommunication Convention 1982 pursuant to Articles 43 and 83 of that Convention;

“CEPT” means the European Conference of Postal and Telecommunications Administrations, and “CEPT country” means a country which is a member of CEPT;

“CEPT amateur radio licence” means a licence issued by a CEPT country, pursuant to and in accordance with the requirements of CEPT recommendation T/R 61—01;

“CEPT Recommendation T/R 61—01” means CEPT Recommendation T/R 61—01 entitled “Concerning the CEPT Amateur Radio Licence”, as adopted by CEPT in Nice in 1985;

“CEPT radio amateur” means a radio amateur who holds a CEPT amateur radio licence issued by a CEPT country, other than the United Kingdom, where that CEPT country permits UK radio amateurs to establish, install and use relevant amateur stations in its territory in accordance with CEPT Recommendation T/R 61—01 without making application in that behalf;

"host country" means, in relation to a radio amateur who holds a CEPT amateur radio licence, a CEPT country, other than the CEPT country which issued that licence, which he is for the time being visiting;

"radio amateur" means a person who, being duly authorised so to do by the country in which he resides, uses the amateur service, or the amateur—satellite service, or both;

"relevant amateur station" means a station for wireless telegraphy, being—

(a) any portable station, including any station using mains electricity at a temporary location;

(b) any mobile station; or

(c) the station of a radio amateur holding a licence in the host country,

in the amateur service, or in the amateur-satellite service, or both; and

"UK radio amateur" means a radio amateur who holds a CEPT amateur radio licence granted under section 1 of the Act.

[4274]

NOTES

The Act: Wireless Telegraphy Act 1949.

3 Exemption

Subject to Regulations 4 and 5, the establishment, installation and use of relevant amateur stations are hereby exempted from the provisions of section 1(1) of the Act.

[4275]

NOTES

The Act: Wireless Telegraphy Act 1949.

4 Terms, provisions and limitations

The exemption provided for in Regulation 3 shall be limited to establishment, installation and use of relevant amateur stations by CEPT radio amateurs.

[4276]

5 The exemption provided for in Regulation 3 shall be subject to the terms, provisions and limitations contained in "Terms and Limitations Booklet BR68" as published in English in October 1988 by the Department of Trade and Industry.

[4277]

WIRELESS TELEGRAPHY APPARATUS (RECEIVERS) (EXEMPTION) REGULATIONS 1989

(SI 1989/123)

NOTES

Made: 27 January 1989.
Authority: Wireless Telegraphy Act 1949, s 1.
Commencement: 27 February 1989.

1 Citation and Commencement

These Regulations may be cited as the Wireless Telegraphy Apparatus (Receivers) (Exemption) Regulations 1989 and shall come into force on 27th February 1989.

[4278]

2 Interpretation

In these Regulations—

"authorised broadcasting station" means a station for the time being duly authorised to conduct a broadcasting service pursuant to the Radio Regulations published by the General Secretariat of the International Telecommunication Union for the time being in force; and

"transmission" means any intentional emission by wireless telegraphy.

[4279]

3 Exemption

Subject to the terms, provisions and limitations contained in regulation 4 and except as provided for in regulations 5 and 6, there are hereby exempted from the provisions of section 1 of the Act—

(a) the establishment or use for wireless telegraphy of any station; and

(b) the installation or use for wireless telegraphy of any apparatus,

which is inherently incapable of transmission.

[4280]

NOTES

The Act: Wireless Telegraphy Act 1949.

4 Terms, provisions and limitations

The terms, provisions and limitations to which the exemption provided for in regulation 3 shall be subject are that the station or apparatus for wireless telegraphy shall not—

(a) infringe any requirements for the time being applied to it by or under any enactment for the purpose of preventing it from causing interference with any wireless telegraphy; or

(b) cause undue interference with any wireless telegraphy.

[4281]

5 Exceptions

The exemption provided for in regulation 3 shall not extend to the establishment or use of any station for wireless telegraphy, or the installation or use of any apparatus for wireless telegraphy—

[(a) which is a television receiver within the meaning of section 1(7) of the Act (as added by paragraph 1(6) of Part I of Schedule 18 to the Broadcasting Act 1990);] or

(b) used for receiving broadcasts from any broadcasting station (other than a space station) which has not been licensed to transmit those broadcasts by the government of any country or territory.

[4282]

NOTES

Words in square brackets substituted by the Wireless Telegraphy (Television Licence Fees) Regulations 1991, SI 1991/436, reg 5(2).

The Act: Wireless Telegraphy Act 1949.

6 The exemption provided for in regulation 3 shall not apply to any station or apparatus for wireless telegraphy which is exempted from the provisions of section 1(1) of the Act by—

(a) the Wireless Telegraphy (Exemption) Regulations 1980; …

(b) …

[4283]

NOTES

Words omitted revoked by the Wireless Telegraphy (Television Licence Fees) Regulations 1991, SI 1991/436, reg 5(3).

The Act: Wireless Telegraphy Act 1949.

PART VI TELECOMMUNICATIONS

WIRELESS TELEGRAPHY APPARATUS (CITIZENS' BAND EUROPEAN USERS) (EXEMPTION) REGULATIONS 1989

(SI 1989/943)

NOTES

Made: 6 June 1989.
Authority: Wireless Telegraphy Act 1949, ss 1, 3, 16.
Commencement: 1 July 1989.

ARRANGEMENT OF REGULATIONS

1 Citation and commencement

These Regulations may be cited as the Wireless Telegraphy Apparatus (Citizens' Band European Users) (Exemption) Regulations 1989 and shall come into force on 1st July 1989.

[4284]

2 Interpretation

In these Regulations—

"the Act" means the Wireless Telegraphy Act 1949;

"authorised person" means any person authorised by the Secretary of State for the purposes of the Wireless Telegraphy Acts of 1949 and 1967 (as amended) and for the purposes of the Telecommunications Act 1984, and in particular for the purposes of section 79(3) thereof;

"CEPT" means the European Conference of Postal and Telecommunications Administrations, and "CEPT country" means a country which is a member of CEPT;

"CEPT Recommendation T/R 20–02" means CEPT Recommendation T/R20–02 entitled "Citizens' Band Radio" as adopted by CEPT on 1st September 1986; and

"relevant CB station" means a station for wireless telegraphy for the provision of voice radiocommunication in the frequency band 26.960 MHz to 27.410 MHz which complies with the requirements of CEPT Recommendation T/R 20–02.

[4285]

3 Exemption

Subject to regulations 4 and 5, the establishment, installation and use of relevant CB stations are hereby exempted from the provisions of section 1(1) of the Act.

[4286]

4 Terms, provisions and limitations

The exemption provided for in regulation 3 shall be limited to—

(a) establishment, installation and use of a relevant CB station by any person who is—

  (i) aged 14 years or over;

  (ii) ordinarily resident in a country listed in Schedule 1; and

  (iii) authorised by the government of that country to use a relevant CB station in its territory;

(hereinafter referred to as a "CEPT CB user"); and

(b) use of a relevant CB station by any person under the supervision of a CEPT CB user.

[4287]

5 The exemption provided for in regulation 3 shall be subject to the terms, provisions and limitations contained in Schedule 2.

[4288]

6 Inspection and restriction on use

The CEPT CB user shall forthwith on the demand of an authorised person—

(a) permit and facilitate the inspection by that authorised person of the relevant CB station;

(b) cause the use of the relevant CB station to—

(i) cease; or

(ii) be restricted in the manner specified by that authorised person.

[4289]

SCHEDULES

SCHEDULE 1
LIST OF COUNTRIES RESIDENTS OF WHICH MAY USE RELEVANT CB STATIONS WITHOUT A LICENCE UNDER SECTION 1(1) OF THE ACT

Regulation 4

Austria
Belgium
Cyprus
Denmark
Finland
France
Germany (Federal Republic)
Greece
Irish Republic
Iceland
Italy
Liechtenstein
Luxembourg
Malta
Monaco
Netherlands
Norway
Portugal
San Marino
Spain
Sweden
Switzerland
Turkey
Vatican City
Yugoslavia

[4290]

SCHEDULE 2
TERMS, PROVISIONS AND LIMITATIONS OF EXEMPTION

Regulation 5

1. A relevant CB station may be used for sending and receiving only—

(a) messages in plain speech; and

(b) signals of—

(i) less than 2.5 seconds in length, which are intended to call up any other relevant CB station; and

(ii) less than 1 second in length, which are intended to identify, or mark the end of a message sent by, any relevant CB station.

2. A relevant CB station shall not be used if, at any time, such use is likely to obstruct the police, any authorised person, or any government department in the carrying out of their duties.

3.—(1) Subject to sub-paragraph (2), only the following ancillary equipment may be connected between the antenna socket of the transceiver of the relevant CB station and its antenna—

(a) devices for suppressing interference;

(b) low pass filters; and

PART VI TELECOMMUNICATIONS

(c) mechanically operated co-axial antenna change over switches.

(2) A meter to measure the transmitter power or Voltage Standing Wave Radio (VSWR) of the antenna may be temporarily inserted between the antenna socket of the transceiver and the antenna for the sole purpose of establishing or testing the relevant CB station provided that such meter is removed before the relevant CB station is used.

4. If the relevant CB station has provision for connection to an external antenna, only a single vertical omnidirectional monopole antenna may be connected, the driven element of which does not exceed 1.65 m in length or 55 mm in diameter, including any loading coils and associated circuitry and casings, but excluding any plates or radial wires or rods designed solely to act as a ground plane.

5. If the relevant CB station is situated within 1 km of the boundary of any aerodrome, the height of the antenna and any supporting mast or structure must not exceed 15 m.

6. The relevant CB station shall not be established, installed or used—
   (a) in any aircraft or other airborne vehicle;
   (b) on board ship or vessel except with the consent of the ship's Master; or
   (c) for the purpose of advertising goods or services of any kind.

7. The relevant CB station shall not cause undue interference with any wireless telegraphy.
[4291]

WIRELESS TELEGRAPHY (TESTING AND DEVELOPMENT UNDER SUPPRESSED RADIATION CONDITIONS) (EXEMPTION) REGULATIONS 1989

(SI 1989/1842)

NOTES
Made: 6 October 1989.
Authority: Wireless Telegraphy Act 1949, ss 1, 3.
Commencement: 1 November 1989.

ARRANGEMENT OF REGULATIONS

1 Citation and commencement

These Regulations may be cited as the Wireless Telegraphy (Testing and Development Under Suppressed Radiation Conditions) (Exemption) Regulations 1989 and shall come into force on 1st November 1989.

[4292]

2 Interpretation

In these Regulations—
"the Act" means the Wireless Telegraphy Act 1949;
"apparatus" means wireless telegraphy apparatus; and "relevant apparatus" means apparatus to which these Regulations apply;
"authorised person" means any person authorised by the Secretary of State for the purposes of the Act, the Wireless Telegraphy Act 1967 and the Telecommunications Act (1984);

"field strength" means the magnitude of a component of the electric or magnetic field;
"premises" includes a vehicle, vessel or aircraft;
"spurious emission" means an emission—
(a) on a frequency which is outside the necessary bandwidth; and
(b) the level of which may be reduced without affecting the corresponding transmission of information;

and, without prejudice to the generality of the foregoing, includes harmonic emissions, parasitic emissions, intermodulation products and frequency conversion products;
"station" means a station for wireless telegraphy; and "relevant station" means a station to which these Regulations apply;
"suppressed radiation conditions" means conditions under which the electromagnetic energy emitted by any station or apparatus is suppressed, reduced or contained at or to such a level that it is incapable, under all reasonably foreseeable operational conditions, of causing interference with any station or apparatus which is situated outside the boundary of the premises in which the first mentioned station or apparatus is situated; and
"testing or development" includes—
(a) modifying, servicing or repairing, and
(b) scientific research, training, instruction or experimentation in radio theory or practice.

[4293]

3 Application

(1) Subject to paragraph (2), these Regulations apply to any station or apparatus for the testing or development of that, or any other, station or apparatus under suppressed radiation conditions.

(2) These Regulations shall not extend to any station or apparatus the establishment, installation or use of which is exempted from the provisions of section 1(1) of the Act by—
(a) the Wireless Telegraphy (Exemption) Regulations 1980;
(b) the Wireless Telegraphy (Exemption) Regulations 1982;
(c) the Wireless Telegraphy (Broadcast Licence Charges and Exemption) Regulations 1984;
(d) the Wireless Telegraphy (Cordless Telephone Apparatus) (Exemption) Regulations 1988;
(e) the Wireless Telegraphy Apparatus (Receivers) (Exemption) Regulations 1989; or
(f) the Wireless Telegraphy Apparatus (Low Power Devices) (Exemption) Regulations 1989.

[4294]

4 Exemption

Subject to regulation 5, the establishment, installation and use of any relevant station or relevant apparatus are hereby exempted from the provisions of section 1(1) of the Act.

[4295]

5 Terms, provisions and limitations

The exemption provided for in regulation 4 shall be subject to the terms, provisions and limitations that the relevant station or relevant apparatus shall—
(a) be operated—
(i) only on those frequencies;
(ii) at a maximum field strength no greater than the limit;
(iii) so as not to radiate spurious emissions in excess of the limits, specified in the Schedule; and
(b) not cause undue interference with any wireless telegraphy.

[4296]

6 Inspection and Restrictions on Use

Where the Secretary of State has reasonable cause to believe that a relevant station or relevant apparatus is—
(a) causing undue interference with any wireless telegraphy; or
(b) emitting signals which are capable of causing interference with any station or

PART VI TELECOMMUNICATIONS

apparatus which is situated outside the boundary of the premises on which the relevant station or relevant apparatus is situated,

any person who is in possession or control of the relevant station or the relevant apparatus shall on the demand of any authorised person:—

(i) permit and facilitate its inspection by that authorised person;

(ii) cause its use to—

(aa) cease; or

(bb) be restricted in the manner specified by the authorised person.

[4297]

7 Measurement of emissions

Any person using a relevant station or relevant apparatus pursuant to the exemption provided for in regulation 4 above shall conduct such measurements as are reasonably necessary to ascertain whether the terms, provisions and limitations set out in the Schedule are being complied with.

[4298]

SCHEDULE

TERMS, PROVISIONS AND LIMITATIONS OF EXEMPTION

Regulation 5

1. Use of relevant stations and relevant apparatus for emission shall be limited to use—

(a) on a frequency within a frequency band specified in table 1 below; and

(b) where the maximum field strength of the emission does not exceed the limit specified in relation to that frequency band when measured at the distance specified in relation thereto.

TABLE 1

Frequency Band (MHz)	*Limit for maximum field strength (dBμ V/m)*	*Distance at which measurement taken (m)*
0.150–0.2835	34	100
0.5265–1.605	34	100
1.605–2.1735	48	100
2.1905–3.950	48	100
22.00–29.999	34	100
30.00–70.50	30	30
71.50–74.60	30	30
75.40–80.00	30	30
84.00–108.00	30	30
137.00–143.00	30	30
144.00–146.00	30	30
148.00–153.00	30	30
156.8375–225.00	30	30
400.00–405.50	30	30
406.50–450.00	30	30
453.00–464.00	30	30
467.00–960.00	30	30

2. Relevant stations and relevant apparatus shall not radiate, in any frequency band, spurious emissions of a maximum field strength in excess of the limit, when measured at the distance specified in table 2 below in relation to each frequency band—

TABLE 2

Frequency Band (MHz)	*Limit for maximum field* strength (dBμ *V/m*)	*Distance at which measurement taken* (*m*)
below 30	23	100
30 and above	23	30

3. In paragraphs 1 and 2 above—
"distance" means the distance from the relevant station or relevant apparatus; and
"measured" means ascertained by making measurements of all components of the emission from such number of directions—
(a) in a horizontal plane; or
(b) where the configuration of the site is such that it is not reasonably practicable to make measurements in an exactly horizontal plane, in a plane which is as near to horizontal as reasonably practicable,

including at least four—
(i) orthogonal directions; or
(ii) where the configuration of the site is such that it is not reasonably practicable to make measurements from exactly orthogonal directions, directions which are as near to orthogonal as reasonably practicable,

as is reasonably necessary to determine the maximum field strength of the emission at the distance specified, and the highest value obtained shall be taken to be the maximum field strength.

[4299]

MULTIPLEX LICENCE (BROADCASTING OF PROGRAMMES IN GAELIC) ORDER 1996

(SI 1996/2758)

NOTES
Made: 30 October 1996.
Authority: Broadcasting Act 1996, s 32(1), (2).
Commencement: 20 November 1996.

1 Citation, commencement and interpretation

(1) This Order may be cited as the Multiplex Licence (Broadcasting of Programmes in Gaelic) Order 1996 and shall come into force on 20th November 1996.

(2) In this Order "the Act" means the Broadcasting Act 1996.

[4300]

2 Condition of licence

The Commission shall include in the multiplex licence granted in respect of the frequency on which digital capacity is reserved for the broadcasting of Channel 5 in digital form and of S4C Digital, being a frequency to which section 28 of the Act applies, a condition requiring the holder of the licence, when broadcasting programmes for reception wholly or mainly in Scotland, to broadcast programmes in Gaelic for at least 30 minutes per day between 1800 hours and 2230 hours.

[4301]

3 Minimum transmission time of programmes provided by suppliers

In complying with the condition specified in article 2, the holder of the licence shall broadcast programmes in Gaelic supplied by each of the persons mentioned in section 32(4)(a) and (c) of the Act amounting to at least 30 hours of transmission time per year in relation to each such person.

[4302]

SATELLITE TELEVISION SERVICE REGULATIONS 1997

(SI 1997/1682)

NOTES

Made: 10 July 1997.
Authority: European Communities Act 1972, s 2(2).
Commencement: 11 July 1997.

1 Citation and commencement

(1) These Regulations may be cited as the Satellite Television Service Regulations 1997.

(2) These Regulations shall come into force on the day after the day on which they are made.

[4303]

2 Amendments of Broadcasting Act 1990

The Broadcasting Act 1990 is amended in accordance with the Schedule to these Regulations.

[4304]

3 Modification of licence conditions

Any licence to provide a non-domestic satellite service (within the meaning of Part I of the Broadcasting Act 1990 as originally enacted) granted before the commencement of these Regulations shall, as from that commencement, for the remainder of the term of the licence—

(a) be taken to be a licence to provide a satellite television service (within the meaning of that Part), and

(b) be taken to include a condition requiring that either—

(i) the holder of the licence is established in the United Kingdom, or

(ii) the holder of the licence is not established in any EEA State and the service is provided in circumstances falling within section 43(2) of that Act.

[4305]

4 Transitional saving for any satellite service becoming licensable on commencement of Regulations

(1) In this Regulation—

"the 1990 Act" means the Broadcasting Act 1990;

"commencement" means the commencement of these Regulations.

(2) Paragraph (3) applies in relation to any service which—

(a) was provided before commencement,

(b) immediately before commencement, was not required by Part I of the 1990 Act to be licensed as a domestic satellite service or a non-domestic satellite service, and

(c) on commencement, is a satellite television service for the purposes of section 43 of the 1990 Act (as amended by these Regulations).

(3) During the period of three months beginning with the day on which these Regulations come into force, section 13 of the 1990 Act (prohibition on providing television services without a licence) shall not apply in relation to any service to which this paragraph applies.

[4306]

5 Saving for existing order under section 79(5) of Broadcasting Act 1990

Until the commencement of the first order made under subsection (5) of section 79 of the Broadcasting Act 1990 after the commencement of these Regulations—

(a) the Broadcasting (Foreign Satellite Programmes) (Specified Countries) Order 1994 shall have effect as if made for the purposes of paragraph (b) of that subsection (which relates to radio), and

(b) the specified countries for the purposes of paragraph (a)(iii) of that subsection (which relates to television) shall be taken to be such of the countries listed in the Schedule to that Order as are not EEA States (within the meaning of the 1990 Act).

[4307]

6 (*Repeals the Broadcasting Act 1990, Sch 10, para 15 and revokes the Broadcasting (Prescribed Countries) Order 1996, SI 1996/904.*)

(*Schedule amends the Broadcasting Act 1990.*)

WIRELESS TELEGRAPHY APPARATUS APPROVAL AND EXAMINATION FEES ORDER 1997

(SI 1997/3050)

NOTES

Made: 17 December 1997.
Authority: Telecommunications Act 1984, s 84(7); Finance Act 1990, s 128.
Commencement: 2 February 1998.

ARRANGEMENT OF ARTICLES

1 Citation and commencement

This Order may be cited as the Wireless Telegraphy Apparatus Approval and Examination Fees Order 1997 and shall come into force on 2nd February 1998.

[4308]

2 Revocation and transitional provisions

(1) Subject to paragraph (2) below, the Wireless Telegraphy Apparatus Approval and Test Fees Order 1992 is hereby revoked.

(2) Where, for the purposes of the determination of an application for approval received by the Secretary of State on or before 1st February 1998, the whole or part of any approval of apparatus is conducted on or after the coming into force hereof, the fee to be charged in respect of the whole of that approval shall be the fee provided for in the Wireless Telegraphy Apparatus Approval and Test Fees Order 1992.

[4309]

3 Interpretation

(1) In this Order—

"the Act" means the Telecommunications Act 1984;

"apparatus" means wireless telegraphy apparatus or apparatus designed or adapted for use in connection with wireless telegraphy apparatus;

"approval" means approval under section 84 of the Act and includes initial approval of apparatus and approval of a technical change or modification to approved apparatus under that section;

"approval fee" shall be construed in accordance with article 6;

"approved apparatus" means apparatus which is approved under section 84 of the Act;

"examination" means the supervision by an officer of a test carried out by a person other than an officer and inspection of apparatus and shall include the carrying out of a test by an officer;

"examination fee" shall be construed in accordance with article 5;

"modification" means any change to approved apparatus which is effected by or on behalf of a person other than the manufacturer of that apparatus;

"non-technical change" means any change to approved apparatus which does not affect or is not capable of affecting the radio frequency characteristics of that apparatus which is effected by or on behalf of the manufacturer;

"officer" means a person engaged in examination on behalf of the Secretary of State; and

"technical change" means any change to approved apparatus which affects or is capable of affecting the radio frequency characteristics of that apparatus which is effected by or on behalf of the manufacturer.

(2) For the purposes of this Order—

(a) the setting up and dismantling of the apparatus examined and any other equipment required to conduct an examination;

(b) the analysis of examination results;

(c) the compiling of an examination report; and

(d) unpacking and repacking the apparatus examined,

shall be treated as part of the examination.

(3) For the purposes of this Order, "visit" means a continuous period of time during which an officer is reasonably absent from his work place for the purposes of conducting an examination and includes time spent in conducting the examination, time reasonably spent in travel wholly undertaken for the purposes of an examination wholly or partly conducted at a place other than the officer's work place, any period in which overnight accommodation (including a berth on a boat or train) is reasonably occupied (an "overnight stay") and any other rest periods reasonably taken whilst so absent.

(4) In calculating an officer's subsistence costs, a visit shall be divided into periods of time in the following order—

(a) each complete period of 24 hours (a "24 hour period");

(b) any—

(i) single period of less than 24 hours; or

(ii) period of less than 24 hours remaining after any 24 hour periods have been taken into account,

which includes an overnight stay (an "overnight period");

(c) where—

(i) the visit does not involve an overnight stay; or

(ii) the visit involves one or more 24 hour periods, but no overnight period is counted,

any period of—

(aa) 10 hours or more but less than 24 hours (a "day period"); or

(bb) 5 hours or more but less than 10 hours (a "half-day period"); and

(d) any remaining period of less than 5 hours, which shall be disregarded.

(5) In calculating an examination fee or variable fee, each period of time taken by each officer involved in conducting an examination shall be counted separately, and the total for each officer be aggregated, and the aggregate for all officers involved divided into complete periods of 15 minutes, with any remaining period of 7.5 minutes or more but less than 15 minutes being counted as a complete period of 15 minutes, and any remaining period of less than 7.5 minutes being disregarded.

[4310]

4 Application

This Order applies to the charging of fees for the purpose of determining an application for approval and in respect of the examination of apparatus for that purpose conducted by the Secretary of State.

[4311]

5 Examination fees

(1) This article applies to the charging of fees, "examination fees", in respect of the examination of apparatus conducted by the Secretary of State for the purpose of determining an application for approval.

(2) The examination fee shall be the sum of—

(a) the amount calculated in accordance with Schedule 1 hereto; and

(b) an amount equal to the value added tax chargeable on the supply of that examination.

(3) For the purposes of this article, the value of the supply of examination by reference to which value added tax is chargeable shall be the amount calculated in accordance with Schedule 1 hereto.

[4312]

6 Approval fees

(1) This article applies to the charging of fees, "approval fees", in respect of the determination of an application for approval of apparatus by the Secretary of State including the charging of fees in respect of any examination carried out as part of that determination.

(2) The approval fee, which is payable whether or not approval is granted, shall be the sum of—

(a) the sum specified in relation to the type of application appearing in Schedule 2 hereto ("the fixed fee"); and

(b) if the determination of an application for approval includes a visit, the sum of—

(i) the amount calculated in accordance with Schedule 3 hereto ("the variable fee"); and

(ii) an amount equal to the value added tax chargeable on the supply of that examination.

(3) For the purposes of this article, the value of the supply of examination by reference to which value added tax is chargeable shall be the variable fee.

[4313]

7 Timing of payment of fees

(1) Where an examination fee is payable, the Secretary of State shall—

(a) on receipt of an application for examination of apparatus, estimate in complete periods of 15 minutes the time to be taken in conducting the examination and thereby estimate the amount to be payable in accordance with article 5 above, and shall serve an invoice on the applicant for the amount so estimated, which shall thereupon be due and payable to the Secretary of State;

(b) on completion of the examination, the Secretary of State shall—

(i) serve an invoice on the applicant for the final amount of the examination fee, which shall thereupon, and before disclosure of the examination report, be due and payable to the Secretary of State; or

(ii) if the amount received under paragraph (1)(a) above exceeds the final amount of the examination fee, repay the balance to the applicant.

(2) Where a variable fee is payable, the Secretary of State shall on completion of the visit notify the applicant of the amount of the variable fee which shall thereupon, and before disclosure and notification of the result of the application, be due and payable to the Secretary of State.

(3) The fixed fee shall be due and payable on the making of the application for approval.

[4314]

SCHEDULES

SCHEDULE 1
CALCULATION OF EXAMINATION FEES

Article 5

The amount to be included in the examination fee for the purposes of article 5(2)(a) shall be £66 per hour taken in conducting the examination, subject to—

(a) a minimum of £250; and

(b) a maximum of £10,500.

[4315]

PART VI TELECOMMUNICATIONS

SCHEDULE 2
CALCULATION OF FIXED FEES

Article 6(2)

Type of Application	*Fee*
Initial Approval	£400
Modification	£400
Non-technical Change	£200
Technical Change	£200

[4316]

SCHEDULE 3
CALCULATION OF VARIABLE FEES

Article 6(2)

The amount to be included in the variable fee for the purposes of article 6(2)(b)(i) shall be the sum of the following—

(a) £41 per hour for time spent in conducting the examination;
(b) any travelling costs reasonably incurred; and
(c) where an examination involves a visit of 5 hours or more, each officer's reasonable subsistence costs.

[4317]

WIRELESS TELEGRAPHY (CONTROL OF INTERFERENCE FROM VIDEOSENDERS) ORDER 1998

(SI 1998/722)

NOTES

Made: 10 March 1998.
Authority: Wireless Telegraphy Act 1967, s 7(2).
Commencement: 20 April 1998.

1 Citation and commencement

This Order may be cited as the Wireless Telegraphy (Control of Interference from Videosenders) Order 1998 and shall come into force on 20th April 1998.

[4318]

2 (*Revokes the Wireless Telegraphy (Control of Interference from Videosenders) Order 1997, SI 1997/1842.*)

3 Interpretation

In this Order—

"the 1967 Act" means the Wireless Telegraphy Act 1967;

"television set" has the meaning given to it by section 6(1) of the 1967 Act;

"video camera" means apparatus designed or adapted for capturing visual images (with or without sound) and converting the same into signals;

"video recorder" means apparatus designed or adapted to be used for the purposes of making or playing back video recordings;

"video recording" means any disc, magnetic tape or any other device capable of storing data electronically containing information by the use of which the whole or a part of a video work may be produced;

"videosender" means wireless telegraphy apparatus which is designed or adapted, or is capable of being adapted, for the purpose of transmitting visual images (with or without sound) in the frequency band 470–854 MHz from a video camera, a video recorder or other equipment to a television set or other receiving apparatus and which is neither licensed under the provisions of section 1(1) of the Wireless Telegraphy Act 1949 nor exempt therefrom; and

"video work" means any series of visual images (with or without sound)—

(a) produced electronically by the use of information contained on any disc, magnetic tape or any other device capable of storing data electronically; and

(b) shown as a moving picture.

[4319]

4 Actions restricted

(1) No person shall take any of the actions listed below in relation to videosenders—

(a) manufacture (whether or not for sale);

(b) selling or offering for sale, letting on hire or offering to let on hire, or indicating (whether by display of the apparatus or by any form of advertisement) one's willingness to sell or let on hire;

(c) having in one's custody or control; and

(d) importation.

(2) Nothing in this Article prevents having in one's custody or control and importation of videosenders for the sole purpose of re-export from the United Kingdom.

[4320]

WIRELESS TELEGRAPHY (CITIZENS' BAND AND AMATEUR APPARATUS) (VARIOUS PROVISIONS) ORDER 1998

(SI 1998/2531)

NOTES

Made: 14 October 1998.
Authority: Wireless Telegraphy Act 1967, s 7(2); Telecommunications Act 1984, ss 84, 85(1).
Commencement: 6 November 1998.

ARRANGEMENT OF ARTICLES

1 Citation and commencement

This Order may be cited as the Wireless Telegraphy (Citizens' Band and Amateur Apparatus) (Various Provisions) Order 1998 and shall come into force on 6th November 1998.

[4321]

2 (*Revokes the Wireless Telegraphy* (*Citizens' Band and Amateur Apparatus*) (*Various Provisions*) *Order 1988, SI 1988/1215 and the Wireless Telegraphy* (*Citizens' Band and Amateur Apparatus*) (*Various Provisions*) (*Amendment*) *Order 1995, SI 1995/2588.*)

3 Interpretation

In this Order—

"the 1967 Act" means the Wireless Telegraphy Act 1967;

"the 1984 Act" means the Telecommunications Act 1984;

["the Directive" means Directive 1999/5/EC of the European Parliament and of the Council on radio equipment and telecommunications terminal equipment and the mutual recognition of their conformity;]

"CB apparatus" means wireless telegraphy apparatus known as "Citizens' Band" which is designed or adapted, or has facilities permitting its adaptation, for the purpose of transmitting spoken messages on the frequency band 26.1 MHz to 28 MHz;

"EN45001 and EN45002" means European Standards (Normes Europeene) EN45001 and EN45002 published in September 1989 by the British Standards Institution;

"ETS 300 135" means European Telecommunications Standard 300 135 published in June 1991 by the European Telecommunications Standards Institute;

"ISO guides 25 and 58" means the International Organization for Standardization Guides 25 and 58 published by the International Organisation for Standardisation in December 1990 and September 1993 respectively;

"MPT 1320" means Department of Trade and Industry Performance Specification MPT 1320 published in April 1981 and revised and reprinted in May 1993 and withdrawn in December 1995;

"MPT 1333" means Department of Trade and Industry Performance Specification MPT 1333 published in December 1986 and revised and reprinted in May 1993 and withdrawn in December 1996; …

"MPT 1382" means Department of Trade and Industry Performance Specification MPT 1382 published in March 1995 and revised and reprinted in [January 1997; and]

["United Kingdom Radio Interface Requirement (IR)" means the interface requirement published by the Radiocommunications Agency of the Department of Trade and Industry (RA) in accordance with Article 4.1 of the Directive.]

[4322]

NOTES

Definitions "the Directive" and "United Kingdom Radio Interface Requirement (IR)" inserted, in definition "MPT 1333" word omitted revoked and in definition "MPT 1382" words in square brackets substituted by the Wireless Telegraphy (Citizens' Band and Amateur Apparatus) (Various Provisions) (Amendment) Order 2000, SI 2000/1013, art 3(a).

4 Actions restricted

(1) Subject to paragraph (4) of this article, no person shall take any of the actions listed in paragraph (3) in relation to CB apparatus [prior to 1st May 2000] unless—

(a) the CB apparatus operates in the frequency band 27.59625–27.99625 MHz and—
   (i) complies with the requirements of MPT 1320; or
   (ii) complies with the requirements of MPT 1382; or
   (iii) is approved for the time being by the Secretary of State under section 84 of the 1984 Act for the purposes of this Order,

provided that a person may have CB apparatus in his custody or control or undertake second-hand sale and advertisement of such apparatus, which operates in the frequency band 27.59625–27.99625 MHz and complies with the requirements of MPT 1320, if it was manufactured prior to 1st January 1996; or

(b) the CB apparatus operates in the frequency band 26.960–27.410 MHz and complies with ETS 300 135 by either—
   (i) being approved for the time being by the Secretary of State under section 84 of the 1984 Act for the purposes of this Order; or
   (ii) being approved to ETS 300 135 by the national administration of a country listed in Schedule 1 following type testing at a test laboratory, which has been accredited in accordance with ISO guides 25 and 58 or EN45001 and EN45002 or a national standard conforming to ISO guides 25 and 58 or EN45001 and EN45002,

provided that a person may have CB apparatus in his custody or control or undertake second-hand sale and advertisement of such apparatus, which operates in the frequency band 26.960–27.410 MHz and complies with the requirements of MPT 1333 by being approved for the time being by the Secretary of State under section 84 of the 1984 Act for the purposes of this Order, if it was manufactured prior to 27th October 1995; or

(c) the CB apparatus operates in the frequency bands 26.960–27.410 MHz and 27.59625–27.99625 MHz and—
   (i) complies with the requirements of MPT 1382; or
   (ii) is approved for the time being by the Secretary of State under section 84 of the 1984 Act for the purposes of this Order.

[(1A) After 30th April 2000, subject to paragraphs (1B) and (4) of this article, no person shall take any of the actions listed in paragraph (3) in relation to CB apparatus unless such apparatus complies with IR 2027 entitled "UK Radio Interface Requirement for CB

Transmitters and Receivers for Use in the Citizens' Band Radio Service" published by RA in March 2000, provided that paragraph (3) shall not apply to CB apparatus which complies with article 4(1)(a) to (c) as appropriate and in respect of which the relevant restricted action listed in paragraph (3) has occurred prior to 8th April 2001.

(1B) Notwithstanding paragraph (1A) of this article, a person may have CB apparatus which complies with article 4(1)(a) to (c) as appropriate in his custody or control or undertake second-hand sale and advertisement of such apparatus if the relevant restricted action listed in paragraph (3) has occurred in relation thereto prior to 8th April 2001.]

(2) …

(3) The actions restricted by this article are—

(a) manufacture (whether or not for sale);

(b) selling or offering for sale, letting on hire or offering to let on hire, or indicating (whether by display of the apparatus or by any form of advertisement) one's willingness to sell or let on hire;

(c) having in one's custody or control; and

(d) importation.

(4) Nothing in this article prevents having in one's custody or control and importation of CB apparatus and importation of the wireless telegraphy apparatus specified in paragraph (2) for the sole purpose of re-export from the United Kingdom.

[4323]

NOTES

Para (1): words in square brackets inserted by the Wireless Telegraphy (Citizens' Band and Amateur Apparatus) (Various Provisions) (Amendment) Order 2000, SI 2000/1013, art 3(b).

Paras (1A), (1B): inserted by SI 2000/1013, art 3(c).

Para (2): revoked by SI 2000/1013, art 3(d).

5 Marking

(1) CB apparatus [which complies with article 4(1)(a) to (c) as appropriate prior to 1st May 2000 and in respect of which the relevant restricted action listed in paragraph (3) has occurred prior to 8th April 2001] shall be marked in accordance with the requirements specified in Schedule 2.

(2) No person shall, in the course of any trade or business, supply or offer to supply CB apparatus which does not comply with paragraph (1) of this article.

[4324]

NOTES

Para (1): words in square brackets inserted by the Wireless Telegraphy (Citizens' Band and Amateur Apparatus) (Various Provisions) (Amendment) Order 2000, SI 2000/1013, art 3(e).

6 Channel Islands and Isle of Man

This Order shall not extend to the Channel Islands and the Isle of Man.

[4325]

SCHEDULES

SCHEDULE 1

Article 4(1)(b)(ii)

Country	*Symbol*	*Country*	*Symbol*	*Country*	*Symbol*
Albania	AL	Hungary	H	Portugal	P
Austria	A	Iceland	IS	Romania	RO
Belgium	B	Ireland	IRL	San Marino	RSM
Bosnia and Herzegovina	BH	Italy	I	Slovak Republic	SK

PART VI TELECOMMUNICATIONS

Country	*Symbol*	*Country*	*Symbol*	*Country*	*Symbol*
Bulgaria	BG	Latvia	LV	Slovenia	SLO
Croatia	HR	Liechtenstein	FL	Spain	E
Cyprus	CY	Lithuania	LT	Sweden	S
Czech Republic	CZ	Luxembourg	L	Switzerland	CH
Denmark	DK	Malta	M	Turkey	TR
Estonia	EST	Moldova	MLD	United Kingdom of Great Britain and Northern Ireland	GB
Finland	Fl	Monaco	MC	Vatican City	SCV
France	F	Netherlands	NL		
Germany	D	Norway	N		
Greece	GR	Poland	PL		

[4326]

SCHEDULE 2

Article 5

1. CB apparatus which complies with the requirements of—
   (a) article 4(1)(a)(i) shall be marked as follows—

   (b) article 4(1)(a)(ii) or (iii) shall be marked as follows—

PR 27/94 or CB 27/94

   (c) article 4(1)(b) shall be marked as follows—
   (i)

PR27GB

where the apparatus is manufactured before 12th June 1990 and has been approved under section 84 of the 1984 Act; or
   (ii)

CEPT PR27GB or PR27GB

where the apparatus is manufactured on or after 12th June 1990 and has been approved under section 84 of the 1984 Act; or
   (iii) as specified in paragraph (ii) where the apparatus is manufactured on or after 1st June 1991 and has been approved in a country listed in Schedule 1 except that the symbol "GB" shall be replaced with the relevant symbol listed in that Schedule to indicate the country in which the approval has been obtained; and
   (d) article 4(1)(c) shall be marked as follows—

PR 27/97
FOR USE IN
UK ONLY

2. The marks described in paragraph 1 shall—
   (a) be placed on the CB apparatus in a visible place;
   (b) be legible, tamperproof and durable; and
   (c) have a letter and figure height not less than 2 mm.

[4327]

WIRELESS TELEGRAPHY (VISITING SHIPS AND AIRCRAFT) REGULATIONS 1998

(SI 1998/2970)

NOTES

Made: 30 November 1998.
Authority: Wireless Telegraphy Act 1949, s 6.
Commencement: 24 December 1998.

ARRANGEMENT OF REGULATIONS

PART VI TELECOMMUNICATIONS

1 Citation and commencement

These Regulations may be cited as the Wireless Telegraphy (Visiting Ships and Aircraft) Regulations 1998 and shall come into force on 24th December 1998.

[4328]

2 (*Revokes the Wireless Telegraphy* (*Colonial Ships and Aircraft*) *Regulations 1954, SI 1954/539 and the Wireless Telegraphy* (*Foreign Ships and Aircraft*) *Regulations 1954, SI 1954/540.*)

3 Interpretation

(1) In these Regulations—

"authorised person" means any person authorised by the Secretary of State for the purposes of regulation 7; and

"visiting ship" and "visiting aircraft" mean a ship or aircraft, as the case may be, which, not being registered in the United Kingdom, is registered in a country other than the United Kingdom, the Isle of Man, or any of the Channel Islands and which is for the time being within the limits of the British Islands and the territorial waters adjacent thereto, but does not include a ship or aircraft in the service of the armed forces of any state.

(2) In the application of the definition of "visiting ship" and "visiting aircraft" for the purposes of these Regulations as having effect in the Isle of Man or any of the Channel Islands, for the words "United Kingdom" where they first occur there shall be substituted the name of the Island in which they so have effect.

[4329]

4 Interference

All apparatus for wireless telegraphy on board a visiting ship or visiting aircraft shall be so used as not to interfere with the emitting or receiving of any wireless telegraphy.

[4330]

5 Communication with land stations

All persons using apparatus for wireless telegraphy on board a visiting ship or visiting aircraft for communication with a land station shall comply with the instructions given by the land station in all questions relating to the order and time of transmission, to the choice of frequency and of the class of emission, and to the duration and suspension of communication.

[4331]

6 Distress signals

Nothing in the foregoing Regulations shall restrict the use of wireless telegraphy for the purpose of making or answering signals of distress.

[4332]

7 Inspection and restrictions on use

(1) Where an authorised person has reasonable cause to believe that any apparatus for wireless telegraphy on board a visiting ship or visiting aircraft is not complying with these Regulations, any person who is in possession or control of such apparatus shall, on the demand of that authorised person—

(a) permit and facilitate its inspection by that authorised person; and

(b) cause its use to—

(i) cease; or

(ii) be restricted in the manner specified by that authorised person,

for a period of time ending either on a date or on the occurrence of an event specified by that authorised person.

(2) Any authorised person exercising powers under paragraph (1) shall produce evidence of his authority, if so required by the person in possession or control of such apparatus.

[4333]

8 Penalties

(1) Any person who contravenes any provision of these Regulations shall be guilty of an offence and shall be liable on summary conviction for each such offence to a fine not exceeding level 5 on the standard scale, and upon such conviction the court may order that any apparatus for wireless telegraphy in respect of which the offence was committed shall be forfeited.

(2) For the purposes of any proceedings under these Regulations, the master or person being or appearing to be in command or charge of any visiting ship or aircraft shall be deemed to have authorised and to be responsible for the use of any apparatus for wireless telegraphy on board such ship or aircraft.

(3) Any summons, complaint or other document in any proceedings under these Regulations shall be deemed to have been duly served on the person to whom the same is addressed by being left with the person being or appearing to be in command or charge of the visiting ship or visiting aircraft in which the offence is charged to have been committed.

[4334]

9 Application to Northern Ireland

(1) In the application of these Regulations to Northern Ireland, the expression "summary conviction" means conviction subject to and in accordance with the Summary Jurisdiction Acts, within the meaning of the Interpretation Act (Northern Ireland) 1954.

[4335]

NOTES

Note: this regulation is reproduced as it appears in the Queen's Printer's copy.

10 Application to the Isle of Man

In the application of these Regulations to the Isle of Man, the expression "summary conviction" means conviction subject to and in accordance with the Summary Jurisdiction Acts, within the meaning of the Interpretation Act 1976.

[4336]

11 Application to the Channel Islands

In the application of these Regulations to the Channel Islands, the word "summary" in regulation 8(1) shall be omitted, and, in relation to the Bailiwick of Jersey, the reference therein to "level 5 on the standard scale" shall be construed as a reference to level 4 on the standard scale of fines in the Schedule to the Criminal Justice (Standard Scale of Fines) (Jersey) Law 1993 as that scale has effect at any time.

[4337]

RADIO EQUIPMENT AND TELECOMMUNICATIONS TERMINAL EQUIPMENT REGULATIONS 2000

(SI 2000/730)

NOTES

Made: 9 March 2000.
Authority: European Communities Act 1972, s 2(2).
Commencement: 8 April 2000.

ARRANGEMENT OF REGULATIONS

PART I
INTRODUCTORY

PART II
GENERAL PRINCIPLES

PART III
COMPLIANCE

PART IV
ENFORCEMENT

PART I
INTRODUCTORY

1 Citation, commencement, revocations and disapplications

(1) These Regulations may be cited as the Radio Equipment and Telecommunications Terminal Equipment Regulations 2000 and shall come into force on 8th April 2000.

(2) …

(3) Sections 22 and 84 of the Act, … and the Electrical Equipment (Safety) Regulations 1994, except for regulations 5 and 7, shall cease to apply to apparatus covered by these Regulations.

[4338]

NOTES

Para (2): revokes the Telecommunication Apparatus (Advertisements) Order 1982, SI 1982/490, the Telecommunication Apparatus (Advertisements) Order 1985, SI 1985/719, the Telecommunication Apparatus (Advertisements) (Amendments) Order 1985, SI 1985/1030, the Telecommunication Apparatus (Marking and Labelling) Order 1982, SI 1982/491, the Telecommunication Apparatus (Marking and Labelling) Order 1985, SI 1985/718, the Telecommunication Apparatus (Marking and Labelling) (Amendment) Order 1985, SI 1985/1031, the Telecommunication Apparatus (Bell Noise Labelling) Order 1985, SI 1985/718, the Telecommunication Apparatus (Approval Fees) (British Approvals Board for Telecommunications) Order 1990, SI 1990/1679, the Telecommunication Apparatus (Approval Fees) (British Approvals Board for Telecommunications) Order 1992, SI 1992/1875, the Telecommunications Terminal Equipment Regulations 1992, SI 1992/2423, the Telecommunications Terminal Equipment (Amendment and Extension) Regulations 1994, SI 1994/3129 and the Telecommunications Terminal Equipment (Amendment) Regulations 1995, SI 1995/144.

Para (3): words omitted revoked by the Electromagnetic Compatibility Regulations 2005, SI 2005/281, reg 104.

2 Interpretation

(1) In these Regulations (except in Schedule 9)—

"the Act" means the Telecommunications Act 1984;

"active implantable medical device" shall have the meaning in Article 1 of Council Directive 90/385/EEC of 20 June 1990 on the approximation of the laws of the Member States relating to active implantable medical devices;

"apparatus" means any equipment that is either radio equipment or telecommunications terminal equipment or both;

"the CE marking" has the meaning given in regulation 10;

"the Commission" means the Commission of the European Communities;

"a component or a separate technical unit of a vehicle" shall have the meaning in Article 2 of Council Directive 92/61/EEC;

"the Directive" means Directive 1999/5/EC of the European Parliament and of the Council on radio equipment and telecommunications terminal equipment and the mutual recognition of their conformity;

"the Director" means the Director General of Telecommunications appointed under section 1 of the Act;

"enforcement authority" has the meaning given in paragraphs 1 and 2 of Schedule 9;

"equipment class" means a class identifying particular types of apparatus which under the Directive are considered similar and those interfaces for which the apparatus is designed. Apparatus may belong to more than one equipment class;

"harmful interference" means interference which endangers the functioning of a radio navigation service or of other safety services or which otherwise seriously degrades, obstructs or repeatedly interrupts a radio communications service operating in accordance with the applicable Community or national regulations;

"harmonised standard" means a technical specification adopted by a recognised standards body under a mandate from the Commission in conformity with the procedures laid down in Directive 98/34/EC of the European Parliament and of the Council for the purpose of establishing a European requirement, compliance with which is not compulsory;

"interface" means either or both of—

(i) a network termination point which is a physical connection point at which a user is provided with access to public telecommunications network, and

(ii) an air interface specifying the radio path between radio equipment

and their technical specifications;

"medical device" shall have the meaning in Article 1 of Council Directive 93/42/EEC of 14 June 1993 concerning medical devices;

["OFCOM" means the Office of Communications established under the Office of Communications Act 2002;]

"public telecommunications networks" means telecommunications networks used wholly or partly for the provision of publicly available telecommunications services;

"radio equipment" means a product, or a relevant component thereof, capable of communication by means of the emission and/or reception of radio waves utilising the spectrum allocated to terrestrial/space radio communication;

"radio waves" means electromagnetic waves of frequencies from 9 kHz to 3,000 GHz, propagated in space without artificial guide;

"responsible person" means the manufacturer of apparatus or his authorised representative within the Community, or any other person who places the apparatus on the market;

"technical construction file" means a file describing the apparatus and providing information and explanations as to how the essential requirements (within the meaning of regulation 4) applicable to the apparatus have been met;

"telecommunications terminal equipment" means a product enabling communication, or a relevant component thereof, which is intended to be connected directly or indirectly by any means whatsoever to interfaces of public telecommunications networks;

and any other expression used in these Regulations which is also used in the Directive has the same meaning in these Regulations as it has in the Directive.

(2) For the purposes of these Regulations, unless the context otherwise requires, a reference to a numbered regulation or Schedule is a reference to the regulation or Schedule so numbered in these Regulations and a reference—

(i) in a regulation to a paragraph is a reference to a paragraph in that regulation;
(ii) to an Annex is a reference to an Annex of the Directive.

(3) For the purposes of these Regulations, Annexes I, II, III, IV, V, VI and VII are respectively set out in Schedules 1, 2, 3, 4, 5, 6 and 7, and a reference to a paragraph in an Annex is a reference to a paragraph in that Annex as set out in the respective Schedule.

[(4) Except for the references to the European Communities in the definition of "the Commission" and in relation to the Official Journal, a reference to the Community includes a reference to the EEA, and a reference to a member State includes a reference to an EEA State: for this purpose—

(a) the "EEA" means the European Economic Area;
(b) an "EEA State" means a State which is a contracting party to the EEA Agreement; and
(c) the "EEA Agreement" means the Agreement on the European Economic Area signed at Oporto on 2nd May 1992 as adjusted by the Protocol signed at Brussels on 17th March 1993.]

[4339]

NOTES

Para (1): definition "OFCOM" inserted by the Radio Equipment and Telecommunications Terminal Equipment (Amendment No 2) Regulations 2003, SI 2003/3144, reg 2(1), (3).

Para (4): added by the Radio Equipment and Telecommunications Terminal Equipment (Amendment) Regulations 2003, SI 2003/1903, reg 2(1), (3).

PART II
GENERAL PRINCIPLES

3 Scope and Exclusions

(1) Subject to paragraphs (4) and (5), these Regulations shall apply to all apparatus.

(2) Where apparatus incorporates, as an integral part or as an accessory—

(a) a medical device; or
(b) an active implantable medical device,

[the apparatus shall be governed by these Regulations without prejudice to] the application of Council Directive 93/42/EEC of 14 June 1993; or Council Directive 90/385/EEC of 20 June 1990; or the Medical Devices Regulations 1994; or the Active Implantable Medical Devices Regulations 1992.

(3) Where apparatus constitutes a component or a separate technical unit of a vehicle, [the apparatus shall be governed by these Regulations without prejudice to] the application of Council Directive 72/245/EEC of 20 June 1972; or Council Directive 92/61/EEC of 30 June 1992; or the Motor Vehicles (Type Approval) Regulations 1980; or the Motorcycle (EC Type Approval) Regulations 1995.

(4) These Regulations shall not apply to apparatus exclusively used for the purposes of public security, defence, State security (including the economic well-being of the State) or the activities of the State in the area of criminal law.

(5) These Regulations shall not apply to equipment listed in Schedule 1.

[4340]

NOTES

Paras (2), (3): words in square brackets substituted by the Radio Equipment and Telecommunications Terminal Equipment (Amendment) Regulations 2003, SI 2003/1903, reg 2(1), (4).

4 Essential Requirements

(1) Apparatus when properly installed and maintained and used for its intended purpose shall satisfy the essential requirements set out in this regulation.

(2) The following essential requirements shall apply to all apparatus—

(a) the protection of the health and safety of the user and any other person, including the objectives with respect to safety requirements contained in Council Directive 73/23/EEC (but as if there were no voltage limit);

(b) the protection requirements with respect to electromagnetic compatibility contained in Council Directive 89/336/EEC;

(3) In addition, radio equipment shall be so constructed that it effectively uses the spectrum allocated to terrestrial/space radio communication and orbital resources so as to avoid harmful interference.

(4) When a measure has been adopted by the Commission pursuant to Articles 3.3, 6.2 and 15 of the Directive and published in the Official Journal of the European Communities determining that apparatus shall be so constructed that—

(a) it interworks via networks with other apparatus and that it can be connected to interfaces of the appropriate type throughout the community; or that

(b) it does not harm the network or its functioning nor misuse network resources, thereby causing an unacceptable degradation of service; or that

(c) it incorporates safeguards to ensure that the personal data and privacy of the user and of the subscriber are protected; or that

(d) it supports certain features ensuring avoidance of fraud; or that

(e) it supports certain features ensuring access to emergency services; or that

(f) it supports certain features in order to facilitate its use by users with a disability,

apparatus within the scope of that measure shall meet the requirements of that measure from the date specified in that measure.

[4341]

PART III
COMPLIANCE

5 General duty relating to the placing on the market and putting into service of apparatus

(1) Subject to [paragraph (4) and] regulations 6, 7 and 8, no person shall place on the market or put into service any apparatus unless the requirements of paragraph (2) and (in the case of radio equipment) the requirements of paragraph (3) have been complied with in relation to it.

(2) The requirements in respect of any apparatus are that—

(a) it satisfies the essential requirements set out in regulation 4: and without prejudice to other means of complying for the purpose of satisfying those requirements, where a harmonised standard covers one or more of the relevant essential requirements, any apparatus or part thereof constructed in accordance with that harmonised standard or part thereof shall be presumed to comply with that or, as the case may be, those essential requirements;

(b) the information has been provided in accordance with regulation 11;

(c) the appropriate conformity assessment procedures in respect of the apparatus have been carried out in accordance with regulation 9;

[(d) the requirements of regulation 10 and Schedule 7 (CE and other marking) have been complied with;] and

(e) a declaration of conformity has been drawn up in respect of it by the manufacturer of the apparatus or other responsible person in accordance with Schedule 2, 3, 4 or 5.

(3) In respect of radio equipment using frequency bands whose use is not harmonised throughout the Community it is also a requirement that notification of intention to place it on the market shall have been given in accordance with regulation 12.

[(4) Paragraph (1) does not prohibit the putting into service of apparatus in relation to which the requirements of paragraphs (2)(b), (c), (d) and (e) have not been complied with.]

[4342]

NOTES

Para (1): words in square brackets inserted by the Radio Equipment and Telecommunications Terminal Equipment (Amendment) Regulations 2003, SI 2003/1903, reg 2(1), (5)(a).

Para (2): sub-para (d) substituted by SI 2003/1903, reg 2(1), (5)(b).

Para (4): added by SI 2003/1903, reg 2(1), (5)(c).

6 Exceptions in respect of placing on the market and putting into service

(1) For the purposes of regulation 5, apparatus shall not be regarded as being placed on the market where that apparatus—

(a) is intended to be exported to a country outside the Community; or

(b) is imported into the Community for re-export to a country outside the Community; or

(c) is transferred from the manufacturer in a third country to his authorised representative established within the Community who is responsible on behalf of the manufacturer for ensuring compliance with the Directive; or

(d) is transferred to a manufacturer for further processing (for example, to modify the product or to integrate it into another product, or to put his own name on the product);

save that this paragraph shall not apply if the CE marking, or any inscription liable to be confused therewith, is affixed thereto.

[(2) Subject to paragraph (3), no offence under the Act or the Wireless Telegraphy Acts 1949 to 1967, nor any offence of incitement to commit such an offence, shall be committed by reason only that apparatus which does not comply with these Regulations is displayed at a trade fair, exhibition or demonstration if a notice is displayed in relation to the apparatus to the effect

(a) that it does not satisfy the provisions of these Regulations; and

(b) that it may not be placed on the market or put into service until those provisions are satisfied by a responsible person.

(3) Paragraph (2) does not apply in any case in which radio equipment is switched on and thereby causes harmful interference or endangers public health.

(4) The Secretary of State and [OFCOM] shall so exercise their respective functions under Part VI of the Act and the Wireless Telegraphy Acts 1949 to 1967 that the putting into service of radio equipment which complies with these Regulations is restricted only for reasons related to the effective and appropriate use of the radio spectrum, avoidance or harmful interference of public health.]

[4343]

NOTES

Paras (2), (3): substituted, together with para (4), for original para (2), by the Radio Equipment and Telecommunications Terminal Equipment (Amendment) Regulations 2003, SI 2003/1903, reg 2(1), (6).

Para (4): substituted, together with paras (2), (3), for original para (2), by SI 2003/1903, reg 2(1), (6); word in square brackets substituted by the Radio Equipment and Telecommunications Terminal Equipment (Amendment No 2) Regulations 2003, SI 2003/3144, reg 2(1), (2).

[7 The right to connect

(1) Operators of public telecommunications networks

(a) shall connect or permit the connection, at an interface, of any telecommunications terminal equipment which meets the requirements of regulation 4 or is equipment which was placed on the market before 8th April 2001 and complied with the

provisions of Directive 98/13/EC, the Telecommunication Terminal Equipment Regulations 1992 or section 22 or 84 of the Telecommunications Act 1984;
(b) shall not discontinue such connection lawfully made of any such equipment.

(2) No apparatus is required under sub-paragraphs (1)(a) and (b) or otherwise to be, or to be permitted to be, connected or kept connected if that apparatus
(a) met the requirements of regulation 4 at the time when the connection was made but no longer does so;
(b) was placed on the market before 8th April 2001 and complied with the provisions of Directive 98/13/EC, the Telecommunication Terminal Equipment Regulations 1992 or section 22 or 84 of the Telecommunications Act 1984 at the time when the connection was made but no longer does so;
(c) causes serious damage to a network or harmful radio interference or harm to the network or its functioning; and the operator may refuse connection of that apparatus, disconnect that apparatus or withdraw that apparatus from service provided the operator at the earliest practical opportunity informs the Secretary of State and [OFCOM] of its action; or
(d) is, in case of emergency, required to be disconnected to protect the network, provided that
(i) the user may be offered, without delay and without costs, an alternative solution; and
(ii) the operator immediately informs the Secretary of State and [OFCOM].

(3) In any case in which a public telecommunications operator
(a) refuses connection of apparatus declared to be compliant with the provisions of the Directive; or
(b) disconnects such apparatus; or
(c) withdraws it from service

the Secretary of State and [OFCOM] may, if they are of the opinion that the apparatus would not cause serious damage to a network or harmful interference or harm to the network or its functioning, require the operator to provide connection, reconnect the apparatus or restore it to service (as the case may be).]

[4344]

NOTES

Commencement: 25 July 2003.

Substituted by the Radio Equipment and Telecommunications Terminal Equipment (Amendment) Regulations 2003, SI 2003/1903, reg 2(1), (7).

Paras (2), (3): words in square brackets substituted by the Radio Equipment and Telecommunications Terminal Equipment (Amendment No 2) Regulations 2003, SI 2003/3144, reg 2(1), (2).

8 Transitional provisions in respect of placing on the market and putting into service

Notwithstanding the provisions of regulation 5, apparatus may be placed on the market before 8 April 2001, and apparatus so placed on the market may be put into service, if (in either case) it is in accordance with the provisions of Council Directive 98/13/EC, the Telecommunications Terminal Equipment Regulations 1992, or section 22 or 84 of the Act.

[4345]

9 Conformity assessment procedures for apparatus

(1) For the purposes of regulation 5(2)(c), the appropriate conformity assessment procedure for apparatus shall, subject to paragraph (2), be chosen from the procedures set out in Schedules 2, 3, 4 and 5 as follows—
(a) for telecommunications terminal equipment which does not make use of the spectrum allocated to terrestrial/space radio communications and for the receiving parts of radio equipment, the conformity assessment procedures which may be chosen from are those laid down in Schedules 2, 4 and 5;
(b) where radio equipment is not within the scope of subparagraph (a) above and the manufacturer has fully applied harmonised standards, the conformity assessment procedures which may be chosen from are those laid down in Schedules 3, 4 and 5;
(c) where radio equipment is not within the scope of subparagraph (a) above and the manufacturer has not applied harmonised standards or has applied them only in part, the conformity assessment procedures which may be chosen from are those laid down in Schedules 4 and 5.

(2) As an alternative to the procedures set out in paragraph (1), compliance of the apparatus with the essential requirements identified in—

(a) regulation 4(2)(a) may be demonstrated by using the procedures specified in Council Directive 73/23/EEC, and

(b) regulation 4(2)(b) may be demonstrated by using the procedures specified in Article 10(1) and 10(2) of Directive 89/336/EEC,

where apparatus is within the scope of either of those Directives.

(3) Any technical documentation or other information in relation to apparatus required to be retained under the conformity assessment procedure used shall be retained by the person specified in that respect in that conformity assessment procedure for the appropriate period specified in that procedure.

[4346]

10 CE marking

(1) In these Regulations, "the CE marking" means a marking in the form set out in paragraph 1 of Annex VII as set out in Schedule 7.

(2) The CE marking shall be accompanied by—

(a) the identification number of all notified bodies used where the conformity assessment procedure is carried out in accordance with Schedule 3, 4 or 5;

(b) in the case of radio equipment, the equipment class identifier where one has been assigned.

[(3) There shall be marked on the apparatus

(a) the name of the responsible person;

(b) the type identification of the apparatus; and

(c) the batch or serial number assigned to the apparatus by the manufacturer.]

(4) Where apparatus is subject to other directives concerning other aspects and which also provide for the affixing of the CE marking, the markings shall indicate that the apparatus in question is also presumed to conform to the provisions of those other directives. However, should one or more of those directives allow the manufacturer, during a transitional period, to choose which arrangements to apply, the CE marking shall indicate conformity to the provisions only of those directives applied by the manufacturer. In this case the particulars of those directives, as published in the Official Journal, must be given in the documents, notices or instructions required by those directives and accompanying such products.

(5) Subject to paragraph (6) any other marking may be affixed to apparatus provided that the visibility and legibility of the CE marking is not thereby reduced.

(6) The affixing of markings on apparatus which are likely to mislead third parties as to the meaning or form of the CE marking is prohibited.

[4347]

NOTES

Para (3): substituted by the Radio Equipment and Telecommunications Terminal Equipment (Amendment) Regulations 2003, SI 2003/1903, reg 2(1), (8).

11 Information accompanying apparatus

There shall be prominently displayed on or accompany the apparatus information for the user as follows—

(a) in the case of all apparatus—

(i) its intended use; and

(ii) a declaration of its conformity to the applicable essential requirements;

(b) in the case of radio equipment, sufficient information on the packaging and the instructions for use to identify the Member States or the geographical area within the Member States where it is intended to be used; and marking on the apparatus as provided for in paragraph 5 of Schedule 7 shall be used when appropriate to alert the user that restrictions or requirements for authorisation of the use of the radio equipment apply in certain Member States;

(c) in the case of telecommunications terminal equipment, sufficient information to identify the interfaces of public telecommunications networks to which the equipment is intended to be connected.

[4348]

12 Notice to be given to [OFCOM] before placing radio equipment on the market

(1) The responsible person shall, not less than four weeks before the date it is intended to place on the market in the United Kingdom radio equipment using frequency bands whose use is not harmonised throughout the Community, give notice in writing to the [OFCOM] which contains—

(a) such information as is required by the [OFCOM] about the radio characteristics of the equipment, in particular its frequency bands, channel spacing, type of modulation and RF power; and

(b) where appropriate the identification number of all the notified bodies used.

(2) Notice given under paragraph (1) shall be effective in respect of all items of equipment, whether placed on the market at the same time or at different times, which are in all material respects identical to each other.

[4349]

NOTES

Section heading, para (1): words in square brackets substituted by the Radio Equipment and Telecommunications Terminal Equipment (Amendment No 2) Regulations 2003, SI 2003/3144, reg 2(1), (4).

[13 Publication of and access to information

(1) Subject to paragraph (7) below, each public telecommunications network operator shall, in relation to all interfaces in use by the operator at the time this regulation comes into force, notify such interfaces to [OFCOM] and publish within 90 days of this regulation coming into force, in an accurate and adequate manner, the technical specifications of the interfaces in accordance with paragraph (5) below.

(2) Before services are provided through any interface which is not published under paragraph (1) above the public telecommunications network operator shall

(a) notify such interface to [OFCOM]; and

(b) publish the technical specification of the interface in an accurate and adequate manner and in accordance with paragraph (5) below.

(3) Where any interface to which paragraph (1) or (2) above applies is modified by the public telecommunications network operator

(a) he shall notify such modification to [OFCOM] and publish such modification in an accurate and adequate manner and in accordance with paragraph (5) below; and

(b) the modification shall include any change in the description of any interface which may affect the maintenance of effective interoperability of services by means of the interface.

(4) Where any interface to which paragraph (1) or (2) above applies is withdrawn, the public telecommunications network operator shall notify such withdrawal to [OFCOM] and publish such withdrawal in accordance with paragraph (5) below.

(5) The requirements as to publication are that

(a) the interface specification published shall

(i) be in sufficient detail to permit the design of telecommunications terminal equipment capable of utilising all services provided through the corresponding interface;

(ii) detail any changes in existing interfaces; and

(iii) include, inter alia, all the information necessary to allow manufacturers to carry out, at their choice, the relevant tests for the essential requirements applicable to the telecommunications terminal equipment; and

(b) the interface specification shall be made readily available by the public telecommunications network operator.

[(6) If, following any representation made to it OFCOM concludes that any interface specification contains insufficient information for the purpose of paragraph (5), OFCOM may direct the public telecommunications network operator to

(a) amend the interface specification in order to remedy the defect; and

(b) publish the amended interface specification in accordance with the provisions of paragraph (5).]

(7) Nothing in this regulation shall require the public telecommunications network operator to publish or send to [OFCOM] information which it has already published or sent to [OFCOM].]

[4350]

NOTES

Commencement: 25 July 2003.

Substituted by the Radio Equipment and Telecommunications Terminal Equipment (Amendment) Regulations 2003, SI 2003/1903, reg 2(1), (9).

Paras (1)–(4), (7): words in square brackets substituted by the Radio Equipment and Telecommunications Terminal Equipment (Amendment No 2) Regulations 2003, SI 2003/3144, reg 2(1), (2).

Para (6): substituted by SI 2003/3144, reg 2(1), (5).

14 Notified bodies

For the purposes of these Regulations, a notified body is a body which has been—

(a) appointed as a notified body pursuant to regulation 15; or

(b) appointed by a Member State other than the United Kingdom and notified to the Commission and the other Member States pursuant to Article 11 of the Directive

[(c) recognised for the purpose of carrying out those functions by inclusion in a mutual recognition agreement relating to the Directive or a similar agreement (including a Protocol to the Europe Agreement, or other Agreement, on Conformity Assessment and Acceptance of Industrial Products) which has been concluded between the European Union and a State other than an EEA State.]

[4351]

NOTES

Para (c) added by the Radio Equipment and Telecommunications Terminal Equipment (Amendment) Regulations 2003, SI 2003/1903, reg 2(1), (10).

15 Notified bodies appointed by the Secretary of State

(1) The Secretary of State, applying the criteria in Schedule 6 and such other criteria as he thinks fit, may from time to time appoint such persons as he thinks fit to be notified bodies.

(2) An appointment—

(a) may relate to such descriptions of apparatus as the Secretary of State may from time to time determine;

(b) may be made subject to such conditions as the Secretary of State may from time to time determine, and such conditions may include conditions which are to apply upon or following termination of the appointment;

(c) shall, without prejudice to the generality of subparagraph (b) and subject to paragraph (4), require the appointed body to carry out the procedures and specific tasks for which it has been appointed including (where so provided as part of those procedures) surveillance to ensure that the responsible person duly fulfils the obligations arising out of the relevant conformity assessment procedure;

(d) shall be terminated upon 90 days' notice in writing given to the Secretary of State by the notified body; and

(e) may be terminated if it appears to the Secretary of State that any of the conditions of the appointment are not complied with.

(3) Subject to paragraph (2)(d) and (e), an appointment under this regulation may be for the time being or for such period as may be specified in the appointment.

(4) A notified body appointed by the Secretary of State shall not be required to carry out the functions referred to in paragraph (2)(c) if—

(a) the documents submitted to it in relation to carrying out such functions are not in English or another language acceptable to that body; or

(b) the responsible person has not submitted with his application the amount of the fee which the body requires to be submitted with the application pursuant to regulation 16.

(5) If for any reason the appointment of a notified body is terminated under this regulation, the Secretary of State may—

(a) give such directions (either to the body the subject of the termination or to another notified body) for the purpose of making such arrangements for the determination of outstanding applications as he considers appropriate; and

(b) without prejudice to the generality of the foregoing, authorise another notified body to take over its functions in respect of such cases as he may specify.

[4352]

16 Fees

(1) A notified body appointed by the Secretary of State may charge such fees in connection with, or incidental to, the performance of its functions as it may determine: provided that such fees shall not exceed the sum of the following—

(a) the costs incurred or to be incurred by the notified body in performing the relevant function; and

(b) an amount on account of profit which is reasonable in the circumstances having regard to—

(i) the character and extent of the work done or to be done by the body on behalf of the applicant; and

(ii) the commercial rate normally charged on account of profit for that work or similar work.

(2) A notified body may require the payment of fees or a reasonable estimate thereof in advance of carrying out the work requested by the applicant.

[4353]

17 (*Revoked by the Radio Equipment and Telecommunications Terminal Equipment (Amendment) Regulations 2003, SI 2003/1903, reg 2(1), (11).*)

PART IV
ENFORCEMENT

18 Enforcement Notices

(1) [Subject to paragraphs (2) and (5),] Schedule 9 shall have effect for the purposes of providing for the enforcement of these Regulations and for matters incidental thereto.

(2) Except in the case of apparatus which, in the opinion of an enforcement authority, is liable to endanger the safety of persons and, where appropriate, of property, where an enforcement authority has reasonable grounds for suspecting that the CE marking has been affixed to apparatus in relation to which any provision of these Regulations has not been complied with, it may serve notice in writing on—

(a) the manufacturer of the apparatus or his authorised representative established within the Community; or

(b) in a case where neither the manufacturer of the apparatus nor his authorised representative established within the Community has placed the apparatus on the market, the person who places it on the market in the United Kingdom;

and subject to paragraph (3), no other action pursuant to Schedule 9 may be taken in respect of apparatus until such notice has been given and the person to whom it is given has failed to comply with its requirements.

(3) Notwithstanding the provisions of paragraph (2), for the purpose of ascertaining whether or not the CE marking has been correctly affixed, action may be taken pursuant to [paragraph 8 of Schedule 9].

(4) A notice which is given under paragraph (2) shall—

(a) state that the enforcement authority suspects that the CE marking has not been correctly affixed to the apparatus;

(b) specify the respect in which it is so suspected and give particulars thereof;

(c) require the person to whom the notice is given—

(i) to secure that any apparatus to which the notice relates conforms as regards the provisions concerning the correct affixation of the CE marking within such period as may be specified in the notice; or

(ii) to provide evidence within that period, to the satisfaction of the enforcement authority, that the CE marking has been correctly affixed; and

(d) warn that person that if the non-conformity continues after, or if satisfactory evidence has not been provided within, the period specified in the notice, further action may be taken under the Regulations in respect of that apparatus or apparatus of the same type placed on the market by that person.

[(5) Sections 94–97 [and section 98(1)–(3)] of the Communications Act 2003 shall apply for the purposes of the enforcement of regulations 7 and 13 above as if the requirements in those regulations were conditions set under section 45 of that Act.]

[4354]

NOTES

Para (1): words in square brackets substituted by the Radio Equipment and Telecommunications Terminal Equipment (Amendment) Regulations 2003, SI 2003/1903, reg 2(1), (12)(a).

Para (3): words in square brackets substituted by the Radio Equipment and Telecommunications Terminal Equipment (Amendment No 2) Regulations 2003, SI 2003/3144, reg 2(1), (6)(a).

Para (5): added by SI 2003/1903, reg 2(1), (12)(b); words in square brackets inserted by SI 2003/3144, reg 2(1), (6)(b).

[18A Duty of enforcement authority to inform Secretary of State of action taken

An enforcement authority shall, where action has been taken by it to prohibit or restrict the supply or taking into service (whether under these Regulations or otherwise) of any relevant apparatus, forthwith inform the Secretary of State of the action taken, and the reasons for it, with a view to this information being passed by her to the Commission.]

[4355]

NOTES

Commencement: 29 December 2003.

Inserted by the Radio Equipment and Telecommunications Terminal Equipment (Amendment No 2) Regulations 2003, SI 2003/3144, reg 2(1), (7).

19 Offences

[(1)] Any person who—

(a) [(subject to paragraph (2))] contravenes or fails to comply with regulation 5(1) or 12; or

(b) fails to supply or retain a copy of the appropriate documentation as required by regulation 9(3),

shall be guilty of an offence.

[(2) No offence shall be committed merely by reason of failure to comply with regulation 12 in respect of equipment which uses frequency bands the use of which by that equipment is consistent with the United Kingdom Plan for Frequency Authorisation published under section 153 of the Communications Act 2003.]

[4356]

NOTES

Para (1): numbered as such, and words in square brackets inserted, by the Radio Equipment and Telecommunications Terminal Equipment (Amendment) Regulations 2003, SI 2003/1903, reg 2(1), (13)(a), (b).

Para (2): added by SI 2003/1903, reg 2(1), (13)(c).

20 Penalties

(1) A person guilty of an offence under regulation 19(a) shall be liable on summary conviction—

(a) to imprisonment for a term not exceeding 3 months; or

(b) to a fine not exceeding level 5 on the standard scale,

or to both.

(2) A person guilty of an offence under regulation 19(b) shall be liable on summary conviction to a fine not exceeding level 5 on the standard scale.

[4357]

21 Defence of due diligence

(1) Subject to the following provisions of this regulation, in proceedings against any person for an offence under regulation 19 [or paragraph 11(1) of Schedule 9] above it shall be a defence for that person to show that he took all reasonable steps and exercised all due diligence to avoid committing the offence.

(2) Where in any proceedings against any person for such an offence the defence provided in paragraph (1) involves an allegation that the commission of the offence was due—

(a) to the act or default of another; or

(b) to reliance on information given by another,

that person shall not, without the leave of the court, be entitled to rely on the defence unless, not less than seven clear days before the hearing of the proceedings (or, in Scotland, the trial diet), he has served a notice under paragraph (3) on the person bringing the proceedings.

(3) A notice under this paragraph shall give such information identifying or assisting in the identification of the person who committed the act or default or gave the information as is in the possession of the person serving the notice at the time he serves it.

(4) It is hereby declared that a person shall not be entitled to rely on the defence provided in paragraph (1) by reason of his reliance on information supplied by another, unless he shows that it was reasonable in all the circumstances for him to have relied on the information, having regard in particular—

(a) to the steps which he took, and those which might reasonably have been taken, for the purpose of verifying the information; and

(b) to whether he had any reason to disbelieve the information.

[4358]

NOTES

Para (1): words in square brackets inserted by the Radio Equipment and Telecommunications Terminal Equipment (Amendment No 2) Regulations 2003, SI 2003/3144, reg 2(1), (8).

22 Liability of persons other than the principal offender

(1) Where the commission by any person of an offence under regulation 19 [or paragraph 11(1) of Schedule 9] is due to the act or default committed by some other person in the course of any business of his, the other person shall be guilty of the offence and may be proceeded against and punished by virtue of this paragraph whether or not proceedings are taken against the first-mentioned person.

(2) Where a body corporate is guilty of an offence under these Regulations (including where it is so guilty by virtue of paragraph (1)) in respect of any act or default which is shown to have been committed with the consent or connivance of, or to be attributable to any neglect on the part of, any director, manager, secretary or other similar officer of the body corporate or any person who was purporting to act in any such capacity he, as well as the body corporate, shall be guilty of that offence and shall be liable to be proceeded against and punished accordingly.

(3) Where the affairs of a body corporate are managed by its members, paragraph (2) shall apply in relation to the acts and defaults of a member in connection with his functions of management as if he were a director of the body corporate.

(4) In this regulation, references to a "body corporate" include references to a partnership in Scotland and, in relation to such partnership, any reference to a director, manager, secretary or other similar officer of a body corporate is a reference to a partner.

[4359]

NOTES

Para (1): words in square brackets inserted by the Radio Equipment and Telecommunications Terminal Equipment (Amendment No 2) Regulations 2003, SI 2003/3144, reg 2(1), (9).

23 Savings for action taken under other enactments

Nothing in these Regulations shall be construed as preventing the taking of any action in respect of any relevant apparatus under the provisions of any other enactment.

[4360]

SCHEDULES

(*Schs 1–7 set out Directive 99/5/EC, Annexes I–VII, at* **[3724]–[3730]***; Sch 8 revoked by the Radio Equipment and Telecommunications Terminal Equipment (Amendment) Regulations 2003, SI 2003/1903, reg 2(1), (14).*)

[SCHEDULE 9
ENFORCEMENT

Regulation 18

PART I

Enforcement authorities

1. It shall be the duty of the following authorities to enforce these Regulations:
   (1) in Great Britain:
      (a) OFCOM, insofar as action taken to enforce a regulation relates to the protection and management of the radio spectrum; and
      (b) a local weights and measures authority within their area; and
   (2) in Northern Ireland:
      (a) OFCOM, insofar as action taken to enforce a regulation relates to the protection and management of the radio spectrum; and
      (b) the district councils within their area.

2. The Secretary of State may enforce these Regulations.

3. In this Schedule—

"Local weights and measures authority" has the meaning given by section 69 of the Weights and Measures Act 1985.

4. Nothing in these Regulations shall authorise any enforcement authority to bring proceedings in Scotland for an offence.]

[4361]

NOTES

Commencement: 29 December 2003.

Substituted by the Radio Equipment and Telecommunications Terminal Equipment (Amendment No 2) Regulations 2003, SI 2003/3144, reg 2(1), (10).

[PART II

Enforcement in Great Britain

5 Suspension notices

(1) Where an enforcement authority has reasonable grounds for suspecting that any regulation has been contravened in relation to any apparatus, the authority may serve a notice ("a suspension notice") prohibiting the person on whom it is served, for such period ending not more than six months after the date of the notice as is specified therein, from doing any of the following things without the consent of the authority, that is to say, supplying the apparatus, offering to supply it, agreeing to supply it or exposing it for supply.

(2) A suspension notice served by an enforcement authority in respect of any apparatus shall—

(a) describe the apparatus in a manner sufficient to identify it;

(b) set out the grounds on which the authority suspects that a regulation has been contravened in relation to the apparatus; and

(c) state that, and the manner in which, the person on whom the notice is served may appeal against the notice under paragraph 6 below.

(3) A suspension notice served by an enforcement authority for the purpose of prohibiting a person for any period from doing the things mentioned in sub-paragraph (1) above in relation to any apparatus may also require that person to keep the authority informed of the whereabouts throughout that period of any of the apparatus in which he has an interest.

(4) Where a suspension notice has been served on any person in respect of any apparatus, no further such notice shall be served on that person in respect of the same apparatus unless—

(a) proceedings against that person for an offence in respect of a contravention in relation to the apparatus of a regulation (not being an offence under this subparagraph); or

PART VI TELECOMMUNICATIONS

(b) proceedings for the forfeiture of the apparatus under paragraph 21 or 22 below,

are pending at the end of the period specified in the first-mentioned notice.

(5) A consent given by an enforcement authority for the purposes of sub-paragraph (1) above may impose such conditions on the doing of anything for which the consent is required as the authority considers appropriate.

(6) Any person who contravenes a suspension notice shall be guilty of an offence and liable on summary conviction to imprisonment for a term not exceeding three months or to a fine not exceeding level 5 on the standard scale or to both.

(7) Where an enforcement authority serves a suspension notice in respect of any apparatus, the authority shall be liable to pay compensation to any person having an interest in the apparatus in respect of any loss or damage caused by reason of the service of the notice if—

- (a) there has been no contravention in relation to the apparatus of any regulation; and
- (b) the exercise of the power is not attributable to any neglect or default by that person.

(8) Any disputed question as to the right to or the amount of any compensation payable under this paragraph shall be determined by arbitration or, in Scotland, by a single arbiter appointed, failing agreement between the parties, by the sheriff.

6 Appeals against suspension notices

(1) Any person having an interest in any apparatus in respect of which a suspension notice is for the time being in force may apply for an order setting aside the notice.

(2) An application under this paragraph may be made—

- (a) to any magistrates' court in which proceedings have been brought in England and Wales or Northern Ireland—
  - (i) for an offence in respect of a contravention in relation to the apparatus of any regulation; or
  - (ii) for the forfeiture of the apparatus under paragraph 21 below;
- (b) where no such proceedings have been so brought, by way of complaint to a magistrates' court; or
- (c) in Scotland, by summary application to the sheriff.

(3) On an application under this paragraph to a magistrates' court in England and Wales or Northern Ireland the court shall make an order setting aside the suspension notice only if the court is satisfied that there has been no contravention in relation to the apparatus of any regulation.

(4) On an application under this paragraph to the sheriff he shall make an order setting aside the suspension notice only if he is satisfied that at the date of making the order—

- (a) proceedings for an offence in respect of a contravention in relation to the apparatus of any regulation; or
- (b) proceedings for the forfeiture of the apparatus under paragraph 22 below,

have not been brought or, having been brought, have been concluded.

(5) Any person aggrieved by an order made under this paragraph by a magistrates' court in England and Wales or Northern Ireland, or by a decision of such a court not to make such an order, may appeal against that order or decision—

- (a) in England and Wales, to the Crown Court;
- (b) in Northern Ireland, to the county court;

and an order so made may contain such provision as appears to the court to be appropriate for delaying the coming into force of the order pending the making and determination of any appeal (including any application under section 111 of the Magistrates' Courts Act 1980 or Article 146 of the Magistrates' Courts (Northern Ireland) Order 1981 (statement of case)).

7 Test purchases

(1) An enforcement authority shall have power, for the purpose of ascertaining whether any regulation has been contravened in relation to any apparatus to make, or to authorise an officer of the authority to make, any purchase of any apparatus.

(2) Where—

- (a) any apparatus purchased under this paragraph by or on behalf of an enforcement authority is submitted to a test; and

(b) the test leads to—
   (i) the bringing of proceedings for an offence in respect of a contravention in relation to the apparatus of any regulation or for the forfeiture of the apparatus under paragraph 21 or 22 below; or
   (ii) the serving of a suspension notice in respect of any apparatus; and
(c) the authority is requested to do so and it is practicable for the authority to comply with the request,

the authority shall allow the person from whom the apparatus was purchased or any person who is a party to the proceedings or has an interest in any apparatus to which the notice relates to have the apparatus tested.

8 Powers of search etc

(1) Subject to the following provisions of this Part, a duly authorised officer of an enforcement authority may at any reasonable hour and on production, if required, of his credentials exercise any of the powers conferred by the following provisions of this paragraph.

(2) The officer may, for the purposes of ascertaining whether there has been any contravention of any regulation, inspect any apparatus and enter any premises other than premises occupied only as a person's residence.

(3) The officer may, for the purpose of ascertaining whether there has been any contravention of any regulation, examine any procedure (including any arrangements for carrying out a test) connected with the production of any apparatus.

(4) If the officer has reasonable grounds for suspecting that there has been a contravention in relation to any apparatus of any regulation, he may—
(a) for the purpose of ascertaining whether there has been any such contravention, require any person carrying on a business, or employed in connection with a business, to produce any documents or information relating to the business;
(b) for the purpose of ascertaining (by testing or otherwise) whether there has been any such contravention, seize and detain the apparatus;
(c) take copies of, or any entry in, any records produced by virtue of sub-paragraph (a) above.

(5) The officer may seize and detain—
(a) any apparatus or records which he has reasonable grounds for believing may be required as evidence in proceedings for an offence in respect of a contravention of any regulation;
(b) any apparatus which he has reasonable grounds for suspecting may be liable to be forfeited under paragraph 21 or 22 below.

(6) If and to the extent that it is reasonably necessary to do so to prevent a contravention of any regulation, the officer may, for the purpose of exercising his power under sub-paragraph (4) or (5) above to seize any apparatus or documents or information—
(a) require any person having authority to do so to open any container; and
(b) himself open or break open any such container where a requirement made under sub-paragraph (a) above in relation to the container has not been complied with.

9 Provisions supplemental to paragraph 8

(1) An officer seizing any apparatus or records under paragraph 8 above shall inform the following persons that the apparatus or documents or information have been so seized, that is to say—
(a) the person from whom they are seized; and
(b) in the case of imported apparatus seized on any premises under the control of the Commissioners of Customs and Excise, the importer of the apparatus (within the meaning of the Customs and Excise Management Act 1979).

(2) If a justice of the peace—
(a) is satisfied by any written information on oath that there are reasonable grounds for believing either—
   (i) that any apparatus or documents or information which any officer has power to inspect under paragraph 8 above are on any premises and that their inspection is likely to disclose evidence that there has been a contravention of any regulation; or
   (ii) that such a contravention has taken place, is taking place or is about to take place on any premises; and

PART VI TELECOMMUNICATIONS

(b) is also satisfied by any such information either—

(i) that admission to the premises has been or is likely to be refused and that notice of intention to apply for a warrant under this sub-paragraph has been given to the occupier; or

(ii) that an application for admission, or the giving of such a notice, would defeat the object of the entry or that the premises are unoccupied or that the occupier is temporarily absent and it might defeat the object of the entry to await his return,

the justice may by warrant under his hand, which shall continue in force for a period of one month, authorise any officer of an enforcement authority to enter the premises, if need be by force.

(3) An officer entering any premises by virtue of paragraph 8 above or a warrant under sub-paragraph (2) above may take with him such other persons and such equipment as may appear to him necessary.

(4) On leaving any premises which a person is authorised to enter by a warrant under sub-paragraph (2) above, that person shall, if the premises are unoccupied or the occupier is temporarily absent, leave the premises as effectively secured against trespassers as he found them.

(5) If any person who is not an officer of an enforcement authority purports to act as such under paragraph 8 or this paragraph he shall be guilty of an offence and liable on summary conviction to a fine not exceeding level 5 on the standard scale.

(6) Where any apparatus seized by an officer under paragraph 8 above is submitted to a test, the officer shall inform the persons mentioned in sub-paragraph (1) above of the result of the test and, if—

(a) proceedings are brought for an offence in respect of a contravention in relation to the apparatus of any regulation or for the forfeiture of the apparatus under paragraph 21 or 22, or a suspension notice is served in respect of any apparatus; and

(b) the officer is requested to do so and it is practicable to comply with the request,

the officer shall allow any person who is a party to the proceedings or, as the case may be, has an interest in the apparatus to which the notice relates to have the apparatus tested.

(7) In the application of this paragraph to Scotland, the reference in sub-paragraph (2) above to a justice of the peace shall include a reference to a sheriff and the references to written information on oath shall be construed as references to evidence on oath.

(8) In the application of this paragraph to Northern Ireland, the references in sub-paragraph (2) above to any information on oath shall be construed as references to any complaint on oath.

10 Power of customs officer to detain apparatus

(1) A customs officer may, for the purpose of facilitating the exercise by an enforcement authority or officer of such an authority of any functions conferred on the authority or officer by or under this Schedule in its application for the purposes of these Regulations, seize any imported apparatus and detain it for not more than two working days.

(2) Anything seized and detained under this paragraph shall be dealt with during the period of its detention in such manner as the Commissioners of Customs and Excise may direct.

(3) In sub-paragraph (1) above the reference to two working days is a reference to a period of forty-eight hours calculated from the time when the apparatus in question is seized but disregarding so much of any period as falls on a Saturday or Sunday or on Christmas Day, Good Friday or a day which is a bank holiday under the Banking and Financial Dealings Act 1971 in the part of the United Kingdom where the apparatus is seized.

(4) In this paragraph and paragraph 11 below "customs officer" means any officer within the meaning of the Customs and Excise Management Act 1979.

11 Obstruction of authorised officer

(1) Subject to regulations 21 and 22 any person who—

(a) intentionally obstructs any officer of an enforcement authority who is acting in pursuance of any provision of this Part or any customs officer who is so acting; or

(b) intentionally fails to comply with any requirement made of him by any officer of an enforcement authority under any provision of this Part of this Schedule; or

(c) without reasonable cause fails to give any officer of an enforcement authority who is so acting any other assistance or information which the officer may reasonably require of him for the purposes of the exercise of the officer's functions under any provision of this Part of this Schedule,

shall be guilty of an offence and liable on summary conviction to a fine not exceeding level 5 on the standard scale.

(2) A person shall be guilty of an offence if, in giving any information which is required of him by virtue of sub-paragraph (1)(c) above—

(a) he makes any statement which he knows is false in a material particular; or

(b) he recklessly makes a statement which is false in a material particular.

(3) A person guilty of an offence under sub-paragraph (2) above shall be liable—

(a) on conviction on indictment, to a fine;

(b) on summary conviction, to a fine not exceeding the statutory maximum.

12 Appeals against detention of apparatus

(1) Any person having an interest in any apparatus which is for the time being detained under any provision of this Part of this Schedule by an enforcement authority or by an officer of such an authority may apply for an order requiring the apparatus to be released to him or to another person.

(2) An application under this paragraph may be made—

(a) to any magistrates' court in which proceedings have been brought in England and Wales or Northern Ireland—

(i) for an offence in respect of a contravention in relation to the apparatus of any regulation; or

(ii) for the forfeiture of the apparatus under paragraph 21;

(b) where no such proceedings have been so brought, by way of complaint to a magistrates' court; or

(c) in Scotland, by summary application to the sheriff.

(3) On an application under this paragraph to a magistrates' court or to the sheriff, an order requiring apparatus to be released shall be made only if the court or sheriff is satisfied—

(a) that proceedings—

(i) for an offence in respect of a contravention in relation to the apparatus of any regulation; or

(ii) for the forfeiture of the apparatus under paragraph 21 or 22,

have not been brought or, having been brought, have been concluded without the apparatus being forfeited; and

(b) where no such proceedings have been brought, that more than six months have elapsed since the apparatus was seized.

(4) Any person aggrieved by an order made under this paragraph by a magistrates' court in England and Wales or Northern Ireland, or by a decision of such a court not to make such an order, may appeal against that order or decision—

(a) in England and Wales, to the Crown Court;

(b) in Northern Ireland, to the county court;

and an order so made may contain such provision as appears to the court to be appropriate for delaying the coming into force of the order pending the making and determination of any appeal (including any application under section 111 of the Magistrates' Courts Act 1980 or Article 146 of the Magistrates' Courts (Northern Ireland) Order 1981 (statement of case)).

13 Compensation for seizure and detention

(1) Where an officer of an enforcement authority exercises any power under paragraph 8 above to seize and detain apparatus, the enforcement authority shall be liable to pay compensation to any person having an interest in the apparatus in respect of any loss or damage caused by reason of the exercise of the power if—

(a) there has been no contravention in relation to the apparatus of any regulation; and

(b) the exercise of the power is not attributable to any neglect or default by that person.

(2) Any disputed question as to the right to or the amount of any compensation payable under this paragraph shall be determined by arbitration or, in Scotland, by a single arbiter appointed, failing agreement between the parties, by the sheriff.

14 Recovery of expenses of enforcement

(1) This paragraph shall apply where a court—
- (a) convicts a person of an offence in respect of a contravention in relation to any apparatus of any regulation; or
- (b) makes an order under paragraph 21 or 22 for the forfeiture of any apparatus.

(2) The court may (in addition to any other order it may make as to costs or expenses) order the person convicted or, as the case may be, any person having an interest in the apparatus to reimburse an enforcement authority for any expenditure which has been or may be incurred by that authority—
- (a) in connection with any seizure or detention of the apparatus by or on behalf of the authority; or
- (b) in connection with any compliance by the authority with directions given by the court for the purposes of any order for the forfeiture of the apparatus.

15 Power of Commissioners of Customs and Excise to disclose information

(1) If they think it appropriate to do so for the purpose of facilitating the exercise by any person to whom sub-paragraph (2) below applies of any functions conferred on that person by or under these Regulations, the Commissioners of Customs and Excise may authorise the disclosure to that person of any information obtained for the purposes of the exercise by the Commissioners of their functions in relation to imported apparatus.

(2) This sub-paragraph applies to an enforcement authority and to any officer of an enforcement authority.

(3) A disclosure of information made to any person under sub-paragraph (1) above shall be made in such manner as may be directed by the Commissioners of Customs and Excise and may be made through such persons acting on behalf of that person as may be so directed.

(4) Information may be disclosed to a person under sub-paragraph (1) above whether or not the disclosure of the information has been requested by or on behalf of that person.

16 Service of documents etc

(1) Any document required or authorised by virtue of this Schedule to be served on a person may be so served—
- (a) by delivering it to him or by leaving it at his proper address or by sending it by post to him at that address; or
- (b) if a person is a body corporate, by serving it in accordance with paragraph (a) above on the secretary or clerk of that body; or
- (c) if the person is a partnership, by serving it in accordance with that paragraph on a partner or on a person having control or management of the partnership business.

(2) For the purposes of sub-paragraph (1) above, and for the purposes of section 7 of the Interpretation Act 1978 (which relates to the service of documents by post) in its application to that sub-paragraph, the proper address of any person on whom a document is to be served by virtue of this Schedule shall be his last known address except that—
- (a) in the case of service on a body corporate or its secretary or clerk, it shall be the address of the registered or principal office of the body corporate;
- (b) in the case of service on a partnership or a partner or a person having the control or management of a partnership business, it shall be the principal office of the partnership;

and for the purposes of this sub-paragraph the principal office of a company registered outside the United Kingdom or of a partnership carrying on business outside the United Kingdom is its principal office within the United Kingdom.

17 Savings for certain privileges

(1) Nothing in this Schedule shall be taken as requiring any person to produce any records if he would be entitled to refuse to produce those records in any proceedings in any court on the grounds that they are the subject of legal professional privilege or, in Scotland, that they contain a confidential communication made by or to an advocate or solicitor in that capacity, or as authorising any person to take possession of any records which are in the possession of a person who would be so entitled.

(2) Nothing in this Schedule shall be construed as requiring a person to answer any question or give any information if to do so would incriminate that person or that person's spouse.

18 Commencement of proceedings

In England and Wales, a magistrates' court may try an information in respect of an offence committed under these Regulations if the information is laid within twelve months from the time when the offence is committed, and in Scotland summary proceedings for such an offence may be begun at any time within twelve months from the time when the offence is committed.

Enforcement in Northern Ireland

19 The provisions of paragraphs 5 to 17 shall have effect.

20 Commencement of proceedings

A magistrates' court may try a complaint in respect of an offence committed under these Regulations if the complaint is made within twelve months from the time when the offence is committed.

21 Forfeiture of apparatus: England and Wales and Northern Ireland

(1) An enforcement authority in England and Wales or Northern Ireland may apply under this paragraph for an order for the forfeiture of any apparatus on the grounds that there has been a contravention in relation thereto of regulation 5.

(2) An application under this paragraph may be made—

(a) where proceedings have been brought in a magistrates' court in respect of an offence in relation to some or all of the apparatus under regulation 19 to that court; and

(b) where no application for the forfeiture of the apparatus has been made under sub-paragraph (a), by way of complaint to a magistrates' court.

(3) On an application under this paragraph the court shall make an order for the forfeiture of the apparatus if it is satisfied that there has been a contravention in relation thereto of regulation 5.

(4) For the avoidance of doubt it is hereby declared that a court may infer for the purposes of this paragraph that there has been a contravention in relation to any apparatus of regulation 5 if it is satisfied that that regulation has been contravened in relation to any apparatus (whether by reason of being of the same design or part of the same consignment or batch or otherwise).

(5) Any person aggrieved by an order made under this paragraph by a magistrates' court, or by a decision of such court not to make such an order, may appeal against that order or decision—

(a) in England and Wales, to the Crown Court

(b) in Northern Ireland, to the county court,

and an order so made may contain such provision as appears to the court to be appropriate for delaying the coming into force of an order pending the making and determination of any appeal (including any application under paragraph 111 of the Magistrates' Courts Act 1980, or article 146 of the Magistrates' Courts (Northern Ireland) Order 1981 (statement of case)).

(6) Subject to sub-paragraph (7), where any apparatus is forfeited under this paragraph it shall be destroyed in accordance with such directions as the court may give.

(7) On making an order under this paragraph a magistrates' court may, if it considers it appropriate to do so, direct that the apparatus to which the order relates shall (instead of being destroyed) be released, to such person as the court may specify, on condition that that person—

(a) does not supply the apparatus to any person otherwise than—

(i) to a person who carries on a business of buying apparatus of the same description as the first mentioned product and repairing or reconditioning it; or

(ii) as scrap (that is to say, for the value of materials included in the apparatus rather than for the value of the apparatus itself); and

(b) complies with any order to pay costs or expenses which has been made against that person in the proceedings for the order for forfeiture.

22 Forfeiture of apparatus: Scotland

(1) In Scotland a sheriff may make an order for forfeiture of any apparatus for private use or consumption in relation to which there has been a contravention of any provision of regulation 5—

(a) on an application by the procurator-fiscal made in the manner specified in section 134 of the Criminal Procedure (Scotland) Act 1995, or

(b) where a person is convicted of any offence in respect of any such contravention, in addition to any other penalty which the sheriff may impose.

(2) The procurator-fiscal making an application under sub-paragraph (1)(a) shall serve on any person appearing to him to be the owner of, or otherwise to have an interest in, the apparatus to which the application relates a copy of the application, together with a notice giving him the opportunity to appear at the hearing of the application to show cause why the apparatus should not be forfeited.

(3) Service under sub-paragraph (2) shall be carried out, and such service may be proved, in the manner specified for citation of an accused in summary proceedings under the Criminal Procedure (Scotland) Act 1995.

(4) Any person upon whom a notice is served under sub-paragraph (2) and any other person claiming to be the owner of, or otherwise to have an interest in, the apparatus to which an application under this paragraph relates shall be entitled to appear at the hearing of the application to show cause why the apparatus should not be forfeited.

(5) The sheriff shall not make an order following an application under sub-paragraph (1)(a)—

(a) if any person on whom notice is served under sub-paragraph (2) does not appear, unless service of the notice on that person is proved; or

(b) if no notice under sub-paragraph (2) has been served, unless the court is satisfied that in the circumstances it was reasonable not to serve notice on any person.

(6) The sheriff shall make an order under this paragraph only if he is satisfied that there has been a contravention in relation to the apparatus of regulation 5.

(7) For the avoidance of doubt it is declared that the sheriff may infer for the purposes of this paragraph that there has been a contravention in relation to any apparatus of regulation 5 if he is satisfied that that regulation has been contravened in relation to an item of apparatus which is representative of that apparatus (whether by reason of being of the same design or part of the same consignment or batch or otherwise).

(8) Where an order for the forfeiture of any apparatus is made following an application by the procurator-fiscal under sub-paragraph (1)(a), any person who appeared, or was entitled to appear, to show cause why it should not be forfeited may, within twenty-one days of the making of the order, appeal to the High Court by Bill of Suspension on the ground of an alleged miscarriage of justice; and section 182(5)(a) to (e) of the Criminal Procedure (Scotland) Act 1995 shall apply to an appeal under this sub-paragraph as it applies to a stated case under Part X of that Act.

(9) An order following an application under sub-paragraph (1)(a) shall not take effect—

(a) until the end of the period of twenty-one days beginning with the day after the day on which the order was made; or

(b) if an appeal is made under sub-paragraph (8) within that period, until the appeal is determined or abandoned.

(10) An order under sub-paragraph (1)(b) shall not take effect—

(a) until the end of the period within which an appeal against the order could be brought under the Criminal Procedure (Scotland) Act 1995; or

(b) if an appeal is made within that period, until the appeal is determined or abandoned.

(11) Subject to sub-paragraph (12), apparatus forfeited under this paragraph shall be destroyed in accordance with such directions as the sheriff may give.

(12) If he thinks fit, the sheriff may direct the apparatus to be released to such person as he may specify, on condition that that person does not supply it to any person otherwise than—

(a) to a person who carries on a business of buying apparatus of the same description as the first-mentioned apparatus and repairing or re-conditioning it; or

(b) as scrap (that is to say, for the value of material included in the apparatus rather than for the value of the apparatus).]

[4362]

NOTES

Commencement: 29 December 2003.

Substituted by the Radio Equipment and Telecommunications Terminal Equipment (Amendment No 2) Regulations 2003, SI 2003/3144, reg 2(1), (10).

WIRELESS TELEGRAPHY (BROADBAND FIXED WIRELESS ACCESS LICENCES) REGULATIONS 2000

(SI 2000/2039)

NOTES

Made: 27 July 2000.

Authority: Wireless Telegraphy Act 1998, ss 3, 6.

Commencement: 18 August 2000.

ARRANGEMENT OF REGULATIONS

1 Citation and commencement

These Regulations may be cited as the Wireless Telegraphy (Broadband Fixed Wireless Access Licences) Regulations 2000 and shall come into force on 18th August 2000.

[4363]

2 Interpretation

In these Regulations—

"Broadband Fixed Wireless Access" means the provision by means of a wireless communications system of two-way wireless communications link over which data may be transmitted and received at rates of at least 2Mbits/second on demand and whereby end users gain access to other telecommunication systems;

"the licences" means in respect of each region of the United Kingdom as specified in Part 1 of the Schedule hereto three wireless telegraphy licences to establish or use radio transmitting and receiving stations or install or use apparatus for Broadband Fixed Wireless Access at the frequencies specified in Part 2 of the Schedule hereto and to be granted subject to the terms, conditions and limitations specified in a notice issued pursuant to regulation 4;

"Radiocommunications Agency's Internet Website" means the Radiocommunications Agency's website located at http://www.radio.gov.uk on the Internet; and

"wireless telegraphy licence" means any licence under the Wireless Telegraphy Act 1949 other than a television licence as defined in section 1(7) of that Act.

[4364]

3 Application of the Regulations

These Regulations shall have effect in relation to applications for, procedures for the grant of, and the provision of refunds of fees payable in accordance with the terms of, the licences.

[4365]

4 Notice

(1) Applications for the grant of the licences shall only be made in accordance with a procedure which is set out in a notice issued by the Secretary of State under these Regulations.

(2) A notice issued pursuant to paragraph (1) above shall—

(a) invite any body corporate to make an application to the Secretary of State to bid for a licence, in accordance with a specified procedure;

(b) specify criteria by which the Secretary of State shall determine whether an applicant is qualified to participate in a bidding procedure;

(c) specify criteria to determine whether a qualified applicant is associated with one or more other qualified applicants;

(d) specify criteria to determine whether any qualified applicants who fall within sub-paragraph (c) above shall be entitled to participate in the procedure referred to in sub-paragraph (e) below;

(e) specify a procedure by which qualified applicants may submit bids for licences;

(f) specify reserve prices for each of the licences;

(g) provide for the Secretary of State to determine minimum and maximum bids for each of the licences during the bidding procedure referred to in sub-paragraph (e) above;

(h) provide for payment of a deposit on submission of an application and for payment of one of or more additional deposits before a qualified applicant may submit a bid for a licence;

(i) provide for the payment of interest on the deposit and on any additional deposits;

(j) provide for the circumstances in which all, or part, of any deposit, and all, or part, of any interest which accrues to a deposit, is not to be refunded;

(k) specify the conditions which must be satisfied before a licence may be issued to a qualified applicant who submits the highest valid bid for a licence;

(l) provide for a qualified applicant who submits the highest valid bid for a licence to elect whether he wishes to pay such sum—

(i) as a single cash sum on issue of the licence; or

(ii) as one half of such sum on issue of the licence with the balance payable as periodic sums calculated in accordance with a specified formula;

(m) specify a guarantee which a qualified applicant who elects to pay the licence fee other than as a single cash sum is to provide to the Secretary of State on issue of the licence;

(n) provide for the other terms, provisions and limitations subject to which each of the licences is to be issued; and

(o) provide for the other conditions with which qualified applicants must comply to participate, or continue to participate, in the procedures referred to in sub-paragraph (e) above.

(3) A notice which is issued pursuant to paragraph (1) above shall be published by the Secretary of State on the Radiocommunications Agency's Internet Website.

[4366]

5 Refunds

The Secretary of State may, in such cases as he thinks fit, refund, in whole or in part, sums which have been paid to him in accordance with any provision of the licences.

[4367]

SCHEDULE

Regulation 2

PART 1
DESCRIPTION OF THE REGIONS

Column 1	*Column 2*
Region A	That area of the United Kingdom comprising Greater London;

Column 1	*Column 2*
Region B	That area of the United Kingdom comprising Greater Manchester, Merseyside and the county of Cheshire;
Region C	That area of the United Kingdom comprising the West Midlands, and the counties of Warwickshire, Staffordshire, Worcestershire, Shropshire and Herefordshire;
Region D	That area of the United Kingdom comprising the Isle of Wight and the counties of Hampshire, Berkshire and Oxfordshire;
Region E	That area of the United Kingdom comprising the counties of Essex, Hertfordshire and Buckinghamshire;
Region F	That area of the United Kingdom comprising the counties of Suffolk, Norfolk, Bedfordshire, Cambridgeshire and Northamptonshire;
Region G	That area of the United Kingdom comprising the counties of Derbyshire, Lincolnshire (other than the areas of the North Lincolnshire District Council and the North East Lincolnshire District Council), Leicestershire, Nottinghamshire and Rutland;
Region H	That area of the United Kingdom comprising the counties of Kent, Surrey, East Sussex and West Sussex;
Region I	That area of the United Kingdom comprising the East Riding of Yorkshire, North Yorkshire, South Yorkshire, West Yorkshire and the areas of the North Lincolnshire District Council and the North East Lincolnshire District Council;
Region J	That area of the United Kingdom comprising Tyne and Wear, and the counties of Durham, Northumberland, Cumbria and Lancashire;
Region K	That area of the United Kingdom comprising Bristol and the counties of Devon, Cornwall and the Isles of Scilly, Dorset, Somerset, Wiltshire and Gloucestershire;
Region L	Scotland
Region M	Wales
Region N	Northern Ireland

[4368]

PART 2
DESCRIPTION OF THE FREQUENCIES FOR EACH OF THE LICENCES IN EACH OF THE REGIONS SPECIFIED IN PART 1 ABOVE

Column	*1*	*2*
	(GHz)	(GHz)
Licence 1	28.0525–28.1645	29.0605–29.1725
Licence 2	28.1925–28.3045	29.2005–29.3125
Licence 3	28.3325–28.4445	29.3405–29.4525

[4369]

WIRELESS TELEGRAPHY (PUBLIC FIXED WIRELESS ACCESS LICENCES) REGULATIONS 2002

(SI 2002/1911)

NOTES
Made: 22 July 2002.
Authority: Wireless Telegraphy Act 1998, ss 3, 6.
Commencement: 12 August 2002.

ARRANGEMENT OF REGULATIONS

1 Citation and commencement

These Regulations may be cited as the Wireless Telegraphy (Public Fixed Wireless Access Licences) Regulations 2002 and shall come into force on 12th August 2002.

[4370]

NOTES
Commencement: 12 August 2002.

2 Interpretation

In these Regulations—

"the licences" means, in respect of each region of the United Kingdom as designated in the first column of Part I of the Schedule hereto and described by reference to the postcode areas and part areas (hereinafter referred to as "sectors") specified in the second column thereof, the wireless telegraphy licences specified in the third column thereof being licences to establish or use radio transmitting and receiving stations or install or use apparatus for Public Fixed Wireless Access at the frequencies specified in relation to each licence in Part II of the Schedule hereto and to be granted subject to the terms, provisions and limitations specified in a notice issued pursuant to regulation 4;

"Public Fixed Wireless Access" means the provision by means of a wireless communications system of wireless communications links over which data may be transmitted and received on demand and whereby end-users gain access to other telecommunication systems;

"Radiocommunications Agency's Internet Website" means the Radiocommunications Agency's website located at www.radio.gov.uk on the Internet;

"telecommunication system" has the same meaning as in section 4(1) of the Telecommunications Act 1984; and

"wireless telegraphy licence" means any licence granted under the Wireless Telegraphy Act 1949 other than a television licence as defined in section 1(7) of that Act.

[4371]

NOTES
Commencement: 12 August 2002.

3 Application of the Regulations

These Regulations shall have effect in relation to applications for, procedures for the grant of, and the provision of refunds of fees payable in accordance with the terms of, the licences.

[4372]

NOTES
Commencement: 12 August 2002.

4 Notice

(1) Applications for the grant of the licences shall only be made in accordance with a procedure which is set out in a notice issued by the Secretary of State under these Regulations.

(2) A notice issued pursuant to paragraph (1) shall—
- (a) invite any body corporate to make an application to the Secretary of State to bid for a licence, in accordance with a specified procedure;
- (b) specify criteria by which the Secretary of State shall determine whether an applicant is qualified to participate in a bidding procedure;
- (c) specify criteria to determine whether a qualified applicant is associated with one or more other qualified applicants;
- (d) specify criteria to determine whether any qualified applicants who fall within sub-paragraph (c) above shall be entitled to participate in the procedure referred to in sub-paragraph (e) below;
- (e) specify a procedure by which qualified applicants may submit bids for licences;
- (f) specify reserve prices for each of the licences;
- (g) provide for the Secretary of State to determine minimum bids for each of the licences during the bidding procedure referred to in sub-paragraph (e) above;
- (h) provide for the payment of a deposit on submission of an application and for payment of one or more additional deposits before a qualified applicant may submit a bid for each licence;
- (i) provide for the payment of interest on the deposit and on any additional deposits;
- (j) provide for the circumstances in which all, or part, of any deposit, and all, or part, of any interest which accrues to a deposit, is not to be refunded;
- (k) specify the conditions which must be satisfied before a licence may be issued to a qualified applicant who submits the highest valid bid for a licence;
- (l) provide for a qualified applicant who submits the highest valid bid for a licence to pay such sum on such date as shall be specified in or determined under the said notice;
- (m) provide for the qualified applicant referred to in sub-paragraph (l) above to have the option to renew the licence for two successive periods of five years on such terms as shall be specified in or determined under the said notice;
- (n) provide for the other terms, provisions and limitations subject to which each of the licences is to be issued; and
- (o) provide for the other conditions with which qualified applicants must comply to participate, or to continue to participate, in the procedures referred to in sub-paragraph (e) above.

(3) A notice which is issued pursuant to paragraph (1) above shall be published by the Secretary of State on the Radiocommunications Agency's Internet Website.

[4373]

NOTES
Commencement: 12 August 2002.

5 Refunds

The Secretary of State may, in such cases as she thinks fit, refund, in whole or in part, sums which have been paid to her in accordance with any provision of the licences.

[4374]

NOTES
Commencement: 12 August 2002.

6 Channel Islands and Isle of Man

These Regulations shall not extend to the Channel Islands and the Isle of Man.

[4375]

NOTES

Commencement: 12 August 2002.

SCHEDULE

Regulation 2

PART I
THE REGIONS

Designation	*Region of the United Kingdom*								*Licences available*
Metropolitan Regions									
Central Scotland	EH1	EH19	EH51	G12	G46	G77	PA3		One
	EH2	EH20	EH52	G13	G51	G78	PA4		
	EH3	EH21	EH53	G14	G52	G81	PA5		
	EH4	EH22	EH54	G15	G53	G82	PA6		
	EH5	EH23	EH55	G20	G60	KY3	PA7		
	EH6	EH24	FK1	G21	G61	KY4	PA8		
	EH7	EH25	FK2	G22	G62	KY11	PA9		
	EH8	EH26	FK3	G23	G64	KY12	PA10		
	EH9	EH27	FK4	G31	G65	ML1	PA11		
	EH10	EH28	FK5	G32	G66	ML2	PA15		
	EH11	EH29	FK6	G33	G67	ML3	PA16		
	EH12	EH30	FK10	G34	G68	ML4	PA19		
	EH13	EH33	G1	G40	G69	ML5	G76		
	EH14	EH34	G2	G41	G71	ML6	PA14		
	EH15	EH35	G3	G42	G72	ML7			
	EH16	EH47	G4	G43	G73	ML9			
	EH17	EH48	G5	G44	G74	PA1			
	EH18	EH49	G11	G45	G75	PA2			
Greater London	**Areas**	AL	KT	SW	CR	IG	TW	SM	
		BR	NW	UB	DA	N	WC	HA	
		E	SE	W	EC	SL	WD	EN	
	Sectors	CM12	GU1	GU15	GU23	HP6	HP15	ME1	One
		CM13	GU2	GU16	GU24	HP7	LU1	ME2	
		CM14	GU4	GU17	GU25	HP8	LU2	ME3	
	RM9	CM15	GU9	GU18	GU46	HP9	LU3	ME4	
	RM10	CM16	GU11	GU19	GU47	HP10	LU4	ME5	
	RM11	CM18	GU12	GU20	HP1	HP11	LU5	ME6	
	RM12	CM19	GU13	GU21	HP2	HP12	RH1	ME7	
	RM13	CM20	GU14	GU22	HP3	HP13	RH2	ME8	
	RM14	RG1	RG30	RM1	SS0	TN13	RH3	ME14	
	RM15	RG2	RG31	RM2	SS1	TN14	RH4	ME15	
	RM16	RG4	RG40	RM3	SS2	TN15	RH8	ME16	

Designation	*Region of the United Kingdom*								*Licences available*
	RM17	RG5	RG41	RM5	SS6	TN16	RH9	ME19	
	RM18	RG6	RG42	RM6	SS7	SS11	SS14	ME20	
	RM19	RG10	RG45	RM7	SS8	SS12	SS15	SS17	
	RM20	RG12		RM8	SS9	SS13	SS16		
Midlands	B1	B23	B46	B78	CV13	DY5	NG8	WS11	One
	B2	B24	B47	B79	DE1	DY6	NG9	WS12	
	B3	B25	B48	B90	DE3	DY8	NG10	WS13	
	B4	B26	B60	B91	DE5	LE3	NG11	WS14	
	B5	B27	B61	B92	DE7	LE4	NG15	WV1	
	B6	B28	B62	B93	DE11	LE5	NG16	WV2	
	B7	B29	B63	B94	DE12	LE6	NG17	WV3	
	B8	B30	B64	B97	DE14	LE9	NG18	WV4	
	B9	B31	B65	B98	DE15	LE11	NG19	WV5	
	B10	B32	B66	CV1	DE21	LE12	ST19	WV6	
	B11	B33	B67	CV2	DE22	LE18	WS1	WV7	
	B12	B34	B68	CV3	DE23	LE65	WS2	WV8	
	B13	B35	B69	CV4	DE24	LE67	WS3	WV9	
	B14	B36	B70	CV5	DE72	NG1	WS4	WV10	
	B15	B37	B71	CV6	DE74	NG2	WS5	WV11	
	B16	B38	B72	CV7	DE75	NG3	WS6	WV12	
	B17	B40	B73	CV9	DY1	NG4	WS7	WV13	
	B18	B42	B74	CV10	DY2	NG5	WS8	WV14	
	B19	B43	B75	CV11	DY3	NG6	WS9	LE1	
	B20	B44	B76	CV12	DY4	NG7	WS10	LE2	
	B21	B45	B77						
Northern	**Areas**	L	M	OL	WF	WN			
	Sectors	DN1	LS1	PR1	S32	CH1	SK7	WF15	One
		DN2	LS2	PR2	S33	CH2	SK8	WF16	
		DN3	LS3	PR4	S35	CH4	SK9	WF17	
		DN4	LS4	PR5	S36	CH41	SK10	BB1	
		DN5	LS5	PR6	S40	CH42	SK12	BB2	
		DN6	LS6	PR7	S41	CH43	SK13	BB3	
	BD16	DN11	LS7	PR8	S60	CH44	SK14	BB4	
	BD17	FY1	LS8	PR9	S61	CH45	SK15	BB5	
	BD18	FY2	LS9	S1	S62	CH46	SK16	BB6	
	BD19	FY3	LS10	S2	S63	CH47	SK22	BB8	
	BD20	FY4	LS11	S3	S64	CH48	SK23	BB9	
	BD21	FY5	LS12	S4	S65	CH49	WA1	BB10	
	BD22	FY7	LS13	S5	S66	CH60	WA2	BB11	
	BL0	FY8	LS14	S6	S70	CH61	WA3	BB12	
	BL1	HD1	LS15	S7	S71	CH62	WA4	BB18	
	BL2	HD2	LS16	S8	S72	CH63	WA5	BD1	
	BL3	HD3	LS17	S9	S73	CH65	WA6	BD2	
	BL4	HD4	LS18	S10	S74	CH66	WA7	BD3	

PART VI TELECOMMUNICATIONS

Designation	Region of the United Kingdom								Licences available
	BL5	HD5	LS19	S11	S75	BD11	WA8	BD4	
	BL6	HD6	LS20	S12	SK1	BD12	WA9	BD5	
	BL7	HD7	LS26	S13	SK2	BD13	WA10	BD6	
	BL8	HD8	LS27	S14	SK3	BD14	WA11	BD7	
	BL9	HX1	LS28	S17	SK4	BD15	WA12	BD8	
	HX5	HX2	LS29	S18	SK5	DN12	WA13	BD9	
	HX6	HX3	S26	S20	SK6	WA15	WA14	BD10	
	HX7	HX4	S25						
Severnside	BS1	BS6	BS11	BS20	BS31	CF10	CF24	NP10	One
	BS2	BS7	BS13	BS21	BS32	CF11	CF38	NP18	
	BS3	BS8	BS14	BS22	BS34	CF14	CF62	NP19	
	BS4	BS9	BS15	BS23	CF3	CF15	CF63	NP20	
	BS5	BS10	BS16	BS30	CF5	CF23	CF64	NP26	
South Coast	BN9	BN41	PO8	PO19	SO18	SO52	BH9	BH23	One
	BN10	BN42	PO9	PO20	SO19	SO53	BH10	BH24	
	BN11	BN43	PO10	PO21	SO30	BH1	BH11	BH25	
	BN12	PO1	PO11	PO22	SO31	BH2	BH12	BN1	
	BN13	PO2	PO12	RH15	SO40	BH3	BH13	BN2	
	BN14	PO3	PO13	RH16	SO41	BH4	BH14	BN3	
	BN15	PO4	PO14	SO14	SO42	BH5	BH15	BN6	
	BN16	PO5	PO15	SO15	SO43	BH6	BH17	BN7	
	BN17	PO6	PO16	SO16	SO45	BH7	BH18	BN8	
	BN18	PO7	PO18	SO17	SO50	BH8	BH22	PO30	
	PO33		PO35	PO39	PO31	PO32	PO40	PO41	
	PO34		PO36						
			PO37						
			PO38						
Tyne-Tees	DH1	DL5	NE7	NE23	NE34	SR1	TS4	TS19	One
	DH2	DL14	NE8	NE24	NE35	SR2	TS5	TS20	
	DH3	DL15	NE9	NE25	NE36	SR3	TS6	TS21	
	DH4	DL16	NE10	NE26	NE37	SR4	TS7	TS22	
	DH5	DL17	NE11	NE27	NE38	SR5	TS8	TS23	
	DH6	NE1	NE12	NE28	NE39	SR6	TS10	TS24	
	DH7	NE2	NE15	NE29	NE40	SR7	TS11	TS25	
	DH9	NE3	NE16	NE30	NE41	SR8	TS12	TS26	
	DL1	NE4	NE17	NE31	NE62	TS1	TS14	TS27	
	DL3	NE5	NE21	NE32	NE63	TS2	TS17	TS28	
	DL4	NE6	NE22	NE33	NE64	TS3	TS18	TS29	
	TS13								

Designation	*Region of the United Kingdom*	*Licences available*
Provincial Regions		
Midlands and Mid Wales	**Areas** LE WS TF B WR DE NN DY ST WV CV NG SY LD HR Except the postcodes in the Midlands Metropolitan Region	One
Northern Ireland	**Area** BT	One
North of England	**Areas** DL CA TS DH LA NE Except the postcodes in the Tyne-Tees Metropolitan Region	One
North West, Yorkshire and North Wales	**Areas** LL SK S HU FY BB CH WA YO PR DN LN HX CW BD LS HD HG BL Except the postcodes in the Northern Metropolitan Regions	One
Scotland	**Areas** ML TD PA KY DD HS EH KA G FK AB KW PH IV ZE DG Except the postcodes in the Central Scotland Metropolitan Region	One
South East	**Areas** PE HP TN CO SG MK NR LU ME CM RG RM IP OX CT CB GU RH Except the postcodes in the Greater London and South Coast Metropolitan Regions and the Southern Provincial Region	One
Southern	**Areas** DT SP PO BN Except the postcodes in the South Coast Metropolitan Region Plus Sectors RH13 GU32 TN22 TN21 TN34 TN39 RH14 RH17 GU36 TN20 TN19 TN35 TN40 RH20 … GU31 TN37 TN32 TN36 GU29 GU27 GU28 TN31 TN33 TN38	One
South West and South Wales	**Areas** TR TA SN CF NP EX TQ BA GL SA BS PL Except the postcodes in the Severnside Metropolitan Region	One

[4376]

NOTES

Commencement: 12 August 2002.

In region "Southern" in column 2 sector omitted revoked by the Wireless Telegraphy (Public Fixed Wireless Access Licences) (Amendment) Regulations 2003, SI 2003/397, reg 2.

PART II
THE FREQUENCIES FOR EACH OF THE LICENCES IN EACH OF THE REGIONS SPECIFIED IN PART I

3480–3500 MHz and 3580–3600 MHz

[4377]

NOTES

Commencement: 12 August 2002.

ELECTRONIC COMMUNICATIONS (UNIVERSAL SERVICE) REGULATIONS 2003

(SI 2003/33)

NOTES

Made: 9 January 2003.
Authority: European Communities Act 1972, s 2(2)
Commencement: 1 February 2003.
For transitional provisions relating to universal service matters, see the Communications Act 2003, s 406(6), Sch 18, para 7 at **[3434]**, **[3460]**.

ARRANGEMENT OF REGULATIONS

1 Citation and commencement

These Regulations may be cited as the Electronic Communications (Universal Service) Regulations 2003 and shall come into force on 1st February 2003.

[4378]

NOTES

Commencement: 1 February 2003.

2 Interpretation

In these Regulations—

"the Director" means the Director General of Telecommunications appointed under section 1 of the Telecommunications Act 1984;

"the Framework Directive" means Directive 2002/21/EC of the European Parliament and of the Council of 7 March 2002 on a common regulatory framework for electronic communications networks and services;

"the universal service" means the provision in the United Kingdom of the services and facilities set out in Articles 4, 5, 6, 7 and 9(2) of the Universal Service Directive;

"the Universal Service Directive" means Directive 2002/22/EC of the European Parliament and of the Council of 7 March 2002 on universal service and users' rights relating to electronic communications networks and services; and

"universal service provider" means person who is designated as a person who provides the whole or part of the universal service.

[4379]

NOTES

Commencement: 1 February 2003.
The Director General of Telecommunications: on such a day as may be appointed under the Communications Act 2003, s 31(4)(a) at **[3108]**, the office of the Director is abolished. As to the transfer of the Director's functions, etc, see s 2 of the 2003 Act at **[3079]**.

3 Policy objectives and regulatory principles

(1) It shall be the duty of the Director in carrying out any of the functions set out in these Regulations to act in accordance with the policy objectives and regulatory principles in Article 8 of the Framework Directive.

(2) Where it appears to the Director that any of those policy objectives or regulatory principles conflict with each other, he must secure that the conflict is resolved in the manner he thinks best in the circumstances.

(3) Where it appears to the Director that any of his duties in section 3 of the Telecommunications Act 1984 conflict with one or more of those policy objectives or regulatory principles, priority must be given to those objectives and principles.

[4380]

NOTES

Commencement: 1 February 2003.

4 Designation of Universal Service Provider

(1) The Director shall be under a duty to make proposals to secure, as far as practicable, the universal service.

(2) In order to fulfil the duty in paragraph (1), the Director may propose the designation of such persons as he considers appropriate as universal service providers.

(3) Proposals for designating any person as a universal service provider shall be by means of a notification published by the Director—

- (a) stating that he is proposing to designate that person as a universal service provider;
- (b) giving the reasons for making the proposal;
- (c) inviting expressions of interest from any other person to be designated as a universal service provider instead of the person stated in the notification; and
- (d) specifying the period within which representations about the proposal or expressions of interest may be made.

(4) The notification may also set out the following—

- (a) the conditions that the Director is proposing to set on a person designated as a universal service provider in accordance with Articles 4, 5, 6, 7, 9, 10 and 11 of the Universal Service Directive;
- (b) the effect of those conditions; and
- (c) the reasons for setting those conditions.

(5) The period specified for the purposes of paragraph (3)(d) must be one of not less than one month, beginning with the day after the day on which the notification was published.

(6) The Director shall send a copy of each notification published under paragraph (3) to the Secretary of State.

(7) The publication of a notification under this regulation must be in such manner as appears to the Director to be appropriate for bringing it to the attention of the persons who, in the Director's opinion, are likely to have an interest in, or be affected by, it.

(8) Where following publication of a notification in accordance with paragraph (3), the Director, within the period specified for the purposes of paragraph (3)(d), receives an expression of interest from a person to be designated as a universal service provider instead of the person stated in the notice he shall—

- (a) consider that expression of interest; and
- (b) determine whether or not, in his opinion, it would be appropriate to propose to designate that person as a universal service provider instead of the person stated in the notification.

(9) Where the Director determines, in accordance with paragraph (8)(b), that it would be appropriate to propose to designate another person as a universal service provider instead of the person stated in the notification, he must, before confirming that proposal, publish a notification in accordance with paragraph (3).

(10) If—

- (a) he has considered every representation about the proposals set out in a notification published under paragraph (3) that is made to him within the period specified in the notification; and
- (b) he has determined, in accordance with paragraph 8(b), that it would not be appropriate to propose to designate another person as a universal service provider instead of the person stated in the notification,

the Director may, by publication of a further notification, set out the proposals, with or without modification, as he intends that effect would be given to them upon the coming into force of any enactment (including an enactment contained in subordinate legislation) which implements the provision of the Universal Service [Directive] to which the proposals relate; and reference in this regulation to confirmation of a proposal is reference to publication of such a notification setting out a proposal.

(11) Where the Director has confirmed any proposal by the publication of a notification under paragraph (10), he may, by publication of a further notification, withdraw that proposal.

(12) Any proposed conditions which the Director sets out in a notification published under paragraphs (3) or (10) must comply with, and be necessary for satisfying requirements in, Articles 4, 5, 6, 7, 9, 10 and 11 of the Universal Service Directive.

[4381]

NOTES

Commencement: 1 February 2003.

Para 10: word in square brackets substituted by the Electronic Communications (Market Analysis) Regulations 2003, SI 2003/330, reg 3.

5 Notifications for conditions set on universal service providers

(1) Following the publication of a notification under paragraph (3) of regulation 4, the Director may publish further notifications setting out conditions or, where the notification under paragraph (3) sets out proposals for setting conditions, further conditions that he is proposing to set on a person designated as a universal service provider in accordance with Articles 4, 5, 6, 7, 9, 10 and 11 of the Universal Service Directive.

(2) A further notification must set out—

(a) the conditions or further conditions that the Director is proposing to set on a person designated as a universal service provider in accordance with Articles 4, 5, 6, 7, 9, 10 and 11 of the Universal Service Directive;
(b) the effect of those conditions;
(c) the reasons for setting those conditions; and
(d) the period within which representations may be made to the Director about the proposals set out in his notification.

(3) The period specified for the purpose of paragraph (2)(d) must be one of not less than one month, beginning with the day after the day on which the notification is published.

(4) If he has considered every representation about the proposals set out in a notification published under this regulation that is made to him within the period specified in the notification the Director may, by publication of a further notification, set out the proposals with or without modification, as he intends that effect would be given to them upon the coming into force of any enactment (including an enactment contained in subordinate legislation) which implements the provision of the Universal Service Directive to which the proposals relate; and reference in this regulation to confirmation of a proposal is reference to publication of such a notification setting out a proposal.

(5) Where the Director has confirmed any proposal by the publication of a notification under paragraph (4) he may, by publication of a further notification, withdraw that proposal.

(6) The publication of a notification under this regulation must be in such manner as appears to the Director to be appropriate for bringing it to the attention of the persons who, in the Director's opinion, are likely to have an interest in, or be affected by, it.

(7) Any proposed conditions which the Director sets out in a notification published under this regulation must comply with, and be necessary for satisfying requirements in, Articles 4, 5, 6, 7, 9, 10 and 11 of the Universal Service Directive.

[4382]

NOTES

Commencement: 1 February 2003.

6 Appeals

Section 46B of the Telecommunications Act 1984 shall apply to decisions made by the Director.

[4383]

NOTES

Commencement: 1 February 2003.

WIRELESS TELEGRAPHY (EXEMPTION) REGULATIONS 2003

(SI 2003/74)

NOTES

Made: 20 January 2003.
Authority: Wireless Telegraphy Act 1949, ss 1(1), 3(1)(a), (b).
Commencement: 12 February 2003.

ARRANGEMENT OF REGULATIONS

1 Citation and commencement

These Regulations may be cited as the Wireless Telegraphy (Exemption) Regulations 2003 and shall come into force on 12th February 2003.

[4384]

NOTES

Commencement: 12 February 2003.

2 Revocation

The Regulations specified in Schedule 1 are hereby revoked.

[4385]

NOTES

Commencement: 12 February 2003.

3 Interpretation

(1) In these Regulations

"the 1949 Act" means the Wireless Telegraphy Act 1949;

"the 1984 Act" means the Telecommunications Act 1984;

"apparatus" means wireless telegraphy apparatus or apparatus designed or adapted for use in connection with wireless telegraphy apparatus;

…

…

"eirp" means equivalent isotropically radiated power, as defined in the Radio Regulations;

"EN45001 and EN45002" means European Standards (Normes Européenne) EN45001 and EN45002 published in September 1989 by the British Standards Institution;

…

"ETSI" means the European Telecommunications Standards Institute;

"Interface Requirement" means an interface requirement published by [OFCOM] in accordance with Article 4.1 of Directive 1999/5/EC of the European Parliament and of the Council on radio equipment and telecommunications terminal equipment and the mutual recognition of their conformity;

"ISO guides 25 and 58" means the International Organization for Standardization Guides 25 and 58 published by the International Organization for Standardization in 1990 and 1993 respectively;

"national administration" means the national administration of a country listed in Schedule 2;

…

"the Radio Regulations" means [the 2004 edition] of the Radio Regulations made under Article 13 of the Constitution of the International Telecommunication Union;

"relevant apparatus" means the prescribed apparatus as defined in [Schedules 3 to 10] hereto;

"station" means a station for wireless telegraphy; and

"test laboratory" means a test laboratory which has been accredited in accordance with ISO guides 25 and 58 or EN45001 and EN45002 or a national standard conforming to ISO guides 25 and 58 or EN45001 and EN45002.

(2) …

[4386]

NOTES

Commencement: 12 February 2003.

Para (1): definitions "authorised person", "CEPT", "erp" and "RA" (omitted) revoked, and words in square brackets in definitions "Interface Requirement", "the Radio Regulations", and "relevant apparatus" substituted, by the Wireless Telegraphy (Exemption) (Amendment) Regulations 2006, SI 2006/2994, reg 3.

Para (2): revoked by the Communications Act (Consequential Amendments) Order 2003, SI 2003/2155, art 3(2), Sch 2, Table 2.

4 Exemption

(1) Subject to regulation 5, the establishment, installation and use of the relevant apparatus are hereby exempted from the provisions of section 1(1) of the 1949 Act.

(2) With the exception of relevant apparatus operating in the frequency bands specified in paragraph (3), the exemption in paragraph (1) shall not apply to relevant apparatus which is established, installed or used to provide or to be capable of providing a wireless telegraphy link between [electronic communications apparatus] or [an electronic communications network] and other such apparatus or system, by means of which [an electronic communications service] is provided by way of business to another person.

(3) The frequency bands specified for the purposes of paragraph (2) are—

(a) 2400.0 to 2483.5 MHz;

(b) 5150 to 5350 MHz;

(c) 5470 to 5725 MHz;

(d) 57.1 to 58.9 GHz.

[(4) The exemption provided in the case of relevant apparatus operating in the frequency bands specified in paragraph (3) shall not apply unless such apparatus complies with the appropriate following Interface Requirement—

(a) in the case of the frequency bands specified at sub-paragraph (a), IR 2005—UK Radio Interface Requirement for Wideband Transmission Systems operating in the 2.4 GHz ISM Band and Using Wide Band Modulation Techniques, published by OFCOM in November 2006;

(b) in the case of the frequency bands specified at sub-paragraphs (b) and (c), IR 2006—UK Interface Requirement 2006 for Wireless Access Systems (WAS) including RLANs operating in the frequency range 5150–5725 MHz, published by OFCOM in November 2006;

(c) in the case of the frequency band specified at sub-paragraph (d), IR 2000—UK Interface Requirement 2000 for Point-to-Point Radio-Relay Systems Operating in Fixed Service Frequency Bands Administered by OFCOM, published by OFCOM in July 2005.]

[4387]

NOTES

Commencement: 12 February 2003.

Para (2): words in square brackets substituted by the Communications Act (Consequential Amendments) Order 2003, SI 2003/2155, art 3(1), Sch 1, Pt 5, para 51(1), (2).

Para (4): substituted by the Wireless Telegraphy (Exemption) (Amendment) Regulations 2006, SI 2006/2994, reg 4.

5 Terms, provisions and limitations

(1) The exemption provided in regulation 4(1) shall be subject to the terms, provisions and limitations that—

(a) the relevant apparatus shall not cause or contribute to any undue interference to any wireless telegraphy; and

(b) the use of the relevant apparatus is terrestrial use only, [unless non-terrestrial use is permitted under Part III of Schedule 6].

(2) Such exemption shall also be subject to such additional terms, provisions and limitations as are specified in the Schedules hereto in respect of the relevant apparatus.

[4388]

NOTES

Commencement: 12 February 2003.

Para (1): words in square brackets in sub-para (b) substituted by the Wireless Telegraphy (Exemption) (Amendment) Regulations 2006, SI 2006/2994, reg 5.

6 (*Revoked by the Wireless Telegraphy* (*Inspection and Restrictions on Use of Exempt Stations and Apparatus*) *Regulations 2005, SI 2005/3481, reg 3.*)

(*Sch 1 revokes the Wireless Telegraphy* (*Exemption*) *Regulations 1999, SI 1999/930, the Wireless Telegraphy* (*Exemption*) (*Amendment*) *Regulations 2000, SI 2000/1012, the Wireless*

Telegraphy (Exemption) (Amendment) Regulations 2001, SI 2001/730, the Wireless Telegraphy (Exemption) (Amendment) Regulations 2002, SI 2002/1590.)

SCHEDULE 2
LIST OF NATIONAL ADMINISTRATIONS

Regulation 3(1)

Country	*Symbol*	*Country*	*Symbol*
Albania	AL	Luxembourg	L
Andorra	AND	Malta	M
Austria	A	Moldova	MLD
Belgium	B	Monaco	MC
Bosnia and Herzegovina	BH	Netherlands	NL
Bulgaria	BG	Norway	N
Croatia	HR	Poland	PL
Cyprus	CY	Portugal	P
Czech Republic	CZ	Romania	RO
Denmark	DK	Russian Federation	RUS
Estonia	EST	San Marino	RSM
Finland	FI	Slovak Republic	SK
France	F	Slovenia	SLO
Germany	D	Spain	E
Greece	GR	Sweden	S
Hungary	H	Switzerland	CH
Iceland	IS	The Former Yugoslav Republic of Macedonia	MK
Ireland	IRL	Turkey	TR
Italy	I	Ukraine	UA
Latvia	LV	United Kingdom of Great Britain and Northern Ireland	GB
Liechtenstein	FL	Vatican City	SCV
Lithuania	LT		

[4389]

NOTES

Commencement: 12 February 2003.

SCHEDULE 3
NETWORK USER STATIONS

Regulation 3(1)

PART I
INTERPRETATION

In this Schedule—

"BABT" means the British Approvals Board for Telecommunications;

"BTx" means Base Transmit, the frequency on which a base station transmits and a user station receives;

"CDMA" means Code Division Multiple Access as defined in the Radio Regulations;

"MTx" means Mobile Transmit, the frequency on which a user station transmits and a base station receives;

"prescribed apparatus" means a user station as defined below and any station or apparatus described in the appropriate Interface Requirement referred to in Part IV of this Schedule;

"relevant network" means [an electronic communications network] consisting exclusively of stations established and used under and in accordance with a licence, which has been granted under section 1(1) of the 1949 Act by the Secretary of State and is of a type specified in Part III of this Schedule;

"TDD" means Time Division Duplex as defined in the Radio Regulations; and

"user station" means a mobile station for wireless telegraphy designed or adapted—

(a) to be connected by wireless telegraphy to one or more relevant networks; and

(b) to be used solely for the purpose of sending and receiving messages conveyed by a relevant network by means of wireless telegraphy.

[4390]

NOTES

Commencement: 12 February 2003.

In definition "relevant network" words in square brackets substituted by the Communications Act (Consequential Amendments) Order 2003, SI 2003/2155, art 3(1), Sch 1, Pt 5, para 51(1), (3).

PART II
ADDITIONAL TERMS, PROVISIONS AND LIMITATIONS

1 The prescribed apparatus shall be subject to and comply with the appropriate Interface Requirement referred to in Part IV of this Schedule.

2 Prescribed apparatus taken into service before 1st May 2000 must also comply with the appropriate Common Technical Regulations referred to in Part V of this Schedule, and in the absence of a Common Technical Regulation applying to such apparatus, the prescribed apparatus must—

(a) be approved by the Secretary of State under section 84 of the 1984 Act for the purposes of these Regulations;

(b) be approved to the ETSI standards or the draft ETSI standards referred to in Part V of this Schedule as appropriate by a national administration following type testing at a test laboratory; or

(c) comply with the BABT performance standards referred to in Part V of this Schedule as appropriate,

provided that paragraph (a) above shall not apply in relation to prescribed apparatus situated in the Bailiwick of Jersey.

[4391]

NOTES

Commencement: 12 February 2003.

PART III
TYPE OF LICENCE GRANTED UNDER SECTION 1(1) OF THE 1949 ACT FOR THE ESTABLISHMENT AND USE OF RELEVANT NETWORKS

Public Mobile Operator Licences

1 Public mobile data systems licensed for use in the following frequency bands—

105–165 MHz
174–208 MHz
420–470 MHz

(for non-voice only operation)

2 Meteor burst data systems licensed for use on the following frequencies—

39.025 MHz
39.050 MHz
46.400 MHz
46.950 MHz
46.975 MHz

3 Cellular radiotelephone systems licensed for use in the following services on the relevant frequency bands—

(a) digital cellular radiotelephones:

Global System for Mobile Communications (GSM): 880–915 MHz (MTx)

925–960 MHz (BTx)

(b) digital cellular PCN radiotelephones:

Personal Communications Network (PCN): 1710–1785 MHz (MTx)

1805–1880 MHz (BTx)

(c) Universal Mobile Telephony System radiotelephones (UMTS):

1899.9–1920 MHz (BTx/MTx in TDD)

1920–1980 MHz (MTx)

2110–2170 MHz (BTx)

4 Public access mobile radio systems licensed for use in the following frequency bands—

174–208 MHz

410–430 MHz

5 …

6 Public two-way paging systems licensed for use in the following frequency bands—

169.4–169.8 MHz (MTx) paired with

870–871 MHz (BTx).

Common Base Station Operator Licence

Common base station systems licensed for use in the following frequency bands—

55–56 MHz

81–87 MHz

162–167 MHz

171–191 MHz

209–215 MHz

440–449 MHz

[4392]

NOTES

Commencement: 12 February 2003.

Para 5: revoked by the Wireless Telegraphy (Exemption) (Amendment) Regulations 2006, SI 2006/2994, reg 6(a).

[PART IV
INTERFACE REQUIREMENT

IR 2014—Public Wireless Networks, published by OFCOM in August 2005.

IR 2017—Remote Meter Reading Operator Services, published by OFCOM in October 2004.

IR 2019—Third Generation Mobile, published by OFCOM in June 2005.

IR 2044—12.5 kHz and 25 kHz Channel spacing for Land Mobile Services, Covering CBS, Analogue PAMR, National Paging, Data Networks, TETRA/TEDS Networks, and National & Regional PMBR Authorisations, published by OFCOM in November 2006.]

[4393]

NOTES

Commencement: 8 December 2006.

Substituted by the Wireless Telegraphy (Exemption) (Amendment) Regulations 2006, SI 2006/2994, reg 6(b).

PART V
COMMON TECHNICAL REGULATIONS AND STANDARDS

GSM

CTR 005—Commission Decision of 21st December 1993 on a common technical regulation for the general attachment requirements for public pan-European cellular digital land-based mobile communications, including the ETSI Technical Basis for Regulation (TBR) TBR 005 published in November 1993.

CTR 009—Commission Decision of 21st December 1993 on a common technical regulation for the telephony application requirements for public pan-European cellular digital land-based mobile communications, including TBR 009 published in November 1993.

TBR 019 published by ETSI in October 1996.

TBR 020 published by ETSI in October 1996.

Public mobile data systems

ETS 300 339 published by ETSI in June 1993.

ETS 300 113 published by ETSI in July 1996.

Meteor burst data systems

ETS 300 113 published by ETSI in July 1996.

PCN

BABT Special Investigation Test Schedule (SITS) 92/50 published in March 1991 and revised and reprinted in June 1995.

TBR 031: 1996–02 published by ETSI in February 1996.

TBR 032: 1996–02 published by ETSI in February 1996.

Public access mobile radio systems

ETS 300 086 published by ETSI in January 1991.

ETS 300 113 published by ETSI in July 1996.

I-ETS 300 219 published by ETSI in October 1993.

Common base station systems

ETS 300 086 published by ETSI in January 1991.

ETS 300 113 published by ETSI in July 1996.

[4394]

NOTES

Commencement: 12 February 2003.

SCHEDULE 4
CORDLESS TELEPHONE APPARATUS

Regulation 3(1)

PART I
INTERPRETATION

In this Schedule—

…

"MPTs 1322, 1334, 1371 and 1384" means Department of Trade and Industry Performance Specifications 1322, 1334, 1371 and 1384 referred to in Part IV of this Schedule; and

"prescribed apparatus" means a station or apparatus described in the Interface Requirement referred to in Part III of this Schedule.

[4395]

NOTES

Commencement: 12 February 2003.

Definition "data message" (omitted) revoked by the Wireless Telegraphy (Exemption) (Amendment) Regulations 2006, SI 2006/2994, reg 7(a).

PART II
ADDITIONAL TERMS, PROVISIONS AND LIMITATIONS

1 The prescribed apparatus shall be subject to and comply with the Interface Requirement referred to in Part III of this Schedule.

2 Prescribed apparatus taken into service before 1st May 2000 must also comply with the appropriate Common Technical Regulations referred to in Part IV of this Schedule, and in the absence of a Common Technical Regulation applying to such apparatus, the prescribed apparatus must—

(a) be approved by the Secretary of State under section 84 of the 1984 Act for the purposes of these Regulations;

(b) be approved to the ETSI standards referred to in Part IV of this Schedule as appropriate by a national administration following type testing at a test laboratory; or

(c) comply with the requirements of MPT 1322, MPT 1334, MPT 1371 or MPT 1384 as appropriate in relation to prescribed apparatus taken into service before section 84 of the 1984 Act came into force,

provided that paragraph (a) above shall not apply in relation to prescribed apparatus situated in the Bailiwick of Jersey.

[4396]

NOTES

Commencement: 12 February 2003.

PART III
INTERFACE REQUIREMENT

[IR 2011—UK Interface Requirement 2011 Analogue and digital cordless telephony service, published by OFCOM in June 2005.]

[4397]

NOTES

Commencement: 12 February 2003.

Words in square brackets substituted by the Wireless Telegraphy (Exemption) (Amendment) Regulations 2006, SI 2006/2994, reg 7(b).

PART IV
COMMON TECHNICAL REGULATIONS AND STANDARDS

CT1

Department of Trade and Industry Performance Specification MPT 1322 published in August 1982 and revised and reprinted in August 1994.

Department of Trade and Industry Performance Specification MPT 1384 published in November 1997.

Extended range CT1

Department of Trade and Industry Performance Specification MPT 1371 published in May 1989 and revised and reprinted in August 1994.

CT2

Department of Trade and Industry Performance Specification MPT 1334 published in December 1987 and revised and reprinted in July 1994.

I-ETS 300 131 published by ETSI in April 1992 and revised and reprinted in November 1994.

DECT

CTR 006—Commission Decision of 9th July 1997 on a common technical regulation for the general terminal attachment requirements for DECT, including the ETSI Technical Basis for Regulation TBR 006.

CTR 010—Commission Decision of 9th July 1997 on a common technical regulation for the telephony application requirements for DECT, including the ETSI Technical Basis for Regulation TBR 010.

CTR 022—Commission Decision of 9th July 1997 on a common technical regulation for the attachment requirements for DECT generic access profile (GAP), including the ETSI Technical Basis for Regulation TBR 022.

ETSI Technical Basis for Regulation TBR 006 published in December 1993 and revised and reprinted in December 1995.

[4398]

NOTES

Commencement: 12 February 2003.

SCHEDULE 5
LAND MOBILE-SATELLITE SERVICE STATIONS

Regulation 3(1)

PART I
INTERPRETATION

In this Schedule—

"Eutelsat" means Eutelsat SA whose registered office is situated at 70 rue Ballard, 75502 Paris, Cedex 15, France;

"Globalstar" means Globalstar LP whose registered office is situated at 3200 Zanker Road, GS-06, San Jose, CA 95134, United States of America;

"ICO" means ICO Global Communications (Holdings) Limited whose registered office is situated at Clarendon House, 2 Church Street, Hamilton, Bermuda;

"Inmarsat" means Inmarsat Limited whose registered office is situated at 99 City Road, London EC1Y 1AX;

"Iridium" means Iridium Communications Germany GmbH whose registered office is situated at Jagerhofstrasse 19–20, 40479 Dusseldorf, Germany;

"Italsat" means the satellite network operated by Telespazio spa whose registered office is situated at via Tiburting, 965–00156 Rome, Italy;

"Land Mobile-Satellite Service", "Land Earth Station" and "Land Mobile Earth Station" have the meanings given to them in the Radio Regulations;

"Orbcomm" means Orbcomm LLC whose registered office is situated at 21700 Atlantic Boulevard, Dulles, VA 20166, United States of America;

"prescribed apparatus" means a Land Mobile Earth Station in a Land Mobile-Satellite Service described in the IR referred to in Part III of this Schedule;

"SpaceChecker" means SpaceChecker NV whose registered office is situated at Interleuvenlaan 15A, B-3001 Leuven, Belgium; and

"Thuraya" means Thuraya Satellite Telecommunications Company whose registered office is situated at P.O. Box 33344, Abu Dhabi, United Arab Emirates.

[4399]

NOTES

Commencement: 12 February 2003.

PART II
ADDITIONAL TERMS, PROVISIONS AND LIMITATIONS

1 The prescribed apparatus shall be subject to and comply with the Interface Requirement referred to in Part III of this Schedule.

PART VI TELECOMMUNICATIONS

2 Prescribed apparatus taken into service before 1st May 2000 must also comply with the appropriate Common Technical Regulations referred to in Part IV of this Schedule, and in the absence of a Common Technical Regulation applying to such apparatus, the prescribed apparatus must—

(a) be approved by the Secretary of State under section 84 of the 1984 Act for the purposes of these Regulations; or

(b) be approved to the ETSI standards referred to in Part IV of this Schedule as appropriate by a national administration following type testing at a test laboratory,

provided that paragraph (a) above shall not apply in relation to prescribed apparatus situated in the Bailiwick of Jersey.

3 Prescribed apparatus in the Iridium and Globalstar Land Mobile-Satellite Services described in the Interface Requirement referred to in Part III of this Schedule shall cease operation at or within a distance determined by the Secretary of State for each relevant radioastronomy site for the duration of any radioastronomy observation.

[4400]

NOTES

Commencement: 12 February 2003.

PART III
INTERFACE REQUIREMENT

[IR 2016—UK Radio Interface Requirement for Land Mobile Satellite Systems, published by OFCOM in April 2006.]

[4401]

NOTES

Commencement: 12 February 2003.

Words in square brackets substituted by the Wireless Telegraphy (Exemption) (Amendment) Regulations 2006, SI 2006/2994, reg 8.

PART IV
COMMON TECHNICAL REGULATIONS AND STANDARDS

Inmarsat

Type of Inmarsat station	*Maximum power (eirp)*	*ETSI standard (unless otherwise stated)*	*Date of publication*
A	+37 Dbw	Technical Requirements for Inmarsat Standard—A Ship Earth Stations, edition 3	May 1988
		Ship Earth Station Technical Bulletin 26A	September 1991
		Ship Earth Station Technical Bulletin 27B	May 1998
B	+34 dBW (+1/–2 dB)	EN 301 444	May 1998
C	+16 Dbw	EN 301 426	May 1998
D+	+9 dBW	EN 301 426	May 1998
M	+28 dBW (+3/–3 dB)	EN 301 444	May 1998
Mini M (phone)	+2.7 dBW	EN 201 444	May 1998
M4	26 dBW	EN 301 444	May 1998

Eutelsat

Type of Eutelsat station	*Maximum power (eirp)*	*ETSI standard*	*Date of publication*
Euteltracs (Omnitracs)	19 dBW	EN 301 426	May 1998

Italsat

Type of Italsat station	*Maximum power (eirp)*	*ETSI standard*	*Date of publication*
EMS-PRODAT	12 dBW	EN 301 426	May 1998
EMS-MSSAT	11.5 dBW	EN 301 444	May 1998

Iridium

CTR 41—Commission Decision of 3rd September 1998 on a common technical regulation for Satellite Personal Communications Networks (S-PCN) Mobile Earth Stations (MESs), including hand held earth stations, for S-PCN operating in the 1.6/2.4 GHz frequency bands under the Mobile Satellite Service (MSS).

ICO

CTR 42—Commission Decision of 3rd September 1998 on a common technical regulation for Satellite Personal Communications Networks (S-PCN) Mobile Earth Stations (MESs), including hand held earth stations, for S-PCN operating in the 2.0 GHz frequency bands under the Mobile Satellite Service (MSS).

Globalstar

CTR 41.

Thuraya

Type of Thuraya station	*Maximum power (eirp)*	*ETSI standard*	*Date of publication*
Hand held	7.0 dBW	EN 301 681	December 1999

Orbcomm

Type of Orbcomm station	*Maximum power (eirp)*	*ETSI standard*	*Date of publication*
Hand held	10 dBW/5 KHz	EN 301 721	December 1999

SpaceChecker

Type of SpaceCheker station	*Maximum power (eirp)*	*ETSI standard*	*Date of publication*
Hand held	12.5 dBW/15 KHz	EN 301 426	May 1998

[4402]

NOTES

Commencement: 12 February 2003.

SCHEDULE 6
SHORT RANGE DEVICES

Regulation 3(1)

PART I
INTERPRETATION

In this Schedule, "prescribed apparatus" means a station or apparatus described in the Interface Requirement referred to in Part III of this Schedule.

[4403]

NOTES

Commencement: 12 February 2003.

PART II
ADDITIONAL TERMS, PROVISIONS AND LIMITATIONS

1 The prescribed apparatus shall be subject to and comply with the Interface Requirement referred to in Part III of this Schedule.

2 Prescribed apparatus taken into service before 1st May 2000 must also—

(a) be approved by the Secretary of State under section 84 of the 1984 Act for the purposes of these Regulations; or

(b) be approved to the ETSI standards referred to in Part IV of this Schedule as appropriate by a national administration following type testing at a test laboratory, or otherwise complies with such standards in the case of non-manufactured apparatus used as metal detectors or model control apparatus referred to in the Interface Requirement in Part III of this Schedule,

provided that paragraph (a) above shall not apply in relation to prescribed apparatus situated in the Bailiwick of Jersey.

[4404]

NOTES

Commencement: 12 February 2003.

PART III
INTERFACE REQUIREMENT

IR 2030—UK Radio Interface Requirement for Short Range Devices, [published by OFCOM in November 2006].

[4405]

NOTES

Commencement: 12 February 2003.

Words in square brackets substituted by the Wireless Telegraphy (Exemption) (Amendment) Regulations 2006, SI 2006/2994, reg 9.

PART IV
STANDARDS

European Telecommunications Standard EN 300 220–1 published by ETSI in November 1997.

European Telecommunications Standard EN 300 330 published by ETSI in April 1999.

European Telecommunications Standard EN 300 422 published by ETSI in September 1999.

European Telecommunications Standard I-ETS 300 440 published by ETSI in December 1995 and Corrigendum issued in April 1996.

European Telecommunications Standard EN 300 674 published by ETSI in November 1998.

European Telecommunications Standard EN 300 718 published by ETSI in March 1997.

European Telecommunications Standard EN 300 761 published by ETSI in January 1998.

European Telecommunications Standard EN 301 091 published by ETSI in May 1998.

European Telecommunications Standard EN 301 357, version 1.2.1 (1991) published by ETSI in 1999.

[4406]

NOTES
Commencement: 12 February 2003.

SCHEDULE 7
PMR 446

Regulation 3(1)

PART I
INTERPRETATION

In this Schedule, "prescribed apparatus" means a station or apparatus described in the Interface Requirement referred to in Part III of this Schedule.

[4407]

NOTES
Commencement: 12 February 2003.

PART II
ADDITIONAL TERMS, PROVISIONS AND LIMITATIONS

1 The prescribed apparatus shall be subject to and comply with the Interface Requirement referred to in Part III of this Schedule.

2 Prescribed apparatus taken into service before 1st May 2000 must also—

(a) be approved by the Secretary of State under section 84 of the 1984 Act for the purposes of these Regulations; or

(b) be approved to the standard referred to in Part IV of this Schedule by a national administration following type testing at a test laboratory,

provided that paragraph (a) above shall not apply in relation to prescribed apparatus situated in the Bailiwick of Jersey.

[4408]

NOTES
Commencement: 12 February 2003.

PART III
INTERFACE REQUIREMENT

IR 2009—UK Radio Interface Requirement for Private Business Mobile Radio Operating in the Licence Exempt PMR 446 MHz Band, published by RA in December 2000.

[4409]

NOTES

Commencement: 12 February 2003.

PART IV
STANDARD

ETS 300 296 published by ETSI in December 1994 and revised and reprinted in March 1997.

[4410]

NOTES

Commencement: 12 February 2003.

SCHEDULE 8
FIXED TERRESTRIAL LINKS APPARATUS IN THE 57.1 TO 58.9 GHZ FREQUENCY BAND

Regulation 3(1)

PART I
INTERPRETATION

In this Schedule, "prescribed apparatus" means analogue or digital equipment for High Density Fixed Service (HDFS) applications.

[4411]

NOTES

Commencement: 12 February 2003.

PART II
ADDITIONAL TERMS, PROVISIONS AND LIMITATIONS

1 The prescribed apparatus shall be subject to and comply with the Interface Requirement referred to in Part III of this Schedule for the frequency range 57.1 to 58.9 GHz.

2 Prescribed apparatus taken into service before 1st May 2000 must also—

(a) be approved by the Secretary of State under section 84 of the 1984 Act for the purposes of these Regulations; or

(b) comply with the requirements of the Department of Trade and Industry Performance Specification referred to in Part IV of this Schedule,

provided that paragraph (a) above shall not apply in relation to prescribed apparatus situated in the Bailiwick of Jersey.

[4412]

NOTES

Commencement: 12 February 2003.

PART III
INTERFACE REQUIREMENT

[IR 2000—UK Interface Requirement 2000 for Point-to-Point Radio-Relay Systems Operating in Fixed Service Frequency Bands Administered by OFCOM, published by OFCOM in July 2005.]

[4413]

NOTES

Commencement: 12 February 2003.

Words in square brackets substituted by the Wireless Telegraphy (Exemption) (Amendment) Regulations 2006, SI 2006/2994, reg 10.

PART IV
STANDARD

MPT 1415 published in August 1998.

[4414]

NOTES

Commencement: 12 February 2003.

SCHEDULE 9
[WIRELESS ACCESS SYSTEMS INCLUDING RADIO LOCAL AREA NETWORKS]

Regulation 3(1)

NOTES

Schedule heading substituted by the Wireless Telegraphy (Exemption) (Amendment) Regulations 2006, SI 2006/2994, reg 11(1).

PART I
INTERPRETATION

In this Schedule, "prescribed apparatus" means [apparatus providing wireless access systems including radio local area networks] that provide wideband transmissions and short range broadband services.

[4415]

NOTES

Commencement: 12 February 2003.

Words in square brackets substituted by the Wireless Telegraphy (Exemption) (Amendment) Regulations 2006, SI 2006/2994, reg 11(2).

PART II
ADDITIONAL TERMS, PROVISIONS AND LIMITATIONS

1 The prescribed apparatus shall be subject to and comply with the appropriate Interface Requirement referred to in Part III of this Schedule.

2 Prescribed apparatus taken into service before 1st May 2000 must also—

(a) be approved by the Secretary of State under section 84 of the 1984 Act for the purposes of these Regulations; or

(b) be approved to the ETSI standards referred to in Part IV of this Schedule as appropriate by a national administration following type testing at a test laboratory,

provided that paragraph (a) above shall not apply in relation to prescribed apparatus situated in the Bailiwick of Jersey.

[4416]

NOTES

Commencement: 12 February 2003.

PART III
INTERFACE REQUIREMENT

[IR 2005—UK Interface Requirement for Wideband Transmission Systems operating in the 2400–2483.5 MHz Band, published by OFCOM in November 2006.

IR 2006—UK Interface Requirement 2006 for Wireless Access Systems (WAS) including RLANs operating in the frequency range 5150–5725 MHz, published by OFCOM in November 2006.]

[4417]

NOTES

Commencement: 12 February 2003.

Words in square brackets substituted by the Wireless Telegraphy (Exemption) (Amendment) Regulations 2006, SI 2006/2994, reg 11(3).

PART IV
STANDARDS

European Telecommunications Standard EN 300 328–1 published by ETSI in July 1997.

European Telecommunications Standard EN 300 328–2 published by ETSI in July 1997.

European Telecommunications Standard EN 300 836–1 published by ETSI in May 1998.

[4418]

NOTES

Commencement: 12 February 2003.

[SCHEDULE 10
CITIZENS' BAND RADIO EQUIPMENT

Regulation 3(1)

PART I
INTERPRETATION

In this Schedule "prescribed apparatus" means apparatus described in the Interface Requirement referred to in Part III of this Schedule.

PART II
ADDITIONAL TERMS, PROVISIONS AND LIMITATIONS

The prescribed apparatus shall be subject to and comply with the Interface Requirement referred to in Part III of this Schedule.

PART III
INTERFACE REQUIREMENT

UK Radio Interface Requirement 2027—UK Radio Interface Requirement 2027 for Citizens' Band (CB) radio for use in the Citizens' Band Radio Service, published by OFCOM in November 2006.]

[4419]

NOTES

Commencement: 8 December 2006.

Added by the Wireless Telegraphy (Exemption) (Amendment) Regulations 2006, SI 2006/2994, reg 12.

ELECTRONIC COMMUNICATIONS (MARKET ANALYSIS) REGULATIONS 2003

(SI 2003/330)

NOTES

Made: 19 February 2003.

Authority: European Communities Act 1972, s 2(2).

Commencement: 24 February 2003.

ARRANGEMENT OF REGULATIONS

1 Citation and commencement

These Regulations may be cited as the Electronic Communications (Market Analysis) Regulations 2003 and shall come into force on 24th February 2003.

[4420]

NOTES

Commencement: 24 February 2003.

2 Interpretation

In these Regulations—

"the Access Directive" means Directive 2002/19/EC of the European Parliament and of the Council of 7th March 2002 on access to, and interconnection of, electronic communications networks and associated facilities;

"associated facilities" has the meaning given by Article 2(e) of the Framework Directive;

"the Director" means the Director General of Telecommunications appointed under section 1 of the Telecommunications Act 1984;

"electronic communications network" has the meaning given by Article 2(a) of the Framework Directive;

"electronic communications service" has the meaning given by Article 2(c) of the Framework Directive;

"the Framework Directive" means Directive 2002/21/EC of the European Parliament and of the Council of 7th March 2002 on a common regulatory framework for electronic communications networks and services;

"significant market power" has the meaning given by regulation 5(3) to (7); and

"the Universal Service Directive" means Directive 2002/22/EC of the European Parliament and of the Council of 7th March 2002 on universal service and users' rights relating to electronic communications networks and services.

[4421]

NOTES

Commencement: 24 February 2003.

The Director General of Telecommunications: on such a day as may be appointed under the Communications Act 2003, s 31(4)(a) at **[3108]**, the office of the Director is abolished. As to the transfer of the Director's functions, etc, see s 2 of the 2003 Act at **[3079]**.

3 (*Amends the Electronic Communications* (*Universal Service*) *Regulations 2003, SI 2003/33, reg 4 at* **[4381]**.)

4 Policy objectives and regulatory principles

(1) It shall be the duty of the Director in carrying out any of the functions set out in these Regulations to act in accordance with the policy objectives and regulatory principles in Article 8 of the Framework Directive.

(2) Where it appears to the Director that any of those policy objectives or regulatory principles conflict with each other, he must secure that the conflict is resolved in the manner he thinks best in the circumstances.

(3) Where it appears to the Director that any of his duties in section 3 of the Telecommunications Act 1984 conflict with one or more of those policy objectives or regulatory principles, priority must be given to those objectives and principles.

[4422]

PART VI TELECOMMUNICATIONS

NOTES

Commencement: 24 February 2003.

5 Market identification and analysis

(1) The Director shall—

(a) make proposals for identification (by reference, in particular, to area and locality) of the markets for electronic communications networks, electronic communications services and associated facilities which in his opinion are the ones which in the circumstances of the United Kingdom are the markets in relation to which it is appropriate to consider whether to make a determination that a person has significant market power;

(b) carry out an analysis of the identified markets; and

(c) based on that market analysis, make proposals for determination as to whether any person in the identified markets has significant market power.

(2) In identifying and analysing those markets, and in considering whether to make any such proposals, the Director must take due account of all applicable guidelines and recommendations which—

(a) have been issued or made by the European Commission in pursuance of a Community instrument; and

(b) relate to market analysis or the determination of what constitutes significant market power.

(3) A person shall be taken to have significant market power in relation to a market if he enjoys a position which amounts to or is equivalent to dominance of the market.

(4) References in this regulation to dominance of a market must be construed in accordance with any applicable provisions of Article 14 of the Framework Directive.

(5) A person is to be taken to enjoy a position of dominance of a market if he is one of a number of persons who enjoy such a position in combination with each other.

(6) A person or combination of persons may also be taken to enjoy a position of dominance of a market by reason wholly or partly of his or their position in a closely related market if the links between the two markets allow the market power held in the closely related market to be used in a way that influences the other market so as to strengthen the position in the other market of that person or combination of persons.

(7) The matters which must be taken into account in determining whether a combination of persons enjoys a position of dominance include, in particular, those matters set out in Annex II of the Framework Directive.

[4423]

NOTES

Commencement: 24 February 2003.

6 Notifications for market identification etc

(1) Proposals for identifying a market or making a market power determination shall be made by means of a notification published by the Director.

(2) Notifications for the purposes of paragraph (1)—

(a) may be given separately; or

(b) may be contained in a single notification relating to both the identification of a market and the making of a market power determination.

(3) A notification for the purposes of paragraph (1) must—

(a) state that the Director is proposing to identify the market which is the subject of the proposal or to make that market power determination;

(b) set out the effect of the proposal;

(c) give his reasons for making the proposal; and

(d) specify the period within which representations may be made to the Director about the proposals set out in his notification.

(4) A notification which sets out proposals for the making of a market power determination may also set out the conditions that the Director is proposing to set by reference

to that market power determination so as to bind the person whom the Director is proposing to determine as having significant market power in the identified market.

(5) Where a notification published in accordance with paragraph (1) sets out the conditions that the Director is proposing to set, the notification must set out—

(a) the effect of those conditions; and

(b) the reasons for setting those conditions.

(6) The period specified for the purpose of paragraph (3)(d) must be one of not less than one month, beginning with the day after the day on which the notification is published.

(7) The publication of a notification under this regulation must be in such manner as appears to the Director to be appropriate for bringing it to the attention of the persons who, in the Director's opinion, are likely to have an interest in, or be affected by, it.

(8) Any proposed conditions which the Director sets out in a notification published under this regulation must comply with, and be necessary for satisfying requirements in, Article 16 of the Framework Directive, Articles 7 to 13 of the Access Directive and Articles 16 to 19 of the Universal Service Directive.

[4424]

NOTES

Commencement: 24 February 2003.

7 Notifications for conditions set by reference to market power determination

(1) Following the publication of a notification under regulation 6 which sets out proposals about the making of a market power determination ("the market power notification"), the Director may publish further notifications setting out one or more of the following—

(a) conditions or further conditions that he is proposing to set by reference to the market power determination proposed in the market power notification; and

(b) modifications which he is proposing to make to the proposals to set conditions set out in the market power notification.

(2) A further notification must set out—

(a) the market power determination proposed in the market power notification;

(b) where the market power notification included proposals for the setting of conditions in accordance with paragraph (4) of regulation 6—

(i) any modification (if any) of those proposals which the Director is proposing to make; and

(ii) any further conditions (if any) the Director is proposing to set by reference to the market power determination proposed in the market power notification;

(c) where the market power notification did not include proposals for the setting of conditions in accordance with paragraph (4) of regulation 6, any conditions which the Director is proposing to set by reference to the market power determination proposed in the market power notification;

(d) the effect of making those modifications and setting those conditions;

(e) the reasons for proposing to make those modifications and set those conditions; and

(f) the period within which representations about the proposals set out in the further notification in accordance with paragraphs (b) and (c) may be made to the Director.

(3) The period specified for the purpose of paragraph (2)(f) must be one of not less than one month, beginning with the day after the day on which the notification is published.

(4) The Director may give effect, with or without modifications, to a proposal to make a modification to proposals to set conditions in the market power notification, only if he has considered every representation about the proposal that is made to him within the period specified in the notification; and the way in which the Director gives effect to such a proposal is by the publication of a notification.

(5) The publication of a notification under this regulation must be in such manner as appears to the Director to be appropriate for bringing it to the attention of the persons who, in the Director's opinion, are likely to have an interest in, or be affected by, it.

(6) Any proposed conditions or modification to conditions which the Director sets out in a notification published under this regulation must comply with, and be necessary for satisfying requirements in, Article 16 of the Framework Directive, Articles 7 to 13 of the Access Directive and Articles 16 to 19 of the Universal Service Directive.

[4425]

NOTES

Commencement: 24 February 2003.

8 Confirmation of proposals

(1) This regulation applies to—

(a) any proposals set out in a notification published under regulation 6 to the extent that they have not been modified by a notification published under regulation 7(4);

(b) any proposals to set conditions which have been modified by a notification published under regulation 7(4); and

(c) any proposals to set conditions set out in a notification published under regulation 7(1)(a).

(2) Subject to regulation 9, and if he has considered every representation about the proposals, set out in a notification, to which this regulation applies that is made to him within the period specified in the notification, the Director may, by publication of a further notification, set out the proposals, with or without modification, as he intends that effect would be given to them upon the coming into force of any enactment (including an enactment contained in subordinate legislation) which implements the provision of the Framework Directive, the Access Directive or the Universal Service Directive to which the proposal relates; and reference in this regulation to confirmation of proposals is a reference to publication of such a further notification.

(3) Where the Director has confirmed any proposals under paragraph (2), he may, by publication of a further notification, withdraw part or all of those proposals.

(4) Any proposed conditions which the Director sets out in a notification published under this regulation must comply with, and be necessary for satisfying requirements in, Article 16 of the Framework Directive, Articles 7 to 13 of the Access Directive and Articles 16 to 19 of the Universal Service Directive.

[4426]

NOTES

Commencement: 24 February 2003.

9 European Commission's control of market identification and analysis

(1) The Director shall send a copy of each notification published under regulations 6 and 7 to—

(a) the Secretary of State; and

(b) where the proposal in the notification would, in the opinion of the Director, affect trade between member States, to the European Commission and to the national regulatory authorities (as defined in Article 2(g) of the Framework Directive) of every other member State.

(2) If, within the representations period, the Director is notified by the European Commission for the purposes of Article 7(4) of the Framework Directive (market identifications that do not conform to Commission recommendations and determinations that affect trade between member States)—

(a) that the Commission considers that giving effect to the proposal would create a barrier in relation to the single European market, or

(b) that the Commission has serious doubts as to whether giving effect to the proposal would be compatible with the requirements of any Community obligations,

the Director is not to confirm the proposal, in accordance with regulation 8, before the end of a further two months beginning with the end of the representations period.

(3) Where, before the end of that two month period, the European Commission makes a decision in accordance with Article 7(4) of the Framework Directive that the proposal should be withdrawn, the Director—

(a) must withdraw it; and

(b) shall not be entitled to confirm it in accordance with regulation 8.

(4) In this regulation "the representations period", in relation to a notification under regulations 6 and 7, means the period specified in that notification for the making of representations about the proposals contained in it.

[4427]

NOTES

Commencement: 24 February 2003.

10 Information requirements for carrying out market analysis

For the purposes of regulations 5, 6, 7, 8 and 9, section 53 of the Telecommunications Act 1984 shall apply as if the exercise by the Director of the functions under those regulations was a relevant purpose under subsection (6) of that section.

[4428]

NOTES

Commencement: 24 February 2003.

11 Appeals

Section 46B of the Telecommunications Act 1984 shall apply to decisions made by the Director under these Regulations as it applies to the decisions set out in subsection (1) of that section.

[4429]

NOTES

Commencement: 24 February 2003.

WIRELESS TELEGRAPHY (INTERCEPTION AND DISCLOSURE OF MESSAGES) (DESIGNATION) REGULATIONS 2003

(SI 2003/3104)

NOTES

Made: 28 November 2003.
Authority: Wireless Telegraphy Act 1949, s 5(7)(c), (12)(c).
Commencement: 29 December 2003.

1 Citation and commencement

These Regulations may be cited as the Wireless Telegraphy (Interception and Disclosure of Messages) (Designation) Regulations 2003 and shall come into force on 29th December 2003.

[4430]

NOTES

Commencement: 29 December 2003.

2 (*Revokes the Wireless Telegraphy* (*Interception and Disclosure of Messages*) (*Designation*) *Regulations 2000, SI 2000/2409.*)

3 Designation of persons

The persons for the time being who hold the respective positions of Operations Director and Head of Field Operations of the Office of Communications established under the Office of Communications Act 2002 are hereby designated for the purposes of section 5(7)(c) and (12)(c) of the Wireless Telegraphy Act 1949.

[4431]

NOTES

Commencement: 29 December 2003.

ELECTROMAGNETIC COMPATIBILITY REGULATIONS 2005

(SI 2005/281)

NOTES

Made: 2 February 2005.
Authority: European Communities Act 1972, s 2(2).
Commencement: 7 March 2005.

ARRANGEMENT OF REGULATIONS

PART I
PRELIMINARY

PART II
APPLICATION

General Application

Modified application

Exclusions

Apparatus covered by other Directives

PART III
GENERAL REQUIREMENTS

PART IV
THE STANDARDS ROUTE TO COMPLIANCE

PART V
THE TECHNICAL CONSTRUCTION FILE ROUTE TO COMPLIANCE

General

United Kingdom competent bodies

EC declaration of conformity

Final Provisions

PART VI
THE EC TYPE-EXAMINATION ROUTE TO COMPLIANCE FOR RADIOCOMMUNICATION TRANSMISSION APPARATUS

General

United Kingdom notified bodies

EC declaration of conformity

Final provisions

PART VII
ENFORCEMENT

Enforcement authorities and powers

Offences

Powers of the court

PART I
PRELIMINARY

1 Citation and commencement

These Regulations may be cited as the Electromagnetic Compatibility Regulations 2005, and shall come into force on 7th March 2005.

[4432]

NOTES

Commencement: 7 March 2005.

2 Repeal and disapplication

(1) The following Regulations are hereby revoked—

(a) the Electromagnetic Compatibility Regulations 1992;
(b) the Electromagnetic Compatibility (Amendment) Regulations 1994; and
(c) the Electromagnetic Compatibility (Amendment) Regulations 1995.

(2) The regulations made under section 10 of the Wireless Telegraphy Act 1949 listed in Schedule 1, to the extent that they impose electromagnetic compatibility requirements which must be complied with if relevant apparatus is—

(a) to be supplied or taken into service and
(b) used for the purpose for which it was intended,

shall cease to have effect, but nothing in these Regulations shall affect the said regulations to the extent that they impose requirements for radio frequency spectrum planning or for the prevention of undue interference to wireless telegraphy from relevant apparatus in use.

[4433]

NOTES

Commencement: 7 March 2005.

3 Interpretation

(1) In these Regulations,

"the 1949 Act" means the Wireless Telegraphy Act 1949;

"the 1984 Act" means the Telecommunications Act 1984;

"the EMC Directive" means Council Directive 89/336/EEC on the approximation of the laws of the member States relating to electromagnetic compatibility as amended by

(a) Council Directive 92/31/EEC; and

(b) Articles 5, 14.1 and 14.2 of Council Directive 93/68/EEC (the CE Marking Directive);

"affixed" in relation to the CE marking, or any inscription which is liable to be confused therewith, or which is likely to deceive third parties as to the meaning and form thereof, means affixed to one of the items mentioned in regulation 35(2) below or to any other item such that it is referable to any apparatus;

"authorised representative" means a person established within the Community appointed by the manufacturer (whether or not established in the Community) to act on his behalf in fulfilling his obligations under the EMC Directive as implemented by these Regulations;

"business" includes a profession and an undertaking, and a supply in the course of a business includes any supply by a business;

"CE marking" and "CE conformity marking" shall be construed in accordance with regulation 35 below;

"the Commission" means the Commission of the European Communities;

"the Community" means the European Community;

"competent body" shall be construed in accordance with regulation 47 below;

"conformity assessment requirements" shall be construed in accordance with regulation 33 below;

"EC declaration of conformity" has the meaning given in regulation 36(1) below;

"EC type-examination certificate" in relation to the EC type-examination route to compliance in respect of radiocommunication transmission apparatus means an EC type-examination certificate issued by—

(a) a United Kingdom notified body pursuant to regulation 66 below; or

(b) a notified body of an EEA state other than the United Kingdom pursuant to Article 10.5 of the EMC Directive;

"the EC type-examination route to compliance" in relation to radiocommunication transmission apparatus shall be construed in accordance with regulation 33(b) below;

"education and training equipment" means any relevant apparatus (including a kit)—

(a) supplied or possessed for supply to education or training establishments or manufactured in such an establishment for the purposes of experimentation, learning or practical training; and

(b) the usual electromagnetic environment of which is a classroom, laboratory, study area or similar such place;

"electrical apparatus" shall be construed in accordance with regulation 7(2) below;

"enforcement authority" in relation to any relevant apparatus means any person who is, pursuant to the provisions of regulation 75 below, authorised to act as an enforcement authority in relation to that relevant apparatus;

"end user" means

(a) a manufacturer who first uses electrical apparatus which he has manufactured for the purpose for which it is designed, but excludes a manufacturer who uses the apparatus by incorporating it into other apparatus; and

(b) any other person who uses the electrical apparatus;

"excluded installation" has the meaning giving by regulation 12(2);

"immunity" means immunity to electromagnetic disturbance;

"kit" means a collection of all or substantially all the necessary components, for supply as a single commercial unit, required for the construction of an item of electrical apparatus and intended for such use, whether or not accompanied by instructions. For the purposes of the definition of "system" in this paragraph and of the application of regulation 7 below, a kit shall be considered to be a system with an intrinsic function intended for the end user notwithstanding that, when it is supplied, it is not yet assembled;

"manufacture" means manufacture in the course of a business, and includes—

(a) assembly;

(b) finishing;

(c) reconditioning;

(d) modification which substantially alters the electromagnetic compatibility characteristics of the apparatus;

but does not include repair or the assembly of relevant apparatus from a kit;

"medical device" has the meaning given by regulation 22(3) below;

"notified body" shall be construed in accordance with regulation 63 below;

"OFCOM" means the Office of Communications established under the Office of Communications Act 2002;

"presumption of conformity" shall be construed in accordance with regulation 34 below;

"protection requirements" has the meaning given by regulation 5 below;

"radio amateur apparatus" means wireless telegraphy apparatus designed or adapted for use in the amateur service, but excludes citizens' band apparatus, and in this definition—

(a) "amateur service" has the meaning given by Article 1, definition 1.56 of the 2001 edition of the Radio Regulations annexed to the International Telecommunication Constitution 1992 pursuant to Articles 4 and 54 of that Constitution; and

(b) "citizen's band apparatus" means wireless telegraphy apparatus designed or adapted exclusively for the provision of voice radiocommunication in the frequency bands 26.960 MHz to 27.410 MHz and 27.60125 MHz to 27.99125 MHz;

"radiocommunication transmission apparatus" has the meaning given by regulation 61(2) below;

"radio frequency spectrum" means that part of the electromagnetic spectrum at frequencies not exceeding 3,000 GHz; and requirements of regulations made under section 10 of the 1949 Act shall be taken to concern radio frequency spectrum planning if they concern the frequency allocation for any apparatus (whether wireless telegraphy apparatus or other apparatus which operates by emitting electromagnetic radiation in the radio frequency spectrum) and the necessary characteristics of any signal or emission authorised by such regulations;

"relevant apparatus" shall be construed in accordance with regulation 6 below;

"responsible person" in relation to relevant apparatus means—

(a) the manufacturer;

(b) the manufacturer's authorised representative; or

(c) where the manufacturer is not established in the Community and he has not appointed an authorised representative, the person who supplies the relevant apparatus;

"the standards route to compliance" in relation to relevant apparatus other than radiocommunication transmission apparatus shall be construed in accordance with regulation 33(a)(i) below;

"supply" means the first making available of relevant apparatus in the Community including, offering to supply, agreeing to supply, exposing for supply and possessing for supply such apparatus; but relevant apparatus shall not be regarded as having been supplied by reason only of its having been displayed at a trade fair or exhibition or advertised for supply when not available for supply;

"system" means an item of equipment, or a combination of items of equipment, containing—

(a) electrical components;

(b) electronic components; or

(c) both (a) and (b),

and includes a kit but excludes any such equipment containing a medical device;

"technical certificate" in relation to the technical construction file route to compliance in respect of relevant apparatus other than radiocommunication transmission apparatus means a technical certificate issued by—

(a) a United Kingdom competent body in accordance with regulation 52 below; or

(b) a competent body of an EEA State other than the United Kingdom pursuant to Article 10.2 of the EMC Directive;

"technical construction file" shall be construed in accordance with regulation 45 below;

"the technical construction file route to compliance" in relation to relevant apparatus other than radiocommunication transmission apparatus shall be construed in accordance with regulation 33(a)(ii) below;

"technical report" in relation to the technical construction file route to compliance in respect of relevant apparatus other than radiocommunication transmission apparatus means a technical report issued by—

(a) a United Kingdom competent body in accordance with regulation 52 below; or

(b) a competent body of an EEA State other than the United Kingdom pursuant to Article 10.2 of the EMC Directive;

PART VI TELECOMMUNICATIONS

"test apparatus" means relevant apparatus designed or adapted to generate or be susceptible to electromagnetic disturbance for the specific purpose of conducting any test or measurement in relation to—

(a) any relevant apparatus; or

(b) any other thing, matter or phenomenon;

"United Kingdom competent body" shall be construed in accordance with regulation 48 below;

"United Kingdom notified body" shall be construed in accordance with regulation 64 below; and

"wireless telegraphy", "wireless telegraphy apparatus" and "station for wireless telegraphy" have the meanings given respectively by section 19(1) of the 1949 Act.

(2) For the purpose of these Regulations—

(a) "electromagnetic compatibility" ("EMC") is the ability of relevant apparatus to function satisfactorily in its electromagnetic environment without introducing intolerable electromagnetic disturbance to anything in that environment;

(b) the electromagnetic ("EM") characteristics of relevant apparatus comprise—

(i) the propensity of that apparatus to generate electromagnetic disturbance; and

(ii) the adequacy of the immunity of that apparatus to external electromagnetic disturbance;

(c) a reference to an applicable EM characteristic of relevant apparatus is a reference to—

(i) in the case of apparatus to which regulations 27 to 29 below apply, any EM characteristic thereof which falls within the scope of these Regulations; and

(ii) in the case of any other apparatus, any EM characteristic thereof;

(d) "applicable EMC standard", "harmonised standard", "recognised national standard" and "transposed harmonised standard" shall be construed in accordance with regulation 40 below;

(e) an electromagnetic environment is the totality of electromagnetic phenomena existing at a given location, and

(i) a reference to the immediate electromagnetic environment in relation to education and training equipment or test apparatus ("disturbance permissible apparatus") is a reference to a sufficient space for that apparatus to—

(aa) operate as intended, where the object of the study or test as the case may be is that it should generate electromagnetic disturbance;

(bb) be subjected to electromagnetic disturbance, where the object of the study or test as the case may be is that it should be the victim of electromagnetic disturbance,

without preventing other relevant apparatus (other than any apparatus involved in the study or test) from operating as intended; and in this definition, "sufficient space" means a space no greater in size than is reasonably necessary having regard to all the circumstances, to enable the disturbance permissible apparatus to be so operated or so subjected, and having regard in particular to the steps which might reasonably be taken to insulate the site at which the disturbance permissible apparatus is being used against the escape of emissions therefrom;

(ii) a reference to a sealed electromagnetic environment is a reference to an electromagnetic environment which prevents relevant apparatus therein from causing electromagnetic disturbance to relevant apparatus outside that electromagnetic environment and includes an anechoic chamber, an electromagnetic anechoic room or a Faraday cage; and

(iii) a reference to the usual electromagnetic environment of apparatus is a reference to—

(aa) where the apparatus is manufactured or supplied for the purpose of being used at a specific location, the totality of electromagnetic phenomena which exist at that location under normal circumstances at the time when it is first used; or

(bb) where sub-paragraph (aa) above does not apply, the totality of electromagnetic phenomena which might reasonably be expected to exist at the usual range of locations at which that relevant apparatus might reasonably be expected to be used, having regard to all the circumstances, and in particular to—

(iv) the electromagnetic phenomena associated with that relevant apparatus and other relevant apparatus which might reasonably be expected to be in sufficient proximity to the first mentioned relevant apparatus to be affected thereby; and

(v) any indication by the manufacturer or supplier of the applications for which the first-mentioned relevant apparatus is suitable; and

(f) relevant apparatus other than a kit is taken into service when it is first used by the person who assembled it or the person who imported it from a country or territory other than a member State; but relevant apparatus shall not be regarded as having been taken into service by reason only of its having been operated by or on behalf of the manufacturer at a trade fair or exhibition or by a supplier for demonstration purposes.

(3) In these Regulations, with respect to matters arising on and after 1st January 1994, a reference to the Community includes a reference to the EEA States, and for the purposes of this paragraph an EEA state means a member State, Norway, Iceland or Liechtenstein.

[4434]

NOTES

Commencement: 7 March 2005.

4 Electromagnetic disturbance

In these Regulations, "electromagnetic disturbance" means, subject to paragraphs (2) to (6) below, any electromagnetic phenomenon which is liable to degrade the performance of relevant apparatus.

(1) Without prejudice to the generality of paragraph (1) above, the following phenomena shall be regarded as electromagnetic disturbance (being phenomena expressly stated to be such in Article 1.2 of the EMC Directive):—

(a) electromagnetic noise;
(b) unwanted signals; and
(c) changes in the propagation medium.

(2) Without prejudice to the generality of paragraph (1) above and in addition to the phenomena regarded as electromagnetic disturbance pursuant to paragraph (2) above, the phenomena and effects listed in Schedule 2 hereto may be regarded as electromagnetic disturbance.

(3) A signal or emission which is a necessary function, or consequence of the operation, of relevant apparatus shall not be taken to be electromagnetic disturbance if, in relation to that apparatus, that signal or emission is permitted, and does not exceed the limits specified, by—

(a) the applicable EMC standard;
(b) a condition of the technical report or technical certificate;
(c) where the apparatus is radiocommunication transmission apparatus—
  (i) a condition of the EC type-examination certificate; or
  (ii) a term, provision or limitation of—
    (aa) a licence granted under section 1 of the 1949 Act; or
    (bb) regulations made under that section; or
(d) where the apparatus is—
  (i) radiocommunication transmission apparatus; or
  (ii) apparatus other than wireless telegraphy apparatus which operates by emitting electromagnetic radiation in the radio frequency spectrum,

any relevant provisions of regulations made under section 10 of the 1949 Act concerning radio frequency spectrum planning.

(4) A nuclear electromagnetic pulse ("NEMP") shall not be regarded as electromagnetic disturbance.

(5) Without prejudice to the generality of the foregoing provisions of this regulation, the performance of relevant apparatus shall be taken to be degraded if any of the following types of interference with its function occur—

(a) permanent, temporary or intermittent—
  (i) total loss of function;
  (ii) significant impairment of function; or
(b) where the apparatus is information storage or retrieval equipment, destruction or corruption of information stored thereby.

[4435]

PART VI TELECOMMUNICATIONS

NOTES

Commencement: 7 March 2005.

5 Protection requirements

(1) A reference to "protection requirements" in relation to relevant apparatus is a reference to the requirements set out in the following provisions of this regulation.

(2) Subject to paragraphs (3) to (5) below, relevant apparatus shall be so constructed that—

(a) the electromagnetic disturbance it generates does not exceed a level allowing other relevant apparatus to operate as intended; and

(b) it has a level of intrinsic immunity which is adequate to enable it to operate as intended,

when it is—

(i) properly installed and maintained; and

(ii) used for the purpose for which it was intended.

(3) Nothing in paragraph (2) above shall be taken to require relevant apparatus, not being apparatus specifically designed for use at a given location, to be constructed in such a manner as to—

(a) prevent the generation of electromagnetic disturbance to, or

(b) provide for intrinsic immunity to electromagnetic disturbance generated by,

other relevant apparatus which would not reasonably be expected to be present in its usual electromagnetic environment.

(4) Without prejudice to the generality of paragraph (2)(a), the electromagnetic disturbance generated by relevant apparatus shall—

(a) not exceed a level allowing radio and telecommunications equipment to operate as intended; and

(b) be such as not to hinder the use of apparatus of any of the descriptions listed in Schedule 3 hereto (being descriptions listed in the illustrative list of the principal protection requirements in Annex III of the EMC Directive) where that apparatus is constructed in such a way that it has an adequate level of immunity in its usual electromagnetic environment so as to allow its unhindered operation taking into account the levels of electromagnetic disturbance generated by relevant apparatus complying with applicable EMC standards.

(5) Without prejudice to the generality of paragraph (2)(b)—

(a) relevant apparatus shall be constructed in such a way that it has an adequate level of immunity in its usual electromagnetic environment so as to allow its unhindered operation taking into account the levels of electromagnetic disturbance generated by other relevant apparatus which might reasonably be expected to be present in that environment and which complies with the protection requirements; and

(b) whether the level of intrinsic immunity of relevant apparatus is adequate is to be considered having regard to all the circumstances of the case, and in particular to—

(i) the level of performance reasonably expected of that apparatus having regard to its function or intended function;

(ii) any specification for an acceptable level of degradation of performance provided to the end user by the manufacturer;

(iii) the consequences of degradation of performance,

but nothing in this sub-paragraph shall authorise a level of intrinsic immunity which could permit the operation of the apparatus to be dangerous (either to persons or property) in any reasonably foreseeable circumstances.

(6) The information required to enable use in accordance with the intended purpose of the relevant apparatus must be contained in the manufacturer's instructions accompanying the apparatus.

[4436]

NOTES

Commencement: 7 March 2005.

PART II
APPLICATION

General Application

6 Relevant apparatus

(1) Subject to paragraph (2) below, this Part shall have effect for the purposes of providing for the application of these Regulations, and apparatus to which these Regulations apply shall be relevant apparatus.

(2) In addition to applying to relevant apparatus, the following provisions of these Regulations apply as follows:—

(a) Part I, and regulations 35(6), 36(4), 76 to 79, 82, 83, 84(c) and (d), 86 to 88, 91 to 93 and 95 to 99, apply to electrical apparatus other than relevant apparatus; and

(b) Part I and regulations 7(2), 82, 83, 86, 92, 93, 95, and 99 apply to an excluded installation as a unit (without prejudice to the application of the provisions referred to in sub-paragraph (a) above to such installation or any part thereof on the ground that it is electrical apparatus).

[4437]

NOTES

Commencement: 7 March 2005.

7 General conditions of application

(1) Subject to regulations 8 and 9 below, these Regulations apply to electrical apparatus unless, pursuant to regulations 10 to 29 below, it falls outside the scope of these Regulations.

(2) For the purposes of these Regulations, electrical apparatus consists of a product—

(a) with an intrinsic function intended for the end user; and

(b) supplied or intended for supply or taken into service or intended to be taken into service as a single commercial unit,

which is—

(i) an electrical appliance;

(ii) an electronic appliance; or

(iii) a system.

[4438]

NOTES

Commencement: 7 March 2005.

Modified application

8 Education and training equipment

(1) This regulation applies to education and training equipment which would not, except for the provisions of this regulation, conform with the protection requirements under normal conditions of use in its usual electromagnetic environment.

(2) Education and training equipment to which this regulation applies shall be deemed to conform with the protection requirements if it satisfies the following conditions—

(a) in relation to supply, the apparatus is accompanied by a declaration in English stating that the use of the apparatus outside the classroom, laboratory, study area or similar such place invalidates conformity with the protection requirements of the EMC Directive and could lead to prosecution; and

(b) the equipment when operated does not cause electromagnetic disturbance to apparatus situated outside its immediate electromagnetic environment.

[4439]

NOTES

Commencement: 7 March 2005.

9 Test apparatus

In the application of these Regulations to test apparatus, a reference to the protection requirements—

(a) insofar as it relates to the electromagnetic disturbance generated by that apparatus shall be construed as a reference to that disturbance capable of preventing relevant apparatus situated outside the immediate electromagnetic environment of that apparatus from operating as intended; and

(b) insofar as it relates to the immunity of that apparatus, shall not be taken to refer to any susceptibility to electromagnetic disturbance which is a necessary feature of that apparatus to facilitate the conducting of the test.

[4440]

NOTES

Commencement: 7 March 2005.

Exclusions

10 Apparatus supplied or taken into service before 28th October 1992

These Regulations do not apply to an item of electrical apparatus supplied or taken into service in the Community before 28th October 1992.

[4441]

NOTES

Commencement: 7 March 2005.

11 Apparatus for export to a third country outside the Community

(1) Subject to paragraph (2) below, these Regulations do not apply to any apparatus which the supplier believes (with reasonable cause) will not be used either in the United Kingdom or elsewhere in the Community.

(2) Paragraph (1) above shall not apply if the CE mark or any inscription liable to be confused therewith is affixed to the apparatus.

[4442]

NOTES

Commencement: 7 March 2005.

12 Excluded installations

(1) These Regulations do not apply to excluded installations; but the extent to which any apparatus or system comprised or to be comprised therein is relevant apparatus shall be determined in accordance with the provisions of this Part.

(2) In this regulation "excluded installation" means two or more combined items of relevant apparatus or systems put together at a given place (whether or not in combination with any other item) to fulfil a specific objective but not designed by the manufacturer (or manufacturers, where the items are made by different manufacturers) for supply as a single functional unit.

[4443]

NOTES

Commencement: 7 March 2005.

13 Spare parts

(1) Subject to paragraph (2), these Regulations do not apply to spare parts.

(2) Nothing in this regulation shall be taken to affect the application of these Regulations to apparatus into which a spare part has been incorporated.

(3) In this regulation, "spare part" means a component or combination of components intended for use in replacing parts of electrical apparatus.

[4444]

NOTES

Commencement: 7 March 2005.

14 Supply to the authorised representative

These Regulations do not apply to the supply of apparatus by the manufacturer thereof to his authorised representative.

[4445]

NOTES

Commencement: 7 March 2005.

15 Second-hand apparatus

(1) Subject to paragraph (2) below, these Regulations do not apply to second-hand apparatus.

(2) Nothing in paragraph (1) above shall be taken to disapply these Regulations to—

(a) the supply of second-hand apparatus which has, since it was last used, been subjected to further manufacture within the meaning of sub-paragraphs (c) or (d) of the definition of manufacture in regulation 3(1) above;

(b) the supply or taking into service of such apparatus following such further manufacture; or

(c) the supply or taking into service in the Community of apparatus which has previously been supplied or used in a country or territory outside the Community.

(3) In this regulation, "second-hand apparatus" means apparatus which has previously been used by an end user.

[4446]

NOTES

Commencement: 7 March 2005.

16 Electromagnetically benign apparatus

These Regulations do not apply to apparatus the inherent qualities of which are such that neither is it liable to cause, nor is its performance liable to be degraded by, electromagnetic disturbance.

[4447]

NOTES

Commencement: 7 March 2005.

17 Apparatus for use in a sealed electromagnetic environment

These Regulations do not apply to—

(a) the supply of any apparatus—

(i) for which the usual electromagnetic environment is a sealed electromagnetic environment; and

(ii) which is accompanied by instructions which state that the apparatus is suitable for use only in a sealed electromagnetic environment; or

(b) the taking into service of any apparatus in such an environment.

[4448]

NOTES

Commencement: 7 March 2005.

18 Radio amateur apparatus

(1) These Regulations do not apply to radio amateur apparatus which is not available commercially.

PART VI TELECOMMUNICATIONS

(2) In this regulation, "available commercially" means manufactured in the course of a business of manufacture of relevant apparatus.

[4449]

NOTES

Commencement: 7 March 2005.

19 Military equipment

(1) These Regulations do not apply to military equipment.

(2) In this regulation, "military equipment" means apparatus which is designed for use as arms, munitions or war material within the meaning of Article 223.1(b) of the Treaty establishing the European Community (notwithstanding that it may be capable of other applications), but does not include apparatus which is designed both for such use and for other applications.

[4450]

NOTES

Commencement: 7 March 2005.

Apparatus covered by other Directives

20 Active implantable medical devices

(1) These Regulations do not apply to active implantable medical devices.

(2) In this regulation "active implantable medical device" has the meaning given by Article 1.2(c) of Council Directive 90/385/EEC on the approximation of laws of the member States relating to active implantable medical devices.

[4451]

NOTES

Commencement: 7 March 2005.

21 In vitro medical devices

(1) These Regulations do not apply to in vitro medical devices and their accessories.

(2) In this regulation "in vitro medical device" has the meaning given by Article 1.2(b) of Directive 98/79/EC concerning in vitro medical devices and "accessory" has the meaning given in Article 1.2(c) of that Directive.

[4452]

NOTES

Commencement: 7 March 2005.

22 Medical devices

(1) These Regulations do not apply to medical devices.

(2) Insofar as the Wireless Telegraphy (Control of Interference from Electro Medical Apparatus) Regulations 1963 impose electromagnetic compatibility requirements which must be complied with if a relevant medical device is to be supplied, used or taken into service, those Regulations shall cease to apply except where the manufacturer elects to comply with the Wireless Telegraphy (Control of Interference from Electro Medical Apparatus) Regulations 1963 if applicable.

(3) In this regulation "medical device" has the meaning given by Article 1.2(a) of Directive 93/42/EEC concerning medical devices.

[4453]

NOTES

Commencement: 7 March 2005.

23 Vehicles, components and separate technical units

(1) These Regulations do not apply to vehicles, components or separate technical units.

(2) In this regulation, in accordance with Council Directive 72/245/EEC relating to the radio interference (electromagnetic compatibility) of vehicles as adapted to technical progress and amended by Commission Directive 95/54/EC, "vehicle", "component" and "separate technical unit" have the meanings respectively given to them by Article 2 of Council Directive 70/156/EEC on the approximation of the laws of the member States relating to the type-approval of motor vehicles and their trailers, as amended by Council Directive 92/53/EEC.

[4454]

NOTES

Commencement: 7 March 2005.

24 Agricultural or forestry tractors

(1) These Regulations do not apply to agricultural or forestry tractors insofar as the electromagnetic disturbance generated by them is liable to cause radio interference.

(2) In this regulation, "agricultural or forestry tractor" has the meaning given to "vehicle" in Article 1 of Council Directive 75/322/EEC on the suppression of radio interference produced by agricultural or forestry tractors (electromagnetic compatibility) as amended by Commission Directive 2000/2/EC of 14 January 2000.

[4455]

NOTES

Commencement: 7 March 2005.

25 Two and three-wheel motor vehicles

(1) These Regulations do not apply to two and three-wheel motor vehicles.

(2) In this regulation, in accordance with Directive 97/24/EC on certain components and characteristics of two and three-wheel motor vehicles, "two and three-wheel motor vehicles" has the meaning given to two or three-wheel motor vehicles referred to in Article 1 of Directive 2002/24/EC relating to the type approval of two and three-wheel vehicles.

[4456]

NOTES

Commencement: 7 March 2005.

26 Marine Equipment

(1) These Regulations do not apply to marine equipment.

(2) In this regulation, "marine equipment" has the meaning given to "equipment", as defined in Article 2 (b) of Directive 96/98/EC on marine equipment, for use on board as provided for in Article 3 of that Directive.

[4457]

NOTES

Commencement: 7 March 2005.

27 Electrical Energy Meters

(1) These Regulations do not apply to electrical energy meters as regards the immunity thereof.

(2) In this regulation, "electrical energy meter" means any new directly connected induction meter, with single or multiple tariffs, designed to measure active energy single-phase or polyphase current at 53 Hz frequency mentioned or referred to in Article 2 of Council Directive 76/891/EEC on the approximation of the laws of the member States relating to electrical energy meters.

[4458]

NOTES
Commencement: 7 March 2005.

28 Non-automatic weighing instruments

(1) These Regulations do not apply to non-automatic weighing instruments as regards the immunity thereof.

(2) In this regulation, "non-automatic weighing instrument" has the meaning given by the second indent of Article 1.1 read in conjunction with Article 1.2(a) of Council Directive 90/384/EEC on the harmonisation of the laws of the member States relating to non-automatic weighing instruments.

[4459]

NOTES
Commencement: 7 March 2005.

[29 Radio equipment and telecommunications terminal equipment

These Regulations do not apply to equipment covered by Directive 1999/5/EC of the European Parliament and of the Council on radio equipment and telecommunications terminal equipment and the mutual recognition of their conformity as amended by Regulation (EC) No 1882/2003 of the European Parliament and of the Council.]

[4460]

NOTES
Commencement: 28 June 2006.
Substituted by the Electromagnetic Compatibility (Amendment) Regulations 2006, SI 2006/1449, reg 2.

[29A The Measuring Instruments Directive

(1) These Regulations do not apply to a measuring instrument or sub-assembly covered by Directive 2004/22/EC of the European Parliament and of the Council on measuring instruments which bear the—

(a) CE marking;
(b) M marking; and
(c) identification number of the notified body responsible for carrying out the conformity assessment of the instrument or sub-assembly

in accordance with the requirements of that Directive, as regards the immunity of such instrument or sub-assembly.

(2) For the purposes of this regulation, "measuring instrument" and "sub-assembly" have the meanings defined in that Directive.]

[4461]

NOTES
Commencement: 30 October 2006.
Inserted by the Measuring Instruments (Automatic Gravimetric Filling Instruments) Regulations 2006, SI 2006/1258, reg 33.

PART III
GENERAL REQUIREMENTS

30 General duty for supply

No person shall supply relevant apparatus unless the requirements of regulation 32 below are complied with in relation to such apparatus.

[4462]

NOTES
Commencement: 7 March 2005.

31 General duty for taking into service

No person shall take into service relevant apparatus unless that apparatus conforms with the protection requirements.

[4463]

NOTES

Commencement: 7 March 2005.

32 Requirements for supply

The requirements of this regulation are that—

(a) the relevant apparatus conforms with the protection requirements;

(b) the conformity assessment requirements have been complied with;

(c) the CE marking has been properly affixed by the manufacturer or his authorised representative in relation to the relevant apparatus in accordance with regulation 35 below; and

(d) the manufacturer or his authorised representative has properly issued an EC declaration of conformity in respect of the relevant apparatus in accordance with the requirements of regulation 36 below.

[4464]

NOTES

Commencement: 7 March 2005.

33 Conformity assessment requirements—the three routes to compliance

The conformity assessment requirements are that—

(a) in the case of relevant apparatus other than radiocommunication transmission apparatus, the requirements of—

(i) Part IV (in these Regulations referred to as "the standards route to compliance"); or

(ii) Part V (in these Regulations referred to as "the technical construction file route to compliance")

of these Regulations are complied with; and

(b) in the case of radiocommunication transmission apparatus, the requirements of Part VI (in these Regulations referred to as "the EC type-examination route to compliance") of these Regulations are complied with.

[4465]

NOTES

Commencement: 7 March 2005.

34 Presumption of conformity

Where in relation to any relevant apparatus—

(a) such apparatus conforms to the applicable EMC standard, or all applicable EMC standards, which make provision for that apparatus; or

(b) the conformity assessment requirements are complied with pursuant to the technical construction file route to compliance,

there shall be a presumption ("the presumption of conformity") that, until the contrary is proved, that relevant apparatus complies with the protection requirements.

[4466]

NOTES

Commencement: 7 March 2005.

35 The CE marking

(1) For the purposes of these Regulations, the CE marking shall be regarded as properly affixed in relation to relevant apparatus if the requirements of this regulation are complied with.

(2) The CE marking shall be affixed in relation to any relevant apparatus by being affixed to one of the following—

(a) the apparatus; or

(b) the apparatus'—

(i) packaging;

(ii) instructions for use; or

(iii) guarantee certificate.

(3) Subject to paragraph (4) below, where the apparatus is the subject of other Community Directives covering other aspects and which also provide for the CE conformity marking, the latter shall indicate that the apparatus is also presumed to conform to those other Directives.

(4) Where one or more of the other Directives referred to in paragraph (3) above allow the manufacturer, during a transitional period, to choose which arrangements to apply, the CE marking shall indicate conformity only to the Directives applied by the manufacturer. In this case, particulars of the Directives applied, as published in the Official Journal of the European Communities, must be given in the documents, notices or instructions required by the Directives and accompanying such apparatus.

(5) No person shall affix to relevant apparatus, its packaging, the instructions for use or the guarantee certificate any marking which is likely to deceive third parties as to the meaning and form of the CE marking. Any other marking may be affixed to the apparatus, its packaging, the instructions for use or the guarantee certificate provided that the visibility and legibility of the CE marking are not thereby reduced.

(6) No person shall affix the CE marking, or any other inscription liable to be confused with it, in relation to any relevant apparatus, unless—

(a) the apparatus complies with the protection requirements; and

(b) the conformity assessment requirements have been complied with.

(7) Except as provided in paragraph (3) above, no person shall affix the CE marking, or any other inscription liable to be confused with it, to any electrical apparatus other than relevant apparatus.

(8) The CE marking shall comply with the form requirements set out in Schedule 4 to these Regulations.

(9) In these Regulations, "CE marking" means the CE conformity marking, being a mark—

(a) consisting of the initials "CE";

(b) taking the form set out in paragraph 1 of Schedule 4 hereto; and

(c) which, when used in relation to the EMC Directive, indicates conformity to all the provisions of that Directive, including the conformity assessment requirements.

[4467]

NOTES

Commencement: 7 March 2005.

---

36 EC declaration of conformity

(1) For the purposes of these Regulations, an EC declaration of conformity is a declaration which indicates that apparatus conforms with the protection requirements of the EMC Directive (howsoever expressed).

(2) For the purposes of these Regulations, an EC declaration of conformity shall be regarded as properly issued in relation to relevant apparatus if the following requirements are complied with—

(a) the apparatus conforms with the protection requirements;

(b) the conformity assessment requirements are complied with;

(c) in the case of a declaration issued in the United Kingdom—

(i) in the case of a declaration issued pursuant to the standards route to compliance, it complies with the requirements of regulation 42 below;

(ii) in the case of a declaration issued pursuant to the technical construction file route to compliance, it complies with the requirements of regulation 59 below;

(iii) in the case of a declaration issued pursuant to the EC type-examination route to compliance, it complies with the requirements of regulation 72 below;

(d) in the case of a declaration issued other than in the United Kingdom, the declaration is issued by the manufacturer or his authorised representative and contains the following—

(i) a description of the apparatus to which it refers;

(ii) reference to the specifications or harmonised standards or both under which conformity is declared, and where appropriate, to the national measures or recognised national standards or both, as the case may be, implemented to ensure the conformity of the apparatus with the provisions of the EMC Directive;

(iii) identification of the signatory empowered to bind the manufacturer or his authorised representative; and

(iv) where appropriate, reference to the EC type-examination certificate issued by a notified body.

(3) No person shall (in the United Kingdom) issue an EC declaration of conformity in relation to relevant apparatus unless—

(a) the apparatus to which it relates conforms with the protection requirements;

(b) the conformity assessment requirements have been complied with; and

(c) the requirements of paragraph (2)(c) above are complied with.

(4) No person shall (in the United Kingdom) issue an EC declaration of conformity in relation to any electrical apparatus other than relevant apparatus.

[4468]

NOTES

Commencement: 7 March 2005.

37 Retention of documentation

(1) A responsible person shall hold an EC declaration of conformity in relation to relevant apparatus at the disposal of the Secretary of State for ten years beginning with the date on which the latest item of relevant apparatus to be supplied in the Community to which the declaration relates was so supplied.

(2) Where the EC declaration of conformity is made pursuant to Part V or VI of these Regulations, the responsible person shall hold the technical construction file, or EC type-examination certificate, as the case may be, at the disposal of the Secretary of State for ten years beginning with the date on which the latest item of relevant apparatus to be supplied in the Community to which the technical construction file or EC type-examination certificate relates was so supplied.

(3) Any documentation to be retained by the responsible person pursuant to the requirements of paragraphs (1) and (2) above may be kept by recording the matters in question in any form, provided that adequate precautions shall be taken for guarding against falsification.

(4) The power conferred on a responsible person in paragraph (3) above includes power to keep the documentation by recording those matters otherwise than in legible form, so long as the recording is capable of being reproduced in a legible form.

(5) If the responsible person records the documentation in question otherwise than in a legible form, any duty imposed on him by these Regulations to allow inspection of, or to furnish a copy of, the documentation or any part of it is to be treated as a duty to allow inspection of, or to furnish, a reproduction of the document or of the relevant part of it in legible form.

[4469]

NOTES

Commencement: 7 March 2005.

PART IV
THE STANDARDS ROUTE TO COMPLIANCE

38 Application of Part IV

(1) Subject to paragraph (2) below, this Part shall have effect for the purposes of providing for the manner in which the conformity assessment requirements may be complied with where the manufacturer has chosen the standards route to compliance.

(2) This Part does not, save for regulation 40, apply to radiocommunication transmission apparatus.

[4470]

NOTES

Commencement: 7 March 2005.

39 The standards route to compliance

The conformity assessment requirements are complied with pursuant to the standards route to compliance if the manufacturer has applied an applicable EMC standard which makes, or all applicable EMC standards which make, complete provision in respect of the apparatus.

[4471]

NOTES

Commencement: 7 March 2005.

40 Applicable EMC standards

(1) This regulation shall have effect for the purpose of making provision in respect of the standards which are to be recognised for the purposes of Article 7 of the EMC Directive.

(2) Except for regulation 49(4) below, a harmonised standard is a technical specification (European standard or harmonisation document)—

(a) adopted for the purposes of Article 7.1(a) of the EMC Directive by the European Committee for Electrotechnical Standardisation (CENELEC) or the European Telecommunications Standards Institute (ETSI) upon a remit from the Commission in accordance with the provisions of Council Directive 83/189/EEC laying down a procedure for the provision of information in the field of technical standards and regulations or Directive 98/34/EC as amended by Directive 98/48/EC;

(b) the reference number of which has been published in the Official Journal of the European Communities pursuant to that sub-article.

(3) A transposed harmonised standard is a national standard of a Member State—

(a) which transposes a harmonised standard; and

(b) the reference number of which has been published—

(i) by the relevant member State pursuant to Article 7.1(a) of the EMC Directive; or

(ii) in the case of a transposed harmonised standard of the United Kingdom, pursuant to regulation 41(1) below.

(4) A recognised national standard is a standard of a member State—

(a) which applies to relevant apparatus for which no harmonised standard has been adopted;

(b) which is recognised as a national standard for the purposes of Article 7.1(b) of the EMC Directive, the Commission having notified the member States pursuant to Articles 7.2 and 8.2 of that Directive that that standard enjoys the presumption of conformity with the protection requirements for the time being and published its reference number in the Official Journal pursuant to Article 7.2 of the Directive; and

(c) in the case of a recognised national standard of—

(i) a member State other than the United Kingdom, the reference number of which has been published by the relevant member State pursuant to the said Article 7.2;

(ii) the United Kingdom, the reference number of which has been published (and not withdrawn) pursuant to regulation 41(2) below.

(5) In relation to any description of relevant apparatus, an applicable EMC standard is either a transposed harmonised standard or a recognised national standard within the scope of which that description of relevant apparatus falls.

[4472]

NOTES

Commencement: 7 March 2005.

41 Publication of reference numbers of standards

(1) The Secretary of State shall from time to time publish pursuant to this paragraph, lists of the reference numbers of standards which are to be regarded as the transposed harmonised standards of the United Kingdom for the time being for the purposes of Article 7.1(a) of the EMC Directive.

(2) The Secretary of State shall from time to time publish pursuant to this paragraph lists of the reference numbers of standards which are to be regarded as the recognised national standards of the United Kingdom for the time being for the purposes of Article 7.1(b) of the EMC Directive.

(3) The Secretary of State shall from time to time publish lists of the reference numbers of standards which are for the time being transposed harmonised standards and recognised national standards of the member States other than the United Kingdom.

[4473]

NOTES

Commencement: 7 March 2005.

42 EC declaration of conformity pursuant to the standards route to compliance

(1) This regulation shall have effect for prescribing the form of an EC declaration of conformity issued in the United Kingdom in respect of relevant apparatus in relation to which the conformity assessment requirements have been complied with pursuant to the standards route to compliance.

(2) An EC declaration of conformity to which this regulation applies shall—

- (a) be in English;
- (b) give the name and address—
  - (i) of the responsible person;
  - (ii) where that person is not the manufacturer, of the manufacturer;
- (c) be signed by or on behalf of the manufacturer or his authorised representative and identify that signatory;
- (d) bear the date of issue;
- (e) give particulars of the relevant apparatus to which it relates sufficient to identify it;
- (f) state the numbers and titles of the applicable EMC standards applied by the manufacturer; and
- (g) certify that the apparatus to which it relates conforms with the protection requirements of the EMC Directive.

[4474]

NOTES

Commencement: 7 March 2005.

PART V
THE TECHNICAL CONSTRUCTION FILE ROUTE TO COMPLIANCE

General

43 Application of Part V

This Part shall have effect for the purposes of providing for—

- (a) the circumstances and manner in which the conformity assessment requirements may be complied with pursuant to the technical construction file route to compliance; and

(b) the appointment of United Kingdom competent bodies to exercise functions in relation thereto, and matters incidental to such appointment and exercise.

[4475]

NOTES

Commencement: 7 March 2005.

44 Applicability of the technical construction file route to compliance

(1) Subject to paragraph (2) below, the conformity assessment requirements may be complied with pursuant to the technical construction file route to compliance where—

(a) there are applicable EMC standards which make complete provision in respect of the apparatus, but the manufacturer has chosen not to apply all or any of those standards either as regards the whole or part thereof;

(b) there is no applicable EMC standard; or

(c) there are applicable EMC standards and the manufacturer has applied all or any of them as regards the whole or part thereof, but they do not make complete provision in respect of the apparatus.

(2) The technical construction file route to compliance shall not apply in respect of radiocommunication transmission apparatus.

[4476]

NOTES

Commencement: 7 March 2005.

45 Technical construction files

(1) A technical construction file is a file which—

(a) describes the apparatus to which it relates;

(b) contains information about the design, manufacture and operation thereof;

(c) sets out the procedures used to ensure the conformity of the apparatus with the protection requirements in respect of the applicable EM characteristics of the apparatus in respect of which the manufacturer has not applied an applicable EMC standard; and

(d) includes a technical report or technical certificate.

(2) A technical construction file may be composed in relation to—

(a) a single item of apparatus;

(b) where a number of items are to be produced, a specimen representative of the production envisaged (a "representative"); or

(c) a number of items of apparatus or representatives of each such item or representative being variants of the same basic design (each such item or representative being referred to as a "variant").

(3) Without prejudice to the generality of paragraph (1) above, a technical construction file composed in the United Kingdom shall—

(a) be in material form;

(b) be in—

  (i) English where application for the technical report or technical certificate is made to a United Kingdom competent body; or

  (ii) any official Community language acceptable to the competent body where such application is made to a competent body of another member State;

(c) give the name and address—

  (i) of the responsible person;

  (ii) where that person is not the manufacturer, of the manufacturer;

(d) contain such information as is sufficient, in all the circumstances of the case, to enable the enforcement authority to—

  (i) identify the apparatus to which it relates; and

  (ii) ascertain whether the apparatus to which it relates conforms with the protection requirements;

(e) state the numbers and titles of the applicable EMC standards, and any other standards, specifications or codes of practice, applied by the manufacturer; and

(f) contain particulars of the electromagnetic environment for which the apparatus is suitable.

[4477]

NOTES

Commencement: 7 March 2005.

46 The technical construction file route to compliance

The conformity assessment requirements are complied with in relation to relevant apparatus pursuant to the technical construction file route to compliance if the manufacturer or his authorised representative has composed a technical construction file in respect of the apparatus.

[4478]

NOTES

Commencement: 7 March 2005.

47 Competent bodies

For the purposes of these Regulations, a competent body is a body responsible for issuing technical reports and technical certificates pursuant to Article 10.2 of the EMC Directive either for all descriptions of relevant apparatus (other than radiocommunication transmission apparatus) or for specific descriptions thereof, and which is for the time being—

(a) a United Kingdom competent body pursuant to appointment under regulation 48 below;

(b) a competent body of a member State other than the United Kingdom; or

(c) recognised for the purpose of carrying out those functions by inclusion in a mutual recognition agreement relating to the EMC Directive or a similar agreement (including a Protocol to the Europe Agreement, or other Agreement, on Conformity Assessment and Acceptance of Industrial Products) which has been concluded between the Community and a State other than an EEA State.

[4479]

NOTES

Commencement: 7 March 2005.

United Kingdom competent bodies

48 Appointment

(1) Subject to regulation 49 below, the Secretary of State may appoint a person as a United Kingdom competent body in accordance with the following provisions of this regulation.

(2) An appointment under this regulation shall be in writing and shall, subject to regulations 50(5) and 51(3) below, be subject to such conditions as the Secretary of State may impose for the time being, and such conditions may include conditions which are to apply on or following the termination or expiry of the appointment.

(3) Subject to regulation 49(2) below, an appointment under this regulation shall have effect in respect of such descriptions of relevant apparatus as the Secretary of State may for the time being authorise, and in this Part, "authorised" shall be construed accordingly.

(4) In exercising the power conferred by paragraph (1) above, the Secretary of State may (in addition to the matters of which she is required to satisfy herself pursuant to regulation 49(2) below) have regard to any matter appearing to her to be relevant, and, without prejudice to the generality of the foregoing, she may have regard to any standards relating to the accreditation of laboratories or certification bodies appearing to her to be appropriate.

(5) Subject to regulation 50 below, an appointment under this regulation may be for—

(a) the time being; or

(b) such period as may be specified in the appointment.

PART VI TELECOMMUNICATIONS

(6) The Secretary of State shall from time to time publish lists of United Kingdom competent bodies indicating the descriptions of relevant apparatus in respect of which each body is authorised; and such lists may include information concerning any condition to which the appointment of any competent body is for the time being subject.

[4480]

NOTES

Commencement: 7 March 2005.

49 Eligibility and verification

(1) Subject to paragraph (2) below, the following persons shall be eligible for appointment as United Kingdom competent bodies—

(a) the Secretary of State; and

(b) any person resident, incorporated, or carrying on a business in the United Kingdom.

(2) The criteria listed in Schedule 5 hereto (being the criteria for the assessment of the bodies to be notified listed in Annex II of the EMC Directive and the criteria which competent bodies are required by Article 1.5 of that Directive to meet) ("the minimum criteria") must be satisfied in relation to any person if that person is to be appointed or remain a United Kingdom competent body, and accordingly the Secretary of State shall not—

(a) make an appointment under regulation 48(1) above unless she is satisfied that the person concerned meets the minimum criteria; or

(b) authorise under regulation 48(3) above the appointment to have effect in relation to any description of relevant apparatus unless she is satisfied that the body meets the minimum criteria in respect of that description of apparatus.

(3) The Secretary of State shall from time to time verify that each United Kingdom competent body meets the minimum criteria listed in paragraphs 1 and 2 of Schedule 5 hereto.

(4) A person who complies with the assessment criteria fixed by a standard which is a relevant harmonised standard within the meaning of Article 10.6 of the EMC Directive shall be presumed to meet the minimum criteria.

(5) An appointment under regulation 48 above may be subject to the condition that only a defined part of the undertaking of the appointed person may exercise the functions of a competent body, and where an appointment is, or is to be, subject to such a condition—

(a) a reference in these Regulations to a person's meeting the minimum criteria shall be construed in relation to that person as a reference to the part of that person's undertaking so defined meeting those criteria; and

(b) the conditions of the appointment shall include provision for ensuring that the confidentiality of confidential information held by the part of the undertaking so defined in pursuance of its function as a United Kingdom competent body is protected from disclosure to other parts of the undertaking.

(6) Upon the expiry of an appointment under regulation 48 above, the United Kingdom competent body shall be eligible for re-appointment.

[4481]

NOTES

Commencement: 7 March 2005.

50 Termination of appointment and transfer of functions

(1) The Secretary of State, by notice in writing (a "notice of termination")—

(a) shall terminate the appointment of a United Kingdom competent body where—

(i) the body so requests; or

(ii) it appears to the Secretary of State that—

(aa) the body no longer satisfies the minimum criteria; or

(bb) it is necessary in the interests of manufacturers, suppliers or end users of relevant apparatus to terminate the body's appointment; and

(b) may terminate such appointment if the body is in breach of a condition of appointment.

(2) Where the Secretary of State exercises the power conferred by paragraph (1) above—

(a) the notice of termination shall take effect on such date as shall be specified therein; and
(b) the Secretary of State shall inform the appropriate authorities of the other member States and the Commission.

(3) Where the Secretary of State—
(a) withdraws the authorisation of a United Kingdom competent body to exercise functions in relation to any description of apparatus pursuant to regulation 48(3) above; or
(b) terminates the appointment of such a body pursuant to paragraph (1) of this regulation,

she may give such directions (either to the body the subject of the withdrawal or termination, as the case may be, or to another authorised United Kingdom competent body) for the purposes of making such arrangements for the determination of outstanding applications as she considers appropriate.

(4) Without prejudice to the generality of the power conferred by paragraph (3) above, such directions may include the manner in which fees already received pursuant to regulation 51 below in respect of outstanding applications by the body the subject of the withdrawal or termination, as the case may be, are to be disposed of, having regard to the work already done on such applications by that body.

(5) The Secretary of State shall, where she takes an action referred to in paragraph (3)(a) or (b) above in relation to a United Kingdom competent body, give such directions as she considers appropriate to provide for the exercise by another United Kingdom competent body or herself of the powers conferred by regulations 56(3) and 57 below exercisable by the first mentioned United Kingdom competent body, and where such directions have been given, a reference in those provisions to the United Kingdom competent body which issued a technical certificate or technical report shall be construed as a reference to that other United Kingdom competent body or to the Secretary of State, as the case may be.

[4482]

NOTES

Commencement: 7 March 2005.

51 Power of competent body other than the Secretary of State to charge fees

(1) Without prejudice to the power of the Secretary of State, where she is a United Kingdom competent body, to charge fees pursuant to regulations made under section 56 of the Finance Act 1973 and subject to paragraphs (2) and (3) below, a United Kingdom competent body other than the Secretary of State may charge applicants for technical reports or technical certificates such fees in connection with or incidental to the consideration of applications therefor as the body may determine; and such fees may include an amount on account of profit which is reasonable in the circumstances having regard to—
(a) the character and extent of the work done or to be done by the body in the determination of such applications; and
(b) the commercial rate normally charged on account of profit for that work or similar work.

(2) The power in paragraph (1) above includes power to require the payment of fees or a reasonable estimate thereof with the application.

(3) Without prejudice to the generality of regulation 48(2) above, the conditions to which an appointment under regulation 48(1) may be subject may include a requirement to publish from time to time the scale of fees which the United Kingdom competent body charges pursuant to this regulation, or such information about the basis of calculation thereof as may be specified in the condition.

[4483]

NOTES

Commencement: 7 March 2005.

52 Applications for technical reports and technical certificates

(1) Subject to regulation 53 below, a United Kingdom competent body shall determine applications made thereto for the issue of technical reports and technical certificates in respect of relevant apparatus of authorised descriptions.

(2) In determining such applications, the United Kingdom competent body—

(a) shall have regard to the actual or usual electromagnetic environment of the apparatus; and

(b) may have regard to any standards (whether applicable EMC standards or otherwise) or other technical criteria appearing to it to be relevant.

(3) Where in the opinion of the United Kingdom competent body the apparatus to which an application relates conforms with the protection requirements, it shall issue a technical report or technical certificate, as the case may be, which complies with the requirements of regulation 55 below.

(4) Subject to regulation 58 below, where in the opinion of the United Kingdom competent body the apparatus to which the application relates does not conform with the protection requirements, it shall refuse to issue a technical report or technical certificate, as the case may be, giving written reasons for the refusal.

[4484]

NOTES

Commencement: 7 March 2005.

53 Limitations on duty to exercise functions

(1) A United Kingdom competent body shall not accept any application for a technical report or technical certificate in respect of any apparatus unless the application—

(a) is in writing;

(b) is accompanied by a draft technical construction file, that is to say, a file containing such information as will, when the technical report or technical certificate as the case may be is added thereto, be sufficient to constitute the file as a technical construction file;

(c) includes particulars of which applicable EMC standards the manufacturer has applied or proposes to apply in respect of the apparatus, and in respect of which applicable EM characteristics; and

(d) contains a declaration by the applicant that no application to another competent body for a technical report or technical certificate in respect of that apparatus is outstanding.

(2) A United Kingdom competent body shall not be required to—

(a) accept an application for a technical report or technical certificate where—

(i) the application, and the draft technical construction file, are not in English or another language acceptable to that body;

(ii) the applicant has not submitted with the application the amount of the fee which the competent body (not being the Secretary of State) requires to be submitted with the application pursuant to regulation 51(2) above; or

(iii) the body reasonably believes that, having regard to the number of applications for technical reports or technical certificates made to it which are outstanding, it will be unable to determine the application within three months of receiving the application;

(b) determine an application for a technical report or technical certificate where the manufacturer has not—

(i) granted the body access to the apparatus to which the application relates or the production facilities for the apparatus (including where applicable the production envisaged in relation to a representative) to the extent that the body reasonably requests; and

(ii) made available to the body such information as it may reasonably require to determine the application; or

(c) having determined the application, inform the applicant of the result thereof or, in the case of a successful application, issue the technical report or technical certificate, unless the applicant has paid any fees chargeable pursuant to regulation 51 above or in accordance with regulations made under section 56 of the Finance Act 1973, as the case may be.

[4485]

NOTES

Commencement: 7 March 2005.

54 Contractors etc

(1) Subject to paragraphs (2) and (3) below, a United Kingdom competent body may, in exercising its functions—

(a) arrange for some other person to carry out any test, assessment or inspection on its behalf; or

(b) require the applicant to satisfy another person with respect to any matter at the applicant's expense.

(2) Nothing in paragraph (1) above authorises a United Kingdom competent body to rely on the opinion of another person with regard to whether any relevant apparatus conforms with the protection requirements.

(3) Nothing in these Regulations shall preclude a person referred to in paragraph (1)(a) or (b) above from charging any fee in respect of any work undertaken by him in pursuance of those sub-paragraphs.

[4486]

NOTES

Commencement: 7 March 2005.

55 Form of technical reports and technical certificates

A technical report or technical certificate issued by a United Kingdom competent body shall be in writing and shall—

(a) be in English;

(b) give the name and address—

(i) of the applicant;

(ii) where that person is not the manufacturer, of the manufacturer;

(c) be signed on behalf of the body and identify the signatory;

(d) bear—

(i) the date of issue; and

(ii) the number of the report or certificate;

(e) give particulars of the relevant apparatus (where applicable, in relation to each variant) to which it relates sufficient to identify it, and shall state whether the apparatus to which it relates is a single item or a representative, or a number of variants thereof, as the case may be;

(f) certify that the apparatus to which it relates conforms with the protection requirements of the EMC Directive.

[4487]

NOTES

Commencement: 7 March 2005.

56 Conditions of technical reports or technical certificates

(1) Subject to regulation 58 below and paragraphs (2) and (3) of this regulation, a technical report or technical certificate issued by a United Kingdom competent body may be unconditional or subject to such conditions, which must be complied with if the report or certificate as the case may be is to apply, as the body considers appropriate.

(2) Without prejudice to the generality of paragraph (1) above, such conditions may include—

(a) a limitation on the electromagnetic environment for which the apparatus may be stated to be suitable; or

(b) a limitation that the apparatus is only to be installed at a specific site.

(3) The conditions imposed pursuant to paragraph (1) above may be varied by the United Kingdom competent body which issued the technical report or technical certificate, and a variation under this paragraph may include the imposition of new conditions or the removal of conditions.

[4488]

NOTES

Commencement: 7 March 2005.

57 Withdrawal of technical reports or technical certificates

(1) Subject to regulation 58 below and paragraph (2) of this regulation, the United Kingdom competent body which issued a technical report or technical certificate shall withdraw that report or certificate as the case may be if it appears that the apparatus to which it relates does not conform with the protection requirements.

(2) A withdrawal of a technical report or technical certificate shall be by notice in writing stating the reasons for the withdrawal.

[4489]

NOTES

Commencement: 7 March 2005.

58 Procedure where United Kingdom competent body is minded to make an unfavourable decision

Before making an unfavourable decision in respect of an applicant, that is to say—

(a) refusing to grant a technical report or technical certificate pursuant to regulation 52(4) above;

(b) the imposition of a condition of a technical report or technical certificate or the making of a restrictive variation of a condition thereof pursuant to regulation 56 above in circumstances where the applicant has not indicated in writing that the apparatus concerned is suitable for use subject to that condition;

(c) the withdrawal of a technical report or technical certificate pursuant to regulation 57 above,

the United Kingdom competent body shall—

(i) give notice in writing to the applicant, or holder of the technical report or technical certificate concerned, as the case may be ("the person concerned"), of the reasons why it proposes to make the unfavourable decision; and

(ii) give the person concerned the opportunity of making representations within a period of 28 days of the notice being given as to why that body should make a favourable decision, and consider any representations which are made by that person within that period.

[4490]

NOTES

Commencement: 7 March 2005.

EC declaration of conformity

59 EC declaration of conformity where conformity assessment requirements are complied with by reference to a technical construction file

(1) This regulation shall have effect for prescribing the form of an EC declaration of conformity issued in the United Kingdom in respect of relevant apparatus in relation to which the conformity assessment requirements have been complied with pursuant to the technical construction file route to compliance.

(2) An EC declaration of conformity to which this regulation applies shall—

(a) be in English;

(b) give the name and address—

(i) of the responsible person;

(ii) where that person is not the manufacturer, of the manufacturer;

(c) be signed by or on behalf of the manufacturer or his authorised representative and identify that signatory;

(d) bear the date of issue;

(e) give particulars of the relevant apparatus to which it relates sufficient to identify it;

(f) identify the technical construction file relating thereto, and give the name and address of the competent body which issued the technical report or technical certificate, and the date and any number thereof;

(g) state the numbers and titles of the applicable EMC standards, if any, applied by the manufacturer; and

(h) certify that the apparatus to which it relates conforms with the protection requirements of the EMC Directive.

[4491]

NOTES

Commencement: 7 March 2005.

Final Provisions

60 Interpretation of Part V

(1) In this Part—

"authorised" in relation to any description of apparatus shall be construed in accordance with regulation 48(3);

"minimum criteria" shall be construed in accordance with regulation 49(2);

"representative" shall be construed in accordance with regulation 45(2)(b); and

"variant" shall be construed in accordance with regulation 45(2)(c).

[4492]

NOTES

Commencement: 7 March 2005.

PART VI
THE EC TYPE-EXAMINATION ROUTE TO COMPLIANCE FOR RADIOCOMMUNICATION TRANSMISSION APPARATUS

General

61 Application of Part VI

(1) This Part shall have effect for the purposes of providing for—

(a) the manner in which the conformity assessment requirements shall be complied with in relation to radiocommunication transmission apparatus pursuant to the EC type-examination route to compliance; and

(b) United Kingdom notified bodies to exercise functions in relation thereto, and matters incidental to such exercise.

(2) For the purposes of these Regulations, "radiocommunication transmission apparatus" is wireless telegraphy apparatus for—

(a) transmitting; or

(b) both transmitting and receiving,

other than—

(i) radio amateur apparatus designed, and intended by the manufacturer, for use exclusively by radio amateurs;

(ii) apparatus neither designed nor intended by the manufacturer to be used for transmitting in conjunction with other wireless telegraphy apparatus; or

(iii) apparatus which is dependent for its operation on a magnetic as distinct from an electromagnetic field.

[4493]

NOTES

Commencement: 7 March 2005.

62 The EC type-examination route to compliance

The conformity assessment requirements are complied with in relation to radiocommunication transmission apparatus pursuant to the EC type-examination route to compliance if there is in force an EC type-examination certificate obtained by the responsible person from a notified body in respect of the applicable EM characteristics of the apparatus.

[4494]

NOTES

Commencement: 7 March 2005.

63 Notified bodies

For the purposes of these Regulations, a notified body is a body responsible for issuing EC type-examination certificates pursuant to Article 10.5 of the EMC Directive either for all descriptions of radiocommunication transmission apparatus or for specific descriptions thereof, and which is—

(a) a United Kingdom notified body pursuant to regulation 64 below;

(b) for the time being a notified body of a member State other than the United Kingdom having been notified as a notified body by the member State concerned to the Commission and the other member States pursuant to Article 10.6 of the EMC Directive; or

(c) recognised for the purpose of carrying out those functions by inclusion in a mutual recognition agreement relating to the EMC Directive or a similar agreement (including a Protocol to the Europe Agreement, or other Agreement, on Conformity Assessment and Acceptance of Industrial Products) which has been concluded between the Community and a State other than an EEA State.

[4495]

NOTES

Commencement: 7 March 2005.

United Kingdom notified bodies

64 Bodies and scope of authority

The following shall be United Kingdom notified bodies in relation to the descriptions ("authorised descriptions") of radiocommunication transmission apparatus referred to in relation thereto in Schedule 6—

(a) the Civil Aviation Authority ("the CAA");

(b) OFCOM.

[4496]

NOTES

Commencement: 7 March 2005.

65 Power of CAA and OFCOM to charge fees

(1) Subject to paragraph (2) below, the CAA and OFCOM may charge applicants for EC type-examination certificates such fees as they may determine provided that such fees shall not exceed the sum of the following—

(a) the costs incurred or to be incurred by the notified body in performing the relevant function; and

(b) an amount on account of profit which is reasonable in the circumstances having regard to—

(i) the character and extent of the work done or to be done by the body on behalf of the applicant; and

(ii) the commercial rate normally charged on account of profit for that work or similar work.

(2) The power in paragraph (1) above includes power to require the payment of fees or a reasonable estimate thereof with the application.

(3) The CAA and OFCOM shall each publish from time to time the scale of fees charged by it, or such information about the basis of calculation thereof as the Secretary of State may direct.

[4497]

NOTES

Commencement: 7 March 2005.

66 Applications for EC type-examination certificates

(1) It shall be the function of a United Kingdom notified body to determine applications made to it in writing for the issue of EC type-examination certificates from the manufacturer or his authorised representative in respect of authorised descriptions of radiocommunication transmission apparatus.

(2) Subject to regulation 67, a United Kingdom notified body shall, following receipt of an application in respect of an authorised description of apparatus—

(a) examine the apparatus and the design thereof;

(b) subject the apparatus or cause it to be subjected to such tests as the body considers appropriate to determine whether or not the apparatus conforms with the protection requirements in all the circumstances (having regard, without prejudice to the generality of the foregoing, to the actual or usual electromagnetic environment in which the apparatus is to be used), and, where there is a relevant transposed harmonised standard or a recognised national standard and the body considers it appropriate to apply that standard, such tests as may be provided for thereby.

(3) Following examination and testing pursuant to paragraph (2) above, the United Kingdom notified body shall determine whether or not the apparatus to which the application relates conforms with the protection requirements.

(4) Where in the opinion of the United Kingdom notified body the apparatus to which an application relates conforms with the protection requirements, it shall issue an EC type-examination certificate in respect thereof.

(5) Subject to regulation 71 below, where in the opinion of the United Kingdom notified body the apparatus to which the application relates does not conform with the protection requirements, it shall refuse to issue the EC type-examination certificate, giving written reasons for the refusal.

(6) An EC type-examination certificate may relate to—

(a) a single item of apparatus;

(b) where a number of items are to be produced, a specimen representative of the production envisaged (a "representative"); or

(c) a number of items or representatives of each such item or representative being variants of the same basic design.

[4498]

NOTES

Commencement: 7 March 2005.

67 Limitations on duty to exercise functions

(1) Nothing in these Regulations shall require a United Kingdom notified body to determine a relevant application—

(a) which is not in English or another language acceptable to that body; or

(b) where the applicant has not—

(i) granted the body access to the radiocommunication transmission apparatus to which the application relates or the production facilities for the apparatus (including where applicable, the production envisaged in relation to a representative) to the extent that the body reasonably requests; and

(ii) made available to the body such information as it may reasonably require to determine the application.

(2) Nothing in these Regulations shall require a United Kingdom notified body to—

(a) determine a relevant application; or

(b) having determined the application, inform the applicant of the result thereof or, in the case of a successful application, issue the EC type-examination certificate,

unless the applicant has paid the fees charged pursuant to regulation 65 above.

[4499]

NOTES

Commencement: 7 March 2005.

PART VI TELECOMMUNICATIONS

68 Contractors etc

(1) Subject to paragraphs (2) and (3) below, a United Kingdom notified body may, in exercising its functions—

(a) arrange for some other person to carry out any test, assessment or inspection on its behalf; or

(b) require the applicant to satisfy another person with respect to any matter at the applicant's expense.

(2) Nothing in paragraph (1) above authorises a United Kingdom notified body to rely on the opinion of another person with regard to whether any radiocommunication transmission apparatus conforms with the protection requirements.

(3) Nothing in these Regulations shall preclude a person referred to in sub-paragraph (1)(a) or (b) above from charging any fee in respect of any work undertaken by him in pursuance of those sub-paragraphs.

[4500]

NOTES

Commencement: 7 March 2005.

69 Conditions of EC type-examination certificates

(1) Subject to regulation 71 below and paragraphs (2) and (3) of this regulation, an EC type-examination certificate issued by a United Kingdom notified body may be unconditional or subject to such conditions, which must be complied with if the certificate is to apply, as the body considers appropriate.

(2) Without prejudice to the generality of paragraph (1) above, such conditions may include—

(a) a limitation on the electromagnetic environment for which the apparatus may be stated to be suitable; or

(b) a limitation that the apparatus is only to be installed at a specific site.

(3) The conditions imposed pursuant to paragraph (1) above may be varied by the United Kingdom notified body which issued the EC type-examination certificate, and a variation under this paragraph may include the imposition of new conditions or the withdrawal of conditions.

[4501]

NOTES

Commencement: 7 March 2005.

70 Withdrawal of EC type-examination certificates

(1) Subject to regulation 71 below and paragraph (2) of this regulation, the United Kingdom notified body which issued an EC type-examination certificate shall withdraw that certificate if it appears that the apparatus to which it relates does not conform with the protection requirements.

(2) A withdrawal of an EC type-examination certificate shall be by notice in writing stating the reasons for the withdrawal.

[4502]

NOTES

Commencement: 7 March 2005.

71 Procedure where United Kingdom notified body is minded to make a decision unfavourable to the applicant

Before making an unfavourable decision in respect of an applicant, that is to say—

(a) refusing to grant an EC type-examination certificate pursuant to regulation 66(5) above;

(b) the imposition of a condition of an EC type-examination certificate or the making of a restrictive variation of a condition thereof pursuant to regulation 69 above in

circumstances where the applicant has not indicated in writing that the apparatus concerned is suitable for use subject to that condition;
- (c) the withdrawal of an EC type-examination certificate pursuant to regulation 70 above,

the United Kingdom notified body shall—
- (i) give notice in writing to the applicant, or holder of the EC type-examination certificate concerned, as the case may be ("the person concerned"), of the reasons why it proposes to make the unfavourable decision; and
- (ii) give the person concerned the opportunity of making representations within a period of 28 days of the notice being given as to why that body should make a favourable decision, and consider any representations which are made by that person within that period.

[4503]

NOTES

Commencement: 7 March 2005.

EC declaration of conformity

72 EC declaration of conformity for radiocommunication transmission apparatus

(1) This regulation shall have effect for prescribing the form of an EC declaration of conformity issued in the United Kingdom in respect of radiocommunication transmission apparatus.

(2) An EC declaration of conformity to which this regulation applies shall—
- (a) be in English;
- (b) give the name and address—
  - (i) of the responsible person;
  - (ii) where that person is not the manufacturer, of the manufacturer;
- (c) be signed by or on behalf of the manufacturer or his authorised representative and identify that signatory;
- (d) bear the date of issue;
- (e) give particulars of the relevant apparatus to which it relates sufficient to identify it;
- (f) identify the EC type-examination certificate relating thereto, and give the name and address of the notified body which issued it, and the date and any number thereof; and
- (g) certify that the apparatus to which it relates conforms with the protection requirements of the EMC Directive.

[4504]

NOTES

Commencement: 7 March 2005.

Final provisions

73 Savings

(1) For the avoidance of doubt, it is hereby declared that nothing in this Part shall be construed as dispensing with any requirement—
- (a) of a licence granted under—
  - (i) section 1 of the 1949 Act to establish and use any station for wireless telegraphy or to install and use any wireless telegraphy apparatus;
  - (ii) Part I of the Broadcasting Act 1990;
  - (iii) Part III of the Broadcasting Act 1990 to provide independent radio services within the meaning of that Part; or
  - (iv) the Broadcasting Act 1996;
- (b) that apparatus be approved under section 84 of the 1984 Act;
- (c) of regulations made under section 1 of the 1949 Act;
- (d) of an order made under—
  - (i) section 7of the Wireless Telegraphy Act 1967; or

(ii) section 85 or 86 of the 1984 Act; or

(e) of a continuation notice under paragraph 9 of Schedule 18 to the Communications Act 2003 given to a person who was a holder of a licence granted under section 7 of the 1984 Act.

(2) Nothing in this Part shall affect the validity of an EC-type examination certificate lawfully issued by a notified body pursuant to regulation 60 of the Electromagnetic Compatibility Regulations 1992.

[4505]

NOTES

Commencement: 7 March 2005.

74 Interpretation of Part VI

In this Part—

"authorised description" shall be construed in accordance with regulation 64 above;

"examine" includes, where a UK notified body considers appropriate, the disassembly of apparatus.

[4506]

NOTES

Commencement: 7 March 2005.

PART VII
ENFORCEMENT

Enforcement authorities and powers

75 Enforcement authorities

(1) Except in relation to the descriptions of apparatus mentioned in paragraph (3) below, it shall be the duty of the following authorities to enforce these Regulations—

(a) in Great Britain:
  (i) OFCOM insofar as action taken to enforce a regulation relates to the protection and management of the radio spectrum; and
  (ii) local weights and measures authorities within their area; and

(b) in Northern Ireland:
  (i) OFCOM insofar as action taken to enforce a regulation relates to the protection and management of the radio spectrum; and
  (ii) the Department of Enterprise, Trade and Investment.

(2) Except in relation to the descriptions of apparatus mentioned in paragraph (3) below, the Secretary of State may enforce these Regulations.

(3) These Regulations may be enforced—

(a) by the CAA, in relation to wireless telegraphy apparatus of a description listed in paragraph 1 of Schedule 6 hereto; and

(b) in relation to electricity meters other than those which are wireless telegraphy apparatus—
  (i) in Great Britain, by the Gas and Electricity Markets Authority; and
  (ii) in Northern Ireland, by the Northern Ireland Authority for Energy Regulation.

(4) Nothing in this regulation shall authorise any enforcement authority to bring proceedings in Scotland for an offence.

[4507]

NOTES

Commencement: 7 March 2005.

76 Test purchases

(1) An enforcement authority shall have power, for the purpose of ascertaining whether any relevant apparatus complies with the requirements of regulation 32 above to make, or to authorise an officer of the authority to make, any purchase of electrical apparatus.

(2) Where—

(a) any apparatus purchased under this regulation by or on behalf of any enforcement authority is submitted to a test; and

(b) the test leads to—

(i) the bringing of proceedings for an offence under regulation 85, 86 or 88 below in relation to the apparatus or the forfeiture of apparatus of the same description under regulation 97 or 98 below; or

(ii) the serving of a suspension notice in respect of any apparatus; and

(c) the authority is requested to do so and it is practicable for the authority to comply with the request,

the authority shall allow the person from whom the apparatus was purchased or any person who is a party to the proceedings or has an interest in any apparatus to which the notice relates to have the apparatus tested.

[4508]

NOTES

Commencement: 7 March 2005.

77 Powers of search etc

(1) Subject to regulation 78 below, a duly authorised officer of an enforcement authority may at any reasonable hour and on production, if required, of his credentials exercise any of the powers conferred by the following provisions of this regulation.

(2) The officer may, for the purpose of ascertaining whether there has been a contravention of any of the requirements of Part III of these Regulations—

(a) inspect any electrical apparatus and enter any premises other than premises occupied only as a person's residence; or

(b) examine any procedure (including any arrangements for carrying out a test) connected with the production of any electrical apparatus.

(3) If the officer has reasonable grounds for suspecting that there has been a contravention of any of the requirements of Part III of these Regulations, he may for the purpose of ascertaining (by testing or otherwise) whether there has been any such contravention, seize and detain any electrical apparatus.

(4) The officer may seize and detain—

(a) any electrical apparatus, any document, record or information which the officer may require production of under regulation 84 below, or any other thing, which he has reasonable grounds for believing may be required—

(i) as evidence in proceedings for an offence under these Regulations;

(ii) by a competent authority of a member State other than the United Kingdom for the purpose of the exercise of its functions; or

(b) any electrical apparatus which he has reasonable grounds for suspecting may be liable to be forfeited under regulation 97 or 98 below.

(5) The officer may, for the purpose of the exercise of his powers under paragraphs (3) or (4) above to seize any electrical apparatus, any document or record or any other thing—

(a) require any person having authority to do so to open any container; and

(b) himself open or break open any such container where a requirement made under paragraph (a) above in relation to the container has not been complied with.

[4509]

NOTES

Commencement: 7 March 2005.

78 Provisions supplemental to regulation 77

(1) An officer seizing any electrical apparatus, records, documents, information or other thing under regulation 77 above shall inform the person from whom they are seized that such apparatus, records or other thing have been so seized.

PART VI TELECOMMUNICATIONS

(2) If a justice of the peace—

(a) is satisfied by any written information on oath that there are reasonable grounds for believing either—

(i) that any electrical apparatus, documents, records, information or other thing which any officer has power to inspect under regulation 77 above are on any premises (which may be premises occupied only as a person's residence) and that, if their inspection reveals that the apparatus is relevant apparatus or that the documents, records, information or any other thing relates to relevant apparatus, such inspection is likely to disclose evidence that there has been a contravention of any provision of Part III of these Regulations; or

(ii) that such a contravention has taken place, is taking place or is about to take place on any premises; and

(b) is also satisfied by any such information either—

(i) that admission to the premises has been or is likely to be refused and that notice of intention to apply for a warrant under this paragraph has been given to the occupier; or

(ii) that an application for admission, or the giving of such a notice, would defeat the object of the entry or that the premises are unoccupied or that the occupier is temporarily absent and it might defeat the object of the entry to await his return,

the justice may by warrant under his hand, which shall continue in force for one month, authorise any officer of an enforcement authority to enter the premises, if need be by force.

(3) An officer entering any premises by virtue of regulation 77 above or a warrant under paragraph (2) of this regulation may take with him such other persons and such equipment as may appear to him necessary.

(4) On leaving any premises which a person is authorised to enter by a warrant under paragraph (2) of this regulation, that person shall, if the premises are unoccupied or the occupier is temporarily absent, leave the premises as effectively secured against trespassers as he found them.

(5) Where any apparatus seized by an officer under regulation 77 above is submitted to a test, the officer shall inform the persons mentioned in paragraph (1) of this regulation of the result of the test and, if—

(a) proceedings are brought for an offence in respect of a contravention in relation to any relevant apparatus of any provision of these Regulations or for the forfeiture of any relevant apparatus under regulation 97 or 98 below, or a suspension notice is served in respect of any relevant apparatus; and

(b) the officer is requested to do so and it is practicable to comply with the request,

the officer shall allow any person who is a party to the proceedings or, as the case may be, has an interest in the relevant apparatus to which the notice relates to have the relevant apparatus tested.

(6) In the application of this regulation to Scotland, the reference in paragraph (2) above to a justice of the peace shall include a reference to a sheriff and the references to written information on oath shall be construed as references to evidence on oath.

(7) In the application of this regulation to Northern Ireland, the references in paragraph (2) above to any information on oath shall be construed as references to any complaint on oath.

[4510]

NOTES

Commencement: 7 March 2005.

79 Appeals against detention of apparatus

(1) Any person having an interest in any apparatus, document, record, information or other thing which is for the time being detained under any provision of this Part by an enforcement authority or by an officer of such an authority may apply for an order requiring the apparatus to be released to him or to another person.

(2) An application under this regulation may be made—

(a) to any magistrates' court in which proceedings have been brought in England and Wales and Northern Ireland—

(i) for an offence under regulation 85, 86 or 88 below; or
(ii) for the forfeiture of the apparatus under regulation 97 below;

(b) where no such proceedings have been so brought, by way of complaint to a magistrates' court; or

(c) in Scotland, by summary application to the sheriff.

(3) On an application under this regulation to a magistrates' court or to the sheriff, an order requiring apparatus to be released shall be made only if the court or sheriff is satisfied—

(a) that proceedings—
(i) for an offence under regulation 85, 86 or 88 below in respect of the apparatus; or
(ii) for the forfeiture of the apparatus under regulation 97 or 98 below,

have not been brought or, having been brought, have been concluded without the apparatus being forfeited; and

(b) where no such proceedings have been brought, that more than six months have elapsed since the apparatus was seized.

(4) Any person aggrieved by an order made under this regulation by a magistrates' court in England and Wales or Northern Ireland, or by a decision of such a court not to make such an order, may appeal against that order or decision—

(a) in England and Wales, to the Crown Court;

(b) in Northern Ireland, to the county court,

and an order so made may contain such provision as appears to the court appropriate for delaying the coming into force of the order pending the making and determination of any appeal (including any application under section 111 of the Magistrates' Courts Act 1980 or article 146 of the Magistrates' Courts (Northern Ireland) Order 1981 (statement of case)).

[4511]

NOTES

Commencement: 7 March 2005.

80 Compliance notices

(1) Subject to paragraph (4) below, in the relevant circumstances, no notice may be served pursuant to regulation 81 or 82 below, and no proceedings may be commenced pursuant to regulation 85, 88, 97 or 98 below, unless the requirements of this regulation are satisfied.

(2) The relevant circumstances are that it is established that the CE mark or CE marking has been affixed unduly to electrical apparatus.

(3) The requirements of this regulation are that—

(a) there has been served upon the manufacturer or his authorised representative a notice in writing obliging the person on whom the notice is served to make the electrical apparatus conform as regards the provisions concerning the CE mark or CE marking and its due affixation and to end the infringement under conditions imposed in, or in relation to, the said notice; and

(b) the non-conformity continues after the period specified in, or in relation to, the said notice during which the infringement must be ended has expired.

(4) Without prejudice to paragraph 3(a) and (b), a notice served pursuant to paragraph (1) above shall include, but not by way of limitation,

(a) a description of the electrical apparatus in respect of which the notice is served on the manufacturer or his authorised representative in a manner sufficient to identify it;

(b) a statement that the CE mark or CE marking affixed to either the electrical apparatus or the apparatus' packaging, instructions for use or guarantee certificate is unduly affixed, or that the CE mark or CE marking is affixed to some other item accompanying the apparatus;

(c) a statement of the grounds upon which it is established that the CE mark or CE marking has been or is being unduly affixed in relation to the electrical apparatus; and

(d) an indication as to which of the following procedures cannot be commenced unless the requirements of this regulation are satisfied:—
(i) a notice pursuant to regulation 81 or 82 below; or
(ii) proceedings pursuant to regulation 85, 88, 97 or 98 below,

and may include such other information as may be considered expedient to enable the person to whom the notice is addressed to decide what action should be taken to end the particular infringement.

(5) This regulation does not apply where it is found that apparatus bearing the CE mark or CE marking does not comply with the protection requirements.

[4512]

NOTES

Commencement: 7 March 2005.

81 Prohibition notices

(1) The Secretary of State may serve on—

(a) the manufacturer or supplier of any relevant apparatus which the Secretary of State considers does not comply with the protection requirements or the requirements of regulation 32 above as the case may be; or

(b) the user of relevant apparatus which the Secretary of State considers did not so comply at the time when it was supplied or taken into service as the case may be,

a notice ("a prohibition notice") prohibiting that manufacturer, supplier or user from manufacturing, supplying, taking into service or using that apparatus as the case may be, except with the consent of the Secretary of State.

(2) Schedule 7 hereto shall have effect with respect to prohibition notices.

(3) A consent given by the Secretary of State for the purposes of a prohibition notice may impose such conditions on the doing of anything for which the consent is required as the Secretary of State considers appropriate.

[4513]

NOTES

Commencement: 7 March 2005.

82 Suspension notices

(1) Where an enforcement authority has reasonable grounds for suspecting that regulation 30, 31 or 36(4) above has been, is being or is likely to be contravened, the authority may serve a notice ("a suspension notice")—

(a) in relation to relevant apparatus or electrical apparatus other than relevant apparatus, prohibiting the manufacturer, supplier or user on whom it is served, for such period ending not more than six months after the date of the notice as is specified therein, from manufacturing, supplying, taking into service or using the apparatus; or

(b) in relation to an excluded installation, where the enforcement authority is unable to establish upon reasonable inquiry which item of relevant apparatus or system incorporated therein the suspected contravention relates to, for such period ending not more than six months after the date of the notice as is specified therein, from taking into service or using the excluded installation,

without the consent of that authority.

(2) A suspension notice served by an enforcement authority in respect of any apparatus or excluded installation shall—

(a) describe the apparatus or installation to which it relates in a manner sufficient to identify it;

(b) set out the grounds on which the authority suspects that regulation 30, 31 or 36(4) above has been, is being or is likely to be contravened, as the case may be; and

(c) state that, and the manner in which, the person on whom the notice is served may appeal against the notice under regulation 83 below.

(3) A consent given by an enforcement authority for the purposes of a suspension notice may impose such conditions on the doing of anything for which the consent is required as that authority considers appropriate.

(4) A suspension notice may require the person on whom it is served to keep the enforcement authority which served the notice informed of the whereabouts throughout the period during which the notice has effect of any of the apparatus, or the excluded installation, in which that person has an interest.

(5) Where a suspension notice has been served on any person in respect of any apparatus or excluded installation, no further such notice shall be served on that person in respect of the same apparatus unless—

(a) proceedings against that person for an offence under regulation 85, 86 or 88 below; or

(b) proceedings for the forfeiture of the apparatus under regulation 97 or 98 below,

are pending at the end of the period specified in the first-mentioned notice.

[4514]

NOTES

Commencement: 7 March 2005.

83 Appeals against suspension notices

(1) Any person having an interest in any apparatus or excluded installation in respect of which a suspension notice is for the time being in force may apply for an order setting aside the notice.

(2) An application under this regulation may be made—

(a) in England and Wales or Northern Ireland—

(i) to any magistrates' court in which proceedings have been brought—

(aa) for an offence under regulation 85, 86 or 88 below; or

(bb) for the forfeiture of the apparatus under regulation 97 below; or

(ii) where no such proceedings have been so brought, by way of complaint to a magistrates' court; or

(b) in Scotland, by summary application to the sheriff.

(3) On an application under this regulation to a magistrates' court in England and Wales or Northern Ireland the court shall make an order setting aside the suspension notice only if the court is satisfied that there has been no contravention in relation to the apparatus, or any item of relevant apparatus or system included in the excluded installation, of regulation 30, 31 or 36(4) above as the case may be.

(4) On an application under this regulation to the sheriff he shall make an order setting aside the suspension notice only if he is satisfied that at the date of making the order—

(a) proceedings for an offence under regulation 85, 86 or 88 below; or

(b) proceedings for the forfeiture of the apparatus under regulation 98 below,

have not been brought or, having been brought, have been concluded.

(5) Any person aggrieved by an order made under this regulation by a magistrates' court in England and Wales or Northern Ireland, or by a decision of such a court not to make such an order, may appeal against that order or decision—

(a) in England and Wales, to the Crown Court;

(b) in Northern Ireland, to the county court,

and an order so made may contain such provision as appears to the court appropriate for delaying the coming into force of the order pending the making and determination of any appeal (including any application under section 111 of the Magistrates' Courts Act 1980 or article 146 of the Magistrates' Courts (Northern Ireland) Order 1981 (statement of case)).

[4515]

NOTES

Commencement: 7 March 2005.

84 Power to require production of documents and information etc

An officer of an enforcement authority may, for the purposes of exercising his functions under this Part, require—

(a) any person who is required by regulation 37 above to retain an EC declaration of conformity, technical construction file or EC type-examination certificate, during the period in which that person is required to retain that document, to produce such document;

(b) any person who is in possession of an EC declaration of conformity, technical construction file or EC type-examination certificate, or of a copy of such document, at any time to produce it;

(c) a responsible person, or a manufacturer, importer, supplier or user of electrical apparatus to produce such documents or records relating to such apparatus as are in his possession or under his control; or

(d) a responsible person, or a manufacturer, importer, supplier or user of any electrical apparatus, to give him such information as he may reasonably require,

and such officer may inspect any thing which he may require to be produced under this regulation, and take a copy thereof or of any part thereof.

[4516]

NOTES

Commencement: 7 March 2005.

Offences

85 Supplying or taking into service apparatus in contravention of regulation 30 or 31

Any person who supplies or takes into service relevant apparatus in contravention of regulation 30 or 31 above shall be guilty of an offence.

[4517]

NOTES

Commencement: 7 March 2005.

86 Contravention of prohibition notice or suspension notice

Any person who contravenes a prohibition notice or a suspension notice shall be guilty of an offence.

[4518]

NOTES

Commencement: 7 March 2005.

87 False or misleading information

Any person who, in giving any information which he is required to give under regulation 84(c) or (d) above—

(a) makes any statement which he knows is false or misleading in a material particular; or

(b) recklessly makes any statement which is false or misleading in a material particular,

shall be guilty of an offence.

[4519]

NOTES

Commencement: 7 March 2005.

88 Misuse of the CE marking etc

(1) Any person who, in relation to any relevant apparatus, or any electrical apparatus other than relevant apparatus, affixes the CE marking or any other inscription or marking in contravention of regulation 35(5), (6) or (7) above, shall be guilty of an offence.

(2) Any person who issues an EC declaration of conformity in relation to—

(a) any relevant apparatus in contravention of regulation 36(3) above; or

(b) any electrical apparatus in contravention of regulation 36(4) above,

shall be guilty of an offence.

[4520]

NOTES

Commencement: 7 March 2005.

89 Obstruction etc of officers of enforcement authorities etc

(1) Any person who—

(a) intentionally obstructs any officer of an enforcement authority who is acting in pursuance of any provision of this Part;

(b) intentionally fails or refuses to comply with any requirement made of him by any officer of an enforcement authority under any provision of this Part;

(c) without reasonable cause fails or refuses to give any officer of an enforcement authority who is so acting any other assistance which the officer may reasonably require of him for the purposes of the exercise of the officer's functions under any provision of this Part; or

(d) fails to comply with a court order under regulation 96 below,

shall be guilty of an offence.

(2) Any person who falsely pretends to be an officer of an enforcement authority shall be guilty of an offence.

[4521]

NOTES

Commencement: 7 March 2005.

90 Failure to retain documentation

Any person who contravenes regulation 37 above shall be guilty of an offence.

[4522]

NOTES

Commencement: 7 March 2005.

91 Defence of due diligence

(1) Subject to the following provisions of this regulation, in proceedings against any person for an offence under regulation 85 or 88 above it shall be a defence for that person to show that he took all reasonable steps and exercised all due diligence to avoid committing the offence.

(2) Where in any proceedings against any person for such an offence the defence provided by paragraph (1) above involves an allegation that the commission of the offence was due—

(a) to the act or default of another; or

(b) to reliance on information given by another,

that person shall not, without the leave of the court, be entitled to rely on the defence unless, not less than seven clear days before the hearing of the proceedings (or, in Scotland the trial diet), he has served a notice under paragraph (3) below on the person bringing the proceedings.

(3) A notice under this paragraph shall give such information identifying or assisting in the identification of the person who committed the act or default or gave the information as is in the possession of the person serving the notice at the time he serves it.

(4) It is hereby declared that a person shall not be entitled to rely on the defence provided by paragraph (1) above by reason of his reliance on information supplied by another, unless he shows that it was reasonable in all the circumstances for him to have relied on the information, having regard in particular—

(a) to the steps which he took, and those which might reasonably have been taken, for the purpose of verifying the information; and

(b) to whether he had any reason to disbelieve the information.

[4523]

NOTES

Commencement: 7 March 2005.

92 Liability of persons other than the principal offender

(1) Where the commission by any person of an offence under any of regulations 85 to 90 above is due to the act or default committed by some other person in the course of any

business of his, the other person shall be guilty of the offence and may be proceeded against and punished by virtue of this paragraph whether or not proceedings are taken against the first-mentioned person.

(2) Where a body corporate is guilty of an offence under these Regulations (including where it is so guilty by virtue of paragraph (1) above) in respect of any act or default which is shown to have been committed with the consent or connivance of, or to be attributable to any neglect on the part of, any director, manager, secretary or other similar officer of the body corporate or any person who was purporting to act in any such capacity he, as well as the body corporate, shall be guilty of that offence and shall be liable to be proceeded against and punished accordingly.

(3) Where the affairs of a body corporate are managed by its members, paragraph (2) above shall apply in relation to the acts and defaults of a member in connection with his functions of management as if he were a director of the body corporate.

(4) In this regulation, references to a "body corporate" include references to a partnership in Scotland and, in relation to such partnership, any reference to a director, manager, secretary or other similar officer of a body corporate is a reference to a partner.

[4524]

NOTES

Commencement: 7 March 2005.

93 Extension of time for bringing summary proceedings

Notwithstanding section 127 of the Magistrates' Courts Act 1980 and section 136 of the Criminal Procedure (Scotland) Act 1995, proceedings for an offence under regulations 85 to 90 above may be commenced at any time within three years from the date of the offence, or one year from the date on which there comes to the knowledge of the prosecutor evidence sufficient to justify a prosecution for that offence, whichever is the earlier; and for the purposes of this regulation—

(a) a certificate of the prosecutor stating that such evidence came to his knowledge on a specified date shall be conclusive evidence of that fact; and

(b) a document purporting to be such a certificate and to be signed by or on behalf of the prosecutor in question shall be presumed to be such a certificate unless the contrary is proved.

[4525]

NOTES

Commencement: 7 March 2005.

94 Inference of condition of apparatus at time of supply or taking into service

In any proceedings in which it is in issue whether any relevant apparatus complied with the protection requirements or the requirements of regulation 32 above as the case may be at the time when it was supplied or taken into service as the case may be, a court may infer that such apparatus did not so comply at that time if—

(a) it is proved that it does not so comply or did not so comply at a time subsequent to its having been supplied or taken into service; and

(b) having regard to all the circumstances of the case, it appears to the court that the failure of the apparatus to comply at the time referred to in sub-paragraph (a) above is not attributable to any cause arising subsequent to its having been supplied or taken into service.

[4526]

NOTES

Commencement: 7 March 2005.

Powers of the court

95 Penalties

(1) A person guilty of an offence under regulation 86, 87 or 89(2) above shall be liable on summary conviction—

(a) to imprisonment for a term not exceeding three months; or
(b) to a fine not exceeding level 5 on the standard scale,

or to both.

(2) A person guilty of an offence under regulation 85, 88, 89(1) or 90 above shall be liable on summary conviction to a fine not exceeding level 5 on the standard scale.

[4527]

NOTES

Commencement: 7 March 2005.

96 Power of the court to require matter to be remedied

(1) Where a person is convicted of an offence under regulation 85 or 88 above in respect of any matters which appear to the court to be matters which it is in his power to remedy, the court may, in addition to or instead of imposing any punishment, order him, within such time as may be fixed by the order, to take such steps as may be specified in the order for remedying the said matters.

(2) The time fixed by an order under paragraph (1) above may be extended or further extended by order of the court on an application made before the end of that time as originally fixed or as extended under this paragraph, as the case may be.

(3) Where a person is ordered under paragraph (1) above to remedy any matters, that person shall not be guilty of an offence under regulation 85 or 88 above as the case may be in respect of those matters in so far as they continue during the time fixed by the order or any further time allowed under paragraph (2) above.

[4528]

NOTES

Commencement: 7 March 2005.

97 Forfeiture: England and Wales and Northern Ireland

(1) An enforcement authority in England and Wales or Northern Ireland may apply under this regulation for an order for the forfeiture of any—

(a) relevant apparatus on the grounds that there has been a contravention in relation thereto of regulation 30 or 31 above; or
(b) electrical apparatus other than relevant apparatus, on the grounds that the CE marking, or an inscription liable to be confused therewith, is affixed in relation to it in contravention of regulation 35(7) above.

(2) An application under this regulation may be made—

(a) where proceedings have been brought in a magistrates' court in respect of an offence in relation to some or all of the apparatus under regulation 85, 86 or 88, to that court;
(b) where an application with respect to some or all of the apparatus has been made to a magistrates' court under regulation 79 or 83 above, to that court; and
(c) where no application for the forfeiture of the apparatus has been made under sub-paragraph (a) or (b) above, by way of complaint to a magistrates' court.

(3) On an application under this regulation the court shall make an order for the forfeiture of the apparatus only if it is satisfied that there has been a contravention in relation thereto of regulation 30, 31 or 35(6) above as the case may be.

(4) For the avoidance of doubt it is hereby declared that a court may infer for the purposes of this regulation that there has been a contravention in relation to any apparatus of regulation 30, 31 or 35(6) above as the case may be if it is satisfied that that provision has been contravened in relation to apparatus which is representative of that apparatus (whether by reason of being of the same design or part of the same consignment or batch or otherwise).

(5) Any person aggrieved by an order made under this regulation by a magistrates' court, or by a decision of such court not to make such an order, may appeal against that order or decision—

(a) in England and Wales, to the Crown Court;
(b) in Northern Ireland, to the county court,

and an order so made may contain such provision as appears to the court to be appropriate for delaying the coming into force of an order pending the making and determination of any appeal (including any application under section 111 of the Magistrates' Courts Act 1980 or article 146 of the Magistrates' Courts (Northern Ireland) Order 1981 (statement of case)).

(6) Subject to paragraph (7) below, where any apparatus is forfeited under this regulation it shall be destroyed in accordance with such directions as the court may give.

(7) On making an order under this regulation a magistrates' court may, if it considers it appropriate to do so, direct that the apparatus to which the order relates shall (instead of being destroyed) be released, to such person as the court may specify, on condition that that person—

(a) does not supply the apparatus to any person otherwise than—

(i) to a person who carries on a business of buying apparatus of the same description as the first mentioned apparatus and repairing or reconditioning it; or

(ii) as scrap (that is to say, for the value of materials included in the apparatus rather than for the value of the apparatus itself); and

(b) complies with any order to pay costs or expenses (including any order under regulation 99 below) which has been made against that person in the proceedings for the order for forfeiture.

[4529]

NOTES

Commencement: 7 March 2005.

98 Forfeiture: Scotland

(1) In Scotland an order for forfeiture of any—

(a) relevant apparatus in relation to which there has been a contravention of regulation 30 or 31 above as the case may be; or

(b) electrical apparatus other than relevant apparatus, on the grounds that the CE marking, or an inscription liable to be confused therewith, is affixed in relation to it in contravention of regulation 35(7) above,

may be made by the sheriff—

(i) on an application by the procurator-fiscal made in the manner specified in section 134 of the Criminal Procedure (Scotland) Act 1995; or

(ii) where a person is convicted of any offence in respect of any such contravention, in addition to any other penalty which the sheriff may impose.

(2) The procurator-fiscal making an application under paragraph (1)(i) above shall serve on any person appearing to him to be the owner of, or otherwise to have an interest in, the apparatus to which the application relates a copy of the application, together with a notice giving him the opportunity to appear at the hearing of the application to show cause why the apparatus should not be forfeited.

(3) Service under paragraph (2) above shall be carried out, and such service may be proved, in the manner specified for citation of an accused in summary proceedings under the Criminal Procedure (Scotland) Act 1995.

(4) Any person upon whom a notice is served under paragraph (2) above and any other person claiming to be the owner of, or otherwise to have an interest in, the apparatus to which an application under this regulation relates shall be entitled to appear at the hearing of the application to show cause why the apparatus should not be forfeited.

(5) The sheriff shall not make an order following an application under paragraph (1)(i) above—

(a) if any person on whom notice is served under paragraph (2) above does not appear, unless service of the notice on that person is proved; or

(b) if no notice under paragraph (2) above has been served, unless the court is satisfied that in the circumstances it was reasonable not to serve notice on any person.

(6) The sheriff shall make an order under this regulation only if he is satisfied that there has been a contravention in relation to the apparatus of regulation 30, 31 or 35(6) above as the case may be.

(7) For the avoidance of doubt it is hereby declared that the sheriff may infer for the purposes of this regulation that there has been a contravention in relation to any apparatus of regulation 30, 31 or 35(6) above if he is satisfied that that provision has been contravened in relation to apparatus which is representative of that apparatus (whether by reason of being of the same design or part of the same consignment or batch or otherwise).

(8) Where an order for the forfeiture of any apparatus is made following an application by the procurator-fiscal under paragraph (1)(i) above, any person who appeared, or was entitled to appear, to show cause why it should not be forfeited may, within twenty-one days of the making of the order, appeal to the High Court by Bill of Suspension on the ground of an alleged miscarriage of justice; and section 182(5)(a) to (e) of the Criminal Procedure (Scotland) Act 1995 shall apply to an appeal under this paragraph as it applies to a stated case under Part X of that Act.

(9) An order following an application under paragraph (1)(i) above shall not take effect—

(a) until the end of the period of twenty-one days beginning with the day after the day on which the order is made; or

(b) if an appeal is made under paragraph (8) above within that period, until the appeal is determined or abandoned.

(10) An order under paragraph (1)(ii) shall not take effect—

(a) until the end of the period within which an appeal against the order could be brought under the Criminal Procedure (Scotland) Act 1995; or

(b) if an appeal is made within that period, until the appeal is determined or abandoned.

(11) Subject to paragraph (12) below, apparatus forfeited under this regulation shall be destroyed in accordance with such directions as the sheriff may give.

(12) If he thinks fit, the sheriff may direct the apparatus to be (instead of being destroyed) released to such person as he may specify, on condition that that person does not supply it to any person otherwise than—

(a) to a person who carries on a business of buying apparatus of the same description as the first-mentioned apparatus and repairing or reconditioning it; or

(b) as scrap (that is to say, for the value of materials included in the apparatus rather than for the value of the apparatus itself).

[4530]

NOTES

Commencement: 7 March 2005.

99 Recovery of expenses of enforcement

(1) This regulation applies where a court—

(a) convicts a person of an offence under regulation 85, 86 or 88 above; or

(b) makes an order under regulation 97 or 98 above for the forfeiture of any apparatus.

(2) The court may (in addition to any other order it may make as to costs or expenses) order the person convicted or, as the case may be, any person having an interest in the apparatus the subject of the order for forfeiture, to reimburse an enforcement authority for any expenditure which has been or may be incurred by that authority—

(a) in investigating the offence, and, without prejudice to the generality of the foregoing, in having the apparatus tested;

(b) in connection with any seizure or detention of the apparatus by or on behalf of the authority; or

(c) in connection with any compliance by that authority with directions given by the court for the purposes of any order for the forfeiture of the apparatus.

[4531]

NOTES

Commencement: 7 March 2005.

PART VI TELECOMMUNICATIONS

PART VIII
MISCELLANEOUS AND SUPPLEMENTAL

100 Service of documents etc

(1) Any document required or authorised by these Regulations to be served on a person may be so served—

(a) by delivering it to him or by leaving it at his proper address or by sending it by post to him at that address;

(b) if the person is a body corporate, by serving it in accordance with sub-paragraph (a) above on the secretary or clerk of that body; or

(c) if the person is a partnership, by serving it in accordance with that sub-paragraph on a partner or on a person having control or management of the partnership business.

(2) For the purposes of paragraph (1) above, and for the purposes of section 7 of the Interpretation Act 1978 (which relates to the service of documents by post) in its application to that paragraph, the proper address of any person on whom a document is to be served by virtue of these Regulations shall be his last known address except that—

(a) in the case of service on a body corporate or its secretary or clerk, it shall be the address of the registered or principal office of the body corporate;

(b) in the case of service on a partnership or a partner or a person having the control or management of a partnership business, it shall be the principal office of the partnership,

and for the purposes of this paragraph the principal office of a company registered outside the United Kingdom or of a partnership carrying on business outside the United Kingdom is its principal office within the United Kingdom.

[4532]

NOTES

Commencement: 7 March 2005.

101 Duty of enforcement authority to inform the Secretary of State of action taken

An enforcement authority shall, where action has been taken by it to prohibit or restrict the supply or taking into service (whether under these Regulations or otherwise) of any relevant apparatus, forthwith inform the Secretary of State of the action taken, and the reasons for it, with a view to this information being passed by her to the Commission.

[4533]

NOTES

Commencement: 7 March 2005.

102 Savings for certain privileges

(1) Nothing in these Regulations shall be taken as requiring any person to produce any documents or records if he would be entitled to refuse to produce those documents or records in any proceedings in any court on the grounds that they are the subject of legal professional privilege or, in Scotland, that they contain a confidential communication made by or to an advocate or solicitor in that capacity, or as authorising any person to take possession of any documents or records which are in the possession of a person who would be so entitled.

(2) Nothing in these Regulations shall be construed as requiring a person to answer any question or give any information if to do so would incriminate that person or that person's spouse.

[4534]

NOTES

Commencement: 7 March 2005.

103 Savings for action taken under other enactments

Nothing in these Regulations shall be construed as preventing the taking of any action in respect of any relevant apparatus under the provisions of any other enactment.

[4535]

NOTES
Commencement: 7 March 2005.

104, 105 (*Reg 104 amends the Radio Equipment and Telecommunications Terminal Equipment Regulations 2000, SI 2000/730, reg 1 at* **[4338]***; reg 105 amends the Enterprise Act 2002* (*Part 9 Restrictions on Disclosure of Information*) (*Specification*) *Order 2004, SI 2004/693, Sch 1.*)

SCHEDULE 1
REGULATIONS UNDER SECTION 10 OF THE WIRELESS TELEGRAPHY ACT 1949
Regulation 2(2)

1 The Wireless Telegraphy (Control of Interference from Ignition Apparatus) Regulations 1952;

2 The Wireless Telegraphy (Control of Interference from Electro Medical Apparatus) Regulations 1966;

3 The Wireless Telegraphy (Control of Interference from Radio Frequency Heating Apparatus) Regulations 1971;

4 The Wireless Telegraphy (Control of Interference from Household Appliances, Portable Tools, etc) Regulations 1978;

5 The Wireless Telegraphy (Control of Interference from Fluorescent Lighting Apparatus) Regulations 1978; and

6 The Wireless Telegraphy (Control of Interference from Citizens' Band Radio Apparatus) Regulations 1982.

[4536]

NOTES
Commencement: 7 March 2005.

SCHEDULE 2
PHENOMENA AND EFFECTS WHICH MAY BE REGARDED AS ELECTROMAGNETIC DISTURBANCE
Regulation 4(3)

1 Conducted low-frequency phenomena
—harmonics, interharmonics;
—signalling voltages;
—voltage fluctuations;
—voltage dips and interruptions;
—voltage unbalance;
—power-frequency variations;
—induced low-frequency voltages;
—DC in AC networks; and
—DC ground circuits;

2 Radiated low-frequency phenomena—
—magnetic fields; and
—electric fields;

3 Conducted high-frequency phenomena—
—induced continuous wave (CW) voltages or currents;
—unidirectional transients; and
—oscillatory transients;

4 Radiated high frequency phenomena—
—magnetic fields;

—electric fields;
—electromagnetic fields;
—continuous waves; and
—transients; and

5 Electrostatic discharge phenomena (ESD).

[4537]

NOTES
Commencement: 7 March 2005.

SCHEDULE 3
DESCRIPTIONS OF APPARATUS THE OPERATION OF WHICH MUST NOT BE HINDERED BY RELEVANT APPARATUS

Regulation 5(4)(b)

1 domestic radio and television receivers;

2 industrial manufacturing equipment;

3 mobile radio equipment;

4 mobile radio and commercial radiotelephone equipment;

5 medical and scientific apparatus;

6 information technology equipment;

7 domestic appliances and household electronic equipment;

8 aeronautical and marine radio apparatus;

9 subject to regulation 8, educational electronic equipment;

10 telecommunications networks and apparatus;

11 radio and television broadcast transmitters; and

12 lights and fluorescent lamps.

[4538]

NOTES
Commencement: 7 March 2005.

SCHEDULE 4
THE CE MARKING

Regulation 35

1 In the CE marking, the initials CE shall take the following form—

The grid providing the background in the above graduated drawing is not part of the CE marking.

2 If the CE marking is reduced or enlarged the proportions given in the above graduated drawing must be respected.

3 The various components of the CE marking must have substantially the same vertical dimension, which may not be less than 5 millimetres.

[4539]

NOTES

Commencement: 7 March 2005.

SCHEDULE 5
MINIMUM CRITERIA FOR THE ASSESSMENT OF UNITED KINGDOM COMPETENT BODIES

Regulation 49

1 availability of personnel and of the necessary means and equipment;

2 technical competence and professional integrity of personnel;

3 independence, in carrying out the tests, preparing the reports, issuing the certificates and performing the verification function provided for in the EMC Directive, of staff and technical personnel in relation to all circles, groups or persons directly or indirectly concerned with the product in question;

4 maintenance of professional secrecy by personnel; and

5 possession of civil liability insurance unless such liability is covered by the government of the United Kingdom.

[4540]

NOTES

Commencement: 7 March 2005.

SCHEDULE 6
DESCRIPTIONS OF APPARATUS FOR WHICH UNITED KINGDOM NOTIFIED BODIES ARE AUTHORISED

Regulations 64, 75(3)(a)

1 The CAA is authorised (as a United Kingdom notified body for radiocommunication transmission apparatus and as an enforcement authority for wireless telegraphy apparatus) in relation to aeronautical apparatus of the following descriptions—

—aeronautical mobile—
—associated ground communications;
—EPIRB/ELT (Emergency Position Indicating Radio Beacon/Emergency Locating Transmitter);
—ground and airborne equipment for primary and secondary radar for—
—the CAA;
—the Ministry of Defence; and
—private airfield operators;
—general communications—
—ground/air;
—ground/ground; and
—air/air; and
—aeronautical earth station equipment;
—radio navigation—
—radio altimeters;
—ILS (Instrument Landing System); and
—aeronautical radiobeacons;
—satellite aeronautical mobile radio—
—EPIRB/ELT; and
—voice, medium speed data and low speed data in each case via INMARSAT (satellite operated by the International Maritime Satellite Organisation);
—aeronautical radionavigation—
—ILS/MLS (Microwave Landing System);
—ATC (Air Traffic Control) marker beacons for aircraft;
—radionavigation satellite equipment on board aircraft;

PART VI TELECOMMUNICATIONS

—hyperbolic navigation aids;
—NDB;
—VOR (VHF Omnidirectional Range);
—TACAN/DME (Tactical Air Navigation/Distance Measuring Equipment); and
—satellite navigation systems—
—ADS (Automatic Dependent Surveillance); and
—CIS (Co-operative Independent Surveillance); and
—radiolocation and radiodetermination—
—radar—
—primary;
—OTHR (Over the Horizon Radar);
—secondary;
—ground; and
—airborne; and

any other apparatus not subject to Directive 1999/5/EC on Radio Equipment and Telecommunications Terminal Equipment by virtue of Annex 1, paragraphs 5 and 6 of that Directive.

2 OFCOM is authorised (as a United Kingdom notified body) in relation to every description of radiocommunication transmission apparatus not provided for in paragraph 1 above.

[4541]

NOTES

Commencement: 7 March 2005.

SCHEDULE 7
PROHIBITION NOTICES

Regulation 81(2)

1 A prohibition notice in respect of any relevant apparatus shall—
- (a) state that the Secretary of State considers that—
  - (i) where the notice is served on a manufacturer or supplier, the relevant apparatus does not comply with the protection requirements or the requirements of regulation 32 as the case may be; or
  - (ii) where the notice is served on a user, the relevant apparatus did not so comply at the time when it was supplied;
- (b) set out the reasons why the Secretary of State so considers;
- (c) specify the day on which the notice is to come into force; and
- (d) state that the manufacturer, supplier or user as the case may be may at any time make representations in writing to the Secretary of State for the purpose of establishing that that apparatus so complies or did so comply, as the case may require.

2(1) If representations in writing about a prohibition notice are made by the manufacturer, supplier or user to the Secretary of State, it shall be the duty of the Secretary of State to consider whether to revoke the notice and—
- (a) if she decides to revoke it, to do so;
- (b) in any other case, to appoint a person to consider those representations, any further representations made (whether in writing or orally) by the notified person about the notice and the statements of any witnesses examined under this Schedule.

(2) Where the Secretary of State has appointed a person to consider representations about a prohibition notice, she shall serve a notification on the notified person which—
- (a) states that the notified person may make oral representations to the appointed person for the purpose of establishing that the relevant apparatus to which the notice relates complies or did comply as the case may require with the protection requirements or regulation 32 as the case may be; and
- (b) specifies the place and time at which the oral representations may be made.

(3) The time specified in a notification served under sub-paragraph (2) above shall not be before the end of the period of twenty-one days beginning with the day on which the notification is served, unless the notified person otherwise agrees.

(4) A person on whom a notification has been served under sub-paragraph (2) above or his representative may, at the place and time specified in the notification—

(a) make oral representations to the appointed person for the purpose of establishing that the apparatus in question complies or did so comply as the case may require; and

(b) call and examine witnesses in connection with the representations.

3(1) Where representations in writing about a prohibition notice are made by the notified person to the Secretary of State at any time after a person has been appointed to consider representations about that notice, then, whether or not the appointed person has made a report to the Secretary of State, the following provisions of this paragraph shall apply instead of paragraph 2 above.

(2) The Secretary of State shall, before the end of the period of one month beginning with the day on which she receives the representations, serve a notification on the notified person which states—

(a) that the Secretary of State has decided to revoke the notice, has decided to vary it or, as the case may be, has decided neither to revoke nor to vary it; or

(b) that, a person having been appointed to consider representations about the notice, the notified person may, at a place and time specified in the notification, make oral representations to the appointed person for the purpose of establishing that the apparatus to which the notice relates complies or did so comply as the case may require with the protection requirements or regulation 32 as the case may be.

(3) The time specified in a notification served for the purposes of sub-paragraph (2)(b) above shall not be before the end of the period of twenty-one days beginning with the day on which the notification is served, unless the notified person otherwise agrees or the time is the time already specified for the purposes of paragraph 2(2)(b) above.

(4) A person on whom a notification has been served for the purposes of sub-paragraph (2)(b) above or his representative may, at the place and time specified in the notification—

(a) make oral representations to the appointed person for the purpose of establishing that the apparatus in question complies or did so comply as the case may require; and

(b) call and examine witnesses in connection with the representations.

4(1) Where a person is appointed to consider representations about a prohibition notice, it shall be his duty to consider—

(a) any written representations made by the notified person about the notice, other than those in respect of which a notification is served under paragraph 3(2)(a) above;

(b) any oral representations made under paragraph 2(4) or 3(4) above; and

(c) any statements made by witnesses in connection with the oral representations,

and, after considering any matters under this paragraph, to make a report (including recommendations) to the Secretary of State about the matters considered by her and the notice.

(2) It shall be the duty of the Secretary of State to consider any report made to her under sub-paragraph (1) above and, after considering the report, to inform the notified person of her decision with respect to the prohibition notice to which the report relates.

5(1) The Secretary of State may revoke or vary a prohibition notice by serving on the notified person a notification stating that the notice is revoked or, as the case may be, is varied as specified in the notification.

(2) The Secretary of State shall not vary a prohibition notice so as to make the effect of the notice more restrictive for the notified person.

(3) The service of a notification under sub-paragraph (l) above shall be sufficient to satisfy the requirement of paragraph 4(2) above that the notified person shall be informed of the Secretary of State's decision.

6(1) Where in a notification served on any person under this Schedule the Secretary of State has appointed a time for the making of oral representations or the examination of witnesses, she may, by giving that person such notification as the Secretary of State considers appropriate, change that time to a later time or appoint further times at which further representations may be made or the examination of witnesses may be continued; and paragraphs 2(4) and 3(4) above shall have effect accordingly.

(2) For the purposes of this Schedule the Secretary of State may appoint a person (instead of the appointed person) to consider any representations or statements, if the person originally appointed, or last appointed under this sub-paragraph, to consider those representations or statements has died or appears to the Secretary of State to be otherwise unable to act.

7 In this Schedule—

"the appointed person" in relation to a prohibition notice means the person for the time being appointed under this Schedule to consider representations about the notice;

"notification" means a notification in writing; and

"notified person", in relation to a prohibition notice, means the manufacturer, supplier or user on whom the notice is or was served.

[4542]

NOTES

Commencement: 7 March 2005.

WIRELESS TELEGRAPHY (LICENCE CHARGES) REGULATIONS 2005

(SI 2005/1378)

NOTES

Made: 19 May 2005.
Authority: Wireless Telegraphy Act 1998, ss 1, 2(2); Communications Act 2003, s 403(7).
Commencement: 13 June 2005.

ARRANGEMENT OF REGULATIONS

1 Citation and commencement

These Regulations may be cited as the Wireless Telegraphy (Licence Charges) Regulations 2005 and shall come into force on 13th June 2005.

[4543]

NOTES

Commencement: 13 June 2005.

2 Revocation

The Regulations set out in Schedule 1 are hereby revoked.

[4544]

NOTES

Commencement: 13 June 2005.

3 Interpretation

(1) In these Regulations—

"the 1998 Act" means the Wireless Telegraphy Act 1998;

"the 2003 Act" means the Communications Act 2003;

"the "2004 Regulations" means the Wireless Telegraphy (Spectrum Trading) Regulations 2004;

"apparatus" means apparatus for wireless telegraphy;

"base station" means a station which facilitates or controls communications between a mobile station and—

(a) itself;
(b) another mobile station;
(c) a fixed mobile station; or
(d) any electronic communications network;

"channel" means a part of the radio frequency spectrum intended to be used for a transmission of signals, and defined by—

(a) two specified frequency limits; or
(b) by its centre frequency and the associated bandwidth,

or by an indication equivalent to (a) or (b);

"co-channel" means apparatus operating in an identical frequency or channel;

"congested area" and "heavily congested area" means such part of the British Islands considered by OFCOM to have respectively congested and heavily congested use of the radio frequency spectrum for a specified class of licence and identified as such in Schedules 3 to 6 by reference to the grid squares of the 2nd series of Landranger maps published by the Ordnance Survey, and "non-congested area" shall be construed accordingly;

"cross-polar" means the use of orthogonal polarisation to permit the re-use of identical frequencies or channels in the same area;

"earth station" means a radio station situated either on the earth's surface or within the earth's atmosphere and is intended for communication with one or more:

(c) radio stations which are situated beyond, or are intended to be situated beyond, the earth's atmosphere; or
(d) radio stations of the same kind by means of one or more reflecting satellites or other objects in space;

"fixed link" means a connection by wireless telegraphy designed for use between two fixed points;

PART VI TELECOMMUNICATIONS

"fixed mobile station" means a control point configured to operate in the manner of a mobile station;

"hub" means a single fixed site connected to more than one fixed station via wireless telegraphy links operating in the same frequency bands;

"licence" means a wireless telegraphy licence;

"licensee" means the person to whom a licence is issued;

"medium wave broadcasting band" means that part of the radio frequency spectrum between 526.5 kHz and 1606.5 kHz;

"mobile station" means a station (other than a base station) intended to be used while in motion or during halts at unspecified points;

"national channel" means a channel which the licensee is authorised to use throughout the United Kingdom;

"prescribed payment interval" has the meaning given by regulation 4(1);

"prescribed sum" means a fixed sum or variable sum which is payable to OFCOM under regulation 4(1)(c) or (d);

"prescribed time" means the time when a sum is payable to OFCOM under regulation 4(1);

"slot" means the smallest unit of the radio frequency spectrum used in the construction of a frequency plan, such that all bands, sub-bands, blocks and channels which are used in such plan are integer multiples of the slot size;

"station" means a station for wireless telegraphy;

"time slot" means a recurring time delimited proportion of a channel within which the transmission must be initiated and completed;

"UHF Band I" means that part of the radio frequency spectrum between 410.00000 MHz and 449.49375 MHz;

"UHF Band II" means that part of the radio frequency spectrum between 453.00625 MHz and 466.08750 MHz;

"VHF broadcasting band" means that part of the radio frequency spectrum between 87.5 MHz and 108.0 MHz;

"VHF High Band" means that part of the radio frequency spectrum between 165.04375 MHz and 173.09375 MHz;

"VHF Low Band" means that part of the radio frequency spectrum between 68.08125 MHz and 87.49375 MHz; and

"VHF Mid Band" means that part of the radio frequency spectrum between 137.96250 MHz and 165.04375 MHz.

(2) Where these Regulations provide for the prescribed sum to be calculated by reference to a number of any of the following things—

(a) base stations;
(b) channels;
(c) fixed links;
(d) mobile stations;
(e) national channels;
(f) population;
(g) regional channels;
(h) slots;
(i) stations,

the number shall be taken to be the number the use of which is authorised by the licence at the prescribed time.

(3) In relation to a Transmission of National and Local Radio Broadcasting Services Licence and a Community Radio Licence, a reference to the licensee's coverage is a reference to the total population covered by the transmitters which the licensee is authorised to use in the medium wave broadcasting band or the VHF broadcasting band (as the case may be) as specified in the licence granted to the licensee, and "covered" shall be construed accordingly.

(4) In relation to a Business Radio (Public Access Mobile Radio) Licence, a Business Radio (Public Wide Area Paging) Licence, a Business Radio (Public Mobile Data, Non-Voice) Licence and a Business Radio (Remote Meter Reading Operator) Licence, "regional channel" means a channel used for transmission at stations situated in an area specified in the licence.

(5) In relation to a Coastal Station Radio (International) Licence and a Coastal Station Radio (UK) Licence—

(a) "channels designated for emergency use" means channels 0, 00, 16, 67, 70 and 73 when used solely to assist Her Majesty's Coastguard, and channels 10, 16 and 70 when used solely to assist the Secretary of State with oil pollution control activities; and

(b) a reference to an international maritime channel means a channel specified in the table in Appendix 18 to the 2004 edition of the Radio Regulations.

(6) In relation to a Programme Making and Special Events Fixed Site Licence, a Programme Making and Special Events Link Licence, a Programme Making and Special Events Low Power Licence, a UK Wireless Microphone (Annual) Licence and a UK Wireless Microphone (Biennial) Licence—

(a) "area" in relation to a channel specified in such a licence refers to an area with a population coverage below 2 million individuals;

(b) "designated website" means the website address (at www.jfmg.co.uk or at such other website address as may be notified by OFCOM to persons who, in their opinion, are likely to be affected by any change of address by publishing such a notice on OFCOM's website, www.ofcom.org.uk) of OFCOM's agents managing and licensing in the classes of licence set out under the heading of Programme Making and Special Events in Schedule 2;

(c) "multi use type (1)" in relation to a channel specified in such a licence refers to a maximum of 60 periods with each such period not exceeding 48 hours;

(d) "multi use type (2)" in relation to a channel specified in such a licence refers to a maximum of 480 periods with each such period not exceeding 48 hours;

(e) "occasional use" in relation to a channel specified in such a licence refers to a period not exceeding 48 hours;

(f) "premium case" means a case where at the applicant's request such a licence is granted or varied outside office hours; and for the purposes of this definition "office hours" means 09.00 to 17.00 hours from Monday to Friday other than on a day which is a bank holiday in England and Wales;

(g) "primary" in relation to a channel specified in such a licence refers to use at any time;

(h) "programme making" includes the making of a programme for broadcast, the making of a film presentation, advertisement or audio or video tape, and the staging or performance of an entertainment, sporting or other public event;

(i) "programme sound link" in relation to a channel specified in such a licence refers to a channel used to transmit the material produced in programme making from a fixed transmission station to a fixed receiving station;

(j) "regional" in relation to a channel specified in such a licence refers to an area with a population coverage of 2 million individuals or more but below 12 million individuals;

(k) "restricted service programme sound link" in relation to a channel specified in such a licence refers to a channel used to transmit the material produced in programme making from a fixed transmission station to a fixed receiving station where the transmission is for a period not exceeding thirty consecutive days;

(l) "secondary" in relation to a channel specified in such a licence refers to use when the channel or band is not being used by another licensee under a licence which authorises such use as a primary channel;

(m) "shared" in relation to a channel specified in such a licence refers to use at the same time as such a channel may be used by a licensee under another licence; and

(n) "variation" in relation to such a licence refers to the addition of a channel to the channel specified in such licence;

and for the purpose of determining "population coverage" as referred to above, reference shall be made as appropriate to—

(i) the estimated mid-year resident population for England and Wales for 2000 as shown in the "Office of National Statistics Population Estimates Mid-2000 for England and Wales" published in August 2001;

(ii) the estimated mid-year resident population for Scotland for 2000 as shown in the "Mid-Year Population Estimates, Scotland" published in June 2001; and

(iii) the estimated mid-year resident population for Northern Ireland for 2000 as shown in the "Annual Report of the Registrar General for Northern Ireland" published in November 2001.

(7) In relation to a Satellite (Aircraft Earth Station) Licence, a Satellite (Earth Station Network) Licence and a Satellite (Earth Station on board Vessel) Licence, "network" means a

uni- or bi-directional service from any number of earth station terminals to a single geo-stationary orbit satellite transponder transmitting in the earth to space direction.

[4545]

NOTES

Commencement: 13 June 2005.

4 Licence charges and time of payment

(1) Subject to paragraphs (2) to (10) and to regulations 5 and 6, there shall be paid to OFCOM by the licensee—

(a) on the issue of the licence and on the variation of the licence where such variation is prescribed in Schedule 2; and

(b) on the last day of the period of twelve, twenty-four, thirty-six or (as the case may be) sixty months prescribed in Schedule 2, if any, in respect of the class of licence in question ("prescribed payment interval") and on the last day of each subsequent prescribed payment interval thereafter (the first prescribed payment interval having begun on the day of the issue of the licence) for which the licence continues in force,

in relation to a licence of a class listed in Schedule 2—

(c) the fixed sum specified in; or

(d) the variable sum determined in accordance with the provisions of,

that Schedule.

(2) Except for the classes of licence listed under the heading "Programme Making and Special Events" in Schedule 2, where a licence is issued for a period less than a year, the sum payable shall be such sum as represents one-twelfth of the prescribed sum multiplied by the number of complete and part-complete months to the expiry of the licence.

(3) The sum payable in accordance with paragraph (2) shall not be less than £20, and where such sum represents a fraction of a whole pound sterling then such sum shall be rounded up to the nearest pound sterling.

(4) Paragraph (2) shall only apply to a licence in respect of which the fee otherwise payable for such licence is greater than £75 per annum.

(5) Paragraph (7) shall apply to a licensee where—

(a) a prescribed sum is payable by that licensee in respect of a licence under paragraph (1);

(b) the licence is of one of the following classes—

(i) the classes listed under the heading "Broadcasting" in Schedule 2;

(ii) the classes listed under the heading "Fixed Links" in Schedule 2;

(iii) the classes listed under the heading "Public Wireless Networks" in Schedule 2;

(iv) the classes listed under the heading "Satellite Services" in Schedule 2; or

(v) the classes listed under the heading "Business Radio" in Schedule 2;

(c) the licence is granted for a period of a year or longer; and

(d) the prescribed sum due for payment by the licensee is in excess of £100,000.

(6) Paragraph (7) shall also apply to a licensee where—

(a) prescribed sums are payable by that licensee under paragraph (1) in respect of more than one licence where all of those licences are of the same class and that class is one of the classes listed in paragraph (5)(b);

(b) each of those prescribed sums is due for payment by the licensee at the same prescribed time in accordance with paragraph (1);

(c) each of the prescribed sums is in respect of licences granted for a period of a year or longer; and

(d) the total of the prescribed sums due for payment by the licensee are in excess of £100,000.

(7) If OFCOM receive notice from a licensee to which this paragraph applies of the licensee's intention to make payment in ten equal instalments of a sum equal to the prescribed sum referred to in paragraph (5) or equal to the total of the prescribed sums referred to in paragraph (6)(d), the licensee—

(a) shall not be required to make payment at the prescribed time other than in accordance with this paragraph; and

(b) shall make payment of the sum in ten equal instalment payments with the first instalment to be paid to OFCOM on the day which shall be the same day as the prescribed time when the prescribed sum or the prescribed sums were to be paid to OFCOM and each subsequent instalment to be paid on the same day in each of the nine consecutive months thereafter (or in a month in which there is no such day, on the last day of the month).

(8) Where at any time the licensee fails to make payment in accordance with paragraph (7), the total of the outstanding instalment payments shall become immediately due for payment.

(9) No sums shall be payable to OFCOM in respect of the issue of a licence in order to effect a transfer of rights and obligations under a licence to another person under regulation 8(5) of the 2004 Regulations.

(10) For any licence issued in order to effect a transfer under the 2004 Regulations, the prescribed payment interval shall be treated as to commence and expire at the times when the corresponding prescribed payment interval would have commenced and expired under the licence from which the rights and obligations were transferred had the transfer not been made.

[4546]

NOTES

Commencement: 13 June 2005.

5 Concessionary licence charges

(1) This regulation applies where a relevant licence is granted to an applicant, or held by a licensee, which—

(a) is a charity; and
(b) has as its object the safety of human life in an emergency.

(2) The sum to be paid by a qualifying charity to OFCOM under section 1 of the 1998 Act on the issue of a relevant licence, and on the last day of each of the prescribed payment intervals (if any), shall be one half of the prescribed sum. Where the sum so payable to OFCOM represents a fraction of a whole pound sterling then the sum payable by the qualifying charity shall be rounded up to the nearest whole pound sterling.

(3) In this regulation—

"charity" means a person who—

(a) being subject to the laws of England and Wales, or Scotland, or Northern Ireland, is a charity within the meaning of section 506(1) of the Income and Corporation Taxes Act 1988;
(b) being subject to the laws of the Isle of Man, is registered as a charity under the Charities Registration Act 1989;
(c) being subject to the laws of Guernsey, is a member for the time being of the Association of Guernsey Charities; or
(d) being subject to the laws of Jersey, is a member for the time being of the Association of Jersey Charities; and

"qualifying charity" is a body falling within paragraph (1); and

"relevant licence" means a licence of one of the following classes—

(i) all of the classes listed under the heading "Aeronautical" in Schedule 2;
(ii) all of the classes listed under the heading "Maritime" in Schedule 2 [apart from Ship Radio and Ship Portable Radio]; and
(iii) all of the classes listed under the heading "Business Radio" in Schedule 2.

[4547]

NOTES

Commencement: 13 June 2005.

Para (3): words in square brackets in definition "relevant licence" inserted by the Wireless Telegraphy (Licence Charges) (Amendment) Regulations 2006, SI 2006/2894, reg 2(a).

6 Other licence charges

Where a sum is not prescribed by regulations made under section 1 of the 1998 Act whether on the issue of a licence or subsequently, there shall be paid to OFCOM such sum as OFCOM may in the particular case determine.

[4548]

NOTES

Commencement: 13 June 2005.

(Sch 1 revokes the Wireless Telegraphy (Licence Charges) Regulations 2002, SI 2002/1700, the Wireless Telegraphy (Licence Charges) (Amendment) Regulations 2003, SI 2003/2983, and the Wireless Telegraphy (Licence Charges) (Amendment) (Channel Islands and Isle of Man) Regulations 2003, SI 2003/2984.)

SCHEDULE 2
LICENCE CHARGES AND PAYMENT INTERVALS

Regulation 4

The sum payable on the issue of the licence and on the expiry of each prescribed payment interval

Class of licence	*Fixed sums*	*Variable sums*	*Prescribed payment interval*
Aeronautical			
Aeronautical Ground Station (Air Traffic/ Ground Movement Control)	£150		12 months
Aeronautical Ground Station (Air/Ground Communications Services)	£100		12 months
Aeronautical Ground Station (Airfield Flight Information Service)	£100		12 months
Aeronautical Ground Station (Operations Control)	£250		12 months
Aeronautical Ground Station (General Aviation)	£25		12 months
Aeronautical Ground Station (Fire)	£25		12 months
Aeronautical Ground Station (High Frequency)	£350		12 months
Aeronautical Ground Station (Offshore Platform)	£250		12 months
Aeronautical Radar	£50		12 months
Aeronautical Navigation Aid Stations		£50 for each navigational aid station.	12 months
Aircraft		(a) £20 for each aircraft which has an approved maximum take-off weight of not more than 3,200 kg.	12 months

		(b) £150 for each aircraft which has an approved maximum take-off weight of more than 3,200 kg but not more than 14,000 kg.	12 months
		(c) £350 for each aircraft which has an approved maximum take-off weight of more than 14,000 kg.	12 months
Aircraft (Transportable)	£15		12 months
Amateur and Citizens' Band			
Amateur Radio		[£20 for each licence that is not applied for electronically; no charge for persons aged 75 years or over.]	…
Citizens' Band Radio		£15 per person aged 21 years or over; no charge for persons aged under 21 years or aged 75 years or over.	12 months
Broadcasting			
Restricted Radio Services Transmission (Class A—Freely Radiating)		(a) £15 per day for each medium wave broadcasting band frequency.	
		(b) £25 per day where the power of transmission does not exceed 1 W erp for each VHF broadcasting band frequency.	
		(c) £40 per day where the power of transmission exceeds 1 W erp for each VHF broadcasting band frequency.	
Restricted Radio Services Transmission (Class B—Radiating Cable)	£100		12 months
Restricted Radio Services Transmission (Class C—Freely Radiating Very Low Power)	£100		12 months
Transmission of National and Local Radio Broadcasting Services		(a) For any number of transmitters in the medium wave broadcasting band—	12 months

		(i) £226, where coverage is of fewer than 100,000 people;	
		(ii) £339 per complete 100,000 people covered, any final group of fewer than 100,000 people being disregarded, where coverage is of 100,000 people or more.	
		(b) For any number of transmitters in the VHF broadcasting band—	12 months
		(i) £339, where coverage is of fewer than 100,000 people;	
		(ii) £509 per complete 100,000 people covered, any final group of fewer than 100,000 people being disregarded, where coverage is of 100,000 people or more.	
Community Radio		(a) For any number of transmitters in the medium wave broadcasting band—	12 months
		(i) £226, where coverage is of fewer than 100,000 people;	
		(ii) £339 per complete 100,000 people covered, any final group of fewer than 100,000 people being disregarded, where coverage is of 100,000 people or more.	
		(b) For any number of transmitters in the VHF broadcasting band—	12 months
		(i) £339, where coverage is of fewer than 100,000 people;	
		(ii) £509 per complete 100,000 people covered, any final group of fewer than 100,000 people being disregarded, where coverage is of 100,000 people or more.	
Business Radio			
Business Radio (GSM-R Railway use)		£158,400 for each 2 x 200 kHz channel.	12 months
Business Radio (National and Regional)		(a) Subject to paragraph (f), for each 2 x 12.5 kHz channel—	12 months

(i) £9,900 in respect of a channel in the VHF High Band, UHF Band I or UHF Band II in the United Kingdom;	
(ii) £8,250 in respect of a channel in any frequency bands in the United Kingdom other than those specified in paragraph (a)(i).	
(b) Subject to paragraph (f), for each 2 x 12.5 kHz channel—	12 months
(i) £6,435 in respect of a channel in the VHF High Band, UHF Band I or UHF Band II in England;	
(ii) £5,363 in respect of a channel in any frequency bands in England other than those specified in paragraph (b)(i);	
(iii) £990 in respect of a channel in the VHF High Band, UHF Band I or UHF Band II in Wales;	
(iv) £825 in respect of a channel in any frequency bands in Wales other than those specified in paragraph (b)(iii);	
(v) £1,485 in respect of a channel in the VHF High Band, UHF Band I or UHF Band II in Scotland;	
(vi) £1,237 in respect of a channel in any frequency bands in Scotland other than those specified in paragraph (b)(v);	
(vii) £990 in respect of a channel in the VHF High Band, UHF Band I or UHF Band II in Northern Ireland;	
(viii) £825 in respect of a channel in any frequency bands in Northern Ireland other than those specified in paragraph (b)(vii).	

(c) Subject to paragraph (f), for each 1 x 12.5 kHz channel, 50 per cent of the prescribed sum specified in paragraphs (a) or (b) depending on the applicable frequency band and territorial extent.	12 months
(d) Subject to paragraph (f), for each channel of less than or equal to 2 x 6.25 kHz, 50 per cent of the prescribed sum specified in paragraphs (a) or (b) depending on the applicable frequency band and territorial extent.	12 months
(e) Subject to paragraph (f), for each 2 x 25 kHz channel, 200 per cent of the prescribed sum specified in paragraphs (a) or (b) depending on the applicable frequency band and territorial extent.	12 months
(f) Where OFCOM are satisfied that technologies associated with the use of the channel complies with section 154(2)(a) of the 2003 Act—	
(i) 20 per cent of the prescribed sum in paragraphs (a) to (e) is payable on the issue of the licence;	
(ii) 40 per cent of the prescribed sum in paragraphs (a) to (e) is payable on the first anniversary of the issue of the licence;	
(iii) 60 per cent of the prescribed sum in paragraphs (a) to (e) is payable on the second anniversary of the issue of the licence;	

	(iv) 80 per cent of the prescribed sum in paragraphs (a) to (e) is payable on the third anniversary of the issue of the licence; (v) the full prescribed sum in paragraphs (a) to (e) is payable on the fourth and each subsequent anniversary of the issue of the licence.	
Business Radio (On-Site Hospital Paging and Emergency Speech Systems)	£150 for each channel per site.	36 months
Business Radio (On-Site Local Communications Systems)	Depending on whether use of the channel is being licensed in a heavily congested, congested, or non-congested area designated in Schedule 3— (i) £200 for each channel per site in a heavily congested area; (ii) £100 for each channel per site in a congested area; (iii) £75 for each channel per site in a non-congested area.	12 months
Business Radio (On-Site One-Way Paging and Speech Systems)	£75 for each channel per site.	36 months
Business Radio (On-Site Speech and Data Systems)	(a) For each 2 x 12.5 kHz channel or for each channel of less than or equal to 1 x 12.5 kHz per site in the VHF High Band, UHF Band I or UHF Band II, the following sums depending on whether use of the channel is being licensed in a heavily congested, congested or non-congested area designated in Schedule 3— (i) £200 for each channel per site in a heavily congested area;	12 months

PART VI TELECOMMUNICATIONS

	(ii) £100 for each channel per site in a congested area;	
	(iii) £75 for each channel per site in a non-congested area.	
	(b) £75 for each 2 x 12.5 kHz channel or for each channel of less than or equal to 1 x 12.5 kHz per site in any bands other than those specified in paragraph (a).	12 months
Business Radio (IR 2008 Data)	(a) For each 12.5 kHz channel per site in the VHF High Band, UHF Band I or UHF Band II, the following sums per 250 millisecond or 500 millisecond time slot depending on whether use of the channel is being licensed in a heavily congested, congested, or non-congested area designated in Schedule 4—	12 months
	(i) £100 per mobile station transmit frequency time slot in a heavily congested area;	
	(ii) £100 per base station transmit frequency time slot in a heavily congested area;	
	(iii) £50 per mobile station transmit frequency time slot in a congested area;	
	(iv) £50 per base station transmit frequency time slot in a congested area;	
	(v) £25 per mobile station transmit frequency time slot in a non-congested area;	
	(vi) £25 per base station transmit frequency time slot in a non-congested area.	

		(b) £25 for each 12.5 kHz channel per site in any band other than those specified in paragraph (a) per 250 millisecond or 500 millisecond mobile station, or per 250 millisecond or 500 millisecond base station, transmit frequency time slot.	12 months
Business Radio (Suppliers)	£200		12 months
Business Radio (UK General)	£60		36 months
Business Radio (Standard)		(a) For channels other than 6.25 kHz channels— (i) £140 for up to 10 mobile stations; (ii) £250 for 11–25 mobile stations; (iii) £500 for 26–60 mobile stations; (iv) £1,000 for 61–100 mobile stations; (v) £1,750 for 101–200 mobile stations; (vi) £3,500 for 201–500 mobile stations; (vii) £7,000 for 501–1,000 mobile stations; (viii) for more than 1,000 mobile stations, £7,000 for the first 1,000 plus £5,000 for each successive group of 500 and £5,000 for any final group of less than 500.	12 months
		(b) For 6.25 kHz channels, 50 per cent of the prescribed sum specified in paragraph (a)(i) to (viii) for channels other than 6.25 kHz channels depending on the number of mobile stations.	12 months
Business Radio (Self-Select)		£50 for each one-way paging system site.	36 months

PART VI TELECOMMUNICATIONS

Business Radio (Wide Area Distress Alarm Systems)		For each 1 x 12.5 kHz channel per site, the following sums depending on whether use of the channel is being licensed in a heavily congested, congested or non-congested area designated in Part 2 of Schedule 5— (i) £100 for each channel per site in a heavily congested area; (ii) £75 for each channel per site in a congested area; (iii) £75 for each channel per site in a non-congested area.	12 months
Business Radio (Wide Area One-Way Paging and Speech Systems)		(a) For each 1 x 25kHz channel per site, the following sums depending on whether use of the channel is being licensed in a heavily congested, congested or non-congested area designated in Part 2 of Schedule 5— (i) £200 for each channel per site in a heavily congested area; (ii) £100 for each channel per site in a congested area; (iii) £75 for each channel per site in a non-congested area.	12 months
		(b) For each 1 x 12.5 kHz channel, 50 per cent of the prescribed sum specified in paragraph (a) depending upon whether the channel is being licensed in a heavily congested, congested or non-congested area designated in Part 2 of Schedule 5.	12 months

Business Radio (Wide Area Speech and Data Systems)	(a) Subject to paragraph (f), for each 2 x 12.5 kHz channel in the VHF High Band, UHF Band I or UHF Band II, the appropriate sum payable in accordance with Part 1 of Schedule 5 as determined by whether use of the channel is being licensed in a heavily congested, congested or non-congested area designated in Part 2, and by the applicable category (having regard to the number of mobile stations per channel in use) specified in Part 3, of that Schedule.	12 months
	(b) Subject to paragraph (f), for each 2 x 12.5 kHz channel in any bands other than those specified in paragraph (a), the appropriate sum applying in respect of a channel licensed in a non-congested area payable in accordance with Part 1 of Schedule 5 as determined by the applicable category (having regard to the number of mobile stations per channel in use) specified in Part 3 of that Schedule.	12 months
	(c) Subject to paragraph (f), for each 1 x 12.5 kHz channel, 50 per cent of the prescribed sum specified in paragraphs (a) or (b) depending on the frequency band in which the channel falls.	12 months
	(d) Subject to paragraph (f), for each channel of less than or equal to 2 x 6.25 kHz, 50 per cent of the prescribed sum specified in paragraphs (a) or (b) depending on the frequency band in which the channel falls.	12 months

	(e) Subject to paragraph (f), for each 2 x 25 kHz channel, 200 per cent of the prescribed sum specified in paragraphs (a) or (b) depending on the frequency band in which the channel falls.	12 months
	(f) Where the sum payable in paragraphs (a) to (e) would otherwise be less than £75, a minimum fee of £75 shall be payable.	
Business Radio (Common Base Station)	(a) £407 for each 2 x 12.5 kHz channel in the VHF Low Band designated for use within the defined coverage area of the licensed common base station service.	12 months
	(b) For each 2 x 12.5 kHz channel in the VHF Mid Band or VHF High Band for common base station assignments on designated downgraded channels shared with wide area business radio systems, the following sums depending on whether use of the channel is being licensed in a heavily congested, congested or non-congested area designated in Schedule 6— (i) £1,141 for each channel in a heavily congested area; (ii) £570 for each channel in a congested area; (iii) £285 for each channel in a non-congested area.	12 months
	(c) For each 2 x 12.5 kHz channel in the 55–67 MHz and 171–191 MHz bands, £103 on the issue of the licence and thereafter— (i) £206 on the first anniversary of the issue of the licence;	12 months

	(ii) £309 on the second anniversary of the issue of the licence;	
	(iii) £412 on the third anniversary of the issue of the licence;	
	(iv) £618 on the fourth anniversary of the issue of the licence;	
	(v) £824 on the fifth and each subsequent anniversary of the issue of the licence.	
	(d) For each 2 x 12.5 kHz channel in any bands other than those specified in paragraphs (a) to (c) above designated for use within the defined coverage area of the licensed common base station service, the following sums depending on whether use of the channel is being licensed in a heavily congested, congested or non-congested area designated in Schedule 6—	12 months
	(i) £1,630 for each channel in a heavily congested area;	
	(ii) £815 for each channel in a congested area;	
	(iii) £407 for each channel in a non-congested area.	
	(e) For each 1 x 12.5 channel, 50 per cent of the prescribed sum specified in paragraphs (a) to (d) depending on the frequency band in which the channel falls and whether use of the channel is being licensed in a heavily congested, congested or non-congested area designated in Schedule 6.	12 months

Business Radio (Public Access Mobile Radio)	(a) £5,544 for each 2 x 12.5 kHz national channel in the 174–208 MHz band.	12 months
	(b) £1,109 for each 2 x 12.5 kHz regional channel in the 174–208 MHz band subject to a maximum fee of £3,000 where the same channel is licensed to the same licensee in more than one location.	12 months
	(c) For each 1 x 12.5 kHz channel, 50 per cent of the prescribed sum specified in paragraphs (a) or (b) depending on whether the channel is a national channel or a regional channel.	12 months
Business Radio (Public Wide Area Paging)	(a) £9,900 for each 1 x 25 kHz national channel in the 137–172 MHz, 449–470 MHz or 870–871 MHz bands.	12 months
	(b) £1,980 for each 1 x 25 kHz regional channel in the 137–172 MHz, 449–470 MHz or 870–871 MHz bands.	12 months
	(c) For each 1 x 12.5 kHz channel, 50 per cent of the prescribed sum specified in paragraphs (a) or (b) depending on whether the channel is a national channel or a regional channel.	12 months
Business Radio (Public Mobile Data, Non-Voice)	(a) £9,900 for each 2 x 12.5 kHz national channel in the 105–165 MHz band.	12 months
	(b) £7,920 for each 2 x 12.5 kHz national channel in the 174–208 MHz band.	12 months
	(c) £7,920 for each 2 x 12.5 kHz national channel in the 420–450 MHz band.	12 months
	(d) £9,900 for each 2 x 12.5 kHz national channel in the 450–470 MHz band.	12 months

	(e) For each 1 x 12.5 kHz national channel, 50 per cent of the prescribed sum specified in paragraphs (a) to (d) depending on the frequency band in which the channel falls.	12 months
	(f) £9,900 for each national channel in the 133–147 kHz band.	
Business Radio (Remote Meter Reading Operator)	(a) £80,000 for each exclusive 200 kHz national channel in the 183.5–184.5 MHz band.	12 months
	(b) £8,000 for each shared 200 kHz national channel in the 183.5–184.5 MHz band.	12 months
	(c) £1,600 for each shared 200 kHz regional channel in the 183.5–184.5 MHz band.	12 months
	(d) £1,000 for each shared 25 kHz national channel in the 183.5–184.5 MHz band.	12 months
	(e) £200 for each shared 25kHz regional channel in the 183.5–184.5 MHz band.	12 months
Fixed Links		
Point to Point Security CCTV Services	(a) £720 for each hub with a bandwidth less than or equal to 56 MHz.	12 months
	(b) £885 for each hub with a bandwidth greater than 56 MHz but less than, or equal to, 140 MHz.	12 months
	(c) £1,030 for each hub with a bandwidth greater than 140 MHz but less than, or equal to, 250 MHz.	12 months
	(d) £1,155 for each hub with a bandwidth greater than 250 MHz but less than, or equal to, 308 MHz.	12 months

PART VI TELECOMMUNICATIONS

	(e) Where a hub listed in paragraphs (a) to (d) is added after the issue of the licence, such sum as represents one-twelfth of the prescribed sum on the issue of the licence, multiplied by the number of complete calendar months beginning with the date of the addition of the hub to the next anniversary of the issue of the licence.	
Point to Point Fixed Links	(a) Subject to paragraphs (b) and (d), for each co-ordinated bi-directional fixed link, the appropriate sum calculated in accordance with the formula set out in Part 1 of Schedule 7.	12 months
	(b) For each co-ordinated bi-directional fixed link added after the issue of the licence and where the additional links are operating co-channel and cross-polar, 50 per cent of the prescribed sum specified in paragraph (a).	12 months
	(c) For each uni-directional fixed link, 75 per cent of the prescribed sum specified in paragraph (a).	12 months
	(d) Where a temporary co-ordinated bi-directional or uni-directional fixed link (other than an additional link referred to in paragraph (b)) is added after the issue of the licence, such sum as represents one-twelfth of the prescribed sum on the issue of the licence, multiplied by the number of complete calendar months beginning with the date of the addition of the link to the next anniversary of the issue of the licence.	
Self Co-ordinated Links	£50 for each 65 GHz fixed link.	12 months

Scanning Telemetry		(a) £410 for each channel used at a base station hub which is not subject to national channel arrangements.	12 months
		(b) For each 2 x 12.5 kHz national channel, £6,440 on the issue of the licence and on the first anniversary of issue of the licence, and £7,920 on the second and on any subsequent anniversary of the issue of the licence.	12 months
		(c) For each 1 x 12.5 kHz channel, 50 per cent of the prescribed sum specified in paragraphs (a) or (b) depending on whether or not the channel is used at a base station hub which is not subject to national channel arrangements.	12 months
Fixed Wireless Access			
Fixed Wireless Access (3.4, 3.6–4.2 GHz—Guernsey)	£5,000		60 months
Fixed Wireless Access (3.4, 3.6–4.2 GHz—Isle of Man)	£5,000		60 months
Fixed Wireless Access (3.4, 3.6–4.2 GHz—Jersey)	£5,000		60 months
Fixed Wireless Access (3.6–4.2 GHz)		(a) £8,436 for each 1 MHz national slot, where co-ordination is required with earth stations.	12 months
		(b) £2,226 for each 1 MHz national slot, where co-ordination is required with earth stations and fixed links.	12 months
Fixed Wireless Access (5.8 GHz)		£1 for each terminal, subject to a minimum fee of £50 for up to 49 terminals.	12 months
Fixed Wireless Access (28 GHz Guernsey)		(a) £1,800 for each 2 x 112 MHz channel in the 28.0525–28.1645 GHz, paired with 29.0605–29.1725 GHz, bands.	12 months

PART VI TELECOMMUNICATIONS

	(b) £1,800 for each 2 x 112 MHz channel in the 28.1925–28.3045 GHz, paired with 29.2005–29.3125 GHz, bands.	12 months
	(c) £1,800 for each 2 x 112 MHz channel in the 28.3325–28.4445 GHz, paired with 29.3405–29.4525 GHz, bands.	12 months
Fixed Wireless Access (28 GHz Isle of Man)	(a) £2,133 for each 2 x 112 MHz channel in the 28.0525–28.1645 GHz, paired with 29.0605–29.1725 GHz, bands.	12 months
	(b) £2,133 for each 2 x 112 MHz channel in the 28.1925–28.3045 GHz, paired with 29.2005–29.3125 GHz, bands.	12 months
	(c) £2,133 for each 2 x 112 MHz channel in the 28.3325–28.4445 GHz, paired with 29.3405–29.4525 GHz, bands.	12 months
Fixed Wireless Access (28 GHz Jersey)	(a) £2,533 for each 2 x 112 MHz channel in the 28.0525–28.1645 GHz, paired with 29.0605–29.1725 GHz, bands.	12 months
	(b) £2,533 for each 2 x 112 MHz channel in the 28.1925–28.3045 GHz, paired with 29.2005–29.3125 GHz, bands.	12 months
	(c) £2,533 for each 2 x 112 MHz channel in the 28.3325–28.4445 GHz, paired with 29.3405–29.4525 GHz, bands.	12 months
Maritime		
Coastal Station Radio (Marina)	£75 for each base station in respect of channels M (157.850 MHz), M2 (161.425 MHz) and channel 80 (157.025 MHz).	12 months
Coastal Station Radio (International)	£100 for each international maritime channel (except channel 80 (157.025 MHz)) per base station, provided that channels designated for emergency use shall not be taken into account.	12 months

Coastal Station Radio (UK)		£180 for each channel in respect of non-international maritime channels per base station (including associated mobile stations).	12 months
Coastal Station Radio (Training School)	£50		12 months
Differential Global Positioning System		(a) £250 for each channel per VHF station.	12 months
		(b) £1,000 for each channel per MF or UHF station.	12 months
Maritime Navigational Aids and Radar		(a) £40 for each frequency per navigational aid or radar station, except for the use of a pair of VHF channels AI51 and AI52.	12 months
		(b) £40 for each pair of VHF channels AI51 and AI52.	12 months
Maritime Radio (Suppliers and Demonstration)	£50		12 months
Ship Portable Radio	…	[£20 for each licence that is not applied for electronically.]	…
Ship Radio	…	[£20 for each licence that is not applied for electronically.]	…
Programme Making and Special Events			
Programme Making and Special Events Fixed Site		(a) For the issue of a licence— (i) £24 for each channel per site in respect of a single channel talk-back or a single channel radio microphone; (ii) £96 for each channel per site in respect of a multi-channel talk-back, a multi-channel radio microphone or a wideband channel; plus— (iii) in a premium case, £55. (b) For the variation of a licence—	

PART VI TELECOMMUNICATIONS

		(i) subject to paragraph (b)(ii), where a channel listed in paragraph (a)(i) to(ii) is added, such sum as represents one-twelfth of the sum payable for the issue of a licence for the type of channel to which the additional channel belongs, multiplied by the number of complete and part-complete calendar months beginning with the day of the addition of the channel to the next anniversary of the issue of the licence; (ii) where the aggregate sum payable for a variation of a licence in this paragraph in any case other than a premium case would otherwise be less than £24, a charge of £24 only; plus— (iii) in a premium case, £55.
Programme Making and Special Events Link		(a) Subject to paragraph (a)(liii), for the issue of a licence— (i) £2.25 for each channel of 12.5 kHz in the band 26–65 MHz for occasional use; (ii) £7 for each channel of 12.5 kHz in the band 65–470 MHz for occasional use; (iii) £2.25 for each channel of the 12.5 kHz in the band 470–1,000 MHz for occasional use; (iv) £14 for each channel (not being a telemetry or telecommand channel) of 0.5 MHz in the band 1–2 GHz for occasional use; (v) £14 for each telemetry or telecommand channel of 5MHz in the band 1–2 GHz for occasional use;

(vi) £23 for each channel of 5 MHz in the band 2–5 GHz for occasional use;

(vii) £14 for each channel of 5 MHz in the band 5–8 GHz for occasional use;

(viii) £7 for each channel of 5 MHz in the band 8–20 GHz for occasional use;

(ix) £4.50 for each channel of 5 MHz in the band 20–40 GHz for occasional use;

(x) £2.25 for each channel of 5 MHz in the band above 40 GHz for occasional use;

(xi) £125 for each channel of 12.5 kHz in the band 26–65 MHz for multi use type (1) channels;

(xii) £388 for each channel of 12.5 kHz in the band 65–470 MHz for multi use type (1) channels;

(xiii) £125 for each channel of 12.5 kHz in the band 470–1,000 MHz for multi use type (1) channels;

(xiv) £777 for each channel of 0.5 MHz in the band 1–2 GHz for multi use type (1) channels;

(xv) £1,276 for each channel of 5 MHz in the band 2–5 GHz for multi use type (1) channels;

(xvi) £777 for each channel of 5 MHz in the band 5–8 GHz for multi use type (1) channels;

(xvii) £388 for each channel of 5 MHz in the band 8–20 GHz for multi use type (1) channels;

(xviii) £249 for each channel of 5 MHz in the band 20–40 GHz for multi use type (1) channels;

(xix) £125 for each channel of 5 MHz in the band above 40 GHz for multi use type (1) channels;

(xx) £810 for each channel of 12.5 kHz in the band 26–65 MHz for multi use type (2) channels;

(xxi) £2,520 for each channel of 12.5 kHz in the band 65–470 MHz for multi use type (2) channels;

(xxii) £810 for each channel of 12.5 kHz in the band 470–1,000 MHz for multi use type (2) channels;

(xxiii) £5,040 for each channel of 0.5 MHz in the band 1–2 GHz for multi use type (2) channels;

(xxiv) £8,280 for each channel of 5 MHz in the band 2–5 GHz for multi use type (2) channels;

(xxv) £5,040 for each channel of 5 MHz in the band 5–8 GHz for multi use type (2) channels;

(xxvi) £2,520 for each channel of 5 MHz in the band 8–20 GHz for multi use type (2) channels;

(xxvii) £1,620 for each channel of 5 MHz in the band 20–40 GHz for multi use type (2) channels;

(xxviii) £810 for each channel of 5 MHz in the band above 40 GHz for multi use type (2) channels;

(xxix) £72 for each channel of 12.5 kHz in the band 26–65 MHz for primary regional channels;

(xxx) £225 for each channel of 12.5 kHz in the band 65–470 MHz for primary regional channels;

(xxxi) £72 for each channel of 12.5 in the band 470–1,000 MHz for primary regional channels;

(xxxii) £432 for each channel of 0.5 MHz in the band 1–2 GHz for primary regional channels;

(xxxiii) £750 for each channel of 5MHz in the band 2–5 GHz for primary regional channels;

(xxxiv) £432 for each channel of 5MHz in the band 5–8 GHz for primary regional channels;

(xxxv) £216 for each channel of 5 MHz in the band 8–20 GHz for primary regional channels;

(xxxvi) £144 for each channel of 5 MHz in the band 20–40 GHz for primary regional channels;

(xxxvii) £72 for each channel of 5 MHz in the band above 40 GHz for primary regional channels;

(xxxviii) £29 for each channel of 12.5 kHz in the band 26–65 MHz for secondary regional channels and primary area channels;

(xxxix) £90 for each channel of 12.5 kHz in the band 65–470 MHz for secondary regional channels and primary area channels;

(xl) £29 for each channel of 12.5 kHz in the band 470–1,000 MHz for secondary regional channels and primary area channels;

(xli) £172 for each channel of 0.5 MHz in the band 1–2 GHz for secondary regional channels and primary area channels;

(xlii) £300 for each channel of 5 MHz in the band 2–5 GHz for secondary regional channels and primary area channels;

(xliii) £172 for each channel of 5 MHz in the band 5–8 GHz for secondary regional channels and primary area channels;

(xliv) £86 for each channel of 5 MHz in the band 8–20 GHz for secondary regional channels and primary area channels;

(xlv) £58 for each channel of 5 MHz in the band 20–40 GHz for secondary regional channels and primary area channels;

(xlvi) £29 for each channel of 5 MHz in the band above 40 GHz for secondary regional channels and primary area channels;

(xlvii) £43 for each channel of 12.5 kHz in the band 26–65 MHz for programme sound link use;

(xlviii) £205 for each channel of 0.5 MHz in the band 1517–1525 MHz for programme sound link use;

(xlix) £12 for each channel of 12.5 kHz in the band 26–65 MHz for restricted service programme sound link use;

(l) £36 for each channel of 12.5 kHz in the band 65–470 MHz for restricted service programme sound link use;

(li) £12 for each channel of 12.5 kHz in the band 470–1,000 MHz for restricted service programme sound link use;

	(lii) £100 for each channel of 0.5 MHz in the band 1517–1525 MHz for restricted service programme sound link use; (liii) where the aggregate sum payable on the issue of a licence in this paragraph in any case other than a premium case would otherwise be less than £24, a charge of £24 only; plus— (liv) in a premium case, £55. (b) For the variation of a licence— (i) subject to paragraph (b)(ii), where a channel listed in paragraph (a)(xxix) to(xlviii) is added, such sum as represents one-twelfth of the sum payable for the issue of a licence for the type of channel to which the additional channel belongs, multiplied by the number of complete and part-complete calendar months beginning with the day of the addition of the channel to the next anniversary of the issue of the licence; (ii) where the aggregate sum payable for a variation of a licence in this paragraph in any case other than a premium case would otherwise be less than £24, a charge of £24 only; plus— (iii) in a premium case, £55.
Programme Making and Special Events Low Power	(a) Subject to paragraph (a)(xi), for the issue of a licence— (i) £8 for each occasional use channel for a single channel radio microphone;

(ii) £444 for each multi use type (1) channel for a single channel radio microphone;

(iii) £2,880 for each multi use type (2) channel for a single channel radio microphone;

(iv) £1,152 per primary channel in the British Islands for a single channel radio microphone;

(v) £288 for each primary regional channel for a single channel radio microphone;

(vi) £115 for each primary area channel for a single channel radio microphone;

(vii) £460 for each secondary channel in the British Islands for a single channel radio microphone;

(viii) £115 for each secondary regional channel for a single channel radio microphone;

(ix) £48 for each occasional use of a multi-channel radio microphone or a single wideband channel;

(x) £2,664 for each multi-use type (1) channel of a multi-channel radio microphone or a single wideband channel; plus—

(xi) where the aggregate sum payable on the issue of a licence in this paragraph in any case other than a premium case would otherwise be less than £24, a charge of £24 only; plus—

(xii) in a premium case, £55.

(b) For the variation of a licence—

	(i) subject to paragraph (b)(ii), where a channel listed in paragraph (a)(iv) to(viii) is added, such sum as represents one-twelfth of the sum payable for the issue of a licence for the type of channel to which the additional channel belongs, multiplied by the number of complete and part-complete calendar months beginning with the day of the addition of the channel to the next anniversary of the issue of the licence;	
	(ii) where the aggregate sum payable for a variation of a licence in this paragraph in any case other than a premium case would otherwise be less than £24, a charge of £24 only; plus—	
	(ii) in a premium case, £55.	
UK Wireless Microphone (Annual)	(a) £75 for each shared Multi-channel or wideband channel in the British Islands, where the licensee has applied for the licence using the facilities for application and payment on the designated website.	12 months
	(b) In any case other than that specified in paragraph (a), £80 for each shared Multi-channel or wideband channel in the British Islands.	12 months
UK Wireless Microphone (Biennial)	(a) £135 for each shared Multi-channel or wideband channel in the British Islands, where the licensee has applied for the licence using the facilities for application and payment on the designated website.	24 months

		(b) In any case other than that specified in paragraph (a), £145 for each shared Multi-channel or wideband channel in the British Islands.	24 months
Public Wireless Networks			
Public Wireless Networks (2G Cellular Operator)		(a) £142,560 for each 2 x 200 kHz national channel in the 880.0–960.0 MHz band.	12 months
		(b) £110,880 for each 2 x 200 kHz national channel in the 1710.0–1880.0 MHz band.	12 months
Public Wireless Networks (2G and 3G Cellular Operator—Guernsey)		£320 for each 2 x 200 kHz channel or slot.	12 months
Public Wireless Networks (2G and 3G Cellular Operator—Jersey)		£320 for each 2 x 200 kHz channel or slot.	12 months
Public Wireless Networks (2G and 3G Cellular Operator—Isle of Man)		£320 for each 2 x 200 kHz channel or slot.	12 months
Satellite Services			
Satellite (Aircraft Earth Station)		For each network of earth stations installed in aircraft and operating in the 14.0–14.25 GHz band, the appropriate sum calculated in accordance with the formula set out in Part 1 of Schedule 8.	12 months
Satellite (Earth Station Network)		For each network of earth stations operating in the 14.0–14.25 GHz and 29.5–30.0 GHz bands, the appropriate sum calculated in accordance with the formula set out in Part 1 of Schedule 8.	12 months
Satellite (Earth Station—Non-Fixed Satellite Service)	£500.		12 months
Satellite (Earth Station—Non-Geostationary)	£500.		12 months

Satellite (Earth Station on board Vessel)	For each network of earth stations installed on board vessels and operating in the 14.0–14.25 GHz band, the appropriate sum calculated in accordance with the formula set out in Part 1 of Schedule 8.	12 months
Satellite (Permanent Earth Station)	For each site (the area contained within a circle of a radius of 500 metres centred on a point defined by the licensee), the appropriate sum calculated in accordance with the formula set out in Part 2 of Schedule 8.	12 months
Satellite (Transportable Earth Station)	For each earth station operating in the 14.0–14.5 GHz band, the appropriate sum payable in accordance with Part 4 of Schedule 8 as determined by the power and bandwidth of the earth station.	12 months
Science and Technology		
Non-Operational Temporary Use	£50 for each channel per location each month.	
Non-Operational Development	£50 for each station or apparatus per location.	12 months.

[4549]

NOTES

Commencement: 13 June 2005.

In categories "Amateur and Citizens' Band" and "Maritime", words in square brackets substituted and words omitted revoked by the Wireless Telegraphy (Licence Charges) (Amendment) Regulations 2006, SI 2006/2894, reg 2(b).

SCHEDULE 3
DESIGNATIONS OF HEAVILY CONGESTED, CONGESTED AND NON-CONGESTED AREAS FOR THE BUSINESS RADIO (ON-SITE LOCAL COMMUNICATIONS SYSTEMS) AND (ON-SITE SPEECH AND DATA SYSTEMS) LICENCES

Schedule 2

Designation of area	*National Grid References for 10km x 10km areas*
Heavily congested	TQ 200700; TQ 200800; TQ 300700; TQ 300800
Congested	TQ 100700; TQ 100800; TQ 200900; TQ 300900; TQ 400700; TQ 400800
Non-congested	All National Grid References for 10 km x 10 km areas other than those designated as heavily congested or congested

[4550]

NOTES

Commencement: 13 June 2005.

SCHEDULE 4
DESIGNATIONS OF HEAVILY CONGESTED, CONGESTED AND NON-CONGESTED AREAS FOR THE BUSINESS RADIO (IR 2008 DATA) LICENCE
Schedule 2

Designation of area	*National Grid References for 10km x 10km areas*
Heavily congested	TQ 200700; TQ 200800; TQ 300700; TQ 300800
Congested	TQ 100700; TQ 100800; TQ 200900; TQ 300900; TQ 400700; TQ 400800
Non-congested	All National Grid References for 10 km x 10 km areas other than those designated as heavily congested or congested

[4551]

NOTES

Commencement: 13 June 2005.

SCHEDULE 5
DESIGNATIONS OF HEAVILY CONGESTED, CONGESTED AND NON-CONGESTED AREAS FOR THE BUSINESS RADIO (WIDE AREA DISTRESS ALARM SYSTEMS), (WIDE AREA ONE-WAY PAGING AND SPEECH SYSTEMS), AND (WIDE AREA SPEECH AND DATA SYSTEMS) LICENCES AND FEES PAYABLE FOR THE BUSINESS RADIO (WIDE AREA SPEECH AND DATA SYSTEMS) LICENCE
Schedule 2

PART 1
FEES PAYABLE FOR THE BUSINESS RADIO (WIDE AREA SPEECH AND DATA SYSTEMS) LICENCE

Fee £			
Category	*Heavily congested*	*Congested*	*Non-congested*
A	1,640	820	410
B	820	410	205
C	328	164	82
D	200	100	75

[4552]

NOTES

Commencement: 13 June 2005.

PART 2
DESIGNATIONS OF HEAVILY CONGESTED, CONGESTED AND NON-CONGESTED AREAS

Designation of area	*National Grid References for 10km x 10km areas*
Heavily congested	TQ 200700; TQ 200800; TQ 300700; TQ 300800
Congested	TQ 100700; TQ 100800; TQ 200900; TQ 300900; TQ 400700; TQ 400800
Non-congested	All National Grid References for 10 km x 10 km areas other than those designated as heavily congested or congested

[4553]

NOTES

Commencement: 13 June 2005.

PART 3
DETERMINATION OF CATEGORY FOR FEES PAYABLE UNDER PART 1

Number of mobile stations per channel location for relevant type of business use as declared by the licensee on application for a licence

Category	*Data dominant and data only users*	*Local government, and users of the 177 MHz-207.5 MHz frequency band*	*Taxi, minicab and courier companies*	*All other private business users*
A	>375	>180	>113	>75
B	151–375	73–180	46–113	31–75
C	39–150	19–72	12–45	9–30
D	1–38	1–18	1–11	1–8

[4554]

NOTES

Commencement: 13 June 2005.

SCHEDULE 6
DESIGNATIONS OF HEAVILY CONGESTED, CONGESTED AND NON-CONGESTED AREAS FOR THE BUSINESS RADIO (COMMON BASE STATION) LICENCE

Schedule 2

Designation of Area

National Grid References for 10km x 10 km areas

Heavily Congested	TQ 000500	TQ 100 500	TQ 200 500	TQ 300 500	TQ 400 500	TQ 500 600
	TQ 000600	TQ 100 600	TQ 200 600	TQ 300 600	TQ 400 600	TQ 500 700

Designation of Area	*National Grid References for 10km x 10 km areas*					
	TQ 000700	TQ 100 700	TQ 200 700	TQ 300 700	TQ 400 700	TQ 500 800
	TQ 000800	TQ 100 800	TQ 200 800	TQ 300 800	TQ 400 800	TQ 500 900
	TQ 000900	TQ 100 900	TQ 200 900	TQ 300 900	TQ 400 900	
Congested	NX 300 000	NX 400 000				
	SC 100 600	SC 200 600	SC 300 600	SC 200 700	SC 300 700	SC 400 700
	SC 200 800	SC 300 800	SC 400 800	SC 300 900	SC 400 900	
	SD 200 000	SD 300 000	SD 400 000	SD 500 000	SD 600 000	SD 700 000
	SD 800 000	SD 900 000	SD 200 100	SD 300 100	SD 400 100	SD 500 100
	SD 600 100	SD 700 100	SD 800 100	SD 900 100		
	SE 000 000	SD 000100				
	SH 600 600	SH 700 600	SH 800 600	SH 900 600	SH 600 700	SH 700 700
	SH 800 700	SH 900 700	SH 600 800	SH 700 800	SH 800 800	
	SJ 000 000	SJ 400 000	SJ 500 000	SJ 600 000	SJ 700 000	SJ 800 000
	SJ 900 000	SJ 400 100	SJ 500 100	SJ 600 100	SJ 700 100	SJ 800 100
	SJ 900 100	SJ 200 200	SJ 300 200	SJ 400 200	SJ 500 200	SJ 600 200
	SJ 700 200	SJ 800 200	SJ 900 200	SJ 000300	SJ 100 300	SJ 200 300
	SJ 300 300	SJ 400 300	SJ 500 300	SJ 600 300	SJ 700 300	SJ 800 300
	SJ 900 300	SJ 000400	SJ 100 400	SJ 200 400	SJ 300 400	SJ 400 400
	SJ 500 400	SJ 600 400	SJ 700 400	SJ 800 400	SJ 900 400	SJ 000500
	SJ 100 500	SJ 200 500	SJ 300 500	SJ 400 500	SJ 500 500	SJ 600 500
	SJ 700 500	SJ 800 500	SJ 900 500	SJ 000600	SJ 100 600	SJ 200 600
	SJ 300 600	SJ 400 600	SJ 500 600	SJ 600 600	SJ 700 600	SJ 800 600
	SJ 900 600	SJ 000700	SJ 100 700	SJ 200 700	SJ 300 700	SJ 400 700
	SJ 500 700	SJ 600 700	SJ 700 700	SJ 800 700	SJ 900 700	SJ 000800

Designation of Area					
National Grid References for 10km x 10 km areas					
SJ 100 800	SJ 200 800	SJ 300 800	SJ 400 800	SJ 500 800	SJ 600 800
SJ 700 800	SJ 800 800	SJ 900 800	SJ 200 900	SJ 300 900	SJ 400 900
SJ 500 900	SJ 600 900	SJ 700 900	SJ 800 900	SJ 900 900	
SK 000 000	SK 100 000	SK 200 000	SK 300 000	SK 400 000	SK 500 000
SK 600 000	SK 000100	SK 100 100	SK 200 100	SK 300 100	SK 400 100
SK 500 100	SK 000200	SK 100 200	SK 200 200	SK 300 200	SK 400 200
SK 500 200	SK 000300	SK 100 300	SK 200 300	SK 300 300	SK 400 300
SK 000400	SK 100 400	SK 200 400	SK 300 400	SK 000500	SK 100 500
SK 200 500	SK 300 500	SK 000600	SK 100 600	SK 200 600	SK 000700
SK 100 700	SK 000800	SK 100 800	SK 000900		
SO 600 400	SO 700 400	SO 800 400	SO 900 400	SO 600 500	SO 700 500
SO 800 500	SO 900 500	SO 500 600	SO 600 600	SO 700 600	SO 800 600
SO 900 600	SO 500 700	SO 600 700	SO 700 700	SO 800 700	SO 900 700
SO 500 800	SO 600 800	SO 700 800	SO 800 800	SO 900 800	SO 400 500
SO 500 900	SO 600 900	SO 700 900	SO 800 900	SO 900 900	
SP 100 000	SP 200 000	SP 300 000	SP 400 000	SP 500 000	SP 600 000
SP 700 000	SP 800 000	SP 900 000	SP 000100	SP 100 100	SP 200 100
SP 300 100	SP 400 100	SP 500 100	SP 600 100	SP 700 100	SP 800 100
SP 900 100	SP 000200	SP 100 200	SP 200 200	SP 300 200	SP 400 200
SP 500 200	SP 600 200	SP 700 200	SP 800 200	SP 900 200	SP 000300
SP 100 300	SP 200 300	SP 300 300	SP 400 300	SP 500 300	SP 600 300
SP 700 300	SP 800 300	SP 900 300	SP 000400	SP 100 400	SP 200 400
SP 300 400	SP 400 400	SP 500 400	SP 600 400	SP 700 400	SP 800 400
SP 900 400	SP 000500	SP 100 500	SP 200 500	SP 300 500	SP 400 500

PART VI TELECOMMUNICATIONS

Designation of Area					
National Grid References for 10km x 10 km areas					
SP 500 500	SP 600 500	SP 700 500	SP 800 500	SP 900 500	SP 000600
SP 100 600	SP 200 600	SP 300 600	SP 400 600	SP 500 600	SP 600 600
SP 700 600	SP 800 600	SP 000700	SP 100 700	SP 200 700	SP 300 700
SP 400 700	SP 500 700	SP 600 700	SP 700 700	SP 800 700	SP 000800
SP 100 800	SP 200 800	SP 300 800	SP 400 800	SP 500 800	SP 600 800
SP 700 800	SP 000900	SP 100 900	SP 200 900	SP 300 900	SP 400 900
SP 500 900	SP 600 900				
SU 300 000	SU 400 000	SU 500 000	SU 600 000	SU 700 000	SU 800 000
SU 900 000	SU 300 100	SU 400 100	SU 500 100	SU 600 100	SU 700 100
SU 800 100	SU 900 100	SU 300 200	SU 400 200	SU 500 200	SU 600 200
SU 700 200	SU 800 200	SU 900 200	SU 300 300	SU 400 300	SU 500 300
SU 600 300	SU 700 300	SU 800 300	SU 900 300	SU 300 400	SU 400 400
SU 500 400	SU 600 400	SU 700 400	SU 800 400	SU 900 400	SU 300 500
SU 400 500	SU 500 500	SU 600 500	SU 700 500	SU 800 500	SU 900 500
SU 300 600	SU 400 600	SU 500 600	SU 600 600	SU 700 600	SU 800 600
SU 900 600	SU 200 700	SU 300 700	SU 400 700	SU 500 700	SU 600 700
SU 700 700	SU 800 700	SU 900 700	SU 200 800	SU 300 800	SU 400 800
SU 500 800	SU 600 800	SU 700 800	SU 800 800	SU 900 800	SU 100 900
SU 200 900	SU 300 900	SU 400 900	SU 500 900	SU 600 900	SU 700 900
SU 800 900	SU 900 900				
SZ 400 700	SZ 500 700	SZ 600 800	SZ 300 800	SZ 400 800	SZ 500 800
SZ 600 900	SZ 700 900	SZ 800 900	SZ 900 900	SZ 300 900	SZ 400 900
SZ 500 900					
TL 000 000	TL 100 000	TL 200 000	TL 300 000	TL 400 00	TL 500 000

Designation of Area	*National Grid References for 10km x 10 km areas*					
	TL 600 000	TL 700 000	TL 800 000	TL 900 000	TL 000100	TL 100 100
	TL 200 100	TL 300 100	TL 400 100	TL 500 100	TL 600 100	TL 700 100
	TL 800 100	TL 900 100	TL 000200	TL 100 200	TL 200 200	TL 300 200
	TL 400 200	TL 500 200	TL 600 200	TL 700 200	TL 800 200	TL 900 200
	TR 000100	TR 000200	TR 000300	TR 100 300	TR 200 300	TR 000400
	TR 100 400	TR 200 400	TR 300 400	TR 000500	TR 100 500	TR 200 500
	TR 300 500	TR 000600	TR 100 600	TR 200 600	TR 300 600	TR 400 600
	TR 000700	TR 300 700				
	TQ 000 000	TQ 100 000	TQ 200 000	TQ 300 000	TQ 400 000	TQ 500 000
	TQ 600 000	TQ 700 000	TQ 800 000	TQ 000100	TQ 100 100	TQ 200 100
	TQ 300 100	TQ 400 100	TQ 500 100	TQ 600 100	TQ 700 100	TQ 800 100
	TQ 900 100	TQ 000200	TQ 100 200	TQ 200 200	TQ 300 200	TQ 400 200
	TQ 500 200	TQ 600 200	TQ 700 200	TQ 800 200	TQ 900 200	TQ 000300
	TQ 100 300	TQ 200 300	TQ 300 300	TQ 400 300	TQ 500 300	TQ 600 300
	TQ 700 300	TQ 800 300	TQ 900 300	TQ 000400	TQ 100 400	TQ 200 400
	TQ 300 400	TQ 400 400	TQ 500 400	TQ 600 400	TQ 700 400	TQ 800 400
	TQ 900 400	TQ 500 500	TQ 600 500	TQ 700 500	TQ 800 500	TQ 900 500
	TQ 600 600	TQ 700 600	TQ 800 600	TQ 900 600	TQ 600 700	TQ 700 700
	TQ 800 700	TQ 900 700	TQ 600 800	TQ 700 800	TQ 800 800	TQ 900 800
	TQ 600 900	TQ 700 900	TQ 800 900	TQ 900 900		
	TV 400 900	TV 500 900	TV 600 900			
Non-Congested	All National Grid References for 10 km x 10 km areas other than those designated as heavily congested or congested					

[4555]

NOTES

Commencement: 13 June 2005.

SCHEDULE 7
FORMULA FOR CALCULATING THE APPROPRIATE SUM FOR THE POINT TO POINT FIXED LINKS LICENCE

Schedule 2

PART 1
FORMULA

1 In this Schedule—

(a) "the appropriate sum" means the amount in pounds sterling, which is payable for a Point to Point Fixed Links Licence, calculated in accordance with the formula set out in paragraph 2; and

(b) *"Availability"* means the minimum percentage of time that the fixed link is capable of functioning as set out in the licensee's licence.

2 The formula is *AS = Sp x Bwf x Bf x Plf x Avf*

where—

"AS" means the appropriate sum;

"Avf" means the Availability Factor, being the number in Column 2 of the table set out in Part 5 as determined by the Availability (in per cent) as set out in Column 1 of that table;

"Bf" means the Band Factor, being the number in Column 2 of the table set out in Part 2 as determined by the range of frequency band (in GHz), if any, of a fixed link set out in Column 1 of that table in which the licensee's band falls as declared by the licensee on application for a licence;

"Bwf" means the Bandwidth Factor, subject to paragraph 3, being the number corresponding to the bandwidth (in MHz) of a co-ordinated bi-directional fixed link (or a part thereof) as declared by the licensee on application for a licence;

"*MPL*" means the Minimum Path Length, being the number corresponding to the applicable (depending on the amount of data that can be transmitted over the bandwidth ("the data rate") or over the channel width for analogue systems) length of the path (in kilometres) specified in Columns 2 and 3 of tables 1 or 2 set out in Part 4 as determined by the range of frequency band (in GHz), if any, of a fixed link set out in Column 1 of those respective tables in which the licensee's band falls as declared by the licensee on application for a licence;

"*PL*" means the Path Length, being the number corresponding to the distance (in kilometres) between two fixed points of the link as declared by the licensee on application for a licence;

"Plf" means the Path Length Factor, being the number in Column 2 of the table set out in Part 3 as determined by the relationship between the *PL* and the *MPL* as set out in Column 1 of that table; and

"Sp" means the Spectrum Price, being a fixed sum of £88 per 2 x 1 MHz bandwidth for each co-ordinated bi-directional fixed link.

3 Where the number of the bandwidth (in MHz) of a co-ordinated bi-directional fixed link (or a part thereof) as set out in the licensee's licence is less than 1.0, the number of the Bandwidth Factor shall be 1.0.

[4556]

NOTES

Commencement: 13 June 2005.

PART 2
BAND FACTOR

Column 1: Range of frequency band (fb) (in GHz)	*Column 2: Band Factor*
1.35 ≤ fb < 2.69	1.0
3.60 ≤ fb < 4.20	1.0

5.92 ≤ fb < 7.13	0.74
7.42 ≤ fb < 7.90	0.74
10.70 ≤ fb < 11.70	0.43
12.75 ≤ fb < 15.35	0.43
17.30 ≤ fb < 19.70	0.30
21.20 ≤ fb < 23.60	0.30
24.50 ≤ fb < 29.06	0.26
31.00 ≤ fb < 31.80	0.26
31.80 ≤ fb < 33.40	0.26
37.00 ≤ fb < 39.50	0.26
49.20 ≤ fb < 57.00	0.17

[4557]

NOTES

Commencement: 13 June 2005.

PART 3
PATH LENGTH FACTOR

Column 1: Relationship between PL and MPL	*Column 2: Path Length Factor*
MPL ≤ PL	1
MPL > PL	Smaller of $(MPL / PL)^{0.5}$ and 4

[4558]

NOTES

Commencement: 13 June 2005.

PART 4
MINIMUM PATH LENGTH

Table 1

Column 1: Range of frequency band (fb) (in GHz)	*Column 2: MPL (km) where the data rate is < 2 MBit/s or, for analogue systems, where the channel width is < 2 MHz*	*Column 3: MPL (km) where the data rate is ≥2 MBit/s or, for analogue systems, where the channel width is ≥ 2 MHz*
1.35 ≤ fb < 2.69	0	30

Table 2

Column 1: Range of frequency band (fb) (in GHz)	*Column 2: MPL (km) where the data rate is < 140 MBit/s or, for analogue systems, where the channel width is < 140 MHz*	*Column 3: MPL (km) where the data rate is ≥140 MBit/s or, for analogue systems, where the channel width is ≥140 MHz*
3.60 ≤ fb < 4.20	24.5	16
5.92 ≤ fb < 7.13	24.5	16
7.42 ≤ fb < 7.90	15.5	9.5
10.70 ≤ fb < 11.70	10	6
12.75 ≤ fb < 15.35	9.5	5.5
17.30 ≤ fb < 19.70	4	2.5
21.20 ≤ fb < 23.60	4	2
24.50 ≤ fb < 29.06	3	2
31.00 ≤ fb < 31.80	0	0
31.80 ≤ fb < 33.40	2	1.5
37.00 ≤ fb < 39.50	0	0
49.20 ≤ fb < 57.00	0	0

[4559]

NOTES

Commencement: 13 June 2005.

PART 5
AVAILABILITY FACTOR

Column 1: The percentage of Availability	*Column 2: Availability Factor*
Availability ≤ 99.9%	0.7
99.9% < Availability < 99.99%	0.7 + (Availability x 100 – 99.9) x (0.3 / 0.09)
99.99% ≤ Availability	1.0 + (Availability x 100 – 99.99) x (0.4 / 0.009)

[4560]

NOTES

Commencement: 13 June 2005.

SCHEDULE 8
FEES PAYABLE FOR THE SATELLITE (AIRCRAFT EARTH STATION), (EARTH STATION NETWORK), (EARTH STATION ON BOARD VESSEL), (PERMANENT EARTH STATION) AND (TRANSPORTABLE EARTH STATION) LICENCES

Schedule 2

PART 1
FORMULA FOR CALCULATING THE APPROPRIATE SUM FOR THE SATELLITE (AIRCRAFT EARTH STATION), (EARTH STATION NETWORK) AND (EARTH STATION ON BOARD VESSEL) LICENCES

4 In this Part, "the appropriate sum" means the amount in pounds sterling, which is payable for a Satellite (Aircraft Earth Station), (Earth Station Network) and (Earth Station on board Vessel) Licence, calculated in accordance with the formula set out in paragraph 2.

5 The formula is—

$$AS = \sqrt{433.4 \times \sum_{n} (P_n \times BW_n \times MOD_n)}$$

where—

> *"AS"* means the appropriate sum;
>
> *"n"* means, subject to paragraph 3, the number corresponding to the number of earth station terminals licensed for each network;
>
> *"BWn"* means the number corresponding to the number of aggregated accessible transmit bandwidth (in MHz) available to each earth station terminal as declared by the licensee on application for a licence;
>
> *"MODn"* means the Modifier Value of 0.5; and
>
> *"Pn"* means the number corresponding to the number of the Transmit Peak power (in Watts) appearing at the flange of the network terminal antennas as declared by the licensee on application for a licence.

6 Where the number of earth station terminals licensed in the network is less than 50, the number for *"n"* shall be 50 for each licence.

[4561]

NOTES

Commencement: 13 June 2005.

Note that the Queen's Printer's version of these Regulations does not contain paragraphs 1–3.

PART 2
FORMULA FOR CALCULATING THE APPROPRIATE SUM FOR THE SATELLITE (PERMANENT EARTH STATION) LICENCE

7 In this Part, subject to paragraph 3, "the appropriate sum" means the amount in pounds sterling, which is payable for a Satellite (Permanent Earth Station) Licence, calculated in accordance with the formula set out in paragraph 2.

8 The formula is—

$$AS = \sqrt{433.4 \times \sum_{ijk} (P_{ijk} \times BW_{ijk} \times MOD_{ijk})}$$

where—

> *"AS"* means the appropriate sum;
>
> *"i"* means the number corresponding to the number of earth station terminals on a site as declared by the licensee on application for a licence;
>
> *"j"* means the number corresponding to the number of satellites as declared by the licensee on application for a licence;
>
> *"k"* means the number corresponding to the number of transmission paths as declared by the licensee on application for a licence;
>
> *"BWijk"* means the number corresponding to number of the Transmit Authorised bandwidth (in MHz) as declared by the licensee on application for a licence;

PART VI TELECOMMUNICATIONS

"MODijk" means Modifier Value, being the number in Column 2 of the table set out in Part 3 as determined by the range of frequency (in MHz), if any, of the earth station set out in Column 1 of that table in which the licensee's band falls as declared by the licensee on application for a licence; and

"Pijk" means the number corresponding to the number of the Transmit Peak power (in Watts) at the flange of the antenna of the earth station as declared by the licensee on application for a licence.

9 Where the amount in pounds sterling calculated in accordance with the formula set out in paragraph 2 is less than £500, the appropriate sum shall be £500.

[4562]

NOTES

Commencement: 13 June 2005.

Note that the Queen's Printer's version of these Regulations does not contain paragraphs 1–3.

PART 3
MODIFIER VALUE FOR CALCULATING THE APPROPRIATE SUM FOR THE SATELLITE (PERMANENT EARTH STATION) LICENCE

Column 1: Range of frequency band (fb) (in MHz)	*Column 2: Modifier Value*
5850 ≤ fb < 7075	1
12500 ≤ fb < 12750	0.5
12750 ≤ fb < 13250	1
13750 ≤ fb < 14250	0.5
14250 ≤ fb < 14500	1
17300 ≤ fb < 17700	0.5
17700 ≤ fb < 29500	1
29500 ≤ fb < 30000	0.5

[4563]

NOTES

Commencement: 13 June 2005.

PART 4
FEE PAYABLE FOR THE SATELLITE (TRANSPORTABLE EARTH STATION) LICENCE

10 The appropriate sum is the amount in pounds sterling, which is payable for each earth station of a Satellite (Transportable Earth Station) Licence, specified in Column 2 of the table as determined by the range of *p* specified in Column 1 of the table in which the licensee's network falls.

11 In this Part—

(a) *"OMP"* means the number corresponding to the number of the Operational Maximum Power (in Watts) as declared by the licensee on application for each earth station licence;

(b) *"p"* means the total sum of *OMP* multiplied by *WBW*; and

(c) *"WBW"* means the number corresponding to the number of the widest bandwidth (in MHz) as declared by the licensee on application for a licence.

Column 1: Range of p	*Column 2: Fee (£) per earth station*
$0 < p \leq 100$	200
$100 < p \leq 2,500$	1,000
$p > 2,500$	3,000

[4564]

NOTES

Commencement: 13 June 2005.

WIRELESS TELEGRAPHY (LICENSING PROCEDURES) REGULATIONS 2006

(SI 2006/2785)

NOTES

Made: 16 October 2006.
Authority: Wireless Telegraphy Act 1949, s 1D(3).
Commencement: 16 November 2006.

ARRANGEMENT OF REGULATIONS

1 Citation and commencement

These Regulations may be cited as the Wireless Telegraphy (Licensing Procedures) Regulations 2006 and shall come into force on 16th November 2006.

[4565]

NOTES

Commencement: 16 November 2006.

2 Interpretation

In these Regulations—

"apparatus" means apparatus for wireless telegraphy;

"earth station" means a station situated either on the earth's surface or within the earth's atmosphere which is intended for communication with a station beyond the earth's atmosphere;

"equipment" means a station or apparatus;

"fixed station" means a station which only transmits from a fixed location;

"licence" means a licence under section 1 of the Wireless Telegraphy Act 1949;

"mobile station" means a station which transmits while in motion; and

"station" means a station for wireless telegraphy.

[4566]

NOTES

Commencement: 16 November 2006.

3 Time limits for dealing with the grant of licences

A decision on an application for the grant of a licence shall be made, notified to the applicant and published—

(a) in the case of any licence relating to radio frequencies allocated for use in the United Kingdom Plan for Frequency Authorisation, not more than six weeks after the day of the receipt of the application; and

(b) in any other case as soon as possible after the day of the receipt of the application.

[4567]

NOTES

Commencement: 16 November 2006.

4 Requirements that must be met for the grant of a licence

(1) Licences shall be granted by OFCOM, either—

(a) in relation to particular equipment; or

(b) in relation to any equipment falling within the description specified in the licence and expressed by reference to such factors (including factors confined to the manner in which it is established, installed or used), as are described in the licence.

(2) An applicant for the grant of a licence (whether in respect of a station or apparatus) must complete the licence application form which is appropriate for the class of licence being applied for and must provide—

(a) the name and address of the applicant;

(b) where the duration for which the licence is required is less than twelve months, the duration; and

(c) where information is specified as being required in the Schedule to these Regulations for the class of licence concerned, that information.

(3) An applicant for the grant of a licence in respect of a station must also provide—

(a) the frequencies on which the applicant wishes to operate the station;

(b) the location of any proposed fixed station;

(c) the position of any remote control point for a fixed station;

(d) the purpose or type of service for which the proposed station is intended;

(e) the type of station proposed for use;

(f) the intended geographical range of operation;

(g) the type, position, direction, signal strength, output power and signal beam width of each antenna forming part of the proposed station;

(h) the modulation characteristics and data bit rate of—

(i) transmissions by the proposed station; and

(ii) any transmissions which are for the purpose of station recognition;

(i) the call sign desired by the applicant;

(j) information required for station site clearance in accordance with the publication UK Radio Site Clearance Procedure published by OFCOM;

(k) in the case of an application in respect of a mobile station, an indication of whether or not the station is to be established on board—

(i) an aircraft,

(ii) a ship; or

(iii) a train; and

(l) if the application is in relation to more than one fixed station, the length and direction of proposed transmission signal paths between stations.

[4568]

NOTES

Commencement: 16 November 2006.

5 Particulars of the terms, provisions and limitations of licences

(1) Licences are granted subject to—

(a) a limitation as to the type of equipment which is authorised;
(b) a limitation as to the circumstances of use;
(c) a term providing for the licence to commence on the date of its grant and continue in force until revoked by OFCOM or surrendered by the licensee;
(d) terms, as to the circumstances in which OFCOM may revoke or vary the licence;
(e) terms providing for the manner and payment of fees;
(f) a term as to access and inspection by OFCOM of equipment;
(g) terms as to the modification or restriction in use of equipment and the circumstances in which OFCOM may require any such equipment to be temporarily closed down; and
(h) terms, provisions and limitations as to strength and type of signal.

(2) Licences are also granted subject to the other terms, provisions and limitations in the case of any particular licence which are contained in the publication Wireless Telegraphy Act Licences (Terms, Provisions and Limitations) published by OFCOM.

[4569]

NOTES

Commencement: 16 November 2006.

SCHEDULE
ADDITIONAL INFORMATION REQUIRED FOR THE GRANT OF A LICENCE

Regulation 4(2)(c)

PART 1
AERONAUTICAL

1 For the licence classes Aeronautical Ground Station (Air traffic/Ground Movement Control), Aeronautical Ground Station (Air/Ground Communications Services), Aeronautical Ground Station (Airfield Flight Information Service), Aeronautical Ground Station (General Aviation), Aeronautical Ground Station (Fire), Aeronautical Ground Station (High Frequency), Aeronautical Ground Station (Offshore Platform), Aeronautical Navigation Aid Stations, Aeronautical Radar, and Aeronautical Ground Station (Operations Controls), the following information shall be provided—

(a) whether authorisation of a temporary or permanent station is sought;
(b) the number of aircraft with which the station is intended to communicate in any day; and
(c) the level of radio traffic for which authorisation is sought.

2 For the licence classes Aircraft and Aircraft (Transportable) the following information shall be provided—

(a) the make, model, and serial number of station or apparatus for which authorisation is sought;
(b) the registration number and make and model of the aircraft on which the station will be established or apparatus installed; and
(c) the take off weight of that aircraft and the intended use of that aircraft.

[4570]

NOTES

Commencement: 16 November 2006.

PART 2
MARITIME

3 For the licence class Ship Radio the following information shall be provided—

(a) the current name and any previous name and registration number of the vessel on which a station will be established or apparatus installed;
(b) the type of vessel, its gross tonnage or approximate weight and the maximum number of persons the vessel is capable of carrying;

(c) the intended use of the vessel;
(d) the current and any previous call sign of the vessel;
(e) whether digital selective calling is to be used by the station; and
(f) for emergency position indicating radio beacon equipment and personal locator beacon equipment, the type of beacon equipment for which authorisation is sought, its code which identifies its country of authorisation, its manufacturer, its serial number, and whether or not it operates using a global positioning system.

4 For the licence class Ship Portable Radio applicants shall specify if authorisation of emergency position indicating radio beacon equipment or personal locator beacon equipment is sought and if so the type of beacon equipment for which authorisation is sought, its code which identifies its country of authorisation, its manufacturer, its serial number, and whether or not it operates using a global positioning system.

[4571]

NOTES
Commencement: 16 November 2006.

PART 3
PROGRAMME MAKING AND SPECIAL EVENTS

5 For the licence classes Programme Making and Special Events Fixed Site, Programme Making and Special Events Link, Programme Making and Special Events Low Power, UK Wireless Microphone (Annual) and UK Wireless Microphone (Biennial) the following information shall be provided—
(a) the location or proposed area of apparatus use; and
(b) the proposed dates and times of apparatus use.

[4572]

NOTES
Commencement: 16 November 2006.

PART 4
SATELLITE SERVICES

6 For the licence class Satellite (Earth Station Network) the following information shall be provided—
(a) the date when satellite network operations will start;
(b) the name of the satellite network which the earth station will use;
(c) the orbital longitude of all satellites in the network;
(d) the satellite beam service area;
(e) the maximum bandwidth which is accessible by the earth station;
(f) identification of any other earth stations which are associated with the station; and
(g) a postal address for the control centre for the satellite network and the name of the person controlling the network at that address.

7 For the licence class Satellite (Aircraft Earth Station) the following information shall be provided—
(a) the name of the satellite network which the aircraft earth station will use;
(b) the orbital longitude of all satellites in the network;
(c) the satellite beam service area;
(d) the maximum bandwidth which is accessible by the earth station;
(e) identification of any other earth stations which are associated with the earth station;
(f) a postal address for the control centre for the satellite network and the name of the person controlling the network at that address; and
(g) in the case of an aircraft which it is proposed will carry an earth station which will use the satellite network, in relation to that aircraft—
(i) the aircraft call sign;
(ii) the model of the aircraft;
(iii) the name of the aircraft operator; and
(iv) the country in which the aircraft is registered.

8 For the licence class Satellite (Earth Station On Board Vessel) the following information shall be provided—

(a) the name of the satellite network to be used by the earth station which is proposed to be carried on board the vessel;
(b) the orbital longitude of the satellites in the network;
(c) the satellite beam service area;
(d) the maximum bandwidth which is accessible by the earth station;
(e) identification of any other earth stations which are associated with the station;
(f) a postal address for the control centre for the satellite network and the name of the person controlling the network at that address; and
(g) in the case of a vessel which it is proposed will carry an earth station which will use the satellite network, in relation to that vessel—
  (i) the name of the vessel;
  (ii) the vessel call sign;
  (iii) the maritime mobile service identity number of the vessel; and
  (iv) the country in which the vessel is registered.

9 For the licence classes Satellite (Permanent Earth Station), Satellite (Earth Station—Non-Fixed Satellite Service), and Satellite (Earth Station Non-Geostationary) the following information shall be provided—

(a) the name and location of the proposed earth stations;
(b) the range of frequencies;
(c) the direction and power required for each earth station;
(d) the name and location of any associated satellite transponders together with their operating angles or their range of operating angles;
(e) whether any satellite transmission signals are to be received by earth stations; and
(f) in relation to the signals to be received at the earth station, the International Telecommunication Union classification of emissions and necessary bandwidths set out in Appendix 1 of the Appendices to the Radio Regulations of the International Telecommunication Union.

[4573]

NOTES

Commencement: 16 November 2006.

PART 5
SCIENCE AND TECHNOLOGY

10 For the licence classes Non-Operational Temporary Use, Non-Operational Development, and Ground Probing Radar the applicant shall provide a description of the configuration of any apparatus for which authorisation is sought, the purpose for which it will transmit and the intended geographical range of operation.

[4574]

NOTES

Commencement: 16 November 2006.

EUROPEAN PARLIAMENT AND COUNCIL REGULATION

of 18 December 2000

on unbundled access to the local loop

(2887/2000/EC)

(Text with EEA relevance)

NOTES

Date of publication in OJ: OJ L336, 30.12.2000, p 4.

THE EUROPEAN PARLIAMENT AND THE COUNCIL OF THE EUROPEAN UNION,

Having regard to the Treaty establishing the European Community, and in particular Article 95 thereof,

Having regard to the proposal from the Commission,

Having regard to the opinion of the Economic and Social Committee,[1]

Acting in accordance with the procedure laid down in Article 251 of the Treaty,[2]

Whereas—

(1) The conclusions of the European Council of Lisbon of 23 and 24 March 2000 note that, for Europe to fully seize the growth and job potential of the digital, knowledge-based economy, businesses and citizens must have access to an inexpensive, world-class communications infrastructure and a wide range of services. The Member States, together with the Commission, are called upon to work towards introducing greater competition in local access networks before the end of 2000 and unbundling the local loop, in order to help bring about a substantial reduction in the costs of using the Internet. The Feira European Council of 20 June 2000 endorsed the proposed "e-Europe" Action Plan which identifies unbundled access to the local loop as a short-term priority.

(2) Local loop unbundling should complement the existing provisions in Community law guaranteeing universal service and affordable access for all citizens by enhancing competition, ensuring economic efficiency and bringing maximum benefit to users.

(3) The "local loop" is the physical twisted metallic pair circuit in the fixed public telephone network connecting the network termination point at the subscriber's premises to the main distribution frame or equivalent facility. As noted in the Commission's Fifth Report on the implementation of the telecommunications regulatory package, the local access network remains one of the least competitive segments of the liberalised telecommunications market. New entrants do not have widespread alternative network infrastructures and are unable, with traditional technologies, to match the economies of scale and the coverage of operators designated as having significant market power in the fixed public telephone network market. This results from the fact that these operators rolled out their metallic local access infrastructures over significant periods of time protected by exclusive rights and were able to fund investment costs through monopoly rents.

(4) The European Parliament Resolution of 13 June 2000 on the Commission communication on the 1999 Communications review stresses the importance of enabling the sector to develop infrastructures which promote the growth of electronic communications and e-commerce and the importance of regulating in a way that supports this growth. It notes that the unbundling of the local loop currently concerns mainly the metallic infrastructure of a dominant entity and that investment in alternative infrastructures must have the possibility of ensuring a reasonable rate of return, since that might facilitate the expansion of these infrastructures in areas where their penetration is still low.

(5) The provision of new loops with high capacity optical fibre directly to major users is a specific market that is developing under competitive conditions with new investments. This Regulation therefore addresses access to metallic local loops, without prejudice to national obligations regarding other types of access to local infrastructures.

(6) It would not be economically viable for new entrants to duplicate the incumbent's metallic local access infrastructure in its entirety within a reasonable time. Alternative infrastructures such as cable television, satellite, wireless local loops do not generally offer the same functionality or ubiquity for the time being, though situations in Member States may differ.

(7) Unbundled access to the local loop allows new entrants to compete with notified operators in offering high bit-rate data transmission services for continuous Internet access and for multimedia applications based on digital subscriber line (DSL) technology as well as voice telephony services. A reasonable request for unbundled access implies that the access is necessary for the provision of the services of the beneficiary, and that refusal of the request would prevent, restrict or distort competition in this sector.

(8) This Regulation mandates unbundled access to the metallic local loops only of notified operators that have been designated by their national regulatory authorities as having significant market power in the fixed public telephone network supply market under the relevant Community provisions (hereinafter referred to as "notified operators"). Member States have already notified to the Commission the names of those fixed public network operators which have significant market power under Annex I, Part 1, of Directive 97/33/EC of the European Parliament and of the Council of 30 June 1997 on interconnection in telecommunications with regard to ensuring universal service and interoperability through application of the principles of open network provision (ONP),[3] and Directive 98/10/EC of the European Parliament and of the Council of 26 February 1998 on the application of open network provision to voice telephony and on universal service for telecommunications in a competitive environment.[4]

(9) A notified operator cannot be required to provide types of access which are not within its powers to provide, for example where fulfilment of a request would cause a violation of the legal rights of an independent third party. The obligation to provide unbundled access to the local loop does not imply that notified operators have to install entirely new local network infrastructure specifically to meet beneficiaries' requests.

(10) Although commercial negotiation is the preferred method for reaching agreement on technical and pricing issues for local loop access, experience shows that in most cases regulatory intervention is necessary due to imbalance in negotiating power between the new entrant and the notified operator, and lack of other alternatives. In certain circumstances the national regulatory authority may, in accordance with Community law, intervene on its own initiative in order to ensure fair competition, economic efficiency and maximum benefit for end-users. Failure of the notified operator to meet lead times should entitle the beneficiary to receive compensation.

(11) Costing and pricing rules for local loops and related facilities should be transparent, non-discriminatory and objective to ensure fairness. Pricing rules should ensure that the local loop provider is able to cover its appropriate costs in this regard plus a reasonable return, in order to ensure the long term development and upgrade of local access infrastructure. Pricing rules for local loops should foster fair and sustainable competition, bearing in mind the need for investment in alternative infrastructures, and ensure that there is no distortion of competition, in particular no margin squeeze between prices of wholesale and retail services of the notified operator. In this regard, it is considered important that competition authorities be consulted.

(12) Notified operators should provide information and unbundled access to third parties under the same conditions and of the same quality as they provide for their own services or to their associated companies. To this end, the publication by the notified operator of an adequate reference offer for unbundled access to the local loop, within a short time-frame and ideally on the Internet, and under the supervisory control of the national regulatory authority, would contribute to the creation of transparent and non-discriminatory market conditions.

(13) In its Recommendation 2000/417/EC of 25 May 2000 on unbundled access to the local loop enabling the competitive provision of a full range of electronic communications services including broadband multimedia and high-speed Internet[5] and its Communication of 26 April 2000,[6] the Commission set out detailed guidance to assist national regulatory authorities on the fair regulation of different forms of unbundled access to the local loop.

(14) In accordance with the principle of subsidiarity as set out in Article 5 of the Treaty, the objective of achieving a harmonised framework for unbundled access to the local loop in order to enable the competitive provision of an inexpensive, world-class communications infrastructure and a wide range of services for all businesses and citizens in the Community cannot be achieved by the Member States in a secure, harmonised and timely manner and can therefore be better achieved by the Community. In accordance with the principle of proportionality as set out in that Article, the provisions of this Regulation do not go beyond what is necessary in order to achieve this objective for that purpose. They are adopted without prejudice to national provisions complying with Community law which set out more detailed measures, for example dealing with virtual collocation.

(15) This Regulation complements the regulatory framework for telecommunications, in particular Directives 97/33/EC and 98/10/EC. The new regulatory framework for electronic communications should include appropriate provisions to replace this Regulation,

NOTES

1 Opinion delivered on 19 October 2000 (not yet published in the Official Journal).
2 Opinion of the European Parliament of 26 October 2000 (not yet published in the Official Journal) and Decision of the Council of 5 December 2000.
3 OJ L199, 26.7.1997, p 32. Directive as amended by Directive 98/61/EC (OJ L268, 3.10.1998, p 37).
4 OJ L101, 1.4.1998, p 24.
5 OJ L156, 29.6.2000, p 44.
6 OJ C272, 23.9.2000, p 55.

HAVE ADOPTED THIS REGULATION—

Article 1

Aim and Scope

1. This Regulation aims at intensifying competition and stimulating technological innovation on the local access market, through the setting of harmonised conditions for unbundled access to the local loop, to foster the competitive provision of a wide range of electronic communications services.

2. This Regulation shall apply to unbundled access to the local loops and related facilities of notified operators as defined in Article 2(a).

3. This Regulation shall apply without prejudice to the obligations for notified operators to comply with the principle of non-discrimination, when using the fixed public telephone network in order to provide high speed access and transmission services to third parties in the same manner as they provide for their own services or to their associated companies, in accordance with Community provisions.

4. This Regulation is without prejudice to the rights of Member States to maintain or introduce measures in conformity with Community law which contain more detailed provisions than those set out in this Regulation and/or are outside the scope of this Regulation *inter alia* with respect to other types of access to local infrastructures.

[4575]

Article 2

Definitions

For the purposes of this Regulation the following definitions apply—

(a) "notified operator" means operators of fixed public telephone networks that have been designated by their national regulatory authority as having significant market power in the provision of fixed public telephone networks and services under Annex I, Part 1, of Directive 97/33/EC or Directive 98/10/EC;

(b) "beneficiary" means a third party duly authorised in accordance with Directive 97/13/EC[1] or entitled to provide communications services under national legislation, and which is eligible for unbundled access to a local loop;

(c) "local loop" means the physical twisted metallic pair circuit connecting the network termination point at the subscriber's premises to the main distribution frame or equivalent facility in the fixed public telephone network;

(d) "local sub-loop" means a partial local loop connecting the network termination point at the subscriber's premises to a concentration point or a specified intermediate access point in the fixed public telephone network;

(e) "unbundled access to the local loop" means full unbundled access to the local loop and shared access to the local loop; it does not entail a change in ownership of the local loop;

(f) "full unbundled access to the local loop" means the provision to a beneficiary of access to the local loop or local sub loop of the notified operator authorising the use of the full frequency spectrum of the twisted metallic pair;

(g) "shared access to the local loop" means the provision to a beneficiary of access to the local loop or local sub loop of the notified operator, authorising the use of the non-voice band frequency spectrum of the twisted metallic pair; the local loop continues to be used by the notified operator to provide the telephone service to the public;

(h) "collocation" means the provision of physical space and technical facilities necessary to reasonably accommodate and connect the relevant equipment of a beneficiary, as mentioned in Section B of the Annex;

(i) "related facilities" means the facilities associated with the provision of unbundled access to the local loop, notably collocation, cable connections and relevant information technology systems, access to which is necessary for a beneficiary to provide services on a competitive and fair basis.

[4576]

NOTES

[1] Directive 97/13/EC of the European Parliament and of the Council of 10 April 1997 on a common framework for general authorisations and individual licences in the field of telecommunications services (OJ L117, 7.5.1997, p 15).

Article 3

Provision of unbundled access

1. Notified operators shall publish from 31 December 2000, and keep updated, a reference offer for unbundled access to their local loops and related facilities, which shall include at least the items listed in the Annex. The offer shall be sufficiently unbundled so that the beneficiary does not have to pay for network elements or facilities which are not necessary for the supply of its services, and shall contain a description of the components of the offer, associated terms and conditions, including charges.

2. Notified operators shall from 31 December 2000 meet reasonable requests from beneficiaries for unbundled access to their local loops and related facilities, under transparent, fair and non-discriminatory conditions. Requests shall only be refused on the basis of objective criteria, relating to technical feasibility or the need to maintain network integrity. Where access is refused, the aggrieved party may submit the case to the dispute resolution procedure referred to in Article 4(5). Notified operators shall provide beneficiaries with facilities equivalent to those provided for their own services or to their associated companies, and with the same conditions and timescales.

3. Without prejudice to Article 4(4), notified operators shall charge prices for unbundled access to the local loop and related facilities set on the basis of cost-orientation.

[4577]

Article 4

Supervision by the national regulatory authority

1. The national regulatory authority shall ensure that charging for unbundled access to the local loop fosters fair and sustainable competition.

2. The national regulatory authority shall have the power to—

(a) impose changes on the reference offer for unbundled access to the local loop and related facilities, including prices, where such changes are justified; and

(b) require notified operators to supply information relevant for the implementation of this Regulation.

3. The national regulatory authority may, where justified, intervene on its own initiative in order to ensure non-discrimination, fair competition, economic efficiency and maximum benefit for users.

4. When the national regulatory authority determines that the local access market is sufficiently competitive, it shall relieve the notified operators of the obligation laid down in Article 3(3) for prices to be set on the basis of cost-orientation.

5. Disputes between undertakings concerning issues included in this Regulation shall be subject to the national dispute resolution procedures established in conformity with Directive 97/33/EC and shall be handled promptly, fairly and transparently.

[4578]

Article 5

Entry into force

This Regulation shall enter into force on the third day following that of its publication in the *Official Journal of the European Communities*.

This Regulation shall be binding in its entirety and directly applicable in all Member States.

[4579]

Done at Brussels, 18 December 2000.

ANNEX

MINIMUM LIST OF ITEMS TO BE INCLUDED IN A REFERENCE OFFER FOR UNBUNDLED ACCESS TO THE LOCAL LOOP TO BE PUBLISHED BY NOTIFIED OPERATORS

A. Conditions for unbundled access to the local loop

1. Network elements to which access is offered covering in particular the following elements—

(a) access to local loops;

(b) access to non-voice band frequency spectrum of a local loop, in the case of shared access to the local loop;

2. Information concerning the locations of physical access sites,[1] availability of local loops in specific parts of the access network;
3. Technical conditions related to access and use of local loops, including the technical characteristics of the twisted metallic pair in the local loop;
4. Ordering and provisioning procedures, usage restrictions.

B. Collocation services

1. Information on the notified operator's relevant sites;[1]
2. Collocation options at the sites indicated under point 1 (including physical collocation and, as appropriate, distant collocation and virtual collocation);
3. Equipment characteristics: restrictions, if any, on equipment that can be collocated;
4. Security issues: measures put in place by notified operators to ensure the security of their locations;
5. Access conditions for staff of competitive operators;
6. Safety standards;
7. Rules for the allocation of space where collocation space is limited;
8. Conditions for beneficiaries to inspect the locations at which physical collocation is available, or sites where collocation has been refused on grounds of lack of capacity.

C. Information systems

Conditions for access to notified operator's operational support systems, information systems or databases for pre-ordering, provisioning, ordering, maintenance and repair requests and billing.

D. Supply conditions

1. Lead time for responding to requests for supply of services and facilities; service level agreements, fault resolution, procedures to return to a normal level of service and quality of service parameters;
2. Standard contract terms, including, where appropriate, compensation provided for failure to meet lead times;
3. Prices or pricing formulae for each feature, function and facility listed above.

[4580]

NOTES

[1] Availability of this information may be restricted to interested parties only, in order to avoid public security concerns.

DIRECTIVE OF THE EUROPEAN PARLIAMENT AND OF THE COUNCIL

of 7 March 2002

on access to, and interconnection of, electronic communications networks and associated facilities (Access Directive)

(2002/19/EC)

NOTES

Date of publication in OJ: OJ L108, 24.4.2002, p 7.

THE EUROPEAN PARLIAMENT AND THE COUNCIL OF THE EUROPEAN UNION,

Having regard to the Treaty establishing the European Community, and in particular Article 95 thereof,

Having regard to the proposal from the Commission,[1]

Having regard to the opinion of the Economic and Social Committee,[2]

Acting in accordance with the procedure laid down in Article 251 of the Treaty,[3]

Whereas—

(1) Directive 2002/21/EC of the European Parliament and of the Council of 7 March 2002 on a common regulatory framework for electronic communications networks and services (Framework Directive)[4] lays down the objectives of a regulatory framework to cover electronic communications networks and services in the Community, including fixed and mobile telecommunications networks, cable television networks, networks used for terrestrial broadcasting, satellite networks and Internet networks, whether used for voice, fax, data or images. Such networks may have been authorised by Member States under Directive 2002/20/EC of the European Parliament and of the Council of 7 March 2002 on the authorisation of electronic communications networks and services (Authorisation Directive)[5] or have been authorised under previous regulatory measures. The provisions of this Directive apply to those networks that are used for the provision of publicly available electronic communications services. This Directive covers access and interconnection arrangements between service suppliers. Non-public networks do not have obligations under this Directive except where, in benefiting from access to public networks, they may be subject to conditions laid down by Member States.

(2) Services providing content such as the offer for sale of a package of sound or television broadcasting content are not covered by the common regulatory framework for electronic communications networks and services.

(3) The term "access" has a wide range of meanings, and it is therefore necessary to define precisely how that term is used in this Directive, without prejudice to how it may be used in other Community measures. An operator may own the underlying network or facilities or may rent some or all of them.

(4) Directive 95/47/EC of the European Parliament and of the Council of 24 October 1995 on the use of standards for the transmission of television signals[6] did not mandate any specific digital television transmission system or service requirement, and this opened up an opportunity for the market actors to take the initiative and develop suitable systems. Through the Digital Video Broadcasting Group, European market actors have developed a family of television transmission systems that have been adopted by broadcasters throughout the world. These transmissions systems have been standardised by the European Telecommunications Standards Institute (ETSI) and have become International Telecommunication Union recommendations. In relation to wide-screen digital television, the 16:9 aspect ratio is the reference format for wide-format television services and programmes, and is now established in Member States' markets as a result of Council Decision 93/424/EEC of 22 July 1993 on an action plan for the introduction of advanced television services in Europe.[7]

(5) In an open and competitive market, there should be no restrictions that prevent undertakings from negotiating access and interconnection arrangements between themselves, in particular on cross-border agreements, subject to the competition rules of the Treaty. In the context of achieving a more efficient, truly pan-European market, with effective competition, more choice and competitive services to consumers, undertakings which receive requests for access or interconnection should in principle conclude such agreements on a commercial basis, and negotiate in good faith.

(6) In markets where there continue to be large differences in negotiating power between undertakings, and where some undertakings rely on infrastructure provided by others for delivery of their services, it is appropriate to establish a framework to ensure that the market functions effectively. National regulatory authorities should have the power to secure, where commercial negotiation fails, adequate access and interconnection and interoperability of services in the interest of end-users. In particular, they may ensure end-to-end connectivity by imposing proportionate obligations on undertakings that control access to end-users. Control of means of access may entail ownership or control of the physical link to the end-user (either fixed or mobile), and/or the ability to change or withdraw the national number or numbers needed to access an end-user's network termination point. This would be the case for example if network operators were to restrict unreasonably end-user choice for access to Internet portals and services.

(7) National legal or administrative measures that link the terms and conditions for access or interconnection to the activities of the party seeking interconnection, and specifically to the degree of its investment in network infrastructure, and not to the interconnection or access services provided, may cause market distortion and may therefore not be compatible with competition rules.

(8) Network operators who control access to their own customers do so on the basis of unique numbers or addresses from a published numbering or addressing range. Other network operators need to be able to deliver traffic to those customers, and so need to be able to interconnect directly or indirectly to each other. The existing rights and obligations to negotiate interconnection should therefore be maintained. It is also appropriate to maintain the obligations formerly laid down in Directive 95/47/EC requiring fully digital electronic communications networks used for the distribution of television services and open to the

public to be capable of distributing wide-screen television services and programmes, so that users are able to receive such programmes in the format in which they were transmitted.

(9) Interoperability is of benefit to end-users and is an important aim of this regulatory framework. Encouraging interoperability is one of the objectives for national regulatory authorities as set out in this framework, which also provides for the Commission to publish a list of standards and/or specifications covering the provision of services, technical interfaces and/or network functions, as the basis for encouraging harmonisation in electronic communications. Member States should encourage the use of published standards and/or specifications to the extent strictly necessary to ensure interoperability of services and to improve freedom of choice for users.

(10) Competition rules alone may not be sufficient to ensure cultural diversity and media pluralism in the area of digital television. Directive 95/47/EC provided an initial regulatory framework for the nascent digital television industry which should be maintained, including in particular the obligation to provide conditional access on fair, reasonable and non-discriminatory terms, in order to make sure that a wide variety of programming and services is available. Technological and market developments make it necessary to review these obligations on a regular basis, either by a Member State for its national market or the Commission for the Community, in particular to determine whether there is justification for extending obligations to new gateways, such as electronic programme guides (EPGs) and application program interfaces (APIs), to the extent that is necessary to ensure accessibility for end-users to specified digital broadcasting services. Member States may specify the digital broadcasting services to which access by end-users must be ensured by any legislative, regulatory or administrative means that they deem necessary.

(11) Member States may also permit their national regulatory authority to review obligations in relation to conditional access to digital broadcasting services in order to assess through a market analysis whether to withdraw or amend conditions for operators that do not have significant market power on the relevant market. Such withdrawal or amendment should not adversely affect access for end-users to such services or the prospects for effective competition.

(12) In order to ensure continuity of existing agreements and to avoid a legal vacuum, it is necessary to ensure that obligations for access and interconnection imposed under Articles 4, 6, 7, 8, 11, 12, and 14 of Directive 97/33/EC of the European Parliament and of the Council of 30 June 1997 on interconnection in telecommunications with regard to ensuring universal service and interoperability through application of the principles of open network provision (ONP),[8] obligations on special access imposed under Article 16 of Directive 98/10/EC of the European Parliament and of the Council of 26 February 1998 on the application of open network provision (ONP) to voice telephony and on universal service for telecommunications in a competitive environment,[9] and obligations concerning the provision of leased line transmission capacity under Council Directive 92/44/EEC of 5 June 1992 on the application of open network provision to leased lines,[10] are initially carried over into the new regulatory framework, but are subject to immediate review in the light of prevailing market conditions. Such a review should also extend to those organisations covered by Regulation (EC) No 2887/2000 of the European Parliament and of the Council of 18 December 2000 on unbundled access to the local loop.[11]

(13) The review should be carried out using an economic market analysis based on competition law methodology. The aim is to reduce *ex ante* sector specific rules progressively as competition in the market develops. However the procedure also takes account of transitional problems in the market such as those related to international roaming and of the possibility of new bottlenecks arising as a result of technological development, which may require *ex ante* regulation, for example in the area of broadband access networks. It may well be the case that competition develops at different speeds in different market segments and in different Member States, and national regulatory authorities should be able to relax regulatory obligations in those markets where competition is delivering the desired results. In order to ensure that market players in similar circumstances are treated in similar ways in different Member States, the Commission should be able to ensure harmonised application of the provisions of this Directive. National regulatory authorities and national authorities entrusted with the implementation of competition law should, where appropriate, coordinate their actions to ensure that the most appropriate remedy is applied. The Community and its Member States have entered into commitments on interconnection of telecommunications networks in the context of the World Trade Organisation agreement on basic telecommunications and these commitments need to be respected.

(14) Directive 97/33/EC laid down a range of obligations to be imposed on undertakings with significant market power, namely transparency, non-discrimination, accounting separation, access, and price control including cost orientation. This range of possible obligations should be maintained but, in addition, they should be established as a set of

maximum obligations that can be applied to undertakings, in order to avoid over-regulation. Exceptionally, in order to comply with international commitments or Community law, it may be appropriate to impose obligations for access or interconnection on all market players, as is currently the case for conditional access systems for digital television services.

(15) The imposition of a specific obligation on an undertaking with significant market power does not require an additional market analysis but a justification that the obligation in question is appropriate and proportionate in relation to the nature of the problem identified.

(16) Transparency of terms and conditions for access and interconnection, including prices, serve to speed-up negotiation, avoid disputes and give confidence to market players that a service is not being provided on discriminatory terms. Openness and transparency of technical interfaces can be particularly important in ensuring interoperability. Where a national regulatory authority imposes obligations to make information public, it may also specify the manner in which the information is to be made available, covering for example the type of publication (paper and/or electronic) and whether or not it is free of charge, taking into account the nature and purpose of the information concerned.

(17) The principle of non-discrimination ensures that undertakings with market power do not distort competition, in particular where they are vertically integrated undertakings that supply services to undertakings with whom they compete on downstream markets.

(18) Accounting separation allows internal price transfers to be rendered visible, and allows national regulatory authorities to check compliance with obligations for non-discrimination where applicable. In this regard the Commission published Recommendation 98/322/EC of 8 April 1998 on interconnection in a liberalised telecommunications market (Part 2 – accounting separation and cost accounting).[12]

(19) Mandating access to network infrastructure can be justified as a means of increasing competition, but national regulatory authorities need to balance the rights of an infrastructure owner to exploit its infrastructure for its own benefit, and the rights of other service providers to access facilities that are essential for the provision of competing services. Where obligations are imposed on operators that require them to meet reasonable requests for access to and use of networks elements and associated facilities, such requests should only be refused on the basis of objective criteria such as technical feasibility or the need to maintain network integrity. Where access is refused, the aggrieved party may submit the case to the dispute resolutions procedure referred to in Articles 20 and 21 of Directive 2002/21/EC (Framework Directive). An operator with mandated access obligations cannot be required to provide types of access which are not within its powers to provide. The imposition by national regulatory authorities of mandated access that increases competition in the short-term should not reduce incentives for competitors to invest in alternative facilities that will secure more competition in the long-term. The Commission has published a Notice on the application of the competition rules to access agreements in the telecommunications sector[13] which addresses these issues. National regulatory authorities may impose technical and operational conditions on the provider and/or beneficiaries of mandated access in accordance with Community law. In particular the imposition of technical standards should comply with Directive 98/34/EC of the European Parliament and of the Council of 22 June 1998 laying down a procedure for the provision of information in the field of technical standards and regulations and of rules of Information Society Services.[14]

(20) Price control may be necessary when market analysis in a particular market reveals inefficient competition. The regulatory intervention may be relatively light, such as an obligation that prices for carrier selection are reasonable as laid down in Directive 97/33/EC, or much heavier such as an obligation that prices are cost oriented to provide full justification for those prices where competition is not sufficiently strong to prevent excessive pricing. In particular, operators with significant market power should avoid a price squeeze whereby the difference between their retail prices and the interconnection prices charged to competitors who provide similar retail services is not adequate to ensure sustainable competition. When a national regulatory authority calculates costs incurred in establishing a service mandated under this Directive, it is appropriate to allow a reasonable return on the capital employed including appropriate labour and building costs, with the value of capital adjusted where necessary to reflect the current valuation of assets and efficiency of operations. The method of cost recovery should be appropriate to the circumstances taking account of the need to promote efficiency and sustainable competition and maximise consumer benefits.

(21) Where a national regulatory authority imposes obligations to implement a cost accounting system in order to support price controls, it may itself undertake an annual audit to ensure compliance with that cost accounting system, provided that it has the necessary qualified staff, or it may require the audit to be carried out by another qualified body, independent of the operator concerned.

(22) Publication of information by Member States will ensure that market players and potential market entrants understand their rights and obligations, and know where to find the

relevant detailed information. Publication in the national gazette helps interested parties in other Member States to find the relevant information.

(23) In order to ensure that the pan-European electronic communications market is effective and efficient, the Commission should monitor and publish information on charges which contribute to determining prices to end-users.

(24) The development of the electronic communications market, with its associated infrastructure, could have adverse effects on the environment and the landscape. Member States should therefore monitor this process and, if necessary, take action to minimise any such effects by means of appropriate agreements and other arrangements with the relevant authorities.

(25) In order to determine the correct application of Community law, the Commission needs to know which undertakings have been designated as having significant market power and what obligations have been placed upon market players by national regulatory authorities. In addition to national publication of this information, it is therefore necessary for Member States to send this information to the Commission. Where Member States are required to send information to the Commission, this may be in electronic form, subject to appropriate authentication procedures being agreed.

(26) Given the pace of technological and market developments, the implementation of this Directive should be reviewed within three years of its date of application to determine if it is meeting its objectives.

(27) The measures necessary for the implementation of this Directive should be adopted in accordance with Council Decision 1999/468/EC of 28 June 1999 laying down the procedures for the exercise of implementing powers conferred on the Commission.[15]

(28) Since the objectives of the proposed action, namely establishing a harmonised framework for the regulation of access to and interconnection of electronic communications networks and associated facilities, cannot be sufficiently achieved by the Member States and can therefore, by reason of the scale and effects of the action, be better achieved at Community level, the Community may adopt measures, in accordance with the principle of subsidiarity as set out in Article 5 of the Treaty. In accordance with the principle of proportionality, as set out in that Article, this Directive does not go beyond what is necessary in order to achieve those objectives,

NOTES

1 OJ C365E, 19.12.2000, p 215 and OJ C270E, 25.9.2001, p 161.
2 OJ C123, 25.4.2001, p 50.
3 Opinion of the European Parliament of 1 March 2001 (OJ C277, 1.10.2001, p 72), Council Common Position of 17 September 2001 (OJ C337, 30.11.2001, p 1) and Decision of the European Parliament of 12 December 2001 (not yet published in the Official Journal). Council Decision of 14 February 2002.
4 See page 33 of this Official Journal.
5 See page 21 of this Official Journal.
6 OJ L281, 23.11.1995, p 51.
7 OJ L196, 5.8.1993, p 48.
8 OJ L199, 26.7.1997, p 32. Directive as last amended by Directive 98/61/EC (OJ L268, 3.10.1998, p 37).
9 OJ L101, 1.4.1998, p 24.
10 OJ L165, 19.6.1992, p 27. Directive as last amended by Commission Decision No 98/80/EC (OJ L14, 20.1.1998, p 27).
11 OJ L366, 30.12.2000, p 4.
12 OJ L141, 13.5.1998, p 6.
13 OJ C265, 22.8.1998, p 2.
14 OJ L204, 21.7.1998, p 37. Directive as amended by Directive 98/48/EC (OJ L217, 5.8.1998, p 18).
15 OJ L184, 17.7.1999, p 23.

HAVE ADOPTED THIS DIRECTIVE—

CHAPTER I
SCOPE, AIM AND DEFINITIONS

Article 1

Scope and aim

1. Within the framework set out in Directive 2002/21/EC (Framework Directive), this Directive harmonises the way in which Member States regulate access to, and interconnection

of, electronic communications networks and associated facilities. The aim is to establish a regulatory framework, in accordance with internal market principles, for the relationships between suppliers of networks and services that will result in sustainable competition, interoperability of electronic communications services and consumer benefits.

2. This Directive establishes rights and obligations for operators and for undertakings seeking interconnection and/or access to their networks or associated facilities. It sets out objectives for national regulatory authorities with regard to access and interconnection, and lays down procedures to ensure that obligations imposed by national regulatory authorities are reviewed and, where appropriate, withdrawn once the desired objectives have been achieved. Access in this Directive does not refer to access by end-users.

[4581]

Article 2

Definitions

For the purposes of this Directive the definitions set out in Article 2 of Directive 2002/21/EC (Framework Directive) shall apply.

The following definitions shall also apply—

(a) "access" means the making available of facilities and/or services, to another undertaking, under defined conditions, on either an exclusive or non-exclusive basis, for the purpose of providing electronic communications services. It covers *inter alia*: access to network elements and associated facilities, which may involve the connection of equipment, by fixed or non-fixed means (in particular this includes access to the local loop and to facilities and services necessary to provide services over the local loop), access to physical infrastructure including buildings, ducts and masts; access to relevant software systems including operational support systems, access to number translation or systems offering equivalent functionality, access to fixed and mobile networks, in particular for roaming, access to conditional access systems for digital television services; access to virtual network services;

(b) "interconnection" means the physical and logical linking of public communications networks used by the same or a different undertaking in order to allow the users of one undertaking to communicate with users of the same or another undertaking, or to access services provided by another undertaking. Services may be provided by the parties involved or other parties who have access to the network. Interconnection is a specific type of access implemented between public network operators;

(c) "operator" means an undertaking providing or authorised to provide a public communications network or an associated facility;

(d) "wide-screen television service" means a television service that consists wholly or partially of programmes produced and edited to be displayed in a full height wide-screen format. The 16:9 format is the reference format for wide-screen television services;

(e) "local loop" means the physical circuit connecting the network termination point at the subscriber's premises to the main distribution frame or equivalent facility in the fixed public telephone network.

[4582]

CHAPTER II
GENERAL PROVISIONS

Article 3

General framework for access and interconnection

1. Member States shall ensure that there are no restrictions which prevent undertakings in the same Member State or in different Member States from negotiating between themselves agreements on technical and commercial arrangements for access and/or interconnection, in accordance with Community law. The undertaking requesting access or interconnection does not need to be authorised to operate in the Member State where access or interconnection is requested, if it is not providing services and does not operate a network in that Member State.

2. Without prejudice to Article 31 of Directive 2002/22/EC of the European Parliament and of the Council of 7 March 2002 on universal service and users' rights relating to

electronic communications networks and services (Universal Service Directive),[1] Member States shall not maintain legal or administrative measures which oblige operators, when granting access or interconnection, to offer different terms and conditions to different undertakings for equivalent services and/ or imposing obligations that are not related to the actual access and interconnection services provided without prejudice to the conditions fixed in the Annex of Directive 2002/20/EC (Authorisation Directive).

[4583]

NOTES

[1] See page 51 of this Official Journal.

Article 4

Rights and obligations for undertakings

1. Operators of public communications networks shall have a right and, when requested by other undertakings so authorised, an obligation to negotiate interconnection with each other for the purpose of providing publicly available electronic communications services, in order to ensure provision and interoperability of services throughout the Community. Operators shall offer access and interconnection to other undertakings on terms and conditions consistent with obligations imposed by the national regulatory authority pursuant to Articles 5, 6, 7 and 8.

2. Public electronic communications networks established for the distribution of digital television services shall be capable of distributing wide-screen television services and programmes. Network operators that receive and redistribute wide-screen television services or programmes shall maintain that wide-screen format.

3. Without prejudice to Article 11 of Directive 2002/20/EC (Authorisation Directive), Member States shall require that undertakings which acquire information from another undertaking before, during or after the process of negotiating access or interconnection arrangements use that information solely for the purpose for which it was supplied and respect at all times the confidentiality of information transmitted or stored. The received information shall not be passed on to any other party, in particular other departments, subsidiaries or partners, for whom such information could provide a competitive advantage.

[4584]

Article 5

Powers and responsibilities of the national regulatory authorities with regard to access and interconnection

1. National regulatory authorities shall, acting in pursuit of the objectives set out in Article 8 of Directive 2002/21/EC (Framework Directive), encourage and where appropriate ensure, in accordance with the provisions of this Directive, adequate access and interconnection, and interoperability of services, exercising their responsibility in a way that promotes efficiency, sustainable competition, and gives the maximum benefit to end-users.

In particular, without prejudice to measures that may be taken regarding undertakings with significant market power in accordance with Article 8, national regulatory authorities shall be able to impose—

(a) to the extent that is necessary to ensure end-to-end connectivity, obligations on undertakings that control access to end-users, including in justified cases the obligation to interconnect their networks where this is not already the case;

(b) to the extent that is necessary to ensure accessibility for end-users to digital radio and television broadcasting services specified by the Member State, obligations on operators to provide access to the other facilities referred to in Annex I, Part II on fair, reasonable and non-discriminatory terms.

2. When imposing obligations on an operator to provide access in accordance with Article 12, national regulatory authorities may lay down technical or operational conditions to be met by the provider and/or beneficiaries of such access, in accordance with Community law, where necessary to ensure normal operation of the network. Conditions that refer to implementation of specific technical standards or specifications shall respect Article 17 of Directive 2002/21/EC (Framework Directive).

3. Obligations and conditions imposed in accordance with paragraphs 1 and 2 shall be objective, transparent, proportionate and non-discriminatory, and shall be implemented in accordance with the procedures referred to in Articles 6 and 7 of Directive 2002/21/EC (Framework Directive).

4. With regard to access and interconnection, Member States shall ensure that the national regulatory authority is empowered to intervene at its own initiative where justified or, in the absence of agreement between undertakings, at the request of either of the parties involved, in order to secure the policy objectives of Article 8 of Directive 2002/21/EC (Framework Directive), in accordance with the provisions of this Directive and the procedures referred to in Articles 6 and 7, 20 and 21 of Directive 2002/21/EC (Framework Directive).

[4585]

CHAPTER III
OBLIGATIONS ON OPERATORS AND MARKET REVIEW PROCEDURES

Article 6

Conditional access systems and other facilities

1. Member States shall ensure that, in relation to conditional access to digital television and radio services broadcast to viewers and listeners in the Community, irrespective of the means of transmission, the conditions laid down in Annex I, Part I apply.

2. In the light of market and technological developments, Annex I may be amended in accordance with the procedure referred to in Article 14(3).

3. Notwithstanding the provisions of paragraph 1, Member States may permit their national regulatory authority, as soon as possible after the entry into force of this Directive and periodically thereafter, to review the conditions applied in accordance with this Article, by undertaking a market analysis in accordance with the first paragraph of Article 16 of Directive 2002/21/EC (Framework Directive) to determine whether to maintain, amend or withdraw the conditions applied.

Where, as a result of this market analysis, a national regulatory authority finds that one or more operators do not have significant market power on the relevant market, it may amend or withdraw the conditions with respect to those operators, in accordance with the procedures referred to in Articles 6 and 7 of Directive 2002/21/EC (Framework Directive), only to the extent that—

(a) accessibility for end-users to radio and television broadcasts and broadcasting channels and services specified in accordance with Article 31 of Directive 2002/22/EC (Universal Service Directive) would not be adversely affected by such amendment or withdrawal, and

(b) the prospects for effective competition in the markets for—
   (i) retail digital television and radio broadcasting services, and
   (ii) conditional access systems and other associated facilities,

would not be adversely affected by such amendment or withdrawal.

An appropriate period of notice shall be given to parties affected by such amendment or withdrawal of conditions.

4. Conditions applied in accordance with this Article are without prejudice to the ability of Member States to impose obligations in relation to the presentational aspect of electronic programme guides and similar listing and navigation facilities.

[4586]

Article 7

Review of former obligations for access and interconnection

1. Member States shall maintain all obligations on undertakings providing public communications networks and/or services concerning access and interconnection that were in force prior to the date of entry into force of this Directive under Articles 4, 6, 7, 8, 11, 12, and 14 of Directive 97/33/EC, Article 16 of Directive 98/10/EC, and Articles 7 and 8 of Directive 92/44/EC, until such time as these obligations have been reviewed and a determination made in accordance with paragraph 3.

2. The Commission will indicate relevant markets for the obligations referred to in paragraph 1 in the initial recommendation on relevant product and service markets and the Decision identifying transnational markets to be adopted in accordance with Article 15 of Directive 2002/21/EC (Framework Directive).

3. Member States shall ensure that, as soon as possible after the entry into force of this Directive, and periodically thereafter, national regulatory authorities undertake a market analysis, in accordance with Article 16 of Directive 2002/21/EC (Framework Directive) to determine whether to maintain, amend or withdraw these obligations. An appropriate period of notice shall be given to parties affected by such amendment or withdrawal of obligations.

[4587]

Article 8

Imposition, amendment or withdrawal of obligations

1. Member States shall ensure that national regulatory authorities are empowered to impose the obligations identified in Articles 9 to 13.

2. Where an operator is designated as having significant market power on a specific market as a result of a market analysis carried out in accordance with Article 16 of Directive 2002/21/EC (Framework Directive), national regulatory authorities shall impose the obligations set out in Articles 9 to 13 of this Directive as appropriate.

3. Without prejudice to—

— the provisions of Articles 5(1), 5(2) and 6,

— the provisions of Articles 12 and 13 of Directive 2002/21/EC (Framework Directive), Condition 7 in Part B of the Annex to Directive 2002/20/EC (Authorisation Directive) as applied by virtue of Article 6(1) of that Directive, Articles 27, 28 and 30 of Directive 2002/22/EC (Universal Service Directive) and the relevant provisions of Directive 97/66/EC of the European Parliament and of the Council of 15 December 1997 concerning the processing of personal data and the protection of privacy in the telecommunications sector[1] containing obligations on undertakings other than those designated as having significant market power, or

— the need to comply with international commitments,

national regulatory authorities shall not impose the obligations set out in Articles 9 to 13 on operators that have not been designated in accordance with paragraph 2.

In exceptional circumstances, when a national regulatory authority intends to impose on operators with significant market power other obligations for access or interconnection than those set out in Articles 9 to 13 in this Directive it shall submit this request to the Commission. The Commission, acting in accordance with Article 14(2), shall take a decision authorising or preventing the national regulatory authority from taking such measures.

4. Obligations imposed in accordance with this Article shall be based on the nature of the problem identified, proportionate and justified in the light of the objectives laid down in Article 8 of Directive 2002/21/EC (Framework Directive). Such obligations shall only be imposed following consultation in accordance with Articles 6 and 7 of that Directive.

5. In relation to the third indent of the first subparagraph of paragraph 3, national regulatory authorities shall notify decisions to impose, amend or withdraw obligations on market players to the Commission, in accordance with the procedure referred to in Article 7 of Directive 2002/21/EC (Framework Directive).

[4588]

NOTES

[1] OJ L24, 30.1.1998, p 1.

Article 9

Obligation of transparency

1. National regulatory authorities may, in accordance with the provisions of Article 8, impose obligations for transparency in relation to interconnection and/or access, requiring operators to make public specified information, such as accounting information, technical specifications, network characteristics, terms and conditions for supply and use, and prices.

2. In particular where an operator has obligations of non-discrimination, national regulatory authorities may require that operator to publish a reference offer, which shall be sufficiently unbundled to ensure that undertakings are not required to pay for facilities which are not necessary for the service requested, giving a description of the relevant offerings

broken down into components according to market needs, and the associated terms and conditions including prices. The national regulatory authority shall, *inter alia*, be able to impose changes to reference offers to give effect to obligations imposed under this Directive.

3. National regulatory authorities may specify the precise information to be made available, the level of detail required and the manner of publication.

4. Notwithstanding paragraph 3, where an operator has obligations under Article 12 concerning unbundled access to the twisted metallic pair local loop, national regulatory authorities shall ensure the publication of a reference offer containing at least the elements set out in Annex II.

5. In the light of market and technological developments, Annex II may be amended in accordance with the procedure referred to in Article 14(3).

[4589]

Article 10

Obligation of non-discrimination

1. A national regulatory authority may, in accordance with the provisions of Article 8, impose obligations of non-discrimination, in relation to interconnection and/or access.

2. Obligations of non-discrimination shall ensure, in particular, that the operator applies equivalent conditions in equivalent circumstances to other undertakings providing equivalent services, and provides services and information to others under the same conditions and of the same quality as it provides for its own services, or those of its subsidiaries or partners.

[4590]

Article 11

Obligation of accounting separation

1. A national regulatory authority may, in accordance with the provisions of Article 8, impose obligations for accounting separation in relation to specified activities related to interconnection and/or access.

In particular, a national regulatory authority may require a vertically integrated company to make transparent its wholesale prices and its internal transfer prices *inter alia* to ensure compliance where there is a requirement for non-discrimination under Article 10 or, where necessary, to prevent unfair cross-subsidy. National regulatory authorities may specify the format and accounting methodology to be used.

2. Without prejudice to Article 5 of Directive 2002/21/EC (Framework Directive), to facilitate the verification of compliance with obligations of transparency and non-discrimination, national regulatory authorities shall have the power to require that accounting records, including data on revenues received from third parties, are provided on request. National regulatory authorities may publish such information as would contribute to an open and competitive market, while respecting national and Community rules on commercial confidentiality.

[4591]

Article 12

Obligations of access to, and use of, specific network facilities

1. A national regulatory authority may, in accordance with the provisions of Article 8, impose obligations on operators to meet reasonable requests for access to, and use of, specific network elements and associated facilities, *inter alia* in situations where the national regulatory authority considers that denial of access or unreasonable terms and conditions having a similar effect would hinder the emergence of a sustainable competitive market at the retail level, or would not be in the end-user's interest.

Operators may be required *inter alia*—

(a) to give third parties access to specified network elements and/or facilities, including unbundled access to the local loop;
(b) to negotiate in good faith with undertakings requesting access;
(c) not to withdraw access to facilities already granted;
(d) to provide specified services on a wholesale basis for resale by third parties;

(e) to grant open access to technical interfaces, protocols or other key technologies that are indispensable for the interoperability of services or virtual network services;

(f) to provide co-location or other forms of facility sharing, including duct, building or mast sharing;

(g) to provide specified services needed to ensure interoperability of end-to-end services to users, including facilities for intelligent network services or roaming on mobile networks;

(h) to provide access to operational support systems or similar software systems necessary to ensure fair competition in the provision of services;

(i) to interconnect networks or network facilities.

National regulatory authorities may attach to those obligations conditions covering fairness, reasonableness and timeliness.

2. When national regulatory authorities are considering whether to impose the obligations referred in paragraph 1, and in particular when assessing whether such obligations would be proportionate to the objectives set out in Article 8 of Directive 2002/21/EC (Framework Directive), they shall take account in particular of the following factors—

(a) the technical and economic viability of using or installing competing facilities, in the light of the rate of market development, taking into account the nature and type of interconnection and access involved;

(b) the feasibility of providing the access proposed, in relation to the capacity available;

(c) the initial investment by the facility owner, bearing in mind the risks involved in making the investment;

(d) the need to safeguard competition in the long term;

(e) where appropriate, any relevant intellectual property rights;

(f) the provision of pan-European services.

[4592]

Article 13

Price control and cost accounting obligations

1. A national regulatory authority may, in accordance with the provisions of Article 8, impose obligations relating to cost recovery and price controls, including obligations for cost orientation of prices and obligations concerning cost accounting systems, for the provision of specific types of interconnection and/or access, in situations where a market analysis indicates that a lack of effective competition means that the operator concerned might sustain prices at an excessively high level, or apply a price squeeze, to the detriment of end-users. National regulatory authorities shall take into account the investment made by the operator and allow him a reasonable rate of return on adequate capital employed, taking into account the risks involved.

2. National regulatory authorities shall ensure that any cost recovery mechanism or pricing methodology that is mandated serves to promote efficiency and sustainable competition and maximise consumer benefits. In this regard national regulatory authorities may also take account of prices available in comparable competitive markets.

3. Where an operator has an obligation regarding the cost orientation of its prices, the burden of proof that charges are derived from costs including a reasonable rate of return on investment shall lie with the operator concerned. For the purpose of calculating the cost of efficient provision of services, national regulatory authorities may use cost accounting methods independent of those used by the undertaking. National regulatory authorities may require an operator to provide full justification for its prices, and may, where appropriate, require prices to be adjusted.

4. National regulatory authorities shall ensure that, where implementation of a cost accounting system is mandated in order to support price controls, a description of the cost accounting system is made publicly available, showing at least the main categories under which costs are grouped and the rules used for the allocation of costs. Compliance with the cost accounting system shall be verified by a qualified independent body. A statement concerning compliance shall be published annually.

CHAPTER IV
PROCEDURAL PROVISIONS

[4593]

Article 14

Committee

1. The Commission shall be assisted by the Communications Committee set up by Article 22 of Directive 2002/21/EC (Framework Directive).

2. Where reference is made to this paragraph, Articles 3 and 7 of Decision 1999/468/EC shall apply, having regard to the provisions of Article 8 thereof.

3. Where reference is made to this paragraph, Articles 5 and 7 of Decision 1999/468/EC shall apply, having regard to the provisions of Article 8 thereof.

The period laid down in Article 5(6) of Decision 1999/468/EC shall be set at three months.

4. The Committee shall adopt its rules of procedure.

[4594]

Article 15

Publication of, and access to, information

1. Member States shall ensure that the specific obligations imposed on undertakings under this Directive are published and that the specific product/service and geographical markets are identified. They shall ensure that up-to-date information, provided that the information is not confidential and, in particular, does not comprise business secrets, is made publicly available in a manner that guarantees all interested parties easy access to that information.

2. Member States shall send to the Commission a copy of all such information published. The Commission shall make this information available in a readily accessible form, and shall distribute the information to the Communications Committee as appropriate.

[4595]

Article 16

Notification

1. Member States shall notify to the Commission by at the latest the date of application referred to in Article 18(1) second subparagraph the national regulatory authorities responsible for the tasks set out in this Directive.

2. National regulatory authorities shall notify to the Commission the names of operators deemed to have significant market power for the purposes of this Directive, and the obligations imposed upon them under this Directive. Any changes affecting the obligations imposed upon undertakings or of the undertakings affected under the provisions of this Directive shall be notified to the Commission without delay.

[4596]

Article 17

Review procedures

The Commission shall periodically review the functioning of this Directive and report to the European Parliament and to the Council, on the first occasion not later than three years after the date of application referred to in Article 18(1), second subparagraph. For this purpose, the Commission may request from the Member States information, which shall be supplied without undue delay.

[4597]

Article 18

Transposition

1. Member States shall adopt and publish the laws, regulations and administrative provisions necessary to comply with this Directive by not later than 24 July 2003. They shall forthwith inform the Commission thereof.

They shall apply those measures from 25 July 2003.

When Member States adopt these measures, they shall contain a reference to this Directive or be accompanied by such a reference on the occasion of their official publication. The methods of making such reference shall be laid down by Member States.

2. Member States shall communicate to the Commission the text of the provisions of national law which they adopt in the field governed by this Directive and of any subsequent amendments to those provisions.

[4598]

Article 19

Entry into force

This Directive shall enter into force on the day of its publication in the *Official Journal of the European Communities*.

[4599]

Article 20

Addressees

This Directive is addressed to the Member States.

[4600]

Done at Brussels, 7 March 2002.

ANNEX I
CONDITIONS FOR ACCESS TO DIGITAL TELEVISION AND RADIO SERVICES BROADCAST TO VIEWERS AND LISTENERS IN THE COMMUNITY

PART I:
CONDITIONS FOR CONDITIONAL ACCESS SYSTEMS TO BE APPLIED IN ACCORDANCE WITH ARTICLE 6(1)

In relation to conditional access to digital television and radio services broadcast to viewers and listeners in the Community, irrespective of the means of transmission, Member States must ensure in accordance with Article 6 that the following conditions apply—

(a) conditional access systems operated on the market in the Community are to have the necessary technical capability for cost-effective transcontrol allowing the possibility for full control by network operators at local or regional level of the services using such conditional access systems;

(b) all operators of conditional access services, irrespective of the means of transmission, who provide access services to digital television and radio services and whose access services broadcasters depend on to reach any group of potential viewers or listeners are to—
- offer to all broadcasters, on a fair, reasonable and non-discriminatory basis compatible with Community competition law, technical services enabling the broadcasters' digitally-transmitted services to be received by viewers or listeners authorised by means of decoders administered by the service operators, and comply with Community competition law,
- keep separate financial accounts regarding their activity as conditional access providers;

(c) when granting licences to manufacturers of consumer equipment, holders of industrial property rights to conditional access products and systems are to ensure that this is done on fair, reasonable and non-discriminatory terms. Taking into account technical and commercial factors, holders of rights are not to subject the granting of licences to conditions prohibiting, deterring or discouraging the inclusion in the same product of—
- a common interface allowing connection with several other access systems, or
- means specific to another access system, provided that the licensee complies with the relevant and reasonable conditions ensuring, as far as he is concerned, the security of transactions of conditional access system operators.

[4601]

PART II: OTHER FACILITIES TO WHICH CONDITIONS MAY BE APPLIED UNDER ARTICLE 5(1)(B)

(a) Access to application program interfaces (APIs);

(b) Access to electronic programme guides (EPGs).

[4602]

ANNEX II MINIMUM LIST OF ITEMS TO BE INCLUDED IN A REFERENCE OFFER FOR UNBUNDLED ACCESS TO THE TWISTED METALLIC PAIR LOCAL LOOP TO BE PUBLISHED BY NOTIFIED OPERATORS

For the purposes of this Annex the following definitions apply—

(a) "local sub-loop" means a partial local loop connecting the network termination point at the subscriber's premises to a concentration point or a specified intermediate access point in the fixed public telephone network;

(b) "unbundled access to the local loop" means full unbundled access to the local loop and shared access to the local loop; it does not entail a change in ownership of the local loop;

(c) "full unbundled access to the local loop" means the provision to a beneficiary of access to the local loop or local sub-loop of the notified operator authorising the use of the full frequency spectrum of the twisted metallic pair;

(d) "shared access to the local loop" means the provision to a beneficiary of access to the local loop or local sub-loop of the notified operator, authorising the use of the non-voice band frequency spectrum of the twisted metallic pair; the local loop continues to be used by the notified operator to provide the telephone service to the public;

A. Conditions for unbundled access to the local loop

1. Network elements to which access is offered covering in particular the following elements—
   (a) access to local loops;
   (b) access to non-voice band frequency spectrum of a local loop, in the case of shared access to the local loop;
2. Information concerning the locations of physical access sites,[1] availability of local loops in specific parts of the access network;
3. Technical conditions related to access and use of local loops, including the technical characteristics of the twisted metallic pair in the local loop;
4. Ordering and provisioning procedures, usage restrictions.

B. Co-location services

1. Information on the notified operator's relevant sites.[1]
2. Co-location options at the sites indicated under point 1 (including physical co-location and, as appropriate, distant co-location and virtual co-location).
3. Equipment characteristics: restrictions, if any, on equipment that can be co-located.
4. Security issues: measures put in place by notified operators to ensure the security of their locations.
5. Access conditions for staff of competitive operators.
6. Safety standards.
7. Rules for the allocation of space where co-location space is limited.
8. Conditions for beneficiaries to inspect the locations at which physical co-location is available, or sites where co-location has been refused on grounds of lack of capacity.

C. Information systems

Conditions for access to notified operator's operational support systems, information systems or databases for pre-ordering, provisioning, ordering, maintenance and repair requests and billing.

D. Supply conditions

1. Lead time for responding to requests for supply of services and facilities; service level agreements, fault resolution, procedures to return to a normal level of service and quality of service parameters.
2 Standard contract terms, including, where appropriate, compensation provided for failure to meet lead times.

3. Prices or pricing formulae for each feature, function and facility listed above.

[4603]

NOTES

[1] Availability of this information may be restricted to interested parties only, in order to avoid public security concerns.

DIRECTIVE OF THE EUROPEAN PARLIAMENT AND OF THE COUNCIL

of 7 March 2002

on the authorisation of electronic communications networks and services (Authorisation Directive)

(2002/20/EC)

NOTES

Date of publication in OJ: OJ L108, 24.4.2002, p 21.

THE EUROPEAN PARLIAMENT AND THE COUNCIL OF THE EUROPEAN UNION,

Having regard to the Treaty establishing the European Community, and in particular Article 95 thereof,

Having regard to the proposal from the Commission,[1]

Having regard to the opinion of the Economic and Social Committee,[2]

Acting in accordance with the procedure laid down in Article 251 of the Treaty,[3]

Whereas—

(1) The outcome of the public consultation on the 1999 review of the regulatory framework for electronic communications, as reflected in the Commission communication of 26 April 2000, and the findings reported by the Commission in its communications on the fifth and sixth reports on the implementation of the telecommunications regulatory package, has confirmed the need for a more harmonised and less onerous market access regulation for electronic communications networks and services throughout the Community.

(2) Convergence between different electronic communications networks and services and their technologies requires the establishment of an authorisation system covering all comparable services in a similar way regardless of the technologies used.

(3) The objective of this Directive is to create a legal framework to ensure the freedom to provide electronic communications networks and services, subject only to the conditions laid down in this Directive and to any restrictions in conformity with Article 46(1) of the Treaty, in particular measures regarding public policy, public security and public health.

(4) This Directive covers authorisation of all electronic communications networks and services whether they are provided to the public or not. This is important to ensure that both categories of providers may benefit from objective, transparent, non-discriminatory and proportionate rights, conditions and procedures.

(5) This Directive only applies to the granting of rights to use radio frequencies where such use involves the provision of an electronic communications network or service, normally for remuneration. The self-use of radio terminal equipment, based on the non-exclusive use of specific radio frequencies by a user and not related to an economic activity, such as use of a citizen's band by radio amateurs, does not consist of the provision of an electronic communications network or service and is therefore not covered by this Directive. Such use is covered by the Directive 1999/5/EC of the European Parliament and of the Council of 9 March 1999 on radio equipment and telecommunications terminal equipment and the mutual recognition of their conformity.[4]

(6) Provisions regarding the free movement of conditional access systems and the free provision of protected services based on such systems are laid down in Directive 98/84/EC of the European Parliament and of the Council of 20 November 1998 on the legal protection of services based on, or consisting of, conditional access.[5] The authorisation of such systems and services therefore does not need to be covered by this Directive.

(7) The least onerous authorisation system possible should be used to allow the provision of electronic communications networks and services in order to stimulate the development of

new electronic communications services and pan-European communications networks and services and to allow service providers and consumers to benefit from the economies of scale of the single market.

(8) Those aims can be best achieved by general authorisation of all electronic communications networks and services without requiring any explicit decision or administrative act by the national regulatory authority and by limiting any procedural requirements to notification only. Where Member States require notification by providers of electronic communication networks or services when they start their activities, they may also require proof of such notification having been made by means of any legally recognised postal or electronic acknowledgement of receipt of the notification. Such acknowledgement should in any case not consist of or require an administrative act by the national regulatory authority to which the notification must be made.

(9) It is necessary to include the rights and obligations of undertakings under general authorisations explicitly in such authorisations in order to ensure a level playing field throughout the Community and to facilitate cross-border negotiation of interconnection between public communications networks.

(10) The general authorisation entitles undertakings providing electronic communications networks and services to the public to negotiate interconnection under the conditions of Directive 2002/19/EC of the European Parliament and of the Council of 7 March 2002 on access to, and interconnection of, electronic communication networks and associated facilities (Access Directive).[6] Undertakings providing electronic communications networks and services other than to the public can negotiate interconnection on commercial terms.

(11) The granting of specific rights may continue to be necessary for the use of radio frequencies and numbers, including short codes, from the national numbering plan. Rights to numbers may also be allocated from a European numbering plan, including for example the virtual country code "3883" which has been attributed to member countries of the European Conference of Post and Telecommunications (CEPT). Those rights of use should not be restricted except where this is unavoidable in view of the scarcity of radio frequencies and the need to ensure the efficient use thereof.

(12) This Directive does not prejudice whether radio frequencies are assigned directly to providers of electronic communication networks or services or to entities that use these networks or services. Such entities may be radio or television broadcast content providers. Without prejudice to specific criteria and procedures adopted by Member States to grant rights of use for radio frequencies to providers of radio or television broadcast content services, to pursue general interest objectives in conformity with Community law, the procedure for assignment of radio frequencies should in any event be objective, transparent, non-discriminatory and proportionate. In accordance with case law of the Court of Justice, any national restrictions on the rights guaranteed by Article 49 of the Treaty should be objectively justified, proportionate and not exceed what is necessary to achieve general interest objectives as defined by Member States in conformity with Community law. The responsibility for compliance with the conditions attached to the right to use a radio frequency and the relevant conditions attached to the general authorisation should in any case lie with the undertaking to whom the right of use for the radio frequency has been granted.

(13) As part of the application procedure for granting rights to use a radio frequency, Member States may verify whether the applicant will be able to comply with the conditions attached to such rights. For this purpose the applicant may be requested to submit the necessary information to prove his ability to comply with these conditions. Where such information is not provided, the application for the right to use a radio frequency may be rejected.

(14) Member States are neither obliged to grant nor prevented from granting rights to use numbers from the national numbering plan or rights to install facilities to undertakings other than providers of electronic communications networks or services.

(15) The conditions, which may be attached to the general authorisation and to the specific rights of use, should be limited to what is strictly necessary to ensure compliance with requirements and obligations under Community law and national law in accordance with Community law.

(16) In the case of electronic communications networks and services not provided to the public it is appropriate to impose fewer and lighter conditions than are justified for electronic communications networks and services provided to the public.

(17) Specific obligations which may be imposed on providers of electronic communications networks and services in accordance with Community law by virtue of their significant market power as defined in Directive 2002/21/EC of the European Parliament and of the Council of 7 March 2002 on a common regulatory framework for electronic

communications networks and services (Framework Directive)[7] should be imposed separately from the general rights and obligations under the general authorisation.

(18) The general authorisation should only contain conditions which are specific to the electronic communications sector. It should not be made subject to conditions which are already applicable by virtue of other existing national law which is not specific to the electronic communications sector. Nevertheless, the national regulatory authorities may inform network operators and service providers about other legislation concerning their business, for instance through references on their websites.

(19) The requirement to publish decisions on the granting of rights to use frequencies or numbers may be fulfilled by making these decisions publicly accessible via a website.

(20) The same undertaking, for example a cable operator, can offer both an electronic communications service, such as the conveyance of television signals, and services not covered under this Directive, such as the commercialisation of an offer of sound or television broadcasting content services, and therefore additional obligations can be imposed on this undertaking in relation to its activity as a content provider or distributor, according to provisions other than those of this Directive, without prejudice to the list of conditions laid in the Annex to this Directive.

(21) When granting rights of use for radio frequencies, numbers or rights to install facilities, the relevant authorities may inform the undertakings to whom they grant such rights of the relevant conditions in the general authorisation.

(22) Where the demand for radio frequencies in a specific range exceeds their availability, appropriate and transparent procedures should be followed for the assignment of such frequencies in order to avoid any discrimination and optimise use of those scarce resources.

(23) National regulatory authorities should ensure, in establishing criteria for competitive or comparative selection procedures, that the objectives in Article 8 of Directive 2002/21/EC (Framework Directive) are met. It would therefore not be contrary to this Directive if the application of objective, non-discriminatory and proportionate selection criteria to promote the development of competition would have the effect of excluding certain undertakings from a competitive or comparative selection procedure for a particular radio frequency.

(24) Where the harmonised assignment of radio frequencies to particular undertakings has been agreed at European level, Member States should strictly implement such agreements in the granting of rights of use of radio frequencies from the national frequency usage plan.

(25) Providers of electronic communications networks and services may need a confirmation of their rights under the general authorisation with respect to interconnection and rights of way, in particular to facilitate negotiations with other, regional or local, levels of government or with service providers in other Member States. For this purpose the national regulatory authorities should provide declarations to undertakings either upon request or alternatively as an automatic response to a notification under the general authorisation. Such declarations should not by themselves constitute entitlements to rights nor should any rights under the general authorisation or rights of use or the exercise of such rights depend upon a declaration.

(26) Where undertakings find that their applications for rights to install facilities have not been dealt with in accordance with the principles set out in Directive 2002/21/EC (Framework Directive) or where such decisions are unduly delayed, they should have the right to appeal against decisions or delays in such decisions in accordance with that Directive.

(27) The penalties for non-compliance with conditions under the general authorisation should be commensurate with the infringement. Save in exceptional circumstances, it would not be proportionate to suspend or withdraw the right to provide electronic communications services or the right to use radio frequencies or numbers where an undertaking did not comply with one or more of the conditions under the general authorisation. This is without prejudice to urgent measures which the relevant authorities of the Member States may need to take in case of serious threats to public safety, security or health or to economic and operational interests of other undertakings. This Directive should also be without prejudice to any claims between undertakings for compensation for damages under national law.

(28) Subjecting service providers to reporting and information obligations can be cumbersome, both for the undertaking and for the national regulatory authority concerned. Such obligations should therefore be proportionate, objectively justified and limited to what is strictly necessary. It is not necessary to require systematic and regular proof of compliance with all conditions under the general authorisation or attached to rights of use. Undertakings have a right to know the purposes for which the information they should provide will be used. The provision of information should not be a condition for market access. For statistical purposes a notification may be required from providers of electronic communication networks or services when they cease activities.

(29) This Directive should be without prejudice to Member States' obligations to provide any information necessary for the defence of Community interests within the context of international agreements. This Directive should also be without prejudice to any reporting obligations under legislation which is not specific to the electronic communications sector such as competition law.

(30) Administrative charges may be imposed on providers of electronic communications services in order to finance the activities of the national regulatory authority in managing the authorisation system and for the granting of rights of use. Such charges should be limited to cover the actual administrative costs for those activities. For this purpose transparency should be created in the income and expenditure of national regulatory authorities by means of annual reporting about the total sum of charges collected and the administrative costs incurred. This will allow undertakings to verify that administrative costs and charges are in balance.

(31) Systems for administrative charges should not distort competition or create barriers for entry into the market. With a general authorisation system it will no longer be possible to attribute administrative costs and hence charges to individual undertakings, except for the granting of rights to use numbers, radio frequencies and for rights to install facilities. Any applicable administrative charges should be in line with the principles of a general authorisation system. An example of a fair, simple and transparent alternative for these charge attribution criteria could be a turnover related distribution key. Where administrative charges are very low, flat rate charges, or charges combining a flat rate basis with a turnover related element could also be appropriate.

(32) In addition to administrative charges, usage fees may be levied for the use of radio frequencies and numbers as an instrument to ensure the optimal use of such resources. Such fees should not hinder the development of innovative services and competition in the market. This Directive is without prejudice to the purpose for which fees for rights of use are employed. Such fees may for instance be used to finance activities of national regulatory authorities that cannot be covered by administrative charges. Where, in the case of competitive or comparative selection procedures, fees for rights of use for radio frequencies consist entirely or partly of a one-off amount, payment arrangements should ensure that such fees do not in practice lead to selection on the basis of criteria unrelated to the objective of ensuring optimal use of radio frequencies. The Commission may publish on a regular basis benchmark studies with regard to best practices for the assignment of radio frequencies, the assignment of numbers or the granting of rights of way.

(33) Member States may need to amend rights, conditions, procedures, charges and fees relating to general authorisations and rights of use where this is objectively justified. Such changes should be duly notified to all interested parties in good time, giving them adequate opportunity to express their views on any such amendments.

(34) The objective of transparency requires that service providers, consumers and other interested parties have easy access to any information regarding rights, conditions, procedures, charges, fees and decisions concerning the provision of electronic communications services, rights of use of radio frequencies and numbers, rights to install facilities, national frequency usage plans and national numbering plans. The national regulatory authorities have an important task in providing such information and keeping it up to date. Where such rights are administered by other levels of government the national regulatory authorities should endeavour to create a user-friendly instrument for access to information regarding such rights.

(35) The proper functioning of the single market on the basis of the national authorisation regimes under this Directive should be monitored by the Commission.

(36) In order to arrive at a single date of application of all elements of the new regulatory framework for the electronic communications sector, it is important that the process of national transposition of this Directive and of alignment of the existing licences with the new rules take place in parallel. However, in specific cases where the replacement of authorisations existing on the date of entry into force of this Directive by the general authorisation and the individual rights of use in accordance with this Directive would lead to an increase in the obligations for service providers operating under an existing authorisation or to a reduction of their rights, Member States may avail themselves of an additional nine months after the date of application of this Directive for alignment of such licences, unless this would have a negative effect on the rights and obligations of other undertakings.

(37) There may be circumstances under which the abolition of an authorisation condition regarding access to electronic communications networks would create serious hardship for one or more undertakings that have benefited from the condition. In such cases further transitional arrangements may be granted by the Commission, upon request by a Member State.

(38) Since the objectives of the proposed action, namely the harmonisation and simplification of electronic communications rules and conditions for the authorisation of networks and services cannot be sufficiently achieved by the Member States and can therefore, by reason of the scale and effects of the action, be better achieved at Community level, the Community may adopt measures in accordance with the principle of subsidiarity as set out in Article 5 of the Treaty. In accordance with the principle of proportionality, as set out in that Article, this Directive does not go beyond what is necessary for those objectives,

NOTES

1 OJ C365E, 19.12.2000, p 230 and OJ C270E, 25.9.2001, p 182.
2 OJ C123, 25.4.2001, p 55.
3 Opinion of the European Parliament of 1 March 2001 (OJ C277, 1.10.2001, p 116), Council Common Position of 17 September 2001 (OJ C337, 30.11.2001, p 18) and Decision of the European Parliament of 12 December 2001 (not yet published in the Official Journal). Council Decision of 14 February 2002.
4 OJ L91, 7.4.1999, p 10.
5 OJ L320, 28.11.1998, p 54.
6 See page 7 of this Official Journal.
7 See page 33 of this Official Journal.

HAVE ADOPTED THIS DIRECTIVE—

Article 1

Objective and scope

1. The aim of this Directive is to implement an internal market in electronic communications networks and services through the harmonisation and simplification of authorisation rules and conditions in order to facilitate their provision throughout the Community.

2. This Directive shall apply to authorisations for the provision of electronic communications networks and services.

[4604]

Article 2

Definitions

1. For the purposes of this Directive, the definitions set out in Article 2 of Directive 2002/21/EC (Framework Directive) shall apply.

2. The following definitions shall also apply—

(a) "general authorisation" means a legal framework established by the Member State ensuring rights for the provision of electronic communications networks or services and laying down sector specific obligations that may apply to all or to specific types of electronic communications networks and services, in accordance with this Directive;

(b) "harmful interference" means interference which endangers the functioning of a radionavigation service or of other safety services or which otherwise seriously degrades, obstructs or repeatedly interrupts a radiocommunications service operating in accordance with the applicable Community or national regulations.

[4605]

Article 3

General authorisation of electronic communications networks and services

1. Member States shall ensure the freedom to provide electronic communications networks and services, subject to the conditions set out in this Directive. To this end, Member States shall not prevent an undertaking from providing electronic communications networks or services, except where this is necessary for the reasons set out in Article 46(1) of the Treaty.

2. The provision of electronic communications networks or the provision of electronic communications services may, without prejudice to the specific obligations referred to in Article 6(2) or rights of use referred to in Article 5, only be subject to a general authorisation. The undertaking concerned may be required to submit a notification but may not be required

to obtain an explicit decision or any other administrative act by the national regulatory authority before exercising the rights stemming from the authorisation. Upon notification, when required, an undertaking may begin activity, where necessary subject to the provisions on rights of use in Articles 5, 6 and 7.

3. The notification referred to in paragraph 2 shall not entail more than a declaration by a legal or natural person to the national regulatory authority of the intention to commence the provision of electronic communication networks or services and the submission of the minimal information which is required to allow the national regulatory authority to keep a register or list of providers of electronic communications networks and services. This information must be limited to what is necessary for the identification of the provider, such as company registration numbers, and the provider's contact persons, the provider's address, a short description of the network or service, and an estimated date for starting the activity.

[4606]

Article 4

Minimum list of rights derived from the general authorisation

1. Undertakings authorised pursuant to Article 3, shall have the right to—
   (a) provide electronic communications networks and services;
   (b) have their application for the necessary rights to install facilities considered in accordance with Article 11 of Directive 2002/21/EC (Framework Directive).

2. When such undertakings provide electronic communications networks or services to the public the general authorisation shall also give them the right to—
   (a) negotiate interconnection with and where applicable obtain access to or interconnection from other providers of publicly available communications networks and services covered by a general authorisation anywhere in the Community under the conditions of and in accordance with Directive 2002/19/EC (Access Directive);
   (b) be given an opportunity to be designated to provide different elements of a universal service and/or to cover different parts of the national territory in accordance with Directive 2002/22/EC of the European Parliament and of the Council of 7 March 2002 on universal service and users' rights relating to electronic communications networks and services (Universal Service Directive).

[4607]

Article 5

Rights of use for radio frequencies and numbers

1. Member States shall, where possible, in particular where the risk of harmful interference is negligible, not make the use of radio frequencies subject to the grant of individual rights of use but shall include the conditions for usage of such radio frequencies in the general authorisation.

2. Where it is necessary to grant individual rights of use for radio frequencies and numbers, Member States shall grant such rights, upon request, to any undertaking providing or using networks or services under the general authorisation, subject to the provisions of Articles 6, 7 and 11(1)(c) of this Directive and any other rules ensuring the efficient use of those resources in accordance with Directive 2002/21/EC (Framework Directive).

Without prejudice to specific criteria and procedures adopted by Member States to grant rights of use of radio frequencies to providers of radio or television broadcast content services with a view to pursuing general interest objectives in conformity with Community law, such rights of use shall be granted through open, transparent and non-discriminatory procedures. When granting rights of use, Member States shall specify whether those rights can be transferred at the initiative of the right holder, and under which conditions, in the case of radio frequencies, in accordance with Article 9 of Directive 2002/21/EC (Framework Directive). Where Member States grant rights of use for a limited period of time, the duration shall be appropriate for the service concerned.

3. Decisions on rights of use shall be taken, communicated and made public as soon as possible after receipt of the complete application by the national regulatory authority, within three weeks in the case of numbers that have been allocated for specific purposes within the national numbering plan and within six weeks in the case of radio frequencies that have been allocated for specific purposes within the national frequency plan. The latter time limit shall be without prejudice to any applicable international agreements relating to the use of radio frequencies or of orbital positions.

4. Where it has been decided, after consultation with interested parties in accordance with Article 6 of Directive 2002/21/EC (Framework Directive), that rights for use of numbers of exceptional economic value are to be granted through competitive or comparative selection procedures, Member States may extend the maximum period of three weeks by up to three weeks.

With regard to competitive or comparative selection procedures for radio frequencies Article 7 shall apply.

5. Member States shall not limit the number of rights of use to be granted except where this is necessary to ensure the efficient use of radio frequencies in accordance with Article 7.

[4608]

Article 6

Conditions attached to the general authorisation and to the rights of use for radio frequencies and for numbers, and specific obligations

1. The general authorisation for the provision of electronic communications networks or services and the rights of use for radio frequencies and rights of use for numbers may be subject only to the conditions listed respectively in parts A, B and C of the Annex. Such conditions shall be objectively justified in relation to the network or service concerned, non-discriminatory, proportionate and transparent.

2. Specific obligations which may be imposed on providers of electronic communications networks and services under Articles 5(1), 5(2), 6 and 8 of Directive 2002/19/EC (Access Directive) and Articles 16, 17, 18 and 19 of Directive 2002/22/EC (Universal Service Directive) or on those designated to provide universal service under the said Directive shall be legally separate from the rights and obligations under the general authorisation. In order to achieve transparency for undertakings, the criteria and procedures for imposing such specific obligations on individual undertakings shall be referred to in the general authorisation.

3. The general authorisation shall only contain conditions which are specific for that sector and are set out in Part A of the Annex and shall not duplicate conditions which are applicable to undertakings by virtue of other national legislation.

4. Member States shall not duplicate the conditions of the general authorisation where they grant the right of use for radio frequencies or numbers.

[4609]

Article 7

Procedure for limiting the number of rights of use to be granted for radio frequencies

1. Where a Member State is considering whether to limit the number of rights of use to be granted for radio frequencies, it shall *inter alia*—

(a) give due weight to the need to maximise benefits for users and to facilitate the development of competition;

(b) give all interested parties, including users and consumers, the opportunity to express their views on any limitation in accordance with Article 6 of Directive 2002/21/EC (Framework Directive);

(c) publish any decision to limit the granting of rights of use, stating the reasons therefor;

(d) after having determined the procedure, invite applications for rights of use; and

(e) review the limitation at reasonable intervals or at the reasonable request of affected undertakings.

2. Where a Member State concludes that further rights of use for radio frequencies can be granted, it shall publish that conclusion and invite applications for such rights.

3. Where the granting of rights of use for radio frequencies needs to be limited, Member States shall grant such rights on the basis of selection criteria which must be objective, transparent, non-discriminatory and proportionate. Any such selection criteria must give due weight to the achievement of the objectives of Article 8 of Directive 2002/21/EC (Framework Directive).

4. Where competitive or comparative selection procedures are to be used, Member States may extend the maximum period of six weeks referred to in Article 5(3) for as long as

necessary to ensure that such procedures are fair, reasonable, open and transparent to all interested parties, but by no longer than eight months.

These time limits shall be without prejudice to any applicable international agreements relating to the use of radio frequencies and satellite coordination.

5. This Article is without prejudice to the transfer of rights of use for radio frequencies in accordance with Article 9 of Directive 2002/21/EC (Framework Directive).

[4610]

Article 8

Harmonised assignment of radio frequencies

Where the usage of radio frequencies has been harmonised, access conditions and procedures have been agreed, and undertakings to which the radio frequencies shall be assigned have been selected in accordance with international agreements and Community rules, Member States shall grant the right of use for such radio frequencies in accordance therewith. Provided that all national conditions attached to the right to use the radio frequencies concerned have been satisfied in the case of a common selection procedure, Member States shall not impose any further conditions, additional criteria or procedures which would restrict, alter or delay the correct implementation of the common assignment of such radio frequencies.

[4611]

Article 9

Declarations to facilitate the exercise of rights to install facilities and rights of interconnection

At the request of an undertaking, national regulatory authorities shall, within one week, issue standardised declarations, confirming, where applicable, that the undertaking has submitted a notification under Article 3(2) and detailing under what circumstances any undertaking providing electronic communications networks or services under the general authorisation has the right to apply for rights to install facilities, negotiate interconnection, and/or obtain access or interconnection in order to facilitate the exercise of those rights for instance at other levels of government or in relation to other undertakings. Where appropriate such declarations may also be issued as an automatic reply following the notification referred to in Article 3(2).

[4612]

Article 10

Compliance with the conditions of the general authorisation or of rights of use and with specific obligations

1. National regulatory authorities may require undertakings providing electronic communications networks or services covered by the general authorisation or enjoying rights of use for radio frequencies or numbers to provide information necessary to verify compliance with the conditions of the general authorisation or of rights of use or with the specific obligations referred to in Article 6(2), in accordance with Article 11.

2. Where a national regulatory authority finds that an undertaking does not comply with one or more of the conditions of the general authorisation, or of rights of use or with the specific obligations referred to in Article 6(2), it shall notify the undertaking of those findings and give the undertaking a reasonable opportunity to state its views or remedy any breaches within—

- — one month after notification, or
- — a shorter period agreed by the undertaking or stipulated by the national regulatory authority in case of repeated breaches, or
- — a longer period decided by the national regulatory authority.

3. If the undertaking concerned does not remedy the breaches within the period as referred to in paragraph 2, the relevant authority shall take appropriate and proportionate measures aimed at ensuring compliance. In this regard, Member States may empower the relevant authorities to impose financial penalties where appropriate. The measures and the reasons on which they are based shall be communicated to the undertaking concerned within one week of their adoption and shall stipulate a reasonable period for the undertaking to comply with the measure.

4. Notwithstanding the provisions of paragraphs 2 and 3, Member States may empower the relevant authority to impose financial penalties where appropriate on undertakings for

PART VI TELECOMMUNICATIONS

failure to provide information in accordance with obligations imposed under Article 11(1)(a) or (b) of this Directive or Article 9 of Directive 2002/19/EC (Access Directive) within a reasonable period stipulated by the national regulatory authority.

5. In cases of serious and repeated breaches of the conditions of the general authorisation, the rights of use or specific obligations referred to in Article 6(2), where measures aimed at ensuring compliance as referred to in paragraph 3 of this Article have failed, national regulatory authorities may prevent an undertaking from continuing to provide electronic communications networks or services or suspend or withdraw rights of use.

6. Irrespective of the provisions of paragraphs 2, 3 and 5, where the relevant authority has evidence of a breach of the conditions of the general authorisation, rights of use or specific obligations referred to in Article 6(2) that represents an immediate and serious threat to public safety, public security or public health or will create serious economic or operational problems for other providers or users of electronic communications networks or services, it may take urgent interim measures to remedy the situation in advance of reaching a final decision. The undertaking concerned shall thereafter be given a reasonable opportunity to state its view and propose any remedies. Where appropriate, the relevant authority may confirm the interim measures.

7. Undertakings shall have the right to appeal against measures taken under this Article in accordance with the procedure referred to in Article 4 of Directive 2002/21/EC (Framework Directive).

[4613]

Article 11

Information required under the general authorisation, for rights of use and for the specific obligations

1. Without prejudice to information and reporting obligations under national legislation other than the general authorisation, national regulatory authorities may only require undertakings to provide information under the general authorisation, for rights of use or the specific obligations referred to in Article 6(2) that is proportionate and objectively justified for—

(a) systematic or case-by-case verification of compliance with conditions 1 and 2 of Part A, condition 6 of Part B and condition 7 of Part C of the Annex and of compliance with obligations as referred to in Article 6(2);
(b) case-by-case verification of compliance with conditions as set out in the Annex where a complaint has been received or where the national regulatory authority has other reasons to believe that a condition is not complied with or in case of an investigation by the national regulatory authority on its own initiative;
(c) procedures for and assessment of requests for granting rights of use;
(d) publication of comparative overviews of quality and price of services for the benefit of consumers;
(e) clearly defined statistical purposes;
(f) market analysis for the purposes of Directive 2002/19/EC (Access Directive) or Directive 2002/22/EC (Universal Service Directive).

The information referred to in points (a), (b), (d), (e) and (f) of the first subparagraph may not be required prior to or as a condition for market access.

2. Where national regulatory authorities require undertakings to provide information as referred to in paragraph 1, they shall inform them of the specific purpose for which this information is to be used.

[4614]

Article 12

Administrative charges

1. Any administrative charges imposed on undertakings providing a service or a network under the general authorisation or to whom a right of use has been granted shall—

(a) in total, cover only the administrative costs which will be incurred in the management, control and enforcement of the general authorisation scheme and of rights of use and of specific obligations as referred to in Article 6(2), which may include costs for international cooperation, harmonisation and standardisation, market analysis, monitoring compliance and other market control, as well as regulatory work involving preparation and enforcement of secondary legislation and administrative decisions, such as decisions on access and interconnection; and

(b) be imposed upon the individual undertakings in an objective, transparent and proportionate manner which minimises additional administrative costs and attendant charges.

2. Where national regulatory authorities impose administrative charges, they shall publish a yearly overview of their administrative costs and of the total sum of the charges collected. In the light of the difference between the total sum of the charges and the administrative costs, appropriate adjustments shall be made.

[4615]

Article 13

Fees for rights of use and rights to install facilities

Member States may allow the relevant authority to impose fees for the rights of use for radio frequencies or numbers or rights to install facilities on, over or under public or private property which reflect the need to ensure the optimal use of these resources. Member States shall ensure that such fees shall be objectively justified, transparent, non-discriminatory and proportionate in relation to their intended purpose and shall take into account the objectives in Article 8 of Directive 2002/21/EC (Framework Directive).

[4616]

Article 14

Amendment of rights and obligations

1. Member States shall ensure that the rights, conditions and procedures concerning general authorisations and rights of use or rights to install facilities may only be amended in objectively justified cases and in a proportionate manner. Notice shall be given in an appropriate manner of the intention to make such amendments and interested parties, including users and consumers, shall be allowed a sufficient period of time to express their views on the proposed amendments, which shall be no less than four weeks except in exceptional circumstances.

2. Member States shall not restrict or withdraw rights to install facilities before expiry of the period for which they were granted except where justified and where applicable in conformity with relevant national provisions regarding compensation for withdrawal of rights.

[4617]

Article 15

Publication of information

1. Member States shall ensure that all relevant information on rights, conditions, procedures, charges, fees and decisions concerning general authorisations and rights of use is published and kept up to date in an appropriate manner so as to provide easy access to that information for all interested parties.

2. Where information as referred to in paragraph 1 is held at different levels of government, in particular information regarding procedures and conditions on rights to install facilities, the national regulatory authority shall make all reasonable efforts, bearing in mind the costs involved, to create a user-friendly overview of all such information, including information on the relevant levels of government and the responsible authorities, in order to facilitate applications for rights to install facilities.

[4618]

Article 16

Review procedures

The Commission shall periodically review the functioning of the national authorisation systems and the development of cross-border service provision within the Community and report to the European Parliament and to the Council on the first occasion not later than three years after the date of application of this Directive referred to in Article 18(1), second subparagraph. For this purpose, the Commission may request from the Member States information, which shall be supplied without undue delay.

[4619]

Article 17

Existing authorisations

1. Member States shall bring authorisations already in existence on the date of entry into force of this Directive into line with the provisions of this Directive by at the latest the date of application referred to in Article 18(1), second subparagraph.

2. Where application of paragraph 1 results in a reduction of the rights or an extension of the obligations under authorisations already in existence, Member States may extend the validity of those rights and obligations until at the latest nine months after the date of application referred to in Article 18(1), second subparagraph, provided that the rights of other undertakings under Community law are not affected thereby. Member States shall notify such extensions to the Commission and state the reasons therefor.

3. Where the Member State concerned can prove that the abolition of an authorisation condition regarding access to electronic communications networks, which was in force before the date of entry into force of this Directive, creates excessive difficulties for undertakings that have benefited from mandated access to another network, and where it is not possible for these undertakings to negotiate new agreements on reasonable commercial terms before the date of application referred to in Article 18(1), second subparagraph, Member States may request a temporary prolongation of the relevant condition(s). Such requests shall be submitted by the date of application referred to in Article 18(1), second subparagraph, at the latest, and shall specify the condition(s) and period for which the temporary prolongation is requested.

The Member State shall inform the Commission of the reasons for requesting a prolongation. The Commission shall consider such a request, taking into account the particular situation in that Member State and of the undertaking(s) concerned, and the need to ensure a coherent regulatory environment at a Community level. It shall take a decision on whether to grant or reject the request, and where it decides to grant the request, on the scope and duration of the prolongation to be granted. The Commission shall communicate its decision to the Member State concerned within six months after receipt of the application for a prolongation. Such decisions shall be published in the *Official Journal of the European Communities.*

[4620]

Article 18

Transposition

1. Member States shall adopt and publish the laws, regulations and administrative provisions necessary to comply with this Directive by 24 July 2003 at the latest. They shall forthwith inform the Commission thereof.

They shall apply those measures from 25 July 2003.

When Member States adopt these measures, they shall contain a reference to this Directive or be accompanied by such reference on the occasion of their official publication. The methods of making such reference shall be laid down by Member States.

2. Member States shall communicate to the Commission the text of the provisions of national law which they adopt in the field governed by this Directive and of any subsequent amendments to those provisions.

[4621]

Article 19

Entry into force

This Directive shall enter into force on the day of its publication in the *Official Journal of the European Communities.*

[4622]

Article 20

Addressees

This Directive is addressed to the Member States.

[4623]

Done at Brussels, 7 March 2002.

ANNEX

The conditions listed in this Annex provide the maximum list of conditions which may be attached to general authorisations (Part A), rights to use radio frequencies (Part B) and rights to use numbers (Part C) as referred to in Article 6(1) and Article 11(1)(a).

A. **Conditions which may be attached to a general authorisation**

1. Financial contributions to the funding of universal service in conformity with Directive 2002/22/EC (Universal Service Directive).
2. Administrative charges in accordance with Article 12 of this Directive.
3. Interoperability of services and interconnection of networks in conformity with Directive 2002/19/EC (Access Directive).
4. Accessibility of numbers from the national numbering plan to end-users including conditions in conformity with Directive 2002/22/EC (Universal Service Directive).
5. Environmental and town and country planning requirements, as well as requirements and conditions linked to the granting of access to or use of public or private land and conditions linked to co-location and facility sharing in conformity with Directive 2002/22/EC (Framework Directive) and including, where applicable, any financial or technical guarantees necessary to ensure the proper execution of infrastructure works.
6. "Must carry" obligations in conformity with Directive 2002/22/EC (Universal Service Directive).
7. Personal data and privacy protection specific to the electronic communications sector in conformity with Directive 97/66/EC of the European Parliament and of the Council of 15 December 1997 concerning the processing of personal data and the protection of privacy in the telecommunications sector.[1]
8. Consumer protection rules specific to the electronic communications sector including conditions in conformity with Directive 2002/22/EC (Universal Service Directive).
9. Restrictions in relation to the transmission of illegal content, in accordance with Directive 2000/31/EC of the European Parliament and of the Council of 8 June 2000 on certain legal aspects of information society services, in particular electronic commerce, in the internal market[2] and restrictions in relation to the transmission of harmful content in accordance with Article 2a(2) of Council Directive 89/552/EEC of 3 October 1989 on the coordination of certain provisions laid down by law, regulation or administrative action in Member States concerning the pursuit of television broadcasting activities.[3]
10. Information to be provided under a notification procedure in accordance with Article 3(3) of this Directive and for other purposes as included in Article 11 of this Directive.
11. Enabling of legal interception by competent national authorities in conformity with Directive 97/66/EC and Directive 95/46/EC of the European Parliament and of the Council of 24 October 1995 on the protection of individuals with regard to the processing of personal data and on the free movement of such data.[4]
12. Terms of use during major disasters to ensure communications between emergency services and authorities and broadcasts to the general public.
13. Measures regarding the limitation of exposure of the general public to electromagnetic fields caused by electronic communications networks in accordance with Community law.
14. Access obligations other than those provided for in Article 6(2) of this Directive applying to undertakings providing electronic communications networks or services, in conformity with Directive 2002/19/EC (Access Directive).
15. Maintenance of the integrity of public communications networks in accordance with Directive 2002/19/EC (Access Directive) and Directive 2002/22/EC (Universal Service Directive) including by conditions to prevent electromagnetic interference between electronic communications networks and/or services in accordance with Council Directive 89/336/EEC of 3 May 1989 on the approximation of the laws of the Member States relating to electromagnetic compatibility.[5]
16. Security of public networks against unauthorised access according to Directive 97/66/EC.
17. Conditions for the use of radio frequencies, in conformity with Article 7(2) of Directive 1999/5/EC, where such use is not made subject to the granting of individual rights of use in accordance with Article 5(1) of this Directive.

PART VI TELECOMMUNICATIONS

18. Measures designed to ensure compliance with the standards and/or specifications referred to in Article 17 of Directive 2002/21/EC (Framework Directive).

B. **Conditions which may be attached to rights of use for radio frequencies**

1. Designation of service or type of network or technology for which the rights of use for the frequency has been granted, including, where applicable, the exclusive use of a frequency for the transmission of specific content or specific audiovisual services.
2. Effective and efficient use of frequencies in conformity with Directive 2002/21/EC (Framework Directive), including, where appropriate, coverage requirements.
3. Technical and operational conditions necessary for the avoidance of harmful interference and for the limitation of exposure of the general public to electromagnetic fields, where such conditions are different from those included in the general authorisation.
4. Maximum duration in conformity with Article 5 of this Directive, subject to any changes in the national frequency plan.
5. Transfer of rights at the initiative of the right holder and conditions for such transfer in conformity with Directive 2002/21/EC (Framework Directive).
6. Usage fees in accordance with Article 13 of this Directive.
7. Any commitments which the undertaking obtaining the usage right has made in the course of a competitive or comparative selection procedure.
8. Obligations under relevant international agreements relating to the use of frequencies.

C. **Conditions which may be attached to rights of use for numbers**

1. Designation of service for which the number shall be used, including any requirements linked to the provision of that service.
2. Effective and efficient use of numbers in conformity with Directive 2002/21/EC (Framework Directive).
3. Number portability requirements in conformity with Directive 2002/22/EC (Universal Service Directive).
4. Obligation to provide public directory subscriber information for the purposes of Articles 5 and 25 of Directive 2002/22/EC (Universal Service Directive).
5. Maximum duration in conformity with Article 5 of this Directive, subject to any changes in the national numbering plan.
6. Transfer of rights at the initiative of the right holder and conditions for such transfer in conformity with Directive 2002/21/EC (Framework Directive).
7. Usage fees in accordance with Article 13 of this Directive.
8. Any commitments which the undertaking obtaining the usage right has made in the course of a competitive or comparative selection procedure.
9. Obligations under relevant international agreements relating to the use of numbers.

[4624]

NOTES

[1] OJ L24, 30.1.1998, p 1.

[2] OJ L178, 17.7.2000, p 1.

[3] OJ L298, 17.10.1989, p 23. Directive as amended by Directive 97/36/EC of the European Parliament and of the Council (OJ L202, 30.7.1997, p 60).

[4] OJ L281, 23.11.1995, p 31.

[5] OJ L139, 23.5.1989, p 19. Directive as last amended by Directive 93/68/EEC (OJ L220, 30.8.1993, p 1).

DIRECTIVE OF THE EUROPEAN PARLIAMENT AND OF THE COUNCIL

of 7 March 2002

on a common regulatory framework for electronic communications networks and services (Framework Directive)

(2002/21/EC)

THE EUROPEAN PARLIAMENT AND THE COUNCIL OF THE EUROPEAN UNION,

Having regard to the Treaty establishing the European Community, and in particular Article 95 thereof,

Having regard to the proposal from the Commission,[1]

Having regard to the opinion of the Economic and Social Committee,[2]

Acting in accordance with the procedure laid down in Article 251 of the Treaty,[3]

Whereas—

(1) The current regulatory framework for telecommunications has been successful in creating the conditions for effective competition in the telecommunications sector during the transition from monopoly to full competition.

(2) On 10 November 1999, the Commission presented a communication to the European Parliament, the Council, the Economic and Social Committee and the Committee of the Regions entitled "Towards a new framework for electronic communications infrastructure and associated services – the 1999 communications review". In that communication, the Commission reviewed the existing regulatory framework for telecommunications, in accordance with its obligation under Article 8 of Council Directive 90/387/EEC of 28 June 1990 on the establishment of the internal market for telecommunications services through the implementation of open network provision.[4] It also presented a series of policy proposals for a new regulatory framework for electronic communications infrastructure and associated services for public consultation.

(3) On 26 April 2000 the Commission presented a communication to the European Parliament, the Council, the Economic and Social Committee and the Committee of the Regions on the results of the public consultation on the 1999 communications review and orientations for the new regulatory framework. The communication summarised the public consultation and set out certain key orientations for the preparation of a new framework for electronic communications infrastructure and associated services.

(4) The Lisbon European Council of 23 and 24 March 2000 highlighted the potential for growth, competitiveness and job creation of the shift to a digital, knowledge-based economy. In particular, it emphasised the importance for Europe's businesses and citizens of access to an inexpensive, world-class communications infrastructure and a wide range of services.

(5) The convergence of the telecommunications, media and information technology sectors means all transmission networks and services should be covered by a single regulatory framework. That regulatory framework consists of this Directive and four specific Directives: Directive 2002/20/EC of the European Parliament and of the Council of 7 March 2002 on the authorisation of electronic communications networks and services (Authorisation Directive),[5] Directive 2002/19/EC of the European Parliament and of the Council of 7 March 2002 on access to, and interconnection of, electronic communications networks and associated facilities (Access Directive),[6] Directive 2002/22/EC of the European Parliament and of the Council of 7 March 2002 on universal service and users' rights relating to electronic communications networks and services (Universal Service Directive),[7] Directive 97/66/EC of the European Parliament and of the Council of 15 December 1997 concerning the processing of personal data and the protection of privacy in the telecommunications sector,[8] (hereinafter referred to as "the Specific Directives"). It is necessary to separate the regulation of transmission from the regulation of content. This framework does not therefore cover the content services delivered over electronic communications networks using electronic communications services, such as broadcasting content, financial services and certain information society services, and is therefore without prejudice to measures taken at Community or national level in respect of such services, in compliance with Community law, in order to promote cultural and linguistic diversity and to ensure the defence of media pluralism. The content of television programmes is covered by Council Directive 89/552/EEC of 3 October 1989 on the coordination of certain provisions laid down by law, regulation or administrative action in Member States concerning the pursuit of television broadcasting activities.[9] The separation between the regulation of transmission and the regulation of

content does not prejudice the taking into account of the links existing between them, in particular in order to guarantee media pluralism, cultural diversity and consumer protection.

(6) Audiovisual policy and content regulation are undertaken in pursuit of general interest objectives, such as freedom of expression, media pluralism, impartiality, cultural and linguistic diversity, social inclusion, consumer protection and the protection of minors. The Commission communication "Principles and guidelines for the Community's audio-visual policy in the digital age", and the Council conclusions of 6 June 2000 welcoming this communication, set out the key actions to be taken by the Community to implement its audio-visual policy.

(7) The provisions of this Directive and the Specific Directives are without prejudice to the possibility for each Member State to take the necessary measures to ensure the protection of its essential security interests, to safeguard public policy and public security, and to permit the investigation, detection and prosecution of criminal offences, including the establishment by national regulatory authorities of specific and proportional obligations applicable to providers of electronic communications services.

(8) This Directive does not cover equipment within the scope of Directive 1999/5/EC of the European Parliament and of the Council of 9 March 1999 on radio equipment and telecommunications terminal equipment and the mutual recognition of their conformity,[10] but does cover consumer equipment used for digital television. It is important for regulators to encourage network operators and terminal equipment manufacturers to cooperate in order to facilitate access by disabled users to electronic communications services.

(9) Information society services are covered by Directive 2000/31/EC of the European Parliament and of the Council of 8 June 2000 on certain legal aspects of information society services, in particular electronic commerce, in the internal market (Directive on electronic commerce).[11]

(10) The definition of "information society service" in Article 1 of Directive 98/34/EC of the European Parliament and of the Council of 22 June 1998 laying down a procedure for the provision of information in the field of technical standards and regulations and of rules of information society services[12] spans a wide range of economic activities which take place on-line. Most of these activities are not covered by the scope of this Directive because they do not consist wholly or mainly in the conveyance of signals on electronic communications networks. Voice telephony and electronic mail conveyance services are covered by this Directive. The same undertaking, for example an Internet service provider, can offer both an electronic communications service, such as access to the Internet, and services not covered under this Directive, such as the provision of web-based content.

(11) In accordance with the principle of the separation of regulatory and operational functions, Member States should guarantee the independence of the national regulatory authority or authorities with a view to ensuring the impartiality of their decisions. This requirement of independence is without prejudice to the institutional autonomy and constitutional obligations of the Member States or to the principle of neutrality with regard to the rules in Member States governing the system of property ownership laid down in Article 295 of the Treaty. National regulatory authorities should be in possession of all the necessary resources, in terms of staffing, expertise, and financial means, for the performance of their tasks.

(12) Any party who is the subject of a decision by a national regulatory authority should have the right to appeal to a body that is independent of the parties involved. This body may be a court. Furthermore, any undertaking which considers that its applications for the granting of rights to install facilities have not been dealt with in accordance with the principles set out in this Directive should be entitled to appeal against such decisions. This appeal procedure is without prejudice to the division of competences within national judicial systems and to the rights of legal entities or natural persons under national law.

(13) National regulatory authorities need to gather information from market players in order to carry out their tasks effectively. Such information may also need to be gathered on behalf of the Commission, to allow it to fulfil its obligations under Community law. Requests for information should be proportionate and not impose an undue burden on undertakings. Information gathered by national regulatory authorities should be publicly available, except in so far as it is confidential in accordance with national rules on public access to information and subject to Community and national law on business confidentiality.

(14) Information that is considered confidential by a national regulatory authority, in accordance with Community and national rules on business confidentiality, may only be exchanged with the Commission and other national regulatory authorities where such exchange is strictly necessary for the application of the provisions of this Directive or the Specific Directives. The information exchanged should be limited to that which is relevant and proportionate to the purpose of such an exchange.

(15) It is important that national regulatory authorities consult all interested parties on proposed decisions and take account of their comments before adopting a final decision. In order to ensure that decisions at national level do not have an adverse effect on the single market or other Treaty objectives, national regulatory authorities should also notify certain draft decisions to the Commission and other national regulatory authorities to give them the opportunity to comment. It is appropriate for national regulatory authorities to consult interested parties on all draft measures which have an effect on trade between Member States. The cases where the procedures referred to in Articles 6 and 7 apply are defined in this Directive and in the Specific Directives. The Commission should be able, after consulting the Communications Committee, to require a national regulatory authority to withdraw a draft measure where it concerns definition of relevant markets or the designation or not of undertakings with significant market power, and where such decisions would create a barrier to the single market or would be incompatible with Community law and in particular the policy objectives that national regulatory authorities should follow. This procedure is without prejudice to the notification procedure provided for in Directive 98/34/EC and the Commission's prerogatives under the Treaty in respect of infringements of Community law.

(16) National regulatory authorities should have a harmonised set of objectives and principles to underpin, and should, where necessary, coordinate their actions with the regulatory authorities of other Member States in carrying out their tasks under this regulatory framework.

(17) The activities of national regulatory authorities established under this Directive and the Specific Directives contribute to the fulfilment of broader policies in the areas of culture, employment, the environment, social cohesion and town and country planning.

(18) The requirement for Member States to ensure that national regulatory authorities take the utmost account of the desirability of making regulation technologically neutral, that is to say that it neither imposes nor discriminates in favour of the use of a particular type of technology, does not preclude the taking of proportionate steps to promote certain specific services where this is justified, for example digital television as a means for increasing spectrum efficiency.

(19) Radio frequencies are an essential input for radio-based electronic communications services and, in so far as they relate to such services, should therefore be allocated and assigned by national regulatory authorities according to a set of harmonised objectives and principles governing their action as well as to objective, transparent and non-discriminatory criteria, taking into account the democratic, social, linguistic and cultural interests related to the use of frequency. It is important that the allocation and assignment of radio frequencies is managed as efficiently as possible. Transfer of radio frequencies can be an effective means of increasing efficient use of spectrum, as long as there are sufficient safeguards in place to protect the public interest, in particular the need to ensure transparency and regulatory supervision of such transfers. Decision No 676/2002/EC of the European Parliament and of the Council of 7 March 2002 on a regulatory framework for radio spectrum policy in the European Community (Radio Spectrum Decision)[13] establishes a framework for harmonisation of radio frequencies, and action taken under this Directive should seek to facilitate the work under that Decision.

(20) Access to numbering resources on the basis of transparent, objective and non-discriminatory criteria is essential for undertakings to compete in the electronic communications sector. All elements of national numbering plans should be managed by national regulatory authorities, including point codes used in network addressing. Where there is a need for harmonisation of numbering resources in the Community to support the development of pan-European services, the Commission may take technical implementing measures using its executive powers. Where this is appropriate to ensure full global interoperability of services, Member States should coordinate their national positions in accordance with the Treaty in international organisations and fora where numbering decisions are taken. The provisions of this Directive do not establish any new areas of responsibility for the national regulatory authorities in the field of Internet naming and addressing.

(21) Member States may use, *inter alia*, competitive or comparative selection procedures for the assignment of radio frequencies as well as numbers with exceptional economic value. In administering such schemes, national regulatory authorities should take into account the provisions of Article 8.

(22) It should be ensured that procedures exist for the granting of rights to install facilities that are timely, non-discriminatory and transparent, in order to guarantee the conditions for fair and effective competition. This Directive is without prejudice to national provisions governing the expropriation or use of property, the normal exercise of property rights, the normal use of the public domain, or to the principle of neutrality with regard to the rules in Member States governing the system of property ownership.

(23) Facility sharing can be of benefit for town planning, public health or environmental reasons, and should be encouraged by national regulatory authorities on the basis of voluntary agreements. In cases where undertakings are deprived of access to viable alternatives, compulsory facility or property sharing may be appropriate. It covers *inter alia*: physical co-location and duct, building, mast, antenna or antenna system sharing. Compulsory facility or property sharing should be imposed on undertakings only after full public consultation.

(24) Where mobile operators are required to share towers or masts for environmental reasons, such mandated sharing may lead to a reduction in the maximum transmitted power levels allowed for each operator for reasons of public health, and this in turn may require operators to install more transmission sites to ensure national coverage.

(25) There is a need for *ex ante* obligations in certain circumstances in order to ensure the development of a competitive market. The definition of significant market power in the Directive 97/33/EC of the European Parliament and of the Council of 30 June 1997 on interconnection in telecommunications with regard to ensuring universal service and interoperability through application of the principles of open network provision (ONP)[14] has proved effective in the initial stages of market opening as the threshold for *ex ante* obligations, but now needs to be adapted to suit more complex and dynamic markets. For this reason, the definition used in this Directive is equivalent to the concept of dominance as defined in the case law of the Court of Justice and the Court of First Instance of the European Communities.

(26) Two or more undertakings can be found to enjoy a joint dominant position not only where there exist structural or other links between them but also where the structure of the relevant market is conducive to coordinated effects, that is, it encourages parallel or aligned anti-competitive behaviour on the market.

(27) It is essential that *ex ante* regulatory obligations should only be imposed where there is not effective competition, ie in markets where there are one or more undertakings with significant market power, and where national and Community competition law remedies are not sufficient to address the problem. It is necessary therefore for the Commission to draw up guidelines at Community level in accordance with the principles of competition law for national regulatory authorities to follow in assessing whether competition is effective in a given market and in assessing significant market power. National regulatory authorities should analyse whether a given product or service market is effectively competitive in a given geographical area, which could be the whole or a part of the territory of the Member State concerned or neighbouring parts of territories of Member States considered together. An analysis of effective competition should include an analysis as to whether the market is prospectively competitive, and thus whether any lack of effective competition is durable. Those guidelines will also address the issue of newly emerging markets, where de facto the market leader is likely to have a substantial market share but should not be subjected to inappropriate obligations. The Commission should review the guidelines regularly to ensure that they remain appropriate in a rapidly developing market. National regulatory authorities will need to cooperate with each other where the relevant market is found to be transnational.

(28) In determining whether an undertaking has significant market power in a specific market, national regulatory authorities should act in accordance with Community law and take into the utmost account the Commission guidelines.

(29) The Community and the Member States have entered into commitments in relation to standards and the regulatory framework of telecommunications networks and services in the World Trade Organisation.

(30) Standardisation should remain primarily a market-driven process. However there may still be situations where it is appropriate to require compliance with specified standards at Community level to ensure interoperability in the single market. At national level, Member States are subject to the provisions of Directive 98/34/EC. Directive 95/47/EC of the European Parliament and of the Council of 24 October 1995 on the use of standards for the transmission of television signals[15] did not mandate any specific digital television transmission system or service requirement. Through the Digital Video Broadcasting Group, European market players have developed a family of television transmission systems that have been standardised by the European Telecommunications Standards Institute (ETSI) and have become International Telecommunication Union recommendations. Any decision to make the implementation of such standards mandatory should follow a full public consultation. Standardisation procedures under this Directive are without prejudice to the provisions of Directive 1999/5/EC, Council Directive 73/23/EEC of 19 February 1973 on the harmonisation of the laws of Member States relating to electrical equipment designed for use within certain voltage limits[16] and Council Directive 89/336/EEC of 3 May 1989 on the approximation of the laws of the Member States relating to electromagnetic compatibility.[17]

(31) Interoperability of digital interactive television services and enhanced digital television equipment, at the level of the consumer, should be encouraged in order to ensure the free flow of information, media pluralism and cultural diversity. It is desirable for

consumers to have the capability of receiving, regardless of the transmission mode, all digital interactive television services, having regard to technological neutrality, future technological progress, the need to promote the take-up of digital television, and the state of competition in the markets for digital television services. Digital interactive television platform operators should strive to implement an open application program interface (API) which conforms to standards or specifications adopted by a European standards organisation. Migration from existing APIs to new open APIs should be encouraged and organised, for example by Memoranda of Understanding between all relevant market players. Open APIs facilitate interoperability, ie the portability of interactive content between delivery mechanisms, and full functionality of this content on enhanced digital television equipment. However, the need not to hinder the functioning of the receiving equipment and to protect it from malicious attacks, for example from viruses, should be taken into account.

(32) In the event of a dispute between undertakings in the same Member State in an area covered by this Directive or the Specific Directives, for example relating to obligations for access and interconnection or to the means of transferring subscriber lists, an aggrieved party that has negotiated in good faith but failed to reach agreement should be able to call on the national regulatory authority to resolve the dispute. National regulatory authorities should be able to impose a solution on the parties. The intervention of a national regulatory authority in the resolution of a dispute between undertakings providing electronic communications networks or services in a Member State should seek to ensure compliance with the obligations arising under this Directive or the Specific Directives.

(33) In addition to the rights of recourse granted under national or Community law, there is a need for a simple procedure to be initiated at the request of either party in a dispute, to resolve cross-border disputes which lie outside the competence of a single national regulatory authority.

(34) A single Committee should replace the "ONP Committee" instituted by Article 9 of Directive 90/387/EEC and the Licensing Committee instituted by Article 14 of Directive 97/13/ EC of the European Parliament and of the Council of 10 April 1997 on a common framework for general authorisations and individual licences in the field of telecommunications services.[18]

(35) National regulatory authorities and national competition authorities should provide each other with the information necessary to apply the provisions of this Directive and the Specific Directives, in order to allow them to cooperate fully together. In respect of the information exchanged, the receiving authority should ensure the same level of confidentiality as the originating authority.

(36) The Commission has indicated its intention to set up a European regulators group for electronic communications networks and services which would constitute a suitable mechanism for encouraging cooperation and coordination of national regulatory authorities, in order to promote the development of the internal market for electronic communications networks and services, and to seek to achieve consistent application, in all Member States, of the provisions set out in this Directive and the Specific Directives, in particular in areas where national law implementing Community law gives national regulatory authorities considerable discretionary powers in application of the relevant rules.

(37) National regulatory authorities should be required to cooperate with each other and with the Commission in a transparent manner to ensure consistent application, in all Member States, of the provisions of this Directive and the Specific Directives. This cooperation could take place, *inter alia*, in the Communications Committee or in a group comprising European regulators. Member States should decide which bodies are national regulatory authorities for the purposes of this Directive and the Specific Directives.

(38) Measures that could affect trade between Member States are measures that may have an influence, direct or indirect, actual or potential, on the pattern of trade between Member States in a manner which might create a barrier to the single market. They comprise measures that have a significant impact on operators or users in other Member States, which include, *inter alia*: measures which affect prices for users in other Member States; measures which affect the ability of an undertaking established in another Member State to provide an electronic communications service, and in particular measures which affect the ability to offer services on a transnational basis; and measures which affect market structure or access, leading to repercussions for undertakings in other Member States.

(39) The provisions of this Directive should be reviewed periodically, in particular with a view to determining the need for modification in the light of changing technological or market conditions.

(40) The measures necessary for the implementation of this Directive should be adopted in accordance with Council Decision 1999/468/EC of 28 June 1999 laying down the procedures for the exercise of implementing powers conferred on the Commission.[19]

(41) Since the objectives of the proposed action, namely achieving a harmonised framework for the regulation of electronic communications services, electronic communications networks, associated facilities and associated services cannot be sufficiently achieved by the Member States and can therefore, by reason of the scale and effects of the action, be better achieved at Community level, the Community may adopt measures in accordance with the principle of subsidiarity as set out in Article 5 of the Treaty. In accordance with the principle of proportionality, as set out in that Article, this Directive does not go beyond what is necessary for those objectives.

(42) Certain directives and decisions in this field should be repealed.

(43) The Commission should monitor the transition from the existing framework to the new framework, and may in particular, at an appropriate time, bring forward a proposal to repeal Regulation (EC) No 2887/2000 of the European Parliament and of the Council of 18 December 2000 on unbundled access to the local loop,[20]

NOTES

1 OJ C365E, 19.12.2000, p 198 and OJ C270E, 25.9.2001, p 199.

2 OJ C123, 25.4.2001, p 56.

3 Opinion of the European Parliament of 1 March 2001 (OJ C277, 1.10.2001, p 91), Council Common Position of 17 September 2001 (OJ C337, 30.11.2001, p 34) and Decision of the European Parliament of 12 December 2001 (not yet published in the Official Journal). Council Decision of 14 February 2002.

4 OJ L192, 24.7.1990, p 1. Directive as amended by Directive 97/51/EC of the European Parliament and of the Council (OJ L295, 29.10.1997, p 23).

5 See page 21 of this Official Journal.

6 See page 7 of this Official Journal.

7 See page 51 of this Official Journal.

8 OJ L24, 30.1.1998, p 1.

9 OJ L298, 17.10.1989, p 23. Directive as amended by Directive 97/36/EC of the European Parliament and of the Council (OJ L202, 30.7.1997, p 60).

10 OJ L91, 7.4.1999, p 10.

11 OJ L178, 17.7.2000, p 1.

12 OJ L204, 21.7.1998, p 37. Directive as amended by Directive 98/48/EC (OJ L217, 5.8.1998, p 18).

13 See page 1 of this Official Journal.

14 OJ L199, 26.7.1997, p 32. Directive as amended by Directive 98/61/EC (OJ L268, 3.10.1998, p 37).

15 OJ L281, 23.11.1995, p 51.

16 OJ L77, 26.3.1973, p 29.

17 OJ L139, 23.5.1989, p 19.

18 OJ L117, 7.5.1997, p 15.

19 OJ L184, 17.7.1999, p 23.

20 OJ L336, 30.12.2000, p 4.

HAVE ADOPTED THIS DIRECTIVE—

CHAPTER I
SCOPE, AIM AND DEFINITIONS

Article 1

Scope and aim

1. This Directive establishes a harmonised framework for the regulation of electronic communications services, electronic communications networks, associated facilities and associated services. It lays down tasks of national regulatory authorities and establishes a set of procedures to ensure the harmonised application of the regulatory framework throughout the Community.

2. This Directive as well as the Specific Directives are without prejudice to obligations imposed by national law in accordance with Community law or by Community law in respect of services provided using electronic communications networks and services.

3. This Directive as well as the Specific Directives are without prejudice to measures taken at Community or national level, in compliance with Community law, to pursue general interest objectives, in particular relating to content regulation and audio-visual policy.

4. This Directive and the Specific Directives are without prejudice to the provisions of Directive 1999/5/EC.

[4625]

Article 2

Definitions

For the purposes of this Directive—

(a) "electronic communications network" means transmission systems and, where applicable, switching or routing equipment and other resources which permit the conveyance of signals by wire, by radio, by optical or by other electromagnetic means, including satellite networks, fixed (circuit-and packet-switched, including Internet) and mobile terrestrial networks, electricity cable systems, to the extent that they are used for the purpose of transmitting signals, networks used for radio and television broadcasting, and cable television networks, irrespective of the type of information conveyed;

(b) "transnational markets" means markets identified in accordance with Article 15(4) covering the Community or a substantial part thereof;

(c) "electronic communications service" means a service normally provided for remuneration which consists wholly or mainly in the conveyance of signals on electronic communications networks, including telecommunications services and transmission services in networks used for broadcasting, but exclude services providing, or exercising editorial control over, content transmitted using electronic communications networks and services; it does not include information society services, as defined in Article 1 of Directive 98/34/EC, which do not consist wholly or mainly in the conveyance of signals on electronic communications networks;

(d) "public communications network" means an electronic communications network used wholly or mainly for the provision of publicly available electronic communications services;

(e) "associated facilities" means those facilities associated with an electronic communications network and/or an electronic communications service which enable and/or support the provision of services via that network and/ or service. It includes conditional access systems and electronic programme guides;

(f) "conditional access system" means any technical measure and/or arrangement whereby access to a protected radio or television broadcasting service in intelligible form is made conditional upon subscription or other form of prior individual authorisation;

(g) "national regulatory authority" means the body or bodies charged by a Member State with any of the regulatory tasks assigned in this Directive and the Specific Directives;

(h) "user" means a legal entity or natural person using or requesting a publicly available electronic communications service;

(i) "consumer" means any natural person who uses or requests a publicly available electronic communications service for purposes which are outside his or her trade, business or profession;

(j) "universal service" means the minimum set of services, defined in Directive 2002/22/EC (Universal Service Directive), of specified quality which is available to all users regardless of their geographical location and, in the light of specific national conditions, at an affordable price;

(k) "subscriber" means any natural person or legal entity who or which is party to a contract with the provider of publicly available electronic communications services for the supply of such services;

(l) "Specific Directives" means Directive 2002/20/EC (Authorisation Directive), Directive 2002/19/EC (Access Directive), Directive 2002/22/EC (Universal Service Directive) and Directive 97/66/EC;

(m) "provision of an electronic communications network" means the establishment, operation, control or making available of such a network;

(n) "end-user" means a user not providing public communications networks or publicly available electronic communications services;

(o) "enhanced digital television equipment" means set-top boxes intended for connection to television sets or integrated digital television sets, able to receive digital interactive television services;

(p) "application program interface (API)" means the software interfaces between applications, made available by broadcasters or service providers, and the resources in the enhanced digital television equipment for digital television and radio services.

[4626]

CHAPTER II
NATIONAL REGULATORY AUTHORITIES

Article 3

National regulatory authorities

1. Member States shall ensure that each of the tasks assigned to national regulatory authorities in this Directive and the Specific Directives is undertaken by a competent body.

2. Member States shall guarantee the independence of national regulatory authorities by ensuring that they are legally distinct from and functionally independent of all organisations providing electronic communications networks, equipment or services. Member States that retain ownership or control of undertakings providing electronic communications networks and/or services shall ensure effective structural separation of the regulatory function from activities associated with ownership or control.

3. Member States shall ensure that national regulatory authorities exercise their powers impartially and transparently.

4. Member States shall publish the tasks to be undertaken by national regulatory authorities in an easily accessible form, in particular where those tasks are assigned to more than one body. Member States shall ensure, where appropriate, consultation and cooperation between those authorities, and between those authorities and national authorities entrusted with the implementation of competition law and national authorities entrusted with the implementation of consumer law, on matters of common interest. Where more than one authority has competence to address such matters, Member States shall ensure that the respective tasks of each authority are published in an easily accessible form.

5. National regulatory authorities and national competition authorities shall provide each other with the information necessary for the application of the provisions of this Directive and the Specific Directives. In respect of the information exchanged, the receiving authority shall ensure the same level of confidentiality as the originating authority.

6. Member States shall notify to the Commission all national regulatory authorities assigned tasks under this Directive and the Specific Directives, and their respective responsibilities.

[4627]

Article 4

Right of appeal

1. Member States shall ensure that effective mechanisms exist at national level under which any user or undertaking providing electronic communications networks and/or services who is affected by a decision of a national regulatory authority has the right of appeal against the decision to an appeal body that is independent of the parties involved. This body, which may be a court, shall have the appropriate expertise available to it to enable it to carry out its functions. Member States shall ensure that the merits of the case are duly taken into account and that there is an effective appeal mechanism. Pending the outcome of any such appeal, the decision of the national regulatory authority shall stand, unless the appeal body decides otherwise.

2. Where the appeal body referred to in paragraph 1 is not judicial in character, written reasons for its decision shall always be given. Furthermore, in such a case, its decision shall be subject to review by a court or tribunal within the meaning of Article 234 of the Treaty.

[4628]

Article 5

Provision of information

1. Member States shall ensure that undertakings providing electronic communications networks and services provide all the information, including financial information, necessary for national regulatory authorities to ensure conformity with the provisions of, or decisions made in accordance with, this Directive and the Specific Directives. These undertakings shall provide such information promptly on request and to the timescales and level of detail required by the national regulatory authority. The information requested by the national regulatory authority shall be proportionate to the performance of that task. The national regulatory authority shall give the reasons justifying its request for information.

2. Member States shall ensure that national regulatory authorities provide the Commission, after a reasoned request, with the information necessary for it to carry out its tasks under the Treaty. The information requested by the Commission shall be proportionate to the performance of those tasks. Where the information provided refers to information previously provided by undertakings at the request of the national regulatory authority, such undertakings shall be informed thereof. To the extent necessary, and unless the authority that provides the information has made an explicit and reasoned request to the contrary, the Commission shall make the information provided available to another such authority in another Member State.

Subject to the requirements of paragraph 3, Member States shall ensure that the information submitted to one national regulatory authority can be made available to another such authority in the same or different Member State, after a substantiated request, where necessary to allow either authority to fulfil its responsibilities under Community law.

3. Where information is considered confidential by a national regulatory authority in accordance with Community and national rules on business confidentiality, the Commission and the national regulatory authorities concerned shall ensure such confidentiality.

4. Member States shall ensure that, acting in accordance with national rules on public access to information and subject to Community and national rules on business confidentiality, national regulatory authorities publish such information as would contribute to an open and competitive market.

5. National regulatory authorities shall publish the terms of public access to information as referred to in paragraph 4, including procedures for obtaining such access.

[4629]

Article 6

Consultation and transparency mechanism

Except in cases falling within Articles 7(6), 20 or 21 Member States shall ensure that where national regulatory authorities intend to take measures in accordance with this Directive or the Specific Directives which have a significant impact on the relevant market, they give interested parties the opportunity to comment on the draft measure within a reasonable period. National regulatory authorities shall publish their national consultation procedures. Member States shall ensure the establishment of a single information point through which all current consultations can be accessed. The results of the consultation procedure shall be made publicly available by the national regulatory authority, except in the case of confidential information in accordance with Community and national law on business confidentiality.

[4630]

Article 7

Consolidating the internal market for electronic communications

1. In carrying out their tasks under this Directive and the Specific Directives, national regulatory authorities shall take the utmost account of the objectives set out in Article 8, including in so far as they relate to the functioning of the internal market.

2. National regulatory authorities shall contribute to the development of the internal market by cooperating with each other and with the Commission in a transparent manner to ensure the consistent application, in all Member States, of the provisions of this Directive and the Specific Directives. To this end, they shall, in particular, seek to agree on the types of instruments and remedies best suited to address particular types of situations in the market place.

3. In addition to the consultation referred to in Article 6, where a national regulatory authority intends to take a measure which—

(a) falls within the scope of Articles 15 or 16 of this Directive, Articles 5 or 8 of Directive 2002/19/EC (Access Directive) or Article 16 of Directive 2002/22/EC (Universal Service Directive), and

(b) would affect trade between Member States,

it shall at the same time make the draft measure accessible to the Commission and the national regulatory authorities in other Member States, together with the reasoning on which the measure is based, in accordance with Article 5(3), and inform the Commission and other national regulatory authorities thereof. National regulatory authorities and the Commission may make comments to the national regulatory authority concerned only within one month or within the period referred to in Article 6 if that period is longer. The one-month period may not be extended.

4. Where an intended measure covered by paragraph 3 aims at—

(a) defining a relevant market which differs from those defined in the recommendation in accordance with Article 15(1), or

(b) deciding whether or not to designate an undertaking as having, either individually or jointly with others, significant market power, under Article 16(3), (4) or (5),

and would affect trade between Member States and the Commission has indicated to the national regulatory authority that it considers that the draft measure would create a barrier to the single market or if it has serious doubts as to its compatibility with Community law and in particular the objectives referred to in Article 8, then the draft measure shall not be adopted for a further two months. This period may not be extended. Within this period the Commission may, in accordance with the procedure referred to in Article 22(2), take a decision requiring the national regulatory authority concerned to withdraw the draft measure. This decision shall be accompanied by a detailed and objective analysis of why the Commission considers that the draft measure should not be adopted together with specific proposals for amending the draft measure.

5. The national regulatory authority concerned shall take the utmost account of comments of other national regulatory authorities and the Commission and may, except in cases covered by paragraph 4, adopt the resulting draft measure and, where it does so, shall communicate it to the Commission.

6. In exceptional circumstances, where a national regulatory authority considers that there is an urgent need to act, by way of derogation from the procedure set out in paragraphs 3 and 4, in order to safeguard competition and protect the interests of users, it may immediately adopt proportionate and provisional measures. It shall, without delay, communicate those measures, with full reasons, to the Commission and the other national regulatory authorities. A decision by the national regulatory authority to render such measures permanent or extend the time for which they are applicable shall be subject to the provisions of paragraphs 3 and 4.

[4631]

CHAPTER III
TASKS OF NATIONAL REGULATORY AUTHORITIES

Article 8

Policy objectives and regulatory principles

1. Member States shall ensure that in carrying out the regulatory tasks specified in this Directive and the Specific Directives, the national regulatory authorities take all reasonable measures which are aimed at achieving the objectives set out in paragraphs 2, 3 and 4. Such measures shall be proportionate to those objectives.

Member States shall ensure that in carrying out the regulatory tasks specified in this Directive and the Specific Directives, in particular those designed to ensure effective competition, national regulatory authorities take the utmost account of the desirability of making regulations technologically neutral.

National regulatory authorities may contribute within their competencies to ensuring the implementation of policies aimed at the promotion of cultural and linguistic diversity, as well as media pluralism.

2. The national regulatory authorities shall promote competition in the provision of electronic communications networks, electronic communications services and associated facilities and services by *inter alia*—

(a) ensuring that users, including disabled users, derive maximum benefit in terms of choice, price, and quality;

(b) ensuring that there is no distortion or restriction of competition in the electronic communications sector;

(c) encouraging efficient investment in infrastructure, and promoting innovation; and

(d) encouraging efficient use and ensuring the effective management of radio frequencies and numbering resources.

3. The national regulatory authorities shall contribute to the development of the internal market by *inter alia*—

(a) removing remaining obstacles to the provision of electronic communications networks, associated facilities and services and electronic communications services at European level;
(b) encouraging the establishment and development of trans-European networks and the interoperability of pan-European services, and end-to-end connectivity;
(c) ensuring that, in similar circumstances, there is no discrimination in the treatment of undertakings providing electronic communications networks and services;
(d) cooperating with each other and with the Commission in a transparent manner to ensure the development of consistent regulatory practice and the consistent application of this Directive and the Specific Directives.

4. The national regulatory authorities shall promote the interests of the citizens of the European Union by *inter alia*—
(a) ensuring all citizens have access to a universal service specified in Directive 2002/22/EC (Universal Service Directive);
(b) ensuring a high level of protection for consumers in their dealings with suppliers, in particular by ensuring the availability of simple and inexpensive dispute resolution procedures carried out by a body that is independent of the parties involved;
(c) contributing to ensuring a high level of protection of personal data and privacy;
(d) promoting the provision of clear information, in particular requiring transparency of tariffs and conditions for using publicly available electronic communications services;
(e) addressing the needs of specific social groups, in particular disabled users; and
(f) ensuring that the integrity and security of public communications networks are maintained.

[4632]

Article 9

Management of radio frequencies for electronic communications services

1. Member States shall ensure the effective management of radio frequencies for electronic communication services in their territory in accordance with Article 8. They shall ensure that the allocation and assignment of such radio frequencies by national regulatory authorities are based on objective, transparent, non-discriminatory and proportionate criteria.

2. Member States shall promote the harmonisation of use of radio frequencies across the Community, consistent with the need to ensure effective and efficient use thereof and in accordance with the Decision No 676/2002/EC (Radio Spectrum Decision).

3. Member States may make provision for undertakings to transfer rights to use radio frequencies with other undertakings.

4. Member States shall ensure that an undertaking's intention to transfer rights to use radio frequencies is notified to the national regulatory authority responsible for spectrum assignment and that any transfer takes place in accordance with procedures laid down by the national regulatory authority and is made public. National regulatory authorities shall ensure that competition is not distorted as a result of any such transaction. Where radio frequency use has been harmonised through the application of Decision No 676/2002/EC (Radio Spectrum Decision) or other Community measures, any such transfer shall not result in change of use of that radio frequency.

[4633]

Article 10

Numbering, naming and addressing

1. Member States shall ensure that national regulatory authorities control the assignment of all national numbering resources and the management of the national numbering plans. Member States shall ensure that adequate numbers and numbering ranges are provided for all publicly available electronic communications services. National regulatory authorities shall establish objective, transparent and non-discriminatory assigning procedures for national numbering resources.

2. National regulatory authorities shall ensure that numbering plans and procedures are applied in a manner that gives equal treatment to all providers of publicly available electronic communications services. In particular, Member States shall ensure that an undertaking

allocated a range of numbers does not discriminate against other providers of electronic communications services as regards the number sequences used to give access to their services.

3. Member States shall ensure that the national numbering plans, and all subsequent additions or amendments thereto, are published, subject only to limitations imposed on the grounds of national security.

4. Member States shall support the harmonisation of numbering resources within the Community where that is necessary to support the development of pan European services. The Commission may, in accordance with the procedure referred to in Article 22(3), take the appropriate technical implementing measures on this matter.

5. Where this is appropriate in order to ensure full global interoperability of services, Member States shall coordinate their positions in international organisations and forums in which decisions are taken on issues relating to the numbering, naming and addressing of electronic communications networks and services.

[4634]

Article 11

Rights of way

1. Member States shall ensure that when a competent authority considers—

— an application for the granting of rights to install facilities on, over or under public or private property to an undertaking authorised to provide public communications networks, or

— an application for the granting of rights to install facilities on, over or under public property to an undertaking authorised to provide electronic communications networks other than to the public,

the competent authority—

— acts on the basis of transparent and publicly available procedures, applied without discrimination and without delay, and

— follows the principles of transparency and non-discrimination in attaching conditions to any such rights.

The abovementioned procedures can differ depending on whether the applicant is providing public communications networks or not.

2. Member States shall ensure that where public or local authorities retain ownership or control of undertakings operating electronic communications networks and/or services, there is effective structural separation of the function responsible for granting the rights referred to in paragraph 1 from activities associated with ownership or control.

3. Member States shall ensure that effective mechanisms exist to allow undertakings to appeal against decisions on the granting of rights to install facilities to a body that is independent of the parties involved.

[4635]

Article 12

Co-location and facility sharing

1. Where an undertaking providing electronic communications networks has the right under national legislation to install facilities on, over or under public or private property, or may take advantage of a procedure for the expropriation or use of property, national regulatory authorities shall encourage the sharing of such facilities or property.

2. In particular where undertakings are deprived of access to viable alternatives because of the need to protect the environment, public health, public security or to meet town and country planning objectives, Member States may impose the sharing of facilities or property (including physical co-location) on an undertaking operating an electronic communications network or take measures to facilitate the coordination of public works only after an appropriate period of public consultation during which all interested parties must be given an opportunity to express their views. Such sharing or coordination arrangements may include rules for apportioning the costs of facility or property sharing.

[4636]

Article 13
Accounting separation and financial reports

1. Member States shall require undertakings providing public communications networks or publicly available electronic communications services which have special or exclusive rights for the provision of services in other sectors in the same or another Member State to—

(a) keep separate accounts for the activities associated with the provision of electronic communications networks or services, to the extent that would be required if these activities were carried out by legally independent companies, so as to identify all elements of cost and revenue, with the basis of their calculation and the detailed attribution methods used, related to their activities associated with the provision of electronic communications networks or services including an itemised breakdown of fixed asset and structural costs, or

(b) have structural separation for the activities associated with the provision of electronic communications networks or services.

Member States may choose not to apply the requirements referred to in the first subparagraph to undertakings the annual turnover of which in activities associated with electronic communications networks or services in the Member States is less than EUR 50 million.

2. Where undertakings providing public communications networks or publicly available electronic communications services are not subject to the requirements of company law and do not satisfy the small and medium-sized enterprise criteria of Community law accounting rules, their financial reports shall be drawn up and submitted to independent audit and published. The audit shall be carried out in accordance with the relevant Community and national rules.

This requirement shall also apply to the separate accounts required under paragraph 1(a).
[4637]

CHAPTER IV
GENERAL PROVISIONS

Article 14

Undertakings with significant market power

1. Where the Specific Directives require national regulatory authorities to determine whether operators have significant market power in accordance with the procedure referred to in Article 16, paragraphs 2 and 3 of this Article shall apply.

2. An undertaking shall be deemed to have significant market power if, either individually or jointly with others, it enjoys a position equivalent to dominance, that is to say a position of economic strength affording it the power to behave to an appreciable extent independently of competitors, customers and ultimately consumers.

In particular, national regulatory authorities shall, when assessing whether two or more undertakings are in a joint dominant position in a market, act in accordance with Community law and take into the utmost account the guidelines on market analysis and the assessment of significant market power published by the Commission pursuant to Article 15. Criteria to be used in making such an assessment are set out in Annex II.

3. Where an undertaking has significant market power on a specific market, it may also be deemed to have significant market power on a closely related market, where the links between the two markets are such as to allow the market power held in one market to be leveraged into the other market, thereby strengthening the market power of the undertaking.
[4638]

Article 15

Market definition procedure

1. After public consultation and consultation with national regulatory authorities the Commission shall adopt a recommendation on relevant product and service markets (hereinafter "the recommendation"). The recommendation shall identify in accordance with Annex I hereto those product and service markets within the electronic communications

sector, the characteristics of which may be such as to justify the imposition of regulatory obligations set out in the Specific Directives, without prejudice to markets that may be defined in specific cases under competition law. The Commission shall define markets in accordance with the principles of competition law.

The Commission shall regularly review the recommendation.

2. The Commission shall publish, at the latest on the date of entry into force of this Directive, guidelines for market analysis and the assessment of significant market power (hereinafter "the guidelines") which shall be in accordance with the principles of competition law.

3. National regulatory authorities shall, taking the utmost account of the recommendation and the guidelines, define relevant markets appropriate to national circumstances, in particular relevant geographic markets within their territory, in accordance with the principles of competition law. National regulatory authorities shall follow the procedures referred to in Articles 6 and 7 before defining the markets that differ from those defined in the recommendation.

4. After consultation with national regulatory authorities the Commission may, acting in accordance with the procedure referred to in Article 22(3), adopt a Decision identifying transnational markets.

[4639]

Article 16

Market analysis procedure

1. As soon as possible after the adoption of the recommendation or any updating thereof, national regulatory authorities shall carry out an analysis of the relevant markets, taking the utmost account of the guidelines. Member States shall ensure that this analysis is carried out, where appropriate, in collaboration with the national competition authorities.

2. Where a national regulatory authority is required under Articles 16, 17, 18 or 19 of Directive 2002/22/EC (Universal Service Directive), or Articles 7 or 8 of Directive 2002/19/EC (Access Directive) to determine whether to impose, maintain, amend or withdraw obligations on undertakings, it shall determine on the basis of its market analysis referred to in paragraph 1 of this Article whether a relevant market is effectively competitive.

3. Where a national regulatory authority concludes that the market is effectively competitive, it shall not impose or maintain any of the specific regulatory obligations referred to in paragraph 2 of this Article. In cases where sector specific regulatory obligations already exist, it shall withdraw such obligations placed on undertakings in that relevant market. An appropriate period of notice shall be given to parties affected by such a withdrawal of obligations.

4. Where a national regulatory authority determines that a relevant market is not effectively competitive, it shall identify undertakings with significant market power on that market in accordance with Article 14 and the national regulatory authority shall on such undertakings impose appropriate specific regulatory obligations referred to in paragraph 2 of this Article or maintain or amend such obligations where they already exist.

5. In the case of transnational markets identified in the Decision referred to in Article 15(4), the national regulatory authorities concerned shall jointly conduct the market analysis taking the utmost account of the guidelines and decide on any imposition, maintenance, amendment or withdrawal of regulatory obligations referred to in paragraph 2 of this Article in a concerted fashion.

6. Measures taken according to the provisions of paragraphs 3, 4 and 5 of this Article shall be subject to the procedures referred to in Articles 6 and 7.

[4640]

Article 17

Standardisation

1. The Commission, acting in accordance with the procedure referred to in Article 22(2), shall draw up and publish in the *Official Journal of the European Communities* a list of standards and/or specifications to serve as a basis for encouraging the harmonised provision of electronic communications networks, electronic communications services and associated

facilities and services. Where necessary, the Commission may, acting in accordance with the procedure referred to in Article 22(2) and following consultation of the Committee established by Directive 98/34/EC, request that standards be drawn up by the European standards organisations (European Committee for Standardisation (CEN), European Committee for Electrotechnical Standardisation (CENELEC), and European Telecommunications Standards Institute (ETSI)).

2. Member States shall encourage the use of the standards and/or specifications referred to in paragraph 1, for the provision of services, technical interfaces and/or network functions, to the extent strictly necessary to ensure interoperability of services and to improve freedom of choice for users.

As long as standards and/or specifications have not been published in accordance with paragraph 1, Member States shall encourage the implementation of standards and/or specifications adopted by the European standards organisations.

In the absence of such standards and/or specifications, Member States shall encourage the implementation of international standards or recommendations adopted by the International Telecommunication Union (ITU), the International Organisation for Standardisation (ISO) or the International Electrotechnical Commission (IEC).

Where international standards exist, Member States shall encourage the European standards organisations to use them, or the relevant parts of them, as a basis for the standards they develop, except where such international standards or relevant parts would be ineffective.

3. If the standards and/or specifications referred to in paragraph 1 have not been adequately implemented so that interoperability of services in one or more Member States cannot be ensured, the implementation of such standards and/or specifications may be made compulsory under the procedure laid down in paragraph 4, to the extent strictly necessary to ensure such interoperability and to improve freedom of choice for users.

4. Where the Commission intends to make the implementation of certain standards and/or specifications compulsory, it shall publish a notice in the *Official Journal of the European Communities* and invite public comment by all parties concerned. The Commission, acting in accordance with the procedure referred to in Article 22(3), shall make implementation of the relevant standards compulsory by making reference to them as compulsory standards in the list of standards and/or specifications published in the *Official Journal of the European Communities*.

5. Where the Commission considers that standards and/or specifications referred to in paragraph 1 no longer contribute to the provision of harmonised electronic communications services, or that they no longer meet consumers' needs or are hampering technological development, it shall, acting in accordance with the procedure referred to in Article 22(2), remove them from the list of standards and/or specifications referred to in paragraph 1.

6. Where the Commission considers that standards and/or specifications referred to in paragraph 4 no longer contribute to the provision of harmonised electronic communications services, or that they no longer meet consumers' needs or are hampering technological development, it shall, acting in accordance with the procedure referred to in Article 22(3), remove them from this list of standards and/or specifications referred to in paragraph 1.

7. This Article does not apply in respect of any of the essential requirements, interface specifications or harmonised standards to which the provisions of Directive 1999/5/EC apply.
[4641]

Article 18

Interoperability of digital interactive television services

1. In order to promote the free flow of information, media pluralism and cultural diversity, Member States shall encourage, in accordance with the provisions of Article 17(2)—

(a) providers of digital interactive television services for distribution to the public in the Community on digital interactive television platforms, regardless of the transmission mode, to use an open API;

(b) providers of all enhanced digital television equipment deployed for the reception of digital interactive television services on interactive digital television platforms to comply with an open API in accordance with the minimum requirements of the relevant standards or specifications.

PART VI TELECOMMUNICATIONS

2. Without prejudice to Article 5(1)(b) of Directive 2002/19/EC (Access Directive), Member States shall encourage proprietors of APIs to make available on fair, reasonable and non-discriminatory terms, and against appropriate remuneration, all such information as is necessary to enable providers of digital interactive television services to provide all services supported by the API in a fully functional form.

3. Within one year after the date of application referred to in Article 28(1), second subparagraph, the Commission shall examine the effects of this Article. If interoperability and freedom of choice for users have not been adequately achieved in one or more Member States, the Commission may take action in accordance with the procedure laid down in Article 17(3) and (4).

[4642]

Article 19

Harmonisation procedures

1. Where the Commission, acting in accordance with the procedure referred to in Article 22(2), issues recommendations to Member States on the harmonised application of the provisions in this Directive and the Specific Directives in order to further the achievement of the objectives set out in Article 8, Member States shall ensure that national regulatory authorities take the utmost account of those recommendations in carrying out their tasks. Where a national regulatory authority chooses not to follow a recommendation, it shall inform the Commission giving the reasoning for its position.

2. Where the Commission finds that divergence at national level in regulations aimed at implementing Article 10(4) creates a barrier to the single market, the Commission may, acting in accordance with the procedure referred to in Article 22(3), take the appropriate technical implementing measures.

[4643]

Article 20

Dispute resolution between undertakings

1. In the event of a dispute arising in connection with obligations arising under this Directive or the Specific Directives between undertakings providing electronic communications networks or services in a Member State, the national regulatory authority concerned shall, at the request of either party, and without prejudice to the provisions of paragraph 2, issue a binding decision to resolve the dispute in the shortest possible time frame and in any case within four months except in exceptional circumstances. The Member State concerned shall require that all parties cooperate fully with the national regulatory authority.

2. Member States may make provision for national regulatory authorities to decline to resolve a dispute through a binding decision where other mechanisms, including mediation, exist and would better contribute to resolution of the dispute in a timely manner in accordance with the provisions of Article 8. The national regulatory authority shall inform the parties without delay. If after four months the dispute is not resolved, and if the dispute has not been brought before the courts by the party seeking redress, the national regulatory authority shall issue, at the request of either party, a binding decision to resolve the dispute in the shortest possible time frame and in any case within four months.

3. In resolving a dispute, the national regulatory authority shall take decisions aimed at achieving the objectives set out in Article 8. Any obligations imposed on an undertaking by the national regulatory authority in resolving a dispute shall respect the provisions of this Directive or the Specific Directives.

4. The decision of the national regulatory authority shall be made available to the public, having regard to the requirements of business confidentiality. The parties concerned shall be given a full statement of the reasons on which it is based.

5. The procedure referred to in paragraphs 1, 3 and 4 shall not preclude either party from bringing an action before the courts.

[4644]

Article 21

Resolution of cross-border disputes

1. In the event of a cross-border dispute arising under this Directive or the Specific Directives between parties in different Member States, where the dispute lies within the

competence of national regulatory authorities from more than one Member State, the procedure set out in paragraphs 2, 3 and 4 shall be applicable.

2. Any party may refer the dispute to the national regulatory authorities concerned. The national regulatory authorities shall coordinate their efforts in order to bring about a resolution of the dispute, in accordance with the objectives set out in Article 8. Any obligations imposed on an undertaking by the national regulatory authority in resolving a dispute shall respect the provisions of this Directive or the Specific Directives.

3. Member States may make provision for national regulatory authorities jointly to decline to resolve a dispute where other mechanisms, including mediation, exist and would better contribute to resolution of the dispute in a timely manner in accordance with the provisions of Article 8. They shall inform the parties without delay. If after four months the dispute is not resolved, if the dispute has not been brought before the courts by the party seeking redress, and if either party requests it, the national regulatory authorities shall coordinate their efforts in order to bring about a resolution of the dispute, in accordance with the provisions set out in Article 8.

4. The procedure referred to in paragraph 2 shall not preclude either party from bringing an action before the courts.

[4645]

Article 22

Committee

1. The Commission shall be assisted by a Committee ("the Communications Committee").

2. Where reference is made to this paragraph, Articles 3 and 7 of Decision 1999/468/EC shall apply, having regard to the provisions of Article 8 thereof.

3. Where reference is made to this paragraph, Articles 5 and 7 of Decision 1999/468/EC shall apply, having regard to the provisions of Article 8 thereof.

The period laid down in Article 5(6) of Decision 1999/468/EC shall be three months.

4. The Committee shall adopt its rules of procedure.

[4646]

Article 23

Exchange of information

1. The Commission shall provide all relevant information to the Communications Committee on the outcome of regular consultations with the representatives of network operators, service providers, users, consumers, manufacturers and trade unions, as well as third countries and international organisations.

2. The Communications Committee shall, taking account of the Community's electronic communications policy, foster the exchange of information between the Member States and between the Member States and the Commission on the situation and the development of regulatory activities regarding electronic communications networks and services.

[4647]

Article 24

Publication of information

1. Member States shall ensure that up-to-date information pertaining to the application of this Directive and the Specific Directives is made publicly available in a manner that guarantees all interested parties easy access to that information. They shall publish a notice in their national official gazette describing how and where the information is published. The first such notice shall be published before the date of application referred to in Article 28(1), second subparagraph, and thereafter a notice shall be published whenever there is any change in the information contained therein.

2. Member States shall send to the Commission a copy of all such notices at the time of publication. The Commission shall distribute the information to the Communications Committee as appropriate.

[4648]

Article 25

Review procedures

1. The Commission shall periodically review the functioning of this Directive and report to the European Parliament and to the Council, on the first occasion not later than three years after the date of application referred to in Article 28(1), second subparagraph. For this purpose, the Commission may request information from the Member States, which shall be supplied without undue delay.

[4649]

CHAPTER V
FINAL PROVISIONS

Article 26

Repeal

The following Directives and Decisions are hereby repealed with effect from the date of application referred to in Article 28(1), second subparagraph—

- — Directive 90/387/EEC,
- — Council Decision 91/396/EEC of 29 July 1991 on the introduction of a single European emergency call number,[1]
- — Council Directive 92/44/EEC of 5 June 1992 on the application of open network provision to leased lines,[2]
- — Council Decision 92/264/EEC of 11 May 1992 on the introduction of a standard international telephone access code in the Community,[3]
- — Directive 95/47/EC,
- — Directive 97/13/EC,
- — Directive 97/33/EC,
- — Directive 98/10/EC of the European Parliament and of the Council of 26 February 1998 on the application of open network provision (ONP) to voice telephony and on universal service for telecommunications in a competitive environment.[4]

[4650]

NOTES

1 OJ L217, 6.8.1991, p 31.
2 OJ L165, 19.6.1992, p 27. Directive as last amended by Commission Decision 98/80/EC (OJ L14, 20.1.1998, p 27).
3 OJ L137, 20.5.1992, p 21.
4 OJ L101, 1.4.1998, p 24.

Article 27

Transitional measures

Member States shall maintain all obligations under national law referred to in Article 7 of Directive 2002/19/EC (Access Directive) and Article 16 of Directive 2002/22/EC (Universal Service Directive) until such time as a determination is made in respect of those obligations by a national regulatory authority in accordance with Article 16 of this Directive.

Operators of fixed public telephone networks that were designated by their national regulatory authority as having significant market power in the provision of fixed public telephone networks and services under Annex I, Part 1 of Directive 97/33/EC or Directive 98/10/EC shall continue to be considered "notified operators" for the purposes of Regulation (EC) No 2887/2000 until such a time as the market analysis procedure referred to in Article 16 has been completed. Thereafter they shall cease to be considered "notified operators" for the purposes of the Regulation.

[4651]

Article 28

Transposition

1. Member States shall adopt and publish the laws, regulations and administrative provisions necessary to comply with this Directive not later than 24 July 2003. They shall forthwith inform the Commission thereof.

They shall apply those measures from 25 July 2003.

2. When Member States adopt these measures, they shall contain a reference to this Directive or be accompanied by such a reference on the occasion of their official publication. The methods of making such a reference shall be laid down by the Member States.

3. Member States shall communicate to the Commission the text of the provisions of national law which they adopt in the field governed by this Directive and of any subsequent amendments to those provisions.

[4652]

Article 29

Entry into force

This Directive shall enter into force on the day of its publication in the *Official Journal of the European Communities.*

[4653]

Article 30

Addressees

This Directive is addressed to the Member States.

[4654]

Done at Brussels, 7 March 2002.

ANNEX I
LIST OF MARKETS TO BE INCLUDED IN THE INITIAL COMMISSION RECOMMENDATION ON RELEVANT PRODUCT AND SERVICE MARKETS REFERRED TO IN ARTICLE 15

1. *Markets referred to in Directive 2002/22/EC* (*Universal Service Directive*)

Article 16 – Markets defined under the former regulatory framework, where obligations should be reviewed.

The provision of connection to and use of the public telephone network at fixed locations.

The provision of leased lines to end users.

2. *Markets referred to in Directive 2002/19/EC* (*Access Directive*)

Article 7 – Markets defined under the former regulatory framework, where obligations should be reviewed.

Interconnection (Directive 97/33/EC)

call origination in the fixed public telephone network
call termination in the fixed public telephone network
transit services in the fixed public telephone network
call origination on public mobile telephone networks
call termination on public mobile telephone networks
leased line interconnection (interconnection of part circuits)

Network access and special network access (Directive 97/33/EC, Directive 98/10/EC)

access to the fixed public telephone network, including unbundled access to the local loop
access to public mobile telephone networks, including carrier selection

Wholesale leased line capacity (Directive 92/44/EEC)

wholesale provision of leased line capacity to other suppliers of electronic communications networks or services

3. *Markets referred to in Regulation* (*EC*) *No 2887/2000*

Services provided over unbundled (twisted metallic pair) loops.

4. *Additional markets*

The national market for international roaming services on public mobile telephone networks.

[4655]

ANNEX II
CRITERIA TO BE USED BY NATIONAL REGULATORY AUTHORITIES IN MAKING AN ASSESSMENT OF JOINT DOMINANCE IN ACCORDANCE WITH ARTICLE 14(2), SECOND SUBPARAGRAPH

Two or more undertakings can be found to be in a joint dominant position within the meaning of Article 14 if, even in the absence of structural or other links between them, they operate in

PART VI TELECOMMUNICATIONS

a market the structure of which is considered to be conducive to coordinated effects. Without prejudice to the case law of the Court of Justice on joint dominance, this is likely to be the case where the market satisfies a number of appropriate characteristics, in particular in terms of market concentration, transparency and other characteristics mentioned below—

- — mature market,
- — stagnant or moderate growth on the demand side,
- — low elasticity of demand,
- — homogeneous product,
- — similar cost structures,
- — similar market shares,
- — lack of technical innovation, mature technology,
- — absence of excess capacity,
- — high barriers to entry,
- — lack of countervailing buying power,
- — lack of potential competition,
- — various kinds of informal or other links between the undertakings concerned,
- — retaliatory mechanisms,
- — lack or reduced scope for price competition.

The above is not an exhaustive list, nor are the criteria cumulative. Rather, the list is intended to illustrate only the sorts of evidence that could be used to support assertions concerning the existence of joint dominance.

[4656]

DIRECTIVE OF THE EUROPEAN PARLIAMENT AND OF THE COUNCIL

of 7 March 2002

on universal service and users' rights relating to electronic communications networks and services (Universal Service Directive)

(2002/22/EC)

NOTES

Date of publication in OJ: OJ L108, 24.4.2002, p 51.

THE EUROPEAN PARLIAMENT AND THE COUNCIL OF THE EUROPEAN UNION,

Having regard to the Treaty establishing the European Community, and in particular Article 95 thereof,

Having regard to the proposal from the Commission,[1]

Having regard to the opinion of the Economic and Social Committee,[2]

Having regard to the opinion of the Committee of the Regions,[3]

Acting in accordance with the procedure laid down in Article 251 of the Treaty,[4]

Whereas—

(1) The liberalisation of the telecommunications sector and increasing competition and choice for communications services go hand in hand with parallel action to create a harmonised regulatory framework which secures the delivery of universal service. The concept of universal service should evolve to reflect advances in technology, market developments and changes in user demand. The regulatory framework established for the full liberalisation of the telecommunications market in 1998 in the Community defined the minimum scope of universal service obligations and established rules for its costing and financing.

(2) Under Article 153 of the Treaty, the Community is to contribute to the protection of consumers.

(3) The Community and its Member States have undertaken commitments on the regulatory framework of telecommunications networks and services in the context of the World Trade Organisation (WTO) agreement on basic telecommunications. Any member of the WTO has the right to define the kind of universal service obligation it wishes to maintain. Such obligations will not be regarded as anti-competitive per se, provided they are administered in a transparent, non-discriminatory and competitively neutral manner and are not more burdensome than necessary for the kind of universal service defined by the member.

(4) Ensuring universal service (that is to say, the provision of a defined minimum set of services to all end-users at an affordable price) may involve the provision of some services to some end-users at prices that depart from those resulting from normal market conditions. However, compensating undertakings designated to provide such services in such circumstances need not result in any distortion of competition, provided that designated undertakings are compensated for the specific net cost involved and provided that the net cost burden is recovered in a competitively neutral way.

(5) In a competitive market, certain obligations should apply to all undertakings providing publicly available telephone services at fixed locations and others should apply only to undertakings enjoying significant market power or which have been designated as a universal service operator.

(6) The network termination point represents a boundary for regulatory purposes between the regulatory framework for electronic communication networks and services and the regulation of telecommunication terminal equipment. Defining the location of the network termination point is the responsibility of the national regulatory authority, where necessary on the basis of a proposal by the relevant undertakings.

(7) Member States should continue to ensure that the services set out in Chapter II are made available with the quality specified to all end-users in their territory, irrespective of their geographical location, and, in the light of specific national conditions, at an affordable price. Member States may, in the context of universal service obligations and in the light of national conditions, take specific measures for consumers in rural or geographically isolated areas to ensure their access to the services set out in the Chapter II and the affordability of those services, as well as ensure under the same conditions this access, in particular for the elderly, the disabled and for people with special social needs. Such measures may also include measures directly targeted at consumers with special social needs providing support to identified consumers, for example by means of specific measures, taken after the examination of individual requests, such as the paying off of debts.

(8) A fundamental requirement of universal service is to provide users on request with a connection to the public telephone network at a fixed location, at an affordable price. The requirement is limited to a single narrowband network connection, the provision of which may be restricted by Member States to the end-user's primary location/residence, and does not extend to the Integrated Services Digital Network (ISDN) which provides two or more connections capable of being used simultaneously. There should be no constraints on the technical means by which the connection is provided, allowing for wired or wireless technologies, nor any constraints on which operators provide part or all of universal service obligations. Connections to the public telephone network at a fixed location should be capable of supporting speech and data communications at rates sufficient for access to online services such as those provided via the public Internet. The speed of Internet access experienced by a given user may depend on a number of factors including the provider(s) of Internet connectivity as well as the given application for which a connection is being used. The data rate that can be supported by a single narrowband connection to the public telephone network depends on the capabilities of the subscriber's terminal equipment as well as the connection. For this reason it is not appropriate to mandate a specific data or bit rate at Community level. Currently available voice band modems typically offer a data rate of 56 kbit/s and employ automatic data rate adaptation to cater for variable line quality, with the result that the achieved data rate may be lower than 56 kbit/s. Flexibility is required on the one hand to allow Member States to take measures where necessary to ensure that connections are capable of supporting such a data rate, and on the other hand to allow Member States where relevant to permit data rates below this upper limit of 56 kbits/s in order, for example, to exploit the capabilities of wireless technologies (including cellular wireless networks) to deliver universal service to a higher proportion of the population. This may be of particular importance in some accession countries where household penetration of traditional telephone connections remains relatively low. In specific cases where the connection to the public telephony network at a fixed location is clearly insufficient to support satisfactory Internet access, Member States should be able to require the connection to be brought up to the level enjoyed by the majority of subscribers so that it supports data rates sufficient for access to the Internet. Where such specific measures produce a net cost burden for those consumers concerned, the net effect may be included in any net cost calculation of universal service obligations.

(9) The provisions of this Directive do not preclude Member States from designating different undertakings to provide the network and service elements of universal service. Designated undertakings providing network elements may be required to ensure such construction and maintenance as are necessary and proportionate to meet all reasonable requests for connection at a fixed location to the public telephone network and for access to publicly available telephone services at a fixed location.

(10) Affordable price means a price defined by Member States at national level in the light of specific national conditions, and may involve setting common tariffs irrespective of location or special tariff options to deal with the needs of low-income users. Affordability for individual consumers is related to their ability to monitor and control their expenditure.

(11) Directory information and a directory enquiry service constitute an essential access tool for publicly available telephone services and form part of the universal service obligation. Users and consumers desire comprehensive directories and a directory enquiry service covering all listed telephone subscribers and their numbers (including fixed and mobile numbers) and want this information to be presented in a non-preferential fashion. Directive 97/66/EC of the European Parliament and of the Council of 15 December 1997 concerning the processing of personal data and the protection of privacy in the telecommunications sector[5] ensures the subscribers' right to privacy with regard to the inclusion of their personal information in a public directory.

(12) For the citizen, it is important for there to be adequate provision of public pay telephones, and for users to be able to call emergency telephone numbers and, in particular, the single European emergency call number ("112") free of charge from any telephone, including public pay telephones, without the use of any means of payment. Insufficient information about the existence of "112" deprives citizens of the additional safety ensured by the existence of this number at European level especially during their travel in other Member States.

(13) Member States should take suitable measures in order to guarantee access to and affordability of all publicly available telephone services at a fixed location for disabled users and users with special social needs. Specific measures for disabled users could include, as appropriate, making available accessible public telephones, public text telephones or equivalent measures for deaf or speech-impaired people, providing services such as directory enquiry services or equivalent measures free of charge for blind or partially sighted people, and providing itemised bills in alternative format on request for blind or partially sighted people. Specific measures may also need to be taken to enable disabled users and users with special social needs to access emergency services "112" and to give them a similar possibility to choose between different operators or service providers as other consumers. Quality of service standards have been developed for a range of parameters to assess the quality of services received by subscribers and how well undertakings designated with universal service obligations perform in achieving these standards. Quality of service standards do not yet exist in respect of disabled users. Performance standards and relevant parameters should be developed for disabled users and are provided for in Article 11 of this Directive. Moreover, national regulatory authorities should be enabled to require publication of quality of service performance data if and when such standards and parameters are developed. The provider of universal service should not take measures to prevent users from benefiting fully from services offered by different operators or service providers, in combination with its own services offered as part of universal service.

(14) The importance of access to and use of the public telephone network at a fixed location is such that it should be available to anyone reasonably requesting it. In accordance with the principle of subsidiarity, it is for Member States to decide on the basis of objective criteria which undertakings have universal service obligations for the purposes of this Directive, where appropriate taking into account the ability and the willingness of undertakings to accept all or part of the universal service obligations. It is important that universal service obligations are fulfilled in the most efficient fashion so that users generally pay prices that correspond to efficient cost provision. It is likewise important that universal service operators maintain the integrity of the network as well as service continuity and quality. The development of greater competition and choice provide more possibilities for all or part of the universal service obligations to be provided by undertakings other than those with significant market power. Therefore, universal service obligations could in some cases be allocated to operators demonstrating the most cost-effective means of delivering access and services, including by competitive or comparative selection procedures. Corresponding obligations could be included as conditions in authorisations to provide publicly available services.

(15) Member States should monitor the situation of consumers with respect to their use of publicly available telephone services and in particular with respect to affordability. The affordability of telephone service is related to the information which users receive regarding telephone usage expenses as well as the relative cost of telephone usage compared to other services, and is also related to their ability to control expenditure. Affordability therefore means giving power to consumers through obligations imposed on undertakings designated as having universal service obligations. These obligations include a specified level of itemised billing, the possibility for consumers selectively to block certain calls (such as high-priced

calls to premium services), the possibility for consumers to control expenditure via pre-payment means and the possibility for consumers to offset up-front connection fees. Such measures may need to be reviewed and changed in the light of market developments. Current conditions do not warrant a requirement for operators with universal service obligations to alert subscribers where a predetermined limit of expenditure is exceeded or an abnormal calling pattern occurs. Review of the relevant legislative provisions in future should consider whether there is a possible need to alert subscribers for these reasons.

(16) Except in cases of persistent late payment or non-payment of bills, consumers should be protected from immediate disconnection from the network on the grounds of an unpaid bill and, particularly in the case of disputes over high bills for premium rate services, should continue to have access to essential telephone services pending resolution of the dispute. Member States may decide that such access may continue to be provided only if the subscriber continues to pay line rental charges.

(17) Quality and price are key factors in a competitive market and national regulatory authorities should be able to monitor achieved quality of service for undertakings which have been designated as having universal service obligations. In relation to the quality of service attained by such undertakings, national regulatory authorities should be able to take appropriate measures where they deem it necessary. National regulatory authorities should also be able to monitor the achieved quality of services of other undertakings providing public telephone networks and/or publicly available telephone services to users at fixed locations.

(18) Member States should, where necessary, establish mechanisms for financing the net cost of universal service obligations in cases where it is demonstrated that the obligations can only be provided at a loss or at a net cost which falls outside normal commercial standards. It is important to ensure that the net cost of universal service obligations is properly calculated and that any financing is undertaken with minimum distortion to the market and to undertakings, and is compatible with the provisions of Articles 87 and 88 of the Treaty.

(19) Any calculation of the net cost of universal service should take due account of costs and revenues, as well as the intangible benefits resulting from providing universal service, but should not hinder the general aim of ensuring that pricing structures reflect costs. Any net costs of universal service obligations should be calculated on the basis of transparent procedures.

(20) Taking into account intangible benefits means that an estimate in monetary terms, of the indirect benefits that an undertaking derives by virtue of its position as provider of universal service, should be deducted from the direct net cost of universal service obligations in order to determine the overall cost burden.

(21) When a universal service obligation represents an unfair burden on an undertaking, it is appropriate to allow Member States to establish mechanisms for efficiently recovering net costs. Recovery via public funds constitutes one method of recovering the net costs of universal service obligations. It is also reasonable for established net costs to be recovered from all users in a transparent fashion by means of levies on undertakings. Member States should be able to finance the net costs of different elements of universal service through different mechanisms, and/or to finance the net costs of some or all elements from either of the mechanisms or a combination of both. In the case of cost recovery by means of levies on undertakings, Member States should ensure that that the method of allocation amongst them is based on objective and non-discriminatory criteria and is in accordance with the principle of proportionality. This principle does not prevent Member States from exempting new entrants which have not yet achieved any significant market presence. Any funding mechanism should ensure that market participants only contribute to the financing of universal service obligations and not to other activities which are not directly linked to the provision of the universal service obligations. Recovery mechanisms should in all cases respect the principles of Community law, and in particular in the case of sharing mechanisms those of non-discrimination and proportionality. Any funding mechanism should ensure that users in one Member State do not contribute to universal service costs in another Member State, for example when making calls from one Member State to another.

(22) Where Member States decide to finance the net cost of universal service obligations from public funds, this should be understood to comprise funding from general government budgets including other public financing sources such as state lotteries.

(23) The net cost of universal service obligations may be shared between all or certain specified classes of undertaking. Member States should ensure that the sharing mechanism respects the principles of transparency, least market distortion, non-discrimination and proportionality. Least market distortion means that contributions should be recovered in a way that as far as possible minimises the impact of the financial burden falling on end-users, for example by spreading contributions as widely as possible.

(24) National regulatory authorities should satisfy themselves that those undertakings benefiting from universal service funding provide a sufficient level of detail of the specific

elements requiring such funding in order to justify their request. Member States' schemes for the costing and financing of universal service obligations should be communicated to the Commission for verification of compatibility with the Treaty. There are incentives for designated operators to raise the assessed net cost of universal service obligations. Therefore Member States should ensure effective transparency and control of amounts charged to finance universal service obligations.

(25) Communications markets continue to evolve in terms of the services used and the technical means used to deliver them to users. The universal service obligations, which are defined at a Community level, should be periodically reviewed with a view to proposing that the scope be changed or redefined. Such a review should take account of evolving social, commercial and technological conditions and the fact that any change of scope should be subject to the twin test of services that become available to a substantial majority of the population, with a consequent risk of social exclusion for those who can not afford them. Care should be taken in any change of the scope of universal service obligations to ensure that certain technological choices are not artificially promoted above others, that a disproportionate financial burden is not imposed on sector undertakings (thereby endangering market developments and innovation) and that any financing burden does not fall unfairly on consumers with lower incomes. Any change of scope automatically means that any net cost can be financed via the methods permitted in this Directive. Member States are not permitted to impose on market players financial contributions which relate to measures which are not part of universal service obligations. Individual Member States remain free to impose special measures (outside the scope of universal service obligations) and finance them in conformity with Community law but not by means of contributions from market players.

(26) More effective competition across all access and service markets will give greater choice for users. The extent of effective competition and choice varies across the Community and varies within Member States between geographical areas and between access and service markets. Some users may be entirely dependent on the provision of access and services by an undertaking with significant market power. In general, for reasons of efficiency and to encourage effective competition, it is important that the services provided by an undertaking with significant market power reflect costs. For reasons of efficiency and social reasons, end-user tariffs should reflect demand conditions as well as cost conditions, provided that this does not result in distortions of competition. There is a risk that an undertaking with significant market power may act in various ways to inhibit entry or distort competition, for example by charging excessive prices, setting predatory prices, compulsory bundling of retail services or showing undue preference to certain customers. Therefore, national regulatory authorities should have powers to impose, as a last resort and after due consideration, retail regulation on an undertaking with significant market power. Price cap regulation, geographical averaging or similar instruments, as well as non-regulatory measures such as publicly available comparisons of retail tariffs, may be used to achieve the twin objectives of promoting effective competition whilst pursuing public interest needs, such as maintaining the affordability of publicly available telephone services for some consumers. Access to appropriate cost accounting information is necessary, in order for national regulatory authorities to fulfil their regulatory duties in this area, including the imposition of any tariff controls. However, regulatory controls on retail services should only be imposed where national regulatory authorities consider that relevant wholesale measures or measures regarding carrier selection or pre-selection would fail to achieve the objective of ensuring effective competition and public interest.

(27) Where a national regulatory authority imposes obligations to implement a cost accounting system in order to support price controls, it may itself undertake an annual audit to ensure compliance with that cost accounting system, provided that it has the necessary qualified staff, or it may require the audit to be carried out by another qualified body, independent of the operator concerned.

(28) It is considered necessary to ensure the continued application of the existing provisions relating to the minimum set of leased line services in Community telecommunications legislation, in particular in Council Directive 92/44/EEC of 5 June 1992 on the application of open network provision to leased lines,[6] until such time as national regulatory authorities determine, in accordance with the market analysis procedures laid down in Directive 2002/21/EC of the European Parliament and of the Council of 7 March 2002 on a common regulatory framework for electronic communications networks and services (Framework Directive),[7] that such provisions are no longer needed because a sufficiently competitive market has developed in their territory. The degree of competition is likely to vary between different markets of leased lines in the minimum set, and in different parts of the territory. In undertaking the market analysis, national regulatory authorities should make separate assessments for each market of leased lines in the minimum set, taking into account their geographic dimension. Leased lines services constitute mandatory services to be

provided without recourse to any compensation mechanisms. The provision of leased lines outside of the minimum set of leased lines should be covered by general retail regulatory provisions rather than specific requirements covering the supply of the minimum set.

(29) National regulatory authorities may also, in the light of an analysis of the relevant market, require mobile operators with significant market power to enable their subscribers to access the services of any interconnected provider of publicly available telephone services on a call-by-call basis or by means of pre-selection.

(30) Contracts are an important tool for users and consumers to ensure a minimum level of transparency of information and legal security. Most service providers in a competitive environment will conclude contracts with their customers for reasons of commercial desirability. In addition to the provisions of this Directive, the requirements of existing Community consumer protection legislation relating to contracts, in particular Council Directive 93/13/EEC of 5 April 1993 on unfair terms in consumer contracts[8] and Directive 97/7/EC of the European Parliament and of the Council of 20 May 1997 on the protection of consumers in respect of distance contracts,[9] apply to consumer transactions relating to electronic networks and services. Specifically, consumers should enjoy a minimum level of legal certainty in respect of their contractual relations with their direct telephone service provider, such that the contractual terms, conditions, quality of service, condition for termination of the contract and the service, compensation measures and dispute resolution are specified in their contracts. Where service providers other than direct telephone service providers conclude contracts with consumers, the same information should be included in those contracts as well. The measures to ensure transparency on prices, tariffs, terms and conditions will increase the ability of consumers to optimise their choices and thus to benefit fully from competition.

(31) End-users should have access to publicly available information on communications services. Member States should be able to monitor the quality of services which are offered in their territories. National regulatory authorities should be able systematically to collect information on the quality of services offered in their territories on the basis of criteria which allow comparability between service providers and between Member States. Undertakings providing communications services, operating in a competitive environment, are likely to make adequate and up-to-date information on their services publicly available for reasons of commercial advantage. National regulatory authorities should nonetheless be able to require publication of such information where it is demonstrated that such information is not effectively available to the public.

(32) End-users should be able to enjoy a guarantee of interoperability in respect of all equipment sold in the Community for the reception of digital television. Member States should be able to require minimum harmonised standards in respect of such equipment. Such standards could be adapted from time to time in the light of technological and market developments.

(33) It is desirable to enable consumers to achieve the fullest connectivity possible to digital television sets. Interoperability is an evolving concept in dynamic markets. Standards bodies should do their utmost to ensure that appropriate standards evolve along with the technologies concerned. It is likewise important to ensure that connectors are available on television sets that are capable of passing all the necessary elements of a digital signal, including the audio and video streams, conditional access information, service information, application program interface (API) information and copy protection information. This Directive therefore ensures that the functionality of the open interface for digital television sets is not limited by network operators, service providers or equipment manufacturers and continues to evolve in line with technological developments. For display and presentation of digital interactive television services, the realisation of a common standard through a market-driven mechanism is recognised as a consumer benefit. Member States and the Commission may take policy initiatives, consistent with the Treaty, to encourage this development.

(34) All end-users should continue to enjoy access to operator assistance services whatever organisation provides access to the public telephone network.

(35) The provision of directory enquiry services and directories is already open to competition. The provisions of this Directive complement the provisions of Directive 97/66/EC by giving subscribers a right to have their personal data included in a printed or electronic directory. All service providers which assign telephone numbers to their subscribers are obliged to make relevant information available in a fair, cost-oriented and non-discriminatory manner.

(36) It is important that users should be able to call the single European emergency number "112", and any other national emergency telephone numbers, free of charge, from any telephone, including public pay telephones, without the use of any means of payment. Member States should have already made the necessary organisational arrangements best

PART VI TELECOMMUNICATIONS

suited to the national organisation of the emergency systems, in order to ensure that calls to this number are adequately answered and handled. Caller location information, to be made available to the emergency services, will improve the level of protection and the security of users of "112" services and assist the emergency services, to the extent technically feasible, in the discharge of their duties, provided that the transfer of calls and associated data to the emergency services concerned is guaranteed. The reception and use of such information should comply with relevant Community law on the processing of personal data. Steady information technology improvements will progressively support the simultaneous handling of several languages over the networks at a reasonable cost. This in turn will ensure additional safety for European citizens using the "112" emergency call number.

(37) Easy access to international telephone services is vital for European citizens and European businesses. "00" has already been established as the standard international telephone access code for the Community. Special arrangements for making calls between adjacent locations across borders between Member States may be established or continued. The ITU has assigned, in accordance with ITU Recommendation E.164, code "3883" to the European Telephony Numbering Space (ETNS). In order to ensure connection of calls to the ETNS, undertakings operating public telephone networks should ensure that calls using "3883" are directly or indirectly interconnected to ETNS serving networks specified in the relevant European Telecommunications Standards Institute (ETSI) standards. Such interconnection arrangements should be governed by the provisions of Directive 2002/19/EC of the European Parliament and of the Council of 7 March 2002 on access to, and interconnection of, electronic communications networks and associated facilities (Access Directive).[10]

(38) Access by end-users to all numbering resources in the Community is a vital pre-condition for a single market. It should include freephone, premium rate, and other non-geographic numbers, except where the called subscriber has chosen, for commercial reasons, to limit access from certain geographical areas. Tariffs charged to parties calling from outside the Member State concerned need not be the same as for those parties calling from inside that Member State.

(39) Tone dialling and calling line identification facilities are normally available on modern telephone exchanges and can therefore increasingly be provided at little or no expense. Tone dialling is increasingly being used for user interaction with special services and facilities, including value added services, and the absence of this facility can prevent the user from making use of these services. Member States are not required to impose obligations to provide these facilities when they are already available. Directive 97/66/EC safeguards the privacy of users with regard to itemised billing, by giving them the means to protect their right to privacy when calling line identification is implemented. The development of these services on a pan-European basis would benefit consumers and is encouraged by this Directive.

(40) Number portability is a key facilitator of consumer choice and effective competition in a competitive telecommunications environment such that end-users who so request should be able to retain their number(s) on the public telephone network independently of the organisation providing service. The provision of this facility between connections to the public telephone network at fixed and non-fixed locations is not covered by this Directive. However, Member States may apply provisions for porting numbers between networks providing services at a fixed location and mobile networks.

(41) The impact of number portability is considerably strengthened when there is transparent tariff information, both for end-users who port their numbers and also for end-users who call those who have ported their numbers. National regulatory authorities should, where feasible, facilitate appropriate tariff transparency as part of the implementation of number portability.

(42) When ensuring that pricing for interconnection related to the provision of number portability is cost-oriented, national regulatory authorities may also take account of prices available in comparable markets.

(43) Currently, Member States impose certain "must carry" obligations on networks for the distribution of radio or television broadcasts to the public. Member States should be able to lay down proportionate obligations on undertakings under their jurisdiction, in the interest of legitimate public policy considerations, but such obligations should only be imposed where they are necessary to meet general interest objectives clearly defined by Member States in conformity with Community law and should be proportionate, transparent and subject to periodical review. "Must carry" obligations imposed by Member States should be reasonable, that is they should be proportionate and transparent in the light of clearly defined general interest objectives, and could, where appropriate, entail a provision for proportionate remuneration. Such "must carry" obligations may include the transmission of services specifically designed to enable appropriate access by disabled users.

(44) Networks used for the distribution of radio or television broadcasts to the public include cable, satellite and terrestrial broadcasting networks. They might also include other networks to the extent that a significant number of end-users use such networks as their principal means to receive radio and television broadcasts.

(45) Services providing content such as the offer for sale of a package of sound or television broadcasting content are not covered by the common regulatory framework for electronic communications networks and services. Providers of such services should not be subject to universal service obligations in respect of these activities. This Directive is without prejudice to measures taken at national level, in compliance with Community law, in respect of such services.

(46) Where a Member State seeks to ensure the provision of other specific services throughout its national territory, such obligations should be implemented on a cost efficient basis and outside the scope of universal service obligations. Accordingly, Member States may undertake additional measures (such as facilitating the development of infrastructure or services in circumstances where the market does not satisfactorily address the requirements of end-users or consumers), in conformity with Community law. As a reaction to the Commission's e-Europe initiative, the Lisbon European Council of 23 and 24 March 2000 called on Member States to ensure that all schools have access to the Internet and to multimedia resources.

(47) In the context of a competitive environment, the views of interested parties, including users and consumers, should be taken into account by national regulatory authorities when dealing with issues related to end-users' rights. Effective procedures should be available to deal with disputes between consumers, on the one hand, and undertakings providing publicly available communications services, on the other. Member States should take full account of Commission Recommendation 98/257/EC of 30 March 1998 on the principles applicable to the bodies responsible for out-of-court settlement of consumer disputes.[11]

(48) Co-regulation could be an appropriate way of stimulating enhanced quality standards and improved service performance. Co-regulation should be guided by the same principles as formal regulation, ie it should be objective, justified, proportional, non-discriminatory and transparent.

(49) This Directive should provide for elements of consumer protection, including clear contract terms and dispute resolution, and tariff transparency for consumers. It should also encourage the extension of such benefits to other categories of end-users, in particular small and medium-sized enterprises.

(50) The provisions of this Directive do not prevent a Member State from taking measures justified on grounds set out in Articles 30 and 46 of the Treaty, and in particular on grounds of public security, public policy and public morality.

(51) Since the objectives of the proposed action, namely setting a common level of universal service for telecommunications for all European users and of harmonising conditions for access to and use of public telephone networks at a fixed location and related publicly available telephone services and also achieving a harmonised framework for the regulation of electronic communications services, electronic communications networks and associated facilities, cannot be sufficiently achieved by the Member States and can therefore by reason of the scale or effects of the action be better achieved at Community level, the Community may adopt measures in accordance with the principles of subsidiarity as set out in Article 5 of the Treaty. In accordance with the principle of proportionality, as set out in that Article, this Directive does not go beyond what is necessary in order to achieve those objectives.

(52) The measures necessary for the implementation of this Directive should be adopted in accordance with Council Decision 1999/468/EC of 28 June 1999 laying down the procedures for the exercise of implementing powers conferred on the Commission,[12]

NOTES

1 OJ C365E, 19.12.2000, p 238 and OJ C332E, 27.11.2001, p 292.

2 OJ C139, 11.5.2001, p 15.

3 OJ C144, 16.5.2001, p 60.

4 Opinion of the European Parliament of 13 June 2001 (not yet published in the Official Journal), Council Common Position of 17 September 2001 (OJ C337, 30.11.2001, p 55) and Decision of the European Parliament of 12 December 2001 (not yet published in the Official Journal). Council Decision of 14 February 2002.

5 OJ L24, 30.1.1998, p 1.

6 OJ L165, 19.6.1992, p 27. Directive as last amended by Commission Decision No 98/80/EC (OJ L14, 20.1.1998, p 27).

7 See page 33 of this Official Journal.

8 OJ L95, 21.4.1993, p 29.

[9] OJ L144, 4.6.1997, p 19.
[10] See page 7 of this Official Journal.
[11] OJ L115, 17.4.1998, p 31.
[12] OJ L184, 17.7.1999, p 23.

HAVE ADOPTED THIS DIRECTIVE—

CHAPTER I
SCOPE, AIMS AND DEFINITIONS

Article 1

Scope and aims

1. Within the framework of Directive 2002/21/EC (Framework Directive), this Directive concerns the provision of electronic communications networks and services to end-users. The aim is to ensure the availability throughout the Community of good quality publicly available services through effective competition and choice and to deal with circumstances in which the needs of end-users are not satisfactorily met by the market.

2. This Directive establishes the rights of end-users and the corresponding obligations on undertakings providing publicly available electronic communications networks and services. With regard to ensuring provision of universal service within an environment of open and competitive markets, this Directive defines the minimum set of services of specified quality to which all end-users have access, at an affordable price in the light of specific national conditions, without distorting competition. This Directive also sets out obligations with regard to the provision of certain mandatory services such as the retail provision of leased lines.

[4657]

Article 2

Definitions

For the purposes of this Directive, the definitions set out in Article 2 of Directive 2002/21/EC (Framework Directive) shall apply.

The following definitions shall also apply—

(a) "public pay telephone" means a telephone available to the general public, for the use of which the means of payment may include coins and/or credit/debit cards and/or pre-payment cards, including cards for use with dialling codes;

(b) "public telephone network" means an electronic communications network which is used to provide publicly available telephone services; it supports the transfer between network termination points of speech communications, and also other forms of communication, such as facsimile and data;

(c) "publicly available telephone service" means a service available to the public for originating and receiving national and international calls and access to emergency services through a number or numbers in a national or international telephone numbering plan, and in addition may, where relevant, include one or more of the following services: the provision of operator assistance, directory enquiry services, directories, provision of public pay phones, provision of service under special terms, provision of special facilities for customers with disabilities or with special social needs and/or the provision of non-geographic services;

(d) "geographic number" means a number from the national numbering plan where part of its digit structure contains geographic significance used for routing calls to the physical location of the network termination point (NTP);

(e) "network termination point" (NTP) means the physical point at which a subscriber is provided with access to a public communications network; in the case of networks involving switching or routing, the NTP is identified by means of a specific network address, which may be linked to a subscriber number or name;

(f) "non-geographic numbers" means a number from the national numbering plan that is not a geographic number.

It includes *inter alia* mobile, freephone and premium rate numbers.

[4658]

CHAPTER II
UNIVERSAL SERVICE OBLIGATIONS INCLUDING SOCIAL OBLIGATIONS

Article 3

Availability of universal service

1. Member States shall ensure that the services set out in this Chapter are made available at the quality specified to all end-users in their territory, independently of geographical location, and, in the light of specific national conditions, at an affordable price.

2. Member States shall determine the most efficient and appropriate approach for ensuring the implementation of universal service, whilst respecting the principles of objectivity, transparency, non-discrimination and proportionality. They shall seek to minimise market distortions, in particular the provision of services at prices or subject to other terms and conditions which depart from normal commercial conditions, whilst safeguarding the public interest.

[4659]

Article 4

Provision of access at a fixed location

1. Member States shall ensure that all reasonable requests for connection at a fixed location to the public telephone network and for access to publicly available telephone services at a fixed location are met by at least one undertaking.

2. The connection provided shall be capable of allowing end-users to make and receive local, national and international telephone calls, facsimile communications and data communications, at data rates that are sufficient to permit functional Internet access, taking into account prevailing technologies used by the majority of subscribers and technological feasibility.

[4660]

Article 5

Directory enquiry services and directories

1. Member States shall ensure that—

(a) at least one comprehensive directory is available to end-users in a form approved by the relevant authority, whether printed or electronic, or both, and is updated on a regular basis, and at least once a year;

(b) at least one comprehensive telephone directory enquiry service is available to all end-users, including users of public pay telephones.

2. The directories in paragraph 1 shall comprise, subject to the provisions of Article 11 of Directive 97/66/EC, all subscribers of publicly available telephone services.

3. Member States shall ensure that the undertaking(s) providing the services referred to in paragraph 1 apply the principle of non-discrimination to the treatment of information that has been provided to them by other undertakings.

[4661]

Article 6

Public pay telephones

1. Member States shall ensure that national regulatory authorities can impose obligations on undertakings in order to ensure that public pay telephones are provided to meet the reasonable needs of end-users in terms of the geographical coverage, the number of telephones, the accessibility of such telephones to disabled users and the quality of services.

2. A Member State shall ensure that its national regulatory authority can decide not to impose obligations under paragraph 1 in all or part of its territory, if it is satisfied that these facilities or comparable services are widely available, on the basis of a consultation of interested parties as referred to in Article 33.

3. Member States shall ensure that it is possible to make emergency calls from public pay telephones using the single European emergency call number "112" and other national emergency numbers, all free of charge and without having to use any means of payment.

[4662]

Article 7

Special measures for disabled users

1. Member States shall, where appropriate, take specific measures for disabled end-users in order to ensure access to and affordability of publicly available telephone services, including access to emergency services, directory enquiry services and directories, equivalent to that enjoyed by other end-users.

2. Member States may take specific measures, in the light of national conditions, to ensure that disabled end-users can also take advantage of the choice of undertakings and service providers available to the majority of end-users.

[4663]

Article 8

Designation of undertakings

1. Member States may designate one or more undertakings to guarantee the provision of universal service as identified in Articles 4, 5, 6 and 7 and, where applicable, Article 9(2) so that the whole of the national territory can be covered. Member States may designate different undertakings or sets of undertakings to provide different elements of universal service and/or to cover different parts of the national territory.

2. When Member States designate undertakings in part or all of the national territory as having universal service obligations, they shall do so using an efficient, objective, transparent and non-discriminatory designation mechanism, whereby no undertaking is a priori excluded from being designated. Such designation methods shall ensure that universal service is provided in a cost-effective manner and may be used as a means of determining the net cost of the universal service obligation in accordance with Article 12.

[4664]

Article 9

Affordability of tariffs

1. National regulatory authorities shall monitor the evolution and level of retail tariffs of the services identified in Articles 4, 5, 6 and 7 as falling under the universal service obligations and provided by designated undertakings, in particular in relation to national consumer prices and income.

2. Member States may, in the light of national conditions, require that designated undertakings provide tariff options or packages to consumers which depart from those provided under normal commercial conditions, in particular to ensure that those on low incomes or with special social needs are not prevented from accessing or using the publicly available telephone service.

3. Member States may, besides any provision for designated undertakings to provide special tariff options or to comply with price caps or geographical averaging or other similar schemes, ensure that support is provided to consumers identified as having low incomes or special social needs.

4. Member States may require undertakings with obligations under Articles 4, 5, 6 and 7 to apply common tariffs, including geographical averaging, throughout the territory, in the light of national conditions or to comply with price caps.

5. National regulatory authorities shall ensure that, where a designated undertaking has an obligation to provide special tariff options, common tariffs, including geographical averaging, or to comply with price caps, the conditions are fully transparent and are published and applied in accordance with the principle of non-discrimination. National regulatory authorities may require that specific schemes be modified or withdrawn.

[4665]

Article 10

Control of expenditure

1. Member States shall ensure that designated undertakings, in providing facilities and services additional to those referred to in Articles 4, 5, 6, 7 and 9(2), establish terms and

conditions in such a way that the subscriber is not obliged to pay for facilities or services which are not necessary or not required for the service requested.

2. Member States shall ensure that designated undertakings with obligations under Articles 4, 5, 6, 7 and 9(2) provide the specific facilities and services set out in Annex I, Part A, in order that subscribers can monitor and control expenditure and avoid unwarranted disconnection of service.

3. Member States shall ensure that the relevant authority is able to waive the requirements of paragraph 2 in all or part of its national territory if it is satisfied that the facility is widely available.

[4666]

Article 11

Quality of service of designated undertakings

1. National regulatory authorities shall ensure that all designated undertakings with obligations under Articles 4, 5, 6, 7 and 9(2) publish adequate and up-to-date information concerning their performance in the provision of universal service, based on the quality of service parameters, definitions and measurement methods set out in Annex III. The published information shall also be supplied to the national regulatory authority.

2. National regulatory authorities may specify, *inter alia*, additional quality of service standards, where relevant parameters have been developed, to assess the performance of undertakings in the provision of services to disabled end-users and disabled consumers. National regulatory authorities shall ensure that information concerning the performance of undertakings in relation to these parameters is also published and made available to the national regulatory authority.

3. National regulatory authorities may, in addition, specify the content, form and manner of information to be published, in order to ensure that end-users and consumers have access to comprehensive, comparable and user-friendly information.

4. National regulatory authorities shall be able to set performance targets for those undertakings with universal service obligations at least under Article 4. In so doing, national regulatory authorities shall take account of views of interested parties, in particular as referred to in Article 33.

5. Member States shall ensure that national regulatory authorities are able to monitor compliance with these performance targets by designated undertakings.

6. Persistent failure by an undertaking to meet performance targets may result in specific measures being taken in accordance with Directive 2002/20/EC of the European Parliament and of the Council of 7 March 2002 on the authorisation of electronic communications networks and services (Authorisation Directive). National regulatory authorities shall be able to order independent audits or similar reviews of the performance data, paid for by the undertaking concerned, in order to ensure the accuracy and comparability of the data made available by undertakings with universal service obligations.

[4667]

Article 12

Costing of universal service obligations

1. Where national regulatory authorities consider that the provision of universal service as set out in Articles 3 to 10 may represent an unfair burden on undertakings designated to provide universal service, they shall calculate the net costs of its provision.

For that purpose, national regulatory authorities shall—

(a) calculate the net cost of the universal service obligation, taking into account any market benefit which accrues to an undertaking designated to provide universal service, in accordance with Annex IV, Part A; or

(b) make use of the net costs of providing universal service identified by a designation mechanism in accordance with Article 8(2).

2. The accounts and/or other information serving as the basis for the calculation of the net cost of universal service obligations under paragraph 1(a) shall be audited or verified by the national regulatory authority or a body independent of the relevant parties and approved by the national regulatory authority. The results of the cost calculation and the conclusions of the audit shall be publicly available.

[4668]

Article 13

Financing of universal service obligations

1. Where, on the basis of the net cost calculation referred to in Article 12, national regulatory authorities find that an undertaking is subject to an unfair burden, Member States shall, upon request from a designated undertaking, decide—

(a) to introduce a mechanism to compensate that undertaking for the determined net costs under transparent conditions from public funds; and/or

(b) to share the net cost of universal service obligations between providers of electronic communications networks and services.

2. Where the net cost is shared under paragraph 1(b), Member States shall establish a sharing mechanism administered by the national regulatory authority or a body independent from the beneficiaries under the supervision of the national regulatory authority. Only the net cost, as determined in accordance with Article 12, of the obligations laid down in Articles 3 to 10 may be financed.

3. A sharing mechanism shall respect the principles of transparency, least market distortion, non-discrimination and proportionality, in accordance with the principles of Annex IV, Part B. Member States may choose not to require contributions from undertakings whose national turnover is less than a set limit.

4. Any charges related to the sharing of the cost of universal service obligations shall be unbundled and identified separately for each undertaking. Such charges shall not be imposed or collected from undertakings that are not providing services in the territory of the Member State that has established the sharing mechanism.

[4669]

Article 14

Transparency

1. Where a mechanism for sharing the net cost of universal service obligations as referred to in Article 13 is established, national regulatory authorities shall ensure that the principles for cost sharing, and details of the mechanism used, are publicly available.

2. Subject to Community and national rules on business confidentiality, national regulatory authorities shall ensure that an annual report is published giving the calculated cost of universal service obligations, identifying the contributions made by all the undertakings involved, and identifying any market benefits, that may have accrued to the undertaking(s) designated to provide universal service, where a fund is actually in place and working.

[4670]

Article 15

Review of the scope of universal service

1. The Commission shall periodically review the scope of universal service, in particular with a view to proposing to the European Parliament and the Council that the scope be changed or redefined. A review shall be carried out, on the first occasion within two years after the date of application referred to in Article 38(1), second subparagraph, and subsequently every three years.

2. This review shall be undertaken in the light of social, economic and technological developments, taking into account, *inter alia*, mobility and data rates in the light of the prevailing technologies used by the majority of subscribers. The review process shall be undertaken in accordance with Annex V. The Commission shall submit a report to the European Parliament and the Council regarding the outcome of the review.

[4671]

CHAPTER III
REGULATORY CONTROLS ON UNDERTAKINGS WITH SIGNIFICANT MARKET POWER IN SPECIFIC MARKETS

Article 16

Review of obligations

1. Member States shall maintain all obligations relating to—

(a) retail tariffs for the provision of access to and use of the public telephone network, imposed under Article 17 of Directive 98/10/EC of the European Parliament and of the Council of 26 February 1998 on the application of open network provision (ONP) to voice telephony and on universal service for telecommunications in a competitive environment;[1]

(b) carrier selection or pre-selection, imposed under Directive 97/33/EC of the European Parliament and of the Council of 30 June 1997 on interconnection in telecommunications with regard to ensuring universal service and interoperability through application of the principles of open network provision (ONP);[2]

(c) leased lines, imposed under Articles 3, 4, 6, 7, 8 and 10 of Directive 92/ 44/EEC,

until a review has been carried out and a determination made in accordance with the procedure in paragraph 3 of this Article.

2. The Commission shall indicate relevant markets for the obligations relating to retail markets in the initial recommendation on relevant product and service markets and the Decision identifying transnational markets to be adopted in accordance with Article 15 of Directive 2002/21/EC (Framework Directive).

3. Member States shall ensure that, as soon as possible after the entry into force of this Directive, and periodically thereafter, national regulatory authorities undertake a market analysis, in accordance with the procedure set out in Article 16 of Directive 2002/21/EC (Framework Directive) to determine whether to maintain, amend or withdraw the obligations relating to retail markets. Measures taken shall be subject to the procedure referred to in Article 7 of Directive 2002/21/EC (Framework Directive).

[4672]

NOTES

1 OJ L101, 1.4.1998, p 24.

2 OJ L199, 26.7.1997, p 32. Directive as amended by Directive 98/61/EC (OJ L268, 3.10.1998, p 37).

Article 17

Regulatory controls on retail services

1. Member States shall ensure that, where—

(a) as a result of a market analysis carried out in accordance with Article 16(3) a national regulatory authority determines that a given retail market identified in accordance with Article 15 of Directive 2002/21/EC (Framework Directive) is not effectively competitive, and

(b) the national regulatory authority concludes that obligations imposed under Directive 2002/19/EC (Access Directive), or Article 19 of this Directive would not result in the achievement of the objectives set out in Article 8 of Directive 2002/21/EC (Framework Directive),

national regulatory authorities shall impose appropriate regulatory obligations on undertakings identified as having significant market power on a given retail market in accordance with Article 14 of Directive 2002/21/EC (Framework Directive).

2. Obligations imposed under paragraph 1 shall be based on the nature of the problem identified and be proportionate and justified in the light of the objectives laid down in Article 8 of Directive 2002/21/EC (Framework Directive). The obligations imposed may include requirements that the identified undertakings do not charge excessive prices, inhibit market entry or restrict competition by setting predatory prices, show undue preference to specific end-users or unreasonably bundle services. National regulatory authorities may apply to such undertakings appropriate retail price cap measures, measures to control individual tariffs, or measures to orient tariffs towards costs or prices on comparable markets, in order to protect end-user interests whilst promoting effective competition.

3. National regulatory authorities shall, on request, submit information to the Commission concerning the retail controls applied and, where appropriate, the cost accounting systems used by the undertakings concerned.

4. National regulatory authorities shall ensure that, where an undertaking is subject to retail tariff regulation or other relevant retail controls, the necessary and appropriate cost accounting systems are implemented. National regulatory authorities may specify the format and accounting methodology to be used. Compliance with the cost accounting system shall be

verified by a qualified independent body. National regulatory authorities shall ensure that a statement concerning compliance is published annually.

5. Without prejudice to Article 9(2) and Article 10, national regulatory authorities shall not apply retail control mechanisms under paragraph 1 of this Article to geographical or user markets where they are satisfied that there is effective competition.

[4673]

Article 18

Regulatory controls on the minimum set of leased lines

1. Where, as a result of the market analysis carried out in accordance with Article 16(3), a national regulatory authority determines that the market for the provision of part or all of the minimum set of leased lines is not effectively competitive, it shall identify undertakings with significant market power in the provision of those specific elements of the minimum set of leased lines services in all or part of its territory in accordance with Article 14 of Directive 2002/21/EC (Framework Directive). The national regulatory authority shall impose obligations regarding the provision of the minimum set of leased lines, as identified in the list of standards published in the *Official Journal of the European Communities* in accordance with Article 17 of Directive 2002/21/EC (Framework Directive), and the conditions for such provision set out in Annex VII to this Directive, on such undertakings in relation to those specific leased line markets.

2. Where as a result of the market analysis carried out in accordance with Article 16(3), a national regulatory authority determines that a relevant market for the provision of leased lines in the minimum set is effectively competitive, it shall withdraw the obligations referred to in paragraph 1 in relation to this specific leased line market.

3. The minimum set of leased lines with harmonised characteristics, and associated standards, shall be published in the *Official Journal of the European Communities* as part of the list of standards referred to in Article 17 of Directive 2002/21/EC (Framework Directive). The Commission may adopt amendments necessary to adapt the minimum set of leased lines to new technical developments and to changes in market demand, including the possible deletion of certain types of leased line from the minimum set, acting in accordance with the procedure referred to in Article 37(2) of this Directive.

[4674]

Article 19

Carrier selection and carrier pre-selection

National regulatory authorities shall require undertakings notified as having significant market power for the provision of connection to and use of the public telephone network at a fixed location in accordance with Article 16(3) to enable their subscribers to access the services of any interconnected provider of publicly available telephone services—

(a) on a call-by-call basis by dialling a carrier selection code; and

(b) by means of pre-selection, with a facility to override any pre-selected choice on a call-by-call basis by dialling a carrier selection code.

2. User requirements for these facilities to be implemented on other networks or in other ways shall be assessed in accordance with the market analysis procedure laid down in Article 16 of Directive 2002/21/EC (Framework Directive) and implemented in accordance with Article 12 of Directive 2002/19/EC (Access Directive).

3. National regulatory authorities shall ensure that pricing for access and interconnection related to the provision of the facilities in paragraph 1 is cost oriented and that direct charges to subscribers, if any, do not act as a disincentive for the use of these facilities.

[4675]

CHAPTER IV
END-USER INTERESTS AND RIGHTS

Article 20

Contracts

1. Paragraphs 2, 3 and 4 apply without prejudice to Community rules on consumer protection, in particular Directives 97/7/EC and 93/13/EC, and national rules in conformity with Community law.

2. Member States shall ensure that, where subscribing to services providing connection and/or access to the public telephone network, consumers have a right to a contract with an undertaking or undertakings providing such services. The contract shall specify at least—

(a) the identity and address of the supplier;

(b) services provided, the service quality levels offered, as well as the time for the initial connection;

(c) the types of maintenance service offered;

(d) particulars of prices and tariffs and the means by which up-to-date information on all applicable tariffs and maintenance charges may be obtained;

(e) the duration of the contract, the conditions for renewal and termination of services and of the contract;

(f) any compensation and the refund arrangements which apply if contracted service quality levels are not met; and

(g) the method of initiating procedures for settlement of disputes in accordance with Article 34.

Member States may extend these obligations to cover other end-users.

3. Where contracts are concluded between consumers and electronic communications services providers other than those providing connection and/or access to the public telephone network, the information in paragraph 2 shall also be included in such contracts. Member States may extend this obligation to cover other end-users.

4. Subscribers shall have a right to withdraw from their contracts without penalty upon notice of proposed modifications in the contractual conditions. Subscribers shall be given adequate notice, not shorter than one month, ahead of any such modifications and shall be informed at the same time of their right to withdraw, without penalty, from such contracts, if they do not accept the new conditions.

[4676]

Article 21

Transparency and publication of information

1. Member States shall ensure that transparent and up-to-date information on applicable prices and tariffs, and on standard terms and conditions, in respect of access to and use of publicly available telephone services is available to end-users and consumers, in accordance with the provisions of Annex II.

2. National regulatory authorities shall encourage the provision of information to enable end-users, as far as appropriate, and consumers to make an independent evaluation of the cost of alternative usage patterns, by means of, for instance, interactive guides.

[4677]

Article 22

Quality of service

1. Member States shall ensure that national regulatory authorities are, after taking account of the views of interested parties, able to require undertakings that provide publicly available electronic communications services to publish comparable, adequate and up-to-date information for end-users on the quality of their services. The information shall, on request, also be supplied to the national regulatory authority in advance of its publication.

2. National regulatory authorities may specify, *inter alia*, the quality of service parameters to be measured, and the content, form and manner of information to be published, in order to ensure that end-users have access to comprehensive, comparable and user-friendly information. Where appropriate, the parameters, definitions and measurement methods given in Annex III could be used.

[4678]

Article 23

Integrity of the network

Member States shall take all necessary steps to ensure the integrity of the public telephone network at fixed locations and, in the event of catastrophic network breakdown or in cases of *force majeure*, the availability of the public telephone network and publicly available telephone services at fixed locations. Member States shall ensure that undertakings providing publicly available telephone services at fixed locations take all reasonable steps to ensure uninterrupted access to emergency services.

[4679]

Article 24

Interoperability of consumer digital television equipment

In accordance with the provisions of Annex VI, Member States shall ensure the interoperability of the consumer digital television equipment referred to therein.

[4680]

Article 25

Operator assistance and directory enquiry services

1. Member States shall ensure that subscribers to publicly available telephone services have the right to have an entry in the publicly available directory referred to in Article 5(1)(a).

2. Member States shall ensure that all undertakings which assign telephone numbers to subscribers meet all reasonable requests to make available, for the purposes of the provision of publicly available directory enquiry services and directories, the relevant information in an agreed format on terms which are fair, objective, cost oriented and non-discriminatory.

3. Member States shall ensure that all end-users provided with a connection to the public telephone network can access operator assistance services and directory enquiry services in accordance with Article 5(1)(b).

4. Member States shall not maintain any regulatory restrictions which prevent end-users in one Member State from accessing directly the directory enquiry service in another Member State.

5. Paragraphs 1, 2, 3 and 4 apply subject to the requirements of Community legislation on the protection of personal data and privacy and, in particular, Article 11 of Directive 97/66/EC.

[4681]

Article 26

Single European emergency call number

1. Member States shall ensure that, in addition to any other national emergency call numbers specified by the national regulatory authorities, all end-users of publicly available telephone services, including users of public pay telephones, are able to call the emergency services free of charge, by using the single European emergency call number "112".

2. Member States shall ensure that calls to the single European emergency call number "112" are appropriately answered and handled in a manner best suited to the national organisation of emergency systems and within the technological possibilities of the networks.

3. Member States shall ensure that undertakings which operate public telephone networks make caller location information available to authorities handling emergencies, to the extent technically feasible, for all calls to the single European emergency call number "112".

4. Member States shall ensure that citizens are adequately informed about the existence and use of the single European emergency call number "112".

[4682]

Article 27

European telephone access codes

1. Member States shall ensure that the "00" code is the standard international access code. Special arrangements for making calls between adjacent locations across borders between Member States may be established or continued. The end-users of publicly available telephone services in the locations concerned shall be fully informed of such arrangements.

2. Member States shall ensure that all undertakings that operate public telephone networks handle all calls to the European telephony numbering space, without prejudice to the need for an undertaking that operates a public telephone network to recover the cost of the conveyance of calls on its network.

[4683]

Article 28

Non-geographic numbers

Member States shall ensure that end-users from other Member States are able to access non-geographic numbers within their territory where technically and economically feasible, except where a called subscriber has chosen for commercial reasons to limit access by calling parties located in specific geographical areas.

[4684]

Article 29

Provision of additional facilities

1. Member States shall ensure that national regulatory authorities are able to require all undertakings that operate public telephone networks to make available to end-users the facilities listed in Annex I, Part B, subject to technical feasibility and economic viability.

2. A Member State may decide to waive paragraph 1 in all or part of its territory if it considers, after taking into account the views of interested parties, that there is sufficient access to these facilities.

3. Without prejudice to Article 10(2), Member States may impose the obligations in Annex I, Part A, point (e), concerning disconnection as a general requirement on all undertakings.

[4685]

Article 30

Number portability

1. Member States shall ensure that all subscribers of publicly available telephone services, including mobile services, who so request can retain their number(s) independently of the undertaking providing the service—

(a) in the case of geographic numbers, at a specific location; and

(b) in the case of non-geographic numbers, at any location.

This paragraph does not apply to the porting of numbers between networks providing services at a fixed location and mobile networks.

2. National regulatory authorities shall ensure that pricing for interconnection related to the provision of number portability is cost oriented and that direct charges to subscribers, if any, do not act as a disincentive for the use of these facilities.

3. National regulatory authorities shall not impose retail tariffs for the porting of numbers in a manner that would distort competition, such as by setting specific or common retail tariffs.

[4686]

Article 31

"Must carry" obligations

1. Member States may impose reasonable "must carry" obligations, for the transmission of specified radio and television broadcast channels and services, on undertakings under their jurisdiction providing electronic communications networks used for the distribution of radio or television broadcasts to the public where a significant number of end-users of such networks use them as their principal means to receive radio and television broadcasts. Such obligations shall only be imposed where they are necessary to meet clearly defined general interest objectives and shall be proportionate and transparent. The obligations shall be subject to periodical review.

2. Neither paragraph 1 of this Article nor Article 3(2) of Directive 2002/19/EC (Access Directive) shall prejudice the ability of Member States to determine appropriate remuneration, if any, in respect of measures taken in accordance with this Article while ensuring that, in similar circumstances, there is no discrimination in the treatment of undertakings providing electronic communications networks. Where remuneration is provided for, Member States shall ensure that it is applied in a proportionate and transparent manner.

[4687]

CHAPTER V
GENERAL AND FINAL PROVISIONS

Article 32

Additional mandatory services

Member States may decide to make additional services, apart from services within the universal service obligations as defined in Chapter II, publicly available in its own territory but, in such circumstances, no compensation mechanism involving specific undertakings may be imposed.

[4688]

Article 33

Consultation with interested parties

1. Member States shall ensure as far as appropriate that national regulatory authorities take account of the views of end-users, and consumers (including, in particular, disabled users), manufacturers, undertakings that provide electronic communications networks and/or services on issues related to all end-user and consumer rights concerning publicly available electronic communications services, in particular where they have a significant impact on the market.

2. Where appropriate, interested parties may develop, with the guidance of national regulatory authorities, mechanisms, involving consumers, user groups and service providers, to improve the general quality of service provision by, *inter alia*, developing and monitoring codes of conduct and operating standards.

[4689]

Article 34

Out-of-court dispute resolution

1. Member States shall ensure that transparent, simple and inexpensive out-of-court procedures are available for dealing with unresolved disputes, involving consumers, relating to issues covered by this Directive. Member States shall adopt measures to ensure that such procedures enable disputes to be settled fairly and promptly and may, where warranted, adopt a system of reimbursement and/or compensation. Member States may extend these obligations to cover disputes involving other end-users.

2. Member States shall ensure that their legislation does not hamper the establishment of complaints offices and the provision of on-line services at the appropriate territorial level to facilitate access to dispute resolution by consumers and end-users.

3. Where such disputes involve parties in different Member States, Member States shall coordinate their efforts with a view to bringing about a resolution of the dispute.

4. This Article is without prejudice to national court procedures.

[4690]

Article 35

Technical adjustment

Amendments necessary to adapt Annexes I, II, III, VI and VII to technological developments or to changes in market demand shall be adopted by the Commission, acting in accordance with the procedure referred to in Article 37(2).

[4691]

Article 36

Notification, monitoring and review procedures

1. National regulatory authorities shall notify to the Commission by at the latest the date of application referred to in Article 38(1), second subparagraph, and immediately in the event of any change thereafter in the names of undertakings designated as having universal service obligations under Article 8(1).

The Commission shall make the information available in a readily accessible form, and shall distribute it to the Communications Committee referred to in Article 37.

2. National regulatory authorities shall notify to the Commission the names of operators deemed to have significant market power for the purposes of this Directive, and the obligations imposed upon them under this Directive. Any changes affecting the obligations imposed upon undertakings or of the undertakings affected under the provisions of this Directive shall be notified to the Commission without delay.

3. The Commission shall periodically review the functioning of this Directive and report to the European Parliament and to the Council, on the first occasion not later than three years after the date of application referred to in Article 38(1), second subparagraph. The Member States and national regulatory authorities shall supply the necessary information to the Commission for this purpose.

[4692]

Article 37

Committee

1. The Commission be assisted by the Communications Committee, set up by Article 22 of Directive 2002/21/EC (Framework Directive).

2. Where reference is made to this paragraph, Articles 5 and 7 of Decision 1999/468/EC shall apply, having regard to the provisions of Article 8 thereof.

The period laid down in Article 5(6) of Decision 1999/468/EC shall be three months.

3. The Committee shall adopt its rules of procedure.

[4693]

Article 38

Transposition

1. Member States shall adopt and publish the laws, regulations and administrative provisions necessary to comply with this Directive by 24 July 2003 at the latest. They shall forthwith inform the Commission thereof.

They shall apply those measures from 25 July 2003.

2. When Member States adopt these measures, they shall contain a reference to this Directive or be accompanied by such a reference on the occasion of their official publication. The methods of making such a reference shall be laid down by the Member States.

3. Member States shall communicate to the Commission the text of the provisions of national law which they adopt in the field governed by this Directive and of any subsequent modifications to those provisions.

[4694]

Article 39

Entry into force

This Directive shall enter into force on the day of its publication in the *Official Journal of the European Communities*.

[4695]

Article 40

Addressees

This Directive is addressed to the Member States.

[4696]

Done at Brussels, 7 March 2002.

PART VI
TELECOMMUNICATIONS

ANNEX I
DESCRIPTION OF FACILITIES AND SERVICES REFERRED TO IN ARTICLE 10 (CONTROL OF EXPENDITURE) AND ARTICLE 29 (ADDITIONAL FACILITIES)

PART A:
FACILITIES AND SERVICES REFERRED TO IN ARTICLE 10

(a) *Itemised billing*

Member States are to ensure that national regulatory authorities, subject to the requirements of relevant legislation on the protection of personal data and privacy, may lay down the basic level of itemised bills which are to be provided by designated undertakings (as established in Article 8) to consumers free of charge in order that they can—

(i) allow verification and control of the charges incurred in using the public telephone network at a fixed location and/or related publicly available telephone services, and

(ii) adequately monitor their usage and expenditure and thereby exercise a reasonable degree of control over their bills.

Where appropriate, additional levels of detail may be offered to subscribers at reasonable tariffs or at no charge.

Calls which are free of charge to the calling subscriber, including calls to helplines, are not to be identified in the calling subscriber's itemised bill.

(b) *Selective call barring for outgoing calls, free of charge*

Ie the facility whereby the subscriber can, on request to the telephone service provider, bar outgoing calls of defined types or to defined types of numbers free of charge.

(c) *Pre-payment systems*

Member States are to ensure that national regulatory authorities may require designated undertakings to provide means for consumers to pay for access to the public telephone network and use of publicly available telephone services on pre-paid terms.

(d) *Phased payment of connection fees*

Member States are to ensure that national regulatory authorities may require designated undertakings to allow consumers to pay for connection to the public telephone network on the basis of payments phased over time.

(e) *Non-payment of bills*

Member States are to authorise specified measures, which are to be proportionate, non-discriminatory and published, to cover non-payment of telephone bills for use of the public telephone network at fixed locations. These measures are to ensure that due warning of any consequent service interruption or disconnection is given to the subscriber beforehand. Except in cases of fraud, persistent late payment or non-payment, these measures are to ensure, as far as is technically feasible, that any service interruption is confined to the service concerned. Disconnection for non-payment of bills should take place only after due warning is given to the subscriber. Member States may allow a period of limited service prior to complete disconnection, during which only calls that do not incur a charge to the subscriber (e g "112" calls) are permitted.

[4697]

PART B:
LIST OF FACILITIES REFERRED TO IN ARTICLE 29

(a) *Tone dialling or DTMF (dual-tone multi-frequency operation)*

Ie the public telephone network supports the use of DTMF tones as defined in ETSI ETR 207 for end-to-end signalling throughout the network both within a Member State and between Member States.

(b) *Calling-line identification*

Ie the calling party's number is presented to the called party prior to the call being established.

This facility should be provided in accordance with relevant legislation on protection of personal data and privacy, in particular Directive 97/66/EC.

To the extent technically feasible, operators should provide data and signals to facilitate the offering of calling-line identity and tone dialling across Member State boundaries.

[4698]

ANNEX II
INFORMATION TO BE PUBLISHED IN ACCORDANCE WITH ARTICLE 21 (TRANSPARENCY AND PUBLICATION OF INFORMATION)

The national regulatory authority has a responsibility to ensure that the information in this Annex is published, in accordance with Article 21. It is for the national regulatory authority to decide which information is to be published by the undertakings providing public telephone networks and/or publicly available telephone services and which information is to be published by the national regulatory authority itself, so as to ensure that consumers are able to make informed choices.

1. Name(s) and address(es) of undertaking(s).

Ie names and head office addresses of undertakings providing public telephone networks and/ or publicly available telephone services.

2. Publicly available telephone services offered.

2.1. Scope of the publicly available telephone service.

Description of the publicly available telephone services offered, indicating what is included in the subscription charge and the periodic rental charge (e g operator services, directories, directory enquiry services, selective call barring, itemised billing, maintenance, etc).

2.2. Standard tariffs covering access, all types of usage charges, maintenance, and including details of standard discounts applied and special and targeted tariff schemes.

2.3. Compensation/refund policy, including specific details of any compensation/refund schemes offered.

2.4. Types of maintenance service offered.

2.5. Standard contract conditions, including any minimum contractual period, if relevant.

3. Dispute settlement mechanisms including those developed by the undertaking.

4. Information about rights as regards universal service, including the facilities and services mentioned in Annex I.

[4699]

ANNEX III
QUALITY OF SERVICE PARAMETERS

Supply-time and quality-of-service parameters, definitions and measurement methods referred to Articles 11 and 22

Parameter[1]	*Definition*	*Measurement method*
Supply time for initial connection	ETSI EG 201 769–1	ETSI EG 201 769–1
Fault rate per access line	ETSI EG 201 769–1	ETSI EG 201 769–1
Fault repair time	ETSI EG 201 769–1	ETSI EG 201 769–1
Unsuccessful call ratio[2]	ETSI EG 201 769–1	ETSI EG 201 769–1
Call set up time[2]	ETSI EG 201 769–1	ETSI EG 201 769–1
Response times for operator services	ETSI EG 201 769–1	ETSI EG 201 769–1
Response times for directory enquiry services	ETSI EG 201 769–1	ETSI EG 201 769–1
Proportion of coin and card operated public pay telephones in working order	ETSI EG 201 769–1	ETSI EG 201 769–1
Bill correctness complaints	ETSI EG 201 769–1	ETSI EG 201 769–1

[4700]

[1] Parameters should allow for performance to be analysed at a regional level (i e no less than Level 2 in the Nomenclature of Territorial Units for Statistics (NUTS) established by Eurostat)

[2] Member States may decide not to require that up-to-date information concerning the performance for these two parameters be kept, if evidence is available to show that performance in these two areas is satisfactory

Note: Version number of ETSI EG 201 769–1 is 1.1.1 (April 2000).

ANNEX IV
CALCULATING THE NET COST, IF ANY, OF UNIVERSAL SERVICE OBLIGATIONS AND ESTABLISHING ANY RECOVERY OR SHARING MECHANISM IN ACCORDANCE WITH ARTICLES 12 AND 13

PART A: CALCULATION OF NET COST

Universal service obligations refer to those obligations placed upon an undertaking by a Member State which concern the provision of a network and service throughout a specified geographical area, including, where required, averaged prices in that geographical area for the provision of that service or provision of specific tariff options for consumers with low incomes or with special social needs.

National regulatory authorities are to consider all means to ensure appropriate incentives for undertakings (designated or not) to provide universal service obligations cost efficiently. In undertaking a calculation exercise, the net cost of universal service obligations is to be calculated as the difference between the net cost for a designated undertaking of operating with the universal service obligations and operating without the universal service obligations. This applies whether the network in a particular Member State is fully developed or is still undergoing development and expansion. Due attention is to be given to correctly assessing the costs that any designated undertaking would have chosen to avoid had there been no universal service obligation. The net cost calculation should assess the benefits, including intangible benefits, to the universal service operator.

The calculation is to be based upon the costs attributable to—

(i) elements of the identified services which can only be provided at a loss or provided under cost conditions falling outside normal commercial standards. This category may include service elements such as access to emergency telephone services, provision of certain public pay telephones, provision of certain services or equipment for disabled people, etc;

(ii) specific end-users or groups of end-users who, taking into account the cost of providing the specified network and service, the revenue generated and any geographical averaging of prices imposed by the Member State, can only be served at a loss or under cost conditions falling outside normal commercial standards.
This category includes those end-users or groups of end-users which would not be served by a commercial operator which did not have an obligation to provide universal service.

The calculation of the net cost of specific aspects of universal service obligations is to be made separately and so as to avoid the double counting of any direct or indirect benefits and costs. The overall net cost of universal service obligations to any undertaking is to be calculated as the sum of the net costs arising from the specific components of universal service obligations, taking account of any intangible benefits. The responsibility for verifying the net cost lies with the national regulatory authority.

[4701]

PART B: RECOVERY OF ANY NET COSTS OF UNIVERSAL SERVICE OBLIGATIONS

The recovery or financing of any net costs of universal service obligations requires designated undertakings with universal service obligations to be compensated for the services they provide under non-commercial conditions. Because such a compensation involves financial transfers, Member States are to ensure that these are undertaken in an objective, transparent, non-discriminatory and proportionate manner. This means that the transfers result in the least distortion to competition and to user demand.

In accordance with Article 13(3), a sharing mechanism based on a fund should use a transparent and neutral means for collecting contributions that avoids the danger of a double imposition of contributions falling on both outputs and inputs of undertakings.

The independent body administering the fund is to be responsible for collecting contributions from undertakings which are assessed as liable to contribute to the net cost of universal service obligations in the Member State and is to oversee the transfer of sums due and/or administrative payments to the undertakings entitled to receive payments from the fund.

[4702]

ANNEX V
PROCESS FOR REVIEWING THE SCOPE OF UNIVERSAL SERVICE IN ACCORDANCE WITH ARTICLE 15

In considering whether a review of the scope of universal service obligations should be undertaken, the Commission is to take into consideration the following elements—

- social and market developments in terms of the services used by consumers,
- social and market developments in terms of the availability and choice of services to consumers,
- technological developments in terms of the way services are provided to consumers.

In considering whether the scope of universal service obligations be changed or redefined, the Commission is to take into consideration the following elements—

- are specific services available to and used by a majority of consumers and does the lack of availability or non-use by a minority of consumers result in social exclusion, and
- does the availability and use of specific services convey a general net benefit to all consumers such that public intervention is warranted in circumstances where the specific services are not provided to the public under normal commercial circumstances?

[4703]

ANNEX VI
INTEROPERABILITY OF DIGITAL CONSUMER EQUIPMENT REFERRED TO IN ARTICLE 24

1. *The common scrambling algorithm and free-to-air reception*

All consumer equipment intended for the reception of digital television signals, for sale or rent or otherwise made available in the Community, capable of descrambling digital television signals, is to possess the capability to—

- allow the descrambling of such signals according to the common European scrambling algorithm as administered by a recognised European standards organisation, currently ETSI;
- display signals that have been transmitted in clear provided that, in the event that such equipment is rented, the rentee is in compliance with the relevant rental agreement.

2. *Interoperability for analogue and digital television sets*

Any analogue television set with an integral screen of visible diagonal greater than 42 cm which is put on the market for sale or rent in the Community is to be fitted with at least one open interface socket, as standardised by a recognised European standards organisation, e g as given in the CENELEC EN 50 049–1:1997 standard, permitting simple connection of peripherals, especially additional decoders and digital receivers.

Any digital television set with an integral screen of visible diagonal greater than 30 cm which is put on the market for sale or rent in the Community is to be fitted with at least one open interface socket (either standardised by, or conforming to a standard adopted by, a recognised European standards organisation, or conforming to an industry-wide specification) e g the DVB common interface connector, permitting simple connection of peripherals, and able to pass all the elements of a digital television signal, including information relating to interactive and conditionally accessed services.

[4704]

ANNEX VII
CONDITIONS FOR THE MINIMUM SET OF LEASED LINES REFERRED TO IN ARTICLE 18

Note: In accordance with the procedure in Article 18, provision of the minimum set of leased lines under the conditions established by Directive 92/44/EC should continue until such time as the national regulatory authority determines that there is effective competition in the relevant leased lines market.

National regulatory authorities are to ensure that provision of the minimum set of leased lines referred to in Article 18 follows the basic principles of non-discrimination, cost orientation and transparency.

1. *Non discrimination*

National regulatory authorities are to ensure that the organisations identified as having significant market power pursuant to Article 18(1) adhere to the principle of non-discrimination when providing leased lines referred to in Article 18. Those organisations are to apply similar conditions in similar circumstances to organisations providing similar services, and are to provide leased lines to others under the same conditions and of the same quality as they provide for their own services, or those of their subsidiaries or partners, where applicable.

2. *Cost orientation*

National regulatory authorities are, where appropriate, to ensure that tariffs for leased lines referred to in Article 18 follow the basic principles of cost orientation.

To this end, national regulatory authorities are to ensure that undertakings identified as having significant market power pursuant to Article 18(1) formulate and put in practice a suitable cost accounting system.

National regulatory authorities are to keep available, with an adequate level of detail, information on the cost accounting systems applied by such undertakings. They are to submit this information to the Commission on request.

3. *Transparency*

National regulatory authorities are to ensure that the following information in respect of the minimum set of leased lines referred to in Article 18 is published in an easily accessible form.

3.1. Technical characteristics, including the physical and electrical characteristics as well as the detailed technical and performance specifications which apply at the network termination point.

3.2. Tariffs, including the initial connection charges, the periodic rental charges and other charges. Where tariffs are differentiated, this must be indicated.

Where, in response to a particular request, an organisation identified as having significant market power pursuant to Article 18(1) considers it unreasonable to provide a leased line in the minimum set under its published tariffs and supply conditions, it must seek the agreement of the national regulatory authority to vary those conditions in that case.

3.3. Supply conditions, including at least the following elements—

— information concerning the ordering procedure,

— the typical delivery period, which is the period, counted from the date when the user has made a firm request for a leased line, in which 95% of all leased lines of the same type have been put through to the customers.

This period will be established on the basis of the actual delivery periods of leased lines during a recent time interval of reasonable duration. The calculation must not include cases where late delivery periods were requested by users,

— the contractual period, which includes the period which is in general laid down in the contract and the minimum contractual period which the user is obliged to accept,

— the typical repair time, which is the period, counted from the time when a failure message has been given to the responsible unit within the undertaking identified as having significant market power pursuant to Article 18(1) up to the moment in which 80% of all leased lines of the same type have been re-established and in appropriate cases notified back in operation to the users. Where different classes of quality of repair are offered for the same type of leased lines, the different typical repair times shall be published,

— any refund procedure.

In addition where a Member State considers that the achieved performance for the provision of the minimum set of leased lines does not meet users' needs, it may define appropriate targets for the supply conditions listed above.

[4705]

COMMISSION DIRECTIVE

of 16 September 2002

on competition in the markets for electronic communications networks and services

(2002/77/EC)

(Text with EEA relevance)

NOTES

Date of publication in OJ: OJ L249, 17.9.2002, p 21.

THE COMMISSION OF THE EUROPEAN COMMUNITIES,

Having regard to the Treaty establishing the European Community, and in particular Article 86(3) thereof,

Whereas—

(1) Commission Directive 90/388/EEC of 28 June 1990 on competition in the markets for telecommunications services,[1] as last amended by Directive 1999/64/EC,[2] has been substantially amended several times. Since further amendments are to be made, it should be recast in the interest of clarity.

(2) Article 86 of the Treaty entrusts the Commission with the task of ensuring that, in the case of public undertakings and undertakings enjoying special or exclusive rights, Member States comply with their obligations under Community law. Pursuant to Article 86(3), the Commission can specify and clarify the obligations arising from that Article and, in that framework, set out the conditions which are necessary to allow the Commission to perform effectively the duty of surveillance imposed upon it by that paragraph.

(3) Directive 90/388/EEC required Member States to abolish special and exclusive rights for the provision of telecommunications services, initially for other services than voice telephony, satellite services and mobile radiocommunications, and then it gradually established full competition in the telecommunications market.

(4) A number of other Directives in this field have also been adopted under Article 95 of the Treaty by the European Parliament and the Council aiming, principally, at the establishment of an internal market for telecommunications services through the implementation of open network provision and the provision of a universal service in an environment of open and competitive markets. Those Directives should be repealed with effect from 25 July 2003 when the new regulatory framework for electronic communications networks and services is applied.

(5) The new electronic communications regulatory framework consists of one general Directive, Directive 2002/21/EC of the European Parliament and of the Council of 7 March 2002 on a common regulatory framework for electronic communications networks and services (Framework Directive)[3] and four specific Directives: Directive 2002/20/EC of the European Parliament and of the Council of 7 March 2002 on the authorisation of electronic communications networks and services (Authorisation Directive),[4] Directive 2002/19/EC of the European Parliament and of the Council of 7 March 2002 on access to, and interconnection of, electronic communications networks and associated facilities (Access Directive),[5] Directive 2002/22/EC of the European Parliament and of the Council of 7 March 2002 on universal service and users' rights relating to electronic communications networks and services (Universal Service Directive),[6] and Directive 2002/58/EC of the European Parliament and of the Council of 12 July 2002 concerning the processing of personal data and the protection of privacy in the electronic communications (Directive on privacy and electronic communications) sector.[7]

(6) In the light of the developments which have marked the liberalisation process and the gradual opening of the telecommunications markets in Europe since 1990, certain definitions used in Directive 90/388/EEC and its amending acts should be adjusted in order to reflect the latest technological developments in the telecommunications field, or replaced in order to take account of the convergence phenomenon which has shaped the information technology, media

PART VI TELECOMMUNICATIONS

and telecommunications industries over recent years. The wording of certain provisions should, where possible, be clarified in order to facilitate their application, taking into account, where appropriate, the relevant Directives adopted under Article 95 of the Treaty, and the experience acquired through the implementation of Directive 90/388/EEC as amended.

(7) This Directive makes reference to "electronic communications services" and "electronic communications networks" rather than the previously used terms "telecommunications services" and "telecommunications networks". These new definitions are indispensable in order to take account of the convergence phenomenon by bringing together under one single definition all electronic communications services and/or networks which are concerned with the conveyance of signals by wire, radio, optical or other electromagnetic means (ie fixed, wireless, cable television, satellite networks). Thus, the transmission and broadcasting of radio and television programmes should be recognised as an electronic communication service and networks used for such transmission and broadcasting should likewise be recognised as electronic communications networks. Furthermore, it should be made clear that the new definition of electronic communications networks also covers fibre networks which enable third parties, using their own switching or routing equipment, to convey signals.

(8) In this context, it should be made clear that Member States must remove (if they have not already done so) exclusive and special rights for the provision of all electronic communications networks, not just those for the provision of electronic communications services and should ensure that undertakings are entitled to provide such services without prejudice to the provisions of Directives 2002/19/EC, 2002/20/EC, 2002/21/EC and 2002/22/EC. The definition of electronic communications networks should also mean that Member States are not permitted to restrict the right of an operator to establish, extend and/or provide a cable network on the ground that such network could also be used for the transmission of radio and television programming. In particular, special or exclusive rights which amount to restricting the use of electronic communications networks for the transmission and distribution of television signals are contrary to Article 86(1), read in conjunction with Article 43 (right of establishment) and/or Article 82(b) of the EC Treaty insofar as they have the effect of permitting a dominant undertaking to limit "production, markets or technical development to the prejudice of consumers". This is, however, without prejudice to the specific rules adopted by the Member States in accordance with Community law, and, in particular, in accordance with Council Directive 89/552/EEC of 3 October 1989,[8] on the coordination of certain provisions laid down by law, regulation or administrative action in Member States concerning the pursuit of television broadcasting activities, as amended by Directive 97/36/EC of the European Parliament and of the Council,[9] governing the distribution of audiovisual programmes intended for the general public.

(9) Pursuant to the principle of proportionality, Member States should no longer make the provision of electronic communications services and the establishment and provision of electronic communications networks subject to a licensing regime but to a general authorisation regime. This is also required by Directive 2002/20/EC, according to which electronic communications services or networks should be provided on the basis of a general authorisation and not on the basis of a license. An aggrieved party should have the right to challenge a decision preventing him from providing electronic communications services or networks before an independent body and, ultimately, before a court or a tribunal. It is a fundamental principle of Community law that an individual is entitled to effective judicial protection whenever a State measure violates rights conferred upon him by the provisions of a Directive.

(10) Public authorities may exercise a dominant influence on the behaviour of public undertakings, as a result either of the rules governing the undertaking or of the manner in which the shareholdings are distributed. Therefore, where Member States control vertically integrated network operators which operate networks which have been established under special or exclusive rights, those Member States should ensure that, in order to avoid potential breaches of the Treaty competition rules, such operators, when they enjoy a dominant position in the relevant market, do not discriminate in favour of their own activities. It follows that Member States should take all measures necessary to prevent any discrimination between such vertically integrated operators and their competitors.

(11) This Directive should also clarify the principle derived from Commission Directive 96/ 2/EC of 16 January 1996 amending Directive 90/388/EC with regard to mobile and personal communications,[10] by providing that Member States should not grant exclusive or special rights of use of radio frequencies and that the rights of use of those frequencies should be assigned according to objective, non-discriminatory and transparent procedures. This should be without prejudice to specific criteria and procedures adopted by Member States to grant such rights to providers of radio or television broadcast content services with a view to pursuing general interest objectives in conformity with Community law.

(12) Any national scheme pursuant to Directive 2002/22/EC, serving to share the net cost of the provision of universal service obligations shall be based on objective, transparent and non-discriminatory criteria and shall be consistent with the principles of proportionality and of least market distortion. Least market distortion means that contributions should be recovered in a way that as far as possible minimises the impact of the financial burden falling on end-users, for example by spreading contributions as widely as possible.

(13) Where rights and obligations arising from international conventions setting up international satellite organisations are not compatible with the competition rules of the Treaty, Member States should take, in accordance with Article 307 of the EC Treaty, all appropriate steps to eliminate such incompatibilities. This Directive should clarify this obligation because Article 3 of Directive 94/46/EC,[11] merely required Member States to "communicate to the Commission" the information they possessed on such incompatibilities. Article 11 of this Directive should clarify the obligation on Member States to remove any restrictions which could still be in force because of those international conventions.

(14) This Directive should maintain the obligation imposed on Member States by Directive 1999/64/EC, so as to ensure that dominant providers of electronic communications networks and publicly available telephone services operate their public electronic communication network and cable television network as separate legal entities.

(15) This Directive should be without prejudice to obligations of the Member States concerning the time limits set out in Annex I, Part B, within which the Member States are to comply with the preceding Directives.

(16) Member States should supply to the Commission any information which is necessary to demonstrate that existing national implementing legislation reflects the clarifications provided for in this Directive as compared with Directives 90/388/EC, 94/46/EC, 95/51/EC,[12] 96/2/EC, 96/19/EC[13] and 1999/64/EC.

(17) In the light of the above, Directive 90/388/EC should be repealed,

NOTES

1 OJ L192, 24.7.1990, p 10.
2 OJ L175, 10.7.1999, p 39.
3 OJ L108, 24.4.2002, p 33.
4 OJ L108, 24.4.2002, p 21.
5 OJ L108, 24.4.2002, p 7.
6 OJ L108, 24.4.2002, p 51.
7 OJ L201, 31.7.2002, p 37.
8 OJ L298, 17.10.1989, p 23.
9 OJ L202, 30.7.1997, p 60.
10 OJ L20, 26.1.1996, p 59.
11 OJ L268, 19.10.1994, p 15.
12 OJ L256, 26.10.1995, p 49.
13 OJ L74, 22.3.1996, p 13.

HAS ADOPTED THIS DIRECTIVE—

Article 1

Definitions

For the purposes of this Directive the following definitions shall apply—

1. "electronic communications network" shall mean transmission systems and, where applicable, switching or routing equipment and other resources which permit the conveyance of signals by wire, by radio, by optical or by other electromagnetic means, including satellite networks, fixed (circuit- and packet-switched, including Internet) and mobile terrestrial networks, and electricity cable systems, to the extent that they are used for the purpose of transmitting signals, networks used for radio and television broadcasting, and cable television networks, irrespective of the type of information conveyed;
2. "public communications network" shall mean an electronic communications network used wholly or mainly for the provision of public electronic communications services;
3. "electronic communications services" shall mean a service normally provided for remuneration which consists wholly or mainly in the conveyance of signals on electronic communications networks, including telecommunications services and transmission services in networks used for broadcasting but exclude services providing or exercising editorial control over, content transmitted using electronic communications networks and services; it does not include information society

PART VI TELECOMMUNICATIONS

services as defined in Article 1 of Directive 98/34/EC which do not consist wholly or mainly in the conveyance of signals on electronic communications networks;

4. "publicly available electronic communications services" shall mean electronic communications services available to the public;
5. "exclusive rights" shall mean the rights that are granted by a Member State to one undertaking through any legislative, regulatory or administrative instrument, reserving it the right to provide an electronic communications service or to undertake an electronic communications activity within a given geographical area;
6. "special rights" shall mean the rights that are granted by a Member State to a limited number of undertakings through any legislative, regulatory or administrative instrument which, within a given geographical area—
   (a) designates or limits to two or more the number of such undertakings authorised to provide an electronic communications service or undertake an electronic communications activity, otherwise than according to objective, proportional and non-discriminatory criteria, or
   (b) confers on undertakings, otherwise than according to such criteria, legal or regulatory advantages which substantially affect the ability of any other undertaking to provide the same electronic communications service or to undertake the same electronic communications activity in the same geographical area under substantially equivalent conditions;
7. "satellite earth station network" shall mean a configuration of two or more earth stations which interwork by means of a satellite;
8. "cable television networks" shall mean any mainly wire-based infrastructure established primarily for the delivery or distribution of radio or television broadcast to the public.

[4706]

Article 2

Exclusive and special rights for electronic communications networks and electronic communications services

1. Member States shall not grant or maintain in force exclusive or special rights for the establishment and/or the provision of electronic communications networks, or for the provision of publicly available electronic communications services.

2. Member States shall take all measures necessary to ensure that any undertaking is entitled to provide electronic communications services or to establish, extend or provide electronic communications networks.

3. Member States shall ensure that no restrictions are imposed or maintained on the provision of electronic communications services over electronic communications networks established by the providers of electronic communications services, over infrastructures provided by third parties, or by means of sharing networks, other facilities or sites without prejudice to the provisions of Directives 2002/19/EC, 2002/20/EC, 2002/21/EC and 2002/22/EC.

4. Member States shall ensure that a general authorisation granted to an undertaking to provide electronic communications services or to establish and/or provide electronic communications networks, as well as the conditions attached thereto, shall be based on objective, non-discriminatory, proportionate and transparent criteria.

5. Reasons shall be given for any decision taken on the grounds set out in Article 3(1) of Directive 2002/20/EC preventing an undertaking from providing electronic communications services or networks.

Any aggrieved party should have the possibility to challenge such a decision before a body that is independent of the parties involved and ultimately before a court or a tribunal.

[4707]

Article 3

Vertically integrated public undertakings

In addition to the requirements set out in Article 2(2), and without prejudice to Article 14 of Directive 2002/21/EC, Member States shall ensure that vertically integrated public undertakings which provide electronic communications networks and which are in a dominant position do not discriminate in favour of their own activities.

[4708]

Article 4

Rights of use of frequencies

Without prejudice to specific criteria and procedures adopted by Member States to grant rights of use of radio frequencies to providers of radio or television broadcast content services with a view to pursuing general interest objectives in conformity with Community law—

1. Member States shall not grant exclusive or special rights of use of radio frequencies for the provision of electronic communications services.
2. The assignment of radio frequencies for electronic communication services shall be based on objective, transparent, non-discriminatory and proportionate criteria.

[4709]

Article 5

Directory services

Member States shall ensure that all exclusive and/or special rights with regard to the establishment and provision of directory services on their territory, including both the publication of directories and directory enquiry services, are abolished.

[4710]

Article 6

Universal service obligations

1. Any national scheme pursuant to Directive 2002/22/EC, serving to share the net cost of the provision of universal service obligations shall be based on objective, transparent and non-discriminatory criteria and shall be consistent with the principle of proportionality and of least market distortion. In particular, where universal service obligations are imposed in whole or in part on public undertakings providing electronic communications services, this shall be taken into consideration in calculating any contribution to the net cost of universal service obligations.

2. Member States shall communicate any scheme of the kind referred to in paragraph 1 to the Commission.

[4711]

Article 7

Satellites

1. Member States shall ensure that any regulatory prohibition or restriction on the offer of space segment capacity to any authorised satellite earth station network operator are abolished, and shall authorise within their territory any space segment supplier to verify that the satellite earth station network for use in connection with the space segment of the supplier in question is in conformity with the published conditions for access to such person's space segment capacity.

2. Member States which are party to international conventions setting up international satellite organisations shall, where such conventions are not compatible with the competition rules of the EC Treaty, take all appropriate steps to eliminate such incompatibilities.

[4712]

Article 8

Cable television networks

1. Each Member State shall ensure that no undertaking providing public electronic communications networks operates its cable television network using the same legal entity as it uses for its other public electronic communications network, when such undertaking—

(a) is controlled by that Member State or benefits from special rights; and

(b) is dominant in a substantial part of the common market in the provision of public electronic communications networks and publicly available telephone services; and

(c) operates a cable television network which has been established under special or exclusive right in the same geographic area.

2. The term "publicly available telephone services" shall be considered synonymous with the term "public voice telephony services" referred to in Article 1 of Directive 1999/64/EC.

3. Member States which consider that there is sufficient competition in the provision of local loop infrastructure and services in their territory shall inform the Commission accordingly.

Such information shall include a detailed description of the market structure. The information provided shall be made available to any interested party on demand, regard being had to the legitimate interest of undertakings in the protection of their business secrets.

4. The Commission shall decide within a reasonable period, after having heard the comments of these parties, whether the obligation of legal separation may be ended in the Member State concerned.

5. The Commission shall review the application of this Article not later than 31 December 2004.

[4713]

Article 9

Member States shall supply to the Commission not later than 24 July 2003 such information as will allow the Commission to confirm that the provisions of this Directive have been complied with.

[4714]

Article 10

Repeal

Directive 90/388/EC, as amended by the Directives listed in Annex I, Part A, is repealed with effect from 25 July 2003, without prejudice to the obligations of the Member States in respect of the time limits for transposition laid down in Annex I, Part B.

References to the repealed Directives shall be construed as references to this Directive and shall be read in accordance with the correlation table in Annex II.

[4715]

Article 11

This Directive shall enter into force on the 20th day following that of its publication in the *Official Journal of the European Communities*.

[4716]

Article 12

This Directive is addressed to the Member States.

[4717]

Done at Brussels, 16 September 2002.

ANNEX I

PART A

LIST OF DIRECTIVES TO BE REPEALED

Directive 90/388/EEC (OJ L192, 24.7.1990, p 10)

Articles 2 and 3 of Directive 94/46/EC (OJ L268, 19.1.1994, p 15)

Directive 95/51/EC (OJ L256, 26.10.1995, p 49)

Directive 96/2/EC (OJ L20, 26.1.1996, p 59)

Directive 96/19/EC (OJ L74, 22.3.1996, p 13)

Directive 1999/64/EC (OJ L175, 10.7.1999, p 39)

PART B
TRANSPOSITION DATES FOR THE ABOVE DIRECTIVES

Directive 90/388/EEC: transposition date:	31 December 1990
Directive 94/46/EC: transposition date:	8 August 1995
Directive 95/51/EC: transposition date:	1 October 1996
Directive 96/2/EC: transposition date:	15 November 1996
Directive 96/19/EC: transposition date:	11 January 1997
Directive 1999/64/EC: transposition date:	30 April 2000

[4718]

ANNEX II
CORRELATION TABLE

This Directive	Directive 90/388/EEC
Article 1 (Definitions)	Article 1
Article 2 (withdrawal of exclusive/special rights)	Article 2
Article 3 (vertically integrated public undertakings)	Article 3(a)(ii)
Article 4 (rights of use of radio frequencies)	Article 3(b)
Article 5 (directory services)	Article 4(b)
Article 6 (universal service obligations)	Article 4(c)
Article 7 (satellites)	Article 3 of Directive 94/46/EC
Article 8 (cable networks)	Article 9

[4719]–[5000]

PART VII
MISCELLANEOUS

UNFAIR CONTRACT TERMS ACT 1977

(1977 c 50)

ARRANGEMENT OF SECTIONS

PART I
AMENDMENT OF LAW FOR ENGLAND AND WALES AND NORTHERN IRELAND

Introductory

Avoidance of liability for negligence, breach of contract, etc

Liability arising from sale or supply of goods

Other provisions about contracts

PART II
AMENDMENT OF LAW FOR SCOTLAND

PART III
PROVISIONS APPLYING TO WHOLE OF UNITED KINGDOM

Miscellaneous

PART VII MISCELLANEOUS

General

An Act to impose further limits on the extent to which under the law of England and Wales and Northern Ireland civil liability for breach of contract, or for negligence or other breach of duty, can be avoided by means of contract terms and otherwise, and under the law of Scotland civil liability can be avoided by means of contract terms

[26 October 1977]

PART I
AMENDMENT OF LAW FOR ENGLAND AND WALES AND NORTHERN IRELAND

Introductory

1 Scope of Part I

(1) For the purposes of this Part of this Act, "negligence" means the breach—

(a) of any obligation, arising from the express or implied terms of a contract, to take reasonable care or exercise reasonable skill in the performance of the contract;

(b) of any common law duty to take reasonable care or exercise reasonable skill (but not any stricter duty);

(c) of the common duty of care imposed by the Occupiers' Liability Act 1957 or the Occupiers' Liability Act (Northern Ireland) 1957.

(2) This Part of this Act is subject to Part III; and in relation to contracts, the operation of sections 2 to 4 and 7 is subject to the exceptions made by Schedule 1.

(3) In the case of both contract and tort, sections 2 to 7 apply (except where the contrary is stated in section 6(4)) only to business liability, that is liability for breach of obligations or duties arising—

(a) from things done or to be done by a person in the course of a business (whether his own business or another's); or

(b) from the occupation of premises used for business purposes of the occupier;

and references to liability are to be read accordingly [but liability of an occupier of premises for breach of an obligation or duty towards a person obtaining access to the premises for recreational or educational purposes, being liability for loss or damage suffered by reason of the dangerous state of the premises, is not a business liability of the occupier unless granting that person such access for the purposes concerned falls within the business purposes of the occupier].

(4) In relation to any breach of duty or obligation, it is immaterial for any purpose of this Part of this Act whether the breach was inadvertent or intentional, or whether liability for it arises directly or vicariously.

[5001]

NOTES

Sub-s (3): words in square brackets inserted by the Occupiers' Liability Act 1984, s 2.

Avoidance of liability for negligence, breach of contract, etc

2 Negligence liability

(1) A person cannot by reference to any contract term or to a notice given to persons generally or to particular persons exclude or restrict his liability for death or personal injury resulting from negligence.

(2) In the case of other loss or damage, a person cannot so exclude or restrict his liability for negligence except in so far as the term or notice satisfies the requirement of reasonableness.

(3) Where a contract term or notice purports to exclude or restrict liability for negligence a person's agreement to or awareness of it is not of itself to be taken as indicating his voluntary acceptance of any risk.

[5002]

3 Liability arising in contract

(1) This section applies as between contracting parties where one of them deals as consumer or on the other's written standard terms of business.

(2) As against that party, the other cannot by reference to any contract term—

- (a) when himself in breach of contract, exclude or restrict any liability of his in respect of the breach; or
- (b) claim to be entitled—
  - (i) to render a contractual performance substantially different from that which was reasonably expected of him, or
  - (ii) in respect of the whole or any part of his contractual obligation, to render no performance at all,

except in so far as (in any of the cases mentioned above in this subsection) the contract term satisfies the requirement of reasonableness.

[5003]

4 Unreasonable indemnity clauses

(1) A person dealing as consumer cannot by reference to any contract term be made to indemnify another person (whether a party to the contract or not) in respect of liability that may be incurred by the other for negligence or breach of contract, except in so far as the contract term satisfies the requirement of reasonableness.

(2) This section applies whether the liability in question—

- (a) is directly that of the person to be indemnified or is incurred by him vicariously;
- (b) is to the person dealing as consumer or to someone else.

[5004]

Liability arising from sale or supply of goods

5 "Guarantee" of consumer goods

(1) In the case of goods of a type ordinarily supplied for private use or consumption, where loss or damage—

- (a) arises from the goods proving defective while in consumer use; and
- (b) results from the negligence of a person concerned in the manufacture or distribution of the goods,

liability for the loss or damage cannot be excluded or restricted by reference to any contract term or notice contained in or operating by reference to a guarantee of the goods.

(2) For these purposes—

- (a) goods are to be regarded as "in consumer use" when a person is using them, or has them in his possession for use, otherwise than exclusively for the purposes of a business; and
- (b) anything in writing is a guarantee if it contains or purports to contain some promise or assurance (however worded or presented) that defects will be made good by complete or partial replacement, or by repair, monetary compensation or otherwise.

(3) This section does not apply as between the parties to a contract under or in pursuance of which possession or ownership of the goods passed.

[5005]

6 Sale and hire-purchase

(1) Liability for breach of the obligations arising from—

(a) [section 12 of the Sale of Goods Act 1979] (seller's implied undertakings as to title, etc);

(b) section 8 of the Supply of Goods (Implied Terms) Act 1973 (the corresponding thing in relation to hire-purchase),

cannot be excluded or restricted by reference to any contract term.

(2) As against a person dealing as consumer, liability for breach of the obligations arising from—

(a) [section 13, 14 or 15 of the 1979 Act] (seller's implied undertakings as to conformity of goods with description or sample, or as to their quality or fitness for a particular purpose);

(b) section 9, 10 or 11 of the 1973 Act (the corresponding things in relation to hire-purchase),

cannot be excluded or restricted by reference to any contract term.

(3) As against a person dealing otherwise than as consumer, the liability specified in subsection (2) above can be excluded or restricted by reference to a contract term, but only in so far as the term satisfies the requirement of reasonableness.

(4) The liabilities referred to in this section are not only the business liabilities defined by section 1(3), but include those arising under any contract of sale of goods or hire-purchase agreement.

[5006]

NOTES

Sub-ss (1), (2): words in square brackets substituted by the Sale of Goods Act 1979, s 63, Sch 2, para 19.

7 Miscellaneous contracts under which goods pass

(1) Where the possession or ownership of goods passes under or in pursuance of a contract not governed by the law of sale of goods or hire-purchase, subsections (2) to (4) below apply as regards the effect (if any) to be given to contract terms excluding or restricting liability for breach of obligation arising by implication of law from the nature of the contract.

(2) As against a person dealing as consumer, liability in respect of the goods' correspondence with description or sample, or their quality or fitness for any particular purpose, cannot be excluded or restricted by reference to any such term.

(3) As against a person dealing otherwise than as consumer, that liability can be excluded or restricted by reference to such a term, but only in so far as the term satisfies the requirement of reasonableness.

[(3A) Liability for breach of the obligations arising under section 2 of the Supply of Goods and Services Act 1982 (implied terms about title etc in certain contracts for the transfer of the property in goods) cannot be excluded or restricted by references to any such term.]

(4) Liability in respect of—

(a) the right to transfer ownership of the goods, or give possession; or

(b) the assurance of quiet possession to a person taking goods in pursuance of the contract,

cannot [(in a case to which subsection (3A) above does not apply)] be excluded or restricted by reference to any such term except in so far as the term satisfies the requirement of reasonableness.

(5) …

[5007]

NOTES

Sub-s (3A): inserted by the Supply of Goods and Services Act 1982, s 17(2), (3).

Sub-s (4): words in square brackets inserted by the Supply of Goods and Services Act 1982, s 17(2), (3).

Sub-s (5): repealed in relation to England and Wales by the Regulatory Reform (Trading Stamps) Order 2005, SI 2005/871, art 6, Schedule, and in relation to Northern Ireland by the Law Reform (Miscellaneous Provisions) (Northern Ireland) Order 2005, SI 2005/1452, art 24, Sch 2.

Other provisions about contracts

8 (*Substitutes the Misrepresentation Act 1967, s 3, and the Misrepresentation Act (Northern Ireland) 1967, s 3.*)

9 Effect of breach

(1) Where for reliance upon it a contract term has to satisfy the requirement of reasonableness, it may be found to do so and be given effect accordingly notwithstanding that the contract has been terminated either by breach or by a party electing to treat it as repudiated.

(2) Where on a breach the contract is nevertheless affirmed by a party entitled to treat it as repudiated, this does not of itself exclude the requirement of reasonableness in relation to any contract term.

[5008]

10 Evasion by means of secondary contract

A person is not bound by any contract term prejudicing or taking away rights of his which arise under, or in connection with the performance of, another contract, so far as those rights extend to the enforcement of another's liability which this Part of this Act prevents that other from excluding or restricting.

[5009]

Explanatory provisions

11 The "reasonableness" test

(1) In relation to a contract term, the requirement of reasonableness for the purposes of this Part of this Act, section 3 of the Misrepresentation Act 1967 and section 3 of the Misrepresentation Act (Northern Ireland) 1967 is that the term shall have been a fair and reasonable one to be included having regard to the circumstances which were, or ought reasonably to have been, known to or in the contemplation of the parties when the contract was made.

(2) In determining for the purposes of section 6 or 7 above whether a contract term satisfies the requirement of reasonableness, regard shall be had in particular to the matters specified in Schedule 2 to this Act; but this subsection does not prevent the court or arbitrator from holding, in accordance with any rule of law, that a term which purports to exclude or restrict any relevant liability is not a term of the contract.

(3) In relation to a notice (not being a notice having contractual effect), the requirement of reasonableness under this Act is that it should be fair and reasonable to allow reliance on it, having regard to all the circumstances obtaining when the liability arose or (but for the notice) would have arisen.

(4) Where by reference to a contract term or notice a person seeks to restrict liability to a specified sum of money, and the question arises (under this or any other Act) whether the term or notice satisfies the requirement of reasonableness, regard shall be had in particular (but without prejudice to subsection (2) above in the case of contract terms) to—

- (a) the resources which he could expect to be available to him for the purpose of meeting the liability should it arise; and
- (b) how far it was open to him to cover himself by insurance.

(5) It is for those claiming that a contract term or notice satisfies the requirement of reasonableness to show that it does.

[5010]

12 "Dealing as consumer"

(1) A party to a contract "deals as consumer" in relation to another party if—

- (a) he neither makes the contract in the course of a business nor holds himself out as doing so; and
- (b) the other party does make the contract in the course of a business; and
- (c) in the case of a contract governed by the law of sale of goods or hire-purchase, or by section 7 of this Act, the goods passing under or in pursuance of the contract are of a type ordinarily supplied for private use or consumption.

[(1A) But if the first party mentioned in subsection (1) is an individual paragraph (c) of that subsection must be ignored.]

[(2) But the buyer is not in any circumstances to be regarded as dealing as consumer—

(a) if he is an individual and the goods are second hand goods sold at public auction at which individuals have the opportunity of attending the sale in person;

(b) if he is not an individual and the goods are sold by auction or by competitive tender.]

(3) Subject to this, it is for those claiming that a party does not deal as consumer to show that he does not.

[5011]

NOTES

Sub-s (1A): inserted by the Sale and Supply of Goods to Consumers Regulations 2002, SI 2002/3045, reg 14(1), (2).

Sub-s (2): substituted by SI 2002/3045, reg 14(1), (3).

13 Varieties of exemption clause

(1) To the extent that this Part of this Act prevents the exclusion or restriction of any liability it also prevents—

(a) making the liability or its enforcement subject to restrictive or onerous conditions;

(b) excluding or restricting any right or remedy in respect of the liability, or subjecting a person to any prejudice in consequence of his pursuing any such right or remedy;

(c) excluding or restricting rules of evidence or procedure;

and (to that extent) sections 2 and 5 to 7 also prevent excluding or restricting liability by reference to terms and notices which exclude or restrict the relevant obligation or duty.

(2) But an agreement in writing to submit present or future differences to arbitration is not to be treated under this Part of this Act as excluding or restricting any liability.

[5012]

14 Interpretation of Part I

In this Part of this Act—

"business" includes a profession and the activities of any government department or local or public authority;

"goods" has the same meaning as in [the Sale of Goods Act 1979];

"hire-purchase agreement" has the same meaning as in the Consumer Credit Act 1974;

"negligence" has the meaning given by section 1(1);

"notice" includes an announcement, whether or not in writing, and any other communication or pretended communication; and

"personal injury" includes any disease and any impairment of physical or mental condition.

[5013]

NOTES

Words in square brackets in definition "goods" substituted by the Sale of Goods Act 1979, s 63, Sch 2, para 20.

PART II
AMENDMENT OF LAW FOR SCOTLAND

15 Scope of Part II

(1) This Part of this Act … is subject to Part III of this Act and does not affect the validity of any discharge or indemnity given by a person in consideration of the receipt by him of compensation in settlement of any claim which he has.

(2) Subject to subsection (3) below, sections 16 to 18 of this Act apply to any contract only to the extent that the contract—

(a) relates to the transfer of the ownership or possession of goods from one person to another (with or without work having been done on them);

(b) constitutes a contract of service or apprenticeship;

(c) relates to services of whatever kind, including (without prejudice to the foregoing generality) carriage, deposit and pledge, care and custody, mandate, agency, loan and services relating to the use of land;

(d) relates to the liability of an occupier of land to persons entering upon or using that land;

(e) relates to a grant of any right or permission to enter upon or use land not amounting to an estate or interest in the land.

(3) Notwithstanding anything in subsection (2) above, sections 16 to 18—

(a) do not apply to any contract to the extent that the contract—

(i) is a contract of insurance (including a contract to pay an annuity on human life);

(ii) relates to the formation, constitution or dissolution of any body corporate or unincorporated association or partnership;

(b) apply to—
a contract of marine salvage or towage;
a charter party of a ship or hovercraft;
a contract for the carriage of goods by ship or hovercraft; or,
a contract to which subsection (4) below relates,
only to the extent that—

(i) both parties deal or hold themselves out as dealing in the course of a business (and then only in so far as the contract purports to exclude or restrict liability for breach of duty in respect of death or personal injury); or

(ii) the contract is a consumer contract (and then only in favour of the consumer).

(4) This subsection relates to a contract in pursuance of which goods are carried by ship or hovercraft and which either—

(a) specifies ship or hovercraft as the means of carriage over part of the journey to be covered; or

(b) makes no provision as to the means of carriage and does not exclude ship or hovercraft as that means,

in so far as the contract operates for and in relation to the carriage of the goods by that means.
[5014]

NOTES

Sub-s (1): words omitted repealed by the Law Reform (Miscellaneous Provisions) (Scotland) Act 1990, ss 68(1), (2), 74(2), Sch 9.

16 Liability for breach of duty

(1) [Subject to subsection (1A) below,] where a term of a contract[, or a provision of a notice given to persons generally or to particular persons] purports to exclude or restrict liability for breach of duty arising in the course of any business or from the occupation of any premises used for business purposes of the occupier, that term [or provision]—

(a) shall be void in any case where such exclusion or restriction is in respect of death or personal injury;

(b) shall, in any other case, have no effect if it was not fair and reason-able to incorporate the term in the contract [or, as the case may be, if it is not fair and reasonable to allow reliance on the provision].

[(1A) Nothing in paragraph (b) of subsection (1) above shall be taken as implying that a provision of a notice has effect in circumstances where, apart from that paragraph, it would not have effect.]

(2) Subsection (1)(a) above does not affect the validity of any discharge and indemnity given by a person, on or in connection with an award to him of compensation for pneumoconiosis attributable to employment in the coal industry, in respect of any further claim arising from his contracting that disease.

(3) Where under subsection (1) above a term of a contract [or a provision of a notice] is void or has no effect, the fact that a person agreed to, or was aware of the term [or provision] shall not of itself be sufficient evidence that he knowingly and voluntarily assumed any risk.
[5015]

NOTES

Sub-ss (1), (3): words in square brackets inserted by the Law Reform (Miscellaneous Provisions) (Scotland) Act 1990, s 68(1), (3)(a), (c).

Sub-s (1A): inserted by the Law Reform (Miscellaneous Provisions) (Scotland) Act 1990, s 68(1), (3)(b).

17 Control of unreasonable exemptions in consumer or standard form contracts

(1) Any term of a contract which is a consumer contract or a standard form contract shall have no effect for the purpose of enabling a party to the contract—

(a) who is in breach of a contractual obligation, to exclude or restrict any liability of his to the consumer or customer in respect of the breach;

(b) in respect of a contractual obligation, to render no performance, or to render a performance substantially different from that which the consumer or customer reasonably expected from the contract;

if it was not fair and reasonable to incorporate the term in the contract.

(2) In this section "customer" means a party to a standard form contract who deals on the basis of written standard terms of business of the other party to the contract who himself deals in the course of a business.

[5016]

18 Unreasonable indemnity clauses in consumer contracts

(1) Any term of a contract which is a consumer contract shall have no effect for the purpose of making the consumer indemnify another person (whether a party to the contract or not) in respect of liability which that other person may incur as a result of breach of duty or breach of contract, if it was not fair and reasonable to incorporate the term in the contract.

(2) In this section "liability" means liability arising in the course of any business or from the occupation of any premises used for business purposes of the occupier.

[5017]

19 "Guarantee" of consumer goods

(1) This section applies to a guarantee—

(a) in relation to goods which are of a type ordinarily supplied for private use or consumption; and

(b) which is not a guarantee given by one party to the other party to a contract under or in pursuance of which the ownership or possession of the goods to which the guarantee relates is transferred.

(2) A term of a guarantee to which this section applies shall be void in so far as it purports to exclude or restrict liability for loss or damage (including death or personal injury)—

(a) arising from the goods proving defective while—

(i) in use otherwise than exclusively for the purposes of a business; or

(ii) in the possession of a person for such use; and

(b) resulting from the breach of duty of a person concerned in the manufacture or distribution of the goods.

(3) For the purposes of this section, any document is a guarantee if it contains or purports to contain some promise or assurance (however worded or presented) that defects will be made good by complete or partial replacement, or by repair, monetary compensation or otherwise.

[5018]

20 Obligations implied by law in sale and hire-purchase contracts

(1) Any term of a contract which purports to exclude or restrict liability for breach of the obligations arising from—

(a) section 12 of the Sale of Goods Act [1979] (seller's implied undertakings as to title etc);

(b) section 8 of the Supply of Goods (Implied Terms) Act 1973 (implied terms as to title in hire-purchase agreements),

shall be void.

(2) Any term of a contract which purports to exclude or restrict liability for breach of the obligations arising from—

(a) section 13, 14 or 15 of the said Act of [1979] (seller's implied undertakings as to conformity of goods with description or sample, or as to their quality or fitness for a particular purpose);

(b) section 9, 10 or 11 of the said Act of 1973 (the corresponding provisions in relation to hire-purchase),

shall—

(i) in the case of a consumer contract, be void against the consumer;

(ii) in any other case, have no effect if it was not fair and reasonable to incorporate the term in the contract.

[5019]

NOTES

Dates in square brackets substituted by the Sale of Goods Act 1979, s 63(1), Sch 2, para 21.

21 Obligations implied by law in other contracts for the supply of goods

(1) Any term of a contract to which this section applies purporting to exclude or restrict liability for breach of an obligation—

(a) such as is referred to in subsection (3)(a) below—

(i) in the case of a consumer contract, shall be void against the consumer, and

(ii) in any other case, shall have no effect if it was not fair and reasonable to incorporate the term in the contract;

(b) such as is referred to in subsection (3)(b) below, shall have no effect if it was not fair and reasonable to incorporate the term in the contract.

(2) This section applies to any contract to the extent that it relates to any such matter as is referred to in section 15(2)(a) of this Act, but does not apply to—

(a) a contract of sale of goods or a hire-purchase agreement; or

(b) a charter party of a ship or hovercraft unless it is a consumer contract (and then only in favour of the consumer).

(3) An obligation referred to in this subsection is an obligation incurred under a contract in the course of a business and arising by implication of law from the nature of the contract which relates—

(a) to the correspondence of goods with description or sample, or to the quality or fitness of goods for any particular purpose; or

(b) to any right to transfer ownership or possession of goods, or to the enjoyment of quiet possession of goods.

[(3A) Notwithstanding anything in the foregoing provisions of this section, any term of a contract which purports to exclude or restrict liability for breach of the obligations arising under section 11B of the Supply of Goods and Services Act 1982 (implied terms about title, freedom from encumbrances and quiet possession in certain contracts for the transfer of property in goods) shall be void.]

(4) …

[5020]

NOTES

Sub-s (3A): inserted by the Supply of Goods and Services Act 1982, s 11B(6) (as inserted by the Sale and Supply of Goods Act 1994, s 6, Sch 1, para 1).

Sub-s (4): repealed by the Regulatory Reform (Trading Stamps) Order 2005, SI 2005/871, art 6, Schedule.

22 Consequence of breach

For the avoidance of doubt, where any provision of this Part of this Act requires that the incorporation of a term in a contract must be fair and reasonable for that term to have effect—

(a) if that requirement is satisfied, the term may be given effect to notwithstanding that the contract has been terminated in consequence of breach of that contract;

(b) for the term to be given effect to, that requirement must be satisfied even where a party who is entitled to rescind the contract elects not to rescind it.

[5021]

PART VII MISCELLANEOUS

23 Evasion by means of secondary contract

Any term of any contract shall be void which purports to exclude or restrict, or has the effect of excluding or restricting—

(a) the exercise, by a party to any other contract, of any right or remedy which arises in respect of that other contract in consequence of breach of duty, or of obligation, liability for which could not by virtue of the provisions of this Part of this Act be excluded or restricted by a term of that other contract;

(b) the application of the provisions of this Part of this Act in respect of that or any other contract.

[5022]

24 The "reasonableness" test

(1) In determining for the purposes of this Part of this Act whether it was fair and reasonable to incorporate a term in a contract, regard shall be had only to the circumstances which were, or ought reasonably to have been, known to or in the contemplation of the parties to the contract at the time the contract was made.

(2) In determining for the purposes of section 20 or 21 of this Act whether it was fair and reasonable to incorporate a term in a contract, regard shall be had in particular to the matters specified in Schedule 2 to this Act; but this subsection shall not prevent a court or arbiter from holding, in accordance with any rule of law, that a term which purports to exclude or restrict any relevant liability is not a term of the contract.

[(2A) In determining for the purposes of this Part of this Act whether it is fair and reasonable to allow reliance on a provision of a notice (not being a notice having contractual effect), regard shall be had to all the circumstances obtaining when the liability arose or (but for the provision) would have arisen.]

(3) Where a term in a contract [or a provision of a notice] purports to restrict liability to a specified sum of money, and the question arises for the purposes of this Part of this Act whether it was fair and reasonable to incorporate the term in the contract [or whether it is fair and reasonable to allow reliance on the provision], then, without prejudice to subsection (2) above [in the case of a term in a contract], regard shall be had in particular to—

(a) the resources which the party seeking to rely on that term [or provision] could expect to be available to him for the purpose of meeting the liability should it arise;

(b) how far it was open to that party to cover himself by insurance.

(4) The onus of proving that it was fair and reasonable to incorporate a term in a contract [or that it is fair and reasonable to allow reliance on a provision of a notice] shall lie on the party so contending.

[5023]

NOTES

Sub-s (2A): inserted by the Law Reform (Miscellaneous Provisions) (Scotland) Act 1990, s 68(1), (4)(a).

Sub-ss (3), (4): words in square brackets inserted by the Law Reform (Miscellaneous Provisions) (Scotland) Act 1990, s 68(1), (4)(b), (c).

25 Interpretation of Part II

(1) In this Part of this Act

"breach of duty" means the breach—

(a) of any obligation, arising from the express or implied terms of a contract, to take reasonable care or exercise reasonable skill in the performance of the contract;

(b) of any common law duty to take reasonable care or exercise reasonable skill;

(c) of the duty of reasonable care imposed by section 2(1) of the Occupiers' Liability (Scotland) Act 1960;

"business" includes a profession and the activities of any government department or local or public authority;

"consumer" has the meaning assigned to that expression in the definition in this section of "consumer contract";

"consumer contract" means [subject to subsections (1A) and (1B) below] a contract … in which—

(a) one party to the contract deals, and the other party to the contract ("the consumer") does not deal or hold himself out as dealing, in the course of a business, and

(b) in the case of a contract such as is mentioned in section 15(2)(a) of this Act, the goods are of a type ordinarily supplied for private use or consumption;

and for the purposes of this Part of this Act the onus of proving that a contract is not to be regarded as a consumer contract shall lie on the party so contending;

"goods" has the same meaning as in [the Sale of Goods Act 1979];

"hire-purchase agreement" has the same meaning as in section 189(1) of the Consumer Credit Act 1974;

["notice" includes an announcement, whether or not in writing, and any other communication or pretended communication;]

"personal injury" includes any disease and any impairment of physical or mental condition.

[(1A) Where the consumer is an individual, paragraph (b) in the definition of "consumer contract" in subsection (1) must be disregarded.

(1B) The expression of "consumer contract" does not include a contract in which—

(a) the buyer is an individual and the goods are second hand goods sold by public auction at which individuals have the opportunity of attending in person; or

(b) the buyer is not an individual and the goods are sold by auction or competitive tender.]

(2) In relation to any breach of duty or obligation, it is immaterial for any purpose of this Part of this Act whether the act or omission giving rise to that breach was inadvertent or intentional, or whether liability for it arises directly or vicariously.

(3) In this Part of this Act, any reference to excluding or restricting any liability includes—

(a) making the liability or its enforcement subject to any restrictive or onerous conditions;

(b) excluding or restricting any right or remedy in respect of the liability, or subjecting a person to any prejudice in consequence of his pursuing any such right or remedy;

(c) excluding or restricting any rule of evidence or procedure;

(d) …

but does not include an agreement to submit any question to arbitration.

(4) …

(5) In sections 15 and 16 and 19 to 21 of this Act, any reference to excluding or restricting liability for breach of an obligation or duty shall include a reference to excluding or restricting the obligation or duty itself.

[5024]

NOTES

Sub-s (1): in definition "consumer contract" words in square brackets inserted and words omitted repealed by the Sale and Supply of Goods to Consumers Regulations 2002, SI 2002/3045, reg 14(1), (4)(a); words in square brackets in definition "goods" substituted by the Sale of Goods Act 1979, s 63(1), Sch 2, para 22; definition "notice" inserted by the Law Reform (Miscellaneous Provisions) (Scotland) Act 1990, s 68(1), (5)(a).

Sub-ss (1A), (1B): inserted by SI 2002/3045, reg 14(1), (4)(b).

Sub-s (3): para (d) repealed by the Law Reform (Miscellaneous Provisions) (Scotland) Act 1990, ss 68(1), (5)(b), 74(2), Sch 9.

Sub-s (4): repealed by the Law Reform (Miscellaneous Provisions) (Scotland) Act 1990, ss 68(1), (5)(b), 74(2), Sch 9.

PART III
PROVISIONS APPLYING TO WHOLE OF UNITED KINGDOM

Miscellaneous

26 International supply contracts

(1) The limits imposed by this Act on the extent to which a person may exclude or restrict liability by reference to a contract term do not apply to liability arising under such a contract as is described in subsection (3) below.

(2) The terms of such a contract are not subject to any requirement of reasonableness under section 3 or 4: and nothing in Part II of this Act shall require the incorporation of the terms of such a contract to be fair and reasonable for them to have effect.

(3) Subject to subsection (4), that description of contract is one whose characteristics are the following—

(a) either it is a contract of sale of goods or it is one under or in pursuance of which the possession or ownership of goods passes; and

(b) it is made by parties whose places of business (or, if they have none, habitual residences) are in the territories of different States (the Channel Islands and the Isle of Man being treated for this purpose as different States from the United Kingdom).

(4) A contract falls within subsection (3) above only if either—

(a) the goods in question are, at the time of the conclusion of the contract, in the course of carriage, or will be carried, from the territory of one State to the territory of another; or

(b) the acts constituting the offer and acceptance have been done in the territories of different States; or

(c) the contract provides for the goods to be delivered to the territory of a State other than that within whose territory those acts were done.

[5025]

27 Choice of law clauses

(1) Where the [law applicable to] a contract is the law of any part of the United Kingdom only by choice of the parties (and apart from that choice would be the law of some country outside the United Kingdom) sections 2 to 7 and 16 to 21 of this Act do not operate as part [of the law applicable to the contract].

(2) This Act has effect notwithstanding any contract term which applies or purports to apply the law of some country outside the United Kingdom, where (either or both)—

(a) the term appears to the court, or arbitrator or arbiter to have been imposed wholly or mainly for the purpose of enabling the party imposing it to evade the operation of this Act; or

(b) in the making of the contract one of the parties dealt as consumer, and he was then habitually resident in the United Kingdom, and the essential steps necessary for the making of the contract were taken there, whether by him or by others on his behalf.

(3) In the application of subsection (2) above to Scotland, for paragraph (b) there shall be substituted—

> "(b) the contract is a consumer contract as defined in Part II of this Act, and the consumer at the date when the contract was made was habitually resident in the United Kingdom, and the essential steps necessary for the making of the contract were taken there, whether by him or by others on his behalf."

[5026]

NOTES

Sub-s (1): words in square brackets substituted by the Contracts (Applicable Law) Act 1990, s 5, Sch 4, para 4.

---

28 Temporary provision for sea carriage of passengers

(1) This section applies to a contract for carriage by sea of a passenger or of a passenger and his luggage where the provisions of the Athens Convention (with or without modification) do not have, in relation to the contract, the force of law in the United Kingdom.

(2) In a case where—

(a) the contract is not made in the United Kingdom, and

(b) neither the place of departure nor the place of destination under it is in the United Kingdom,

a person is not precluded by this Act from excluding or restricting liability for loss or damage, being loss or damage for which the provisions of the Convention would, if they had the force of law in relation to the contract, impose liability on him.

(3) In any other case, a person is not precluded by this Act from excluding or restricting liability for that loss or damage—

(a) in so far as the exclusion or restriction would have been effective in that case had the provisions of the Convention had the force of law in relation to the contract; or

(b) in such circumstances and to such extent as may be prescribed, by reference to a prescribed term of the contract.

(4) For the purposes of subsection (3) (*a*), the values which shall be taken to be the official values in the United Kingdom of the amounts (expressed in gold francs) by reference to which liability under the provisions of the Convention is limited shall be such amounts in sterling as the Secretary of State may from time to time by order made by statutory instrument specify.

(5) In this section,—

(a) the references to excluding or restricting liability include doing any of those things in relation to the liability which are mentioned in section 13 or section 25 (3) and (5); and

(b) "the Athens Convention" means the Athens Convention relating to the Carriage of Passengers and their Luggage by Sea, 1974; and

(c) "prescribed" means prescribed by the Secretary of State by regulations made by statutory instrument;

and a statutory instrument containing the regulations shall be subject to annulment in pursuance of a resolution of either House of Parliament.

[5027]

NOTES

Orders: As a result of the coming into force of the 1976 Protocol to the Athens Convention, which replaced the references to gold francs in the Convention by references to special drawing rights, no equivalent for gold francs are now provided for by order under this section.

29 Saving for other relevant legislation

(1) Nothing in this Act removes or restricts the effect of, or prevents reliance upon, any contractual provision which—

(a) is authorised or required by the express terms or necessary implication of an enactment; or

(b) being made with a view to compliance with an international agreement to which the United Kingdom is a party, does not operate more restrictively than is contemplated by the agreement.

(2) A contract term is to be taken—

(a) for the purposes of Part I of this Act, as satisfying the requirement of reasonableness; and

(b) for those of Part II, to have been fair and reasonable to incorporate,

if it is incorporated or approved by, or incorporated pursuant to a decision or ruling of, a competent authority acting in the exercise of any statutory jurisdiction or function and is not a term in a contract to which the competent authority is itself a party.

(3) In this section—

"competent authority" means any court, arbitrator or arbiter, government department or public authority;

"enactment" means any legislation (including subordinate legislation) of the United Kingdom or Northern Ireland and any instrument having effect by virtue of such legislation; and

"statutory" means conferred by an enactment.

[5028]

30 (*Repealed by the Consumer Safety Act 1978, s 10(1), Sch 3.*)

General

31 Commencement; amendments; repeals

(1) This Act comes into force on 1st February 1978.

(2) Nothing in this Act applies to contracts made before the date on which it comes into force; but subject to this, it applies to liability for any loss or damage which is suffered on or after that date.

(3) The enactments specified in Schedule 3 to this Act are amended as there shown.

(4) The enactments specified in Schedule 4 to this Act are repealed to the extent specified in column 3 of that Schedule.

[5029]

32 Citation and extent

(1) This Act may be cited as the Unfair Contract Terms Act 1977.

(2) Part I of this Act extends to England and Wales and to Northern Ireland; but it does not extend to Scotland.

(3) Part II of this Act extends to Scotland only.

(4) This Part of this Act extends to the whole of the United Kingdom.

[5030]

SCHEDULES

SCHEDULE 1
SCOPE OF SECTIONS 2 TO 4 AND 7

Section 1(2)

1. Sections 2 to 4 of this Act do not extend to—
   (a) any contract of insurance (including a contract to pay an annuity on human life);
   (b) any contract so far as it relates to the creation or transfer of an interest in land, or to the termination of such an interest, whether by extinction, merger, surrender, forfeiture or otherwise;
   (c) any contract so far as it relates to the creation or transfer of a right or interest in any patent, trade mark, copyright [or design right], registered design, technical or commercial information or other intellectual property, or relates to the termination of any such right or interest;
   (d) any contract so far as it relates—
      (i) to the formation or dissolution of a company (which means any body corporate or unincorporated association and includes a partnership), or
      (ii) to its constitution or the rights or obligations of its corporators or members;
   (e) any contract so far as it relates to the creation or transfer of securities or of any right or interest in securities.

2. Section 2(1) extends to—
   (a) any contract of marine salvage or towage;
   (b) any charter party of a ship or hovercraft; and
   (c) any contract for the carriage of goods by ship or hovercraft;

but subject to this sections 2 to 4 and 7 do not extend to any such contract except in favour of a person dealing as consumer.

3. Where goods are carried by ship or hovercraft in pursuance of a contract which either—
   (a) specifies that as the means of carriage over part of the journey to be covered, or
   (b) makes no provision as to the means of carriage and does not exclude that means,

then sections 2(2), 3 and 4 do not, except in favour of a person dealing as consumer, extend to the contract as it operates for and in relation to the carriage of the goods by that means.

4. Section 2(1) and (2) do not extend to a contract of employment, except in favour of the employee.

5. Section 2(1) does not affect the validity of any discharge and indemnity given by a person, on or in connection with an award to him of compensation for pneumoconiosis attributable to employment in the coal industry, in respect of any further claim arising from his contracting that disease.

[5031]

NOTES

Para 1: the reference to a trade mark in sub-para (c) includes a reference to a service mark, by virtue of the Patents, Designs and Marks Act 1986, s 2(3), Sch 2, Part I; words in square brackets inserted by the Copyright, Designs and Patents Act 1988, s 303(1), Sch 7, para 24.

References to trade marks or registered trade marks within the meaning of the Trade Marks Act 1938 shall, unless the context otherwise requires, be construed as references to trade marks or registered trade marks within the meaning of the Trade Marks Act 1994; see the Trade Marks Act 1994, Sch 4, para 1.

SCHEDULE 2
"GUIDELINES" FOR APPLICATION OF REASONABLENESS TEST

Sections 11(2), 24(2)

The matters to which regard is to be had in particular for the purposes of sections 6(3), 7(3) and (4), 20 and 21 are any of the following which appear to be relevant—

(a) the strength of the bargaining positions of the parties relative to each other, taking into account (among other things) alternative means by which the customer's requirements could have been met;

(b) whether the customer received an inducement to agree to the term, or in accepting it had an opportunity of entering into a similar contract with other persons, but without having to accept a similar term;

(c) whether the customer knew or ought reasonably to have known of the existence and extent of the term (having regard, among other things, to any custom of the trade and any previous course of dealing between the parties);

(d) where the term excludes or restricts any relevant liability if some condition is not complied with, whether it was reasonable at the time of the contract to expect that compliance with that condition would be practicable;

(e) whether the goods were manufactured, processed or adapted to the special order of the customer.

[5032]

(Schs 3, 4 contain amendments and repeals outside the scope of this work.)

PART VII MISCELLANEOUS

COMPUTER MISUSE ACT 1990

(1990 c 18)

ARRANGEMENT OF SECTIONS

Computer misuse offences

Jurisdiction

Miscellaneous and general

An Act to make provision for securing computer material against unauthorised access or modification; and for connected purposes

[29 June 1990]

Computer misuse offences

1 Unauthorised access to computer material

(1) A person is guilty of an offence if—

(a) he causes a computer to perform any function with intent to secure access to any program or data held in any computer[, or to enable any such access to be secured];

(b) the access he intends to secure[, or to enable to be secured,] is unauthorised; and

(c) he knows at the time when he causes the computer to perform the function that that is the case.

(2) The intent a person has to have to commit an offence under this section need not be directed at—

(a) any particular program or data;

(b) a program or data of any particular kind; or

(c) a program or data held in any particular computer.

(3) A person guilty of an offence under this section shall be liable on summary conviction to imprisonment for a term not exceeding six months or to a fine not exceeding level 5 on the standard scale or to both.

[5033]

NOTES

Sub-s (1): words in square brackets inserted by the Police and Justice Act 2006, s 35(1), (2), as from a day to be appointed, subject to transitional provisions in s 38(1) of the 2006 Act; as to which, see the "Transitional Provisions" note below.

Sub-s (3): substituted by the Police and Justice Act 2006, s 35(1), (3), as from a day to be appointed (subject to transitional provisions in s 38(2), (6)(a) of the 2006 Act; as to which, see the "Transitional Provisions" note below), as follows:

"(3) A person guilty of an offence under this section shall be liable—

(a) on summary conviction in England and Wales, to imprisonment for a term not exceeding 12 months or to a fine not exceeding the statutory maximum or to both;

(b) on summary conviction in Scotland, to imprisonment for a term not exceeding six months or to a fine not exceeding the statutory maximum or to both;

(c) on conviction on indictment, to imprisonment for a term not exceeding two years or to a fine or to both.".

Transitional provisions: the Police and Justice Act 2006, s 38, makes transitional and savings provisions in relation to the amendments that the 2006 Act makes to this Act, and provides as follows:

"38 Transitional and saving provision

(1) The amendments made by—

(a) subsection (2) of section 35, and

(b) paragraphs 19(2), 25(2) and 29(2) of Schedule 14,

apply only where every act or other event proof of which is required for conviction of an offence under section 1 of the 1990 Act takes place after that subsection comes into force.

(2) The amendments made by—

(a) subsection (3) of section 35, and

(b) paragraphs 23, 24, 25(4) and (5), 26, 27(2) and (7) and 28 of Schedule 14,

do not apply in relation to an offence committed before that subsection comes into force.

(3) An offence is not committed under the new section 3 unless every act or other event proof of which is required for conviction of the offence takes place after section 36 above comes into force.

(4) In relation to a case where, by reason of subsection (3), an offence is not committed under the new section 3—

(a) section 3 of the 1990 Act has effect in the form in which it was enacted;

(b) paragraphs 19(3), 25(3) to (5), 27(4) and (5) and 29(3) and (4) of Schedule 14 do not apply.

(5) An offence is not committed under the new section 3A unless every act or other event proof of which is required for conviction of the offence takes place after section 37 above comes into force.

(6) In the case of an offence committed before section 154(1) of the Criminal Justice Act 2003 (c 44) comes into force, the following provisions have effect as if for "12 months" there were substituted "six months"—

(a) paragraph (a) of the new section 1(3);

(b) paragraph (a) of the new section 2(5);

(c) subsection (6)(a) of the new section 3;

(d) subsection (5)(a) of the new section 3A.

(7) In this section—

(a) "the new section 1(3)" means the subsection (3) substituted in section 1 of the 1990 Act by section 35 above;

(b) "the new section 2(5)" means the subsection (5) substituted in section 2 of the 1990 Act by paragraph 17 of Schedule 14 to this Act;

(c) "the new section 3" means the section 3 substituted in the 1990 Act by section 36 above;

(d) "the new section 3A" means the section 3A inserted in the 1990 Act by section 37 above.".

---

2 Unauthorised access with intent to commit or facilitate commission of further offences

(1) A person is guilty of an offence under this section if he commits an offence under section 1 above ("the unauthorised access offence") with intent—

(a) to commit an offence to which this section applies; or

(b) to facilitate the commission of such an offence (whether by himself or by any other person);

and the offence he intends to commit or facilitate is referred to below in this section as the further offence.

(2) This section applies to offences—

(a) for which the sentence is fixed by law; or

(b) for which a person *of twenty-one years of age or over* (*not previously convicted*) may be sentenced to imprisonment for a term of five years (or, in England and Wales, might be so sentenced but for the restrictions imposed by section 33 of the Magistrates' Courts Act 1980).

(3) It is immaterial for the purposes of this section whether the further offence is to be committed on the same occasion as the unauthorised access offence or on any future occasion.

(4) A person may be guilty of an offence under this section even though the facts are such that the commission of the further offence is impossible.

(*5*) *A person guilty of an offence under this section shall be liable—*

(*a*) *on summary conviction, to imprisonment for a term not exceeding six months or to a fine not exceeding the statutory maximum or to both; and*

(*b*) *on conviction on indictment, to imprisonment for a term not exceeding five years or to a fine or to both.*

[5034]

NOTES

Sub-s (2): for the words in italics in para (b) there are substituted the words "who has attained the age of twenty-one years (eighteen in relation to England and Wales) and has no previous convictions" by the Criminal Justice and Court Services Act 2000, s 74, Sch 7, Pt II, para 98, as from a day to be appointed.

Sub-s (5): substituted by the Police and Justice Act 2006, s 52, Sch 14, para 17, as from a day to be appointed (subject to transitional provisions in s 38(6)(b) of the 2006 Act; as to which, see the "Transitional Provisions" note to s 1 at **[5033]**), as follows:

"(5) A person guilty of an offence under this section shall be liable—

(a) on summary conviction in England and Wales, to imprisonment for a term not exceeding 12 months or to a fine not exceeding the statutory maximum or to both;

(b) on summary conviction in Scotland, to imprisonment for a term not exceeding six months or to a fine not exceeding the statutory maximum or to both;

(c) on conviction on indictment, to imprisonment for a term not exceeding five years or to a fine or to both.".

---

3 Unauthorised modification of computer material

(1) A person is guilty of an offence if—

(a) he does any act which causes an unauthorised modification of the contents of any computer; and

(b) at the time when he does the act he has the requisite intent and the requisite knowledge.

(2) For the purposes of subsection (1)(b) above the requisite intent is an intent to cause a modification of the contents of any computer and by so doing—

(a) to impair the operation of any computer;

(b) to prevent or hinder access to any program or data held in any computer; or

(c) to impair the operation of any such program or the reliability of any such data.

(3) The intent need not be directed at—

(a) any particular computer;

(b) any particular program or data or a program or data of any particular kind; or

(c) any particular modification or a modification of any particular kind.

(4) For the purposes of subsection (1)(b) above the requisite knowledge is knowledge that any modification he intends to cause is unauthorised.

(5) It is immaterial for the purposes of this section whether an unauthorised modification or any intended effect of it of a kind mentioned in subsection (2) above is, or is intended to be, permanent or merely temporary.

(6) For the purposes of the Criminal Damage Act 1971 a modification of the contents of a computer shall not be regarded as damaging any computer or computer storage medium unless its effect on that computer or computer storage medium impairs its physical condition.

(7) A person guilty of an offence under this section shall be liable—

(a) on summary conviction, to imprisonment for a term not exceeding six months or to a fine not exceeding the statutory maximum or to both; and

(b) on conviction on indictment, to imprisonment for a term not exceeding five years or to a fine or to both.

[5035]

NOTES

Substituted by the Police and Justice Act 2006, s 36, as from a day to be appointed (subject to transitional provisions in s 38(3), (4), (6)(c) of the 2006 Act; as to which, see the "Transitional Provisions" note to s 1 at **[5033]**), as follows:

"3 Unauthorised acts with intent to impair, or with recklessness as to impairing, operation of computer, etc

(1) A person is guilty of an offence if—

(a) he does any unauthorised act in relation to a computer;

(b) at the time when he does the act he knows that it is unauthorised; and

(c) either subsection (2) or subsection (3) below applies.

(2) This subsection applies if the person intends by doing the act—

(a) to impair the operation of any computer;

(b) to prevent or hinder access to any program or data held in any computer;

(c) to impair the operation of any such program or the reliability of any such data; or

(d) to enable any of the things mentioned in paragraphs (a) to (c) above to be done.

(3) This subsection applies if the person is reckless as to whether the act will do any of the things mentioned in paragraphs (a) to (d) of subsection (2) above.

(4) The intention referred to in subsection (2) above, or the recklessness referred to in subsection (3) above, need not relate to—

(a) any particular computer;

(b) any particular program or data; or

(c) a program or data of any particular kind.

(5) In this section—

(a) a reference to doing an act includes a reference to causing an act to be done;

(b) "act" includes a series of acts;

(c) a reference to impairing, preventing or hindering something includes a reference to doing so temporarily.

(6) A person guilty of an offence under this section shall be liable—

(a) on summary conviction in England and Wales, to imprisonment for a term not exceeding 12 months or to a fine not exceeding the statutory maximum or to both;

(b) on summary conviction in Scotland, to imprisonment for a term not exceeding six months or to a fine not exceeding the statutory maximum or to both;
(c) on conviction on indictment, to imprisonment for a term not exceeding ten years or to a fine or to both.".

[3A Making, supplying or obtaining articles for use in offence under section 1 or 3

(1) A person is guilty of an offence if he makes, adapts, supplies or offers to supply any article intending it to be used to commit, or to assist in the commission of, an offence under section 1 or 3.

(2) A person is guilty of an offence if he supplies or offers to supply any article believing that it is likely to be used to commit, or to assist in the commission of, an offence under section 1 or 3.

(3) A person is guilty of an offence if he obtains any article with a view to its being supplied for use to commit, or to assist in the commission of, an offence under section 1 or 3.

(4) In this section "article" includes any program or data held in electronic form.

(5) A person guilty of an offence under this section shall be liable—
(a) on summary conviction in England and Wales, to imprisonment for a term not exceeding 12 months or to a fine not exceeding the statutory maximum or to both;
(b) on summary conviction in Scotland, to imprisonment for a term not exceeding six months or to a fine not exceeding the statutory maximum or to both;
(c) on conviction on indictment, to imprisonment for a term not exceeding two years or to a fine or to both.]

[5036]

NOTES

Commencement: to be appointed.
Inserted by the Police and Justice Act 2006, s 37, as from a day to be appointed, subject to transitional provisions in s 38(5), (6)(d) of the 2006 Act (as to which, see the "Transitional Provisions" note to s 1 at **[5033]**).

Jurisdiction

4 Territorial scope of *offences under this Act*

(1) Except as provided below in this section, it is immaterial for the purposes of any offence under section 1 or 3 above—
(a) whether any act or other event proof of which is required for conviction of the offence occurred in the home country concerned; or
(b) whether the accused was in the home country concerned at the time of any such act or event.

(2) Subject to subsection (3) below, in the case of such an offence at least one significant link with domestic jurisdiction must exist in the circumstances of the case for the offence to be committed.

(3) There is no need for any such link to exist for the commission of an offence under section 1 above to be established in proof of an allegation to that effect in proceedings for an offence under section 2 above.

(4) Subject to section 8 below, where—
(a) any such link does in fact exist in the case of an offence under section 1 above; and
(b) commission of that offence is alleged in proceedings for an offence under section 2 above;

section 2 above shall apply as if anything the accused intended to do or facilitate in any place outside the home country concerned which would be an offence to which section 2 applies if it took place in the home country concerned were the offence in question.

(5) This section is without prejudice to any jurisdiction exercisable by a court in Scotland apart from this section.

(6) References in this Act to the home country concerned are references—
(a) in the application of this Act to England and Wales, to England and Wales;

(b) in the application of this Act to Scotland, to Scotland; and
(c) in the application of this Act to Northern Ireland, to Northern Ireland.

[5037]

NOTES

Section heading: for the words in italics there are substituted the words "offences under sections 1 to 3" by the Police and Justice Act 2006, s 52, Sch 14, para 18, as from a day to be appointed.

5 Significant links with domestic jurisdiction

(1) The following provisions of this section apply for the interpretation of section 4 above.

(2) In relation to an offence under section 1, either of the following is a significant link with domestic jurisdiction—

(a) that the accused was in the home country concerned at the time when he did the act which caused the computer to perform the function; or
(b) that any computer containing any program or data to which the accused secured or intended to secure unauthorised access by doing that act was in the home country concerned at that time.

(3) In relation to an offence under section 3, either of the following is a significant link with domestic jurisdiction—

(a) that the accused was in the home country concerned at the time when *he did the act which caused the unauthorised modification*; or
(b) that the unauthorised modification took place in the home country concerned.

[5038]

NOTES

Sub-s (2): para (b) substituted by the Police and Justice Act 2006, s 52, Sch 14, para 19(1), (2), as from a day to be appointed (subject to transitional provisions in s 38(1) of the 2006 Act; as to which, see the "Transitional Provisions" note to s 1 at **[5033]**), as follows:

"(b) that any computer containing any program or data to which the accused by doing that act secured or intended to secure unauthorised access, or enabled or intended to enable unauthorised access to be secured, was in the home country concerned at that time.".

Sub-s (3): for the words in italics in para (a) there are substituted the words "he did the unauthorised act (or caused it to be done)", and para (b) substituted by the Police and Justice Act 2006, s 52, Sch 14, para 19(1), (3), as from a day to be appointed (subject to transitional provisions in s 38(4) of the 2006 Act; as to which, see the "Transitional Provisions" note to s 1 at **[5033]**), as follows:

"(b) that the unauthorised act was done in relation to a computer in the home country concerned.".

6 Territorial scope of inchoate offences related to *offences under this Act*

(1) On a charge of conspiracy to commit an *offence under this Act* the following questions are immaterial to the accused's guilt—

(a) the question where any person became a party to the conspiracy; and
(b) the question whether any act, omission or other event occurred in the home country concerned.

(2) On a charge of attempting to commit an offence under section 3 above the following questions are immaterial to the accused's guilt—

(a) the question where the attempt was made; and
(b) the question whether it had an effect in the home country concerned.

(3) On a charge of incitement to commit an *offence under this Act* the question where the incitement took place is immaterial to the accused's guilt.

(4) This section does not extend to Scotland.

[5039]

NOTES

Section heading: for the words in italics there are substituted the words "offences under sections 1 to 3" by the Police and Justice Act 2006, s 52, Sch 14, para 20(a), as from a day to be appointed.

Sub-ss (1), (3): for the words in italics there are substituted the words "offence under section 1, 2 or 3 above" by the Police and Justice Act 2006, s 52, Sch 14, para 20(b), as from a day to be appointed.

7 Territorial scope of inchoate offences related to offences under external law corresponding to *offences under this Act*

(1)–(3) …

(4) Subject to section 8 below, if any act done by a person in England and Wales would amount to the offence of incitement to commit an *offence under this Act* but for the fact that what he had in view would not be an offence triable in England and Wales—

(a) what he had in view shall be treated as *an offence under this Act* for the purposes of any charge of incitement brought in respect of that act; and

(b) any such charge shall accordingly be triable in England and Wales.

[5040]

NOTES

Section heading: for the words in italics there are substituted the words "offences under sections 1 to 3" by the Police and Justice Act 2006, s 52, Sch 14, para 21(a), as from a day to be appointed.

Sub-ss (1), (2): repealed by the Criminal Justice (Terrorism and Conspiracy) Act 1998, s 9(2), (3), Sch 2, Pt II.

Sub-s (3): inserts the Criminal Attempts Act 1981, s 1(1A), (1B).

Sub-s (4): for the words in italics in both places they appear, there are substituted the words "offence under section 1, 2 or 3 above" by the Police and Justice Act 2006, s 52, Sch 14, para 21(b), as from a day to be appointed.

8 Relevance of external law

(1) A person is guilty of an offence triable by virtue of section 4(4) above only if what he intended to do or facilitate would involve the commission of an offence under the law in force where the whole or any part of it was intended to take place.

(2) …

(3) A person is guilty of an offence triable by virtue of section 1(1A) of the Criminal Attempts Act 1981 or by virtue of section 7(4) above only if what he had in view would involve the commission of an offence under the law in force where the whole or any part of it was intended to take place.

(4) Conduct punishable under the law in force in any place is an offence under that law for the purposes of this section, however it is described in that law.

(5) Subject to subsection (7) below, a condition specified in [subsection (1) or (3)] above shall be taken to be satisfied unless not later than rules of court may provide the defence serve on the prosecution a notice—

(a) stating that, on the facts as alleged with respect to the relevant conduct, the condition is not in their opinion satisfied;

(b) showing their grounds for that opinion; and

(c) requiring the prosecution to show that it is satisfied.

(6) In subsection (5) above "the relevant conduct" means—

(a) where the condition in subsection (1) above is in question, what the accused intended to do or facilitate;

(b) … ; and

(c) where the condition in subsection (3) above is in question, what the accused had in view.

(7) The court, if it thinks fit, may permit the defence to require the prosecution to show that the condition is satisfied without the prior service of a notice under subsection (5) above.

(8) If by virtue of subsection (7) above a court of solemn jurisdiction in Scotland permits the defence to require the prosecution to show that the condition is satisfied, it shall be competent for the prosecution for that purpose to examine any witness or to put in evidence any production not included in the lists lodged by it.

(9) In the Crown Court the question whether the condition is satisfied shall be decided by the judge alone.

(10) In the High Court of Justiciary and in the sheriff court the question whether the condition is satisfied shall be decided by the judge or, as the case may be, the sheriff alone.

[5041]

NOTES

Sub-s (2): repealed by the Criminal Justice (Terrorism and Conspiracy) Act 1998, s 9(1), (2), Sch 1, Pt II, para 6(1)(a), Sch 2, Pt II.

Sub-s (5): words in square brackets substituted by the Criminal Justice (Terrorism and Conspiracy) Act 1998, s 9(1), Sch 1, Pt II, para 6(1)(b).

Sub-s (6): para (b) repealed by the Criminal Justice (Terrorism and Conspiracy) Act 1998, s 9(1), (2), Sch 1, Pt II, para 6(1)(c), Sch 2, Pt II.

9 British citizenship immaterial

(1) In any proceedings brought in England and Wales in respect of any offence to which this section applies it is immaterial to guilt whether or not the accused was a British citizen at the time of any act, omission or other event proof of which is required for conviction of the offence.

(2) This section applies to the following offences—

(a) any *offence under this Act*;

(b) … ;

(c) any attempt to commit an offence under section 3 above; and

(d) incitement to commit an *offence under this Act*.

[5042]

NOTES

Sub-s (2): para (b) repealed by the Criminal Justice (Terrorism and Conspiracy) Act 1998, s 9(1), (2), Sch 1, Pt II, para 6(2), Sch 2, Pt II.

Sub-s (4): for the words in italics in paras (a), (d), there are substituted the words "offence under section 1, 2 or 3 above" by the Police and Justice Act 2006, s 52, Sch 14, para 22, as from a day to be appointed.

Miscellaneous and general

10 Saving for certain law enforcement powers

Section 1(1) above has effect without prejudice to the operation—

(a) in England and Wales of any enactment relating to powers of inspection, search or seizure; and

(b) in Scotland of any enactment or rule of law relating to powers of examination, search or seizure.

[and nothing designed to indicate a withholding of consent to access to any program or data from persons as enforcement officers shall have effect to make access unauthorised for the purposes of the said section 1(1).

In this section "enforcement officer" means a constable or other person charged with the duty of investigating offences; and withholding consent from a person "as" an enforcement officer of any description includes the operation, by the person entitled to control access, of rules whereby enforcement officers of that description are, as such, disqualified from membership of a class of persons who are authorised to have access.]

[5043]

NOTES

Words in square brackets added by the Criminal Justice and Public Order Act 1994, s 162(1).

11 Proceedings for offences under section 1

(1) …

(2) Subject to subsection (3) below, proceedings for an offence under section 1 above may be brought within a period of six months from the date on which evidence sufficient in the opinion of the prosecutor to warrant the proceedings came to his knowledge.

(3) No such proceedings shall be brought by virtue of this section more than three years after the commission of the offence.

(4) For the purposes of this section, a certificate signed by or on behalf of the prosecutor and stating the date on which evidence sufficient in his opinion to warrant the proceedings came to his knowledge shall be conclusive evidence of that fact.

(5) A certificate stating that matter and purporting to be so signed shall be deemed to be so signed unless the contrary is proved.

(6) …

(7) This section does not extend to Scotland.

[5044]

NOTES

Repealed by the Police and Justice Act 2006, s 52, Sch 14, para 23, Sch 15, Pt 4, as from a day to be appointed (subject to transitional provisions in s 38(2) of the 2006 Act; as to which, see the "Transitional Provisions" note to s 1 at **[5033]**).

Sub-s (1): repealed by the Courts Act 2003, s 109(1), (3), Sch 8, para 346, Sch 10, subject to transitional provisions in SI 2005/911, arts 2–5.

Sub-s (6): repealed by the Access to Justice Act 1999, s 106, Sch 15, Pt V, Table (1).

12 Conviction of an offence under section 1 in proceedings for an offence under section 2 or 3

(1) If on the trial on indictment of a person charged with—

(a) an offence under section 2 above; or

(b) an offence under section 3 above or any attempt to commit such an offence;

the jury find him not guilty of the offence charged, they may find him guilty of an offence under section 1 above if on the facts shown he could have been found guilty of that offence in proceedings for that offence brought before the expiry of any time limit under section 11 above applicable to such proceedings.

(2) The Crown Court shall have the same powers and duties in relation to a person who is by virtue of this section convicted before it of an offence under section 1 above as a magistrates' court would have on convicting him of the offence.

(3) This section is without prejudice to section 6(3) of the Criminal Law Act 1967 (conviction of alternative indictable offence on trial on indictment).

(4) This section does not extend to Scotland.

[5045]

NOTES

Repealed by the Police and Justice Act 2006, s 52, Sch 14, para 24, Sch 15, Pt 4, as from a day to be appointed (subject to transitional provisions in s 38(2) of the 2006 Act; as to which, see the "Transitional Provisions" note to s 1 at **[5033]**).

13 Proceedings in Scotland

(1) A sheriff shall have jurisdiction in respect of an offence under section 1 or 2 above if—

(a) the accused was in the sheriffdom at the time when he did the act which caused the computer to perform the function; or

(b) any computer containing any program or data to which the accused secured or intended to secure unauthorised access by doing that act was in the sheriffdom at that time.

(2) A sheriff shall have jurisdiction in respect of an offence under section 3 above if—

(a) the accused was in the sheriffdom at the time when *he did the act which caused the unauthorised modification*; or

(b) the unauthorised modification took place in the sheriffdom.

(3) Subject to subsection (4) below, summary proceedings for an offence under section 1, 2 or 3 above may be commenced within a period of six months from the date on which evidence sufficient in the opinion of the procurator fiscal to warrant proceedings came to his knowledge.

(4) No such proceedings shall be commenced by virtue of this section more than three years after the commission of the offence.

(5) For the purposes of this section, a certificate signed by or on behalf of the procurator fiscal and stating the date on which evidence sufficient in his opinion to warrant the proceedings came to his knowledge shall be conclusive evidence of that fact.

PART VII MISCELLANEOUS

(6) A certificate stating that matter and purporting to be so signed shall be deemed to be so signed unless the contrary is proved.

(7) Subsection (3) of [section 136 of the Criminal Procedure (Scotland) Act 1995] (date of commencement of proceedings) shall apply for the purposes of this section as it applies for the purposes of that section.

(8) In proceedings in which a person is charged with an offence under section 2 or 3 above and is found not guilty or is acquitted of that charge, he may be found guilty of an offence under section 1 above if on the facts shown he could have been found guilty of that offence in proceedings for that offence *commenced before the expiry of any time limit under this section applicable to such proceedings*.

(9) Subsection (8) above shall apply whether or not an offence under section 1 above has been libelled in the complaint or indictment.

(10) A person found guilty of an offence under section 1 above by virtue of subsection (8) above shall be liable, in respect of that offence, only to the penalties set out in section 1.

(11) This section extends to Scotland only.

[5046]

NOTES

Sub-s (1): para (b) substituted by the Police and Justice Act 2006, s 52, Sch 14, para 25(1), (2), as from a day to be appointed (subject to transitional provisions in s 38(1) of the 2006 Act; as to which, see the "Transitional Provisions" note to s 1 at **[5033]**), as follows:

"(b) any computer containing any program or data to which the accused by doing that act secured or intended to secure unauthorised access, or enabled or intended to enable unauthorised access to be secured, was in the sheriffdom at that time.".

Sub-s (2): for the words in italics in para (a) there are substituted the words "he did the unauthorised act (or caused it to be done)", and para (b) substituted by the Police and Justice Act 2006, s 52, Sch 14, para 25(1), (3), as from a day to be appointed (subject to transitional provisions in s 38(4) of the 2006 Act; as to which, see the "Transitional Provisions" note to s 1 at **[5033]**), as follows:

"(b) the unauthorised act was done in relation to a computer in the sheriffdom.".

Sub-ss (3)–(6): repealed by the Police and Justice Act 2006, s 52, Sch 14, para 25(1), (4), Sch 15, Pt 4, as from a day to be appointed (subject to transitional provisions in s 38(2), (4) of the 2006 Act; as to which, see the "Transitional Provisions" note to s 1 at **[5033]**).

Sub-s (7): repealed by the Police and Justice Act 2006, s 52, Sch 14, para 25(1), (4), Sch 15, Pt 4, as from a day to be appointed (subject to transitional provisions in s 38(2), (4) of the 2006 Act; as to which, see the "Transitional Provisions" note to s 1 at **[5033]**); words in square brackets substituted by the Criminal Procedure (Consequential Provisions) (Scotland) Act 1995, s 5, Sch 4, para 77.

Sub-s (8): words in italics repealed by the Police and Justice Act 2006, s 52, Sch 14, para 25(1), (5), Sch 15, Pt 4, as from a day to be appointed (subject to transitional provisions in s 38(2), (4) of the 2006 Act; as to which, see the "Transitional Provisions" note to s 1 at **[5033]**).

14 Search warrants for offences under section 1

(1) Where a circuit judge [or a District Judge (Magistrates' Courts)] is satisfied by information on oath given by a constable that there are reasonable grounds for believing—

(a) that an offence under section 1 above has been or is about to be committed in any premises; and

(b) that evidence that such an offence has been or is about to be committed is in those premises;

he may issue a warrant authorising a constable to enter and search the premises, using such reasonable force as is necessary.

(2) The power conferred by subsection (1) above does not extend to authorising a search for material of the kinds mentioned in section 9(2) of the Police and Criminal Evidence Act 1984 (privileged, excluded and special procedure material).

(3) A warrant under this section—

(a) may authorise persons to accompany any constable executing the warrant; and

(b) remains in force for [three months] from the date of its issue.

(4) In executing a warrant issued under this section a constable may seize an article if he reasonably believes that it is evidence that an offence under section 1 above has been or is about to be committed.

(*5*) *In this section "premises" includes land, buildings, movable structures, vehicles, vessels, aircraft and hovercraft.*

(*6*) *This section does not extend to Scotland.*

[5047]

NOTES

Repealed by the Police and Justice Act 2006, s 52, Sch 14, para 26, Sch 15, Pt 4, as from a day to be appointed, subject to transitional provisions in s 38(2) of the 2006 Act (as to which, see the "Transitional Provisions" note to s 1 at **[5033]**).

Sub-s (1): words in square brackets inserted by the Courts Act 2003, s 65, Sch 4, para 7, as from a day to be appointed.

Sub-s (3): words in square brackets substituted, in relation to England and Wales, for original words "twenty-eight days" by the Serious Organised Crime and Police Act 2005, s 174(1), Sch 16, para 7.

15 (*Repealed by the Extradition Act 2003, ss 219(1), 220, Sch 3, paras 1, 7, Sch 4, except in relation to any request for extradition which is received by the relevant authority in the United Kingdom and an extradition made from or to the United Kingdom on or before 31 December 2003.*)

16 Application to Northern Ireland

(1) The following provisions of this section have effect for applying this Act in relation to Northern Ireland with the modifications there mentioned.

[(1A) In section 1(3)(a)—

(a) the reference to England and Wales shall be read as a reference to Northern Ireland; and

(b) the reference to 12 months shall be read as a reference to six months.]

(2) In section 2(2)(b)—

(a) the reference to England and Wales shall be read as a reference to Northern Ireland; and

(b) the reference to section 33 of the Magistrates' Courts Act 1980 shall be read as a reference to Article 46(4) of the Magistrates' Courts (Northern Ireland) Order 1981.

[(2A) In section 2(5)(a)—

(a) the reference to England and Wales shall be read as a reference to Northern Ireland; and

(b) the reference to 12 months shall be read as a reference to six months.]

(*3*) *The reference in section 3(6) to the Criminal Damage Act 1971 shall be read as a reference to the Criminal Damage (Northern Ireland) Order 1977.*

[(3A) In section 3(6)(a)—

(a) the reference to England and Wales shall be read as a reference to Northern Ireland; and

(b) the reference to 12 months shall be read as a reference to six months.

(3B) In section 3A(5)(a)—

(a) the reference to England and Wales shall be read as a reference to Northern Ireland; and

(b) the reference to 12 months shall be read as a reference to six months.]

(4) [Subsection (7) below shall apply in substitution for subsection (3) of section 7]; and any reference in subsection (4) of that section to England and Wales shall be read as a reference to Northern Ireland.

(5)–(7) …

(8) In section 8—

(a) …

(b) the reference in subsection (3) to section 1(1A) of the Criminal Attempts Act 1981 shall be read as a reference to Article 3(1A) of that Order.

(9) The references in sections 9(1) and 10 to England and Wales shall be read as references to Northern Ireland.

(*10*) *In section 11, [before subsection (2) there shall be inserted]—*

"*(1) A magistrates' court for a county division in Northern Ireland may hear and determine a complaint charging an offence under section 1 above or conduct a preliminary investigation or preliminary inquiry into an offence under that section if—*

- *(a) the accused was in that division at the time when he did the act which caused the computer to perform the function; or*
- *(b) any computer containing any program or data to which the accused secured or intended to secure unauthorised access by doing that act was in that division at that time.*";

...

(11) The reference in section 12(3) to section 6(3) of the Criminal Law Act 1967 shall be read as a reference to section 6(2) of the Criminal Law Act (Northern Ireland) 1967.

(12) In section 14—

- *(a) the reference in subsection (1) to a circuit judge shall be read as a reference to a county court judge; and*
- *(b) the reference in subsection (2) to section 9(2) of the Police and Criminal Evidence Act 1984 shall be read as a reference to Article 11(2) of the Police and Criminal Evidence (Northern Ireland) Order 1989.*

[5048]

NOTES

Sub-ss (1A), (2A), (3A), (3B): inserted by the Police and Justice Act 2006, s 52, Sch 14, para 27(1)–(3), (5), (6), as from a day to be appointed (subject to transitional provisions in s 38(2), (4) of the 2006 Act; as to which, see the "Transitional Provisions" note to s 1 at **[5033]**).

Sub-s (3): repealed by the Police and Justice Act 2006, s 52, Sch 14, para 27(1), (4), Sch 15, Pt 4, as from a day to be appointed (subject to transitional provisions in s 38(4) of the 2006 Act; as to which, see the "Transitional Provisions" note to s 1 at **[5033]**).

Sub-s (4): words in square brackets substituted by the Criminal Justice (Terrorism and Conspiracy) Act 1998, s 9(1), (3), Sch 1, Pt II, para 6(3)(a).

Sub-ss (5), (6): repealed by the Criminal Justice (Terrorism and Conspiracy) Act 1998, s 9(1), (2), Sch 1, Pt II, para 6(3)(b), Sch 2, Pt II.

Sub-s (7): amends the Criminal Attempts and Conspiracy (Northern Ireland) Order 1983, SI 1983/1120.

Sub-s (8): para (a) repealed by the Criminal Justice (Terrorism and Conspiracy) Act 1998, s 9(1), (2), Sch 1, Pt II, para 6(3)(b), Sch 2, Pt II.

Sub-s (10): repealed by the Police and Justice Act 2006, s 52, Sch 14, para 27(1), (7), Sch 15, Pt 4, as from a day to be appointed, subject to transitional provisions in s 38(2) of the 2006 Act (as to which, see the "Transitional Provisions" note to s 1 at **[5033]**); words in square brackets substituted and words omitted repealed, by the Courts Act 2003, s 109(1), (3), Sch 8, para 347, Sch 10.

Sub-ss (11), (12): repealed by the Police and Justice Act 2006, s 52, Sch 14, para 27(1), (7), Sch 15, Pt 4, as from a day to be appointed, subject to transitional provisions in s 38(2) of the 2006 Act (as to which, see the "Transitional Provisions" note to s 1 at **[5033]**).

[16A Northern Ireland: search warrants for offences under section 1

(1) Where a county court judge is satisfied by information on oath given by a constable that there are reasonable grounds for believing—

- (a) that an offence under section 1 above has been or is about to be committed in any premises, and
- (b) that evidence that such an offence has been or is about to be committed is in those premises,

he may issue a warrant authorising a constable to enter and search the premises, using such reasonable force as is necessary.

(2) The power conferred by subsection (1) above does not extend to authorising a search for material of the kinds mentioned in Article 11(2) of the Police and Criminal Evidence (Northern Ireland) Order 1989 (privileged, excluded and special procedure material).

(3) A warrant under this section—

- (a) may authorise persons to accompany any constable executing the warrant; and
- (b) remains in force for twenty-eight days from the date of its issue.

(4) In exercising a warrant issued under this section a constable may seize an article if he reasonably believes that it is evidence that an offence under section 1 above has been or is about to be committed.

(5) In this section "premises" includes land, buildings, movable structures, vehicles, vessels, aircraft and hovercraft.

(6) This section extends only to Northern Ireland.]

[5049]

NOTES

Commencement: to be appointed.

Inserted by the Police and Justice Act 2006, s 52, Sch 14, para 28, as from a day to be appointed, subject to transitional provisions in s 38(2) of the 2006 Act (as to which, see the "Transitional Provisions" note to s 1 at **[5033]**).

17 Interpretation

(1) The following provisions of this section apply for the interpretation of this Act.

(2) A person secures access to any program or data held in a computer if by causing a computer to perform any function he—

(a) alters or erases the program or data;

(b) copies or moves it to any storage medium other than that in which it is held or to a different location in the storage medium in which it is held;

(c) uses it; or

(d) has it output from the computer in which it is held (whether by having it displayed or in any other manner);

and references to access to a program or data (and to an intent to secure such access [or to enable such access to be secured]) shall be read accordingly.

(3) For the purposes of subsection (2)(c) above a person uses a program if the function he causes the computer to perform—

(a) causes the program to be executed; or

(b) is itself a function of the program.

(4) For the purposes of subsection (2)(d) above—

(a) a program is output if the instructions of which it consists are output; and

(b) the form in which any such instructions or any other data is output (and in particular whether or not it represents a form in which, in the case of instructions, they are capable of being executed or, in the case of data, it is capable of being processed by a computer) is immaterial.

(5) Access of any kind by any person to any program or data held in a computer is unauthorised if—

(a) he is not himself entitled to control access of the kind in question to the program or data; and

(b) he does not have consent to access by him of the kind in question to the program or data from any person who is so entitled

[but this subsection is subject to section 10.]

(6) References to any program or data held in a computer include references to any program or data held in any removable storage medium which is for the time being in the computer; and a computer is to be regarded as containing any program or data held in any such medium.

(7) A modification of the contents of any computer takes place if, by the operation of any function of the computer concerned or any other computer—

(a) any program or data held in the computer concerned is altered or erased; or

(b) any program or data is added to its contents;

and any act which contributes towards causing such a modification shall be regarded as causing it.

(8) Such a modification is unauthorised if—

(a) the person whose act causes it is not himself entitled to determine whether the modification should be made; and

(b) he does not have consent to the modification from any person who is so entitled.

(9) References to the home country concerned shall be read in accordance with section 4(6) above.

(10) References to a program include references to part of a program.

[5050]

PART VII MISCELLANEOUS

NOTES

Sub-s (2): words in square brackets inserted by the Police and Justice Act 2006, s 52, Sch 14, para 29(1), (2), as from a day to be appointed, subject to transitional provisions in s 38(1) of the 2006 Act (as to which, see the "Transitional Provisions" note to s 1 at **[5033]**).

Sub-s (5): words in square brackets added by the Criminal Justice and Public Order Act 1994, s 162(2).

Sub-s (7): repealed by the Police and Justice Act 2006, s 52, Sch 14, para 29(1), (3), Sch 15, Pt 4, as from a day to be appointed, subject to transitional provisions in s 38(4) of the 2006 Act (as to which, see the "Transitional Provisions" note to s 1 at **[5033]**).

Sub-s (8): substituted by the Police and Justice Act 2006, s 52, Sch 14, para 29(1), (4), as from a day to be appointed (subject to transitional provisions in s 38(4) of the 2006 Act; as to which, see the "Transitional Provisions" note to s 1 at **[5033]**), as follows:

"(8) An act done in relation to a computer is unauthorised if the person doing the act (or causing it to be done)—

(a) is not himself a person who has responsibility for the computer and is entitled to determine whether the act may be done; and

(b) does not have consent to the act from any such person.

In this subsection "act" includes a series of acts.".

18 Citation, commencement etc

(1) This Act may be cited as the Computer Misuse Act 1990.

(2) This Act shall come into force at the end of the period of two months beginning with the day on which it is passed.

(3) An offence is not committed under this Act unless every act or other event proof of which is required for conviction of the offence takes place after this Act comes into force.

[5051]

ANTI-TERRORISM, CRIME AND SECURITY ACT 2001

(2001 c 24)

ARRANGEMENT OF SECTIONS

PART 11
RETENTION OF COMMUNICATIONS DATA

PART 14
SUPPLEMENTAL

An Act to amend the Terrorism Act 2000; to make further provision about terrorism and security; to provide for the freezing of assets; to make provision about immigration and asylum; to amend or extend the criminal law and powers for preventing crime and enforcing that law; to make provision about the control of pathogens and toxins; to provide for the retention of communications data; to provide for implementation of Title VI of the Treaty on European Union; and for connected purposes

[14 December 2001]

1–101 ((*Pts 1–10*) *outside the scope of this work.*)

PART 11
RETENTION OF COMMUNICATIONS DATA

102 Codes and agreements about the retention of communications data

(1) The Secretary of State shall issue, and may from time to time revise, a code of practice relating to the retention by communications providers of communications data obtained by or held by them.

(2) The Secretary of State may enter into such agreements as he considers appropriate with any communications provider about the practice to be followed by that provider in relation to the retention of communications data obtained by or held by that provider.

(3) A code of practice or agreement under this section may contain any such provision as appears to the Secretary of State to be necessary—
- (a) for the purpose of safeguarding national security; or
- (b) for the purposes of prevention or detection of crime or the prosecution of offenders which may relate directly or indirectly to national security.

(4) A failure by any person to comply with a code of practice or agreement under this section which is for the time being in force shall not of itself render him liable to any criminal or civil proceedings.

(5) A code of practice or agreement under this section which is for the time being in force shall be admissible in evidence in any legal proceedings in which the question arises whether or not the retention of any communications data is justified on the grounds that a failure to retain the data would be likely to prejudice national security, the prevention or detection of crime or the prosecution of offenders.

[5052]

103 Procedure for codes of practice

(1) Before issuing the code of practice under section 102 the Secretary of State shall—
- (a) prepare and publish a draft of the code; and
- (b) consider any representations made to him about the draft;

and the Secretary of State may incorporate in the code finally issued any modifications made by him to the draft after its publication.

(2) Before publishing a draft of the code the Secretary of State shall consult with—
- (a) the Information Commissioner; and
- (b) the communications providers to whom the code will apply.

(3) The Secretary of State may discharge his duty under subsection (2) to consult with any communications providers by consulting with a person who appears to him to represent those providers.

(4) The Secretary of State shall lay before Parliament the draft code of practice under section 102 that is prepared and published by him under this section.

(5) The code of practice issued by the Secretary of State under section 102 shall not be brought into force except in accordance with an order made by the Secretary of State by statutory instrument.

(6) An order under subsection (5) may contain such transitional provisions and savings as appear to the Secretary of State to be necessary or expedient in connection with the coming into force of the code to which the order relates.

(7) The Secretary of State shall not make an order under this section unless a draft of the order has been laid before Parliament and approved by resolution of each House.

(8) The Secretary of State may from time to time—
- (a) revise the whole or any part of the code issued under section 102; and
- (b) issue the revised code.

(9) The preceding provisions of this section shall apply (with appropriate modifications) in relation to the issue of any revised code under section 102 as they apply in relation to the first issuing of the code.

(10) Subsection (9) shall not, in the case of a draft of a revised code, require the Secretary of State to consult under subsection (2) with any communications providers who would not be affected by the proposed revisions.

[5053]

NOTES

Orders: the Retention of Communications Data (Code of Practice) Order 2003, SI 2003/3175.

104 Directions about retention of communications data

(*1*) *If, after reviewing the operation of any requirements contained in the code of practice and any agreements under section 102, it appears to the Secretary of State that it is necessary to do so, he may by order made by statutory instrument authorise the giving of directions under this section for purposes prescribed in section 102(3).*

(*2*) *Where any order under this section is in force, the Secretary of State may give such directions as he considers appropriate about the retention of communications data—*

(*a*) *to communications providers generally;*
(*b*) *to communications providers of a description specified in the direction; or*
(*c*) *to any particular communications providers or provider.*

(*3*) *An order under this section must specify the maximum period for which a communications provider may be required to retain communications data by any direction given under this section while the order is in force.*

(*4*) *Before giving a direction under this section the Secretary of State shall consult—*

(*a*) *with the communications provider or providers to whom it will apply; or*
(*b*) *except in the case of a direction confined to a particular provider, with the persons appearing to the Secretary of State to represent the providers to whom it will apply.*

(*5*) *A direction under this section must be given or published in such manner as the Secretary of State considers appropriate for bringing it to the attention of the communications providers or provider to whom it applies.*

(*6*) *It shall be the duty of a communications provider to comply with any direction under this section that applies to him.*

(*7*) *The duty imposed by subsection* (*6*) *shall be enforceable by civil proceedings by the Secretary of State for an injunction, or for specific performance of a statutory duty under section 45 of the Court of Session Act 1988* (*c 36*), *or for any other appropriate relief.*

(*8*) *The Secretary of State shall not make an order under this section unless a draft of it has been laid before Parliament and approved by a resolution of each House.*

[5054]

NOTES

This section ceases to have effect on 14 December 2007: for the effect of this repeal see s 105(2)–(5) at **[5055]**, the Retention of Communications Data (Extension of Initial Period) Order 2003, SI 2003/3173, art 2 at **[5238]**, and the Retention of Communications Data (Further Extension of Initial Period) Order 2005, SI 2005/3335, art 2 at **[5240]**.

105 Lapsing of powers in section 104

(1) Section 104 shall cease to have effect at the end of the initial period unless an order authorising the giving of directions is made under that section before the end of that period.

(2) Subject to subsection (3), the initial period is the period of two years beginning with the day on which this Act is passed.

(3) The Secretary of State may by order made by statutory instrument extend, or (on one or more occasions) further extend the initial period.

(4) An order under subsection (3)—

(a) must be made before the time when the initial period would end but for the making of the order; and
(b) shall have the effect of extending, or further extending, that period for the period of two years beginning with that time.

(5) The Secretary of State shall not make an order under subsection (3) unless a draft of it has been laid before Parliament and approved by a resolution of each House.

[5055]

NOTES

Orders: the Retention of Communications Data (Extension of Initial Period) Order 2003, SI 2003/3173 at **[5237]**; the Retention of Communications Data (Further Extension of Initial Period) Order 2005, SI 2005/3335 at **[5239]**.

106 Arrangements for payments

(1) It shall be the duty of the Secretary of State to ensure that such arrangements are in force as he thinks appropriate for authorising or requiring, in such cases as he thinks fit, the making to communications providers of appropriate contributions towards the costs incurred by them—

- (a) in complying with the provisions of any code of practice, agreement or direction under this Part, or
- (b) as a consequence of the retention of any communications data in accordance with any such provisions.

(2) For the purpose of complying with his duty under this section, the Secretary of State may make arrangements for the payments to be made out of money provided by Parliament.

[5056]

107 Interpretation of Part 11

(1) In this Part—

"communications data" has the same meaning as in Chapter 2 of Part 1 of the Regulation of Investigatory Powers Act 2000 (c 23);

"communications provider" means a person who provides a postal service or a telecommunications service;

"legal proceedings", "postal service" and "telecommunications service" each has the same meaning as in that Act;

and any reference in this Part to the prevention or detection of crime shall be construed as if contained in Chapter 2 of Part 1 of that Act.

(2) References in this Part, in relation to any code of practice, agreement or direction, to the retention by a communications provider of any communications data include references to the retention of any data obtained by that provider before the time when the code was issued, the agreement made or the direction given, and to data already held by that provider at that time.

[5057]

108–121 ((*Pts 12, 13*) *outside the scope of this work.*)

PART 14
SUPPLEMENTAL

122–126 (*Outside the scope of this work.*)

127 Commencement

(1) Except as provided in subsections (2) to (4), this Act comes into force on such day as the Secretary of State may appoint by order.

(2) The following provisions come into force on the day on which this Act is passed—

- (a) Parts 2 to 6,
- (b) Part 8, except section 78,
- (c) Part 9, except sections 84 and 87,
- (d) sections 89 to 97,
- (e) sections 98 to 100, except so far as they extend to Scotland,
- (f) section 101 and Schedule 7, except so far as they relate to the entries in respect of the Police (Scotland) Act 1967,
- (g) Part 11,
- (h) Part 13, except section 121,
- (i) this Part, except section 125 and Schedule 8 so far as they relate to the entries—
  - (i) in Part 1 of Schedule 8,
  - (ii) in Part 5 of Schedule 8, in respect of the Nuclear Installations Act 1965,

(iii) in Part 6 of Schedule 8, in respect of the British Transport Commission Act 1962 and the Ministry of Defence Police Act 1987, so far as those entries extend to Scotland,
(iv) in Part 7 of Schedule 8, in respect of Schedule 5 to the Terrorism Act 2000.

(3) The following provisions come into force at the end of the period of two months beginning with the day on which this Act is passed—
(a) section 84,
(b) section 87.

(4) The following provisions come into force on such day as the Secretary of State and the Scottish Ministers, acting jointly, may appoint by order—
(a) sections 98 to 100, so far as they extend to Scotland,
(b) section 101 and Schedule 7, so far as they relate to the entries in respect of the Police (Scotland) Act 1967, and
(c) section 125 and Schedule 8, so far as they relate to the entries in Part 6 of Schedule 8 in respect of the British Transport Commission Act 1962 and the Ministry of Defence Police Act 1987, so far as those entries extend to Scotland.

(5) Different days may be appointed for different provisions and for different purposes.

(6) An order under this section—
(a) must be made by statutory instrument, and
(b) may contain incidental, supplemental, consequential or transitional provision.

[5058]

NOTES

Orders: the Anti-terrorism, Crime and Security Act 2001 (Commencement No 1 and Consequential Provisions) Order 2001, SI 2001/4019; the Anti-terrorism, Crime and Security Act 2001 (Commencement No 2) (Scotland) Order 2001, SI 2001/4104; the Anti-terrorism, Crime and Security Act 2001 (Commencement No 3) Order 2002, SI 2002/228; the Anti-terrorism, Crime and Security Act 2001 (Commencement No 4) Order 2002, SI 2002/1279; the Anti-terrorism, Crime and Security Act 2001 (Commencement No 5) Order 2002, SI 2002/1558.

128 Extent

(1) The following provisions do not extend to Scotland—
(a) Part 5,
(b) Part 12,
(c) in Part 6 of Schedule 8, the repeals in the Criminal Justice and Police Order Act 1994 and in the Crime and Disorder Act 1998.

(2) The following provisions do not extend to Northern Ireland—
(a) section 76,
(b) section 100.

(3) Except as provided in subsections (1) and (2), an amendment, repeal or revocation in this Act has the same extent as the enactment amended, repealed or revoked.

[5059]

129 Short title

This Act may be cited as the Anti-terrorism, Crime and Security Act 2001.

[5060]

(*Schs 1–8 outside the scope of this work.*)

ENTERPRISE ACT 2002

(2002 c 40)

ARRANGEMENT OF SECTIONS

PART 8
ENFORCEMENT OF CERTAIN CONSUMER LEGISLATION

Introduction

Enforcement Procedure

Information

Miscellaneous

Interpretation

Crown

PART 11
SUPPLEMENTARY

Establish and provide for the functions of the Office of Fair Trading, the Competition Appeal Tribunal and the Competition Service; to make provision about mergers and market structures and conduct; to amend the constitution and functions of the Competition Commission; to create an offence for those entering into certain anti-competitive agreements; to provide for the disqualification of directors of companies engaging in certain anti-competitive practices; to make other provision about competition law; to amend the law relating to the protection of the collective interests of consumers; to make further provision about the disclosure of information obtained under competition and consumer legislation; to amend the Insolvency Act 1986 and make other provision about insolvency; and for connected purposes

[7 November 2002]

1–209 ((*Pts 1–7*) *outside the scope of this work.*)

PART 8
ENFORCEMENT OF CERTAIN CONSUMER LEGISLATION

Introduction

210 Consumers

(1) In this Part references to consumers must be construed in accordance with this section.

(2) In relation to a domestic infringement a consumer is an individual in respect of whom the first and second conditions are satisfied.

(3) The first condition is that—

(a) goods are or are sought to be supplied to the individual (whether by way of sale or otherwise) in the course of a business carried on by the person supplying or seeking to supply them, or

(b) services are or are sought to be supplied to the individual in the course of a business carried on by the person supplying or seeking to supply them.

(4) The second condition is that—

(a) the individual receives or seeks to receive the goods or services otherwise than in the course of a business carried on by him, or

(b) the individual receives or seeks to receive the goods or services with a view to carrying on a business but not in the course of a business carried on by him.

(5) For the purposes of a domestic infringement it is immaterial whether a person supplying goods or services has a place of business in the United Kingdom.

(6) In relation to a Community infringement a consumer is a person who is a consumer for the purposes of—

(a) the Injunctions Directive, and

(b) the listed Directive concerned.

(7) A Directive is a listed Directive—

(a) if it is a Directive of the Council of the European Communities or of the European Parliament and of the Council, and

(b) if it is specified in Schedule 13 or to the extent that any of its provisions is so specified.

(8) A business includes—

(a) a professional practice;

(b) any other undertaking carried on for gain or reward;

(c) any undertaking in the course of which goods or services are supplied otherwise than free of charge.

(9) The Secretary of State may by order modify Schedule 13.

(10) An order under this section must be made by statutory instrument subject to annulment in pursuance of a resolution of either House of Parliament.

[5061]

NOTES

Commencement: 20 June 2003.

Order: the Enterprise Act 2002 (Part 8 Community Infringements Specified UK Laws) Order 2003, SI 2003/1374.

---

211 Domestic infringements

(1) In this Part a domestic infringement is an act or omission which—

(a) is done or made by a person in the course of a business,
(b) falls within subsection (2), and
(c) harms the collective interests of consumers in the United Kingdom.

(2) An act or omission falls within this subsection if it is of a description specified by the Secretary of State by order and consists of any of the following—

(a) a contravention of an enactment which imposes a duty, prohibition or restriction enforceable by criminal proceedings;
(b) an act done or omission made in breach of contract;
(c) an act done or omission made in breach of a non-contractual duty owed to a person by virtue of an enactment or rule of law and enforceable by civil proceedings;
(d) an act or omission in respect of which an enactment provides for a remedy or sanction enforceable by civil proceedings;
(e) an act done or omission made by a person supplying or seeking to supply goods or services as a result of which an agreement or security relating to the supply is void or unenforceable to any extent;
(f) an act or omission by which a person supplying or seeking to supply goods or services purports or attempts to exercise a right or remedy relating to the supply in circumstances where the exercise of the right or remedy is restricted or excluded under or by virtue of an enactment;
(g) an act or omission by which a person supplying or seeking to supply goods or services purports or attempts to avoid (to any extent) liability relating to the supply in circumstances where such avoidance is restricted or prevented under an enactment.

(3) But an order under this section may provide that any description of act or omission falling within subsection (2) is not a domestic infringement.

(4) For the purposes of subsection (2) it is immaterial—

(a) whether or not any duty, prohibition or restriction exists in relation to consumers as such;
(b) whether or not any remedy or sanction is provided for the benefit of consumers as such;
(c) whether or not any proceedings have been brought in relation to the act or omission;
(d) whether or not any person has been convicted of an offence in respect of the contravention mentioned in subsection (2)(a);
(e) whether or not there is a waiver in respect of the breach of contract mentioned in subsection (2)(b).

(5) References to an enactment include references to subordinate legislation (within the meaning of the Interpretation Act 1978 (c 30)).

(6) The power to make an order under this section must be exercised by statutory instrument.

(7) But no such order may be made unless a draft of it has been laid before Parliament and approved by a resolution of each House.

[5062]

NOTES

Commencement: 20 June 2003.

Order: the Enterprise Act 2002 (Part 8 Community Infringements Specified UK Laws) Order 2003, SI 2003/1593.

212 Community infringements

(1) In this Part a Community infringement is an act or omission which harms the collective interests of consumers and which—

(a) contravenes a listed Directive as given effect by the laws, regulations or administrative provisions of an EEA State, or
(b) contravenes such laws, regulations or administrative provisions which provide additional permitted protections.

(2) The laws, regulations or administrative provisions of an EEA State which give effect to a listed Directive provide additional permitted protections if—

PART VII MISCELLANEOUS

(a) they provide protection for consumers which is in addition to the minimum protection required by the Directive concerned, and
(b) such additional protection is permitted by that Directive.

(3) The Secretary of State may by order specify for the purposes of this section the law in the United Kingdom which—
(a) gives effect to the listed Directives;
(b) provides additional permitted protections.

(4) References to a listed Directive must be construed in accordance with section 210.

(5) An EEA State is a State which is a contracting party to the Agreement on the European Economic Area signed at Oporto on 2nd May 1992 as adjusted by the Protocol signed at Brussels on 17th March 1993.

(6) An order under this section must be made by statutory instrument subject to annulment in pursuance of a resolution of either House of Parliament.

[5063]

NOTES

Commencement: 20 June 2003.

Orders: the Enterprise Act 2002 (Part 8 Community Infringements Specified UK Laws) Order 2003, SI 2003/1374; the Enterprise Act 2002 (Part 8 Community Infringements Specified UK Laws) (Amendment) Order 2005, SI 2005/2418.

213 Enforcers

(1) Each of the following is a general enforcer—
(a) the OFT;
(b) every local weights and measures authority in Great Britain;
(c) the Department of Enterprise, Trade and Investment in Northern Ireland.

(2) A designated enforcer is any person or body (whether or not incorporated) which the Secretary of State—
(a) thinks has as one of its purposes the protection of the collective interests of consumers, and
(b) designates by order.

(3) The Secretary of State may designate a public body only if he is satisfied that it is independent.

(4) The Secretary of State may designate a person or body which is not a public body only if the person or body (as the case may be) satisfies such criteria as the Secretary of State specifies by order.

(5) A Community enforcer is a qualified entity for the purposes of the Injunctions Directive—
(a) which is for the time being specified in the list published in the Official Journal of the European Communities in pursuance of Article 4.3 of that Directive, but
(b) which is not a general enforcer or a designated enforcer.

(6) An order under this section may designate an enforcer in respect of—
(a) all infringements;
(b) infringements of such descriptions as are specified in the order.

(7) An order under this section may make different provision for different purposes.

(8) The designation of a body by virtue of subsection (3) is conclusive evidence for the purposes of any question arising under this Part that the body is a public body.

(9) An order under this section must be made by statutory instrument subject to annulment in pursuance of a resolution of either House of Parliament.

(10) If requested to do so by a designated enforcer which is designated in respect of one or more Community infringements the Secretary of State must notify the Commission of the European Communities—
(a) of its name and purpose;
(b) of the Community infringements in respect of which it is designated.

(11) The Secretary of State must also notify the Commission—

(a) of the fact that a person or body in respect of which he has given notice under subsection (10) ceases to be a designated enforcer;
(b) of any change in the name or purpose of a designated enforcer in respect of which he has given such notice;
(c) of any change to the Community infringements in respect of which a designated enforcer is designated.

[5064]

NOTES

Commencement: 20 June 2003.

Orders: the Enterprise Act 2002 (Part 8 Designated Enforcers: Criteria for Designation, Designation of Public Bodies as Designated Enforcers and Transitional Provisions) Order 2003, SI 2003/1399; the Enterprise Act 2002 (Part 8) (Designation of the Financial Services Authority as a Designated Enforcer) Order 2004, SI 2004/935; the Enterprise Act 2002 (Part 8) (Designation of the Consumers' Association) Order 2005, SI 2005/917; the Enterprise Act 2002 (Water Services Regulation Authority) Order 2006, SI 2006/522.

Enforcement procedure

214 Consultation

(1) An enforcer must not make an application for an enforcement order unless he has engaged in appropriate consultation with—
(a) the person against whom the enforcement order would be made, and
(b) the OFT (if it is not the enforcer).

(2) Appropriate consultation is consultation for the purpose of—
(a) achieving the cessation of the infringement in a case where an infringement is occurring;
(b) ensuring that there will be no repetition of the infringement in a case where the infringement has occurred;
(c) ensuring that there will be no repetition of the infringement in a case where the cessation of the infringement is achieved under paragraph (a);
(d) ensuring that the infringement does not take place in the case of a Community infringement which the enforcer believes is likely to take place.

(3) Subsection (1) does not apply if the OFT thinks that an application for an enforcement order should be made without delay.

(4) Subsection (1) ceases to apply—
(a) for the purposes of an application for an enforcement order at the end of the period of 14 days beginning with the day after the person against whom the enforcement order would be made receives a request for consultation from the enforcer;
(b) for the purposes of an application for an interim enforcement order at the end of the period of seven days beginning with the day after the person against whom the interim enforcement order would be made receives a request for consultation from the enforcer.

(5) The Secretary of State may by order make rules in relation to consultation under this section.

(6) Such an order must be made by statutory instrument subject to annulment in pursuance of a resolution of either House of Parliament.

(7) In this section (except subsection (4)) and in sections 215 and 216 references to an enforcement order include references to an interim enforcement order.

[5065]

NOTES

Commencement: 20 June 2003.

Order: the Enterprise Act 2002 (Part 8 Request for Consultation) Order 2003, SI 2003/1375.

215 Applications

(1) An application for an enforcement order must name the person the enforcer thinks—

(a) has engaged or is engaging in conduct which constitutes a domestic or a Community infringement, or
(b) is likely to engage in conduct which constitutes a Community infringement.

(2) A general enforcer may make an application for an enforcement order in respect of any infringement.

(3) A designated enforcer may make an application for an enforcement order in respect of an infringement to which his designation relates.

(4) A Community enforcer may make an application for an enforcement order in respect of a Community infringement.

(5) The following courts have jurisdiction to make an enforcement order—
(a) the High Court or a county court if the person against whom the order is sought carries on business or has a place of business in England and Wales or Northern Ireland;
(b) the Court of Session or the sheriff if the person against whom the order is sought carries on business or has a place of business in Scotland.

(6) If an application for an enforcement order is made by a Community enforcer the court may examine whether the purpose of the enforcer justifies its making the application.

(7) If the court thinks that the purpose of the Community enforcer does not justify its making the application the court may refuse the application on that ground alone.

(8) The purpose of a Community enforcer must be construed by reference to the Injunctions Directive.

(9) An enforcer which is not the OFT must notify the OFT of the result of an application under this section.

[5066]

NOTES
Commencement: 20 June 2003.

216 Applications: directions by OFT

(1) This section applies if the OFT believes that an enforcer other than the OFT intends to apply for an enforcement order.

(2) In such a case the OFT may direct that if an application in respect of a particular infringement is to be made it must be made—
(a) only by the OFT, or
(b) only by such other enforcer as the OFT directs.

(3) If the OFT directs that only it may make an application that does not prevent—
(a) the OFT or any enforcer from accepting an undertaking under section 219, or
(b) the OFT from taking such other steps it thinks appropriate (apart from making an application) for the purpose of securing that the infringement is not committed, continued or repeated.

(4) The OFT may vary or withdraw a direction given under this section.

(5) The OFT must take such steps as it thinks appropriate to bring a direction (or a variation or withdrawal of a direction) to the attention of enforcers it thinks may be affected by it.

(6) But this section does not prevent an application for an enforcement order being made by a Community enforcer.

[5067]

NOTES
Commencement: 20 June 2003.

217 Enforcement orders

(1) This section applies if an application for an enforcement order is made under section 215 and the court finds that the person named in the application has engaged in conduct which constitutes the infringement.

(2) This section also applies if such an application is made in relation to a Community infringement and the court finds that the person named in the application is likely to engage in conduct which constitutes the infringement.

(3) If this section applies the court may make an enforcement order against the person.

(4) In considering whether to make an enforcement order the court must have regard to whether the person named in the application—

(a) has given an undertaking under section 219 in respect of conduct such as is mentioned in subsection (3) of that section;

(b) has failed to comply with the undertaking.

(5) An enforcement order must—

(a) indicate the nature of the conduct to which the finding under subsection (1) or (2) relates, and

(b) direct the person to comply with subsection (6).

(6) A person complies with this subsection if he—

(a) does not continue or repeat the conduct;

(b) does not engage in such conduct in the course of his business or another business;

(c) does not consent to or connive in the carrying out of such conduct by a body corporate with which he has a special relationship (within the meaning of section 222(3)).

(7) But subsection (6)(a) does not apply in the case of a finding under subsection (2).

(8) An enforcement order may require a person against whom the order is made to publish in such form and manner and to such extent as the court thinks appropriate for the purpose of eliminating any continuing effects of the infringement—

(a) the order;

(b) a corrective statement.

(9) If the court makes a finding under subsection (1) or (2) it may accept an undertaking by the person—

(a) to comply with subsection (6), or

(b) to take steps which the court believes will secure that he complies with subsection (6).

(10) An undertaking under subsection (9) may include a further undertaking by the person to publish in such form and manner and to such extent as the court thinks appropriate for the purpose of eliminating any continuing effects of the infringement—

(a) the terms of the undertaking;

(b) a corrective statement.

(11) If the court—

(a) makes a finding under subsection (1) or (2), and

(b) accepts an undertaking under subsection (9),

it must not make an enforcement order in respect of the infringement to which the undertaking relates.

(12) An enforcement order made by a court in one part of the United Kingdom has effect in any other part of the United Kingdom as if made by a court in that part.

[5068]

NOTES

Commencement: 20 June 2003.

218 Interim enforcement order

(1) The court may make an interim enforcement order against a person named in the application for the order if it appears to the court—

(a) that it is alleged that the person is engaged in conduct which constitutes a domestic or Community infringement or is likely to engage in conduct which constitutes a Community infringement,

(b) that if the application had been an application for an enforcement order it would be likely to be granted,

(c) that it is expedient that the conduct is prohibited or prevented (as the case may be) immediately, and

(d) if no notice of the application has been given to the person named in the application that it is appropriate to make an interim enforcement order without notice.

(2) An interim enforcement order must—

(a) indicate the nature of the alleged conduct, and

(b) direct the person to comply with subsection (3).

(3) A person complies with this subsection if he—

(a) does not continue or repeat the conduct;

(b) does not engage in such conduct in the course of his business or another business;

(c) does not consent to or connive in the carrying out of such conduct by a body corporate with which he has a special relationship (within the meaning of section 222(3)).

(4) But subsection (3)(a) does not apply in so far as the application is made in respect of an allegation that the person is likely to engage in conduct which constitutes a Community infringement.

(5) An application for an interim enforcement order against a person may be made at any time before an application for an enforcement order against the person in respect of the same conduct is determined.

(6) An application for an interim enforcement order must refer to all matters—

(a) which are known to the applicant, and

(b) which are material to the question whether or not the application is granted.

(7) If an application for an interim enforcement order is made without notice the application must state why no notice has been given.

(8) The court may vary or discharge an interim enforcement order on the application of—

(a) the enforcer who applied for the order;

(b) the person against whom it is made.

(9) An interim enforcement order against a person is discharged on the determination of an application for an enforcement order made against the person in respect of the same conduct.

(10) If it appears to the court as mentioned in subsection (1)(a) to (c) the court may instead of making an interim enforcement order accept an undertaking from the person named in the application—

(a) to comply with subsection (3), or

(b) to take steps which the court believes will secure that he complies with subsection (3).

(11) An interim enforcement order made by a court in one part of the United Kingdom has effect in any other part of the United Kingdom as if made by a court in that part.

[5069]

NOTES

Commencement: 20 June 2003.

219 Undertakings

(1) This section applies if an enforcer has power to make an application under section 215.

(2) In such a case the enforcer may accept from a person to whom subsection (3) applies an undertaking that the person will comply with subsection (4).

(3) This subsection applies to a person who the enforcer believes—

(a) has engaged in conduct which constitutes an infringement;

(b) is engaging in such conduct;

(c) is likely to engage in conduct which constitutes a Community infringement.

(4) A person complies with this subsection if he—

(a) does not continue or repeat the conduct;

(b) does not engage in such conduct in the course of his business or another business;

(c) does not consent to or connive in the carrying out of such conduct by a body corporate with which he has a special relationship (within the meaning of section 222(3)).

(5) But subsection (4)(a) does not apply in the case of an undertaking given by a person in so far as subsection (3) applies to him by virtue of paragraph (c).

(6) If an enforcer accepts an undertaking under this section it must notify the OFT—

(a) of the terms of the undertaking;

(b) of the identity of the person who gave it.

[5070]

NOTES

Commencement: 20 June 2003.

220 Further proceedings

(1) This section applies if the court—

(a) makes an enforcement order under section 217,

(b) makes an interim enforcement order under section 218, or

(c) accepts an undertaking under either of those sections.

(2) In such a case the OFT has the same right to apply to the court in respect of a failure to comply with the order or undertaking as the enforcer who made the application for the order.

(3) An application to the court in respect of a failure to comply with an undertaking may include an application for an enforcement order or for an interim enforcement order.

(4) If the court finds that an undertaking is not being complied with it may make an enforcement order or an interim enforcement order (instead of making any other order it has power to make).

(5) In the case of an application for an enforcement order or for an interim enforcement order as mentioned in subsection (3) sections 214 and 216 must be ignored and sections 215 and 217 or 218 (as the case may be) apply subject to the following modifications—

(a) section 215(1)(b) must be ignored;

(b) section 215(5) must be ignored and the application must be made to the court which accepted the undertaking;

(c) section 217(9) to (11) must be ignored;

(d) section 218(10) must be ignored.

(6) If an enforcer which is not the OFT makes an application in respect of the failure of a person to comply with an enforcement order, an interim enforcement order or an undertaking given under section 217 or 218 the enforcer must notify the OFT—

(a) of the application;

(b) of any order made by the court on the application.

[5071]

NOTES

Commencement: 20 June 2003.

221 Community infringements: proceedings

(1) Subsection (2) applies to—

(a) every general enforcer;

(b) every designated enforcer which is a public body.

(2) An enforcer to which this subsection applies has power to take proceedings in EEA States other than the United Kingdom for the cessation or prohibition of a Community infringement.

(3) Subsection (4) applies to—

(a) every general enforcer;

(b) every designated enforcer.

(4) An enforcer to which this subsection applies may co-operate with a Community enforcer—

(a) for the purpose of bringing proceedings mentioned in subsection (2);
(b) in connection with the exercise by the Community enforcer of its functions under this Part.

(5) An EEA State is a State which is a contracting party to the Agreement on the European Economic Area signed at Oporto on 2nd May 1992 as adjusted by the Protocol signed at Brussels on 17th March 1993.

[5072]

NOTES

Commencement: 20 June 2003.

222 Bodies corporate: accessories

(1) This section applies if the person whose conduct constitutes a domestic infringement or a Community infringement is a body corporate.

(2) If the conduct takes place with the consent or connivance of a person (an accessory) who has a special relationship with the body corporate, the consent or connivance is also conduct which constitutes the infringement.

(3) A person has a special relationship with a body corporate if he is—

(a) a controller of the body corporate, or
(b) a director, manager, secretary or other similar officer of the body corporate or a person purporting to act in such a capacity.

(4) A person is a controller of a body corporate if—

(a) the directors of the body corporate or of another body corporate which is its controller are accustomed to act in accordance with the person's directions or instructions, or
(b) either alone or with an associate or associates he is entitled to exercise or control the exercise of one third or more of the voting power at any general meeting of the body corporate or of another body corporate which is its controller.

(5) An enforcement order or an interim enforcement order may be made against an accessory in respect of an infringement whether or not such an order is made against the body corporate.

(6) The court may accept an undertaking under section 217(9) or 218(10) from an accessory in respect of an infringement whether or not it accepts such an undertaking from the body corporate.

(7) An enforcer may accept an undertaking under section 219 from an accessory in respect of an infringement whether or not it accepts such an undertaking from the body corporate.

(8) Subsection (9) applies if—

(a) an order is made as mentioned in subsection (5), or
(b) an undertaking is accepted as mentioned in subsection (6) or (7).

(9) In such a case for subsection (6) of section 217, subsection (3) of section 218 or subsection (4) of section 219 (as the case may be) there is substituted the following subsection—

"( ) A person complies with this subsection if he—

(a) does not continue or repeat the conduct;
(b) does not in the course of any business carried on by him engage in conduct such as that which constitutes the infringement committed by the body corporate mentioned in section 222(1);
(c) does not consent to or connive in the carrying out of such conduct by another body corporate with which he has a special relationship (within the meaning of section 222(3))."

(10) A person is an associate of an individual if—

(a) he is the spouse [or civil partner] of the individual;
(b) he is a relative of the individual;
(c) he is a relative of the individual's spouse [or civil partner];
(d) he is the spouse [or civil partner] of a relative of the individual;

(e) he is the spouse [or civil partner] of a relative of the individual's spouse [or civil partner];

(f) he lives in the same household as the individual otherwise than merely because he or the individual is the other's employer, tenant, lodger or boarder;

(g) he is a relative of a person who is an associate of the individual by virtue of paragraph (f);

(h) he has at some time in the past fallen within any of paragraphs (a) to (g).

(11) A person is also an associate of—

(a) an individual with whom he is in partnership;

(b) an individual who is an associate of the individual mentioned in paragraph (a);

(c) a body corporate if he is a controller of it or he is an associate of a person who is a controller of the body corporate.

(12) A body corporate is an associate of another body corporate if—

(a) the same person is a controller of both;

(b) a person is a controller of one and persons who are his associates are controllers of the other;

(c) a person is a controller of one and he and persons who are his associates are controllers of the other;

(d) a group of two or more persons is a controller of each company and the groups consist of the same persons;

(e) a group of two or more persons is a controller of each company and the groups may be regarded as consisting of the same persons by treating (in one or more cases) a member of either group as replaced by a person of whom he is an associate.

(13) A relative is a brother, sister, uncle, aunt, nephew, niece, lineal ancestor or lineal descendant.

[5073]

NOTES

Commencement: 20 June 2003.

Sub-s (10): words in square brackets inserted by the Civil Partnership Act 2004, s 261(1), Sch 27, para 169.

223 Bodies corporate: orders

(1) This section applies if a court makes an enforcement order or an interim enforcement order against a body corporate and—

(a) at the time the order is made the body corporate is a member of a group of interconnected bodies corporate,

(b) at any time when the order is in force the body corporate becomes a member of a group of interconnected bodies corporate, or

(c) at any time when the order is in force a group of interconnected bodies corporate of which the body corporate is a member is increased by the addition of one or more further members.

(2) The court may direct that the order is binding upon all of the members of the group as if each of them were the body corporate against which the order is made.

(3) A group of interconnected bodies corporate is a group consisting of two or more bodies corporate all of whom are interconnected with each other.

(4) Any two bodies corporate are interconnected—

(a) if one of them is a subsidiary of the other, or

(b) if both of them are subsidiaries of the same body corporate.

(5) "Subsidiary" must be construed in accordance with section 736 of the Companies Act 1985 (c 6).

[5074]

NOTES

Commencement: 20 June 2003.

Information

224 OFT

(1) The OFT may for any of the purposes mentioned in subsection (2) give notice to any person requiring the person to provide it with the information specified in the notice.

(2) The purposes are—

(a) to enable the OFT to exercise or to consider whether to exercise any function it has under this Part;

(b) to enable a designated enforcer to which section 225 does not apply to consider whether to exercise any function it has under this Part;

(c) to enable a Community enforcer to consider whether to exercise any function it has under this Part;

(d) to ascertain whether a person has complied with or is complying with an enforcement order, an interim enforcement order or an undertaking given under section 217(9), 218(10) or 219.

[5075]

NOTES

Commencement: 20 June 2003.

225 Other enforcers

(1) This section applies to—

(a) every general enforcer (other than the OFT);

(b) every designated enforcer which is a public body.

(2) An enforcer to which this section applies may for any of the purposes mentioned in subsection (3) give notice to any person requiring the person to provide the enforcer with the information specified in the notice.

(3) The purposes are—

(a) to enable the enforcer to exercise or to consider whether to exercise any function it has under this Part;

(b) to ascertain whether a person has complied with or is complying with an enforcement order or an interim enforcement order made on the application of the enforcer or an undertaking given under section 217(9) or 218(10) (as the case may be) following such an application or an undertaking given to the enforcer under section 219.

[5076]

NOTES

Commencement: 20 June 2003.

226 Notices: procedure

(1) This section applies to a notice given under section 224 or 225.

(2) The notice must—

(a) be in writing;

(b) specify the purpose for which the information is required.

(3) If the purpose is as mentioned in section 224(2)(a), (b) or (c) or 225(3)(a) the notice must specify the function concerned.

(4) A notice may specify the time within which and manner in which it is to be complied with.

(5) A notice may require the production of documents or any description of documents.

(6) An enforcer may take copies of any documents produced in compliance with such a requirement.

(7) A notice may be varied or revoked by a subsequent notice.

(8) But a notice must not require a person to provide any information or produce any document which he would be entitled to refuse to provide or produce—

(a) in proceedings in the High Court on the grounds of legal professional privilege;
(b) in proceedings in the Court of Session on the grounds of confidentiality of communications.

[5077]

NOTES

Commencement: 20 June 2003.

227 Notices: enforcement

(1) If a person fails to comply with a notice given under section 224 or 225 the enforcer who gave the notice may make an application under this section.

(2) If it appears to the court that the person to whom the notice was given has failed to comply with the notice the court may make an order under this section.

(3) An order under this section may require the person to whom the notice was given to do anything the court thinks it is reasonable for him to do for any of the purposes mentioned in section 224 or 225 (as the case may be) to ensure that the notice is complied with.

(4) An order under this section may require the person to meet all the costs or expenses of the application.

(5) If the person is a company or association the court in proceeding under subsection (4) may require any officer of the company or association who is responsible for the failure to meet the costs or expenses.

(6) The court is a court which may make an enforcement order.

(7) In subsection (5) an officer of a company is a person who is a director, manager, secretary or other similar officer of the company.

[5078]

NOTES

Commencement: 20 June 2003.

Miscellaneous

228 Evidence

(1) Proceedings under this Part are civil proceedings for the purposes of—

(a) section 11 of the Civil Evidence Act 1968 (c 64) (convictions admissible as evidence in civil proceedings);
(b) section 10 of the Law Reform (Miscellaneous Provisions) (Scotland) Act 1968 (c 70) (corresponding provision in Scotland);
(c) section 7 of the Civil Evidence Act (Northern Ireland) 1971 (c 36 (NI)) (corresponding provision in Northern Ireland).

(2) In proceedings under this Part any finding by a court in civil proceedings that an act or omission mentioned in section 211(2)(b), (c) or (d) or 212(1) has occurred—

(a) is admissible as evidence that the act or omission occurred;
(b) unless the contrary is proved, is sufficient evidence that the act or omission occurred.

(3) But subsection (2) does not apply to any finding—

(a) which has been reversed on appeal;
(b) which has been varied on appeal so as to negative it.

[5079]

NOTES

Commencement: 20 June 2003.

229 Advice and information

(1) As soon as is reasonably practicable after the passing of this Act the OFT must prepare and publish advice and information with a view to—

PART VII MISCELLANEOUS

(a) explaining the provisions of this Part to persons who are likely to be affected by them, and

(b) indicating how the OFT expects such provisions to operate.

(2) The OFT may at any time publish revised or new advice or information.

(3) Advice or information published in pursuance of subsection (1)(b) may include advice or information about the factors which the OFT may take into account in considering how to exercise the functions conferred on it by this Part.

(4) Advice or information published by the OFT under this section is to be published in such form and in such manner as it considers appropriate.

(5) In preparing advice or information under this section the OFT must consult such persons as it thinks are representative of persons affected by this Part.

(6) If any proposed advice or information relates to a matter in respect of which another general enforcer or a designated enforcer may act the persons to be consulted must include that enforcer.

[5080]

NOTES

Commencement: 20 June 2003.

230 Notice to OFT of intended prosecution

(1) This section applies if a local weights and measures authority in England and Wales intends to start proceedings for an offence under an enactment or subordinate legislation specified by the Secretary of State by order for the purposes of this section.

(2) The authority must give the OFT—

(a) notice of its intention to start the proceedings;

(b) a summary of the evidence it intends to lead in respect of the charges.

(3) The authority must not start the proceedings until whichever is the earlier of the following—

(a) the end of the period of 14 days starting with the day on which the authority gives the notice;

(b) the day on which it is notified by the OFT that the OFT has received the notice and summary given under subsection (2).

(4) The authority must also notify the OFT of the outcome of the proceedings after they are finally determined.

(5) But such proceedings are not invalid by reason only of the failure of the authority to comply with this section.

(6) Subordinate legislation has the same meaning as in section 21(1) of the Interpretation Act 1978 (c 30).

(7) An order under this section must be made by statutory instrument subject to annulment in pursuance of a resolution of either House of Parliament.

[5081]

NOTES

Commencement: 20 June 2003.
Order: the Enterprise Act 2002 (Part 8 Notice to OFT of Intended Prosecution Specified Enactments, Revocation and Transitional Provision) Order 2003, SI 2003/1376.

231 Notice of convictions and judgments to OFT

(1) This section applies if—

(a) a person is convicted of an offence by or before a court in the United Kingdom, or

(b) a judgment is given against a person by a court in civil proceedings in the United Kingdom.

(2) The court may make arrangements to bring the conviction or judgment to the attention of the OFT if it appears to the court—

(a) having regard to the functions of the OFT under this Part or under the Estate Agents Act 1979 (c 38) that it is expedient for the conviction or judgment to be brought to the attention of the OFT, and
(b) without such arrangements the conviction or judgment may not be brought to the attention of the OFT.

(3) For the purposes of subsection (2) it is immaterial that the proceedings have been finally disposed of by the court.

(4) Judgment includes an order or decree and references to the giving of the judgment must be construed accordingly.

[5082]

NOTES

Commencement: 20 June 2003.

Interpretation

232 Goods and services

(1) References in this Part to goods and services must be construed in accordance with this section.

(2) Goods include—
(a) buildings and other structures;
(b) ships, aircraft and hovercraft.

(3) The supply of goods includes—
(a) supply by way of sale, lease, hire or hire purchase;
(b) in relation to buildings and other structures, construction of them by one person for another.

(4) Goods or services which are supplied wholly or partly outside the United Kingdom must be taken to be supplied to or for a person in the United Kingdom if they are supplied in accordance with arrangements falling within subsection (5).

(5) Arrangements fall within this subsection if they are made by any means and—
(a) at the time the arrangements are made the person seeking the supply is in the United Kingdom, or
(b) at the time the goods or services are supplied (or ought to be supplied in accordance with the arrangements) the person responsible under the arrangements for effecting the supply is in or has a place of business in the United Kingdom.

[5083]

NOTES

Commencement: 20 June 2003.

233 Person supplying goods

(1) This section has effect for the purpose of references in this Part to a person supplying or seeking to supply goods under—
(a) a hire-purchase agreement;
(b) a credit-sale agreement;
(c) a conditional sale agreement.

(2) The references include references to a person who conducts any antecedent negotiations relating to the agreement.

(3) The following expressions must be construed in accordance with section 189 of the Consumer Credit Act 1974 (c 39)—
(a) hire-purchase agreement;
(b) credit-sale agreement;
(c) conditional sale agreement;
(d) antecedent negotiations.

[5084]

NOTES

Commencement: 20 June 2003.

234 Supply of services

(1) References in this Part to the supply of services must be construed in accordance with this section.

(2) The supply of services does not include the provision of services under a contract of service or of apprenticeship whether it is express or implied and (if it is express) whether it is oral or in writing.

(3) The supply of services includes—

(a) performing for gain or reward any activity other than the supply of goods;

(b) rendering services to order;

(c) the provision of services by making them available to potential users.

(4) The supply of services includes making arrangements for the use of computer software or for granting access to data stored in any form which is not readily accessible.

(5) The supply of services includes making arrangements by means of a relevant agreement (within the meaning of [paragraph 29 of Schedule 2 to the Telecommunications Act 1984]) for sharing the use of telecommunications apparatus.

(6) The supply of services includes permitting or making arrangements to permit the use of land in such circumstances as the Secretary of State specifies by order.

(7) The power to make an order under subsection (6) must be exercised by statutory instrument.

(8) But no such order may be made unless a draft of it has been laid before Parliament and approved by a resolution of each House.

[5085]

NOTES

Commencement: 20 June 2003.

Sub-s (5): words in square brackets substituted by the Communications Act 2003, s 406(1), Sch 17, para 174(1), (6).

Order: the Enterprise Act 2002 (Supply of Services) Order 2003, SI 2003/1594.

235 Injunctions Directive

In this Part the Injunctions Directive is Directive 98/27/EC of the European Parliament and of the Council on injunctions for the protection of consumers' interests.

[5086]

NOTES

Commencement: 20 June 2003.

Crown

236 Crown

This Part binds the Crown.

[5087]

NOTES

Commencement: 20 June 2003.

237–272 ((*Pts 9, 10*) *outside the scope of this work.*)

PART 11
SUPPLEMENTARY

273–278 (*Outside the scope of this work.*)

279 Commencement

The preceding provisions of this Act shall come into force on such day as the Secretary of State may by order made by statutory instrument appoint; and different days may be appointed for different purposes.

[5088]

NOTES

Commencement: 7 November 2002.

Orders: the Enterprise Act 2002 (Commencement No 1) Order 2003, SI 2003/765; the Enterprise Act 2002 (Commencement No 2, Transitional and Transitory Provisions) Order 2003, SI 2003/766; the Enterprise Act 2002 (Commencement No 3, Transitional and Transitory Provisions and Savings) Order 2003, SI 2003/1397; the Enterprise Act 2002 (Commencement No 4 and Transitional Provisions and Savings) Order 2003, SI 2003/2093; the Enterprise Act 2002 (Commencement No 5 and Amendment) Order 2003, SI 2003/3340; the Enterprise Act 2002 (Commencement No 6) Order 2004, SI 2004/1866; the Enterprise Act 2002 (Commencement No 7 and Transitional Provisions and Savings) Order 2004, SI 2004/3233.

280 Extent

(1) Sections 256 to 265, 267, 269 and 272 extend only to England and Wales.

(2) Sections 204, 248 to 255 and 270 extend only to England and Wales and Scotland (but subsection (3) of section 415A as inserted by section 270 extends only to England and Wales).

(3) Any other modifications by this Act of an enactment have the same extent as the enactment being modified.

(4) Otherwise, this Act extends to England and Wales, Scotland and Northern Ireland.

[5089]

NOTES

Commencement: 7 November 2002.

281 Short title

This Act may be cited as the Enterprise Act 2002.

[5090]

NOTES

Commencement: 7 November 2002.

(*Schs 1–12 outside the scope of this work.*)

SCHEDULE 13
LISTED DIRECTIVES

Section 210

PART 1
DIRECTIVES

1 Council Directive 84/450/EEC of 10 September 1984 relating to the approximation of the laws, regulations and administrative provisions of the Member States concerning misleading advertising.

2 Council Directive 85/577/EEC of 20 December 1985 to protect the consumer in respect of contracts negotiated away from business premises.

PART VII MISCELLANEOUS

3 Council Directive 87/102/EEC of 22 December 1986 for the approximation of the laws, regulations and administrative provisions of the Member States concerning consumer credit as last amended by Directive 98/7/EC.

4 Council Directive 90/314/EEC of 13 June 1990 on package travel, package holidays and package tours.

5 Council Directive 93/13/EEC of 5 April 1993 on unfair terms in consumer contracts.

6 Directive 94/47/EC of the European Parliament and of the Council of 26 October 1994 on the protection of purchasers in respect of certain aspects of contracts relating to the purchase of the right to use immovable properties on a timeshare basis.

7 Directive 97/7/EC of the European Parliament and of the Council of 20 May 1997 on the protection of consumers in respect of distance contracts.

8 Directive 1999/44/EC of the European Parliament and of the Council of 25 May 1999 on certain aspects of the sale of consumer goods and associated guarantees.

9 Directive 2000/31/EC of the European Parliament and of the Council of 8 June 2000 on certain legal aspects of information society services, in particular electronic commerce, in the Internal Market ("Directive on electronic commerce").

[9A Directive 2002/65/EC of the European Parliament and of the Council of 23 September 2002 concerning the distance marketing of consumer financial services and amending Council Directive 90/619/EEC and Directives 97/7/EC and 98/27/EC.]

[5091]

NOTES

Commencement: 20 June 2003.

Para 9A: added by the Financial Services (Distance Marketing) Regulations 2004, SI 2004/2095, reg 26.

PART 2
PROVISIONS OF DIRECTIVES

10 Articles 10 to 21 of Council Directive 89/552/EEC of 3 October 1989 on the co-ordination of certain provisions laid down by law, regulation or administrative action in Member States concerning the pursuit of television broadcasting activities as amended by Directive 97/36/EC.

[11 Articles 83 to 100 of the Directive 2001/83/EC of the European Parliament and of the Council of 6 November 2001 on the Community Code relating to medicinal products for human use as read with—

(a) Directive 2004/24/EC of the European Parliament and of the Council amending, as regards traditional herbal medicinal products, the code, and

(b) Directive 2004/27/EC of the European Parliament and of the Council also amending the code.]

[5092]

NOTES

Commencement: 20 June 2003.

Para 11: substituted by the Medicines (Marketing Authorisations Etc) Amendment Regulations 2005, SI 2005/2759, reg 4, Schedule, para 19.

(*Schs 14–26 outside the scope of this work.*)

FRAUD ACT 2006

(2006 c 35)

ARRANGEMENT OF SECTIONS

Fraud

PART VII MISCELLANEOUS

An Act to make provision for, and in connection with, criminal liability for fraud and obtaining services dishonestly.

[8 November 2006]

Fraud

1 Fraud

(1) A person is guilty of fraud if he is in breach of any of the sections listed in subsection (2) (which provide for different ways of committing the offence).

(2) The sections are—
(a) section 2 (fraud by false representation),
(b) section 3 (fraud by failing to disclose information), and
(c) section 4 (fraud by abuse of position).

(3) A person who is guilty of fraud is liable—
(a) on summary conviction, to imprisonment for a term not exceeding 12 months or to a fine not exceeding the statutory maximum (or to both);
(b) on conviction on indictment, to imprisonment for a term not exceeding 10 years or to a fine (or to both).

(4) Subsection (3)(a) applies in relation to Northern Ireland as if the reference to 12 months were a reference to 6 months.

[5093]

NOTES
Commencement: 15 January 2007.

2 Fraud by false representation

(1) A person is in breach of this section if he—

(a) dishonestly makes a false representation, and
(b) intends, by making the representation—
(i) to make a gain for himself or another, or
(ii) to cause loss to another or to expose another to a risk of loss.

(2) A representation is false if—
(a) it is untrue or misleading, and
(b) the person making it knows that it is, or might be, untrue or misleading.

(3) "Representation" means any representation as to fact or law, including a representation as to the state of mind of—
(a) the person making the representation, or
(b) any other person.

(4) A representation may be express or implied.

(5) For the purposes of this section a representation may be regarded as made if it (or anything implying it) is submitted in any form to any system or device designed to receive, convey or respond to communications (with or without human intervention).

[5094]

NOTES

Commencement: 15 January 2007.

3 Fraud by failing to disclose information

A person is in breach of this section if he—
(a) dishonestly fails to disclose to another person information which he is under a legal duty to disclose, and
(b) intends, by failing to disclose the information—
(i) to make a gain for himself or another, or
(ii) to cause loss to another or to expose another to a risk of loss.

[5095]

NOTES

Commencement: 15 January 2007.

4 Fraud by abuse of position

(1) A person is in breach of this section if he—
(a) occupies a position in which he is expected to safeguard, or not to act against, the financial interests of another person,
(b) dishonestly abuses that position, and
(c) intends, by means of the abuse of that position—
(i) to make a gain for himself or another, or
(ii) to cause loss to another or to expose another to a risk of loss.

(2) A person may be regarded as having abused his position even though his conduct consisted of an omission rather than an act.

[5096]

NOTES

Commencement: 15 January 2007.

5 "Gain" and "loss"

(1) The references to gain and loss in sections 2 to 4 are to be read in accordance with this section.

(2) "Gain" and "loss"—
(a) extend only to gain or loss in money or other property;
(b) include any such gain or loss whether temporary or permanent;

and "property" means any property whether real or personal (including things in action and other intangible property).

(3) "Gain" includes a gain by keeping what one has, as well as a gain by getting what one does not have.

(4) "Loss" includes a loss by not getting what one might get, as well as a loss by parting with what one has.

[5097]

NOTES

Commencement: 15 January 2007.

6 Possession etc of articles for use in frauds

(1) A person is guilty of an offence if he has in his possession or under his control any article for use in the course of or in connection with any fraud.

(2) A person guilty of an offence under this section is liable—

(a) on summary conviction, to imprisonment for a term not exceeding 12 months or to a fine not exceeding the statutory maximum (or to both);

(b) on conviction on indictment, to imprisonment for a term not exceeding 5 years or to a fine (or to both).

(3) Subsection (2)(a) applies in relation to Northern Ireland as if the reference to 12 months were a reference to 6 months.

[5098]

NOTES

Commencement: 15 January 2007.

7 Making or supplying articles for use in frauds

(1) A person is guilty of an offence if he makes, adapts, supplies or offers to supply any article—

(a) knowing that it is designed or adapted for use in the course of or in connection with fraud, or

(b) intending it to be used to commit, or assist in the commission of, fraud.

(2) A person guilty of an offence under this section is liable—

(a) on summary conviction, to imprisonment for a term not exceeding 12 months or to a fine not exceeding the statutory maximum (or to both);

(b) on conviction on indictment, to imprisonment for a term not exceeding 10 years or to a fine (or to both).

(3) Subsection (2)(a) applies in relation to Northern Ireland as if the reference to 12 months were a reference to 6 months.

[5099]

NOTES

Commencement: 15 January 2007.

8 "Article"

(1) For the purposes of—

(a) sections 6 and 7, and

(b) the provisions listed in subsection (2), so far as they relate to articles for use in the course of or in connection with fraud,

"article" includes any program or data held in electronic form.

(2) The provisions are—

(a) section 1(7)(b) of the Police and Criminal Evidence Act 1984 (c 60),

(b) section 2(8)(b) of the Armed Forces Act 2001 (c 19), and

(c) Article 3(7)(b) of the Police and Criminal Evidence (Northern Ireland) Order 1989 (SI 1989/1341 (NI 12));

(meaning of "prohibited articles" for the purposes of stop and search powers).

[5100]

NOTES

Commencement: 15 January 2007.

9 Participating in fraudulent business carried on by sole trader etc

(1) A person is guilty of an offence if he is knowingly a party to the carrying on of a business to which this section applies.

(2) This section applies to a business which is carried on—

(a) by a person who is outside the reach of section 458 of the Companies Act 1985 (c 6) or Article 451 of the Companies (Northern Ireland) Order 1986 (SI 1986/1032) (NI 6)) (offence of fraudulent trading), and

(b) with intent to defraud creditors of any person or for any other fraudulent purpose.

(3) The following are within the reach of section 458 of the 1985 Act—

(a) a company (within the meaning of that Act);

(b) a person to whom that section applies (with or without adaptations or modifications) as if the person were a company;

(c) a person exempted from the application of that section.

(4) The following are within the reach of Article 451 of the 1986 Order—

(a) a company (within the meaning of that Order);

(b) a person to whom that Article applies (with or without adaptations or modifications) as if the person were a company;

(c) a person exempted from the application of that Article.

(5) "Fraudulent purpose" has the same meaning as in section 458 of the 1985 Act or Article 451 of the 1986 Order.

(6) A person guilty of an offence under this section is liable—

(a) on summary conviction, to imprisonment for a term not exceeding 12 months or to a fine not exceeding the statutory maximum (or to both);

(b) on conviction on indictment, to imprisonment for a term not exceeding 10 years or to a fine (or to both).

(7) Subsection (6)(a) applies in relation to Northern Ireland as if the reference to 12 months were a reference to 6 months.

[5101]

NOTES

Commencement: 15 January 2007.

10 (*Amends the Companies Act 1985, Sch 24, and the Companies (Northern Ireland) Order 1986, SI 1986/1032, Sch 23; outside the scope of this work.*)

Obtaining services dishonestly

11 Obtaining services dishonestly

(1) A person is guilty of an offence under this section if he obtains services for himself or another—

(a) by a dishonest act, and

(b) in breach of subsection (2).

(2) A person obtains services in breach of this subsection if—

(a) they are made available on the basis that payment has been, is being or will be made for or in respect of them,

(b) he obtains them without any payment having been made for or in respect of them or without payment having been made in full, and

(c) when he obtains them, he knows—

(i) that they are being made available on the basis described in paragraph (a), or

(ii) that they might be,

but intends that payment will not be made, or will not be made in full.

(3) A person guilty of an offence under this section is liable—

(a) on summary conviction, to imprisonment for a term not exceeding 12 months or to a fine not exceeding the statutory maximum (or to both);

(b) on conviction on indictment, to imprisonment for a term not exceeding 5 years or to a fine (or to both).

(4) Subsection (3)(a) applies in relation to Northern Ireland as if the reference to 12 months were a reference to 6 months.

[5102]

NOTES

Commencement: 15 January 2007.

Supplementary

12 Liability of company officers for offences by company

(1) Subsection (2) applies if an offence under this Act is committed by a body corporate.

(2) If the offence is proved to have been committed with the consent or connivance of—

(a) a director, manager, secretary or other similar officer of the body corporate, or

(b) a person who was purporting to act in any such capacity,

he (as well as the body corporate) is guilty of the offence and liable to be proceeded against and punished accordingly.

(3) If the affairs of a body corporate are managed by its members, subsection (2) applies in relation to the acts and defaults of a member in connection with his functions of management as if he were a director of the body corporate.

[5103]

NOTES

Commencement: 15 January 2007.

13 Evidence

(1) A person is not to be excused from—

(a) answering any question put to him in proceedings relating to property, or

(b) complying with any order made in proceedings relating to property,

on the ground that doing so may incriminate him or his spouse or civil partner of an offence under this Act or a related offence.

(2) But, in proceedings for an offence under this Act or a related offence, a statement or admission made by the person in—

(a) answering such a question, or

(b) complying with such an order,

is not admissible in evidence against him or (unless they married or became civil partners after the making of the statement or admission) his spouse or civil partner.

(3) "Proceedings relating to property" means any proceedings for—

(a) the recovery or administration of any property,

(b) the execution of a trust, or

(c) an account of any property or dealings with property,

and "property" means money or other property whether real or personal (including things in action and other intangible property).

(4) "Related offence" means—

(a) conspiracy to defraud;

(b) any other offence involving any form of fraudulent conduct or purpose.

[5104]

NOTES

Commencement: 15 January 2007.

14 Minor and consequential amendments etc

(1) Schedule 1 contains minor and consequential amendments.

(2) Schedule 2 contains transitional provisions and savings.

(3) Schedule 3 contains repeals and revocations.

[5105]

NOTES

Commencement: 15 January 2007.

15 Commencement and extent

(1) This Act (except this section and section 16) comes into force on such day as the Secretary of State may appoint by an order made by statutory instrument; and different days may be appointed for different purposes.

(2) Subject to subsection (3), sections 1 to 9 and 11 to 13 extend to England and Wales and Northern Ireland only.

(3) Section 8, so far as it relates to the Armed Forces Act 2001 (c 19), extends to any place to which that Act extends.

(4) Any amendment in section 10 or Schedule 1, and any related provision in section 14 or Schedule 2 or 3, extends to any place to which the provision which is the subject of the amendment extends.

[5106]

NOTES

Commencement: 8 November 2006.
Order: the Fraud Act 2006 (Commencement) Order 2006, SI 2006/3200.

16 Short title

This Act may be cited as the Fraud Act 2006.

[5107]

NOTES

Commencement: 8 November 2006.

(*Sch 1 contains minor and consequential amendments; outside the scope of this work.*)

SCHEDULE 2
TRANSITIONAL PROVISIONS AND SAVINGS

Section 14(2)

Maximum term of imprisonment for offences under this Act

1 In relation to an offence committed before the commencement of section 154(1) of the Criminal Justice Act 2003 (c 44), the references to 12 months in sections 1(3)(a), 6(2)(a), 7(2)(a), 9(6)(a) and 11(3)(a) are to be read as references to 6 months.

2–11 …

[5108]–[5200]

NOTES

Commencement: 15 January 2007.
Paras 2–11: outside the scope of this work (transitional provisions and savings in relation to the amendments made by s 10 of, and Sch 1 to, this Act).

(*Sch 3 contains repeals and revocations; outside the scope of this work.*)

HEALTH AND SAFETY (DISPLAY SCREEN EQUIPMENT) REGULATIONS 1992

(SI 1992/2792)

NOTES

Made: 5 November 1992.
Authority: Health and Safety at Work etc Act 1974, ss 15(1), (2), (5)(b), (9), 82(3)(a), Sch 3, paras 1(1)(a), (c), (2), 7, 8(1), 9, 14.
Commencement: 1 January 1993.

ARRANGEMENT OF REGULATIONS

PART VII MISCELLANEOUS

1 Citation, commencement, interpretation and application

(1) These Regulations may be cited as the Health and Safety (Display Screen Equipment) Regulations 1992 and shall come into force on 1st January 1993.

(2) In these Regulations—

(a) "display screen equipment" means any alphanumeric or graphic display screen, regardless of the display process involved;

(b) "operator" means a self-employed person who habitually uses display screen equipment as a significant part of his normal work;

(c) "use" means use for or in connection with work;

(d) "user" means an employee who habitually uses display screen equipment as a significant part of his normal work; and

(e) "workstation" means an assembly comprising—

(i) display screen equipment (whether provided with software determining the interface between the equipment and its operator or user, a keyboard or any other input device),

(ii) any optional accessories to the display screen equipment,

(iii) any disk drive, telephone, modem, printer, document holder, work chair, work desk, work surface or other item peripheral to the display screen equipment, and

(iv) the immediate work environment around the display screen equipment.

(3) Any reference in these Regulations to—

(a) a numbered regulation is a reference to the regulation in these Regulations so numbered; or

(b) a numbered paragraph is a reference to the paragraph so numbered in the regulation in which the reference appears.

(4) Nothing in these Regulations shall apply to or in relation to—

(a) drivers' cabs or control cabs for vehicles or machinery;

(b) display screen equipment on board a means of transport;

(c) display screen equipment mainly intended for public operation;

(d) portable systems not in prolonged use;

(e) calculators, cash registers or any equipment having a small data or measurement display required for direct use of the equipment; or

(f) window typewriters.

[5201]

2 Analysis of workstations

(1) Every employer shall perform a suitable and sufficient analysis of those workstations which—

(a) (regardless of who has provided them) are used for the purposes of his undertaking by users; or

(b) have been provided by him and are used for the purposes of his undertaking by operators,

for the purpose of assessing the health and safety risks to which those persons are exposed in consequence of that use.

(2) Any assessment made by an employer in pursuance of paragraph (1) shall be reviewed by him if—

(a) there is reason to suspect that it is no longer valid; or

(b) there has been a significant change in the matters to which it relates;

and where as a result of any such review changes to an assessment are required, the employer concerned shall make them.

(3) The employer shall reduce the risks identified in consequence of an assessment to the lowest extent reasonably practicable.

(4) The reference in paragraph (3) to "an assessment" is a reference to an assessment made by the employer concerned in pursuance of paragraph (1) and changed by him where necessary in pursuance of paragraph (2).

[5202]

[3 Requirements of workstations

Every employer shall ensure that any workstation which may be used for the purposes of his undertaking meets the requirements laid down in the Schedule to these Regulations, to the extent specified in paragraph 1 thereof.]

[5203]

NOTES

Commencement: 17 September 2002.

Substituted by the Health and Safety (Miscellaneous Amendments) Regulations 2002, SI 2002/2174, reg 3(a).

4 Daily work routine of users

Every employer shall so plan the activities of users at work in his undertaking that their daily work on display screen equipment is periodically interrupted by such breaks or changes of activity as reduce their workload at that equipment.

[5204]

5 Eyes and eyesight

[(1) Where a person—

(a) is a user in the undertaking in which he is employed; or

(b) is to become a user in the undertaking in which he is, or is to become, employed,

the employer who carries on the undertaking shall, if requested by that person, ensure that an appropriate eye and eyesight test is carried out on him by a competent person within the time specified in paragraph (2).

(2) The time referred to in paragraph (1) is—

(a) in the case of a person mentioned in paragraph (1)(a), as soon as practicable after the request; and

(b) in the case of a person mentioned in paragraph (1)(b), before he becomes a user.]

(3) At regular intervals after an employee has been provided [(whether before or after becoming an employee)] with an eye and eyesight test in accordance with paragraphs (1) and (2), his employer shall, subject to paragraph (6), ensure that he is provided with a further eye and eyesight test of an appropriate nature, any such test to be carried out by a competent person.

(4) Where a user experiences visual difficulties which may reasonably be considered to be caused by work on display screen equipment, his employer shall ensure that he is provided

at his request with an appropriate eye and eyesight test, any such test to be carried out by a competent person as soon as practicable after being requested as aforesaid.

(5) Every employer shall ensure that each user employed by him is provided with special corrective appliances appropriate for the work being done by the user concerned where—

(a) normal corrective appliances cannot be used; and

(b) the result of any eye and eyesight test which the user has been given in accordance with this regulation shows such provision to be necessary.

(6) Nothing in paragraph (3) shall require an employer to provide any employee with an eye and eyesight test against that employee's will.

[5205]

NOTES

Paras (1), (2): substituted by the Health and Safety (Miscellaneous Amendments) Regulations 2002, SI 2002/2174, reg 3(b).

Para (3): words in square brackets inserted by SI 2002/2174, reg 3(c).

6 Provision of training

[(1) Where a person—

(a) is a user in the undertaking in which he is employed; or

(b) is to become a user in the undertaking in which he is, or is to become, employed,

the employer who carries on the undertaking shall ensure that he is provided with adequate health and safety training in the use of any workstation upon which he may be required to work.

(1A) In the case of a person mentioned in sub-paragraph (b) of paragraph (1) the training shall be provided before he becomes a user.]

(2) Every employer shall ensure that each user at work in his undertaking is provided with adequate health and safety training whenever the organisation of any workstation in that undertaking upon which he may be required to work is substantially modified.

[5206]

NOTES

Paras (1), (1A): substituted, for original para (1), by the Health and Safety (Miscellaneous Amendments) Regulations 2002, SI 2002/2174, reg 3(d).

7 Provision of information

(1) Every employer shall ensure that operators and users at work in his undertaking are provided with adequate information about—

(a) all aspects of health and safety relating to their workstations; and

(b) such measures taken by him in compliance with his duties under regulations 2 and 3 as relate to them and their work.

(2) Every employer shall ensure that users at work in his undertaking are provided with adequate information about such measures taken by him in compliance with his duties under regulations 4 and 6(2) as relate to them and their work.

(3) Every employer shall ensure that users employed by him are provided with adequate information about such measures taken by him in compliance with his duties under regulations 5 and 6(1) as relate to them and their work.

[5207]

8 Exemption certificates

(1) The Secretary of State for Defence may, in the interests of national security, exempt any of the home forces, any visiting force or any headquarters from any of the requirements imposed by these Regulations.

(2) Any exemption such as is specified in paragraph (1) may be granted subject to conditions and to a limit of time and may be revoked by the Secretary of State for Defence by a further certificate in writing at any time.

(3) In this regulation—

(a) "the home forces" has the same meaning as in section 12(1) of the Visiting Forces Act 1952;
(b) "headquarters" has the same meaning as in article 3(2) of the Visiting Forces and International Headquarters (Application of Law) Order 1965; and
(c) "visiting force" has the same meaning as it does for the purposes of any provision of Part I of the Visiting Forces Act 1952.

[5208]

9 Extension outside Great Britain

These Regulations shall, subject to regulation 1(4), apply to and in relation to the premises and activities outside Great Britain to which sections 1 to 59 and 80 to 82 of the Health and Safety at Work etc Act 1974 apply by virtue of the Health and Safety at Work etc Act 1974 (Application Outside Great Britain) Order 1989 as they apply within Great Britain.

[5209]

THE SCHEDULE
(WHICH SETS OUT THE MINIMUM REQUIREMENTS FOR WORKSTATIONS WHICH ARE CONTAINED IN THE ANNEX TO COUNCIL DIRECTIVE 90/270/EEC ON THE MINIMUM SAFETY AND HEALTH REQUIREMENTS FOR WORK WITH DISPLAY SCREEN EQUIPMENT)

Regulation 3

1. Extent to which employers must ensure that workstations meet the requirements laid down in this schedule

An employer shall ensure that a workstation meets the requirements laid down in this Schedule to the extent that—

(a) those requirements relate to a component which is present in the workstation concerned;
(b) those requirements have effect with a view to securing the health, safety and welfare of persons at work; and
(c) the inherent characteristics of a given task make compliance with those requirements appropriate as respects the workstation concerned.

2. Equipment

(a) *General comment*

The use as such of the equipment must not be a source of risk for operators or users.

(b) *Display screen*

The characters on the screen shall be well-defined and clearly formed, of adequate size and with adequate spacing between the characters and lines.

The image on the screen should be stable, with no flickering or other forms of instability.

The brightness and the contrast between the characters and the background shall be easily adjustable by the operator or user, and also be easily adjustable to ambient conditions.

The screen must swivel and tilt easily and freely to suit the needs of the operator or user.

It shall be possible to use a separate base for the screen or an adjustable table.

The screen shall be free of reflective glare and reflections liable to cause discomfort to the operator or user.

(c) *Keyboard*

The keyboard shall be tiltable and separate from the screen so as to allow the operator or user to find a comfortable working position avoiding fatigue in the arms or hands.

The space in front of the keyboard shall be sufficient to provide support for the hands and arms of the operator or user.

The keyboard shall have a matt surface to avoid reflective glare.

The arrangement of the keyboard and the characteristics of the keys shall be such as to facilitate the use of the keyboard.

The symbols on the keys shall be adequately contrasted and legible from the design working position.

(d) *Work desk or work surface*

The work desk or work surface shall have a sufficiently large, low-reflectance surface and allow a flexible arrangement of the screen, keyboard, documents and related equipment.

The document holder shall be stable and adjustable and shall be positioned so as to minimise the need for uncomfortable head and eye movements.
There shall be adequate space for operators or users to find a comfortable position.

(e) *Work chair*
The work chair shall be stable and allow the operator or user easy freedom of movement and a comfortable position.
The seat shall be adjustable in height.
The seat back shall be adjustable in both height and tilt.
A footrest shall be made available to any operator or user who wishes one.

3. Environment

(a) *Space requirements*
The workstation shall be dimensioned and designed so as to provide sufficient space for the operator or user to change position and vary movements.

(b) *Lighting*
Any room lighting or task lighting provided shall ensure satisfactory lighting conditions and an appropriate contrast between the screen and the background environment, taking into account the type of work and the vision requirements of the operator or user.
Possible disturbing glare and reflections on the screen or other equipment shall be prevented by co-ordinating workplace and workstation layout with the positioning and technical characteristics of the artificial light sources.

(c) *Reflections and glare*
Workstations shall be so designed that sources of light, such as windows and other openings, transparent or translucid walls, and brightly coloured fixtures or walls cause no direct glare and no distracting reflections on the screen.
Windows shall be fitted with a suitable system of adjustable covering to attenuate the daylight that falls on the workstation.

(d) *Noise*
Noise emitted by equipment belonging to any workstation shall be taken into account when a workstation is being equipped, with a view in particular to ensuring that attention is not distracted and speech is not disturbed.

(e) *Heat*
Equipment belonging to any workstation shall not produce excess heat which could cause discomfort to operators or users.

(f) *Radiation*
All radiation with the exception of the visible part of the electromagnetic spectrum shall be reduced to negligible levels from the point of view of the protection of operators' or users' health and safety.

(g) *Humidity*
An adequate level of humidity shall be established and maintained.

4. Interface between computer and operator/user

In designing, selecting, commissioning and modifying software, and in designing tasks using display screen equipment, the employer shall take into account the following principles—

(a) software must be suitable for the task;

(b) software must be easy to use and, where appropriate, adaptable to the level of knowledge or experience of the operator or user; no quantitative or qualitative checking facility may be used without the knowledge of the operators or users;

(c) systems must provide feedback to operators or users on the performance of those systems;

(d) systems must display information in a format and at a pace which are adapted to operators or users;

(e) the principles of software ergonomics must be applied, in particular to human data processing.

[5210]

NOTES

Council Directive 90/270/EEC: OJ L156, 21.6.90, p 14.

UNFAIR TERMS IN CONSUMER CONTRACTS REGULATIONS 1999

(SI 1999/2083)

NOTES

Made: 22 July 1999.
Authority: European Communities Act 1972, s 2(2).
Commencement: 1 October 1999.

ARRANGEMENT OF REGULATIONS

1 Citation and commencement

These Regulations may be cited as the Unfair Terms in Consumer Contracts Regulations 1999 and shall come into force on 1st October 1999.

[5211]

2 (*Revokes the Unfair Terms in Consumer Contracts Regulations 1994, SI 1994/3159.*)

3 Interpretation

(1) In these Regulations—

"the Community" means the European Community;

"consumer" means any natural person who, in contracts covered by these Regulations, is acting for purposes which are outside his trade, business or profession;

"court" in relation to England and Wales and Northern Ireland means a county court or the High Court, and in relation to Scotland, the Sheriff or the Court of Session;

"[OFT]" means [the Office of Fair Trading];

"EEA Agreement" means the Agreement on the European Economic Area signed at Oporto on 2nd May 1992 as adjusted by the protocol signed at Brussels on 17th March 1993;

"Member State" means a State which is a contracting party to the EEA Agreement;

"notified" means notified in writing;

"qualifying body" means a person specified in Schedule 1;

"seller or supplier" means any natural or legal person who, in contracts covered by these Regulations, is acting for purposes relating to his trade, business or profession, whether publicly owned or privately owned;

"unfair terms" means the contractual terms referred to in regulation 5.

[(1A) The references—

(a) in regulation 4(1) to a seller or a supplier, and

(b) in regulation 8(1) to a seller or supplier,

include references to a distance supplier and to an intermediary.

(1B) In paragraph (1A) and regulation 5(6)—

"distance supplier" means—

(a) a supplier under a distance contract within the meaning of the Financial Services (Distance Marketing) Regulations 2004, or

(b) a supplier of unsolicited financial services within regulation 15 of those Regulations; and

"intermediary" has the same meaning as in those Regulations.]

(2) In the application of these Regulations to Scotland for references to an "injunction" or an "interim injunction" there shall be substituted references to an "interdict" or "interim interdict" respectively.

[5212]

NOTES

Para (1): words in square brackets substituted by virtue of the Enterprise Act 2002, s 2.

Paras (1A), (1B): inserted by the Financial Services (Distance Marketing) Regulations 2004, SI 2004/2095, reg 24(1), (2).

4 Terms to which these Regulations apply

(1) These Regulations apply in relation to unfair terms in contracts concluded between a seller or a supplier and a consumer.

(2) These Regulations do not apply to contractual terms which reflect—

(a) mandatory statutory or regulatory provisions (including such provisions under the law of any Member State or in Community legislation having effect in the United Kingdom without further enactment);

(b) the provisions or principles of international conventions to which the Member States or the Community are party.

[5213]

5 Unfair Terms

(1) A contractual term which has not been individually negotiated shall be regarded as unfair if, contrary to the requirement of good faith, it causes a significant imbalance in the parties' rights and obligations arising under the contract, to the detriment of the consumer.

(2) A term shall always be regarded as not having been individually negotiated where it has been drafted in advance and the consumer has therefore not been able to influence the substance of the term.

(3) Notwithstanding that a specific term or certain aspects of it in a contract has been individually negotiated, these Regulations shall apply to the rest of a contract if an overall assessment of it indicates that it is a pre-formulated standard contract.

(4) It shall be for any seller or supplier who claims that a term was individually negotiated to show that it was.

(5) Schedule 2 to these Regulations contains an indicative and non-exhaustive list of the terms which may be regarded as unfair.

[(6) Any contractual term providing that a consumer bears the burden of proof in respect of showing whether a distance supplier or an intermediary complied with any or all of the obligations placed upon him resulting from the Directive and any rule or enactment implementing it shall always be regarded as unfair.

(7) In paragraph (6)—

"the Directive" means Directive 2002/65/EC of the European Parliament and of the Council of 23 September 2002 concerning the distance marketing of consumer financial services and amending Council Directive 90/619/EEC and Directives 97/7/EC and 98/27/EC; and

"rule" means a rule made by the Financial Services Authority under the Financial Services and Markets Act 2000 or by a designated professional body within the meaning of section 326(2) of that Act.]

[5214]

NOTES

Paras (6), (7): added by the Financial Services (Distance Marketing) Regulations 2004, SI 2004/2095, reg 24(1), (3).

6 Assessment of unfair terms

(1) Without prejudice to regulation 12, the unfairness of a contractual term shall be assessed, taking into account the nature of the goods or services for which the contract was concluded and by referring, at the time of conclusion of the contract, to all the circumstances attending the conclusion of the contract and to all the other terms of the contract or of another contract on which it is dependent.

(2) In so far as it is in plain intelligible language, the assessment of fairness of a term shall not relate—

(a) to the definition of the main subject matter of the contract, or

(b) to the adequacy of the price or remuneration, as against the goods or services supplied in exchange.

[5215]

7 Written contracts

(1) A seller or supplier shall ensure that any written term of a contract is expressed in plain, intelligible language.

(2) If there is doubt about the meaning of a written term, the interpretation which is most favourable to the consumer shall prevail but this rule shall not apply in proceedings brought under regulation 12.

[5216]

8 Effect of unfair term

(1) An unfair term in a contract concluded with a consumer by a seller or supplier shall not be binding on the consumer.

(2) The contract shall continue to bind the parties if it is capable of continuing in existence without the unfair term.

[5217]

9 Choice of law clauses

These Regulations shall apply notwithstanding any contract term which applies or purports to apply the law of a non-Member State, if the contract has a close connection with the territory of the Member States.

[5218]

10 Complaints—consideration by [OFT]

(1) It shall be the duty of the [OFT] to consider any complaint made to [it] that any contract term drawn up for general use is unfair, unless—

(a) the complaint appears to the [OFT] to be frivolous or vexatious; or

(b) a qualifying body has notified the [OFT] that it agrees to consider the complaint.

(2) The [OFT] shall give reasons for [its] decision to apply or not to apply, as the case may be, for an injunction under regulation 12 in relation to any complaint which these Regulations require [it] to consider.

(3) In deciding whether or not to apply for an injunction in respect of a term which the [OFT] considers to be unfair, [it] may, if [it] considers it appropriate to do so, have regard to any undertakings given to [it] by or on behalf of any person as to the continued use of such a term in contracts concluded with consumers.

[5219]

NOTES

Words in square brackets substituted by virtue of the Enterprise Act 2002, s 2.

11 Complaints—consideration by qualifying bodies

(1) If a qualifying body specified in Part One of Schedule 1 notifies the [OFT] that it agrees to consider a complaint that any contract term drawn up for general use is unfair, it shall be under a duty to consider that complaint.

(2) Regulation 10(2) and (3) shall apply to a qualifying body which is under a duty to consider a complaint as they apply to the [OFT].

[5220]

NOTES

Words in square brackets substituted by virtue of the Enterprise Act 2002, s 2.

12 Injunctions to prevent continued use of unfair terms

(1) The [OFT] or, subject to paragraph (2), any qualifying body may apply for an injunction (including an interim injunction) against any person appearing to the [OFT] or that body to be using, or recommending use of, an unfair term drawn up for general use in contracts concluded with consumers.

(2) A qualifying body may apply for an injunction only where—

(a) it has notified the [OFT] of its intention to apply at least fourteen days before the date on which the application is made, beginning with the date on which the notification was given; or

(b) the [OFT] consents to the application being made within a shorter period.

(3) The court on an application under this regulation may grant an injunction on such terms as it thinks fit.

(4) An injunction may relate not only to use of a particular contract term drawn up for general use but to any similar term, or a term having like effect, used or recommended for use by any person.

[5221]

NOTES

Paras (1), (2): words in square brackets substituted by virtue of the Enterprise Act 2002, s 2.

13 Powers of the [OFT] and qualifying bodies to obtain documents and information

(1) The [OFT] may exercise the power conferred by this regulation for the purpose of—

(a) facilitating [its] consideration of a complaint that a contract term drawn up for general use is unfair; or

(b) ascertaining whether a person has complied with an undertaking or court order as to the continued use, or recommendation for use, of a term in contracts concluded with consumers.

(2) A qualifying body specified in Part One of Schedule 1 may exercise the power conferred by this regulation for the purpose of—

(a) facilitating its consideration of a complaint that a contract term drawn up for general use is unfair; or

(b) ascertaining whether a person has complied with—

(i) an undertaking given to it or to the court following an application by that body, or

(ii) a court order made on an application by that body,

as to the continued use, or recommendation for use, of a term in contracts concluded with consumers.

(3) The [OFT] may require any person to supply to [it], and a qualifying body specified in Part One of Schedule 1 may require any person to supply to it—

(a) a copy of any document which that person has used or recommended for use, at the time the notice referred to in paragraph (4) below is given, as a pre-formulated standard contract in dealings with consumers;

(b) information about the use, or recommendation for use, by that person of that document or any other such document in dealings with consumers.

(4) The power conferred by this regulation is to be exercised by a notice in writing which may—

(a) specify the way in which and the time within which it is to be complied with; and

(b) be varied or revoked by a subsequent notice.

(5) Nothing in this regulation compels a person to supply any document or information which he would be entitled to refuse to produce or give in civil proceedings before the court.

(6) If a person makes default in complying with a notice under this regulation, the court may, on the application of the [OFT] or of the qualifying body, make such order as the court thinks fit for requiring the default to be made good, and any such order may provide that all the costs or expenses of and incidental to the application shall be borne by the person in default or by any officers of a company or other association who are responsible for its default.

[5222]

NOTES

Words in square brackets substituted by virtue of the Enterprise Act 2002, s 2.

14 Notification of undertakings and orders to [OFT]

A qualifying body shall notify the [OFT]—

(a) of any undertaking given to it by or on behalf of any person as to the continued use of a term which that body considers to be unfair in contracts concluded with consumers;

(b) of the outcome of any application made by it under regulation 12, and of the terms of any undertaking given to, or order made by, the court;

(c) of the outcome of any application made by it to enforce a previous order of the court.

[5223]

NOTES

Words in square brackets substituted by virtue of the Enterprise Act 2002, s 2.

15 Publication, information and advice

(1) The [OFT] shall arrange for the publication in such form and manner as [it] considers appropriate, of—

(a) details of any undertaking or order notified to [it] under regulation 14;

(b) details of any undertaking given to [it] by or on behalf of any person as to the continued use of a term which the [OFT] considers to be unfair in contracts concluded with consumers;

(c) details of any application made by [it] under regulation 12, and of the terms of any undertaking given to, or order made by, the court;

(d) details of any application made by the [OFT] to enforce a previous order of the court.

(2) The [OFT] shall inform any person on request whether a particular term to which these Regulations apply has been—

(a) the subject of an undertaking given to the [OFT] or notified to [it] by a qualifying body; or

(b) the subject of an order of the court made upon application by [it] or notified to [it] by a qualifying body;

and shall give that person details of the undertaking or a copy of the order, as the case may be, together with a copy of any amendments which the person giving the undertaking has agreed to make to the term in question.

(3) The [OFT] may arrange for the dissemination in such form and manner as [it] considers appropriate of such information and advice concerning the operation of these Regulations as may appear to [it] to be expedient to give to the public and to all persons likely to be affected by these Regulations.

[5224]

NOTES

Words in square brackets substituted by virtue of the Enterprise Act 2002, s 2.

[16 The functions of the Financial Services Authority

The functions of the Financial Services Authority under these Regulations shall be treated as functions of the Financial Services Authority under the [Financial Services and Markets Act 2000].]

[5225]

NOTES

Inserted by the Unfair Terms in Consumer Contracts (Amendment) Regulations 2001, SI 2001/1186, reg 2(a).

Words in square brackets substituted by the Financial Services and Markets Act 2000 (Consequential Amendments and Repeals) Order 2001, SI 2001/3649, art 583.

SCHEDULE 1
QUALIFYING BODIES

Regulation 3

PART ONE

[1 The Information Commissioner.

2 The Gas and Electricity Markets Authority.

3 The Director General of Electricity Supply for Northern Ireland.

4 The Director General of Gas for Northern Ireland.

5 [The Office of Communications].

6 [The Water Services Regulation Authority].

7 [The Office of Rail Regulation].

8 Every weights and measures authority in Great Britain.

9 The Department of Enterprise, Trade and Investment in Northern Ireland.

10 The Financial Services Authority.]

[5226]

NOTES

Substituted by the Unfair Terms in Consumer Contracts (Amendment) Regulations 2001, SI 2001/1186, reg 2(b).

Entry 5: words in square brackets substituted by the Communications Act 2003 (Consequential Amendments No 2) Order 2003, SI 2003/3182, art 2.

Entry 6: words in square brackets substituted by the Unfair Terms in Consumer Contracts (Amendment) and Water Act 2003 (Transitional Provision) Regulations 2006, SI 2006/523, reg 2, subject to transitional provisions in reg 3 thereof.

Entry 7: words in square brackets substituted by virtue of the Railways and Transport Safety Act 2003, s 16(4), (5), Sch 3, para 4.

PART TWO

11 Consumers' Association

[5227]

SCHEDULE 2
INDICATIVE AND NON-EXHAUSTIVE LIST OF TERMS WHICH MAY BE REGARDED AS UNFAIR

Regulation 5(5)

1 Terms which have the object or effect of—

(a) excluding or limiting the legal liability of a seller or supplier in the event of the death of a consumer or personal injury to the latter resulting from an act or omission of that seller or supplier;

(b) inappropriately excluding or limiting the legal rights of the consumer vis-à-vis the seller or supplier or another party in the event of total or partial non-performance or inadequate performance by the seller or supplier of any of the contractual obligations, including the option of offsetting a debt owed to the seller or supplier against any claim which the consumer may have against him;

(c) making an agreement binding on the consumer whereas provision of services by the seller or supplier is subject to a condition whose realisation depends on his own will alone;

(d) permitting the seller or supplier to retain sums paid by the consumer where the

PART VII MISCELLANEOUS

latter decides not to conclude or perform the contract, without providing for the consumer to receive compensation of an equivalent amount from the seller or supplier where the latter is the party cancelling the contract;

(e) requiring any consumer who fails to fulfil his obligation to pay a disproportionately high sum in compensation;

(f) authorising the seller or supplier to dissolve the contract on a discretionary basis where the same facility is not granted to the consumer, or permitting the seller or supplier to retain the sums paid for services not yet supplied by him where it is the seller or supplier himself who dissolves the contract;

(g) enabling the seller or supplier to terminate a contract of indeterminate duration without reasonable notice except where there are serious grounds for doing so;

(h) automatically extending a contract of fixed duration where the consumer does not indicate otherwise, when the deadline fixed for the consumer to express his desire not to extend the contract is unreasonably early;

(i) irrevocably binding the consumer to terms with which he had no real opportunity of becoming acquainted before the conclusion of the contract;

(j) enabling the seller or supplier to alter the terms of the contract unilaterally without a valid reason which is specified in the contract;

(k) enabling the seller or supplier to alter unilaterally without a valid reason any characteristics of the product or service to be provided;

(l) providing for the price of goods to be determined at the time of delivery or allowing a seller of goods or supplier of services to increase their price without in both cases giving the consumer the corresponding right to cancel the contract if the final price is too high in relation to the price agreed when the contract was concluded;

(m) giving the seller or supplier the right to determine whether the goods or services supplied are in conformity with the contract, or giving him the exclusive right to interpret any term of the contract;

(n) limiting the seller's or supplier's obligation to respect commitments undertaken by his agents or making his commitments subject to compliance with a particular formality;

(o) obliging the consumer to fulfil all his obligations where the seller or supplier does not perform his;

(p) giving the seller or supplier the possibility of transferring his rights and obligations under the contract, where this may serve to reduce the guarantees for the consumer, without the latter's agreement;

(q) excluding or hindering the consumer's right to take legal action or exercise any other legal remedy, particularly by requiring the consumer to take disputes exclusively to arbitration not covered by legal provisions, unduly restricting the evidence available to him or imposing on him a burden of proof which, according to the applicable law, should lie with another party to the contract.

2 Scope of paragraphs 1(g), (j) and (l)

(a) Paragraph 1(g) is without hindrance to terms by which a supplier of financial services reserves the right to terminate unilaterally a contract of indeterminate duration without notice where there is a valid reason, provided that the supplier is required to inform the other contracting party or parties thereof immediately.

(b) Paragraph 1(j) is without hindrance to terms under which a supplier of financial services reserves the right to alter the rate of interest payable by the consumer or due to the latter, or the amount of other charges for financial services without notice where there is a valid reason, provided that the supplier is required to inform the other contracting party or parties thereof at the earliest opportunity and that the latter are free to dissolve the contract immediately.

Paragraph 1(j) is also without hindrance to terms under which a seller or supplier reserves the right to alter unilaterally the conditions of a contract of indeterminate duration, provided that he is required to inform the consumer with reasonable notice and that the consumer is free to dissolve the contract.

(c) Paragraphs 1(g), (j) and (l) do not apply to:

— transactions in transferable securities, financial instruments and other products or services where the price is linked to fluctuations in a stock exchange quotation or index or a financial market rate that the seller or supplier does not control;

— contracts for the purchase or sale of foreign currency, traveller's cheques or international money orders denominated in foreign currency.

(d) Paragraph 1(1) is without hindrance to price indexation clauses, where lawful, provided that the method by which prices vary is explicitly described.

[5228]

CONSUMER CREDIT (CREDIT REFERENCE AGENCY) REGULATIONS 2000

(SI 2000/290)

NOTES

Made: 8 February 2000.

Authority: Data Protection Act 1998, s 9(3); Consumer Credit Act 1974, ss 157(1), 158(1), (2), 159(5), 160(3), 182(2).

Commencement: 1 March 2000.

ARRANGEMENT OF REGULATIONS

1 Title, commencement, revocation and savings

(1) These Regulations may be cited as the Consumer Credit (Credit Reference Agency) Regulations 2000 and shall come into force on 1st March 2000.

(2) Subject to paragraph (3) below, the Consumer Credit (Credit Reference Agency) Regulations 1977 are revoked.

(3) The Consumer Credit (Credit Reference Agency) Regulations 1977 shall continue to apply—

(a) in any case where a credit reference agency has, on or before 29th February 2000, received a request under section 158(1) of the 1974 Act (other than a request made by reference to the 1998 Act) but does not, until after that date, comply with section 158(1) and (2) of that Act or deal with the request under section 160(3); and

(b) in any case where a credit reference agency has received a request under section 158(1) of the 1974 Act and has complied with section 158(1) and (2) of that Act or dealt with the request under section 160(3) before 1st March 2000.

[5229]

2 Interpretation

In these Regulations—

"the 1974 Act" means the Consumer Credit Act 1974;

"the 1998 Act" means the Data Protection Act 1998;

"agency" means a credit reference agency; and

"business consumer" means a consumer carrying on a business who has been given information under section 160 of the 1974 Act.

[5230]

3 Prescribed period for the purposes of sections 157(1), 158(1) and 160(3) of the 1974 Act

The period of seven working days is prescribed for the purposes of sections 157(1), 158(1) and 160(3) of the 1974 Act.

[5231]

PART VII MISCELLANEOUS

4 Statement of rights under sections 159 and 160 of the 1974 Act

(1) The form in Schedule 1, completed in accordance with the footnotes, is prescribed for the purposes of section 9(3) of the 1998 Act.

(2) The form in Schedule 2, completed in accordance with the footnotes, is prescribed for the purposes of section 158(2) of the 1974 Act.

(3) The form in Schedule 3, completed in accordance with the footnotes, is prescribed for the purposes of section 160(3) of the 1974 Act.

[5232]

5 Applications to the relevant authority under section 159(5) of the 1974 Act

(1) This regulation prescribes the manner in which applications under section 159(5) of the 1974 Act by—

(a) objectors,
(b) business consumers, and
(c) agencies

shall be made to the relevant authority.

(2) An application by an objector, a business consumer or an agency shall state the name and address of the agency and of the objector or business consumer and shall give an indication of when the notice of correction under section 159(3) of the 1974 Act was served by the objector or business consumer on the agency.

(3) An application by an objector or a business consumer shall give particulars of the entry in the file or, as the case may be, of the information received by him from the agency and shall state why he considers the entry or information to be incorrect and why, if it is not corrected, he considers that he is likely to be prejudiced.

(4) An application by an agency shall be accompanied by—

(a) a copy of the file given by the agency to the objector, or of the information given by the agency to the business consumer under section 160(3) of the 1974 Act;
(b) a copy of the notice of correction; and
(c) a copy of related correspondence and other documents which have passed between the agency and the objector or business consumer;

and shall state the grounds upon which it appears to the agency that it would be improper for it to publish the notice of correction.

[5233]

SCHEDULES

SCHEDULE 1
CREDIT REFERENCE AGENCY FILES INDIVIDUALS (INCLUDING SOLE TRADERS)

Regulation 4(1)

YOUR RIGHTS UNDER SECTION 159 OF THE CONSUMER CREDIT ACT 1974, AND UNDER THE DATA PROTECTION ACT 1998, IF YOU THINK ANY ENTRY IN OUR FILE IS WRONG

This statement of your rights is provided by [**Note 1**] together with all the information we hold about you on our files. Our postal address is [**Note 2**].

Your rights are as follows—

If you think that any of the information we have sent you is wrong and that you are likely to suffer because it is wrong, you can ask us to correct it or remove it from our file.

You need to write to us telling us what you want us to do. You should explain why you think the information is wrong.

If you write to us, we have to reply in writing within 28 days.

Our reply will tell you whether we have corrected the information, removed it from our file or done nothing. If we tell you that we have corrected the information, you will get a copy.

If our reply says that we have done nothing, or if we fail to reply within 28 days, or if we correct the information but you are not happy with the correction, you can write your own note of correction and ask for it to be included on our file.

To do this, you will need to write to us within 28 days of receiving our reply. If you did not get a reply from us and you want the information we sent you to be corrected, you will need to write to us within 8 weeks of the letter you wrote to us in which you asked us to correct the information or remove it from our file.

Your letter will need to—

- include the note of correction you have written. It must not be more than 200 words long and should give a clear and accurate explanation of why you think the information is wrong. If the information is factually correct but you think it creates a misleading impression, your note of correction can explain why.
- ask us to add your note of correction to our file and to include a copy of it whenever we give anyone any of the information you think is wrong or any information based on it.

If we accept your note of correction, we have to tell you in writing within 28 days that we are going to add it to our file.

If we think it would be wrong to add your note of correction to our file, we have to apply for a ruling from [the Information Commissioner].

We will apply for a ruling if we do not want to include your note of correction because we think it is wrong, or because we think it is defamatory, frivolous or scandalous, or unsuitable for publication for some other reason. We can only refuse to include your note of correction if the Commissioner agrees with us.

If we have not written to you within 28 days of receiving your note of correction, or if we have written telling you that we are not going to add your note of correction to our file, you can appeal to the [the Information Commissioner].

If you want to do this, you will have to write to the following address [**Note 3**]—

[The Information Commissioner]
Wycliffe House
Water Lane
Wilmslow
Cheshire
SK9 5AF
Telephone no 01625–545700
Fax no 01625–524510
email: data@wycliffe.demon.co uk

When you write, you must give the following details—

- your full name and address
- our name and address
- details of the information you think is wrong, including—
  why you think it is wrong,
  why you think you are likely to suffer because it is wrong, and
  an indication of when you sent us your note of correction.

It would be helpful to the Commissioner if you could include a copy of your note of correction.

Before deciding what to do, the Commissioner may ask us for our side of the story and send us a copy of your letter. In return, you will be sent any comments we make.

The Commissioner can make any order she thinks fit when she has considered your appeal. For example, she can order us to accept your note of correction and add it to our file.

If at any stage we fail to correct or remove wrong information, you can ask [the Information Commissioner] to check whether we are meeting the requirements of the Data Protection Act 1998.

The Data Protection Act 1998 requires us to take reasonable steps to check the accuracy of personal information. If you think we have failed to correct or remove wrong information about you, you have the right to ask [the Information Commissioner], at the above address, to check whether our dealing with your information has met this requirement.

IMPORTANT NOTE: The various time limits referred to in this statement (mostly 28 days) start with the day following receipt and end with the day of delivery. That means (for example) that if you have 28 days to reply to a letter from us, the period starts with the day after you receive our letter; and you then have to make sure that your reply is delivered to us no later than 28 days from that date. In order to avoid the risk of losing your rights you should therefore allow for postal delays.

Note 1: insert the name of the credit reference agency issuing the statement.

Note 2: insert the credit reference agency's postal address.

Note 3: if the address, telephone number, fax number or email address of [the Information Commissioner] have changed, substitute the correct details.

[5234]

NOTES

Words "the Information Commissioner" in square brackets substituted by virtue of the Freedom of Information Act 2000, s 18(4), Sch 2, Pt I, para 1(1).

SCHEDULE 2
CREDIT REFERENCE AGENCY FILES PARTNERSHIPS AND OTHER UNINCORPORATED BODIES

Regulation 4(2)

YOUR RIGHTS UNDER SECTION 159 OF THE CONSUMER CREDIT ACT 1974 IF YOU THINK ANY ENTRY IN YOUR FILE IS WRONG

This statement of your rights is provided by [**Note 1**] together with all the information we hold about you on our files. Our postal address is [**Note 2**].

Your rights are as follows—

If you think that any of the information we have sent you is wrong and that you are likely to suffer because it is wrong, you can ask us to correct it or remove it from our file.

You need to write to us telling us what you want us to do. You should explain why you think the information is wrong.

If you write to us, we have to reply in writing within 28 days.

Our reply will tell you whether we have corrected the information, removed it from our file or done nothing. If we tell you that we have corrected the information, you will get a copy.

If our reply says that we have done nothing, or if we fail to reply within 28 days, or if we correct the information but you are not happy with the correction, you can write your own note of correction and ask for it to be included on our file.

To do this, you will need to write to us within 28 days of receiving our reply. If you did not get a reply from us and you want the information we sent you to be corrected, you will need to write to us within 8 weeks of the letter you wrote to us in which you asked us to correct the information or remove it from our file.

Your letter will need to—

— include the note of correction you have written. It must not be more than 200 words long and should give a clear and accurate explanation of why you think the information is wrong. If the information is factually correct but you think it creates a misleading impression, your note of correction can explain why.

— ask us to add your note of correction to our file and to include a copy of it whenever we give anyone any of the information you think is wrong or any information based on it.

If we accept your note of correction, we have to tell you in writing within 28 days that we are going to add it to our file.

If we think it would be wrong to add your note of correction to our file, we have to apply for a ruling from [the Office of Fair Trading].

We will apply for a ruling if we do not want to include your note of correction because we think it is wrong, or because we think it is defamatory, frivolous or scandalous, or unsuitable for publication for some other reason. We can only refuse to include your note of correction if [the Office of Fair Trading] agrees with us.

If we have not written to you within 28 days of receiving your note of correction, or if we have written telling you that we are not going to add your note of correction to our file, you can appeal to [the Office of Fair Trading].

If you want to do this, you will have to write to the following address [**Note 3**]—

...
Office of Fair Trading
Fleetbank House
2/6 Salisbury Square
London
EC4Y 8JX
Telephone no [020 7]211 8000
Fax no [020 7]211 8800
email: enquiries@oft.gov.uk

When you write, you must give the following details—

— your full name and address
— our name and address
— details of the information you think is wrong, including—
why you think it is wrong,
why you think you are likely to suffer because it is wrong, and
an indication of when you sent us your note of correction.

It would be helpful to [the Office of Fair Trading] if you could include a copy of your note of correction.

Before deciding what to do, [the Office of Fair Trading] may ask us for our side of the story and send us a copy of your letter. In return, you will be sent any comments we make.

[The Office of Fair Trading] can make any order [it] thinks fit when [it] has considered your appeal. For example, [it] can order us to accept your note of correction and add it to our file.

IMPORTANT NOTE: The various time limits referred to in this statement (mostly 28 days) start with the day following receipt and end with the day of delivery. That means (for example) that if you have 28 days to reply to a letter from us, the period starts with the day after you receive our letter; and you then have to make sure that your reply is delivered to us no later than 28 days from that date. In order to avoid the risk of losing your rights you should therefore allow for postal delays.

Note 1: insert the name of the credit reference agency issuing the statement.
Note 2: insert the credit reference agency's postal address.
Note 3: if the address, telephone number, fax number or email address of the Director General of Fair Trading have changed, substitute the correct details.

[5235]

NOTES

The Enterprise Act 2002, s 2(1) provides that, as from 1 April 2003, the functions of the Director General of Fair Trading, his property, rights and liabilities are transferred to the Office of Fair Trading. By virtue of s 2(2), (3) of the 2002 Act, the office of the Director is abolished, and any reference to the Director in any enactment, instrument or other document passed or made before 1 April 2003 shall, in so far as is necessary, have effect as if it were a reference to the Office of Fair Trading. Accordingly, the references to "the Office of Fair Trading" and "it" in this Schedule were substituted, and the words omitted from the postal address were repealed, by virtue of s 2 of the 2002 Act.

SCHEDULE 3
CREDIT REFERENCE AGENCY FILES BUSINESS CONSUMERS (PARTNERSHIPS AND OTHER UNINCORPORATED BODIES ONLY)

Regulation 4(3)

YOUR RIGHTS UNDER SECTIONS 159 AND 160 OF THE CONSUMER CREDIT ACT 1974

This statement of your rights is provided by [**Note 1**]. Our postal address is [**Note 2**].

You asked us for a copy of all the information we hold about you on our files. Under section 160 of the Consumer Credit Act 1974, we have obtained a ruling from [the Office of Fair Trading] which means that we do not have to give you all of that information. We are allowed to withhold some of that information because [the Office of Fair Trading] is satisfied that letting you have a copy of it would adversely affect the service we provide to our customers.

We are therefore providing you with some of the information we hold about you on our files or information based on it.

Sections 159 and 160 of the Consumer Credit Act 1974 give you certain rights and this statement tells you what those rights are.

RIGHTS UNDER SECTION 159

Your rights under section 159 of the Consumer Credit Act 1974 exist where you think that any of the information we have sent you is wrong and that you are likely to suffer because it is wrong.

These rights are available to you whether or not you have appealed to [the Office of Fair Trading] under section 160 (see the section headed "RIGHTS UNDER SECTION 160" below).

If you think that any of the information we have sent you is wrong and that you are likely to suffer because it is wrong, you can ask us to correct it or remove it from our file.

You need to write to us telling us what you want us to do. You should explain why you think the information is wrong.

If you write to us, we have to reply in writing within 28 days.

Our reply will tell you whether we have corrected the information, removed it from our file or done nothing. If we tell you that we have corrected the information, you will get a copy.

If our reply says that we have done nothing, or if we fail to reply within 28 days, or if we correct the information but you are not happy with the correction, you can write your own note of correction and ask for it to be included on our file.

To do this, you will need to write to us within 28 days of receiving our reply. If you did not get a reply from us and you want the information we sent you to be corrected, you will need to write to us within 8 weeks of the letter you wrote to us in which you asked us to correct the information or remove it from our file.

Your letter will need to—

— include the note of correction you have written. It must not be more than 200 words long and should give a clear and accurate explanation of why you think the information is wrong. If the information is factually correct but you think it creates a misleading impression, your note of correction can explain why.

— ask us to add your note of correction to our file and to include a copy of it whenever we give anyone any of the information you think is wrong or any information based on it.

If we accept your note of correction, we have to tell you in writing within 28 days that we are going to add it to our file.

If we think it would be wrong to add your note of correction to our file, we have to apply for a ruling from [the Office of Fair Trading].

We will apply for a ruling if we do not want to include your note of correction because we think it is wrong, or because we think it is defamatory, frivolous or scandalous, or unsuitable for publication for some other reason. We can only refuse to include your note of correction if [the Office of Fair Trading] agrees with us.

If we have not written to you within 28 days of receiving your note of correction, or if we have written telling you that we are not going to add your note of correction to our file, you can appeal to [the Office of Fair Trading].

If you want to do this, you will have to write to the following address [**Note 3**]—

…

Office of Fair Trading
Fleetbank House
2/6 Salisbury Square
London
EC4Y 8JX

Telephone no [020 7]211 8000
Fax no [020 7]211 8800
email: enquiries@oft.gov.uk

When you write, you must give the following details—

— your full name and address

— our name and address

— details of the information you think is wrong, including—
why you think it is wrong,
why you think you are likely to suffer because it is wrong, and
an indication of when you sent us your note of correction.

It would be helpful to [the Office of Fair Trading] if you could include a copy of your note of correction.

Before deciding what to do, [the Office of Fair Trading] may ask us for our side of the story and send us a copy of your letter. In return, you will be sent any comments we make.

[The Office of Fair Trading] can make any order [it] thinks fit when [it] has considered your appeal. For example, [it] can order us to accept your note of correction and add it to our file.

RIGHTS UNDER SECTION 160

If you are not happy with the information we have sent you because it is incomplete (rather than wrong), you can appeal to [the Office of Fair Trading], but you must first of all get in touch with us, telling us why you are unhappy and asking us to help you.

You may be unhappy with the information because, for example, you cannot work out whether it is accurate without seeing information which we have apparently withheld.

You can appeal by writing to [the Office of Fair Trading] at the address set out above.

You will need to—

— give [the Office of Fair Trading] a copy of the information you have received and tell [the OFT] the date you received it,

— tell [the OFT] why you are unhappy with the information, and

— say what steps you have taken to persuade us to help you.

You need to do all this within 28 days of receiving the information from us. If you cannot write within 28 days, do so as soon as you can and explain why you could not write earlier.

If [the Office of Fair Trading] thinks that you have taken all reasonable steps to get a satisfactory response from us without success, [it] can tell us to send [the OFT] a copy of all the information we hold about you on our files. [The Office of Fair Trading] can then pass all or some of that information on to you.

Your rights under section 160 are available whether or not you have written to us under section 159.

IMPORTANT NOTE: The various time limits referred to in this statement (mostly 28 days) start with the day following receipt and end with the day of delivery. That means that (for example) if you have 28 days to reply to a letter from us, the period starts with the day after you receive our letter; and you then have to make sure that your reply is delivered to us no later than 28 days from that date. In order to avoid the risk of losing your rights you should therefore allow for postal delays.

Note 1: insert the name of the credit reference agency issuing the statement.

Note 2: insert the credit reference agency's postal address.

Note 3: if the address, telephone number, fax number or email address of [the Office of Fair Trading] have changed, substitute the correct details.

[5236]

NOTES

The Enterprise Act 2002, s 2(1) provides that, as from 1 April 2003, the functions of the Director General of Fair Trading, his property, rights and liabilities are transferred to the Office of Fair Trading. By virtue of s 2(2), (3) of the 2002 Act, the office of the Director is abolished, and any reference to the Director in any enactment, instrument or other document passed or made before 1 April 2003 shall, in so far as is necessary, have effect as if it were a reference to the Office of Fair Trading. Accordingly, the references to "the Office of Fair Trading" and "it" in this Schedule were substituted, and the words omitted from the postal address were repealed, by virtue of s 2 of the 2002 Act.

RETENTION OF COMMUNICATIONS DATA (EXTENSION OF INITIAL PERIOD) ORDER 2003

(SI 2003/3173)

NOTES

Made: 4 December 2003.
Authority: Anti-terrorism, Crime and Security Act 2001, s 105(3).
Commencement: 5 December 2003.

1 This Order may be cited as the Retention of Communications Data (Extension of Initial Period) Order 2003 and shall come into force on the day after the day on which it is made.

[5237]

NOTES

Commencement: 5 December 2003.

2 The initial period specified in section 105(2) of the Anti-terrorism, Crime and Security Act 2001 shall be extended for the period of two years beginning with the time when that period would end but for the making of this Order.

[5238]

NOTES

Commencement: 5 December 2003.

RETENTION OF COMMUNICATIONS DATA (FURTHER EXTENSION OF INITIAL PERIOD) ORDER 2005

(SI 2005/3335)

NOTES

Made: 5 December 2005.
Authority: Anti-terrorism, Crime and Security Act 2001, s 105(3).
Commencement: 6 December 2005.

1 This Order may be cited as the Retention of Communications Data (Further Extension of Initial Period) Order 2005 and shall come into force on the day after the day on which it is made.

[5239]

NOTES

Commencement: 6 December 2005.

2 The initial period specified in section 105(2) of the Anti-terrorism, Crime and Security Act 2001, as extended by the Retention of Communications Data (Extension of Initial Period) Order 2003, shall be extended for a further period of two years beginning with the time when that period would end but for the making of this Order.

[5240]

NOTES

Commencement: 6 December 2005.

RETENTION OF COMMUNICATIONS DATA UNDER PART 11: ANTI-TERRORISM, CRIME & SECURITY ACT 2001

Voluntary Code of Practice

NOTES

Authority: Anti-terrorism, Crime and Security Act 2001, s 103(5). This Code of Practice came into force on 5 December 2003 (see the Retention of Communications Data (Code of Practice) Order 2003, SI 2003/3175).

FOREWORD

The Anti-Terrorism, Crime & Security Act was passed in December of 2001 (the Act) Part 11 of the Act aims to allow for the retention of communications data to ensure that the UK security, intelligence and law enforcement agencies have sufficient information available to them to assist them in protecting the UK's national security and to investigate terrorism.

Communications data are retained by the communications service providers to enable them to carry out their business effectively. Such information could be divided into three broad categories these being subscriber information (identifies user); traffic data (identifies whom was called etc); and use made of service (identifies what services are used). The Act recognises that communications data are an essential tool for the security, intelligence and law enforcement agencies in carrying out their work to safeguard United Kingdom national security. These agencies, which are authorised to acquire communications data under statutory provisions, would be greatly assisted if they could rely on the communications data being available when they required it.

Part 11 of the Act provides only for the retention of data that communication service providers already retain for business purposes. Its object is not to enlarge the fields of data which a communication service provider may (or must) retain, but to encourage communication service providers to retain that data for longer than they would otherwise need to do so for their own commercial purposes. The Act identifies that the purpose of the retention period is the safeguarding of national security or for the prevention or detection of crime or the prosecution of offences which relate directly or indirectly to national security.

This Code of Practice relates specifically to the need for communications service providers to retain data for extended periods of time in order to assist the security, intelligence and law enforcement agencies in carrying out their work of safeguarding national security or in the prevention or detection of crime or the prosecution of offences which relate directly or indirectly to national security.

This Code of Practice does not address issues relating to disclosure of data, it simply addresses the issues of what types of data can be retained and for how long it will be retained beyond a particular company's existing business practice. The Code explains why communications service providers have the ability to retain data beyond their normal business purposes for the reasons outlined in the Act.

Communications data may be obtained by security, intelligence and law enforcement agencies under the Regulation of Investigatory Powers Act 2000 and other statutory powers. This Code does not deal with these provisions.

The Data Protection Act 1998 requires that personal data are processed lawfully. In retaining communications data for longer than needed for their own business purposes and for the purposes identified in the Act communication service providers will process personal data. The Information Commissioner's Office (ICO) has accepted that such processing will not, on human rights grounds, contravene this requirement of the Act.

However, individual communication service providers must satisfy themselves that the processing is "necessary" for one of a range of functions. In doing so they are entitled to rely heavily on the Secretary of State's assurance that the retention of communications data for the periods as specified in this Code is necessary for the government's function of safeguarding national security, and on the fact that the Code has been approved by Parliament.

The ICO has though expressed concern about such retained data being acquired for purposes that do not relate to national security. Acquisition of communications data is not addressed in the Act and therefore is not within the proper ambit of this Code.

PART VII MISCELLANEOUS

CONTENTS

PURPOSE OF THE CODE

1. In section 102 of the Act, Parliament has given the Secretary of State the power to issue a Code of Practice relating to the retention of communications data by communication service providers. This Code of Practice is intended to outline how communication service providers can assist in the fight against terrorism by meeting agreed time periods for retention of communications data that may be extended beyond those periods for which their individual company currently retains data for business purposes.

2. After consultation with the security, intelligence and law enforcement agencies, the Secretary of State has determined that retention of communications data by communication service providers in line with the Appendix to this Code of Practice is necessary for the purposes set out in section 102(3) of the Act, namely;
   (a) the purposes of safeguarding national security
   (b) the purposes of prevention or detection of crime or the prosecution of offenders which may relate directly or indirectly to national security.

3. The Code of Practice is intended to ensure that communication service providers may retain data for the two purposes identified at 2 a & b, after the need for retention for business purposes has elapsed and there is otherwise an obligation to erase or anonymise retained data. It does not provide guidance on the manner in which data retained for these purposes should be processed; nor does the Secretary of State consider it necessary to impose new standards on the conditions in which the data are stored, e g technical media, security, ease of access, indexing or other.

4. The Code does not relate to the powers of public authorities to obtain communications data retained in accordance with the Appendix to the Code. Acquisition of communications data is provided for by Chapter II of Part I of the Regulation of Investigatory Powers Act 2000, as well as other relevant statutory powers. See paragraphs 25 to 28.

HUMAN RIGHTS AND DATA PROTECTION CONSIDERATIONS

5. This Code has been drawn up in accordance with existing legislation, including the Human Rights Act 1998, and the Data Protection Act 1998, and the Telecommunications (Data Protection and Privacy) Regulations 1999, together with their parent directives.

6. Data retained under the Code are subject to the data protection principles found in the Data Protection Act 1998. Under the first data protection principle personal data may only be processed if at least one of the conditions in Schedule 2 to the 1998 Act is met. The processing of data retained under this Code falls within paragraph 5 of Schedule 2 of the Data Protection Act 1998 in that it is necessary for the communication service provider to retain data to enable the Secretary of State to fulfil his function for the protection of national security. Some communications data may in certain circumstances constitute sensitive personal data. Processing of such data is permitted by virtue of Schedule 3, paragraph 7 of the 1998 Act.

7. Data retained under the Code will, at least for a certain period, be data that are needed by the communication service provider for business purposes. Its processing will therefore initially be undertaken for a dual purpose: (a) business purposes, (b) national security purposes, where "national security purposes" includes both the purposes set out in section 102(3) of the Act. Since both purposes of retention will apply to all data

simultaneously during the "business purpose time period, there is no need for separate storage systems for "business data" and "national security data" under this dual-purpose scheme.

However, once an individual company has exceeded the business purpose time period then data will be retained specifically for the purposes described in Section 102(3) of the Act. The system deployed by individual companies will need to identify that the data has exceeded the business purpose time period. Individual communication service providers will need to ensure that they do not access those data for their own purposes. At the end of the retention period necessary for "business purposes" the only data that a communication service provider should retain are that data identified in the "Technical Specification" attached as Appendix A to this Code.

8. The fifth data protection principle provides that personal data processed for any purpose or purposes shall not be kept for any longer than is necessary for that purpose or those purposes. The periods for which it appears necessary to the Secretary of State for communication service providers to retain communications data for national security purposes are those set out in Appendix A. The periods for which it is necessary for communication service providers to retain communications data for business purposes is a matter for each communication service provider, and they might be longer or shorter than the retention periods the Secretary of State has set out are necessary for national security. Compliance with the fifth data protection principle under the dual-purpose scheme requires that after the expiry of the shorter of these two periods, communications data may only be retained further for the period required by the remaining purpose. When the retention periods for both purposes have expired, the data must be either anonymised or erased.

9. As indicated the Secretary of State considers the retention of data in accordance with Appendix A to be necessary for the purpose of national security and accordingly retention for those periods should comply with the fifth data protection principle. However, because the purpose of retention is to safeguard national security were it to be suggested that retention in accordance with this Code did not comply with the fifth principle, the national security exemption in s 28 of the Data Protection Act 1998 could be relied on to exempt such data from the fifth principle so enabling it to be retained in accordance with the Code. If necessary the Secretary of State would issue a certificate under s 28.2 confirming the same.

10. The data subject access provisions set out in the Data Protection Act 1998 continue to apply to communications data retained under this Code, that is to say that data subjects may request access to their personal data whether it is held for national security purposes or for the communication service provider's business purposes. In addition, subscribers should be notified where their personal data will be retained for the purpose of the Act, as well as for the communication service providers business purposes, and that it may be disclosed to relevant public authorities, as set out in paragraph 27 of this Code. Every effort should be made to ensure that this is brought to the attention of the subscriber for example this could be added to billing information or sent by way of text message or e-mail.

NB. Communication service providers will need to ensure that their entry in the register of data controllers maintained by the Information Commissioner describes the processing of personal data involved in retention of communications data for the national security purposes. The Information Commissioner's advice is that they should notify that they are processing for the following purpose:

> ***"NATIONAL SECURITY:~ Retention of communications data for the purpose of safeguarding national security or for the purposes of prevention or detection of crime or the prosecution of offenders which may relate directly or indirectly to national security"***

This is not one of the standard purpose descriptions that the Information Commissioner provides so communication service providers will need to complete it in full, together with details of the associated data subjects, classes and recipients, when they apply to add a new purpose to their existing notification.

11. The retention specification set out in Appendix A to this Code has been drafted taking into account a number of factors, including the right to respect for private life under Article 8 of the European Convention of Human Rights. The Secretary of State considers the retention periods set out in Appendix A to be both necessary and proportionate in light of the individual's right to respect for private life and the national security purposes for which the retention of data is required.

JURISDICTION AND TYPES OF OPERATORS COVERED BY THE CODE OF PRACTICE

12. The Code of Practice applies to all communication service providers who, provide a public telecommunications service in the United Kingdom as defined in section 2 of the Regulation of Investigatory Powers Act 2000, and who retain communications data in line with the provisions of the Act. The Secretary of State considers it necessary for the national security purposes outlined in the Act, for communications data held by communication service providers, which relates to subscribers resident in the UK or subscribing to or using a UK-based service, to be retained in accordance with the provisions of the Code, whether the data are generated or processed in the UK or abroad. However, if data relating to a service provided in the UK are stored in a foreign jurisdiction it may be subject to conflicting legal requirements prohibiting the retention of data in accordance with this Code. In such cases, it is accepted that it may not be possible to adhere to the terms of this Code in respect of that communications data.

13. The data categories and retention periods in the Appendix to this Code have been determined with regard to considerations of necessity and proportionality. The data categories and retention periods relate to communications data generated and retained by communication service providers who provide a service to the general public in the United Kingdom. This Code is not intended to apply to individuals or organisations who do not provide such a public service (e g private networks).

14. In some cases, two or more legal entities may be involved in the provision of a public telecommunications service, e g backbone/virtual service provider model. In such cases, the provisions of this Code apply to data retained by each legal entity for their own business purposes.

TYPES OF DATA AND RETENTION PERIODS

15. Communications data can be divided into three broad categories, corresponding to the definitions in section 21(4) of the Regulation of Investigatory Powers Act 2000, which can be summarised as follows:

a) **traffic data** – including telephone numbers called, email addresses, and location data etc.
b) **use made of service** – including services subscribed to, etc.
c) **other information relating to the subscriber** – including installation address, etc.

"communications data" as defined by RIPA means any of the following—

(i) any traffic data comprised in or attached to a communication (whether by the sender or otherwise) for the purposes of any postal service or telecommunication system by means of which it is being or may be transmitted;

(ii) any information which includes none of the contents of a communication [apart from any information falling within paragraph (i)] and is about the use made by any person
 (1) of any telecommunications service; or
 (2) in connection with the provision to or use by any person of any telecommunications service, of any part of a telecommunication system;

(iii) any information not falling within paragraph (i) or (ii) that is held or obtained, in relation to persons to whom he provides the service, by a person providing a telecommunications service.

"traffic data", as defined by the Regulation of Investigatory Powers Act 2000 in relation to any communication, means—

(i) any data identifying, or purporting to identify, any person, apparatus or location to or from which the communication is or may be transmitted,

(ii) any data identifying or selecting, or purporting to identify or select, apparatus through which, or by means of which, the communication is or may be transmitted,

(iii) any data comprising signals for the actuation of apparatus used for the purposes of a telecommunication system for effecting (in whole or in part) the transmission of any communication, and

(iv) any data identifying the data or other data as data comprised in or attached to a particular communication, but that expression includes data identifying a computer file or computer program access to which is obtained, or which is run, by means of the communication to the extent only that the file or program is identified by reference to the apparatus in which it is stored.

References, in relation to traffic data comprising signals for the actuation of apparatus, to a telecommunication system by means of which a communication is being or may be transmitted include references to any telecommunication system in which that apparatus is comprised; and references to traffic data being attached to a communication include references to the data and the communication being logically associated with each other.

16. The maximum retention period for data held under the provisions of this Code is 12 months, without prejudice to any longer retention period which may be justified by the business practices of the communication service provider.

17. For data categories 15(a) and 15(b) above the period of retention begins at the point when the call ends, for subscriber-related data category 15(c) the period of retention begins when the data are changed or subscriber leaves the service.

18. The retention periods given in Appendix A recognise that types of communications data, as personal data, vary with respect both to their usefulness to the agencies, and to their sensitivity. It is recognised that the usefulness of different types of communications data for the purpose of safeguarding national security will vary and this is reflected in the different retention periods.

19. The data categories listed in Appendix A will not all be relevant to every communication service provider. Whether or not a data type will be relevant to a communication service provider and therefore retained will depend on the services which it provides, for example, an internet service provider will not retain IMEI data. Communication service providers will not be expected to retain additional categories of data to those which they routinely retain for business purposes. In other words if a data type is not already captured for the business purposes of an individual company then there will be no expectation that this data type is retained for the purposes of the Act.

AGREEMENTS

20. The Secretary of State may enter into agreements with individual communication service providers who receive requests for communications data stored under these provisions. The purpose of these agreements is to communicate the retention practices of those communication service provider to public authorities listed in Chapter II of Part I of the Regulation of Investigatory Powers Act 2000. They will play the role of Service Level Agreements (SLAs) and will include any arrangements for payments to cover retention costs. These SLAs will be based on an open document outlining the agreement between the Secretary of State and the company concerned. Each of these will differ with respect to the appendices which will outline the services that a particular provider is able to deliver. Those parts of these agreements that do not contain commercially sensitive material will be publicly available. The appendices will remain commercially sensitive.

21. The agreements will be drafted within the framework provided by this Code. An agreement may not set a retention period for any type of data which is greater than the period set out in Appendix A to this Code.

22. Any agreement will be made between the Secretary of State and the communication service provider and must be entered into voluntarily by both sides. It may be terminated by either side subject to a period of notice set out in the agreement.

COSTS ARRANGEMENTS

23. Where the period of retention of data for national security purposes is not substantially larger than the period of retention for business purposes, the retention costs will continue to be borne by the communication service provider.

24. Where data retention periods are significantly longer for national security purposes than for business purposes, the Secretary of State will contribute a reasonable proportion of the marginal cost as appropriate. Marginal costs may include, for example, the design and production of additional storage and searching facilities. This may be in the form of capital investment into retention and retrieval equipment or may include running costs.

ACQUISITION OF DATA RETAINED UNDER THE TERMS OF THIS CODE OF PRACTICE

25. It is outside of the scope of this Code of Practice to address the issue of acquisition of data after it has been retained. It can only address the issue of retention of data for the purposes of the Act. The Act establishes the framework for communication service providers to retain data for the purposes of safeguarding national security and for the prevention or detection of crime and prosecution of offenders which may relate directly or indirectly to national security.

26. The Code sets out a retention specification which is designed to meet the two aims set out above, both relating to national security. That is to say that any particular piece of data is retained because it belongs to a certain data type, and it is necessary to retain all data of that type for the purpose of safeguarding national security or for the purpose of the prevention or detection of crime or the prosecution of offenders which may relate directly or indirectly to national security.

27. The retention of such data is necessary so that it is available to be acquired by relevant public authorities under Chapter II of Part I of the Regulation of Investigatory Powers Act 2000, or otherwise, to assist them in safeguarding national security. However, whilst restrictions exist elsewhere, this Code cannot itself place restrictions on the ability of these bodies or other persons to acquire data retained under the Code for other purposes through the exercise of any statutory power. In particular, this Code cannot place any restrictions on the ability of the public authorities listed in Chapter II of Part I of the Regulation of Investigatory Powers Act 2000 to acquire data retained under this Code for any of the purposes set out in section 22 of that Act which do not relate to national security.

28. In addition data access requests can also be received from data subjects under the Data Protection Act 1998 and from civil litigants.

OVERSIGHT MECHANISM

29. The retention of communications data is a form of personal data processing. As such, it is subject to the Data Protection Act 1998. Oversight of the 1998 Act is by the Information Commissioner.

TRANSITIONAL ARRANGEMENTS

30. All data collected after the communication service provider adopts the Code should be processed in accordance with both the national security purposes and the business purposes from the point that it is generated. Data already held by the communication service providers at the time of adopting the Code will be processed only in accordance with the purpose for which it was originally collected.

31. Subscribers should be notified of the new purpose for which data is being retained. This may be done by sending out a general notification to all customers. The national security purpose must be made clear to any new subscribers at the time they subscribe.

32. During the period of time that a communications service provider is building the technical capacity to extend retention of specified data beyond their normal business time periods, the company's standard retention practice takes precedence. Once the individual communication service provider has the technical capacity to retain data for the extended time periods set out in this voluntary Code of Practice, then the communication service provider shall inform existing and new customers that the purpose for retention and the periods of retention have been varied to meet with the needs of the Act. Only after this information has been passed on to existing customers and new customers can the communication service provider then retain the data for the extended time periods for the purposes of national security. There may be a period after the communication service provider has adopted the Code when he cannot retain data for the full period set out in Appendix A owing to the need to introduce technical adaptations. The agreement with the communication service provider will set out how long it will take to reach full compliance.

CRITERIA FOR ASSESSING THE EFFECTIVENESS OF THE CODE OF PRACTICE

33. The Code will be reviewed three months from the date when it first receives parliamentary approval, in accordance with the following criteria:

(a) Has it improved investigative work?
(b) How many request for data have been made?
(c) Is the voluntary system working?
(d) What percentage of the market is covered by communication service providers who have adopted the Code of Practice?
(e) Are sectors of the industry which have not adopted the Code enjoying an unfair commercial advantage?

The SLAs introduced under this Code will require communication service providers to keep records of all enquiries made for data retained under the Act from the date an individual service provider enters into a voluntary agreement with the Secretary of State, in order to enable a comprehensive survey to be undertaken.

[5241]

APPENDIX A

Data retention: expansion of data categories

SUBSCRIBER INFORMATION **12 months**

(From end of subscription/last change)

Subscriber details relating to the person

e g Name, date of birth, installation and billing address, payment methods, account/ credit card details

Contact information (information held about the subscriber but not verified by the CSP)

e g Telephone number, email address

Identity of services subscribed to (information determined by the communication service provider)

e g Customer reference/account number, list of services subscribed to

Telephony:	telephone number(s), IMEI, IMSI(s)
Email:	email address(es), IP at registration
Instant messaging:	Internet Message Handle, IP at registration
ISP – dial-in:	Log-in, CLI at registration (if kept)
ISP – always-on:	Unique identifiers,-MAC address-(if kept), ADSL end points

IP tunnel address

TELEPHONY DATA **12 months**

e g All numbers (or other identifiers e g name@bt) associated with call (e g physical/ presentational/network assigned CLI, DNI, IMSI, IMEI, exchange/divert numbers)

Date and time of start of call

Duration of call/date and time of end of call

Type of call (if available)

Location data at start and/or end of call, in form of lat/long reference.

Cell site data from time cell ceases to be used.

IMSI/MSISDN/IMEI mappings.

For GPRS & 3G, date and time of connection, IMSI, IP address assigned.

Mobile data exchanged with foreign operators; IMSI & MSISDN, sets of GSM triples, sets of 3G quintuples, global titles of equipment communicating with or about the subscriber.

SMS, EMS and MMS DATA **6 months**

e g Calling number, IMEI

Called number, IMEI

Date and time of sending

Delivery receipt – if available

Location data when messages sent and received, in form of lat/long reference.

EMAIL DATA **6 months**

e g Log-on (authentication user name, date and time of log-in/log-off, IP address logged-in from)

Sent email (authentication user name, from/to/cc email addresses, date and time sent)

Received email (authentication user name, from/to email addresses, date and time received)

ISP DATA **6 months**

e g Log-on (authentication user name, date and time of log-in/log-off, IP address assigned)

Dial-up: CLI and number dialled

Always-on: ADSL end point/MAC address (If available)

WEB ACTIVITY LOGS **4 days**

e g Proxy server logs (date/time, IP address used, URL's visited, services) The data types here will be restricted **solely to Communications Data and exclude content of communication**. This will mean that storage under this code can only take place to the level of www.homeoffice.gov.uk/.......

OTHER SERVICES **Retention relative to service provided**

e g Instant Message Type Services (log-on/off time) If available.

COLLATERAL DATA **Retention relative to data to which it is related**

e g Data needed to interpret other communications data, for example – the mapping between cellmast identifiers and their location – translation of dialling (as supported by IN networks)

Notes:

All times should include an indication of which time zone is being used (Universal Co-ordinated Time is preferred).

An indication should also be given of the accuracy of the timing.

To assist in the interpretation of Internet terminology the Home Office have, with the permission of the Internet Crime Forum, reproduced at Appendix C the document written by the Data Retention Project Group of the Internet Crime Forum.

The Home Office recognises the effort that has gone into producing this document and would thank all those responsible for its production.

[5242]

APPENDIX B

Agreements

To be written as single document outlining voluntary agreement and requirements of Appendix A. To include separate appendices relative to individual company's additional storage.

[5243]

APPENDIX C

PRINCIPAL CURRENT DATA TYPES

Howard Lamb
Chair
ICF Data Retention Project Group

1. Introduction

1.1 In December 2001, the Internet Crime Forum (ICF) established a project group the primary aim of which was to identify current data types in use by subscribers who have access to the Internet.

1.2 The group was not tasked with debating the legal issues in relation to the data types identified. There are many legal issues relating to data retention and these will undoubtedly be discussed in other documents.

1.3 The group was established with a view to producing a document that would provide a better understanding of the technology used and the information that law enforcement is seeking from its investigations. It is not intended to be a standard or a best practice document. The document is intended to be a reference to what data may be available and which of those data types are likely to be useful to law enforcement when conducting an investigation.

2. Group Members

2.1 The group is restricted to technical and investigation experts, as explained in 1.2, this group does not hold a view on the value or legality of access to this data.

2.2 The ICF Data Retention Project Group called upon experts from the Internet industry who gave advice on the numerous data types that are created when a subscriber connects to and communicates via the Internet. This connection could be through an Internet Service Provider (ISP), a Virtual Internet Service Provider (VISP) or by other connection to the Internet.

2.3 The group also engaged the services of Computer Forensic experts whose work regularly involves liaising with various Law Enforcement Agencies and assisting with their investigation involving the Internet. Representatives of various Trade Associations were involved in the process together with several members of various Law Enforcement Agencies.

3. Acknowledgements

3.1 I would like to acknowledge the support given to this project by Chief Superintendent Len Hynds of the National High Tech Crime Unit, members of the Internet Crime Forum and to those experts from the Internet and Forensics Industry who have assisted in the process. All participants gave freely of their time as they agreed it was vital that this type of work be carried out.

4. Current Data Types

4.1 This document seeks to identify the principal known Data Types that a subscriber to an Internet Service may create whilst they are actively subscribing and utilising their Internet account.

4.2 It is accepted that this document could not be a definitive document of all data types due to the rapid development of technology.

5. Service Providers

It must be appreciated by the reader of this document that not all Internet Service Providers retain the data types that are mentioned within this document.

Each service provider is aware of their current data retention practices and may be able to advise on the detail. Communication should in the first instance be routed through a Law Enforcement Single Point of Contact for Law Enforcement personnel. Requests for data retention policies made from outside the SPOC regime may be liable to conditions determined by individual ISPs.

There are service providers, known as Virtual Internet Service Providers (VISPs), who utilise most, if not all, the infrastructure of a large service provider. They may utilise various elements of a service, such as mail, sign up servers, radius servers, web cache and news and badge them as their own. In these cases the data that a subscriber generates may be spread across several companies.

Even amongst traditional ISPs some parts of their service may be provided by third parties. In this case as well, information may be held by many different companies and may or may not be accessible to the primary ISP.

Furthermore, some data types for example, web server log information, may be owned by and under the control of the customer rather than the ISP.

6. Glossary

There is a glossary attached to this document that informs the reader of what the various data types are and it is advisable that this is read in conjunction with the rest of the document.

7. Subscriber Data Types

7.1 This next section of the document identifies the principal data types that may be created when a subscriber accesses the Internet.

7.2 The data types have been broken down into two main areas. The first being the activity of the subscriber and the second the resources that a subscriber could utilise.

PART VII MISCELLANEOUS

7.3 When matching events on the Internet with details recorded in ISP logs it is absolutely essential to ensure that time and date information is correctly recorded. It is Best Practice for ISPs to synchronize their systems with global time standards using protocols such as NTP, however consideration should always be given to this not being the case for particular logs. Equally it is essential that enquiries about logging information provide accurate timing information. A frequently encountered pitfall is incorrect handling of timezone offset information and careful attention should be paid to this.

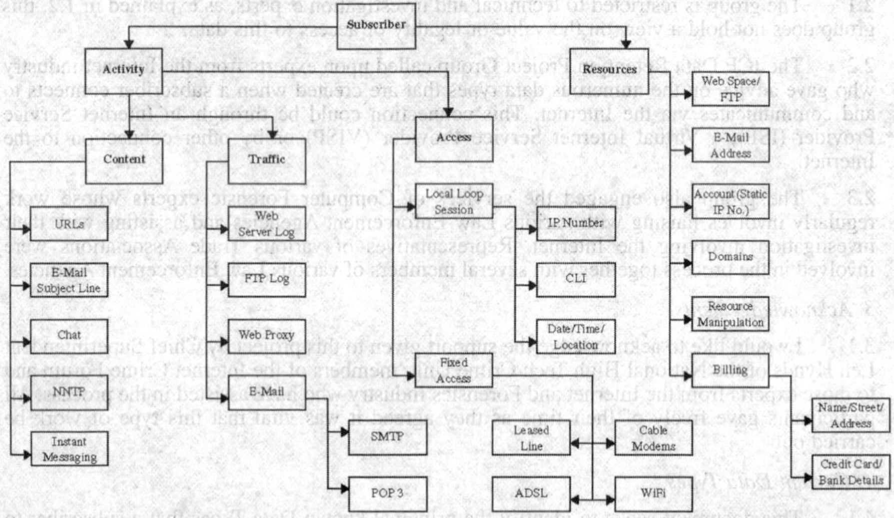

8. Potential Value

8.1 This section of the document identifies and details the potential value of the various data types to investigations. This is not a definitive list of data types and it must be appreciated that advances in technology may well mean that some of the data types that are currently of little value may at some stage in the future generate logs that could be useful for the purposes of investigations.

8.2 The table below identifies each of the data types and the data that could be generated by the subscriber.

8.3 Data can only be obtained in accordance with UK Law and international treaties. This document does not address this issue any further.

8.4 Internet Service Providers retain data for business purposes. The procedures surrounding this data retention may affect the way in which data could be used for evidential purposes.

Activity	Data Type	Comment
Content		
	URLs	A URL (Uniform/Unique Resource Locator) is the address of a file (resource) accessible on the Internet. The type of resource depends on the Internet application protocol. Using the World Wide Web's protocol, the Hypertext Transfer Protocol (**HTTP**), the resource can be an **HTML** page, an image file, a program such as a **common gateway interface** (CGI) application or Java **applet**, or any other file supported by HTTP. The URL contains the name of the protocol required to access the resource, a host name that identifies a specific computer on the Internet, and a hierarchical description of a file location on the computer. The host name can be used to determine the physical location of the computer and its logical ownership.

Activity	Data Type	Comment
Content		
	E-mail	ISPs may hold e-mail on behalf of subscribers. Much of the e-mail is content and a number of different legal regimes apply to the divulgence of this. Some of the header is communications data. In addition details of what e-mail has been sent and received may be recorded in logs. Some of the information in these logs may be content.
	Chat	Depending upon the technology the service provider will not normally retain the content of an individual Chat Room session but individual participants will be able to make their own record. It may be possible to trace and identify participants in a chat session providing the IP address or for some ISPs the screen name is obtained together with an accurate time stamp.
	NNTP/Usenet	In order to trace the author of a Usenet article, the article headers will need to be inspected. These will usually contain the posting IP address and time stamp. The system through which it was originally posted should then be able to identify the account responsible for creating the posting. Provision of Usenet services is increasingly performed by third parties so it may be necessary to make further enquiries with a connectivity ISP to determine where the account was used from. The content of an NNTP (Usenet) session will not be retained by a service provider. Therefore the readership of an article is unlikely to be available. Usenet postings are commonly exchanged between ISPs. This means that an article may well have been hosted on a different service provider from the one on which it is read.
	Instant messaging	Instant Messaging (sometimes called IM or Iming) is the ability to easily see whether a chosen friend or co-worker is connected to the Internet and, if they are, to exchange messages with them. Instant messaging differs from ordinary **e-mail** in the immediacy of the message exchange and also makes a continued exchange simpler than sending e-mail back and forth. Most exchanges are text-only. However, some services allow attachments. In order for Iming to work, both users (who must subscribe to the service) must be online at the same time, and the intended recipient must be willing to accept instant messages. (It is possible to set your software to reject messages.) An attempt to send an IM to someone who is not online, or who is not willing to accept Ims, will result in notification that the transmission cannot be completed. The ISPs will not in general have any records of the messages which have been exchanged because they flow directly between the participants (Peer to Peer). If a "rendez-vous" server is involved in the initial connection between the participants then some logging information about their identities may be retained. The rendez-vous server may be totally independent of any connectivity ISP.

PART VII MISCELLANEOUS

Activity	Data Type	Comment
Content		
Traffic		
	Web Server Logs	These typically contain the source IP address, requested content, submitted data e g username, password and previous site visited. Some of the data may be content rather than traffic data. Some of the data may be anonymised in near real time. Some of the IP addresses may be proxy caches rather than the actual requestor.
	FTP Logs	These contain source IP, account details and details of the file names uploaded into or downloaded from. Although most sites appear to have a username/password login, anonymous guest accounts are also common and although an e-mail address is traditionally provided as identification there is seldom any validation of this whatsoever. Some of the data may be content rather than traffic data. It is quite common for customers to upload the content of their web pages using FTP.
	Web proxy	A proxy server is a **server** that acts as an intermediary between a user and the Internet. A proxy server receives a request for an Internet service (such as a Web page request) from a user. If it passes filtering requirements, the proxy server will access the remote site and pass the information to the user. A Web **cache** maintains a store of previously downloaded items from the Web such as an HTML page. If it is asked for a page that is already in its store, then it returns it to the user without needing to forward the request to the Internet, though it may need to check if its cached copy remains up-to-date. If the page is not in the cache then the cache server acting as a client, on behalf of the user, uses one of its own IP addresses to request the page from the server out on the Internet. When the page is returned, the proxy server relates it to the original request and forwards it on to the user. The user's general impression of using both proxy servers and caches will be of a direct connection to the remote site. In the ISP context it is usual to combine these two functions, and the result may be, rather confusingly, called a web cache, a web proxy or indeed a proxy-cache. Some ISPs use a "transparent" scheme that intercepts, for example, all HTTP (port 80) traffic and sends it via a proxy-cache. In other cases the use of a proxy-cache is entirely under the users' control, though the ISP may encourage usage by means of the default configurations shipped to its customers.

Activity	Data Type	Comment
Content		
		These servers can produce logs of the data handled, giving the local customer IP address, details of the requested content and details of any connections made to remote sites. Complete logging may only be enabled for troubleshooting, but even incomplete logging can create very substantial volumes of data and these logs are not kept for long periods of time. The presence of a proxy may mean that the user never accesses the target web site. The access that is made will show the IP address of the server. The server may be configured to pass information to the target web site giving some details of the user, but some servers are configured specifically to obscure the true identity of the user. Some web pages are designed so that they cannot be cached and so this traffic will flow directly and hence proxy-cache logs will be incomplete. Similar effects will be caused by the use of protocols such as HTTPS which often avoid the use of a proxy-caches altogether.
E-mail		SMTP (Simple Mail Transfer Protocol) is a **TCP protocol** used in sending and receiving e-mail between permanently connected machines. However, because mail is "pushed" rather than "pulled" it works very poorly with intermittently connected machines. Therefore is usual to provide mail delivery to dialup customers via **POP3** or **IMAP**. These provide a store and forward system, so that users can periodically "pull" any new e-mail. SMTP is the standard method for ISP customers to send their e-mail. Although delivery can be made directly to remote systems it is common to relay e-mail traffic via an SMTP server at the ISP called a "smart host". Some ISPs will intercept outgoing SMTP (port 25) traffic and force it to use the smart host. POP3 is a relatively simple protocol for e-mail reception. It is usual to configure clients to delete the e-mail once it has been fetched. If it is not deleted then the ISP will delete it after a preset period. Long term storage is done on the client machine. IMAP is somewhat more complex and provides a client/server implementation of a fully featured e-mail interface – with all the e-mail held on the server machine, possibly for very long periods. IMAP clients will hold very little state from one session to another.

PART VII MISCELLANEOUS

Activity	Data Type	Comment
Content		
	SMTP	Mail will be held on the server until it can be passed to a destination but most service providers do not routinely keep content thereafter. A service provider may retain summary logging details of e-mail that has been received from or sent to their customers. This would include a unique message identifier, who the mail was alleged to be from, who the mail was addressed to, the IP address of the immediately previous hop and the time and date the mail was sent. Further information such as size and content such as the subject line may sometimes be recorded. When the intended destination of e-mail is unavailable it may be routed via intermediate machines (using lower priority MX records). This will reduce the usefulness of IP address logging details. It is also essential to view the "from" details with caution since they are trivial to forge. Finally, many ISPs have outsourced virus scanning and "spam" deletion services. Initial delivery is made to a third party who will only forward genuine e-mail to the ISP's systems. In all cases, the e-mail itself should contain full details of all the machines it has passed through, but these machines will almost invariably only record one part of its journey.
	IMAP & POP3	IMAP & POP3 logs typically contain just brief summary details of connections. These may extend as far as recording the connecting IP address and how many e-mails were read or deleted. It would be very unusual indeed to record anything which references the content, sender or path associated with transmission of the e-mail. IMAP & POP3 servers can usually be accessed from anywhere on the Internet so any IP address recorded may well require further tracing to be useful.
	Webmail	Acesss to e-mail via a web interface ("webmail") may be provided as a front end to POP3 services or as a service in its own right. Logging will typically record the IP address that accesses the mail box and may record which items of mail were looked at. Webmail services are almost invariably designed to be used from any Internet address.
Access Circuit Switched		
	IP Address	An IP address can either be static (allocated on permanent basis) or dynamic (a different IP address allocated each time authentication is made). When mapping a dynamic address to an account it is therefore essential to provide accurate timing information (date, time and timezone).

Activity	Data Type	Comment
Content		
	Account Usage	Logging of account usage will record the date and time that the connection was established, and the date and time that it. Further details such as the number of packets transferred may also be available from some ISPs. Account authorisation if often done using a system called RADIUS so these logs are often referred to as RADIUS logs. Further logs, holding much the same information, from the Network Access Servers (NASs) may also be available at some ISPs.. A number of different versions of RADIUS are in use, so that the actual format of the logs (and indeed the format of the time and date information) may vary from ISP to ISP.
	CLI	If CLI is captured by the service provider it is most likely to be recorded within the RADIUS logs. Not all types of accounts will require CLI to be presented to the ISP. Some types of account will require access only from authorised CLI. At present, ISP equipment will not usually record the CLI if it is marked to be withheld.
Fixed access		Unlike circuit switched (dial-up) services which may be provided "free", fixed access systems are invariably charged for. This means that a valid billing address will be present in the ISP's accounting systems. In addition an installation address will be recorded, though in some cases the service may be moved to another address without the ISP becoming aware of it or bothering to record the change.
	Leased Line	A leased line is a link via the local exchange that has been provided for private use. In some contexts, it's called a *dedicated* line. A leased line is usually contrasted with a *switched line or dial-up line*.
	Cable Modem	The connection may be a dedicated modem or integrated into a television set top box.
	ADSL	A method of providing broadband access over a standard local loop. Within the UK this is mainly provided by British Telecom who route the traffic over an ATM cloud and provide an IP data connection to the ISP.
	Satellite	A system designed for rural areas to provide high bandwidth Internet access. The return path from the user to the ISP may be direct or via the satellite.
	WiFi	A fixed base station is connected by one of the previously described methods to the Internet. Clients may access by wireless within a limited distance. Currently these systems are insecure even where encryption has been used to protect the connection. Logs may only show that someone (necessarily physically close to the base station) has been using the system but local logging may provide further traceability. Some WiFi installations are deliberately made open for public access and some commercial operations provide access for payment, which may be made in cash.

PART VII MISCELLANEOUS

Activity	Data Type	Comment
Content		
Resources		
	Shell Sessions	Details pertaining to telnet and other "shell" login sessions may be held in several files (telnet connections are typically logged in "last" and "messages" files on UNIX based systems). Shell sessions may log a variety of data including start/stop and source IP.
	Web/ FTP Space	Web and FTP Space may be provided separately or as part of a service package. All of the remarks relating to billing (to identify the owner) to server logs (to identify readers) and to FTP Logs (to identify up loaders) apply to this section.
	E-mail Addresses	There is a mapping between the e-mail address and the account. This may vary between ISPs. An account may have one or more e-mail addresses associated with it. Users may have the ability to change e-mail addresses at will. Some ISPs may not hold data on previous e-mail addresses.
	Domains	ISPs provide Domain Name Service (DNS) to allow mapping between domain names and IP addresses as well as information such as where to deliver e-mail. Details of who actually owns the domain name will be held by the appropriate registrar. The ISP will have some records as to which of their customers is controlling it. There may be limited records of historical settings.
	Resource manipulation	Many services provided by ISPs and particularly those provided by third parties can be configured by the user for example e-mail may be redirected to another account, web space requests may be directed to another server or DNS settings may be rearranged. The system that is used for this configuration may keep logs that allow historic configurations to be reconstructed.
Billing		Many forms of access are paid for. Billing data may relate to an individual or could also be that of an organization. Some systems may be sub-let and billing records will relate to the "letting company". Many services are re-sold. Some systems may be insecure and used without permission.
	Name, Street, Address	A service provider does not necessarily verify a subscriber's name and address details. This is dependant upon the service a subscriber utilises whilst on the Internet. In many instances the subscriber will provide CLI (Caller Line Identifier) as a part of the authentication process prior to their use of that service. This CLI can often be mapped to a geographical location by the appropriate telco.
	Credit Card/ Bank DetailsD	For accounts where payments are made, credit -card, debit card, direct debit, cheques or standing order will provide traceability through the banking system. Where postal orders or cash payments are made or accepted, these will not always be verified. It should be noted that billing information may not be retained by the backbone ISP but by the Virtual ISP who has ownership of the customer.

[5244]

GLOSSARY OF TERMS USED WITHIN THIS DOCUMENT

Access	Data access is being able to get to (usually having permission to use) particular data on a computer
ADSL	Asymmetric Digital Subscriber Line is a technology for transmitting **digital** information at a high **bandwidth** on existing phone lines
ATM	Asynchronous Transfer Mode. A switching technology for transferring packets of data. ATM was originally developed for voice application, but is now used for Internet transports and underpins current broadband technologies.
Cable Modem	A cable modem is a device that enables you to hook up your PC to a local **cable TV** connection in order to send and receive data packets.
CGI	Common Gateway Interface. A method of providing dynamic content within "web pages".
Chat	Facility to talk with others whilst on line.
CLI	Calling Line Identifier is the telephone number that a person has used to access their required service
DNS	Domain Name System. Protocol for providing mappings from domain names to resource identifiers such as IP addresses.
Domain name	A domain name is a user-friendly method of identifying the location of resources on the Internet.
E-mail	E-mail is the exchange of text-based electronic messages by telecommunication.
E-mail Subject Line	A conventional e-mail header that is intended to provide a brief description of the contents of an e-mail.
FTP	File Transfer Protocol. A standard TCP protocol for transferring files between machines. FTP is often used to upload the content of web sites onto servers.
HTML	Hypertext Markup Language. This is the language which is used for "web pages" to indicate the structure of documents so that browsers can display them in a standardised manner.
HTTP	Hypertext Transport Protocol. A standard TCP protocol for transferring "web pages" from one machine to another.
HTTPS	Secure HTTP. Transfer of "web pages" over an encrypted transport protocol.
ICF	Internet Crime Forum. A body formed "To promote, maintain and enhance an effective working relationship between industry and law enforcement to tackle crime and foster business and public confidence in the use of the Internet in ways that respect human rights and are sympathetic to the needs of industry."
Instant Messaging	A quick and easy way of exchanging messages with others who are also online.
IM	Instant Messaging.
IMAP	Internet Message Access Protocol. A standard TCP protocol for accessing e-mail that is received, organised and stored on a remote server.
MX record	DNS record entry that indicates where e-mail for a domain is to be delivered.

PART VII MISCELLANEOUS

IP	Internet Protocol. The basic protocol used for communication between computers on the Internet.
IP address	Internet Protocol Address. A numeric value that serves to uniquely identify an interface that is connected to the Internet.
ISP	Internet Service Provider. An organisation that makes Internet services to its customers. ISPs usually provide connectivity, often many other services as well.
Java applet	A way of providing "mobile code" on web pages so as to enable extra functionality on web pages.
Leased Line	A method of providing a fixed connection to the Internet.
Local Loop	In telephony, a local loop is the wired connection from a telephone company's **central office** in a locality to its customers' telephones at homes and businesses
NNTP	Network News Transfer Protocol. A standard TCP protocol for transferring Usenet articles over the Internet.
POP3	Post Office Protocol 3. A standard TCP protocol for collecting e-mail from a server.
RADIUS	Remote Authentication Dial-in User Service. A standard TCP protocol for communicating authentication information and establishing parameters for dial-up connections to the Internet.
SMTP	Simple Mail Transfer Protocol. A standard **protocol** used for the transport of e-mail over the Internet.
SPOC	Single Point of Contact. A scheme whereby requests from law enforcement organisations are funnelled through a single part of that organisation and passed to a single contact point within ISPs
TCP	Transport Control Protocol. A protocol layered over IP that provides a reliable delivery service for data.
URL	Unique/Uniform Resource Locator. A stylised naming system for web resources.
VISP	Virtual ISP. An ISP whose infrastructure is completely provided by third parties.
Web Cache	A cache is a server that retains copies of web content so as to provide timely local delivery for repeat requests.
Web Proxy	A proxy is a **server** that acts as an intermediary between a workstation user and the Internet
WiFi	Wireless systems (such as 802.11) that provide Internet connectivity.

[5245]

COUNCIL REGULATION

of 22 December 2000

on jurisdiction and the recognition and enforcement of judgments in civil and commercial matters

(44/2001/EC)

NOTES

Date of publication in OJ: OJ L12, 16.1.2001, p 1.
Incorporating the Corrigendum from OJ L307 24.11.2001.

THE COUNCIL OF THE EUROPEAN UNION,

Having regard to the Treaty establishing the European Community, and in particular Article 61(c) and Article 67(1) thereof,

Having regard to the proposal from the Commission,[1]

Having regard to the opinion of the European Parliament,[2]

Having regard to the opinion of the Economic and Social Committee,[3]

Whereas:

(1) The Community has set itself the objective of maintaining and developing an area of freedom, security and justice, in which the free movement of persons is ensured. In order to establish progressively such an area, the Community should adopt, amongst other things, the measures relating to judicial cooperation in civil matters which are necessary for the sound operation of the internal market.

(2) Certain differences between national rules governing jurisdiction and recognition of judgments hamper the sound operation of the internal market. Provisions to unify the rules of conflict of jurisdiction in civil and commercial matters and to simplify the formalities with a view to rapid and simple recognition and enforcement of judgments from Member States bound by this Regulation are essential.

(3) This area is within the field of judicial cooperation in civil matters within the meaning of Article 65 of the Treaty.

(4) In accordance with the principles of subsidiarity and proportionality as set out in Article 5 of the Treaty, the objectives of this Regulation cannot be sufficiently achieved by the Member States and can therefore be better achieved by the Community. This Regulation confines itself to the minimum required in order to achieve those objectives and does not go beyond what is necessary for that purpose.

(5) On 27 September 1968 the Member States, acting under Article 293, fourth indent, of the Treaty, concluded the Brussels Convention on Jurisdiction and the Enforcement of Judgments in Civil and Commercial Matters, as amended by Conventions on the Accession of the New Member States to that Convention (hereinafter referred to as the "Brussels Convention").[4] On 16 September 1988 Member States and EFTA States concluded the Lugano Convention on Jurisdiction and the Enforcement of Judgments in Civil and Commercial Matters, which is a parallel Convention to the 1968 Brussels Convention. Work has been undertaken for the revision of those Conventions, and the Council has approved the content of the revised texts. Continuity in the results achieved in that revision should be ensured.

(6) In order to attain the objective of free movement of judgments in civil and commercial matters, it is necessary and appropriate that the rules governing jurisdiction and the recognition and enforcement of judgments be governed by a Community legal instrument which is binding and directly applicable.

(7) The scope of this Regulation must cover all the main civil and commercial matters apart from certain well-defined matters.

(8) There must be a link between proceedings to which this Regulation applies and the territory of the Member States bound by this Regulation. Accordingly common rules on jurisdiction should, in principle, apply when the defendant is domiciled in one of those Member States.

(9) A defendant not domiciled in a Member State is in general subject to national rules of jurisdiction applicable in the territory of the Member State of the court seised, and a defendant domiciled in a Member State not bound by this Regulation must remain subject to the Brussels Convention.

(10) For the purposes of the free movement of judgments, judgments given in a Member State bound by this Regulation should be recognised and enforced in another Member State bound by this Regulation, even if the judgment debtor is domiciled in a third State.

(11) The rules of jurisdiction must be highly predictable and founded on the principle that jurisdiction is generally based on the defendant's domicile and jurisdiction must always be available on this ground save in a few well-defined situations in which the subject-matter of the litigation or the autonomy of the parties warrants a different linking factor. The domicile of a legal person must be defined autonomously so as to make the common rules more transparent and avoid conflicts of jurisdiction.

(12) In addition to the defendant's domicile, there should be alternative grounds of jurisdiction based on a close link between the court and the action or in order to facilitate the sound administration of justice.

(13) In relation to insurance, consumer contracts and employment, the weaker party should be protected by rules of jurisdiction more favourable to his interests than the general rules provide for.

(14) The autonomy of the parties to a contract, other than an insurance, consumer or employment contract, where only limited autonomy to determine the courts having jurisdiction is allowed, must be respected subject to the exclusive grounds of jurisdiction laid down in this Regulation.

(15) In the interests of the harmonious administration of justice it is necessary to minimise the possibility of concurrent proceedings and to ensure that irreconcilable judgments will not be given in two Member States. There must be a clear and effective mechanism for resolving cases of lis pendens and related actions and for obviating problems flowing from national differences as to the determination of the time when a case is regarded as pending. For the purposes of this Regulation that time should be defined autonomously.

(16) Mutual trust in the administration of justice in the Community justifies judgments given in a Member State being recognised automatically without the need for any procedure except in cases of dispute.

(17) By virtue of the same principle of mutual trust, the procedure for making enforceable in one Member State a judgment given in another must be efficient and rapid. To that end, the declaration that a judgment is enforceable should be issued virtually automatically after purely formal checks of the documents supplied, without there being any possibility for the court to raise of its own motion any of the grounds for non-enforcement provided for by this Regulation.

(18) However, respect for the rights of the defence means that the defendant should be able to appeal in an adversarial procedure, against the declaration of enforceability, if he considers one of the grounds for non-enforcement to be present. Redress procedures should also be available to the claimant where his application for a declaration of enforceability has been rejected.

(19) Continuity between the Brussels Convention and this Regulation should be ensured, and transitional provisions should be laid down to that end. The same need for continuity applies as regards the interpretation of the Brussels Convention by the Court of Justice of the European Communities and the 1971 Protocol[5] should remain applicable also to cases already pending when this Regulation enters into force.

(20) The United Kingdom and Ireland, in accordance with Article 3 of the Protocol on the position of the United Kingdom and Ireland annexed to the Treaty on European Union and to the Treaty establishing the European Community, have given notice of their wish to take part in the adoption and application of this Regulation.

(21) Denmark, in accordance with Articles 1 and 2 of the Protocol on the position of Denmark annexed to the Treaty on European Union and to the Treaty establishing the European Community, is not participating in the adoption of this Regulation, and is therefore not bound by it nor subject to its application.

(22) Since the Brussels Convention remains in force in relations between Denmark and the Member States that are bound by this Regulation, both the Convention and the 1971 Protocol continue to apply between Denmark and the Member States bound by this Regulation.

(23) The Brussels Convention also continues to apply to the territories of the Member States which fall within the territorial scope of that Convention and which are excluded from this Regulation pursuant to Article 299 of the Treaty.

(24) Likewise for the sake of consistency, this Regulation should not affect rules governing jurisdiction and the recognition of judgments contained in specific Community instruments.

(25) Respect for international commitments entered into by the Member States means that this Regulation should not affect conventions relating to specific matters to which the Member States are parties.

(26) The necessary flexibility should be provided for in the basic rules of this Regulation in order to take account of the specific procedural rules of certain Member States. Certain provisions of the Protocol annexed to the Brussels Convention should accordingly be incorporated in this Regulation.

(27) In order to allow a harmonious transition in certain areas which were the subject of special provisions in the Protocol annexed to the Brussels Convention, this Regulation lays down, for a transitional period, provisions taking into consideration the specific situation in certain Member States.

(28) No later than five years after entry into force of this Regulation the Commission will present a report on its application and, if need be, submit proposals for adaptations.

(29) The Commission will have to adjust Annexes I to IV on the rules of national jurisdiction, the courts or competent authorities and redress procedures available on the basis of the amendments forwarded by the Member State concerned; amendments made to Annexes V and VI should be adopted in accordance with Council Decision 1999/468/EC of 28 June 1999 laying down the procedures for the exercise of implementing powers conferred on the Commission,[6]

NOTES

[1] OJ C376, 28.12.1999, p 1.
[2] Opinion delivered on 21 September 2000 (not yet published in the Official Journal).
[3] OJ C117, 26.4.2000, p 6.
[4] OJ L299, 31.12.1972, p 32.
OJ L304, 30.10.1978, p 1.
OJ L388, 31.12.1982, p 1.
OJ L285, 3.10.1989, p 1.
OJ C15, 15.1.1997, p 1.
For a consolidated text, see OJ C27, 26.1.1998, p 1.
[5] OJ L204, 2.8.1975, p 28.
OJ L304, 30.10.1978, p 1.
OJ L388, 31.12.1982, p 1.
OJ L285, 3.10.1989, p 1.
OJ C15, 15.1.1997, p 1.
For a consolidated text see OJ C27, 26.1.1998, p 28.
[6] OJ L184, 17.7.1999, p 23.

HAS ADOPTED THIS REGULATION:

CHAPTER I
SCOPE

Article 1

1. This Regulation shall apply in civil and commercial matters whatever the nature of the court or tribunal. It shall not extend, in particular, to revenue, customs or administrative matters.

2. The Regulation shall not apply to:

(a) the status or legal capacity of natural persons, rights in property arising out of a matrimonial relationship, wills and succession;

(b) bankruptcy, proceedings relating to the winding-up of insolvent companies or other legal persons, judicial arrangements, compositions and analogous proceedings;

(c) social security;

(d) arbitration.

3. In this Regulation, the term "Member State" shall mean Member States with the exception of Denmark.

[5246]

CHAPTER II
JURISDICTION

SECTION 1
GENERAL PROVISIONS

Article 2

1. Subject to this Regulation, persons domiciled in a Member State shall, whatever their nationality, be sued in the courts of that Member State.

2. Persons who are not nationals of the Member State in which they are domiciled shall be governed by the rules of jurisdiction applicable to nationals of that State.

[5247]

Article 3

1. Persons domiciled in a Member State may be sued in the courts of another Member State only by virtue of the rules set out in Sections 2 to 7 of this Chapter.

2. In particular the rules of national jurisdiction set out in Annex I shall not be applicable as against them.

[5248]

Article 4

1. If the defendant is not domiciled in a Member State, the jurisdiction of the courts of each Member State shall, subject to Articles 22 and 23, be determined by the law of that Member State.

2. As against such a defendant, any person domiciled in a Member State may, whatever his nationality, avail himself in that State of the rules of jurisdiction there in force, and in particular those specified in Annex I, in the same way as the nationals of that State.

[5249]

SECTION 2
SPECIAL JURISDICTION

Article 5

A person domiciled in a Member State may, in another Member State, be sued:

1.
   (a) in matters relating to a contract, in the courts for the place of performance of the obligation in question;
   (b) for the purpose of this provision and unless otherwise agreed, the place of performance of the obligation in question shall be:
      — in the case of the sale of goods, the place in a Member State where, under the contract, the goods were delivered or should have been delivered,
      — in the case of the provision of services, the place in a Member State where, under the contract, the services were provided or should have been provided,
   (c) if subparagraph (b) does not apply then subparagraph (a) applies;

2. in matters relating to maintenance, in the courts for the place where the maintenance creditor is domiciled or habitually resident or, if the matter is ancillary to proceedings concerning the status of a person, in the court which, according to its own law, has jurisdiction to entertain those proceedings, unless that jurisdiction is based solely on the nationality of one of the parties;

3. in matters relating to tort, *delict* or *quasi-delict*, in the courts for the place where the harmful event occurred or may occur;

4. as regards a civil claim for damages or restitution which is based on an act giving rise to criminal proceedings, in the court seised of those proceedings, to the extent that that court has jurisdiction under its own law to entertain civil proceedings;

5. as regards a dispute arising out of the operations of a branch, agency or other establishment, in the courts for the place in which the branch, agency or other establishment is situated;

6. as settlor, trustee or beneficiary of a trust created by the operation of a statute, or by a written instrument, or created orally and evidenced in writing, in the courts of the Member State in which the trust is domiciled;

7. as regards a dispute concerning the payment of remuneration claimed in respect of the salvage of a cargo or freight, in the court under the authority of which the cargo or freight in question:
   (a) has been arrested to secure such payment, or
   (b) could have been so arrested, but bail or other security has been given;

provided that this provision shall apply only if it is claimed that the defendant has an interest in the cargo or freight or had such an interest at the time of salvage.

[5250]

Article 6

A person domiciled in a Member State may also be sued:

1. where he is one of a number of defendants, in the courts for the place where any one of them is domiciled, provided the claims are so closely connected that it is expedient to hear and determine them together to avoid the risk of irreconcilable judgments resulting from separate proceedings;

2. as a third party in an action on a warranty or guarantee or in any other third party proceedings, in the court seised of the original proceedings, unless these were instituted solely with the object of removing him from the jurisdiction of the court which would be competent in his case;

3. on a counter-claim arising from the same contract or facts on which the original claim was based, in the court in which the original claim is pending;

4. in matters relating to a contract, if the action may be combined with an action against the same defendant in matters relating to rights *in rem* in immovable property, in the court of the Member State in which the property is situated.

[5251]

Article 7

Where by virtue of this Regulation a court of a Member State has jurisdiction in actions relating to liability from the use or operation of a ship, that court, or any other court substituted for this purpose by the internal law of that Member State, shall also have jurisdiction over claims for limitation of such liability.

[5252]

Articles 8–14

((*Jurisdiction in matters relating to insurance*) *outside the scope of this work.*)

SECTION 4
JURISDICTION OVER CONSUMER CONTRACTS

Article 15

1. In matters relating to a contract concluded by a person, the consumer, for a purpose which can be regarded as being outside his trade or profession, jurisdiction shall be determined by this Section, without prejudice to Article 4 and point 5 of Article 5, if:
   (a) it is a contract for the sale of goods on instalment credit terms; or
   (b) it is a contract for a loan repayable by instalments, or for any other form of credit, made to finance the sale of goods; or
   (c) in all other cases, the contract has been concluded with a person who pursues commercial or professional activities in the Member State of the consumer's domicile or, by any means, directs such activities to that Member State or to several States including that Member State, and the contract falls within the scope of such activities.

2. Where a consumer enters into a contract with a party who is not domiciled in the Member State but has a branch, agency or other establishment in one of the Member States, that party shall, in disputes arising out of the operations of the branch, agency or establishment, be deemed to be domiciled in that State.

3. This Section shall not apply to a contract of transport other than a contract which, for an inclusive price, provides for a combination of travel and accommodation.

[5253]

Article 16

1. A consumer may bring proceedings against the other party to a contract either in the courts of the Member State in which that party is domiciled or in the courts for the place where the consumer is domiciled.

2. Proceedings may be brought against a consumer by the other party to the contract only in the courts of the Member State in which the consumer is domiciled.

3. This Article shall not affect the right to bring a counter-claim in the court in which, in accordance with this Section, the original claim is pending.

[5254]

Article 17

The provisions of this Section may be departed from only by an agreement:

1. which is entered into after the dispute has arisen; or

2. which allows the consumer to bring proceedings in courts other than those indicated in this Section; or

3. which is entered into by the consumer and the other party to the contract, both of whom are at the time of conclusion of the contract domiciled or habitually resident in the same Member State, and which confers jurisdiction on the courts of that Member State, provided that such an agreement is not contrary to the law of that Member State.

[5255]

SECTION 5
JURISDICTION OVER INDIVIDUAL CONTRACTS OF EMPLOYMENT

Article 18

1. In matters relating to individual contracts of employment, jurisdiction shall be determined by this Section, without prejudice to Article 4 and point 5 of Article 5.

2. Where an employee enters into an individual contract of employment with an employer who is not domiciled in a Member State but has a branch, agency or other establishment in one of the Member States, the employer shall, in disputes arising out of the operations of the branch, agency or establishment, be deemed to be domiciled in that Member State.

[5256]

Article 19

An employer domiciled in a Member State may be sued:

1. in the courts of the Member State where he is domiciled; or

2. in another Member State:

   (a) in the courts for the place where the employee habitually carries out his work or in the courts for the last place where he did so, or

   (b) if the employee does not or did not habitually carry out his work in any one country, in the courts for the place where the business which engaged the employee is or was situated.

[5257]

Article 20

1. An employer may bring proceedings only in the courts of the Member State in which the employee is domiciled.

2. The provisions of this Section shall not affect the right to bring a counter-claim in the court in which, in accordance with this Section, the original claim is pending.

[5258]

Article 21

The provisions of this Section may be departed from only by an agreement on jurisdiction:

1. which is entered into after the dispute has arisen; or

2. which allows the employee to bring proceedings in courts other than those indicated in this Section.

[5259]

SECTION 6
EXCLUSIVE JURISDICTION

Article 22

The following courts shall have exclusive jurisdiction, regardless of domicile:

1. in proceedings which have as their object rights in rem in immovable property or tenancies of immovable property, the courts of the Member State in which the property is situated.

However, in proceedings which have as their object tenancies of immovable property concluded for temporary private use for a maximum period of six consecutive months, the courts of the Member State in which the defendant is domiciled shall also have jurisdiction, provided that the tenant is a natural person and that the landlord and the tenant are domiciled in the same Member State;

2. in proceedings which have as their object the validity of the constitution, the nullity or the dissolution of companies or other legal persons or associations of natural or legal persons, or of the validity of the decisions of their organs, the courts of the Member State in which the company, legal person or association has its seat. In order to determine that seat, the court shall apply its rules of private international law;

3. in proceedings which have as their object the validity of entries in public registers, the courts of the Member State in which the register is kept;

4. in proceedings concerned with the registration or validity of patents, trade marks, designs, or other similar rights required to be deposited or registered, the courts of the Member State in which the deposit or registration has been applied for, has taken place or is under the terms of a Community instrument or an international convention deemed to have taken place.

Without prejudice to the jurisdiction of the European Patent Office under the Convention on the Grant of European Patents, signed at Munich on 5 October 1973, the courts of each Member State shall have exclusive jurisdiction, regardless of domicile, in proceedings concerned with the registration or validity of any European patent granted for that State;

5. in proceedings concerned with the enforcement of judgments, the courts of the Member State in which the judgment has been or is to be enforced.

[5260]

SECTION 7
PROROGATION OF JURISDICTION

Article 23

1. If the parties, one or more of whom is domiciled in a Member State, have agreed that a court or the courts of a Member State are to have jurisdiction to settle any disputes which have arisen or which may arise in connection with a particular legal relationship, that court or those courts shall have jurisdiction. Such jurisdiction shall be exclusive unless the parties have agreed otherwise. Such an agreement conferring jurisdiction shall be either:

(a) in writing or evidenced in writing; or

(b) in a form which accords with practices which the parties have established between themselves; or

(c) in international trade or commerce, in a form which accords with a usage of which the parties are or ought to have been aware and which in such trade or commerce is widely known to, and regularly observed by, parties to contracts of the type involved in the particular trade or commerce concerned.

2. Any communication by electronic means which provides a durable record of the agreement shall be equivalent to "writing".

3. Where such an agreement is concluded by parties, none of whom is domiciled in a Member State, the courts of other Member States shall have no jurisdiction over their disputes unless the court or courts chosen have declined jurisdiction.

4. The court or courts of a Member State on which a trust instrument has conferred jurisdiction shall have exclusive jurisdiction in any proceedings brought against a settlor, trustee or beneficiary, if relations between these persons or their rights or obligations under the trust are involved.

5. Agreements or provisions of a trust instrument conferring jurisdiction shall have no legal force if they are contrary to Articles 13, 17 or 21, or if the courts whose jurisdiction they purport to exclude have exclusive jurisdiction by virtue of Article 22.

[5261]

Article 24

Apart from jurisdiction derived from other provisions of this Regulation, a court of a Member State before which a defendant enters an appearance shall have jurisdiction. This rule shall not apply where appearance was entered to contest the jurisdiction, or where another court has exclusive jurisdiction by virtue of Article 22.

[5262]

SECTION 8
EXAMINATION AS TO JURISDICTION AND ADMISSIBILITY

Article 25

Where a court of a Member State is seised of a claim which is principally concerned with a matter over which the courts of another Member State have exclusive jurisdiction by virtue of Article 22, it shall declare of its own motion that it has no jurisdiction.

[5263]

Article 26

1. Where a defendant domiciled in one Member State is sued in a court of another Member State and does not enter an appearance, the court shall declare of its own motion that it has no jurisdiction unless its jurisdiction is derived from the provisions of this Regulation.

2. The court shall stay the proceedings so long as it is not shown that the defendant has been able to receive the document instituting the proceedings or an equivalent document in sufficient time to enable him to arrange for his defence, or that all necessary steps have been taken to this end.

3. Article 19 of Council Regulation (EC) No 1348/2000 of 29 May 2000 on the service in the Member States of judicial and extrajudicial documents in civil or commercial matters[1] shall apply instead of the provisions of paragraph 2 if the document instituting the proceedings or an equivalent document had to be pursuant to this Regulation.

4. Where the provisions of Regulation (EC) No 1348/2000 are not applicable, Article 15 of the Hague Convention of 15 November 1965 on the Service Abroad of Judicial and Extrajudicial Documents in Civil or Commercial Matters shall apply if the document instituting the proceedings or an equivalent document had to be transmitted pursuant to that Convention.

[5264]

NOTES

[1] OJ L160, 30.6.2000, p 37.

SECTION 9
LIS PENDENS—RELATED ACTIONS

Article 27

1. Where proceedings involving the same cause of action and between the same parties are brought in the courts of different Member States, any court other than the court first seised shall of its own motion stay its proceedings until such time as the jurisdiction of the court first seised is established.

2. Where the jurisdiction of the court first seised is established, any court other than the court first seised shall decline jurisdiction in favour of that court.

[5265]

Article 28

1. Where related actions are pending in the courts of different Member States, any court other than the court first seised may stay its proceedings.

2. Where these actions are pending at first instance, any court other than the court first seised may also, on the application of one of the parties, decline jurisdiction if the court first seised has jurisdiction over the actions in question and its law permits the consolidation thereof.

3. For the purposes of this Article, actions are deemed to be related where they are so closely connected that it is expedient to hear and determine them together to avoid the risk of irreconcilable judgments resulting from separate proceedings.

[5266]

Article 29

Where actions come within the exclusive jurisdiction of several courts, any court other than the court first seised shall decline jurisdiction in favour of that court.

[5267]

Article 30

For the purposes of this Section, a court shall be deemed to be seised:

1. at the time when the document instituting the proceedings or an equivalent document is lodged with the court, provided that the plaintiff has not subsequently failed to take the steps he was required to take to have service effected on the defendant, or

2. if the document has to be served before being lodged with the court, at the time when it is received by the authority responsible for service, provided that the plaintiff has not subsequently failed to take the steps he was required to take to have the document lodged with the court.

[5268]

SECTION 10
PROVISIONAL, INCLUDING PROTECTIVE, MEASURES

Article 31

Application may be made to the courts of a Member State for such provisional, including protective, measures as may be available under the law of that State, even if, under this Regulation, the courts of another Member State have jurisdiction as to the substance of the matter.

[5269]

CHAPTER III
RECOGNITION AND ENFORCEMENT

Article 32

For the purposes of this Regulation, "judgment" means any judgment given by a court or tribunal of a Member State, whatever the judgment may be called, including a decree, order, decision or writ of execution, as well as the determination of costs or expenses by an officer of the court.

[5270]

SECTION 1
RECOGNITION

Article 33

1. A judgment given in a Member State shall be recognised in the other Member States without any special procedure being required.

2. Any interested party who raises the recognition of a judgment as the principal issue in a dispute may, in accordance with the procedures provided for in Sections 2 and 3 of this Chapter, apply for a decision that the judgment be recognised.

3. If the outcome of proceedings in a court of a Member State depends on the determination of an incidental question of recognition that court shall have jurisdiction over that question.

[5271]

Article 34

A judgment shall not be recognised:

1. if such recognition is manifestly contrary to public policy in the Member State in which recognition is sought;

2. where it was given in default of appearance, if the defendant was not served with the document which instituted the proceedings or with an equivalent document in sufficient time and in such a way as to enable him to arrange for his defence, unless the defendant failed to commence proceedings to challenge the judgment when it was possible for him to do so;

3. if it is irreconcilable with a judgment given in a dispute between the same parties in the Member State in which recognition is sought;

4. if it is irreconcilable with an earlier judgment given in another Member State or in a third State involving the same cause of action and between the same parties, provided that the earlier judgment fulfils the conditions necessary for its recognition in the Member State addressed.

[5272]

Article 35

1. Moreover, a judgment shall not be recognised if it conflicts with Sections 3, 4 or 6 of Chapter II, or in a case provided for in Article 72.

2. In its examination of the grounds of jurisdiction referred to in the foregoing paragraph, the court or authority applied to shall be bound by the findings of fact on which the court of the Member State of origin based its jurisdiction.

3. Subject to the paragraph 1, the jurisdiction of the court of the Member State of origin may not be reviewed. The test of public policy referred to in point 1 of Article 34 may not be applied to the rules relating to jurisdiction.

[5273]

Article 36

Under no circumstances may a foreign judgment be reviewed as to its substance.

[5274]

Article 37

1. A court of a Member State in which recognition is sought of a judgment given in another Member State may stay the proceedings if an ordinary appeal against the judgment has been lodged.

2. A court of a Member State in which recognition is sought of a judgment given in Ireland or the United Kingdom may stay the proceedings if enforcement is suspended in the State of origin, by reason of an appeal.

[5275]

SECTION 2
ENFORCEMENT

Article 38

1. A judgment given in a Member State and enforceable in that State shall be enforced in another Member State when, on the application of any interested party, it has been declared enforceable there.

2. However, in the United Kingdom, such a judgment shall be enforced in England and Wales, in Scotland, or in Northern Ireland when, on the application of any interested party, it has been registered for enforcement in that part of the United Kingdom.

[5276]

Article 39

1. The application shall be submitted to the court or competent authority indicated in the list in Annex II.

2. The local jurisdiction shall be determined by reference to the place of domicile of the party against whom enforcement is sought, or to the place of enforcement.

[5277]

Article 40

1. The procedure for making the application shall be governed by the law of the Member State in which enforcement is sought.

2. The applicant must give an address for service of process within the area of jurisdiction of the court applied to. However, if the law of the Member State in which enforcement is sought does not provide for the furnishing of such an address, the applicant shall appoint a representative ad litem.

3. The documents referred to in Article 53 shall be attached to the application.

[5278]

Article 41

The judgment shall be declared enforceable immediately on completion of the formalities in Article 53 without any review under Articles 34 and 35. The party against whom enforcement is sought shall not at this stage of the proceedings be entitled to make any submissions on the application.

[5279]

Article 42

1. The decision on the application for a declaration of enforceability shall forthwith be brought to the notice of the applicant in accordance with the procedure laid down by the law of the Member State in which enforcement is sought.

2. The declaration of enforceability shall be served on the party against whom enforcement is sought, accompanied by the judgment, if not already served on that party.

[5280]

Article 43

1. The decision on the application for a declaration of enforceability may be appealed against by either party.

2. The appeal is to be lodged with the court indicated in the list in Annex III.

3. The appeal shall be dealt with in accordance with the rules governing procedure in contradictory matters.

4. If the party against whom enforcement is sought fails to appear before the appellate court in proceedings concerning an appeal brought by the applicant, Article 26(2) to (4) shall apply even where the party against whom enforcement is sought is not domiciled in any of the Member States.

5. An appeal against the declaration of enforceability is to be lodged within one month of service thereof. If the party against whom enforcement is sought is domiciled in a Member State other than that in which the declaration of enforceability was given, the time for appealing shall be two months and shall run from the date of service, either on him in person or at his residence. No extension of time may be granted on account of distance.

[5281]

Article 44

The judgment given on the appeal may be contested only by the appeal referred to in Annex IV.

[5282]

Article 45

1. The court with which an appeal is lodged under Article 43 or Article 44 shall refuse or revoke a declaration of enforceability only on one of the grounds specified in Articles 34 and 35. It shall give its decision without delay.

2. Under no circumstances may the foreign judgment be reviewed as to its substance.

[5283]

Article 46

1. The court with which an appeal is lodged under Article 43 or Article 44 may, on the application of the party against whom enforcement is sought, stay the proceedings if an ordinary appeal has been lodged against the judgment in the Member State of origin or if the time for such an appeal has not yet expired; in the latter case, the court may specify the time within which such an appeal is to be lodged.

2. Where the judgment was given in Ireland or the United Kingdom, any form of appeal available in the Member State of origin shall be treated as an ordinary appeal for the purposes of paragraph 1.

3. The court may also make enforcement conditional on the provision of such security as it shall determine.

[5284]

Article 47

1. When a judgment must be recognised in accordance with this Regulation, nothing shall prevent the applicant from availing himself of provisional, including protective, measures in accordance with the law of the Member State requested without a declaration of enforceability under Article 41 being required.

2. The declaration of enforceability shall carry with it the power to proceed to any protective measures.

3. During the time specified for an appeal pursuant to Article 43(5) against the declaration of enforceability and until any such appeal has been determined, no measures of enforcement may be taken other than protective measures against the property of the party against whom enforcement is sought.

[5285]

Article 48

1. Where a foreign judgment has been given in respect of several matters and the declaration of enforceability cannot be given for all of them, the court or competent authority shall give it for one or more of them.

2. An applicant may request a declaration of enforceability limited to parts of a judgment.

[5286]

Article 49

A foreign judgment which orders a periodic payment by way of a penalty shall be enforceable in the Member State in which enforcement is sought only if the amount of the payment has been finally determined by the courts of the Member State of origin.

[5287]

Article 50

An applicant who, in the Member State of origin has benefited from complete or partial legal aid or exemption from costs or expenses, shall be entitled, in the procedure provided for in this Section, to benefit from the most favourable legal aid or the most extensive exemption from costs or expenses provided for by the law of the Member State addressed.

[5288]

Article 51

No security, bond or deposit, however described, shall be required of a party who in one Member State applies for enforcement of a judgment given in another Member State on the ground that he is a foreign national or that he is not domiciled or resident in the State in which enforcement is sought.

[5289]

Article 52

In proceedings for the issue of a declaration of enforceability, no charge, duty or fee calculated by reference to the value of the matter at issue may be levied in the Member State in which enforcement is sought.

[5290]

SECTION 3
COMMON PROVISIONS

Article 53

1. A party seeking recognition or applying for a declaration of enforceability shall produce a copy of the judgment which satisfies the conditions necessary to establish its authenticity.

2. A party applying for a declaration of enforceability shall also produce the certificate referred to in Article 54, without prejudice to Article 55.

[5291]

Article 54

The court or competent authority of a Member State where a judgment was given shall issue, at the request of any interested party, a certificate using the standard form in Annex V to this Regulation.

[5292]

Article 55

1. If the certificate referred to in Article 54 is not produced, the court or competent authority may specify a time for its production or accept an equivalent document or, if it considers that it has sufficient information before it, dispense with its production.

2. If the court or competent authority so requires, a translation of the documents shall be produced. The translation shall be certified by a person qualified to do so in one of the Member States.

[5293]

Article 56

No legalisation or other similar formality shall be required in respect of the documents referred to in Article 53 or Article 55(2), or in respect of a document appointing a representative *ad litem*.

[5294]

CHAPTER IV
AUTHENTIC INSTRUMENTS AND COURT SETTLEMENTS

Article 57

1. A document which has been formally drawn up or registered as an authentic instrument and is enforceable in one Member State shall, in another Member State, be declared enforceable there, on application made in accordance with the procedures provided for in Articles 38, et seq. The court with which an appeal is lodged under Article 43 or Article 44 shall refuse or revoke a declaration of enforceability only if enforcement of the instrument is manifestly contrary to public policy in the Member State addressed.

2. Arrangements relating to maintenance obligations concluded with administrative authorities or authenticated by them shall also be regarded as authentic instruments within the meaning of paragraph 1.

3. The instrument produced must satisfy the conditions necessary to establish its authenticity in the Member State of origin.

4. Section 3 of Chapter III shall apply as appropriate. The competent authority of a Member State where an authentic instrument was drawn up or registered shall issue, at the request of any interested party, a certificate using the standard form in Annex VI to this Regulation.

[5295]

Article 58

A settlement which has been approved by a court in the course of proceedings and is enforceable in the Member State in which it was concluded shall be enforceable in the State addressed under the same conditions as authentic instruments. The court or competent authority of a Member State where a court settlement was approved shall issue, at the request of any interested party, a certificate using the standard form in Annex V to this Regulation.

[5296]

CHAPTER V
GENERAL PROVISIONS

Article 59

1. In order to determine whether a party is domiciled in the Member State whose courts are seised of a matter, the court shall apply its internal law.

2. If a party is not domiciled in the Member State whose courts are seised of the matter, then, in order to determine whether the party is domiciled in another Member State, the court shall apply the law of that Member State.

[5297]

Article 60

1. For the purposes of this Regulation, a company or other legal person or association of natural or legal persons is domiciled at the place where it has its:

(a) statutory seat, or

(b) central administration, or

(c) principal place of business.

2. For the purposes of the United Kingdom and Ireland "statutory seat" means the registered office or, where there is no such office anywhere, the place of incorporation or, where there is no such place anywhere, the place under the law of which the formation took place.

3. In order to determine whether a trust is domiciled in the Member State whose courts are seised of the matter, the court shall apply its rules of private international law.

[5298]

Article 61

Without prejudice to any more favourable provisions of national laws, persons domiciled in a Member State who are being prosecuted in the criminal courts of another Member State of which they are not nationals for an offence which was not intentionally committed may be defended by persons qualified to do so, even if they do not appear in person. However, the court seised of the matter may order appearance in person; in the case of failure to appear, a judgment given in the civil action without the person concerned having had the opportunity to arrange for his defence need not be recognised or enforced in the other Member States.

[5299]

Article 62

In Sweden, in summary proceedings concerning orders to pay (*betalningsföreläggande*) and assistance (*handräckning*), the expression "court" includes the "Swedish enforcement service" (*kronofogdemyndighet*).

[5300]

Article 63

1. A person domiciled in the territory of the Grand Duchy of Luxembourg and sued in the court of another Member State pursuant to Article 5(1) may refuse to submit to the jurisdiction of that court if the final place of delivery of the goods or provision of the services is in Luxembourg.

2. Where, under paragraph 1, the final place of delivery of the goods or provision of the services is in Luxembourg, any agreement conferring jurisdiction must, in order to be valid, be accepted in writing or evidenced in writing within the meaning of Article 23(1)(a).

3. The provisions of this Article shall not apply to contracts for the provision of financial services.

4. The provisions of this Article shall apply for a period of six years from entry into force of this Regulation.

[5301]

Article 64

1. In proceedings involving a dispute between the master and a member of the crew of a seagoing ship registered in Greece or in Portugal, concerning remuneration or other conditions of service, a court in a Member State shall establish whether the diplomatic or consular officer responsible for the ship has been notified of the dispute. It may act as soon as that officer has been notified.

2. The provisions of this Article shall apply for a period of six years from entry into force of this Regulation.

[5302]

[Article 65

1. The jurisdiction specified in Article 6(2) and Article 11 in actions on a warranty of guarantee or in any other third party proceedings may not be resorted to Germany, Austria and Hungary. Any person domiciled in another Member State may be sued in the courts:

(a) of Germany, pursuant to Articles 68 and 72 to 74 of the Code of Civil Procedure (Zivilprozessordnung) concerning third-party notices;

(b) of Austria, pursuant to Article 21 of the Code of Civil Procedure (Zivilprozessordnung) concerning third-party notices;

(c) of Hungary, pursuant to Articles 58 to 60 of the Code of Civil Procedure (Polgári perrendtartás) concerning third-party notices.

(2) Judgments given in other Member States by virtue of Article 6(2), or Article 11 shall be recognised and enforced in Germany, Austria and Hungary in accordance with Chapter III. Any effects which judgments given in these States may have on third parties by application of the provisions in paragraph 1 shall also be recognised in the other Member States.]

[5303]

NOTES

Substituted by AA5, as from 1 May 2004.

CHAPTER VI
TRANSITIONAL PROVISIONS

Article 66

1. This Regulation shall apply only to legal proceedings instituted and to documents formally drawn up or registered as authentic instruments after the entry into force thereof.

2. However, if the proceedings in the Member State of origin were instituted before the entry into force of this Regulation, judgments given after that date shall be recognised and enforced in accordance with Chapter III,

(a) if the proceedings in the Member State of origin were instituted after the entry into force of the Brussels or the Lugano Convention both in the Member State or origin and in the Member State addressed;

(b) in all other cases, if jurisdiction was founded upon rules which accorded with those provided for either in Chapter II or in a convention concluded between the Member State of origin and the Member State addressed which was in force when the proceedings were instituted.

[5304]

PART VII MISCELLANEOUS

CHAPTER VII
RELATIONS WITH OTHER INSTRUMENTS

Article 67

This Regulation shall not prejudice the application of provisions governing jurisdiction and the recognition and enforcement of judgments in specific matters which are contained in Community instruments or in national legislation harmonised pursuant to such instruments.

[5305]

Article 68

1. This Regulation shall, as between the Member States, supersede the Brussels Convention, except as regards the territories of the Member States which fall within the territorial scope of that Convention and which are excluded from this Regulation pursuant to Article 299 of the Treaty.

2. In so far as this Regulation replaces the provisions of the Brussels Convention between Member States, any reference to the Convention shall be understood as a reference to this Regulation.

[5306]

Article 69

Subject to Article 66(2) and Article 70, this Regulation shall, as between Member States, supersede the following conventions and treaty concluded between two or more of them:

— the Convention between Belgium and France on Jurisdiction and the Validity and Enforcement of Judgments, Arbitration Awards and Authentic Instruments, signed at Paris on 8 July 1899,

— the Convention between Belgium and the Netherlands on Jurisdiction, Bankruptcy, and the Validity and Enforcement of Judgments, Arbitration Awards and Authentic Instruments, signed at Brussels on 28 March 1925,

— the Convention between France and Italy on the Enforcement of Judgments in Civil and Commercial Matters, signed at Rome on 3 June 1930,

— the Convention between the United Kingdom and the French Republic providing for the reciprocal enforcement of judgements in civil and commercial matters, with Protocol, signed at Paris on 18 January 1934,

— the Convention between the United Kingdom and the Kingdom of Belgium providing for the reciprocal enforcement of judgements in civil and commercial matters, with Protocol, signed at Brussels on 2 May 1934,

— the Convention between Germany and Italy on the Recognition and Enforcement of Judgments in Civil and Commercial Matters, signed at Rome on 9 March 1936,

— the Convention between Belgium and Austria on the Reciprocal Recognition and Enforcement of Judgments and Authentic Instruments relating to Maintenance Obligations, signed at Vienna on 25 October 1957,

— the Convention between Germany and Belgium on the Mutual Recognition and Enforcement of Judgments, Arbitration Awards and Authentic Instruments in Civil and Commercial Matters, signed at Bonn on 30 June 1958,

— the Convention between the Netherlands and Italy on the Recognition and Enforcement of Judgments in Civil and Commercial Matters, signed at Rome on 17 April 1959,

— the Convention between Germany and Austria on the Reciprocal Recognition and Enforcement of Judgments, Settlements and Authentic Instruments in Civil and Commercial Matters, signed at Vienna on 6 June 1959,

— the Convention between Belgium and Austria on the Reciprocal Recognition and Enforcement of Judgments, Arbitral Awards and Authentic Instruments in Civil and Commercial Matters, signed at Vienna on 16 June 1959,

— the Convention between the United Kingdom and the Federal Republic of Germany for the reciprocal recognition and enforcement of judgements in civil and commercial matters signed at Bonn on 14 July 1960,

— the Convention between the United Kingdom and Austria providing for the reciprocal recognition and enforcement of judgements in civil and commercial matters, signed at Vienna on 14 July 1961, with amending Protocol signed at London on 6 March 1970,

— the Convention between Greece and Germany for the Reciprocal Recognition and

Enforcement of Judgments, Settlements and Authentic Instruments in Civil and Commercial Matters, signed in Athens on 4 November 1961,

— the Convention between Belgium and Italy on the Recognition and Enforcement of Judgments and other Enforceable Instruments in Civil and Commercial Matters, signed at Rome on 6 April 1962,

— the Convention between the Netherlands and Germany on the Mutual Recognition and Enforcement of Judgments and Other Enforceable Instruments in Civil and Commercial Matters, signed at The Hague on 30 August 1962,

— the Convention between the Netherlands and Austria on the Reciprocal Recognition and Enforcement of Judgments and Authentic Instruments in Civil and Commercial Matters, signed at The Hague on 6 February 1963,

— the Convention between the United Kingdom and the Republic of Italy for the reciprocal enforcement of judgements in civil and commercial matters, signed at Rome on 7 February 1964, with amending Protocol signed at Rome on 14 July 1970,

— the Convention between France and Austria on the Recognition and Enforcement of Judgments and Authentic Instruments in Civil and Commercial Matters, signed at Vienna on 15 July 1966,

— the Convention between the United Kingdom and the Kingdom of the Netherlands providing for the reciprocal recognition and enforcement of judgements in civil matters, signed at The Hegue on 17 November 1967,

— the Convention between Spain and France on the Recognition and Enforcement of Judgment Arbitration Awards in Civil and Commercial Matters, signed at Paris on 28 May 1969,

— the Convention between Luxembourg and Austria on the Recognition and Enforcement of Judgments and Authentic Instruments in Civil and Commercial Matters, signed at Luxembourg on 29 July 1971,

— the Convention between Italy and Austria on the Recognition and Enforcement of Judgments in Civil and Commercial Matters, of Judicial Settlements and of Authentic Instruments, signed at Rome on 16 November 1971,

— the Convention between Spain and Italy regarding Legal Aid and the Recognition and Enforcement of Judgments in Civil and Commercial Matters, signed at Madrid on 22 May 1973,

— the Convention between Finland, Iceland, Norway, Sweden and Denmark on the Recognition and Enforcement of Judgments in Civil Matters, signed at Copenhagen on 11 October 1977,

— the Convention between Austria and Sweden on the Recognition and Enforcement of Judgments in Civil Matters, signed at Stockholm on 16 September 1982,

— the Convention between Spain and the Federal Republic of Germany on the Recognition and Enforcement of Judgments, Settlements and Enforceable Authentic Instruments in Civil and Commercial Matters, signed at Bonn on 14 November 1983,

— the Convention between Austria and Spain on the Recognition and Enforcement of Judgments, Settlements and Enforceable Authentic Instruments in Civil and Commercial Matters, signed at Vienna on 17 February 1984,

— the Convention between Finland and Austria on the Recognition and Enforcement of Judgments in Civil Matters, signed at Vienna on 17 November 1986, and

— the Treaty between Belgium, the Netherlands and Luxembourg in Jurisdiction, Bankruptcy, and the Validity and Enforcement of Judgments, Arbitration Awards and Authentic Instruments, signed at Brussels on 24 November 1961, in so far as it is in force.

[— the Convention between the Czechoslovak Republic and Portugal on the Recognition and Enforcement of Court Decisions, signed at Lisbon on 23 November 1927, still in force between the Czech Republic and Portugal,

— the Convention between the Federative People's Republic of Yugoslavia and the Republic of Austria on Mutual Judicial Cooperation, signed at Vienna on 16 December 1954,

— the Convention between the Polish People's Republic and the Hungarian People's Republic on the Legal Assistance in Civil, Family and Criminal Matters, signed at Budapest on 6 March 1959,

— the Convention between the Federative People's Republic of Yugoslavia and the Kingdom of Greece on the Mutual Recognition and Enforcement of Judgments, signed at Athens on 18 June 1959,

— the Convention between the Polish People's Republic and the Federative People's

Republic of Yugoslavia on the Legal Assistance in Civil and Criminal Matters, signed at Warsaw on 6 February 1960, now in force between Poland and Slovenia,
- the Agreement between the Federative People's Republic of Yugoslavia and the Republic of Austria on the Mutual Recognition and Enforcement of Arbitral Awards and Arbitral Settlements in Commercial Matters, signed at Belgrade on 18 March 1960,
- the Agreement between the Federative People's Republic of Yugoslavia and the Republic of Austria on the Mutual Recognition and Enforcement of Decisions in Alimony Matters, signed at Vienna on 10 October 1961,
- the Convention between Poland and Austria on Mutual Relations in Civil Matters and on Documents, signed at Vienna on 11 December 1963,
- the Treaty between the Czechoslovak Socialist Republic and the Socialist Federative Republic of Yugoslavia on Settlement of Legal Relations in Civil, Family and Criminal Matters, signed at Belgrade on 20 January 1964, still in force between the Czech Republic, Slovakia and Slovenia,
- the Convention between Poland and France on Applicable Law, Jurisdiction and the Enforcement of Judgments in the Field of Personal and Family Law, concluded in Warsaw on 5 April 1967,
- the Convention between the Governments of Yugoslavia and France on the Recognition and Enforcement of Judgments in Civil and Commercial Matters, signed at Paris on 18 May 1971,
- the Convention between the Federative Socialist Republic of Yugoslavia and the Kingdom of Belgium on the Recognition and Enforcement of Court Decisions in Alimony Matters, signed at Belgrade on 12 December 1973,
- the Convention between Hungary and Greece on Legal Assistance in Civil and Criminal Matters, signed at Budapest on 8 October 1979,
- the Convention between Poland and Greece on Legal Assistance in Civil and Criminal Matters, signed at Athens on 24 October 1979,
- the Convention between Hungary and France on Legal Assistance in Civil and Family Law, on the Recognition and Enforcement of Decisions and on Legal Assistance in Criminal Matters and on Extradition, signed at Budapest on 31 July 1980,
- the Treaty between the Czechoslovak Socialist Republic and the Hellenic Republic on Legal Aid in Civil and Criminal Matters, signed at Athens on 22 October 1980, still in force between the Czech Republic, Slovakia and Greece,
- the Convention between the Republic of Cyprus and the Hungarian People's Republic on Legal Assistance in Civil and Criminal Matters, signed at Nicosia on 30 November 1981,
- the Treaty between the Czechoslovak Socialistic Republic and the Republic of Cyprus on Legal Aid in Civil and Criminal Matters, signed at Nicosia on 23 April 1982, still in force between the Czech Republic, Slovakia and Cyprus,
- the Agreement between the Republic of Cyprus and the Republic of Greece on Legal Cooperation in Matters of Civil, Family, Commercial and Criminal Law, signed at Nicosia on 5 March 1984,
- the Treaty between the Government of the Czechoslovak Socialist Republic and the Government of the Republic of France on Legal Aid and the Recognition and Enforcement of Judgments in Civil, Family and Commercial Matters, signed at Paris on 10 May 1984, still in force between the Czech Republic, Slovakia and France,
- the Agreement between the Republic of Cyprus and the Socialist Federal Republic of Yugoslavia on Legal Assistance in Civil and Criminal Matters, signed at Nicosia on 19 September 1984, now in force between Cyprus and Slovenia,
- the Treaty between the Czechoslovak Socialist Republic and the Italian Republic on Legal Aid in Civil and Criminal Matters, signed at Prague on 6 December 1985, still in force between the Czech Republic, Slovakia and Italy,
- the Treaty between the Czechoslovak Socialist Republic and the Kingdom of Spain on Legal Aid, Recognition and Enforcement of Court Decisions in Civil Matters, signed at Madrid on 4 May 1987, still in force between the Czech Republic, Slovakia and Spain,
- the Treaty between the Czechoslovak Socialist Republic and the Polish People's Republic on Legal Aid and Settlement of Legal Relations in Civil, Family, Labour and Criminal Matters, signed at Warsaw on 21 December 1987, still in force between the Czech Republic, Slovakia and Poland,
- the Treaty between the Czechoslovak Socialist Republic and the Hungarian People's Republic on Legal Aid and Settlement of Legal Relations in Civil,

Family and Criminal Matters, signed at Bratislava on 28 March 1989, still in force between the Czech Republic, Slovakia and Hungary,
- the Convention between Poland and Italy on Judicial Assistance and the Recognition and Enforcement of Judgments in Civil Matters, signed at Warsaw on 28 April 1989,
- the Treaty between the Czech Republic and the Slovak Republic on Legal Aid provided by Judicial Bodies and on Settlements of Certain Legal Relations in Civil and Criminal Matters, signed at Prague on 29 October 1992,
- the Agreement between the Republic of Latvia, the Republic of Estonia and the Republic of Lithuania on Legal Assistance and Legal Relationships, signed at Tallinn on 11 November 1992,
- the Agreement between the Republic of Poland and the Republic of Lithuania on Legal Assistance and Legal Relations in Civil, Family, Labour and Criminal Matters, signed in Warsaw on 26 January 1993,
- the Agreement between the Republic of Latvia and the Republic of Poland on Legal Assistance and Legal Relationships in Civil, Family, Labour and Criminal Matters, signed at Riga on 23 February 1994,
- the Agreement between the Republic of Cyprus and the Republic of Poland on Legal Cooperation in Civil and Criminal Matters, signed at Nicosia on 14 November 1996,
- the Agreement between Estonia and Poland on Granting Legal Assistance and Legal Relations on Civil, Labour and Criminal Matters, signed at Tallinn on 27 November 1998.]

[5307]

NOTES

Entries in square brackets added by AA5, as from 1 May 2004.

Article 70

1. The Treaty and the Conventions referred to in Article 69 shall continue to have effect in relation to matters to which this Regulation does not apply.

2. They shall continue to have effect in respect of judgments given and documents formally drawn up or registered as authentic instruments before the entry into force of this Regulation.

[5308]

Article 71

1. This Regulation shall not affect any conventions to which the Member States are parties and which in relation to particular matters, govern jurisdiction or the recognition or enforcement of judgments.

2. With a view to its uniform interpretation, paragraph 1 shall be applied in the following manner:

(a) this Regulation shall not prevent a court of a Member State, which is a party to a convention on a particular matter, from assuming jurisdiction in accordance with that convention, even where the defendant is domiciled in another Member State which is not a party to that convention. The court hearing the action shall, in any event, apply Article 26 of this Regulation;

(b) judgments given in a Member State by a court in the exercise of jurisdiction provided for in a convention on a particular matter shall be recognised and enforced in the other Member States in accordance with this Regulation.

Where a convention on a particular matter to which both the Member State of origin and the Member State addressed are parties lays down conditions for the recognition or enforcement of judgments, those conditions shall apply. In any event, the provisions of this Regulation which concern the procedure for recognition and enforcement of judgments may be applied.

[5309]

Article 72

This Regulation shall not affect agreements by which Member States undertook, prior to the entry into force of this Regulation pursuant to Article 59 of the Brussels Convention, not to

PART VII MISCELLANEOUS

recognise judgments given, in particular in other Contracting States to that Convention, against defendants domiciled or habitually resident in a third country where, in cases provided for in Article 4 of that Convention, the judgment could only be founded on a ground of jurisdiction specified in the second paragraph of Article 3 of that Convention.

[5310]

CHAPTER VIII
FINAL PROVISIONS

Article 73

No later than five years after the entry into force of this Regulation, the Commission shall present to the European Parliament, the Council and the Economic and Social Committee a report on the application of this Regulation. The report shall be accompanied, if need be, by proposals for adaptations to this Regulation.

[5311]

Article 74

1. The Member States shall notify the Commission of the texts amending the lists set out in Annexes I to IV. The Commission shall adapt the Annexes concerned accordingly.

2. The updating or technical adjustment of the forms, specimens of which appear in Annexes V and VI, shall be adopted in accordance with the advisory procedure referred to in Article 75(2).

[5312]

Article 75

1. The Commission shall be assisted by a committee.

2. Where reference is made to this paragraph, Articles 3 and 7 of Decision 1999/468/EC shall apply.

3. The Committee shall adopt its rules of procedure.

[5313]

Article 76

This Regulation shall enter into force on l March 2002.

This Regulation is binding in its entirety and directly applicable in the Member States in accordance with the Treaty establishing the European Community.

[5314]

Done at Brussels, 22 December 2000.

ANNEX I
RULES OF JURISDICTION REFERRED TO IN ARTICLE 3(2) AND ARTICLE 4(2)

The rules of jurisdiction referred to in Article 3(2) and Article 4(2) are the following:

— in Belgium: Article 15 of the Civil Code (*Code civil/Burgerlijk Wetboek*) and Article 638 of the Judicial Code (*Code judiciaire/Gerechtelijk Wetboek*);

[— in the Czech Republic: Article 86 of Act No 99/1963 Coll., the Code of Civil Procedure (obcanský soudní rád), as amended,]

— in Germany: Article 23 of the Code of Civil Procedure (*Zivilprozessordnung*),

[— in Estonia: Article 139, paragraph 2 of the Code of Civil Procedure (tsiviilkohtumenetluse seadustik),]

— in Greece, Article 40 of the Code of Civil Procedure (Κώδικας Πολιτικής Δικονομίας);

— in France: Articles 14 and 15 of the Civil Code (*Code civil*),

— in Ireland: the rules which enable jurisdiction to be founded on the document instituting the proceedings having been served on the defendant during his temporary presence in Ireland,

— in Italy: Articles 3 and 4 of Act 218 of 31 May 1995,

[— in Cyprus: section 21(2) of the Courts of Justice Law No 14 of 1960, as amended,

[— in Latvia: section 27 and paragraphs 3, 5, 6 and 9 of section 28 of the Civil Procedure Law (Civilprocesa likums),]

— in Lithuania: Article 31 of the Code of Civil Procedure (Civilinio proceso kodeksas),]
— in Luxembourg: Articles 14 and 15 of the Civil Code (*Code civil*),
[— in Hungary: Article 57 of Law Decree No. 13 of 1979 on International Private Law (a nemzetközi magánjogról szóló 1979. évi 13. törvényereju rendelet),
— in Malta: Articles 742, 743 and 744 of the Code of Organisation and Civil Procedure-Cap. 12 (Kodici ta' Organizzazzjoni u Procedura Civili-Kap. 12) and Article 549 of the Commercial Code-Cap. 13 (Kodici tal-kummerc-Kap. 13),]
…
— in Austria: Article 99 of the Court Jurisdiction Act (*Jurisdiktionsnorm*),
[— in Poland: Articles 1103 and 1110 of the Code of Civil Procedure (Kodeks postepowania cywilnego),]
— in Portugal: Articles 65 and 65A of the Code of Civil Procedure (*Código de Processo Civil*) and Article 11 of the Code of Labour Procedure (*Código de Processo de Trabalho*),
[— in Slovenia: Article 48(2) of the Private International Law and Procedure Act (Zakon o medarodnem zasebnem pravu in postopku) in relation to Article 47(2) of Civil Procedure Act (Zakon o pravdnem postopku) and Article 58(1) of the Private International Law and Procedure Act (Zakon o medarodnem zasebnem pravu in postopku) in relation to Article 57(1) and 47(2) of Civil Procedure Act (Zakon o pravdnem postopku),]
[— in Slovakia: Articles 37 to 37e of Act No 97/1963 on Private International Law and the Rules of Procedure relating thereto,]
— in Finland: the second, third and fourth sentences of the first paragraph of Section 1 of Chapter 10 of the Code of Judicial Procedure (*oikeudenkäymiskaari/ rättegångsbalken*),
— in Sweden: the first sentence of the first paragraph of Section 3 of Chapter 10 of the Code of Judicial Procedure (*rättegångsbalken*),
— in the United Kingdom: rules which enable jurisdiction to be founded on:
(a) the document instituting the proceedings having been served on the defendant during his temporary presence in the United Kingdom; or
(b) the presence within the United Kingdom of property belonging to the defendant; or
(c) the seizure by the plaintiff of property situated in the United Kingdom.

[5315]

NOTES

Entries relating to the Czech Republic, Estonia, Cyprus, Latvia, Lithuania, Hungary, Malta, Poland, Slovenia and Slovakia inserted by AA5, as from 1 May 2004.

Entries relating to Latvia, Slovenia and Slovakia substituted by Commission Regulation 2245/2004/EC, Art 1(1), as from 4 January 2005.

Entry omitted repealed by Commission Regulation 1496/2002/EC, Art 1, as from 29 August 2002.

ANNEX II

The courts or competent authorities to which the application referred to in Article 39 may be submitted are the following:
— in Belgium, the "*tribunal de première instance*" or "*rechtbank van eerste aanleg*" or "*erstinstanzliches Gericht*",
[— in the Czech Republic, the "okresní soud" or "soudní exekutor",]
— [in Germany:
(a) the presiding Judge of a chamber of the "Landgericht";
(b) a notary ("…") in a procedure of declaration of enforceability of an authentic instrument.]
[— in Estonia, the "maakohus" or the "linnakohus",]
— in Greece, the "Μονομελές Πρωτδικείο",
— in Spain, the "*Juzgado de Primera Instancia*",
[— in France:
(a) the "greffier en chef du tribunal de grande instance",
(b) the "président de la chambre départementale des notaires" in the case of application for a declaration of enforceability of a notarial authentic instrument.]
— in Ireland, the High Court,
— in Italy, the "*Corte d'appello*",
[— in Cyprus, the "Επαρχιακό Δικαστήριο" or in the case of a maintenance judgment the "Οικογενειακό Δικαστήριο",

— in Latvia, the "rajona (pilsetas) tiesa",
— in Lithuania, the "Lietuvos apeliacinis teismas",]
— in Luxembourg, the presiding judge of the "*tribunal d'arrondissement*",
[— in Hungary, the "megyei bíróság székhelyén muködo helyi bíróság", and in Budapest the "Budai Központi Kerületi Bíróság",
— in Malta, the "Prim' Awla tal-Qorti Civili" or "Qorti tal-Magistrati ta' Ghawdex fil-gurisdizzjoni superjuri taghha", or, in the case of a maintenance judgment, the "Registratur tal-Qorti" on transmission by the "Ministru responsabbli ghall-Gustizzja",]
— [in the Netherlands, the "voorzieningenrechter van de rechtbank",]
— in Austria, the "*Bezirksgericht*",
[— in Poland, the "Sad Okregowy",]
— in Portugal, the "*Tribunal de Comarca*",
[— in Slovenia, the "okrožno sodišče",]
[— in Slovakia, the "okresný súd",]
— in Finland, the "*käräjäoikeus/tingsrätt*",
— in Sweden, the "*Svea hovrätt*",
— in the United Kingdom:
(a) in England and Wales, the High Court of Justice, or in the case of a maintenance judgment, the Magistrate's Court on transmission by the Secretary of State;
(b) in Scotland, the Court of Session, or in the case of a maintenance judgment, the Sheriff Court on transmission by the Secretary of State;
(c) in Northern Ireland, the High Court of Justice, or in the case of a maintenance judgment, the Magistrate's Court on transmission by the Secretary of State;
(d) in Gibraltar, the Supreme Court of Gibraltar, or in the case of a maintenance judgment, the Magistrates' Court on transmission by the Attorney General of Gibraltar.

[5316]

NOTES

Entries relating to the Czech Republic, Estonia, Cyprus, Latvia, Lithuania, Hungary, Malta, Poland, Slovenia and Slovakia inserted by AA5, as from 1 May 2004.

Entries relating to France, Slovenia and Slovakia substituted by Commission Regulation 2245/2004/EC, Art 1(2), as from 4 January 2005.

Entries relating to Germany and the Netherlands substituted by Commission Regulation 1496/2002/EC, Arts 2, 3, as from 29 August 2002.

ANNEX III

The courts with which appeals referred to in Article 43(2) may be lodged are the following:

— in Belgium,
(a) as regards appeal by the defendant: the "tribunal de première instance" or "rechtbank van eerste aanleg" or "erstinstanzliches Gericht",
(b) as regards appeal by the applicant: the "Cour d'appel" or "hof van beroep",
[— in the Czech Republic, the "okresní soud",]
— in the Federal Republic of Germany, the "*Oberlandesgericht*",
[— in Estonia, the "ringkonnakohus",]
— in Greece, the "Εφετείο",
— in Spain, the "*Audiencia Provincial*",
[— in France:
(a) the "cour d'appel" on decisions allowing the application,
(b) the presiding judge of the "tribunal de grande instance", on decisions rejecting the application.]
— in Ireland, the High Court,
— in Italy, the "*corte d'appello*",
[— in Cyprus, the "Επαρχιακό Δικαστήριο" or in the case of a maintenance judgment the "Οικογενειακό Δικαστήριο",
— in Latvia, the "Apgabaltiesa",
[— in Lithuania, the "Lietuvos apeliacinis teismas",]]
— in Luxembourg, the "*Cour supérieure de Justice*" sitting as a court of civil appeal,
[— in Hungary, the "megyei bíróság"; in Budapest, the "Fovárosi Bíróság",
— in Malta, the "Qorti ta' l-Appell" in accordance with the procedure laid down for appeals in the Kodici ta' Organizzazzjoni u Procedura Civili-Kap.12 or in the case

of a maintenance judgment by "citazzjoni" before the "Prim' Awla tal-Qorti ivili jew il-Qorti tal-Magistrati ta' Ghawdex fil-gurisdizzjoni superjuri taghha'",]

— in the Netherlands:
 (a) for the defendant: the "*arrondissementsrechtbank*",
 (b) for the applicant: the "*gerechtshof*",

— in Austria, the "*Bezirksgericht*",

[— in Poland, the "Sad Apelacyjny",]

— in Portugal, the "*Tribunal de Relação*",

[— in Slovenia, the "okrožno sodišče",]

[— in Slovakia, the "okresný súd",]

— in Finland, the "*hovioikeus/hovrätt*",

— in Sweden, the "*Svea hovrätt*",

— in the United Kingdom:
 (a) in England and Wales, the High Court of Justice, or in the case of a maintenance judgment, the Magistrate's Court;
 (b) in Scotland, the Court of Session, or in the case of a maintenance judgment, the Sheriff Court;
 (c) in Northern Ireland, the High Court of Justice, or in the case of a maintenance judgment, the Magistrate's Court;
 (d) in Gibraltar, the Supreme Court of Gibraltar, or in the case of a maintenance judgment, the Magistrates' Court.

[5317]

NOTES

Entries relating to the Czech Republic, Estonia, Cyprus, Latvia, Lithuania, Hungary, Malta, Poland, Slovenia and Slovakia inserted by AA5, as from 1 May 2004.

Entries relating to France, Lithuania, Slovenia and Slovakia substituted by Commission Regulation 2245/2004/EC, Art 1(3), as from 4 January 2005.

ANNEX IV

The appeals which may be lodged pursuant to Article 44 are the following

— in Belgium, Greece, Spain, France, Italy, Luxembourg and the Netherlands, an appeal in cassation,

[— in the Czech Republic, a "dovolání" and a "žaloba pro zmatecnost",]

— in Germany, a "*Rechtsbeschwerde*",

[— in Estonia, a "kassatsioonkaebus",]

— in Ireland, an appeal on a point of law to the Supreme Court,

[— in Cyprus, an appeal to the Supreme Court,

— in Latvia, an appeal to the "Augstaka tiesa",

[— in Lithuania, an appeal to the "Lietuvos Aukščiausiasis Teismas",]

— in Hungary, "felülvizsgálati kérelem",

— in Malta, no further appeal lies to any other court; in the case of a maintenance judgment the "Qorti ta' l-Appell" in accordance with the procedure laid down for appeal in the "kodici ta' Organizzazzjoni u Procedura Civili-Kap. 12",]

— in Austria, a "*Revisionsrekurs*",

[— in Poland, by an appeal in cassation to the "Sad Najwyzszy",]

— in Portugal, an appeal on a point of law,

[— in Slovenia, an appeal to the "Vrhovno sodišče Republike Slovenije",]

[— in Slovakia, the "dovolanie",]

— in Finland, an appeal to the "*korkein oikeus/högsta domstolen*",

— in Sweden, an appeal to the "*Högsta domstolen*",

— in the United Kingdom, a single further appeal on a point of law.

[5318]

NOTES

Entries relating to the Czech Republic, Estonia, Cyprus, Latvia, Lithuania, Hungary, Malta, Poland, Slovenia and Slovakia inserted by AA5, as from 1 May 2004.

Entries relating to Lithuania, Slovenia and Slovakia substituted by Commission Regulation 2245/2004/EC, Art 1(4), as from 4 January 2005.

PART VII MISCELLANEOUS

ANNEX V
CERTIFICATE REFERRED TO IN ARTICLES 54 AND 58 OF THE REGULATION ON JUDGMENTS AND COURT SETTLEMENTS

(English, inglés, anglais, inglese, …)

1. Member State of origin
2. Court or competent authority issuing the certificate
   2.1. Name
   2.2. Address
   2.3. Tel./fax/e-mail
3. Court which delivered the judgment/approved the court settlement(*)
   3.1. Type of court
   3.2. Place of court
4. Judgment/court settlement(*)
   4.1. Date
   4.2. Reference number
   4.3. The parties to the judgment/court settlement(*)
      4.3.1. Name(s) of plaintiff(s)
      4.3.2. Name(s) of defendant(s)
      4.3.3. Name(s) of other party(ies), if any
   4.4. Date of service of the document instituting the proceedings where judgment was given in default of appearance
   4.5. Text of the judgment/court settlement(*) as annexed to this certificate
5. Names of parties to whom legal aid has been granted

The judgment/court settlement(*) is enforceable in the Member State of origin (Articles 38 and 58 of the Regulation) against:

Name:

Done at .... , date ....

Signature and/or stamp ....

(*) Delete as appropriate.

[5319]

ANNEX VI
CERTIFICATE REFERRED TO IN ARTICLE 57(4) OF THE REGULATION ON AUTHENTIC INSTRUMENTS

(English, inglés, anglais, inglese, …)

1. Member State of origin
2. Competent authority issuing the certificate
   2.1. Name
   2.2. Address
   2.3. Tel./fax/e-mail
3. Authority which has given authenticity to the instrument
   3.1. Authority involved in the drawing up of the authentic instrument (if applicable)
      3.1.1. Name and designation of authority
      3.1.2. Place of authority
   3.2. Authority which has registered the authentic instrument (if applicable)
      3.2.1. Type of authority
      3.2.2. Place of authority
4. Authentic instrument
   4.1. Description of the instrument
   4.2. Date
      4.2.1. on which the instrument was drawn up
      4.2.2. if different: on which the instrument was registered
   4.3. Reference number
   4.4. Parties to the instrument
      4.4.1. Name of the creditor
      4.4.2. Name of the debtor

5. Text of the enforceable obligation as annexed to this certificate

The authentic instrument is enforceable against the debtor in the Member State of origin (Article 57(1) of the Regulation)

Done at .... , date ....

Signature and/or stamp ....

[5320]

COUNCIL DIRECTIVE

of 7 May 2002

amending and amending temporarily Directive 77/388/EEC as regards the value added tax arrangements applicable to radio and television broadcasting services and certain electronically supplied services

(2002/38/EEC)

NOTES

Date of publication in OJ: OJ L128, 15.5.2002, p 41.

THE COUNCIL OF THE EUROPEAN UNION,

Having regard to the Treaty establishing the European Community, and in particular Article 93 thereof,

Having regard to the proposal from the Commission,[1]

Having regard to the opinion of the European Parliament,[2]

Having regard to the opinion of the Economic and Social Committee,[3]

Whereas:

(1) The rules currently applicable to VAT on radio and television broadcasting services and on electronically supplied services, under Article 9 of the sixth Council Directive 77/388/EEC of 17 May 1977 on the harmonisation of the laws of the Member States relating to turnover taxes — Common system of value added tax: uniform basis of assessment,[4] are inadequate for taxing such services consumed within the Community and for preventing distortions of competition in this area.

(2) In the interests of the proper functioning of the internal market, such distortions should be eliminated and new harmonised rules introduced for this type of activity. Action should be taken to ensure, in particular, that such services where effected for consideration and consumed by customers established in the Community are taxed in the Community and are not taxed if consumed outside the Community.

(3) To this end, radio and television broadcasting services and electronically supplied services provided from third countries to persons established in the Community or from the Community to recipients established in third countries should be taxed at the place of the recipient of the services.

(4) To define electronically supplied services, examples of such services should be included in an annex to the Directive.

(5) To facilitate compliance with fiscal obligations by operators providing electronically supplied services, who are neither established nor required to be identified for tax purposes within the Community, a special scheme should be established. In applying this scheme any operator supplying such services by electronic means to non-taxable persons within the Community, may, if he is not otherwise identified for tax purposes within the Community, opt for identification in a single Member State.

(6) The non-established operator wishing to benefit from the special scheme should comply with the requirements laid down therein, and with any relevant existing provision in the Member State where the services are consumed.

(7) The Member State of identification must under certain conditions be able to exclude a non-established operator from the special scheme.

(8) Where the non-established operator opts for the special scheme, any input value added tax that he has paid with respect to goods and services used by him for the purpose of his taxed activities falling under the special scheme, should be refunded by the Member State where the input value added tax was paid, in accordance with the arrangements of the thirteenth Council Directive 86/560/EEC of 17 November 1986 on the harmonisation of the

PART VII MISCELLANEOUS

laws of the Member States relating to turnover taxes — arrangements for the refund of value added tax to taxable persons not established in Community territory.[5] The optional restrictions for refund in Article 2(2) and (3) and Article 4(2) of the same Directive should not be applied.

(9) Subject to conditions which they lay down, Member States should allow certain statements and returns to be made by electronic means, and may also require that electronic means are used.

(10) Those provisions pertaining to the introduction of electronic tax returns and statements should be adopted on a permanent basis. It is desirable to adopt all other provisions for a temporary period of three years which may be extended for practical reasons but should, in any event, based on experience, be reviewed within three years from 1 July 2003.

(11) Directive 77/388/EEC should therefore be amended accordingly,

NOTES

1 OJ C337 E, 28.11.2000, p 65.
2 OJ C232, 17.8.2001, p 202.
3 OJ C116, 20.4.2001, p 59.
4 OJ L145, 13.6.1977, p 1. Directive as last amended by Council Directive 2001/115/EC (OJ L15, 17.1.2002, p 24).
5 OJ L326, 21.11.1986, p 40.

HAS ADOPTED THIS DIRECTIVE:

Article 1

Directive 77/388/EEC is hereby temporarily amended as follows:

1. in Article 9:

(a) in paragraph (2)(e), a comma shall replace the final full stop and the following indents shall be added:

"— radio and television broadcasting services,

— electronically supplied services, inter alia, those described in Annex L."

(b) in paragraph 2, the following point shall be added:

"(f) the place where services referred to in the last indent of subparagraph (e) are supplied when performed for non-taxable persons who are established, have their permanent address or usually reside in a Member State, by a taxable person who has established his business or has a fixed establishment from which the service is supplied outside the Community or, in the absence of such a place of business or fixed establishment, has his permanent address or usually resides outside the Community, shall be the place where the non-taxable person is established, has his permanent address or usually resides."

(c) in paragraph 3, the introductory phrase shall be replaced by the following:

"3. In order to avoid double taxation, non-taxation or the distortion of competition, the Member States may, with regard to the supply of services referred to in paragraph 2(e), except for the services referred to in the last indent when supplied to non-taxable persons, and also with regard to the hiring out of forms of transport consider:"

(d) paragraph 4 shall be amended as follows:

"4. In the case of telecommunications services and radio and television broadcasting services referred to in paragraph 2(e) when performed for non-taxable persons who are established, have their permanent address or usually reside in a Member State, by a taxable person who has established his business or has a fixed establishment from which the service is supplied outside the Community, or in the absence of such a place of business or fixed establishment, has his permanent address or usually resides outside the Community, Member States shall make use of paragraph 3(b)."

2. in Article 12(3)(a), the following fourth subparagraph shall be added:

"The third subparagraph shall not apply to the services referred to in the last indent of Article 9(2)(e)."

3. the following Article shall be added:

"Article 26c

Special scheme for non-established taxable persons supplying electronic services to non-taxable persons

A. *Definitions*

For the purposes of this Article, the following definitions shall apply without prejudice to other Community provisions:

(a) "non-established taxable person" means a taxable person who has neither established his business nor has a fixed establishment within the territory of the Community and who is not otherwise required to be identified for tax purposes under Article 22;

(b) "electronic services" and "electronically supplied services" means those services referred to in the last indent of Article 9(2)(e);

(c) "Member State of identification" means the Member State which the non-established taxable person chooses to contact to state when his activity as a taxable person within the territory of the Community commences in accordance with the provisions of this Article;

(d) "Member State of consumption" means the Member State in which the supply of the electronic services is deemed to take place according to Article 9(2)(f);

(e) "value added tax return" means the statement containing the information necessary to establish the amount of tax that has become chargeable in each Member State.

B. *Special scheme for electronically supplied services*

1. Member States shall permit a non-established taxable person supplying electronic services to a non-taxable person who is established or has his permanent address or usually resides in a Member State to use a special scheme in accordance with the following provisions. The special scheme shall apply to all those supplies within the Community.

2. The non-established taxable person shall state to the Member State of identification when his activity as a taxable person commences, ceases or changes to the extent that he no longer qualifies for the special scheme. Such a statement shall be made electronically.

The information from the non-established taxable person to the Member State of identification when his taxable activities commence shall contain the following details for the identification: name, postal address, electronic addresses, including websites, national tax number, if any, and a statement that the person is not identified for value added tax purposes within the Community. The non-established taxable person shall notify the Member State of identification of any changes in the submitted information.

3. The Member State of identification shall identify the non-established taxable person by means of an individual number. Based on the information used for this identification, Member States of consumption may keep their own identification systems.

The Member State of identification shall notify the non-established taxable person by electronic means of the identification number allocated to him.

4. The Member State of identification shall exclude the non-established taxable person from the identification register if:

(a) he notifies that he no longer supplies electronic services, or

(b) it otherwise can be assumed that his taxable activities have ended, or

(c) he no longer fulfils the requirements necessary to be allowed to use the special scheme, or

(d) he persistently fails to comply with the rules concerning the special scheme.

5. The non-established taxable person shall submit by electronic means to the Member State of identification a value added tax return for each calendar quarter whether or not electronic services have been supplied. The return shall be submitted within 20 days following the end of the reporting period to which the return refers.

The value added tax return shall set out the identification number and, for each Member State of consumption where tax has become due, the total value, less value added tax, of supplies of electronic services for the reporting period and total amount of the corresponding tax. The applicable tax rates and the total tax due shall also be indicated.

PART VII MISCELLANEOUS

6. The value added tax return shall be made in euro. Member States which have not adopted the euro may require the tax return to be made in their national currencies. If the supplies have been made in other currencies, the exchange rate valid for the last date of the reporting period shall be used when completing the value added tax return. The exchange shall be done following the exchange rates published by the European Central Bank for that day, or, if there is no publication on that day, on the next day of publication.

7. The non-established taxable person shall pay the value added tax when submitting the return. Payment shall be made to a bank account denominated in euro, designated by the Member State of identification. Member States which have not adopted the euro may require the payment to be made to a bank account denominated in their own currency.

8. Notwithstanding Article 1(1) of Directive 86/560/EEC, the non-established taxable person making use of this special scheme shall, instead of making deductions under Article 17(2) of this Directive, be granted a refund according to Directive 86/560/EEC. Articles 2(2), 2(3) and 4(2) of Directive 86/560/EEC shall not apply to the refund related to electronic supplies covered by this special scheme.

9. The non-established taxable person shall keep records of the transactions covered by this special scheme in sufficient detail to enable the tax administration of the Member State of consumption to determine that the value added tax return referred to in paragraph 5 is correct. These records should be made available electronically on request to the Member State of identification and to the Member State of consumption. These records shall be maintained for a period of 10 years from the end of the year when the transaction was carried out.

10. Article 21(2)(b) shall not apply to a non-established taxable person who has opted for this special scheme."

[5321]

Article 2

Article 22, contained in Article 28h of Directive 77/388/EEC, is hereby amended as follows:

1. in paragraph 1, point (a) shall be replaced by the following:
   "(a) Every taxable person shall state when his activity as a taxable person commences, changes or ceases. Member States shall, subject to conditions which they lay down, allow the taxable person to make such statements by electronic means, and may also require that electronic means are used."
2. in paragraph 4, point (a) shall be replaced by the following:
   "(a) Every taxable person shall submit a return by a deadline to be determined by Member States. That deadline may not be more than two months later than the end of each tax period. The tax period shall be fixed by each Member State at one month, two months or a quarter. Member States may, however, set different periods provided that they do not exceed one year. Member States shall, subject to conditions which they lay down, allow the taxable person to make such returns by electronic means, and may also require that electronic means are used."
3. in paragraph 6, point (a) shall be replaced by the following:
   "(a) Member States may require a taxable person to submit a statement, including all the particulars specified in paragraph 4, concerning all transactions carried out in the preceding year. That statement shall provide all the information necessary for any adjustments. Member States shall, subject to conditions which they lay down, allow the taxable person to make such statements by electronic means, and may also require that electronic means are used."
4. in paragraph 6, the second paragraph in point (b) shall be replaced by:
"The recapitulative statement shall be drawn up for each calendar quarter within a period and in accordance with procedures to be determined by the Member States, which shall take the measures necessary to ensure that the provisions concerning administrative cooperation in the field of indirect taxation are in any event complied with. Member States shall, subject to conditions which they lay down, allow the taxable person to make such statements by electronic means, and may also require that electronic means are used."

[5322]

Article 3

1. Member States shall bring into force the laws, regulations and administrative provisions necessary to comply with this Directive on 1 July 2003. They shall forthwith inform the Commission thereof.

When Member States adopt these measures, they shall contain a reference to this Directive or shall be accompanied by such reference on the occasion of their official publication. Member States shall determine how such reference is to be made.

2. Member States shall communicate to the Commission the text of the provisions of domestic law which they adopt in the field covered by this Directive.

[5323]

[Article 4

Article 1 shall apply until 31 December 2006.]

[5324]

NOTES

Substituted by Council Directive 2006/58/EC, Art 1.

Article 5

The Council, on the basis of a report from the Commission, shall review the provisions of Article 1 of this Directive before 30 June 2006 and shall either, acting in accordance with Article 93 of the Treaty, adopt measures on an appropriate electronic mechanism on a non-discriminatory basis for charging, declaring, collecting and allocating tax revenue on electronically supplied services with taxation in the place of consumption or, if considered necessary for practical reasons, acting unanimously on the basis of a proposal from the Commission, extend the period mentioned in Article 4.

[5325]

Article 6

This Directive shall enter into force on the day of its publication in the *Official Journal of the European Communities*.

[5326]

Article 7

This Directive is addressed to the Member States.

[5327]

Done at Brussels, 7 May 2002.

ANNEX

"ANNEX L
ILLUSTRATIVE LIST OF ELECTRONICALLY SUPPLIED SERVICES REFERRED TO IN ARTICLE 9(2)(E)

1. Website supply, web-hosting, distance maintenance of programmes and equipment.

2. Supply of software and updating thereof.

3. Supply of images, text and information, and making databases available.

4. Supply of music, films and games, including games of chance and gambling games, and of political, cultural, artistic, sporting, scientific and entertainment broadcasts and events.

5. Supply of distance teaching.

Where the supplier of a service and his customer communicates via electronic mail, this shall not of itself mean that the service performed is an electronic service within the meaning of the last indent of Article 9(2)(e)."

[5328]

TREATY ON PRINCIPLES GOVERNING THE ACTIVITIES OF STATES IN THE EXPLORATION AND USE OF OUTER SPACE, INCLUDING THE MOON AND OTHER CELESTIAL BODIES

London, Moscow and Washington, 27 January 1967

Treaty Series No 10 (1968)

THE STATES PARTIES TO THIS TREATY,

Inspired by the great prospects opening up before mankind as a result of man's entry into outer space,

Recognising the common interest of all mankind in the progress of the exploration and use of outer space for peaceful purposes,

Believing that the exploration and use of outer space should be carried on for the benefit of all peoples irrespective of the degree of their economic or scientific development,

Desiring to contribute to broad international co-operation in the scientific as well as the legal aspects of the exploration and use of outer space for peaceful purposes,

Believing that such co-operation will contribute to the development of mutual understanding and to the strengthening of friendly relations between States and peoples,

Recalling resolution 1962 (XVIII), entitled "Declaration of Legal Principles Governing the Activities of States in the Exploration and Use of Outer Space", which was adopted unanimously by the United Nations General Assembly on 13 December 1963,

Recalling resolution 1884 (XVIII), calling upon States to refrain from placing in orbit around the earth any objects carrying nuclear weapons or any other kinds of weapons of mass destruction or from installing such weapons on celestial bodies, which was adopted unanimously by the United Nations General Assembly on 17 October 1963,

Taking account of United Nations General Assembly resolution 110 (II) of 3 November 1947, which condemned propaganda designed or likely to provoke or encourage any threat to the peace, breach of the peace or act of aggression, and considering that the aforementioned resolution is applicable to outer space,

Convinced that a Treaty on Principles Governing the Activities of States in the Exploration and Use of Outer Space, including the Moon and Other Celestial Bodies, will further the Purposes and Principles of the Charter of the United Nations,

HAVE AGREED ON THE FOLLOWING—

Article I

The exploration and use of outer space, including the moon and other celestial bodies, shall be carried out for the benefit and in the interests of all countries, irrespective of their degree of economic or scientific development, and shall be the province of all mankind.

Outer space, including the moon and other celestial bodies, shall be free for exploration and use by all States without discrimination of any kind, on a basis of equality and in accordance with international law, and there shall be free access to all areas of celestial bodies.

There shall be freedom of scientific investigation in outer space, including the moon and other celestial bodies, and States shall facilitate and encourage international co-operation in such investigation.

[5329]

Article II

Outer space, including the moon and other celestial bodies, is not subject to national appropriation by claim of sovereignty, by means of use or occupation, or by any other means.

[5330]

Article III

States Parties to the Treaty shall carry on activities in the exploration and use of outer space, including the moon and other celestial bodies, in accordance with international law, including the Charter of the United Nations[1] in the interest of maintaining international peace and security and promoting international co-operation and understanding.

[5331]

NOTES

[1] Treaty Series No 67 (1946), Cmd 7015.

Article IV

States Parties to the Treaty undertake not to place in orbit around the earth any objects carrying nuclear weapons or any other kinds of weapons of mass destruction, instal such weapons on celestial bodies, or station such weapons in outer space in any other manner.

The moon and other celestial bodies shall be used by all States Parties to the Treaty exclusively for peaceful purposes. The establishment of military bases, installations and fortifications, the testing of any type of weapons and the conduct of military manoeuvres on celestial bodies shall be forbidden. The use of military personnel for scientific research or for any other peaceful purposes shall not be prohibited. The use of any equipment or facility necessary for peaceful exploration of the moon and other celestial bodies shall also not be prohibited.

[5332]

Article V

States Parties to the Treaty shall regard astronauts as envoys of mankind in outer space and shall render to them all possible assistance in the event of accident, distress, or emergency landing on the territory of another State Party or on the high seas. When astronauts make such a landing, they shall be safely and promptly returned to the State of registry of their space vehicle.

In carrying on activities in outer space and on celestial bodies, the astronauts of one State Party shall render all possible assistance to the astronauts of other States Parties.

States Parties to the Treaty shall immediately inform the other States Parties to the Treaty or the Secretary-General of the United Nations of any phenomena they discover in outer space, including the moon and other celestial bodies, which could constitute a danger to the life or health of astronauts.

[5333]

Article VI

States Parties to the Treaty shall bear international responsibility for national activities in outer space, including the moon and other celestial bodies, whether such activities are carried on by governmental agencies or by non-governmental entities, and for assuring that national activities are carried out in conformity with the provisions set forth in the present Treaty. The activities of non-governmental entities in outer space, including the moon and other celestial bodies, shall require authorisation and continuing supervision by the appropriate State Party to the Treaty. When activities are carried on in outer space, including the moon and other celestial bodies, by an international organisation, responsibility for compliance with this Treaty shall be borne both by the international organisation and by the States Parties to the Treaty participating in such organisation.

[5334]

Article VII

Each State Party to the Treaty that launches or procures the launching of an object into outer space, including the moon and other celestial bodies, and each State Party from whose territory or facility an object is launched, is internationally liable for damage to another State Party to the Treaty or to its natural or juridical persons by such object or its component parts on the Earth, in air space or in outer space, including the moon and other celestial bodies.

[5335]

Article VIII

A State Party to the Treaty on whose registry an object launched into outer space is carried shall retain jurisdiction and control over such object, and over any personnel thereof, while in outer space or on a celestial body. Ownership of objects launched into outer space, including objects landed or constructed on a celestial body, and of their component parts, is not affected by their presence in outer space or on a celestial body or by their return to the Earth. Such objects or component parts found beyond the limits of the State Party to the Treaty on whose registry they are carried shall be returned to that State Party, which shall, upon request, furnish identifying data prior to their return.

[5336]

Article IX

In the exploration and use of outer space, including the moon and other celestial bodies, States Parties to the Treaty shall be guided by the principle of co-operation and mutual assistance and shall conduct all their activities in outer space, including the moon and other celestial bodies, with due regard to the corresponding interests of all other States Parties to the Treaty. States Parties to the Treaty shall pursue studies of outer space, including the moon and other celestial bodies, and conduct exploration of them so as to avoid their harmful contamination and also adverse changes in the environment of the Earth resulting from the introduction of extraterrestrial matter and, where necessary, shall adopt appropriate measures for this purpose. If a State Party to the Treaty has reason to believe that an activity or experiment planned by it or its nationals in outer space, including the moon and other celestial bodies, would cause potentially harmful interference with activities of other States Parties in the peaceful exploration and use of outer space, including the moon and other celestial bodies, it shall undertake appropriate international consultations before proceeding with any such activity or experiment. A State Party to the Treaty which has reason to believe that an activity or experiment planned by another State Party in outer space, including the moon and other celestial bodies, would cause potentially harmful interference with activities in the peaceful exploration and use of outer space, including the moon and other celestial bodies, may request consultation concerning the activity or experiment.

[5337]

Article X

In order to promote international co-operation in the exploration and use of outer space, including the moon and other celestial bodies, in conformity with the purposes of this Treaty, the States Parties to the Treaty shall consider on a basis of equality any requests by other States Parties to the Treaty to be afforded an opportunity to observe the flight of space objects launched by those States.

The nature of such an opportunity for observation and the conditions under which it could be afforded shall be determined by agreement between the States concerned.

[5338]

Article XI

In order to promote international co-operation in the peaceful exploration and use of outer space, States Parties to the Treaty conducting activities in outer space, including the moon and other celestial bodies, agree to inform the Secretary-General of the United Nations as well as the public and the international scientific community, to the greatest extent feasible and practicable, of the nature, conduct, locations and results of such activities. On receiving the said information, the Secretary-General of the United Nations should be prepared to disseminate it immediately and effectively.

[5339]

Article XII

All stations, installations, equipment and space vehicles on the moon and other celestial bodies shall be open to representatives of other States Parties to the Treaty on a basis of reciprocity. Such representatives shall give reasonable advance notice of a projected visit, in order that appropriate consultations may be held and that maximum precautions may be taken to assure safety and to avoid interference with normal operations in the facility to be visited.

[5340]

Article XIII

The provisions of this Treaty shall apply to the activities of States Parties to the Treaty in the exploration and use of outer space, including the moon and other celestial bodies, whether such activities are carried on by a single State Party to the Treaty or jointly with other States, including cases where they are carried on within the framework of international inter-governmental organisations.

Any practical questions arising in connection with activities carried on by international inter-governmental organisations in the exploration and use of outer space, including the moon and other celestial bodies, shall be resolved by the States Parties to the Treaty either with the appropriate international organisation or with one or more States members of that international organisation, which are Parties to this Treaty.

[5341]

Article XIV

1. This Treaty shall be open to all States for signature. Any State which does not sign this Treaty before its entry into force in accordance with paragraph 3 of this Article may accede to it at any time.

2. This Treaty shall be subject to ratification by signatory States. Instruments of ratification and instruments of accession shall be deposited with the Governments of the United Kingdom of Great Britain and Northern Ireland, the Union of Soviet Socialist Republics and the United States of America, which are hereby designated the Depositary Governments.

3. This Treaty shall enter into force upon the deposit of instruments of ratification by five Governments including the Governments designated as Depositary Governments under this Treaty.[1]

4. For States whose instruments of ratification or accession are deposited subsequent to the entry into force of this Treaty, it shall enter into force on the date of the deposit of their instruments of ratification or accession.

5. The Depositary Governments shall promptly inform all signatory and acceding States of the date of each signature, the date of deposit of each instrument of ratification of and accession to this Treaty, the date of its entry into force and other notices.

6. This Treaty shall be registered by the Depositary Governments pursuant to Article 102 of the Charter of the United Nations.

[5342]

NOTES

[1] The Treaty entered into force on 10 October, 1967.

Article XV

Any State Party to the Treaty may propose amendments to this Treaty. Amendments shall enter into force for each State Party to the Treaty accepting the amendments upon their acceptance by a majority of the States Parties to the Treaty and thereafter for each remaining State Party to the Treaty on the date of acceptance by it.

[5343]

Article XVI

Any State Party to the Treaty may give notice of its withdrawal from the Treaty one year after its entry into force by written notification to the Depositary Governments. Such withdrawal shall take effect one year from the date of receipt of this notification.

[5344]

Article XVII

This Treaty, of which the English, Russian, French, Spanish and Chinese texts are equally authentic, shall be deposited in the archives of the Depositary Governments. Duly certified copies of this Treaty shall be transmitted by the Depositary Governments to the Governments of the signatory and acceding States

[5345]

RATIFICATIONS DEPOSITED IN LONDON

Country	*Date of deposit*
Australia	10 October 1967
Bulgaria	19 April 1967
Canada	10 October 1967
Czechoslovakia	11 May 1967
Denmark	10 October 1967
Finland	12 July 1967

Country	Date of deposit
Hungary	26 June 1967
Japan	10 October 1967
Nepal	10 October 1967
Niger	17 April 1967
Sierra Leone	25 October 1967
Sweden	11 October 1967
Union of Soviet Socialist Republics	10 October 1967
United Kingdom[1]	10 October 1967
United States	10 October 1967

[5346]

NOTES

[1] The United Kingdom's ratification is in respect of the United Kingdom of Great Britain and Northern Ireland, the Associated States (Antigua, Dominica, Grenada, Saint Christopher-Nevis-Anguilla and Saint Lucia) and Territories under the territorial sovereignty of the United Kingdom, as well as the State of Brunei, the Kingdom of Swaziland, the Kingdom of Tonga and the British Solomon Islands Protectorate. On depositing its Instrument of Ratification the United Kingdom declared that it reserves the right not to apply the Treaty to Southern Rhodesia unless and until the United Kingdom informs the other depositary Governments that it is in a position to ensure that the obligations imposed by the Treaty in respect of that territory can be fully implemented.

ACCESSIONS DEPOSITED IN LONDON

Country	Date of deposit
Morocco	21 December 1967
Nigeria	14 November 1967

[5347]

THE FOLLOWING COUNTRIES SIGNED IN MOSCOW

Country	Date of deposit
Afghanistan	30 January 1967
Argentina	18 April 1967
Austria	20 February 1967
Belgium	27 January 1967
Brazil	30 January 1967
Bulgaria	27 January 1967
Burma	22 May 1967
Byelorussia	10 February 1967
Canada	27 January 1967
Chile	20 February 1967
Congo (Kinshasa)	29 April 1967
Cyprus	15 February 1967
Czechoslovakia	27 January 1967
Denmark	27 January 1967

Country	*Date of deposit*
Ecuador	7 June 1967
Ethiopia	10 February 1967
Finland	27 January 1967
France	25 September 1967
Federal Republic of Germany	27 January 1967
German Democratic Republic	27 January 1967
Ghana	15 February 1967
Hungary	27 January 1967
Iceland	27 January 1967
India	3 March 1967
Indonesia	30 January 1967
Iraq	9 March 1967
Israel	27 January 1967
Italy	27 January 1967
Jamaica	29 June 1967
Japan	27 January 1967
Laos	2 February 1967
Lebanon	23 February 1967
Luxembourg	27 January 1967
Malaysia	3 May 1967
Mexico	27 January 1967
Mongolia	27 January 1967
Nepal	3 February 1967
Netherlands	10 February 1967
New Zealand	27 January 1967
Norway	3 February 1967
Pakistan	12 September 1967
Philippines	29 April 1967
Poland	27 January 1967
Rumania	27 January 1967
San Marino	6 June 1967
Sierra Leone	27 January 1967
Soviet Union	27 January 1967
Sweden	27 January 1967
Switzerland	30 January 1967
Thailand	27 January 1967
Trinidad and Tobago	17 August 1967
Tunisia	15 February 1967
Turkey	27 January 1967
Ukraine	10 February 1967
United Arab Republic	27 January 1967
United Kingdom	27 January 1967
United States	27 January 1967

Country	Date of deposit
Uruguay	30 January 1967
Yugoslavia	27 January 1967

[5348]

RATIFICATIONS DEPOSITED IN MOSCOW

Country	Date of deposit
Australia	10 October 1967
Bulgaria	28 March 1967
Byelorussia	31 October 1967
Canada	10 October 1967
Czechoslovakia	18 May 1967
Denmark	10 October 1967
Finland	12 July 1967
German Democratic Republic	2 February 1967
Hungary	26 June 1967
Japan	10 October 1967
Mongolia	10 October 1967
Nepal	16 October 1967
Sierra Leone	13 July 1967
Soviet Union	10 October 1967
Sweden	11 October 1967
Ukraine	31 October 1967
United Kingdom[1]	10 October 1967
United States	10 October 1967

[5349]

NOTES

[1] See footnote 1 at para **[5346]** above.

ACCESSIONS DEPOSITED IN MOSCOW

Country	Date of deposit
Morocco	21 December 1967

[5350]

THE FOLLOWING COUNTRIES SIGNED IN WASHINGTON

Country	Date of signature
Afghanistan	27 January 1967
Argentina	27 January 1967

Country	*Date of signature*
Australia	27 January 1967
Austria	20 February 1967
Belgium	2 February 1967
Bolivia	27 January 1967
Botswana	27 January 1967
Brazil	2 February 1967
Bulgaria	27 January 1967
Burma	22 May 1967
Burundi	27 January 1967
Cameroon	27 January 1967
Canada	27 January 1967
Central African Republic	27 January 1967
Chile	27 January 1967
China	27 January 1967
Colombia	27 January 1967
Congo (Kinshasa)	27 January 1967
Cyprus	27 January 1967
Czechoslovakia	27 January 1967
Denmark	27 January 1967
Dominican Republic	27 January 1967
Ecuador	27 January 1967
El Salvador	27 January 1967
Ethiopia	27 January 1967
Finland	27 January 1967
France	25 September 1967
Federal Republic of Germany	27 January 1967
Ghana	27 January 1967
Greece	27 January 1967
Guyana	3 February 1967
Haiti	27 January 1967
Honduras	27 January 1967
Hungary	27 January 1967
Iceland	27 January 1967
India	3 March 1967
Indonesia	27 January 1967
Iraq	27 February 1967
Ireland	27 January 1967
Israel	27 January 1967
Italy	27 January 1967
Jamaica	29 June 1967
Japan	27 January 1967
Jordan	2 February 1967
Korea	27 January 1967

Country	Date of signature
Laos	27 January 1967
Lebanon	23 February 1967
Lesotho	27 January 1967
Luxembourg	27 January 1967
Malaysia	20 February 1967
Mexico	27 January 1967
Nepal	3 February 1967
Netherlands	10 February 1967
New Zealand	27 January 1967
Nicaragua	27 January 1967
Niger	1 February 1967
Norway	3 February 1967
Pakistan	12 September 1967
Panama	27 January 1967
Peru	30 June 1967
Philippines	27 January 1967
Poland	27 January 1967
Rumania	27 January 1967
Rwanda	27 January 1967
San Marino	21 April 1967
Sierra Leone	16 May 1967
Somalia	2 February 1967
South Africa	1 March 1967
Soviet Union	27 January 1967
Sweden	27 January 1967
Switzerland	27 January 1967
Thailand	27 January 1967
Togo	27 January 1967
Trinidad and Tobago	28 September 1967
Tunisia	27 January 1967
Turkey	27 January 1967
United Arab Republic	27 January 1967
United Kingdom	27 January 1967
United States	27 January 1967
Upper Volta	3 March 1967
Uruguay	27 January 1967
Venezuela	27 January 1967
Viet-Nam	27 January 1967
Yugoslavia	27 January 1967

[5351]

RATIFICATIONS DEPOSITED IN WASHINGTON

Country	*Date of deposit*
Australia	10 October 1967
Bulgaria	11 April 1967
Canada	10 October 1967
Czechoslovakia	22 May 1967
Denmark	10 October 1967
Finland	12 July 1967
Hungary	26 June 1967
Japan	10 October 1967
Republic of Korea	13 October 1967
Nepal	22 November 1967
Niger	3 May 1967
Sierra Leone	14 July 1967
Soviet Union	10 October 1967
Sweden	11 October 1967
United Arab Republic	10 October 1967
United Kingdom[1]	10 October 1967
United States	10 October 1967

[5352]

NOTES

[1] See footnote 1 at para **[5346]** above.

ACCESSION IN WASHINGTON

Country	*Date of deposit*
Morocco	22 December 1967

[5353]

UN GENERAL ASSEMBLY RESOLUTION

of 16 December 1970

International co-operation in the peaceful uses of outer space

2733 (XXV)

A

THE GENERAL ASSEMBLY,

Recalling its resolution 2453 B (XXIII) of 20 December 1968 whereby it established a Working Group of the Committee on the Peaceful Uses of Outer Space to study and report on the technical feasibility of communication by direct broadcast from satellites and the current and foreseeable developments in this field, as well as the implications of such developments in the social, cultural, legal and other areas,

PART VII MISCELLANEOUS

Taking note with appreciation of the reports prepared by the Working Group on Direct Broadcast Satellites during its three sessions,[1]

Noting that the first satellite-borne instructional television experiment for direct reception into community receivers will be undertaken in India as early as 1973/1974, thereby making it possible to enrich life in isolated communities,

Noting that the potential benefits of satellite broadcasting have particular significance with regard to better understanding among peoples, the expansion of the flow of information and the wider dissemination of knowledge in the world, and the promotion of cultural exchanges,

Recognising that the use of satellite-borne television for educational and training purposes, particularly in developing countries, can in many instances contribute towards national programmes of integration and community development and economic, social and cultural development in such areas as formal and adult education, agriculture, health and family planning,

Taking note of the concern of the Committee on the Peaceful Uses of Outer Space in considering the practical interests of all States, in particular the interests of the developing countries, regarding the efficient use of the geostationary orbit and the frequency spectrum,

Recognising that the effective deployment and use of direct satellite broadcasting requires large-scale international and regional co-operation and that further consideration may have to be given to the legal principles applicable in this field,

Endorsing the Working Group's conclusions on the applicability to such broadcasting of certain existing international legal instruments, including the Charter of the United Nations, the Treaty on Principles Governing the Activities of States in the Exploration and Use of Outer Space, including the Moon and Other Celestial Bodies and the applicable provisions of the International Telecommunication Convention[2] and Radio Regulations,

NOTES

1 *Official Records of the General Assembly, Twenty-fourth Session, Supplement No 21A* (A/7621/Add.1), annexes III and IV; and *ibid, Twenty fifth Session, Supplement No 20* (A/8020), paras 48–59.

2 Signed at Montreux on 12 November 1965.

1. *Recommends,* on the basis of the probable patterns of use of satellite broadcasting systems outlined by the Working Group on Direct Broadcast Satellites of the Committee on the Peaceful Uses of Outer Space, that Member States, regional and international organisations, including broadcasting associations, should promote and encourage international co-operation at regional and other levels in order, *inter alia,* to allow all participating parties to share in the establishment and operation of regional satellite broadcasting services and/or in programme planning and production;

2. *Draws the attention* of Member States, specialised agencies and other interested international organisations to the potential benefits to be derived from direct broadcast satellite services, especially in developing countries, for improving their telecommunications infrastructure, thereby contributing to general economic and social development;

3. *Recommends,* with a view to making available the benefits of this new technology to countries, regardless of the degree of their social and economic development, that Member States, the United Nations Development Programme and other international agencies should promote international co-operation in this field in order to assist interested countries to develop the skills and techniques that may be necessary for its application;

4. *Requests* the Committee on the Peaceful Uses of Outer Space to keep under review the question of reconvening the Working Group on Direct Broadcast Satellites at such time as additional material of substance on which further useful studies might be based may have become available;

5. *Recommends* that the Committee on the Peaceful Uses of Outer Space should study through its Legal Sub-Committee, giving priority to the convention on liability, the work carried out by the Working Group on Direct Broadcast Satellites, under the item on the implications of space communications;

6. *Invites* the International Telecommunication Union to continue to take the necessary steps to promote the use of satellite broadcasting services by Member States and to consider at the 1971 World Administrative Radio Conference for Space Telecommunications the appropriate provisions under which satellite broadcasting services may be established;

7. *Requests* the International Telecommunication Union to transmit, when available, to the Committee on the Peaceful Uses of Outer Space all information about the use of the geostationary orbit and the frequency spectrum;

8. *Invites* the United Nations Educational, Scientific and Cultural Organisation to continue to promote the use of satellite broadcasting for the advancement of education and training, science and culture and, in consultation with appropriate intergovernmental and non-governmental organisations and broadcasting associations, to direct its efforts towards the solution of problems falling within its mandate.

1932nd plenary meeting,
16 December 1970.

[5354]

B

THE GENERAL ASSEMBLY,

Recognising the importance of international co-operation in developing the rule of law in the exploration and peaceful uses of outer space,

Recalling that, in its resolutions 1963 (XVIII) of 13 December 1963, 2130 (XX) of 21 December 1965 and 2222 (XXI) of 19 December 1966, it requested the Committee on the Peaceful Uses of Outer Space to prepare a draft convention on liability for damage caused by objects launched into outer space,

Recalling that in its resolution 2345 (XXII) of 19 December 1967, in which it commended the Agreement on the Rescue of Astronauts, the Return of Astronauts and the Return of Objects Launched into Outer Space, it also called upon the Committee on the Peaceful Uses of Outer Space to complete urgently the draft convention on liability,

Recalling also its resolution 2453 B (XXIII) of 20 December 1968, in which it requested the Committee on the Peaceful Uses of Outer Space to complete urgently the draft convention on liability and to submit it to the General Assembly at its twenty-fourth session,

Recalling further its resolution 2601 B (XXIV) of 16 December 1969, in which it urged the Committee on the Peaceful Uses of Outer Space to complete the draft convention on liability in time for final consideration by the General Assembly during its twenty-fifth session and emphasised that the convention was intended to establish international rules and procedures concerning liability for damage caused by the launching of objects into outer space and to ensure, in particular, prompt and equitable compensation for damage,

Affirming that until an effective convention is concluded an unsatisfactory situation will exist in which the remedies for damage caused by space objects are inadequate for the needs of the nations and peoples of the world,

Aware that various proposals have been submitted to the Committee on the Peaceful Uses of Outer Space and that a number of provisions have been agreed upon, although subject to certain conditions and reservations, in its Legal Sub-Committee,

1. *Takes note* of the efforts made by the Committee on the Peaceful Uses of Outer Space and its Legal Sub-Committee at their sessions in 1970 to complete the preparation of a draft convention on liability,[1] for submission to the General Assembly at its current session;

NOTES

1 See *Official Records of the General Assembly, Twenty-fifth Session, Supplement No 20* (A/8020), annex IV.

2. *Expresses its deep regret* that, notwithstanding some progress towards this objective, the Committee on the Peaceful Uses of Outer Space has not yet been able to complete the drafting of a convention on liability, a subject which it has had under consideration for the past seven years;

3. *Affirms* that the early conclusion of an effective and generally acceptable convention on liability should remain the firm priority task of the Committee on the Peaceful Uses of Outer Space and urges the Committee to intensify its efforts to reach agreement;

4. *Notes* in this connexion that the main obstacle to agreement lies in differences of opinion within the Committee on the Peaceful Uses of Outer Space on two main issues: the legal rules to be applied for determining compensation payable to the victims of damage and the procedures for the settlement of claims;

5. *Expresses the view* that a condition of a satisfactory convention on liability is that it should contain provisions which would ensure the payment of a full measure of compensation to victims and effective procedures which would lead to the prompt and equitable settlement of claims;

6. *Urges* the Committee on the Peaceful Uses of Outer Space to make a decisive effort to reach early agreement on texts embodying the principles outlined in paragraph 5 above with a view to submitting a draft convention on liability to the General Assembly at its twenty-sixth session.

1932nd plenary meeting,
16 December 1970.

[5355]

C

THE GENERAL ASSEMBLY,

Recalling its resolutions 2600 (XXIV) and 2601 (XXIV) of 16 December 1969,

Having considered the report of the Committee on the Peaceful Uses of Outer Space,[1]

Reaffirming the common interest of mankind in furthering the exploration and use of outer space for peaceful purposes,

Recognising the importance of international co-operation in developing the rule of law in the exploration and peaceful uses of outer space,

Convinced of the need for increased efforts to promote applications of space technology for the benefit of all countries, particularly the developing countries,

Believing that the benefits of space exploration can be extended to States at all stages of economic and scientific development if Member States conduct their space programmes in a manner designed to promote the maximum international co-operation, including the widest possible exchange and practical application of information in this field,

NOTES

1 *Official Records of the General Assembly, Twenty fifth Session, Supplement No 20* (A/8020).

1. *Endorses* the recommendations and decisions contained in the report of the Committee on the Peaceful Uses of Outer Space;

2. *Requests* the Committee on the Peaceful Uses of Outer Space to continue to study questions relative to the definition of outer space and the utilisation of outer space and celestial bodies, including various implications of space communications, as well as those comments which may be brought to the attention of the Committee by specialised agencies and the International Atomic Energy Agency as a result of their examination of problems that have arisen or that may arise from the use of outer space in the fields within their competence;

3. *Invites* those States which have not yet become parties to the Treaty on Principles Governing the Activities of States in the Exploration and Use of Outer Space, including the Moon and Other Celestial Bodies and the Agreement on the Rescue of Astronauts, the Return of Astronauts and the Return of Objects Launched into Outer Space to give consideration to ratifying or acceding to those agreements so that they may have the broadest possible effect;

4. *Reaffirms its belief,* as expressed in its resolution 1721 D (XVI) of 20 December 1961, that communication by means of satellites should be available to the nations of the world as soon as practicable on a global and non-discriminatory basis, and recommends that States parties to negotiations regarding international arrangements in the field of satellite communication should constantly bear this principle in mind so that its ultimate realisation may be achieved;

5. *Welcomes* the intensified efforts of the Committee on the Peaceful Uses of Outer Space to encourage international programmes to promote such practical applications of space technology as earth resources surveying, for the benefit of both developed and developing countries, and commends to the attention of Member States, specialised agencies and interested United Nations bodies the new programmes and proposals to promote international benefits from space applications noted by the Committee in its report, such as the organisation of technical panels, the utilisation of internationally sponsored education and training

opportunities in the practical applications of space technology and the conduct of experiments in the transfer of space-generated technology to non-space applications;

6. *Takes note* of the recommendation of the Scientific and Technical Sub-Committee of the Committee on the Peaceful Uses of Outer Space that the travel and subsistence of participants in the technical panels mentioned in paragraph 5 above should be funded by their own Governments, but that the United Nations may give timely assistance in exceptional cases within the existing programmes of the United Nations where this appears necessary both to defray costs and to stimulate interest in special areas;

7. *Welcomes* the efforts of Member States to share with other interested Member States the practical benefits which may be derived from their programmes in space technology, including earth resources surveying;

8. *Requests* the Scientific and Technical Sub-Committee, as authorised by the Committee on the Peaceful Uses of Outer Space, to determine at its next session whether, at what time and in what specific frame of reference to convene a working group on earth resources surveying, with special reference to satellites, and in so doing to take into account the importance of appropriate co-ordination with the Committee on Natural Resources, established under Economic and Social Council resolution 1535 (XLIX) of 27 July 1970;

9. *Welcomes* the efforts of Member States to keep the Committee on the Peaceful Uses of Outer Space fully informed of their activities and invites all Member States to do so;

10. *Notes with appreciation* the report of the Expert on Applications of Space Technology concerning the promotion of space applications;[1]

NOTES

1 *Official Records of the General Assembly, Twenty fifth Session, Supplement No 20* (A/8020), annex II.

11. *Recalls* the recommendation[1] that Member States give consideration to designating specific offices or individuals, within their Governments, as a point of contact for communications regarding the promotion of the application of space technology and thereafter inform the Secretary-General of such designations, and urges those Member States which have not yet designated a point of contact to do so;

NOTES

1 *Official Records of the General Assembly, Twenty-fourth Session, Supplement No 21A* (A7621Add.1), annex II, para 25.

12. *Takes note* of the report provided by the Secretary-General to the Committee on the Peaceful Uses of Outer Space concerning improved co-ordination of Secretariat activities in the field of outer space;[1]

NOTES

1 *Official Records of the General Assembly, Twenty-fifth Session, Supplement No 20* (A/8020), annex III.

13. *Endorses* the suggestion of the Scientific and Technical Sub-Committee that the Secretary-General should bring to the attention of Member States all relevant documents relating to applications of space technology submitted to the Sub-Committee by Member States, the United Nations, the specialised agencies and other bodies;

14. *Approves* the continuing sponsorship by the United Nations of the Thumba Equatorial Rocket Launching Station and the CELPA Mar del Plata Station and recommends that Member States should give consideration to the use of these facilities for appropriate space research activities;

15. *Notes* that, in accordance with General Assembly resolution 1721 B (XVI) of 20 December 1961, the Secretary-General continues to maintain a public registry of objects launched into orbit or beyond on the basis of information furnished by Member States;

16. *Endorses* the recommendation of the Committee on the Peaceful Uses of Outer Space that the Secretary-General be requested to issue an index of existing internatio[nal] instruments—conventions, treaties and agreements—relating to or bearing upon broadca[st] satellite services;

17. *Requests* the specialised agencies and the International Atomic Energy Agency to furnish the Committee on the Peaceful Uses of Outer Space with progress reports on their work in the field of the peaceful uses of outer space, and to examine and report to the Committee on the particular problems which arise or may arise from the use of outer space in the fields within their competence and which should in their opinion be brought to the attention of the Committee;

18. *Requests* the Committee on the Peaceful Uses of Outer Space to continue its work as set out in the present resolution and in previous resolutions of the General Assembly, and to report to the Assembly at its twenty-sixth session.

1932nd plenary meeting,
16 December 1970.

[5356]

D

THE GENERAL ASSEMBLY,

Concerned over the devastating and harmful effects of typhoons and storms in various parts of the world, particularly in Asia,

Believing that man's present scientific and technical capabilities that have conquered space could help conquer this environmental scourge,

Recalling its resolutions 1721 (XVI) of 20 December 1961 and 1802 (XVII) of 14 December 1962, and noting the work being undertaken and progress achieved in response to them, as indicated by the World Meteorological Organisation in its annual reports to the Committee on the Peaceful Uses of Outer Space,

Noting further the co-ordinating role in this field of the joint Typhoon Committee of the World Meteorological Organisation and the Economic Commission for Asia and the Far East, the discussions on this subject held in that forum and the recent decision to transfer the Typhoon Committee secretariat to Manila,

1. Recommends that the World Meteorological Organisation take, if necessary, further appropriate action for mobilising capable scientists, technologists and other pertinent resources from any or all nations with a view to obtaining basic meteorological data and discovering ways and means of mitigating the harmful effects of these storms and removing or minimising their destructive potentials;

2. *Calls upon* Member States to exert efforts within their means to implement fully the World Weather Watch plan of the World Meteorological Organisation;

3. *Requests* the World Meteorological Organisation to submit a report through the Secretary-General to the Committee on the Peaceful Uses of Outer Space at its next session, and to such other United Nations bodies as may be appropriate, on the steps taken pursuant to the present and other resolutions.

1932nd plenary meeting,
16 December 1970.

[5357]

CONVENTION ON CYBERCRIME

Budapest, 23.XI.2001

(European Treaty Series No 185)

…es of the Council of Europe and the other States signatory hereto,

… the aim of the Council of Europe is to achieve a greater unity between its

… value of fostering co-operation with the other States parties to this

Convinced of the need to pursue, as a matter of priority, a common criminal policy aimed at the protection of society against cybercrime, *inter alia*, by adopting appropriate legislation and fostering international co-operation;

Conscious of the profound changes brought about by the digitalisation, convergence and continuing globalisation of computer networks;

Concerned by the risk that computer networks and electronic information may also be used for committing criminal offences and that evidence relating to such offences may be stored and transferred by these networks;

Recognising the need for co-operation between States and private industry in combating cybercrime and the need to protect legitimate interests in the use and development of information technologies;

Believing that an effective fight against cybercrime requires increased, rapid and well-functioning international co-operation in criminal matters;

Convinced that the present Convention is necessary to deter action directed against the confidentiality, integrity and availability of computer systems, networks and computer data as well as the misuse of such systems, networks and data by providing for the criminalisation of such conduct, as described in this Convention, and the adoption of powers sufficient for effectively combating such criminal offences, by facilitating their detection, investigation and prosecution at both the domestic and international levels and by providing arrangements for fast and reliable international co-operation;

Mindful of the need to ensure a proper balance between the interests of law enforcement and respect for fundamental human rights as enshrined in the 1950 Council of Europe Convention for the Protection of Human Rights and Fundamental Freedoms, the 1966 United Nations International Covenant on Civil and Political Rights and other applicable international human rights treaties, which reaffirm the right of everyone to hold opinions without interference, as well as the right to freedom of expression, including the freedom to seek, receive, and impart information and ideas of all kinds, regardless of frontiers, and the rights concerning the respect for privacy;

Mindful also of the right to the protection of personal data, as conferred, for example, by the 1981 Council of Europe Convention for the Protection of Individuals with regard to Automatic Processing of Personal Data;

Considering the 1989 United Nations Convention on the Rights of the Child and the 1999 International Labour Organisation Worst Forms of Child Labour Convention;

Taking into account the existing Council of Europe conventions on co-operation in the penal field, as well as similar treaties which exist between Council of Europe member States and other States, and stressing that the present Convention is intended to supplement those conventions in order to make criminal investigations and proceedings concerning criminal offences related to computer systems and data more effective and to enable the collection of evidence in electronic form of a criminal offence;

Welcoming recent developments which further advance international understanding and cooperation in combating cybercrime, including action taken by the United Nations, the OECD, the European Union and the G8;

Recalling Committee of Ministers Recommendations No R (85) 10 concerning the practical application of the European Convention on Mutual Assistance in Criminal Matters in respect of letters rogatory for the interception of telecommunications, No R (88) 2 on piracy in the field of copyright and neighbouring rights, No R (87) 15 regulating the use of personal data in the police sector, No R (95) 4 on the protection of personal data in the area of telecommunication services, with particular reference to telephone services, as well as No R (89) 9 on computer-related crime providing guidelines for national legislatures concerning the definition of certain computer crimes and No R (95) 13 concerning problems of criminal procedural law connected with information technology;

Having regard to Resolution No 1 adopted by the European Ministers of Justice at their 21st Conference (Prague, 10 and 11 June 1997), which recommended that the Committee of Ministers support the work on cybercrime carried out by the European Committee on Crime Problems (CDPC) in order to bring domestic criminal law provisions closer to each other and enable the use of effective means of investigation into such offences, as well as to Resolution No 3 adopted at the 23rd Conference of the European Ministers of Justice (London, 8 and 9 June 2000), which encouraged the negotiating parties to pursue their efforts with a view to finding appropriate solutions to enable the largest possible number of States to become parties to the Convention and acknowledged the need for a swift and efficient system of international co-operation, which duly takes into account the specific requirements of the fight against cybercrime;

Having also regard to the Action Plan adopted by the Heads of State and Government of the Council of Europe on the occasion of their Second Summit (Strasbourg, 10 and 11 October 1997), to seek common responses to the development of the new information technologies based on the standards and values of the Council of Europe;

Have agreed as follows—

CHAPTER I
USE OF TERMS

Article 1

Definitions

For the purposes of this Convention—

(a) "computer system" means any device or a group of interconnected or related devices, one or more of which, pursuant to a program, performs automatic processing of data;

(b) "computer data" means any representation of facts, information or concepts in a form suitable for processing in a computer system, including a program suitable to cause a computer system to perform a function;

(c) "service provider" means—

(i) any public or private entity that provides to users of its service the ability to communicate by means of a computer system, and

(ii) any other entity that processes or stores computer data on behalf of such communication service or users of such service;

(d) "traffic data" means any computer data relating to a communication by means of a computer system, generated by a computer system that formed a part in the chain of communication, indicating the communication's origin, destination, route, time, date, size, duration, or type of underlying service.

[5358]

CHAPTER II
MEASURES TO BE TAKEN AT THE NATIONAL LEVEL

SECTION 1—SUBSTANTIVE CRIMINAL LAW

TITLE 1—OFFENCES AGAINST THE CONFIDENTIALITY, INTEGRITY AND AVAILABILITY OF COMPUTER DATA AND SYSTEMS

Article 2

Illegal access

Each Party shall adopt such legislative and other measures as may be necessary to establish as criminal offences under its domestic law, when committed intentionally, the access to the whole or any part of a computer system without right. A Party may require that the offence be committed by infringing security measures, with the intent of obtaining computer data or other dishonest intent, or in relation to a computer system that is connected to another computer system.

Article 3

Illegal interception

Each Party shall adopt such legislative and other measures as may be necessary to establish as criminal offences under its domestic law, when committed intentionally, the interception without right, made by technical means, of non-public transmissions of computer data to, from or within a computer system, including electromagnetic emissions from a computer system carrying such computer data. A Party may require that the offence be committed with dishonest intent, or in relation to a computer system that is connected to another computer system.

Article 4

Data interference

1. Each Party shall adopt such legislative and other measures as may be necessary to establish as criminal offences under its domestic law, when committed intentionally, the damaging, deletion, deterioration, alteration or suppression of computer data without right.

2. A Party may reserve the right to require that the conduct described in paragraph 1 result in serious harm.

Article 5

System interference

Each Party shall adopt such legislative and other measures as may be necessary to establish as criminal offences under its domestic law, when committed intentionally, the serious hindering without right of the functioning of a computer system by inputting, transmitting, damaging, deleting, deteriorating, altering or suppressing computer data.

Article 6

Misuse of devices

1. Each Party shall adopt such legislative and other measures as may be necessary to establish as criminal offences under its domestic law, when committed intentionally and without right—

(a) the production, sale, procurement for use, import, distribution or otherwise making available of—

(i) a device, including a computer program, designed or adapted primarily for the purpose of committing any of the offences established in accordance with the above Articles 2–5;

(ii) a computer password, access code, or similar data by which the whole or any part of a computer system is capable of being accessed,

with intent that it be used for the purpose of committing any of the offences established in Articles 2–5; and

(b) the possession of an item referred to in paragraphs (a)(i) or (ii) above, with intent that it be used for the purpose of committing any of the offences established in Articles 2–5. A Party may require by law that a number of such items be possessed before criminal liability attaches.

2. This article shall not be interpreted as imposing criminal liability where the production, sale, procurement for use, import, distribution or otherwise making available or possession referred to in paragraph 1 of this article is not for the purpose of committing an offence established in accordance with Articles 2–5 of this Convention, such as for the authorised testing or protection of a computer system.

3. Each Party may reserve the right not to apply paragraph 1 of this article, provided that the reservation does not concern the sale, distribution or otherwise making available of the items referred to in paragraph 1(a)(ii) of this article.

TITLE 2—COMPUTER-RELATED OFFENCES

Article 7

Computer-related forgery

Each Party shall adopt such legislative and other measures as may be necessary to establish as criminal offences under its domestic law, when committed intentionally and without right, the input, alteration, deletion, or suppression of computer data, resulting in inauthentic data with the intent that it be considered or acted upon for legal purposes as if it were authentic, regardless whether or not the data is directly readable and intelligible. A Party may require an intent to defraud, or similar dishonest intent, before criminal liability attaches.

Article 8

Computer-related fraud

Each Party shall adopt such legislative and other measures as may be necessary to establish as criminal offences under its domestic law, when committed intentionally and without right, the causing of a loss of property to another person by—

(a) any input, alteration, deletion or suppression of computer data;

(b) any interference with the functioning of a computer system,

with fraudulent or dishonest intent of procuring, without right, an economic benefit for oneself or for another person.

TITLE 3—CONTENT-RELATED OFFENCES

Article 9

Offences related to child pornography

1. Each Party shall adopt such legislative and other measures as may be necessary to establish as criminal offences under its domestic law, when committed intentionally and without right, the following conduct—

(a) producing child pornography for the purpose of its distribution through a computer system;
(b) offering or making available child pornography through a computer system;
(c) distributing or transmitting child pornography through a computer system;
(d) procuring child pornography through a computer system for oneself or for another person;
(e) possessing child pornography in a computer system or on a computer-data storage medium.

2. For the purpose of paragraph 1 above, the term "child pornography" shall include pornographic material that visually depicts—

(a) a minor engaged in sexually explicit conduct;
(b) a person appearing to be a minor engaged in sexually explicit conduct;
(c) realistic images representing a minor engaged in sexually explicit conduct.

3. For the purpose of paragraph 2 above, the term "minor" shall include all persons under 18 years of age. A Party may, however, require a lower age-limit, which shall be not less than 16 years.

4. Each Party may reserve the right not to apply, in whole or in part, paragraphs 1, sub-paragraphs (d) and (e), and 2, sub-paragraphs (b) and (c).

TITLE 4—OFFENCES RELATED TO INFRINGEMENTS OF COPYRIGHT AND RELATED RIGHTS

Article 10

Offences related to infringements of copyright and related rights

1. Each Party shall adopt such legislative and other measures as may be necessary to establish as criminal offences under its domestic law the infringement of copyright, as defined under the law of that Party, pursuant to the obligations it has undertaken under the Paris Act of 24 July 1971 revising the Bern Convention for the Protection of Literary and Artistic Works, the Agreement on Trade-Related Aspects of Intellectual Property Rights and the WIPO Copyright Treaty, with the exception of any moral rights conferred by such conventions, where such acts are committed wilfully, on a commercial scale and by means of a computer system.

2. Each Party shall adopt such legislative and other measures as may be necessary to establish as criminal offences under its domestic law the infringement of related rights, as defined under the law of that Party, pursuant to the obligations it has undertaken under the International Convention for the Protection of Performers, Producers of Phonograms and Broadcasting Organisations (Rome Convention), the Agreement on Trade-Related Aspects of Intellectual Property Rights and the WIPO Performances and Phonograms Treaty, with the exception of any moral rights conferred by such conventions, where such acts are committed wilfully, on a commercial scale and by means of a computer system.

3. A Party may reserve the right not to impose criminal liability under paragraphs 1 and 2 of this article in limited circumstances, provided that other effective remedies are available and that such reservation does not derogate from the Party's international obligations set forth in the international instruments referred to in paragraphs 1 and 2 of this article.

TITLE 5—ANCILLARY LIABILITY AND SANCTIONS

Article 11

Attempt and aiding or abetting

1. Each Party shall adopt such legislative and other measures as may be necessary to establish as criminal offences under its domestic law, when committed intentionally, aiding or

abetting the commission of any of the offences established in accordance with Articles 2–10 of the present Convention with intent that such offence be committed.

2. Each Party shall adopt such legislative and other measures as may be necessary to establish as criminal offences under its domestic law, when committed intentionally, an attempt to commit any of the offences established in accordance with Articles 3–5, 7, 8, and 9.1(a) and (c) of this Convention.

3. Each Party may reserve the right not to apply, in whole or in part, paragraph 2 of this article.

Article 12

Corporate liability

1. Each Party shall adopt such legislative and other measures as may be necessary to ensure that legal persons can be held liable for a criminal offence established in accordance with this Convention, committed for their benefit by any natural person, acting either individually or as part of an organ of the legal person, who has a leading position within it, based on—

(a) a power of representation of the legal person;
(b) an authority to take decisions on behalf of the legal person;
(c) an authority to exercise control within the legal person.

2. In addition to the cases already provided for in paragraph 1 of this article, each Party shall take the measures necessary to ensure that a legal person can be held liable where the lack of supervision or control by a natural person referred to in paragraph 1 has made possible the commission of a criminal offence established in accordance with this Convention for the benefit of that legal person by a natural person acting under its authority.

3. Subject to the legal principles of the Party, the liability of a legal person may be criminal, civil or administrative.

4. Such liability shall be without prejudice to the criminal liability of the natural persons who have committed the offence.

Article 13

Sanctions and measures

1. Each Party shall adopt such legislative and other measures as may be necessary to ensure that the criminal offences established in accordance with Articles 2–11 are punishable by effective, proportionate and dissuasive sanctions, which include deprivation of liberty.

2. Each Party shall ensure that legal persons held liable in accordance with Article 12 shall be subject to effective, proportionate and dissuasive criminal or non-criminal sanctions or measures, including monetary sanctions.

SECTION 2—PROCEDURAL LAW

TITLE 1—COMMON PROVISIONS

Article 14

Scope of procedural provisions

1. Each Party shall adopt such legislative and other measures as may be necessary to establish the powers and procedures provided for in this section for the purpose of specific criminal investigations or proceedings.

2. Except as specifically provided otherwise in Article 21, each Party shall apply the powers and procedures referred to in paragraph 1 of this article to—

(a) the criminal offences established in accordance with Articles 2–11 of this Convention;
(b) other criminal offences committed by means of a computer system; and
(c) the collection of evidence in electronic form of a criminal offence.

3.

(a) Each Party may reserve the right to apply the measures referred to in Article 20 only to offences or categories of offences specified in the reservation, provided that the range of such offences or categories of offences is not more restricted than the range of offences to which it applies the measures referred to in Article 21. Each Party shall consider restricting such a reservation to enable the broadest application of the measure referred to in Article 20.

(b) Where a Party, due to limitations in its legislation in force at the time of the adoption of the present Convention, is not able to apply the measures referred to in Articles 20 and 21 to communications being transmitted within a computer system of a service provider, which system—
   (i) is being operated for the benefit of a closed group of users, and
   (ii) does not employ public communications networks and is not connected with another computer system, whether public or private,

that Party may reserve the right not to apply these measures to such communications. Each Party shall consider restricting such a reservation to enable the broadest application of the measures referred to in Articles 20 and 21.

Article 15

Conditions and safeguards

1. Each Party shall ensure that the establishment, implementation and application of the powers and procedures provided for in this Section are subject to conditions and safeguards provided for under its domestic law, which shall provide for the adequate protection of human rights and liberties, including rights arising pursuant to obligations it has undertaken under the 1950 Council of Europe Convention for the Protection of Human Rights and Fundamental Freedoms, the 1966 United Nations International Covenant on Civil and Political Rights, and other applicable international human rights instruments, and which shall incorporate the principle of proportionality.

2. Such conditions and safeguards shall, as appropriate in view of the nature of the procedure or power concerned, *inter alia*, include judicial or other independent supervision, grounds justifying application, and limitation of the scope and the duration of such power or procedure.

3. To the extent that it is consistent with the public interest, in particular the sound administration of justice, each Party shall consider the impact of the powers and procedures in this section upon the rights, responsibilities and legitimate interests of third parties.

TITLE 2—EXPEDITED PRESERVATION OF STORED COMPUTER DATA

Article 16

Expedited preservation of stored computer data

1. Each Party shall adopt such legislative and other measures as may be necessary to enable its competent authorities to order or similarly obtain the expeditious preservation of specified computer data, including traffic data, that has been stored by means of a computer system, in particular where there are grounds to believe that the computer data is particularly vulnerable to loss or modification.

2. Where a Party gives effect to paragraph 1 above by means of an order to a person to preserve specified stored computer data in the person's possession or control, the Party shall adopt such legislative and other measures as may be necessary to oblige that person to preserve and maintain the integrity of that computer data for a period of time as long as necessary, up to a maximum of ninety days, to enable the competent authorities to seek its disclosure. A Party may provide for such an order to be subsequently renewed.

3. Each Party shall adopt such legislative and other measures as may be necessary to oblige the custodian or other person who is to preserve the computer data to keep confidential the undertaking of such procedures for the period of time provided for by its domestic law.

4. The powers and procedures referred to in this article shall be subject to Articles 14 and 15.

Article 17

Expedited preservation and partial disclosure of traffic data

1. Each Party shall adopt, in respect of traffic data that is to be preserved under Article 16, such legislative and other measures as may be necessary to—

(a) ensure that such expeditious preservation of traffic data is available regardless of whether one or more service providers were involved in the transmission of that communication; and

(b) ensure the expeditious disclosure to the Party's competent authority, or a person designated by that authority, of a sufficient amount of traffic data to enable the Party to identify the service providers and the path through which the communication was transmitted.

2. The powers and procedures referred to in this article shall be subject to Articles 14 and 15.

TITLE 3—PRODUCTION ORDER

Article 18

Production order

1. Each Party shall adopt such legislative and other measures as may be necessary to empower its competent authorities to order—

(a) a person in its territory to submit specified computer data in that person's possession or control, which is stored in a computer system or a computer-data storage medium; and

(b) a service provider offering its services in the territory of the Party to submit subscriber information relating to such services in that service provider's possession or control.

2. The powers and procedures referred to in this article shall be subject to Articles 14 and 15.

3. For the purpose of this article, the term "subscriber information" means any information contained in the form of computer data or any other form that is held by a service provider, relating to subscribers of its services other than traffic or content data and by which can be established—

(a) the type of communication service used, the technical provisions taken thereto and the period of service;

(b) the subscriber's identity, postal or geographic address, telephone and other access number, billing and payment information, available on the basis of the service agreement or arrangement;

(c) any other information on the site of the installation of communication equipment, available on the basis of the service agreement or arrangement.

TITLE 4—SEARCH AND SEIZURE OF STORED COMPUTER DATA

Article 19

Search and seizure of stored computer data

1. Each Party shall adopt such legislative and other measures as may be necessary to empower its competent authorities to search or similarly access—

(a) a computer system or part of it and computer data stored therein; and

(b) a computer-data storage medium in which computer data may be stored in its territory.

2. Each Party shall adopt such legislative and other measures as may be necessary to ensure that where its authorities search or similarly access a specific computer system or part of it, pursuant to paragraph 1(a), and have grounds to believe that the data sought is stored in another computer system or part of it in its territory, and such data is lawfully accessible from or available to the initial system, the authorities shall be able to expeditiously extend the search or similar accessing to the other system.

3. Each Party shall adopt such legislative and other measures as may be necessary to empower its competent authorities to seize or similarly secure computer data accessed according to paragraphs 1 or 2. These measures shall include the power to—

(a) seize or similarly secure a computer system or part of it or a computer-data storage medium;

(b) make and retain a copy of those computer data;

(c) maintain the integrity of the relevant stored computer data;

(d) render inaccessible or remove those computer data in the accessed computer system.

4. Each Party shall adopt such legislative and other measures as may be necessary to empower its competent authorities to order any person who has knowledge about the functioning of the computer system or measures applied to protect the computer data therein to provide, as is reasonable, the necessary information, to enable the undertaking of the measures referred to in paragraphs 1 and 2.

5. The powers and procedures referred to in this article shall be subject to Articles 14 and 15.

TITLE 5—REAL-TIME COLLECTION OF COMPUTER DATA

Article 20

Real-time collection of traffic data

1. Each Party shall adopt such legislative and other measures as may be necessary to empower its competent authorities to—

(a) collect or record through the application of technical means on the territory of that Party, and

(b) compel a service provider, within its existing technical capability—

(i) to collect or record through the application of technical means on the territory of that Party; or

(ii) to co-operate and assist the competent authorities in the collection or recording of,

traffic data, in real-time, associated with specified communications in its territory transmitted by means of a computer system.

2. Where a Party, due to the established principles of its domestic legal system, cannot adopt the measures referred to in paragraph 1(a), it may instead adopt legislative and other measures as may be necessary to ensure the real-time collection or recording of traffic data associated with specified communications transmitted in its territory, through the application of technical means on that territory.

3. Each Party shall adopt such legislative and other measures as may be necessary to oblige a service provider to keep confidential the fact of the execution of any power provided for in this article and any information relating to it.

4. The powers and procedures referred to in this article shall be subject to Articles 14 and 15.

Article 21

Interception of content data

1. Each Party shall adopt such legislative and other measures as may be necessary, in relation to a range of serious offences to be determined by domestic law, to empower its competent authorities to—

(a) collect or record through the application of technical means on the territory of that Party, and

(b) compel a service provider, within its existing technical capability—

(i) to collect or record through the application of technical means on the territory of that Party, or

(ii) to co-operate and assist the competent authorities in the collection or recording of,

content data, in real-time, of specified communications in its territory transmitted by means of a computer system.

2. Where a Party, due to the established principles of its domestic legal system, cannot adopt the measures referred to in paragraph 1(a), it may instead adopt legislative and other measures as may be necessary to ensure the real-time collection or recording of content data on specified communications in its territory through the application of technical means on that territory.

3. Each Party shall adopt such legislative and other measures as may be necessary to oblige a service provider to keep confidential the fact of the execution of any power provided for in this article and any information relating to it.

4. The powers and procedures referred to in this article shall be subject to Articles 14 and 15.

SECTION 3—JURISDICTION

Article 22

Jurisdiction

1. Each Party shall adopt such legislative and other measures as may be necessary to establish jurisdiction over any offence established in accordance with Articles 2–11 of this Convention, when the offence is committed—
   (a) in its territory; or
   (b) on board a ship flying the flag of that Party; or
   (c) on board an aircraft registered under the laws of that Party; or
   (d) by one of its nationals, if the offence is punishable under criminal law where it was committed or if the offence is committed outside the territorial jurisdiction of any State.

2. Each Party may reserve the right not to apply or to apply only in specific cases or conditions the jurisdiction rules laid down in paragraphs 1(b)–1(d) of this article or any part thereof.

3. Each Party shall adopt such measures as may be necessary to establish jurisdiction over the offences referred to in Article 24, paragraph 1, of this Convention, in cases where an alleged offender is present in its territory and it does not extradite him or her to another Party, solely on the basis of his or her nationality, after a request for extradition.

4. This Convention does not exclude any criminal jurisdiction exercised by a Party in accordance with its domestic law.

5. When more than one Party claims jurisdiction over an alleged offence established in accordance with this Convention, the Parties involved shall, where appropriate, consult with a view to determining the most appropriate jurisdiction for prosecution.

[5359]

CHAPTER III
INTERNATIONAL CO-OPERATION

SECTION 1—GENERAL PRINCIPLES

TITLE 1—GENERAL PRINCIPLES RELATING TO INTERNATIONAL CO-OPERATION

Article 23

General principles relating to international co-operation

The Parties shall co-operate with each other, in accordance with the provisions of this chapter, and through the application of relevant international instruments on international co-operation in criminal matters, arrangements agreed on the basis of uniform or reciprocal legislation, and domestic laws, to the widest extent possible for the purposes of investigations or proceedings concerning criminal offences related to computer systems and data, or for the collection of evidence in electronic form of a criminal offence.

TITLE 2—PRINCIPLES RELATING TO EXTRADITION

Article 24

Extradition

1.
   (a) This article applies to extradition between Parties for the criminal offences established in accordance with Articles 2–11 of this Convention, provided that they are punishable under the laws of both Parties concerned by deprivation of liberty for a maximum period of at least one year, or by a more severe penalty.
   (b) Where a different minimum penalty is to be applied under an arrangement agreed

on the basis of uniform or reciprocal legislation or an extradition treaty, including the European Convention on Extradition (ETS No 24), applicable between two or more parties, the minimum penalty provided for under such arrangement or treaty shall apply.

2. The criminal offences described in paragraph 1 of this article shall be deemed to be included as extraditable offences in any extradition treaty existing between or among the Parties. The Parties undertake to include such offences as extraditable offences in any extradition treaty to be concluded between or among them.

3. If a Party that makes extradition conditional on the existence of a treaty receives a request for extradition from another Party with which it does not have an extradition treaty, it may consider this Convention as the legal basis for extradition with respect to any criminal offence referred to in paragraph 1 of this article.

4. Parties that do not make extradition conditional on the existence of a treaty shall recognise the criminal offences referred to in paragraph 1 of this article as extraditable offences between themselves.

5. Extradition shall be subject to the conditions provided for by the law of the requested Party or by applicable extradition treaties, including the grounds on which the requested Party may refuse extradition.

6. If extradition for a criminal offence referred to in paragraph 1 of this article is refused solely on the basis of the nationality of the person sought, or because the requested Party deems that it has jurisdiction over the offence, the requested Party shall submit the case at the request of the requesting Party to its competent authorities for the purpose of prosecution and shall report the final outcome to the requesting Party in due course. Those authorities shall take their decision and conduct their investigations and proceedings in the same manner as for any other offence of a comparable nature under the law of that Party.

7.

(a) Each Party shall, at the time of signature or when depositing its instrument of ratification, acceptance, approval or accession, communicate to the Secretary General of the Council of Europe the name and address of each authority responsible for making or receiving requests for extradition or provisional arrest in the absence of a treaty.

(b) The Secretary General of the Council of Europe shall set up and keep updated a register of authorities so designated by the Parties. Each Party shall ensure that the details held on the register are correct at all times.

TITLE 3—GENERAL PRINCIPLES RELATING TO MUTUAL ASSISTANCE

Article 25

General principles relating to mutual assistance

1. The Parties shall afford one another mutual assistance to the widest extent possible for the purpose of investigations or proceedings concerning criminal offences related to computer systems and data, or for the collection of evidence in electronic form of a criminal offence.

2. Each Party shall also adopt such legislative and other measures as may be necessary to carry out the obligations set forth in Articles 27–35.

3. Each Party may, in urgent circumstances, make requests for mutual assistance or communications related thereto by expedited means of communication, including fax or e-mail, to the extent that such means provide appropriate levels of security and authentication (including the use of encryption, where necessary), with formal confirmation to follow, where required by the requested Party. The requested Party shall accept and respond to the request by any such expedited means of communication.

4. Except as otherwise specifically provided in articles in this chapter, mutual assistance shall be subject to the conditions provided for by the law of the requested Party or by applicable mutual assistance treaties, including the grounds on which the requested Party may refuse co-operation. The requested Party shall not exercise the right to refuse mutual assistance in relation to the offences referred to in Articles 2–11 solely on the ground that the request concerns an offence which it considers a fiscal offence.

5. Where, in accordance with the provisions of this chapter, the requested Party is permitted to make mutual assistance conditional upon the existence of dual criminality, that

condition shall be deemed fulfilled, irrespective of whether its laws place the offence within the same category of offence or denominate the offence by the same terminology as the requesting Party, if the conduct underlying the offence for which assistance is sought is a criminal offence under its laws.

Article 26

Spontaneous information

1. A Party may, within the limits of its domestic law and without prior request, forward to another Party information obtained within the framework of its own investigations when it considers that the disclosure of such information might assist the receiving Party in initiating or carrying out investigations or proceedings concerning criminal offences established in accordance with this Convention or might lead to a request for co-operation by that Party under this chapter.

2. Prior to providing such information, the providing Party may request that it be kept confidential or only used subject to conditions. If the receiving Party cannot comply with such request, it shall notify the providing Party, which shall then determine whether the information should nevertheless be provided. If the receiving Party accepts the information subject to the conditions, it shall be bound by them.

TITLE 4—PROCEDURES PERTAINING TO MUTUAL ASSISTANCE REQUESTS IN THE ABSENCE OF APPLICABLE INTERNATIONAL AGREEMENTS

Article 27

Procedures pertaining to mutual assistance requests in the absence of applicable international agreements

1. Where there is no mutual assistance treaty or arrangement on the basis of uniform or reciprocal legislation in force between the requesting and requested Parties, the provisions of paragraphs 2–9 of this article shall apply. The provisions of this article shall not apply where such treaty, arrangement or legislation exists, unless the Parties concerned agree to apply any or all of the remainder of this article in lieu thereof.

2.
(a) Each Party shall designate a central authority or authorities responsible for sending and answering requests for mutual assistance, the execution of such requests or their transmission to the authorities competent for their execution.
(b) The central authorities shall communicate directly with each other.
(c) Each Party shall, at the time of signature or when depositing its instrument of ratification, acceptance, approval or accession, communicate to the Secretary General of the Council of Europe the names and addresses of the authorities designated in pursuance of this paragraph.
(d) The Secretary General of the Council of Europe shall set up and keep updated a register of central authorities designated by the Parties. Each Party shall ensure that the details held on the register are correct at all times.

3. Mutual assistance requests under this article shall be executed in accordance with the procedures specified by the requesting Party, except where incompatible with the law of the requested Party.

4. The requested Party may, in addition to the grounds for refusal established in Article 25, paragraph 4, refuse assistance if—
(a) the request concerns an offence which the requested Party considers a political offence or an offence connected with a political offence, or
(b) it considers that execution of the request is likely to prejudice its sovereignty, security, *ordre public* or other essential interests.

5. The requested Party may postpone action on a request if such action would prejudice criminal investigations or proceedings conducted by its authorities.

6. Before refusing or postponing assistance, the requested Party shall, where appropriate after having consulted with the requesting Party, consider whether the request may be granted partially or subject to such conditions as it deems necessary.

7. The requested Party shall promptly inform the requesting Party of the outcome of the execution of a request for assistance. Reasons shall be given for any refusal or postponement

of the request. The requested Party shall also inform the requesting Party of any reasons that render impossible the execution of the request or are likely to delay it significantly.

8. The requesting Party may request that the requested Party keep confidential the fact of any request made under this chapter as well as its subject, except to the extent necessary for its execution. If the requested Party cannot comply with the request for confidentiality, it shall promptly inform the requesting Party, which shall then determine whether the request should nevertheless be executed.

9.

(a) In the event of urgency, requests for mutual assistance or communications related thereto may be sent directly by judicial authorities of the requesting Party to such authorities of the requested Party. In any such cases, a copy shall be sent at the same time to the central authority of the requested Party through the central authority of the requesting Party.

(b) Any request or communication under this paragraph may be made through the International Criminal Police Organisation (Interpol).

(c) Where a request is made pursuant to sub-paragraph (a) of this article and the authority is not competent to deal with the request, it shall refer the request to the competent national authority and inform directly the requesting Party that it has done so.

(d) Requests or communications made under this paragraph that do not involve coercive action may be directly transmitted by the competent authorities of the requesting Party to the competent authorities of the requested Party.

(e) Each Party may, at the time of signature or when depositing its instrument of ratification, acceptance, approval or accession, inform the Secretary General of the Council of Europe that, for reasons of efficiency, requests made under this paragraph are to be addressed to its central authority.

Article 28

Confidentiality and limitation on use

1. When there is no mutual assistance treaty or arrangement on the basis of uniform or reciprocal legislation in force between the requesting and the requested Parties, the provisions of this article shall apply. The provisions of this article shall not apply where such treaty, arrangement or legislation exists, unless the Parties concerned agree to apply any or all of the remainder of this article in lieu thereof.

2. The requested Party may make the supply of information or material in response to a request dependent on the condition that it is—

(a) kept confidential where the request for mutual legal assistance could not be complied with in the absence of such condition, or

(b) not used for investigations or proceedings other than those stated in the request.

3. If the requesting Party cannot comply with a condition referred to in paragraph 2, it shall promptly inform the other Party, which shall then determine whether the information should nevertheless be provided. When the requesting Party accepts the condition, it shall be bound by it.

4. Any Party that supplies information or material subject to a condition referred to in paragraph 2 may require the other Party to explain, in relation to that condition, the use made of such information or material.

SECTION 2—SPECIFIC PROVISIONS

TITLE 1—MUTUAL ASSISTANCE REGARDING PROVISIONAL MEASURES

Article 29

Expedited preservation of stored computer data

1. A Party may request another Party to order or otherwise obtain the expeditious preservation of data stored by means of a computer system, located within the territory of that other Party and in respect of which the requesting Party intends to submit a request for mutual assistance for the search or similar access, seizure or similar securing, or disclosure of the data.

2. A request for preservation made under paragraph 1 shall specify—

(a) the authority seeking the preservation;
(b) the offence that is the subject of a criminal investigation or proceedings and a brief summary of the related facts;
(c) the stored computer data to be preserved and its relationship to the offence;
(d) any available information identifying the custodian of the stored computer data or the location of the computer system;
(e) the necessity of the preservation; and
(f) that the Party intends to submit a request for mutual assistance for the search or similar access, seizure or similar securing, or disclosure of the stored computer data.

3. Upon receiving the request from another Party, the requested Party shall take all appropriate measures to preserve expeditiously the specified data in accordance with its domestic law. For the purposes of responding to a request, dual criminality shall not be required as a condition to providing such preservation.

4. A Party that requires dual criminality as a condition for responding to a request for mutual assistance for the search or similar access, seizure or similar securing, or disclosure of stored data may, in respect of offences other than those established in accordance with Articles 2–11 of this Convention, reserve the right to refuse the request for preservation under this article in cases where it has reasons to believe that at the time of disclosure the condition of dual criminality cannot be fulfilled.

5. In addition, a request for preservation may only be refused if—
(a) the request concerns an offence which the requested Party considers a political offence or an offence connected with a political offence, or
(b) the requested Party considers that execution of the request is likely to prejudice its sovereignty, security, *ordre public* or other essential interests.

6. Where the requested Party believes that preservation will not ensure the future availability of the data or will threaten the confidentiality of or otherwise prejudice the requesting Party's investigation, it shall promptly so inform the requesting Party, which shall then determine whether the request should nevertheless be executed.

7. Any preservation effected in response to the request referred to in paragraph 1 shall be for a period not less than sixty days, in order to enable the requesting Party to submit a request for the search or similar access, seizure or similar securing, or disclosure of the data. Following the receipt of such a request, the data shall continue to be preserved pending a decision on that request.

Article 30

Expedited disclosure of preserved traffic data

1. Where, in the course of the execution of a request made pursuant to Article 29 to preserve traffic data concerning a specific communication, the requested Party discovers that a service provider in another State was involved in the transmission of the communication, the requested Party shall expeditiously disclose to the requesting Party a sufficient amount of traffic data to identify that service provider and the path through which the communication was transmitted.

2. Disclosure of traffic data under paragraph 1 may only be withheld if—
(a) the request concerns an offence which the requested Party considers a political offence or an offence connected with a political offence; or
(b) the requested Party considers that execution of the request is likely to prejudice its sovereignty, security, *ordre public* or other essential interests.

TITLE 2—MUTUAL ASSISTANCE REGARDING INVESTIGATIVE POWERS

Article 31

Mutual assistance regarding accessing of stored computer data

1. A Party may request another Party to search or similarly access, seize or similarly secure, and disclose data stored by means of a computer system located within the territory of the requested Party, including data that has been preserved pursuant to Article 29.

2. The requested Party shall respond to the request through the application of international instruments, arrangements and laws referred to in Article 23, and in accordance with other relevant provisions of this chapter.

PART VII MISCELLANEOUS

3. The request shall be responded to on an expedited basis where—
   (a) there are grounds to believe that relevant data is particularly vulnerable to loss or modification; or
   (b) the instruments, arrangements and laws referred to in paragraph 2 otherwise provide for expedited co-operation.

Article 32

Trans-border access to stored computer data with consent or where publicly available

A Party may, without the authorisation of another Party—

(a) access publicly available (open source) stored computer data, regardless of where the data is located geographically; or

(b) access or receive, through a computer system in its territory, stored computer data located in another Party, if the Party obtains the lawful and voluntary consent of the person who has the lawful authority to disclose the data to the Party through that computer system.

Article 33

Mutual assistance in the real-time collection of traffic data

1. The Parties shall provide mutual assistance to each other in the real-time collection of traffic data associated with specified communications in their territory transmitted by means of a computer system. Subject to the provisions of paragraph 2, this assistance shall be governed by the conditions and procedures provided for under domestic law.

2. Each Party shall provide such assistance at least with respect to criminal offences for which real-time collection of traffic data would be available in a similar domestic case.

Article 34

Mutual assistance regarding the interception of content data

The Parties shall provide mutual assistance to each other in the real-time collection or recording of content data of specified communications transmitted by means of a computer system to the extent permitted under their applicable treaties and domestic laws.

TITLE 3—24/7 NETWORK

Article 35

24/7 Network

1. Each Party shall designate a point of contact available on a twenty-four hour, seven-day-a-week basis, in order to ensure the provision of immediate assistance for the purpose of investigations or proceedings concerning criminal offences related to computer systems and data, or for the collection of evidence in electronic form of a criminal offence. Such assistance shall include facilitating, or, if permitted by its domestic law and practice, directly carrying out the following measures—

(a) the provision of technical advice;

(b) the preservation of data pursuant to Articles 29 and 30;

(c) the collection of evidence, the provision of legal information, and locating of suspects.

2. (a) A Party's point of contact shall have the capacity to carry out communications with the point of contact of another Party on an expedited basis.

(b) If the point of contact designated by a Party is not part of that Party's authority or authorities responsible for international mutual assistance or extradition, the point of contact shall ensure that it is able to co-ordinate with such authority or authorities on an expedited basis.

3. Each Party shall ensure that trained and equipped personnel are available, in order to facilitate the operation of the network.

[5360]

CHAPTER IV
FINAL PROVISIONS

Article 36

Signature and entry into force

1. This Convention shall be open for signature by the member States of the Council of Europe and by non-member States which have participated in its elaboration.

2. This Convention is subject to ratification, acceptance or approval. Instruments of ratification, acceptance or approval shall be deposited with the Secretary General of the Council of Europe.

3. This Convention shall enter into force on the first day of the month following the expiration of a period of three months after the date on which five States, including at least three member States of the Council of Europe, have expressed their consent to be bound by the Convention in accordance with the provisions of paragraphs 1 and 2.

4. In respect of any signatory State which subsequently expresses its consent to be bound by it, the Convention shall enter into force on the first day of the month following the expiration of a period of three months after the date of the expression of its consent to be bound by the Convention in accordance with the provisions of paragraphs 1 and 2.

Article 37

Accession to the Convention

1. After the entry into force of this Convention, the Committee of Ministers of the Council of Europe, after consulting with and obtaining the unanimous consent of the Contracting States to the Convention, may invite any State which is not a member of the Council and which has not participated in its elaboration to accede to this Convention. The decision shall be taken by the majority provided for in Article 20(d) of the Statute of the Council of Europe and by the unanimous vote of the representatives of the Contracting States entitled to sit on the Committee of Ministers.

2. In respect of any State acceding to the Convention under paragraph 1 above, the Convention shall enter into force on the first day of the month following the expiration of a period of three months after the date of deposit of the instrument of accession with the Secretary General of the Council of Europe.

Article 38

Territorial application

1. Any State may, at the time of signature or when depositing its instrument of ratification, acceptance, approval or accession, specify the territory or territories to which this Convention shall apply.

2. Any State may, at any later date, by a declaration addressed to the Secretary General of the Council of Europe, extend the application of this Convention to any other territory specified in the declaration. In respect of such territory the Convention shall enter into force on the first day of the month following the expiration of a period of three months after the date of receipt of the declaration by the Secretary General.

3. Any declaration made under the two preceding paragraphs may, in respect of any territory specified in such declaration, be withdrawn by a notification addressed to the Secretary General of the Council of Europe. The withdrawal shall become effective on the first day of the month following the expiration of a period of three months after the date of receipt of such notification by the Secretary General.

Article 39

Effects of the Convention

1. The purpose of the present Convention is to supplement applicable multilateral or bilateral treaties or arrangements as between the Parties, including the provisions of—

— the European Convention on Extradition, opened for signature in Paris, on 13 December 1957 (ETS No 24);

— the European Convention on Mutual Assistance in Criminal Matters, opened for signature in Strasbourg, on 20 April 1959 (ETS No 30);
— the Additional Protocol to the European Convention on Mutual Assistance in Criminal Matters, opened for signature in Strasbourg, on 17 March 1978 (ETS No 99).

2. If two or more Parties have already concluded an agreement or treaty on the matters dealt with in this Convention or have otherwise established their relations on such matters, or should they in future do so, they shall also be entitled to apply that agreement or treaty or to regulate those relations accordingly. However, where Parties establish their relations in respect of the matters dealt with in the present Convention other than as regulated therein, they shall do so in a manner that is not inconsistent with the Convention's objectives and principles.

3. Nothing in this Convention shall affect other rights, restrictions, obligations and responsibilities of a Party.

Article 40

Declarations

By a written notification addressed to the Secretary General of the Council of Europe, any State may, at the time of signature or when depositing its instrument of ratification, acceptance, approval or accession, declare that it avails itself of the possibility of requiring additional elements as provided for under Articles 2, 3, 6 paragraph 1(b), 7, 9 paragraph 3, and 27, paragraph 9(e).

Article 41

Federal clause

1. A federal State may reserve the right to assume obligations under Chapter II of this Convention consistent with its fundamental principles governing the relationship between its central government and constituent States or other similar territorial entities provided that it is still able to co-operate under Chapter III.

2. When making a reservation under paragraph 1, a federal State may not apply the terms of such reservation to exclude or substantially diminish its obligations to provide for measures set forth in Chapter II. Overall, it shall provide for a broad and effective law enforcement capability with respect to those measures.

3. With regard to the provisions of this Convention, the application of which comes under the jurisdiction of constituent States or other similar territorial entities, that are not obliged by the constitutional system of the federation to take legislative measures, the federal government shall inform the competent authorities of such States of the said provisions with its favourable opinion, encouraging them to take appropriate action to give them effect.

Article 42

Reservations

By a written notification addressed to the Secretary General of the Council of Europe, any State may, at the time of signature or when depositing its instrument of ratification, acceptance, approval or accession, declare that it avails itself of the reservation(s) provided for in Article 4, paragraph 2, Article 6, paragraph 3, Article 9, paragraph 4, Article 10, paragraph 3, Article 11, paragraph 3, Article 14, paragraph 3, Article 22, paragraph 2, Article 29, paragraph 4, and Article 41, paragraph 1. No other reservation may be made.

Article 43

Status and withdrawal of reservations

1. A Party that has made a reservation in accordance with Article 42 may wholly or partially withdraw it by means of a notification addressed to the Secretary General of the Council of Europe. Such withdrawal shall take effect on the date of receipt of such notification by the Secretary General. If the notification states that the withdrawal of a reservation is to take effect on a date specified therein, and such date is later than the date on which the notification is received by the Secretary General, the withdrawal shall take effect on such a later date.

2. A Party that has made a reservation as referred to in Article 42 shall withdraw such reservation, in whole or in part, as soon as circumstances so permit.

3. The Secretary General of the Council of Europe may periodically enquire with Parties that have made one or more reservations as referred to in Article 42 as to the prospects for withdrawing such reservation(s).

Article 44

Amendments

1. Amendments to this Convention may be proposed by any Party, and shall be communicated by the Secretary General of the Council of Europe to the member States of the Council of Europe, to the non-member States which have participated in the elaboration of this Convention as well as to any State which has acceded to, or has been invited to accede to, this Convention in accordance with the provisions of Article 37.

2. Any amendment proposed by a Party shall be communicated to the European Committee on Crime Problems (CDPC), which shall submit to the Committee of Ministers its opinion on that proposed amendment.

3. The Committee of Ministers shall consider the proposed amendment and the opinion submitted by the CDPC and, following consultation with the non-member States Parties to this Convention, may adopt the amendment.

4. The text of any amendment adopted by the Committee of Ministers in accordance with paragraph 3 of this article shall be forwarded to the Parties for acceptance.

5. Any amendment adopted in accordance with paragraph 3 of this article shall come into force on the thirtieth day after all Parties have informed the Secretary General of their acceptance thereof.

Article 45

Settlement of disputes

1. The European Committee on Crime Problems (CDPC) shall be kept informed regarding the interpretation and application of this Convention.

2. In case of a dispute between Parties as to the interpretation or application of this Convention, they shall seek a settlement of the dispute through negotiation or any other peaceful means of their choice, including submission of the dispute to the CDPC, to an arbitral tribunal whose decisions shall be binding upon the Parties, or to the International Court of Justice, as agreed upon by the Parties concerned.

Article 46

Consultations of the Parties

1. The Parties shall, as appropriate, consult periodically with a view to facilitating—

(a) the effective use and implementation of this Convention, including the identification of any problems thereof, as well as the effects of any declaration or reservation made under this Convention;

(b) the exchange of information on significant legal, policy or technological developments pertaining to cybercrime and the collection of evidence in electronic form;

(c) consideration of possible supplementation or amendment of the Convention.

2. The European Committee on Crime Problems (CDPC) shall be kept periodically informed regarding the result of consultations referred to in paragraph 1.

3. The CDPC shall, as appropriate, facilitate the consultations referred to in paragraph 1 and take the measures necessary to assist the Parties in their efforts to supplement or amend the Convention. At the latest three years after the present Convention enters into force, the European Committee on Crime Problems (CDPC) shall, in co-operation with the Parties, conduct a review of all of the Convention's provisions and, if necessary, recommend any appropriate amendments.

4. Except where assumed by the Council of Europe, expenses incurred in carrying out the provisions of paragraph 1 shall be borne by the Parties in the manner to be determined by them.

5. The Parties shall be assisted by the Secretariat of the Council of Europe in carrying out their functions pursuant to this article.

Article 47

Denunciation

1. Any Party may, at any time, denounce this Convention by means of a notification addressed to the Secretary General of the Council of Europe.

2. Such denunciation shall become effective on the first day of the month following the expiration of a period of three months after the date of receipt of the notification by the Secretary General.

Article 48

Notification

The Secretary General of the Council of Europe shall notify the member States of the Council of Europe, the non-member States which have participated in the elaboration of this Convention as well as any State which has acceded to, or has been invited to accede to, this Convention of—

(a) any signature;
(b) the deposit of any instrument of ratification, acceptance, approval or accession;
(c) any date of entry into force of this Convention in accordance with Articles 36 and 37;
(d) any declaration made under Article 40 or reservation made in accordance with Article 42;
(e) any other act, notification or communication relating to this Convention.

In witness whereof the undersigned, being duly authorised thereto, have signed this Convention.

Done at Budapest, this 23rd day of November 2001, in English and in French, both texts being equally authentic, in a single copy which shall be deposited in the archives of the Council of Europe. The Secretary General of the Council of Europe shall transmit certified copies to each member State of the Council of Europe, to the non-member States which have participated in the elaboration of this Convention, and to any State invited to accede to it.

(*For chart of Signatures, Ratifications, etc see www.conventions.coe.int*)

[5361]

ADDITIONAL PROTOCOL TO THE CONVENTION ON CYBERCRIME, CONCERNING THE CRIMINALISATION OF ACTS OF A RACIST AND XENOPHOBIC NATURE COMMITTED THROUGH COMPUTER SYSTEMS

Strasbourg, 28.I.2003

(European Treaty Series No 189)

The member States of the Council of Europe and the other States Parties to the Convention on Cybercrime, opened for signature in Budapest on 23 November 2001, signatory hereto;

Considering that the aim of the Council of Europe is to achieve a greater unity between its members;

Recalling that all human beings are born free and equal in dignity and rights;

Stressing the need to secure a full and effective implementation of all human rights without any discrimination or distinction, as enshrined in European and other international instruments;

Convinced that acts of a racist and xenophobic nature constitute a violation of human rights and a threat to the rule of law and democratic stability;

Considering that national and international law need to provide adequate legal responses to propaganda of a racist and xenophobic nature committed through computer systems;

Aware of the fact that propaganda to such acts is often subject to criminalisation in national legislation;

Having regard to the Convention on Cybercrime, which provides for modern and flexible means of international co-operation and convinced of the need to harmonise substantive law provisions concerning the fight against racist and xenophobic propaganda;

Aware that computer systems offer an unprecedented means of facilitating freedom of expression and communication around the globe;

Recognising that freedom of expression constitutes one of the essential foundations of a democratic society, and is one of the basic conditions for its progress and for the development of every human being;

Concerned, however, by the risk of misuse or abuse of such computer systems to disseminate racist and xenophobic propaganda;

Mindful of the need to ensure a proper balance between freedom of expression and an effective fight against acts of a racist and xenophobic nature;

Recognising that this Protocol is not intended to affect established principles relating to freedom of expression in national legal systems;

Taking into account the relevant international legal instruments in this field, and in particular the Convention for the Protection of Human Rights and Fundamental Freedoms and its Protocol No. 12 concerning the general prohibition of discrimination, the existing Council of Europe conventions on co-operation in the penal field, in particular the Convention on Cybercrime, the United Nations International Convention on the Elimination of All Forms of Racial Discrimination of 21 December 1965, the European Union Joint Action of 15 July 1996 adopted by the Council on the basis of Article K.3 of the Treaty on European Union, concerning action to combat racism and xenophobia;

Welcoming the recent developments which further advance international understanding and co-operation in combating cybercrime and racism and xenophobia;

Having regard to the Action Plan adopted by the Heads of State and Government of the Council of Europe on the occasion of their Second Summit (Strasbourg, 10–11 October 1997) to seek common responses to the developments of the new technologies based on the standards and values of the Council of Europe;

Have agreed as follows—

CHAPTER I
COMMON PROVISIONS

Article 1

Purpose

The purpose of this Protocol is to supplement, as between the Parties to the Protocol, the provisions of the Convention on Cybercrime, opened for signature in Budapest on 23 November 2001 (hereinafter referred to as "the Convention"), as regards the criminalisation of acts of a racist and xenophobic nature committed through computer systems.

Article 2

Definition

1. For the purposes of this Protocol—

"*racist and xenophobic material*" means any written material, any image or any other representation of ideas or theories, which advocates, promotes or incites hatred, discrimination or violence, against any individual or group of individuals, based on race, colour, descent or national or ethnic origin, as well as religion if used as a pretext for any of these factors.

2. The terms and expressions used in this Protocol shall be interpreted in the same manner as they are interpreted under the Convention.

[5362]

CHAPTER II
MEASURES TO BE TAKEN AT NATIONAL LEVEL

Article 3

Dissemination of racist and xenophobic material through computer systems

1. Each Party shall adopt such legislative and other measures as may be necessary to establish as criminal offences under its domestic law, when committed intentionally and without right, the following conduct—

distributing, or otherwise making available, racist and xenophobic material to the public through a computer system.

2. A Party may reserve the right not to attach criminal liability to conduct as defined by paragraph 1 of this article, where the material, as defined in Article 2, paragraph 1, advocates, promotes or incites discrimination that is not associated with hatred or violence, provided that other effective remedies are available.

3. Notwithstanding paragraph 2 of this article, a Party may reserve the right not to apply paragraph 1 to those cases of discrimination for which, due to established principles in its national legal system concerning freedom of expression, it cannot provide for effective remedies as referred to in the said paragraph 2.

Article 4

Racist and xenophobic motivated threat

Each Party shall adopt such legislative and other measures as may be necessary to establish as criminal offences under its domestic law, when committed intentionally and without right, the following conduct—

threatening, through a computer system, with the commission of a serious criminal offence as defined under its domestic law, (i) persons for the reason that they belong to a group, distinguished by race, colour, descent or national or ethnic origin, as well as religion, if used as a pretext for any of these factors, or (ii) a group of persons which is distinguished by any of these characteristics.

Article 5

Racist and xenophobic motivated insult

1. Each Party shall adopt such legislative and other measures as may be necessary to establish as criminal offences under its domestic law, when committed intentionally and without right, the following conduct—

insulting publicly, through a computer system, (i) persons for the reason that they belong to a group distinguished by race, colour, descent or national or ethnic origin, as well as religion, if used as a pretext for any of these factors; or (ii) a group of persons which is distinguished by any of these characteristics.

2. A Party may either—

(a) require that the offence referred to in paragraph 1 of this article has the effect that the person or group of persons referred to in paragraph 1 is exposed to hatred, contempt or ridicule; or

(b) reserve the right not to apply, in whole or in part, paragraph 1 of this article.

Article 6

Denial, gross minimisation, approval or justification of genocide or crimes against humanity

1. Each Party shall adopt such legislative measures as may be necessary to establish the following conduct as criminal offences under its domestic law, when committed intentionally and without right—

distributing or otherwise making available, through a computer system to the public, material which denies, grossly minimises, approves or justifies acts constituting genocide or crimes against humanity, as defined by international law and recognised as such by final and binding decisions of the International Military Tribunal, established by the London Agreement of 8 August 1945, or of any other international court established by relevant international instruments and whose jurisdiction is recognised by that Party.

2. A Party may either—
   (a) require that the denial or the gross minimisation referred to in paragraph 1 of this article is committed with the intent to incite hatred, discrimination or violence against any individual or group of individuals, based on race, colour, descent or national or ethnic origin, as well as religion if used as a pretext for any of these factors, or otherwise
   (b) reserve the right not to apply, in whole or in part, paragraph 1 of this article.

Article 7

Aiding and abetting

Each Party shall adopt such legislative and other measures as may be necessary to establish as criminal offences under its domestic law, when committed intentionally and without right, aiding or abetting the commission of any of the offences established in accordance with this Protocol, with intent that such offence be committed.

[5363]

CHAPTER III
RELATIONS BETWEEN THE CONVENTION AND THIS PROTOCOL

Article 8

Relations between the Convention and this Protocol

1. Articles 1, 12, 13, 22, 41, 44, 45 and 46 of the Convention shall apply, *mutatis mutandis*, to this Protocol.

2. The Parties shall extend the scope of application of the measures defined in Articles 14 to 21 and Articles 23 to 35 of the Convention, to Articles 2 to 7 of this Protocol.

[5364]

CHAPTER IV
FINAL PROVISIONS

Article 9

Expression of consent to be bound

1. This Protocol shall be open for signature by the States which have signed the Convention, which may express their consent to be bound by either—
   (a) signature without reservation as to ratification, acceptance or approval; or
   (b) signature subject to ratification, acceptance or approval, followed by ratification, acceptance or approval.

2. A State may not sign this Protocol without reservation as to ratification, acceptance or approval, or deposit an instrument of ratification, acceptance or approval, unless it has already deposited or simultaneously deposits an instrument of ratification, acceptance or approval of the Convention.

3. The instruments of ratification, acceptance or approval shall be deposited with the Secretary General of the Council of Europe.

Article 10

Entry into force

1. This Protocol shall enter into force on the first day of the month following the expiration of a period of three months after the date on which five States have expressed their consent to be bound by the Protocol, in accordance with the provisions of Article 9.

2. In respect of any State which subsequently expresses its consent to be bound by it, the Protocol shall enter into force on the first day of the month following the expiration of a period of three months after the date of its signature without reservation as to ratification, acceptance or approval or deposit of its instrument of ratification, acceptance or approval.

Article 11

Accession

1. After the entry into force of this Protocol, any State which has acceded to the Convention may also accede to the Protocol.

2. Accession shall be effected by the deposit with the Secretary General of the Council of Europe of an instrument of accession which shall take effect on the first day of the month following the expiration of a period of three months after the date of its deposit.

Article 12

Reservations and declarations

1. Reservations and declarations made by a Party to a provision of the Convention shall be applicable also to this Protocol, unless that Party declares otherwise at the time of signature or when depositing its instrument of ratification, acceptance, approval or accession.

2. By a written notification addressed to the Secretary General of the Council of Europe, any Party may, at the time of signature or when depositing its instrument of ratification, acceptance, approval or accession, declare that it avails itself of the reservation(s) provided for in Articles 3, 5 and 6 of this Protocol. At the same time, a Party may avail itself, with respect to the provisions of this Protocol, of the reservation(s) provided for in Article 22, paragraph 2, and Article 41, paragraph 1, of the Convention, irrespective of the implementation made by that Party under the Convention. No other reservations may be made.

3. By a written notification addressed to the Secretary General of the Council of Europe, any State may, at the time of signature or when depositing its instrument of ratification, acceptance, approval or accession, declare that it avails itself of the possibility of requiring additional elements as provided for in Article 5, paragraph 2(a), and Article 6, paragraph 2(a), of this Protocol.

Article 13

Status and withdrawal of reservations

1. A Party that has made a reservation in accordance with Article 12 above shall withdraw such reservation, in whole or in part, as soon as circumstances so permit. Such withdrawal shall take effect on the date of receipt of a notification addressed to the Secretary General of the Council of Europe. If the notification states that the withdrawal of a reservation is to take effect on a date specified therein, and such date is later than the date on which the notification is received by the Secretary General, the withdrawal shall take effect on such a later date.

2. The Secretary General of the Council of Europe may periodically enquire with Parties that have made one or more reservations in accordance with Article 12 as to the prospects for withdrawing such reservation(s).

Article 14

Territorial application

1. Any Party may at the time of signature or when depositing its instrument of ratification, acceptance, approval or accession, specify the territory or territories to which this Protocol shall apply.

2. Any Party may, at any later date, by a declaration addressed to the Secretary General of the Council of Europe, extend the application of this Protocol to any other territory specified in the declaration. In respect of such territory, the Protocol shall enter into force on the first day of the month following the expiration of a period of three months after the date of receipt of the declaration by the Secretary General.

3. Any declaration made under the two preceding paragraphs may, in respect of any territory specified in such declaration, be withdrawn by a notification addressed to the Secretary General of the Council of Europe. The withdrawal shall become effective on the first day of the month following the expiration of a period of three months after the date of receipt of such notification by the Secretary General.

Article 15

Denunciation

1. Any Party may, at any time, denounce this Protocol by means of a notification addressed to the Secretary General of the Council of Europe.

2. Such denunciation shall become effective on the first day of the month following the expiration of a period of three months after the date of receipt of the notification by the Secretary General.

Article 16

Notification

The Secretary General of the Council of Europe shall notify the member States of the Council of Europe, the non-member States which have participated in the elaboration of this Protocol as well as any State which has acceded to, or has been invited to accede to, this Protocol of—

(a) any signature;

(b) the deposit of any instrument of ratification, acceptance, approval or accession;

(c) any date of entry into force of this Protocol in accordance with its Articles 9, 10 and 11;

(d) any other act, notification or communication relating to this Protocol.

In witness whereof the undersigned, being duly authorised thereto, have signed this Protocol.

Done at Strasbourg, this 28 January 2003, in English and in French, both texts being equally authentic, in a single copy which shall be deposited in the archives of the Council of Europe. The Secretary General of the Council of Europe shall transmit certified copies to each member State of the Council of Europe, to the non-member States which have participated in the elaboration of this Protocol, and to any State invited to accede to it.

(*For chart of Signatures, Ratifications, etc see www.conventions.coe.int*)

[5365]

Index